STANLEY GIBBONS

PRICED POSTAGE STAMP CATALOGUE

Part One

British Commonwealth

Ireland and South Africa

69th edition

1967

STANLEY GIBBONS LTD.
391 STRAND
LONDON WC2
Telephone TEMple Bar 9707

By appointment
to H.M. the Queen
Philatelists

Retail Price: 35/- in U.K.: $5 U.S.A.

Made and Printed in Great Britain
by Brightype litho by
Taylor Garnett Evans & Co. Ltd. at the
Mayflower Press, Watford

INDEX

INTRODUCTION

Some of the pointers mentioned in the Introduction to the 1966 edition of this Catalogue have borne fruit if sales are anything to go by. Although we printed a record number of that edition, it was obvious before publication that we had grossly underestimated the demand and a substantial reprint had to be ordered, which in turn sold out. Taken in conjunction with the rocketing circulation of *Gibbons Stamp Monthly* (now selling 67,000 copies a month) and the record attendance at " Stampex ", it is no wonder that stamp prices are booming. Another important fillip to the popularity of the hobby has been given by the more progressive stamp-issuing policy of the present Postmaster General.

We cannot recall any period during which catalogue prices in general have been so difficult to determine, many countries having been repriced two or three times during the course of production, and the number of changes make last year's edition as obsolete as an out-of-date London telephone directory.

Attention should be drawn to several editorial innovations. As prices for rare stamps escalate there has been a growing demand for these stamps with " Specimen " overprints and so we have started introducing quotations for those with a face value of £1 or more (shown in brackets after the colours as " S " followed by the price). Miniature sheets are given abbreviated listing with a distinctive " **MS** " Catalogue number and prices. The growing number of " missing colours " errors has presented certain problems which we have attempted to solve in the following ways. Stamps with major portions of the design missing are listed in this volume as well as in the *Elizabethan Catalogue*, but stamps which are not so startling are given Elizabethan listing only. There is a third category, sometimes resulting in major omissions, which is not due to failure to print the colour but is caused by a major shift of colour so that some stamps in the sheet may be without colour and others will have it misplaced. In general these will receive Elizabethan recognition but are outside the scope of this Catalogue. As an experiment the Georgian key type Dies in the Script watermark in *Nigeria* have been rewritten on the lines suggested by Mr. Wall in a *G.S.M.* article. This clarifies the philatelic story behind these issues and if the new listing meets with general approval we are willing to treat other countries similarly, although the problems are not always the same.

Coming now to specific editiorial revision, after India there are references to the wartime stamps issued by the Japanese authorities in the *Andaman and Nicobar Islands* and to those issued by the Indian National Army in *Imphal*. We are indebted to Mr. C. T. Sturton for the addition of a number of varieties in the *Indian Native States* and for a new detailed listing of the 1914–41 issues of *Bundi*. With the assistance of Mr. E. W. Proud we have made further revision in *Japanese Occupation of Malaya* incorporating a number of additional varieties and listing the handstamped seals of the Japanese commanders. Stamps formerly listed under the Japanese Occupation of Kelantan are now correctly designated *Thai Occupation of Kelantan* and the *Thai Occupation of Malaya* set has been transferred from Part III. Following the researches of Commander F. W. Collins, R.N. into the papers and printings of the *Mauritius* " POST PAID ", this classic issue has been rewritten. A number of additions will be found in *Rhodesia* on the advice of Mr. Bernard Livermore and for convenience the stamps of Southern Rhodesia with the name altered to Rhodesia now follow the old Rhodesia list although the two Rhodesias do not represent the same geographical area. Lt.-Col. G. H. C. Napier's researches have resulted in a reclassification of colours of the 2d. imperf. of *South Australia*.

New issues in the body of the Catalogue account for an increase of 67 pages as against 51 pages added in the last edition although this year we are publishing a month earlier than usual. It is perhaps worth mentioning that within the year we have had four omnibus issues (I.T.U., I.C.Y., Churchill and Royal Visit) and before the volume is published there will be another for the World Football Cup.

TERMS OF SALE AND HOW TO ORDER

GUARANTEE.—Every effort is made to ensure that all stamps sold by us, unless otherwise described, shall be in all respects genuine originals and they are offered for sale as such. If not as described, and if returned to us by the purchaser within six years, we undertake to refund the price paid to us and our liability in respect thereof shall be limited accordingly. If any stamp is certified as genuine by the Expert Committee of the Royal Philatelic Society, London, or of the British Philatelic Association Ltd., the purchaser shall not be entitled to make any claim against us in respect of any error, omission or mistake in such certificate.

All purchases from us are to be deemed to be subject to the above conditions.

(*N.B. The above form of guarantee is that approved by the Royal Philatelic Society and by the British Philatelic Association Ltd.*)

PRICES AND PRICE ALTERATIONS.—Our prices in this Catalogue are for stamps in fine condition. In the case of the older " classic " issues which vary greatly in condition, our prices are for stamps in fine condition, superb copies being supplied at special prices. *Less perfect copies of those issues in which " condition " varies greatly can be supplied at prices much below those quoted in this Catalogue.*

The prices quoted are those current when the Catalogue was revised, but that is some months before publication. A number of price alterations are notified each month in *Gibbons' Stamp Monthly.*

We reserve the right to raise or lower the prices quoted in this Catalogue without notice, and we give no guarantee to supply all stamps priced.

Prices for unused stamps are in the left-hand column and those for used in the right. Exceptions in G.B. Controls and South African countries are indicated at the head of the columns.

The prices quoted for the albums and publications, etc., advertised in this catalogue are also subject to alteration without notice.

All our prices are " postage extra ".

HOW TO ORDER STAMPS.—In ordering stamps from this Catalogue, it is essential to give the name of country, the number in the left hand column, and, if there are two sets of price columns, the letter or other indication at the head of the price column indicating the variety desired, and to state if required used or unused. **It is not sufficient to give the date of issue or the number of the illustration.** All orders should be written on slips of paper, on one side only, *separately from the letter that accompanies them*, or on our own Want List forms supplied free of charge; the original order will then be returned with the stamps. Please mention the name and edition of the Catalogue.

YOUR FULL AND CLEARLY WRITTEN NAME AND ADDRESS with *every* communication will much oblige, also your account number if you have dealt with us before. Printing your name in block letters is always helpful.

WANT LISTS.—Collectors' want lists are welcomed, provided that they do not consist of stamps all priced at 1s. or less (minimum order 10s., plus return postage). We have a large and varied stock and supply many thousands of pounds worth of stamps every year in this way. Postage is extra. For orders totalling more than £5 from the U.K. or 20s. from abroad, an extra 1s. 9d. for registration should be included.

APPROVAL SELECTIONS.—We have a wide range of approval books of individual countries available for general circulation and can arrange to send selections at any stipulated interval. An average purchase of at least £1 is expected to be made from each despatch.

SPECIALISTS FILE.—Specialist collectors are catered for through the medium of our Specialists File and selections of such stamps can be made up to suit individual requirements. In the case of new clients we request the usual banker's reference.

RARE STAMPS.—A wonderful stock of rare stamps is readily available for inspection at 391 Strand and can be sent, on approval, to collectors (banker's reference requested from new clients).

STOCK BOOKS.—Our stock books have now been completely revised and contain a full range of stamps in catalogue order, including shades and postmarks, also proofs, essays and minor varieties. These are available for immediate inspection in our shop at 391 Strand and will prove of inestimable value to all collectors.

BRITISH COMMONWEALTH NEW ISSUES.—Details of our service for the regular supply of new issues of the British Commonwealth to collectors will be sent on request.

GIFT TOKENS.—An ideal solution to the problem of giving presents enabling the recipient to choose any stamps, albums, or publications needed from the Gibbons stock. Available in units of £1, £5 and £10 and redeemable within six months.

TERMS OF SALE.—*Net Cash in advance*, except in the case of clients known to us, or furnishing the usual business references.

HOW TO REMIT.—Remittances must be made free of costs, preferably by cheque, payable on a Bank in the United Kingdom, or by Banker's Draft. Cheques, Money Orders and Postal Orders should be made payable to "Stanley Gibbons Ltd." and crossed "Lloyds Bank Ltd." Foreign cheques will be sold, and the proceeds only credited to the customer.

In their own interests customers in the U.K. are advised not to send currency notes or coin. Foreign Bank Notes should be registered and any that our bankers are unable to negotiate will have to be returned to the customer.

Remittances from abroad *apart* from the British Commonwealth (except Canada), Burma, Iceland, the Irish Republic, Jordan, Kuwait, Libya, the Republic of South Africa, South West Africa and Western Samoa, should be made by International Money Order or by Banker's Draft. Before remitting by any other method than a Money Order, it is advisable to consult a banker.

Unused, current British Commonwealth or Foreign stamps or reply coupons cannot be accepted as remittances.

CORRESPONDENCE in English, French, German, Spanish and Italian.

EXAMINATION AND IDENTIFICATION OF STAMPS.—We beg to state that we do not give opinions as to the genuineness of stamps, nor do we identify stamps or number them by our Catalogue.

EXPERT COMMITTEES.—The recognized Expert Committees in this country are those of the Royal Philatelic Society, 41 Devonshire Place, London, W.1, and of the British Philatelic Association Ltd., 446 Strand, London, W.C.2. The R.P.S. Committee expertises all British Commowealth stamps but does not handle foreign stamps issued after 1913. These Expert Committees do not undertake valuation under any circumstances.

FILM STRIPS AND SLIDES FOR HIRE.—We have several 35 mm. film strips and sets of slides on popular philatelic subjects, with accompanying lectures, which can be hired by philatelic societies and other bodies in Great Britain. Particulars will be sent on receipt of a stamped addressed envelope.

SUPPLEMENTS TO THIS CATALOGUE.—Our magazine, *Gibbons Stamp Monthly* (price 1s. a copy from your newsagent or 15s. 6d. a year for overseas subscribers), includes, in addition to articles and features, a monthly illustrated supplement to this Catalogue.

LETTERS FOR THE EDITOR.—Correspondence on editorial matters connected with this Catalogue should be addressed to the Catalogue Editor, the Editorial and Publishing Division, Stanley Gibbons Ltd., Drury House, Russell St., Drury Lane, London, W.C.2. Orders for stamps, etc., should NOT be sent in the same letter as they will be delayed. The Editor and Publishers can accept no responsibility for stamps sent by correspondents, though care will, of course, be taken.

¶*All enquiries to the Editor must be accompanied by stamped addressed envelope for reply*, and where stamps are sent an extra 1s. 9d. for registration should be added.

OUR STAMP-BUYING DEPARTMENT

We are daily buying collections of all kinds, single rarities, stamps on cover and quantities of sets and single stamps required for our general stock. We welcome offers of all such items, with the exception of collections consisting mainly of common stamps, and pay cash down for anything we buy.

VALUATIONS.—In the case of important collections of any countries needed to replenish our stocks we will gladly send our Chief Buyer to any part of the country to carry out a valuation and make an offer.

Please WRITE in the first instance to The Buying Dept., Stanley Gibbons Ltd., 391 Strand, W.C.2, giving general particulars, before sending stamps or asking for our Valuer to make a visit.

OUR ADDRESSES AND HOURS OF BUSINESS

HEAD OFFICE—

STANLEY GIBBONS LTD.
391 STRAND,
LONDON, W.C.2.

Telephone: TEMple Bar 9707.
Telegrams: Philatelic, London, W.C.2.
Cables: Stangib, London, W.C.2.
Code: A.B.C. (6th Edition).

SHOP DEPARTMENT—

Our only retail shop is at
391 Strand, W.C.2.

Open from Monday to Friday 9 a.m. to 5.30 p.m.
and on Saturday 9.30 a.m. to 12.30 p.m.

EDITORIAL AND PUBLISHING DIVISION AND TRADE WAREHOUSE—

STANLEY GIBBONS LTD.
DRURY HOUSE,
RUSSELL ST.,
DRURY LANE,
LONDON, W.C.2.

Telephones:
TEMple Bar 4136 (Editorial and Publishing)
TEMple Bar 2005 (Trade Warehouse).

De La Rue Dies (Victorian and Georgian)

Types of the General Plates used by Messrs. De La Rue & Co. for printing British Colonial Stamps.

I. VICTORIAN KEY TYPE

Die I

Die II

Die I

1. The ball of decoration on the second point of the Crown appears as a dark mass of lines.
2. Dark vertical shading separates the front hair from the bun.
3. The vertical line of colour outlining the front of the throat stops at the sixth line of shading on the neck.
4. The white space in the coil of the hair above the curl is roughly the shape of a pin's head.

Die II

1. There are very few lines of colour in the ball and it appears almost white.
2. A white vertical strand of hair appears in place of the dark shading.
3. The line stops at the eighth line of shading.
4. The white space is oblong, with a line of colour partially dividing it at the left end.

Plates numbered 1 and 2 are both Die I. Plates 3 and 4 are Die II.

II. GEORGIAN KEY TYPE

Die I

Die II

Die I

A. The second (thick) line below the name of the country is cut slanting, conforming roughly to the shape of the Crown on each side.

B. The labels of solid colour bearing the words "POSTAGE" and "& REVENUE" are square at the inner top corners.

C. There is a projecting "bud" on the outer spiral of the ornament in each of the lower corners.

Die II

A. The second line is cut vertically on each side of the Crown.

B. The labels curve inwards at the top.

C. There is no "bud" in this position.

Unless otherwise stated in the lists, all stamps with wmk. Multiple Crown CA are Die I while those with wmk. Multiple Script CA are Die II.

Sterling into U.S. Dollars with this easy-to-use Conversion Table

The £1 sterling is here converted at the rate of $2.80 with the U.S. equivalents rounded off upwards so as to avoid half cents, etc. When ordering, the sterling prices should be added up and the total converted at the current rate of exchange. Before making payment please see " How to remit " on page vii.

12 pence=1 shilling. 20 shillings=£1 (pound).

Sterling	*U.S.*	*Sterling*	*U.S.*	*Sterling*	*U.S.*	*Sterling*	*U.S.*
0 1	2	5 9	81	47 6	$6.65	£32	$90
0 2	3	6 0	84	50 0	7.00	£35	98
0 3	4	6 3	88	52 6	7.35	£38	106
0 4	5	6 6	91	55 0	7.70	£40	112
0 5	6	6 9	95	57 6	8.05	£45	126
0 6	7	7 0	98	60 0	8.40	£48	135
0 7	8	7 3	$1.02	62 6	8.75	£50	140
0 8	9	7 6	1.05	65 0	9.10	£55	155
0 9	10	7 9	1.09	67 6	9.45	£60	170
0 10	11	8 0	1.12	70 0	9.80	£65	182
0 11	12	8 6	1.19	75 0	10.50	£70	196
1 0	14	8 9	1.23	80 0	11.20	£75	210
1 1	15	9 0	1.26	85 0	11.90	£80	225
1 2	16	9 6	1.33	90 0	12.60	£85	240
1 3	18	10 0	1.40	95 0	13.30	£90	255
1 4	19	10 6	1.47	£5	14.00	£95	265
1 5	20	11 0	1.54	105 0	14.70	£100	280
1 6	21	11 6	1.61	110 0	15.40	£105	295
1 7	22	12 0	1.68	115 0	16.10	£110	310
1 8	24	12 6	1.75	£6	16.80	£120	335
1 9	25	13 0	1.82	125 0	17.50	£125	350
1 10	26	13 3	1.86	130 0	18.20	£130	365
1 11	27	13 6	1.89	£7	19.60	£140	395
2 0	28	14 0	1.96	150 0	21.00	£150	420
2 1	30	14 6	2.03	£8	22.40	£160	450
2 2	31	15 0	2.10	170 0	23.80	£170	475
2 3	32	15 6	2.17	175 0	24.50	£175	490
2 4	33	16 0	2.24	£9	25.20	£180	505
2 5	34	16 6	2.31	190 0	26.60	£190	535
2 6	35	17 0	2.38	£10	28.00	£200	560
2 7	37	17 6	2.45	£11	30.80	£210	590
2 8	38	18 0	2.52	£12	33.60	£220	615
2 9	39	18 6	2.60	£13	36.40	£225	630
2 10	40	19 0	2.66	£14	39.20	£240	670
2 11	41	19 6	2.73	£15	42.00	£250	700
3 0	42	20 0	2.80	£16	45.00	£275	770
3 2	45	20 6	2.87	£17	48.00	£300	840
3 3	46	21 0	2.94	£18	51.00	£350	980
3 4	47	22 0	3.08	£19	54.00	£400	1,120
3 6	49	22 6	3.15	£20	56.00	£450	1,260
3 9	53	24 0	3.36	£21	59.00	£500	1,400
4 0	56	25 0	3.50	£22	62.00	£550	1,540
4 2	59	27 6	3.85	£23	65.00	£600	1,680
4 3	60	30 0	4.20	£24	68.00	£650	1,820
4 6	63	32 6	4.60	£25	70.00	£700	1,960
4 9	67	35 0	4.90	£26	73.00	£750	2,100
5 0	70	37 6	5.25	£27	76.00	£800	2,240
5 3	74	40 0	5.60	£28	78.00	£850	2,380
5 4	75	42 6	5.95	£29	82.00	£900	2,520
5 6	77	45 0	6.30	£30	84.00	£1,000	2,800

CANADIAN CONVERSION TABLE OVERLEAF

CANADA

Sterling into Canadian Dollars with this easy-to-use Conversion Table

The £1 sterling is here converted at the rate of $3 with the Canadian equivalents rounded off upwards so as to avoid half cents, etc. When ordering, the sterling prices should be added up and the total converted at the current rate of exchange. Before making payment please see " How to remit " on page vii.

12 pence=1 shilling. 20 shillings=£1 (pound).

Sterling	*Canada*	*Sterling*	*Canada*	*Sterling*	*Canada*	*Sterling*	*Canada*
0 1	2	5 9	87	47 6	$7.15	£32	$96
0 2	3	6 0	90	50 0	7.50	£35	105
0 3	4	6 3	94	52 6	7.90	£38	114
0 4	5	6 6	98	55 0	8.25	£40	120
0 5	7	6 9	$1.02	57 6	8.65	£45	135
0 6	8	7 0	1.05	60 0	9.00	£48	144
0 7	9	7 3	1.09	62 6	9.40	£50	150
0 8	10	7 6	1.13	65 0	9.75	£55	165
0 9	12	7 9	1.17	67 6	10.15	£60	180
0 10	13	8 0	1.20	70 0	10.50	£65	195
0 11	14	8 6	1.28	75 0	11.25	£70	210
1 0	15	8 9	1.32	80 0	12.00	£75	225
1 1	17	9 0	1.35	85 0	12.75	£80	240
1 2	18	9 6	1.45	90 0	13.50	£85	255
1 3	19	10 0	1.50	95 0	14.25	£90	270
1 4	20	10 6	1.60	£5	15.00	£95	285
1 5	22	11 0	1.65	105 0	15.75	£100	300
1 6	23	11 6	1.75	110 0	16.50	£105	315
1 7	24	12 0	1.80	115 0	17.25	£110	330
1 8	25	12 6	1.90	£6	18.00	£120	360
1 9	27	13 0	1.95	125 0	18.75	£125	375
1 10	28	13 3	2.00	130 0	19.50	£130	390
1 11	29	13 6	2.05	£7	20.00	£140	420
2 0	30	14 0	2.10	150 0	22.50	£150	450
2 1	32	14 6	2.20	£8	24.00	£160	480
2 2	33	15 0	2.25	170 0	25.50	£170	510
2 3	34	15 6	2.35	175 0	26.25	£175	525
2 4	35	16 0	2.40	£9	27.00	£180	540
2 5	37	16 6	2.50	190 0	28.50	£190	570
2 6	38	17 0	2.55	£10	30.00	£200	600
2 7	39	17 6	2.65	£11	33.00	£210	630
2 8	40	18 0	2.70	£12	36.00	£220	660
2 9	42	18 6	2.80	£13	39.00	£225	675
2 10	43	19 0	2.85	£14	42.00	£240	720
2 11	44	19 6	2.95	£15	45.00	£250	750
3 0	45	20 0	3.00	£16	48.00	£275	825
3 2	48	20 6	3.10	£17	51.00	£300	900
3 3	49	21 0	3.15	£18	54.00	£350	1,050
3 4	50	22 0	3.30	£19	57.00	£400	1,200
3 6	53	22 6	3.40	£20	60.00	£450	1,350
3 9	57	24 0	3.60	£21	63.00	£500	1,500
4 0	60	25 0	3.75	£22	66.00	£550	1,650
4 2	63	27 6	4.15	£23	69.00	£600	1,800
4 3	64	30 0	4.50	£24	72.00	£650	1,950
4 6	68	32 6	4.90	£25	75.00	£700	2,100
4 9	72	35 0	5.25	£26	78.00	£750	2,250
5 0	75	37 6	5.65	£27	81.00	£800	2,400
5 3	79	40 0	6.00	£28	84.00	£850	2,550
5 4	80	42 6	6.40	£29	87.00	£900	2,700
5 6	83	45 0	6.75	£30	90.00	£1,000	3,000

AMERICAN CONVERSION TABLE OVERLEAF

WATERMARKS

w. 1

w. 2

The watermarks in the stamps printed by Messrs. Perkins Bacon and Co. for various British possessions were (w. **1**) *Large Star*, measuring from 15 to 16 mm. across the star from point to point, and about 27 mm. from centre to centre vertically; (w. **2**) *Small Star* of similar design, but measuring from 12 to 13½ mm. from point to point, and 24 mm. from centre to centre vertically; and (w. **3**) Broad Star, in which the points are broader. The Large Star paper was made for long stamps like Ceylon and St. Helena, the Small Star paper for ordinary size stamps, as Grenada, Barbados, etc.; consequently, when the former was used for the smaller stamps, the watermark only occasionally comes in the centre of the paper, and frequently is so misplaced as to show portions of two stars above and below (this eccentricity will very often determine the watermark when it would be difficult otherwise to test it). The watermarks in the stamps printed by Messrs. De La Rue and Co. for various British possessions—not exclusively used for one colony—are (w. **4**) a Crown over " CC " (Crown Colonies) for the stamps of ordinary size, (w. **5**) for the stamps of larger size and (w. **6**) a Crown over " CA " (Crown Agents). There is another (w. **7**) properly described as " CA over Crown ". This watermark was specially made for paper on which it was intended to print long fiscal stamps of the size and shape of those (which have been used postally) in Sierra Leone, Western Australia, etc. It occupies twice the space of the ordinary Crown CA watermark. When stamps of normal size are printed on paper with this watermark, the watermark is *sideways*, and it takes a horizontal pair of postage stamps to show the entire watermark.

w. 3

w. 4

w. 5

w. 6

w. 7

w. 8

w. 9

In 1904 a new watermark (w. **8**), described as " Multiple Crown CA ", was introduced. On stamps of the ordinary size portions of 2 or 3 watermarks appear, and on the large-sized stamps a greater number can be observed.

In 1921 yet another change was made, resulting in what is known as the " Multiple Script CA " watermark, in which the letters are in Script character, while the Crown is of distinctly different shape (Type w. **9**).

w. 9*a*

w. 9*b*

WATERMARKS—Continued

As a result of a crown falling away from two of the dandy rolls (the rolls which impress the watermark in the paper pulp) and their subsequent replacement by crowns of a different type known as St. Edward's crown, four varieties of the Script CA watermark recur among the 1950–52 printings of several colonies. On one dandy roll the mishap occurred in a " Crown " row as shown in Types w. **9***a* and w. **9***b* and the resulting faulty paper was used for Seychelles, Johore and the postage due stamps of nine colonies. On the other dandy roll the error was in a " Crown CA " row and produced varieties in Bahamas, St. Kitts-Nevis and Singapore.

w. **12**

w. **13**

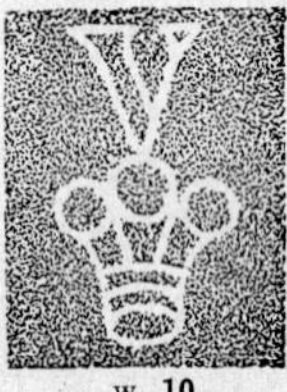

w. **10**

w. **11**

The " Multiple St. Edward's Crown CA " watermark (Type w. **12**) was introduced for Colonial issues in 1957. Besides the change in the Crown the " CA " reverted to the block capitals.

Type w. **13**, " Multiple PTM ", was introduced for new Malayan issues in November, 1961.

We also illustrate here two watermarks which are found in the stamps of the Australian states, to avoid frequent repetition of them in the text.

Kindly Note. Watermarks are normally shown as seen from the FRONT of the stamp.

Where no watermark is noted, the stamps are without distinctive watermark.

We do not normally list inverted or reversed watermarks as separate varieties in this Catalogue but such varieties in the Commonwealth stamps of the present reign are listed in the more specialised *Elizabethan Catalogue* and, of course, in the *Great Britain Specialised Catalogue.*

PERFORATIONS

Stamps not described as " imperf." or " perf." are to be taken as imperforate.

Imperf. Errors of normally perforated stamps are usually listed only in pairs, but not always (e.g. Great Britain).

Perforations are normally given to the nearest half and the *Instanta* Gauge is our standard. Where perfs. are exactly on the Quarter or Threequarter measurement, the Catalogue quotes the higher figures, i.e. $11\frac{3}{4} \times 12\frac{1}{4} = 12 \times 12\frac{1}{2}$.

The various perforations are therefore expressed as follows:—

Perf. 14: Perforated alike on all sides.

Perf. 14 × 15: Compound perforation. The first figure refers to top and bottom, the second to left and right sides.

Perf. 14, 14½: Perforated approximately 14¼.

Perf. 14–15: Perforations are irregular in the sheet, and stamps may measure anything between 14 and 15.

Perf. compound of 14 *and* 15: This is a general description indicating that two gauges of perforation have been used, but not *necessarily* on opposite sides of the stamp. It could be one side in one gauge and three in the other; or two adjacent sides with the same gauge. Where more precise detail is required we give the perforations starting with that at the top and proceeding clockwise: i.e. 14 × 14 × 15 × 14 indicates perf. 15 at bottom and perf. 14 on the other three sides.

Perf. 11 *and* 14 *mixed*: This indicates stamps that were perforated in one gauge, and re-perforated in another.

☛ PLEASE NOTE THAT . . . .

(i) Stamps not listed in this Catalogue (unless they are new issues) are almost certainly not adhesive postage stamps but Revenue, Local or other issues outside its scope.

(ii) We regret we cannot undertake the identification or numbering of stamps.

(iii) We do not give opinions as to the genuineness of stamps.

NOTES

Colonial "Chalky" and Coloured Papers

"Ordinary" and "Chalk-surfaced" Papers.—In Great Britain and its Colonies the availability of many postage stamps for revenue purposes made it necessary to provide some safeguard against the illegitimate re-use of stamps with removable cancellations. This was at first secured by the use, where necessary, of fugitive inks and later by the introduction of chalk-surfaced paper, both of which made it difficult to remove any form of obliteration without also damaging the stamp design.

With some exceptions we *do not list* the varieties on chalk-surfaced paper separately, but we have indicated the existence of the papers by the letters "O" (ordinary) and "C" (*chalky*) after the description of all stamps where the chalky paper may be found. The two letters together, signify that the stamp exists on both papers; if a date is given it is that of the first-mentioned paper and the price quoted is that of the cheaper variety. Where no indication is given, the paper is "ordinary".

Our definition of chalk-surfaced paper applies to a coated paper which shows a black line when touched with silver. The paper used during the Second World War for high values, as in Bermuda, the Leeward Is., etc., was thinly coated with some kind of surfacing which does not react to silver and is therefore regarded (and listed) as "ordinary".

Another paper introduced during the war as a substitute for "chalky" is rather thick, very white, and glossy, and shows little or no watermark, nor does it show a black line when touched with silver. In the Bahamas high values this paper might be mistaken for the "chalky" (which is thinner and poorer-looking) but for the silver test.

British Colonial Green and Yellow Papers.—The issue of stamps printed on paper with coloured surface and white back (commonly called "white-backs") necessitated a special method of indicating their existence in the Catalogue lists. Owing to further variations in the Colonial green and yellow papers the lists are now extended, as many of these stamps show one colour on the surface of the paper and another at the back. While there are many variations which will not fall within any hard-and-fast classification, we have adopted the following grouping as being the least likely to cause confusion.

YELLOW PAPER

(*a*) The original *yellow* paper, usually bright in colour.
(*b*) The "*white backs*".
(*c*) A bright *lemon* paper. Only stamps with the greenish tinge of true lemons have been put in this group, otherwise they belong to Group (*a*). Stamps of Group (*a*) printed in green sometimes make the paper appear *lemon*, and allowance must be made for this.
(*d*) An *orange-buff* paper, with a distinct brownish (coffee) tinge, not to be confused with a muddy yellow belonging to Group (*a*).
(*e*) The *pale yellow* paper, which has a creamy tone.

GREEN PAPER

(*m*) The original *green* paper, varying considerably through shades of bluish and yellowish green.
(*n*) The "*white backs*".
(*p*) A paper bluish green on the surface, with "*pale*" or "*olive*" *back*.
(*q*) Paper with a bright green surface, commonly called "*emerald-surfaced*", with the olive back of Group (*p*).
(*r*) The paper with "*emerald back*". As (*q*), but with the bright colour at back and front.

ABBREVIATIONS USED IN THIS PART

Anniv. .	denotes	Anniversary.
B.W. & Co.	,,	Bradbury, Wilkinson & Co.
C, c. . .	,,	Chalky paper
c. . . .	,,	Cancelled to order.
Des. . .	,,	Designer; designed.
Diag. . .	,,	Diagonal; diagonally.
D. L. R. & Co.	,,	De La Rue & Co.
Eng. . .	,,	Engraver; engraved.
F.C. . .	,,	Fiscally cancelled.
Horiz. . .	,,	Horizontal; horizontally.
Imp., Imperf.	,,	Imperforate (not Perforated).
Inscr. . .	,,	Inscribed.
L. . . .	,,	Left.
Litho. . .	,,	Lithographed.
mm. . .	,,	Millimetres.
O, o. . .	,,	Ordinary paper.
Opt(d) . .	,,	Overprint (ed).
P.-c. or Pen-c.	,,	Pen-cancelled.
P., Perf. or Pf.	,,	Perforated.
Pr. . . .	,,	Pair.
Percé en arc	,,	Perforated in curves.
Percé en scie	,,	Perforated with a saw-edge.
Photo. . .	,,	Photogravure.
Pin-Perf. .	,,	Perforated without removing any paper.
Ptd. . .	,,	Printed.
R. . . .	,,	Right.
Recess. . .	,,	Recess-printed.
Roul. . .	,,	Rouletted—a broken line of cuts.
S. . . .	,,	SPECIMEN (overprint).
Surch. . .	,,	Surcharged.
T. . . .	,,	Type.
Typo. . .	,,	Typographed.
Un. . . .	,,	Unused.
Us. . . .	,,	Used.
Vert. . .	,,	Vertical; vertically.
W. or Wmk.	,,	Watermark.
W'low & Sons.	,,	Waterlow & Sons.
Wmk. s. .	,,	Watermark sideways.

/between colours means "on" and the colour following is that of the paper on which the stamp is printed.

PRICES. †(or * in lists of controls) = does not exist.

—(or a blank in the price column) means exists, but price cannot be quoted.

Prices for stamps with "SPECIMEN" overprints are expressed thus: (S. £5). Where more than one type of overprint exists the price is for the cheapest.

COLOURS. The following and similar abbreviations are in general use throughout the Catalogue where exigencies of space necessitate them: Bl. (blue); blk. (black); bwn., brn. (brown); car., carm. (carmine); choc. (chocolate); clar. (claret); emer. (emerald); grn. (green); ind. (indigo); mag. (magenta); mar. (maroon); mve. (mauve); ol. (olive); orge., or. (orange); pk. (pink); pur. (purple); scar. (scarlet); sep. (sepia); turq. (turquoise); ultram. (ultramarine); verm. (vermilion); vio. (violet); yell. (yellow).

In the case of stamps printed in two or more colours, the central portion of the design is in the first colour given, unless otherwise stated.

Where stamps are printed from "head" and "duty" plates, the colour of the portions printed from the "duty" plate (e.g. the name of the country and the value, or tablet of value) is usually given second.

COLOURS OF OVERPRINTS AND SURCHARGES. All overprints and surcharges are in black unless otherwise stated, either in the heading or by abbreviations in brackets after the description of the stamp, thus (B.) = blue, (Br.) = brown, (C.) = carmine, (G.) = green, (Mag.) = magenta, (Mve.) = mauve, (O.) = orange, (Ol.) = olive, (P.) = purple, (Pk.) = pink, (R.) = red, (Sil.) = silver, (V.) = violet, (Vm.) or (Verm.) = vermilion; (W.) = white, (Y.) = yellow.

SIMPLIFICATION TABLES

We realise that the lists of the early issues of some countries which have been written by specialists for specialists, are possibly somewhat too complicated for the average collector and tend to turn him against stamps which are really very interesting.

We have introduced at the beginning of each of the more complicated lists a table headed "**SIMPLIFICATION**" which gives the catalogue numbers of the stamps of the earlier issues which the non-specialist collector is likely to need. The general basis is as follows, but common sense has been taken as a guide rather than any rigid rule and each country has been dealt with on its merits.

Plates and dies. Where differences in plate or die make a clearly appreciable difference in the appearance of the stamp, they are included.

Colours. Where shades are included these are usually so pronounced that they may be regarded as a real difference in colour, clearly apparent to the untrained eye.

Watermarks. All major differences of watermarks are included.

Perforations. Stamps imperf. and perf. are regarded as separate varieties. Varieties in gauge or perforation are not usually included, though there are exceptions where there is a great difference in the general *appearance* of the perforation.

Errors and Varieties are not included.

The tables are shown as groups of catalogue numbers, main groups or issues being separated by full stops, while the end of a sub-group is indicated by a colon.

HOW TO USE THE TABLES

The catalogue numbers are not placed in catalogue order, but in the order in which we suggest that a straightforward collection might be arranged. **They thus provide a guide to arrangement as well as to simplification.**

Generally speaking, the numbers selected represent the cheapest variety (shade, perf. etc.), but sometimes the stamp which, though not the lowest priced, is likely to be the easiest to obtain. Only one number is given, even though there may be several at the same price. The collector must select his own alternatives.

We particularly urge collectors not to use these tables as a rigid guide but only as a basis on which to superimpose their own individual ideas. The Simplification Table represents the " middle line ". The collector who likes perfs. or shades or errors should amplify the tables for himself, while the " simple lifer " will no doubt cut out many of the shades and other items which we have included.

The whole art of collecting is to please yourself. The catalogue lists and the table are only guides, each useful in its way, but should not be slavishly followed if full enjoyment is to be gained from the hobby.

CATALOGUE NUMBERS ALTERED IN THIS EDITION

We give below a list of catalogue numbers which have been altered in this edition as a result of revision of the lists, together with the numbers now allotted to them.

Old	New
GREAT BRITAIN	
N12/13	N13/14
S2/3	S3/4
W2/3	W3/4
BAHAMAS	
103a	103b
103b	103a
BASUTOLAND	
D8a	D8b
D8b	D8a
BRITISH GUIANA	
501/12	O1/12
BRITISH HONDURAS	
34	35b
36	35c
BURMA (Jap Occ.)	
J79a	J79b
J79b	J79a
CEYLON	
O9/15	O1/7
O16	O11
O17/18	O8/9
O21	O10
O22/7	O12/17
GAMBIA	
11a	11b
29b	28a
INDIAN STATES	
Bhopal	
83/7	84/8
88/100	89/98 A or B
101/2	99/100
319c	319b
321a	321b
326a	326b
326b	326a
327a	327b
331*c*	331*d*
332a/b	332b/c
332c	332a
335*a*	335*b*
336*b*	336c
336c	336d
Bundi	
18/42*a*	*Rewritten*
49/56	79/92
O1/45	*Rewritten*
O46/51	O53/9
Cochin	
7aa	*7ab*
O104a	O104b
O104ab	O104ba
Hyderabad	
35a	35b
36a	36b
36*b*	36*c*
40a	40b
42a	42c
Soruth	
35*b*	36
35c	36c
36	35b
MALAYA	
Johore	
3a	3b
Perak	
75a	76
Japanese Occ.	
J241a	J248a
JD8/21	JD13/26
JD23/4	JD27/8
JD26/38	JD29/41
JKP1/5	TK1/5
JK1/10	JK17/25
JK11/13	JK13/15
JK14/15	JK1/2
JK15*a*	JK3
JK16/20	JK4/8
JK20*a*	JK9
JK21/3	JK10/12
MALTA	
24*a*	25
25/8	26/9
29	27a
MAURITIUS	
2a/25*a*	*Rewritten*
MONTSERRAT	
159/61	157/9
NAURU	
56*a*	57
57/60	58/61
60*a*	62
61	63
61*a*	64
NIGERIA	
15*a*	25*a*
16a	25*b*
17a	25*c*
19	20
19a	29*b*
20	21
20a	25*e*
21/2	22/3
23a	29*d*
24	25
24a	29*e*
25/6	26/7
27	29*a*
27a	28
28	19
28a	25*d*
NORTH BORNEO	
253b	253d
253d	253dd
253e	253b
253f	253*e*
RHODESIA	
S. Rhod.	Rhod.
106/8	351/3
ST. VINCENT	
216/21	215/20
224/33	221/30
SARAWAK	
17	18
18/27	22/31
28	17
29/31	19/21
207	206
209/10	207/8
212/3	210/1
SEYCHELLES	
192	175*a*
SOUTH AUSTRALIA	
4/7	3/6
VICTORIA	
193aa	193bb
199*b*	199*a*

LIST OF CATALOGUE NUMBERS OF STAMPS

ADDED TO THIS EDITION BUT NOT LISTED IN *G.S.M.* SUPPLEMENTS

Great Britain. 653a, 661*a*, 667a, 667pa, 679a, z1152*a*, z1568*a*.

Australia. 327a, 346a, 358a, 359a, 372a/b, 379a.

Br. Guiana. 90b.

Br. Honduras. 204a.

Br. Levant. 47a.

Burma (Jap. Occ.). J72b, J82*c*, J83*c*, J84*c*.

Canada. 27*b*, 28*a*, O38a, O45a, O46a.

Cape of Good Hope (Mafeking). 18a.

Cook Is. 87*a*/*d*.

Dominica. 55b.

Fiji. 97*a*.

Gambia. 11a.

India. 467a.
—**Bhopal.** 81a, 83, 99a, 301b/c, 302a, 307a, 313ca, 320a, 321a, 321ba, 321c, 321ca, 324c, 325a/d, 326ba, 327a, 327ba, 327c, 327ca, 327cb, 327cc, 331b/c, 331e/g, 332ca, 335a, 336b, 337a/c, 340a/c, 352c.
—**Bundi.** 11*a*, 17*a*, O1/52 rewritten.
—**Charkhari.** 51*a*.
—**Cochin.** 116a, 121a, 123a, O16a, O50a, O104a.
—**Hyderabad.** 13cc, 18a, 25b, 27a, 27*b*, 34b, 35a, 36a, 40a, 42a/b, 54a, 57ab, 58a, 60a, O22c, O30b, O31a, O33b, O35*a*, O40b/c, O43b, O44b, O46b, O47b, O48a, O49a.
—**Indore.** 30a, S4a.
—**Jaipur.** O3c.
—**Kishargarh.** 19a.
—**Soruth.** 36a/b, 39c, 41d, 60c, 61a.

Jamaica. 226a.

Malaya.
—**Johore.** 3a, 3ba, 4a.
—**Malayan P.U.** D15ba.
—**Perak.** 15*a*, 24a.
—**Straits Settlements.** 91a.
—**Sungei Ujong.** 31*a*, 42a.
—**Jap. Occ.** J32c, J35a, J38b, J42c, J45c, J58c, J59c, J67a, J72a, J79b, J87b, J92b, J93b, J95a, J98b, J101b, J104b, J111a, J136a, J203*b*/*v*, J204a, J270*a*/*g*, JD8/12, JD8a/12a, JK16.

Malta. 300a, 341a, 345a.

Nauru. 20a.

Newfoundland. 198a, 263aB.

New Guinea.—15b.

New South Wales. 33d.

New Zealand. 376*a*, 810a, 818a. 837a.
—**King Edward VII Land.** A1*b*.
—**Aitutaki.** 10*b*, 10c.

Nigeria. 139a.

North Borneo. 242*a*, 253da, 253db, 253dc, 253f/k, 272a, 274ab.

Northern Rhodesia. 67a.

Pakistan. O82a.

Palestine. D4b.

Rhodesia. 217*a*, 236*a*, 254*a*, 279*d*, 303*a*, 366a.

St. Lucia. D2b.

Sarawak. 21*a*/*c*.

Sierra Leone. 330a, 333a.

Singapore. 65a, 69a, 71a.

Somaliland Prot. 104a.

South Africa. 246a.

South Australia. 7.

S. Rhodesia. 93a, 99a.

Tanganyika. 118a.

Tasmania. 10a, 139a.

Togo. 31a.

Turks and Caicos Is. 264a.

Victoria. 38b, 193*b*, 429*a*.

INTERNATIONAL PHILATELIC GLOSSARY

Including the 100 colour names shown in the Stanley Gibbons Colour Guide

English	*French*	*German*	*Spanish*	*Italian*
Agate	Agate	Achat	Ágata	Agata
Air stamp	Timbre de la poste aérienne	Flugpostmarke	Sello de correo aéreo	Francobollo per posta aerea
Apple-green	Vert-pomme	Apfelgrün	Verde manzana	Verde mela
Barred	Annulé par barres	Balkenentwertung	Anulado con barras	Sbarrato
Bisected	Timbre coupé	Halbiert	Partido en dos	Frazionato
Bistre	Bistre	Bister	Bistre	Bistro
Bistre-brown	Brun-bistre	Bisterbraun	Castaño bistre	Bruno-bistro
Black	Noir	Schwarz	Negro	Nero
Blackish Brown	Brun-noir	Schwärzlichbraun	Castaño negruzco	Bruno nerastro
Blackish Green	Vert foncé	Schwärzlichgrün	Verde negruzco	Verde nerastro
Blackish Olive	Olive foncé	Schwärzlicholiv	Oliva negruzco	Oliva nerastro
Block of four	Bloc de quatre	Viererblock	Bloque de cuatro	Bloco di quattro
Blue	Bleu	Blau	Azul	Azzurro
Blue-green	Vert-bleu	Blaugrün	Verde azul	Verde azzurro
Bluish Violet	Violet bleuâtre	Bläulichviolett	Violeta azulado	Violetto azzurrastro
Booklet	Carnet	Heft	Cuardernillo	Libretto
Bright Blue	Bleu vif	Lebhaftblau	Azul vivo	Azzurro vivo
Bright Green	Vert vif	Lebhaftgrün	Verde vivo	Verde vivo
Bright Purple	Mauve vif	Lebhaftpurpur	Púrpura vivo	Porpora vivo
Bronze-green	Vert-bronze	Bronzegrün	Verde bronce	Verde bronzo
Brown	Brun	Braun	Castaño	Bruno
Brown-lake	Carmin-brun	Braunlack	Laca castaño	Lacca bruno
Brown-purple	Pourpre-brun	Braunpurpur	Púrpura castaño	Porpora bruno
Brown-red	Rouge-brun	Braunrot	Rojo castaño	Rosso bruno
Buff	Chamois	Sämisch	Anteado	Camoscio
Cancellation	Oblitération	Entwertung	Cancelación	Annullamento
Cancelled	Annulé, oblitéré	Gestempelt	Cancelado	Annullato
Carmine	Carmin	Karmin	Carmín	Carminio
Carmine-red	Rouge-carmin	Karminrot	Rojo carmín	Rosso carminio
Centred	Centré	Zentriert	Centrado	Centrato
Cerise	Rouge-cerise	Kirschrot	Color de ceresa	Color Ciliegia
Chalk-surfaced paper	Papier couché	Kreidepapier	Papel estucado	Carta gessata
Chalky Blue	Bleu terne	Kreideblau	Azul turbio	Azzurro smorto
Charity stamp	Timbre de bienfaisance	Wohltätigkeitsmarke	Sello de beneficenza	Francobollo di beneficenza
Chestnut	Marron	Kastanienbraun	Castaño rojo	Marrone
Chocolate	Chocolat	Schokoladen	Chocolate	Cioccolato
Cinnamon	Cannelle	Zimtbraun	Canela	Cannella
Claret	Grenat	Weinrot	Rojo vinoso	Vinaccia
Cobalt	Cobalt	Kobalt	Cobalto	Cobalto
Colour	Couleur	Farbe	Color	Colore
Comb-perforation	Dentelure en peigne	Kammzähnung, Reihenzähnung	Dentado de peine	Dentellatura a pettine
Commemorative stamp	Timbre commémoratif	Gedenkmarke	Sello conmemorativo	Francobollo commemorativo
Crimson	Cramoisi	Karmesin	Carmesí	Cremisi

Deep Blue	Bleu foncé	Dunkelblau	Azul oscuro	Azzurro scuro
Deep Bluish Green	Vert-bleu foncé	Dunkelbläulichgrün	Verde azulado oscuro	Verde azzurro scuro
Design	Dessin	Markenbild	Diseño	Disegno
Die	Matrice	Urstempel, Type, Platte	Cuño	Conio, Matrice
Double	Double	Doppelt	Doble	Doppio
Drab	Olive terne	Trüboliv	Oliva turbio	Oliva smorto
Dull Green	Vert terne	Trübgrün	Verde turbio	Verde smorto
Dull Purple	Mauve terne	Trübpurpur	Púrpura turbio	Porpora smorto
Embossing	Impression en relief	Prägedruck	Impresión en relieve	Impressione a rilievo
Emerald	Vert-eméraude	Smaragdgrün	Esmeralda	Smeraldo
Engraved	Gravé	Graviert	Grabado	Inciso
Error	Erreur	Fehler, Fehldruck	Error	Errore
Essay	Essai	Probedruck	Ensayo	Saggio
Express letter stamp	Timbre pour lettres par exprès	Eilmarke	Sello de urgencia	Francobollo per espresso
Fiscal-postal	Timbre fiscal-postal	Stempelmarke als Postmarke verwendet	Sello fiscal-postal	Fiscale postale
Fiscal stamp	Timbre fiscal	Stempelmarke	Sello fiscal	Francobollo fiscale
Flesh	Chair	Fleischfarben	Carne	Carnicino
Forgery	Faux, Falsification	Fälschung	Falsificación	Falso, falsificazione
Frame	Cadre	Rahmen	Marco	Cornice
Granite paper	Papier avec fragments de fils de soie	Faserpapier	Papel con filamentos	Carta con fili di seta
Green	Vert	Grün	Verde	Verde
Greenish Blue	Bleu verdâtre	Grünlichblau	Azul verdoso	Azzurro verdastro
Greenish Yellow	Jaune-vert	Grünlichgelb	Amarillo verdoso	Giallo verdastro
Grey	Gris	Grau	Gris	Grigio
Grey-blue	Bleu-gris	Graublau	Azul gris	Azzurro grigio
Grey-green	Vert-gris	Graugrün	Verde gris	Verde grigio
Gum	Gomme	Gummi	Goma	Gomma
Gutter	Interpanneau	Zwischensteg	Espacio blanco entre dos grupos	Ponte
Imperforate	Non-dentelé	Geschnitten	Sin dentar	Non dentellato
Indigo	Indigo	Indigo	Axul índigo	Indaco
Inscription	Inscription	Inschrift	Inscripción	Dicitura
Inverted	Renversé	Kopfstehend	Invertido	Capovolto
Issue	Émission	Ausgabe	Emisión	Emissione
Laid	Vergé	Gestreift	Listado	Vergato
Lake	Lie de vin	Lackfarbe	Laca	Lacca
Lake-brown	Brun-carmin	Lackbraun	Castaño laca	Bruno lacca
Lavender	Bleu-lavande	Lavendel	Color de alhucema	Lavanda
Lemon	Jaune-citron	Zitrongelb	Limón	Limone
Light Blue	Bleu clair	Hellblau	Azul claro	Azzurro chiaro
Lilac	Lilas	Lila	Lila	Lilla
Line perforation	Dentelure en lignes	Linienzähnung	Dentado en linea	Dentellatura lineare
Lithography	Lithographie	Steindruck	Litografía	Litografia
Local	Timbre de poste locale	Lokalpostmarke	Emisión local	Emissione locale
Lozenge roulette	Percé en losanges	Rautenförmiger Durchstich	Picadura en rombos	Perforazione a losanghe
Magenta	Magenta	Magentarot	Magenta	Magenta
Margin	Marge	Rand	Borde	Margine
Maroon	Marron pourpré	Dunkelrotpurpur	Púrpura rojo oscuro	Marrone rossastro

English	French	German	Spanish	Italian
Mauve	Mauve	Malvenfarbe	Malva	Malva
Multicoloured	Polychrome	Mehrfarbig	Multicolores	Policromo
Myrtle-green	Vert myrte	Myrtengrün	Verde mirto	Verde mirto
New Blue*	Bleu ciel vif	Neublau	Azul nuevo	Azzurro nuovo
Newspaper stamp	Timbre pour journaux	Zeitungsmarke	Sello para periódicos	Francobollo per giornali
Obliteration	Oblitération	Abstempelung	Matasellado	Annullamento
Obsolete	Hors (de) cours	Ausser Kurs	Fuera de curso	Fuori corso
Ochre	Ocre	Ocker	Ocre	Ocra
Official stamp	Timbre de service	Dienstmarke	Sello di servicio	Francobollo di servizio
Olive-brown	Brun-olive	Olivbraun	Castaño oliva	Bruno oliva
Olive-green	Vert-olive	Olivgrün	Verde oliva	Verde oliva
Olive-grey	Gris-olive	Olivgrau	Gris oliva	Grigio oliva
Olive-yellow	Jaune-olive	Olivgelb	Amarillo oliva	Giallo oliva
Orange	Orange	Orange	Naranja	Arancio
Orange-brown	Brun-orange	Orangebraun	Castaño naranja	Bruno arancio
Orange-red	Rouge-orange	Orangerot	Rojo naranja	Rosso arancio
Orange-yellow	Jaune-orange	Orangegelb	Amarillo naranja	Giallo arancio
Overprint	Surcharge	Aufdruck	Sobrecarga	Soprastampa
Pair	Paire	Paar	Pareja	Coppia
Pale	Pâle	Blass	Pálido	Pallido
Pane	Panneau	Gruppe	Grupo	Gruppo
Paper	Papier	Papier	Papel	Carta
Parcel post stamp	Timbre pour colis postaux	Paketmarke	Sello para paquete postale	Francobollo per pacchi postali
Pen-cancelled	Oblitéré à plume	Federzugentwertung	Cancelado a pluma	Annullato a penna
Percé en arc	Percé en arc	Bogenförmiger Durchstich	Picadura en forma de arco	Perforazione ad arco
Percé en scie	Percé en scie	Bogenförmiger Durchstich	Picado en sierra	Foratura a sega
Perforated	Dentelé	Gezähnt	Dentado	Dentellato
Perforation	Dentelure	Zähnung	Dentar	Dentellatura
Photogravure	Photogravure, Heliogravure	Rastertiefdruck	Fotograbado	Rotocalco
Pin perforation	Percé en points	In Punkten durchstochen	Horadado con alfileres	Perforato a punti
Plate	Planche	Platte	Plancha	Lastra
Plum	Prune	Pflaumenfarbe	Color de ciruela	Prugna
Postage Due stamp	Timbre-taxe	Portomarke	Sello de tasa	Segnatasse
Postage	Timbre-poste	Briefmarke, Freimarke, Postmarke	Sello de correos	Francobollo postale
Postmark	Oblitération postale	Poststempel	Matasello	Bollo
Printing	Impression	Druck	Impresión	Stampa
Proof	Épreuve	Druckprobe	Prueba de impresión	Prova
Provisionals	Timbres provisoires	Provisorische Marken Provisorien	Provisionales	Provvisori
Prussian Blue	Bleu de Prusse	Preussischblau	Azul de Prusia	Azzurro di Prussia
Purple	Pourpre	Purpur	Púrpura	Porpora
Purple-brown	Brun-pourpre	Purpurbraun	Castaño púrpura	Bruno porpora
Recess-printing	Impression en taille douce	Tiefdruck	Grabado	Incisione
Red	Rouge	Rot	Rojo	Rosso
Red-brown	Brun-rouge	Rotbraun	Castaño rojizo	Bruno rosso
Reddish Lilac	Lilas rougeâtre	Rötlichlila	Lila rojizo	Lilla rossastro
Reddish Purple	Pourpre-rouge	Rötlichpurpur	Púrpura rojizo	Porpora rossastro
Reddish Violet	Violet rougeâtre	Rötlichviolett	Violeta rojizo	Violetto rossastro
Red-orange	Orange rougeâtre	Rotorange	Naranja rojizo	Arancio rosso

Registration stamp	Timbre pour lettre chargée (recommandée)	Einschreibemarke	Sello de certificado	Francobollo per lettere raccomandate
Reprint	Réimpression	Neudruck	Reimpresión	Ristampa
Reversed	Retourné	Umgekehrt	Invertido	Rovesciato
Rose	Rose	Rosa	Rosa	Rosa
Rose-red	Rouge rosé	Rosarot	Rojo rosado	Rosso rosa
Rosine	Rose vif	Lebhaftrosa	Rosa vivo	Rosa vivo
Roulette	Perçage	Durchstich	Picadura	Foratura
Rouletted	Percé	Durchstochen	Picado	Forato
Royal Blue	Bleu-roi	Königblau	Azul real	Azzurro reale
Sage-green	Vert-sauge	Salbeigrün	Verde salvia	Verde salvia
Salmon	Saumon	Lachs	Salmón	Salmone
Scarlet	Ecarlate	Scharlach	Escarlata	Scarlatto
Sepia	Sépia	Sepia	Sepia	Seppia
Serpentine roulette	Percé en serpentin	Schlangenlieniger Durchstich	Picado a serpentina	Perforazione a serpentina
Shade	Nuance	Tönung	Tono	Gradazione di colore
Sheet	Feuille	Bogen	Hoja	Foglio
Slate	Ardoise	Schiefer	Pizarra	Ardesia
Slate-blue	Bleu-ardoise	Schieferblau	Azul pizarra	Azzuro ardesia
Slate-green	Vert-ardoise	Schiefergrün	Verde pizarra	Verde ardesia
Slate-lilac	Lilas-gris	Schieferlila	Lila pizarra	Lilla ardesia
Slate-purple	Mauve-gris	Schieferpurpur	Púrpura pizzara	Porpora ardesia
Slate-violet	Violet-gris	Schieferviolett	Violeta pizarra	Violetto ardesia
Special delivery stamp	Timbres pour exprès	Eilmarke	Sello de urgencia	Francobollo per espressi
Specimen	Spécimen	Muster	Muestra	Saggio
Steel Blue	Bleu acier	Stahlblau	Azul acero	Azzurro acciaio
Strip	Bande	Streifen	Tira	Striscia
Surcharge	Surcharge	Aufdruck	Sobrecarga	Soprastampa
Tête-Bêche	Tête-bêche	Kehrdruck	Tête-bêche	Tête-bêche
Tinted paper	Papier teinté	Getöntes papier	Papel coloreado	Carta tinto
Too-late stamp	Timbre pour lettres en retard	Verspätungsmarke	Sello para cartas retardadas	Francobollo per le lettere in ritarde
Turquoise-blue	Bleu-turquoise	Turkisblau	Azul turquesa	Azzurro turchese
Turquoise-green	Vert-turquoise	Turkisgrün	Verde turquesa	Verde turchese
Typography	Typographie	Buchdruck	Tipografia	Tipografia
Ultramarine	Outremer	Ultramarin	Ultramar	Oltremare
Unused	Neuf	Ungebraucht	Nuevo	Nuovo
Used	Oblitéré, usé	Gebraucht	Usado	Usato
Venetian Red	Rouge-brun terne	Venezianischrot	Rojo veneciano	Rosso veneziano
Vermilion	Vermillon	Zinnober	Cinabrio	Vermiglione
Violet	Violet	Violett	Violeta	Violetto
Violet-blue	Bleu-violet	Violettblau	Azul violeta	Azzurro violetto
Watermark	Filigrane	Wasserzeichen	Filigrana	Filigrana
Watermark sideways	Filigrane couché	Wasserzeichen liegend	Filigrana acostado	Filigrana coricata
Wove paper	Papier ordinaire, Papier uni	Einfaches papier	Papel avitelado	Carta unita
Yellow	Jaune	Gelb	Amarillo	Giallo
Yellow-brown	Brun-jaune	Gelbbraun	Castaño amarillo	Bruno giallo
Yellow-green	Vert-jaune	Gelbgrün	Verde amarillo	Verde giallo
Yellow-olive	Olive jaunâtre	Gelboliv	Oliva amarillo	Oliva giallastro
Yellow-orange	Orange jaunâtre	Gelborange	Naranja amarillo	Arancio giallastro
Zig-zag roulette	Percé en zigzag	Sägezahnartiger Durchstich	Picado en zigzig	Perforazione a zigzag

** "New Blue" is a colour name introduced in the Stanley Gibbons Colour Guide to describe a colour used in the modern issues of Germany, Poland, Switzerland, etc.*

THE S. G. CATALOGUES

The STANLEY GIBBONS' CATALOGUE

This Catalogue is published in three parts as follows:—

PART		*U.K. Price* s. d.	*Post & pack.* U.K. Abroad
I.	BRITISH COMMONWEALTH OF NATIONS (1967 edition)	35 0	3 0 2 7
II.	FOREIGN—EUROPE AND COLONIES (1967 edition). Due for issue, September 1966	Prices on application	
III.	FOREIGN—REST OF THE WORLD (1967 edition). Due for issue, September 1966	Prices on application	

'ELIZABETHAN' CATALOGUE

Comprehensive listing of all the Commonwealth stamps of the current reign. Full of revutionary new features, including hundreds of new varieties, new shades, modern typography and large pages (6⅞" × 9"), withdrawal and invalidation dates, tabulated printings and plate numbers, alphabetical arrangement, basic Catalogue Nos. as in Part One, **with prices in dollars as well as sterling.** 336 pages; 1,000 varieties; 3,000 illustrations; 5,500 stamps listed.

1966 edition. *Price* **15/-.** *Post U.K.* 1/7, abd. 2/1.

GREAT BRITAIN SPECIALISED CATALOGUE

VOL. I QUEEN VICTORIA

The first edition of this section is now out of print. **A fully revised second edition is expected to be published early in 1967.**

VOL. II KING EDWARD VII — KING GEORGE VI

The first edition of this section, covering the stamps of King Edward VII, King George V, King Edward VIII and King George VI is in active preparation. **Due for publication Autumn 1966—please write for details.**

STANLEY GIBBONS' "SIMPLIFIED" CATALOGUE

This catalogue, which does not differentiate between watermarks and perfs., is the only whole world single volume catalogue now published in Britain. Published annually. Write for details of the 1967 edition (due for issue, November, 1966).

All Catalogue prices *are postage extra*, and we emphasise that the prices quoted above are the *British* net retail prices at which the books are available at stamp dealers, booksellers, stationers and stores throughout Great Britain. These prices, or their equivalent in local currency, are not necessarily those at which the catalogues are available overseas, but in no case must any Stanley Gibbons catalogues be sold at less than the British prices, or their equivalents.

CATALOGUE SUPPLEMENTS

together with informative and helpful articles, stamp news from all over the world, and many attractive stamp offers, appear each month in

GIBBONS STAMP MONTHLY

which can be sent by post overseas for 15s. 6d. per annum, post free. Price 1s. per month from your local newsagent or stamp dealer.

NOTE. The first Supplement containing new issues not in this Catalogue or the Addenda appeared in the July, 1966 number of *Gibbons Stamp Monthly*.

GREAT BRITAIN.

GENERAL NOTES.—LINE-ENGRAVED ISSUES.

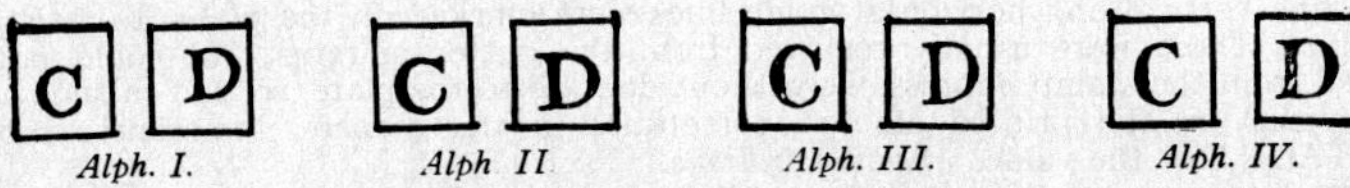

Alph. I. *Alph II* *Alph. III.* *Alph. IV.*

Typical Corner Letters of the four Alphabets.

Alphabets. Four different letterings were used for the corner letters on stamps prior to the issue with letters in all four corners, these being known to collectors as:—

Alphabet I. Used for all plates made from 1840 to the end of 1851. Letters small.

Alphabet II. Plates from 1852 to mid-1855. Letters larger, heavier and broader.

Alphabet III. Plates from mid-1855 to end of period. Letters tall and more slender.

Alphabet IV. 1861. 1d. Die II, Plates 50 and 51 only. Letters were hand-engraved instead of being punched on the plate. They are therefore inconsistent in shape and size but generally larger and outstanding.

While the general descriptions and the illustrations of typical letters given above may be of some assistance, only long experience can enable every stamp to be allotted to its particular Alphabet without hesitation, as certain letters in each are similar to those in one of the others.

Blued Paper. The blueing of the paper of the earlier issues is believed to be due to the presence of prussiate of potash in the printing ink, or in the paper, which, under certain conditions, tended to colour the paper when the sheets were damped for printing.

Corner Letters. The corner letters on the early British stamps were intended as a safeguard against forgery, each stamp in the sheet having a different combination of letters. Taking the first 1d. stamp, printed in 20 horizontal rows of 12, as an example, we have lettering as follows—

Row 1. A A, A B, A C, etc. to A L.
Row 2. B A, B B, B C, etc. to B L.
and so on to
Row 20. T A, T B, T C, etc. to T L.

On the stamps with four corner letters, those in the upper corners are in the reverse positions to those in the lower corners. Thus in a sheet of 240 (12×20) we have:—

Row 1.	A A B A C A A A A B A C	etc.	to	L A A L
Row 2.	A B B B C B B A B B B C	etc.	to	L B B L
	and so on to			
Row 20.	A T B T C T T A T B T C	etc.	to	L T T L

Dies. (*See illustrations on page* 5.) The first Die of the 1d. was used for making the original Die of the 2d. which was used for both the No Lines and White Lines issues. In 1855 the 1d. Die I was amended by retouching the head and deepening the lines on a transferred impression of the original. This later version, known to collectors as Die II, was used for making the dies for the 1d. and 2d. with letters in all four corners and also for the 1½d.

Double letter.

Guide line in corner.

Guide line through value.

NOTE.—*The above illustrations and that illustrating a re-entry, below, show typical examples of the varieties described, but there are numerous stamps showing double letters, guide lines or re-entries of differing importance, intensity and value.*

Double Corner Letters. These are due to the workman placing his letter punch in the wrong position at the first attempt, when lettering the plate, and then correcting the mistake, or to a slight shifting of the punch when struck. If a wrong letter was struck in the first instance, traces of a wrong letter may appear in a corner in addition to the correct one.

Guide Lines and Dots. When laying down the impressions of the design on the early plates, fine vertical and horizontal guide lines were marked on the plates to assist the operative. These were usually removed from the gutter margins, but could not be removed from the stamp impressions without damage to the plate, so that in such cases they appear on the printed stamps, sometimes in the corners, sometimes through " POSTAGE " or the value. (*See illustrations.*)

Guide dots or cuts were similarly made to indicate the spacing of the guide lines. These too sometimes appear on the stamps.

Inverted " S ". The corner letter " S " is inverted on the 1d. red-brown (and shades) as follows :—

Die I (Imperf.)
Plates 78, 105, 107 : S A to S L
Plate 140 : S A and S B
Plate 142 : S B
Plate 143 : S A

Die II (Perf. 16 and 14, Small and Large Crown, Blue paper)
Plate 5 : S D to S L

Ivory head.

" Ivory Head." The so-called " ivory head " variety (*see illustration*) in which the Queen's Head shows white on the back of the stamp is due to the comparative absence of ink in the head portion of the design, with consequent absence of blueing. (*See* " Blued Paper " note above.)

Plates. Until the introduction of the stamps with letters in all four corners, the number of the plate was not indicated in the design of the stamp, but was printed on the sheet margin. By long study of identifiable blocks and of the minor variations in the design, coupled with the position of the corner letters, philatelists are now able to allot many of these stamps to their respective plates.

Maltese Cross.

Type of Town postmark.

Type of 1844 postmark.

Postmarks. The so-called " Maltese Cross " design was the first employed for obliterating British postage stamps and was in use from 1840 to 1844. Being hand-cut, the obliterating stamps varied greatly in detail and some distinctive types can be allotted to particular towns or offices. Local types, such as those used at Manchester,

Norwich, Leeds, etc., are keenly sought for. A red ink was first employed, but was superseded by black, after some earlier experiments, in February, 1841. Maltese Cross obliterations in other colours are rare.

Obliterations of this type, numbered 1 to 12 in the centre, were used at the London Chief Office in 1843 and 1844.

In 1844 the Maltese Cross design was superseded by numbered obliterators of various types, one of which is illustrated above. This is naturally comparatively scarce on the first 1d. and 2d. stamps. Like the Maltese Cross it is found in various colours, some of which are rare.

Re-cut " R ". On several plates the letter " R " is formed from the letter " P ", the tail having been hand cut. It occurs on the Penny Plate 10 in black and in red and also on Plates 30, 31, 32, 33 ; 58, 83, 86 and 87.

Re-entry.

" Union Jack " re-entry.

Re-entries. Re-entries on the plate show as a doubling of part of the design of the stamp generally at top or bottom. Many re-entries are very slight while others are most marked. (*See illustration.*)

The " *Union Jack* " *re-entry*, so called owing to the effect of the re-entry on the appearance of the corner stars (*see illustration*) occurs on stamp L K of Plate 75 of the 1d. red, Die I.

T A (T L) M A (M L)

Varieties to the Large Crown Watermark.

I II

Two states of the Large Crown Watermark.

Watermarks. Two watermark varieties, consisting of crowns of entirely different shape, are found in sheets of the Large Crown paper and fall on stamps lettered M A and T A (or M L and T L when the paper is printed on the wrong side). Both varieties are found on the 1d. rose-red of 1857, while the M A (M L) variety comes also on some plates of the 1d. of 1864 (Nos. 43, 44) up to about Plate 96. On the 2d. the T A (T L) variety is known on plates 8 and 9, and the M A (M L) on later prints of plate 9. These varieties may exist inverted, or inverted reversed on stamps lettered A A and A L and H A and H L, and some are known. (*See illustrations.*)

In 1861 a minor alteration was made in the Large Crown watermark by the removal of the two small vertical strokes, representing *fleurs-de-lis*, which projected upwards from the uppermost of the three horizontal curves at the base of the Crown. (*See illustration.*)

QUEEN VICTORIA, 1837–1901.

MULREADY ENVELOPES AND COVERS, which were issued concurrently with the first British adhesive postage stamps, can be supplied as follows:

1d. black.

Envelopes: 75*s. unused*; 70*s. used.*
Covers: 65*s. unused*; 50*s. used.*

2d. blue.

Envelopes: 95*s. unused*; £22 *used.*
Covers: 95*s. unused*; £20 *used.*

1.—LINE-ENGRAVED STAMPS

1

2. Small Crown.

Engraved by Mr. Frederick Heath and printed by Messrs. Perkins Bacon & Co.)

1840 (6 May). *Letters in lower corners. Wmk. Small Crown, T* **2**. *Imperf.*

No.	*Type.*		*Un.* *s. d.*	*Used.* *s. d.*
1	**1**	1d. intense black	£40	85 0
2	,,	1d. black	£35	75 0
3	,,	1d. grey-black (worn plate)	£45	95 0
4	,,	2d. deep full blue	£120	£20
5	,,	2d. blue	£120	£16
6	,,	2d. pale blue	£160	£25

The 1d. stamp in black was printed from Plates 1 to 11. Plate 1 was printed from in two states (known to collectors as 1*a* and 1*b*), the latter being the result of extensive repairs.

Repairs were also made to plates 2, 5, 6, 8, 9, 10 and 11, and certain impressions exist in a second and third state. See *Stanley Gibbons Specialised Cat., Vol. I.*

Plates. 1d. black.

Plate.	*Un.* *s. d.*	*Used.* *s. d.*	*Plate.*	*Un.* *s. d.*	*Used.* *s. d.*
1*a*.	£45	£7	6.	£36	75 0
1*b*.	£40	85 0	7.	£35	85 0
2.	£40	80 0	8.	£42	80 0
3.	£45	95 0	9.	£55	£5
4.	£40	80 0	10.	£60	£10
5.	£45	80 0	11.	£75	£40

Varieties. 1d. black.

		Un.	*Used.*
a.	*On bleuté paper*	—	£8
b.	*Double letter in corner*	£45	£8
bb.	*Re-entry*	£48	£7
bc.	"PB" *re-entry* (*Plate* 5, *3rd state*) ..	—	£500
cc.	*Large letters in each corner* (I L *and* J C) (*Plate* 1*b*)	£90	£22
c.	*Guide line in corner*	£40	80 0
d.	,, ,, *through value*	£50	£7
e.	*Wmk. inverted*	£80	£15
f.	*Reconstructed plate of* 240 *stamps* ..	—	£850
g.	*Oblit. red Maltese Cross*		75 0
h.	,, *black* ,, ...		75 0
i.	,, *blue* ,, ...		£70
k.	,, *magenta* ,, ...		£50
m.	,, *yellow* ,, ...		£200
n.	*Number* (1 *to* 12) *in Maltese Cross* .. *from*		£110
o.	*Town oblit. in black on stamp* ..		£20
p.	*Town oblit. in yellow* ,, ..		£50
q.	*Town oblit. in red* ,, ..		£35
r.	*Penny Post oblit. in black* ,, ..		£20
s.	*Oblit. of* 1844 *in black* ,, ..		£20

The so-called "Royal reprint" of the 1d. black was made in 1864, from Plate 66, Die II, on paper with Large Crown watermark, inverted. A printing was also made in carmine, on paper with the same watermark, normal.

For 1d. black with "VR" in upper corners see No. V1 following the Postage Dues.

The 2d. stamps were printed from Plates 1 and 2.

Plates.	2d. blue.	*Un.*	*Used.*
Plate 1	*Shades from*	£120	£16
Plate 2	*Shades from*	£140	£20

Varieties. 2d. blue.

		Un.	*Used.*
a.	*Double letter in corner*	—	£25
aa.	*Re-entry*	—	£30
b.	*Guide line in corner*	—	£20
c.	,, ,, *through value*	—	£26
d.	*Wmk. inverted*	—	£40

Varieties. 2d. blue (*contd.*)

		Used.
e.	*Oblit. red Maltese Cross*	£16
f.	,, *black* ,, ...	£16
g.	,, *blue* ,, ...	£75
h.	,, *magenta* ,, ...	£65
i.	,, *number* (1 *to* 12) *in Maltese Cross* *from*	£80
k.	*Town oblit. in black on stamp*	£45
l.	*Oblit. of* 1844 *in black* ,, ...	£40
m	,, ,, ,, *blue* ,, ...	£100
n.	*Penny Post oblit. in black* ,, ...	£55

1841 (10 Feb.). *Wmk. T* **2**. *Paper more or less blued. Imperf.*

8	**1**	1d. red-brown	60 0	4 0
8*a*	,,	1d. red-brown on very blue paper	£5	6 0
9	,,	1d. pale red-brown (worn plate)	£6	10 0
10	,,	1d. deep red-brown ..	65 0	10 0
11	,,	1d. lake-red	£8	40 0
12	,,	1d. orange-brown ..	£12	70 0

Old No. 7 (deep orange-brown on *white* paper) has been deleted, as all copies are believed to have been manipulated by later removal of the original blueing.

Error. No letter "A" *in right lower corner.* (*Stamp* B (A), *Plate* 77).

12*a*	**1**	1d. red-brown	—	£700

Early printings of 1d. red-brown, etc. *from* "*Black plates*" (*see* Notes *on page* 5).

Plate.	*Un.* *s. d.*	*Used.* *s. d.*	*Plate.*	*Un.* *s. d.*	*Used.* *s. d.*
1*b*.	£60	110 0	9.	£16	17 6
2.	£60	90 0	10.	£15	30 0
5.	£20	30 0	11.	£16	17 6
8.	£20	20 0			

Varieties. 1d. red-brown, etc.

		Un.	*Used.*
aa.	*Re-entry*	—	35 0
ab.	"PB" *re-entry* (*Plate* 5, *3rd state*) ..	—	£50
b.	*Double letter in corner*	—	35 0
ba.	*Double Star* (*Plate* 75) "*Union Jack*" *re-entry* (*see page* 3) ..	—	£35
c.	*Guide line in corner*	—	8 6
d.	,, ,, *through value*	—	45 0
e.	*Thick outer frame to stamp*	—	17 6
f.	*Ivory head*	—	15 0
g.	*Wmk. inverted*	£20	30 0
ga.	*Left corner letter* "S" *inverted* ..	—	85 0
gb.	P *converted to* R	—	55 0
h.	*Oblit. red Maltese Cross*		£45
i.	,, *black* ,, ,, ...		6 0
k.	,, *blue* ,, ,, ...		80 0
m.	*Oblit. No.* 1 *in Maltese Cross*		15 0
	,, ,, 2 ,, ,, ,, ...		12 6
	,, ,, 3 ,, ,, ,, ...		18 6
	,, ,, 4 ,, ,, ,, ...		50 0
	,, ,, 5 ,, ,, ,, ...		15 0
	,, ,, 6 ,, ,, ,, ...		12 6
	,, ,, 7 ,, ,, ,, ...		12 6
	,, ,, 8 ,, ,, ,, ...		12 6
	,, ,, 9 ,, ,, ,, ...		12 6
	,, ,, 10 ,, ,, ,, ...		15 0
	,, ,, 11 ,, ,, ,, ...		20 0
	,, ,, 12 ,, ,, ,, ...		40 0
n.	*Oblit.* "*Penny Post*" *on stamp* ..		£5
o.	*Town oblit. in black* ,, ,, ..		£6
p.	,, ,, *blue* ,, ,, ..		£20
q.	,, ,, *green* ,, ,, ..		£35
r.	,, ,, *yellow* ,, ,, ..		£225
ra.	,, ,, *red* ,, ,, ..		£200
s.	*Oblit. of* 1844 *in blue* ,, ,, ..		25 0
t.	,, ,, ,, *red* ,, ,, ..		£45
u.	,, ,, ,, *green* ,, ,, ..		80 0
v.	,, ,, ,, *violet* ,, ,, ..		£25
w.	,, ,, ,, *black* ,, ,, ..		4 0

NOTES. Early printings of the 1d. in red were made from some of the plates previously used for the 1d. black. They were plates 1b, 2, 5, 8, 9, 10 and 11 and, in this connection, are known to collectors as the " black plates ".

The error " No letter A in right corner " was due to the omission to insert this letter on stamp B A of Plate 77. The error was discovered some months after the plate was registered and was then corrected.

Stamps with thick outer frame to the design are from plates on which the frame-lines have been strengthened or recut, particularly Plates 76 and 90.

There are innumerable variations in the colour and shade of the 1d. " red " and those given in the above list represent colour groups each covering a wide range.

For " Union Jack " re-entry, " Inverted S ", etc., see General Notes above.

3. White lines added.

1841 (13 March). *White lines added. Wmk. T 2. Paper more or less blued. Imperf.*

			Un.	Used.
13	**3**	2d. pale blue	£35	40 0
14	„	2d. blue	£35	20 0
15	„	2d. deep full blue	£35	40 0
15*aa*	„	2d. violet-blue	£85	£25

The 2d. stamp with white lines was printed from Plates 3 and 4.

Plates.	2d. blue.	*Un.*	*Used.*
Plate 3.	*Shades from*	£35	20 0
„ 4.	*Shades from*	£40	25 0

Varieties. 2d. blue.

		Un.	Used.
a.	*Guide line in corner*	—	30 0
b.	„ „ *through value*	—	35 0
bb.	*Double letter in corner*	—	70 0
bc.	*Re-entry*	—	£7
c.	*Ivory head*	£40	35 0
d.	*Wmk. inverted*	£65	£15
e.	*Oblit. red Maltese Cross*		
f.	„ *black* „ „		40 0
g.	„ *blue* „ „		£20
i.	„ *No.* 1 *in Maltese Cross*		£5
	„ „ 2 „ „ „		95 0
	„ „ 3 „ „ „		£5
	„ „ 4 „ „ „		80 0

		Used.
i.	*Oblit. No.* 5 *in Maltese Cross*	£6
	„ „ 6 „ „ „	£5
	„ „ 7 „ „ „	£5
	„ „ 8 „ „ „	£6
	„ „ 9 „ „ „	£9
	„ „ 10 „ „ „	£18
	„ „ 11 „ „ „	£16
	„ „ 12 „ „ „	65 0
k.	*Oblit. of* 1844 *in black on stamp* ..	20 0
l.	„ „ „ *blue* „	£6
m.	„ „ „ *red* „	£65
n.	„ „ „ *green* „	£40
p.	*Town oblit. in black* „	£12
q.	„ „ „ *blue* „	£25

1841 (April). *Trial printing (unissued) on Dickinson silk-thread paper. Imperf.*

16 **1** 1d. red-brown (Plate 11) £95

Eight sheets were printed on this paper, six being gummed, two ungummed.

1848. *Rouletted* 12 *by Henry Archer.*

16*a* **1** 1d. red-brown (Plates 70, 71) £150

1850. *P* 16, *by Henry Archer.*

16*b* **1** 1d. red-brown (Alph. I) (from Plates 71, 79, 90–101 and 105. Also Pl. 8, unused only) £30 £9

Stamp on cover, dated prior to Feb. 1854 (*price* £28); dated Feb. and after 1854 (*price* £18).

1853. *Government Trial Perforations.*

16*c* **1** 1d. red-brown (*perf.* 16) (Alph. II) (*on cover*) .. .. † £350

16*d* „ 1d. „ (*perf.* 14) (Alph. I) £150

NOTES. Although the various trials of machines for rouletting and perforating were unofficial, Archer had the consent of the authorities in making his experiments, and sheets so experimented upon were afterwards put in use by the Post Office.

As Archer ended his experiments in 1850 and plates with corner letters of Alphabet II did not come into issue until 1852, perforated stamps with corner letters of Alphabet I may safely be assumed to be Archer productions, if genuine.

The Government trial perforations were done on Napier machines in 1853. As Alphabet II was by that time in use, the trials can only be distinguished from the perforated stamps listed below by being dated prior to January 28th, 1854, the date when the perforated stamps were officially issued.

Die I.

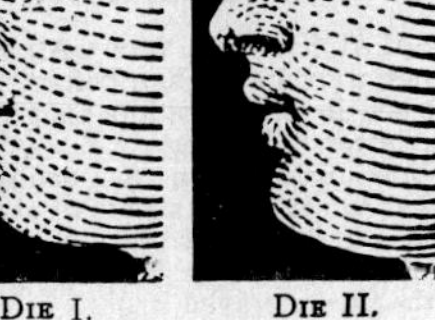

Die II.

Die I is the original die, used from 1840 to 1855. The features of the portrait are lightly shaded and consequently lack emphasis.

Die II is Die I retouched by Mr. William Humphrys in which the lines of the features have been deepened and appear stronger.

The eye is deeply shaded and made more lifelike. The nostril and lips are more clearly defined, the latter appearing much thicker. A strong downward stroke of colour marks the corner of the mouth. There is a deep indentation of colour between lower lip and chin. The band running from the back of the ear to the chignon has a bolder horizontal line below it than in Die I.

4. Large Crown.

1854–57. *Paper more or less blued.* (i.) *Wmk. Small Crown, T* **2.** *P* 16.

No.	Type	Description	Unused	Used
17	1	1d. red-brown (Die I) (February, 1854)	70 0	4 0
18	,,	1d. yellowish brown (Die I)	90 0	8 6
19	3	2d. deep blue (Plate 4) (13 March, 1854)	£35	17 6
20	,,	2d. pale blue (Plate 4)	£40	50 0
20a	,,	2d. blue (Plate 5) (28 August, 1855)	£110	£12
21	1	1d. red-brown (Die II) (5 March, 1855)	£5	20 0
		a. Imperf.	—	£100

(ii.) *Wmk. Small Crown, T* **2.** *P* 14.

No.	Type	Description	Unused	Used
22	1	1d. red-brown (Die I) (January, 1855)	£20	25 0
23	3	2d. blue (Plate 4) (4 March, 1855)	£60	30 0
23a	,,	2d. blue (Plate 5) (5 July, 1855)	£65	45 0
		b. Imperf. (Plate 5)		
24	1	1d. red-brown (Die II) (28 February, 1855)	90 0	17 6
24a	,,	1d. deep red-brown (very blue paper) (Die II)	£6	25 0
25	,,	1d. orange-brown (Die II)	£40	£5

(iii.) *Wmk. Large Crown, T* **4.** *P* 16.

No.	Type	Description	Unused	Used
26	1	1d. red-brown (Die II) (15 May, 1855)	£32	50 0
27	3	2d. blue (Plate 5) (20 July, 1855)	£140	£12
		a. Imperf.		

(iv.) *Wmk. Large Crown, T* **4.** *P* 14.

No.	Type	Description	Unused	Used
29	1	1d. red-brown (Die II) (18 August, 1855)	40 0	1 9
		a. Imperf. (*shades*)	£35	£50
30	,,	1d. brick-red (Die II)	50 0	12 6
31	,,	1d. plum (Die II) (February, 1857)	£12	40 0
32	,,	1d. brown-rose (Die II)	65 0	17 6
33	,,	1d. orange-brown (Die II) (March, 1857)	£20	50 0
34	3	2d. blue (Plate 5) (20 July, 1855)	£18	15 0
35	,,	2d. blue (Plate 6) (2 July, 1857)	£19	17 6

1856–58. *Paper no longer blued.* (i). *Wmk. Large Crown, T* **4.** *P* 16.

No.	Type	Description	Unused	Used
36	1	1d. rose-red (Die II) (29 December, 1857)	£20	14 0
36a	3	2d. blue (Plate 6) (1 February 1858)	£120	65 0

(ii.) (Die II) *Wmk. Large Crown, T* **4.** *P* 14.

No.	Type	Description	Unused	Used
37	1	1d. red-brown (November, 1856)	£5	20 0
38	,,	1d. pale red (9 April, 1857)	80 0	7 6
		a. Imperf.	£30	
39	,,	1d. pale rose (March, 1857)	50 0	3 6
40	,,	1d. rose-red (July, 1857)	15 0	0 4
		a. Imperf.	£35	£40
		b. Reserve plates 15 or 16 (Alphabet II)	*from* 80 0	7 6
41	,,	1d. deep rose-red (August, 1857)	15 0	0 8

1861. *Letters engraved on plate instead of punched* (Alphabet IV).

No.	Type	Description	Unused	Used
42	1	1d. rose-red (Die II) (Plates 50 and 51)	80 0	7 6
		a. Imperf.	—	£125

NOTES. 1d. The numbering of the 1d. plates recommenced at 1 on the introduction of Die II. Corner letters of Alphabet III appear on Plate 22 and onwards.

As an experiment, the corner letters were engraved by hand on Plates 50 and 51 in 1856, instead of being punched (Alphabet IV), but punching was again resorted to on Plate 52 and onwards. Plates 50 and 51 were not put into use until 1861.

2d. Plates 3 and 4 of the 2d. had corner letters of Alphabet I, Plate 5 Alphabet II and Plate 6 Alphabet III. In Plate 6 the white lines are thinner than before.

In both values varieties may be found as described in the preceding issues—ivory heads, inverted watermarks, re-entries, and double letters in corners.

The change of perforation from 16 to 14 was decided upon late in 1854 owing to the fact that the closer holes of the former gauge tended to cause the sheets of stamps to break up when handled, but for a time both gauges were in concurrent use. Owing to faulty alignment of the impressions on the plates and to shrinkage of the paper when damped badly perforated stamps are plentiful in the line-engraved issues.

5

6

Plate 191.

Showing position of the plate number on the 1d. *and* 2d. *values.*

1858–64. *Letters in all four corners. Wmk. Large Crown, T* **4.** *Die* II (*1d. and 2d.*). *P* 14.

43	5	1d. rose-red (1 April, 1864)	..	4 6		0 6
44	„	1d. lake-red	..	4 6		0 6

Plate No.	*Un. s. d.*	*Used. s. d.*	*Plate No.*	*Un. s. d.*	*Used. s. d.*	*Plate No.*	*Un. s. d.*	*Used. s. d.*	*Plate No.*	*Un. s. d.*	*Used. s. d.*
71.	7 6	0 6	110.	7 6	0 6	150.	5 0	0 6	188.	10 0	0 6
72.	7 6	0 6	111.	7 6	0 6	151.	12 6	1 0	189.	15 0	2 0
73.	8 6	0 6	112.	25 0	0 8	152.	6 0	0 6	190.	4 6	0 6
74.	10 0	0 8	113.	8 6	0 6	153.	30 0	8 0	191.	4 6	0 6
76.	10 0	0 6	114.	20 0	1 0	154.	7 6	0 6	192.	4 6	0 6
77.	£3000	£2000	115.	35 0	1 6	155.	8 0	1 6	193.	4 6	0 6
78.	6 0	0 6	116.	12 6	0 6	156.	6 6	0 6	194.	6 0	0 6
79.	4 6	0 6	117.	7 6	0 6	157.	6 0	0 6	195.	7 6	0 6
80.	8 6	0 6	118.	7 6	0 6	158.	5 0	0 6	196.	4 6	0 6
81.	27 6	0 6	119.	7 6	0 6	159.	6 0	0 6	197.	10 0	0 6
82.	30 0	3 0	120.	5 0	0 6	160.	4 6	0 6	198.	5 0	0 6
83.	£10	8 6	121.	6 0	0 6	161.	25 0	4 6	199.	5 0	0 6
84.	6 0	0 6	122.	5 0	0 6	162.	7 6	0 6	200.	5 0	0 6
85.	6 6	0 6	123.	5 0	0 6	163.	7 6	0 6	201.	4 6	0 6
86.	20 0	0 6	124.	5 0	0 6	164.	5 0	0 6	202.	5 0	0 8
87.	6 0	0 6	125.	6 0	0 6	165.	5 0	0 6	203.	5 0	0 6
88.	90 0	7 6	127.	6 0	0 6	166.	6 6	0 6	204.	6 0	0 6
89.	6 0	0 6	129.	5 0	0 6	167.	4 6	0 6	205.	6 6	0 6
90.	15 0	0 6	130.	6 0	0 6	168.	6 0	0 6	206.	6 0	0 6
91.	7 6	0 6	131.	8 6	0 6	169.	12 6	2 6	207.	5 0	0 6
92.	8 0	0 6	132.	£6	20 0	170.	5 0	0 6	208.	8 0	0 6
93.	7 6	0 6	133.	90 0	8 6	171.	4 6	0 6	209.	10 0	0 6
94.	12 6	0 6	134.	5 0	0 8	172.	5 0	0 6	210.	15 0	1 0
95.	10 0	0 6	135.	7 6	0 6	173.	4 6	0 6	211.	22 6	6 0
96.	17 6	0 8	136.	7 6	0 6	174.	4 6	0 6	212.	6 0	1 0
97.	10 0	0 6	137.	7 6	0 8	175.	4 6	0 6	213.	6 0	1 0
98.	10 0	0 6	138.	5 0	0 6	176.	10 0	2 0	214.	7 6	1 0
99.	10 0	0 6	139.	6 0	0 8	177.	4 6	0 6	215.	7 6	1 0
100.	10 0	0 6	140.	4 6	0 6	178.	10 6	2 0	216.	6 0	1 0
101.	12 6	0 6	141.	30 0	2 6	179.	6 0	0 6	217.	8 6	2 6
102.	7 6	0 6	142.	12 6	0 6	180.	12 6	2 0	218.	6 0	2 6
103.	7 6	0 6	143.	12 6	0 6	181.	6 6	0 6	219.	25 0	20 0
104.	17 6	4 6	144.	12 0	0 6	182.	15 0	2 6	220.	6 0	3 6
105.	35 0	5 0	145.	5 0	0 6	183.	5 0	0 6	221.	15 0	7 6
106.	10 0	0 8	146.	5 0	0 6	184.	4 6	0 8	222.	15 0	7 6
107.	25 0	0 6	147.	5 0	0 6	185.	7 6	2 0	223.	27 6	20 0
108.	25 0	1 6	148.	5 0	0 6	186.	15 0	2 0	224.	22 6	20 0
109.	40 0	0 6	149.	8 0	0 6	187.	6 0	0 6	225.	£20	£10

Variety. Imperf. Issued at Cardiff (Plate 116).

44*b* **5** 1d. rose-red (18.1.70) £80 £150

The following plate numbers are also known imperf. and used:—79, 81, 82, 83, 86, 88, 90, 91, 92, 93, 97, 100, 102, 103, 104, 105, 107, 108. 109, 112, 114, 117, 120, 121, 122, 136, 137, 142, 146, 148, 158, 162, 164, 166, 171, 174 and 191. *Prices from £30 each.*

NOTES. The numbering of this series of plates follows after that of the previous 1d. stamp, last printed from Plate 68.

Plates 69, 70, 75, 126 and 128 were prepared for this issue but rejected owing to defects, and stamps from these plates do not exist, so that specimens which appear to be from these plates (like many of those which optimistic collectors believe to be from Plate 77) bear other plate numbers. Owing to faulty engraving or printing it is not always easy to identify the plate number. Plate 77 was also rejected but some stamps printed from it were used. One specimen is in the Tapling Collection and six or seven others are known. Plates 226 to 228 were made but not used.

Specimens from most of the plates are known with inverted watermark. The variety of watermark described in the General Notes occurs on stamp M A (or M L) on plates up to about 96. (*Prices from £15 used.*)

Re-entries in this issue are few, the best being on stamps M K and T K of Plate 71 and on S L and T L, Plate 83.

45	**6**	2d. blue (thick lines) (July, 1858) ..	.. 35 0	2 6
		a. Imperf. (Plate 9) ..	—	£350

Plate No.	Un. s. d.	Used. s. d.	Plate No.	Un. s. d.	Used. s. d.
7.	.. £10	6 6	9.	.. 35 0	2 6
8.	.. £10	5 0	12.	.. £7	25 0

46	**6**	2d. blue (thin lines) (1 July, 1869) ..	.. 35 0	5 0
47	,,	2d. deep blue (thin lines) ..	.. 40 0	6 0
		a. Imperf. (Plate 13) ..	.. £30	

Plate No.	Un. s. d.	Used. s. d.
13.	.. 35 0	5 0
14.	.. 50 0	7 6
15.	.. 45 0	7 6

NOTES. Plate 10 and 11 were prepared but rejected. Plates 13 to 15 were laid down from a new roller impression on which the white lines were thinner.

There are some marked re-entries and repairs, particularly on Plates 7, 8, 9 and 12.

Stamps with inverted watermark may be found and also the T A (T L) and M A (M L) watermark varieties (see General Notes).

Though the paper is normally white, some printings showed blueing and stamps showing the " ivory head " may therefore be found.

7

9

Showing the plate number (20).

1870 (1 Oct.). *Wmk. T* **9**, *extending over three stamps.* *P* 14.

48	**7**	½d. rose-red ..	.. 15 0	4 0
49	,,	½d. rose ..	.. 15 0	4 0

Plate No.	Un. s. d.	Used. s. d.	Plate No.	Un. s. d.	Used. s. d.	Plate No.	Un. s. d.	Used. s. d.	Plate No.	Un. s. d.	Used. s. d.
1.	.. 40 0	25 0	6.	.. 15 0	4 0	11.	.. 15 0	4 0	15.	.. 15 0	5 0
3.	.. 15 0	5 6	8.	.. 95 0	40 0	12.	.. 15 0	4 0	19.	.. 50 0	7 6
4.	.. 15 0	4 6	9.	.. £35	£12	13.	.. 15 0	4 0	20.	.. 25 0	7 6
5.	.. 15 0	4 0	10.	.. 15 0	4 0	14.	.. 15 0	4 0			

The following plate numbers are known imperf. and used: 1, 4, 5, 6, 8 and 14.

NOTES. The ½d. was printed in sheets of 480 (24 × 20) so that the check letters run from AA/AA to XT/TX.

Plates 2, 7, 16, 17, and 18 were not completed while Plates 21 and 22, though made, were not used.

Owing to the method of perforating, the outer side of stamps in either the A or X row (i.e. the left or right side of the sheet) is imperf.

Stamps may be found with watermark inverted or reversed, or without watermark, the latter due to misplacement of the paper when printing.

8

1870 (1 Oct.). *Wmk. T* **4.** *P* 14.

51	**8**	1½d. rose-red ..	.. 70 0	10 0
52	,,	1½d. lake-red ..	.. 70 0	10 0
		a. Imperf. (Plate 1 and 3) ..	..	

Error of lettering. **OP-PC** *for* **CP-PC** (*Plate* 1).

53	**8**	1½d. rose-red ..	.. £225	£45

Plate No.	Un. s. d.	Used. s. d.
(1)	.. 75 0	15 0
3	.. 70 0	10 0

NOTES. Owing to a proposed change in the postal rates, 1½d. stamps were first printed in 1860, in rosy mauve, No. 53*a*, but the change was not approved and the greater part of the stock was destroyed.

In 1870 a 1½d. stamp was required and was issued in rose-red.

Plate 1 did not have the plate number in the design of the stamps, but on stamps from Plate 3 the number will be found in the curved pattern a little above the lower corner letter at each side.

Plate 2 was defective and was not used.

The error of lettering O P-P C on Plate 1 was apparently not noticed by the printers, and therefore not corrected. It was not noticed by collectors until 1894.

1860. *Prepared for use but not issued; blued paper.*

No.	Type	Description	Unused	Used
53*a*	**8**	1½d. rosy mauve (Plate 1)	£45	
		b. Error of lettering, OP-PC for CP-PC		

II.—EMBOSSED STAMPS.

10 11 12

13 Showing position of die number.

(Primary die engraved at the Royal Mint by Mr. William Wyon. Stamps printed at Somerset House.)

1847–54. *Imperf.* (For paper and wmk. see footnote.)

No.	Type	Description	Unused	Used
54	**10**	1s. pale green (11 September, 1847)	£60	£7
55	,,	1s. green	£60	£8
56	,,	1s. deep green	£90	£22
		Die 1. **1847**	£60	£7
		Die 2. **1854**	£60	£7
57	**11**	10d. brown (6 November, 1848)	£60	£18
		Die 1. **1848**	—	£25
		No die number	—	—
		Die 2. **1850**	£55	£18
		Die 3. **1853**	£55	£18
		Die 4. **1854**	£65	£20
58	**12**	6d. mauve (1 March, 1854)	£40	£8
59	,,	6d. dull lilac	£40	£6
60	,,	6d. purple	£60	£7
61	,,	6d. violet	£95	£20

NOTES. The 1s. and 10d. are on "Dickinson" paper with silk threads. The 6d. is on paper watermarked V R in single-lined letters, Type **13**, which may be found in four ways—upright, inverted, upright reversed, and inverted reversed; none is scarce.

The die numbers are indicated on the base of the bust. Only Die 1 (1 WW) of the 6d. was used for the adhesive stamps. The 10d. is from Die 1 (W.W. 1 on stamps), and Dies 2 to 4 (2 W.W., 3 W.W., 4 W.W.) but the number and letters on stamps from Die 1 are seldom clear and many specimens are known without any trace of them. That they are from Die 1 is proved by the existence of blocks showing stamps with and without the die number. The 1s. is from Dies 1 and 2 (W.W.1, W.W.2).

The normal arrangement of the silk threads in the paper was in pairs running down each vertical row of the sheet, the space between the threads of each pair being approximately 5 mm. and between pairs of threads 20 mm. Varieties due to misplacement of the paper in printing show a single thread on the first stamp from the sheet margin and two threads 20 mm. apart on the other stamps of the row. Faulty manufacture is the cause of stamps with a single thread in the middle.

Through bad spacing of the impressions, which were hand-struck, all values may be found with two impressions more or less overlapping. Owing to the small margin allowed for variation of spacing, specimens with good margins on all sides are not common.

Double impressions are known of all values.

Later printings of the 6d. had the gum tinted green to enable the printer to distinguish the gummed side of the paper.

GENERAL NOTES.—SURFACE-PRINTED ISSUES.

" Abnormals ". The majority of the great rarities in the surface-printed group of issues are the so-called " abnormals ", whose existence is due to the practice of printing six sheets from every plate as soon as made, one of which was kept for record purposes at Somerset House, while the others were perforated and usually issued. If such plates were not used for general production or if, before they came into full use, a change of watermark or colour took place, the six sheets originally printed would differ from the main issue in plate, colour or watermark and, if issued, would be extremely rare.

The abnormal stamps of this class listed in this Catalogue and distinguished, where not priced, by a star (*) are:—

3d. Plate 3 (with white dots). 4d. vermilion, Plate 16. 4d. sage-green, Plate 17. 6d. mauve, Plate 10. 6d. pale chestnut, Plate 12. 6d. pale buff, Plate 13. 9d., Plate 3 (hair lines). 9d., Plate 5. 10d., Plate 2. 1s., Plate 3 (Plate No. 2). 1s. green, Plate 14. 2s. blue, Plate 3.

Those which may have been issued, but of which no specimens are known, are 2½d. wmk. Anchor, Plates 4 and 5; 3d. wmk. Emblems, Plate 5; 3d. wmk. Spray, Plate 21; 6d. grey, wmk. Spray, Plate 18; 8d. orange, Plate 2; 1s. wmk. Emblems, Plate 5; 5s. wmk. Maltese Cross, Plate 4.

The 10d. Plate 1, wmk. Emblems, is sometimes reckoned among the abnormals, but was probably an error, due to the use of the wrong paper.

Corner Letters. With the exception of the 4d., 6d. and 1s. of 1855–57, the ½d., 1½d., 2d. and 5d. of 1880, the 1d. lilac of 1881 and the £5 (which had letters in lower corners only, and in the reverse order to the normal), all the surface-printed stamps issued prior to 1887 had letters in all four corners, as in the later line-engraved stamps. The arrangement is the same, the letters running in sequence right across and down the sheets, whether these were divided into panes or not. The corner letters existing naturally depend on the number of stamps in the sheet and their arrangement.

Plate Numbers. All stamps from No. 75 to No. 163 bear in their designs either the plate number or, in one or two earlier instances, some other indication by which one plate can be distinguished from another. With the aid of these and of the corner letters it is thus possible to " reconstruct " a sheet of stamps from any plate of any issue or denomination—a task undertaken by many collectors.

Wing Margins. As the vertical gutters (spaces) between the panes, into which sheets of stamps of most values were divided until the introduction of the Imperial Crown watermark, were perforated through the centre with a single row of holes, instead of each vertical row of stamps on the inner side of the panes having its own line of perforation as is now usual, a proportion of the stamps in each sheet have what is called a " wing margin " about 5 mm. wide on one or other side.

The stamps with " wing margins " are the watermark Emblems and Spray of Rose series (3d. 6d. 9d. 10d. 1s. and 2s.) with letters D, E, H or I in S.E. corner, and the watermark Garter series (4d. and 8d.) with letters F or G in S.E. corner. Knowledge of this lettering will enable collectors to guard against stamps with wing margin cut down and re-perforated, but note that wing margin stamps of Nos. 62 to 73 are also to be found re-perforated.

Perforations. All the surface-printed issues of Queen Victoria are Perf. 14, with the exception of Nos. 126 to 129.

III.—SURFACE-PRINTED STAMPS.

(Printed by Messrs. De La Rue & Co., until 1911.)

14

15. Small.

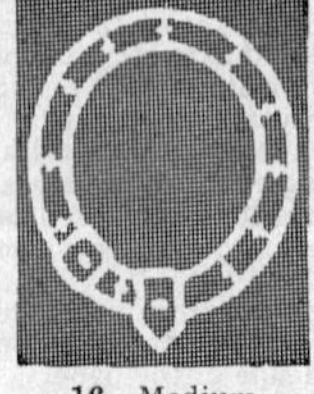

16. Medium.

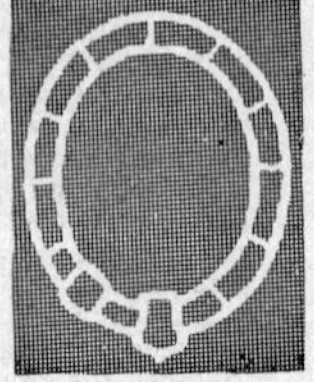

17. Large.

1855-57

I. *Wmk. SMALL Garter*, T **15.** *Highly glazed, deeply blued paper* (31 July 1855).

62	**14**	4d. carmine (*shades*)	£60	90 0
		a. Paper slightly blued	£70	90 0
		b. White paper	£250	£28

II. *Wmk. MEDIUM Garter*, *T* **16**.
(*a*) *Thick, blued highly glazed paper* (25 Feb. 1856).

No.	Type	Description	Unused	Used
63	**14**	4d. carmine (*shades*)	£75	£12
		a. White paper		

(*b*) *Ordinary thin white paper* (Sept. 1856).

No.	Type	Description	Unused	Used
64	**14**	4d. pale carmine	£55	70 0

(*c*) *Ordinary white paper, specially prepared ink* (1 Nov. 1856).

No.	Type	Description	Unused	Used
65	**14**	4d. rose *or* deep rose	£55	70 0

III. *Wmk. LARGE Garter*, *T* **17**. *Ordinary white paper* (Jan. 1857).

No.	Type	Description	Unused	Used
66	**14**	4d. rose-carmine	£36	30 0
		a. Rose	£30	27 6
		b. Thick glazed paper	£50	80 0

18 **19** **20** **20***a*. Error.

Wmk. Emblems, *T* **20**.

No.	Type	Description	Unused	Used
69	**18**	6d. deep lilac (21 October, 1856)	£22	35 0
70	,,	6d. pale lilac	£18	25 0
		a. Azure paper	£95	£15
		b. Thick paper	£30	97 6
71	**19**	1s. deep green (1 November, 1856)	£50	95 0
72	,,	1s. green	£28	60 0
73	,,	1s. pale green	£30	70 0
		a. Azure paper	—	£35
		b. Thick paper	—	£16

21 **22** **23** **24** **25.** Plate 2.

A. White dots added. B. Hair lines.

1862–64. *A small uncoloured letter in each corner, the 4d. wmk. Large Garter, T* **17**, *the others Emblems, T* **20**.

No.	Type	Description	Unused	Used
75	**21**	3d. deep carmine-rose (Plate 2) (1 May, 1862)	£50	£7
76	,,	3d. bright carmine-rose	£18	70 0
77	,,	3d. pale carmine-rose	£18	75 0
		a. Error. Wmk. three roses and shamrock (Type 20a)	—	£55
		b. Thick paper	—	£17
78	,,	3d rose (with white dots, Type A, Plate 3) (August, '62)	*	£250
79	**22**	4d. bright red (Plate 3) (15 January, 1862)	£18	30 0
80	,,	4d. pale red	£15	25 0
81	,,	4d bright red (Hair lines, Type B, Plate 4) (16 October, '63)	£15	30 0
82	,,	4d pale red (Hair lines, Type B, Plate 4)	£15	25 0
		a. Imperf. (Plate 4)	£24	
83	**23**	6d deep lilac (Plate 3) (1 December, 1862)	£18	40 0
84	,,	6d lilac	£15	35 0
		a. Azure paper	—	£50
		b. Thick paper	—	£7
85	,,	6d. lilac (Hair lines, Plate 4) (20 April, '64)	£25	50 0
		a. Imperf.	£30	
		c. Thick paper	£30	
86	**24**	9d. bistre (Plate 2) (15 January, 1862)	£22	£6
87	,,	9d. straw	£22	£7
		a. On azure paper		
		b. Thick paper	—	£25
88	,,	9d. bistre (Hair lines, Plate 3) (May, '62)	£150	£300
89	**25**	1s. deep green (Plate No. 1 = Plate 2) (1 December, 1862)	£40	90 0

90 **25** 1s. green (Plate No. 1 = Plate 2) £22 60 0
a. " K " in lower left corner in white circle .. .. — £55
b. On azure paper .. ..
c. Thick paper £20
ca. Thick paper, " K " in circle as No. 90a .. .. — £175
91 ,, 1s. deep green (Plate No. 2 = Plate 3) .. .. £900 *
a. Imperf. £50

NOTES. The 3d., as T **21**, but with network background in the spandrels, which is found overprinted " SPECIMEN ", was never issued.

The plates of this issue may be distinguished as follows:—

3d. Plate 2. No white dots. Plate 3. White dots as Illustration A.
4d. Plate 3. No hair lines. Roman I next to lower corner letters. Plate 4. Hair lines in corners. (Illustration B.) Roman II.
6d. Plate 3. No hair lines. Plate 4. Hair lines in corners.
9d. Plate 2. No hair lines. Plate 3. Hair lines in corners. Beware of faked lines.
1s. Plate 2. Numbered 1 on stamps. Plate 3. Numbered 2 on stamps and with hair lines. Of Plate 3 only one pane of 20 was perforated and the stamp was never issued.

The variety " K " in circle, found on stamps lettered K D, is due to the K plug not being driven home when the plate was being lettered, so that there was a slight circular indentation which appeared as an uncoloured line on the stamps. Unused, only two copies are known.

The 9d. on azure paper (No. 87a) is very rare, only one specimen being known.

The watermark variety " three roses and a shamrock " illustrated in Type **20*a*** was evidently due to the substitution of an extra rose for the thistle in a faulty watermark bit. It is found on stamp T A of Plates 2 and 4 of the 3d., Plates 5 and 6 of the 6d., Plate 4 of the 9d. and Plate 4 of the 1s.

26 27 28 29 30 31

1865–67. *Large uncoloured corner letters. Wmk. Large Garter, (4d.); others Emblems.*

92 **26** 3d. rose (Plate No. 4) (1 March, 1865) £18 37 6
a. Error. Wmk. three roses and shamrock (Type 20a) £80 £60
b. Thick paper £35 80 0
93 **27** 4d. dull vermilion (4 July, 1865) 95 0 22 6
94 ,, 4d. vermilion 80 0 22 6
95 ,, 4d. deep vermilion 90 0 25 0

Plate No.	7	**1865**	£6	22	6	Plate No.	11	**1869**	80 0	22	6
,, ,,	8	**1866**	95 0	22	6	,, ,,	12	**1870**	80 0	22	6
,, ,,	9	**1867**	85 0	25	0	,, ,,	13	**1872**	90 0	25	0
,, ,,	10	**1868**	97 6	27	6	,, ,,	14	**1873**	80 0	25	0

96 **28** 6d. deep lilac (with hyphen) (1 April, 1865) £18 50 0
97 ,, 6d. lilac (with hyphen) £12 35 0
a. Thick paper £25 80 0
b. Stamp doubly printed (Plate 6) .. .. — £250
c. Error. Wmk. three roses and shamrock (Type 20a, Plates 5, 6) .. .. .. — £65

Plate No. 5 .. **1865** .. £12 35 0 | Plate No. 6 .. **1867** .. £50 70 0

98 **29** 9d. straw (1 December, 1865) £60 £28
a. Thick paper £95 £80
b. Error. Wmk. three roses and shamrock (Type 20a, Plate 4) £300 £110

Plate No. 4 .. **1865** .. £60 £28 | Plate No. 5 .. **1866** .. £600 *

99 **30** 10d. red-brown (Plate No. 1) (11.11.67) .. .. * £1500
101 **31** 1s. green (Plate No. 4) (February, 1865) £14 30 0
a. Error. Wmk. three roses and shamrock (Type 20a) .. .. — £85
b. Thick paper £30 £12
c. Imperf. between (vert. pr.) .. ..

NOTES ON 1865-67 ISSUE. From mid-1866 to about the end of 1871 4d. stamps of this issue appeared generally with watermark inverted.

The 10d. stamps, No. 99, were printed in *error* on paper wmkd. " Emblems " instead of on paper wmkd. " Spray "

32

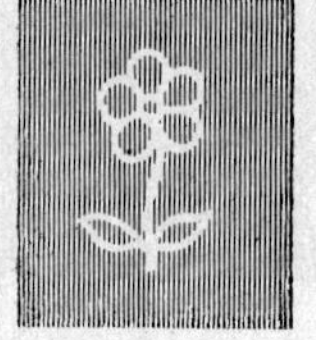
33

34

1867–80. *Wmk. Spray of Rose, T* **33.**

102 **26** 3d. deep rose (12 July, 1867) .. 75 0 22 6
103 ,, 3d. rose .. 75 0 22 6
a. Imperf. (Plates 5, 6, 9) .. £30

Plate No.						Plate No.				
4	**1867**	£17	60 0			8	**1872**	80 0	22 6
5	**1868**	75 0	22 6			9	,,	£5	30 0
6	**1870**	75 0	22 6			10	**1873**	£6	45 0
7	**1871**	85 0	25 0						

104 **28** 6d. lilac (with hyphen between " SIX-PENCE ") (Plate No. 6) (21 June, '67) £14 35 0
105 ,, 6d. deep lilac (with hyphen between " SIX-PENCE ") (Plate No. 6) .. £14 45 0
106 ,, 6d. purple (with hyphen between " SIX-PENCE ") (Plate No. 6) .. £16 60 0
107 ,, 6d. bright violet (with hyphen) (Plate No. 6) (22 July, 1868) .. £15 55 0
108 ,, 6d. dull violet (without hyphen) (Plate No. 8) (13 March, 1869) .. £12 32 6
109 ,, 6d. mauve (without hyphen) .. £12 25 0
a. Imperf. (Plate Nos. 8 and 9) .. £22 £26

Plate No.				
8	**1869**	mauve	£12	32 6
9	**1870**	mauve	£12	25 0
10	**1869**	mauve	*	£1200

110 **29** 9d. straw (Plate No. 4) (3 October, 1867) .. £18 80 0
111 ,, 9d. pale straw (Plate No. 4) .. £15 80 0
a. Imperf. (Plate 4) .. £30
112 **30** 10d. red-brown (1 July, 1867) .. £27 95 0
113 ,, 10d. pale red-brown .. £35 97 6
114 ,, 10d. deep red-brown .. £40 £14
a. Imperf. (Plate 1) ..

Plate No.					Plate No.			
1	**1867**	£27	95 0		2	**1867**	*	£450

115 **31** 1s. deep green (13 July, 1867) .. £14 15 0
117 ,, 1s. pale green .. £14 12 6
a. Imperf. between (pair) (Plate 7) ..
b. Imperf. (Plate 4) .. £22 £28

Plate No.					Plate No.			
4	**1867**	£14	15 0		6	**1872**	£16	12 6
5	**1871**	£14	12 6		7	**1873**	£18	40 0

118 **32** 2s. dull blue (1 July, 1867) .. £25 55 0
119 ,, 2s. deep blue .. £25 47 6
a. Imperf. (Plate 1) .. £32
120 **32** 2s. pale blue .. £25 97 6
120*a* ,, 2s. cobalt .. £200 £30
120*b* ,, 2s. milky blue .. £60 £17

Plate No.			
1	**1867**	£25	47 6
3	**1868**	*	£600

121 **32** 2s. brown (Plate No. 1) (27 February, 1880) .. £100 £65

1872–73. *Uncoloured letters in corners. Wmk. Spray, T* **33.**

122 **34** 6d. deep chestnut (12 April, 1872) .. £16 30 0
123 ,, 6d. chestnut (23 May, 1872) .. £15 30 0
124 ,, 6d. pale buff (26 Oct., 1872) .. £16 £8

Plate No.				
11	**1872**	deep chestnut	£16	30 0
11	,,	chestnut	£15	30 0
11	,,	pale buff	£16	£8
12	,,	pale chestnut†	*	£200
12	,,	chestnut †	*	£200
12	,,	pale buff	£30	£9

(†) The prices quoted are for the true pale chestnut and chestnut shades which are very rare (in this plate).

125 **34** 6d. grey (Plate No. 12) (24 April, 1873) .. £8 50 0
a. Imperf. ..

35

36

37

38

39

40

1867–83. *Uncoloured letters in corners.*

(i.) *Wmk. Maltese Cross, T* **39.** *P* 15½×15.

126	**35**	5s. rose (1 July, 1867)	£55	95 0
127	,,	5s. pale rose	£55	95 0
		a. Imperf. (Plate 1)		

Plate No. 1 .. **1867** .. £55 95 0
,, ,, 2 .. **1874** .. £60 £9

128	**36**	10s. greenish grey (Plate No. 1) (26 September, 1878)	£250	£45
129	**37**	£1 brown-lilac (Plate No. 1) (26 September, 1878)	£400	£55

(ii.) *Wmk. Anchor T* **40.** *P* 14. **(a) *Blued paper.***

130	**35**	5s. rose (Plate No. 4) (25 November, 1882)	£90	£32
131	**36**	10s. grey-green (Plate No. 1) (February, 1883)	£425	£65
132	**37**	£1 brown-lilac (Plate No. 1) (December, 1882)	£500	£100
133	**38**	£5 orange (Plate No. 1) (21 March, 1882)	£600	£150

(b) *White paper.*

134	**35**	5s. rose (Plate No. 4)	£150	£50
135	**36**	10s. greenish grey (Plate No. 1)	£500	£75
136	**37**	£1 brown-lilac (Plate No. 1)	£700	£85
137	**38**	£5 orange (Plate No. 1)	£150	£65

41

42

43

44

45

46

47

48

1873–80. *Large coloured letters in the corners.*

(i.) *Wmk. Anchor, T* **47.**

No.	Type	Description	Unused	Used
138	**41**	2½d. rosy mauve (*blued paper*) (1 July, 1875)	£10	55 0
139	,,	2½d. rosy mauve (*white paper*)	80 0	25 0

Plate	Year	Unused	Used
Plate No. 1 (*blued paper*)	**1875**	£10	55 0
,, ,, 1 (*white paper*)	,,	80 0	25 0
,, ,, 2 (*blued paper*)	,,	£150	£45
,, ,, 2 (*white paper*)	,,	80 0	25 0
,, ,, 3 (*white paper*)	,,	£17	35 0
,, ,, 3 (*blued paper*)	,,	—	£45

Error of Lettering L H—F L for L H—H L (*Plate No.* 2).

No.	Type	Description	Unused	Used
140	**41**	2½d. rosy mauve	£165	£50

(ii.) *Wmk. Orb, T* **48.**

No.	Type	Description	Unused	Used
141	**41**	2½d. rosy mauve (16 May, 1876)	60 0	25 0

Plate	Year	Unused	Used	Plate	Year	Unused	Used
Plate No. 3	**1876**	£20	50 0	Plate No. 11	**1878**	70 0	25 0
,, ,, 4	,,	80 0	25 0	,, ,, 12	,,	60 0	27 6
,, ,, 5	,,	80 0	27 6	,, ,, 13	,,	60 0	27 6
,, ,, 6	,,	65 0	25 0	,, ,, 14	**1879**	55 0	25 0
,, ,, 7	**1877**	70 0	25 0	,, ,, 15	,,	60 0	25 0
,, ,, 8	,,	75 0	27 6	,, ,, 16	,,	55 0	25 0
,, ,, 9	,,	60 0	25 0	,, ,, 17	**1880**	£6	90 0
,, ,, 10	**1878**	90 0	35 0				

No.	Type	Description	Unused	Used
142	**41**	2½d. blue (5 February, 1880)	50 0	10 0

Plate	Year	Unused	Used	Plate	Year	Unused	Used
Plate No. 17	**1880**	50 0	17 6	Plate No. 19	**1880**	50 0	10 0
,, ,, 18	,,	65 0	15 0	,, ,, 20	,,	60 0	10 6

(iii.) *Wmk. Spray, T* **33.**

No.	Type	Description	Unused	Used
143	**42**	3d. rose (5 July, 1873)	42 6	20 0
144	,,	3d. pale rose	42 6	30 0

Plate	Year	Unused	Used	Plate	Year	Unused	Used
Plate No. 11	**1873**	65 0	20 0	Plate No. 17	**1875**	70 0	25 0
,, ,, 12	,,	90 0	22 6	,, ,, 18	,,	60 0	30 0
,, ,, 14	**1874**	80 0	22 6	,, ,, 19	**1876**	42 6	30 0
,, ,, 15	,,	75 0	30 0	,, ,, 20	**1879**	80 0	40 0
,, ,, 16	**1875**	75 0	30 0				

No.	Type	Description	Unused	Used
145	**43**	6d. pale buff (Plate No. 13) (15 March, 1873)	*	£380
146	,,	6d. deep grey (31 March, 1874)	60 0	27 6
147	,,	6d. grey	60 0	27 6

Plate	Year	Unused	Used	Plate	Year	Unused	Used
Plate No. 13	**1874**	65 0	30 0	Plate No. 16	**1878**	65 0	27 6
,, ,, 14	**1875**	65 0	30 0	,, ,, 17	**1880**	70 0	40 0
,, ,, 15	**1876**	60 0	27 6				

No.	Type	Description	Unused	Used
148	**44**	1s. deep green (1 September, 1873)	£9	27 6
150	,,	1s. pale green	90 0	27 6

Plate	Year	Unused	Used	Plate	Year	Unused	Used
Plate No. 8	**1873**	£9	27 6	Plate No. 12	**1875**	90 0	27 6
,, ,, 9	**1874**	£9	30 0	,, ,, 13	**1877**	90 0	27 6
,, ,, 10	,,	£9	30 0	,, ,, 14	**1876**	*	£1250
,, ,, 11	**1875**	£9	30 0				

No.	Type	Description	Unused	Used
151	**44**	1s. orange-brown (Plate No. 13) (14 October, 1880)	£22	£7

(iv.) *Wmk. Large Garter, T* **17.**

No.	Type	Description	Unused	Used
152	**45**	4d. vermilion (1 March, 1876)	£25	£12

Plate	Year	Unused	Used
Plate No. 15	**1876**	£25	£12
,, ,, 16	**1874**	*	£1500

No.	Type	Description	Unused	Used
153	**45**	4d. sage-green (12 March, 1877)	£8	75 0
		a. Imperf. (Plate No. 15)	£20	

Plate	Year	Unused	Used
Plate No. 15	**1877**	£8	75 0
,, ,, 16	,,	£8	75 0
,, ,, 17	,,	*	£900

No.	Type	Description	Unused	Used
154	**45**	4d. grey-brown (Plate No. 17) (15 August, 1880)	£12	65 0
156	**46**	8d. orange (Plate No. 1) (11 September, 1876)	£14	70 0

1876 (July). *Prepared for use but not issued.*

No.	Type	Description	Unused	Used
156a	**46**	8d. purple-brown (Plate No. 1)	£35	

49

3d..

(50)

1880–83. *Wmk. Imperial Crown, T* **49.**

157 **41** 2½d. blue (23 March, 1881) 30 0 7 6
a. Imperf. (Plate No. 23) .. ..

Plate No. 21 .. **1881** .. 65 0 8 0
" " 22 .. " .. 30 0 7 6
" " 23 .. " .. 32 0 7 6

158 **42** 3d. rose (February, 1881) 45 0 20 0

Plate No. 20 .. **1881** .. 70 0 50 0
" " 21 .. " .. 45 0 20 0

159 **42** 3d. lilac (*carmine* surcharge—*T* **50**) (Plate No. 21) (1 January, 1883) .. 65 0 40 0

160 **45** 4d. grey-brown (10 December, 1880) 65 0 20 0

Plate No. 17 .. **1880** .. 65 0 20 0
" " 18 .. **1882** .. 65 0 20 0

161 **43** 6d. grey (1 January, 1881) 45 0 22 6

Plate No. 17 .. **1881** .. 60 0 22 6
" " 18 .. **1882** .. 45 0 22 6

162 **43** 6d. lilac (*carmine* surcharge—as *T* **50**) (Plate No. 18) (1 January, 1883) .. 65 0 40 0
a. A F. Slanting dots £28 £15
b. M H. Late state. Slanting dots—first dot very small £35 £15
c. O I. Slanting dots (first state) £25 £12
d. O I. Left dot only (second state) £35 £15
e. P H. Late state. Slanting dots £25 £12
f. S J. Slanting dots £25 £12
g. T F. Second dot divided into two halves £50 £30
h. M I. Slanting dots .. .. — £15
i. D C. Slanting dots £25 £12

163 **44** 1s. orange-brown (29 May, 1881) 90 0 40 0
a. Imperf. (Plate No. 14) .. ..

Plate No. 13 .. **1881** .. 90 0 40 0
" " 14 .. **1881** .. 90 0 45 0

The 1s. Plates 13 and 14 are known in purple, but were not issued thus. They come from the Souvenir Album prepared for members of the "Stamp Committee of 1884".

52  53  54  55  56

1880–81. *Wmk. Imperial Crown, T* **49.**

164 **52** ½d. deep green (14 October, 1880) 8 6 3 0
a. Imperf. £8
165 **52** ½d. pale green 8 6 2 6
166 **53** 1d. Venetian red (1 January, 1880) 2 6 0 4
a. Imperf. 90 0
167 **54** 1½d. Venetian red (14 October, 1880) 30 0 15 0
168 **55** 2d. pale rose (8 December, 1880) 60 0 20 0
168*a* " 2d. deep rose 60 0 20 0
169 **56** 5d. indigo (15 March, 1881) 75 0 20 0

Die I.  57  Die II.

1881. *Wmk. Imperial Crown, T* **49.** (*a*) 14 *dots in each corner,* Die I (12 *July*).

170 **57** 1d. lilac 45 0 8 6
171 " 1d. pale lilac 35 0 7 6

(*b*) 16 *dots in each corner,* Die II (12 *December*).

172 **57** 1d. lilac 1 0 0 3
172*a* " 1d. bluish lilac £8 50 0
b. Blued paper £50
173 " 1d. deep purple 1 6 0 4
a. Printed both sides .. .. £40 †
b. Frame broken at bottom £35 £40
c. Printed on gummed side .. .. £32 †
d. Imperf. three sides (pair) .. .. £85 †
e. Printed both sides but impression on back inverted .. .. £65 †
f. No watermark £12

174	**57**	1d. mauve	1 0	0 3
		a. Imperf. (pair)	£6	

1d. stamps with the words "PEAR'S SOAP" printed on back in *orange, blue* or *mauve* price *from* 50s., *unused.*

The variety "frame broken at bottom" shows a white space just inside the bottom frame-line from between the "N" and "E" of "ONE" to below the first "N" of "PENNY", breaking the pearls and cutting into the lower part of the oval below "PEN".

58  59  60

1883–84. *Coloured letters in the corners. Wmk. Anchor, T* **40.**

(i) *Blued paper.*

175	**58**	2s. 6d. lilac (2 July, 1883)	£40	£12
176	**59**	5s. rose (1 April, 1884)	£110	£35
177	**60**	10s. ultramarine (1 April, 1884)	£300	£60
177*a*	,,	10s. cobalt (May, 1884)	£350	£135

(ii) *White paper.*

178	**58**	2s. 6d. lilac	75 0	30 0
179	,,	2s. 6d. deep lilac	50 0	25 0
		a. Deep lilac, blued paper (issued during "white paper" period)	£50	
180	**59**	5s. rose	£8	20 0
181	,,	5s. crimson	65 0	25 0
182	**60**	10s. cobalt	£250	£100
183	,,	10s. ultramarine	£10	60 0
183*a*	,,	10s. pale ultramarine	£10	60 0

61

A.

B.

1884 (1 APRIL). *Wmk.* 3 *Imperial Crowns, T* **49.**

185	**61**	£1 brown-lilac	£160	£32
		a. Frame broken. Plate 2, letters JC (ill. A) or TA (ill. B)	£300	£75

1888 (1 FEB.). *Wmk.* 3 *Orbs, T* **48.**

186	**61**	£1 brown-lilac	£325	£55
		a. Frame broken. Plate 2, letters JC (ill. A) or TA (ill. B)	—	£120

62  63  64

65  66

1883 (1 Aug.) (*9d.*) *or* **1884** (1 April) (*others*). *Wmk. Imperial Crown*, *T* **49** (*sideways on horiz. designs*).

No.	Type	Description	Unused	Used
187	**52**	½d. slate-blue	6 0	2 0
188	**62**	1½d. lilac	20 0	12 6
189	**63**	2d. lilac	40 0	15 0
190	**64**	2½d. lilac	15 0	4 6
191	**65**	3d. lilac	35 0	17 6
192	**66**	4d. dull green	90 0	55 0
193	**62**	5d. dull green	55 0	45 0
194	**63**	6d. dull green	50 0	45 0
195	**64**	9d. dull green (1 August, 1883)	£10	£9
196	**65**	1s. dull green	£6	80 0

The above prices are for stamps in the true dull green colour. Stamps which have been soaked, causing the colour to run, are almost valueless.

Stamps of the above set and No. 180 are also found perf. 12; these are official perforations, but were never issued. A second variety of the 5d. is known with a line instead of a stop under the "d" in the value; this was never issued and is therefore only known *unused*. (*Price* £100.)

71 72 73 74 75 76 77 78 79 80 81 82

Plate I Plate II

Plate I: Square dots to right of "d".

Plate II: Thin vertical lines to right of "d".

1887 (1 Jan.)–**1892**. "*Jubilee*" *issue. New types. The bicoloured stamps have the value tablets, or the frames including the value tablets, in the second colour. Wmk. Imperial Crown, T* **49**.

No.	Type	Description	Unused	Used
197	**71**	½d. vermilion	0 6	0 4
		a. Printed on gummed side	£35	†
197*b*	,,	½d. orange-vermilion	0 6	0 4
198	**72**	1½d. dull purple and green	4 0	2 0
		a. Purple part of design double		
199	**73**	2d. green and vermilion	£18	£12
200	,,	2d. green and carmine	6 0	3 6
201	**74**	2½d. purple/*blue*	3 0	1 0
		a. Printed on gummed side	—	†
202	**75**	3d. purple/*yellow*	12 6	1 3
203	,,	3d deep purple/*yellow*	9 0	1 3
204	,,	3d. deep purple/*orange* (1891)	£15	£10
205	**76**	4d. green and purple-brown	12 6	4 0
205*a*	,,	4d. green and deep brown	12 6	4 0
206	**77**	4½d. green and carmine (15 September, 1892)	7 0	6 0
206*a*	,,	4½d. green and aniline carmine	£10	
207	**78**	5d. dull purple and blue (Duty-plate I)	£7	60 0
207*a*	,,	5d. dull purple and blue (Duty-plate II)	7 6	4 6
208	**79**	6d. purple/*rose-red*	12 0	6 0
208*a*	,,	6d. deep purple/*rose-red*	6 0	3 6
209	**80**	9d. dull purple and blue	15 0	10 0

210 **81** 10d. dull purple and carmine (24 February, 1890) 16 0 16 0
210*a* ,, 10d. dull purple and aniline carmine £10 £7
211 **82** 1s. green 27 6 15 0
212 **61** £1 green (27 January, 1891) £45 £35
a. Frame broken. Plate 2, letters JC (ill. A) or TA (ill. B) £175 £90

½d. stamps with "PEARS' SOAP" printed on back in *orange, blue,* or *mauve,* price *from* 60s. each.

1900. *Wmk. Imperial Crown, T* **49.** *Colours changed.*

213 **71** ½d. blue-green* (17 April) 0 6 0 6
a. Printed on the gummed side .. ..
214 **82** 1s. green and carmine (11 July) 17 6 30 0

* The ½d. No. 213, in bright blue, is a colour changeling.

KING EDWARD VII, 1901 (22 Jan.)–1910 (6 May).

83  84  85  86

87  88  89  90

91  92  93

94  95  96

97  97*a*

1902 (1 Jan.)–**10.** *T* **83** *(½d., 1d. and 6d.) to* **97.** *Printed by Messrs. De La Rue & Co. Wmks. Imperial Crown (½d. to 1s.); Anchor (2s. 6d. to 10s.); Three Crowns (£1). P 14.*

O = "Ordinary" paper. C = Chalk-surfaced paper.

215 ½d. dull blue-green, O (1 January, 1902) 1 0 0 4
216 ½d. blue-green, O 1 0 0 6
217 ½d. pale yellow-green, O (26 November, 1904) 0 9 0 4

No.	Description	Unused	Used
218	½d. yellow-green, O	0 9	0 4
	a. Stamp from booklet with cross attached (pair)	90 0	£6
	b. Doubly printed (bottom row on one pane) (Control H9)	£285	
219	1d. scarlet, O (1 January, 1902)	0 10	0 4
220	1d. bright scarlet, O	0 10	0 4
	a. Imperf. (pair).	£300	
221	1½d. dull purple and yellow-green, O (21 March, 1902)	10 0	3 6
222	1½d. slate-purple and yellow-green, O	12 0	3 6
223	1½d. dull purple and green, C (September, 1905)	12 0	3 6
224	1½d. slate-purple and green, C	8 0	3 6
225	2d. yellow-green and carmine, O (25 March, 1902)	12 0	8 6
226	2d. grey-green and carmine, O (March, 1903)	17 6	8 6
227	2d. green and carmine, C (September, 1905)	10 0	7 6
228	2d. deep green and carmine, C (July, 1910)	12 0	8 6
229	2d. pale blue-green and carmine, C	80 0	27 6
230	2½d. deep bright blue, O (1 January, 1902)	3 6	1 6
231	2½d. pale bright blue, O	3 6	1 6
232	3d. dull purple/*orange-yellow*, O (20 March, 1902)	10 0	2 0
232*a*	3d. deep purple/*orange-yellow*, O	12 6	2 0
232*b*	3d. pale reddish purple/*orange-yellow*, C (March, 1906)	65 0	12 6
233	3d. dull purple/*orange-yellow*, C	90 0	17 6
233*a*	3d. dull reddish purple/*lemon*, C	60 0	10 0
233*b*	3d. pale purple/*lemon*, C	7 6	3 6
234	3d. purple/*lemon*, C	6 0	3 0
235	4d. pale green and grey-brown, O (27 March, 1902)	17 6	3 6
236	4d. green and chocolate-brown, O	20 0	5 0
237	4d. green and chocolate-brown, C (January, 1906)	12 6	6 0
238	4d. deep green and chocolate-brown, C	10 6	5 0
239	4d. brown-orange, O (1 November, 1909)	40 0	25 0
240	4d. pale orange, O (December, 1909)	6 6	6 0
241	4d. orange-red, O (December, 1910)	5 0	5 0
242	5d. purple and blue, O (14 May, 1902)	10 6	6 0
243	5d. dull purple and blue, C	12 6	7 6
244	5d. slate-purple and blue, C (May, 1906)	10 0	7 6
245	6d. pale dull purple, O (1 January, 1902)	10 0	5 0
246	6d. dull purple, O	7 6	4 0
247	6d. reddish purple, C (October, 1905)	10 0	5 0
248	6d. dull purple (to deep), C	6 0	5 0
249	7d. grey-black, O (4 May, 1910)	5 0	5 0
249*a*	7d. deep grey-black, O	30 0	15 0
250	9d. dull purple and blue, O (7 April, 1902)	27 6	12 6
251	9d. slate-purple and blue, O	30 0	12 6
252	9d. dull purple and blue, C (29 June, 1905)	25 0	22 6
253	9d. slate-purple and blue, C	12 6	17 6
254	10d. dull purple and carmine, O (3 July, 1902)	25 0	20 0
	a. No cross on crown	£15	£12
255	10d. dull purple and carmine, C (September, 1905)	30 0	20 0
	a. No cross on crown	£12	£12
256	10d. dull purple and scarlet, C (September, 1910)	50 0	40 0
	a. No cross on crown	£15	£12
257	1s. green and carmine, O (24 March, 1902)	15 0	5 0
258	1s. green and carmine, C (September, 1905)	42 6	6 0
259	1s. green and scarlet, C (1910)	12 6	10 0
260	2s. 6d. dull purple, O (5 April, 1902)	75 0	40 0
261	2s. 6d. reddish purple, C (October, 1905)	65 0	40 0
262	2s. 6d. dull purple, C	65 0	40 0
263	5s. carmine, O (5 April, 1902)	80 0	35 0
264	5s. deep carmine O	£5	50 0
265	10s. ultramarine, O (5 April, 1902)	£12	£10
266	£1 green, O (16 June, 1902)	£35	£18

1910 (May). *T* **97***a*. ***Prepared for use, but not issued.***

No.	Description	Unused	Used
266*a*	2d. Tyrian plum	£1750	

One copy of this stamp is known used, but it was never issued to the public.

To distinguish De La Rue printings from the provisional printings of the same values made either by Messrs. Harrison & Sons or at Somerset House, the following hints may be helpful. The 6*d*. is the only value *on chalk-surfaced paper*, printed by De La Rue and also at Somerset House. The latter printing can be distinguished by the shade and impression.

Of the stamps *on ordinary paper*, the De La Rue impressions are usually clearer and of a higher finish than those of the other printers. The shades are markedly different except in some printings of the 4*d*., 6*d*., and 7*d*. and in the 5*s*., 10*s*., and £1. With a little experience the collector should have no difficulty in allotting mint specimens of any value to their respective printings.

1911. *Printed by Messrs. Harrison & Sons.* "*Ordinary*" *paper. Wmk. Imp. Crown.* (*a*) *P* 14.

No.	Description	Unused	Used
267	½d. dull yellow-green (3 May, 1911)	2 0	1 0
268	½d. dull green	2 6	1 0
269	½d. deep dull green	7 6	4 0
270	½d. pale bluish green	7 0	5 0
	a. From booklet, with cross attached (pair)	£8	£8
	b. Wmk. sideways		
	c. Imperf. (pair)		
271	½d. bright green (very clear printing) (June, 1911)	£12	£10

272	1d. rose-red (May, 1911)	2 6	1 6
	a. No wmk.	£18	£18
273	1d. deep rose-red	2 6	1 6
274	1d. rose-carmine	80 0	30 0
275	1d. aniline pink (May, 1911)	£15	£8
275a	1d. aniline rose	£6	70 0
276	2½d. bright blue (July, 1911)	15 0	15 0
277	3d. dull purple/*lemon* (Sept. 1911)	35 0	£6
278	4d. bright orange (July, 1911)	17 6	15 0

(*b*) *P* 15×14.

279	½d. pale bluish green (October, 1911)	6 0	10 0
279a	½d. green	15 0	25 0
280	1d. rose-red (October, 1911)	25 0	20 0
281	1d. rose-carmine	3 6	3 0
282	1d. pale rose-carmine	3 6	3 6
283	2½d. bright blue (October, 1911)	5 0	2 0
284	2½d. blue	4 6	2 0
285	3d. dull purple/*lemon* (September, 1911)	2 6	2 0
285a	3d. grey/*lemon*	£125	£110
286	4d. bright orange (November, 1911)	4 0	4 0

1911–13. *Printed at Somerset House.* ***Ordinary paper, unless marked* C (=*chalk-surfaced paper*).** *Wmks. as* 1902–10. *P* 14.

287	1½d. pale reddish purple and yellow-green (13 July, 1911)	20 0	20 0
288	1½d. purple and green	5 0	3 6
289	1½d. slate-purple and green (September, 1912)	10 0	6 0
290	2d. dull green and red (August, 1911)	7 6	7 6
291	2d. dull green and carmine (December, 1911)	10 0	6 0
292	2d. grey-green and carmine (carmine shows clearly on back) (1912)	3 0	7 6
293	5d. reddish purple and bright blue (August, 1911)	5 0	4 0
294	5d. purple and bright blue	8 0	7 0
295	6d. Royal purple, O (31 October, 1911)	12 6	37 6
296	6d. bright magenta, C	£85	
297	6d. dull purple, O	7 6	5 0
298	6d. reddish purple, O	6 0	4 0
299	6d. deep plum, O	20 0	12 6
300	6d. dark purple, O (March, 1912)	15 0	17 6
301	6d. dull purple, C (March, 1913)	35 0	35 0
303	6d. deep plum, C (July, 1913)	10 0	35 0
	a. No cross on crown (*various shades*) *from*	£15	£15
305	7d. slate-grey (August, 1912)	6 0	7 6
306	9d. pale reddish purple and pale blue (July, 1911)	55 0	45 0
307	9d. reddish purple and blue (October, 1911)	7 6	7 6
307a	9d. purple (to deep) and blue	6 6	7 6
308	9d. blackish purple and bright blue (March, 1912)	60 0	45 0
309	10d. dull purple and scarlet (9 October, 1911)	25 0	20 0
310	10d. dull purple and aniline pink (October, 1911)	£15	£12
311	10d. dull purple and carmine (May, 1912)	15 0	12 6
312	1s. deep green and scarlet (19 July, 1911)	30 0	12 6
313	1s. green and scarlet (October, 1911)	30 0	12 6
314	1s. green and carmine (April, 1912)	6 0	5 0
315	2s. 6d. dull purple (September, 1911)	£12	90 0
316	2s. 6d. reddish purple (1912)	60 0	45 0
317	2s. 6d. blackish purple (1912)	80 0	55 0
318	5s. carmine (February, 1912)	95 0	55 0
319	10s. bright ultramarine (January, 1912)	£12	£10
320	£1 deep green (September, 1911)	£40	£20

KING GEORGE V, 1910 (6 MAY)–1936 (20 JAN.).

WATERMARK VARIETIES.
For note *re* watermark varieties see after No. 429.

PRINTERS. *T* **98** *to* **102** *were typographed by Harrison & Sons, with the exception of certain preliminary printings, referred to in the footnote below No.* 343.

98

99

A

B

A

B

(Des. Bertram Mackennal (T **98/106**, **109**), G. W. Eve (T **107/8**).)

1911–12. *T* **98** *and* **99**. *Wmk. Imperial Crown, T* **49**. *P* 15 × 14.

No.	Description	Unused	Used
321	½d. pale yellow-green (Die A) (22.6.11)	4 0	2 6
322	½d. yell.-grn. (Die A) (22.6.11)	2 0	2 6
323	½d. bluish green (Die A)	£7	70 0
	a. Error. Perf. 14	£350	£40
324	½d. yellow-green (Die B)	2 0	1 0
325	½d. green (Die B)	1 9	1 0
	a. Wmk. sideways	—	£450
326	½d. bluish green (Die B)	£10	£8
327	1d. deep rose-red (Die A) (June, 1911)	3 6	1 6
	a. Error. Perf. 14	£600	
	b. Experimental ptg. chalk-surfaced paper (Control A.11)	£17	
328	1d. carmine (Die A) (22.6.11)	6 0	2 6
	a. No Cross on Crown	£15	£20
329	1d. carmine (Die B)	1 6	0 9
330	1d. pale carmine (Die B)	2 0	0 6
	a. No Cross on Crown	£15	£15
331	1d. rose-pink (Die B)	35 0	15 0
332	1d. scarlet (Die B) (June, 1912)	20 0	17 6
333	1d. aniline scarlet (Die B)*	£10	£7

Die A (in the case of each value) is the original and Die B the altered Die.

HALFPENNY.—In Die A of the ½d. the three upper scales on the body of the right-hand dolphin form a triangle, while in Die B the uppermost of the three is incomplete.

PENNY.—In Die A the second line of shading on the ribbon to right of the Crown is long, extending right across the wreath. In Die B the shading on the ribbon consists of short broken lines.

* For note re anilines see below No. 343.

100

1912 (AUG.). *T* **98** *and* **99** (*Dies B.*) *Wmk. Royal Cypher* ("*Simple*"), *T* **100**. *Booklet stamps. P* 15 × 14.

No.	Description	Unused	Used
334	½d. pale green	7 0	6 0
335	½d. green	6 0	6 0
336	1d. scarlet	6 0	4 0
337	1d. bright scarlet	6 0	6 0

101

102

1912 (1 JAN.). *T* **101** *and* **102**. *Wmk. Imperial Crown, T* **49**. *P* 15 × 14.

No.	Description	Unused	Used
338	½d. deep green	15 0	6 0
339	½d. green	1 0	0 4
340	½d. yellow-green	1 6	0 6
	a. No Cross on Crown	60 0	30 0
341	1d. bright scarlet	0 8	0 4
	a. No Cross on Crown	30 0	17 6
342	1d. scarlet	0 6	0 3
343	1d. aniline scarlet*	£10	£5
	a. No Cross on Crown	£25	

HALFPENNY.—In T **98** the ornament between the dolphins' heads has two thin lines of colour to the left of the centre, where it breaks the rim of the medallion. In T **101** it has one thick line.

PENNY.—In T **99** the body of the lion is white (unshaded). In T **102** it is shaded all over.

A preliminary printing, from the plates of the 1d. (both types), was made at Somerset House before the plates were handed over to Messrs. Harrison & Sons, but these can only be distinguished with certainty when the control is attached, this being lettered "A. 11," "B. 11," or "B. 12," whereas the Harrison control lacks the period after the letter. The ½d. and 1d. wmk., T **103**, with period after the letter, were also printed at Somerset House.

* Our prices for the aniline scarlet 1d. stamps, Nos. 333 and 343, are for specimens in which the colour is suffused on the surface of the stamp and shows through clearly on the back. Specimens without these characteristics, but which show "aniline" reactions under the quartz lamp are relatively common.

1912 (AUG.). *Types* **101** *and* **102**. *Wmk. Royal Cypher* ("*Simple*"), *T* **100**. *P* 15 × 14.

No.	Description	Unused	Used
344	½d. green	1 6	0 4
	a. No Cross on Crown	£12	90 0
345	1d. scarlet	1 3	0 4
	a. No Cross on Crown	95 0	27 6

103

1912 (OCT). *T* **101** *and* **102**. *Wmk. Royal Cypher* ("*Multiple*"), *T* **103**. *P* 15 × 14.

No.	Description	Unused	Used
346	½d. green	1 6	1 6
	a. No Cross on Crown	£18	£6
	b. Imperf.	£8	
	c. Wmk. sideways		
347	½d. bright green	7 6	2 6
348	½d. pale green	5 0	2 6
349	1d. bright scarlet	6 0	3 0
350	1d. scarlet	3 0	2 0
	a. No Cross on Crown	£6	45 0
	b. Imperf.	£6	
	c. Wmk. sideways	£7	£8
	d. Wmk. sideways. No Cross on Crown	£60	

104

105

106

107

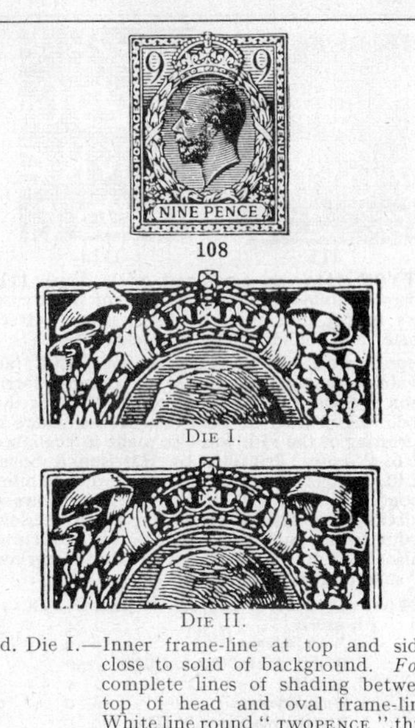

108

Die I.

Die II.

2d. Die I.—Inner frame-line at top and sides close to solid of background. *Four* complete lines of shading between top of head and oval frame-line. White line round " TWOPENCE ".thin.

Die II.—Inner frame-line farther from solid of background. *Three* lines between top of head and oval. White line round " TWOPENCE " thicker.

(Typo. by Harrison & Sons, except the 6d. printed by the Stamping Department of the Board of Inland Revenue, Somerset House. The latter also made printings of other values which can only be distinguished by the " controls," *q.v.*)

1912–22. *Wmk. Royal Cypher, T* **100.** *P* 15 × 14.

No.	Type	Description	Unused	Used
351	**105**	½d. green (Jan. 1913)	0 6	0 3
		a. Doubly printed (Control G.15)		
352	,,	½d. bright green ..	0 8	0 4
353	,,	½d. deep green ..	7 6	2 6
354	,,	½d. yellow-green ..	8 6	3 6
355	,,	½d. bright yellow-(Cyprus) green ..	£45	
356	,,	½d. blue-green ..	70 0	40 0
357	**104**	1d. bright scarlet (Oct., 1912)	0 6	0 4
		a. " Q " for " O " in " ONE "	£15	£15
358	,,	1d. scarlet	0 6	0 3
359	,,	1d. pale rose-red ..	2 0	0 6
360	,,	1d. carmine-red ..	12 6	5 0
361	,,	1d. scarlet-vermilion	60 0	50 0
		a. Printed on back ..	—	†
362	**105**	1½d. red-brn. (Oct., '12)	0 9	0 3
		a. Error " PENCF " ..	95 0	97 6
		b. Booklet pane. Four stamps plus two printed labels	£8	
363	,,	1½d. chocolate-brown ..	1 6	1 3
		a. Without wmk. ..	£7	
364	,,	1½d. chestnut	4 0	0 4
		a. Error. " PENCF " ..	65 0	70 0
365	,,	1½d. yellow-brown ..	25 0	20 0
366	**106**	2d. orange-yellow (Die I.) (Aug., 1912) ..	5 0	3 0
367	,,	2d. reddish orange (Die I.) (Nov., 1913) ..	2 0	0 6
368	**106**	2d. orange (Die I.) ..	1 0	0 4
369	,,	2d. bright oran. (Die I.)	2 6	0 4
370	,,	2d. orange (Die II.) (Sept., 1921) ..	3 6	1 6
371	**104**	2½d. bright ultramarine (Oct., 1912) ..	1 0	0 6
372	,,	2½d. blue	1 0	0 6
373	,,	2½d. deep dull blue ..	£50	£50
373*a*	,,	2½d. Prussian blue* ..	£10	£10
374	**106**	3d. reddish violet (Oct., 1912)	7 6	2 6
375	,,	3d. violet	2 6	0 6
376	,,	3d. bluish violet (Nov., 1913)	2 6	0 3
377	,,	3d. pale bluish violet	4 0	0 6
378	,,	4d. deep grey-green (Jan., 1913) ..	20 0	5 0
379	,,	4d. grey-green ..	2 0	0 8
380	,,	4d. pale grey-green ..	5 0	0 8
381	**107**	5d. brown (June, 1913)	4 0	1 0
382	,,	5d. yellow-brown ..	4 6	1 0
		a. Without wmk. ..	£18	
383	,,	5d. bistre-brown ..	20 0	15 0
384	,,	6d. dull pur., C (Aug., 1913)	20 0	15 0
385	,,	6d. reddish purple, C	2 6	1 0
		a. Perf. 14 (1921) ..	15 0	20 0
386	,,	6d. deep reddish pur., C	4 6	1 3
387	,,	7d. paleolive (Aug.,'13)	10 0	8 0
388	,,	7d. deep olive ..	25 0	12 6
389	,,	7d. sage-green ..	16 0	10 0
390	,,	8d. black/*yellow* (Aug., 1913)	10 0	8 6
391	,,	8d. black/*yellow-buff* (*granite*) (May, '17)	12 6	8 6
392	**108**	9d. agate (June, 1913)	10 0	4 0
393	,,	9d. deep agate ..	12 6	2 6
393*a*	,,	9d. olive-green (Sept., 1922)	18 6	8 6
393*b*	,,	9d. pale olive-green ..	22 6	15 0
394	,,	10d. turq.-bl. (Aug. '13)	10 0	8 6
394*a*	,,	10d. deep turq.-blue ..	15 0	17 6
395	,,	1s. pale bistre-brown (Aug., 1913) ..	7 6	2 0
396	,,	1s. olive-bistre ..	10 0	2 0

For the 2d., T **106**, bisected, see " Channel Islands ".

1913 (Aug.). *Wmk. Royal Cypher* (" *Multiple* "), *T* **103.** *P* 15 × 14.

No.	Type	Description	Unused	Used
397	**105**	½d. bright green	55 0	50 0
398	**104**	1d. dull scarlet	80 0	65 0

Both these stamps were originally issued in rolls only. Subsequently sheets were found, so that horizontal pairs and blocks are known but are of considerable rarity.

109

A

110

*No. 373 is the stamp we described until the 1952 edition of this catalogue as Prussian blue, but this is a distinctive deep dull blue and is quite unlike any of the other numerous shades of this value. The new No. 373*a* is a truer Prussian blue.

Nos. 400*a* and 408*a*. No. 415*b*.

Major Re-entries on 2s. 6d.

T **109.** *Background around portrait consists of horizontal lines. Recess. Wmk. Single Cypher, T* **110.** *P* 11 × 12.

1913 (July). *Printed by Waterlow Bros. & Layton.*

No.		Unused	Used
399	2s. 6d. deep sepia-brown ..	£7	35 0
400	2s. 6d. sepia-brown ..	£5	30 0
	a. Re-entry	£70	£55
401	5s. rose-carmine	£6	35 0
402	10s. indigo-blue	£12	£7
403	£1 green	£95	£60
404	£1 dull blue-green	£90	£60

1915 (Dec.)–**1918.** *Printed by De La Rue & Co.*

No.		Unused	Used
405	2s. 6d. deep brown ..	90 0	50 0
406	2s. 6d. chestnut-brown ..	70 0	37 6
407	2s. 6d. brown ..	55 0	35 0
408	2s. 6d. grey-brown	50 0	30 0
	a. Re-entry	£70	£60
409	5s. bright carmine ..	£6	37 6
410	5s. pale carmine	£6	45 0
411	10s. deep bright blue ..	£32	£12
412	10s. blue	£17	90 0
413	10s. pale blue	£17	85 0

1918 (Dec.)–**1930.** *Printed by Bradbury, Wilkinson & Co., Ltd.*

No.		Unused	Used
413*a*	2s. 6d. brown	40 0	12 6
414	2s. 6d. chocolate-brown ..	35 0	12 6
415	2s. 6d. red-brown	65 0	25 0
415*a*	2s. 6d. pale brown ('30) ..	55 0	22 6
	b. Major re-entry	£55	£35
416	5s. rose-red	60 0	17 6
417	10s. dull grey-blue	75 0	30 0

For (1934) re-engraved Waterlow printings, see Nos. 450/2.

In the De La Rue printings the gum is usually patchy and yellowish, and the colour of the stamp, particularly in the 5s., tends to show through the back.

The distinguishing characteristics of the Bradbury printings are as follows :—The paper appears whiter owing to use generally of a pure white gum. The holes of the perforation are larger.

In the majority of copies of the Bradbury printings a minute coloured dot appears in the margin just above the middle of the upper frame-line.

A further test for the Bradbury printings is the size ; the stamps printed by Waterlow and De La Rue being almost invariably 22 mm. high, while those printed by Bradbury, Wilkinson measure between 22¾ and 23 mm.

111

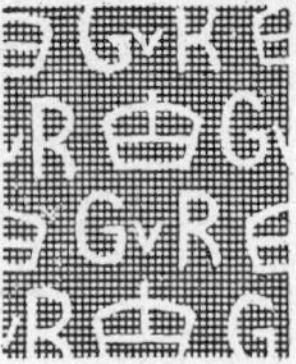

111*a*

TYPE 111*a*, as compared with Type **111**, differs as follows: Closer spacing of horizontal rows to 12½ mm. instead of 14½ mm. Letters shorter and rounder. Wmk. thicker.

(Typographed by Waterlow & Sons, Ltd. (all values except 6d.) and later, 1934–5, by Harrison & Sons, Ltd. (all values). Until 1934 the 6d. was printed at Somerset House where a printing of the 1½d. was also made in 1926 (see No. C 152). Printings by Harrison & Sons, Ltd., in 1934–35 can be identified, when in mint condition, by the fact that the gum shows a streaky appearance vertically, the Waterlow gum being uniformly applied, but Harrison also used up the balance of the Waterlow " smooth gum " paper.)

1924 (April)–**1926.** *T* **104,** *etc. W* **111.** *P* 15 × 14.

No.		Unused	Used
418	½d. green	0 4	0 3
	a. Wmk. sideways	6 0	5 0
	b. Doubly printed (control U34)	£250	
419	1d. scarlet	0 4	0 3
	a. Wmk. sideways	6 0	8 0
	b. Experimental paper, W 111*a*. .	50 0	
420	1½d. chestnut	1 0	0 3
	a. Tête-bêche (pair)	£16	£18
	b. Wmk. sideways	10 0	4 0
	c. Printed on the gummed side	£16	
	d. Booklet pane. Four stamps plus two printed labels ..	22 6	
	e. Ditto. Wmk. sideways ..		
	f. Experimental paper, W 111*a*	85 0	
421	2d. orange (Die II.) ..	1 6	0 3
	a. No wmk.	£9	
	b. Wmk. sideways	12 6	7 6
422	2½d. blue	2 9	0 4
	a. No wmk.	£9	
423	3d. violet	3 6	0 4
424	4d. grey-green	6 0	0 5
	a. Printed on the gummed side	£90	†
425	5d. yellow-brown	6 0	0 5
426	6d. purple, C	8 6	1 0
426*a*	6d purple, O (1926) ..	2 6	0 4
427	9d. olive-green	7 6	1 9
428	10d. turquoise-blue	12 6	7 6
429	1s. bistre	10 0	2 6

There are numerous shades in this issue.

The 6d. on both chalky and ordinary papers was printed by both Somerset House and Harrison. The Harrison printings have streaky gum, differ slightly in shade, and that on chalky paper is printed in a highly fugitive ink. The prices quoted are for the commonest (Harrison) printing in each case.

WATERMARK VARIETIES.

☛ Many *modern* British stamps exist without watermark owing to misplacement of the paper, and with either inverted, reversed, or inverted and reversed watermarks. A proportion of the low value stamps issued in booklets have the wmk. inverted in the normal course of printing. We do not list such wmk. varieties separately, but a number are always in stock. The 1½d. and 5d. 1912–22, and 2d. and 2½d. 1924–26, listed here, are from *whole* sheets without wmk.

Low values with *watermark sideways* are normally from stamp rolls used in machines with sideways delivery or, from April 1961, certain booklets.

112

(Des. H. Nelson. Recess. Waterlow & Sons Ltd.)

1924–25. *British Empire Exhibition.* *W* **111.** *P* 14. (*a*) 23.4.24. *Dated* " 1924 ".

430	**112**	1d. scarlet	10	0	12	6
		a. Bottom margin imperf.. .				
431	"	1½d. brown	12	6	15	0

(*b*) 9.5.25. *Dated* "1925."

432	**112**	1d. scarlet	35	0	40	0
433	"	1½d. brown	60	0	60	0

113

114

115

116

NEW ISSUES

are listed each month in

GIBBONS STAMP MONTHLY

Price **1s.** from your newsagent. (Readers overseas can subscribe by post, price 15s. 6d. per annum, post free.)

117

(Des. J. Farleigh (T **113** and **115**), E. Linzell (T **114**) and H. Nelson (T **116**). Typo. by Waterlow & Sons from plates made at the Royal Mint, except T **116**, recess. by Bradbury, Wilkinson & Co., from die and plate of their own manufacture.)

1929 (10 May). *Ninth Universal Postal Union Congress.* *W* **111.** *P* 15 × 14.

434	**113**	½d. yellow-green ..	2	6	1	3
		a. Wmk. sideways ..	20	0	25	0
435	**114**	1d. scarlet	4	0	3	0
		a. Wmk. sideways ..	35	0	40	0
436	"	1½d. purple-brown ..	2	6	0	9
		a. Wmk. sideways.. ..	30	0	35	0
		b. Booklet pane. Four stamps plus two printed labels ..	80	0		
437	**115**	2½d. blue	17	6	17	6

W **117.** *P* 12.

438	**116**	£1 black	£75	£65

PRINTERS. All subsequent issues are printed in photogravure by Harrison and Sons, Ltd., except where otherwise stated.

118

119

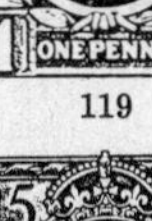

120

121

122

B

1934–36. *W* **111.** *P* 15 × 14.

No.	Type	Description	Unused	Used
439	**118**	½d. green (19.11.34)	0 4	0 3
		a. Wmk. sideways	2 0	2 6
440	**119**	1d. scarlet (24.9.34)	0 4	0 3
		a. Imperf. (pair)	£175	
		b. Ptd. on the gummed side	£30	
		c. Wmk. sideways	4 0	5 0
441	**118**	1½d. red-brown (20.8.34)	0 6	0 3
		a. Imperf. (pair)	£45	
		b. Imp. (three sides) (pair)		
		c. Wmk. sideways	6 0	4 0
		d. Booklet pane. Four stamps plus two printed labels	7 6	
442	**120**	2d. orange (21.1.35)	1 3	0 3
		a. Imperf. (pair)	£200	
		b. Wmk. sideways	12 6	15 0
443	**119**	2½d. ultramarine (18.3.35)	2 0	0 6
444	**120**	3d. violet (18.3.35)	2 0	0 4
445	,,	4d. deep grey-green (2.12.35)	3 0	0 4
446	**121**	5d. yell.-brn. (17.2.36)	5 0	1 0
447	**122**	9d. deep olive-green (2.12.35)	7 6	3 0
448	,,	10d. turquoise-blue (24.2.36)	8 6	3 0
449	,,	1s. bistre-brown (24.2.36)	12 6	1 6

Owing to the need for wider space for the perforations the size of the designs of the ½d. and 2d. were once, and the 1d. and 1½d. twice reduced from that of the first printings.

There are also numerous minor variations, due to the photographic element in the process.

For No. 442 bisected, see "Channel Islands".

(Recess. Waterlow & Sons.)

1934 (Oct.). *T* **109** (*re-engraved*). *Background around portrait consists of horizontal and diagonal lines.* *W* **110.** *P* 11 × 12.

No.	Type	Description	Unused	Used
450	**109**	2s. 6d. chocolate	50 0	15 0
451	,,	5s. bright rose-red	65 0	27 6
452	,,	10s. indigo	90 0	37 6

There are numerous other minor differences in the design of this issue.

123

(Des. B. Freedman.)

1935 (7 May). *Silver Jubilee.* *W* **111.** *P* 15 × 14.

No.	Type	Description	Unused	Used
453	**123**	½d. green	0 9	0 6
454	,,	1d. scarlet	2 6	1 6
455	,,	1½d. red-brown	1 6	0 6
456	,,	2½d. blue	8 6	10 0
456*a*	,,	2½d. Prussian blue	£160	£160

The 1½d. and 2½d. values differ from T **123** in the emblem in the panel at right.

KING EDWARD VIII,
1936 (20 Jan.–10 Dec.)

124

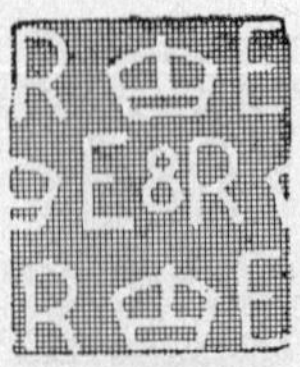

125

1936. *W* **125.** *P* 15 × 14.

No.	Type	Description	Unused	Used
457	**124**	½d. green (1.9.36)	0 3	0 3
458	,,	1d. scarlet (14.9.36)	0 3	0 4
459	,,	1½d. red-brown (1.9.36)	0 4	0 3
		a. Booklet pane. Four stamps plus two printed labels	15 0	
460	,,	2½d. ultramarine (1.9.36)	0 10	1 0

KING GEORGE VI,
1936 (11 Dec.)–**1952** (6 Feb.).

126. King George VI and Queen Elizabeth.

(Des. E. Dulac.)

1937 (13 May). *Coronation.* *W* **127.** *P* 15 × 14.

No.	Type	Description	Unused	Used
461	**126**	1½d. marone	0 6	0 6

127

128

129

130

King George VI and National Emblems.

(Des. T **128/9**, E. Dulac (head) and E. Gill (frames). T **130,** E. Dulac (whole stamp).)

1937–47. *W* **127.** *P* 15 × 14.

No.	Type	Description	Unused	Used
462	**128**	½d. green (10.5.37)	0 4	0 3
		a. Wmk. sideways (-.1.38)	1 0	1 0
		b. Wmk. sideways. Block of 4 (booklet pane)	30 0	30 0
463	,,	1d. scarlet (10.5.37)	0 8	0 3
		a. Wmk. sideways (-.2.38)	5 0	4 0
		b. Wmk. sideways. Block of 4 (booklet pane)	30 0	30 0
464	,,	1½d. red-brown (30.7.37)	0 8	0 3
		a. Wmk. sideways (-.2.38)	1 6	1 3
		b. Booklet pane Four stamps plus two printed labels	20 0	
		c. Imp. three sides (pair)		
465	,,	2d. orange (31.1.38)	3 6	0 4
		a. Wmk. sideways (-.2.38)	12 6	12 6
466	,,	2½d. ultramarine (10.5.37)	1 9	0 3
		a. Wmk. sideways (-.6.40)	10 0	10 0
		b. Tête-bêche (horiz. pr.)		
467	,,	3d. violet (31.1.38)	6 0	0 4
468	**129**	4d. grey-green (21.11.38)	2 9	0 6
		a. Imperf. (pair)	£225	
		b. Imp. three sides (pair)		
469	,,	5d. brown (21.11.38)	1 3	0 6
		a. Imperf. (pair)	£225	
		b. Imp. three sides (pair)		

470 **129** 6d. purple (30.1.39) .. 1 3 0 4

471 **130** 7d. emerald-grn. (27.2.39) 2 0 0 8

a. Imp. three sides (pair) .. £150

472 ,, 8d. bright carm. (27.2.39) 2 0 0 9

473 ,, 9d. deep ol.-grn. (1.5.39) 2 6 0 9

474 ,, 10d. turquoise-blue (1.5.39) 3 0 0 10

aa. Imperf. (pair) .. ..

474*a* ,, 11d. plum (29.12.47) .. 3 0 1 3

475 ,, 1s. bistre-brown (1.5.39) 3 0 0 4

For later printings of the lower values in apparently lighter shades and different colours, see Nos. 485/90 and 503/8.

For No. 465 bisected, see "Channel Islands".

131. King George VI. **132.**

133

(Designed by E. Dulac (T **131**) and Hon. George R. Bellew, M.V.O. (T **132**). Recess. Waterlow & Sons.)

1939–48. *W* **133.** *P* 14.

476 **131** 2s. 6d. brown (4.9.39) .. 25 0 12 6

476*a* ,, 2s. 6d. yell.-grn. (9.3.42) .. 10 0 1 6

477 ,, 5s. red (21.8.39) 15 0 5 6

478 **132** 10s. dark blue (3.10.39) .. 60 0 22 6

478*a* ,, 10s. ultram. (30.11.42) .. 45 0 8 0

478*b* ,, £1 brown (1.10.48) .. 35 0 27 6

134. Queen Victoria and King George VI.

(Des. H. L. Palmer.)

1940 (6 May). *Centenary of First Adhesive Postage Stamps.* *W* **127.** *P* 14½×14.

479 **134** ½d. green 0 9 0 6

480 ,, 1d. scarlet 2 0 1 0

481 ,, 1½d. red-brown 3 6 3 0

482 ,, 2d. orange 3 6 2 6

483 ,, 2½d. ultramarine 5 0 1 0

484 ,, 3d. violet 10 0 10 0

For No. 482 bisected, see "Channel Islands".

1941–42. *Head as Nos. 462/7, but lighter background.* *W* **127.** *P* 15×14.

485 **128** ½d. pale green (1.9.41) .. 0 3 0 3

a. Tête-bêche (horiz. pr.) ..

b. Imperf. (pair) £300

486 ,, 1d. pale scarlet (11.8.41) 0 4 0 3

a. Wmk. sideways (-.10.42) .. 0 8 0 10

b. Imperf. (pair) £225

c. Imperf. three sides (pair) ..

d. Imp. between (vert. pr.) ..

487 ,, 1½d. pale red-brn. (28.9.42) 0 6 0 6

488 ,, 2d. pale orange (6.10.41) 0 6 0 3

a. Wmk. sideways (-.6.42) .. 5 0 5 0

b. Tête-bêche (horiz. pr.) .. £900

c. Imperf. (pair) .. ..

489 ,, 2½d. light ultram. (21.7.41) 0 6 0 3

a. Wmk. sideways (-.8.42) .. 4 0 2 0

b. Tête-bêche (horiz. pr.) ..

c. Imperf. (pair) £225

490 ,, 3d. pale violet (3.11.41) .. 0 6 0 3

The tête-bêche varieties are from defectively made-up stamp booklets.

135

136. Symbols of Peace and Reconstruction.

(Des. H. L. Palmer (T **135**) and Reynolds Stone (T **136**).)

1946 (11 June). *Victory.* *W* **127.** *P* 15×14.

491 **135** 2½d. ultramarine 0 6 0 3

492 **136** 3d. violet 0 8 0 4

137

138. King George VI and Queen Elizabeth.

(Des. G. T. Knipe and Joan Hassall from photographs by Dorothy Wilding.)

1948 (26 Apr.). *Royal Silver Wedding.* *W* **127.** *P* 15 × 14 (2½d.) *or* 14 × 15 (£1).

493	**137**	2½d. ultramarine	0	6	0	3
494	**138**	£1 blue	60	0	70	0

1948 (10 May). Stamps of 1d. and 2½d. showing seaweed-gathering were on sale at eight Head Post Offices elsewhere in Great Britain, but were primarily for use in the Channel Islands and are listed there.

139. Globe and Laurel Wreath.

140. " Speed ".

141. Olympic Symbol.

142. Winged Victory.

(Des. Percy Metcalfe, C.V.O., Abram Games, Stanley D. Scott and Edmund Dulac.)

1948 (29 July). *Olympic Games.* *W* **127.** *P* 15 × 14.

495	**139**	2½d. ultramarine ..	0	9	0	3
496	**140**	3d. violet	0	9	0	8
497	**141**	6d. bright purple ..	1	9	1	9
498	**142**	1s. brown	2	3	2	6

143. Two Hemispheres.

144. U.P.U. Monument, Berne.

145. Goddess Concordia, Globe and Points of Compass.

146. Posthorn and Globe.

(Des. Mary Adshead (T **143**), Percy Metcalfe, C.V.O. (T **144**), H. Fleury (T **145**) and the Hon. George R. Bellew, M.V.O. (T **146**).)

1949 (10 Oct.). *75th Anniv. of Universal Postal Union.* *W* **127.** *P* 15 × 14.

499	**143**	2½d. ultramarine ..	0	10	0	6
500	**144**	3d. violet	2	6	2	0
501	**145**	6d. bright purple ..	4	0	4	0
502	**146**	1s. brown	6	0	6	0

1950–51. *4d. as No. 468 and others as Nos. 485/9, but colours changed.*

503	**128**	½d. pale orange (3.5.51)	0	4	0	3
		a. Imperf. (pair)				
		b. Tête-bêche (horiz. pr.)* ..				
504	,,	1d. light ultram. (3.5.51)	0	4	0	3
		a. Wmk. sideways (-.5.51)	0	6	0	4
		b. Imperf. (pair)	£175			
		c. Imperf. three sides (pr.)	£75			
		d. Booklet pane. Three stamps plus three printed labels	6	0		
505	,,	1½d. pale grn. (3.5.51) ..	0	6	0	3
		a. Wmk. sideways (-.9.51)	0	6	0	8
506	,,	2d. pale red-brn. (3.5.51)	0	6	0	3
		a. Wmk. sideways (-.5.51)	0	10	0	10
		b. Tête-bêche (horiz. pr.) ..	£750			
		c. Imperf. three sides (pr.) ..				
507	,,	2½d. pale scarlet (3.5.51)	0	8	0	3
		a. Wmk. sideways (-.5.51)	1	6	1	0
		b. Tête-bêche (horiz. pr.) ..				
508	**129**	4d. lt. ultram. (2.10.50)	2	6	0	8

*The only known pair is from an imperfect booklet, with one stamp incomplete.

147. H.M.S. *Victory.*

148. White Cliffs of Dover.

149. St. George and the Dragon.

150. Royal Coat-of-Arms.

(Des. Mary Adshead (T **147/8**), Percy Metcalfe, C.V.O. (T **149/50**). Recess. Waterlow & Sons.)

1951 (3 May). *W* **133.** *P* 11×12.

509	**147**	2s. 6d. yellow-green	10	0	2	6
510	**148**	5s. red	17	6	7	6
511	**149**	10s. ultramarine	35	0	12	6
512	**150**	£1 brown	45	0	25	0

151. " Commerce and Prosperity ".

152. Festival Symbol.

(Des. E. Dulac (T **151**), A. Games (T **152**).)

1951 (3 May). *Festival of Britain.* *W* **127.** *P* 15×14.

513	**151**	2½d. scarlet	0	8	0	3
514	**152**	4d. ultramarine	1	6	1	6

QUEEN ELIZABETH II, 6 February, 1952.

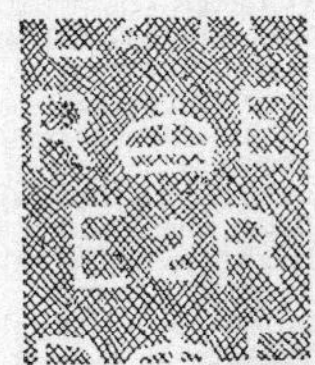

153. Tudor Crown.

154 155 156 157 158 159

160 I. II.

Queen Elizabeth II and National Emblems.

(Des. Miss E. Marx, R.D.I. (T **154**), M. C. Farrar-Bell (T **155/6**), G. Knipe (T **157**), Miss M. Adshead (T **158**), E. Dulac (T **159/60**). Portrait by Dorothy Wilding.)

1952–54. *W* **153.** *P* 15×14.

515	**154**	½d. orange-red (31.8.53)	0	8	0	3
516	,,	1d. ultramarine (31.8.53)	0	4	0	3
		a. Booklet pane. Three stamps plus three printed labels ..	12	6		
517	,,	1½d. green (5.12.52) ..	0	6	0	3
		a. Wmk. sideways (15.10.54)	1	6	2	6
		b. Imperf. pane*				
518	,,	2d. red-brown (31.8.53)	1	3	0	3
		a. Wmk. sideways (8.10.54)	2	9	3	0

No.	Type	Description	Unused s.	d.	Used s.	d.
519	**155**	2½d. carmine-red, Type I (5.12.52)	0	8	0	3
		a. Wmk. sideways (15.11.54)	2	0	2	6
		b. Type II (Booklets) ..	2	0	2	0
520	,,	3d. deep lilac (18.1.54) ..	0	10	0	4
521	**156**	4d. ultramarine (2.11.53)	1	9	0	4
522	**157**	5d. brown (6.7.53) ..	2	6	0	10
523	,,	6d. reddish pur. (18.1.54)	2	0	0	4
		a. Imperf. three sides (pr.)				
524	,,	7d. bright green (18.1.54)	2	0	0	8
525	**158**	8d. magenta (6.7.53) ..	3	0	0	8
526	,,	9d. bronze-green (8.2.54)	6	6	0	10
527	,,	10d. Prussian bl. (8.2.54)	4	0	0	10
528	,,	11d. brn.-purple (8.2.54)	5	0	2	6
529	**159**	1s. bistre-brown (6.7.53)	7	0	0	4
530	**160**	1s. 3d. green (2.11.53) ..	7	6	1	0
531	**159**	1s. 6d. grey-blue (2.11.53)	10	0	1	0

Types of 2½d. Type I :—In the frontal cross of the diadem, the top line is only half the width of the cross. Type II :—The top line extends to the full width of the cross and there are signs of strengthening in other parts of the diadem.

In the above issue Type II is only found in booklets.

* BOOKLET ERROR.—This pane of 6 stamps is *completely* imperf. (cf. No. 540*a*, etc.).

161

162

163

164

(Des. E. G. Fuller (2½d.), M. Goaman (4d.), E. Dulac (1s. 3d.), M. C. Farrar-Bell (1s. 6d.). Portrait (except 1s. 3d.) by Dorothy Wilding.)

1953 (3 JUNE). *Coronation.* *W* **153.** *P* 15 × 14.

No.	Type	Description	Unused s.	d.	Used s.	d.
532	**161**	2½d. carmine-red	2	6	1	0
533	**162**	4d. ultramarine	6	6	8	6
534	**163**	1s. 3d. deep yellow-grn.	25	0	27	6
535	**164**	1s. 6d. deep grey-blue ..	30	0	32	6

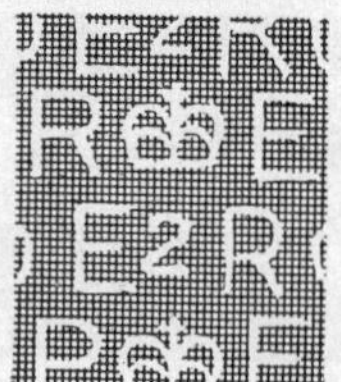

165. St. Edward's Crown.

166. Carrickfergus Castle.

167. Caernarvon Castle.

168. Edinburgh Castle.

169. Windsor Castle.

(Des. L. Lamb. Portrait by Dorothy Wilding Ltd. Recess. Waterlow & Sons Ltd. (until 31.12.57) and De La Rue & Co., Ltd. (subsequently).)

1955–58. *W* **165.** *P* 11 × 12.

No.	Type	Description	Unused s.	d.	Used s.	d.
536	**166**	2s. 6d. blk.-brn. (23.9.55)	15	0	0	9
		a. De La Rue ptg. (17.7.58)	35	0	2	0
537	**167**	5s. rose-red (23.9.55) ..	30	0	2	0
		a. De La Rue ptg. (1.5.58)	65	0	5	0
538	**168**	10s. ultramarine (1.9.55)	60	0	7	6
		a. De La Rue ptg. (1.5.58) ..	£6		12	6
539	**169**	£1 black (1.9.55) ..	£6		15	0
		a. De La Rue ptg. (1.5.58) ..	£14		25	0

On January 1st, 1958, the contract for printing the high values, T **166** to **169** was transferred to De La Rue & Co., Ltd.

The work of the two printers is very similar, but the following notes will be helpful to those attempting to identify Waterlow and De La Rue stamps of the W **165** issue.

The De La Rue sheets are printed in pairs and have a ⊣ or ⊢-shaped guide-mark at the centre of one side-margin opposite the middle row of perforations, indicating left- and right-hand sheets respectively.

The Waterlow sheets have a small circle (sometimes crossed) instead of a " ⊢ " and this is present in both side-margins opposite the 6th row of stamps, though one is sometimes trimmed off. Short dashes are also present in the perforation gutter between the marginal stamps marking the middle of the four sides and a cross is at the centre of the sheet. The four corners of the sheet have two lines forming a right-angle as trimming marks but some are usually trimmed off. All these gutter marks and sheet-trimming marks are absent in the De La Rue printings.

De La Rue used the Waterlow die and no alterations were made to it, so that no difference exists in the design or its size, but the making of new plates at first resulted in slight but measurable variations in the width of the gutters between stamps, particularly the horizontal, as follows:

	W.	D.L.R.
Horiz. gutters, mm ..	3.8 to 4.0	3.4 to 3.8

Later D.L.R. plates were however less distinguishable in this respect.

For a short time in 1959 the D.L.R. 2s. 6d. appeared with one dot in the bottom margin below the first stamp.

It is possible to sort singles with reasonable certainty by general characteristics. The individual lines of the D.L.R. impression are cleaner and devoid of the whiskers of colour of Waterlow's, and the whole impression lighter and softer.

Owing to the closer setting of the horizontal rows the strokes of the perforating comb are closer; this results in the topmost tooth on each side of De La Rue stamps being narrower than the corresponding teeth in Waterlow's which were more than normally broad.

Shades also help. The 2s. 6d. D.L.R. is a warmer, more chocolate shade than the blackish brown of W.; the 5s. a lighter red with less carmine than W's; the 10s. more blue and less ultramarine; the £1 less intense black.

The paper of D.L.R. printings is uniformly white, identical with that of W. printings from February 1957 onwards, but earlier W. printings are on paper which is creamy by comparison.

1955-58. *W* **165.** *P* 15×14.

No.	Type	Description	s.	d.	s.	d.
540	**154**	½d. orange-red (12.12.55)	0	4	0	3
		a. Part perf. pane* ..				
541	,,	1d. ultramarine (19.9.55)	0	4	0	3
		a. Booklet pane, 3 stamps plus 3 printed labels ..	10	0		
		b. Tête-bêche (horiz. pr.) ..				
542	,,	1½d. green (11.10.55) ..	0	6	0	3
		a. Wmk. sideways (7.3.56)	1	3	1	6
		b. Tête-bêche (horiz. pr.) ..				
543	,,	2d. red-brown (6.9.55) ..	0	6	0	4
		aa. Imperf. between (vert. pr.)				
		a. Wmk. sideways ('56) ..	1	3	3	0
		ab. Imperf. between, Wmk. sideways (horiz. pr.) ..				
543*b*	,,	2d. light red-brown (17.10.56)	0	6	0	3
		ba. Tête-bêche (horiz. pr.) ..				
		bb. Imperf. pane*				
		c. Wmk. sideways (5.3.57) ..	3	6	2	0
544	**155**	2½d. carmine-red (Type I) (28.9.55)	0	6	0	3
		a. Wmk. sideways (Type I) (23.3.56)	1	6	1	0
		b. Type II (Sept. '55) ..	0	9	0	9
		ba. Tête-bêche (horiz. pr.) ..				
		bb. Imperf. pane*				
		bc. Part perf. pane* ..				
545	**155**	3d. deep lilac (17.7.56) ..	1	3	0	3
		aa. Tête-bêche (horiz. pr.) ..				
		a. Imp. three sides (pair) ..				
		b. Wmk. sideways (22.11.57)	7	6	7	6
546	**156**	4d. ultram. (14.11.55) ..	1	0	0	3
547	**157**	5d. brown (21.9.55) ..	1	3	1	0
548	,,	6d. reddish purple (20.12.55)	4	0	0	4
		aa. Imperf. three sides (pr.)..				
		a. *Deep claret* (8.5.58) ..	12	6	1	3
		ab. Imperf. three sides (pr.)..				
549	,,	7d. bright green (23.4.56)	2	6	0	6
550	**158**	8d. magenta (21.12.55)..	2	6	0	4
551	,,	9d. bronze-grn. (15.12.55)	3	0	0	4
552	,,	10d. Prussian bl. (22.9.55)	3	0	0	4
553	,,	11d. brn.-pur. (28.10.55)	3	0	1	3
554	**159**	1s. bistre-brn. (3.11.55)	4	0	0	3
555	**160**	1s. 3d. green (27.3.56) ..	4	6	0	6
556	**159**	1s. 6d. grey-bl. (27.3.56)	6	0	0	6

The dates given for Nos. 540/556 are those on which they were first issued by the Supplies Dept. to postmasters.

In December 1956 a completely imperforate sheet of No. 543*b* was noticed by clerks in a Kent post office one of whom purchased it against P.O. regulations. In view of this irregularity we do not consider it properly issued.

Types of 2½d. In this issue, in 1957, Type II formerly only found in stamps from booklets, began to replace Type I on sheet stamps.

* Booklet Errors. Those listed as " imperf. panes " show one row of perforations either at top or bottom of the booklet pane; those as " part perf. panes " have one row of 3 stamps imperf. on three sides.

170. Scout Badge and " Rolling Hitch ".

171. " Scouts coming to Britain ".

172. Globe within a Compass.

(Des. Mary Adshead (2½d.), Pat Keely (4d.), W. H. Brown (1s. 3d.).)

1957 (1 Aug.). *World Scout Jubilee Jamboree. W* **165.** *P* 15×14.

No.	Type	Description	s.	d.	s.	d.
557	**170**	2½d. carmine-red	1	0	0	9
558	**171**	4d. ultramarine	3	6	3	6
559	**172**	1s. 3d. green	12	6	12	6

173

1957 (12 Sept.). *46th Inter Parliamentary Union Conference.* *W* **165.** *P* 15×14.

560	**173**	4d. ultramarine	8	6	10	0

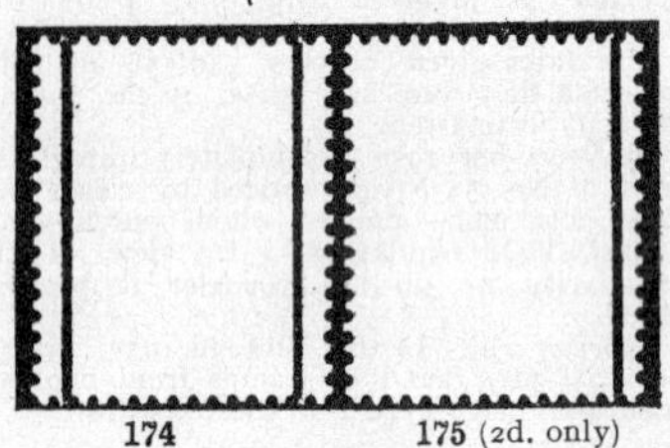

174 **175** (2d. only)

(Stamps viewed from back)

Graphite-Lined and Phosphor Issues.

These are used in connection with automatic sorting machinery, originally experimentally at Southampton but now also operating elsewhere. In such areas phosphor-lined stamps are the normal issue.

The graphite lines were printed in black on the back, beneath the gum; two lines per stamp, except for the 2d. (*see* T **174/5**).

In November 1959, phosphor lines, printed on the front, replaced the Graphite. They are wider than the Graphite, not easy to see, but show as broad vertical bands at certain angles to the light.

Values representing the rate for printed papers have one band and all others have two bands except the large-size commemorative stamps which have three.

In the small stamps the bands are on each side with the single band at left (except where otherwise stated). In the large-size commemorative stamps the three bands are at centre and sides but the single band may be at left, centre or right varying in different issues.

The Phosphor was originally applied typographically and later usually by photogravure, but sometimes by typography.

N.B. *A number of instances of misplaced Phosphor bands have been reported.*

1957 (19 Nov.). *Graphite-lined issue.* *W* **165.** *P* 15×14.

561	**154**	½d. orange-red	0	6	0	6
562	"	1d. ultramarine ..	0	9	0	9
563	"	1½d. green	1	3	1	3
		a. Both lines at left ..	—		£50	
564	"	2d. light red-brown ..	1	6	1	6
		a. Line at left	£75		£75	
565	**155**	2½d. carmine-red (Type II)	1	6	1	9
566	"	3d. deep lilac	1	3	0	6

No. 564*a* results from a misplacement of the line and horizontal pairs exist showing one stamp without line. No. 563*a* results from a similar misplacement.

176. Welsh Dragon.

177. Flag and Games Emblem.

178. Welsh Dragon.

(Des. Reynolds Stone (3d.), W. H. Brown (6d.), Pat Keely (1s. 3d.).)

1958 (18 July). *Sixth British Empire and Commonwealth Games, Cardiff.* *W* **165.** *P* 15×14.

567	**176**	3d. deep lilac	1	6	0	9
568	**177**	6d. reddish purple ..	5	0	5	0
569	**178**	1s. 3d. green	12	6	12	6

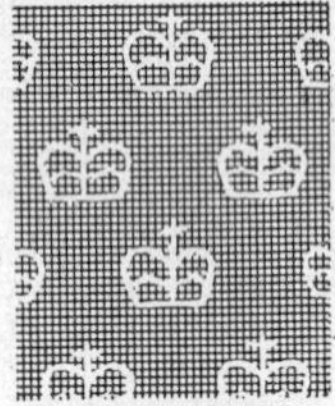

179. Multiple Crowns.

1958–65. *W* **179.** *P* 15×14.

570	**154**	½d. orange-red (25.11.58)	0	1	0	2
		a. Wmk. sideways (-.4.61) ..	0	6	0	6
		c. Part perf. pane* ..				
		d. Tête-bêche (vert. pr.) ..	£275			
		k. Chalky paper (15.7.63) ..	1	6	1	6
		l. Booklet pane (570k×3 *se-tenant* with 574k) ..	6	0	6	0
		m. Booklet pane (570a×2 *se-tenant* with 574l×2) ..	2	0	2	0
571	"	1d. ultram. (-.11.58) ..	0	2	0	2
		aa. Imperf. (vert. pair from coil)				
		a. Wmk. sideways (-.4.61) ..	0	3	0	4
		b. Part perf. pane* ..				
		l. Booklet pane (571a×2 *se-tenant* with 575a×2)†	1	6	1	6
572	"	1½d. green (-.11.58) ..	0	3	0	2
		a. Wmk. sideways (-.4.61) ..	0	6	0	6
573	"	2d. lt. red-brn. (4.12.58)	0	3	0	2
		a. Wmk. sideways (3.4.59) ..	0	4	0	4
574	**155**	2½d. carm.-red (Type II.) (-.11.58)	0	4	0	2
		aa. Imperf. strip of 3 ..				
		ab. Tête-bêche (horiz. pr.) ..				
		ac. Imperf. strip of 6 ..				

a. Wmk. sideways (Type I) (10.11.60) 0 5 0 6
b. Type I (wmk. upright) (-.10.61) 2 6 2 6
k. Type II. Chalky paper (15.7.63) 0 6 0 6
. Wmk. sideways (Type II) Ord. paper (1.7.64) .. 0 6 0 6

575 **155** 3d. deep lilac (-.11.58).. 0 5 0 2
a. Wmk. sideways (24.10.58) 0 5 0 5
b. Imperf. pane* .. ..
c. Part perf. pane* ..
d. Phantom "R".. .. £120

576 **156** 4d. ultram. (29.10.58) .. 0 8 0 4
a. Dp. ultramarine (28.4.65) 0 6 0 2
ab. Wmk. sideways (31.5.65?) 0 6 0 6

577 **156** 4½d. chestnut (9.2.59) .. 0 6 0 3

578 **157** 5d. brown (10.11.58) .. 0 7 0 3

579 „ 6d. dp. claret (23.12.58) 0 8 0 3
a. Imperf. three sides (pr.)..

580 „ 7d. brt. green (26.11.58) 0 9 0 4

581 **158** 8d. magenta (24.2.60) .. 0 11 0 4

582 „ 9d. bronze-grn. (24.3.59) 1 0 0 4

583 „ 10d. Prussian bl. (18.11.58) 1 1 0 6

584 **159** 1s. bistre-brn. (30.10.58) 1 3 0 3

585 **160** 1s. 3d. green (17.6.59) 1 7 0 6

586 **159** 1s. 6d. grey-bl. (16.12.58) 1 11 0 6

* Booklet Errors. See note after No. 556.

†Booklet pane No. 571l comes in two forms, with the 1d. stamps on the left or on the right.

The 1d., 1½d., 2½d. and 3d. first appeared in booklets: 1d. 5/- July '58 booklet (issued Nov. '58); 1½d. 3/- Nov. '58 booklet; 2½d. and 3d. 5/- Nov. '58 booklet. In sheet form they appeared on the following dates: 1d. 24.3.59; 1½d. 30.8.60; 2½d. 15.9.59; 3d. 8.12.58.

Sideways watermark. The 2d., 2½d., 3d. and 4d. come from coils and the ½d., 1d., 1½d., 2½d., 3d. and 4d. come from booklets. In *coil* stamps the sideways watermark shows the top of the watermark to the left. In the *booklet* stamps it comes equally to the left or right.

Nos. 570k and 574k come only from 2s. "Holiday Resort" Experimental undated booklets issued in 1963, in which one page contained 1 × 2½d. *se-tenant* with 3 × ½d. (*See* No. 570l.)

No. 574l comes only from the "Holiday Resort" Experimental booklets dated "1964" comprising four panes each containing two of these 2½d. stamps *se-tenant* vertically with two ½d. No. 570a. (*See* No. 570m.)

2½d. *imperf.* No. 574aa comes from a booklet with watermark upright. No. 574ac is from a coil with sideways watermark.

No. 574b comes from *sheets* bearing cylinder number 42.

Nos. 575d and 615a occurred on the last stamp of the sheet from Cyl. 41 (no stop), where the Jubilee line showed an "R". The cylinder was later twice retouched. The stamps listed show the original, unretouched "R". This variety is best collected in a block of 4 or 6 with full margins in order to be sure that it is not No. 615a with phosphor lines missing.

In *Coil* stamps (2d., 2½d., 3d.) the sideways watermark shows the top of the watermark to the left. In the Booklet stamps (½d., 1d., 1½d., 3d.) it comes equally to left or right.

Whiter paper. On 18th May 1962 the Post Office announced that a whiter paper was being used for the current issue (including Nos. 595/8). The difference is so slight that any attempt at separate listing would only cause confusion. The composition of the paper is unchanged, and there were originally several makings of the "whiter" paper differing in shade.

In 1964 No. 575 was printed on an experimental paper which is distinguishable by an additional watermark letter "T" lying on its side, which occurs about four times in the sheet, usually in the side margins. 48,000 sheets were issued. (*Price of "T" wmk. in marginal block of* 8, 12*s.* 6*d.*)

1958 (24 Nov.)–**61**. *Graphite-lined issue.* *W* **179**. *P* 15 × 14.

587 **154** ½d. orange-red (15.6.59) 8 6 8 6

588 „ 1d. ultramarine (18.12.58) 1 6 1 6
a. Misplaced Graphite lines (July '61)* .. 1 6 2 0

589 „ 1½d. green (4.8.59) .. 22 6 22 6

590 „ 2d. lt. red-brn. (24.11.58) 1 0 1 3

591 **155** 2½d. carm.-red (Type II) (9.6.59) 1 6 2 6

592 „ 3d. deep lilac (24.11.58) 1 6 1 9
a. Misplaced Graphite lines (May '61)* .. ..

593 **156** 4d. ultramarine (29.4.59) 3 6 3 6

594 „ 4½d. chestnut (3.6.59) .. 3 6 3 6

Nos. 587/9 were only issued in booklets or coils (587/8).

* No. 588*a* (in coils) and No. 592*a* (in sheets) result from the use of a residual stock of graphite-lined paper. As the use of graphite lines had ceased, the register of the lines in relation to the stamps was of no importance and numerous misplacements occurred—two lines close together, one line only, etc. No. 592a refers to stamps with two lines only at left and both clear of the perforations.

(Recess. De La Rue (until 31.12.62), then Bradbury, Wilkinson.)

1959–63. *W* **179.** *P* 11 × 12.

595 **166** 2s. 6d. blk.-brn. (22.7.59) 10 0 1 0
a. B.W. ptg. (2.7.63) .. 3 2 0 9

596 **167** 5s. rose-red (15.6.59) .. 20 0 2 0
a. B.W. ptg. (2.9.63) .. 6 3 1 6

597 **168** 10s. blue (21.7.59) .. 40 0 4 0
a. B.W. ptg. *Bright ultramarine* (1.11.63) .. 12 6 3 0

598 **169** £1 black (30.6.59) .. 80 0 10 0
a. B.W. ptg. (2.12.63) .. 25 0 6 0

The B.W. printings have a marginal Plate Number. They are more deeply engraved than the D.L.R., showing more of the Diadem detail and heavier lines on Her Majesty's face. The vertical perf. 11.9 as against D.L.R. 11.8.

1959 (18 Nov.). *Phosphor-Graphite issue.* *P* 15 × 14. (*a*) *W* **165.**

599 **154** ½d. orange-red 12 6 12 6

600 „ 1d. ultramarine.. .. 12 6 12 6

601 „ 1½d. green 12 6 12 6

(*b*) *W* **179.**

605 **154** 2d. lt. red-brn. (1 band) 10 0 10 0
a. Error. W 165 .. 60 0 60 0

606 **155** 2½d. carmine-red (Type II) 12 6 12 6

607 „ 3d. deep lilac 12 6 12 6

608 **156** 4d. ultramarine.. .. 15 0 15 0

609 „ 4½d. chestnut 12 6 12 6

This issue has both Phosphor bands on front and Graphite lines on back. (Except the 2d. value which has one band on front and one line on back.)

1960 (6 July)–**65**. *Phosphor issue.* *W* **179.** *P* 15 × 14.

610 **154** ½d. orange-red.. .. 0 1 0 3
a. Wmk. sideways (-.4.61) 0 6 0 6

611 „ 1d. ultramarine .. 0 2 0 3
a. Wmk. sideways (-.4.61) 0 3 0 5
l. Booklet pane (611a × 2 *se-tenant* with 615d × 2)† 1 9 1 9

612 „ 1½d. green 0 3 0 3
a. Wmk. sideways (-.4.61) 0 8 0 8

613 „ 2d. lt. red-brn. (1 band) 2 6 2 6

613*a* „ 2d. light red brown (two bands) (4.10.61) 0 3 0 4

614 **155** 2½d. carmine-red (Type II) (2 bands)* .. 0 4 0 5

614*a* „ 2½d. carmine-red (Type II) (1 band) (4.10.61) 0 9 0 9

614*b* „ 2½d. carmine-red (Type I) (1 band) (7.11.61).. 4 6 2 0

615 „ 3d. deep lilac (2 bands) 0 8 0 8
a. Phantom "R" .. 90 0
b. Wmk. sideways (-- .61) 0 10 0 9

615*c*	**155**	3d. dp. lilac (1 band) ('65)	0	5	0	4
		d. Wmk. sideways (16.8.65)	0	5	0	6
616	**156**	4d. ultramarine ..	0	8	0	8
		a. Dp. ultramarine (28.4.65)	0	6	0	4
		ab. Wmk. sideways (16.8.65)	0	6	0	6
616*b*	,,	4½d. chestnut (13.9.61)	0	6	0	8
617	**157**	6d. deep claret ..	0	8	0	9
618	**160**	1s. 3d. green	1	7	1	9

The stamps with watermark sideways are from booklets.

*No. 614 with two bands on the creamy paper was originally from cylinder 50 dot and no dot. When the change in postal rates took place in 1965 it was reissued from cylinder 57 dot and no dot on the whiter paper. Some of these latter were also released in error in districts of S.E. London in September 1964. The shade of the reissue is slightly more carmine.

†Booklet pane No. 611l comes in two forms, with the 1d. stamps on the left or on the right. This was printed in this manner to provide for 3d. stamps with only one band.

Unlike previous one-banded phosphor stamps, No. 615*c* has a broad band extending over two stamps so that alternate stamps have the band at left or right (same prices either way).

180. Postboy of 1660.

181. Posthorn of 1660.

(Des. Reynolds Stone (3d.), Faith Jaques (1s. 3d.).)

1960 (7 July). *Tercentenary of Establishment of "General Letter Office".* *W* **179** (*sideways on 1s. 3d.*). *P* 15×14 (3d.) *or* 14×15 (*1s. 3d.*).

619	**180**	3d. deep lilac	1	9	0	6
620	**181**	1s. 3d. green	12	6	12	6

182. Conference Emblem.

(Des. Reynolds Stone (emblem, P. Rahikainen).)

1960 (19 Sept.). *First Anniv. of European Postal and Telecommunications Conference. Chalky paper.* *W* **179.** *P* 15×14.

621	**182**	6d. bronze-grn. & purple	7	6	7	6
622	,,	1s. 6d. brown and blue	15	0	15	0

183. Thrift Plant.

184. " Growth of Savings ".

185. Thrift Plant.

(Des. P. Gauld (2½d.), M. Goaman (others).)

1961 (28 Aug.). *Centenary of Post Office Savings Bank. Chalky paper.* *W* **179** (*sideways on 2½d.*). *P* 14×15 (*2½d.*) *or* 15×14 (*others*).

I. " TIMSON " Machine.

II. " THRISSELL " Machine.

			I.				II.			
623	**183**	2½d. blk. & red	2	0	1	6	10	0	10	0
624	**184**	3d. orge.-brn. & violet	1	6	1	0	4	0	1	0
		a. Oran.-brn. omitd.	—		—		—		—	
		x. Perf. through side sheet margin ..	45	0			†			
		xa. Orge.-brn. omitd.	—		—		†			
625	**185**	1s. 6d. red & blue ..	15	0	15	0	†			

2½d. TIMSON. Cyls. 1E–1F. Deeply shaded portrait (brownish-black).

2½d. THRISSELL. Cyls. 1D–1B or 1D (stop)-1B. Lighter portrait (grey-black).

3d. TIMSON. Cyls. 3D–3E. Clear, well-defined portrait with deep shadows and bright highlights.

3d. THRISSELL. Cyls. 3C–3B or 3C (stop)-3B (stop). Dull portrait, lacking in contrast.

NOTE. Sheet marginal copies *without* single extension perf. hole on the short side of the stamp are always " Timson ", as are those with large punch-hole *not* coincident with printed three-sided box guide mark.

The 3d. " Timson " perforated completely through the right-hand side margin came from a relatively small part of the printing perforated on a sheet-fed machine.

Normally the " Timsons " were perforated in the reel, with three large punch-holes in both long margins and the perforations completely through both short margins. Only one punch-hole coincides with the guide-mark.

The " Thrissells " have one large punch-hole n one long margin, coinciding with guide-mark, and one short margin imperf. (except sometimes for encroachments).

A very small quantity of all values was sold in error at the Chorley, Lancs., P.O. on 21st August, 1961.

186. C.E.P.T. Emblem.

187. Doves and Emblem.

188. Doves and Emblem.

(Des. M. Goaman (doves, T. Kurpershoek).)

1961 (18 Sept.). *European Postal and Telecommunications (C.E.P.T.) Conference, Torquay. Chalky paper. W* **179.** *P* 15 × 14.

626	**186**	2d. orge., pink & brown	1	0	1	0
627	**187**	4d. buff, mve. & ultram.	3	6	3	6
628	**188**	10d. turquoise, pale green and Prussian blue ..	6	0	6	0
		a. Green omitted				
		b. Turquoise omitted ..				

189. Hammer Beam Roof, Westminster Hall.

190. Palace of Westminster.

(Des. Miss F. Jaques.)

1961 (25 Sept.). *Seventh Commonwealth Parliamentary Conference. Chalky paper. W* **179** *(sideways on* 1s. 3*d.). P* 15 × 14 *(6d.) or* 14 × 15 (1s. 3*d.*).

629	**189**	6d. purple and gold ..	3	0	2	0
		a. Gold omitted				
630	**190**	1s. 3d. green and blue ..	12	6	12	6

191. " Units of Productivity ".

192. " National Productivity ".

193. " Unified Productivity ".

(Des. D. Gentleman.)

1962 (14 Nov.). *National Productivity Year. Chalky paper. W* **179** *(inverted on* 2½*d. and* 3*d.). P* 15 × 14.

631	**191**	2½d. deep green and carmine-red (*shades*) ..	1	6	1	0
		p. One phosphor band ..	2	6	2	0
632	**192**	3d. light blue and violet	2	6	1	0
		a. Queen's head omitted ..	£275			
		p. Three phosphor bands ..	3	0	3	0
633	**193**	1s. 3d. carmine, lt. blue and deep green	15	0	15	0
		a. Queen's head omitted ..				
		p. Three phosphor bands ..	17	6	17	6

Small quantities of each value (approx. 60 × 2½d., 350 × 3d. and 20 × 1s. 3d.) were sold in error at a Lewisham, London post office on October 16th and 17th, 1962.

194. Campaign Emblem and Family.

195. Children of Three Races.

(Des. M. Goaman.)

1963 (21 Mar.). *Freedom from Hunger.* *W* **179** (*inverted*). *P* 15 × 14.

634	**194**	2½d. crimson and pink ..	1	6	1	6
		p. One phosphor band ..	2	0	2	0
635	**195**	1s.3d. bis.-brn. & yell.	12	6	12	6
		p. Three phosphor bands	17	6	17	6

196. " Paris Conference ".

(Des. Reynolds Stone.)

1963 (7 May). *Paris Postal Conference Centenary. Chalky paper.* *W* **179** (*inverted*). *P* 15 × 14.

636	**196**	6d. green and mauve ..	3	0	3	0
		a. Green omitted	£350			
		p. Three phosphor bands ..	5	0	5	0

197. Posy of Flowers.

198. Woodland Life.

(Des. S. Scott (3d.), M. Goaman (4½d.).)

1963 (16 May). *National Nature Week. Chalky paper.* *W* **179.** *P* 15 × 14.

637	**197**	3d. yell., grn., brn. & blk.	1	6	1	0
		p. Three phosphor bands ..	2	0	1	6
638	**198**	4½d. black, blue, yellow, magenta & brown-red	4	0	4	0
		p. Three phosphor bands ..	6	0	6	0

199. Rescue at Sea.

200. 19th-century Lifeboat.

201. Lifeboatmen.

(Des. D. Gentleman.)

1963 (31 May). *Ninth International Lifeboat Conference, Edinburgh. Chalky paper.* *W* **179.** *P* 15 × 14.

639	**199**	2½d. blue, black and red ..	1	6	1	0
		p. One phosphor band ..	2	0	1	0
640	**200**	4d. red, yellow, brown, black and blue ..	3	0	3	0
		p. Three phosphor bands ..	4	6	4	6
641	**201**	1s. 6d. sepia, yellow and grey-blue	12	6	12	6
		p. Three phosphor bands ..	17	6	17	6

202. Red Cross.

203

204

(Des. H. Bartram.)

1963 (15 Aug.). *Red Cross Centenary Congress. Chalky paper.* *W* **179.** *P* 15 × 14.

642	**202**	3d. red and deep lilac ..	1 0	0 9
		a. Red omitted ..	..	
		p. Three phosphor bands ..	1 3	1 0
		pa. Red omitted ..	..	
643	**203**	1s. 3d. red, blue and grey	5 0	5 0
		p. Three phosphor bands ..	6 6	6 6
644	**204**	1s. 6d. red, blue & bistre	8 6	8 6
		p. Three phosphor bands ..	12 0	12 0

205. " Commonwealth Cable ".

(Des. P. Gauld.)

1963 (3 Dec.). *Opening of COMPAC (Trans-Pacific Telephone Cable). Chalky paper.* *W* **179.** *P* 15 × 14.

645	**205**	1s. 6d. blue and black ..	10 0	8 6
		a. Black omitted ..	..	
		p. Three phosphor bands ..	12 6	12 6

206. Puck and Bottom (*A Midsummer Night's Dream*).

207. Feste (*Twelfth Night*).

208. Balcony Scene (*Romeo and Juliet*).

209. " Eve of Agincourt " (*Henry V*).

210. Hamlet contemplating Yorick's skull (*Hamlet*) and Queen Elizabeth II.

(Des. D. Gentleman. Photo. Harrison & Sons (3d., 6d., 1s. 3d., 1s. 6d.). Des. C. and R. Ironside. Recess. Bradbury, Wilkinson (2s. 6d.).

1964 (23 April). *Shakespeare Festival. Chalky paper.* *W* **179.** *P* 11 × 12 (*2s. 6d.*) *or* 15 × 14 (*others*).

646	**206**	3d. yellow-bistre, black & deep violet-blue ..	1 0	0 6
		p. Three phosphor bands ..	1 6	1 0
647	**207**	6d. yellow, orange, black and yellow-olive ..	2 6	2 6
		p. Three phosphor bands ..	3 6	3 6
648	**208**	1s. 3d. cerise, turquoise, black and sepia ..	5 0	5 0
		p. Three phosphor bands ..	6 6	6 6
649	**209**	1s. 6d. violet, turquoise, black and blue ..	7 6	7 6
		p. Three phosphor bands ..	10 0	10 0
650	**210**	2s. 6d. deep purple-brown	12 6	12 6

211. Flats, Richmond Park (" Urban Development ").

212. Shipbuilding Yards, Belfast (Industrial Activity ").

213. Beddgelert Forest Park, Snowdonia (" Forestry ").

214. Nuclear Reactor, Dounreay (" Technological Development ").

(Des. D. Bailey.)

1964 (1 July). *20th International Geographical Congress, London. Chalky paper. W* **179.** *P* 15 × 14.

651	**211**	2½d. black, olive-yellow, olive-grey & turq.-bl.	1 0	1 0
		p. One phosphor band ..	1 6	1 6
652	**212**	4d. orge.-brn, red-brown, rose, black and violet	1 9	1 9
		a. Violet omitted	£125	£85
		p. Three phosphor bands ..	2 9	2 9
653	**213**	8d. yellow-brn., emerald, green and black ..	4 0	4 0
		a. Green (lawn) omitted ..		
		p. Three phosphor bands ..	10 0	10 0
654	**214**	1s. 6d. yellow-brn., pale pink, black & brown	7 6	7 6
		p. Three phosphor bands ..	10 0	10 0

215. Spring Gentian.

216. Dog Rose.

217. Honeysuckle.

218. Fringed Water Lily.

(Des. M. and Sylvia Goaman.)

1964 (5 Aug.). *Tenth International Botanical Congress, Edinburgh. Chalky paper. W* **179.** *P* 15 × 14.

655	**215**	3d. violet, blue & sage-grn.	1 0	1 0
		a. Blue omitted		
		p. Three phosphor bands ..	1 3	1 3
656	**216**	6d. apple-green, rose, scarlet and green ..	2 0	2 0
		p. Three phosphor bands ..	2 6	2 6
657	**217**	9d. lemon, green, lake and rose-red	3 0	3 0
		p. Three phosphor bands ..	4 0	4 0
658	**218**	1s. 3d. yell., emerald, reddish violet & grey-grn.	5 6	5 6
		p. Three phosphor bands ..	7 6	7 6

219. Forth Road Bridge.

220. Forth Road and Railway Bridges.

(Des. A. Restall.)

1964 (4 Sept.). *Opening of Forth Road Bridge. Chalky paper. W* **179.** *P* 15 × 14.

659	**219**	3d. blk., bl. & reddish vio.	1 0	1 0
		p. Three phosphor bands ..	1 3	1 3
660	**220**	6d. black, light blue and carmine-red	2 6	2 6
		a. Light blue omitted ..	£400	£400
		p. Three phosphor bands ..	3 6	3 6

221. Sir Winston Churchill.

(Des. D. Gentleman and Rosalind Dease, from photograph by Karsh.)

1965 (8 JULY). *Churchill Commemoration. Chalky paper. W* **179.** *P* 15 × 14.

I. " REMBRANDT " Machine.

661	**221**	4d. black & olive-brown	1 0	1 0
		p. Three phosphor bands ..	1 0	1 0

II. " TIMSON " Machine.

661*a*	**221**	4d. black & olive-brown	1 0	1 0

III. " L. & M. 4 " Machine.

662	–	1s. 3d. black and grey ..	3 6	3 6
		p. Three phosphor bands ..	4 0	4 0

The 1s. 3d. shows a closer view of Churchill's head.

4d. REMBRANDT. Cyls. 1A–1B dot. Lack of shading detail on Churchill's portrait. Queen's portrait appears dull and coarse. This is a new rotary machine which is sheet-fed.

4d. TIMSON. Cyls. 5A–6B no dot. More detail on Churchill's portrait—furrow on forehead, his left eyebrow fully drawn and more shading on cheek. Queen's portrait lighter and sharper. This is a reel-fed, two-colour 12-in. wide rotary machine and the differences in impression are due to the greater pressure applied by this machine.

1s. 3d. Cyls. 1A–1B no dot. The " Linotype and Machinery No. 4 " machine is an ordinary sheet-fed flat plate machine. Besides being used for printing the 1s. 3d. stamps it was also employed for overprinting the phosphor bands on both values.

222. Simon de Montfort's Seal

223. Parliament Buildings (after engraving by Hollar, 1647).

(Des. S. R. Black (6d.), Prof. R. Guyatt (2s. 6d.).)

1965 (19 JULY). *700th Anniv. of Simon de Montfort's Parliament. Chalky paper. W* **179.** *P* 15 × 14.

663	**222**	6d. olive-green	1 0	1 0
		p. Three phosphor bands ..	1 3	1 3
664	**223**	2s. 6d. black & pale drab	6 6	7 6

Both values were accidentally released in the Mill Hill district of London on July 8th, the date of issue of the Churchill stamps. Covers are also known with both values, bearing the " First Day " cancellation of the Philatelic Bureau dated July 8th.

226. Lister's Carbolic Spray.

227. Lister and Chemical Symbols.

224. Bandsmen and Banner.

225. Three Salvationists.

(Des. M. C. Farrar Bell (3d.), G. Trenaman (1s. 6d.).)

1965 (9 AUG.). *Salvation Army Centenary. Chalky paper. W* **179.** *P* 15 × 14.

665	**224**	3d. indigo, grey-blue, cerise, yellow & brown	1 6	1 6
		p. One phosphor band ..	1 9	1 9
666	**225**	1s. 6d. red, blue, yellow and brown	5 0	5 0
		p. Three phosphor bands ..	6 0	6 0

(Des. P. Gauld (4d.), F. Ariss (1s.).)

1965 (1 SEPT.). *Centenary of Joseph Lister's Discovery of Antiseptic Surgery. Chalky paper. W* **179.** *P* 15 × 14.

667	**226**	4d. indigo, brown-red and grey-black	0 8	0 3
		a. Brown-red (tube) omitted		
		b. Indigo omitted		
		p. Three phosphor bands ..	0 9	0 9
		pa. Brown-red (tube) omitted ..		
668	**227**	1s. black, pur. & new blue	1 9	1 9
		p. Three phosphor bands ..	2 0	2 3

228. Trinidad Carnival Dancers.

229. Canadian Folk-dancers.

(Des. D. Gentleman and Rosalind Dease.)

1965 (1 Sept.). *Commonwealth Arts Festival. Chalky paper.* *W* **179.** *P* 15 × 14.

669	**228**	6d. black and orange ..	0 10	1 0
		p. Three phosphor bands ..	1 0	1 3
670	**229**	1s. 6d. black and light reddish violet ..	2 6	2 6
		p. Three phosphor bands ..	2 9	2 9

230. Flight of Spitfires.

231. Pilot in Hurricane.

232. Wing-tips of Spitfire and Messerschmitt "109".

233. Spitfires attacking Heinkel "HE-111" Bomber.

234. Spitfires attacking Stuka Dive-bomber.

235. Hurricanes over Wreck of Dornier. "DO-17z2" Bomber.

236. Anti-aircraft Artillery in Action.

237. Air-battle over St. Paul's Cathedral.

(Des. D. Gentleman and Rosalind Dease (4d. × 6 and 1s. 3d.), A. Restall (9d.).)

1965 (13 Sept.). *25th Anniv. of Battle of Britain. Chalky paper.* *W* **179.** *P* 15 × 14.

671	**230**	4d. yellow-olive & black	0 8	0 4
		p. Three phosphor bands ..	0 8	0 8
672	**231**	4d. yellow-olive, blackish olive and black ..	0 8	0 4
		p. Three phosphor bands ..	0 8	0 8
673	**232**	4d. red, new blue, yellow-olive, olive-grey & blk.	0 8	0 4
		p. Three phosphor bands ..	0 8	0 8
674	**233**	4d. blackish olive, yellow-olive and black ..	0 8	0 4
		p. Three phosphor bands ..	0 8	0 8
675	**234**	4d. blackish olive, yellow-olive and black ..	0 8	0 4
		p. Three phosphor bands ..	0 8	0 8
676	**235**	4d. olive-grey, yellow-olive, new blue and black ..	0 8	0 4
		p. Three phosphor bands ..	0 8	0 8
677	**236**	9d. black, violet, orange and purple-brown ..	1 3	1 3
		p. Three phosphor bands ..	1 6	1 8
678	**237**	1s. 3d. deep blue-green, black and light blue ..	2 0	2 3
		p. Three phosphor bands ..	2 3	2 6

Nos. 671/6 were issued together *se-tenant* in blocks of 6 (3 × 2) within the sheet. *Price per block (ordinary or phosphor), un.* 4s.

238. Tower and Georgian Buildings.

239. Tower and " Nash " Terrace, Regent's Park.

(Des. C. Abbott.)

1965 (8 Oct.). *Opening of Post Office Tower. Chalky paper. W* **179** *(sideways on 3d.). P* 14 × 15 (3*d.*) *or* 15 × 14 (1*s.* 3*d.*).

679	**238**	3d. olive-yellow, new blue and bronze-green ..	0	6	0	8
		a. Olive-yellow(Tower)omitted				
		p. One phosphor band ..	0	6	0	8
680	**239**	1s. 3d. bronze-green, yellow-green and blue ..	2	0	2	3
		p. Three phosphor bands ..	2	3	2	6

240. U.N. Emblem.

241. I.C.Y. Emblem.

(Des. J. Matthews.)

1965 (25 Oct.). *20th Anniv. of U.N.O. and International Co-operation Year. Chalky paper. W* **179.** *P* 15 × 14.

681	**240**	3d. black, yellow-orange and light blue ..	0	6	0	8
		p. One phosphor band ..	0	6	0	8
682	**241**	1s. 6d. black, brt. purple and light blue ..	2	3	2	4
		p. Three phosphor bands ..	2	6	2	9

242. Telecommunications Network.

243. Radio Waves and Switchboard.

(Des. A. Restall.)

1965 (15 Nov.). *I.T.U. Centenary. Chalky paper. W* **179.** *P* 15 × 14.

683	**242**	9d. red, ultram., dp. slate-violet, black and pink ..	2	6	2	6
		p. Three phosphor bands ..	1	3	1	6
684	**243**	1s. 6d. red, greenish blue, indigo, blk. & lt. pink	2	9	3	0
		p. Three phosphor bands ..	5	0	5	0

244. Robert Burns (after Skirving chalk drawing.)

245. Robert Burns (after Nasmyth portrait.)

(Des. G. F. Huntly.)

1966 (25 Jan.). *Burns Commemoration. Chalky paper. W* **179.** *P* 15 × 14.

685	**244**	4d. black, deep violet-blue and new blue ..	0	7	0	3
		p. Three phosphor bands ..	0	7	0	7
686	**245**	1s. 3d. black, grey-blue and yellow-orange ..	2	0	2	0
		p. Three phosphor bands ..	2	0	2	3

246. Westminster Abbey.

247. Fan Vaulting, Henry VII Chapel.

(Des. Sheila Robinson. Photo. Harrison (3d.). Des. and eng. Bradbury, Wilkinson. Recess. (2s. 6d.).)

1966 (28 FEB.). *900th Anniv. of Westminster Abbey. Chalky paper* (3d.). *W* **179.** *P* 15 × 14.

687	**246**	3d. black, red-brown and new blue	0	6	0	6
		p. One phosphor band ..	0	6	0	7
688	**247**	2s. 6d. black	4	6	4	6

REGIONAL ISSUES.

Printers (stamps of all regions) :—Photo. Harrison & Sons. Portrait by Dorothy Wilding Ltd

I. GUERNSEY.

For earlier issues, see *Channel Islands.*

GU 1

GU 2

(Des. E. A. Piprell.)

1958 (18 AUG.)–**66.** *W* **179.** *P* 15 × 14.

GU1	GU **1**	2½d. rose-red (8.6.64) ..	0	6	0	6
GU2	GU **2**	3d. deep lilac ..	0	5	0	5
GU3	,,	4d. ultram. (7.2.66) ..	0	6	0	6

II. ISLE OF MAN.

IM 1

IM 2

(Des. J. H. Nicholson.)

1958 (18 AUG.)–**66.** *W* **179.** *P* 15 × 14.

IM1	IM **1**	2½d. carm.-red (8.6.64)	0	6	0	6
IM2	IM **2**	3d. deep lilac	0	5	0	5
		a. Chalky paper (17.5.63)	0	8	0	8
IM3	,,	4d. ultram. (7.2.66) ..	0	6	0	6

III. JERSEY.

For earlier Jersey issues, see *Channel Islands.*

JE 1

JE 2

(Des. E. Blampied (2½d.), W M. Gardner (3d. 4d.).)

1958 (18 AUG.)–**66.** *W* **179.** *P* 15 × 14.

JE1	JE **1**	2½d. carm.-red (8.6.64)	0	6	0	6
		a. Imperf. three sides (pair)				
JE2	JE **2**	3d. deep lilac	0	5	0	5
JE3	,,	4d. ultram. (7.2.66) ..	0	6	0	6

IV. NORTHERN IRELAND.

N 1

N 2

N 3

(Des. W. Hollywood (3d., 4d.), L. Pilton (6d.) T. Collins (1s. 3d.).)

1958–66. *W* **179.** *P* 15 × 14.

NI1	N **1**	3d. dp. lilac (18.8.58) ..	0	5	0	3
NI2	,,	4d. ultram. (7.2.66) ..	0	6	0	6
NI3	N **2**	6d. deep claret (29.9.58)	0	8	0	8
NI4	N **3**	1s. 3d. green (29.9.58) ..	1	7	1	9

V. SCOTLAND.

S 1

S 2

S 3

(Des. G. F. Huntly (3d., 4d.), J. B. Fleming (6d.) A. B. Imrie (1s. 3d.).)

1958–66. *W* **179.** *P* 15 × 14.

S1	S **1**	3d. deep lilac (18.8.58) ..	0	5	0	3
		p. Two phosphor bands (29.1.63)	0	9	0	6
		pa. One phosphor band ('65) ..	0	5	0	4
S2	,,	4d. ultram. (7.2.66) ..	0	6	0	6
		p. Two phosphor bands ..	0	6	0	8
S3	S **2**	6d. deep claret (29.9.58) ..	0	8	0	8
		p. Two phosphor bands (29.1.63)	0	8	0	9
S4	S **3**	1s. 3d. green (29.9.58) ..	1	7	1	9
		p. Two phosphor bands (29.1.63)	1	7	2	0

VI. WALES AND MONMOUTHSHIRE.

W 1

W 2

W 3

(Des. Reynolds Stone.)

1958–66. *W* **179.** *P* 15×14.

No.	Type	Description				
W1	W 1	3d. deep lilac (18.8.58) ..	0	5	0	3
W2	,,	4d. ultram. (7.2.66)	0	6	0	6
W3	W 2	6d. deep claret (29.9.58)	0	8	0	8
W4	W 3	1s. 3d. green (29.9.58) ..	1	7	1	9

POSTAGE DUE STAMPS.

D 1

D 2

(Typo. by Somerset House (early trial printings of ½d., 1d., 2d. and 5d.; all ptgs. of 1s.) and by Harrison & Sons (later ptgs. of all values except 1s.). Not easily distinguishable except by the control).

1914–23. *Wmk. Royal Cypher, sideways* ("*Simple*"), *T* **100.** *P* 14×15.

No.	Type	Description				
D 1	D 1	½d. emerald	0	6	0	8
D 2	,,	1d. carmine	0	8	0	6
D 3	,,	1d. pale carmine ..	1	0	0	6
D 3*a*	,,	1½d. chestnut (1923) ..	15	0	10	0
D 4	,,	2d. agate	1	0	0	8
D 5	,,	3d. violet (1918) ..	2	3	0	8
D 6	,,	3d. dull violet	2	3	0	8
D 7	,,	4d. dull grey-green (1921)	3	6	0	10
D 8	,,	5d. bistre-brown ..	2	6	0	8
D 9	,,	1s. bright blue (1915) ..	7	6	1	0
D10	,,	1s. deep bright blue ..	7	6	1	0

The 1d. is known bisected and used to make up 1½d. rate on understamped letters from Ceylon (1921).

1924. *As* 1914–23, *but thick chalk-surfaced paper.*

No.	Type	Description				
D10*a*	D 1	1d. carmine	3	0	2	6

(Typo Waterlow & Sons, Ltd., and (from 1934) Harrison & Sons.)

1924–31. *W* **111,** *sideways.* *P* 14×15.

No.	Type	Description				
D10*b*	D 1	½d. emerald	0	6	0	8
D11	,,	1d. carmine	0	6	0	4
D12	,,	1½d. chestnut	30	0	30	0
D13	,,	2d. agate	0	8	0	6
D14	,,	3d. dull violet	1	3	0	10
		a. Printed on gummed side	£12		†	
		b. Experimental paper, W 111*a*	£6		£6	
D15	D 1	4d. dull grey-green ..	1	6	1	3
D16	,,	5d. bistre-brown ('31) ..	6	0	8	6
D17	,,	1s. deep blue	3	6	1	6
D18	D 2	2s. 6d. purple/*yellow* ..	10	0	2	6

1936–37. *W* **125** (E 8 R) *sideways.* *P* 14×15.

No.	Type	Description				
D19	D 1	½d. emerald (June, '37) ..	0	8	1	3
D20	,,	1d. carmine (May, '37) ..	1	0	1	0
D21	,,	2d. agate (May, '37) ..	2	0	2	0
D22	,,	3d. dull violet (Mar., '37)	1	3	1	3
D23	,,	4d. dull grey-green (Dec., '36)	2	6	12	6
D24	,,	5d. bistre-brn. (Nov., '36)	3	6	12	6
D24*a*	,,	5d. yellow-brown ('37) ..	15	0	15	0
D25	,,	1s. deep blue (Dec., '36)	3	6	3	6
D26	D 2	2s. 6d. pur./*yell.* (5.37) ..	15	0	8	6

1937–38. *W* **127** (G VI R) *sideways.* *P* 14×15.

No.	Type	Description				
D27	D 1	½d. emerald ('38) ..	0	10	0	10
D28	,,	1d. carmine ('38) ..	1	0	1	0
D29	,,	2d. agate ('38)	0	10	0	6
D30	,,	3d. violet ('38)	1	0	0	6
D31	,,	4d. dull grey-green ('37)	2	6	1	0
D32	,,	5d. yellow-brown ('38) ..	1	3	0	9
D33	,,	1s. deep blue ('37)	7	6	1	3
D34	D 2	2s. 6d. pur./*yellow* ('38)	12	6	2	0

DATES OF ISSUE:—The following dates are those on which stamps were first issued by the Supplies Dept. to postmasters.

1951–52. *Colours changed and new value* (1½*d.*). *W* **127** (G VI R) *sideways.* *P* 14×15.

No.	Type	Description				
D35	D 1	½d. orange (18.9.51) ..	0	8	0	8
D36	,,	1d. violet-blue (6.6.51)	1	0	1	0
D37	,,	1½d. green (11.2.52) ..	1	3	1	3
D40	,,	4d. blue (14.8.51) ..	3	6	3	6
D42	,,	1s. bistre-brn. (6.12.51)	4	6	3	0

The 1d. is known bisected (Camberley, 6 April, 1954).

1954–55. *W* **153.** (*Mult. Tudor Crown and* E 2 R) *sideways.* *P* 14×15.

No.	Type	Description				
D43	D 1	½d. orange (8.6.55) ..	0	6	0	8
D46	,,	2d. agate (28.7.55) ..	1	3	2	0
D47	,,	3d. violet (4.5.55) ..	4	6	5	6
D48	,,	4d. blue (14.7.55) ..	5	0	4	6
		a. Imperf. (pair)	£70			
D49	,,	5d. yellow-brn. (19.5.55)	5	0	5	0
D51	D 2	2s. 6d. pur.-*yel.* (Dec. '54)	7	6	6	0

1955–57. *W* **165** (*Mult. St. Edward's Crown and* E 2 R) *sideways.* *P* 14×15.

No.	Type	Description				
D52	D 1	½d. orange (16.7.56) ..	0	4	0	4
D53	,,	1d. violet-blue (7.6.56) ..	0	5	0	5
D54	,,	1½d. green (13.2.56) ..	0	6	0	6
D55	,,	2d. agate (22.5.56) ..	1	0	1	0
D56	,,	3d. violet (5.3.56)	1	0	1	0
D57	,,	4d. blue (24.4.56) ..	1	3	1	3
D58	,,	5d. yellow-brn. (23.3.56)	1	3	1	0
D59	,,	1s. bistre-brn. (22.11.55)	2	6	2	6
D60	D 2	2s. 6d. pur./*yell.* (28.6.57)	6	0	6	0
D61	,,	5s. scar./*yellow* (25.11.55)	10	0	3	6

The 2d. is known bisected (June 1956), and also the 4d. (Poplar, London, April 1959).

1959–63. *W* **179** (*Mult. St. Edward's Crown*) *sideways.* *P* 14×15.

No.	Type	Description				
D62	D 1	½d. orange (18.10.61) ..	0	1	0	2
D63	,,	1d. violet-blue (9.5.60) ..	0	2	0	2
D64	,,	1½d. green (5.10.60) ..	0	9	0	9
D65	,,	2d. agate (14.9.59) ..	0	3	0	3
D66	,,	3d. violet (24.3.59) ..	0	5	0	6
D67	,,	4d. blue (17.12.59) ..	0	6	0	6
D68	,,	5d. yell.-brown (6.11.61)	0	7	0	6
D69	,,	6d. purple (29.3.62)	0	8	0	7
D70	,,	1s. bistre-brn. (11.4.60)	1	3	1	3
D71	D 2	2s. 6d. pur./*yell.* (11.5.61)	3	2	2	6
D72	,,	5s. scar./*yell.* (8.5.61) ..	6	3	3	0
D73	,,	10s. blue/*yell.* (2.9.63) ..	12	6	5	0
D74	,,	£1 black/*yell.* (2.9.63) ..	25	0	10	0

Whiter paper. The note after No. 686 also applies to Postage Due stamps.

OFFICIAL STAMPS.

In 1840 the 1d. black (Type **1**), with "V R" in the upper corners, was prepared for official use, but never issued for postal purposes. Obliterated specimens are those which were used for experimental trials of obliterating inks, or those that passed the post by oversight.

V 1

Prepared for use but not issued.
"V" "R" *in upper corners. Imperf.*

V1 V **1** 1d. black £180

All the following were overprinted by De La Rue.

1. INLAND REVENUE.

I.R. OFFICIAL (O **1**) — I. R. OFFICIAL (O **2**)

Optd. with Types O **1** *or* O **2** (5*s*., 10*s*., £1).

1882–1901. *Stamps of Queen Victoria.*

Issues of **1880–81.**

O 1 ½d. green (28.10.82) .. 7 6 3 0
O 3 1d. lilac (Die II) (27.9.82) .. 1 6 0 4
a. Optd. in blue-black 60 0 25 0
b. "OFFICIAL" omitted ..
c. Lines of opts. transposed ..
O 4 6d. grey (30.10.82) 25 0 6 6

Controls. 1d. A *to* X.

Issues of **1884–88.**

O 5 ½d. slate-blue (8.5.85) .. 7 6 2 0
O 6 2½d. lilac (12.3.85) 70 0 40 0
O 7 1s. green (12.3.85) £15 £6
O 8 5s. rose (12.3.85) £25 £18
a. Raised stop after "R" .. £40 £25
b. Optd. in blue-black .. ..
O 9 5s. rose (*blued* paper) (12.3.85) £40 £25
O 9*a* 10s. cobalt (12.3.85) .. £60 £40
O 10 10s. ultramarine (12.3.85) .. £25 £14
a. Raised stop after "R" .. £50 £25
b. Optd. in blue-black .. £90 £60
O 10*c* 10s. ultramarine (*blued* paper) £80 £45
O 11 £1 brn.-lilac (wmk. Crowns) (12.3.85) £450 £400
a. Frame broken .. ..
O 12 £1 brn.-lil. (wmk. Orbs) ('90) £350 £275
a. Frame broken .. ..

Issues of **1887–92.**

O 13 ½d. vermilion (21.1.88) .. 2 0 0 6
a. Without "I.R." .. ..
b. Opt. double (imperf.) .. £40
O 14 1s. green (15.3.89) 40 0 10 0
O 15 2½d. purple/*blue* (20.10.91) .. 30 0 2 0
O 16 £1 green (13.4.92) £45 £16
a. No stop after "R" .. .. — £100
b. Frame broken .. ..

Controls. ½d. A *to* Q.

Nos. O 3, O 13, O 14 and O 16 may be found with two varieties of overprint, viz. 1887 printings, *thin* letters, and 1894 printings, *thicker* letters.

Issues of **1887** *and* **1900.**

O 17 ½d. blue-green (April, '01) .. 6 0 2 0
O 18 6d. pur./*rose-red* (14.6.01) .. £5 15 0
O 19 1s. green & carm. (Dec., '01) £18 £6

Controls. ½d. R.

1902–4. *Stamps of King Edward VII.*

O 20 ½d. blue-green, O (4.2.02) 4 6 1 6
O 21 1d. scarlet, O (4.2.02) .. 2 0 0 6
O 22 2½d. bright blue, O (19.2.02) £10 50 0
O 23 6d. dull purple, O (14.3.04) £3500
O 24 1s. green & car., O (29.4.02) £18 60 0
O 25 5s. carmine, O (29.4.02) .. £160 £90
a. Raised stop after "R" .. £275 £125
O 26 10s. ultram., O (29.4.02) .. £2500 £1600
a. Raised stop after "R" .. £2750 £2000
O 27 £1 green, O (20.4.02) .. £500 £200

Controls. ½d. A *and* B, *continuous.*
1d. A *and* B, *continuous.*

2. OFFICE OF WORKS.

O. W. OFFICIAL (O **3**)

Optd. with Type O **3**.
Stamps of Queen Victoria.

1896.

O 31 ½d. vermilion (24.3.96) .. 30 0 15 0
O 32 1d. lilac (Die II) (24.3.96) .. 20 0 12 0

1901.

O 33 ½d. blue-green (5.11.01) .. 60 0 40 0

Controls. ½d. verm. O
½d. green R
1d. U

1902.

O 34 5d. pur. & blue (II) (29.4.02) £5 70 0
O 35 10d. purple & carm. (28.5.02) £10 £7

1902–03. *Stamps of King Edward VII.*

O 36 ½d. blue-green, O (11.2.02) 50 0 8 0
O 37 1d. scarlet, O (11.2.02) .. 40 0 5 0
O 38 2d. green & car., O (29.3.02) £6 20 0
O 39 2½d. bright blue, O (20.3.02) £7 40 0
O 40 10d. pur. & scar., O (18.5.03) £40 £18

Controls. ½d. A *and* B, *continuous.*
1d. A *and* B, *continuous.*

3. ARMY.

ARMY OFFICIAL (O **4**) — ARMY OFFICIAL (**5**) — ARMY OFFICIAL (O **6**)

Optd. with Type O **4** (½*d*., 1*d*.) *or* O **5** (2½*d*., 6*d*.).
Stamps of Queen Victoria.

1896 (1 Sept.).

O 41 ½d. vermilion 1 0 0 6
a. "OFFICIAI" for "OFFICIAL" 22 6 20 0
O 42 1d. lilac (Die II) 1 0 0 4
a. "OFFICIAI" for "OFFICIAL" 20 0 17 6
O 43 2½d. purple/*blue* 2 6 1 6

Controls. ½d. O, P, Q.
1d. U, V, W, X.

1900–1.

O 46 ½d. blue-green (April, 1900) 1 0 0 4
O 47 6d. pur./*rose-red* (7.11.01) .. 4 0 6 0

Controls. ½d. R.

1902. *Stamps of King Edward VII optd. with Type* O **4**.

O 48 ½d. blue-green, O (11.2.02) 0 8 0 4
O 49 1d. scarlet, O (11.2.02) .. 0 8 0 4
a. Without "ARMY" ..
O 50 6d. dull purple, O (23.8.02) 8 6 10 0

Controls. ½d. A *and* B, *continuous*
1d. A *and* B, *continuous.*

1903 (Sept.). *Optd. with Type* O **6**.

O 52 6d. dull purple, O £16 £14

4. GOVERNMENT PARCELS.

GOVT PARCELS
(O 7)

Overprinted with Type O **7**, *in black.*
Stamps of Queen Victoria.

1883 (1 JULY)–**86.**

No.	Description	Unused		Used	
O 61	1½d. lilac (30.4.86)	45	0	15	0
	a. No dot under "T"	—		£8	
	b. Dot to left of "T"				
O 62	6d. green (30.4.86)	£7		45	0
O 63	9d. green (1.8.83)	90	0	50	0
O 64	1s. brown (*W* Crown, Pl. 13)	75	0	25	0
	a. No dot under "T"	£16		£7	
	b. Dot to left of "T"				
O 64*c*	1s. brown (Pl. 14)	£10		55	0
	d. No dot under "T"	—		£10	

1887–90.

No.	Description	Unused		Used	
O 65	1½d. purple & grn. (29.10.87)	8	6	2	0
	a. No dot under "T"	75	0	12	6
	b. Dot to right of "T" ..	45	0	6	0
	c. Dot to left of "T"	45	0	6	0
O 66	6d. pur./*rose-red* (19.12.87)	15	0	2	0
	a. No dot under "T"	£5		40	0
	b. Dot to right of "T" ..	—		50	0
	c. Dot to left of "T"	—		17	6
O 67	9d. purple & blue (21.8.88)	25	0	6	0
O 68	1s. green (25.3.90)	30	0	7	6
	a. No dot under "T"	—		50	0
	b. Dot to right of "T" ..	—		60	0
	c. Dot to left of "T"	—		45	0
	d. Optd. in blue-black				

1891—1900.

No.	Description	Unused		Used	
O 69	1d. lilac (Die II) (June, '97)	6	0	1	6
	a. No dot under "T"	60	0	17	6
	b. Dot to left of "T"	70	0	20	0
	c. Opt. inverted	£60		£50	
	d. Ditto. Dot to left of "T" ..				
O 70	2d. green & carm. (24.10.91)	12	6	3	6
	a. No dot under "T"	70	0	25	0
	b. Dot to left of "T"	65	0	30	0
O 71	4½d. grn. & carm. (Sept., 1892)	40	0	12	6
O 72	1s. grn. & carm. (Nov. '00)	30	0	17	6
	a. Opt. inverted	—		£700	

Controls. 1d. W *and* X.

1902. *Stamps of King Edward VII.*

No.	Description	Unused		Used	
O 74	1d. scarlet, O (30.10.02) ..	15	0	5	0
O 75	2d. green & car., O (29.4.02)	17	6	5	0
O 76	6d. pull purple, O (19.2.02)	15	0	6	0
O 77	9d. pur. & blue, O (28.8.02)	40	0	12	6
O 78	1s. grn. & car., O (17.12.02)	70	0	22	6

Controls. 1d. A, *continuous.*

5. BOARD OF EDUCATION.

BOARD OF EDUCATION
(O 8)

Overprinted with Type O **8**, *in black.*

1902 (19 FEB.). *Stamps of Queen Victoria.*

No.	Description	Unused		Used	
O 81	5d. purple and blue (II) ..	£10		70	0
O 82	1s. green and carmine ..	£35		£15	

1902–4. *Stamps of King Edward VII.*

No.	Description	Unused		Used	
O 83	½d. blue-green, O (19.2.02)	32	6	5	0
O 84	1d. scarlet, O (19.2.02) ..	27	6	2	6
O 85	2½d. bright blue, O (19.2.02)	£8		35	0
O 86	5d. pur. and blue, O (6.2.04)	£35		£25	
O 87	1s. grn. & car., O (23.12.02)	£2000		£1250	

Controls. ½d. A *and* B, *continuous.*
1d. B, *continuous.*

6. ROYAL HOUSEHOLD.

R.H.

OFFICIAL
(O 9)

1902. *King Edward VII stamps optd. with Type* O **9.**

No.	Description	Unused		Used	
O 91	½d. blue-green, O (29.4.02)	60	0	50	0
O 92	1d. scarlet, O (19.2.02) ..	40	0	25	0

Controls. ½*d. and* 1*d.* A, *continuous.*

7. ADMIRALTY.

ADMIRALTY OFFICIAL (O 10) — **ADMIRALTY OFFICIAL** (O 11)

1903 (3 MAR.). *Stamps of King Edward VII optd. with Type* O **10.**

No.	Description	Unused		Used	
O 101	½d. blue-green, O ..	10	0	4	6
O 102	1d. scarlet, O	5	0	1	0
O 103	1½d. purple and green, O	45	0	20	0
O 104	2d. green and carmine, O	27	6	15	0
O 105	2½d. bright blue, O ..	40	0	27	6
O 106	3d. purple/*yellow*, O ..	27	6	15	0

1903–04. *Stamps of King Edward VII optd. with Type* O **11.**

No.	Description	Unused		Used	
O 107	½d. blue-green O, (9.03)	10	0	4	0
O 108	1d. scarlet, O (11.03) ..	5	0	1	6
O 109	1½d. purple & grn. O (2.04)	£6		50	0
O 110	2d. green & carm. O (3.04)	£15		£7	
O 111	2½d. bright blue, O (3.04)	£25		£16	
O 112	3d. purple/*yellow*, O (2.04)	£7		30	0

Controls. Overprint, Type O **10.**
½d. A *and* B, *continuous.*
1d. A *and* B, *continuous.*
Overprint, Type O **11.**
½d. *and* 1d. B *continuous.*

Stamps of various issues perforated with a Crown and initials ("H.M.O.W.", "O.W.", "B.T." or "S.O.") or with initials only ("H.M.S.O." or "D.S.I.R.") have been used for official purposes, but we do not catalogue or deal in this class of stamp.

CONTROL LETTERS.

PRICES quoted for Nos. C 1 to C 759*m* and for Postage Due controls are for mint single copies, except where pairs, etc., are mentioned. Pairs, strips, or blocks, with control, can be supplied at the prices quoted plus the catalogue price of the extra stamps.

MARGINS. There are two varieties of control, one in which the vertical perforation does not cross the margin of the sheet on which the control appears ("margin imperf.") and the other in which it does ("margin perf."). We price these varieties separately, the price columns being headed I (=Imperf.) and P (=Perf.) respectively. Partially perf. margins are regarded as imperf. * Indicates that the particular variety of margin is not known with the control indicated. A dash (—) means "exists but price cannot be quoted".

Perf. margin.

CONTROL POSITIONS

The Control is beneath the 11th stamp, bottom row, in the Victorian and Edwardian issues, except for the ½d. Edward, when from C onwards it is below the 2nd stamp.

Imperf. margin.

QUEEN VICTORIA.

I. *½d. vermilion.*

(*a*) *Without "Jubilee Line."*†

No.	Control	I.	P.
C 1	½d. *no control, corner pair*†	*	£6
C 2	½d. A ..	*	20 0
C 3	½d. B ..	*	55 0
C 4	½d. C ..	*	30 0
C 5	½d. D ..	*	30 0
C 6	½d. E ..	*	£14

(*b*) *With "Jubilee Line".*

No.	Control	I.	P.
C 7	½d. B ..	*	£12
C 8	½d. C ..	£6	17 6
C 9	½d. D ..	—	16 6
C 10	½d. E ..	—	4 0
C 11	½d. F ..	£5	3 6
C 12	½d. G. ..	£10	7 6
C 13	½d. H ..	5 0	3 6
C 14	½d. I ..	3 6	1 0
C 15	½d. J ..	42 6	1 9
C 16	½d. K ..	35 0	3 6
C 17	½d. L ..	30 0	2 6
C 18	½d. M ..	2 0	1 3
C 19	½d. N ..	1 6	1 0
C 20	½d. O ..	1 6	1 3
C 21	½d. P ..	1 0	3 6
C 22	½d. Q ..	1 0	1 3

II. *½d. green. With line.*

No.	Control	I.	P.
C 23	½d. R ..	1 6	2 6

III. *1d. lilac (16 dots).*

(*a*) *Without "Jubilee Line".*

No.	Control	I.	P.
C 24	1d. *none, corner pair*† ..	*	£12
C 25	1d. A ..	*	£14
C 26	1d. B ..	*	42 6
C 27	1d. C ..	*	85 0
C 28	1d. D ..	*	22 6
C 29	1d. E ..	£15	20 0
C 30	1d. F ..	*	20 0
C 31	1d. G ..	*	10 0
C 32	1d. H ..	*	17 6
C 33	1d. I ..	*	65 0
C 34	1d. J ..	*	40 0

(*b*) *With "Jubilee Line".*

No.	Control	I.	P.
C 34*a*	1d. *none, corner pair*† ..	*	—
C 35	1d. G ..	*	17 6
C 36	1d. H ..	*	12 6
C 37	1d. I ..	*	7 6
C 38	1d. J ..	£15	4 0
C 39	1d. K ..	£15	5 0
C 40	1d. L ..	15 0	3 6
C 41	1d. M ..	12 0	4 6
C 42	1d. N ..	7 6	2 0
C 43	1d. O ..	4 6	2 0
C 44	1d. O over N	£38	£50
C 45	1d. P ..	50 0	2 6
C 46	1d. Q ..	12 6	2 6
C 47	1d. R ..	12 0	3 0
C 48	1d. S ..	2 6	2 0
C 49	1d. T ..	2 3	2 0
C 50	1d. U ..	2 0	2 0
C 51	1d. V ..	2 0	2 0
C 52	1d. W ..	2 0	2 0
C 53	1d. X ..	2 0	5 0

† These are bottom right-hand corner pairs. No. C 34*a* is an error: Nos. C 1 and C 24 are from normal supplies issued before Controls came into use.

The "Jubilee Line" is the coloured line extending round the pane outside the stamps.

When this line is unbroken, as shown in illustration of ½d. vermilion (P) above, it is described as "*continuous*", though in some plates the line has occasional breaks. When the line is composed of short pieces *with gaps exactly opposite the space between the stamps*, as shown above (D 4), it is termed "*Co-extensive.*"

KING EDWARD VII.

De La Rue & Co.

With "Continuous Line."

(i.) *½d. blue-green.*

No.	Control	I.	P.
C 54	½d. A ..	1 9	2 0
C 55	½d. B ..	1 6	3 0
C 56	½d. C ..	3 0	35 0
C 57	½d. C 4 ..	1 6	42 6
C 58	½d. D 4 ..	1 9	£15

(ii.) *½d. yellow-green.*

No.	Control	I.	P.
C 59	½d. D 4 ..	50 0	—

With "Co-extensive Line."

(i.) *½d. blue-green.*

No.	Control	I.	P.
C 60	½d. B ..	75 0	*
C 61	½d. C ..	6 0	—
C 62	½d. C 4 ..	4 0	£10
C 63	½d. D 4 ..	1 6	£12

(ii.) *½d. yellow-green.*

No.	Control	I.	P.
C 64	½d. D 4 ..	1 3	£8
C 65	½d. D 5 ..	1 3	80 0
C 66	½d. E 5 ..	1 3	7 6
C 67	½d. E 6 ..	1 9	—
C 68	½d. F 6 ..	1 3	3 0
C 69	½d. F 7 ..	5 0	6 0
C 70	½d. G 7 ..	1 3	1 3
C 71	½d. G 8 ..	2 0	2 9
C 72	½d. H 8 ..	2 0	2 0
C 73	½d. H 9 ..	2 6	3 6
C 74	½d. I 9 ..	1 3	1 3
C 75	½d. I 10 ..	1 6	1 3
C 76	½d. J 10 ..	1 3	1 3

Harrison & Sons. (*a*) *P* 14.

No.	Control	I.	P.
C 77	½d. A 11 ..	4 0	3 0

(*b*) *P* 15 × 14.

No.	Control	I.	P.
C 78	½d. A 11 ..	8 6	10 6

De La Rue & Co.

With "Continuous Line."

No.	Control	I.	P.
C 79	1d. A ..	1 3	6 0
C 80	1d. B ..	1 3	15 0
C 81	1d. C ..	2 6	47 6
C 82	1d. C 4 ..	1 9	18 6
C 83	1d. D 4 ..	1 6	47 6
C 84	1d. D 5 ..	57 6	—

With "Co-extensive Line."

No.	Control	I.	P.
C 85	1d. C ..	4 0	£14
C 86	1d. C 4 ..	4 0	£10
C 87	1d. D 4 ..	1 3	£12
C 88	1d. D 5 ..	1 3	£15
C 89	1d. E 5 ..	1 3	1 3
C 90	1d. E 6 ..	1 6	£10
C 91	1d. F 6 ..	1 3	1 6
C 92	1d. F 7 ..	4 0	4 0
C 93	1d. G 7 ..	1 3	1 6
C 94	1d. G 8 ..	1 6	1 6
C 95	1d. H 8 ..	1 3	1 3

Somerset House.

Somerset House.

KING GEORGE V TYPOGRAPHED CONTROL POSITIONS

The Control appears below the 2nd stamp, bottom row, except for the 1d. value, where it is beneath the 11th stamp.

Harrison.

		I.	P.
C 96	1d. H 9 ..	1 3	1 3
C 97	1d. I 9 ..	1 3	1 3
C 98	1d. I 10 ..	1 3	1 3
C 99	1d. J 10 ..	1 3	1 6

Harrison & Sons. *P* 14.

		I.	P.
C 100	1d. A 11 (c)	50 0	—
C 100*a*	1d. A 11 (w)	5 0	3 6

P 15 × 14.

		I.	P.
C 101	1d. A 11 (c)	6 0	6 0

(c) "close" and (w) "wide" spacing refer to the distance between the figures which is respectively 1 mm. and 2 mm.

KING GEORGE V.

Printed at Somerset House.
With full stop after letter.
T **99.** *Wmk. Crown.*

		I.	P.
C 102	A 11, Die A. 1d. ..	70 0	75 0

Deepened Die.

		I.	P.
C 103	A.11, Die B, 1d. ..	4 0	4 0

T **101** *and* **102.** *Wmk. Crown.*

		I.	P.
C 104	B 11, 1d...	15 0	14 0
C 104*a*	B 12, ½d...		
C 105	B 12, 1d...	7 6	7 6

Wmk. "GvR," *T* **103.**

		I.	P.
C 105*a*	B.12, ½d...	£30	£30
C 105*b*	B.12, 1d...	£60	£70

T **104** *to* **108.**

Wmk. "GvR," *T* **100** (*all 6d. P* 15 × 14 *unless otherwise stated*), (c) *and* (w) *refer to close and wide spacing.*

		I.	P.
C 106	A. 12, 1½d. (w)	2 0	75 0
C 106*a*	„ 1½d. (c)	3 0	—
C 107	„ 2½d. ..	2 0	£22
C 108	„ 3d. (w)	7 6	£14
C 108*a*	„ 3d. (c)	4 6	10 0
C 109	B.13, ½d...	1 0	£10
C 110	„ 3d...	3 6	5 0
C 111	„ 4d...	20 0	80 0
C 112	„ 5d...	6 0	10 0
C 113	„ 9d...	15 0	*
C 114	C.13, 2d...	4 6	4 0
C 115	„ 3d...	5 6	52 6
C 116	„ 6d. dull pur.	25 0	22 6
C 117	„ 6d. red-pur.	4 6	3 6
C 118	„ 7d...	15 0	*
C 119	„ 8d...	12 6	*
C 120	„ 10d.	15 0	£30
C 121	„ 1s...	10 6	75 0
C 122	D.14, 6d...	4 0	*
C 123	E.14, 6d...	5 0	6 0
C 124	F.15, 6d...	12 6	£22
C 126	G.15, 6d...	4 6	*

		I.	P.
C 127	H.16, 6d...	4 6	*
C 128	I.16, 6d...	4 6	*
C 129	J.17, 6d...	4 6	*
C 130	„ 2½d...	£10	*
C 131	K.17, 6d...	4 6	*
C 132	L.18, 6d...	4 6	55 0
	a. No stop after letter	6 0	*
C 133	M.18, 6d...	4 6	*
C 134	N.19, 6d...	4 6	60 0
C 135	O.19, 6d...	4 6	*
C 136	P.20, 6d...	4 6	*
C 137	Q.20, 6d. (15 × 14)	6 6	*
C 138	„ 6d. (p. 14)	20 0	*
C 139	R.21, 6d. (p. 14)	25 0	*
C 140	„ 6d. (15 × 14)	10 6	*
C 141	S.21, 6d...	5 6	65 0
C 142	T.22, 6d...	5 6	85 0
C 143	U.22, 6d...	5 6	*
C 144	V.23, 6d...	6 0	*
C 145	W.23, 6d...	6 0	*
C 146	A.24, 6d...	6 0	*
C 147	B.24, 6d...	15 0	*

***Wmk. T* 111.**

		I.	P.
C 148	B.24, 6d., C 12	6	*
C 149	C.25, 6d., C 10	6	*
C 150	D.25, 6d., C 10	6	*
C 151	D.25, 6d., O 37	6	*
C 152	E.26, 1½d.	£25	*
C 153	„ 6d., O	5 0	£12
C 154	F.26, 6d., O	5 0	*
C 155	G.27, 6d., O	5 0	*
C 156	H.27, 6d., O	5 0	*
C 157	I.28, 6d., O	6 0	17 6
C 158	J.28, 6d., O	5 0	20 0
C 159	K.29, 6d., O	5 0	*
C 160	L.29, 6d., O	5 0	*
C 161	M.30, 6d., O	5 0	£25
C 162	N.30, 6d., O	5 0	*
C 163	O.31, 6d., O	5 0	*
C 164	P.31, 6d., O	5 0	*
C 165	Q.32, 6d., O	5 0	*
C 166	R.32, 6d., O	5 0	*
C 167	S.33, 6d., O	6 0	*
C 168	T.33, 6d., O	5 0	*

For later 6d. controls, see C 753, etc.

Harrison & Sons.
Without stop after letter.
T **98** *and* **99.** *Wmk. Crown.*

		I.	P
C 231	A 11 (w) ½d. Die A ..	6 6	4 6
	aa. Perf. 14	*	£500
C 231*a*	A 11 (c) ½d. Die A ..		
C 232	A 11 (w) 1d. Die A	7 6	1 6
C 232*a*	A 11 (c) 1d. Die A ..	40 0	£9
C 233	A 11 (w) ½d. Die B ..	6 0	2 6
C 233*a*	A 11 (c) ½d. Die B ..	4 6	3 6
C 234	A 11 (w) 1d. Die B ..	40 0	—
C 234*a*	A 11 (c) 1d. Die B ..	2 6	2 6

(c) "close" and (w) "wide" refer to the space between the figures. (1 mm. and 1½ mm. respectively.)

101 *and* **102.** (*a*) *Wmk. Crown.*

		I.	P.
C 235	B 11, ½d.	1 6	2 6
C 236	„ 1d.	1 0	1 6
C 237	B 12 (c) ½d.	1 6	1 6
C 237*a*	„ (w) ½d.	4 6	3 6
C 238	„ (c) 1d.	1 3	1 3
C 238*a*	„ (w) 1d.	1 3	1 3

(c) "close" and (w) "wide" refer to the space between "B" and the serif of "1". (4½ mm. and 6 mm. respectively.)

Error. Complete lower row of sheet.

		I.	P.
C 239	None ½d. 12 stamps ..	50 0	*

(*b*) *Wmk.* "GvR", *T* **100.**

		I.	P.
C 240	B 12 (c) ½d.	2 0	2 0
C 240*a*	„ (w) ½d.	2 0	2 0
C 241	„ (w) 1d.	1 9	1 9
C 242	B 13, ½d.	2 0	2 0
C 243	„ 1d.	1 9	2 0

(*c*) *Wmk.* "GvR", *T* **103.**

		I.	P.
C 244	B 12 (c) ½d.	2 0	2 6
C 244*a*	„ (w) ½d.	2 6	2 0
C 245	„ 1d.	4 0	5 0
C 245*a*	„ 1d. (350*c*)	*	—

T **104/8** *and* **113/5.**
Wmk. "GvR", *T* **103.**

		I.	P.
C 245*b*	C 13 ½d. ..	—	—
C 245*c*	„ 1d. ..	—	*

Wmk. "GvR", *T* **100.**

All 2d. stamps are Die I only, up to Control R 21; thence to T 22 as stated in brackets; from U 22 onwards, Die II only.

The 9d. is in agate to Control S 22; from T 22 it is in olive-green.

		I.	P.
C 246	C 12, 1d.	0 8	0 8
C 247	None, 2d. *left corner pair*	30 0	30 0
C 248	C 13, ½d.	0 9	0 9
C 249	„ 1d.	0 9	0 9
C 250	„ 1½d.	1 0	1 0
C 251	„ 2½d.	1 6	1 6
C 252	„ 3d. v.	4 0	4 0
C 253	„ 3d. bl. v.	3 6	3 6
C 254	„ 4d.	3 0	3 0
C 255	„ 7d.	13 6	13 6
C 256	C 14, ½d.	1 3	1 3

No.	Control	Value	I.	P.
C 257	C 14,	1d.	0 8	0 8
C 258	,,	2d.	2 6	2 0
C 259	,,	2½d.	1 6	1 6
C 260	,,	5d.	5 6	6 0
C 261	D 14,	½d.	0 9	0 9
C 262	,,	1d.	0 9	0 9
C 263	,,	1½d.	1 0	1 0
C 264	,,	2d.	1 6	1 6
C 265	,,	2½d.	17 6	17 6
C 266	,,	3d.	3 6	4 0
C 267	,,	4d.	3 0	3 0
C 268	,,	5d.	6 0	6 0
C 269	,,	7d.	13 6	13 6
C 270	,,	8d.	12 0	12 0
C 271	,,	10d.	15 0	15 0
C 272	,,	1s.	10 0	10 0
C 273	E 14,	½d.	0 9	0 9
C 274	,,	1d.	1 0	1 0
C 275	,,	2½d.	1 6	1 6
C 276	,,	3d.	3 6	3 6
C 277	,,	9d.	*	15 0
C 278	,,	1s.	£30	£30
C 279	F 15,	½d.	0 9	0 9
C 280	,,	1d.	0 9	0 9
C 281	,,	1½d.	3 6	2 6
C 282	,,	2d.	1 6	3 0
C 284	,,	3d.	3 6	3 6
C 285	,,	4d.	3 0	3 6
C 286	,,	5d.	6 0	6 0
C 287	,,	7d.	17 6	12 6
C 288	,,	8d.	12 6	15 0
C 289	,,	9d.	20 0	60 0
C 290	,,	10d.	20 0	25 0
C 291	,,	1s.	10 0	11 6
C 292	G 15,	½d.	0 9	0 9
C 293	,,	1d.	0 9	0 9
C 294	,,	1½d.	1 0	1 0
C 295	,,	2d.	1 6	1 6
C 296	,,	2½d.	1 6	1 6
C 297	,,	3d.	10 0	3 6
C 298	,,	4d.	3 0	3 0
C 299	,,	5d.	5 6	7 6
C 300	,,	7d.	13 6	13 6
C 301	,,	8d.	12 0	12 0
C 302	G 15,	9d.	15 0	15 0
C 303	,,	10d.	30 0	40 0
C 304	,,	1s.	10 0	10 0
C 305	H 16,	½d.	0 9	1 3
C 306	,,	1d.	0 9	1 0
C 307	,,	1½d.	1 0	1 3
C 308	,,	2d.	1 6	£15
C 309	,,	2½d.	1 6	1 6
C 310	,,	3d.	3 6	10 0
C 311	,,	4d.	4 0	50 0
C 312	,,	5d.	5 6	6 0
C 313	,,	7d.	15 0	15 0
C 314	,,	8d.	12 0	12 0
C 315	,,	9d.	17 6	15 0
C 316	,,	10d.	15 0	40 0
C 317	,,	1s.	10 0	17 6
C 318	I 16,	½d.	0 9	0 9
C 319	,,	1d.	1 0	1 0
C 321	,,	2d.	2 0	20 0
C 322	,,	2½d.	1 6	3 0
C 323	,,	3d.	4 0	3 6
C 324	,,	4d.	3 0	7 6
C 325	,,	5d.	6 0	6 0
C 327	,,	8d.	12 0	12 0
C 328	,,	9d.	15 0	60 0
C 329	,,	10d.	15 0	20 0
C 330	,,	1s.	10 0	20 0
C 331	J 17,	½d.	0 9	0 9
C 332	,,	1d.	0 9	0 9
C 333	,,	1½d.	1 0	1 3
C 334	,,	2d.	1 6	3 0
C 335	,,	2½d.	1 9	3 0
C 336	,,	3d.	3 6	4 6
C 337	,,	4d.	3 0	3 6
C 338	,,	5d.	5 6	6 0
C 339	,,	7d.	15 0	16 6
C 340	,,	8d.	12 6	12 6
	a. Granite paper		17 6	17 6
C 341	J 17,	9d.	15 0	15 0
C 342	,,	10d.	30 0	13 6
C 343	,,	1s.	10 0	15 0
C 344	K 17,	½d.	0 9	1 0
C 345	,,	1d.	0 9	1 0
C 347	,,	2d.	1 6	22 6
C 348	,,	2½d.	1 6	£6
C 350	,,	4d.	3 0	£6
C 351	,,	5d.	5 6	8 6
C 352	,,	9d.	15 0	17 6
C 353	,,	1s.	10 0	85 0
C 354	K 18,	½d.	0 9	1 0
C 355	,,	1d.	0 9	1 0
C 356	,,	1½d.	12 6	12 6
	a. "18" only ("K" omitted)		£15	£20
C 357	K 18,	4d.	3 0	3 6
C 358	,,	8d.	£7	17 6
C 359	,,	9d.	15 0	17 6
C 360	,,	10d.	50 0	10 6

L 18

Letter and figures with serifs.

No.	Control	Value	I.	P.
C 361	L 18,	½d.	0 9	0 9
C 362	,,	1d.	1 0	1 0
C 363	,,	1½d.	1 0	1 6
C 364	,,	2d.	1 6	2 0
C 365	,,	2½d.	1 6	1 6
C 366	,,	3d.	3 6	3 6
C 368	,,	5d.	5 6	5 6
C 370	,,	7d.	17 6	£5
C 371	,,	9d.	15 0	15 0
C 372	,,	1s.	10 6	10 0
C 373	M 18,	½d.	0 9	0 9
C 374	,,	1d.	1 0	1 0
	a. "M" only ("18" omitted)		£30	—
C 375	M 18,	1½d.	1 0	1 0
C 377	,,	2½d.	8 0	7 6
C 378	,,	3d.	3 6	4 0
C 379	,,	4d.	3 0	3 0
C 384	M 19,	½d.	1 0	1 0
C 385	,,	1d.	1 0	1 0
C 386	,,	1½d.	1 0	1 0
C 387	,,	2d.	3 6	8 6
C 388	,,	2½d.	10 0	6 0
C 389	,,	10d.	15 0	15 0
C 390	,,	1s.	20 0	10 6
C 391	N 19,	½d.	0 9	0 10
C 392	,,	1d.	0 9	0 10
C 393	,,	1½d.	1 0	1 0
C 394	,,	2d.	1 6	10 0
C 395	,,	2½d.	2 6	2 0
C 396	,,	3d.	3 6	3 6
C 397	,,	4d.	3 0	3 6
C 398	,,	5d.	6 0	6 0
C 399	,,	9d.	15 0	15 0
C 401	,,	1s.	10 0	10 0
C 402	O 19,	½d.	1 0	1 3
C 403	,,	1d.	0 9	0 10
C 404	,,	1½d.	1 3	1 0
C 405	,,	2d.	2 0	£5
C 406	,,	2½d.	4 0	4 6
C 406*a*	,,	5d.	6 0	5 6
C 407	,,	9d.	15 0	15 0
C 408	,,	10d.	13 6	15 0
C 409	,,	1s.	10 6	10 0
C 410	O 20,	½d.	0 9	0 9
C 411	,,	1d.	1 0	1 0
C 412	,,	1½d.	1 0	1 0
C 413	,,	2d.	1 6	1 6
C 414	,,	2½d.	1 6	1 6
C 415	,,	3d.	3 6	3 6
C 416	,,	4d.	3 0	3 6
C 417	,,	9d.	15 0	15 0
C 418	,,	1s.	12 0	10 0
C 419	P 20,	½d.	0 10	0 9
C 420	,,	1d.	0 9	0 10
C 421	P 20,	2d.	1 6	1 6
C 422	,,	2½d.	2 0	1 6
C 423	,,	3d.	3 6	3 6
C 424	,,	9d.	15 0	15 0
C 425	,,	1s.	10 0	10 0
C 426	Q 20,	½d.	0 9	0 9
C 427	,,	1d.	0 9	0 9
C 428	,,	1½d.	1 6	1 6
C 429	,,	2d.	1 6	1 6
C 430	,,	9d.	15 0	15 0
C 431	,,	1s.	10 0	10 0
C 432	Q 21,	½d.	0 9	0 9
C 433	,,	1d.	0 9	0 9
C 434	,,	1½d.	1 0	1 0
C 435	,,	2d.	1 6	1 9
C 436	,,	2½d.	1 9	1 6
C 437	,,	3d.	3 6	3 6
C 438	,,	4d.	7 6	6 0
C 439	,,	5d.	5 6	6 0
C 440	,,	10d.	15 0	15 0
C 441	R 21,	½d.	0 9	0 9
C 442	,,	1d.	0 9	0 9
C 443	,,	2d.	1 6	1 6
C 444	,,	2½d.	1 9	1 6
C 445	,,	3d.	3 6	3 6
C 446	,,	4d.	3 0	3 0
C 447	,,	5d.	6 0	5 6
C 448	,,	9d.	15 0	15 0
C 449	,,	1s.	10 0	10 0
C 450	S 21,	½d.	1 0	1 0
C 451	,,	1d.	1 0	1 0
C 453	,,	2d. (I)	1 6	1 6
C 454	,,	2d. (II)	4 6	4 6
C 455	,,	2½d.	1 6	1 6
C 456	,,	3d.	3 6	3 6
C 457	,,	4d.	25 0	7 6
C 458	,,	5d.	5 6	6 6
C 459	,,	9d.	15 0	15 0
C 460	,,	10d.	15 0	15 0
C 461	,,	1s.	10 0	10 0
C 462	S 22,	½d.	0 9	0 9
C 463	,,	1d.	0 9	0 9
C 465	,,	2d. (I)	1 6	1 6
C 466	,,	2d. (II)	5 0	4 6
C 467	,,	2½d.	1 6	1 9
C 468	,,	3d.	3 6	3 6
C 469	,,	4d.	4 0	10 0
C 470	,,	5d.	7 6	£6
C 471	,,	9d.	25 0	15 0
C 472	,,	10d.	50 0	13 6
C 473	,,	1s.	10 0	10 6
C 474	T 22,	½d.	0 9	0 9
C 475	,,	1d.	0 9	0 9
C 476	,,	1½d.	1 0	1 0
C 477	,,	2d. (I)	2 6	1 6
C 478	,,	2d. (II)	4 6	5 0
C 479	,,	2½d.	1 6	1 6
C 480	,,	3d.	4 0	3 6
C 481	,,	4d.	3 6	3 0
C 482	,,	5d.	7 6	7 6
C 483	,,	9d.	32 6	32 6
C 484	,,	10d.	15 0	13 6
C 485	,,	1s.	10 0	10 0
C 486	U 22,	½d.	0 9	0 9
C 487	,,	1d.	1 0	0 9
C 488	,,	1½d.	1 0	1 0
C 489	,,	2d.	5 0	4 6
C 490	,,	3d.	4 0	3 6
C 491	,,	4d.	12 0	15 0
C 492	,,	1s.	10 0	10 6
C 493	U 23,	½d.	0 9	0 9
C 494	,,	1d.	0 9	0 9
C 495	,,	1½d.	1 0	1 0
C 496	,,	2d.	4 6	4 6
C 497	,,	2½d.	3 6	3 6
C 498	,,	3d.	3 6	5 0
C 499	,,	4d.	25 0	3 0
C 500	,,	5d.	5 6	5 6
C 501	,,	9d.	32 6	32 6
C 502	,,	10d.	15 0	15 0
C 503	,,	1s.	10 6	10 0
C 504	V 23,	½d.	0 9	0 9
C 505	,,	1d.	0 9	0 9

No.	Type, value	I.	P.
C 506	V 23, 1½d.	1 0	1 0
C 507	,, 2d.	5 0	4 6
C 508	,, 2½d.	1 6	1 6
C 509	,, 3d.	3 6	3 6
C 510	,, 4d.	3 0	3 0
C 511	,, 5d.	5 6	5 6
C 512	,, 9d.	32 6	32 6
C 513	,, 1s.	10 0	10 6
C 514	W 23, ½d.	1 4	1 4
C 515	,, 1d.	2 0	1 6
C 516	,, 1½d.	1 3	1 0
C 517	,, 2d.	5 0	4 6
C 518	,, 3d.	3 6	4 0
C 519	W 24, ½d.	12 6	12 6
C 520	,, 1d.	10 0	10 0
C 521	,, 1½d.	20 0	20 0
C 522	,, 2d.	20 0	25 0

A 24

Without stop. Smaller thick letters and figures, with serifs.

Wmk. "GvR" *T* **111**.

(*a*) Typo. Waterlow & Sons.

No.	Type, value	I.	P.
C 523	A 24, ½d.	0 8	4 6
C 524	,, 1d.	1 0	35 0
C 525	,, 1½d.	1 6	5 0
	a. Wmk. 111*a*	£5	*
C 526	A 24, 2d.	2 0	
C 527	,, 5d.	7 6	8 6
C 528	,, 9d.	12 0	10 0
C 529	,, 10d.	40 0	16 6
C 530	,, 1s.	12 6	35 0
C 531	B 24, ½d.	0 8	40 0
C 532	,, 1d.	0 8	50 0
	a. Wmk. 111*a*	£5	*
C 533	B 24, 1½d.	1 6	£8
	a. Wmk. 111*a*	£6	*
C 534	B 24, 2d.	2 0	£5
C 535	,, 2½d.	4 0	*
C 536	,, 3d.	4 6	*
C 537	,, 4d.	7 6	*
C 538	,, 1s.	12 6	*
C 539	C 25, ½d.	0 8	60 0
C 540	,, 1d.	0 8	20 0
C 541	,, 1½d.	1 6	—
C 542	,, 2d.	2 0	*
C 543	,, 2½d.	3 6	*
C 544	,, 3d.	4 6	*
C 545	,, 4d.	7 6	*
C 546	,, 5d.	7 6	*
C 547	,, 9d.	12 6	*
C 548	D 25, ½d.	0 8	*
C 549	,, 1d.	4 0	*
C 550	,, 1½d.	1 6	*
	a. Wmk. 111*a*	£5	*
C 551	D 25, 2d.	2 0	*
C 552	,, 2½d.	4 0	*
C 553	,, 3d.	4 6	*
C 554	,, 10d.	17 6	*
C 555	,, 1s.	12 6	*
C 556	E 26, ½d.	0 8	£15
C 557	,, 1d.	0 8	*
C 558	,, 1½d.	1 6	*
C 559	,, 2d.	2 0	*
C 560	,, 2½d.	3 6	*
C 561	,, 3d.	4 6	*
C 562	,, 4d.	7 6	*
C 563	F 26, ½d.	0 8	80 0
C 564	,, 1d.	0 8	*
C 565	,, 1½d.	1 6	60 0
C 566	,, 2d.	2 0	*
C 570	,, 5d.	7 6	*
C 571	,, 9d.	15 0	*
C 572	,, 10d.	17 6	*
C 573	,, 1s.	12 6	*
C 574	G 27, ½d.	0 8	35 0
C 575	,, 1d.	0 8	*
C 576	,, 1½d.	1 6	*

No.	Type, value	I.	P.
C 577	G 27, 2d.	2 0	*
C 578	,, 2½d.	4 0	£15
C 579	,, 3d.	4 6	£7
C 580	,, 4d.	7 6	*
C 583	,, 10d.	17 6	*
C 584	H 27, ½d.	0 8	40 0
C 585	,, 1d.	0 8	*
C 586	,, 1½d.	1 6	60 0
C 587	,, 2d.	2 0	*
C 588	,, 2½d.	8 6	*
C 589	,, 5d.	7 6	*
C 590	,, 1s.	12 6	*
C 591	I 28, ½d.	0 8	*
C 592	,, 1d.	0 9	*
C 593	,, 1½d.	1 6	£8
C 594	,, 2d.	2 0	£8
C 595	,, 2½d.	3 6	*
C 596	,, 3d.	6 0	*
C 597	,, 4d.	7 6	*
C 598	,, 5d.	7 6	*
C 599	,, 9d.	12 6	*
C 600	,, 1s.	12 6	*
C 601	J 28, ½d.	0 8	*
C 602	,, 1d.	0 8	*
C 603	,, 1½d.	1 6	*
C 604	,, 2d.	2 0	*
C 609	,, 9d.	12 6	*
C 610	,, 10d.	16 6	*
C 611	,, 1s.	12 6	*
C 612	K 29, ½d.	0 8	*
C 613	,, 1d.	0 8	*
C 614	,, 1½d.	1 6	£7
C 615	,, 2d.	2 0	*
C 616	,, 2½d.	4 0	*
C 617	,, 3d.	4 6	*
C 618	,, 4d.	7 6	*
C 619	,, 5d.	7 6	*
C 622	,, 1s.	12 6	*
C 623	,, ½d. **113**	5 0	*
C 624	,, 1d. **114**	6 0	*
C 625	,, 1½d. ,,	5 0	*
C 626	,, 2½d. **115**	20 0	*
C 627	L 29, ½d. **113**	15 0	*
C 628	,, 1d. **114**	18 0	—
C 629	,, 1½d. ,,	16 0	*
C 630	,, 2½d. **115**	25 0	*
C 631	,, ½d.	0 8	40 0
C 632	,, 1d.	1 0	£6
C 633	,, 1½d.	1 6	*
C 634	,, 2d.	2 0	*
C 638	,, 5d.	7 6	*
C 639	,, 9d.	12 6	*
C 640	,, 10d.	22 6	*
C 641	,, 1s.	12 6	*
C 642	M 30, ½d.	0 8	*
C 643	,, 1d.	0 8	*
C 644	,, 1½d.	1 6	*
C 645	,, 2d.	2 0	*
C 646	,, 2½d.	4 0	*
C 647	,, 3d.	4 6	*
C 648	,, 4d.	7 6	*
C 649	,, 5d.	15 0	*
C 653	N 30, ½d.	0 8	*
C 654	,, 1d.	6 0	*
C 655	,, 1½d.	1 6	—
C 656	,, 2d.	2 0	*
C 657	,, 2½d.	4 6	*
C 658	,, 3d.	5 0	*
C 661	,, 9d.	12 6	*
C 663	,, 1s.	12 6	*
C 664	O 31, ½d.	0 8	—
C 665	,, 1d.	0 9	—
C 666	,, 1½d.	1 6	*
C 667	,, 2d.	2 0	*
C 668	,, 2½d.	£30	*
C 670	,, 4d.	7 6	*
C 671	,, 5d.	8 6	*
C 673	,, 10d.	25 0	*
C 675	P 31, ½d.	0 8	*
C 676	,, 1d.	0 9	*
C 677	,, 1½d.	1 6	*
C 678	,, 2d.	2 0	*

No.	Type, value	I.	P.
C 680	P 31, 3d.	4 6	*
C 683	,, 9d.	12 6	*
C 685	,, 1s.	12 6	*
C 686	Q 32, ½d.	0 8	*
C 687	,, 1d.	0 9	*
C 688	,, 1½d.	1 6	*
C 689	,, 2d.	2 0	*
C 690	,, 2½d.	4 0	*
C 692	,, 4d.	7 6	*
C 693	,, 5d.	17 6	*
C 695	,, 10d.	65 0	*
C 697	R 32, ½d.	0 8	*
C 698	,, 1d.	4 6	*
C 699	,, 1½d.	1 6	*
C 700	,, 2d.	2 0	£12
C 701	,, 2½d.	4 6	*
C 702	,, 3d.	4 6	*
C 703	,, 4d.	7 6	*
C 705	,, 9d.	12 6	*
C 707	,, 1s.	22 6	*
C 708	S 33, ½d.	0 8	*
C 709	,, 1d.	0 9	*
C 710	,, 1½d.	1 6	*
C 711	,, 2d.	2 0	*
C 712	,, 2½d.	10 0	*
C 713	,, 3d.	6 0	*
C 715	,, 5d.	7 6	*
C 717	,, 10d.	16 6	*
C 718	,, 1s.	15 0	*
C 719	T 33, ½d.	0 8	*
C 720	,, 1d.	0 9	*
C 721	,, 1½d.	1 6	*
C 722	,, 2d.	2 0	*
C 723	,, 2½d.	4 0	*
C 724	,, 3d.	4 6	*
C 725	,, 4d.	7 6	*
C 726	,, 5d.	£20	*
C 727	,, 9d.	12 6	*

(*b*) Typo. by both Waterlow and Harrison (smooth gum).

No.	Type, value	I.	P.
C 730	U 34, ½d.	2 0	*
C 731	,, 1d.	3 6	*
C 732	,, 1½d.	1 9	*
C 733	,, 2d.	7 6	*
C 734	,, 5d.	8 6	*
C 735	,, 10d.	50 0	*
C 736	,, 1s.	12 6	*

We do not attempt to distinguish between the Waterlow and Harrison printings of C 730/6, but the former are very rare and, indeed, the Waterlow 2d., U 34, is unknown.

(*c*) Typo. Harrison & Sons (streaky gum).

No.	Type, value	I.	P.
C 737	U 34, ½d.	5 0	*
C 738	,, 1d.	8 6	*
C 739	,, 1½d.	5 0	*
C 740	,, 2d.	4 6	*
C 745	V 34, ½d.	0 8	20 0
C 746	,, 1d.	1 6	20 0
C 747	,, 1½d.	2 6	—
C 748	,, 2d.	3 0	—
C 749	,, 2½d.	25 0	*
C 750	,, 3d.	5 0	*
C 751	,, 4d.	8 6	*
C 752	,, 5d.	8 6	*
C 753	,, 6d., ○	6 0	*
C 754	,, 9d.	10 6	*
C 754*a*	,, 10d.	30 0	*
C 755	,, 1s.	12 6	£7
C 756	W 35, 2½d.	10 0	32 6
C 756*a*	,, 4d.	15 0	*
C 757	,, 6d., ○	10 0	12 6
C 758	,, 9d.	12 6	*
C 758*a*	,, 10d.	17 6	*
C 759	,, 1s.	12 6	*
C 759*a*	X 35, 4d.	7 6	—
C 759*b*	,, 5d.	8 6	*
C 759*c*	,, 6d., ○	5 0	12 6

PHOTOGRAVURE CONTROLS

The Controls are in the left-hand margin, except where stated. At first, they were placed opposite the second row from the bottom of the sheet (viz. V/34 : ½d., 1d. and early printings of 1½d., No. C 769). Later fractional controls (including the final printing of 1½d., V/34, No. C 769*a*) were placed opposite the third row.

PRICES. These fractional controls are best collected in blocks, to show the control, cylinder number and both left and bottom margins.

Our prices quoted below are therefore for blocks of four of the ½d., 1d. and 1½d. (No. C 769) V 34 and for vertical blocks of six of the Silver Jubilee stamps and all numbers from C 769*a* onwards. Where strips, pairs or singles are in stock, they will be supplied at the prices quoted, less an allowance for the reduced number of stamps.

In our list " P " now refers to items where BOTH side and bottom margins are perforated (as illustrated). " I " is where one or both margins are imperf.

Cylinder numbers. The small coloured numbers in the margins indicate the cylinder from which the sheet was printed. **We do not list these separately.**

		I.	P.
C 759*d*	X 35, 9d.	12 6	17 6
C 759*e*	,, 1s.	12 6	*
C 759*f*	Y 36 6d., O	6 0	*
C 759*g*	,, 6d., C	£8	*
C 759*h*	Z 36, 6d., O	6 0	*
C 759*i*	,, 6d., C	10 6	*
C 759*j*	A 37, 6d., O	6 0	*
C 759*k*	B 37, 6d., O	10 6	—
C 759*l*	C 38, 6d., O	6 0	*
C 759*m*	D 38, 6d., O	6 0	7 6

T **123** (*Jubilee*). *W* **111.** "*Fractional*" *control in left-hand margin.*

		I.	P.
C 760	W 35, ½d.	10 0	*
C 761	,, 1d.	25 0	*
C 762	,, 1½d.	17 6	*
C 763	,, 2½d.	60 0	*

T 118 *to* 122. *W* 111.

(*a*) *Control below second stamp in bottom row.*

		I.	P.
C 764	U 34, 1½d.	30 0	35 0
C 765	V 34, 1½d.	15 0	15 0

(*b*) "*Fractional*" *control* (*letter above numeral*) *in left-hand margin.*

		I.	P.
C 767	V 34, ½d.	3 0	7 6
C 768	,, 1d.	4 6	4 6
C 769	,, opp. 2nd row 1½d.	6 0	6 0
C 769*a*	,, opp. 3rd row 1½d.	£8	—
C 770	V 34, 2d.	20 0	80 0
C 771	W 35, ½d.	3 6	20 0
C 772	,, 1d.	£6	*
C 773	,, 1½d.	7 6	12 6
C 774	,, 2d.	12 0	£7
C 775	,, 2½d.	16 6	60 0
C 776	,, 3d.	20 0	20 0
C 777	,, 4d.	—	27 6
C 778	X 35, ½d.	3 6	30 0
C 779	,, 1d.	4 6	35 0
C 780	,, 1½d.	7 6	60 0
C 781	,, 2d.	12 6	*
C 782	,, 3d.	20 0	*
C 783	,, 4d.	30 0	£5
C 783*a*	,, 5d.	£20	*
C 784	,, 9d.	60 0	*
	a. Bar —	60 0	*
	b. Bars ∟	70 0	*
	c. Bars ⊔	70 0	*
	d. Bars □	80 0	*
C 785	Y 36, ½d.	3 0	£5
C 786	,, 1d.	4 6	30 0
C 787	,, 1½d.	7 6	35 0
C 788	,, 2d.	12 6	*
C 789	,, 2½d.	30 0	£5
C 790	,, 3d.	20 0	75 0
C 791	,, 4d.	27 6	*
	a. Bar —	27 6	*
	b. Bars ∟	27 6	*
	c. Bars ⊔	27 6	*
	d. Bars □	27 6	*
C 792	Y 36, 5d.	32 6	£7
C 795	,, 10d.	70 0	*
	a. Bar —	75 0	*
	b. Bars ∟	75 0	*
	c. Bars ⊔	80 0	*
	d. Bars □	95 0	*
C 796	Y 36, 1s.	90 0	*
C 797	Z 36, ½d.	5 0	*
C 798	,, 1½d.	7 6	60 0
C 799	,, 2d.	12 6	75 0
C 800	,, 3d.	20 0	75 0
	a. Bar —	20 0	*
	b. Bars ∟	20 0	*
C 801	Z 36, 5d.	35 0	*
	a. Bar —	35 0	£7
	b. Bars ∟	37 6	*
	c. Bars ⊔	37 6	*
	d. Bars □	37 6	*
C 802	Z 36, 1s.	95 0	*
	a. Bar —	90 0	*
	b. Bars ∟	£5	*
	c. Bars ⊔	£5	*
	d. Bars □	110 0	*
C 803	A 37, 2d.	12 6	*

X
35

Several values of the King George V, King Edward VIII and King George VI photogravure controls were issued successively with bars below control; below and to left; below, to left and to right; and finally all round the control as shown in the accompanying illustration. These represent different control periods and are just as important as the changes in control letters and numbers, but are listed in small type for convenience.

KING EDWARD VIII.

T 124. *W* 125.

		I.	P.
C 804	A 36, ½d.	1 6	35 0
C 805	,, 1d.	2 6	£8
C 806	,, 1½d.	3 0	40 0
C 807	,, 2½d.	7 6	*
	a. Bar —	6 6	*
C 808	A 37, ½d.	1 6	*
C 809	,, 1d.	5 6	*
C 810	,, 1½d.	3 0	*

KING GEORGE VI.

The control is in black on the 6d., 9d., 10d. and 1s., except the 1s., E 39 and G 40 on which it is in the colour of the stamp. On all other values the control is in the colour of the stamp.

In 1937 so-called " Jubilee " or " Co-extensive " lines were introduced in the bottom margin of the sheet in the George VI issue, but we do not list these separately.

T 126, 128 *to* 130 *and* 134 *to* 136. *W* 127.

		I.	P.
C 811	A 37, 1½d. **126**	6 0	*
C 812	,, ½d.	2 6	80 0
C 813	,, 1d.	4 6	*
C 814	,, 1½d.	7 0	*
C 815	,, 2½d.	12 6	*
C 816	B 37, ½d.	2 6	*
C 817	,, 1d.	4 6	£7
C 818	,, 1½d.	5 6	*
C 819	,, 2d.	25 0	*
C 820	,, 2½d.	12 6	*
C 821	C 38, ½d.	2 6	*
C 822	,, 1d.	4 6	*
C 823	,, 1½d.	6 0	*
C 824	,, 2d.	70 0	*
C 825	,, 3d.	27 6	*
C 826	D 38, ½d.	2 6	*
C 827	,, 1d.	4 6	*
C 828	,, 1½d.	6 0	£5
C 829	,, 2d.	25 0	*
C 830	,, 2½d.	12 6	*
C 831	,, 3d.	35 0	*
C 832	,, 4d.	18 6	*
C 833	,, 5d.	11 6	*
C 834	,, 6d.	16 6	*
C 835	E 39, ½d.	2 6	*
C 836	,, 1d.	4 6	*
C 837	,, 1½d.	6 0	£15

			I.	P.
C 838	E 39,	2d.	25 0	*
C 839	,,	2½d.	12 6	*
C 840	,,	3d.	35 0	*
C 841	,,	4d.	18 6	*
C 842	,,	5d	11 6	*
C 843	,,	6d.	11 6	*
C 844	,,	7d.	18 0	*
	a. Bar —		17 0	*
	b. Bars		17 0	*
	c. Bars		17 0	*
	d. Bars		17 0	*
	e. Bars		17 0	*
	f. Bars		17 0	*
C 845	E 39,	8d.	21 6	*
	a. Bar —		19 0	*
	b. Bars		16 6	*
	c. Bars		16 6	*
	d. Bars		16 6	*
	e. Bars		16 6	*
C 846	E 39,	9d.	18 0	*
C 847	,,	10d.	23 0	*
C 848	,,	1s.	25 0	*
C 849	F 39,	½d.	2 6	*
C 850	,,	1d.	4 6	*
C 851	,,	1½d.	6 0	*
C 852	,,	2d.	25 0	*
C 853	,,	6d.	13 6	*
C 854	,,	10d.	21 6	*
C 855	G 40,	½d.	3 0	*
C 856	,,	1d.	4 6	*
C 857	,,	1½d.	10 0	*
C 858	,,	2d.	25 0	*
C 859	,,	2½d.	15 0	*
C 860	,,	3d.	35 0	*
C 861	,,	4d.	18 6	*
C 862	,,	5d.	11 6	*
C 863	,,	6d.	10 0	*
C 866	,,	9d.	18 0	*
C 868	,,	1s.	23 0	*
C 869	,,	½d. **134**	6 6	*
C 870	,,	1d. ,,	15 0	*
C 871	,,	1½d. ,,	27 6	*
C 872	,,	2d. ,,	30 0	*
C 873	,,	2½d. ,,	40 0	*
C 874	,,	3d. ,,	70 0	*
C 876	H 40,	1d.	4 6	*
C 878	,,	2d.	25 0	*
C 879	,,	2½d.	12 6	*
C 880	,,	3d.	35 0	*
C 883	,,	6d.	16 6	*
C 886	,,	9d.	18 0	*
C 887	,,	10d.	21 6	*
C 888	,,	1s.	23 0	*
C 889	I 41,	½d.	2 6	*
C 890	,,	1d.	4 6	*
C 892	,,	2d.	25 0	*
C 893	,,	2½d.	12 6	*
C 895	,,	4d.	18 6	*
C 896	,,	5d.	11 6	*
C 900	,,	9d.	18 0	*
C 901	,,	10d.	21 6	*

The following ½d., 1d., 1½d., 2d., 2½d. and 3d. have lighter background (Nos. 485 to 490).

			I.	P.
C 903	J 41,	½d.	1 6	*
C 904	,,	1d.	2 9	*
C 906	,,	2d.	4 0	*
C 907	,,	2½d.	4 0	*
C 908	,,	3d.	4 0	*
C 911	,,	6d.	11 6	*
C 915	,,	10d.	23 0	*
C 916	,,	1s.	22 6	*
C 917	K 42,	½d.	1 6	*
C 918	,,	1d.	2 6	*
C 920	,,	2d.	4 0	*
C 921	,,	2½d.	4 0	*
C 922	,,	3d.	4 0	*
C 923	,,	4d.	20 0	*
	a. Bar —		18 6	*
	b. Bars		18 6	*
C 924	K 42,	5d.	13 6	*
C 925	,,	6d.	11 6	*
C 928	,,	9d.	18 0	*
C 929	,,	10d.	21 6	*
C 930	,,	1s.	21 0	*
C 931	L 42,	½d.	2 0	*
C 932	,,	1d.	2 6	*
C 933	,,	1½d.	4 0	*
C 934	,,	2d.	4 0	*
C 935	,,	2½d.	4 0	*
C 936	,,	3d.	4 0	*
C 938	,,	5d.	£18	*
	a. Bar —		14 0	*
	b. Bars		11 6	*
	c. Bars		11 6	*
	d. Bars		11 6	*
	e. Bars		11 6	*
C 939	L 42,	6d.	11 6	*
C 942	,,	9d.	18 0	*
C 943	,,	10d.	21 6	*
C 945	M 43,	½d.	2 0	*
C 946	,,	1d.	2 6	*
C 948	,,	2d.	4 0	*
C 949	,,	2½d.	4 0	*
C 950	,,	3d.	4 0	*
C 953	,,	6d.	11 6	*
C 957	,,	10d.	21 6	*
C 958	,,	1s.	21 0	*
C 959	N 43,	½d.	1 6	*
C 960	,,	1d.	2 6	*
C 961	,,	1½d.	4 0	*
C 962	,,	2d.	4 0	*
C 963	,,	2½d.	4 0	*
C 964	,,	3d.	4 0	*
C 967	,,	6d.	11 6	*
C 970	,,	9d.	20 0	*
C 971	,,	10d.	21 6	*
C 973	O 44,	½d.	1 6	*
C 974	,,	1d.	2 6	*
C 975	,,	1½d.	4 0	*
C 976	,,	2d.	4 0	*
C 977	,,	2½d.	4 0	*
C 978	,,	3d.	4 0	*
C 979	,,	4d.	20 0	*
	a. Bar —		18 6	*
	b. Bars		18 6	*
	c. Bars		18 6	*
C 981	O 44	6d.	11 6	*
C 983	,,	8d.	16 6	*
	a. Bar —		19 0	*
C 984	O 44,	9d.	18 6	*
C 985	,,	10d.	21 6	*
C 986	,,	1s.	21 0	*
C 987	P 44,	½d.	1 6	*
C 988	,,	1d.	2 6	*
C 989	,,	1½d.	4 0	*
C 990	,,	2d.	4 0	*
C 991	,,	2½d.	4 0	*
C 992	,,	3d.	4 0	*
C 998	,,	9d.	17 6	*
C 1001	Q 45,	½d.	1 6	*
C 1002	,,	1d.	2 6	*
C 1003	,,	1½d.	4 0	*
C 1004	,,	2d.	4 0	*
C 1005	,,	2½d.	4 0	*
C 1006	,,	3d.	4 0	*
C 1009	,,	6d.	10 0	*
C 1013	,,	10d.	21 6	*
C 1014	,,	1s.	21 0	*
C 1015	R 45,	½d.	1 6	*
C 1016	,,	1d.	2 6	*
C 1017	,,	1½d.	4 0	*
C 1018	,,	2d.	4 0	*
C 1019	,,	2½d.	4 0	*
C 1020	,,	3d.	4 0	*
C 1026	,,	9d.	18 0	*
C 1029	S 46,	½d.	1 6	*
C 1030	,,	1d.	2 6	*
C 1031	,,	1½d.	4 0	*
C 1032	,,	2d.	4 0	*
C 1033	,,	2½d.	4 0	*
C 1038	,,	7d.	15 6	*
C 1039	S 46,	8d.	15 0	*
	a. Bar —		15 0	*
C 1042	S 46,	1s.	21 0	*
C 1043	,,	2½d. **135**	4 0	*
C 1044	,,	3d. **136**	5 6	*
C 1045	T 46,	½d.	1 6	*
C 1046	,,	1d.	2 6	*
C 1048	,,	2d.	4 0	*
C 1049	,,	2½d.	4 0	*
C 1053	,,	6d.	10 0	*
C 1057	,,	10d.	21 6	*
C 1059	U 47,	½d.	1 6	*
C 1060	,,	1d.	2 6	*
C 1061	,,	1½d.	4 6	*
C 1062	,,	2d.	4 0	*
C 1063	,,	2½d.	4 0	*
C 1067	,,	6d.	10 0	*
C 1071	,,	10d.	21 6	*
C 1072	,,	1s.	21 0	*

Controls were discontinued in 1947, the last being U 47. Cylinder numbers still appear.

POSTAGE DUE STAMPS.

☛ (Prices are for single stamp with control attached. The letters "I" and "P" refer to the bottom margins, in all Postage Due Controls, the Control appearing below the 2nd stamp.)

Somerset House. *W* **100.**

Stop after letter.

			I.	P.
CD 1	D.14,	½d.	*	10 0
CD 2	,,	1d.	*	10 0
CD 3	,,	2d.	*	15 0
CD 4	,,	5d.	*	17 6
CD 5	F.15,	1s.	*	20 0
CD 6	O.19,	1s.	*	30 0
CD 7	S.21,	1s.	*	30 0
CD 8	V.23,	1s.	17 6	*

Harrison & Sons. *W* **100.**

No stop after letter.

			I.	P.
CD 21	D 14,	½d.	2 0	2 0
CD 22	,,	1d.	3 6	3 6
CD 23	,,	2d.	5 0	4 0
CD 24	,,	5d.	10 0	£12
CD 25	E 14,	1d.	5 0	1 9
CD 26	G 15,	1d.	3 6	20 0
CD 27	H 16,	2d.	4 6	4 6
CD 28	I 16,	½d.	5 6	5 6
CD 29	,,	1d.	2 6	6 6
CD 30	,,	2d.	4 0	10 0
CD 31	K 17,	1d.	2 6	2 6
CD 32	,,	2d.	12 6	2 6
CD 33	L 18,	3d.	3 0	12 6
CD 34	N 19,	½d.	2 0	3 6
CD 35	,,	1d.	2 6	2 6
CD 37	O 19,	2d.	3 6	5 0
CD 38	O 20,	3d.	2 6	2 6
CD 39	P 20,	1d.	2 0	*
CD 40	,,	2d.	1 6	7 6
CD 41	Q 20,	1d.	12 6	*
CD 42	,,	4d.	6 0	6 0
CD 43	Q 21,	1d.	12 6	20 0
CD 44	R 21,	½d.	3 6	8 6
CD 45	,,	1d.	1 9	5 6
CD 46	,,	2d.	3 0	12 6
CD 47	S 21,	1d.	3 6	3 6
CD 48	S 22,	½d.	*	2 6
CD 49	,,	1d.	3 0	3 0
CD 51	T 22,	1d.	3 6	2 6
CD 52	,,	3d.	5 0	3 0
CD 53	U 22,	½d.	2 6	15 0
CD 54	,,	1½d.	17 6	*
CD 55	U 23,	1d.	2 6	2 6
CD 56	,,	1½d.	17 6	*
CD 57	,,	2d.	25 0	2 6
CD 60	V 23,	1½d.	17 6	17 6
CD 61	,,	3d.	3 6	3 6

No.	Control	Value	I.	P.
CD 62	W 23,	½d.	10 0	12 6
CD 63	,,	3d.	8 6	20 0

Waterlow & Sons.

(*a*) *W* **100.** *Thick chalky paper.*

No.	Control	Value	I.	P.
CD 64	B 24,	1d.	12 6	*
CD 65	C 25,	1d.	6 0	*

(*b*) *W* **111.**

No.	Control	Value	I.	P.
CD 66	A 24,	2d.	3 6	*
CD 67	,,	4d.	45 0	*
CD 68	,,	1s.	£45	*
CD 68*a*	B 24,	½d.	*	2 0
CD 69	,,	1d.	15 0	*
CD 70	,,	1½d.	50 0	*
CD 71	,,	3d.	3 0	*
CD 72	,,	4d.	8 6	*
CD 73	,,	1s.	22 6	*
CD 74	,,	2s. 6d.	30 0	*
CD 76	C 25,	2d.	2 0	*
CD 77	,,	1s.	15 0	*
CD 78	D 25,	3d.	7 6	*
	a. Wmk. 111*a*		—	*
CD 79	E 26,	2d.	3 6	*
CD 80	,,	3d.	5 0	*
CD 81	,,	4d.	12 6	*
CD 82	,,	1s.	—	32 6
CD 83	F 26,	½d.	2 0	*
CD 84	,,	1d.	1 6	7 6
CD 85	,,	2d.	2 0	*
CD 86	,,	3d.	5 0	*
CD 87	,,	4d.	8 6	*
CD 88	,,	1s.	10 0	*
CD 89	G 27,	3d.	2 0	*
CD 90	,,	1s.	11 6	*
CD 91	H 27,	2d.	50 0	*
CD 92	,,	3d.	*	20 0
CD 93	,,	2s. 6d.	40 0	*
CD 94	I 28,	½d.	1 6	*
CD 95	,,	1d.	1 6	*
CD 96	,,	2d.	2 0	*
CD 97	,,	3d.	3 6	*
CD 98	,,	4d.	*	20 0
CD 99	,,	1s.	10 0	*
CD 100	,,	2s. 6d.	45 0	*
CD 101	K 29,	½d.	*	2 0
CD 102	,,	1d.	1 6	40 0
CD 103	,,	2d.	3 0	*
CD 104	,,	3d.	3 6	*
CD 105	,,	4d.	6 0	*
CD 106	,,	1s.	7 6	*
CD 107	,,	2s. 6d.	40 0	—
CD 108	L 29,	½d.	2 0	*
CD 109	,,	1d.	1 6	*
CD 110	,,	2d.	2 0	*
CD 111	,,	3d.	3 6	*
CD 112	,,	4d.	6 0	*
CD 114	,,	2s. 6d.	40 0	*
CD 115	M 30,	½d.	2 0	*
CD 117	,,	2d.	2 0	*
CD 120	,,	1s.	22 6	*
CD 123	N 30,	1d.	1 6	*
CD 125	,,	3d.	3 6	*
CD 126	,,	4d.	5 0	*
CD 127	,,	5d.	10 6	*
CD 128	,,	2s. 6d.	65 0	*
CD 129	O 31,	½d.	3 6	*
CD 130	,,	1d.	3 6	*
CD 131	,,	2d.	3 6	*
CD 132	,,	3d.	3 6	*
CD 133	,,	5d.	10 6	*
CD 134	,,	1s.	22 6	*
CD 135	O 31	2s. 6d.	55 0	*
CD 136	P 31,	½d.	1 3	*
CD 137	,,	2d.	1 6	*
CD 138	Q 32,	½d.	1 3	*
CD 139	,,	1d.	1 3	*
CD 140	,,	2d.	4 0	*
CD 141	,,	3d.	3 6	*
CD 142	,,	4d.	4 0	*
CD 143	,,	5d.	10 6	*
CD 144	,,	1s.	6 0	*
CD 145	,,	2s. 6d.	25 0	*
CD 146	R 32,	2d.	4 0	*
CD 147	,,	3d.	4 6	*
CD 148	,,	4d.	6 6	*
CD 149	,,	1s.	6 0	*
CD 150	,,	2s. 6d.	20 0	*
CD 151	S 33,	½d.	1 0	*
CD 152	,,	1d.	2 0	40 0
CD 154	,,	5d.	30 0	*
CD 155	,,	1s.	25 0	*
CD 156	,,	2s. 6d.	40 0	*
CD 157	T 33,	2d.	50 0	*
CD 158	,,	3d.	3 6	*
CD 159	,,	4d.	£12	*

Harrison & Sons. (*a*) *W* **111.**

No.	Control	Value	I.	P.
CD 160 ‡	U 34	½d.	20 0	*
	a. Streaky gum		4 6	*
CD 161	U 34,	1d.	40 0	40 0
CD 162	,,	5d.	60 0	*
CD 163	,,	1s.	50 0	*
CD 164	,,	2s. 6d.	85 0	*
CD 166	V 34,	2d.	40 0	*
CD 167	,,	4d.	35 0	*
CD 167*a*	,,	2s. 6d.	80 0	*
CD 168	W 35,	½d.	4 0	*
CD 169	,,	1d.	20 0	*
CD 170	,,	3d.	20 0	*
CD 170*a*	,,	5d.	10 0	*
CD 171	,,	1s.	40 0	*
CD 171*a*	X 35,	2d.	3 6	*
CD 171*b*	,,	4d.	30 0	*
CD 172	,,	1s.	40 0	*
CD 173	,,	2s. 6d.	70 0	*
CD 174	Y 36,	½d.	2 6	*
CD 175	,,	1d.	3 6	—
CD 176	,,	2d.	5 0	*
CD 177	,,	3d.	7 6	12 6
CD 178	Z36,	2s. 6d.	40 0	*

‡ No. CD 160 and CD 161/4 are on smooth gummed paper. Later controls and CD 160*a* are on paper with streaky gum (*see* note before No. 418).

(*b*) *W* **125.**

No.	Control	Value	I.	P.
CD 179	A 36,	4d.	5 0	*
CD 180	,,	5d.	15 0	*
CD 181	,,	1s.	12 6	*
CD 182	A 37,	½d.	2 0	*
CD 183	,,	1d.	2 6	*
CD 184	,,	2d.	4 0	*
CD 185	,,	3d.	3 6	*
CD 186	,,	5d.	15 0	*
CD 187	,,	2s. 6d.	35 0	*
CD 188	C38,	2s. 6d.	25 0	*

(*c*) *W* **127** (G VI R).

No.	Control	Value	I.	P.
CD 189	B 37,	3d.	5 0	*
CD 190	,,	4d.	6 0	*
CD 191	,,	1s.	15 0	*
CD 192	C 38,	½d.	3 0	*
CD 193	,,	1d.	4 0	*
CD 194	,,	2d.	6 0	*
CD 195	,,	3d.	5 0	*
CD 196	,,	4d.	12 6	*
CD 197	,,	5d.	7 6	*
CD 198	,,	1s.	15 0	*
CD 199	,,	2s. 6d.	25 0	*
CD 203	D 38,	3d.	6 0	*
CD 207	,,	2s. 6d.	25 0	60 0
CD 208	E 39,	½d.	2 0	*
CD 209	,,	1d.	3 0	*
CD 210	,,	2d.	7 6	*
CD 212	,,	4d.	5 0	*
CD 213	,,	5d.	4 6	*
CD 214	,,	1s.	30 0	*
CD 215	,,	2s. 6d.	27 6	*
CD 219	F 39,	3d.	*	£6
CD 224	G 40,	½d.	£5	£10
CD 225	,,	1d.	6 0	—
CD 226	,,	2d.	—	7 6
CD 228	,,	4d.	*	—
CD 229	,,	5d.	7 6	*
CD 230	,,	1s.	15 0	*
CD 236	H 40,	4d.	£7	*
CD 241	I 41,	1d.	3 0	3 0
CD 242	,,	2d.	—	£5
CD 243	,,	3d.	*	5 0
CD 244	,,	4d.	*	6 6
CD 245	,,	5d.	*	8 6
CD 247	,,	2s. 6d.	£10	*
CD 254	J 41,	1s.	15 0	*
CD 257	K 42,	1d.	*	3 0
CD 258	,,	2d.	—	3 6
CD 259	,,	3d.	110 0	—
CD 260	,,	4d.	*	6 0
CD 262	,,	1s.	15 0	*
CD 263	,,	2s. 6d.	£15	—
CD 271	L 42,	2s. 6d.	£10	*
CD 273	M 43,	1d.	3 0	*
CD 274	,,	2d.	4 0	*
CD 275	,,	3d.	5 0	*
CD 276	,,	4d.	6 0	*
CD 277	,,	5d.	10 0	*
CD 278	,,	1s.	15 0	*
CD 281	O 44,	1d.	4 6	*
CD 282	,,	2d.	£6	*
CD 283	,,	3d.	4 6	*
CD 284	,,	4d.	—	*
CD 285	,,	5d.	10 0	*
CD 286	,,	1s.	15 0	*
CD 287	,,	2s. 6d.	25 0	*
CD 292	P 44,	4d.	6 0	*
CD 293	,,	5d.	8 6	*
CD 294	,,	1s.	15 0	*
CD 295	,,	2s. 6d.	25 0	—
CD 297	Q 44,	1d.	—	*
CD 298	,,	2d.	*	—
CD 305	Q 45,	1d.	£9	*
CD 306	,,	2d.	4 0	*
CD 311	,,	2s. 6d.	—	*
CD 315	R 45,	3d.	6 0	*
CD 318	,,	1s.	15 0	*
CD 326	S 46,	1s.	17 6	*
CD 327	,,	2s. 6d.	—	*
CD 332	T 46,	4d.	6 0	*
CD 333	,,	5d.	8 6	*
CD 335	U 47,	1d.	3 0	*
CD 336	,,	2d.	4 0	*
CD 337	,,	3d.	5 0	—
CD 341	,,	2s. 6d.	—	*

POSTAL FISCALS.

AUTHORISED FOR POSTAL USE 1ST JUNE, 1881

ONE PENNY VALUES. SURFACE-PRINTED. P $15\frac{1}{2}\times 15$

(Printed by Messrs. De La Rue & Co.)

F 1 F 2 F 3 F 4 F 5 F 6

	Date.	Description.	Colour.	Wmk. Type.	Paper.	Type.	Un. s. d.	Used Postally. s. d.
F1	**1853**	Receipt	blue	**F 2** inv.	white	**F 1**	2 6	12 6
F2	**1853**	Draft	brown	,,	white	**F 3**	20 0	17 6
F3	**1854**	Receipt	blue	,,	white	**F 4**	5 0	12 6
F4	**1854**	Receipt	blue	,,	{blue safety}	,,	12 6	17 6
F5	**1855**	{Draft or Receipt}	lilac	,,	,,	**F 5**	25 0	10 0
F6	**1856**	,,	lilac	**F 6**	,,	,,	3 0	4 6
F7	—	,,	lilac	,,	white	,,	3 6	6 0

F 7 F 8 F 9

	Date.	Description.	Colour.	Wmk. Type.	Paper.	Type.	Un. s. d.	Used Postally. s. d.
F9	**1860**	{Draft or Receipt}	lilac		blue	{overpt. "INLAND REVENUE" in red, vertically.}	35 0	35 0

Nos. F1/7 were not specifically authorized for postal use, but as they were passed by the Post Office without question in 1881, they are given here. Nos. F9/56 only were authorized by Acts of Parliament. No. F2 exists *tête-bêche*.

	Date.	Description.	Colour.	Wmk. Type.	Paper.	Type.	Un. s. d.	Used Postally. s. d.
F10	**1860**	{Inland Revenue}	lilac	**F 6**	white	**F 7**	3 0	6 0
F11	—	,,	lilac	,,	blue	,,	3 0	6 0
F12	**1864**	,,	lilac	**40**, 16 mm. high,	bluish	,,	2 6	5 0
F13	—	,,	lilac	,,	white	,,	4 0	4 0
F13*a*	**1867**	,,	lilac	**40**, 18 mm. high,	bluish	,,	7 6	4 0
F13*b*	—	,,	lilac	,,	white	,,		

First Type. (a)

Second Type. (b)

Third Type. (c)*

"Inland Revenue." Small rectangular. P 14.

	Date.	Type.	Colour.	Wmk. Type.	Paper.	Un. s.	Un. d.	Used Postally. s.	Used Postally. d.
F14	**1867**	F **8**	lilac	Anchor, **47**	white	6	0	7	0
F15	**1867**	"	lilac	"	bluish	6	0	7	0
F16	**1868**	F **9** (a)	lilac	"	white	1	0	2	6
F17	**1871**	" "	lilac	"	bluish	1	6	2	6
F18	**1877**	" (b)	lilac	"	white	1	6	4	6
F19	**1877**	" "	lilac	"	bluish	3	0	6	0
F20	**1879**	" (c)	lilac	"	white	1	6	3	6
F21	**1878**	" "	lilac	"	bluish	5	0	3	0
F22	**1881**	" "	lilac	Orb, **48**	white	1	3	1	3
F23	**1881**	" "	lilac	"	bluish	1	6	2	0

* In a the corner ornaments are small; in b they are larger and in c still larger.

F 10

F 13

INLAND
REVENUE
(I)

INLAND
REVENUE
(II)

Embossed. *Type* F **10** *and similar types. Optd.* "inland revenue".

(Made at Somerset House by the Inland Revenue Authorities.)

1883 (1 Jan.).

	Die		Value	Colour	Paper	Perf.	Un.	Used
F24	Die C ..	**1860** ..	3d. ..	pink ..	blue paper ..	imperf. ..	35 0	50 0
F24a	" D ..	" ..	3d. ..	pink ..	blue paper ..	" ..	£9	
F24b	" C ..	" ..	3d. ..	pink ..	blue paper ..	perf. 12½ ..		
F24c	" D ..	" ..	3d. ..	pink ..	blue paper ..	" ..		
F25	" T ..	" ..	6d. ..	pink ..	blue paper ..	imperf. ..	£24	
F25a	" U ..	" ..	6d. ..	pink ..	blue paper ..	" ..	90 0	80 0
F26	" K ..	" ..	2s. ..	pink ..	blue paper ..	" ..	£12	£9

F24aa. *Tête-bêche* pair of No. F24. £38.

1860-82. *Type* F **13**, *and similar types with crown in design, optd.* "inland revenue."

A. "inland revenue" *T* I. Blue *paper.* *No wmk.* *Imperf.* (1860–70.)
B. *Ditto.* *Ditto.* *Perf.* 12½. (1861–73.)
C. "inland revenue" *T* II. White *paper* *Wmk. Anchor.* *Perf.* 12½. (1874.)

		A.		B.		C.	
F27	2d. pink (Die A)	70 0	90 0	£7	£5	–	£8
F28	9d. pink (Die C)	£8		£8	£8	–	–
F29	1s. pink (Die E)	–	£6	£5	95 0	†	
F30	1s. pink (Die F)	70 0	70 0	£5	90 0	£5	£6
	a. Tête-bêche (pair)	£7		†		†	
F31	2s. 6d. pink (Die N)	£12	–	†		†	
F32	2s. 6d. pink (Die O)	30 0	30 0	35 0	35 0	–	£8

F 17

F 18

D. "INLAND REVENUE" *T* II. Blue *or* white *paper.* *Wmk. Anchor.* *P* 12½. (1875–80.)
E. *Ditto.* *T* II. Blue *paper.* *Wmk. Orbs.* *P* 12½. (1882.)

		D.		E.	
F33	2d. vermilion (Die A)	£6	80 0	–	–
F34	9d. vermilion (Die C)	£6	£6	–	–
F35	1s. vermilion (Die E)	50 0	40 0	–	–
F36	1s. vermilion (Die F)	70 0	50 0	†	
F37	2s. 6d. vermilion (Die O)	80 0	70 0	£12	£8

SURFACE-PRINTED STAMPS.
(Printed by Messrs. De La Rue & Co.)

Types F **17** *and* **18**, *bluish to white paper.*

		Wmk. Type.	*Perf.*			
F47	3d. lilac	F **6**	15½ × 15	(1860)	£7	60 0
F48	3d. lilac	**40**, 16 mm. high	,,	(1864)	40 0	30 0
F49	3d. lilac	**40**, 18 mm. ,,	,,	(1867)	15 0	20 0
F50	3d. lilac	**40**, 18 mm. ,,	14	(1881)	£10	£10
F51	3d. lilac	**40**, 20 mm. ,,	14	(1881)	£6	40 0
F52	6d. lilac	F **6**	15½ × 15	(1860)	10 6	20 0
F53	6d. lilac	**40**, 16 mm. ,,	,,	(1864)	8 6	20 0
F54	6d. lilac	**40**, 18 mm. ,,	,,	(1867)	6 0	10 0
F55	6d. lilac	**40**, 18 mm. ,,	14	(1881)	40 0	50 0
F56	6d. lilac	**40**, 20 mm. ,,	14	(1881)	30 0	60 0

BRITISH STAMPS USED ABROAD.

INDEX

INDEX

STAMPS OF GREAT BRITAIN OBLITERATED WITH ONE OF THE FOLLOWING TYPES:—

I. Horizontal oval.

(1)

(2)

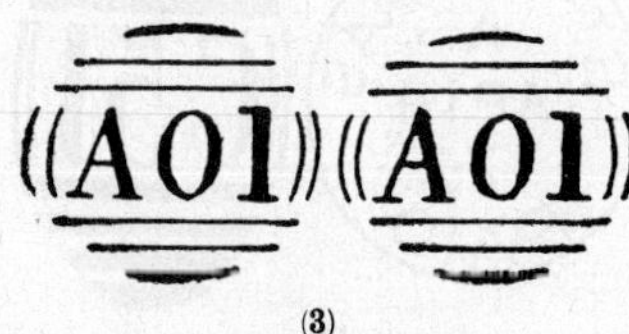

(3)

(4)

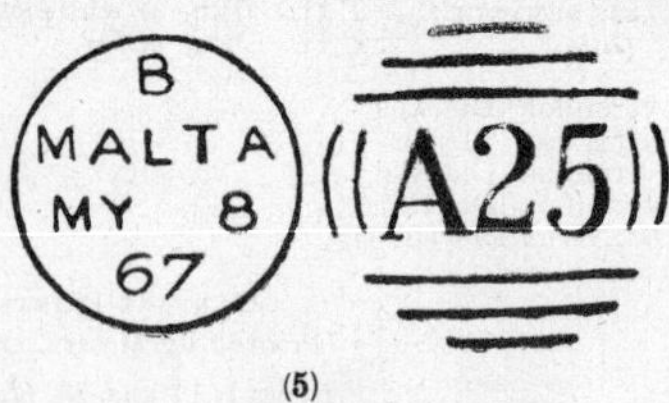

(5)

(6)

(7)

II. Vertical oval.

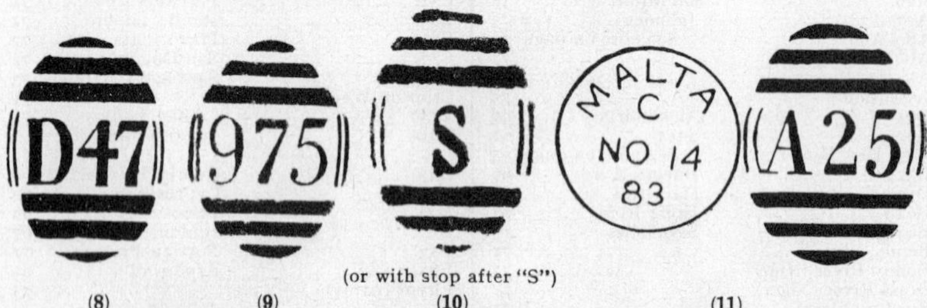

(or with stop after "S")

(8) (9) (10) (11)

(12)

13

(14)

(15)

III. Circular date stamps.

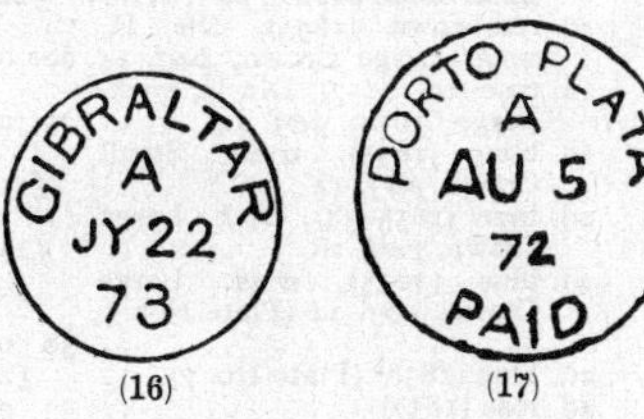

(16) (17)

(18)

(19)

(20)

NOTE.—Prices quoted for British stamps used abroad are for single stamps not on envelopes unless otherwise stated. Stamps on envelopes are worth considerably more in most instances.

In many instances obliterators allotted to post offices abroad were, at a later date, re-allotted to post offices at home. Later issues than those included in our lists can therefore safely be regarded as *not* " used abroad ".

I.

Used in British Possessions in Europe.

MALTA

1857–85.

" M " *Obliteration*, T 1.

z 1 1d. red-brown (1841) £16
z 1a 1d. red-brown, Die I, *wmk.* Small Crown, *perf.* 16 .. .. £6
z 1b 1d. red-brown, Die II, *wmk.* Small Crown, *perf.* 16 .. .. £45
z 1c 1d. red-brown, Die II (1855), *wmk.* Small Crown, *perf.* 14 .. .. £8
z 2 1d. red-brown, Die II (1855), *wmk.* Large Crown, *perf.* 14 .. 90 0
z 3 1d. rose-red (1857), *wmk.* Large Crown, *perf.* 14 .. .. 15 0
z 3a 2d. blue (1841), *imperf.* £45
z 3b 2d. blue (1854), *wmk.* Small Crown, *perf.* 16 (Plate 4) £40
z 4 2d. blue (1855), *wmk.* Large Crown, *perf.* 14 (Plates 5, 6) 30 0
z 5 2d. blue (1858), *wmk.* Large Crown, *perf.* 16 (Plate 6) £8
z 6 2d. bl. (1858) (Pl. Nos. 7, 8, 9) *From* 40 0
z 7 4d. rose (1857) 40 0
z 8 6d. violet (1854), embossed .. £50
z 9 6d. lilac (1856) 35 0
z 10 6d. lilac (1856) (blued *paper*) .. £18
z 11 1s. green (1856) 75 0

"A 25 " *Obliteration as* T 1, 2, 5, 6, 8 *or* 11.

z 12 ½d. rose-red (1870–79) .. *From* 17 6
Plate Nos. 4, 5, 6, 8, 9, 10, 11, 12, 13, 14, 15, 19, 20.
z 13 1d. red-brown (1841), *imperf.* £35
z 13a 1d. red-brown (1854), *wmk.* Small Crown, *perf.* 16 .. .. £18
z 14 1d. red-brown (1855), *wmk.* Large Crown, *perf.* 14 .. .. £7
z 15 1d. rose-red (1857), *wmk.* Large Crown, *perf.* 14 .. .. 7 6
z 15a 1d. rose-red (1861), Alphabet IV ..
z 16 1d. rose-red (1864–79) .. *From* 20 0
Plate Nos. 71, 72, 73, 74, 76, 78, 79, 80, 81, 82, 83, 84, 85, 86, 87, 88, 89, 90, 91, 92, 93, 94, 95, 96, 97, 98, 99, 100, 101, 102, 103, 104, 105, 106, 107, 108, 109, 110, 111, 112, 113, 114, 115, 116, 117, 118, 119, 120, 121, 122, 123, 124, 125, 127, 129, 130, 131, 132, 133, 134, 135, 136, 137, 138, 139, 140, 141, 142, 143, 144, 145, 146, 147, 148, 149, 150, 151, 152, 153, 154, 155, 156, 157, 158, 159, 160, 161, 162, 163, 164, 165, 166, 167, 168, 169, 170, 171, 172, 173, 174, 175, 176, 177, 178, 179, 180, 181, 182, 183, 184, 185, 186, 187, 188, 189, 190, 191, 192, 193, 194, 195, 196, 197, 198, 199, 200, 201, 202, 203, 204, 205, 206, 207, 208, 209, 210, 212, 213, 214, 215, 216, 217, 218, 219, 220, 221, 222, 223, 224.
z 17 1½d. lake-red (1870–79) (Plates, 1, 3) £15
z 17a 2d. blue (1841), *imperf.* £70
z 17b 2d. blue (1855), *wmk.* Large Crown, *perf.* 14 .. .. .. 70 0
z 18 2d. blue (1858–69) .. *From* 15 0
Plate Nos. 7, 8, 9, 12, 13, 14, 15.
z 19 2½d. rosy mauve (1875) (blued *paper*)
Plate Nos. 1, 2. .. *From* 70 0
z 20 2½d. rosy mauve (1875–76) *From* 35 0
Plate Nos. 1, 2, 3.
z 21 2½d. rosy mauve (*Error of Lettering*) £75
z 22 2½d. rosy mauve (1876–79) *From* 32 6
Plate Nos. 3, 4, 5, 6, 7, 8, 9, 10, 11, 12, 13, 14, 15, 16, 17.
z 23 2½d. blue (1880–81) .. .. *From* 15 0
Plate Nos. 17, 18, 19, 20.
z 24 2½d. blue (1881) .. .. *From* 10 6
Plate Nos. 21, 22, 23.
z 25 3d. carmine-rose (1862) 85 0
z 26 3d. rose (1865) (Plate No. 4) .. 50 0
z 27 3d. rose (1867–73) .. *From* 30 0
Plate Nos. 4, 5, 6, 7, 8, 9, 10.
z 28 3d. rose (1873–76) .. *From* 35 0
Plate Nos. 11, 12, 14, 15, 16, 17, 18, 19, 20.
z 29 3d. rose (1881) (Plate Nos. 20, 21) 60 0
z 30 3d. lilac (1883) (3d. *on* 3d.) ..
z 31 4d. rose (1857) 60 0
z 32 4d. red (1862) (Plates 3, 4) *From* 35 0
z 33 4d. vermilion (1865 73) .. " 30 0
Plate Nos. 7, 8, 9, 10, 11, 12, 13, 14.
z 34 4d. vermilion (1876) (Plate No. 15) £15

z 35	4d. sage-green (1877) .. .. Plate Nos 15, 16.	85 0
z 36	4d. grey-brown (1880) *wmk.* Large Garter (Plate No. 17) ..	80 0
z 37	4d. grey-brown (1880) *wmk.* Crown Plate Nos 17, 18.	30 0
z 37a	6d. violet (1854), embossed ..	
z 38	6d. lilac (1856)	35 0
z 39	6d. lilac (1862) (Plates 3, 4) *From*	45 0
z 40	6d. lilac (1865–67) .. „ Plate Nos. 5, 6.	45 0
z 40a	6d. lilac (1865–67) (*Wmk. error*) ..	
z 41	6d. lilac (1867) (Plate No 6) ..	47 6
z 42	6d. violet (1867–70) .. *From* Plate Nos. 6, 8, 9.	40 0
z 43	6d. buff (1872–73) .. *From* Plate Nos. 11, 12.	£12
z 44	6d. chestnut (1872) (Plate No. 11)	35 0
z 45	6d. grey (1873) (Plate No. 12) ..	65 0
z 46	6d. grey (1873–80) .. .. *From* Plate Nos. 13, 14, 15, 16, 17.	35 0
z 47	6d. grey (1881–82) .. .. *From* Plate Nos. 17, 18.	37 6
z 48	6d. lilac (1883) (6d. *on* 6d.) ..	50 0
z 49	8d. orange (1876)	£19
z 50	9d. straw (1862)	£22
z 51	9d. bistre (1862)	£22
z 51a	9d. straw (1865)	£40
z 52	10d. red-brown (1867)	£6
z 52a	1s. (1847), embossed	£40
z 53	1s. green (1856)	75 0
z 54	1s. green (1862)	75 0
z 55	1s. green ("K" *variety*)	
z 56	1s. green (1865) (Plate No. 4) ..	40 0
z 57	1s. green (1867–73) .. *From* Plates Nos. 4, 5, 6, 7.	17 6
z 58	1s. green (1873–77) .. *From* Plate Nos. 8, 9, 10, 11, 12, 13.	35 0
z 59	1s. orange-brown (1880) .. .. Plate No. 13.	£9
z 60	1s. orange-brown (1881) .. *From* Plate Nos. 13, 14.	50 0
z 61	2s. blue (*shades*) (1867) .. *From*	65 0
z 62	2s. brown (1880)	£80
z 63	5s. rose (1867–74) .. .. *From* Plate Nos. 1, 2.	£8
z 64	5s. rose (1882) (Plate No. 4), blue *paper*	£38
z 65	5s. rose (1882) (Plate No. 4), white *paper*	£58
z 66	10s. grey-green (1878)	£85

1880

z 67	½d. deep green	10 0
z 68	½d. pale green	10 0
z 69	1d. Venetian red	8 0
z 69a	1½d. Venetian red	55 0
z 70	2d. pale rose	45 0
z 71	2d. deep rose	45 0
z 72	5d. indigo	40 0

1881

z 73	1d. lilac (14 *dots*)	22 6
z 74	1d. lilac (16 „)	7 6

1883–4

z 75–z 79	½d. slate-blue; 1½d., 2d., 2½d., 3d. .. *From*	10 0
z 80–z 83a	4d., 5d., 6d., 9d., 1s. „	65 0
z 84	5s. rose (blued *paper*)	£44
z 85	5s. rose (white „)	£30

POSTAL FISCALS.

z 86	1d. lilac (1871), *wmk.* Anchor ..	
z 86a	1d. lilac (1881) „ Orb ..	

GIBRALTAR.

1857.

"G" *Obliteration as T 1.*

z 87	1d. red-brown (1854), Die I ..	£12
z 87a	1d. red-brown (1855), Die II, *wmk.* Small Crown, *perf.* 16.	£30
z 88	1d. red-brown (1855), Die II, *wmk.* Small Crown, *perf.* 14...	£12
z 89	1d. red-brown (1855), Die II, *wmk.* Large Crown, *perf.* 14	60 0
z 90	1d. rose-red (1857), Die II, *wmk.* Large Crown, *perf.* 14 ..	25 0
z 91	2d. blue (1855), *wmk.* Small Crown. *perf.* 14	£15
z 92	2d. blue (1855–58), *wmk.* Large Crown, *perf.* 16	£15
z 93	2d. blue (1855), *wmk.* Large Crown, *perf.* 14 (Plate Nos. 5, 6)	30 0
z 94	2d. blue (1858) (Plate No. 7) ..	£8
z 95	4d. rose (1857)	35 0
z 96	6d. lilac (1856)	35 0
z 96a	6d. lilac (1856) (blued *paper*) ..	£35
z 97	1s. green (1856)	70 0
z 97a	1s. green (1856) (blued *paper*) ..	£42

"A 26" *Obliteration as T 2, 5, 11 or 14.*

z 98	½d. rose-red (1870–79) .. *From* Plate Nos. 4, 5, 6, 8, 10, 11, 12, 13, 14, 15, 19, 20.	22 6
z 98a	1d. red-brown (1841), *imperf.*	
z 99	1d. red-brown (1855), *wmk.* Large Crown, *perf.* 14	£9
z 100	1d. rose-red (1857), *wmk.* Large Crown, *perf.* 14	15 0
z 101	1d. rose-red (1864–79) .. *From* Plate Nos. 71, 72, 73, 74, 76, 78, 79, 80, 81, 82, 83, 84, 85, 86, 87, 88, 89, 90, 91, 92, 93, 94, 95, 96, 97, 98, 99, 100, 101, 102, 103, 104, 105, 106, 107, 108, 109, 110, 111, 112, 113, 114, 115, 116, 117, 118, 119, 120, 121, 122, 123, 124, 125, 127, 129, 130, 131, 132, 133, 134, 136, 137, 138, 139, 140, 142, 143, 144, 145, 146, 147, 148, 149, 150, 151, 152, 153, 154, 155, 156, 157, 158, 159, 160, 161, 162, 163, 164, 165, 166, 167, 168, 169, 170, 171, 172, 173, 174, 175, 176, 177, 178, 179, 180, 181, 182, 183, 184, 185, 186, 187, 188, 189, 190, 191, 192, 193, 194, 195, 196, 197, 198, 199, 200, 201, 202, 203, 204, 205, 206, 207, 208, 209, 210, 211, 212, 213, 214, 215, 216, 217, 218, 219, 220, 221, 222, 223, 224, 225.	20 0
z 102	1½d. lake-red (1870) (Pl. 3) ..	
z 103	2d. blue (1855), *wmk.* Large Crown, *perf.* 14 (Plate No. 6)	£7
z 104	2d. blue (1858–69) .. *From* Plate Nos. 7, 8, 9, 12, 13, 14, 15.	17 6
z 105	2½d. rosy mauve (1875) (blued *paper*) (Plate Nos. 1, 2) *From*	£7
z 106	2½d. rosy mauve (1875–76) „ Plate Nos. 1, 2, 3.	35 0
z 107	2½d. rosy mauve (*Error of Lettering*)	
z 108	2½d. rosy mauve (1876–79) *From* Plate Nos 3, 4, 5, 6, 7, 8, 9, 10, 11, 12, 13, 14, 15, 16, 17.	32 6
z 109	2½d. blue (1880–81) .. *From* Plate Nos. 17, 18, 19, 20	17 6
z 110	2½d. blue (1881) .. .. *From* Plate Nos. 21, 22, 23.	10 0
z 111	3d. carmine-rose (1862)	£5
z 112	3d. rose (1865) (Plate No. 4) ..	45 0
z 113	3d. rose (1867–73) .. *From* Plate Nos. 4, 5, 6, 7, 8, 9, 10.	30 0
z 114	3d. rose (1873–76) .. *From* Plate Nos. 11, 12, 14, 15, 16, 17, 18, 19, 20.	30 0
z 115	3d. rose (1881) (Plate Nos. 20, 21)	
z 116	3d. lilac (1883) (3d. *on* 3d.) ..	80 0
z 117	4d. rose (1857)	35 0

z 118 4d. red (1862) (Plates 3, 4) *From* 35 0
z 119 4d. vermilion (1865–73) .. „ 30 0
Plate Nos. 7, 8, 9, 10, 11, 12, 13, 14.
z 120 4d. vermilion (1876) (Plate No. 15) £15
z 121 4d. sage-green (1877) 95 0
Plate Nos. 15, 16.
z 122 4d. grey-brown (1880) *wmk.* Large Garter (Plate No. 17) .. £6
z 123 4d. grey-brown (1880) *wmk.* Crown (Plate Nos. 17, 18) .. *From* 30 0
z 124 6d. lilac (1856) 35 0
z 125 6d. lilac (1862) (Plates 3, 4) *From* 50 0
z 126 6d. lilac (1865–67) .. *From* 42 6
Plate Nos. 5, 6.
z 12 6d lilac (1867) (Plate No. 6) .. 55 0
z 128 6d. violet (1867–70) .. *From* 35 0
Plate Nos. 6, 8, 9.
z 129 6d. buff (1872–73) .. *From* £13
Plate Nos. 11, 12.
z 130 6d. chestnut (1872) (Plate No. 11) 35 0
z 131 6d. grey (1873) (Plate No. 12) 60 0
z 132 6d. grey (1874–80) .. *From* 35 0
Plate Nos. 13, 14, 15, 16, 17.
z 133 6d. grey (1881) (Plates 17, 18) ..
z 134 6d. lilac (1883) (6d. on 6d.) .. 70 0
z 135 8d. orange (1876) £10
z 136 9d. bistre (1862) £10
z 137 9d. straw (1862) .. .. ..
z 138 9d. straw (1865) £35
z 139 9d. straw (1867) 110 0
z 140 10d. red-brown (1867) £10
z 141 1s. green (1856) 70 0
z 142 1s. green (1862) 70 0
z 143 1s. green (1862) ("K" *variety*) ..
z 144 1s. green (1865) (Plate No. 4) .. 37 6
z 145 1s. green (1867–73) .. *From* 17 6
Plate Nos. 4, 5, 6, 7.
z 146 1s. green (1873–77) .. *From* 35 0
Plate Nos. 8, 9, 10 11, 12, 13.
z 146*a* 1s. orange-brown (1880) (Pl. 13) £8
z 147 1s. orange-brown (1881) *From* 50 0
Plate Nos. 13 and 14.
z 148 2s. blue (1867) £7
z 149 5s. rose (1867) (Plate No. 1) .. £20

1880.

z 150 ½d. deep green 10 0
z 151 ½d. pale green 10 0
z 152 1d. Venetian red 8 6
z 153 1½d. Venetian red .. .. ..
z 154 2d. pale rose 40 0
z 155 2d. deep rose .. .. ..
z 156 5d. indigo .. .. ..

1881.

z 157 1d. lilac (14 *dots*) 17 6
z 158 1d. lilac (16 *dots*) 8 6

1884.

z 159–62 ½d. slate-blue; 2d., 2½d., 3d. *From* 10 6
z 163–64 4d., 6d. .. .. „ 70 0

POSTAL FISCAL.

z 173 1d. lilac (1881), *wmk.* Orb ..

IONIAN ISLANDS.

"PAID AT CORFU"

z 174 1d. red-brown (1855) Die II, *wmk.* Large Crown, *perf.* 14 .. £15

VARIOUS TOWNS IN CYPRUS.

LARNACA.

"**942**" *Obliteration as T* **9**.

1878 *to* **1881.**

z 176 ½d. rose-red (1870 79) .. *From* £8
Plate Nos. 11, 12, 13, 14, 15, 19, 20.
z 177 1d. rose-red (1864–79) . *From* 70 0
Plate Nos. 154, 170, 171, 174, 175 176, 177, 178, 179, 181, 182, 183, 184 187, 188, 190, 191, 192, 193, 194, 195, 196, 197, 198, 199, 200, 201, 202, 203, 204, 205, 206, 207, 208, 209, 210, 212, 213, 215, 216, 217, 218, 220, 221, 222, 225.
z 177*a* 1½d. lake-red (1870) (Pl. 3) ..
z 178 2d. blue (1858–69) 65 0
Plate Nos. 9, 14, 15.
z 179 2½d. rosy mauve (1876–79) *From* 32 6
Plate Nos. 5, 6, 8, 10, 11, 12, 13, 14, 15, 16, 17.
z 180 2½d. blue (1880–81) £17
Plate Nos. 17, 18, 19, 20.
z 181 2½d. blue (1881) (Plate No. 21) ..
z 182 4d. sage-green (1877) £18
Plate Nos. 15, 16.
z 183 6d. grey (1874–76) £11
Plate Nos. 15, 16, 17.
z 183*a* 8d. orange (1876) £45
z 184 1s. green (1873–77) £14
Plate Nos. 12, 13.
z 184*a* 1s. orange brown (1881) (Pl. 14)
z 184*b* 5s. rose (1874) (Pl. 2) £140

NICOSIA.

"**969.**" *Obliteration as T* **9**.

1878 *to* **1881.**

z 185 ½d. rose-red (1870–79) £10
Plate Nos. 12, 13, 14, 15, 20.
z 186 1d. rose-red (1864–79) .. *From* 80 0
Plate Nos. 170, 171, 174, 189, 190, 192, 193, 195, 196, 198, 200, 202, 203, 205, 206, 207, 210, 212, 214, 215, 218, 221, 222, 225.
z 187 2d. blue (1858–69) .. ..
Plate Nos. 14 and 15.
z 188 2½d. rosy mauve (1876–79) *From* 55 0
Plate Nos. 10, 11, 12, 13, 14, 15, 16.
z 188*a* 2½d. blue (1880) (Plate No. 20) ..
z 188*b* 2½d. blue (1881) (Plate No. 21) ..
z 188*c* 4d. vermilion (1876) (Pl. No. 15) ..
z 189 4d. sage-green (1877) (Plate No. 16) £13
z 190 6d. grey (1873) (Plate No. 16) ..

KYRENIA

"**974.**" *Obliteration as T* **9**.

1878 *to* **1880**

z 190*a* ½d. rose-red (1870–79) (Plate No. 1)
z 191 1d. rose-red (1864–79) .. *From* £7
Plate Nos. 168, 171, 193, 196, 206, 207, 209, 220.
z 192 2d. blue (1858-69) (Plate No. 15)
z 193 2½d. rosy mauve (1876–79)
Plate Nos. 12, 13, 14, 15
z 193*a* 4d. sage-grn. (1877) (Pl. No. 16) ..
z 193*b* 6d. grey (1874–80) (Pl. No. 16) ..

LIMASSOL.

"**975.**" *Obliteration as T* **9**.

1878 *to* **1880.**

z 194 ½d. rose-red (1870–79) £10
Plate Nos. 11, 13, 15, 19.
z 195 1d. rose-red (1864–79) . *From* 85 0
Plate Nos. 160, 171, 173, 174, 177, 179, 184, 187, 190, 193, 195, 196, 197, 198, 200, 202, 206, 207, 208, 210, 213, 215, 216, 218, 220, 221, 222, 225.
z 196 1½d. lake-red (1870–74) (Plate 3) ..
z 197 2d. blue (1858–69) .. .. *From* 85 0
Plate Nos. 14, 15.
z 198 2½d. rosy-mauve (1876–80) *From* 65 0
Plate Nos. 11, 12, 13, 14, 15, 16.
z 198*a* 2½d. blue (1880) .. .. ..
Plate Nos. 19 and 20.
z 198*b* 4d. sage-green (Plate No. 16) .. £10

PAPHO (PAPHOS).

"981." *Obliteration as T* **9.**

1878 *to* **1881.**

z 198*c* ½d. rose-red (1870–79) .. .. Plate Nos. 13, 15.

z 199 1d. rose-red (1864–79) .. *From* £8 Plate Nos. 196, 201, 202, 204, 206, 213, 217.

z 200 2d. blue (1858–69) (Plate No. 15) £16

z 201 2½d. rosy mauve (1876–79) Plate Nos. 13, 14, 15 ... ... £11

FAMAGUSTA.

"982." *Obliteration as T* **9.**

1878 *to* **1881.**

z 202 ½d. rose-red (1870–79) .. .. Plate No. 13. £8

z 203 1d. rose-red (1864–70) .. .. Plate Nos. 174, 181, 202, 206, 215.

z 204 2d. blue (1858–69) .. .. .. £19 Plate Nos. 13, 14, 15,

z 204*a* 2½d. rosy mauve (1876) (Pl. 16) ..

z 204*b* 6d. grey (1874–80) (Pl. 15). ..

z 204*c* 1s. green (1873–77) (Pl. 12) ..

z 205 1s. orange-brown (1881) .. .. Plate No. 14.

POLYMEDIA.

"D 47." *Obliteration as T* **8.**

1878 *to* **1880.**

z 205*a* ½d. rose-red (1870–79) .. .. Plate No. 11.

z 206 1d. rose-red (1864–79) .. *From* £17 Plate Nos. 175, 192, 197, 205, 206, 207, 208, 209.

z 207 2d. blue (1858–69) (Plate No. 15) £27

HEADQUARTER CAMP (CYPRUS).

"D 48." *Obliteration as T* **8.**

1878 *to* **1880.**

z 207*a* ½d. rose-red (1870–79) .. .. Plate Nos. 13, 20.

z 208 1d. rose-red (1864–79) .. *From* £19 Plate Nos. 171, 174, 177, 201, 204, 205, 214, 218.

z 209 2d. blue (1858–69) (Plate No. 15) £33

II.

British Offices in Turkish Empire.

CONSTANTINOPLE.

"C" *Obliteration or circular postmarks as T* **1, 10,** *or* **19.**

1857.

z 210 ½d. rose-red (1870–79) .. *From* 45 0 Plate Nos. 5, 6, 10, 11, 12, 14, 15, 20.

z 211 1d. red-brown (1854), Die I, *wmk.* Small Crown, *perf.* 16 ..

z 211*a* 1d. red-brown (1855), Die II, *wmk.* Small Crown, *perf.* 14 ..

z 211*b* 1d. red-brown, *wmk.* Large Crown, *perf.* 14 .. .. .. 55 0

z 212 1d. rose-red (1857) 20 0

z 212*a* 1d. rose-red (1861) Alphabet IV ..

z 213 1d. rose-red (1864–79) .. *From* 20 0 Plate Nos. 71, 72, 73, 74, 76, 78, 79, 80, 81, 83, 85, 87, 89, 90, 92, 93, 94, 95, 96, 97, 99, 101, 102, 105, 106, 108, 109, 110, 113, 116, 118, 119, 120, 121, 122, 123, 124, 125, 127, 129, 130, 131, 134, 135, 136, 137, 138, 140, 141, 143, 144, 145, 146, 147, 148, 149, 150, 151, 152, 155, 156, 157, 158, 159, 160, 161, 162, 163, 164, 166, 167, 170, 171, 172, 173, 174, 175, 176, 177, 178, 179, 180, 181, 183, 184, 186, 187, 188, 189, 190, 191, 192, 193, 194, 195, 196, 198, 200, 201, 203, 204, 205, 206, 207, 208, 210, 212, 214, 215, 216, 220, 222, 224.

z 214 1½d. rose-red (1870) (Plate 1) .. £40

z 214*a* 2d. blue (1855), *wmk.* Large Crown, *perf.* 14. Pl. Nos. 5, 6. ..

z 215 2d. blue (1858–69) .. .. *From* 15 0 Plate Nos. 8, 9, 12, 13, 14, 15.

z 216 2½d. rosy mauve (1875–76) (blued *paper*) (Plate Nos. 1, 2) *From* 65 0

z 217 2½d. rosy mauve (1875–76) *From* 35 0 Plate Nos. 1, 2, 3.

z 218 2½d. rosy mauve (*Error of Lettering*)

z 219 2½d. rosy mauve (1876–79) *From* 32 6 Plate Nos. 3, 4, 5, 6, 7, 8, 9, 10, 11, 12, 13, 14, 15, 16, 17.

z 220 2½d. blue (1880–81) .. *From* 17 6 Plate Nos. 17, 18, 19, 20.

z 221 2½d. blue (1881) .. .. „ 10 0 Plate Nos. 21, 22, 23.

z 221*a* 3d. carmine-rose (1862) (Plate 2) .. £15

z 221*b* 3d. rose (1865) (Plate 4) .. £15

z 222 3d. rose (1867–73) .. „ 30 0 Plate Nos. 4, 5, 6, 7, 8, 9, 10.

z 223 3d. rose (1873–76) .. .. 35 0 Plates, 12, 15, 16, 17, 18, 19.

z 224 3d. rose (1881) (Plate No. 21) ..

z 225 4d. rose (1857) 35 0

z 226 4d. red (1862) (Plates 3, 4) *From* 32 6

z 227 4d. vermilion (1865–73) .. *From* 30 0 Plate Nos. 7, 8, 9, 10, 11, 12, 13, 14.

z 228 4d. vermilion (1876) (Plate No. 15) £20

z 229 4d. sage-green (1877) .. .. £5 Plate Nos. 15, 16.

z 230 4d. grey-brown (1880) *wmk.* Large Garter (Plate No. 17)

z 231 4d. grey-brown (1880) *wmk.* Crown .. .. *From* 45 0 Plate Nos. 17, 18.

z 232 6d. lilac (1856) 35 0

z 233 6d. lilac (1862) (Plates 3, 4) *From* 42 6

z 234 6d. lilac (1865–67) .. „ 42 6 Plate Nos. 5, 6.

z 235 6d. lilac (1867) (Plate No. 6) .. 47 6

z 236 6d. violet (1867–70) .. *From* 32 6 Plate Nos. 6, 8, 9.

z 237 6d. buff (1872–73) .. „ £12 Plate Nos. 11, 12.

z 238 6d. chestnut (1872) (Plate No. 11) 37 6

z 239 6d. grey (1873) (Plate No. 12) .. 60 0

z 240 6d. grey (1874–76) .. .. *From* 37 6 Plate Nos. 13, 14, 15, 16.

z 241 6d. grey (1881–82) .. .. „ 50 0 Plate Nos. 17, 18.

z 242 6d. lilac (1883) (Plate No. 18) .. 65 0

a. Dots slanting (Letters MI) .. £22

z 243 8d. orange (1876) £65

z 244 10d. red-brown (1867), *wmk.* Emblems £1500

z 244*a* 10d. red-brown (1867) £6

z 245 1s. green (1856) 75 0

z 246 1s. green (1862) 70 0

z 247 1s. green (1862) ("K" *variety*) ..

z 248 1s. green (1865) (Plate No. 4) .. 37 6

z 249 1s. green (1867–73) .. *From* 17 6 Plate Nos. 4, 5, 6, 7.

z 250 1s. green (1873–77) .. *From* 40 0 Plate Nos. 8, 9, 10, 11, 12, 13.

z 251 1s. orange-brown (1880) .. .. £8 Plate No. 13.

z 252 1s. orange-brown (1881) .. *From* 50 0 Plate Nos. 13, 14.

z 253 2s. blue (1867) 65 0

z 254 5s. rose (1867–74) .. *From* £9 Plate Nos. 1, 2.

z 255 5s. rose (1882) (white *paper*) .. £60
z 256 5s. rose (1882) (blued *paper*) .. £40

1880.
z 257 ½d. deep green 8 6
z 258 ½d. pale green 7 6
z 259 1d. Venetian red 10 6
z 260 2d. pale rose 32 6
z 261 2d. deep rose 35 0

1881.
z 262 1d. lilac (14 *dots*) .. .. ..
z 263 1d. lilac (16 *dots*) 8 6

1883 *to* 1884.
z 264 ½d. slate 20 0
z 265–68 1½d., 2d., 2½d., 3d. .. *From* 8 6
z 269–72 4d., 5d., 6d., 9d., 1s. .. *From* 65 0
z 273 2s. 6d. lilac (blued *paper*) ..
z 274 2s. 6d. lilac (white *paper*) .. 65 0
z 275 5s. rose (blued *paper*) .. ..
z 276 5s. rose (white *paper*) .. ..

1887.
z 276*a–l* ½d., 1½d., 2d., 2½d., 3d., 4d., 4½d., 5d., 6d., 9d., 10d., 1s. .. .. .. *From* 10 6

1900.
z 277–77*a* ½d., 1s. .. .. .. *From* 10 6

1902.
z 278–90*c* ½d., 1d., 1½d., 2d., 2½d., 3d., 4d., 4d. orange, 5d., 6d., 7d., 9d., 10d., 1s., 2s. 6d., 5s. *From* 8 6

1911–18.
z 290*d–u* ½d. (No. 339), ½d. (No. 351), 1d. (No. 330), 1d. (No. 343), 1d. (No. 357), 1½d., 2d., 2½d., 3d., 4d., 5d., 6d., 9d. (No. 392), 9d. (No. 393*a*), 1s., 2s. 6d. (No. 413*a*), 5s. (No. 416), 10s. (No. 417) *From* 10 0

SALONICA.

Office opened in 1900. *Date-stamp with double circle. Issues of* 1887–1900.

z 290*v* ½d. vermilion 30 0
z 291 ½d. green 40 0
z 292 1d. lilac 45 0
z 293 6d. purple/*red* 70 0
z 293*a* 1s. green and carmine .. £6
z 293*b* 5s. rose (white paper) (1883) .. £25

1902.
z 293*c* ½d. blue-green 35 0
z 293*d* ½d. yellow-green 35 0
z 293*e* 1d. scarlet.. .. .. .. 40 0
z 293*f* 2½d. blue 50 0
z 293*g* 1s. green and carmine £5

1911–12.
z 293*h* ½d. (*T* **98**) 30 0
z 293*i* 1d. (*T* **99**) 45 0
z 293*j* 1d. (*T* **102**) 50 0

1912–13.
z 293*k* ½d. (*T* **105**) 30 0
z 293*l* 1d. (*T* **104**) 40 0

STAMBOUL (CONSTANTINOPLE).

" S " *Obliteration as T* **10**.

1884.
z 294 ½d. slate 65 0
z 294*a* 1d. lilac 45 0
z 295 2½d. lilac 45 0
z 296 5d. green £6

1887.
z 296*a* ½d. vermilion 47 6

1911.
z 296*b* ½d. (*T* **98**) etc., and other values of K.G.V. to 1s. .. ..

Circular postmark as T **18**.

z 298 1d. lilac (1881) 32 6
z 299 2½d. lilac (1884) 32 6
z 300 5d. green (1884) 65 0

1887.
z 301–301*k* ½d., 1½d., 2d., 2½d., 3d., 4d., 4½d., 5d., 6d., 9d., 10d., 1s. *From* 17 6

1900.
z 302 ½d. 27 6
z 303 1s. .. .. •

1902–10.
z 304–15*d* ½d., 1d., 1½d., 2d., 2½d., 3d., 4d., 4d. orange, 5d., 6d., 7d., 9d., 10d., 1s., 2s. 6d., 5s. .. .. .. *From* 15 0

1911–13.
z 316–29*d* ½d. (*T* **98**), ½d. (*T* **101**), 1d. (*T* **99**), ½d. (*T* **105**), 1d. (*T* **104**), 1½d., 2d., 2½d., 3d., 4d., 5d., 6d., 7d., 8d., 9d., 10d., 1s., 2s. 6d., 5s. *From* 25 0

ALEXANDRIA (EGYPT).

" B **01**." *Obliteration as T* **2, 8, 12** *or* **15.**

1860 *to* 1879.
z 330 ½d. rose-red (1870–79) .. *From* 40 0
Plate Nos. 5, 6, 8, 10, 13, 20.
z 331 1d. rose-red (1857) 17 6
z 331*a* 1d. rose-red (1861) (Alph. IV) ..
z 332 1d. rose-red (1864–79) .. *From* 17 6
Plate Nos. 71, 72, 73, 74, 76, 78, 79, 80, 81, 82, 83, 84, 85, 86, 87, 88, 89, 90, 91, 92, 93, 94, 95, 96, 97, 98, 99, 101, 102, 103, 104, 106, 107, 108, 109, 110, 111, 112, 113, 114, 115, 117, 118, 119, 120, 121, 122, 123, 125, 127, 129, 130, 131, 133, 134, 136, 137, 138, 139, 140, 142, 143, 144, 145, 146, 147, 148, 149, 154, 156, 157, 158, 159, 160, 162, 163, 165, 168, 169, 170, 171, 172, 174, 175, 177, 179, 180, 181, 182, 183, 185, 188, 190, 198, 200, 203, 210, 220.
z 333 2d. blue (1858–69) .. .. *From* 15 0
Plate Nos. 7, 8, 9, 13, 14, 15.
z 334 2½d. rosy mauve (1875) (blued *paper*)
Plate Nos. 1, 2 .. *From* 65 0
z 335 2½d. rosy mauve (1875–6) 35 0
Plate Nos. 1 2, 3.
z 336 2½d. rosy mauve (*Error of Lettering*) £90
z 337 2½d. rosy mauve (1876–79) .. *From* 32 6
Plate Nos. 3, 4, 5 6, 7, 8, 9.
z 338 3d. carmine-rose (1862) 85 0
z 339 3d. rose (1865) (Plate No. 4) .. 45 0
z 340 3d. rose (1867–73) .. .. *From* 30 0
Plate Nos. 4, 5, 6, 7, 8, 9.
z 341 3d. rose (1875–76) .. *From* 27 6
Plate Nos. 11, 12, 14, 15, 16, 18, 19.
z 341*a* 3d. rose (1881) (Plate No. 20) ..
z 342 4d. rose (1857) 55 0
z 343 4d. red (1862) (Plates 3, 4) *From* 40 0
z 344 4d. vermilion (1865–73) 30 0
Plate Nos. 7, 8, 9, 10, 11, 12, 13, 14.
z 345 4d. vermilion (1876) (Plate No. 15) £15
z 346 4d. sage-green (1877) 85 0
Plate No. 15.
z 347 6d. lilac (1856) 35 0
z 348 6d. lilac (1862) (Plates 3, 4) *From* 45 0
z 349 6d. lilac (1865–67) .. „ 45 0
Plate Nos. 5, 6.
z 350 6d. lilac (1867) (Plate No. 6) .. 50 0
z 351 6d. violet (1867–70) .. *From* 35 0
Plate Nos. 6, 8, 9.
a. Imperf. (Plate No. 8) £50
z 352 6d. buff (1872–73) .. *From* £12
Plate Nos. 11, 12.
z 353 6d. chestnut (1872) (Plate No. 11) 45 0
z 354 6d. grey (1873) (Plate No. 12) .. 60 0
z 355 6d. grey (1874–76) .. .. *From* 35 0
Plate Nos. 13, 14, 15.
z 356 9d. straw (1862) £9

z 357 9d. bistre (1862) .. .. ..
z 358 9d. straw (1867) .. .. ..
z 359 10d. red-brown (1867) £7
z 360 1s. green (1856) 70 0
z 361 1s. green (1862) 70 0
z 361a 1s. green (1862) ("K" *variety*) ..
z 362 1s. green (1865) (Plate No. 4) .. 37 6
z 363 1s. green (1867–73) .. *From* 17 6
Plate Nos. 4, 5, 6, 7.
z 364 1s. green (1873–77) .. *From* 35 0
Plate Nos. 8, 9, 10, 11, 12, 13.
z 365 2s. blue (1867) 65 0
z 366 5s. rose (1867–74) .. *From* £6
Plate Nos. 1, 2.

PORT SAID.

Stamps issued after 1877 can be found with the Egyptian cancellation "Port Said," but these are on letters posted from British ships.

SUEZ (EGYPT).

"B **02**." *Obliteration as T* **2, 8** *and circular date stamp as in T* **5**.

1860 *to* **1879.**

z 367 ½d. rose-red (1870–79) .. ..
Plate Nos. 6, 10, 11, 12, 13, 14.
z 368 1d. rose-red (1857) 40 0
z 369 1d. rose-red (1864–79) .. *From* 30 0
Plate Nos. 73, 74, 79, 80, 81, 83, 84, 86, 87, 91, 94, 96, 97, 100, 101, 106, 110, 113, 119, 120, 121, 122, 123, 124, 125, 129, 131, 134, 137, 138, 140, 143, 144, 145, 147, 148, 149, 150, 151, 153, 154, 156, 158, 159, 161, 162, 163, 164, 165, 166, 167, 168, 170, 174, 176, 177, 178, 179, 180, 181, 182, 184, 185, 186, 187, 189, 190, 205.
z 370 2d. blue (1858–69) .. *From* 50 0
Plate Nos. 8, 9, 13, 14, 15.
z 371 2½d. rosy mauve (1875) (blued *paper*)
Plate Nos. 1 and 2 .. *From* 70 0
z 372 2½d. rosy mauve (1875–76) *From* 37 6
Plate Nos. 1, 2, 3.
z 373 2½d. rosy mauve (*Error of Lettering*) £150
z 374 2½d. rosy mauve (1876–79) *From* 32 6
Plate Nos. 3, 4, 5, 6, 7, 8, 9.
z 375 3d. carmine-rose (1862) 80 0
z 376 3d. rose (1865) (Plate No. 4) .. 65 0
z 377 3d. rose (1867–73) .. ..
Plate Nos. 5, 6, 7, 8.
z 378 3d. rose (1873–76) .. *From* 65 0
Plate Nos. 12, 16.
z 379 4d. rose (1857) 85 0
z 380 4d. red (1862) (Plates 3, 4) .. 75 0
z 381 4d. vermilion (1865–73) .. *From* 30 0
Plate Nos. 7, 8, 9, 10, 11, 12, 13, 14.
z 382 4d. vermilion (1876) (Plate No. 15)
z 383 4d. sage-green (1877) (Plate No. 15) 90 0
z 384 6d. lilac (1856) 40 0
z 385 6d. lilac (1862) (Plates 3, 4) *From* 50 0
z 386 6d. lilac (1865–67) .. *From* 50 0
Plate Nos. 5, 6.
z 387 6d. lilac (1867) (Plate No. 6) .. 55 0
z 388 6d. violet (1867–70) .. *From* 40 0
Plate Nos. 6, 8, 9.
z 389 6d. buff (1872–73) .. *From* £13
Plate Nos. 11, 12.
z 389a 6d. pale chestnut (Plate No. 12) £240
z 390 6d. chestnut (1872) (Plate No. 11) 45 0
z 391 6d. grey (1873) (Plate No. 12) .. 65 0
z 392 6d. grey (1874–76) .. *From* 40 0
Plate Nos. 13, 14, 15, 16.
z 393 8d. orange (1876) .. .. ..
z 394 9d. straw (1862) £11
z 395 9d. bistre (1862) .. .. ..
z 396 9d. straw (1867) .. .. ..
z 397 10d. red-brown (1867) £15
z 398 1s. green (1856) 90 0
z 399 1s. green (1862) 75 0
z 400 1s. green (1862) ("K" *variety*) ..
z 401 1s. green (1865) (Plate No. 4) .. 45 0
z 402 1s. green (1867–73) .. *From* 27 6
Plate Nos. 4, 5, 6, 7.
z 403 1s. green (1873–77) .. *From* 45 0
Plate Nos. 8, 9, 10, 11, 12.
z 404 2s. blue (1867) £5
z 405 5s. rose (1867–74) .. *From* £11
Plate Nos. 1, 2.

SMYRNA.

"F **87**" *Obliteration or circular postmark as T* **8, 16, 18** *or* **19.**

1872.

z 406 ½d. rose-red (1870–79) .. *From* 60 0
Plates 11, 12, 13, 14, 15.
z 407 1d. rose-red (1864–79) .. *From* 30 0
Plate Nos. 120, 124, 134, 137, 138, 139, 140, 142, 143, 145, 146, 148, 149, 150, 151, 152, 153, 155, 156, 157, 158, 159, 160, 161, 162, 163, 164, 166, 167, 168, 169, 170, 171, 172, 173, 174, 175, 176, 177, 178, 183, 184, 185, 186, 187 188, 191, 193, 195, 196, 198, 200, 201, 204, 210, 215, 217, 218.
z 408 1½d. lake-red (1870–74) (Plates 1, 3) *From* £33
z 409 2d. blue (1858) *wmk.* Large Crown, *perf.* 16 .. ..
z 410 2d. blue (1858–69) .. .. *From* 40 0
Plate Nos. 13, 14, 15.
z 411 2½d. rosy mauve (1875) (blued *paper*) 70 0
Plate No. 1.
z 412 2½d. rosy mauve (1875–76) *From* 35 0
Plate Nos. 1, 2, 3.
z 413 2½d. rosy mauve (*Error of lettering*)
z 414 2½d. rosy mauve (1876–79) *From* 32 6
Plate Nos. 3, 4, 5, 6, 7, 8, 9, 10, 11, 12, 13, 14, 15, 16, 17.
z 415 2½d. blue (1880) .. .. *From* 22 6
Plate Nos. 17, 18, 19, 20.
z 416 2½d. blue (1881) 10 6
Plate Nos. 21, 22, 23.
z 417 3d. rose (1867–73) 75 0
Plate Nos. 5, 7, 9, 10.
z 418 3d. rose (1873–76) (Plate No. 14)
z 419 4d. vermilion (1865–73) 35 0
Plate Nos. 12, 13, 14.
z 420 4d. vermilion (1876) (Plate No. 15) £15
z 421 4d. sage-green (1877) 90 0
Plate Nos. 15, 16.
z 422 4d. grey-brown (1880) *wmk.* Large Garter (Plate No. 17) .. ..
z 423 4d. grey-brown (1880) *wmk.* Crown (Plate Nos. 17, 18.) .. *From* 55 0
z 424 6d. buff (1872–73) .. .. *From* £14
Plate Nos. 11, 12.
z 425 6d. chestnut (1872) (Plate No. 11)
z 426 6d. grey (1873) (Plate No. 12) .. £7
z 427 6d. grey (1874–80) .. .. *From* 40 0
Plate Nos. 13, 14, 15, 16, 17.
z 428 6d. grey (1881–82) .. .. ..
Plate Nos. 17, 18.
z 429 6d. lilac (1883) (6d. on 6d.) .. £5
z 430 9d. straw (1867) £8
z 431 10d. red-brown (1867) £8
z 432 1s. green (1867–73) (Plate No. 7)
z 433 1s. green (1873–77) .. *From* 80 0
Plate Nos. 8, 9, 10, 11, 12, 13.
z 434 1s. orange-brown (1880) £13
Plate No. 13.
z 434a 1s. orange-brown (1881) (Plate No. 13, 14) 95 0
z 435 5s. rose (1867–74) (Plate No. 2) ..

1880.

z 436 ½d. deep green 20 0
z 437 ½d. pale green 20 0
z 438 1d. Venetian red 40 0
z 439 1½d. Venetian red £9
z 440 2d. pale rose 70 0

z 441	2d. deep rose	70 0
z 442	5d. indigo	60 0

1881.

z 443	1d. lilac (16 *dots*)	17 6

1884.

z 444	½d. slate blue	35 0
z 445–6	2d., 2½d. .. .. .. *From*	10 6
z 447–9	4d., 5d., 1s. .. .. *From*	60 0

1887.

z 450–7*a*	½d., 1½d., 2d., 2½d., 3d., 4d., 5d., 6d., 1s. .. .. *From*	12 6

1900.

z 458–9	½d., 1s. .. .. .. *From*	17 6

1902–10.

z 460–71*b*	½d., 1d., 1½d., 2d., 2½d., 3d., 4d., 5d., 6d., 7d., 9d., 10d., 1s., 2s. 6d. .. .. *From*	17 6

1911–23.

z 472–86	½d., 1d., 1½d., 2d., 2½d., 3d., 4d., 5d., 6d., 7d., 8d., 9d., 10d., 1s., 2s. 6d. .. *From*	12 6

BEYROUT (LEVANT).

"G **06**." *Obliteration or circular postmark as T* **8, 19,** *or* **20.**

1873.

z 487	½d. rose-red (1870–79) .. *From* Plate Nos. 12, 13, 14, 19, 20.	45 0
z 488	1d. rose-red (1864–79) .. *From* Plate Nos. 1, 7, 118, 130, 140, 145, 148, 155, 157, 162, 167, 177, 179, 180, 184, 185, 186, 195, 198, 200, 204, 211, 213, 215, 218, 220, 222.	35 0
z 489	1½d. lake-red (1870–74) (Plate 3) ..	£55
z 490	2d. blue (1858–69) .. .. *From* Plate Nos. 13, 14, 15.	40 0
z 491	2½d. rosy mauve (1875) (blued *paper*) Plate No. 1.	70 0
z 492	2½d. rosy mauve (1875–76) .. *From* Plate Nos. 1, 2, 3.	35 0
z 493	2½d. rosy mauve (1876–79) .. *From* Plate Nos. 3, 4, 5, 6, 7, 8, 9, 10, 11, 12, 13, 14, 15, 16, 17.	32 6
z 494	2½d. blue (1880) .. .. *From* Plate Nos. 17, 18, 19, 20	20 0
z 495	2½d. blue (1881) .. .. *From* Plate Nos. 21, 22, 23.	20 0
z 496	3d. rose (1867–73) (Plate No. 10)	
z 497	3d. rose (1873–76) .. .. .. Plate Nos. 12, 15, 18, 19.	
z 498	3d. rose (1881) (Plate Nos. 20, 21)	
z 499	4d. vermilion (1865–73) .. *From* Plate Nos. 11, 12, 13, 14.	65 0
z 500	4d. vermilion (1876) (Plate No. 15)	£22
z 501	4d. sage-green (1877) .. .. Plate Nos. 15, 16.	
z 502	4d. grey-brown (1880) *wmk.* Large Garter (Plate No. 17)	
z 503	4d. grey-brown (1880) *wmk.* Crown Plate Nos. 17, 18.	
z 503*a*	6d. mauve (1870) (Plate No. 9) ..	
z 504	6d. buff (1872–73) .. .. *From* Plate Nos. 11, 12.	£12
z 505	6d. chestnut (1872) (Plate No. 11)	40 0
z 506	6d. grey (1873) (Plate No. 12) ..	
z 507	6d. grey (1874–80) .. .. *From* Plate Nos. 13, 14, 15, 16, 17.	55 0
z 507*a*	8d. orange (1876)	
z 508	10d. red-brown (1867)	£8
z 509	1s. green (1867–73) .. .. Plate Nos. 6, 7.	65 0
z 510	1s. green (1873–77) .. *From* Plate Nos. 8, 9, 10, 12, 13.	40 0
z 511	1s. orge.-brn. (1880) (Plate No. 13)	
z 512	1s. orange-brown (1881) .. .. Plate Nos. 13, 14.	85 0
z 513	2s. blue (1867)	75 0
z 514	5s. rose (1867) (Pl. 1, 2) .. *From*	£80

1880.

z 515	½d. deep green	15 0
z 516	½d. pale green	15 0
z 517	1d. Venetian red	17 6
z 518	1½d. Venetian red	£13
z 519	2d. pale rose	35 0
z 520	2d. deep rose	37 6
z 521	5d. indigo	35 0

1881.

z 522	1d. lilac (14 *dots*)	
z 523	1d. lilac (16 *dots*)	

1884.

z 524–529*a*	½d., 1½d., 2d., 2½d., 4d., 5d. 1s. .. .. .. *From*	15 0

1887.

z 530–7*a*	½d., 1½d., 2d., 2½d., 3d., 4½d., 5d., 6d., 1s. .. .. *From*	12 6

1900.

z 538–9	½d., 1s. .. .. .. *From*	15 0

1902–12.

z 540–5	½d., 1d., 2½d., 5d., 10d., 1s. *From*	7 6

1912–13.

z 545*a–b*	½d., 1d. (*T* **105, 104**)	

POSTAL FISCALS

z 546	1d. lilac (*wmk.* Anchor)	
z 547	1d. lilac (*wmk.* Orb)	

III.

BRITISH WEST INDIES.

VARIOUS TOWNS IN JAMAICA.

British stamps were issued to several District post offices between 8 MAY, 1858, and 1 MARCH, 1859 (i.e. before the Obliterators A 27–A 78 were issued). These can only be distinguished (off the cover) when they have the Town's date-stamp on them. They are worth about three times the price of those with an obliteration number.

In the following lists of Jamaica single 1d. stamps on cover are not priced, as usually found in strips of 4 or 6.

KINGSTON

" A **01**." *Obliteration as T* **2.**

1858 (8 MAY)–**1860** (25 AUG.).

			Single stamp.	*Stamp on cover*
J 1	1d. rose-red, *perf.* 16	(No. 36)	—	—
J 2	1d. rose-red, *perf.* 14	(No. 40)	35 0	—
J 3	4d. rose-carmine	(No. 66)	45 0	£15
J 4	4d. rose ..	(No. 66*a*)	45 0	£15
J 5	6d. lilac ..	(No. 70)	45 0	£15
J 6	1s. green ..	(No. 72)	£8	£25

" A **01**." *Obliteration as T* **7** (*Duplex*).

1859 (26 MAY)–**1860** (24 AUG.).

J 7	1d. rose-red, *perf.* 14	(No. 40)	50 0	—
J 8	4d. rose-carmine	(No. 66)	50 0	£8
J 9	4d. rose ..	(No. 66*a*)	50 0	£8
J 10	6d. lilac ..	(No. 70)	45 0	£6
J 11	1s. green ..	(No. 72)	£14	£35

" A **01**." *Obliteration as T* **3.**

1859 (26 MAY)–**1860** (24 AUG.).

J 12	1d. rose-red, *perf.* 14	(No. 40)		
J 13	4d. rose-carmine	(No. 66)	£11	£35
J 14	4d. rose ..	(No. 66*a*)		
J 15	6d. lilac ..	(No. 70)		
J 16	1s. green ..	(No. 72)		

NOTE:—For A **02**, etc., see after A**78**.

" A **27** " *to* " A **78**." *Obliteration as T* **2.**

1859 (1 MAR.)–**1860** (24 AUG.).

A **27.** ALEXANDRIA.

J 17	1d. rose-red, *perf.* 14 (No. 40)		
J 18	4d. rose-carmine (or rose) (Nos. 66 and 66*a*) ..	£16	£40
J 19	6d. lilac (No. 70)		

A **28.** ANNOTTO BAY.

J 20	1d. rose-red	£10	—
J 21	4d. rose-carmine (or rose) ..	£8	£25
J 22	6d. lilac	£9	£28

A 29. BATH.

No.		Single stamp.	Stamp on cover
J 23	1d. rose-red	£13	—
J 24	4d. rose-carmine (or rose)	£9	£28
J 25	6d. lilac		

A 30. BLACK RIVER.

No.		Single stamp.	Stamp on cover
J 26	1d. rose-red	£5	—
J 27	4d. rose-carmine (or rose)	£7	£22
J 28	6d. lilac	£7	£22

A 31. BROWN'S TOWN.

No.		Single stamp.	Stamp on cover
J 29	1d. rose-red	£12	—
J 30	4d. rose-carmine (or rose)	£8	£25
J 31	6d. lilac	£12	£30

A 32. BUFF BAY.

No.		Single stamp.	Stamp on cover
J 32	1d. rose-red	£10	—
J 33	4d. rose-carmine (or rose)	£7	£20
J 34	6d. lilac	£9	£25

A 33. CHAPELTON.

No.		Single stamp.	Stamp on cover
J 35	1d. rose-red		
J 36	4d. rose-carmine (or rose)	£7	—
J 37	6d. lilac	£8	£25

A 34. CLAREMONT.

No.		Single stamp.	Stamp on cover
J 38	1d. rose-red	£12	—
J 39	4d. rose-carmine (or rose)	£9	£25
J 40	6d. lilac	£12	£35

A 35. CLARENDON.
(Near FOUR PATHS.)

No.		Single stamp.	Stamp on cover
J 41	1d. rose-red	£10	—
J 42	4d. rose-carmine (or rose)	£7	£20
J 43	6d. lilac	£10	£30

A 36. DRY HARBOUR.

No.		Single stamp.	Stamp on cover
J 44	1d. rose-red	£16	—
J 45	4d. rose-carmine (or rose)	£13	£30
J 46	6d. lilac	£16	£35

A 37. DUNCANS.

No.		Single stamp.	Stamp on cover
J 47	1d. rose-red		
J 48	4d. rose-carmine (or rose)	£8	£30
J 49	6d. lilac	£7	£30

A 38. EWARTON.

A38 was sent out to EWARTON but it is believed that this office was closed early in 1858 before it arrived as no genuine used specimens have been found on British stamps.

A 39. FALMOUTH.

No.		Single stamp.	Stamp on cover
J 53	1d. rose-red	£5	—
J 54	4d. rose-carmine (or rose)	£5	£15
J 55	6d. lilac	£5	£15
J 56	1s. green (No. 72)	£25	£60

A 40. FLINT RIVER
(Near HOPEWELL.)

No.		Single stamp.	Stamp on cover
J 57	1d. rose-red	£15	—
J 58	4d. rose-carmine (or rose)	£8	£25
J 59	6d. lilac	£11	£35
J 60	1s. green (No. 72)		

A 41. GAYLE.

No.		Single stamp.	Stamp on cover
J 61	1d. rose-red	£13	—
J 62	4d. rose-carmine (or rose)	£8	£25
J 63	6d. lilac	£8	£25
J 64	1s. green (No. 72)	£22	£60

A 42. GOLDEN SPRING.
(Near STONY HILL.)

No.		Single stamp.	Stamp on cover
J 65	1d. rose-red		
J 66	4d. rose-carmine (or rose)		
J 67	6d. lilac	£18	£40
J 68	1s. green (No. 72)	£35	£80

A 43. GORDON TOWN.

No.		Single stamp.	Stamp on cover
J 69	1d. rose-red		
J 70	4d. rose-carmine (or rose)		
J 71	6d. lilac	£18	£50

A 44. GOSHEN.
(Near SANTA CRUZ.)

No.		Single stamp.	Stamp on cover
J 72	1d. rose-red	£8	—
J 73	4d. rose-carmine (or rose)	£8	£25
J 74	6d. lilac	£8	£25

A 45. GRANGE HILL.

No.		Single stamp.	Stamp on cover
J 75	1d. rose-red	£7	—
J 76	4d. rose-carmine (or rose)	£6	£20
J 77	6d. lilac	£7	£22
J 77a	1s. green (No. 72)	£30	—

A 46. GREEN ISLAND.

No.		Single stamp.	Stamp on cover
J 78	1d. rose-red	£12	—
J 79	4d. rose-carmine (or rose)	£8	£25
J 80	6d. lilac	£8	£26
J 81	1s. green (No. 72)	£28	£70

A 47. HIGHGATE.

No.		Single stamp.	Stamp on cover
J 82	1d. rose-red	70 0	—
J 83	4d. rose-carmine (or rose)	£7	£20
J 84	6d. lilac	£8	£25

A 48. HOPE BAY.

No.		Single stamp.	Stamp on cover
J 85	1d. rose-red		
J 86	4d. rose-carmine (or rose)	£16	£40
J 87	6d. lilac	£17	£40

A 49. LILLIPUT.
(Near BALACLAVA.)

No.		Single stamp.	Stamp on cover
J 88	1d. rose-red	£8	—
J 89	4d. rose-carmine (or rose)	£8	£25
J 90	6d. lilac	£12	£30

A 50. LITTLE RIVER.

A50 was sent out for use at LITTLE RIVER, but no specimen has yet been found used on British stamps.

A 51. LUCEA.

No.		Single stamp.	Stamp on cover
J 91	1d. rose-red	£7	—
J 92	4d. rose-carmine (or rose)	£7	£20
J 93	6d. lilac	£7	£22

A 52. MANCHIONEAL.

No.		Single stamp.	Stamp on cover
J 94	1d. rose-red	£9	—
J 95	4d. rose-carmine (or rose)	£8	£25
J 96	6d. lilac		

A 53. MANDEVILLE.

No.		Single stamp.	Stamp on cover
J 97	1d. rose-red	£8	—
J 98	4d. rose-carmine (or rose)	£8	£25
J 99	6d. lilac	£8	£28

A 54. MAY HILL.
(Near SPUR TREE.)

No.		Single stamp.	Stamp on cover
J 100	1d. rose-red	£6	—
J 101	4d. rose-carmine (or rose)	£6	£20
J 102	6d. lilac	£6	£20

A 55. MILE GULLY.

No.		Single stamp.	Stamp on cover
J 103	1d. rose-red	£7	—
J 104	4d. rose-carmine (or rose)	£7	£20
J 105	6d. lilac	£7	£25

A 56. MONEAGUE.

No.		Single stamp.	Stamp on cover
J 106	1d. rose-red	£13	—
J 107	4d. rose-carmine (or rose)	£8	£25
J 108	6d. lilac	£8	£26

A 57. MONTEGO BAY.

No.		Single stamp.	Stamp on cover
J 109	1d. rose-red	£5	—
J 110	4d. rose-carmine (or rose)	80 0	£12
J 111	6d. lilac	£6	£18
J 112	1s. green (No. 72)	£25	£60

A 58. MONTPELIER.

No.		Single stamp.	Stamp on cover
J 113	1d. rose-red		
J 114	4d. rose-carmine (or rose)		
J 115	6d. lilac	£65	

A 59. MORANT BAY.

No.		Single stamp.	Stamp on cover
J 116	1d. rose-red	£8	—
J 117	4d. rose-carmine (or rose)	£7	£20
J 118	6d. lilac	£8	£25

		Single stamp.	*Stamp on cover.*

A **60.** OCHO RIOS.

J 119	1d. rose-red		
J 120	4d. rose-carmine (or rose) ..	£8	£25
J 121	6d. lilac	£9	£26

A **61.** OLD HARBOUR.

J 122	1d. rose-red	£10	—
J 123	4d. rose-carmine (or rose)	£10	£30
J 124	6d. lilac	£10	£35

A **62.** PLANTAIN GARDEN RIVER.
(Now called GOLDEN GROVE.)

J 125	1d. rose-red	£7	—
J 126	4d. rose-carmine (or rose)	£7	£20
J 127	6d. lilac	£8	£25

A **63.** PEAR TREE GROVE.

J 128	1d. rose-red		
J 129	4d. rose-carmine (or rose)		
J 130	6d. lilac	£18	£40

A **64.** PORT ANTONIO.

J 131	1d. rose-red	£9	—
J 132	4d. rose-carmine (or rose)	£9	£25
J 133	6d. lilac	£7	£20

A **65.** PORT MORANT.

J 134	1d. rose-red	£9	—
J 135	4d. rose-carmine (or rose)	£8	£25
J 136	6d. lilac	£9	£28

A **66.** PORT MARIA.

J 137	1d. rose-red	£13	—
J 138	4d. rose-carmine (or rose)	£8	£25
J 139	6d. lilac	£7	£20

A **67.** PORT ROYAL.

J 140	1d. rose-red	£15	—
J 141	4d. rose-carmine (or rose)		
J 142	6d. lilac	£18	£40

A **68.** PORUS.

J 143	1d. rose-red	£10	—
J 144	4d. rose-carmine (or rose)	£10	£30
J 145	6d. lilac	£10	£30

A **69.** RAMBLE.

J 146	1d. rose-red	£8	—
J 147	4d. rose-carmine (or rose) (Nos. 66 and 66*a*) ..	£9	£28
J 148	4d. rose-carmine on thick glazed paper (No. 66b)	£20	£45
J 149	6d. lilac	£12	£35

A **70.** RIO BUENO.

J 150	1d. rose-red		
J 151	4d. rose-carmine (or rose)	£9	£25
J 152	6d. lilac	£8	£25

A **71.** RODNEY HALL.
(Now called LINSTEAD.)

J 153	1d. rose-red	£9	—
J 154	4d. rose-carmine (or rose)	£7	£20
J 155	6d. lilac	£8	£25

A **72.** SAINT DAVID.
(Now called YALLAHS.)

J 156	1d. rose-red	£13	—
J 157	4d. rose-carmine (or rose)	£9	£25
J 158	6d. lilac		

A **73.** ST. ANN'S BAY.

J 159	1d. rose-red	£7	—
J 160	4d. rose-carmine (or rose)	£8	£25
J 161	6d. lilac	£7	£20

A **74.** SALT GUT.
(Near ORACABESSA.)

J 162	1d. rose-red	£9	—
J 163	4d. rose-carmine (or rose)	£9	£28
J 164	6d. lilac	£13	£40

		Single stamp.	*Stamp on cover.*

A **75.** SAVANNA-LA-MAR.

J 165	1d. rose-red	£8	—
J 166	4d. rose-carmine (or rose)	£7	£20
J 167	6d. lilac	£8	£25
J 168	1s. green (No. 72) ..	£30	£60

A **76.** SPANISH TOWN.

J 169	1d. rose-red	£5	—
J 170	4d. rose-carmine (or rose)	£5	£15
J 171	6d. lilac	£7	£20
J 172	1s. green (No. 72) ..	£25	£60

A **77.** STEWART TOWN.

J 173	1d. rose-red		
J 174	4d. rose-carmine (or rose)	£13	£30
J 175	6d. lilac	£16	£35

A **78.** VERE.
(Now called ALLEY.)

J 176	1d. rose-red	£12	—
J 177	4d. rose-carmine (or rose)	£12	£30
J 178	6d. lilac	£12	£30
J 179	1s. green (No. 72) ..	£30	£60

The use of British stamps in JAMAICA after August, 1860, was unauthorised by the P.M.G. of Great Britain.

OTHER TOWNS IN THE WEST INDIES.
"A **02**" *to* "A **15**" *and* "A **18.**"
Obliterations as T **2.**

A **02.** ST. JOHN'S (ANTIGUA).

z 553	1d. rose-red (1857)	£15
z 553*a*	2d. blue (Plate No. 6)	
z 553*b*	2d. blue (1857) *wmk.* Large Crown, *perf.* 14.	
z 554	2d. blue (1858) (Plate Nos. 7, 8, 9)	£20
z 555	4d. rose (1857)	£12
z 556	6d. lilac (1856)	£12
z 557	1s. green (1856)	£50

A **03.** GEORGETOWN *or* DEMERARA (BRITISH GUIANA).

z 558	1d. rose-red (1857)	£9
z 559	4d. rose (1857)	£8
z 560	6d. lilac (1856)	£6
z 561	1s. green (1856)	£40

A **04.** NEW AMSTERDAM *or* BERBICE (BRITISH GUIANA).

z 562	1d. rose-red (1857)	
z 563	2d. blue (1858) (Plate Nos. 7, 8) ..	£12
z 564	4d. rose (1857)	£12
z 565	6d. lilac (1856)	£12
z 566	1s. green (1856)	£50

A **05.** NASSAU (BAHAMAS).

z 567	1d. rose-red (1857)	£20
z 568	2d. blue (1858) (Plate Nos. 7, 8) ..	£20
z 569	4d. rose (1857)	£16
z 570	6d. lilac (1856)	£16
z 571	1s. green (1856)	

A **06.** BRITISH HONDURAS.

z 572	1d. rose-red (1857)	
z 573	4d. rose (1857)	£12
z 574	6d. lilac (1856)	£12
z 575	1s. green (1856)	£50

A **07.** DOMINICA.

z 576	1d. rose-red (1857)	
z 576*a*	2d. blue (1858) (Plate No. 7)	£20
z 577	4d. rose (1857)	£14
z 578	6d. lilac (1856)	£14
z 579	1s. green	£60

A **08.** MONTSERRAT.

z 580	1d. rose-red (1857)	
z 581	4d. rose (1857)	
z 582	6d. lilac (1856)	£25
z 583	1s. green 1856)	

A 09. NEVIS.

z 584 1d. rose-red (1857) £20
z 585 2d. blue (1858) (Plate Nos. 7, 8) ..
z 586 4d. rose (1857) £12
z 587 6d. lilac (1856) £12
z 588 1s. green (1856) .. .. ..

A 10. KINGSTOWN (ST. VINCENT).

z 589 1d. rose-red (1857) £16
z 590 2d. blue (1855) .. .. ..
z 591 4d. rose (1857) £16
z 592 6d. lilac (1856) £20
z 594 1s. green (1856) £60

A 11. CASTRIES (ST. LUCIA).

z 595 1d. rose-red (1857) £90
z 596 2d. blue (1855) .. .. ..
z 597 4d. rose (1857) £20
z 598 6d. lilac (1856) £12
z 599 1s. green (1856) £50

A 12. BASSE-TERRE (ST. CHRISTOPHER).

z 600 1d. rose-red (1857) .. .. ..
z 600a 2d. blue (1858) (Plate No. 7) .. £20
z 601 4d. rose (1857) .. .. ..
z 602 6d. lilac (1856) £12
z 603 1s. green (1856) £50

A 13. TORTOLA (VIRGIN IS.)

z 604 1d. rose-red (1857) .. .. ..
z 605 6d. lilac (1856) .. .. ..
z 606 1s. green (1856) .. .. ..

A 14. SCARBOROUGH (TOBAGO).

z 607 1d. rose-red (1857) £20
z 608 4d. rose (1857) £16
z 609 6d. lilac (1856) £12
z 610 1s. green (1856) £50

A 15. ST. GEORGE (GRENADA).

z 611 1d. rose-red (1857) £16
z 612 2d. blue (1858) (Plate No. 7) ..
z 613 4d. rose (1857) .. .. ..
z 614 6d. lilac (1856) £12
z 615 1s. green (1856) £50

A 18. ENGLISH HARBOUR (ANTIGUA).

z 616 6d. lilac £50
z 616a 1s. green (1856) .. .. ..

IV

Various Foreign Towns in South and Central America and the West Indies.

BUENOS AYRES (ARGENTINA).

"B 32." *Obliteration as T* **2, 12** *or* **13.**

1860 *to* **1873.**

z 736 1d. rose-red (1857) .. .. ..
z 737 1d. rose-red (1864) .. *From* 60 0
Plate Nos. 71, 72, 73, 74, 76, 78, 79, 80, 81, 85, 87, 90, 91, 92, 94, 95, 96, 97, 99, 101, 103, 104, 107, 108, 110, 112, 113, 117, 118, 119, 120, 121, 129, 130, 131, 135, 139, 140, 142, 144, 145, 147, 149, 150, 151, 155, 159, 163, 166, 172.
z 738 2d. blue (1858–69) .. .. *From* 75 0
Plate Nos. 8, 9, 12, 13, 14.
z 739 3d. carmine-rose (1862) 85 0
z 740 3d. rose (1865) (Plate No. 4) .. 75 0
z 741 3d. rose (1867–73) .. .. *From* 50 0
Plate Nos. 4, 5, 6, 7, 8, 9, 10.
z 742 4d. rose (1857) 75 0
z 743 4d. red (1862) (Plate Nos. 3, 4) .. £8
z 744 4d. vermilion (1865–73) .. *From* 45 0
Plate Nos. 7, 8, 9, 10, 11, 12, 13.
z 745 6d. lilac (1856) 85 0
z 746 6d. lilac (1862) (Plate Nos. 3, 4) ..
z 747 6d. lilac (1865–67) .. .. *From* 70 0
Plate Nos. 5, 6.
z 748 6d. lilac (1867) (Plate No. 6) .. 70 0
z 749 6d. violet (1867–70) .. *From* 50 0
Plate Nos. 6, 8, 9.
z 750 6d. buff (1872) (Plate No. 11) .. £15
z 751 6d. chestnut (1872) (Plate No. 11) 85 0
z 752 9d. bistre (1862) .. .. ..
z 753 9d. straw (1862) £13
z 754 9d. straw (1865) £40
z 755 9d. straw (1867) £11
z 756 10d. red-brown (1867) £13
z 757 1s. green (1856) 85 0
z 758 1s. green (1862) 80 0
z 759 1s. green (1865) (Plate No. 4) .. 50 0
z 760 1s. green (1867–73) .. *From* 40 0
Plate Nos. 4, 5, 6, 7.
z 760a 1s. grn. (1873–77) (Plate No. 8)
z 761 2s. blue (1867) £9
z 762 5s. rose (1867) (Plate No. 1) .. £15

MONTEVIDEO (URUGUAY).

"C 28." *Obliteration as T* **4** *or* **12.**

1862 *to* **1872.**

z 763 1d. rose-red (1864) £7
Plate Nos. 73, 93, 119, 148, 171.
z 764 2d. blue (1858–69) (Plate Nos. 9, 13) £7
z 764a 3d. rose (1865) (Plate No. 4) ..
z 765 3d. rose (1867–71) (Plate Nos. 4, 5, 7) £5
z 765a 3d. rose (1873–79) (Plate No. 19)
z 766 4d. rose (1857) .. .. ..
z 766a 4d. red (1862) (Plate 4) .. ..
z 767 4d. vermilion (1865–70) .. *From* 85 0
Plate Nos. 7, 8, 9, 10, 11, 12.
z 768 6d. lilac (1856) .. .. ..
z 768a 6d. lilac (1862) (Pl. 4) .. ..
z 769 6d. lilac (1865–67) (Plate Nos. 5, 6) £5
z 770 6d. lilac (1867) (Plate No. 6) ..
z 771 6d. violet (1867–70) .. *From* £5
Plate Nos. 8, 9.
z 772 6d. buff (1872) .. .. ..
z 773 6d. chestnut (1872) .. .. ..
z 774 9d. straw (1862) .. .. ..
z 775 9d. straw (1865) .. .. ..
z 776 9d. straw (1867) £9
z 777 10d. red-brown (1867) £10
z 778 1s. green (1862) £5
z 779 1s. green (1865) (Plate No. 4) .. 95 0
z 780 1s. green (1867–73) (Plate Nos. 4, 5) 95 0
z 781 2s. blue (1867) £12
z 782 5s. rose (1867) (Plate No. 1) .. £20

VALPARAISO (CHILE).

"C 30." *Obliteration as T* **12** *or as T* **14.**

1865 *to* **1881.**

z 783 ½d. rose-red (1870–79) .. *From* £9
Plate Nos. 6, 11, 12, 13.
z 783a 1d. rose-red (1864–79) *From* 55 0
Plate Nos. 80, 84, 85, 91, 122, 123, 140, 149, 152, 157, 158, 162, 167, 175, 178, 181, 185, 186, 187, 189, 190, 195, 197, 198, 200, 201, 207, 209, 210, 211, 212, 214, 215, 217.
z 784 1½d. lake-red (1870–74) .. *From* £9
Plate Nos. 1 and 3.
z 785 2d. blue (1858–69) £7
Plate Nos. 9, 13, 14, 15.
z 785a 2½d. rosy mauve (1875), white paper (Plate No. 2) £12
z 785b 2½d. rosy mauve (1876) (Pl. No. 4) £9
z 785c 3d. carmine-rose (1862) .. ..
z 785d 3d. rose (1865) (Plate No. 4) ..
z 786 3d. rose (1867–73) .. .. *From* 55 0
Plate Nos. 5, 6, 7, 8, 9, 10.
z 787 3d. rose (1873–76) .. *From* 55 0
Plate Nos. 11, 12, 14, 16, 17, 18, 19.
z 788 4d. vermilion (1865–73) .. *From* 45 0
Pl. Nos. 9, 10, 11, 12, 13, 14.
z 789 4d. vermilion (1876) (Plate No. 15)
z 790 4d. sage-green (1877) £5
Plate Nos. 15, 16.
z 791 4d. grey-brown (1880) *wmk.* Large Garter (Plate No. 17) .. ..
z 792 6d. lilac (1862) (Plates 3, 4) *From* 75 0
z 793 6d. lilac (1865) (Plate Nos. 5, 6) ..
z 794 6d. lilac (1867) (Plate No. 6) ..

z 795 6d. violet (1867–70) .. *From* 60 0
Plate Nos. 6, 8, 9.
z 796 6d. buff (1872–73) .. *From* £9
Plate Nos. 11, 12.
z 797 6d. chestnut (1872) (Plate No. 11) 75 0
z 798 6d. grey (1873) (Plate No. 12) .. 75 0
z 799 6d. grey (1874–80) .. .. *From* 35 0
Plate Nos. 13, 14, 15, 16, 17.
z 800 6d. grey (1881) (Plate No. 17) ..
z 801 8d. orange (1876) £15
z 802 9d. straw (1862) .. .. ..
z 803 9d. straw (1865) .. .. ..
z 804 9d. straw (1867) £5
z 805 10d. red-brown (1867) £8
z 805*a* 1s. green (1865) (Plate No. 4) ..
z 806 1s. green (1867–73) .. *From* 45 0
Plate Nos. 4, 5, 6, 7.
z 807 1s. green (1873–77) .. *From* 35 0
Plate Nos. 8, 9, 10, 11, 12, 13.
z 808 1s. orange-brn. (1880) (Pl No. 13) £10
z 809 2s. blue (1867) 80 0
z 810 2s. brown (1880) £72
z 811 5s. rose (1867–74) .. .. *From* £6
Plate Nos. 1, 2.
z 812 10s. grey-green (1878) (*wmk.* Cross) £70
z 813 20s. brown-vio. (1878) (*wmk.* Cross) £95

1880.
z 814 1d. Venetian red .. .. ..
z 814*a* 1½d. Venetian red .. .. ..

ARICA (*then in* Peru).

"C **36**." *Obliteration as T* **4, 12** *or* **14.**

1865 *to* **1879.**
z 815 ½d. rose-red (1870–79) .. *From* £5
Plate Nos. 5, 6, 10, 11, 13.
z 816 1d. rose-red (1864–79) .. *From* 70 0
Plate Nos. 102, 139, 163, 167.
z 817 1½d. lake-red (1870–74) (Plate No. 3)
z 817*a* 2d. blue (1858–69) (Plate No. 14) .. £16
z 817*b* 3d. rose (1867–73) (Plate No. 5) ..
z 818 3d. rose (1873–76) .. .. *From* £5
Plate Nos. 11, 12, 17, 18, 19.
z 819 4d. vermilion (1865–73) .. *From* 95 0
Plate Nos. 10, 11, 13, 14.
z 820 4d. vermilion (1876) (Plate No. 15)
z 821 4d. sage-green (1877) £8
Plate Nos. 15. 16.
z 822 6d. lilac (1862) (Plates 3, 4) ..
z 822*a* 6d. lilac (1865–67) (Plate No. 5) ..
z 823 6d. violet (1867–70) 90 0
Plate Nos. 6, 8, 9.
z 824 6d. buff (1872) (Plate No. 11) .. £15
z 825 6d. chestnut (1872) (Plate No. 11)
z 825*a* 6d. grey (1873) (Plate No. 12) .. 95 0
z 826 6d. grey (1874–76) .. .. *From* 85 0
Plate Nos. 13, 14, 15, 16.
z 827 8d. orange (1876) .. .. ..
z 828 9d. straw (1862) .. .. ..
z 828*a* 9d. straw (1867) £13
z 829 10d. red-brown (1867) .. ..
z 830 1s. green (1862) .. .. ..
z 830*a* 1s. green (1865) .. .. ..
z 831 1s. green (1867–73) .. *From* 80 0
Plate Nos. 4, 5, 6, 7.
z 832 1s. green (1873–77) .. *From* 75 0
Plate Nos. 8, 9, 10, 11, 12, 13.
z 833 2s. blue (1867) £28
z 834 5s. rose (1867–74) (Plate Nos. 1, 2) £45

CALDERA (CHILE)

"C **37**." *Obliterated as T* **4.**

1865 *to* **1881.**
z 835 1d. rose-red (1864–79) .. *From* 75 0
Plate Nos. 71, 72, 88, 90, 95, 195.
z 836 1½d. lake-red (1870–74) (Plate No. 3)
z 837 2d. blue (1858–69) (Plate No. 9) .. 80 0
z 838 3d. rose (1865) (Plate No. 4) .. 90 0
z 839 3d. rose (1867–73) (Plate Nos. 5, 7)
z 840 3d. rose (1873–76) .. *From* 80 0
Plate Nos. 11, 12, 16, 17, 18, 19.
z 841 4d. red (1862) (Plate 4) .. ..
z 842 4d. vermilion (1865–73) .. *From* 80 0
Plate Nos. 8, 12, 13, 14.
z 843 4d. sage-green (1877) (Plate No. 16)
z 843*a* 6d. lilac (1862) (Plate 4) 90 0
z 844 6d. lilac (1865–67) (Plate No. 6) ..
z 845 6d. violet (1867–70) .. *From* 70 0
Plate Nos. 6, 8, 9.
z 846 6d. buff (1872) (Plate No. 11) ..
z 847 6d. chestnut (1872) (Plate No. 11)
z 848 6d. grey (1873) (Plate No. 12) ..
z 849 6d. grey (1874–80) .. .. *From* 80 0
Plate Nos. 13, 14, 15, 16, 17.
z 850 8d. orange (1876) £22
z 851 9d. straw (1867) £18
z 852 10d. red-brown (1867) £16
z 852*a* 1s. green (1865) (Plate No. 4) ..
z 853 1s. green (1867–73) .. *From* 85 0
Plate Nos. 4, 5, 6.
z 854 1s. green (1873–77) .. *From* 85 0
Plate Nos. 8, 10, 11, 12, 13.
z 855 2s. blue (1867) £28
z 856 2s. brown (1880) £90
z 857 5s. rose (1867–74) (Plate No. 2) .. £65

COBIJA (*then in* Bolivia).

"C **39**." *Obliteration as T* **4, 8** *or* **12.**

1865 *to* **1878.**
z 857*a* 1d. rose-red (Plate Nos. 93, 95) ..
z 858 2d. blue (1858–69) (Plate No. 14)
z 859 3d. rose (1867–73) (Plate No. 6) ..
z 860 3d. rose (1873–76) (Plate No. 16)
z 860*a* 4d. vermilion (1865–73) (Plate 15)
z 860*b* 6d. violet (1867–79) (Plate No. 9) £35
z 861 6d. buff (1872) (Plate No. 11) ..
z 862 6d. grey (1874–76) £35
Plate Nos. 13, 14, 15, 16.
z 863 1s. green (1867–73) (Pl. Nos. 4, 5)
z 864 1s. green (1873–77) £50
Plate Nos. 10, 11, 12, 13.
z 865 2s. blue (1867) £50
z 866 5s. rose (1867–74) (Plate No. 2)

COQUIMBO (CHILE)

"C **40**." *Obliteration as T* **4.**

1865 *to* **1881.**
z 867 1d. rose-red (1857) .. ..
z 867*a* 1d. rose-red (1864–79) (Pl. No. 204)
z 868 2d. blue (1858–69) (Plate Nos. 9, 14)
z 869 3d. rose (1865) .. .. ..
z 869*a* 3d. rose (1872) (Plate No. 8) ..
z 870 3d. rose (1873–76) .. *From* 70 0
Plate Nos. 18, 19.
z 870*a* 4d. red (1862) (Plate No. 4) .. £11
z 871 4d. verm. (1865–73) (Pl. Nos. 12, 14)
z 872 4d. sage-green (1877) .. ..
Plate Nos. 15, 16.
z 873 6d. lilac (1862) (Plate Nos. 3, 4)
z 873*a* 6d. lilac (1867) (Plate No. 6) .. £13
z 874 6d. violet (1867–70) .. *From* 80 0
Plate Nos. 6, 8, 9.
z 875 6d. buff (1872–73) .. .. *From* £14
Plate Nos. 11, 12.
z 876 6d. chestnut (1872) (Plate No. 11)
z 877 6d. grey (1873) (Plate No. 12) .. 70 0
z 878 6d. grey (1874–76) .. .. *From* 60 0
Plate Nos. 13, 14, 15, 16.
z 878*a* 8d. orange (1876) .. .. ..
z 878*b* 9d. straw (1862) .. .. ..
z 879 9d. straw (1867) £9
z 880 10d. red-brown (1867) .. ..
z 881 1s. green (1865) (Plate No. 4) .. £5
z 882 1s. grn. (1867–73) Pl. Nos. 4, 5, 6. £5
z 883 1s. green (1873–77) .. *From* 85 0
Plate Nos. 8, 10, 11, 12, 13.
z 884 2s. blue (1867) £27
z 885 2s. brown (1880) £80
z 886 5s. rose (1867–74) (Pl. Nos. 1, 2) .. £38

IQUIQUE (*then in* PERU).

"D **87**." *Obliteration as T* **12.**

1868 *to* **1878.**
z 886*a* ½d. rose-red (1870–79) (Pl. 5, 6, 14) £7
z 886*b* 1d. rose-red (1864–79) (Pl. No. 179) £7
z 887 2d. blue (1858–69) (Plate Nos. 9, 13)

z 888 3d. rose (1867–73) .. .... *From* £6
Plate Nos. 5, 6, 7, 8, 9.
z 889 3d. rose (1873–76) £13
Plate Nos. 12, 18, 19.
z 890 4d. vermilion (1865–73) .. ..
Plate Nos. 12, 13.
z 890*a* 4d. vermilion (1876) (Plate No. 15) £22
z 890*b* 4d. sage-green (1877) .. *From* £14
Plate Nos. 15, 16.
z 890*c* 6d. mauve (1869) (Plate Nos. 8, 9)
z 891 6d. buff (1872–73) £13
Plate Nos. 11, 12.
z 891*a* 6d. chestnut (1872) (Plate No. 11)
z 892 6d. grey (1875) (Plate No. 12) .. £11
z 893 6d. grey (1874–76) .. .. ..
Plate Nos. 13, 14, 15, 16.
z 893*a* 8d. orange (1876) £30
z 894 9d. straw (1867) £25
z 895 10d. red-brown (1867) .. ..
z 896 1s. green (1867–73) .. *From* £5
Plate Nos. 4, 6, 7.
z 897 1s. green (1873–77) .. *From* £7
Plate Nos. 8, 9, 10, 11, 12, 13.
z 898 2s. blue (1867) .. .. ..

CALLAO (PERU)

"C **38**." *Obliteration as T* **4, 12** *or circular date stamp as in T* **5**.

1865 *to* **1879.**

z 899 ½d. rose-red (1870–79) .. *From* 65 0
Plate Nos. 5, 6, 10, 11, 12, 13, 14.
z 900 1d. rose-red (1864–79) .. *From* 55 0
Plate Nos. 88, 89, 93, 97, 127, 130, 137, 139, 140, 141, 143, 144, 145, 146, 148, 149, 156, 160, 163, 171, 172, 175, 180, 182, 185, 193, 195, 198, 200, 201, 206, 209.
z 901 1½d. lake-red (1870–74) (Plate No. 3)
z 902 2d. blue (1858–69) .. .. *From* 45 0
Plate Nos. 9, 12, 13, 14, 15.
z 903 3d. carmine-rose (1862) .. ..
z 903*a* 3d. rose (1865) (Plate No. 4) .. 55 0
z 904 3d. rose (1867–73) .. .. *From* 45 0
Plate Nos. 5, 6, 7, 8, 9, 10.
z 905 3d. rose (1873–76) .. .. *From* 40 0
Plate Nos. 11, 12, 14, 15, 16, 17, 18, 19.
z 906 4d. red (1862) Plate Nos. 3, 4) ..
z 907 4d. vermilion (1865–73) 40 0
Plate Nos. 8, 10, 11, 12, 13, 14.
z 908 4d. vermilion (1876) (Plate No. 15) £15
z 909 4d. sage-green (1877) 90 0
Plate Nos. 15, 16.
z 910 6d. lilac (1862) (Plate Nos. 3, 4) ..
z 911 6d. lilac (1867) .. .. ..
z 912 6d. violet (1867–70) .. *From* 50 0
Plate Nos. 6, 8, 9.
z 913 6d. buff (1872–73) .. .. *From* £13
Plate Nos. 11, 12.
z 914 6d. chestnut (1872) (Pl. No. 11) .. 45 0
z 915 6d. grey (1873) (Pl. No. 12) .. 65 0
z 916 6d. grey (1874–80) .. .. *From* 35 0
Plate Nos. 13, 14, 15, 16.
z 918 8d. orange (1876) £17
z 918*a* 9d. straw (1862) .. .. ..
z 919 9d. straw (1865) £40
z 920 9d. straw (1867) £5
z 921 10d. red-brown (1867) £9
z 922 1s. green (1865) .. .. ..
z 923 1s. green (1867–73) .. *From* 40 0
Plate Nos. 4, 5, 6, 7.
z 924 1s. green (1873–77) .. *From* 40 0
Plate Nos. 8, 9, 10, 11, 12, 13.
z 925 2s. blue (1867) 80 0
z 926 5s. rose (1867–74) .. *From* £7
Plate Nos. 1, 2.

ISLAY (PERU).

"C **42**." *Obliteration as T* **4**.

1865 *to* **1879.**

z 927 1d. rose-red (1864–79) .. *From* 80 0
Plate Nos. 78, 84, 87, 88, 96, 103, 134.
z 928 1½d. lake-red (1870–74) (Plate No. 3)
z 929 2d. blue (1858–69) 65 0
Plate Nos. 9, 15.
z 929*a* 3d. carmine-rose (1862) .. ..
z 930 3d. rose (1865) .. .. ..
z 931 3d. rose (1867–73) 85 0
Plate Nos. 4, 5, 6, 10.
z 932 4d. red (1862) (Plate Nos. 3, 4) ..
z 933 4d. vermilion (1867–73) .. *From* 55 0
Plate Nos. 9, 10, 11, 12, 13.
z 934 4d. vermilion (1876) (Pl. No. 15) ..
z 935 4d. sage-green (1877) £10
Plate Nos. 15, 16.
z 936 6a. lilac (1862) (Plate Nos. 3, 4) .. £13
z 937 6d. lilac (1865) (Plate No. 5) .. 60 0
z 938 6d. violet (1867–60) .. *From* 60 0
Plate Nos. 6, 8, 9.
z 938*a* 6d. buff (1873) (Plate No. 12) ..
z 939 6d. grey (1873) (Plate No. 12) ..
z 940 6d. grey (1874–76) .. .. *From* 60 0
Plate Nos. 13, 14, 15, 16.
z 941 9d. straw (1865) £40
z 941*a* 9d. straw (1867) £16
z 942 10d. red-brown (1867) £35
z 943 1s. green (1865) (Plate No. 4) ..
z 944 1s. green (1867–73) .. *From* 80 0
Plate Nos. 4, 5, 6, 7.
z 945 1s. green (1873–77) .. *From* 80 0
Plate Nos. 10, 12, 13.
z 946 2s. blue (1867) .. .. ..
z 947 5s. rose (1867) (Plate No. 1) ..

PAITA (PERU)

"C **43**." *Obliteration as T* **4**.

1861 *to* **1879.**

z 947*a* 1d. rose-red (1864–79) (Pl. No. 127)
z 948 2d. blue (1858–69) (Plate Nos. 9, 14)
z 949 3d. rose (1867–73) (Plate Nos. 5, 6) £8
z 949*a* 3d. rose (1876) (Plate Nos. 17, 19) £8
z 950 4d. vermilion (1865–73) .. *From* £5
Plate Nos. 10, 11, 12, 13, 14.
z 951 4d. sage-green (1877) (Plate No. 15)
z 952 6d. lilac (1862) (Plate No. 3) .. £8
z 953 6d. lilac (1865–67) (Plates 5, 6) .. £8
z 954 6d. violet (1867–70) £8
Plate Nos. 6, 8, 9.
z 955 6d. buff (1872–73) .. .. *From* £13
Plate Nos. 11, 12.
z 955*a* 6d. chestnut (Plate No. 11) ..
z 956 6d. grey (1873) .. .. ..
z 957 6d. grey (1874–76) .. .. ..
Plate Nos. 13, 14, 15.
z 957*a* 9d. straw (1862) .. .. ..
z 958 10d. red-brown (1867) £35
z 959 1s. green (1865) (Plate No. 4) ..
z 960 1s. green (1867–73) (Plate No. 4) £7
z 961 1s. green (1873–77) £7
Plate Nos. 8, 9, 10, 13.
z 962 2s. blue (1867) £35
z 963 5s. rose (1867) (Plate No. 1) .. £50

PISCO (PERU).

"D **74**." *Obliteration as T* **12**.

1868 *to* **1870.**

z 963*a* 1d. rose-red (1864–79) (Pl. No. 137)
z 963*b* 2d. blue (1858–69) (Plate No. 9) ..
z 964 4d. vermilion (1865–73) .. ..
Plate Nos. 10, 12, 13.
z 965 6d. violet (1868) (Plate No. 6) .. £70
z 965*a* 1s. green (1867) (Plate No. 4) ..
z 966 2s. blue (1867) £40

PANAMA (COLOMBIA).

"C **35**." *Obliterations as T* **4, 11** *or* **14.**

1865 *to* **1884.**

z 967 ½d. rose-red (1870–79) .. ..
Plate Nos. 10, 11 12, 13, 14, 15, 19.
z 968 1d. rose-red (1864–79) .. *From* 45 0
Plate Nos. 72, 76, 85, 87, 88, 93, 95, 101, 104, 114, 124, 130, 138, 139, 142, 159, 168, 171, 172, 174, 177, 179, 180, 184, 185, 189, 191, 192, 193, 196, 200, 203, 204, 205, 207, 208, 209, 210, 211, 213, 214, 215, 224.

z 969 1½d. lake-red (1870–74) (Plate No. 3) 55 0
z 970 2d. blue (1858–69) .. .. *From* 45 0
Plate Nos. 9, 12, 13, 14, 15.
z 971 2½d. rosy mauve (1875) (Plate 1) ..
z 971*a* 2½d. rosy mauve (1876–80) ..
Plate Nos. 4, 12, 16.
z 971*b* 2½d. blue (1880) (Plate No. 19) ..
z 972 2½d. blue (1881) (Plate Nos. 22, 23)
z 972*a* 3d. carmine-red (1862) .. ..
z 973 3d. rose (1865) (Plate No. 4) ..
z 974 3d. rose (1867–73) .. .. *From* 50 0
Plate Nos. 4, 5, 6, 7, 8, 9.
z 975 3d. rose (1873–76) .. .. *From* 45 0
Plates 14, 15, 16, 17, 18, 19, 20.
z 976 3d. rose (1881) (Plate Nos. 20, 21)
z 977 4d. red (1862) (Plate No. 4) ..
z 978 4d. vermilion (1865–73) .. *From* 45 0
Pl. Nos. 7, 8, 9, 10, 11, 12, 13, 14.
z 979 4d. vermilion (1876) (Plate No. 15) £15
z 980 4d. sage-green (1877) £6
Plate Nos. 15, 16.
z 981 4d. grey-brn. (1880) *wmk.* Crown (Plate Nos. 17, 18) .. *From* 65 0
z 982 6d. lilac (1862) (Plates 3, 4) *From* 55 0
z 983 6d. lilac (1865–67) .. .. *From* 50 0
Plate Nos. 5, 6.
z 984 6d. lilac (1867) (Plate No. 6) ..
z 985 6d. violet (1867–70) 50 0
Plate Nos. 6, 8, 9.
z 986 6d. buff (1872–73) .. .. *From* £13
Plate Nos. 11, 12.
z 987 6d. chestnut (Plate No. 11) .. 75 0
z 988 6d. grey (1873) (Plate No. 12) .. 65 0
z 989 6d. grey (1874–80) .. *From* 50 0
Plate Nos. 13, 14, 15, 16, 17.
z 990 6d. grey (1881) (Plate No. 17) .. £11
z 991 8d. orange (1876) £15
z 992 9d. straw (1862) £17
z 992*a* 9d. straw (1867) £9
z 993 10d. red-brown (1867) £11
z 994 1s. green (1865) (Plate No. 4) .. 45 0
z 995 1s. green (1867–73) .. *From* 40 0
Plate Nos. 4, 5, 6, 7.
z 996 1s. green (1873–77) .. *From* 40 0
Plate Nos. 8, 9, 10, 11, 12, 13.
z 997 1s. orange-brown (1880) (Pl. 13) .. £10
z 998 1s. orge.-brn. (1881) (Plate No. 13) £6
z 999 2s. blue (1867) £5
z 1000 2s. brown (1880) £72
z 1001 5s. rose (1867–74) .. .. *From* £10
Plate Nos. 1, 2.

1880.
z 1001*a* 1d. Venetian red 40 0
z 1002 2d. rose 75 0
z 1003 5d. indigo £5

1881.
z 1004 1d. lilac (14 *dots*) £6
z 1005 1d. lilac (16 *dots*) £5

1884.
z 1006–z 1010 1½d., 2d., 2½d., 4d., 5d *Fr.* 75 0

1887.
z 1010*a* 2d. green and carmine .. ..

The Panama Office was closed to the public in 1881, but remained open as a " transit office " until, at least, 1888.

CARTAGENA (COLOMBIA).
" C **56.**" *Obliterations as T* **4** *or* **13.**

1865 *to* 1881.
z 1010*b* ½d. rose-red (1870–79) (Pl. No. 10)
z 1010*c* 1d. rose-red (1864) .. *From* £6
Plate No. 87, 100, 111, 113, 117, 119, 125, 189, 217.
z 1011 2d. blue (1858–69) .. *From* 80 0
Plate Nos. 9, 11, 14.
z 1011*a* 3d. "*Emblems*" (1865) (Plate No. 4)
z 1012 3d. rose (1865–68) .. ..
Plate Nos. 4, 5.
z 1012*a* 3d. rose (1873–79) .. *From* £10
Plate Nos. 17, 18.
z 1013 4d. vermilion (1865–73) .. *From* 85 0
Plate Nos. 7, 8, 9, 10, 11, 12, 13, 14.
z 1014 4d. vermilion (1876) (Pl. No. 15) £15
z 1014*a* 4d. sage-green .. .. *From* £7
Plate Nos. 15, 16.
z 1015 6d. lilac (1865–67) (Plate Nos. 5, 6)
z 1016 6d. vio. (1867–70) (Pl. 6, 8) *From* £11
z 1017 6d. grey (1873) (Plate No. 12) .. £6
z 1018 6d. grey (1874–76) .. *From* 95 0
Plate Nos. 13, 14, 15, 16.
z 1019 8d. orange (1870) £20
z 1019*a* 9d. straw (1865) .. .. ..
z 1020 1s. green (1865) .. .. ..
z 1021 1s. green (1867–73)
Plate Nos. 4, 5, 7.
z 1022 1s. green (1873–77) .. ..
Plate Nos. 8, 9, 10, 11, 12, 13 95 0
z 1023 1s. orange-brown (1880) .. ..
z 1023*a* 2s. blue (1867) £35
z 1024 5s. rose (1867) (Plate No. 1) .. £65

" C **65** " *error for* " C **56.**"

1866 *to* 1881.
z 1024*a* ½d. rose-red (1870–79) (Pl. 10) ..
z 1024*b* 1d. rose-red (1864–79) .. *From* £13
Plate Nos. 100, 111.
z 1025 2d. blue (1858–69) (Plate No. 9) £5
z 1025*a* 2½d. blue (1880) (Pl. 19) .. ..
z 1025*b* 3d. rose (1867–73) (Plate No. 9)
z 1026 3d. rose (1873–76) (Pl. 17, 19) ..
z 1027 4d. vermilion (1865–73) .. *From* 90 0
Plate Nos. 7, 9, 11, 12, 13, 14.
z 1028 4d. vermilion (1876) (Plate No. 15) £20
z 1028*a* 4d. sage-green (1877) .. *From* £7
Plate Nos. 15, 16.
z 1029 6d. violet (1867–70) (Plates 6, 8)
z 1029*a* 6d. pale buff (1872) (Plate No. 11)
z 1029*b* 6d. grey (1873) (Plate No. 12) .. £13
z 1029*c* 6d. grey (1874–80) (Pl. 13, 15, 16) £13
z 1030 8d. orange (1876) .. .. ..
z 1031 9d. straw (1865) £40
z 1032 1s. green (1865) (Plate No. 4) ..
z 1032*a* 1s. green (1867) (Pls. 4, 5, 6, 7) £5
z 1032*b* 1s. green (1873–77) .. *From* 90 0
Plate Nos. 8, 11, 12, 13.
z 1032*c* 1s. orange-brown (1880) .. ..
z 1032*d* 2s. blue (1867) .. .. ..
z 1033 2s. brown (1880) £90
z 1034 5s. rose (1867) (Plate No. 1) .. £60

SANTA MARTHA (COLOMBIA).
" C **62.**" *Obliteration as T* **4.**

1865 *to* 1881.
z 1034*a* ½d. rose-red (1870–79) (Plate 6) £8
z 1035 1d. rose-red (1864–79) (Pl. No. 106) £8
z 1036 2d. blue (1858–69) (Plate No. 9) £8
z 1037 4d. vermilion (1865–73) .. *From* £6
Plate Nos. 7, 8, 9, 11, 12, 13, 14.
z 1037*a* 4d. sage-green (1877) (Plate 15) £9
z 1037*b* 4d. grey-brown (1880) *wmk.* Large Garter (Plate No. 17) .. £10
z 1037*c* 4d. grey-brown (1880) *wmk.* Crown (Plate No. 17) £7
z 1038 6d. lilac (1865–67) (Plate No. 5)
z 1038*a* 6d. grey (1873) (Plate No. 12) ..
z 1038*b* 6d. grey (1874–76) (Plate No. 14)
z 1039 8d. orange (1876) £20
z 1040 1s. green (1865) (Plate No. 4) .. £7
z 1040*a* 1s. green (1867–73) (Pl. Nos. 5, 7) £7
z 1040*b* 1s. green (1873–77) (Plate No. 8)
z 1041 2s. blue (1867) £35
z 1041*a* 5s. rose (1867) (Plate No. 2) .. £50

ASPINWALL, COLON (COLOMBIA).
" E **88.**" *Obliteration as T* **12.**

1870 *to* 1881.
z 1042 1d. rose-red (1864–79) .. *From* 80 0
Plate Nos. 107, 121, 122, 123, 125, 127, 130, 133, 136, 142, 150, 151, 152, 153, 155, 156, 157, 158, 160, 171, 174, 176, 178, 184, 187, 194, 195, 201, 209, 213, 214, 217.
z 1042*a* 1d. Venetian red (1880) .. ..
z 1043 1½d. lake-red (1870–74) (Pl. No. 3) £13
z 1044 2d. blue (1858–69) (Pl. Nos. 14, 15) £5
z 1045 3d. rose (1867–73) (Plate No. 9)

z 1046 3d. rose (1873–76) £7
Plate Nos. 12, 16, 18, 19, 20.
z 1047 4d. vermilion (1865–73) .. *From* 70 0
Plate Nos. 10, 11, 12, 13, 14.
z 1048 4d. vermilion (1876) (Plate No. 15)
z 1049 4d. sage-grn. (1877) (Pl. Nos. 15, 16) £6
z 1050 4d. grey-brown (1880) *wmk.* Large Garter (Plate No. 17) .. £13
z 1051 4d grey-brown (1880) *wmk.* Crown (Plate No. 17)
z 1052 6d. vio. (1867–70) (Plates 6, 8, 9)
z 1052*a* 6d. buff (1872) (Plate No. 11) ..
z 1053 6d. chestnut (1872) (Plate No. 11) £10
z 1054 6d. grey (1873) (Plate No. 12) ..
z 1055 6d. grey (1874–80) .. *From* 85 0
Plate Nos. 13, 14, 15, 16, 17.
z 1055*a* 8d. orange (1876) .. .. ..
z 1056 9d. straw (1867) .. .. ..
z 1057 1s. green (1867–73) 70 0
Plate Nos. 4, 5, 6, 7.
z 1058 1s. green (1873–77) .. *From* 90 0
Plate Nos. 8, 9, 10, 11, 12, 13.
z 1059 1s. orange-brown (1880) (Plate 13) £22
z 1060 1s. orange-brown (1881) (Plate 13) £6
z 1061 2s. blue (1867) £14
z 1061*a* 2s. brown (1880) £80
z 1061*b* 5s. rose (1867) (Plate Nos. 1, 2) £35

SAVANILLA (COLOMBIA).

" F **69**." *Obliteration as T* **12**.

1872 *to* **1881.**

z 1062 ½d. rose-red (1870–79) (Plate 6) £8
z 1063 1d. rose-red (1864–79) £8
Plate Nos. 122, 171.
z 1064 1½d. lake-red (1870–74) (Pl. No. 3) £13
z 1065 3d. rose (1867–73) (Plate No. 7) ..
z 1066 3d. rose (1873–76) (Plate No. 20)
z 1066*a* 3d. rose (1881) (Plate No. 20) ..
z 1067 4d. vermilion (1865–73) £7
Plate Nos. 12, 13, 14.
z 1068 4d. vermilion (1876) (Plate No. 15)
z 1069 4d. sage-green (1877) £8
Plate Nos. 15, 16.
z 1070 4d. grey-brn. (1880) *wmk.* Large Garter (Plate No. 17)
z 1071 4d. grey-brn. (1880) *wmk.* Crown (Plate No. 17) .. ..
z 1072 6d. buff (1872) (Plate No. 11) ..
z 1072*a* 6d. grey (1878) (Plate No. 16) .. £11
z 1072*b* 8d. orange (1876) £20
z 1073 1s. green (1867–73) (Pl. Nos. 5, 7) £5
z 1074 1s. green (1873–77) .. ..
Plate Nos. 8, 11, 12 and 13.
z 1075 1s. orange-brown (1880) ..
z 1076 2s. blue (1867) .. .. ..
z 1077 5s. rose (1867–74) (Plate No. 2) .. £50

GUAYAQUIL (ECUADOR).

" C **41**." *Obliteration as T* **4**.

1865 *to* **1880.**

z 1078 ½d. rose-red (1870–79) £6
Plate Nos. 5, 6.
z 1079 1d. rose-red (1857) .. ..
z 1080 1d. rose-red (1864–79) 75 0
Plate Nos. 74, 78, 85, 92, 94, 105, 110, 115, 133, 145, 166, 174, 216.
z 1081 1½d. lake-red (1870–74) £5
Plate No. 3.
z 1082 2d. blue (1858–69) .. *From* 80 0
Plate Nos. 9, 13, 14.
z 1082*a* 3d. carmine-rose (1862) £33
z 1083 3d. rose (1865) (Plate No. 4) .. 80 0
z 1084 3d. rose (1867–73) .. *From* 70 0
Plate Nos. 6, 7, 9, 10.
z 1085 3d rose (1873–76) .. *From* 70 0
Plate Nos. 11, 12, 15, 16, 17, 18, 19.
z 1086 4d. red (1862) (Plate Nos. 3, 4) .. £10
z 1087 4d. vermilion (1865–73) .. *From* 70 0
Plate Nos. 7, 8, 9, 10, 11, 12, 13, 14.
z 1088 4d. vermilion (1876) (Pl. No. 15) £16
z 1089 4d. sage-green (1877) £7
Plate Nos. 15, 16.
z 1090 6d. lilac (1862) (Plate No. 4) .. £6
z 1091 6d. lilac (1865–67) (Pl. Nos. 5, 6) 75 0
z 1092 6d. lilac (1867) (Plate No. 6) ..
z 1093 6d. violet (1867–70) .. *From* 75 0
Plate Nos. 6, 8, 9.
z 1094 6d. buff (1872–73) (Pl. Nos. 11, 12)
z 1095 6d. chestnut (1872) .. ..
z 1096 6d. grey (1873) (Plate No. 12) ..
z 1097 6d. grey (1874–76) .. *From* 70 0
Plate Nos. 13, 14, 15, 16.
z 1098 8d. orange (1876) £20
z 1098*a* 9d. straw (1862) £40
z 1098*b* 9d. straw (1867) £10
z 1099 10d. red-brown (1867) £13
z 1100 1s. green (1865) (Plate No. 4) .. 65 0
z 1101 1s. green (1867–73) .. *From* 60 0
Plate Nos. 4, 5, 6, 7.
z 1102 1s. green (1873–77) .. *From* 65 0
Plate Nos. 8, 9, 10, 11, 12, 13.
z 1103 2s. blue (1867) £11
z 1104 2s. brown (1880) £80
z 1105 5s. rose (1867–74) .. *From* £38
Plate Nos. 1, 2.

GREYTOWN (NICARAGUA).

" C **57**. " *Obliteration as T* **4**, **12** *or* **14**.

1865 *to* **1882.**

z 1106 ½d. rose-red (1870–79) £6
Plate Nos. 5, 11.
z 1106*a* 1d. rose-red (1864–79) .. ..
Plate Nos. 197, 210.
z 1107 1½d. lake-red (1870) (Plate No. 3) 90 0
z 1108 2d. blue (1858–69) .. ..
Plate Nos. 9, 14, 15.
z 1109 3d. rose (1873–76) .. ..
Plate Nos. 17, 18, 19, 20.
z 1110 3d. rose (1881) (Plate No. 20) ..
z 1111 4d. vermilion (1865–73) .. *From* 75 0
Plate Nos. 8, 10, 11, 12, 13, 14.
z 1112 4d. vermilion (1876) (Plate No. 15)
z 1113 4d. sage-green (1877) £7
Plate Nos. 15, 16.
z 1114 4d. grey-brn. (1880) *wmk.* Large Garter (Plate No. 17) .. £7
z 1115 4d. grey-brown (1880) *wmk.* Crown (Plate No. 17) £6
z 1116 6d. grey (1874–76) .. ..
Plate Nos. 14, 15, 16.
z 1117 8d. orange (1876) .. ..
z 1117*a* 1s. green (1865) (Plate No. 4) ..
z 1118 1s. green (1867–73) .. ..
Plate Nos. 6, 7.
z 1119 1s. green (1873–77) 80 0
Plate Nos. 8, 12, 13.
z 1120 1s. orange-brown (1880) £13
Plate No. 13.
z 1121 1s. orange-brown (1881) £10
Plate No. 13.
z 1122 2s. blue (1867) £8
z 1123 2s. brown (1880) £75
z 1124 5s. rose (1867–74) (Plate Nos. 1, 2) £17
z 1124*a* 5s. rose (1882) (Plate No. 4), blue *paper* £140
z 1124*b* 10s. greenish grey (1878) £140

1880.

z 1125 1d. Venetian red .. .. ..
z 1126 1½d. Venetian red £13

TAMPICO (MEXICO).

" C **63**. " *Obliteration as T* **4**.

1865 *to* **1876.**

z 1127 1d. rose-red (1864–79) .. *From* £15
Plate Nos. 81, 89, 103, 117, 139, 147.
z 1128 2d. blue (1858–69) £16
Plate Nos. 9, 14.
z 1129 4d. vermilion (1865–73) .. *From* £13
Plate Nos. 7, 8, 10, 11, 12, 13, 14.
z 1130 1s. green (1867–73) .. ..
Plate Nos. 4, 5, 7.
z 1130*a* 2s. blue (1867) £45

LA GUAYRA (VENEZUELA).

" C **60.** " *Obliteration as T* **4,** *circular postmark as T* **16** *or Crowned Circle undated postmark.*

1865 *to* **1880.**

z 1135 ½d. rose-red (1870) (Plate 6) ..
z 1135*a* 1d. rose-red (1864–79) .. *From* 80 0
Plate Nos. 92, 96, 98, 111, 113, 115, 131, 138, 145, 154, 177, 178, 180, 196.
z 1136 1½d. lake-red (1870–74) (Plate 3)
z 1137 2d. blue (1858–69) (Plate No. 14) £8
z 1138 3d. rose (1873–76) .. *From* £11
Plate Nos. 14, 15, 17, 18, 19.
z 1139 4d. vermilion (1865–73) .. *From* 95 0
Plate Nos. 9, 11, 12, 13, 14.
z 1140 4d. vermilion (1876) (Plate No. 15) £16
z 1141 4d. sage-green (1877) £6
Plate Nos. 15, 16.
z 1142 6d. lilac (1865) (Plate No. 5) ..
z 1143 6d. violet (1867–70) (Pl. Nos. 6, 8)
z 1144 6d. buff (1872–73) .. *From* £15
Plate Nos. 11, 12.
z 1145 6d. grey (1873) (Plate No. 12) .. £9
z 1146 6d. grey (1874–76) £11
Plate Nos. 13, 15, 16.
z 1146*a* 8d. orange (1876) £20
z 1146*b* 9d. straw (1862) .. .. ..
z 1146*c* 9d. straw (1867) .. .. ..
z 1147 10d. red-brown (1867) .. ..
z 1147*a* 1s. green (1865) (Plate No. 4) .. £17
z 1148 1s. green (1867–73) (Pl. Nos. 4, 7)
z 1149 1s. green (1873–77) .. *From* £5
Plate Nos. 8, 9, 10, 11, 12, 13.
z 1150 2s. blue (1867) £35
z 1151 5s. rose (1867–74) (Pl. 1, 2) *From* £50

CIUDAD BOLIVAR OR ANGOSTURA (VENEZUELA).

" D **22.**" *Obliteration or circular postmark as T* **12** *or* **17.**

1868 *to* **1880.**

z 1152 1d. rose-red (1864–79) (Pl. No. 133) £11
z 1152*a* 2d. blue (1858–69) (Plate No. 13)
z 1153 3d. rose (1867–73) (Plate No. 5)
z 1153*a* 3d. rose (1873–79) (Plate No. 11) £13
z 1154 4d. vermilion (1865–73) £10
Plate Nos. 9, 12, 14.
z 1155 4d. sage-green (1877) .. *From* £18
Plate Nos. 15, 16.
z 1155*a* 4d. grey-brn. (1880) *wmk.* Crown (Plate No. 17) .. ..
z 1155*b* 9d. straw (1867) .. .. ..
z 1155*c* 10d. red-brown (1867) .. ..
z 1156 1s. green (1867–73) .. *From* £16
Plate Nos. 4, 5, 7.
z 1157 1s. green (1873–77) .. ..
Plate Nos. 10, 12, 13. .. £11
z 1158 2s. blue (1867) £50
z 1158*a* 5s. rose (1867–74) (Pl. Nos. 1, 2) £50

BAHIA (BRAZIL).

" C **81.**" *Obliteration as T* **12.**

1866 *to* **1874.**

z 1159 1d. rose-red (1864) .. *From* 90 0
Plate Nos. 90, 108, 113, 117, 135, 140, 147, 155.
z 1160 1½d. lake-red (1870–74) (Pl. No. 3) £9
z 1161 2d. blue (1858–69) £8
Plate Nos. 9, 12, 13, 14.
z 1162 3d. rose (1865) (Plate No. 4) ..
z 1163 3d. rose (1867–73) £7
Plate Nos. 4, 6, 8, 9, 10.
z 1163*a* 3d. rose (1873–79) (Plate No. 11)
z 1164 4d. vermilion (1865–73) .. *From* 70 0
Plate Nos. 8, 9, 11, 12, 13.
z 1164*a* 6d. lilac (1865–67) (Plate No. 5)
z 1165 6d. lilac (1867) (Plate No. 6) .. 90 0
z 1166 6d. violet (1867–70) .. *From* 90 0
Plate Nos. 6, 8, 9.
z 1166*a* 6d. buff (1872–73) .. *From* £20
Plate Nos. 11, 12.
z 1167 6d. chestnut (1872) (Plate No. 11)
z 1168 6d. grey (1873) (Plate No. 12) ..
z 1169 6d. grey (1874–76) (Plate No. 13)
z 1170 9d. straw (1865) £50
z 1170*a* 9d. straw (1867) £15
z 1171 1s. green (1865) (Plate No. 4) .. £7
z 1172 1s. green (1867–73) .. *From* 95 0
Plate Nos. 4, 5, 6, 7.
z 1173 1s. green (1873–77) .. *From* 95 0
Plate Nos. 8, 9.
z 1174 2s. blue (1867) £17
z 1175 5s. rose (1867) (Plate No. 1) .. £38

PERNAMBUCO (BRAZIL).

" C **82.** " *Obliteration as T* **12.**

1866 *to* **1874.**

z 1176 1d. rose-red (1864) .. *From* £9
Plate Nos. 85, 108, 111, 130, 132, 149, 159, 160.
z 1177 2d. blue (1858–69) .. *From* £10
Plate Nos. 9, 12, 13, 14.
z 1178 3d. rose (1867–73) £9
Plate Nos. 4, 5, 6, 7, 10.
z 1178*a* 3d. rose (1873–77) (Plate No. 11)
z 1179 4d. vermilion (1865–73) .. *From* £6
Plate Nos. 9, 10, 11, 12, 13, 14.
z 1180 6d. lilac (1865–67) (Plate Nos. 5, 6)
z 1181 6d. lilac (1867) (Plate No. 6) ..
z 1182 6d. violet (1867–70) .. *From* £8
Plate Nos. 8, 9.
z 1183 6d. buff (1872–73) .. ..
Plate Nos. 11, 12.
z 1184 6d. chestnut (1872) (Plate No. 11)
z 1185 6d. grey (1873) (Plate No. 12) ..
z 1186 9d. straw (1865) £50
z 1187 9d. straw (1867) £16
z 1188 10d. red-brown (1867) .. ..
z 1189 1s. green (1865) (Plate No. 4) ..
z 1190 1s. green (1867–73) £16
Plate Nos. 4, 5, 6, 7.
z 1191 2s. blue (1867) £17
z 1192 5s. rose (1867–74) (Plate Nos. 1, 2) £55

RIO DE JANEIRO (BRAZIL).

" C **83.**" *Obliteration as T* **12.**

1866 *to* **1874.**

z 1193 1d. rose-red (1857) £8
z 1194 1d. rose-red (1864) .. *From* 85 0
Plates 71, 76, 113, 117, 123, 132, 134, 135, 159, 161, 166.
z 1195 2d. blue (1858–69) .. *From* £6
Plate Nos. 9, 12, 13, 14.
z 1196 3d. rose (1867–73) .. *From* £6
Plate Nos. 4, 5, 6, 7, 8.
z 1197 3d. rose (1873–77) ((Pl. No. 11) ..
z 1198 4d. vermilion (1865–73) .. *From* 70 0
Pl. Nos. 8, 9, 10, 11, 12, 13, 14.
z 1199*a* 6d. lilac (1865–67) (Plate No. 5)
z 1200 6d. lilac (1867) (Plate No. 6) .. £6
z 1201 6d. violet (1867–70) .. *From* 90 0
Plate Nos. 6, 8, 9.
z 1202 6d. buff (1872) (Plate No. 11) ..
z 1203 6d. chestnut (1872) (Plate No. 11)
z 1204 6d. grey (1873) (Plate No. 12) ..
z 1205 9d. straw (1865) £40
z 1206 9d. straw (1867) £22
z 1207 10d. red-brown (1867) .. ..
z 1208 1s. green (1865) (Plate No. 4) .. 75 0
z 1209 1s. green (1867–73) .. *From* 65 0
Plate Nos. 4, 5, 6, 7.
z 1210 1s. green (1873–77) (Pl. Nos. 8, 9) £5
z 1211 2s. blue (1867) £11
z 1212 5s. rose (1867–74) .. *From* £22
Plate Nos. 1, 2.

JACMEL (HAITI).

" C **59.**" *Obliteration as T* **4.**

1865 *to* **1881.**

z 1213 ½d. rose-red (1870–79) .. *From* 80 0
Plate Nos. 4, 5, 6, 10, 11, 12, 14, 15.
z 1214 1d. rose-red (1864–79) .. *From* 70 0
Plate Nos. 74, 87, 95, 107, 122, 136, 137, 139, 148, 150, 151, 152, 156, 157, 159, 160, 162, 164, 166, 170, 171, 179, 181, 186, 187, 189, 192, 194, 200, 204.
z 1215 1½d. lake-red (1870–74) (Plate 3) .. 75 0

z 1216 2d. blue (1858–69) 90 0
Plate Nos. 9, 13, 14, 15.
z 1217 2½d. rosy mauve (1876) (Plate 4)
z 1217*a* 3d. rose (1867–73) .. *From* 90 0
Plate Nos. 5, 6, 8, 9, 10.
z 1218 3d. rose (1873–76) 90 0
Plate Nos. 11, 12, 14, 16, 17, 18, 19.
z 1218*a* 4d. red (1862) (Pl. No. 4) (*Hair lines*) £17
z 1219 4d. vermilion (1865–73) .. *From* 60 0
Plate Nos. 7, 8, 9, 10, 11, 12, 13, 14.
z 1220 4d. vermilion (1876) (Plate No. 15) £16
z 1221 4d. sage-green (1877) £6
Plate Nos. 15, 16.
z 1222 4d. grey-brn. (1880) *wmk.* Large Garter (Plate No. 17) .. £9
z 1223 4d. grey-brn. (1880) *wmk.* Crown (Plate No. 17) 80 0
z 1224 6d. lilac (1867) (Plate No. 6) .. £5
z 1225 6d. vio. (1867–70) (Plate Nos. 8, 9) 75 0
z 1226 6d. buff (1872–73) £13
Plate Nos. 11, 12
z 1227 6d. chestnut (1872) (Plate No. 11)
z 1228 6d. grey (1873) (Plate No. 12) ..
z 1229 6d. grey (1874–76) .. *From* 60 0
Plate Nos. 13, 14, 15, 16, 17.
z 1230 8d. orange (1876) £24
z 1230*a* 9d. straw (1862) £20
z 1231 9d. straw (1867) £14
z 1232 10d. red-brown (1867) .. ..
z 1233 1s. green (1865) (Plate No. 4) .. 65 0
z 1234 1s. green (1867–73) .. *From* 60 0
Plate Nos. 4, 5, 6, 7.
z 1235 1s. green (1873–77) .. *From* 65 0
Plate Nos. 8, 9, 10, 11, 12, 13.
z 1236 1s. orange-brown (1880) £11
Plate No. 13.
z 1237 2s. blue (1867) £13
z 1238 2s. brown (1880) £80
z 1239 5s. rose (1867–74) .. *From* £20
Plate Nos. 1, 2.

1880.

z 1239*a* ½d. green (1880) 95 0
z 1240 1d. Venetian red 80 0
z 1241 1½d. Venetian red £5
z 1242 2d. rose £8

PORT-AU-PRINCE (HAITI).

"E **53**." *Obliteration as T* **11, 12** *or* **14.**

1869 *to* **1881.**

z 1243 ½d. rose-red (1870–79) .. *From* 55 0
Plate Nos. 5, 6, 10, 11, 12, 13.
z 1244 1d. rose-red (1864–79) .. *From* 55 0
Plate Nos. 87, 134, 154, 167, 171, 174, 183, 187, 189, 193, 199, 200, 201, 202, 206, 209, 210, 218.
z 1245 1½d. lake-red (1870–74) (Plate 3) .. 70 0
z 1245*a* 2d. blue (1858–69) (Pl. No. 9) ..
z 1246 2d. blue (1855–69) 95 0
Plate Nos. 14, 15.
z 1247 2½d. rosy mauve (1876–79) .. £15
Plate Nos. 3, 9.
z 1247*a* 3d. rose (1867–73) (Pl. Nos. 6, 7)
z 1248 3d. rose (1873–79) 90 0
Plate Nos. 17, 18, 20.
z 1249 4d. vermilion (1865–73) .. *From* 65 0
Plate Nos. 11, 12, 13, 14.
z 1250 4d. vermilion (1876) (Plate No. 15) £16
z 1251 4d. sage-green (1877) .. *From* £5
Plate Nos. 15, 16.
z 1252 4d. grey-brn. (1880) *wmk.* Large Garter (Plate No. 17) .. £11
z 1253 4d. grey-brown (1880) *wmk.* Crown (Plate No. 17) £5
z 1254 6d. grey (1874–76) (Pl. 15, 16.)
z 1255 8d. orange (1876) £20
z 1256 1s. green (1867–73) .. *From* 65 0
Plate Nos. 4, 5, 6, 7.
z 1257 1s. green (1873–77) .. *From* 65 0
Plate Nos. 9, 10, 11, 12, 13.
z 1258 1s. orge.-brn. (1880) (Plate No. 13) £10
z 1259 1s. orge-brn. (1881) (Plate No. 13) £7
z 1260 2s. blue (1867) £13
z 1261 2s. brown (1880) £80
z 1262 5s. rose (1867–74) £38
Plate Nos. 1, 2.
z 1262*a* 10s. grey-green (1878) £90

1880.

z 1263 ½d. green £7
z 1264 1d. Venetian red 95 0
z 1265 1½d. Venetian red £8
z 1265*a* 2d. rose .. ..

PORTO PLATA (DOMINICAN REPUBLIC).

"C **86**." *Obliteration or circular postmark as T* **8, 12** *or* **17.**

1867 *to* **1869.**

z 1266 ½d. rose-red (1870–79) .. *From* £6
Plate Nos. 10, 12, 14.
z 1267 1d. rose-red (1864–79) .. *From* 90 0
Plate Nos. 123, 130, 136, 146, 151, 178, 199, 200, 205, 217.
z 1268 1½d. lake-red (1870–74) (Pl. 3) .. £7
z 1269 2d. blue (1858–69) (Plate No. 15) £6
z 1270 2½d. rosy mauve (1876–79) *From* £27
Plate Nos. 13, 14.
z 1270*a* 3d. rose (1873–76) (Plate No. 18) £14
z 1270*b* 4d. vermilion (1873) (Plate No. 14) £14
z 1271 4d. vermilion (1876) (Plate No. 15) £16
z 1272 4d. sage-green (1877) (Plate 15) .. £11
z 1272*a* 6d. violet (1867–70) (Plate No. 8)
z 1273 6d. grey (1874–76) (Plate No. 15) £11
z 1273*a* 8d. orange (1876) £25
z 1274 1s. green (1867–73) .. *From* £6
Plate Nos. 4, 7.
z 1275 1s. green (1873–77) .. *From* 95 0
Plate Nos. 11, 12, 13.
z 1276 2s. blue (1867) £30

SAN DOMINGO (DOMINICAN REP.)

"C **87**." *Obliteration or circular postmark as T* **17.**

1867 *or* **1879.**

z 1277 ½d. rose-red (1870–79) .. *From* £6
Plate Nos. 5, 6, 8, 10, 11, 13.
z 1278 1d. rose-red (1864–79) .. *From* £6
Plate Nos. 146, 154, 171, 173, 174, 176, 178, 186, 190, 197, 220.
z 1279 1½d. lake-red (1870–74) £7
Plate No. 3.
z 1280 2d. blue (1858–69) (Pl. 13, 14) .. £7
z 1280*a* 3d. rose (1873–76) (Plate No. 18)
z 1281 4d. vermilion (1865–73) .. *From* £7
Plate Nos. 11, 12, 14.
z 1282 4d. vermilion (1876) (Plate No. 15) £15
z 1282*a* 4d. sage-green (1877) (Plate 15) ..
z 1282*b* 6d. grey (1874–76) (Plate No. 15)
z 1283 9d. straw (1867) .. .. ..
z 1284 1s. green (1867) (Plate No. 4) ..
z 1285 1s. green (1873–77) .. *From* £6
Plate Nos. 10, 11, 12, 13.
z 1285*a* 2s. blue (1867) .. .. ..

ST. THOMAS (D.W.I.).

"C **51**." *Obliteration as T* **4, 12** *or* **14.**

1865 *to* **1879.**

z 1286 ½d. rose-red (1870–79) 80 0
Plate Nos. 5, 6, 8, 10, 11, 12.
z 1286*a* 1d. rose-red (1857) .. ..
z 1287 1d. rose-red (1864–79) .. *From* 50 0
Plate Nos. 71, 72, 79, 81, 84, 85, 86, 87, 88, 89, 90, 93, 94, 95, 96, 97, 98, 100, 101, 102, 105, 106, 107, 110, 112, 113, 114, 117, 118, 119, 120, 121, 122, 123, 124, 125, 127, 129, 130, 131, 133, 134, 136, 137, 138, 139, 140, 141, 142, 144, 145, 146, 147, 148, 149, 150, 151, 152, 154, 155, 156, 157, 158, 159, 160, 161, 162, 163, 164, 165, 166, 167, 169, 170, 171, 172, 173, 174, 175, 176, 177, 178, 179, 180, 181, 182, 184, 185, 186, 187, 189, 190, 197.

z 1288 1½d. lake-red (1870–74) (Pls. 1, 3) 60 0
z 1289 2d. blue (1858–69) .. *From* 45 0
Plate Nos. 9, 12, 13, 14, 15.
z 1290 3d. rose (1865) (Plate No. 4) .. £5
z 1291 3d. rose (1867–73) .. *From* 75 0
Plate Nos. 4, 5, 6, 7, 8, 9, 10.
z 1291*a* 3d. rose (1873–76) .. *From* £5
Plate Nos. 11, 12, 14, 15, 16, 17, 18, 19.
z 1292 4d. red (1862) (Plate Nos. 3, 4)..
z 1293 4d. vermilion (1865–73) .. *From* 45 0
Plate Nos. 7, 8, 9, 10, 11, 12, 13, 14.
z 1294 4d. verm. (1876) (Plate No. 15).. £15
z 1295 4d. sage-green (1877) .. *From* £6
Plate Nos. 15, 16.
z 1295*a* 4d. grey-brown (1880) *wmk.* Large Garter (Plate No. 17) .. £6
z 1296 6d. lilac (1862) (Plate No. 4) .. £8
z 1297 6d. lilac (1865–67) .. *From* 50 0
Plate Nos. 5, 6.
z 1298 6d. lilac (1867) (Plate No. 6) .. 80 0
z 1299 6d. violet (1867–70) .. *From* 45 0
Plate Nos. 6, 8, 9.
z 1300 6d. buff (1872–73) .. *From* £13
Plate Nos. 11, 12.
z 1301 6d. chestnut (1872) (Plate No. 11) 65 0
z 1302 6d. grey (1873) (Plate No. 12) .. 80 0
z 1303 6d. grey (1874–76) 55 0
Plate Nos. 13, 14, 15, 16.
z 1304 8d. orange (1876).. .. .. £11
z 1305 9d. straw (1862) .. .. ..
z 1306 9d. bistre (1862) £10
z 1307 9d. straw (1865) £40
z 1308 9d. straw (1867) £8
z 1309 10d. red-brown (1867) £9
z 1310 1s. green (1865) (Plate No. 4) .. 45 0
z 1311 1s. green (1867–73) .. *From* 30 0
Plate Nos. 4, 5, 6, 7.
z 1312 1s. green (1873–77) .. *From* 40 0
Plate Nos. 8, 9, 10, 11, 12, 13.
z 1313 2s. blue (1867) £6
z 1314 5s. rose (1867–74) .. *From* £16
Plate Nos. 1, 2.

SPANISH MAIL PACKET
ST. THOMAS.

"D **26**." *Obliteration as T* **12**.

1868 *to* **1879** (?).
z 1315 1d. rose-red (1864) (Pls. 98, 125)
z 1316 4d. vermilion (1865–73) £45
Plate Nos. 9, 10, 11.
z 1317 6d. violet (1867–70) (Plate No. 8)

HAVANA (CUBA).

"C **58**." *Obliteration as T* **4** *or* **14**.

1867 *to* **1877**.
z 1318 ½d. rose-red (1870) (Pl. 12) .. £5
z 1319 1d. rose-red (1864) .. ..
Plate Nos. 86, 90, 93, 115, 120, 123, 144, 146, 171, 208.
z 1320 2d. blue (1858–69) .. ..
Plate Nos. 9, 14, 15.
z 1321 3d. rose (1867–73) (Plate No. 4)..
z 1321*a* 3d. rose (1873–76) (Pls. 18, 19)
z 1322 4d. vermilion (1865–73) .. *From* 85 0
Plate Nos. 7, 10, 11, 12, 13, 14.
z 1323 4d. verm. (1876) (Plate No. 15)
z 1324 6d. lilac (1865) (with hyphen)..
Plate No. 5.
z 1324*a* 6d. grey (1874–76) (Pl. No. 15)..
z 1325 8d. orange (1876).. .. ..
z 1325*a* 9d. straw (1867) £33
z 1326 10d. red-brown (1867) .. ..
z 1327 1s. green (1865) (Plate No. 4) ..
z 1328 1s. green (1867–73) .. *From* £5
Plate Nos. 4, 5, 7.
z 1329 1s. green (1873–77) .. *From* 70 0
Plate Nos. 10, 12, 13.
z 1330 2s. blue (1867) £28
z 1331 5s. rose (1867–74) (Plate Nos. 1, 2) £33

SANTIAGO DE CUBA.

"C **88**." *Obliteration as T* **14**.

1866 *to* **1877**.
z 1331*a* ½d. rose-red (1870–79) (Pl. No. 6)
z 1332 1d. rose-red (1864) .. *From* £15
Plate Nos. 100, 105, 106, 109, 120, 123, 144, 146, 171, 208.
z 1333 1½d. lake-red (1870–74) (Pl. No. 3)
z 1334 2d. blue (1858–69) .. ..
Plate Nos. 9, 12, 13, 14.
z 1334*a* 3d. rose (1867) (Plate No. 5) ..
z 1335 4d. vermilion (1865–73) .. *From* £15
Plate Nos. 9, 10, 12, 13, 14.
z 1336 4d. verm. (1876) (Plate No. 15).. £20
z 1337 6d. violet (1867–70) .. *From* £18
Plate Nos. 6, 8, 9.
z 1337*a* 6d. buff (Plate No. 11) .. ..
z 1338 10d. red-brown (1867) £33
z 1339 1s. green (1867–73) .. *From* £35
Plate Nos. 4, 5, 6.
z 1340 1s. green (1873—77) .. ..
Plate Nos. 9, 10, 12, 13.
z 1341 2s. blue (1867) .. .. ..
z 1341*a* 5s. rose (1867) (Plate 1).. ..

PORTO RICO.

"C **61**." *Obliterations as T* **4**, **8** *or* **14**.

1865 *to* **1877**.
z 1342 ½d. rose-red (1870) .. *From* 60 0
Plate Nos. 5, 10, 15.
z 1343 1d. rose-red (1857) .. ..
z 1344 1d. rose-red (1864) .. *From* 40 0
Plate Nos. 73, 81, 84, 90, 100, 102, 107, 122, 124, 125, 127, 130, 137, 138, 139, 140, 145, 146, 149, 153, 156, 159, 160, 162, 163, 169, 171, 172, 173, 175, 179, 180, 182, 186.
z 1345 1½d. lake-red (1870–74) .. *From* £11
Plate Nos. 1, 3.
z 1346 2d. blue (1858–69) .. *From* 50 0
Plate Nos. 9, 13, 14.
z 1347 3d. rose (1865) (Plate No. 4) .. 65 0
z 1348 3d. rose (1867–73) .. *From* 50 0
Plate Nos. 5, 6, 7, 8, 9, 10.
z 1349 3d. rose (1873–76) .. *From* 50 0
Plate Nos. 11, 12, 14, 15, 16, 17, 18.
z 1350 4d. vermilion (1865–73) .. *From* 45 0
Plate Nos. 7, 8, 9, 10, 11, 12, 13, 14.
z 1351 4d. verm. (1876) (Plate No. 15).. £15
z 1352 6d. lilac (1865–67) .. *From* 55 0
Plate Nos. 5, 6.
z 1353 6d. lilac (1867) (Plate No. 6) .. 80 0
z 1354 6d. violet (1867–70) .. *From* 55 0
Plate Nos. 6, 8, 9.
z 1355 6d. buff (1872–73) (Pl. Nos. 11, 12) £13
z 1356 6d. chestnut (1872) (Plate No. 11) 65 0
z 1357 6d. grey (1873) (Plate No. 12) ..
z 1358 6d. grey (1874–76) .. *From* 45 0
Plate Nos. 13, 14, 15.
z 1359 9d. straw (1862) £17
z 1359*a* 9d. straw (1865) £42
z 1360 9d. straw (1867) £10
z 1361 10d. red-brown (1867) £6
z 1362 1s. green (1865) (Plate No. 4) .. 45 0
z 1363 1s. green (1867–73) .. *From* 40 0
Plate Nos. 4, 5, 6, 7.
z 1364 1s. green (1873–77) .. *From* 45 0
Plate Nos. 8, 9, 10, 11, 12, 13.
z 1365 2s. blue (1867) £7
z 1366 5s. rose (1867) (Pls. 1, 2) *From* £9

ARROYO (PORTO RICO).

"F **83**." *Obliteration or circular postmark as T* **8** *or* **17**.

1872 *to* **1877**.
z 1366*a* ½d. rose-red (Plate No. 5) .. £6
z 1367 1d. rose-red (1864) £6
Pl. Nos. 150, 151, 156, 164, 174, 175.
z 1367*a* 1½d. lake-red (1870) (Plate No. 1)
z 1368 2d. blue (1858–69) (Plate No. 14)
z 1369 3d. rose (1867 73) (Pl. Nos 7, 10) £6
z 1370 3d. rose (1873–76) £6
Plate Nos. 12, 14, 18.

z 1371 4d. vermilion (1865–73) 80 0
Plate Nos. 12, 13, 14.
z 1372 4d. verm. (1876) (Plate No. 15) .. £15
z 1372*a* 6d. chestnut (1872) (Plate No. 11)
z 1372*b* 6d. pale buff (1872) (Plate No. 11)
z 1373 6d. grey (1874–76) £6
Plate Nos. 13, 14, 15.
z 1374 9d. straw (1867) £40
z 1375 10d. red-brown (1867) £15
z 1376 1s. green (1865) (Plate No. 4) ..
z 1377 1s. green (1867–73) (Pls. 4, 5, 6, 7) 65 0
z 1378 1s. green (1873–77) .. 60 0
Plate Nos. 8, 9, 10, 11, 12, 13.
z 1379 2s. blue (1867) £40
z 1379*a* 5s. rose (1867–74) (Plate No. 2)

AGUADILLA (PORTO RICO).

" F **84.**" *Obliteration or circular postmark as T* **8** *or* **17.**

1873 *to* **1877.**
z 1380 ½d. rose-red (1870) (Plate No. 6) £6
z 1380*a* 1d. rose-red (1864) £6
Plate Nos. 119, 122, 139, 156.
z 1381 2d. blue (1858–69) (Plate No. 14)
z 1382 3d. rose (1867–73) (Pl. Nos. 7, 8, 9)
z 1383 3d. rose (1873–76) (Plate No. 12)
z 1384 4d. vermilion (1865–73) 85 0
Plate Nos. 12, 13, 14.
z 1385 4d. verm. (1876) (Plate No. 15) £17
z 1386 6d. grey (1874–76) (Pl. Nos. 13, 14)
z 1387 9d. straw (1867) £40
z 1388 10d. red-brown (1867) £15
z 1389 1s. green (1867–73) .. *From* 90 0
Plate Nos. 4, 5, 6, 7.
z 1390 1s. green (1873–77) .. *From* £5
Plate Nos. 8, 9, 10, 11, 12.
z 1390*a* 2s. blue (1867) £40

MAYAGUEZ (PORTO RICO).

" F **85.**" *Obliteration or circular postmark as T* **8** *or* **17.**

1873 *to* **1877.**
z 1391 ½d. rose-red (1870) .. *From* £5
Plate Nos. 4, 5, 6, 8, 10, 11.
z 1392 1d. rose-red (1864) .. *From* 80 0
Plate Nos. 76, 120, 121, 122, 124, 134, 137, 140, 149, 150, 151, 154, 155, 156, 160, 167, 171, 174, 176, 178, 180, 182, 185, 186, 189.
z 1393 1½d. lake-red (1870–74) .. ..
Plate Nos. 1, 3.
z 1394 2d. blue (1858–69) £5
Plate Nos. 13, 14, 15.
z 1395 3d. rose (1867–73) £5
Plate Nos. 7, 8, 9.
z 1396 3d. rose (1873–76) 95 0
Plate Nos. 11, 12, 14, 15, 16, 17, 18, 19.
z 1397 4d. vermilion (1865–73) 75 0
Plate Nos. 11, 12, 13, 14.
z 1398 4d. verm. (1876) (Plate No. 15) .. £15
z 1398*a* 4d. sage-green (1877) (Pl. No. 15)
z 1398*b* 6d. mauve (1870) (Plate No. 9) ..
z 1399 6d. buff (1872) (Plate No. 11) ..
z 1400 6d. chestnut (1872) (Plate No. 11)
z 1401 6d. grey (1873) (Plate No. 12) ..
z 1402 6d. grey (1874–80) .. ..
Plate Nos. 13, 14, 15, 16.
z 1403 8d. orange (1876) £25
z 1404 9d. straw (1867) £27
z 1405 10d. red-brown (1867) £13
z 1406 1s. green (1867–73) 50 0
Plate Nos 4, 5, 6, 7.
z 1407 1s. green (1873–77) .. *From* 50 0
Plate Nos. 8, 9, 10, 11, 12.
z 1408 2s. blue (1867) .. .. ..
z 1409 5s. rose (1867–74) (Plate No. 2)

PONCE (PORTO RICO)

" F **88.**" *Obliteration or circular postmark as T* **8** *or* **17.**

1873 *to* **1877.**
z 1409*a* ½d. rose-red (1870) .. £6
Plate Nos. 5, 10, 12.
z 1410 1d. rose-red (1864) .. *From* 60 0
Plate Nos. 121, 122, 123, 124, 146, 148, 154, 156, 157, 158, 160, 167, 171, 174, 175, 186, 187.
z 1411 1½d. lake-red (1870–74) (Pl. 3) .. £20
z 1412 2d. blue (1858–69) 85 0
Plate Nos. 13, 14.
z 1413 3d. rose (1867–73) (Pl. Nos. 7, 8, 9)
z 1414 3d. rose (1873–76) 85 0
Plate Nos. 16, 17, 18, 19.
z 1415 4d. vermilion (1865–73) .. *From* 60 0
Plate Nos. 8, 9, 12, 13, 14.
z 1416 4d. verm. (1876) (Plate No. 15) .. £15
z 1417 4d. sage-green (1877) .. ..
Plate Nos. 15, 16.
z 1418 6d. buff (1872–73) .. ..
Plate Nos. 11, 12.
z 1419 6d. chestnut (1872) (Plate No. 11) £6
z 1420 6d. grey (1873) (Plate No. 12) ..
z 1421 6d. grey (1874–76) .. *From* 85 0
Plate Nos. 13, 14, 15.
z 1421*a* 9d. straw (1867) £45
z 1422 10d. red-brown (1867) £15
z 1423 1s. green (1867–73) 90 0
Plate Nos. 4, 6, 7.
z 1424 1s. green (1873–77) .. *From* 90 0
Plate Nos. 8, 9, 10, 11, 12, 13.
z 1425 2s. blue (1867) .. ..
z 1426 5s. rose (1867–74) .. *From* £60
Plate Nos. 1, 2.

NAGUABO (PORTO RICO).

" **582.**" *Obliteration as T* **9.**

1875 *to* **1877** (?)
z 1428 ½d. rose-red (1870–79) .. ..
Plate Nos. 5, 12, 14.
z 1429 1d. rose-red (1864–70) .. ..
Plate Nos. 159, 165.
z 1430 3d. rose (1873–76) (Plate No. 18) £40
z 1430*a* 4d. vermilion (1873–76) *From* £35
Plate Nos. 13, 14, 15.
z 1431 6d. grey (1874–76) (Pl. Nos. 14, 15)
z 1432 9d. straw (1867) .. .. ..
z 1433 10d. red-brown (1867) £50
z 1434 1s. green (Plate Nos. 11, 12) ..
z 1435 2s. dull blue (Plate No. 1) .. £45

V.

MISCELLANEOUS

FERNANDO POO.

" **247.**" *Obliteration as T* **9.**

1874 *to* **1877.**
z 1436 4d. vermilion (1865–72) £60
Plate Nos. 13, 14.
z 1437 4d. vermilion (1876) (Plate No. 15)
z 1438 6d. grey (1874–76) £45
Plate Nos. 13, 14, 15, 16.

MAURITIUS.

" B **53.**" *Obliteration as T* **4.**

z 1526 1d. rose-red (1857) £15
z 1527 1d. rose-red (1864) .. *From* £15
Plate Nos. 85, 153, 170, 187.
z 1527*a* 4d. verm. (1865–73) (Pl. No. 10) £11
z 1527*b* 4d. vermilion (1876) (Pl. No. 15) £20
z 1527*c* 6d. lilac (1865–67) (Pl. Nos. 5, 6) £13
z 1528 6d. lilac (1867) (Plate No. 6) .. £13
z 1529 6d. violet (1867–70) £16
Plate Nos. 6, 8, 9.
z 1529*a* 6d. chestnut (1872) (Plate No. 11) £20
z 1529*b* 9d. straw (1867) .. .. ..
z 1530 1s. green (1865) (Plate No. 4) .. £16
z 1531 1s. green (1867) (Plate No. 4) .. £20

HONG KONG.

" B **62.**" *Obliteration as T* **4.**

18(?) *to* **1870.**
z 1535 6d. lilac (1862) (Plate No. 3) ..

z 1536 6d. lilac (1865–67) .. ..
Plate Nos. 5, 6.
z 1537 8d. orange (1876) .. .. ..
z 1539 1s. green (1867) (Plate No. 4) .. £60

SEYCHELLES.

"B **64.**" *Obliteration as T* **2.**

1862.
z 1540 6d. lilac (1862) (Plate No. 3) ..

ASCENSION.

Circular postmarks of various sizes as *T* **16** or oval Registration postmark.

z 1541 1d. red-brown (1855) £30
z 1542 1d. rose-red (1864) .. *From* £13
Plate Nos. 74, 78, 83, 85, 96, 100, 102, 103, 104, 122, 134, 138, 154, 155, 157, 160, 168.
z 1543 6d. lilac (1865) (Plate No. 5) .. £44
z 1544 1s. green (1865) (Plate No. 4) ..
z 1545 1s. green (1867) (Plate No. 7) ..
z 1546 6d. grey (1880) (Plate No. 17) .. £33
z 1547 1d. lilac (1881) (16 *dots*) 15 0
z 1548 ½d. vermilion (1887–92) 15 0
z 1549 1½d. purple and green 22 6
z 1550 2d. green and carmine 22 6
z 1551 2½d. purple/*blue* 20 0
z 1552 3d. purple/*yellow* 30 0
z 1553 4d. green and brown 30 0
z 1553*a* 5d. dull purple and blue 75 0
z 1554 6d. purple/*rose-red* 35 0
z 1555 9d. purple and blue 40 0
z 1556 1s. green 55 0
z 1557 ½d. blue-green (1900) 12 6
z 1558 1s. green and carmine 45 0
z 1559 ½d. green (1902 etc.) 12 6
z 1560 1d. red (1902 etc.) 12 6
z 1561 1½d. purple and green (1902 etc.) .. 20 0
z 1562 2d. green & carmine (1902 etc.) .. 17 6
z 1563 2½d. blue (1902 etc.) 20 0
z 1564 3d. purple/*yellow* (1902 etc.) .. 22 6
z 1565 4d. green and brown (1902 etc.) .. 50 0
z 1566 4d. orange (1902 etc.) 35 0
z 1567 5d. purple and blue (1902 etc.) .. 30 0
z 1568 6d. purple (1902 etc.) 35 0
z 1568*a* 7d. grey-black (1902 etc.) ..
z 1569 9d. purple and blue (1902 etc.) .. 40 0
z 1570 1s. green and carmine (1902 etc.) 35 0
z 1571 ½d. yellow-green (1911–12) .. 30 0
z 1572 ½d. green (1911–12) 30 0
z 1573 1d. scarlet (1911–12) 30 0
z 1574 ½d. green (1912–22) 12 6
z 1575 1d. carmine (1912–22) 10 6
z 1576 1½d. red-brown (1912–22) .. 12 6
z 1577 2d. orange (1912–22) 12 6
z 1578 2½d. blue (1912–22) 17 6
z 1579 3d. violet (1912–22) 17 6
z 1580 4d. grey-green (1912–22) .. 17 6
z 1580*a* 5d. brown (1912–22) 17 6
z 1581 6d. purple (1912–22) 15 0
z 1582 9d. agate (1912–22) 35 0
z 1583 9d. olive-green (1912–22) .. 35 0
z 1583*a* 10d. turquoise-blue (1912–22) .. 30 0
z 1584 1s. bistre (1912–22) 32 6
z 1584*a* 2s. 6d. brown (1918–30) 60 0

MAIL BOAT OBLITERATIONS.

For many years it was supposed that obliterations numbered A **80** to A **99**, B **03**, B **12**, B **56**, B **57** and C **79** were used at Naval Stations abroad (the whereabouts of which were not known), owing to the fact that they are almost invariably found on sailors' letters.

It is definitely known that these obliterations were allotted to mail boats and they are therefore omitted from this Catalogue.

HAVE YOU READ THE NOTES AT THE BEGINNING OF THIS CATALOGUE?

These often provide answers to the enquiries we receive.

VI.

ARMY FIELD OFFICES.

CRIMEA.

1854 *to* **1857.**

Crown between Stars.

z 1585 1d. red-brown (1841), *imperf.* .. £13
z 1586 1d. red-brown (1854), Die I, *wmk.* Small Crown, *perf.* 16 .. £9
z 1587 1d. red-brown (1855), Die II, *wmk.* Small Crown, *perf.* 16. .. £9
z 1588 1d. red-brown, Die I, *wmk.* Small Crown, *perf.* 14 .. ..
z 1589 1d. red-brown (1855), Die II, Small Crown, *perf.* 14 ..
z 1590 2d. blue (1841) *imperf.* £27
z 1591 2d. blue, Small Crown (1854), *perf.* 16, Plate No. 4 .. ..
z 1592 1s. green (1847), embossed .. £30

Star between Cyphers.

z 1593 1d. red-brown (1841), *imperf.* .. £30
z 1594 1d. red-brown (1854), Die I, *wmk.* Small Crown, *perf.* 16 .. £5
z 1595 1d. red-brown (1855), Die II, *wmk.* Small Crown, *perf.* 16 .. £5
z 1596 1d. red-brown (1855), Die I, *wmk.* Small Crown, *perf.* 14 .. £5
z 1597 1d. red-brown (1855), Die II, *wmk.* Small Crown, *perf.* 14 .. £5
z 1597*a* 1d. red-brown (1855), Die II, *wmk.* Large Crown, *perf.* 16 .. £13
z 1598 1d. red-brown (1855), Die II, *wmk.* Large Crown, *perf.* 14 .. 65 0
z 1599 2d. blue (1841), *imperf.* £22
z 1600 2d. blue (1854) *wmk.* Small Crown *perf.* 16, Plate Nos. 4, 5 *From* £13
z 1601 2d. blue (1855) *wmk.* Small Crown *perf.* 14, Plate No. 4 .. .. £11
z 1602 2d. blue (1855) *wmk.* Large Crown *perf.* 16, Plate No. 5 .. .. £19
z 1603 2d. blue (1855) *wmk.* Large Crown. *perf.* 14, Plate No. 5 .. .. £11
z 1604 4d. rose (1857) £45
z 1605 6d. violet (1854), embossed .. £45
z 1606 1s. green (1847), embossed .. £45

EGYPT AND SUDAN.

1882. *Tel-el-Kebir Campaign.*
z 1607 ½d. rose-red (Plate No. 20) ..
z 1608 ½d. green (1880) £24
z 1609 1d. Venetian red (1880) .. ..

z 1610 1d. lilac (1881) £13
z 1611 2½d. blue (1881) (Plate Nos. 21, 22, 23) £5

1885. *Suakim Campaign.*
z 1611*a* 1d. lilac (1881) £15
z 1612 2½d. lilac (1884) £9
z 1613 5d. green (1884) £15

SOUTH AFRICAN WAR.

1899 *to* **1902.**

z 1613*a–n* ½d., 1d., 1½d., 2d., 2½d., 3d., 4d., 4½d., 5d., 6d., 9d., 10d., 1s., 5s. (1881–92) *From* 5 0
z 1614*a–b* ½d., 1s. (1900) .. *From* 35 0
z 1615*a–l* ½d., 1d., 1½d., 2d., 2½d., 3d., 4d., 5d., 6d., 9d., 10d., 1s. (1902) .. *From* 20 0

Many types of cancellation exist besides those shown.

ARMY OFFICIAL.

z 1616 ½d. vermilion £8
z 1617 ½d. green £8
z 1618 1d. lilac £6
z 1619 6d. purple/*red* .. .. ..

VII.

VARIOUS TOWNS ON THE NIGER COAST AND RIVER

(Dates given are those of earliest known postmarks. Colour of postmarks in brackets. Where two or more colours are given, price is for cheapest. Illustrations are reduced to two-thirds linear of the actual size.)

AKASSA.

1. 2.

1888 (6 May). *As T* **2** *but with Maltese cross each side of* " AKASSA ". *Size* 36 × 22 *mm.*
1 **2** 6d. deep purple/*red* £22

1890 (24 June). *Size* 39 × 24 *mm.*
1*a* **1** 2½d. purple/*blue* (V.) £5
1*b* 3d. purple/*yellow* (V.) .. ..
1*c* 5d. dull purple and blue (V.) ..
2 6d. deep purple/*red* (V.) £10
2*a* 10d. dull purple & carmine (V.) ..
2*b* 2s. 6d. lilac (V.) .. .. ..

1895 (7 March). *Size* 39 × 25 *mm.*
3 **2** 2½d. purple/*blue* (V.) £9

3.

1894.
4 **3** 1d. lilac (V.) (July, '94) 95 0
5 2½d. purple/*blue* (V.) (3.10.94) .. 97 6

THE ROYAL NIGER COMPANY
CHARTERED & LIMITED.
7- AUG. 98
POST OFFICE
AKASSA.

4.

1895 (1 June)–**1899.**
6 **4** ½d. vermilion (V.) 45 0
7 1d. lilac (V.) 40 0
7*a* 2d. green and vermilion (V.) .. £15
8 2½d. purple/*blue* (V.) 40 0
9 3d. purple/*yellow* (V.) £10
10 5d. dull purple and blue (V.) .. 50 0
11 6d. deep purple/*red* (V.) 95 0
12 9d. dull purple and blue (V.) .. £8
13 10d. dull purple and carmine (V.) .. 75 0
14 2s. 6d. deep lilac (V.) 85 0

1899 (20 May). *As T* **4**, *but* " CUSTOMS DEPT " *in place of* " POST OFFICE ".
15 1d. lilac (V.) £9
16 2½d. purple/*blue* (V.) £9

THE ROYAL NIGER COMPANY,
CHARTERED & LIMITED.
4 NOV. 1889
POST OFFICE,
AKASSA.

5.

1897 (Jan.)–**1899** (Dec.).
17 **5** ½d. vermilion (V.) 60 0
18 1d. lilac (V.) 55 0
19 2d. green and vermilion (V.) .. £5
20 2½d. purple/*blue* (V.) 65 0
21 3d. purple/*yellow* (V.) £8
22 4d. green and brown (V.) £5
23 4½d. green and carmine (V.) .. £28
24 5d. dull purple and blue (V.) .. 80 0
25 6d. deep purple/*red* (V.) £8
26 9d. dull purple and blue (V.) .. £10
27 10d. dull purple and carmine (V.) .. 95 0
28 1s. green (V.) £17
29 2s. 6d. deep lilac (V.) 95 0

Error. As T **5**, *but* " RECD " *in place of year.*
30 1d. lilac (V.) .. ..

THE ROYAL NIGER COMPANY
Chartered & Limited.
9 JUL 1898
BURUTU

6.

1899 (9 Jan.). *As T* **6**, *but inscribed* " AKASSA ".
31 5d. dull purple and blue (V.) ..

BURUTU.

1898 (9 July)–**1899** (Feb.).
31*a* **6** 1d. lilac (V.) .. .. ..
32 2½d. purple/*blue* (V.) £16

THE ROYAL NIGER COMPANY
CHARTERED & LIMITED.
31 MAR 1898
POST OFFICE.
BURUTU.

7.

1897 (20 Jan.)–**1898** (30 Oct.). *T* **7**, " BURUTU " *in sans-serif caps. Size* 44 × 24 *mm.*
33 **7** ½d. vermilion (V.) 75 0
34 1d. lilac (V.) 60 0
35 1½d. dull purple and green (V.) .. £10
36 2d. green and carmine (V.) .. £5
37 2½d. purple/*blue* (V.) 50 0
38 3d. purple/*yellow* (V.) £8
39 4d. green and brown (V.) £5
40 5d. dull purple and blue (V.) .. 65 0
41 6d. deep purple/*red* (V.) £8
42 9d. dull purple and blue (V.) .. £10
43 10d. dull purple and carmine (V.) .. 90 0
44 1s. green (V.) £16
45 2s. 6d. lilac (V.) 90 0

The 2½d. is also known with this postmark in blue (6.9.97) and violet-black (Apl. 1898) and the ½d., 2½d., 3d., 5d. and 10d. with it in black.

1898–99. *As T* **4**, *but inscribed* " BURUTU " *in seriffed caps. Size* 44 × 27 *mm.*
46 ½d. vermilion (V., Bk.) 75 0
47 1d. lilac (V., Bk.) 65 0
48 2d. green and vermilion (V.) .. £8
49 2½d. purple/*blue* (V., Bk.) 60 0
50 3d. purple/*yellow* (V.) £8
51 4d. green and brown (V.) £5
52 4½d. green and carmine (V.) £30
53 5d. dull purple and blue (V.) .. 85 0
54 6d. deep purple/*red* (V.) £8
55 9d. dull purple and blue (V.) .. £10
56 10d. dull purple and carmine (V., Bk.) 95 0
57 2s. 6d. lilac (V., Bk.) £8

1899 (20 May). *As T* **4**, *but inscribed* " CUSTOMS DEPT. BURUTU ".
58 1d. lilac (V.) £17

1900 (9 Jan.). *Small circular postmark with* " BURUTU " *at top, date in centre and ornament below.*
59 1d. lilac (Bk.) .. ..

LOKOJA.

8.

1899 (30 June)–**1900.**
60 **8** ½d. vermilion (V.) £5
61 1d. lilac (V.) 80 0
62 2½d. purple/*blue* (V.) £16
63 5d. dull purple and blue (V.) .. £16
64 10d. dull purple and carmine (V.) £16
64*a* 2s. 6d. deep lilac (V.) .. ..

ABUTSHI.

1899 (4 Oct.). *As T* **8**, *but inscribed* " THE ROYAL NIGER CO. C. & L. ABUTSHI " *with* " CUSTOMS (date) OFFICE " *in central oval.*
65 ½d. vermilion (V.) £10
66 1d. lilac (V.) £9
67 2½d. purple/*blue* (V.) £15
68 5d. dull purple and blue (V.) .. £22
69 10d. dull purple and carmine (V.) .. £25
70 2s. 6d. deep lilac (V.) £25

BENIN.

1892. *Oval with double-lined frame inscribed* " OIL RIVERS PROTECTORATE BENIN " *with date in central oval.*
71 2½d. purple/*blue* (V.) .. .. ..

BONNY RIVER.

1892. *Name and date in circle.*
72 ½d. vermilion (Bk.) .. .. ..
73 2½d. purple/*blue* (Bk.) .. ..
74 5d. dull purple and blue (Bk.) ..
75 6d. deep purple/*red* (Bk.) .. ..

BRASS RIVER.

1892. *Name and date in circle.*
76 2½d. purple/*blue* (Bk.) £80
77 6d. purple/*red* (Bk.) .. .. ..

FORCADOS RIVER.

1892. *Name and date in circle.*
78 1d. lilac (Bk.) £40
79 5d. dull purple & blue (Bk.) ..
80 10d. dull purple & carmine (Bk.) ..

OLD CALABAR RIVER.

1891. *Name and date in circle.*
81 ½d. vermilion (Bk.) .. .. ..
82 1d. lilac (Bk.) .. .. ..
82*a* 1½d. dull purple & green (Bk.) ..
83 2d. green & vermilion (Bk.) ..
84 2½d. purple/*blue* (Bk.) .. ..
85 5d. dull purple & blue (Bk.) ..
85*a* 6d. purple/*red* (Bk.) .. .. ..
86 1s. green (Bk.) .. .. ..

BRITISH VICE-CONSULATE,
OLD CALABAR.

1891. *Double-lined circle, with Royal Arms in centre, inscribed as above.*
87 2½d. purple/*blue* (V.) £22
88 5d. dull purple & blue (V.) .. ..

VARIOUS OFFICIAL DATE STAMPS.

1894–99. *As T* **8** *but inscribed* " AGENT GENERAL NIGER TERRITORIES ".
89 1d. lilac (V.) (1.6.99) £8
90 2½d. purple/*blue* (V.) (3.10.94) .. £8

1895. (4 Aug.). *As T* **6** *but inscribed as last.*
91 2½d. purple/*blue* (V.) £8

These " AGENT GENERAL " marks were used at Akassa.

ABU DHABI.

An independent Arab Shaikhdom, with a British postal administration until March 1966. Previously used the stamps of Muscat.

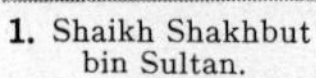

1. Shaikh Shakhbut bin Sultan. **2.** Arabian Gazelle.

3. Ruler's Palace.

4. Oil Rig and Camels.

(Des. M. C. Farrar-Bell. Photo. Harrison (T **1**/**2**). Des. C. T. Kavanagh (T **3**), Miss P. M. Goth (T **4**). Recess. Bradbury, Wilkinson.)

1964 (30 Mar.) *P* 15×14 (5 *to* 75 *n.p.*) *or* 13×13½ (*others*).

1	**1**	5 n.p. green	0	3	0	4
2	,,	15 n.p. red-brown	0	5	0	6
3	,,	20 n.p. ultramarine	0	6	0	8
4	,,	30 n.p. red-orange	0	9	1	0
5	**2**	40 n.p. reddish violet	0	11	1	2
6	,,	50 n.p. bistre	1	1	1	4
7	,,	75 n.p. black	1	8	2	0
8	**3**	1 r. emerald	2	0	2	6
9	,,	2 r. black	4	0	5	0
10	**4**	5 r. carmine-red	10	0	12	6
11	,,	10 r. deep ultramarine	19	6	25	0

5

6

7

Falcons on Gloved Hand.

(Des. V. Whiteley. Photo. Harrison.)

1965 (30 Mar.). *Falconry. P* 14½.

12	**5**	20 n.p. lt. brown & grey-blue	0	6	0	8
13	**6**	40 n.p. light brown and blue	0	11	1	2
14	**7**	2 r. sepia & turquoise-grn.	4	0	5	0

The Abu Dhabi Post Department took over the postal services in March 1966. Later stamp issues will therefore be found in Part III of the Stanley Gibbons Catalogue.

ADEN.

1. Dhow.

(Recess. De La Rue & Co.)

1937 (1 Apr.). *Wmk. Mult. Script CA sideways. P* 13 × 12.

1	**1**	½ a. yellow-green	1	0	1	9
2	,,	9 p. deep green	3	0	4	6
3	,,	1 a. sepia	2	6	2	6
4	,,	2 a. scarlet	5	0	6	0
5	,,	2½ a. bright blue	5	0	7	6
6	,,	3 a. carmine	7	6	12	6
7	,,	3½ a. grey-blue	10	0	16	0
8	,,	8 a. pale purple	12	6	17	6
9	,,	1 r. brown	25	0	27	6
10	,,	2 r. yellow	45	0	50	0
11	,,	5 r. deep purple	£8		£10	
12	,,	10 r. olive-green	£26		£28	

2. King George VI and Queen Elizabeth.

(Recess. De La Rue & Co.)

1937 (12 May). *Coronation. Wmk. Mult. Script CA. P* 14.

13	**2**	1 a. sepia	0	8	1	3
14	,,	2½ a. light blue	3	0	2	6
15	,,	3½ a. grey-blue	5	0	3	9

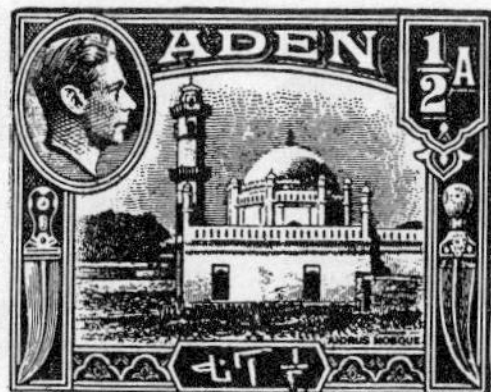

3. Aidrus Mosque, Crater.

4. Adenese Camel Corps.

5. The Harbour.

6. Adenese Dhow.

7. Capture of Aden, 1839.

8. Mukalla.

(Recess. Waterlow & Sons, Ltd.)

1939 (19 Jan.)–**48.** *Wmk. Mult. Script CA. P* 12½.

No.	Type	Description	Unused	Used
16	**3**	½ a. yellowish green ..	0 6	0 10
		a. Bluish green (Sept. '48) ..	2 6	3 6
17	**4**	¾ a. red-brown	0 9	1 6
18	**5**	1 a. pale blue	1 6	1 0
19	**6**	1½ a. scarlet..	2 0	1 6
20	**3**	2 a. sepia	1 0	1 0
21	**8**	2½ a. deep ultramarine ..	2 0	1 6
22	**7**	3 a. sepia and carmine ..	1 6	0 9
23	**8**	8 a. red-orange	3 6	1 6
23*a*	**7**	14 a. sepia and light blue (15.1.45)	3 6	6 0
24	**6**	1 r. emerald-green ..	3 6	5 0
25	**5**	2 r. deep blue and magenta	12 6	7 6
26	**4**	5 r. red-brown & olive-grn.	30 0	17 6
27	**7**	10 r. sepia and violet ..	35 0	40 0

9. Houses of Parliament, London.

(Recess. De La Rue.)

1946 (15 Oct.). *Victory. Wmk. Mult. Script CA. P* 13½×14.

No.	Type	Description	Unused	Used
28	**9**	1½ a. carmine	0 8	1 0
29	,,	2½ a. blue	1 6	1 9

10 **11**

King George VI and Queen Elizabeth.

(T **10**: Photo. Waterlow & Sons, Ltd., T **11**: Design recess; name typo. Bradbury Wilkinson & Co., Ltd.).

1949 (17 Jan.). *Royal Silver Wedding. Wmk. Mult. Script CA.*

No.	Type	Description	Unused	Used
30	**10**	1½ a. scarlet (*p* 14×15) ..	1 0	1 6
31	**11**	10 r. mauve (*p* 11½×11) ..	40 0	42 6

1949 (10 Oct.). *75th Anniv. of Universal Postal Union. As Nos.* 114/7 *of Antigua, surch. with new values.*

No.	Description	Unused	Used
32	2½ a. on 20 c. ultramarine ..	1 9	2 6
33	3 a. on 30 c. carmine-red ..	2 0	3 0
34	8 a. on 50 c. orange	10 0	11 6
35	1 r. on 1s. blue	17 6	20 0

5
CENTS
(12)

13. Queen Elizabeth II.

1951 (1 Oct.). *Currency changed. Surch. with new values, in cents or shillings, as T* **12**, *or in one line between bars* (30 *c.*).

36	**5**	5 c. on 1 a. pale blue ..	1	0	1	6
37	**3**	10 c. on 2 a. sepia ..	1	6	1	9
38	**8**	15 c. on 2½ a. deep ultram.	2	0	3	6
		a. Surch. double	£95			
39	**7**	20 c. on 3 a. sepia & carmine	2	0	3	0
40	**8**	30 c. on 8 a. red-orange (R.)	2	0	2	6
41	,,	50 c. on 8 a. red-orange ..	2	0	3	0
42	**7**	70 c. on 14 a. sepia & lt. blue	4	0	6	6
43	**6**	1s. on 1 r. emerald-green ..	5	0	4	0
44	**5**	2s. on 2 r. dp. bl. & mag.	15	0	12	6
45	**4**	5s. on 5 r. red-brown and olive-green	25	0	20	0
46	**7**	10s. on 10 r. sepia & violet	45	0	45	0

(Des. & eng. B. W. & Co. Recess. D. L. R. & Co.)

1953 2 June). *Coronation. Wmk. Mult. Script CA. P* 13½ × 13.

47	**13**	15 c. black and green ..	2	0	4	0

14. Minaret.

15. Camel Transport.

16. Crater.

18. Dhow.

17. Mosque.

19. Map.

20. Salt Works.

21. Dhow Building.

21a. Colony's Badge.

22. Aden Protectorate Levy.

23. Crater Pass.

24. Tribesman.

25. Aden in 1572.

(Recess. Waterlow, until 1961, then De La Rue.)

1953 (15 June)–**59.** *Wmk. Mult. Script CA. P* 13½ × 13 (20s.), 12 × 13½ (*Nos.* 52*a*, 55*b*, 56*a*, 57*a*) *or* 12 (*others*).

48	**14**	5 c. yellowish green ..	0	4	1	0
48*a*	,,	5 c. bluish green (1.6.55)	0	6	1	6
		ab. Perf. 12 × 13½ (12.4.56) ..	0	3	0	3

49 **15** 10 c. orange 0 10 0 10
49*a* ,, 10 c. vermilion (1.2.55) .. 0 4 0 4
50 **16** 15 c. blue-green 0 10 0 10
50*a* ,, 15 c. slate-green (26.4.59) (*shades*) 0 6 0 7
51 **17** 25 c. carmine-red 1 6 1 6
51*a* ,, 25 c. deep rose-red (15.3.56) (*shades*) 0 6 0 7
52 **18** 35 c. deep ultramarine .. 1 3 1 6
52*a* ,, 35 c. deep blue (15.10.58) (*shades*) 0 9 0 10
53 **19** 50 c. pale blue 2 0 2 0
53*a* ,, 50 c. deep blue (1.7.55) .. 3 6 3 6
ab. Perf. 12 × 13½ (12.4.56) .. 1 6 1 6
54 **20** 70 c. brown-grey 2 6 3 6
54*a* ,, 70 c. black (20.9.54) .. 4 0 4 0
ab. Perf. 12 × 13½ (12.4.56) .. 1 4 1 2
55 **21** 1s. sepia & reddish violet 3 6 3 6
55*a* ,, 1s. black & violet (1.7.55) 1 9 2 0
55*b* **21*a*** 1s. 25 c. blue and black (16.7.56) (*shades*) .. 2 3 2 6
56 **22** 2s. sepia and rose-carmine 5 0 5 0
56*a* ,, 2s. black and carmine-red (1.3.56) (*shades*) .. 3 6 3 6
57 **23** 5s. sepia and pale blue .. 20 0 15 0
57*a* ,, 5s. black and deep blue (11.4.56) (*shades*) .. 7 6 8 6
58 **24** 10s. sepia and olive .. 35 0 40 0
58*a* ,, 10s. black & bronze-green (20.9.54) 15 0 17 6
59 **25** 20s. choc. & reddish lilac 45 0 40 0
59*a* ,, 20s. black and deep lilac (7.1.57) (*shades*) .. 30 0 32 6

On No. 58*a* the tribesman's skirt is shaded with cross-hatching instead of with mainly diagonal lines as in No. 58.

1954 (27 Apr.). *Royal Visit. As No.* 55 *but inscr.* " ROYAL VISIT 1954 " *at top.*
60 **21** 1s. sepia and reddish violet 2 0 3 0

تعديل
الدستور
١٩٥٩
(26)

REVISED
CONSTITUTION
1959
(27)

1959 (26 Jan.). ***Revised Constitution. No.* 50*a* *optd. with T* 26, *and No.* 55*b* *optd. with T* 27, *in red, by Waterlow & Sons.***
61 **16** 15 c. slate-green 1 6 2 0
62 **21*a*** 1s. 25 c. blue and black .. 5 6 6 0

28. " Protein Foods ".

(Des. M. Goaman. Photo. Harrison.)

1963 (4 June). *Freedom from Hunger. W* w.**12.** *P* 14 × 14½.
63 **28** 1s. 25 c. bluish green .. 2 6 3 0

1964 (5 Feb.)–**65.** *As* 1953–59 *but wmk.* w.**12.** *P* 12 (10 *c.*, 15 *c.*, 25 *c.*, 1*s.*) *or* 12 × 13½ (*others*).
64 **14** 5 c. green (16.2.65) .. 0 6 0 6
65 **15** 10 c. bright orange .. 0 4 0 4
66 **16** 15 c. slate-green 0 5 0 6
67 **17** 25 c. carmine-red 0 7 0 9
68 **18** 35 c. indigo-violet 0 9 0 9
69 **19** 50 c. indigo-blue (*shades*) 1 0 1 3
70 **20** 70 c. black (*shades*) .. 1 3 1 9
71 **21** 1s. black and violet (10.3.64) 1 9 2 0
72 **21*a*** 1s. 25 c. ultramarine and black (10.3.64) .. 2 0 2 0
73 **22** 2s. black and carmine-rose (16.2.65) .. 4 0 5 0

The stamps of Aden were withdrawn on 31st March, 1965 and superseded by the stamps of the South Arabian Federation.

KATHIRI STATE OF SEIYUN.

1. Sultan of Seiyun.

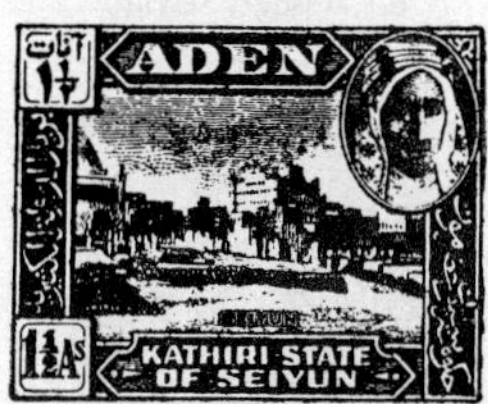

2. Seiyun.

3. Tarim.

4. Mosque, Seiyun.

5. Fortress, Tarim.

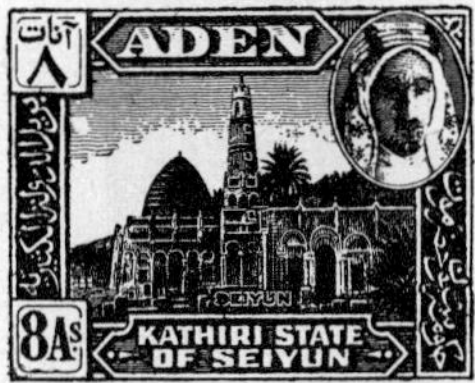

6. Mosque, Seiyun.

7. South Gate, Tarim.

8. Kathiri House.

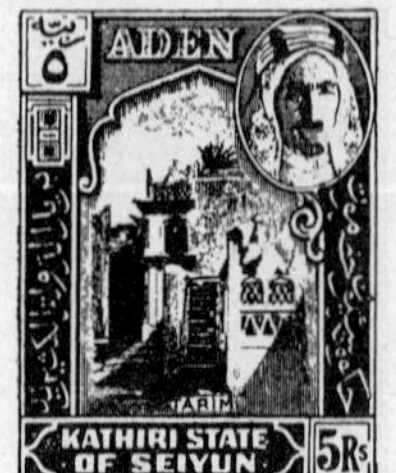

9. Mosque Entrance Tarim.

(Recess. De La Rue & Co.)

1942 (July-Oct.). *Wmk. Mult. Script CA. T* **1**, *perf.* 14; *others, perf.* 12 × 13 (*vert.*) *or* 13 × 12 (*horiz.*).

1	**1**	½ a. blue-green	1	0	1	6
2	,,	¾ a. brown	0	9	2	0
3	,,	1 a. blue	0	9	2	0
4	**2**	1½ a. carmine	1	9	2	6
5	**3**	2 a. sepia	1	3	3	0
6	**4**	2½ a. blue	1	6	3	0
7	**5**	3 a .sepia and carmine ..	1	9	3	0
8	**6**	8 a. red	3	0	4	6
9	**7**	1 r. green	4	0	7	6
10	**8**	2 r. blue and purple ..	12	6	17	6
11	**9**	5 r. brown and green ..	15	0	27	6

VICTORY

ISSUE

8TH JUNE 1946

(**10**)

1946 (15 Oct.). *Victory. No.* 4 *optd. with T* **10** *and No.* 6 *optd. similarly but in four lines.*

12	**2**	1½ a. carmine	0	8	1	0
13	**4**	2½ a. blue (R.)	1	3	1	6
		a. Overprint inverted ..	£135			

1949 (17 Jan.). *Royal Silver Wedding. As Nos.* 30/1 *of Aden.*

14	1½ a. scarlet	0	8	1	0
15	5 r. green	12	6	20	0

1949 (10 Oct.). *75th Anniv. of U.P.U. As Nos.* 114/7 *of Antigua, but inscr.* "ADEN KATHIRI STATE OF SEIYUN" *and surch. with new values.*

16	2½ a. on 20 c. ultramarine ..	1	6	3	0
17	3 a. on 30 c. carmine-red ..	2	0	4	0
18	8 a. on 50 c. orange	7	6	12	6
19	1 r. on 1s. blue	15	0	20	0

5 CTS

(**11**)

50 CENTS

(**12**)

5/-

(**13**)

1951 (1 Oct.). *Currency changed. Surch. as T* **11** (5 *c.*), **12** (20 *c. and* 50 *c.*) *or* **13** (1*s. to* 5*s.*). 10 *c. and* 15 *c. are as T* **12**, *but abbrev.* ("cts").

20	**1**	5 c. on 1 a. blue (R.) ..	1	0	1	6
21	**3**	10 c. on 2 a. sepia	1	3	1	6
22	**4**	15 c. on 2½ a. blue	1	3	3	0
23	**5**	20 c. on 3 a. sepia & carm.	1	6	3	0
24	**6**	50 c. on 8 a. red	2	0	4	0
25	**7**	1s. on 1 r. green	4	0	6	0
26	**8**	2s. on 2 r. blue & purple	8	6	15	0
27	**9**	5s. on 5 r. brown & green	15	0	22	6

1953 (2 June). *Coronation As No.* 47 *of Aden.*

28	15 c. black and deep green ..	1	9	3	0

14. Sultan Hussein.

15. Tarim.

(Recess. De La Rue & Co.).

1954 (15 Jan.). *As T* **1/9** (*but with portrait of Sultan Hussein as in T* **14/5**). *Wmk. Mult. Script CA. T* **14**, *perf.* 12½; *others, perf.* 12×13 (*vert.*) *or* 13×12 (*horiz.*).

No.	Type	Description	Unused s.	Unused d.	Used s.	Used d.
29	**14**	5 c. sepia	0	2	0	2
30	,,	10 c. deep blue	0	3	0	3
31	**2**	15 c. deep bluish green ..	0	4	0	4
32	**15**	25 c. carmine-red	0	6	0	6
33	**4**	35 c. deep blue	0	7	0	8
34	**5**	50 c. dp. brown & carm.-red	0	10	0	10
35	**6**	1s. brown-orange	1	5	1	6
36	**7**	2s. deep yellow-green ..	2	9	3	0
37	**8**	5s. deep blue and violet ..	6	9	8	6
38	**9**	10s. yellow-brown & violet	13	3	15	0

16. Qarn Adh Dhabi.

17. Seiyun.

18. Gheil Omer.

(Recess. De La Rue & Co.)

1964 (1 July). *W* w.**12.** *P* 12×13 (70 *c.*) *or* 13×12 (*others*).

No.	Type	Description	Unused s.	Unused d.	Used s.	Used d.
45	**16**	70 c. black	1	1	1	6
47	**17**	1s. 25 c. blue-green ..	1	9	2	0
48	**18**	1s. 50 c. dp. reddish violet	2	3	2	6

QU'AITI STATE IN HADHRAMAUT.

7. Issues inscr. "SHIHR AND MUKALLA".

1. Sultan of Shihr and Mukalla. **2.** Mukalla Harbour.

3. Gateway of Shihr.

4. Shibam.

5. Outpost of Mukalla.

6. 'Einat.

7. Du'an.

8. Mosque in Hureidha.

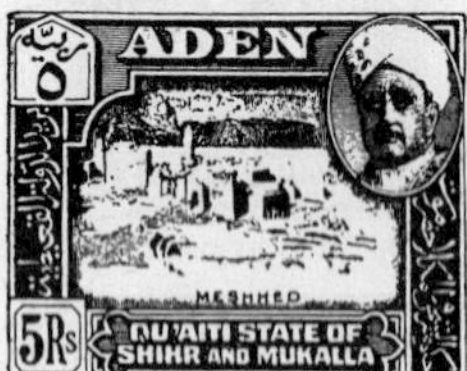

9. Meshhed.

(Recess. De La Rue & Co.)

1942 (JULY)–**46.** *Wmk. Mult. Script CA.* **T1,** *perf.* 14; *others, perf.* 12×13 *(vert.) or* 13×12 *(horiz.).*

1	**1**	½ a. blue-green	0	6	0	9
		a. Olive-green (Dec. '46) ..	25	0	45	0
2	"	¾ a. brown	0	8	1	0
3	"	1 a. blue	0	6	0	8
4	**2**	1½ a. carmine	1	9	2	6
5	**3**	2 a. sepia	1	3	3	0
6	**4**	2½ a. blue	1	6	2	6
7	**5**	3 a. sepia and carmine ..	1	6	3	0
8	**6**	8 a. red	3	0	5	0
9	**7**	1 r. green	4	0	7	6
10	**8**	2 r. blue and purple ..	12	6	17	6
11	**9**	5 r. brown and green ..	15	0	27	6

VICTORY

ISSUE

8TH JUNE

1946

(10)

1946 (15 OCT.). *Victory. No.* 4 *optd. with* T **10** *and No.* 6 *optd. similarly, but in three lines.*

12	**2**	1½ a. carmine	0	8	1	0
13	**4**	2½ a. blue (R.)	1	3	1	6

1949 (17 JAN.). *Royal Silver Wedding. As Nos.* 30/1 *of Aden.*

14	1½ a. scarlet	1	0	1	3
15	5 r. green	12	6	20	0

1949 (10 OCT.). *75th Anniv. of Universal Postal Union. As Nos.* 114/7 *of Antigua, but surch. with new values.*

16	2½ a. on 20 c. ultramarine ..	1	6	3	0
17	3 a. on 30 a. carmine-red ..	2	6	4	0
18	8a. on 50 c. orange	7	6	10	0
19	1r. on 1s. blue	15	0	18	0
	a. Surch. omitted	£250			

1951 (1 OCT.). *Currency changed. Surch. with new values in cents or shillings as T* **11** *to* **13** *of Seiyun.*

20	**1**	5 c. on 1 a. blue (R.) ..	0	8	0	10
21	**3**	10 c. on 2 a sepia	1	3	1	3
22	**4**	15 c. on 2½ a. blue	1	3	1	3
23	**5**	20 c. on 3 a. sepia & carm. ..	1	3	1	6
24	**6**	50 c. on 8 a. red	2	0	2	6
25	**7**	1s. on 1 r. green	3	6	5	0
26	**8**	2s. on 2 r. blue and purple	8	6	12	6
27	**9**	5s. on 5 r. brown & green	15	0	20	0

1953 (2 JUNE). *Coronation. As No.* 47 *of Aden.*

28	15 c. black and deep blue ..	1	9	3	6

II. Issues inscr. " HADHRAMAUT ".

11. Metal Work.

12. Mat-Making.

13. Weaving.

14. Pottery.

15. Building.

16. Date Cultivation.

17. Agriculture.

18. Fisheries.

19. Lime-Burning.

20. Dhow Building.

21. Agriculture.

(Des. Mme. M. de Sturler Raemaekers.
Recess. De La Rue & Co.)

1955 (1 SEPT.). *Wmk. Mult. Script CA. P* 11½×13–13½ *(vert.) or* 14 *(horiz.)*

No.	Type	Description	Unused	Used
29	**11**	5 c. greenish blue	0 4	0 6
30	**12**	10 c. grey-black	0 4	0 6
31	**13**	15 c. deep green *(shades)* ..	0 6	0 6
32	**14**	25 c. carmine-red	0 8	0 10
33	**15**	35 c. blue	0 10	1 0
34	**16**	50 c. orange-red *(shades)* ..	1 3	1 6
35	**17**	90 c. sepia	1 9	2 0
36	**18**	1s. black and deep lilac ..	2 0	2 3
37	**19**	1s. 25, black & red-orange	2 6	3 0
38	**20**	2s. black and indigo ..	3 6	4 6
39	**21**	5s. black and bluish green	8 6	10 0
40	**19**	10s. black and lake ..	17 6	20 0

22. Metal Work.

1963 (20 OCT.). *As T* **11/21**, *but with inset portrait of Sultan Awadh bin Saleh el-Qu'aiti as in T* **22** *and wmk.* w.**12**.

No.	Type	Description	Unused	Used
41	**22**	5 c. greenish blue	0 2	0 2
42	**12**	10 c. grey-black	0 3	0 4
43	**13**	15 c. bronze-green	0 4	0 5
44	**14**	25 c. carmine-red	0 6	0 7
45	**15**	35 c. blue	0 7	0 9
46	**16**	50 c. red-orange	0 10	1 0
47	**17**	70 c. deep brown	1 1	1 6
48	**18**	1s. black and deep lilac ..	1 5	1 10
49	**19**	1s. 25, black & red-orange	1 9	2 0
50	**20**	2s. black and indigo-blue	2 9	4 0
51	**21**	5s. black and bluish green	6 9	7 6
52	**19**	10s. black and lake ..	13 3	15 0

ANTIGUA.

For GREAT BRITAIN stamps used in Antigua, see page 65.

1

3 (Die I)

(Recess. Perkins, Bacon & Co.)

1862 (AUG.). *No wmk.* *(a) Rough perf.* 14 *to* 16.

No.	Type	Description	Unused	Used
1	**1**	6d. blue-green	£35	£25
		(b) P 11 *to* 13.		
2	**1**	6d. blue-green	£300	
		(c) P 14 *to* 16×11 *to* 13.		
3	**1**	6d. blue-green	£100	

Nos. 2 and 3 have not been found *used*.

1863 (JAN.)–**1867**. *Wmk. Small Star, T* w **2**.
(a) Rough perf. 14 *to* 16.

No.	Type	Description	Unused	Used
5	**1**	1d. rosy mauve	£5	60 0
		a. Imperf (pair)	—	£100
6	„	1d. dull rose (1864) ..	£5	75 0
7	„	1d. vermilion (1867) ..	75 0	50 0
		a. Imperf. between (pair) ..	£750	
8	„	6d. green	£14	70 0
		a. Imperf. (pair)	—	£80
9	„	6d. dark green	£10	50 0
10	„	6d. yellow-green	£160	£5
		a. Imperf. (pair)		
		(b) Perf. compound of 11, 12 *and* 14 *to* 16.		
11	**1**	1d. rosy mauve		

This stamp is not known used.

(Recess. De La Rue & Co.)

1872. *Wmk. Crown CC. P* 12½.

13 **1** 1d. lake 65 0 55 0
14 ,, 1d. scarlet £6 50 0
15 ,, 6d. blue-green £28 35 0

1876. *Wmk. Crown CC. P* 14.

16 **1** 1d. lake 65 0 32 6
a. Bisected (½d.) (on cover) .. — £40
17 ,, 1d. lake-rose 65 0 32 6
18 ,, 6d. blue-green £12 35 0

(Recess (T **1**); typo. (T **3**) De La Rue & Co.)

1879. *Wmk. Crown CC. P* 14.

19 **3** 2½d. red-brown £20 £7
a. Large "2" in "2½" with slanting foot £28 £38
20 ,, 4d. blue £12 35 0

1882. *Wmk. Crown CA. P* 14.

21 **3** ½d. dull green 8 0 15 0
22 ,, 2½d. red-brown 90 0 60 0
a. Large "2" in "2½" with slanting foot £38 £27
23 ,, 4d. blue £12 50 0

1884. *Wmk. Crown CA. P* 12.

24 **1** 1d. carmine-red 45 0 35 0

The 1d. scarlet is a colour changeling.

1884–86. *Wmk. Crown CA. P* 14.

25 **1** 1d. carmine-red 8 6 14 0
26 ,, 1d. rose 50 0 42 6
27 **3** 2½d. ultramarine 15 0 25 0
a. Large "2" in "2½" with slanting foot £10 £6
28 ,, 4d. chestnut 12 6 17 6
29 **1** 6d. deep green 70 0 90 0
30 **3** 1s. mauve £18 £15

Nos. 25 and 26 postmarked "A 12" in place of "A 02" were used in St. Christopher *q.v.*

The variety "Large '2' in '2½' with slanting foot" occurs on the first stamp of the seventh row in both left and right panes (in which positions the "NN" of "PENNY" have three vertical strokes shortened) and on the first stamp of the third row of the right hand pane. The "2" varies slightly in each position.

From 31 Oct. 1890 until 1903 Leeward Islands general issues were used. Subsequently both general issues and the following separate issues were in concurrent use, until 1 July, 1956, when the general L.I. stamps were withdrawn.

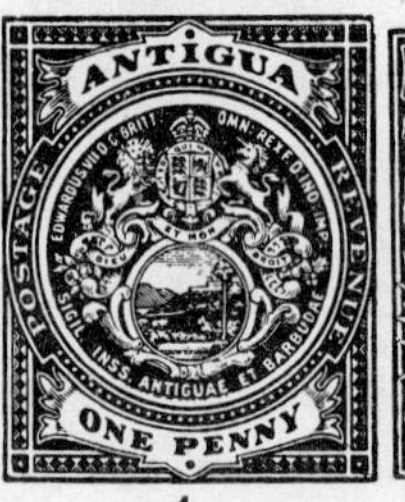

4

5

(Typo. De La Rue & Co.)

1903–9. *T* **4** *and* **5** (5s.). *Wmk. Crown CC. P* 14.

31 ½d. grey-black & grey-grn., O 5 0 5 0
32 1d. grey-black & rose-red, O 7 6 3 6
a. Blue paper (1903) 80 0 90 0
33 2d. dull purple & brown, O .. 20 0 20 0
34 2½d. grey-black & blue, OC .. 17 6 20 0
35 3d. grey-grn. & orange-brn., O 15 0 25 0
36 6d. purple and black, O .. 42 6 47 6
37 1s. blue and dull purple, OC 45 0 50 0
38 2s. grey-grn. & pale violet, O 80 0 85 0
39 2s. 6d. grey-black & pur., O 65 0 70 0
40 5s. grey-green & violet, OC.. £8 £10

1908–12. *T* **4.** *Wmk. Mult. Crown CA. P* 14.

42 ½d. green, O 3 6 4 6
43 1d. red, O 3 6 4 0
43*a* 2d. dull pur. & brn., C (1912) 12 6 15 0
44 2½d. ultramarine, O 12 6 20 0
a. Blue, O 17 6 20 0
45 3d. grey-green and orange-brown, C (1912) .. 10 0 17 6
46 6d. purple & black, C (1911) 15 0 22 6
47 1s. blue and dull purple, C.. 18 6 27 6
48 2s. grey-grn. & vio., C (1912) 90 0 95 0

1913. *As T* **5**, *but portrait of King George V. Wmk. Mult. Crown CA. P* 14.

49 5s. grey-green & violet, C .. £6 £7

1915–17. *Colours changed. Wmk. Mult. Crown CA. P* 14.

50 **4** ½d. blue-green, O (1917) .. 2 6 4 0
51 ,, 1d. scarlet, O (5.8.15) .. 5 0 5 0

WAR STAMP
(7)

8

1916 (Sept.)–**17.** *No.* 42 *optd. in London with T* **7.**

52 **4** ½d. deep green (Bk.) .. 0 10 1 9
53 ,, ½d. deep green (R.) (1.10.17) 1 9 2 6

1918. *Optd. with T* **7.** *Wmk. Mult. Crown CA. P* 14.

54 **4** 1½d. orange 1 0 3 0

(Typo. De La Rue & Co.)

1921–29. *T* **8.** *P* 14.

(*a*) *Wmk. Mult. Crown CA.*

55 3d. purple/*pale yellow*, C .. 7 6 8 6
56 4d. grey-black and red/*pale yellow*, C (Jan., '22) .. 7 0 10 0
57 1s. black/*emerald*, C 12 0 18 6
58 2s. purple and blue/*blue*, C .. 15 0 30 0
59 2s. 6d. black and red/*blue*, C.. 20 0 30 0
60 5s. green and red/*pale yellow*, C (Jan., '22) 45 0 55 0
61 £1 purple & black/*red*, C ('22) £16 £19

(*b*) *Wmk. Mult. Script CA.*

62 ½d. dull green, O 0 6 0 8
63 1d. carmine-red, O 2 0 1 3
64 1d. bright scarlet, O ('29) .. 1 6 1 3
65 1d. bright violet, O 4 6 2 6
66 1d. mauve, O 5 0 3 6
67 1½d. dull orange, O ('22) .. 12 6 17 6
68 1½d. carmine-red, O ('26) .. 2 6 3 6
69 1½d. pale red-brown, O ('29) .. 3 6 4 0
70 2d. grey, O 2 0 2 6
71 2½d. bright blue, O 16 0 22 6
72 2½d. ultramarine, O ('27) .. 5 0 8 6
73 2½d. orange-yellow, O .. 3 6 10 0
74 3d. purple/*pale yellow*, C ('25) 5 0 6 0
75 6d. dull and bright purple, C 5 0 8 0
76 1s. black/*emerald*, C ('29) .. 12 6 10 0
77 2s. pur. & blue/*blue*, C ('27).. 20 0 32 6
78 2s. 6d. blk. & red/*blue*, C ('27) 27 6 37 6
79 3s. green and violet, C ('22).. 35 0 42 6
80 4s. grey-black & red, C ('22).. 35 0 47 6

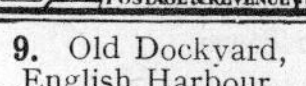

9. Old Dockyard, English Harbour.

12. Sir Thomas Warner's vessel.

10. Government House, St. John's.

11. Nelson's *Victory*.

(Des. and recess Waterlow & Sons, except 5s. des. by Mrs. J. Goodwin.)

1932 (27 Jan.). *Tercentenary. Wmk. Mult. Script CA. P* 12½.

No.	Type					
81	**9**	½d. green	1	3	2	6
82	,,	1d. scarlet	1	6	3	0
83	,,	1½d. brown	4	0	6	0
84	**10**	2d. grey	7	6	17	6
85	,,	2½d. deep blue	10	0	15	0
86	,,	3d. orange	15	0	25	0
87	**11**	6d. violet	25	0	30	0
88	,,	1s. olive-green	37	6	45	0
89	,,	2s. 6d. claret	90	0	95	0
90	**12**	5s. black and chocolate	£16		£18	

13. Windsor Castle.

(Des. H. Fleury. Recess. De La Rue.)

1935 (6 May). *Silver Jubilee. Wmk. Mult. Script CA. P* 13½ × 14.

No.	Type					
91	**13**	1d. deep blue and carmine	1	6	2	0
92	"	1½d. ultramarine and grey	2	0	3	0
93	"	2½d. brown and deep blue	10	0	12	6
94	"	1s. slate and purple	20	0	25	0

1937 (12 May). *Coronation. As Nos.* 13/15 *of Aden, but ptd. by B. W. & Co. P* 11 × 11½.

No.					
95	1d. carmine	0	6	0	8
96	1½d. yellow-brown	1	0	1	6
97	2½d. blue	2	3	3	0

14. English Harbour.

15. St. John's Harbour.

16. Nelson's Dockyard.

17. Fort James.

(Recess. Waterlow.)

1938 (15 Nov.)–**49.** *Wmk. Mult. Script CA. P* 12½.

No.	Type					
98	**14**	½d. green	0	6	0	8
99	**16**	1d. scarlet	0	8	0	9
100	,,	1½d. red-brown	0	9	1	0
		a. Lake-brown (July '49)	45	0	60	0
101	**14**	2d. grey	0	8	0	10
102	**16**	2½d. deep ultramarine	1	0	1	3
103	**17**	3d. orange	1	0	1	3
104	**15**	6d. violet	1	6	1	6
105	,,	1s. black and brown	3	0	3	0
106	**17**	2s. 6d. purple	7	6	8	6
107	**15**	5s. olive-green	12	6	16	0
108	**16**	10s. magenta (Apr. '48)	37	6	42	6
109	**17**	£1 slate-green (Apr. '48)	50	0	55	0

1946 (1 Nov.). *Victory. As Nos.* 28/9 *of Aden.*

No.					
110	1½d. brown	0	6	0	8
111	3d. red-orange	1	0	1	3

1949 (3 Jan.). *Royal Silver Wedding. As Nos.* 30/1 *of Aden.*

No.					
112	2½d. ultramarine	1	0	1	3
113	5s. grey-olive	15	0	20	0

18. Hermes, Globe and Forms of Transport.

19. Hemispheres, Aeroplane and Steamer.

20. Hermes and Globe.

21. U.P.U. Monument.

(T **18** & **21**: Recess., W'low & Sons, Ltd. T **19** & **20**: Design recess, name typo., Bradbury, Wilkinson & Co.)

1949 (10 Oct.). *75th Anniv. of Universal Postal Union. Wmk. Mult. Script. CA.*

114	**18**	2½d. ultram. (*p.* 13½–14) ..	1 9	2 0
115	**19**	3d. orange (*p.* 11 × 11½) ..	2 6	3 0
116	**20**	6d. purple (*p.* 11 × 11½) ..	4 6	5 0
117	**21**	1s. red-brown (*p.* 13½–14)	10 0	12 6

22. Arms of University. **23.** Princess Alice.

(Recess. Waterlow.)

1951 (16 Feb.). *Inauguration of B.W.I. University College. Wmk. Mult. Script CA. P* 14 × 14½.

118	**22**	3 c. black and brown ..	1 6	2 0
119	**23**	12 c. black and violet ..	4 0	4 6

1953 (2 June). *Coronation. As No.* 47 *of Aden.*

120	2 c. black & dp. yellow-green	1 6	1 9

24. Martello Tower.

(Recess. Waterlow until 1961, then De La Rue.)

1953 (2 Nov.)–**61.** *As T* **14/17**, *but with portrait of Queen Elizabeth II in place of King George VI, as in T* **24**. *Wmk. Mult. Script CA. P* 13 × 13½ (*horiz.*) *or* 13½ × 13 (*vert.*).

120*a*	**17**	½ c. brown (3.7.56) ..	0 3	0 4
121	**14**	1 c. slate-grey	0 6	0 8
		a. Slate (7.11.61)	0 4	0 6
122	**16**	2 c. green	0 6	0 8
123	,,	3 c. black & orge.-yellow	0 9	1 0
		a. Blk. & yell.-orge. (5.12.61)	0 8	0 10
124	**14**	4 c. scarlet (*shades*) ..	0 8	0 10
125	**16**	5 c. black & slate-lilac ..	0 10	1 0
126	**17**	6 c. yellow-ochre (*shades*)	1 0	1 2
127	**24**	8 c. deep blue	1 3	1 6
128	**15**	12 c. violet	1 6	1 9
129	,,	24 c. black & chocolate ..	2 0	2 6
130	**24**	48 c. purple & deep blue	2 9	3 6
131	**17**	60 c. maroon	3 6	4 6
132	**15**	$1.20 olive-green (*shades*)	6 9	7 6
133	**16**	$2.40 brt. reddish purple	13 3	15 0
134	**17**	$4.80 slate-blue	25 0	30 0

25. Federation Map.

(Recess. Bradbury, Wilkinson & Co.)

1958 (22 Apr.). *Inauguration of British Caribbean Federation. W* w.**12**. *P* 11½ × 11.

135	**25**	3 c. deep green	0 8	0 8
136	,,	6 c. blue	0 10	1 3
137	,,	12 c. scarlet	1 6	1 9

COMMEMORATION
ANTIGUA
CONSTITUTION
1960

(**26**)

1960 (1 Jan.). *New Constitution. Nos.* 123 *and* 128 *optd. with T* **26**.

138	**16**	3 c. black & orange-yell. (R.)	1 3	1 3
139	**15**	12 c. violet	2 3	2 6

27. Nelson's Dockyard and Admiral Nelson.

(Recess. Bradbury, Wilkinson & Co.)

1961. (14 Nov.) *Restoration of Nelson's Dockyard.* *W* w.**12.** *P* 11½ × 11.

140	**27**	20 c. purple and brown ..	2 6	2 9
141	,,	30 c. green and blue ..	3 3	4 0

28. Stamp of 1862 and R.M.S.P. *Solent* at English Harbour.

(Des. A. W. Morley. Recess. Bradbury, Wilkinson.)

1962 (1 Aug.). *Stamp Centenary.* *W* w**12.** *P* 13½.

142	**28**	3 c. purple & deep green	0 9	1 0
143	,,	10 c. blue & deep green ..	1 3	1 6
144	,,	12 c. dp. sepia & dp. green	1 8	2 0
145	,,	50 c. orge.-brn. & dp. green	4 6	5 0

1963 (4 June). *Freedom from Hunger.* *As No.* 63 *of Aden.*

146	12 c. bluish green	1 0	1 6

INTERNATIONAL RED CROSS CENTENARY 1863 1963 3 CENTS ANTIGUA

29. Red Cross Emblem.

(Des. V. Whiteley. Litho. Bradbury Wilkinson.)

1963 (2 Sept.). *Red Cross Centenary.* *W* w.**12.** *P* 13½.

147	3 c. red and black	0 8	1 0
148	12 c. red and blue	1 3	1 6

(Recess. De La Rue.)

1963 (16 Sept.)–**65.** *As* 1953–61 *but wmk.* w.**12.**

149	**17**	½ c. brown (13.4.65) ..	0 1	0 2
150	**14**	1 c. slate (13.4.65) ..	0 2	0 3
151	**16**	2 c. green	0 3	0 4
152	,,	3 c. black & yell.-orange	0 4	0 5
153	**14**	4 c. brown-red	0 4	0 5
154	**16**	5 c. black and slate-lilac (*shades*)	0 5	0 6
155	**17**	6 c. yellow-ochre ..	0 6	0 7
156	**24**	8 c. deep blue	0 7	0 9
157	**15**	12 c. violet	0 10	1 0
158	,,	24 c. black & dp. chocolate	1 5	1 11

30. Shakespeare and Memorial Theatre, Stratford-upon-Avon.

(Des. R. Granger-Barrett. Photo. Harrison.)

1964 (23 April). *400th Anniv. of Birth of William Shakespeare.* *W* w.**12.** *P* 14×14½.

164	**30**	12 c. orange-brown ..	1 6	1 8

15c.

(**31**)

1965 (1 April). *No.* 157 *surch. with T* **31.**

165	**15**	15 c. on 12 c. violet ..	0 11	1 3

32. I.T.U. Emblem.

(Des. M. Goaman. Litho. Enschedé.)

1965 (17 May). *I.T.U. Centenary.* *W* w.**12.** *P* 11×11½.

166	**32**	2 c. light blue & light red	0 6	0 8
167	,,	50 c. orange-yell. & ultram.	4 0	5 0

33. I.C.Y. Emblem.

(Des. V. Whiteley. Litho. Harrison.)

1965 (25 Oct.). *International Co-operation Year.* *W* w.**12.** *P* 14½.

168	**33**	4 c. reddish purple and turquoise-green ..	0 7	0 9
169	,,	15 c. deep bluish green and lavender	1 6	1 9

34. Sir Winston Churchill, and St. Paul's Cathedral in Wartime.

(Des. Jennifer Toombs. Photo. Harrison.)

1966 (24 Jan.). *Churchill Commemoration. Printed in black, cerise and gold and with background in colours stated.* *W* w.**12.** *P* 14.

170	**34**	½ c. new blue	0 2	0 3
171	,,	4 c. deep green	0 5	0 6
172	,,	25 c. brown	1 10	2 3
173	,,	35 c. bluish violet ..	2 6	3 0

35. Queen Elizabeth II and Duke of Edinburgh.

(Des. H. Baxter. Litho. Bradbury, Wilkinson.)

1966 (4 Feb.). *Royal Visit. W* w.**12.** *P* 11 × 12.

174	**35**	6 c. black & ultramarine	0 7	0 9
175	,,	15 c. black and magenta..	1 1	1 4

ASCENSION.

For GREAT BRITAIN stamps used in Ascension, see page 75.

ASCENSION

(1)

1922. *T* **14** *and* **15** *of St. Helena, optd. with T* **1.**

(a) Wmk. Mult. Script CA.

1	½d. black and green	1 6	5 0
2	1d. green	5 0	7 6
3	1½d. rose-scarlet	10 0	12 6
4	2d. black and grey	8 0	12 6
5	3d. bright blue	15 0	17 6
6	8d. black and dull purple ..	40 0	55 0
7	2s. black and blue/*blue* ..	£5	£6
8	3s. black and violet	£8	£10

(b) Wmk. Mult. Crown CA.

9	1s. black/*green* (R.)	45 0	55 0

2. Badge of St. Helena.

(Typo. De La Rue & Co.)

1924–33. *T* 2. *Wmk. Mult. Script CA. P* 14.

10	½d. grey-black and black, C..	3 0	4 0
11	1d. grey-blk. & dp. bl.-grn., C	2 6	6 0
11*a*	1d. grey-black & bright blue-green, C ('33)	40 0	55 0
12	1½d. rose-red, C	4 6	10 0
13	2d. grey-black and grey, C ..	5 0	6 0
14	3d. blue, C	6 0	7 0
15	4d. grey-blk. & blk./*yellow*, C	20 0	32 6
15*a*	5d. purple & olive-green, C ..	22 6	25 0
16	6d. grey-blk. & bright pur., C	65 0	95 0
17	8d. grey-blk. & bright vio., C	10 0	17 6
18	1s. grey-black and brown, C	15 0	20 0
19	2s. grey-black & blue/*blue*, C	40 0	45 0
20	3s. grey-blk. & blk./*blue*, C ..	65 0	80 0

3. Georgetown.

4. Ascension Island.

5. The Pier.

6. Long Beach.

7. Three Sisters.

8. Sooty Tern and Wideawake Fair.

9. Green Mountain.

(Des. and recess. De La Rue & Co.)

1934 (2 July). *Wmk. Mult. Script CA. P* 14.

21	**3**	½d. black and violet ..	0	9	1	3
22	**4**	1d. black and emerald ..	1	6	2	0
23	**5**	1½d. black and scarlet ..	1	9	2	3
24	**4**	2d. black and orange ..	2	0	2	6
25	**6**	3d. black and ultramarine	2	6	4	0
26	**7**	5d. black and blue ..	5	0	6	0
27	**4**	8d. black and sepia ..	6	0	7	6
28	**8**	1s. black and carmine ..	25	0	27	6
29	**4**	2s. 6d. black & brt. purple	30	0	37	6
30	**9**	5s. black and brown ..	45	0	50	0

1935 (6 May). *Silver Jubilee. As Nos.* 91/4 *of Antigua, but ptd. by Waterlow. P* 11×12.

31	1½d. deep blue and scarlet ..	6	0	7	6
32	2d. ultramarine and grey ..	9	0	11	0
33	5d. green and indigo ..	20	0	25	0
34	1s. slate and purple	60	0	65	0

1937 (19 May). *Coronation. As Nos.* 13/15 *of Aden. P* 14.

35	1d. green	0	8	0	10
36	2d. orange	1	2	1	6
37	3d. bright blue	2	6	3	0

10. The Pier.

(Recess. De La Rue.)

1938 (12 May)–**1953.** *Horiz. designs as T* **3, 6, 7,** *and* **9,** *but modified and with portrait of King George VI as in T* **10.** *Wmk. Mult. Script CA. P* 13½.

38	**3**	½d. black and violet ..	0	6	1	0
		a. Perf. 13. *Black & bluish-violet* ('44)	0	6	1	0
39	**9**	1d. black and green ..	12	6	12	6
39*a*	"	1d. blk. & yell.-orge. ('40)	10	0	17	6
		b. Perf. 13 ('42)	0	10	1	0
		c. Perf. 14 (Feb. '49) ..	3	0	5	0
39*d*	**7**	1d. black and green, p. 13 (1.6.49)	1	0	1	3
40	**10**	1½d. black & vermilion ..	2	0	2	6
		a. Perf. 13 ('44)	1	9	2	0
		b. Perf. 14 (Feb. '49) ..	5	0	10	0
40*c*	"	1½d. black and rose-carm., p. 14 (1.6.49) ..	0	10	1	0
		ca. Perf. 13 (25.2.53) ..	0	10	1	3
		d. *Black and carmine*, p. 14 ..	2	0	2	6
41	**9**	2d. black and red-orange	1	0	1	6
		a. Perf. 13 ('44)	0	10	1	6
		b. Perf. 14 (Feb. '49) ..	8	6	10	6
41*c*	"	2d. black and scarlet, p. 14 (1.6.49)	1	0	1	3
42	**6**	3d. black and ultramarine	37	6	37	6
42*a*	"	3d. black & grey (Jy. '40)	2	0	3	6
		b. Perf. 13 ('44)	1	6	2	0
42*c*	**9**	4d. blk. & ultram. (Jy. '40)	1	6	2	6
		d. Perf. 13 ('44)	1	6	2	9
43	**7**	6d. black and blue ..	2	6	2	6
		a. Perf. 13 ('44)	2	6	3	0
44	**3**	1s. black and sepia ..	4	0	4	6
		a. Perf. 13 ('44)	3	6	4	0
45	**10**	2s. 6d. blk. & deep carm.	12	6	12	6
		a. Perf. 13 ('44)	10	0	12	6
46	**6**	5s. blk. & yellow-brown	17	6	17	6
		a. Perf. 13 ('44)	17	6	20	0
47	**7**	10s. black & bright purple	37	6	45	0
		a. Perf. 13 ('44)	22	6	25	0

1946 (21 Oct.). *Victory. As Nos.* 28/9 *of Aden.*

48	2d. red-orange	0	8	0	10
49	4d. blue	1	6	2	0

1948 (20 Oct.). *Royal Silver Wedding. As Nos.* 30/1 *of Aden.*

50	3d. black	1	3	1	9
51	10s. bright purple	22	6	30	0

1949 (10 Oct.). *75th Anniv. of Universal Postal Union. As Nos.* 114/7 *of Antigua.*

52	3d. carmine	1	3	1	6
53	4d. deep blue	2	0	2	6
54	6d. olive	3	0	4	0
55	1s. blue-black	5	0	6	0

1953 (2 June). *Coronation. As No.* 47 *of Aden.*

56	3d. black and grey-black ..	5	0	6	0

15. Water Catchment.

16. Map of Ascension.

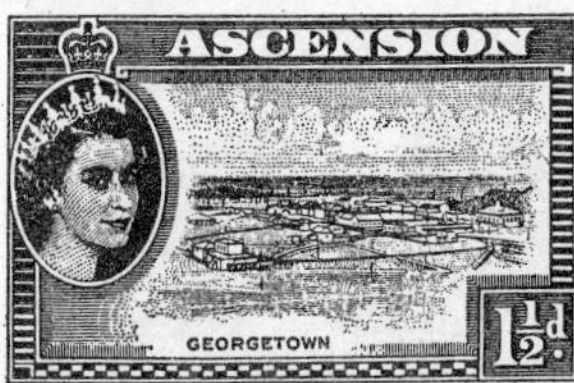

17. View of Georgetown.

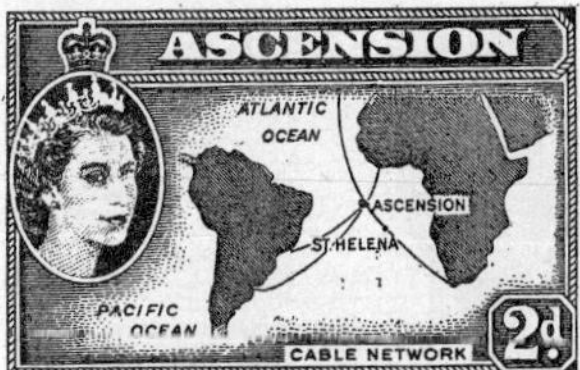

18. Map showing Cable Network.

19. Mountain Road.

20. Boatswain Bird.

21. Long-finned Tunny.

22. Rollers on the Seashore.

23. Young Turtles.

24. Land Crab.

25. Wideawake (Sooty Tern).

26. Perfect Crater.

27. View of Ascension from North-west.

(Recess. Bradbury, Wilkinson & Co.)

1956 (19 Nov.). *Wmk. Mult. Script CA. P* 13.

No.	Type	Description				
57	**15**	½d. black and brown ..	0	3	0	3
58	**16**	1d. black and magenta ..	0	4	0	4
59	**17**	1½d. black and orange ..	0	6	0	6
60	**18**	2d. black and carmine-red	0	6	0	6
61	**19**	2½d. black & orange-brown	0	7	0	8
62	**20**	3d. black and blue ..	1	6	1	9
63	**21**	4d. black & dp. turq.-grn.	1	6	1	9
64	**22**	6d. black and indigo ..	1	0	1	3
65	**23**	7d. black and deep olive ..	2	6	3	0
66	**24**	1s. black and vermilion ..	3	0	3	6
67	**25**	2s. 6d. black & deep dull purple	6	0	7	6
68	**26**	5s. black and blue-green ..	10	0	12	6
69	**27**	10s. black and purple ..	18	0	23	0

28. Brown Booby.

29. Black Noddy.

30. Fairy Tern.

31. Red-billed Tropic Bird.

32. Brown Noddy.

33. Wideawake Tern.

34. Frigate-bird.

35. White Booby.

36. Yellow-billed Tropic Bird.

37. Red-billed Tropic Bird.

38. Madeiran Storm Petrel.

39. Red-footed Booby (brown phase).

40. Frigate-birds.

41. Red-footed Booby (white phase).

(Des. after photos. by N. P. Ashmole. Photo. Harrison.)

1963 (23 MAY). *W* w.**12**. *P* 14×14½.

70	**28**	1d. multicoloured ..	0	3	0	3
71	**29**	1½d. multicoloured ..	0	4	0	4
72	**30**	2d. multicoloured ..	0	4	0	4
73	**31**	3d. multicoloured ..	0	6	0	6
74	**32**	4½d. multicoloured ..	0	8	0	9
75	**33**	6d. multicoloured ..	0	10	1	0
76	**34**	7d. multicoloured ..	0	11	1	0
77	**35**	10d. multicoloured ..	1	3	1	6
78	**36**	1s. multicoloured ..	1	5	1	9
79	**37**	1s. 6d. multicoloured ..	2	0	2	6
80	**38**	2s. 6d. multicoloured ..	3	6	4	0
81	**39**	5s. multicoloured ..	6	9	8	0
82	**40**	10s. multicoloured ..	13	3	16	0
83	**41**	£1 multicoloured ..	25	0	30	0

1963 (4 JUNE). *Freedom from Hunger. As No. 63 of Aden.*

84	1s. 6d. carmine	3	0	4	0

1963 (2 SEPT.). *Red Cross Centenary. As Nos. 147/8 of Antigua.*

85	3d. red and black	0	7	0	9
86	1s. 6d. red and blue	2	6	2	3

1965 (17 May). *I.T.U. Centenary. As Nos.* 166/7 *of Antigua.*

No.	Description	Unused	Used
87	3d. magenta and bluish violet	0 10	1 0
88	6d. turq.-blue & lt. chestnut	1 3	1 9

1965 (25 Oct.). *International Co-operation Year. As Nos.* 168/9 *of Antigua.*

No.	Description	Unused	Used
89	1d. reddish purple and turquoise-green	0 6	0 8
90	6d. dp. bluish green & lavender	1 6	1 9

1966 (24 Jan.). *Churchill Commemoration. As Nos.* 170/3 *of Antigua.*

No.	Description	Unused	Used
91	1d. new blue	0 4	0 6
92	3d. deep green..	0 7	0 10
93	6d. brown	1 0	1 6
94	1s. 6d. bluish violet	2 6	3 6

AUSTRALIA.

AUSTRALIAN STATES. The following States combined to form the Commonwealth of Australia and their issues are listed in alphabetical order in this Catalogue:—

NEW SOUTH WALES
QUEENSLAND
SOUTH AUSTRALIA
TASMANIA
VICTORIA
WESTERN AUSTRALIA

PRINTERS. Except where otherwise stated, all Commonwealth stamps have been printed under Government authority at Melbourne. Until 1918 there were two establishments (both of the Treasury Dept.)—the Note Printing Branch and the Stamp Printing Branch. The former printed T **3** and **4**.

In 1918 the Stamp Printing Branch was closed and all stamps were printed by the Note Printing Branch. In 1926 control was transferred from the Treasury to the Commonwealth Bank of Australia, and on 14 Jan. 1960 the branch was attached to the newly established Reserve Bank of Australia.

Until 1942 stamps bore in the sheet margin the initials or names of successive managers and from 1942 to March 1952 the imprint "Printed by the Authority of the Government of the Commonwealth of Australia". Since November 1952 (or Nos. D129/31 for Postage Dues) imprints have been discontinued. As from the end of 1963 the above printers also used the photogravure process.

1

2

(Des. B. Young. Eng. J. Reading. Typo. J. B. Cooke.)

1913 (Jan.). *W* **2**. *P* 12.

No.	Type	Description	Unused	Used
1	**1**	½d. green	2 6	0 6
2	„	1d. red	2 0	0 3
		a. Wmk. sideways	£8	75 0
2*b*	„	1d. carmine	2 6	0 4
3	„	2d. grey	8 6	1 9
4	„	2½d. indigo	10 0	5 0
5	„	3d. olive (Feb.)	17 6	10 0
5*a*	„	3d. yellow-olive	30 0	7 6
6	„	4d. orange (Feb.)	27 6	18 6
7	„	4d. orange-yellow	60 0	40 0
8	„	5d. chestnut	27 6	17 6
9	**1**	6d. ultramarine	15 0	5 0
		a. Retouched "E"	£50	£16
10	„	9d. violet (Feb.)	20 0	8 6
11	„	1s. emerald	21 0	6 0
11*a*	„	1s. blue-green	27 6	10 0
12	„	2s. brown	60 0	30 0
		a. Double print (O.S. only) ..	£28	
13	„	5s. grey & yellow (Mar.) ..	£10	£5
14	„	10s. grey and pink (Mar.) ..	£18	£10
15	„	£1 brn. and blue (Mar.) ..	£65	£30
16	„	£2 black and rose (April) ..	£125	£45

No. 9*a* shows a badly distorted second "E" in "PENCE", which is unmistakable. It occurs on the last stamp in the sheet.

INVERTED WATERMARKS are met with in some values in this and subsequent issues.

3

4. Kookaburra.

(Recess. T. S. Harrison.)

1913 (Dec.)-**1914**. *No wmk. P* 11.

No.	Type	Description	Unused	Used
17	**3**	1d. red (Dec., 1913)	3 6	6 0
		a. Imp. between (vert. pair) ..	£50	
18	„	1d. pale rose-red (Dec., 1913)	5 0	10 0
		a. Imp. between (vert. pair) ..	£50	
19	**4**	6d. claret (Aug., 1914) ..	60 0	45 0

All printings from Plate 1 were in the shade of No. 18. This plate shows many retouches.

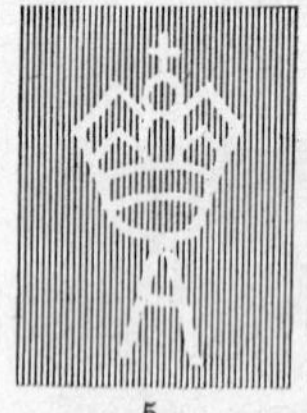
5

1915. *W* **5**. *P* 12.

No.	Type	Description	Unused	Used
20	**1**	2d. grey (2 Jan.)	17 6	4 0
21	„	2½d. indigo (July)	25 0	7 6
23	„	6d. ultramarine (Apr.) ..	35 0	8 0
23*a*	„	6d. bright blue	£10	85 0
24	„	9d. violet (9 July) ..	40 0	12 6
25	„	1s. blue-green (Aug.) ..	40 0	12 6
26	„	2s. brown (Apr.) ..	£8	37 6
27	„	5s. grey & yellow (12 Feb.)	£18	£5
		a. Yellow portion doubly printed	£250	

The watermark in this issue is often misplaced as the paper was made for the portrait stamps.

5a

Die II

Die III

(Dies eng. Perkins Bacon & Co. Typo. J. B. Cooke until 1918, then T. S. Harrison.)

1914–21. *T* 5*a*. *W* 5. *P* 14.

No.	Description	Unused	Used
29	½d. bright green (Jan., 1915)	1 6	0 6
29*a*	½d. yellow-green	5 0	2 0
29*b*	½d. green	2 0	0 6
	c. Fig. '1' in fraction at right thinner	—	£50
30	1d. carm.-red (*shades*) (I) (July 1914)	2 0	1 3
	a. Top of crown missing ..	£8	50 0
31	1d. pale carmine (*shades*) (I)	1 6	0 6
31*a*	1d. carm.-pink (I) (Jan. '18)	40 0	6 6
31*b*	1d. rose-red (I) (Mar., '18) ..	25 0	6 0
31*c*	1d. carm. (aniline) (I) (1921)	12 6	5 0
31*d*	1d. carmine-red (*shades*) (II)	65 0	5 0
	e. Top of crown missing ..	£8	50 0
31*f*	1d. pale red (*shades*) (II) ..	40 0	7 6
32	4d. orange (Jan., 1915) ..	12 6	5 0
33	4d. yellow-orange	15 0	7 6
33*a*	4d. pale orange-yellow ..	30 0	10 6
33*b*	4d. lemon-yellow (1916) ..	25 0	10 6
33*c*	4d. dull orange ..	27 6	5 0
	d. Line through "FOUR PENCE" (*all shades*) .. .. *From*	£8	70 0
34	5d. brown (Feb., 1915) ..	17 6	6 0
34*a*	5d. yellow-brown (1920) ..	22 6	6 6

The variety No. 29*c* was caused by the engraving of a new fraction in a defective electro.

The flaw distinguishing the so-called Die II is now known to be due to a defective roller-die and occurs in 18 impressions on one of the plates. It appears as a white upward projection to right of the base of figure "1" in the shield containing value at left, as shown in the illustration.

The varieties 30*a* and 31*e* are from two clichés, one from each die, which replaced two rusted clichés in one plate.

The 5d. is known printed on the gummed side of the paper.

Two machines were used for the 14 perforation, one an old single line, converted to that gauge, the other a new comb-machine. The former was used mainly for early printings of the 1d. and 5d. and very rarely for later printings of the ½d. and 1d.

6

6*a*

(Typo. J. B. Cooke, T. S. Harrison, A. J. Mullett, or J. Ash.)

1915–28. *W* 6 (*narrow Crown*). *P* 12.

No.	Type	Description	Unused	Used
35	**1**	2d. grey	10 0	1 9
35*a*	"	2d. silver-grey (*shiny paper*)	8 6	4 0
36	"	2½d. indigo	12 6	3 0
		a. "1" of fraction omitted ..	£250	
36*b*	"	2½d. deep blue (1921)	7 6	5 0
37	"	3d. yellow-olive ..	8 6	2 0
37*a*	"	3d. olive-green (1917) ..	7 0	2 0
38	"	6d. ultramarine	22 6	3 6
38*a*	"	6d. dull blue	32 6	5 0
38*b*	"	6d. bright ultram. (1922)	10 6	3 6
		c. Leg of Kangaroo broken	£50	£15
39	"	9d. violet (1916)	10 0	2 0
39*a*	"	9d. bright violet	12 6	1 9
40	"	1s. blue-green (1916) ..	10 0	2 0
		a. Wmk. sideways (1927) ..	60 0	65 0
41	"	2s. brown (1916) ..	50 0	12 6
		a. Imperf. three sides ..	£250	
41*b*	"	2s. red-brown ..	60 0	10 0
42	"	5s. grey & yellow (1916)	90 0	55 0
42*a*	"	5s. grey & orange (1920)	90 0	50 0
42*b*	"	5s. grey & p. yellow (1928)	90 0	50 0
42*c*	"	5s. grey and deep yellow	£6	60 0
		d. Wmk. sideways		
43	"	10s. grey and pink (1917)	£16	£5
43*a*	"	10s. grey & bt. anil. pink	£14	80 0
		ab. Wmk. sideways	—	£55
43*b*	"	10s. grey & p. anil. pink ('28)	£16	90 0
44	"	£1 choc. & dull blue (1916)	£45	£16
45	"	£1 chestnut & bt. bl. ('17)	£50	£16
45*a*	"	£1 bistre-brn. & bt. blue	£50	£12
		b. Wmk. sideways	—	£40
46	"	£2 grey & crimson (1920)	£80	£35
46*a*	"	£2 black and rose ..	£80	£24
46*b*	"	£2 pur.-blk. & p. rose ('24)	£90	£24

Two dies exist in some values but the differences are not very marked.

1916–18. *W* 5. *Rough paper, locally gummed. P* 14.

No.	Type	Description	Unused	Used
47	**5*a***	1d. scarlet (I) (Dec., 1916)	10 0	2 6
48	"	1d. deep red (I) (1917) ..	10 0	1 0
49	"	1d. rose-red (I) (1918)	6 0	1 6
		a. Top of crown missing ..	£8	25 0
49*b*	"	1d. rosine (I) (1918) ..	50 0	15 0
		c. Top of crown missing ..	£14	90 0
50	"	1d. rose-red (II) (1918) ..	60 0	10 0
		aa. Top of crown missing ..	£8	25 0
50*a*	"	1d. rosine (II) (1918) ..	£6	60 0
		ab. Top of crown missing ..	£14	£5
50*b*	"	5d. bright chestnut (Perf. "O.S.") (1918) ..	£45	85 0

For explanations of varieties with top of crown missing, see 3rd paragraph of note below No. 34*a*.

1918 (June). *T* 5*a*, *printed from a new plate* (Die III) *on white unsurfaced paper, locally gummed. W* 5. *P* 14.

No.	Description	Unused	Used
50*c*	1d. rose-red (III)	17 6	15 0
50*d*	1d. rose-carmine (III) ..	20 0	10 0
	e. Printed both sides	£20	

Die III. In 1918 a printing (in sheets of 120) was made on paper prepared for printing War Savings Stamps, with wmk. T **5**. A special plate was made for this printing, differing in detail from those previously used. The shading round the head is even; the solid background of the words "ONE PENNY" is bounded at each end by a *white* vertical line; and there is a horizontal white line cutting the vertical shading lines at left on the King's neck.

(Typographed by J. B. Cooke or T. S. Harrison.)

1918–19. *T* 5*a*. *W* 6*a* (*Mult.*). *P* 14.

No.	Description	Unused	Used
51	½d. green (*shades*) ..	1 0	0 3
	a. Fig. '1' in fraction at right thinner	55 0	45 0
51*b*	1d. carmine-pink (I) (1918) ..	55 0	30 0
52	1d. deep red (I) (1918) ..	£10	£6
53	1d. carmine (I) (Dec., 1919)	12 6	6 0
54	1½d. black-brown (Jan., 1919)	1 9	1 9
	a. Very thin paper (March, 1919)	27 6	20 0
55	1½d. red-brown (April, 1919)	8 6	1 0
56	1½d. chocolate	3 0	1 6

Of the above, No. 51 was printed by Cooke and by Harrison, Nos. 51*b* and 52 by Cooke, and Nos. 53 to 56 by Harrison. Nos. 51*b* and 52 have rather yellowish gum, that of No. 53 being pure white.

1918 (Nov.)–**1919.** *T* **5***a*. *W* **5.** *P* 14.

No.	Description	Unused	Used
57	1½d. black-brown (Nov., 1918)	2 0	0 8
58	1½d. dp. red-brown (June, 1919)	6 6	1 0
59	1½d. chocolate	3 6	1 6

1920–23. *T* **5***a*. *Colours changed.* *W* **5.** *P* 14.

No.	Description	Unused	Used
60	1½d. bright red-brown (1922) ..	8 6	2 0
61	2d. dull orange (Sept., 1920)	6 0	0 6
62	2d. brown-orange	6 0	0 6
63	4d. violet (June, 1921) ..	8 6	6 0
	a. Line through "FOUR PENCE"	£250	£135
	b. "FOUR PENCE" in thinner letters	£12	£5
64	1s. 4d. pale blue (Dec., 1920)	30 0	25 0
65	1s. 4d. dull greenish blue (1923)	30 0	22 6
65*a*	1s. 4d. deep turquoise ..	£24	£18

1922–23. *T* **5***a*. *Colours changed.* *W* **5.** *P* 14.

No.	Description	Unused	Used
66	½d. orange (Nov., 1923) ..	0 8	0 4
67	1d. violet (*shades*)	1 9	0 3
	a. Imperf. three sides	£60	
68	1d. red-violet	2 6	1 3
69	1½d. green (Mar., 1923) ..	2 6	0 6
	a. Rough unsurfaced paper ..	75 0	30 0
70	2d. bright rose-scarlet ..	2 0	0 4
71	2d. dull rose-scarlet	3 6	0 4
72	4d. ultramarine (*shades*) ..	17 6	6 0
	a. "FOUR PENCE" in thinner letters	£8	£5
72*b*	4d. pale milky blue	17 6	8 6

The variety of Nos. 63 and 72 with "FOUR PENCE" thinner, was caused by the correction of a defective cliché (No. 6, 2nd row, right-hand pane), which showed a line running through these words. Variety No. 69*a* was caused by a small residue of the paper used for No. 47–50*d* being used for this value.

(Typo. by T. S. Harrison or A. J. Mullett.)

1923–24. *T* **1.** *W* **6.** *P* 12.

No.	Description	Unused	Used
73	6d. chestnut (Dec., 1923) ..	4 0	2 0
	a. Leg of Kangaroo broken ..	90 0	60 0
74	2s. maroon (May, 1924) ..	20 0	7 6
75	£1 grey (May, 1924)	£25	£9

1924. *T* **5***a*. *P* 14. (*a*) *W* **5.**

No.	Description	Unused	Used
76	1d. sage-green	1 0	0 4
77	1½d. scarlet (*shades*) ..	1 0	0 3
	a. Very thin paper	32 6	25 0
	b. "HALEPENCE"	20 0	17 6
	c. "RAL" of "AUSTRALIA" thin	15 0	12 6
	d. Curved "1" and thin fraction at left	30 0	15 0
78	2d. red-brown	3 9	2 6
78*a*	2d. bright red-brown ..	20 0	10 0
79	3d. dull ultramarine	5 0	0 8
	a. Imperf. three sides ..	£50	
80	4d. olive-yellow	8 6	3 6
80*a*	4d. olive-green	10 0	6 0
81	4½d. violet	10 0	4 0

(*b*) *W* **6***a*.

No.	Description	Unused	Used
82	1d. sage-green	2 6	1 9

(*c*) *No wmk.*

No.	Description	Unused	Used
83	1d. sage-green	2 0	2 6
84	1½d. scarlet	5 0	2 6

In the thin semi-transparent paper of Nos. 54*a* and 77*a* the watermark is almost indistinguishable. Nos. 77*b*, 77*c*, and 77*d* are typical examples of retouching of which there are many others in these issues. In No. 77*c* the letters "RAL" differ markedly from the normal. There is a white stroke cutting the oval frame-line above the "L", and the right-hand outer line of the Crown does not cut the white frame-line above the "A". No. 77*b* is above No. 77*c* in the sheet, so that the varieties may be had *se-tenant*.

7

I.

II.

(Typo. by A. J. Mullett or J. Ash.)

1926–30. *T* **5***a*. *W* **7.** (*a*) *P* 14.

No.	Description	Unused	Used
85	½d. orange	1 0	1 6
86	1d. sage-green	1 0	0 4
87	1½d. scarlet	1 6	0 6
88	1½d. golden scarlet	4 6	1 3
89	2d. red-brown	8 0	5 0
90	3d. dull ultramarine ..	6 0	3 0
91	4d. yellow-olive	8 0	5 0
92	4½d. violet	8 6	5 0
93	1s. 4d. pale greenish blue ..	40 0	40 0

(*b*) *P* 13½ × 12½.

No.	Description	Unused	Used
94	½d. orange	0 8	0 3
95	1d. sage-green (Die I) ..	0 6	0 3
96	1d. sage-green (Die II) ..	40 0	27 6
97	1½d. scarlet	0 9	0 3
98	1½d. golden scarlet	0 8	0 3
98*a*	1½d. red-brown (16.9.30) ..	2 6	2 6
99	2d. red-brown	4 0	3 0
99*a*	2d. golden scarlet (Die I) ..	2 6	1 3
99*b*	2d. golden scarlet (Die II) ..	1 6	0 3
	c. No wmk.	£25	
100	3d. dull ultramarine (Die I)	6 0	0 8
101	3d. deep ultram. (Die II) ..	5 0	0 8
102	4d. yellow-olive	6 0	1 6
103	4½d. violet	12 6	6 0
103*a*	5d. orange-brown ('30) ..	6 0	1 9
104	1s. 4d. turquoise	27 6	15 0

Dies I and II.

1d. For the differences between Dies I and II of this value, see note after No. 34*a*.

2d. *a.* Height of frame. D I, 25.6 mm. D II, 25.1 mm. *b.* The lettering and figures of value in Die I are not so bold as in Die II.

3d. Die II has bolder letters and figures than Die I, as shown in adjoining illustrations.

5d. Nos. 103*a* and 130 are from a new die having a broader figure "5" with flat top. Nos. 34, 34*a*, and 50*b* are from the old die.

The 1½d. with watermark *T* **7** is from steel plates made from a new die. Nos. 88 and 98 are the Ash printings, the ink of which is shiny.

Owing to defective manufacture, part of a sheet of the 2d. (Die II) escaped unwatermarked; while the watermark in other parts of the same sheet was feint or normal.

8. Parliament House, Canberra.

(Des. R. A. Harrison. Die eng. by Waterlow & Sons. Plates and printing by J. Ash.)

1927 (9 May). *Opening of Parliament House, Canberra. No wmk. P* 11.

105 **8** 1½d. brownish lake 1 3 0 8
a. Imp. betwn. (pair) £70

1928 (29 Oct.). *Melbourne Philatelic Exhibition. As T* **4**. *No wmk. P* 11.

106 3d. blue 7 6 8 6

Special sheets of 60 stamps divided into 15 blocks of 4 (5×3) and separated by wide gutters perforated down the middle, were printed and sold at the Exhibition. Block of 4, *unused*, 35s.

(Typo. J. Ash.)

1929–30. *W* **7**. *P* 12.

107 **1** 6d. chestnut 7 6 2 0
108 ,, 9d. violet 14 0 2 6
109 ,, 1s. blue-green 17 6 3 6
110 ,, 2s. maroon 35 0 5 0
111 ,, 5s. grey and yellow .. £6 60 0
112 ,, 10s. grey and pink £13 £8
114 ,, £2 black and rose ('30) .. £70 £15

9

(Des. R. A. Harrison and H. Herbert. Recess. J. Ash.)

1929 (20 May). *Air. No wmk. P* 11.

115 **9** 3d. green (*shades*) 3 6 3 6

10

(Des. Pitt Morrison. Recess. J. Ash.)

1929 (28 Sept.). *Centenary of Western Australia. No wmk. P* 11.

116 **10** 1½d. dull scarlet 3 0 1 6
a. Re-entry ("T" of "AUSTRALIA" clearly double) £7 £6

11. Capt. Chas. Sturt.

TWO

PENCE

(12)

(Recess-printed by John Ash.)

1930 (2 June). *Centenary of Exploration of River Murray by Capt. Sturt. No wmk. P* 11.

117 **11** 1½d. scarlet 1 9 0 10
118 ,, 3d. blue 6 0 6 0

No. 117 with manuscript surcharge "2d. paid P M L H I" was issued by the Postmaster of Lord Howe Island during a shortage of 2d. stamps. A few copies of the 1½d. value No. 98 were also endorsed. These provisionals are not recognized by the Australian postal authorities. (*Price £14 un. or us., either stamp.*)

1930 (1 Aug.). *T* **5a** *surch. as T* **12**. *W* **7**. *P* 13½×12½.

119 2d. on 1½d. golden scarlet .. 1 3 0 8
120 5d. on 4½d. violet 6 0 8 0

No. 120 is from a redrawn die in which the words "FOURPENCE HALFPENNY" are noticeably thicker than in the original die and the figure "4" has square instead of tapering serifs.

Stamps from the redrawn die without the surcharge were printed, but not issued thus. A few stamps, *cancelled to order*, were included in sets supplied by the post office. A few mint copies, which escaped the cancellation, were found and some may have been used postally. The stamps cannot, however, be classed as officially issued.

13. The "Southern Cross" above hemispheres.

(Recess-printed by John Ash.)

1931 (19 Mar.). *Kingsford Smith's flights. No wmk. P* 11. (*a*) *Postage.*

121 **13** 2d. rose-red 2 6 0 10
122 ,, 3d. blue 7 6 8 6

(*b*) *Air. Inscr.* "AIR MAIL SERVICE".

123 **13** 6d. violet 12 6 15 0
a. Re-entry ("FO" of "KINGSFORD" and "LD" of "WORLD" double) .. £9 £9

15

17. Lyre-bird.

(Typo. John Ash.)

1931–36. *W* **15**.

(*a*) *P* 13½×12½.

124 **5a** ½d. orange 1 0 1 0

No.	Type	Description	Unused	Used
125	5a	1d. green (Die I)	0 6	0 3
126	,,	1½d. red-brown ('36) ..	5 0	7 6
127	,,	2d. golden scar. (Die II) ..	1 3	0 3
128	,,	3d. ultramarine (Die II) ..	5 0	1 0
129	,,	4d. yellow-olive	5 0	1 6
130	,,	5d. orange-brown	5 6	0 9
131	,,	1s. 4d. turquoise	27 6	8 6

(b) *P* 12.

No.	Type	Description	Unused	Used
132	1	6d. chestnut	12 6	15 0
133	,,	9d. violet	6 0	0 8
134	,,	2s. maroon ('35) ..	10 0	2 0
135	,,	5s. grey and yellow ..	65 0	30 0
136	,,	10s. grey and pink	£7	60 0
137	,,	£1 grey ('35)	£15	£6
138	,,	£2 black and rose ('34) ..	£70	£15

Stamps as No. 127, without wmk. and perf. 11, are forgeries made in 1932 to defraud the P.O.

For re-engraved type of No. 134, see No. 212.

(Recess. John Ash.)

1931 (4 Nov.). *Air Stamp. As T* **13** *but inscr.* "AIR MAIL SERVICE" *in bottom tablet. No wmk. P* 11.

No.	Type	Description	Unused	Used
139		6d. sepia	11 0	9 6

See note after No. O 3.

(Recess. John Ash.)

1932 (15 Feb.). *No wmk. P* 11.

No.	Type	Description	Unused	Used
140	17	1s. green	30 0	1 6
140a	,,	1s. yellow-green	30 0	3 0

18. Sydney Harbour Bridge.

(Printed by John Ash.)

1932 (14 Mar.). (a) *Recess. No wmk. P* 11.

No.	Type	Description	Unused	Used
141	18	2d. scarlet	2 0	0 6
142	,,	3d. blue	6 0	7 0
143	,,	5s. blue-green	£20	£14

(b) *Typo. W* **15.** *P* 10½ × 11.

No.	Type	Description	Unused	Used
144	18	2d. scarlet	1 9	0 4

Stamps as No. 144 without wmk., and perf. 11 are forgeries made in 1932 to defraud the P.O.

19. Kookaburra.

(Typo. John Ash.)

1932 (1 June). *W* **15.** *P* 13½ × 12½.

No.	Type	Description	Unused	Used
146	19	6d. red-brown	7 6	0 6

20. Melbourne and R. Yarra.

(Recess. John Ash.)

1934 (2 July). *Centenary of Victoria. W* **15.**

No.	Type	Description	I. P 10½ Unused	I. P 10½ Used	II. P 11½ Unused	II. P 11½ Used
147	20	2d. orange-vermilion	1 3	1 0	1 6	0 9
148	,,	3d. blue ..	4 0	2 6	5 0	2 6
149	,,	1s. black ..	27 6	22 6	25 0	20 0

21. Merino Sheep.

(Recess. John Ash.)

1934 (1 Nov.). *Capt. Macarthur Centenary. W* **15.** *P* 11½.

No.	Type	Description	Unused	Used
150	21	2d. carmine-red (A) ..	2 6	0 3
150a	,,	2d. carmine-red (B) ..	15 0	3 6
151	,,	3d. blue	10 0	7 6
152	,,	9d. bright purple ..	35 0	32 6

Type A of the 2d. shows shading on the hill in the background varying from light to dark (as illustrated). Type B has the shading almost uniformly dark.

22. Hermes.

(Recess. John Ash.)

1934–48. (a) *No wmk. P* 11.

No.	Type	Description	Unused	Used
153	22	1s. 6d. dull pur. (1.12.34)	25 0	3 6

(Recess. John Ash or W. C. G. McCracken.)

(b) *W* **15.** *P* 13½ × 14.

No.	Type	Description	Unused	Used
153a	22	1s. 6d. dull pur. (22.10.37)	6 0	1 0
		b. Thin rough paper ('48)	3 6	1 6

23. Cenotaph, Whitehall. **24.** King George V on "Anzac."

(Recess. John Ash.)

1935 (18 Mar.). *20th Anniv. of Gallipoli Landing. W* **15.** *P* 13½ × 12½ *or* 11 (1s.).

No.	Type	Description	Unused	Used
154	23	2d. scarlet	1 0	0 3
155	,,	1s. black (*chalk-surfaced*) ..	35 0	35 0

(Recess. John Ash.)

1935 (2 May.) *Silver Jubilee. Chalk-surfaced paper. W* **15** *sideways. P* 11½.

No.	Type	Description	Unused	Used
156	24	2d. scarlet	1 6	1 0
157	,,	3d. blue	8 0	6 0
158	,,	2s. bright violet	60 0	60 0

25. Amphitrite and Telephone Cable.

(Recess. John Ash.)

1936 (1 Apr.). *Opening of Submarine Telephone Communication to Tasmania.* *W* **15**. *P* 11½.

159	**25**	2d. scarlet	0	8	0	3
160	,,	3d. blue	6	0	4	6

26. Site of Adelaide, 1836; Old Gum Tree, Glenelg; King William St., Adelaide.

(Recess. John Ash.)

1936 (3 Aug.). *Centenary of South Australia.* *W* **15**. *P* 11½.

161	**26**	2d. carmine	0	8	0	3
162	,,	3d. blue	3	6	3	0
163	,,	1s. green	12	6	10	0

27. Kangaroo.

28. Queen Mother.

29. King George VI. **30.**

31

32. Koala.

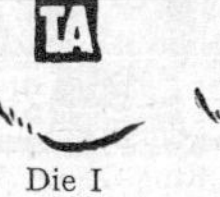

Die I   Die Ia   Die II

33. Merino Ram.

34. Kookaburra.

35. Platypus.

36. Lyre bird.

38. Queen Elizabeth.

39. King George VI.

40. King George VI and Queen Elizabeth.

40*a*. (Background evenly shaded.) **40*b*.**

(Recess. With John Ash, W. C. G. McCracken or " By Authority . . ." imprints.)

1937–49. *W* **15** (*sideways on* 5*d.*, 9*d.*, 5*s. and* 10*s.*).

(*a*) *P* 13½ × 14 (*vert. designs*) *or* 14 × 13½ (*horiz.*).

164	**27**	½d. orange (3.10.38) ..	1	3	0	4
165	**28**	1d. emerald-grn. (10.5.37)	0	8	0	3
166	**29**	1½d. maroon (20.4.38) ..	6	0	3	0
167	**30**	2d. scarlet (10.5.37) ..	0	9	0	3
167*a*	**31**	3d. blue (Die I, 1st ptg.) (2.8.37)	£7		£9	
168	,,	3d. blue (Die I) (2.8.37)..	40	0	12	6
168*a*	,,	3d. blue (Die Ia) (1937)..	60	0	10	0
168*b*	,,	3d. blue (Die II) ('38) ..	65	0	3	0
169	,,	3d. bright blue, *thin paper* (Die II) (21.12.38) ..	40	0	2	0

170	**32**	4d. green (1.2.38) ..	5	0	0	6
171	**33**	5d. purple (1.12.38) ..	4	0	0	9
172	**34**	6d. purple-brown (2.8.37)	3	0	0	4
173	**35**	9d. chocolate (1.9.38) ..	3	6	0	9
174	**36**	1s. grey-green (2.8.37) ..	37	6	1	6
175	**31**	1s. 4d. deep mag. (3.10.38)	7	6	5	0
		a. *Pale magenta*	3	6	3	0
		(*b*) *P* 13½.				
176	**38**	5s. claret (1.4.38) ..	15	0	12	6
		a. Thin rough paper ('48) .	17	6	15	0
177	**39**	10s. dull purple (1.4.38) ..	30	0	30	0
		a. Thin rough paper ('48) ..	35	0	35	0
178	**40**	£1 blue-slate (1.11.38) ..	45	0	45	0
		a. Thin rough paper ('49) ..	50	0	45	0
		(*c*) *P* 15×14 (*vert. designs*) *or* 14×15 (*horiz.*)				
179	**27**	½d. orange (28.1.42) ..	0	6	0	3
		a. Coil pair	6	0		
180	**40*a***	1d. emerald-green (1.8.38)	2	0	0	3
181	,,	1d. maroon (10.12.41) ..	1	0	0	4
		a. Coil pair	8	6		
182	**29**	1½d. maroon (21.11.41) ..	15	0	12	6
183	,,	1½d. emerald-grn. (10.12.41)	1	3	0	6
184	**40*b***	2d. scarlet (11.7.38) ..	1	3	0	2
		a. Coil pair..	£15			
185	,,	2d. bright pur. (10.12.41)	1	0	0	6
		a. Coil pair	8	6		
186	**31**	3d. bright blue (–.11.40)..	27	6	3	6
187	,,	3d. pur.-brown (10.1.42)	0	6	0	4
188	**32**	4d. green (–.10.42) ..	1	0	0	4
188*a*	**33**	5d. purple (–.5.46) ..	3	6	0	8
189	**34**	6d. red-brown (–.6.42) ..	2	0	0	4
		a. *Purple-brown* ('44) ..	1	0	0	3
190	**35**	9d. chocolate (1943) ..	3	0	0	9
191	**36**	1s. grey-green (–.3.41) ..	3	0	0	9

For unwmkd. issue, see Nos. 228/30*d*.

SPECIAL COIL PERFORATION

This special perforation of large and small holes on the narrow sides of the stamps is intended for stamps issued in coils, to facilitate separation. When they exist we list them as "Coil pairs".

The following with "special coil" perforation were placed on sale in *sheets*: Nos. 204*a* (1949), 222*a* (1952), 228, 237, 262 (1953), 309, 311 and 314.

Dies of the 3*d*. In Die I the letters "TA" of "POSTAGE" at right are joined by a white flaw; the outline of the chin consists of separate strokes.

Die Ia is similar, but "T" and "A" have been clearly separated by retouches made on the plate.

In Die II "T" and "A" are separate and a continuous line has been added to the chin. The outline of the cheek extends to about 1 mm. above the lobe of the King's right ear.

No. 167*a* is a preliminary printing made with unsuitable ink and may be detected by the absence of finer details; the King's face appears whitish and the wattles are blank. The greater part of this printing was distributed to the Press with advance notices of the issue.

No. 186 is re-engraved and differs from Nos. 167*a* to 169 in the King's left eyebrow which is shaded downwards from left to right instead of from right to left.

Thin paper. Nos. 176*a*, 177*a*, 178*a*. In these varieties the watermark is more clearly visible on the back and the design is much less sharp.

41. Governor Phillip at Sydney Cove.

(Recess. J. Ash.)

1937 (1 Oct.). 150*th Anniv. of Foundation of New South Wales. W* **15**. *P* 13½×14.

193	**41**	2d. scarlet	1	0	0	4
194	,,	3d. bright blue	5	0	4	0
195	,,	9d. purple	16	0	15	0

42. A.I.F. and Nurse.

(Design from drawing by Virgil Reilly. Recess. W. C. G. McCracken.)

1940 (15 July). *Australian Imperial Forces. W* **15** *sideways. P* 14×13½.

196	**42**	1d. green	2	0	0	9
197	,,	2d. scarlet	2	0	0	6
198	,,	3d. blue	8	6	10	0
199	,,	6d. brown-purple	17	6	15	0

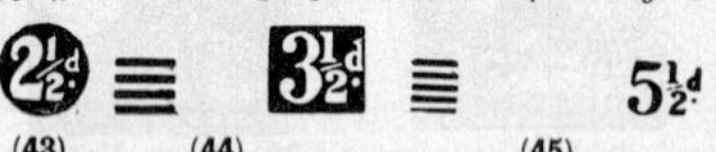

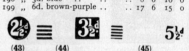

(43) (44) (45)

1941 (10 Dec.). *Nos.* 184, 186 *and* 171 *surch. with T* **43/5**.

200	**40*b***	2½d. on 2d. (V.) ..	1	0	0	6
201	**31**	3½d. on 3d. (Y. on Bk.)..	2	0	2	0
202	**33**	5½d. on 5d. (V.)	5	0	7	6

46. Queen Mother. **46*a*.**

47. King George VI. **48.** King George VI.

49. King George VI. **50.** Emu.

1942–44. *Recess.* *W* **15.** *P* 15×14.

No.	Type	Description	Unused s.	d.	Used s.	d.
203	**46**	1d. brn.-purple (1.1.43)	0	6	0	3
		a. Coil pair	10	0		
204	**46a**	1½d. green (1.12.42)	0	8	0	3
204*a*	**47**	2d. bright pur. (4.12.44)	0	6	0	6
		b. Coil pair	17	6		
205	**48**	2½d. scarlet ('42)	0	6	0	3
206	**49**	3½d. bright blue ('42)	2	0	0	6
		a. Deep blue	6	0	1	6
207	**50**	5½d. slate-blue ('42)	1	3	0	6

For stamps as Nos. 204/*a* but without watermark see Nos. 229/30.

52. Duke and Duchess of Gloucester.

1945 (19 Feb.). *Arrival of Duke and Duchess of Gloucester in Australia.* *Recess.* *W* **15.** *P* 14½.

No.	Type	Description	Unused s.	d.	Used s.	d.
209	**52**	2½d. lake	0	6	0	3
210	,,	3½d. ultramarine	1	0	1	0
211	,,	5½d. indigo	1	6	2	0

A. B.

1946 (3 Jan.). *Kangaroo type, as No.* 134, *but re-engraved as* B. *W* **15.** *P* 12.

No.	Type	Description	Unused s.	d.	Used s.	d.
212	**1**	2s. maroon	5	0	1	6

No. 134 has two background lines between the value circle and "TWO SHILLINGS"; No. 212 has only one line in this position. There are also differences in the shape of the letters.

53

54 **55.** Peace Symbols.

1946 (18 Feb.). *Victory Commemoration.* *Recess.* *W* **15** (*sideways on* 5½*d.*). *P* 14½.

No.	Type	Description	Unused s.	d.	Used s.	d.
213	**53**	2½d. scarlet	0	8	0	4
214	**54**	3½d. blue	1	0	1	3
215	**55**	5½d. green	1	3	1	6

56. Sir Thos. Mitchell and Queensland.

1946 (14 Oct.). *Centenary of Mitchell's Exploration of Central Queensland.* *Recess.* *W* **15.** *P* 14½.

No.	Type	Description	Unused s.	d.	Used s.	d.
216	**56**	2½d. scarlet	0	6	0	4
217	,,	3½d. blue	1	0	1	3
218	,,	1s. grey-olive	2	6	2	6

57. Lt. John Shortland, R.N. **58.** Steel Foundry.

59. Coal Carrier Cranes. **60.** Queen Elizabeth II when Princess.

1947 (8 Sept.). *Sesquicentenary of City of Newcastle, New South Wales.* *Recess.* *W* **15** (*sideways on* 3½*d.*). *P* 14½ *or* 15×14 (2½*d.*).

No.	Type	Description	Unused s.	d.	Used s.	d.
219	**57**	2½d. lake	0	6	0	4
220	**58**	3½d. blue	1	3	1	6
221	**59**	5½d. green	1	6	1	9

The following items are understood to have been the subject of unauthorised leakages from the Commonwealth Note and Stamp Printing Branch and are therefore not listed by us.

It is certain that none of this material was distributed to post offices for issue to the public.

Imperforate all round. 1d. Princess Elizabeth; 1½d. Queen; 2½d. King; 4d. Koala; 6d. Kookaburra; 9d. Platypus; 1s. Lyre-bird (small); 1s. 6d. Air Mail (Type **22**); 2½d. Newcastle.

Also 2½d. Peace, unwatermarked; 2½d. King, *tête-bêche*; 3½d. Newcastle, in dull ultramarine; 2½d. King on "toned" paper.

1947 (20 Nov.)–**1948.** *Marriage of Princess Elizabeth. Recess. P* 14×15.

(*a*) *W* **15** *sideways.*

222 **60** 1d. purple 0 6 0 4

(*b*) *No wmk.*

222*a* **60** 1d. purple ('48) 0 6 0 4

b. Coil pair 7 6

61. Hereford Bull. **61*a*.** Hermes and Globe.

62. Aboriginal Art. **62*a*.** Commonwealth Coat-of-Arms.

(Des. T **61**, F. D. Manley; T **62**, G. Sellheim.)

1948 (16 Feb.)–**56.** *Recess.*

(*a*) *W* **15** *sideways. P* 14½.

223 **61** 1s. 3d. brown-purple .. 4 0 3 0

223*a* **61*a*** 1s. 6d. blackish brown (1.9.49) 2 6 0 8

224 **62** 2s. chocolate 4 0 1 0

(*b*) *W* **15.** *P* 14½×13½.

224*a* **62*a*** 5s. claret (11.4.49) .. 15 0 2 6

224*b* ,, 10s. purple (3.10.49) .. 22 6 5 0

224*c* ,, £1 blue ((28.11.49) .. 40 0 12 6

224*d* ,, £2 green (16.1.50) .. 80 0 40 0

(*c*) *No wmk. P* 14½.

224*e* **61*a*** 1s. 6d. blackish brown (6.12.56) 4 0 1 0

224*f* **62** 2s. chocolate (21.7.56) .. 5 0 1 0

63. William J. Farrer. **64.** F. von Mueller.

1948 (12 July). *William J. Farrer (wheat research). Recess. W* **15.** *P* 15×14.

225 **63** 2½d. scarlet 0 6 0 3

1948 (13 Sept.). *Sir Ferdinand von Mueller (botanist). Recess. W* **15.** *P* 15×14.

226 **64** 2½d. lake 0 6 0 3

65. Boy Scout. **66.** Henry Lawson.

1948 (15 Nov.). *Pan-Pacific Scout Jamboree. Recess. W* **15** *sideways. P* 14×15.

227 **65** 2½d. lake 1 3 0 4

1948–56. *No wmk. P* 15×14 *or* 14×15 (9*d.*).

228 **27** ½d. orange (9.49) .. 0 3 0 3

a. Coil pair 0 8

229 **46*a*** 1½d. green (29.8.49) .. 0 6 0 3

230 **47** 2d. brt. purple (12.48) 0 6 0 3

aa. Coil pair 7 6

230*a* **32** 4d. green (18.8.56) .. 5 0 2 0

230*b* **34** 6d. pur.-brn. (18.8.56) 1 0 0 3

230*c* **35** 9d. chocolate (13.12.56) 2 6 0 8

230*d* **36** 1s. grey-grn. (13.12.56) 2 9 0 8

1949 (17 June). *Anniv. of Birth of Henry Lawson (poet). Recess. P* 15×14.

231 **66** 2½d. maroon 0 6 0 3

67. Mounted Postman and Aeroplane.

1949 (10 Oct.). *75th Anniv. of Founding of U.P.U. Recess. P* 15×14.

232 **67** 3½d. ultramarine 1 9 2 6

68. Lord Forrest of Bunbury. **69.** King George VI.

1949 (28 Nov.). *Lord Forrest of Bunbury (explorer and politician). Recess. W* **15.** *P* 15×14.

233 **68** 2½d. lake 0 6 0 3

1950–51. *Recess. P* 15×14. (*a*) *W* **15.**

234 **69** 2½d. scarlet (12.4.50) .. 0 10 0 3

235 ,, 3d. scarlet (28.2.51) .. 0 10 0 3

aa. Coil pair 7 0

(*b*) *No wmk.*

235*a* **69** 2½d. pur.-brn. (23.5.51) .. 0 10 0 6

235*b* ,, 3d. grey-green (14.11.51) 0 8 0 3

c. Coil pair 5 0

70. Queen Mother. **71.** Aborigine.

1950–51. *Recess.* *P* 15 × 14.
236 **70** 1½d. green (19.6.50) .. 0 6 0 3
237 ,, 2d. yellow-green (28.3.51) 0 8 0 4
a. Coil pair 3 0

1950 (14 Aug.). *Recess.* *W* **15.** *P* 15 × 14.
238 **71** 8½d. brown 2 6 1 6

72. Reproductions of First Stamps of New **73.** South Wales and Victoria.

1950 (27 Sept.). *Centenary of First Adhesive Postage Stamps in Australia. T* **72/3** *alternately in vertical columns throughout the sheet. Recess. P* 15 × 14.
239 **72** 2½d. maroon 0 8 0 4
240 **73** 2½d. maroon 0 8 0 4

> **PRICES** for used horizontal pairs of the issues printed alternately in the sheet are four times the price of a single.

74. Sir Edmund Barton. **75.** Sir Henry Parkes.

76. Opening First Federal Parliament.

77. Federal Parliament House, Canberra.

1951 (1 May). *Golden Jubilee of Commonwealth of Australia. Recess. P* 15 × 14.
241 **74** 3d. lake 0 6 0 6
242 **75** 3d. lake 0 6 0 6
243 **76** 5½d. blue 3 6 5 0
244 **77** 1s. 6d. purple-brown .. 5 0 3 0

Nos. 241/2 are printed alternately in vertical columns throughout the sheet.

78. E. H. Hargraves. **79.** C. J. Latrobe.

1951 (2 July). *Centenary of Discovery of Gold in Australia. Recess. P* 15 × 14.
245 **78** 3d. maroon 0 8 0 8

1951 (2 July). *Centenary of Responsible Government in Victoria. Recess. P* 15 × 14.
246 **79** 3d. maroon 0 8 0 8

Nos. 245/6 are printed alternately in vertical columns throughout the sheet.

80. King George VI. **81.**

1951 (31 Oct.). *Recess.* *W* **15.** *P* 15 × 14.
247 **80** 7½d. blue 2 6 2 0
a. Imperf. 3 sides (vert. pr.)

1951–52. *Recess.* *W* **15.** *P* 15 × 14.
248 **81** 3½d. brown-pur. (28.11.51) 0 8 0 3
249 ,, 4½d. scarlet (20.2.52) .. 1 6 1 6
250 ,, 6½d. brown (20.2.52) .. 2 0 2 0
251 ,, 6½d. emerald-green (9.4.52) 1 3 0 6

82. King George VI.

1952 (19 Mar.)–**65.** *Recess.* *P* 14½.
(*a*) *W* **15** (*sideways*).
252 **82** 1s. 0½d. indigo 2 0 1 0
253 – 2s. 6d. deep brown .. 5 0 2 0
(*b*) *No wmk.*
253*a* – 2s. 6d. deep brn. (30.1.57) 3 6 1 10
b. Sepia (10.65) £5 20 0

Design:—2s. 6d. As T **71** but larger (21 × 25½ *mm.*).

No. 253*b* was an emergency printing and can easily be distinguished from No. 253*a* as it is on white Harrison paper, No. 253*a* being on toned paper.

1952 (19 Nov.). *Pan-Pacific Scout Jamboree, Greystanes. As T* **65**, *but inscr.* "1952–53". *Recess. W* **15** (*sideways*). *P* 14 × 15.
254 3½d. brown-lake 0 8 0 4

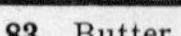

83. Butter.

84. Wheat.

85. Beef.

1953 (11 FEB.). *Food Production. Typo. P* 14½.

255	**83**	3d. emerald	2	6	0	8
256	**84**	3d. emerald	2	6	0	8
257	**85**	3d. emerald	2	6	0	8
258	**83**	3½d. scarlet	2	0	0	8
259	**84**	3½d. scarlet	2	0	0	8
260	**85**	3½d. scarlet	2	0	0	8
		Strips of three 3d. value ..	10	0	10	0
		Strips of three 3½d. value ..	8	0	10	0

The three designs in each denomination appear in rotation, both horizontally and vertically, throughout the sheet.

86. Queen Elizabeth II.

1953–56. *Recess. P* 15 × 14. (*a*) *No wmk.*

261	**86**	1d. purple (19.8.53) ..	0	6	0	3
261*a*	,,	2½d. blue (23.6.54) ..	0	8	0	4
262	,,	3d. deep green (17.6.53)	0	8	0	3
		aa. Coil pair	3	6		
262*a*	,,	3½d. brown-red (2.7.56) ..	0	8	0	3
262*b*	,,	6½d. orange (9.56) ..	1	0	0	10
		(*b*) *W* **15.**				
263	**86**	3½d. brown-red (21.4.53)	0	8	0	3
263*a*	,,	6½d. orange (23.6.54) ..	1	3	1	0

87. Queen Elizabeth II.

1953 (25 MAY). *Coronation. Recess. P* 15 × 14.

264	**87**	3½d. scarlet	0	8	0	4
265	,,	7½d. violet	3	0	3	6
266	,,	2s. dull bluish green ..	5	0	5	0

88. Young Farmers and Calf.

1953 (3 SEPT.). *25th Anniv. of Australian Young Farmers' Clubs. Recess. P* 14½.

267	**88**	3½d. red-brn. & deep grn.	1	6	0	6

89. Lt.-Gov. D. Collins. **90.** Lt.-Gov. W. Paterson.

91. Sullivan Cove, Hobart, 1804.

1953 (23 SEPT.). *150th Anniv. of Settlement in Tasmania. Recess. P* 15 × 14.

268	**89**	3½d. brown-purple ..	1	6	0	8
269	**90**	3½d. brown-purple ..	1	6	0	8
270	**91**	2s. green	10	0	9	0

Nos. 268/9 are printed alternately in vertical columns throughout the sheet.

92. Stamp of 1853.

1953 (11 NOV.). *Tasmanian Postage Stamp Centenary. Recess. P* 14½.

271	**92**	3d. rose-red	1	6	0	6

93. Queen Elizabeth II and Duke of Edinburgh.

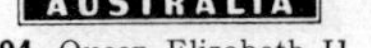

94. Queen Elizabeth II. Re-entry.

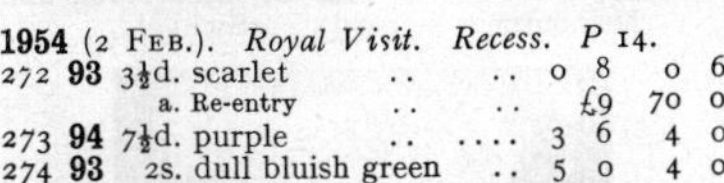

1954 (2 Feb.). *Royal Visit. Recess. P* 14.

272 **93** 3½d. scarlet 0 8 0 6
a. Re-entry £9 70 0
273 **94** 7½d. purple 3 6 4 0
274 **93** 2s. dull bluish green .. 5 0 4 0

95. " Telegraphic Communications ". **96.** Red Cross and Globe.

1954 (7 Apr.). *Australian Telegraph System Centenary. Recess. P* 14.

275 **95** 3½d. brown-red 0 8 0 4

1954 (9 June). *40th Anniv. of Australian Red Cross Society. Design recess, cross typo. P* 14½.

276 **96** 3½d. ultramarine & scarlet 0 8 0 4

97. Black Swan.

1954 (2 Aug.). *Western Australian Postage Stamp Centenary. Recess. P* 14½.

277 **97** 3½d. black 1 0 0 6

98. Locomotives of 1854 and 1954.

1954 (13 Sept.). *Australian Railways Centenary. Recess. P* 14.

278 **98** 3½d. purple-brown .. 0 10 0 6

99. Antarctic Map and Indigenous Flora and Fauna. **100.** Olympic Games Symbol.

(Des. T. Lawrence. Recess.)

1954 (17 Nov.). *Australian Antarctic Research. P* 14½ × 13½.

279 **99** 3½d. grey-black 1 6 0 9

1954–55. *Olympic Games Propaganda. Recess. P* 14.

280 **100** 2s. dp. brt. blue (1.12.54) 7 6 6 0
280*a* ,, 2s. dp. bluish grn. (30.11.55) 5 6 5 0

101. Rotary Symbol, Globe and Flags. **102.** Queen Elizabeth II.

1955 (23 Feb.). *50th Anniv. of Rotary International. Recess. P* 14 × 14½.

281 **101** 3½d. carmine 0 8 0 4

1955 (9 Mar.)–**57.** *Recess. P* 14½. (*a*) *W* **15** (*sideways*).

282 **102** 1s. 0½d. deep blue .. 2 0 0 8

(*b*) *No wmk.*

282*a* **102** 1s. 7d. red-brn. (13.3.57) 3 0 1 3

103. American Memorial, Canberra.

(Des. R. L. Beck. Recess.)

1955 (4 May). *Australian-American Friendship. P* 14 × 14½.

283 **103** 3d. violet-blue 0 10 0 6

104. Cobb & Co. Coach.

1955 (6 July). *Mail-coach Pioneers Commemoration. Recess. P* 14½ × 14.
284 **104** 3½d. blackish brown .. 1 0 0 8
285 ,, 2s. reddish brown .. 8 6 7 6

105. Y.M.C.A. Emblem and Map of the World.

(Des. E. Thake. Design recess; emblem typo.)

1955 (10 Aug.). *World Centenary of Y.M.C.A. P* 14½ × 14.
286 **105** 3½d. dp. bluish grn. & red 0 8 0 3

106. Florence Nightingale and Young Nurse.

107. Queen Victoria.

1955 (21 Sept.). *Nursing Profession Commemoration. Recess. P* 14 × 14½.
287 **106** 3½d. reddish violet .. 0 8 0 4

1955 (17 Oct.). *Centenary of First South Australian Postage Stamps. Recess. P* 14½.
288 **107** 3½d. green 0 8 0 6

108. Badges of New South Wales, Victoria and Tasmania.

1956 (26 Sept.). *Centenary of Responsible Government in New South Wales, Victoria and Tasmania. Recess. P* 14½ × 14.
289 **108** 3½d. brown-lake 0 10 0 6

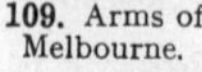

109. Arms of Melbourne.

110. Olympic Torch and Symbol.

111. Collins Street, Melbourne.

112. Melbourne across R. Yarra.

(Nos. 290/1. Recess. Govt. Stamp Ptg. Works, Melbourne. No. 292. Des. M. Murphy and L. Coles. Photo. Harrison & Sons, Ltd., London. No. 293. Des. M. Murphy. Photo. Courvoisier, Switzerland.)

1956 (31 Oct.). *Olympic Games, Melbourne. P* 14½ *(4d.),* 14 × 14½ *(7½d., 1s.) or* 11½ *(2s.).*
290 **109** 4d. carmine-red .. 0 8 0 6
291 **110** 7½d. deep bright blue .. 2 0 3 0
292 **111** 1s. multicoloured .. 2 6 2 6
293 **112** 2s. multicoloured .. 4 0 4 0

113. Queen Elizabeth II.

114. South Australia Coat-of-Arms.

1957. *Recess. P* 15 × 14.
294 **113** 4d. lake (13 Mar.) .. 0 8 0 4
295 ,, 10d. dp. grey-blue (6 Mar.) 1 9 1 3

The 4d. exists in booklet panes of six stamps, with imperf. outer edges, producing single stamps with one or two adjacent sides imperf.

1957 (17 Apr.). *Centenary of Responsible Government in South Australia. Recess. P* 14½.
296 **114** 4d. red-brown 0 10 0 10

115. Map of Australia and Caduceus.

(Des. J. E. Lyle. Recess.)

1957 (21 Aug.). *Flying Doctor Service. P* 14½ × 14.

297	**115**	7d. ultramarine	1 6	0 8

116. "The Spirit of Christmas" (Child, after Sir Joshua Reynolds).

Re-entry (Row 10/1).

1957 (6 Nov.). *Christmas issue. Recess. P* 14½ × 14

298	**116**	3½d. scarlet	0 8	0 4
		a. Re-entry	35 0	25 0
299	„	4d. purple	1 0	0 10

117. Queen Elizabeth II.

1957 (13 Nov.). *Recess. P* 15 × 14.

300	**117**	7½d. violet	3 0	1 6

118. Super-Constellation Airliner.

1958 (6 Jan.). *Inauguration of Australian "Round the World" Air Service. Recess. P* 14½ × 14.

301	**118**	2s. deep blue	4 0	3 0

119. Hall of Memory, Sailor and Airman.

1958 (10 Feb.). *T* **119** *and similar horiz. design. Recess. P* 14½ × 14.

302	**119**	5½d. brown-red	1 6	1 3
303	–	5½d. brown-red	1 6	1 3

No. 303 shows a soldier and service-woman respectively in place of the sailor and airman. Nos. 302/3 are printed alternately in vertical columns throughout the sheet.

120. Sir Charles Kingsford Smith and the "Southern Cross".

(Des. J. E. Lyle. Recess.)

1958 (27 Aug.). *30th Anniv. of First Air Crossing of the Tasman Sea. P* 14 × 14½.

304	**120**	8d. deep ultramarine ..	2 6	3 0

121. Silver Mine, Broken Hill.

(Des. R. H. Evans. Recess.)

1958 (10 Sept.). *75th Anniv. of Founding of Broken Hill. Recess. P* 14½ × 14.

305	**121**	4d. chocolate	0 8	0 4

122. The Nativity.

1958. (5 Nov.). *Christmas. Recess. P* 14½ × 15.

306	**122**	3½d. deep scarlet	0 8	0 4
307	„	4d. deep violet	0 10	0 4

PHOSPHOR STAMPS ("Helecon").

"Helecon" a chemical substance of the zinc sulphide group, has been incorporated in stamps in two different ways, either in the ink with which the stamps are printed, or included in the surface coating of the stamp paper.

Owing to the difficulty of identification without the use of a U.V. lamp we do not list the helecon stamps separately but when in stock can supply them after testing under the lamp.

The first stamp to be issued was the 11d. Bandicoot from an experimental printing of four millions on helecon paper released to the public in December 1963. The next printing on ordinary paper was released in September 1964. The experimental printing was coarse, showing a lot of white dots and the colour is slate-blue, differing from both the ordinary and the later helecon paper.

The following helecon printings have been reported: 2d. (sheets and coils) and 3d. Queen Elizabeth II; 8d. Tiger Cat; 11d. Bandicoot; 1s. Colombo Plan; 1s. 2d. Tasmanian Tiger; 2s. 3d. Wattle (No. 324*a*); and 6d., 9d. and 1s. 6d. Birds (the 2s., 2s. 6d. and 3s. Birds have only been issued on helecon paper). The 5d. Queen Elizabeth II in red (S.G. 354*b*) exists ordinary and with helecon ink. The coil pair was only issued with helecon ink; the booklet is normally with helecon ink but some were printed with ordinary ink by mistake. The Churchill stamp was printed on ordinary and helecon paper. The I.T.U. Centenary, Monash and later commemorative, and all decimal currency stamps were printed on helecon paper only.

123 124

126 127

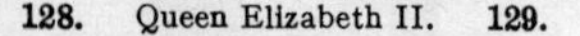

128. Queen Elizabeth II. 129.

Die I.
Short break in outer line to bottom right of "4".

Die II.
Line unbroken.

Die. A.
Four short lines inside "5".

Die B.
Five short lines inside "5".

(Portraits by Baron Studios. Recess.)

1959–62. *P* 14 × 15 (*horiz.*), 15 × 14 (*vert.*).

308	**123**	1d. dp. slate-pur. (2.2.59)	0	4	0	4
309	**124**	2d. brown (21.3.62) ..	0	6	0	4
		a. Coil pair	1	6		
311	**126**	3d. blue-green (20.5.59)	0	6	0	4
		a. Coil pair	2	0		
312	**127**	3½d. deep green (18.3.59)	1	0	0	3
313	**128**	4d. carmine-lake (Die I) (*shades*) (2.2.59) ..	2	6	0	4
		a. Die II (*shades*)	0	9	0	4
314	**129**	5d. deep blue (Die A or B) (1.10.59) ..	0	10	0	4
		a. Vert. *se-tenant* pr. (A and B)	2	6	0	11
		b. Coil pair	2	6		

No. 313. Die I occurs in the upper pane and Die II in the lower pane of the sheet.

No. 314. Both dies occur in alternate horizontal rows in the sheet (Die A in Row 1, Die B in Row 2, and so on), and their value is identical.

The Note after No. 295 also applies to Nos. 313/4.

131. Banded Ant-eater.

132. Tiger Cat (Dasyure).

133. Kangaroos.

134. Rabbit Bandicoot.

135. Platypus.

136. Tasmanian Tiger.

137. Christmas Bells.

138. Flannel Flower.

139. Wattle.

140. Banksia.

141. Waratah.

142. Aboriginal Stockman.

(Des. Eileen Mayo (6d., 8d., 9d., 11d., 1s., 1s. 2d.), Printing Bureau Artists (5s.), Margaret Stones (others). Recess.)

1959–64. *W* **15** (5s.), *no wmk.* (*others*). *P* 14 × 15 (*T* **136**), 15 × 14 (*T* **131/5**) 14½ × 14 (5s.) *or* 14½ (*others*).

316	**131**	6d. brown (30.9.60) ..	1	3	0	6
317	**132**	8d. red-brown (*shades*) (11.5.60)	1	3	0	7
318	**133**	9d. deep sepia (21.10.59)	2	6	1	3
319	**134**	11d. deep blue (3.5.61) ..	2	0	1	3
320	**135**	1s. deep green (9.9.59) ..	2	6	1	0
321	**136**	1s. 2d. deep pur. (21.3.62)	2	6	1	3
322	**137**	1s. 6d. crim/*yell.* (3.2.60)	2	6	1	6
323	**138**	2s. grey-blue (8.4.59) ..	2	9	0	6
324	**139**	2s. 3d. grn./*crm.* (9.9.59)	4	6	1	6
324*a*	,,	2s. 3d. yellow-green (28.10.64)	5	0	1	9
325	**140**	2s. 5d. brn./*yell.* (16.3.60)	4	6	2	0
326	**141**	3s. scarlet (15.7.59) ..	5	0	2	6
327	**142**	5s. red-brown (26.7.61)	12	6	5	0
		a. White paper. *Brown-red* (17.6.64)	20	0	7	6

No. 327a was a late printing on the white paper intended for the Navigators series. No. 324*a* is also on white paper.

143. Postmaster Isaac Nichols boarding the brig *Experiment*.

1959 (22 Apr.). *150th Anniv. of the Australian Post Office. Recess. P* 14½ × 14.

331	**143**	4d. slate	0	7	0	4

144. Parliament House, Brisbane, and Arms of Queensland.

145. "The Approach of the Magi."

1959 (5 June). *Centenary of Self-Government in Queensland. Recess. P* 14 × 14½.

332	**144**	4d. lilac and green ..	0	7	0	6

1959 (4 Nov.). *Christmas Issue. Recess. P* 15 × 14.

333	**145**	5d. deep reddish violet ..	0	9	0	3

146. Girl Guide and Lord Baden-Powell.

1960 (18 Aug.). *Golden Jubilee of Girl Guide Movement. Recess. P* 14½ × 14.

334	**146**	5d. deep ultramarine ..	0	8	0	3

147. "The Overlanders" (after Sir Daryl Lindsay).

1960 (21 Sept.). *Centenary of Northern Territory Exploration. Recess. P* 15 × 14½.

335	**147**	5d. magenta	0	8	0	3

There are two types in this issue. In Type I the horse's mane is rough and in Type II it is smooth. Type II occurs on 94 stamps in the Printer's sheet of 480.

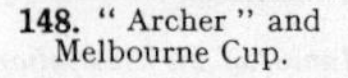

148. " Archer " and Melbourne Cup.

149. Queen Victoria.

(Des. F. D. Manley. Recess.)

1960 (12 OCT.). *100th Melbourne Cup Race Commemoration.* $P\ 14\frac{1}{2}$.
336 **148** 5d. sepia 0 8 0 3

1960 (2 NOV.). *Centenary of First Queensland Postage Stamp.* *Recess.* $P\ 14\frac{1}{2} \times 15$.
337 **149** 5d. dp. myrtle-green .. 0 8 0 6

150. Open Bible and Candle. **151.** Colombo Plan Bureau Emblem.

1960 (9 Nov.). *Christmas Issue. Recess.* $P\ 15 \times 14\frac{1}{2}$.
338 **150** 5d. carmine-red 1 0 0 4

1961 (30 JUNE). *Colombo Plan. Recess.* $P\ 14 \times 14\frac{1}{2}$.
339 **151** 1s. red-brown 1 9 0 6

152. Melba (after bust by Sir Bertram Mackennal).

1961. (20 SEPT.). *Centenary of Birth of Dame Nellie Melba (singer).* *Recess.* $P\ 14\frac{1}{2} \times 15$.
340 **152** 5d. blue 0 9 0 3

153. Open Prayer Book and Text.

1961 (8 Nov.). *Christmas Issue. Recess.* $P\ 14\frac{1}{2} \times 14$.
341 **153** 5d. brown 0 9 0 3

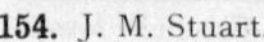

154. J. M. Stuart. **155.** Flynn's Grave and Nursing Sister.

(Des. Walter Jardine. Recess.)

1962 (25 JULY). *Centenary of Stuart's Crossing of Australia from South to North.* $P\ 14\frac{1}{2} \times 15$.
342 **154** 5d. brown-red 1 0 0 6

(Des. F. D. Manley. Photo.)

1962 (5 SEPT.). *50th Anniv. of Australian Inland Mission.* $P\ 13\frac{1}{2}$.
343 **155** 5d. multicoloured .. 1 0 0 4
a. Red printing omitted .. — £100

156. " Woman ". **157.** " Madonna and Child ".

1962 (26 SEPT.). *" Associated Country Women of the World " Conference, Melbourne.* *Recess.* $P\ 14 \times 14\frac{1}{2}$.
344 **156** 5d. deep green 0 9 0 5

1962 (17 OCT.). *Christmas.* *Recess.* $P\ 14\frac{1}{2}$.
345 **157** 5d. violet 0 9 0 5

158. Perth and Kangaroo Paw (plant).

159. Arms of Perth and Running Track.

(Des. R. M. Warner (5d.), G. Hamori (2s. 3d.). Photo. Harrison & Sons.)

1962 (1 Nov.). *Seventh British Empire and Commonwealth Games, Perth.* *P* 14 (5*d.*) *or* 14½ × 14 (2*s.* 3*d.*).

346 **158** 5d. multicoloured .. 1 0 0 9
a. Red omitted .. ..
347 **159** 2s. 3d. black, red, blue and green 11 0 10 0

160. Queen Elizabeth II. **161.** Queen Elizabeth II and Duke of Edinburgh.

(Portraits by Anthony Buckley. Recess.)

1963 (18 Feb.). *Royal Visit.* *P* 14½.

348 **160** 5d. deep green 0 9 0 5
349 **161** 2s. 3d. brown-lake .. 7 6 5 0

162. Arms of Canberra and W. B. Griffin (architect).

1963 (8 Mar.). *50th Anniv. of Canberra.* *Recess.* *P* 14½ × 14.

350 **162** 5d. deep green 0 9 0 6

163. Centenary Emblem.

(Des. G. Hamori. Photo.)

1963 (8 May). *Red Cross Centenary.* *P* 13½ × 13.

351 **163** 5d. red, grey-brn. & blue 0 9 0 6

164. Blaxland, Lawson and Wentworth on Mt. York.

(Des. T. Alban. Recess.)

1963 (28 May). *150th Anniv. of First Crossing of Blue Mountains.* *P* 14½ × 14.

352 **164** 5d. ultramarine 0 9 0 6

165. " Export ".

1963 (28 Aug.). *Recess.* *P* 14½ × 14

353 **165** 5d. red 0 9 0 6

166. Queen Elizabeth II.

(Portrait by Anthony Buckley. Recess.)

1963 (9 Oct.)–**65.** *P* 15 × 14.

354 **166** 5d. deep green 0 9 0 6
a. Imperf. between (horiz. pair) (31.7.64) 2 6 2 6
354*b* ,, 5d. red (30.6.65) 0 10 0 6
c. Coil pair 3 0

The above exist in booklet panes of six stamps, with imperf. outer edges, producing single stamps with one or two adjacent sides imperf.

See illustration of No. 354a on next page.

167. Tasman and Ship.

168. Dampier and *Roebuck*.

169. Captain Cook.

No. 354a comes from sheets of uncut booklet panes containing 288 stamps (16 × 18) with wide margins intersecting the sheet horizontally below each third row, alternate rows of stamps imperforate between vertically and the outer left, right and bottom margins imperforate. This means that in each sheet there are 126 pairs of stamps imperf. between vertically, plus a number with wide imperforate margins attached, as shown in the illustration.

170. Flinders and *Investigator*.

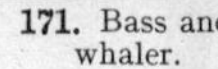

171. Bass and whaler.

172. Admiral King and *Mermaid*.

(Des. W. Jardine. Recess.)

1963–65. *No wmk.* (4s.) *or W* **15** (*others*), (*sideways on* 5s., £1). *P* 14½ × 14 *or* 14½ (5s., £1, £2).

355	**167**	4s. ultramarine (9.10.63)	12 6	10 0
356	**168**	5s. red-brown (25.11.64)	12 6	10 0
357	**169**	7s. 6d. olive (26.8.64) ..	40 0	40 0
358	**170**	10s. brown-pur. (26.2.64)	40 0	30 0
		a. White paper. *Deep brown-purple* (14.1.65)	35 0	25 0
359	**171**	£1 deep reddish violet (26.2.64)	60 0	50 0
		a. White paper. *Deep bluish violet* (16.11.64)	50 0	45 0
360	**172**	£2 sepia (26.8.64) ..	£6	£5

Nos. 358 and 359 were printed on a toned paper but all the other values are on white paper, the 4s. being on rather thicker paper.

173. "Peace on Earth . . ."

(Des. R. M. Warner. Recess.)

1963 (25 Oct.). *Christmas. P* 14½.

361	**173**	5d. greenish blue ..	0 9	0 6

174. "Commonwealth Cable".

1963 (3 Dec.). *Opening of COMPAC (Trans-Pacific Telephone Cable). Chalky paper. Photo. P* 13½.

362	**174**	2s. 3d. red, blue, black and pale blue ..	10 0	10 0

175. Yellow-tailed Thornbill.

176. Black-backed Magpie.

177. Galah (cockatoo).

178. Golden Whistler (Thickhead).

179. Blue Wren.

180. Scarlet Robin.

181. Straw-necked Ibis.

(Des. Mrs. H. Temple-Watts. Photo.)

1964 (11 Mar.)–**65.** *Chalky paper* (*except No.* 367*a*). *P* 13½.

363	**175**	6d. brown, yellow, black and green (19.8.64) ..	1	3	0	9
364	**176**	9d. black, grey & pale grn.	3	0	2	6
365	**177**	1s. 6d. pink, grey, dull purple and black ..	4	6	3	0
366	**178**	2s. yellow, black and pink (21.4.65) ..	4	6	2	0
367	**179**	2s. 5d. dp. royal bl., lt. vio.-blue, yell.-orge., grey and black ..	6	0	3	0
367*a*	,,	2s. 5d. dp. blue, lt. blue, orge.-brn., blue-grey and black (8.65) ..	7	6	4	6
368	**180**	2s. 6d. black, red, grey and green (21.4.65) ..	12	6	6	0
369	**181**	3s. black, red, buff and yellow-green (21.4.65)	15	0	8	0

No. 367*a* is from a printing on unsurfaced Wiggins Teape paper, the rest of the set being on chalk-surfaced Harrison paper. Apart from the differences in shade, the inscriptions, particularly "BLUE WREN", stand out very much more clearly on No. 367*a*.

182. "Bleriot" Aircraft (type flown by M. Guillaux, 1914).

1964 1 (July). *50th Anniv. of First Australian Airmail Flight. Recess. P* 14½ × 14.

370	**182**	5d. olive-green	0	9	0	9
371	,,	2s. 3d. scarlet	4	6	4	6

183. Child looking at Nativity Scene.

184. "Simpson and his Donkey".

(Des. J. Mason. Photo.)

1964 (21 Oct.). *Christmas. Chalky paper. P* 13½.

372	**183**	5d. red, blue, buff & blk.	0	9	0	7
		a. Red omitted				
		b. Black omitted				

The red ink is soluble and can be removed by bleaching and it is therefore advisable to obtain a certificate from a recognised expert committee before purchasing No. 372a.

(Des. C. Andrew (after statue, Shrine of Remembrance, Melbourne). Recess.)

1965 (14 Apr.). *50th Anniv. of Gallipoli Landing. P* 14 × 14½.

373	**184**	5d. drab	0	9	0	9
374	,,	8d. blue	1	2	1	4
375	,,	2s. 3d. reddish purple ..	3	0	3	6

185. "Telecommunications".

186. Sir Winston Churchill.

1965 (10 May). *I.T.U. Centenary. Photo. P* 13½.
376 **185** 5d. black, brown, orange-brown and blue .. 0 9 0 9
a. Black (value and pylon) omitted .. .. ..

(From photo by Karsh. Photo.)

1965 (24 May). *Churchill Commemoration. Chalky paper. P* 13½.
377 **186** 5d. black, pale grey and light blue 0 9 0 9

About half the printing was on helecon impregnated paper, differing slightly in the shade of the blue.

187. General Monash. **189.** I.C.Y. Emblem.

188. Hargrave and " Seaplane " (1902).

(Des. O. Foulkes. Photo.)

1965 (23 June). *Birth Centenary of General Sir John Monash (engineer and soldier). Chalky paper. P* 13½.
378 **187** 5d. multicoloured .. 0 9 0 9

(Des. G. Hamori. Photo.)

1965 (4 Aug.). 50*th Death Anniv. of Lawrence Hargrave (aviation pioneer). Chalky paper. P* 13½.
379 **188** 5d. purple-brown, black, yellow-ochre & purple 0 9 0 9
a. Purple (value) omitted ..

1965 (1 Sept.). *International Co-operation Year. Chalky paper. Photo. P* 13½.
380 **189** 2s. 3d. emer. & lt. blue .. 3 0 3 0

190. " Nativity Scene ".

(Des. J. Mason. Photo.)

1965 (20 Oct.). *Christmas. P* 13½.
381 **190** 5d. multicoloured .. 0 9 0 7

(New currency. 100 cents = 1 dollar.)

191. Queen Elizabeth II. **192.** Blue-faced Honeyeater.

193. Humbug Fish. **194.** Coral Fish.

195. Hermit Crab. **196.** Anemone Fish.

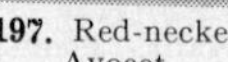

197. Red-necked Avocet. **198.** Azure Kingfisher.

(Des. Mrs. H. Temple-Watts (6 c., 13 c., 24 c.), Eileen Mayo (7 c. to 10 c.). Recess. (1 c. to 4 c., 40 c. to $4). Photo. Chalky paper (others).)

1966. (14 Feb.). *Decimal currency. No wmk. P* 15 × 14 (1 c. *to* 4 c.), 14½ × 14 (40 c., 75 c., $1), 14½ (50 c., $2, $4) *or* 13½ (*others*).
382 **191** 1 c. deep red-brown .. 0 2 0 2
383 ,, 2 c. olive-green 0 4 0 2
384 ,, 3 c. slate-green 0 6 0 3
a. Coil pair (*p.* 13½ × *imp.*) 1 6
385 ,, 4 c. red 0 7 0 3
a. Coil pair (*p.* 13½ × *imp.*) 1 9
386 **175** 5 c. brown, yellow, blk., and green 0 9 0 4
387 **192** 6 c. olive-yellow, black, blue & pale grey .. 0 10 0 5

No.	Type	Description	Unused	Used
388	**193**	7 c. black, grey, salmon and brown	0 11	0 7
389	**194**	8 c. red, yell., blue-grn., and blackish green ..	1 0	0 9
390	**195**	9 c. brown-red, pur.-brn., black & lt. yell.-olive	1 1	0 9
391	**196**	10 c. multicoloured ..	1 3	0 6
392	**197**	13 c. red, black, grey and light turquoise-grn.	1 6	1 0
393	**177**	15 c. rose-carmine, black, grey & lt. bluish grn.	1 8	0 7
394	**178**	20 c. yellow, black & pink	2 3	0 8
395	**198**	24 c. ultramarine, yellow, black & light brown	2 8	1 6
396	**180**	25 c. blk., red, grey & grn.	2 9	1 0
397	**181**	30 c. black, red, buff and light yellow-green ..	3 4	2 0
398	**167**	40 c. ultramarine ..	4 3	2 6
399	**168**	50 c. red-brown	5 4	2 6
400	**169**	75 c. olive	8 0	5 0
401	**170**	$1 brown-purple ..	10 6	6 6
402	**171**	$2 deep reddish violet	21 0	12 6
403	**172**	$4 sepia	40 0	35 0

POSTAGE DUE STAMPS.

POSTAGE DUE PRINTERS. Nos. D1/62 were typographed at the New South Wales Government Printing Office, Sydney.

D 1

D 2

1902 (From JULY). *Type* D **1**, *design of the similar stamps of New South Wales* (*T* **120**), *with the letters at foot removed. Chalk-surfaced paper. Wmk.* D **2**.

(*a*) *P* 11½, 12.

No.	Description	Unused	Used
D 1	½d. emerald-green	2 6	2 6
D 2	1d. emerald-green	3 0	2 6
D 3	2d. emerald-green	3 6	2 6
D 4	3d. emerald-green	5 0	3 6
D 5	4d. emerald-green	6 0	3 6
D 6	6d. emerald-green	7 6	3 6
D 7	8d. emerald-green	17 6	12 6
D 8	5s. emerald-green	40 0	25 0

(*b*) *P* 11½, 12, *compound with* 11.

No.	Description	Unused	Used
D 9	1d. emerald-green	12 6	7 6
D 10	2d. emerald-green	15 0	8 6
D 11	4d. emerald-green	£8	£6

(*c*) *P* 11.

No.	Description	Unused	Used
D 12	1d. emerald-green	65 0	30 0

Stamps may be found showing portions of the letters "N S W" at foot.

D 3

D 4

1902–4. *Type* D **3**, *space at foot filled in. Chalky paper. Wmk.* D **2**. (*a*) *P* 11½, 12.

No.	Description	Unused	Used
D 13	1d. emerald-green	20 0	10 0
D 14	2d. emerald-green	30 0	12 6
D 15	3d. emerald-green	32 6	12 6
D 16	4d. emerald-green		
D 17	5d. emerald-green	3 6	2 6
D 18	10d. emerald-green	10 0	3 0
D 19	1s. emerald-green	10 0	2 0
D 20	2s. emerald-green	15 0	5 0
D 21	5s. emerald-green	£8	80 0

(*b*) *P* 11½, 12, *compound with* 11.

No.	Description	Unused	Used
D 22	½d. emerald-green	5 0	2 0
D 23	1d. emerald-green	2 0	1 0
D 24	2d. emerald-green	3 6	1 0
D 25	3d. emerald-green	3 6	1 0
D 26	4d. emerald-green	7 6	2 6
D 27	5d. emerald-green	8 6	2 6
D 28	6d. emerald-green	8 6	3 0
D 29	8d. emerald-green	12 6	6 0
D 30	10d. emerald-green	12 6	6 0
D 31	1s. emerald-green	12 6	6 6
D 32	2s. emerald-green	35 0	7 6
D 33	5s. emerald-green	40 0	10 0

(*c*) *P* 11.

No.	Description	Unused	Used
D 34	½d. emerald-green	35 0	15 0
D 35	1d. emerald-green	7 6	3 6
D 36	2d. emerald-green	5 0	3 0
D 37	3d. emerald-green	5 0	3 0
D 38	4d. emerald-green	7 6	4 0
D 39	5d. emerald-green	22 6	10 0
D 40	6d. emerald-green	10 0	4 0
D 41	1s. emerald-green	27 6	10 0
D 42	5s. emerald-green	80 0	22 6
D 43	10s. emerald-green	£24	£18
D 44	20s. emerald-green	£30	£20

1906–8. *Chalky paper. Wmk. Type* D **4**.
(*a*) *P* 11½, 12, *compound with* 11.

No.	Type	Description	Unused	Used
D45	D **3**	½d. emerald-green (1907)	2 0	1 6
D46	,,	1d. emerald-green ..	1 6	1 0
D47	,,	2d. emerald-green ..	2 0	1 0
D48	,,	3d. emerald-green ..	17 6	7 6
D49	,,	4d. emerald-green (1907)	6 0	3 0
D50	,,	6d. emerald-green (1908)	8 0	3 0

(*b*) *P* 11.

No.	Type	Description	Unused	Used
D51	D **3**	1d. emerald-green ..	15 0	8 0
D52	,,	4d. emerald-green ..	32 6	25 0

1907. *Chalky paper. Wmk. Type* w.**11**. *P* 11½, 12, *compound with* 11.

No.	Type	Description	Unused	Used
D53	D **3**	½d. emerald-green ..	5 0	2 6
D54	,,	1d. emerald-green ..	5 0	2 6
D55	,,	2d. emerald-green ..	15 0	5 0
D56	,,	4d. emerald-green ..	30 0	12 6
D57	,,	6d. emerald-green ..	30 0	12 6

D 6

D 7

1908–9 (SEPT.). *Stroke after figure of value. Chalky paper. Wmk. Type* D **4.** (*a*) *P* 11½, 12, *compound with* 11.

D 58 D **6** 1s. emerald-grn. (1909) 20 0 7 6
D 59 ,, 5s. emerald-green .. 60 0 15 0

(*b*) *P* 11.

D 60 D **6** 2s. emerald-green .. £8 £6
D 61 ,, 10s. emerald-green .. £25 £14
D 62 ,, 20s. emerald-green .. £45 £24

(Typo. J. B. Cooke, Melbourne.)

1909 (JULY)–**1911.** *Type* D **7.** *Wmk. Crown over A, Type* w.**11.**

(*a*) *P* 12 × 12½ (*comb*) *or* 12½ (*line*).

D 63 ½d. rosine and yellow-green 1 0 2 0
D 64 1d. rosine and yellow-green 2 0 1 0
D 65 2d. rosine and yellow-green 1 6 1 0
D 66 3d. rosine and yellow-green 2 6 2 6
D 67 4d. rosine and yellow-green 2 6 2 0
D 68 6d. rosine and yellow-green 5 0 2 0
D 69 1s. rosine and yellow-green 7 6 3 0
D 70 2s. rosine and yellow-green 17 6 5 0
D 71 5s. rosine and yellow-green 25 0 6 6
D 72 10s. rosine and yellow-green 70 0 30 0
D 73 £1 rosine and yellow-green £8 70 0

Of the 1d. and 2d., two Dies exist differing in the detail of the value-tablet or figure. Subsequent issues are all from the second Dies.

(*b*) *P* 11.

D 74 1d. rose & yellow-grn. (1911) £7 £5
D 75 6d. rose and yellow-green.. £25 £20

The 1d. of this printing is distinguishable from No. D 78 by the colours, the green being very yellow and the rose having less of a carmine tone. The paper is thicker and slightly toned, that of No. D 78 being pure white, the gum is thick and yellowish, No. D 78 having thin white gum.

1912–23. *Type* D **7.** *Thin paper. White gum.* *W* w.**11.** (*a*) *P* 12½ (Dec., 1912).

D 76 ½d. scarlet and pale yell.grn. 6 0 3 6

(*b*) *P* 11 (1913).

D 77 ½d. rosine and apple-green . 3 0 6 0
D 78 1d. rosine and apple-green . 1 0 1 0

(*c*) *P* 14 (Oct., 1914–23).

D 79 1d. scar. & p. yell.-grn. (11.14) 3 6 2 0
D 80 2d. scar. & p. yell.-grn. (4.18) 1 6 2 0
D 81 1s. scar. & p. yell.-grn. (7.23) 4 0 4 0
D 82 10s. scar. & p. yell.-grn. (5.21) 80 0 60 0
D 83 £1 scar. & p. yell.-grn. (5.21) £8 £5

Although printed by Cooke in 1914, the three higher values were not issued until some years later.

1916. *Type* D **7.** *Wmk. Type* w. **11.** *P* 14.

D 84 ½d. rosine and yellow-green 12 6 4 0
D 85 1d. rosine and yellow-green 10 0 4 0

(Typo. T. S. Harrison, Melbourne.)

1918–21. *Type* D **7.** *Wmk. Type* w. **11.** *P* 14.

D 86 ½d. carmine & apple-green 1 6 2 0
D 87 1d. carmine & apple-green 1 6 1 0
D 88 2d. carmine & apple-green 2 6 1 0
D 89 3d. carm. & apple-grn. (1919) 5 0 3 0
D 90 4d. carmine & apple-green (26.4.21) 6 0 4 0

Nos. D 77, D 78 and D 90 exist with wmk. sideways.

(Typo. Harrison, Mullett or Ash.)

1918–30. *W* **6.** (*a*) *P* 14.

D 91 D **7** ½d. carm. & yell.-grn. 0 6 1 0
D 92 ,, 1d. carm. & yell.-grn. 1 6 0 6
D 93 D **7** 1½d. carm. & yell.-grn. (16.3.25) 1 6 3 0
D 94 ,, 2d. carm. & yell.-grn. 1 6 1 0
D 95 ,, 3d. carm. & yell.-grn. 1 6 1 0
D 96 ,, 4d. carm. & yell.-grn. 2 6 3 6
D 97 ,, 6d. carm. & yell.-grn. 4 0 3 0

(*b*) *P* 11 ('30).

D 98 D **7** 4d. carm. & yell.-grn. 1 6 3 0

(Typo. John Ash.)

1931–36. *W* **15.** (*a*) *P* 14.

D 100 D **7** 1d. carm. & yell.-grn. 1 6 1 6
D 102 ,, 2d. carm. & yell.-grn. 1 6 1 6

(*b*) *P* 11.

D 105 D **7** ½d. carm. & yell.-grn. ('34) 2 6 2 6
D 106 ,, 1d. carm. & yell.-grn. 0 9 0 4
D 107 ,, 2d. carm. & yell.-grn. 1 0 0 9
D 108 ,, 3d. carm. & yell.-grn. ('36) 27 6 30 0
D 109 ,, 4d. carm. & yell.-grn. ('34) 1 6 2 6
D 110 ,, 6d. carm. & yell.-grn. ('36) £28 70 0
D 111 ,, 1s. carm. & yell.-grn. ('34) 8 6 5 0

D 8

D 9

A. B.

C.

D.

E.

(Frame recess. Value typo. J. Ash.)

1938. *W* **15.** *P* 14½ × 14.

D 112 D **8** ½d. carm. & green (A) 0 6 1 0
D 113 ,, 1d. carm. & green (A) 1 0 0 9
D 114 ,, 2d. carm. & green (A) 0 10 0 6
D 115 ,, 3d. carm. & green (B) 4 0 6 0
D 116 ,, 4d. carm. & green (A) 3 6 1 6
D 117 ,, 6d. carm. & green (A) 7 6 7 6
D 118 ,, 1s. carm. & green (D) 10 0 5 0

1946–57. *Redrawn as Type* C *and* E (1s.). *W* **15.** *P* 14½ × 14.

D 119 D **9** ½d. carmine & deep green (9.56) .. 3 0 5 0
D 120 ,, 1d. carmine & green (11.1.47) 0 6 0 4
D 121 ,, 2d. carm. & grn. (9.46) 0 6 0 6
D 122 ,, 3d. carmine and green (25.9.46) 0 6 1 0
D 123 ,, 4d. carm. & grn. (11.52) 1 0 1 0
D 124 ,, 5d. carm. & grn. (12.48) 2 0 3 0
D 125 ,, 6d. carm. & grn. (9.47) 1 6 1 3
D 126 ,, 7d. carmine and green (26.8.53) 1 3 2 0

D 127 D **9** 8d. carmine and green (24.4.57) 10 0 12 6
D 128 ,, 1s. carm. & grn. (9.47) 2 6 2 6

The "pence" values differ in the shape of the coloured portion in the middle of the "D". In Type E of the 1s. the "1" is larger, has only three background lines above and the hyphen is more upright.

D 10.

1953 (26 Aug.)-**60.** *W* **15.** *P* 14½ × 14.
D 129 D **10** 1s. carmine and green (17.2.54) 3 6 2 6
D 130 ,, 2s. carmine and green 5 0 4 0
D 131 ,, 5s. carmine and green 12 6 6 0
a. Dp. carm. & dp. grn. ('60) 10 0 4 0

I.

II.

Type I. Numeral, "D" and stop, generally unoutlined.
Type II. Clear white line separates numeral, etc. from background.

1958–60. *No wmk.* *P* 14½ × 14.
D132 D **9** ½d. carmine and deep green (II) (27.2.58) 0 6 0 9
D133 ,, 1d. carmine and deep green (I) (25.2.58) 5 0 8 6
a. Type II ('60) .. 0 6 0 6
D134 ,, 3d. carmine and deep green (II) (25.5.60) 0 6 0 7
D135 ,, 4d. carmine and deep green (I) (27.2.58) 2 0 2 6
a. Type II ('60) .. 10 0 10 0
D136 ,, 5d. carmine and deep green (I) (27.2.58) 4 0 4 6
a. Type II (-.12.59) .. £7 40 0
D137 ,, 6d. carmine and deep green (II) (25.5.60) 1 0 1 0
D138 ,, 8d. carmine and deep green (II) (25.2.58) 7 6 8 6
D139 ,, 10d. carmine and deep green (II) (9.12.59) 1 6 1 9
D140 D **10** 1s. carmine and deep green (8.9.58) .. 3 6 2 6
a. Deep carmine & deep green ('60) 2 0 1 9
D141 ,, 2s. deep carmine and deep green (8.3.60) 3 0 3 0

Nos. D 140*a* and D 141. Value tablets are re-engraved and have thicker and sharper printed lines than before.

The use of Postage Due stamps ceased on 31st January, 1963.

OFFICIAL STAMPS.

Postage stamps perforated "O S" in either large or small letters were used for official purposes. We do not list such varieties separately, but can supply when in stock.

O S

O 1

1931 (4 May). *Overprinted with Type* O **1.**
O 1 **13** 2d. rose-red 35 0 7 6
O 2 ,, 3d. blue £6 80 0

1931 (17 Nov.). *Air. No.* 139 *optd. with Type* O **1.**
O 3 6d. sepia 12 6 7 6

This stamp was on sale at all Post Offices for use by the public and is really a normal postage stamp.

1932–33. *Overprinted as Type* O **1.**
(*a*) *W* **7.** (i.) *P* 13½ × 12½.
O 4 **5a** 2d. golden scarlet (No. 99*b*) 1 0 0 4
O 5 ,, 4d. yellow-olive (Jan. '32) 5 0 1 3
(ii.) *P* 12.
O 6 **1** 6d. chestnut 10 0 8 6
(*b*) *W* **15.** (i.) *P* 13½ × 12½.
O 7 **5a** ½d. orange 1 6 1 0
a. Overprint inverted .. — £25
O 8 ,, 1d. sage-green (Feb. '32) 1 6 0 6
O 9 ,, 2d. golden scarlet (10.2.32) 2 0 0 6
O 10 ,, 3d. ultramarine (Mar. '33) 2 6 2 0
O 11 ,, 5d. orange-brown .. 3 6 5 0
(ii.) *P* 12.
O 13 **1** 6d. chestnut 3 6 7 6
(*c*) *Recess-printed.* *No wmk.* *P* 11.
O 16 **18** 2d. scarlet 1 6 1 0
O 17 ,, 3d. blue 3 6 5 0
O 18 **17** 1s. green 5 0 4 0

Issues of specially overprinted Official stamps became obsolete in 1933 when the various States reverted to the use of stamps with perforated initials.

BRITISH COMMONWEALTH OCCUPATION FORCE (JAPAN).

B.C.O.F.
JAPAN
1946
(1)

B.C.O.F
JAPAN
1946
(2)

1946 (11 Oct.)–**1947** (8 May). *Stamps of Australia optd. as T* **1** (*1d. and 3d.*) *or T* **2** (*other values*).
B1 **27** ½d. orange (No. 179) .. 2 6 3 6
B2 **46** 1d. brown-purple (No. 203) 1 6 2 0
a. Error. Blue overprint .. 30 0 40 0
B3 **31** 3d. purple-brown (No. 187) 1 6 2 0
B4 **34** 6d. purple-brown (No. 189*a*) 4 0 5 0
B5 **36** 1s. grey-green (No. 191) .. 5 0 6 6
B6 **1** 2s. maroon (No. 212) .. 10 6 15 0
B7 **38** 5s. claret (No. 176) .. 50 0 65 0
a. Thin rough paper (No. 176a) 75 0 80 0

The ½d., 1d. and 3d. values were first issued on 11th October, 1946, and withdrawn two days later, but were re-issued together with the other values on 8th May, 1947.

The following values with T **2** opt. in the colours given were from proof sheets, which however were used for postage: ½d. (red), 1d. (red or black) and 3d. (gold, red or black).

The use of B.C.O.F. stamps ceased on March 28, 1949.

AUSTRALIAN ANTARCTIC TERRITORY.

NOTE. All Antarctic Territory stamps are also valid for use in Australia, where they are put on sale for a limited period when first issued.

1. 1954 Expedition at Vestfold Hills and Map.

1957 (27 MAR.). *P* 14½.

1 **1** 2s. ultramarine 3 0 3 0

March 27th was *Australian* date of issue; first territory use 11th December 1957.

2. Members of Shackleton Expedition at South Magnetic Pole, 1909.

3. Weazel and Team.

4. Dog-team and Iceberg.

5. Map of Antarctica and Emperor Penguins.

1959 (16 DEC.). *Recess; value typo.* (*5d., 8d.*). *P* 14½ (*5d.*), 14½ × 14 (*8d.*) *or* 14 × 14½ (*others*).

2 **2** 5d. sepia and black 0 9 1 0
3 **3** 8d. deep blue 0 11 1 0
4 **4** 1s. deep green.. .. .. 1 2 1 3
5 **5** 2s. 3d. green 2 6 2 9

16th December 1959 *Australian* date of issue; first local use 30th January 1960.

6

7. Sir Douglas Mawson (Expedition leader).

1961 (5 JULY). *Recess. P* 14½.

6 **6** 5d. deep blue 0 7 0 8

1961 (18 OCT.). 50*th Anniv.* 1911–14 *Australasian Antarctic Expedition. Recess. P* 14½.

7 **7** 5d. myrtle-green 1 0 1 3

BAGHDAD (BRITISH OCCUPATION).

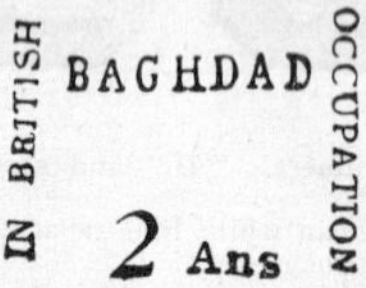

IN BRITISH
BAGHDAD
OCCUPATION
2 Ans

(1)

1917 (SEPT.). *Stamps of Turkey, surch. as* **T 1.**

(*a*) *Pictorial designs of* 1913. **T 32,** *etc., and* **31.**

1 ½ a. on 2 par. claret £6 £5
2 ½ a. on 5 par. dull purple .. 75 0 60 0
a. Value omitted .. ..
3 ½ a. on 10 par. green £10
4 ½ a. on 10 par. green (**T 31**) .. £25 £30
5 1 a. on 20 par. red £10 £10
6 2 a. on 1 pias, bright blue .. £6 £5

(*b*) *As* (*a*), *but overprinted with small Star.*

7 1 a. on 20 par. red (B.) .. £12 £10
a. "OCCUPATION" omitted ..
8 2 a. on 1 pias, bright blue (R.) £80 £65

(*c*) *Postal Jubilee stamps,* **T 56.**

9 ½ a. on 10 par. carmine .. £12 £10
10 1 a. on 20 par. blue £25 £25
a. Value omitted .. ..
11 2 a. on 1 pias, blk. & violet .. 80 0 60 0
a. "BAGHDAD" omitted ..

(*d*) **T 30** *with opt.* **T 26.**

12 2 a. on 1 pias, bright blue .. £10 £9

(*e*) *Stamps optd. with Star and Arabic date* " 1331 " *within Crescent.* **T 53** (*except No.* 16, **T 60**).

13 ½ a. on 10 par. green (**T30**) (R.) 80 0 70 0
14 1 a. on 20 par. rose (**T 30**) .. £18
a. Value omitted £175 £100
b. Overprinted with Type 26 in addition £150 £175
15 1 a. on 20 par. rose (No. 257) £15 £14
a. **Value omitted** ..
16 1 a. on 20 par. carm. (No. N44) £75 £70
17 2 a. on 1 pias. ultram. (**T30**) (R.) £6 90 0
18 2 a. on 1 pias dull blue (No. 218) (R.) £7 £6

(*f*) *Stamps with similar opt., but date between Star and Crescent* (*Nos.* 19 *and* 22, *T* **54**; *others T* **57**).

19 ½ a. on 10 par. grey-green (No. 248) (R.) 85 0 75 0
 a. "OCCUPATION" omitted .. £100
20 ½ a. on 10 par. carm. (T **56**) (B.) £8 £7
21 1 a. on 20 par. rose (T **30**) .. 85 0 80 0
22 1 a. on 20 par. rose (No. 320) £12 £12
23 1 a. on 10 par. on 20 par. claret (No. 638) £10 £9
 a. "OCCUPATION" omitted ..
24 2 a. on 1 pias. ultram. (T**30**) (R.) £8 £7
 a. "OCCUPATION" omitted .. £90
 b. "BAGHDAD" omitted .. £100
25 2 a. on 1 pias. ultram. (No. 323) £30 £30

The last group (*f*) have the Crescent obliterated in violet-black ink, as this included the inscription, "Tax for the relief of children of martyrs".

BAHAMAS.

For GREAT BRITAIN stamps used in Bahamas, see page 65.

1

2

(Engraved and recess. Perkins Bacon & Co.)

1859 (10 JUNE). *No wmk. Imperf.*

(*a*) *Thick paper.*

1 **1** 1d. reddish lake £100 £100
1*a* ,, 1d. brown-lake £60 £70

(*b*) *Thin paper.*

2 **1** 1d. dull lake (*Pen-canc.* 15*s.*) 75 0 £40

Collectors are warned against false postmarks upon the remainder stamps of 1d., imperf., on thin paper.

1860 (OCT.). *No wmk. Clean-cut perf.* 14 *to* 16.

3 **1** 1d. lake £60 £45

1861 (JUNE-DEC.). *No wmk.*

(*a*) *Rough perf.* 14 *to* 16.

4 **1** 1d. lake £20 £10
5 **2** 4d. dull rose (Dec., 1861) .. £80 £30
 a. Imperf. between (pair) ..
6 ,, 6d. grey-lilac (Dec., 1861) .. £75 £25
6*a* ,, 6d. pale dull lilac £70 £25

(*b*) *P* 11 *to* 12.

7 **1** 1d. lake £90

No. 7 was not sent out to the Colony. It is also known part perforated.

(Recess. De La Rue & Co.)

1862. *No wmk.** (*a*) *P* 11½, 12.

8 **1** 1d. carmine-lake £35 £10
9 ,, 1d. lake £30 £15
10 **2** 4d. dull rose £125 £18
11 ,, 6d. lavender-grey .. £130 £30

(*b*) *P* 11½, 12, *compound with* 11.

12 **1** 1d. carmine-lake £60 £50
13 ,, 1d. lake .. .. ..
14 **2** 4d. dull rose .. .. — £120
15 ,, 6d. lavender-grey .. — £80

(*c*) *P* 13.

16 **1** 1d. lake £30 £8
17 ,, 1d. brown-lake £28 £8
18 **2** 4d. dull rose £60 £25
19 ,, 6d. lavender-grey £65 £20
19*a* ,, 6d. lilac £90 £35

*Stamps exist with part of papermaker's sheet wmk. ("T. H. SAUNDERS" and date).

3

(T **3** Typo. De La Rue.

1863-80. *Wmk. Crown CC.* (*a*) *P* 12½.

20 **1** 1d. brown-lake 65 0 65 0
21 ,, 1d. carmine-lake 65 0 65 0
22 ,, 1d. carmine-lake (aniline) £6 £5
23 ,, 1d. rose-red 65 0 65 0
24 ,, 1d. red 50 0 60 0
25 ,, 1d. vermilion 55 0 65 0
26 **2** 4d. dull rose £12 £5
27 ,, 4d. bright rose £9 85 0
28 ,, 4d. brownish rose .. £20 £8
28*a* ,, 6d. rose-lilac .. ..
29 ,, 6d. lilac (*shades*) .. £16 70 0
30 ,, 6d. deep violet (*Pen-c.* 15*s.*) £9 70 0
31 ,, 6d. violet (aniline) .. £12 £6
32 **3** 1s. green (1869?) £75 £15

No. 28*a*, believed to be the shade of the first printing only, is a very rare stamp, not to be confused with No. 29.

(*b*) *P* 14.

33 **1** 1d. scarlet-vermilion .. 55 0 50 0
34 ,, 1d. scarlet (aniline) .. £60 £15
35 **2** 4d. bright rose £35 90 0
36 ,, 4d. dull rose £30 85 0
37 ,, 4d. rose-lake £35 £5
38 **3** 1s. dark green (1863) .. 70 0 35 0
39 ,, 1s. green (thick paper) (1880?) 12 6 17 6

1882 (MARCH). *Wmk. Crown CA.* (*a*) *P* 12.

40 **1** 1d. scarlet-vermilion .. 50 0 50 0
41 **2** 4d. rose £20 85 0

(*b*) *P* 14.

42 **1** 1d. scarlet-vermilion .. £14 80 0
43 **2** 4d. rose £45 95 0
44 **3** 1s. green 55 0 50 0

FOURPENCE
(**4**)

5

1883. *No.* 30 *surch. with T* **4.**
45 **2** 4d. on 6d. deep violet .. £25 £20
a. Surch. inverted £110 £100

The surcharge is also found placed diagonally and in various other positions.

(Typo. De La Rue.)

1884–98. *Wmk. Crown CA. P* 14.
47 **5** 1d. pale rose 30 0 25 0
48 ,, 1d. carmine-rose 15 0 4 6
49 ,, 1d. bright carmine (aniline) 12 6 15 0
50 ,, 2½d. dull blue 45 0 35 0
51 ,, 2½d. blue 45 0 15 0
52 ,, 2½d. ultramarine 7 6 5 0
53 ,, 4d. deep yellow 12 6 10 0
54 ,, 6d. mauve 15 0 17 6
55 **3** 1s. blue-green (1898) .. 32 6 35 0
56 **5** 5s. sage-green 90 0 £6
57 ,, £1 Venetian red £22 £18

6. Queen's Staircase, Nassau. **7.**

(Recess. De La Rue.)

1901–10. *P* 14.
(*a*) *Wmk. Crown CC.* (Sept., 1901)
58 **6** 1d. black and red 6 0 6 0
(*b*) *Wmk. Mult. Crown CA* (1910).
59 **6** 1d. black and red 8 6 8 6
For later shades, see Nos. 93/4.

(Typo. De La Rue.

1902 (Dec.). *Wmk. Crown CA. P* 14.
60 **7** 1d. carmine 5 0 2 6
61 ,, 2½d. ultramarine 22 6 10 0
62 ,, 4d. orange 25 0 40 0
63 ,, 4d. deep yellow 30 0 40 0
64 ,, 6d. brown 25 0 25 0
65 ,, 1s. grey-black & carmine .. 35 0 40 0
66 ,, 1s. brownish grey & carm. 35 0 42 6
67 ,, 5s. dull purple and blue .. £6 £8
68 ,, £1 green and black .. £50 £60

1903. *Wmk. Crown CC. P* 14.
69 **6** 5d. black and orange .. 17 6 27 6
70 ,, 2s. black and blue 30 0 40 0
71 ,, 3s. black and green 40 0 50 0

1906–11. *Wmk. Mult. Crown CA. P* 14.
72 **7** ½d. pale green 5 0 6 0
73 ,, 1d. carmine-rose 5 0 2 0
74 ,, 2½d. ultramarine (1907) .. 22 6 25 0
75 ,, 6d. bistre-brown (1911) .. 65 0 85 0

8 **1.1.17.** **(9)**

(Typo. De La Rue.)

1912–19. *Wmk. Mult. Crown CA. P* 14.
76 **8** ½d. green, O 0 4 0 10
77 ,, ½d. yellow-green, O .. 2 0 2 6
78 **8** 1d. carmine (aniline), O .. 1 0 0 10
79 ,, 1d. deep rose, O 4 0 2 6
80 ,, 1d. rose, O 4 6 3 0
81 ,, 2d. grey, O (1919) .. 5 0 5 0
82 ,, 2½d. ultramarine, O .. 12 6 17 6
83 ,, 2½d. deep dull blue, O .. 15 0 20 0
84 ,, 4d. orange-yellow, O .. 8 6 12 6
85 ,, 4d. yellow, O 5 0 12 6
86 ,, 6d. bistre-brown, O .. 5 0 8 6
87 ,, 1s. grey-blk. & carmine, C 8 6 12 6
88 ,, 1s. jet-black & carmine, C 17 6 22 6
89 ,, 5s. dull purple and blue, C 55 0 60 0
90 ,, 5s. p. dull pur. & dp. bl., C 70 0 75 0
91 ,, £1 dull green and black, C £14 £18
92 ,, £1 green and black, C .. £20 £24

1916–19. *Wmk. Mult. Crown CA. P* 14.
93 **6** 1d. grey-black & scarlet ('16) 3 0 4 0
94 ,, 1d. grey-black and deep carmine-red (1919) 6 0 6 0
95 ,, 3d. purp./*orange* (*thin*) (1917) 22 6 27 6
96 ,, 3d. reddish purple/*yellow* (*thick*) (1.19) 10 0 17 6
97 ,, 5d. black & mauve (18.5.17) 7 6 10 0
98 ,, 2s. black and blue (11.16) .. 45 0 45 0
99 ,, 3s. black and green (8.17) .. 50 0 50 0

1917 (18 May). *No.* 59 *optd. with T* **9.**
100 **6** 1d. black and red (R.) .. 0 6 1 0
a. Long stroke to "7" .. 85 0 90 0

The above stamps were to have been on sale on 1st January, 1917, but owing to delay in shipment they were not issued till May, 1917.

WAR TAX
(10)

1918 (21 Feb.). *Optd. locally at Nassau with T* **10.**
101 **8** ½d. green 6 0 7 6
a. Opt. double £18 £18
b. Opt. inverted £16
102 ,, 1d. carmine 3 6 3 6
a. Opt. double £20 £20
b. Opt. inverted £10
103 **6** 3d. purple/*yellow* 5 0 6 0
a. Opt. double £18 £18
b. Opt. inverted £18 £18
104 **8** 1s. grey-black & carmine .. 60 0 80 0
a. Opt. double £50

1918 (10 July). *Wmk. Mult. Crown CA. Optd. with T* **10.**
105 **6** 1d. black and red 3 6 5 0
a. Opt. double, one inverted .. £28
b. Opt. double £40
c. Opt. inverted £35 £40

No. 105*a* is from a sheet in which the top row was normal and the other five showed this error. No. 105 was on sale for ten days.

WAR TAX **(11)** **WAR CHARITY 3.6.18.** **(13)**

WAR TAX **(12)**

1918 (1 June–20 July). *Optd. in London with T* **11** *or* **12** (3*d*.).
106 **8** ½d. green 0 6 1 0
107 ,, 1d. carmine 0 6 0 9
a. Wmk. sideway £45
108 **6** 3d. purple/*yellow* (20 July) 2 0 4 0
109 **8** 1s. grey-black & carm. (R.) 3 0 7 6

1919 (21 Mar.). *Colour changed. Wmk. Mult. Crown CA. P* 14.
110 **6** 3d. black and brown .. 3 0 4 0

1919 (21 Mar.). *No.* 110 *optd. with T* **12.**
111 **6** 3d. black and brown .. 2 0 4 0

1919 (1 Jan.). *No. 59 optd. with T* **13.**

112	**6**	1d. black and red (R.)	1 0	2 6
		a. Opt. double	£50	

The date is that originally fixed for the issue of the stamp. The year 1918 was also the bicentenary of the appointment of the first Royal governor.

WAR **WAR**

TAX **TAX**

(**14**) (**15**)

1919 (14 July). *Optd. with T* **14.**

113	**8**	½d. green (R.)	0 6	1 0
114	"	1d. carmine..	0 9	1 6
115	"	1s. grey-blk. & carmine (R.)	4 0	8 6

No. 110 optd. with T **15.**

116	**6**	3d. black and brown ..	2 6	5 0

16

(Recess. De La Rue.)

1920 (1 Mar.). *Peace Celebration. Wmk. Mult. Crown CA (sideways). P 14.*

117	**16**	½d. green	1 3	3 0
118	"	1d. carmine	4 0	4 6
119	"	2d. slate-grey	8 6	10 0
120	"	3d. deep brown	12 6	17 6
121	"	1s. deep myrtle-green ..	35 0	45 0

1921–29. *Wmk. Mult. Script CA. P 14.*

Staircase type.

122	**6**	1d. grey and rose-red (29.3.21)	3 6	3 0
122*a*	"	5d. black and purple ('29)	12 6	17 6
123	"	2s. black and blue ('22)	30 0	35 0
123*a*	"	3s. black and green ('24)	45 0	50 0

King George V type.

124	**8**	½d. green, O ('24) ..	0 6	0 8
125	"	1d. carmine, O (8.9.21)..	0 6	0 9
125*a*	"	2d. grey, O (1927) ..	2 6	4 0
126	"	2½d. ultramarine, O ('22)	2 6	2 6
127	"	4d. orange-yellow, O ('24)	2 6	6 0
128	"	6d. bistre-brown, O ('22)	5 0	5 0
129	"	1s. black & carm., C ('26)	6 0	10 0
130	"	5s. dull pur. & bl., C ('24)	40 0	55 0
131	"	£1 green & black, C ('26)	£16	£18

17 **18**

(T **17/8.** Recess. Bradbury, Wilkinson.)

1930 (2 Jan.). *Tercentenary of Colony. Wmk. Mult. Script CA. P 12.*

132	**17**	1d. black & scarlet ..	4 0	6 0
133	,,	3d. black & deep brown ..	6 0	7 6
134	,,	5d. black & deep purple ..	10 0	17 6
135	,,	2s. black & deep blue ..	45 0	60 0
136	,,	3s. black & green	70 0	85 0

1931. *Wmk. Mult. Script CA. P 12.*

137	**18**	2s. black & deep blue ..	3 6	3 6
		a. Slate-purple & deep blue ..	50 0	50 0
138	,,	3s. black & green	6 0	6 0
		a. Slate-purple & green ..	65 0	60 0

1931–37. *Wmk. Mult. Script CA. P 14.*

139	**8**	1½d. red-brown, O ('34) ..	1 0	1 6
140	,,	3d. pur./*pale yellow*, C ('31)	12 6	10 0
		a. Purple/orange-yellow, C ('37)	17 6	20 0

1935 (6 May). *Silver Jubilee. As Nos.* 91/4 *of Antigua. P* 13½ × 14.

141	1½d. deep blue and carmine	1 3	1 6
142	2½d. brown and deep blue ..	3 0	5 0
143	6d. light blue and olive-green	7 0	7 6
144	1s. slate and purple ..	12 6	15 0

19. Flamingoes in flight.

(Recess. Waterlow.)

1935 (22 May). *Wmk. Mult. Script CA. P* 12½.

145	**19**	8d. ultramarine and scarlet	25 0	17 6

1937 (12 May). *Coronation. As Nos.* 13/15 *of Aden. P* 14.

146	½d. green	0 8	0 8
147	1½d. yellow-brown	1 0	1 0
148	2½d. bright blue	3 0	3 9

20. King George VI.

(Typo. De La Rue.)

1938–52. *Wmk. Mult. Script CA. P* 14.

149	**20**	½d. green (11.3.38) ..	0 4	0 6
149*a*	,,	½d. brown-pur. (18.2.52)	0 6	1 6
		c. Error. St. Edward's Crown	£70	
150	,,	1d. carmine (11.3.38) ..	4 0	6 0
150*a*	,,	1d. grey (17.9.41) ..	0 4	0 4

No.	Type					
151	20	1½d. red-brown (19.4.38) ..	0	8	0	10
		a. Pale red-brown (Apr. '48)	0	6	0	10
152	,,	2d. grey (19.4.38) ..	9	0	14	0
152*a*	,,	2d. scarlet (17.9.41) ..	0	9	1	3
152*b*	,,	2d. green (1.5.51) ..	0	9	2	0
153	,,	2½d. blue (11.3.38) ..	4	6	5	6
153*a*	,,	2½d. violet ('43)	0	8	1	6
154	,,	3d. violet (19.4.38) ..	4	0	7	6
154*a*	,,	3d. blue ('43)	1	0	1	0
154*b*	,,	3d. scarlet (1.2.52) ..	1	3	2	6
154*c*	,,	10d. yell.-orange (18.11.46)	2	0	2	0
155	,,	1s. black and carmine CO (15.9.38) ..	3	0	3	6
156	,,	5s. lilac and blue, C (19.4.38)	65	0	75	0
		a. Purple and blue, O ('42) ..	20	0	30	0
		b. Deep purple and bright blue, C ('48)	15	0	22	6
157	,,	£1 green and black, CO (15.9.38)	37	6	50	0

No. 149*c* occurs on a row in the watermark in which the crowns and letters "C A" alternate.

The ordinary paper of Nos. 155/7 is thick, smooth and opaque, and first appeared in 1942 as a substitute for chalk-surfaced paper.

21. Sea Garden, Nassau.

22. Fort Charlotte.

23. Flamingoes in Flight.

(Recess. Waterlow.)

1938 (1 JULY). *Wmk. Mult. Script CA. P* 12½.

No.	Type					
158	21	4d. light blue & red-orange	2	6	2	6
159	22	6d. olive-green & light blue	1	6	2	0
160	23	8d. ultramarine & scarlet	2	6	4	0

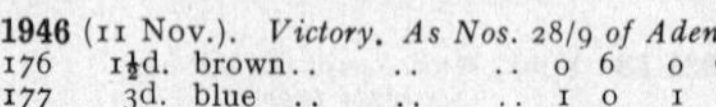

(24) (25)

1940 (28 Nov.). *No.* 153 *surcharged with T* **24.**

No.	Type					
161	20	3d. on 2½d. blue	1	0	2	6

1942 (12 OCT.). 450*th Anniv. of Landing of Columbus in New World. Optd. with T* **25.**

No.	Type					
162	20	½d. green	0	6	0	9
163	,,	1d. grey	0	6	0	9
164	,,	1½d. red-brown	0	8	1	3
165	,,	2d. scarlet	0	9	1	6
166	,,	2½d. blue	0	10	1	6
167	,,	3d. blue	1	0	1	6
168	21	4d. light bl. & red-orange	1	3	2	6
169	22	6d. olive-grn. & light blue	2	0	2	6
170	23	8d. ultramarine & scarlet	2	6	3	0
171	20	1s. black & carmine, CO	3	6	4	6
172	18	2s. black and deep blue..	7	6	8	6
		a. Slate-purple and deep blue	8	6	10	0
173	,,	3s. black and green ..	65	0	55	0
		a. Slate-purple and green ..	12	6	17	6
174	20	5s. purple and blue, CO	15	0	20	0
175	,,	£1 green and black, CO	50	0	60	0

1946 (11 Nov.). *Victory. As Nos.* 28/9 *of Aden.*

No.						
176		1½d. brown..	0	6	0	9
177		3d. blue	1	0	1	6

26. Infant Welfare Clinic.

27. Agriculture.

28. Sisal.

29. Straw Work.

30. Dairy Farm.

31. Fishing Fleet.

32. Island Settlement.

33. Tuna Fishing.

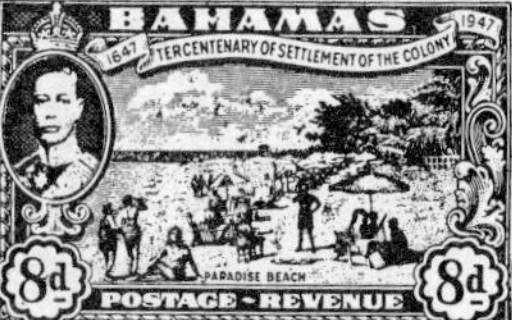

34. Paradise Beach.

35. Modern Hotels.

36. Yacht Racing.

37. Water Sports—Ski-ing.

38. Shipbuilding.

39. Transportation.

40. Salt Production.

41. Parliament Buildings.

(Recess. Canadian Bank Note Co.)

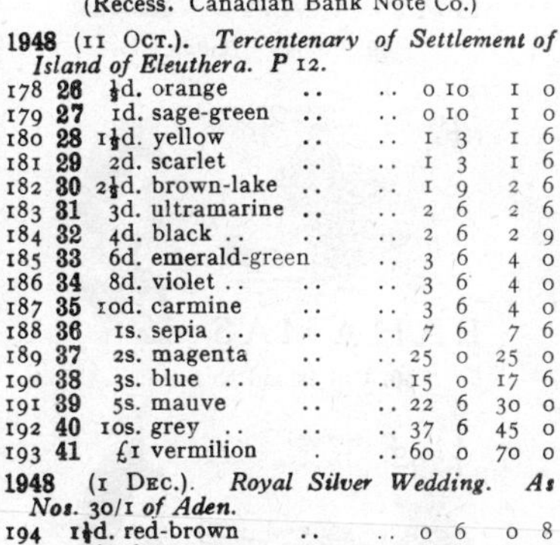

1948 (11 Oct.). *Tercentenary of Settlement of Island of Eleuthera. P* 12.

178	**26**	½d. orange	0	10	1	0
179	**27**	1d. sage-green	0	10	1	0
180	**28**	1½d. yellow	1	3	1	6
181	**29**	2d. scarlet	1	3	1	6
182	**30**	2½d. brown-lake	1	9	2	6
183	**31**	3d. ultramarine	2	6	2	6
184	**32**	4d. black	2	6	2	9
185	**33**	6d. emerald-green	3	6	4	0
186	**34**	8d. violet	3	6	4	0
187	**35**	10d. carmine	3	6	4	0
188	**36**	1s. sepia	7	6	7	6
189	**37**	2s. magenta	25	0	25	0
190	**38**	3s. blue	15	0	17	6
191	**39**	5s. mauve	22	6	30	0
192	**40**	10s. grey	37	6	45	0
193	**41**	£1 vermilion	60	0	70	0

1948 (1 Dec.). *Royal Silver Wedding. As Nos.* 30/1 *of Aden.*

194	1½d. red-brown	0	6	0	8
195	£1 slate-green	45	0	50	0

1949 (10 Oct.). *75th Anniv. of Universal Postal Union. As Nos.* 114/7 *of Antigua.*

196	2½d. violet	1	3	1	3
197	3d. deep blue	1	6	1	9
198	6d. greenish blue	2	6	3	0
199	1s. carmine	4	0	6	0

1953 (3 June). *Coronation. As No.* 47 *of Aden.*

200	6d. black and pale blue	2	0	2	6

42. Infant Welfare Clinic.

(Recess. Bradbury, Wilkinson.)

1954 (1 Jan.). *As T* **26/41** (*but portrait of Queen Elizabeth II in place of King George VI, as in T* **42**, *and commemorative inscr. omitted*). *Wmk. Mult. Script CA. P* 11 × 11½.

201	**42**	½d. black and red-orange	0	3	0	3
202	**27**	1d. olive-green & brown	0	5	0	5
203	**32**	1½d. blue and black	0	5	0	5
204	**29**	2d. yellow-brown and myrtle-green (*shades*)	0	7	0	7
205	**31**	3d. black & carmine-red	0	8	0	8
206	**37**	4d. turquoise-green & dp. reddish purp. (*shades*)	0	9	0	10
207	**30**	5d. red-brown and deep bright blue	1	0	1	0
208	**39**	6d. light blue and black	1	0	1	3
209	**34**	8d. black & reddish lilac (*shades*)	1	3	1	6
210	**35**	10d. blk. & ultram. (*shades*)	1	6	2	0
211	**36**	1s. ultramarine and olive-brown (*shades*)	1	9	2	0
212	**28**	2s. orange-brown & black (*shades*)	3	6	4	0
213	**38**	2s. 6d. black & deep blue	4	3	4	9
214	**33**	5s. bright emerald and orange (*shades*)	8	6	10	0
215	**40**	10s. black and slate-black	17	6	20	0
216	**41**	£1 slate-black and violet	35	0	40	0

43. Queen Elizabeth II.

(Recess. Waterlow & Sons, Ltd.)

1959 (10 June). *Centenary of First Bahamas Postage Stamp. W* w.**12.** *P* 13½.

217	**43**	1d. black and scarlet ..	0 9	0 10
218	,,	2d. black and blue-green	1 0	1 0
219	,,	6d. black and blue ..	1 9	2 0
220	,,	10d. black and chocolate ..	2 9	3 6

44. Christ Church Cathedral.

45. Nassau Public Library.

(Photo. J. Enschedé & Sons.)

1962 (30 Jan.). *Nassau Centenary. P* 14×13.

221	**44**	8d. green	2 0	2 3
222	**45**	10d. bluish violet	2 3	2 6

1963 (4 June). *Freedom from Hunger. As No.* 63 *of Aden.*

223	8d. sepia	1 9	2 0
	a. Name and value omitted ..	£250	

BAHAMAS TALKS 1962 (46)

NEW CONSTITUTION 1964 (47)

1963 (15 July). *Bahamas Talks,* 1962. *Nos.* 209/10 *optd. with T* **46.**

224	**34**	8d. black & reddish lilac	9 0	10 0
225	**35**	10d. black & dp. ultram.	9 6	11 0

1963 (2 Sept.). *Red Cross Centenary. As Nos.* 147/8 *of Antigua.*

226	1d. red and black	0 3	0 4
227	10d. red and blue	1 6	1 9

1964 (7 Jan.). *New Constitution. As Nos.* 201/16 *but W* w.**12**, *optd. with T* **47**, *by Bradbury, Wilkinson & Co.*

228	**42**	½d. black and red-orange	0 3	0 4
229	**27**	1d. olive-green and brown	0 4	0 6
230	**32**	1½d. blue and black ..	0 6	0 6
231	**29**	2d. yellow-brown & deep myrtle-green ..	0 7	0 9
232	**31**	3d. black & carmine-red ..	0 10	1 0
233	**37**	4d. turquoise-blue & deep reddish purple ..	1 0	1 3
234	**30**	5d. red-brn. & dp. brt. bl.	1 3	1 6
235	**39**	6d. deep blue and black ..	1 6	1 7
236	**34**	8d. black & reddish lilac	1 10	2 6
237	**35**	10d. black & dp. ultram. ..	2 3	3 0
238	**36**	1s. ultram. & olive-brown	2 6	3 3
239	**28**	2s. chestnut and black ..	5 0	6 9
240	**38**	2s. 6d. black & dp. blue ..	7 0	8 0
241	**33**	5s. brt. emerald & orange	11 0	12 6
242	**40**	10s. black and slate-black	22 6	25 0
243	**41**	£1 slate-black and violet	45 0	50 0

1964 (23 April). 400*th Anniv. of Birth of William Shakespeare. As No.* 164 *of Antigua.*

244	6d. turquoise	1 6	2 0

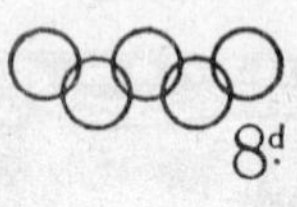

(48)

1964 (1 Oct.). *Olympic Games, Tokio. As No.* 211 *but W* w.**12**, *surch. with T* **48.**

245	**36**	8d. on 1s. ultram. & ol.-brn.	2 6	3 0

1964 (6 Oct.). *As No.* 204, *but wmk.* w.**12.**

246	**29**	2d. yellow-brown and deep myrtle-green	1 6	2 0

49. Colony's Badge.

50. Out Island Regatta.

51. Hospital.

52. High School.

53. Flamingo.

54. *Queen Elizabeth.*

55. " Development ".

56. Yachting.

10d
PUBLIC SQUARE
BAHAMAS

57. Public Square.

58. Sea Garden.

59. Old Cannons at Fort Charlotte.

60. Seaplane and Jet liner.

61. Williamson Film Project (1914) and Undersea Post Office (1939).

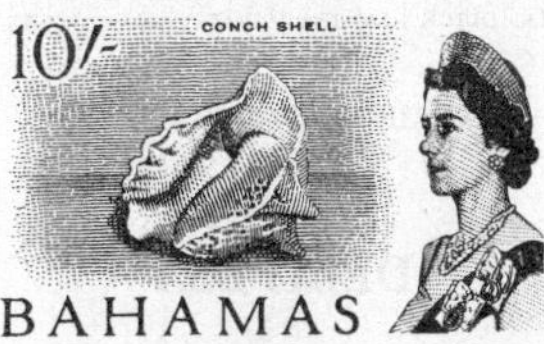

62. Conch Shell.

63. Columbus's Flagship.

(Queen's portrait by Anthony Buckley. Litho. and recess. Bradbury Wilkinson & Co.)

1965 (7 JAN.–14 SEPT.). *W* w.**12**. *P* 13½.

No.	Type	Description	Unused	Used
247	**49**	½d. multicoloured ..	0 2	0 3
248	**50**	1d. slate, lt. blue & orange	0 3	0 4
249	**51**	1½d. rose-red, grn. & brown	0 4	0 4
250	**52**	2d. slate, grn. & turq.-bl.	0 4	0 5
251	**53**	3d. red, lt. blue & purple	0 6	0 7
252	**54**	4d. grn., bl., & orge.-brn.	0 7	0 9
253	**55**	6d. dull green, light blue and rose	0 10	1 0
254	**56**	8d. reddish purple, light blue & bronze-green	1 0	1 5
255	**57**	10d. orange-brown, green and violet	1 3	1 9
256	**58**	1s. red, yellow, turquoise-blue & deep emerald	1 10	2 6
		a. Red, yellow, dull blue and emerald (14.9.65) ..	1 5	1 9
257	**59**	2s. brn., lt. blue & emer.	2 9	3 9
258	**60**	2s. 6d. yellow-olive, blue and carmine	3 6	4 0
259	**61**	5s. orange-brown, ultra-marine and green ..	6 9	7 6
260	**62**	10s. rose, blue & chocolate	13 3	15 0
261	**63**	£1 chest., bl. & rose-red	25 0	30 0

1965 (17 MAY). *I.T.U. Centenary. As Nos.* 166/7 *of Antigua.*

No.	Description	Unused	Used
262	1d. light emerald and orange	0 6	0 8
263	2s. purple and yellow-olive..	4 0	5 0

9d

(**64**)

1965 (12 JULY). *No.* 254 *surch. with T* **64**.

No.	Type	Description	Unused	Used
264	**56**	9d. on 8d. reddish purple, lt. blue & bronze-green	1 1	1 6

1965 (25 OCT.). *International Co-operation Year. As Nos.* 168/9 *of Antigua.*

No.	Description	Unused	Used
265	½d. reddish pur. & turq.-grn.	0 4	0 6
266	1s. dp. bluish grn. & lavender	2 0	2 6

1966 (24 JAN.). *Churchill Commemoration. As Nos.* 170/3 *of Antigua.*

No.	Description	Unused	Used
267	½d. new blue	0 3	0 4
268	2d. deep green	0 5	0 6
269	10d. brown	1 6	2 3
270	1s. bluish violet	1 8	2 6

1966 (4 FEB.). *Royal Visit. As Nos.* 174/5 *of Antigua, but* "to the Caribbean" *omitted.*

No.	Description	Unused	Used
271	6d. black and ultramarine ..	1 0	1 3
272	1s. black and magenta ..	1 8	2 6

SPECIAL DELIVERY STAMPS.

SPECIAL
DELIVERY

(**S 1**)

1916 (JAN.). *Wmk. Crown CC. Optd. locally with Type* S **1**.

No.	Type	Description	Unused	Used
S1	**6**	5d. black and orange ..	£10	
		a. Opt. double	£40	£45
		b. Opt. double, one inverted ..	£40	£45
		c. Opt. inverted	£40	£45
		d. Pair, one without opt. ..	£150	£150

1917 (MARCH). *As last, but* "SPECIAL" *further to right in relation to* "DELIVERY".

No.	Type	Description	Unused	Used
S2	**6**	5d. black and orange ..	40 0	45 0
		a. Opt. double	£35	£35
		b. Opt. double, one inverted ..	£35	£35
		c. Opt. inverted	£40	£40

These two stamps were to facilitate commercial correspondence between the Bahamas and Canada. No. S1 was on sale in Canada, at Ottawa, Toronto, Westmount and Winnipeg. S2, 3 and 4 were on sale in the Bahamas.

Nos. S1 and S2 are difficult to distinguish, but if a line is taken perpendicularly through the "I" of "SPECIAL", stamps with the upright of the second "E" of "DELIVERY" clear on the right of this line are No. S1. 600 were issued of S1; 6,000 of S2.

SPECIAL
DELIVERY

(S **2**)

SPECIAL
DELIVERY

(S **3**)

1917 (2 JULY). *Wmk. Mult. Crown CA. Optd. in London with Type* S **2**.

No.	Type	Description	Unused	Used
S3	**6**	5d. black and orange ..	5 0	7 6

1918. *Optd. with Type* S **3**.

No.	Type	Description	Unused	Used
S4	**6**	5d. black and mauve (R.) ..	2 6	4 0

BAHRAIN.

Bahrain is an independent shaikhdom, but with Indian and, subsequently, British postal administration. This was closed on 1st January, 1966.

BAHRAIN

(**1**)

BAHRAIN

(**2**)

Stamps of India overprinted with T **1** *or T* **2** *(rupee values).*

1933 (10 AUG.). *King George V. Wmk. Mult. Star, T* **69**.

No.	Type	Description	Unused	Used
1	**55**	3 p. slate (Dec. '33) ..	0 6	0 6
2	**56**	½ a. green	4 0	5 0
3	**80**	9 p. deep green	5 0	2 6
4	**57**	1 a. chocolate	3 6	3 0
5	**82**	1 a. 3 p. mauve	3 6	2 0
6	**70**	2 a. vermilion	4 6	5 0
7	**62**	3 a. blue	25 0	30 0
8	**83**	3 a. 6 p. ultramarine ..	4 0	3 0
9	**71**	4 a. sage-green	16 0	17 6
10	**65**	8 a. reddish purple ..	6 0	3 6
11	**66**	12 a. claret	6 0	5 0
12	**67**	1 r. chocolate and green	15 0	8 6
13	,,	2 r. carmine and orange..	30 0	15 0
14	,,	5 r. ultramarine & purple	60 0	75 0

1934–37. *King George V. Wmk. Mult. Star, T* **69**.

No.	Type	Description	Unused	Used
15	**79**	½ a. green ('35)	1 0	0 6
16	**81**	1 a. chocolate ('35)	2 6	0 6
17	**59**	2 a. vermilion ('35) ..	22 6	6 0
17*a*	,,	2 a. verm. (*small die*) ('37)	15 0	3 0
18	**62**	3 a. carmine	6 0	1 0
19	**63**	4 a. sage-green ('35) ..	6 0	2 0

19338–41. *King George VI.*

No.	Type	Description	Unused	Used
20	**91**	3 p. slate (May '38) ..	6 0	4 0
21	,,	½ a. red-brown (May '38)	0 6	0 6
22	,,	9 p. green (May '38) ..	1 6	1 6
23	,,	1 a. carmine (May '38) ..	1 0	0 9
24	**92**	2 a. vermilion ('39) ..	3 6	1 9
26	**94**	3 a. yellow-green ('41) ..	8 6	4 6
27	**95**	3½ a. bright blue (July '38)	4 6	8 6
28	**96**	4 a. brown ('41) ..	70 0	75 0
30	**98**	8 a. slate-violet ('40) ..	75 0	75 0
31	**99**	12 a. lake ('40)	75 0	75 0
32	**100**	1 r. grey & red-brn. ('40)	6 0	3 6
33	,,	2 r. purple & brown ('40)	12 6	8 0
34	,,	5 r. green and blue ('40)	30 0	22 6
35	,,	10 r. purple & claret ('41)	40 0	40 0
36	,,	15 r. brown & green ('41)	55 0	60 0
37	,,	25 r. slate-vio. & pur. ('41)	90 0	90 0

1942–45. *King George VI on white background.*

No.	Type	Description	Unused	Used
38	**100*a***	3 p. slate	0 3	0 6
39	,,	½ a. purple	0 6	0 3

40	**100a**	9 p. green	0	9	1	6
41	,,	1 a. carmine	0	6	0	3
42	**101**	1 a. 3 p. bistre	1	6	5	0
43	,,	1½ a. dull violet	0	10	1	0
44	,,	2 a. vermilion	1	3	0	9
45	,,	3 a. bright violet	2	0	2	6
46	,,	3½ a. bright blue	3	0	4	0
47	**102**	4 a. brown	3	0	1	6
48	,,	6 a. turquoise-green	10	0	5	0
49	,,	8 a. slate-violet	2	6	2	6
50	,,	12 a. lake	4	6	5	0

BAHRAIN
1
ANNA
(3)

BAHRAIN
5 RUPEES
(4)

NOTE. All the following issues until 1960 are surcharged on stamps of GREAT BRITAIN.

For similar surcharges without the name of the country, see MUSCAT.

1948 (1 APR.)–**1949.** *Surch. as T* **3**, **4** (2 *r. and* 5 *r.*) *or similar surch. with bars at foot* (10 *r.*).

51	**128**	½ a. on ½d. pale green	0	4	0	6
52	,,	1 a. on 1d. pale scarlet	0	4	0	4
53	,,	1½ a. on 1½d. pale red-brn.	1	0	2	6
54	,,	2 a. on 2d. pale orange	0	8	1	0
55	,,	2½ a. on 2½d. light ultram.	1	9	2	0
56	,,	3 a. on 3d. pale violet	1	0	1	0
57	**129**	6 a. on 6d. purple	1	3	1	6
58	**130**	1 r. on 1s. bistre-brown	3	0	3	6
59	**131**	2 r. on 2s. 6d. yell.-green	8	6	8	6
60	,,	5 r. on 5s. red	20	0	22	6
60a	**132**	10 r. on 10s. ultram. (4.7.49)	55	0	60	0

BAHRAIN
2½
ANNAS
(5)

BAHRAIN
15
RUPEES
(6)

1948 (26 APR.). *Silver Wedding, surch. as T* **5** *or* **6**.

61	**137**	2½ a. on 2½d. ultramarine	0	9	0	9
62	**138**	15 r. on £1 blue	60	0	65	0

1948 (29 JULY). *Olympic Games, surch. as T* **5**, *but in one line* (6 *a.*) *or two lines* (*others*).

63	**139**	2½ a. on 2½d. ultramarine	1	0	1	6
		a. Surcharge double	£85		£90	
64	**140**	3 a. on 3d. violet	1	6	2	0
65	**141**	6 a. on 6d. bright purple	2	0	2	6
66	**142**	1 r. on 1s. brown	5	0	7	6

BAHRAIN
3 ANNAS
(7)

1949 (10 OCT.). *75th Anniv. of U.P.U., surch. as T* **7**, *in one line* (2½ *a.*) *or in two lines* (*others*).

67	**143**	2½ a. on 2½d. ultram.	1	0	1	0
68	**144**	3 a. on 3d. violet	1	6	2	0
69	**145**	6 a. on 6d. bright purp.	3	0	3	6
70	**146**	1 r. on 1s. brown	6	0	5	0

1950–51. *Surch. as T* **3** *or* **4** (*rupee values*).

71	**128**	½ a. on ½d. pale orange	0	6	0	10
72	,,	1 a. on 1d. light ultram.	0	6	0	6
73	,,	1½ a. on 1½d. pale green	0	8	3	0
74	**128**	2 a. on 2d. pale red-brown	0	9	0	9
75	,,	2½ a. on 2½d. pale scarlet	1	0	3	0
76	**129**	4 a. on 4d. light ultram.	2	6	2	6
77	**147**	2 r. on 2s. 6d. yell.-grn.	6	0	6	0
78	**148**	5 r. on 5s. red	15	0	12	6
79	**149**	10 r. on 10s. ultramarine	27	6	27	6

Dates of issue:—2.10.50, 4 a.; 3.5.51, others.

1952–54. *Q.E. II* (*W* **153**), *surch. as T* **3**.

80	**154**	½ a. on ½d. orange-red	0	4	0	6
		a. Fraction "½" omitted	£55		£60	
81	,,	1 a. on 1d. ultramarine	0	5	0	6
82	,,	1½ a. on 1½d. green	0	7	0	8
83	,,	2 a. on 2d. red-brown	0	8	0	8
84	**155**	2½ a. on 2½d. carmine-red	0	10	1	0
85	,,	3 a. on 3d. deep lilac (B.)	1	0	0	9
86	**156**	4 a. on 4d. ultramarine	2	0	2	6
87	**157**	6 a. on 6d. reddish purple	1	6	1	6
88	**160**	12 a. on 1s. 3d. green	3	6	3	0
89	**159**	1 r. on 1s. 6d. grey-blue	4	0	2	9

The word BAHRAIN is in taller letters on the 1½ a., 2½ a., 3 a. and 6 a.

Dates of issue:—5.12.52, 1½ a., 2½ a.; 31.8.53, ½ a., 1 a., 2 a.; 2.11.53, 4 a., 12 a., 1 r.; 18.1.54, 3 a, 6 a

2½ BAHRAIN
ANNAS
(8)

1953 (3 JUNE). *Coronation, surch. as T* **8**, *or similarly*.

90	**161**	2½ a. on 2½d. carmine-red	3	0	3	0
91	**162**	4 a. on 4d. ultramarine	4	0	5	0
92	**163**	12 a. on 1s. 3d. dp. yell.-grn.	7	6	8	6
93	**164**	1 r. on 1s. 6d. dp. grey-blue	8	6	8	6

BAHRAIN 2 RUPEES I

BAHRAIN 2 RUPEES II

BAHRAIN 2 RUPEES III

(9)

BAHRAIN 5 RUPEES I

BAHRAIN 5 RUPEES II

(10)

BAHRAIN 10 RUPEES I

BAHRAIN 10 RUPEES II

(11)

TYPE I (T **9**/**11**). Type-set opt. Bold, thick letters with sharp corners and straight edges.

TYPE II (T **9/11**). Plate-printed opt. Thinner letters, rounded corners and rough edges. Bars wider apart.

Type III (T **9**). Plate-printed opt. Similar to Type II as regards the position of the bars on all 40 stamps of the sheet, but the letters are thinner and with more rounded corners than in II, while the ink of the surcharge is less black.

The general characteristics of Type II of the 2 r. are less pronounced than in the other values, but a distinguishing test is in the relative position of the bars and the " U " of " RUPEES ". In Type II (except for the 1st stamp, 5th row) the bars start immediately beneath the left-hand edge of the " U ". In Type I they start more to the right.

In the 10 r. the " 1 " and the " 0 " are spaced 0.9 mm. in Type I and only 0.6 mm. in Type II.

1955 (23 SEPT.)–**60.** *T* **166/8** (*Waterlow ptgs.*) *surch. as T* **9/11.**

No.	Type	Description	Unused	Used
94I	**166**	2 r. on 2s. 6d. black-brn.	7 6	7 6
		II. Type II (13.5.58)	25 0	20 0
		III. Type III (No. 536a, D.L.R.) (29.1.60)	65 0	65 0
95I	**167**	5 r. on 5s. rose-red	25 0	25 0
		II. Type II (19.8.57)	75 0	40 0
96I	**168**	10 r. on 10s. ultramarine	30 0	30 0
		II. Type II (13.5.58)	£12	£10

1956–57. *Q.E. II* (*W* **165**), *surch. as T***3.**

No.	Type	Description	Unused	Used
97	**154**	½ a. on ½d. orge.-red ('57)	1 0	2 0
98	**156**	4 a. on 4d. ultramarine	6 0	7 6
99	**157**	6 a. on 6d. reddish purple	2 0	2 6
100	**160**	12 a. on 1s. 3d. green	12 6	12 6
101	**159**	1 r. on 1s. 6d. grey-bl. ('57)	3 0	3 0

New currency. 100 naye paise = 1 rupee.

BAHRAIN BAHRAIN BAHRAIN

NP 1 NP (12) | NP 3 (13) | NP 75 NP (14)

1957 (1 APR.)–**59.** *Q.E. II* (*W* **165**), *surch. as T* **12** (1 *n.p.*, 15 *n.p.*, 25 *n.p.*, 40 *n.p.*, *and* 50 *n.p.*), *T* **14** (75 *n.p.*) *or T* **13** (*others*).

No.	Type	Description	Unused	Used
102	**157**	1 n.p. on 5d. brown	0 6	0 6
103	**154**	3 n.p. on ½d. orge.-red	0 6	0 4
104	,,	6 n.p. on 1d. ultramarine	0 6	0 6
105	,,	9 n.p. on 1½d. green	0 9	0 9
106	,,	12 n.p. on 2d. lt. red-brn.	0 9	0 9
107	**155**	15 n.p. on 2½d. carmine-red (Type I)	1 0	1 0
		a. Type II ('59)	2 0	2 0
108	,,	20 n.p. on 3d. dp. lilac (B.)	0 9	0 9
109	**156**	25 n.p. on 4d. ultramarine	2 0	2 6
110	**157**	40 n.p. on 6d. reddish pur.	1 6	1 6
		a. *Deep claret* ('59)	2 6	2 6
111	**158**	50 n.p. on 9d. bronze-grn.	5 0	6 0
112	**160**	75 n.p. on 1s. 3d. green	3 0	3 6

BAHRAIN
15 NP

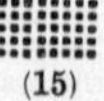

(15)

1957 (1 AUG.). *World Scout Jubilee Jamboree, surch. in two lines as T* **15** (15 *n.p.*), *or in three lines* (*others*).

No.	Type	Description	Unused	Used
113	**170**	15 n.p. on 2½d. carm.-red	0 10	1 0
114	**171**	25 n.p. on 4d. ultram.	1 3	1 6
115	**172**	75 n.p. on 1s. 3d. green	3 0	3 6

1960. *Q.E. II* (*W* **179**), *surch. as T* **12.**

No.	Type	Description	Unused	Used
116	**155**	15 n.p. on 2½d. carmine-red (Type II)	4 6	12 6

16. Shaikh Sulman bin Hamed al-Khalifa. **17.**

(Des. M. C. Farrar-Bell. Photo. Harrison (T **16**). Des. O. C. Meronti. Recess. De La Rue (T **17**).)

1960 (1 JULY). *P* 15 × 14 (*T* **16**) *or* 13½ × 13 (*T* **17**).

No.	Type	Description	Unused	Used
117	**16**	5 n.p. bright blue	0 3	0 3
118	,,	15 n.p. red-orange	0 6	0 10
119	,,	20 n.p. reddish violet	0 7	0 6
120	,,	30 n.p. bistre-brown	0 10	0 9
121	,,	40 n.p. grey	1 1	1 0
122	,,	50 n.p. emerald-green	1 3	1 3
123	,,	75 n.p. chocolate	2 0	2 0
124	**17**	1 r. black	3 0	1 9
125	,,	2 r. rose-red	6 0	4 0
126	,,	5 r. deep blue	14 0	10 0
127	,,	10 r. bronze-green	26 0	17 6

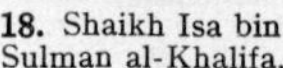

18. Shaikh Isa bin Sulman al-Khalifa. **19.** Air Terminal, Muharraq.

20. Deep Water Harbour.

(Des. M. C. Farrar-Bell. Photo. Harrison & Sons (5 to 75 n.p.). Des. D. C. Rivett. Recess. Bradbury, Wilkinson (others).)

1964 (22 FEB.). *P* 15 × 14 *T* **18** *or* 13½ × 13 *T* **19/20.**

No.	Type	Description	Unused	Used
128	**18**	5 n.p. bright blue ..	0 4	0 4
129	"	15 n.p. orange-red ..	0 6	0 5
130	"	20 n.p. reddish violet ..	0 7	0 6
131	"	30 n.p. olive-brown ..	0 11	0 7
132	"	40 n.p. slate	1 1	0 11
133	"	50 n.p. emerald-green ..	1 4	0 11
134	"	75 n.p. brown	2 0	1 6
135	**19**	1 r. black	2 6	1 6
136	"	2 r. carmine-red ..	4 9	3 3
137	**20**	5 r. ultramarine ..	12 0	9 0
138	"	10 r. myrtle-green ..	22 6	15 0

LOCAL STAMPS.

The following stamps were issued primarily for postage within Bahrain, but apparently also had franking value when used on external mail.

L **1**. Shaikh Sulman bin Hamed al-Khalifa. L **2**.

(Types L **1/2**. Recess. De La Rue.)

1953–56. *P* 12 × 12½.

No.	Type	Description	Unused	Used
L1	L **1**	½ a. deep green (1.10.56)	3 0	4 0
L2	"	1 a. deep blue (1.10.56) ..	3 0	4 0
L3	"	1½ a. carmine (15.3.53)	3 0	4 0

1957 (16 OCT.). *As Nos.* L1/3 *but values in new currency.*

No.	Type	Description	Unused	Used
L4	L **1**	3 p. deep green	6 0	7 6
L5	"	6 p. carmine	6 0	7 6
L6	"	9 p. deep blue	6 0	7 6

1961 (20 MAR.). *P* 12 × 12½.

No.	Type	Description	Unused	Used
L 7	L **2**	5 p. green	4 0	5 0
L 8	"	10 p. carmine-red ..	4 0	5 0
L 9	"	15 p. grey	2 0	2 6
L10	"	20 p. blue	2 6	3 0
L11	"	30 p. sepia	2 9	3 3
L12	"	40 p. ultramarine ..	3 0	3 6

The Bahrain Post Department took over the postal services on 1st January, 1966. Later stamp issues will therefore be found in Part III of the Stanley Gibbons Catalogue.

BANGKOK.

BRITISH POST OFFICES IN SIAM.

B

(1)

1882–85. *Stamps of Straits Settlements optd. with T* **1**.

On issue of 1867.

No.	Type	Description	Unused	Used
1		32 c. on 2 a. yellow ..	£200	£200

On issues of 1867–82. *Wmk. Crown CC.*

No.	Type	Description	Unused	Used
2	**5**	2 c. brown	£20	£20
3	,,	4 c. rose	£12	£14
		a. Overprint double ..		
4	**18**	5 c. purple-brown ..	70 0	80 0
5	**5**	6 c. lilac	50 0	50 0
6	**6**	8 c. orange	£18	65 0
7	**19**	10 c. slate	80 0	50 0
8	**6**	12 c. blue	£10	£6
9	**7**	24 c. green	85 0	50 0
10	**27**	30 c. claret	£80	£70
11	**8**	96 c. grey	£30	£30

On issue of April, 1883.

No.	Type	Description	Unused	Used
12		2 c. on 32 c. (*Wide* "E" (No. 66).) ..	£14	£15
13		2 c. on 32 c. (*Wide* "S" (No. 67).) ..	£20	£22

On issues of 1882–84. *Wmk. Crown CA.*

No.	Type	Description	Unused	Used
14	**5**	2 c. brown	70 0	70 0
15	,,	2 c. rose	15 0	15 0
		a. Overprint inverted	—	£35
		b. Overprint double	£30	
16	,,	4 c. rose	85 0	70 0
17	,,	4 c. brown	35 0	30 0
18	**18**	5 c. blue	70 0	60 0
19	**5**	6 c. lilac	50 0	50 0
20	**6**	8 c. orange	35 0	30 0
		a. Overprint inverted	—	£35
21	**19**	10 c. slate	60 0	60 0
22	**6**	12 c. dull purple ..	80 0	70 0
23	**7**	24 c. green	£20	£16

The use of these stamps ceased 1 July, 1885.

BARBADOS.

— SIMPLIFICATION (see INTRODUCTION)— **Nos. 1 to 84.**

2, 7, 4, 9, 4a, 5, 11, 12a, 13, 14.
20, 21, 24, 25, 29, 31, 35.
43. 65, 66, 45, 46, 61.
56, 52, 63, 49, 50, 54, 64.
72, 74, 75, 68, 76, 77, 79, 81, 82.

1 Britannia. **2**

(Recess. Perkins, Bacon & Co.)

1852 (15 APRIL)–**1855.** *Paper blued. No wmk. Imperf.*

No.	Type	Description	Unused	Used
1	**1**	(½d.) yellow-green ..	—	£35
2	,,	(½d.) deep green ..	£10	£30
3	,,	(1d.) blue	55 0	£18
4	,,	(1d.) deep blue ..	45 0	£10
4a	,,	(2d.) greyish slate ..	£18	
		b. Bisected (1d.) (on cover)	—	£110
5	,,	(4d.) brownish red (1855) ..	95 0	£32

It has now been proved that the stamp in greyish slate was intended for issue as a 2d. stamp. As its use for this rate was extremely limited it was officially bisected and used for the penny rate in August and September, 1854.

Apart from the shade, which is distinctly paler, No. 4*a* can be distinguished from No. 5*b* by the smooth even gum, the gum of No. 5*b* being yellow and patchy, giving a mottled appearance to the back of the stamp. No. 5*a* also has the latter gum.

Prepared for use but not issued.

No.	Type	Description	Unused	Used
5a	**1**	(No value), slate-blue ..	30 0	
5b	,,	(No value), slate ..	£45	

1855–57. *White paper. No wmk. Imperf.*

No.	Type	Description	Unused	Used
7	**1**	(½d.) yellow-green ..	£35	£16
8	,,	(½d.) green	£8	£20
9	,,	(1d.) pale blue ..	£5	£5
10	,,	(1d.) deep blue ..	60 0	£5

1858. *No wmk. Imperf.*

No.	Type	Description	Unused	Used
11	2	6d. pale rose-red	£70	£15
11*a*	,,	6d. deep rose-red	£60	£22
12	,,	1s. brown-black	£18	£12
12*a*	,,	1s. black	£10	£6

1860. *No wmk.* (*a*) *Pin-perf.* 14.

No.	Type	Description	Unused	Used
13	1	(½d.) yellow-green	£80	£28
14	,,	(1d.) pale blue	£80	£8
15	,,	(1d.) deep blue	£85	£8
		(*b*) *Pin-perf.* 12½.		
16	1	(½d.) yellow-green	£165	£40
16*a*	,,	(1d.) blue	—	£50
		(*c*) *Pin-perf.* 14 × 12½.		
16*b*	1	(½d.) yellow-green		

1861. *No wmk. Clean-cut perf.* 14 *to* 16.

No.	Type	Description	Unused	Used
17	1	(½d.) deep green	£5	45 0
18	,,	(1d.) pale blue	£75	85 0
19	,,	(1d.) blue	£85	90 0
		a. Bisected (½d.) (on cover)	—	£60

1861–70. *No wmk. Rough perf.* 14 *to* 16.

No.	Type	Description	Unused	Used
20	1	(½d.) deep green	50 0	45 0
21	,,	(½d.) green	35 0	37 6
21*a*	,,	(½d.) blue-green	£10	£14
		b. Imperf. (pair)	£40	
22	,,	(½d.) grass-green	65 0	50 0
		a. Imperf. (pair)	£40	
23	,,	(1d.) blue (1861)	£5	30 0
		a. Imperf. (pair)	£40	£30
24	,,	(1d.) deep blue	70 0	22 6
		a. Bisect. diag. (½d.) (on cover)	—	£50
25	,,	(4d.) dull rose-red (1861)	£8	90 0
		a. Imperf. (pair)	£45	£40
26	,,	(4d.) dull brown-red (1865)	£16	80 0
		a. Imperf. (pair)	£90	
27	,,	(4d.) lake-rose (1868)	£8	£6
		a. Imperf. (pair)	£90	
28	,,	(4d.) dull vermilion (1869)	£24	£9
		a. Imperf. (pair)	£90	
29	2	6d. rose-red (1861)	£20	55 0
30	,,	6d. orange-red (1864)	£9	55 0
31	,,	6d. brt. orge.-verm. (1868)	£5	60 0
32	,,	6d. dull orge.-verm. (1870)	£5	45 0
		a. Imperf. (pair)	£24	£50
33	,,	6d. orange (1870)	£8	65 0
34	,,	1s. brown-black (1863)	£5	35 0
35	,,	1s. black (1866)	70 0	60 0
		a. Imperf. between (horiz. pr.)	£250	

Variety. P 11 *to* 12.

No.	Type	Description	Unused	Used
36	1	(½d.) green	£260	
37	,,	(1d.) blue	£120	

Nos. 36 and 37 are only known unused.

Error of colour.

No.	Type	Description	Unused	Used
38	2	1s. blue	£850	

1870. *Wmk. Large Star, Type* w. **1**. *Rough perf.* 14 *to* 16.

No.	Type	Description	Unused	Used
43	1	(½d.) green	£9	60 0
		a. Imperf. (pair)	£35	
43*b*	,,	(½d.) yellow-green	—	£8
44	,,	(1d.) blue	£80	£5
		a. Blue paper	—	£6
45	,,	(4d.) dull vermilion	£48	£7
46	2	6d. orange-vermilion	£45	90 0
47	,,	1s. black	£20	60 0

1871. *Wmk. Small Star, Type* w. **2**. *Rough perf.* 14 *to* 16.

No.	Type	Description	Unused	Used
48	1	(1d.) blue	£8	25 0
49	,,	(4d.) dull rose-red	£65	£5
50	2	6d. orange-vermilion	£24	65 0
51	,,	1s. black	£14	70 0

1872. *Wmk. Small Star, Type* w. **2**.

(*a*) *Clean-cut perf.* 14½ *to* 15½.

No.	Type	Description	Unused	Used
52	1	(1d.) blue	£18	20 0
		a. Bisect. diag. (½d.) (on cover)		
53	2	6d. orange-vermilion	£30	£5
54	,,	1s. black	£8	40 0
		(*b*) *P* 11 *to* 13 × 14½ *to* 15½.		
56	1	(½d.) green	£18	50 0
57	,,	(4d.) dull vermilion	£22	£6

1873. *Wmk. Large Star, Type* w. **1**. *Clean-cut perf.* 14½ *to* 15½.

No.	Type	Description	Unused	Used
58	1	(½d.) green	£15	65 0
59	,,	(4d.) dull rose-red	£42	£14
60	2	6d. orange-vermilion	£32	£5
		a. Imperf. between (horiz. pair)	£70	
		b. Imperf. (pair)	£20	
61	,,	1s. black	£7	40 0

Two used singles of No. 60*b* have been seen.

(Date?) *No wmk. Clean-cut perf.* 14½ *to* 15½.

No.	Type	Description	Unused	Used
62	1	(½d.) pale green	—	£225

1873 (June). *Wmk. Small Star, Type* w. **2** (*two points upwards*). *P* 14.

No.	Type	Description	Unused	Used
63	2	3d. brown-purple	£28	£10

3

1873. *Wmk. Small Star, Type* w. **2**. *P* 15½ × 15.

No.	Type	Description	Unused	Used
64	3	5s. dull rose	£70	£45

1874 (May). *Wmk. Large Star, Type* w. **1**.

(*a*) *Perf.* 14.

No.	Type	Description	Unused	Used
65	2	½d. deep green	60 0	40 0
66	,,	1d. deep blue	85 0	20 0
		(*b*) *Clean-cut perf.* 14½ *to* 15½.		
66*a*	2	1d. deep blue	—	£225
		(*c*) *Imperf.* (*pair*).		
66*b*	2	1d. deep blue		

(Recess. De La Rue and Co.)

1875–78. *Wmk. Crown CC* (*sideways on* 6d. *and* 1s.). (*a*) *P* 12½.

No.	Type	Description	Unused	Used
67	2	½d. bright green	40 0	25 0
68	,,	4d. deep red	£18	55 0
69	,,	6d. bright yellow (aniline)	£45	£5
70	,,	6d. chrome-yellow	£42	£5
71	,,	1s. violet (aniline)	£32	60 0
		(*b*) *P* 14.		
72	2	½d. bright green (1876)	25 0	12 6
73	,,	1d. dull blue	70 0	5 0
		a. Bisected (½d.) (on cover)	—	£35
74	,,	1d. grey-blue	80 0	5 0
		a. Wmk. sideways	—	£175
75	,,	3d. mauve-lilac (1878)	£8	60 0
76	,,	4d. red (1878)	£10	60 0
77	,,	4d. carmine	£12	25 0
78	,,	4d. crimson-lake	£20	27 6
79	,,	6d. chrome-yellow (1876)	£8	27 6
80	,,	6d. yellow	£12	60 0
81	,,	1s. purple (1876)	£8	30 0
82	,,	1s. violet (aniline)	£125	£5
83	,,	1s. dull mauve	£20	25 0
		a. Bisected (6d.) (on cover)	—	£175
		Variety. Perf. 14 × 12½.		
84	2	4d. red	£300	

Very few specimens of No. 84 have been found unused. One used specimen is known.

HAVE YOU READ THE NOTES AT THE BEGINNING OF THIS CATALOGUE?

These often provide answers to the enquiries we receive.

1^D. 1^D. 1^D.
(A) (B) (C)

1878 (March). *No. 64, with lower label removed, divided vertically by perforation, and each half surch. sideways in black.*

(A) *Large numeral "* **1** *", 7 mm. high with curved serif, and large letter " D ", 2¾ mm. high.*

86 **3** 1d. on half 5s. dull rose .. £100 £45
a. Unsevered pair (both No. 86) £450 £125
b. Ditto, Nos. 86 and 87 ..
c. Ditto, Nos. 86 and 88 ..
d. As 86b without dividing perf.

(B) *As last, but numeral with straight serif.*

87 **3** 1d. on half 5s. dull rose .. £185 £100
a. Unsevered pair . .. — £225

(C) *Smaller numeral "* **1** *", 6 mm. high and smaller " D ", 2½ mm. high.*

88 **3** 1d. on half 5s. dull rose .. £185 £85
a. Unsevered pair £700 £175

All types of the surcharge are found reading upwards as well as downwards, and there are minor varieties of the type.

4

(Typo. De La Rue.)

1882–86. *Wmk. Crown CA. P* 14.

89 **4** ½d. dull green (1882) .. 7 6 2 6
90 ,, ½d. green 7 6 2 6
91 ,, 1d. rose (1882) .. 20 0 3 6
a. Bisected (½d.) (on cover) — £22
92 ,, 1d. carmine 10 0 3 0
93 ,, 2½d. ultramarine (1882) .. 45 0 5 0
94 ,, 2½d. deep blue 45 0 5 0
95 ,, 3d. deep purple (1885) .. 85 0 55 0
96 ,, 3d. reddish purple .. 12 6 17 6
97 ,, 4d. grey (1882) .. £7 20 0
98 ,, 4d. pale brown (1885) .. 15 0 12 6
99 ,, 4d. deep brown 10 6 6 0
100 ,, 6d. olive-black (1886) .. 35 0 37 6
102 ,, 1s. chestnut (1886) .. 37 6 35 0
103 ,, 5s. bistre (1886) £20 £22

HALF-PENNY

(5)

1892. *No. 99 surch. with T* **5.**

104 **4** ½d. on 4d. deep brown .. 2 0 2 6
a. No hyphen.. .. 10 0 15 0
b. Surch. double (R. + Bk.) .. £45 £50
ba. Do. No hyphen £125 £125

6. Seal of Colony.

(Typo. De La Rue.)

1892–99. *Wmk. Crown CA. P* 14.

107 **6** ½d. slate-grey & carm. (1896) 1 6 1 0
108 ,, ½d. dull green 1 3 1 0
109 ,, 1d. carmine 2 0 0 4
109*a* ,, 2d. slate-black & orange (1899) 10 0 10 6
110 ,, 2½d. ultramarine 7 6 2 0
111 ,, 5d. grey-olive 12 6 12 6
112 ,, 6d. mauve and carmine .. 12 6 15 0
113 ,, 8d. orange & ultramarine 12 6 30 0
114 ,, 10d. dull blue-grn. & carm. 25 0 30 0
115 ,, 2s. 6d. blue-blk. & orange 50 0 55 0

7

8. Nelson Monument.

(Typo. De La Rue.)

1897–98. *Diamond Jubilee. T* **7.** *Wmk. Crown CC. P* 14.

(*a*) *White paper* (1897).

116 ½d. grey and carmine .. 1 6 1 9
117 ½d. dull green 3 0 2 0
118 1d. rose 5 0 3 0
119 2½d. ultramarine 15 0 7 6
120 5d. olive-brown 30 0 30 0
121 6d. mauve and carmine .. 37 6 35 0
122 8d. orange and ultramarine 35 0 35 0
123 10d. blue-green and carmine 50 0 55 0
124 2s. 6d. blue-black and orange 55 0 65 0

(*b*) *Paper blued* (1898).

125 ½d. grey and carmine .. 35 0 50 0
126 ½d. dull green 40 0 40 0
127 1d. carmine 50 0 40 0
128 2½d. ultramarine 50 0 50 0
129 5d. olive-brown £17 £17
130 6d. mauve and carmine .. £6 £7
131 8d. orange and ultramarine £6 £7
132 10d. dull green and carmine £12 £14
133 2s. 6d. blue-blk. and orange £5 £6

1903. *Wmk. Crown CA. P* 14.

134 **6** 2s. 6d. violet and green .. £5 £7

1904–5. *Wmk. Mult. Crown CA. P* 14.

135 **6** ½d. slate-grey and carmine 1 6 1 6
136 ,, ½d. dull green 4 0 0 3
137 ,, 1d. carmine 4 0 0 9
139 ,, 2½d. blue 15 0 4 0
141 ,, 6d. mauve and carmine .. 40 0 42 6
142 ,, 8d. orange & ultramarine 65 0 80 0
144 ,, 2s. 6d. violet and green .. 80 0 90 0

(Des. G. Goodman. Recess. De La Rue.)

1906. *Nelson Centenary. Wmk. Crown CC. P* 14.

145 **8** ½d. black and grey .. 4 0 4 0
146 ,, ½d. black and pale green .. 5 0 3 6
147 ,, 1d. black and red .. 4 6 3 0
148 ,, 2d. black and yellow .. 22 6 22 6
149 ,, 2½d. black and bright blue 22 6 25 0
150 ,, 6d. black and mauve .. 40 0 50 0
151 ,, 1s. black and rose .. 45 0 55 0

Two sets may be made of the above: one on thick, opaque, creamy white paper; the other on thin, rather transparent, bluish white paper.

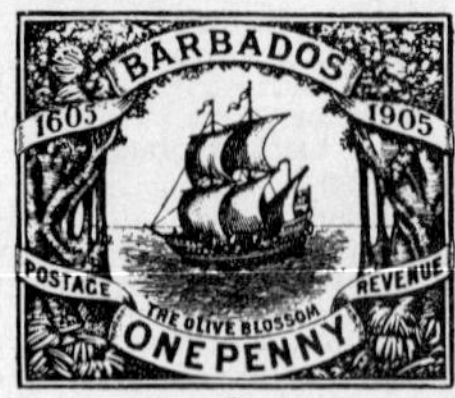

9

(Des. Lady Carter. Recess. De La Rue.)

1906 (15 Aug.). *Tercentenary of Annexation. Wmk. Multiple Crown CA (sideways). P 14.*

152 **9** 1d. black, blue and green .. 15 0 10 6

Kingston Relief Fund. 1d.

(**10**)

1907 (25 Jan.). *Kingston Relief Fund. No. 109a surch. with T* **10.**

153 **6** 1d. on 2d. slate-black and orange (R.) 7 6 10 0

a. Surch. inverted (25.2.07) .. 7 6 8 0

b. Surch. double £90

c. Surch. double, both inverted .. £90

d. Surch. tête-bêche (pair) .. £95

e. No stop after "1d" .. 35 0 40 0

ea. Do., surch. inverted (25.2.07) 30 0 35 0

The above stamp was sold for 2d., of which 1d. was retained for postal revenue, and the other 1d. given to a fund for the relief of the sufferers by the earthquake in Jamaica.

1907 (6 July). *Nelson Centenary. Wmk. Mult. Crown CA. P 14.*

158 **8** ¼d. black and grey .. 5 0 7 6

161 ,, 2d. black and yellow .. 25 0 30 0

162 ,, 2½d. black & bright blue .. 35 0 40 0

162a ,, 2½d. black and indigo .. £85 £90

1909–10. *Wmk. Mult. Crown CA. P 14.*

163 **6** ¼d. brown 2 0 1 6

164 ,, ½d. blue-green 5 0 1 6

165 ,, 1d. red 2 6 0 6

166 ,, 2d. greyish slate ('10) .. 35 0 40 0

167 ,, 2½d. bright blue ('10) .. 22 6 6 0

168 ,, 6d. dull & brt. purple ('10) 35 0 35 0

169 ,, 1s. black/*green* ('10) .. 55 0 60 0

11 12

13 14

(Typo. De La Rue.)

1912 (23 July–13 Aug.). *Wmk. Mult. Crown CA. P 14.*

170 **11** ¼d. brown (23 July) .. 0 9 0 6

170a ,, ¼d. pale brown 1 0 0 6

171 ,, ½d. green (23 July) .. 1 6 1 6

172 ,, 1d. red 2 6 0 8

172a ,, 1d. scarlet 12 6 1 6

173 ,, 2d. greyish slate 10 0 15 0

174 ,, 2½d. bright blue 10 0 5 0

175 **12** 3d. purple/*yellow* 10 0 10 6

176 ,, 4d. red & black/*yellow* .. 12 6 12 6

177 ,, 6d. purple & dull purple .. 17 6 20 0

178 **13** 1s. black/*green* 27 6 30 0

179 ,, 2s. blue & purple/*blue* .. £6 £6

180 ,, 3s. violet and green .. £7 £8

(Recess. De La Rue.)

1916 (16 June)–**1920.** *T* **14.** *Wmk. Mult. Crown CA. P 14.*

181 ¼d. deep brown 0 9 0 8

182 ¼d. chestnut-brown (Apl., '18) 2 0 0 8

183 ¼d. sepia-brown (Nov., '18) .. 1 6 2 6

184 ½d. green 1 9 2 0

185 ½d. deep green (Apl., '18) .. 1 6 1 6

186 ½d. pale green (Oct., '18) .. 3 0 2 0

187 1d. deep red 27 6 10 0

187a 1d. bright carmine-red .. 4 0 1 3

188 1d. pale carm.-red (July, '17) 3 6 1 0

189 2d. grey 17 6 12 6

190 2½d. ultramarine 7 6 7 6

191 3d. purple/*yellow* (*thin paper*) 10 0 12 6

191a 3d. dp. purple/*yellow* (*thick paper*) ('20) 50 0 60 0

192 4d. red/*yellow* (*thin paper*) (23.6.16) 10 0 20 0

193 6d. purple 10 0 12 6

194 1s. black/*green* 17 6 20 0

195 2s. purple/*blue* 60 0 42 6

196 3s. deep violet (23.6.16) .. £9 £10

WAR TAX

(**15**)

1917 (10 Oct.)–**18.** *War Tax. Optd. in London with T* **15.**

197 **11** 1d. bright red 0 6 0 6

a. Imperf. (pair) £140

Thicker bluish paper.

198 **11** 1d. pale red (Apr. '18) .. 0 6 0 8

1918 (18 Feb.). *Colours changed. Wmk. Mult. Crown CA. P 14.*

199 **14** 4d. black and red .. 5 0 10 0

200 ,, 3s. green & deep violet .. 85 0 £5

200a ,, 3s. green & bright violet .. £28 £32

The centres of these are from a new die having no circular border line.

16 17

(Recess. De La Rue.)

1920 (9 Sept.)–**21.** *Victory. P 14. (a) Wmk. Mult. Crown CA (sideways on T* **17**).

201 **16** ¼d. black & bistre-brown 1 6 1 6

202 ,, ½d. black & brt. yell.-grn. 2 0 2 0

203 ,, 1d. black and vermilion .. 2 0 1 6

No.	Type	Description	Unused	Used
204	**16**	2d. black and grey ..	8 6	15 0
205	„	2½d. indigo and ultramarine	12 6	15 0
206	„	3d. black and purple ..	8 6	15 0
207	„	4d. black and blue-green ..	10 0	12 6
208	„	6d. black & brown-orange	10 6	15 0
209	**17**	1s. black and bright green	22 6	27 6
210	„	2s. black and brown ..	50 0	55 0
211	„	3s. black and dull orange ..	85 0	95 0
		(*b*) *Wmk. Mult. Script CA.*		
212	**16**	1d. black & verm. (22.8.21)	7 6	4 0

18

19

(Recess. De La Rue.)

1921 (14 Nov.)–**24.** *P* 14.

No.	Type	Description	Unused	Used
		(*a*) *Wmk. Mult. Crown CA.*		
213	**18**	3d. purple/*pale yellow* ..	5 0	6 0
214	„	4d. red/*pale yellow* ..	8 6	10 0
215	„	1s. black/*emerald* ..	32 6	37 6
		(*b*) *Wmk. Mult. Script CA.*		
217	**18**	¼d. brown	1 3	1 3
219	„	½d. green	0 10	1 3
220	„	1d. red	1 3	0 4
		a. Bright rose-carmine ..	1 6	0 4
221	„	2d. grey	2 6	3 0
222	„	2½d. ultramarine	7 6	6 0
225	„	6d. reddish purple ..	8 6	12 6
226	„	1s. black/*emer.* (18.9.24)	60 0	65 0
227	„	2s. purple/*blue*	70 0	70 0
228	„	3s. deep violet	80 0	85 0

1925–35. T **19.** *Wmk. Mult. Script CA.* (I) *P* 14. (II) *P* 13½×12½ ('32).

No.	Description	I. Unused	I. Used	II. Unused	II. Used
229	¼d. brown ..	0 4	0 6	†	
230	½d. green ..	0 3	0 3	1 0	0 6
231	1d. scarlet ..	0 9	0 3	2 0	0 6
231*a*	1½d. orange ..	8 6	1 6	3 0	1 6
232	2d. grey ..	1 6	3 6	†	
233	2½d. blue ..	5 0	2 6	†	
233*a*	2½d. bt. ultram.	5 0	1 0	10 0	2 6
234	3d. pur./*p. yellow*	3 6	2 6	†	
234*a*	3d. reddish pur./*yellow* ('35)	5 0	4 0	†	
235	4d. red/*p. yellow*	4 0	4 6	†	
236	6d. purple ..	7 6	7 6	†	
237	1s. blk./*emerald*	12 6	8 6	25 0	25 0
237*a*	1s. brownish blk./*bt. yell.-grn.*	17 6	17 6	†	
238	2s. purple/*blue*	22 6	20 0	†	
238*a*	2s. 6d. car./*blue*	60 0	75 0	†	
239	3s. deep violet	40 0	50 0	†	

20. King Charles I and King George V.

(Recess. Bradbury, Wilkinson.)

1927 (17 Feb.). *Tercentenary of Settlement of Barbados. Wmk. Mult. Script CA. P* 12½.

No.	Type	Description	Unused	Used
240	**20**	1d. carmine	5 0	5 0

1935 (6 May). *Silver Jubilee. As Nos.* 91/4 *of Antigua, but ptd. by Waterlow. P* 11×12.

No.	Description	Unused	Used
241	1d. deep blue and scarlet ..	0 9	1 0
242	1½d. ultramarine and grey ..	1 0	1 3
243	2½d. brown and deep blue ..	6 6	7 0
244	1s. slate and purple	15 0	20 0

1937 (14 May). *Coronation. As Nos.* 13/15 *of Aden. P* 14.

No.	Description	Unused	Used
245	1d. scarlet	0 9	1 0
246	1½d. yellow-brown	1 0	1 2
247	2½d. bright blue	2 0	2 0

21. Badge of the Colony.

(Recess. De La Rue.)

1938 (3 Jan.)–**1947.** *Wmk. Mult. Script CA. P* 13½×13.

No.	Type	Description	Unused	Used
248	**21**	½d. green	0 6	0 3
		a. Perf. 14 ('42)	£5	8 0
248*b*	„	½d. yellow-bistre ('42) ..	0 4	0 3
249	„	1d. scarlet	£8	10 0
		a. Perf. 14 ('38)	10 0	1 6
249*b*	„	1d. blue-green (42) ..	2 0	0 3
		c. Perf. 14 ('42)	0 6	0 3
250	„	1½d. orange	0 8	0 8
		a. Perf. 14 ('42)	5 0	1 6
250*b*	„	2d. claret (June, '41) ..	3 6	1 6
250*c*	„	2d. carmine ('43) ..	0 10	0 8
		d. Perf. 14 ('44)	1 0	1 6
251	„	2½d. ultramarine	1 0	2 0
		a. Blue ('44)	2 6	6 0
252	„	3d. brown	2 0	2 0
		a. Perf. 14 ('41)	2 0	1 3
252*b*	„	3d. blue (1.4.47) ..	1 6	0 9
253	„	4d. black	1 0	0 10
		a. Perf. 14 ('44)	1 0	1 3
254	„	6d. violet	1 6	1 0
254*a*	„	8d. magenta (9.12.46) ..	7 6	5 0
255	„	1s. olive-green ..	30 0	17 6
		a. Brown-olive	4 0	2 0
256	„	2s. 6d. purple	7 6	5 0
256*a*	„	5s. indigo (June, '41) ..	15 0	10 0

No. 249*a* was perforated by two machines, one gauging 14.1, the other 13.8×14.1.

22. Kings Charles I, George VI, Assembly Chamber and Mace.

(Recess. De La Rue.)

1939 (27 June). *Tercentenary of Genera Assembly. Wmk. Mult. Script CA. P* 13½×14.

No.	Type	Description	Unused	Used
257	**22**	½d. green	2 0	1 9
258	„	1d. scarlet	2 6	2 0
259	„	1½d. orange	4 0	4 0
260	„	2½d. bright ultramarine ..	10 0	10 0
261	„	3d. brown	10 0	15 0

1946 (18 Sept.). *Victory. As Nos.* 28/9 *of Aden.*

262	1½d. red-orange	0	6	0	6
263	3d. brown	0	8	1	0

ONE
PENNY
(**23**)

(Surcharged by Barbados Advocate Co.)

1947 (21 Apr.). *Surch. with T* **23**.

(*a*) *Perf.* 14.

264	**21** 1d. on 2d. carmine ..	3	0	5	0

(*b*) *P* 13½ × 13.

264*a*	**21** 1d. on 2d. carmine ..	4	6	6	6

1948 (24 Nov.). *Royal Silver Wedding. As Nos.* 30/1 *of Aden.*

265	1½d. orange	0	6	0	6
266	5s. indigo	12	6	12	6

1949 (10 Oct.). *75th Anniv. of Universal Postal Union. As Nos.* 114/7 *of Antigua.*

267	1½d. red-orange	0	8	0	8
268	3d. deep blue..	1	6	1	9
269	4d. grey	2	0	2	0
270	1s. olive	4	0	4	6

24. Dover Fort.

25. Sugar Cane Breeding.

26. Public Buildings.

27. Statue of Nelson.

28. Casting Net.

29. Inter-Colonial Schooner.

30. Flying Fish.

31. Old Main Guard Garrison.

32. The Cathedral. **34.** Map of Barbados and Wireless Mast.

33. Careenage.

35. Arms of Barbados.

(Recess. Bradbury, Wilkinson.)

1950 (1 May). *Wmk. Mult. Script CA. P* 11 × 11½ (*horiz.*), 13½ (*vert.*).

No.	Type	Description	Unused s.	d.	Used s.	d.
271	**24**	1 c. indigo	0	6	1	0
272	**25**	2 c. emerald-green	0	6	0	10
273	**26**	3 c. reddish brn. & bl.-grn.	0	8	0	10
274	**27**	4 c. carmine	0	8	0	10
275	**28**	6 c. light blue	1	0	0	10
276	**29**	8 c. bright bl. & pur.-brn.	1	9	1	3
277	**30**	12 c. greenish blue and brown-olive	3	6	2	0
278	**31**	24 c. scarlet and black ..	3	6	2	0
279	**32**	48 c. violet	5	0	6	6
280	**33**	60 c. green and claret ..	6	0	7	6
281	**34**	$1.20, carm. & olive-grn.	10	6	10	6
282	**35**	$2.40, black	25	0	27	6

1951 (16 Feb.). *Inauguration of B.W.I. University College. As Nos.* 118/9 *of Antigua.*

No.	Description	Unused s.	d.	Used s.	d.
283	3 c. brown and blue-green ..	0	8	0	8
284	12 c. blue-green & brn.-olive	3	0	2	6

36. King George VI and Stamp of 1852.

(Recess. Waterlow & Sons.)

1952 (15 Apr.). *Barbados Stamp Centenary. Wmk. Mult. Script CA. P* 13½.

No.	Type	Description	Unused s.	d.	Used s.	d.
285	**36**	3 c. green and slate-green	1	3	1	6
286	,,	4 c. blue and carmine ..	1	6	2	0
287	,,	12 c. slate-grn. & brt. grn.	2	6	3	0
288	,,	24 c. red-brown & brownish black	4	0	5	0

1953 (4 June). *Coronation. As No.* 47 *of Aden.*

No.	Description	Unused s.	d.	Used s.	d.
289	4 c. black and red-orange ..	1	3	1	3

37. Harbour Police.

(Recess. Bradbury, Wilkinson & Co.)

1953 (13 Apr.)–**57.** *As T* **24/34** (*but with portrait or cypher* ($2.40) *of Queen Elizabeth II in place of that of King George VI, as in T* **37**). *Wmk. Mult. Script CA. P* 11 × 11½ (*horiz.*) *or* 13½ (*vert.*).

No.	Type	Description	Unused s.	d.	Used s.	d.
290	**24**	1 c. indigo	0	4	0	6
291	**25**	2 c. orange and deep turquoise (15.4.54) ..	0	4	0	4
292	**26**	3 c. blk. & emer. (15.4.54)	0	5	0	4
293	**27**	4 c. black and orange (*shades*) (15.4.54) ..	0	6	0	4
294	**37**	5 c. blue & deep carmine-red (4.1.54)	0	6	0	5
295	**28**	6 c. red-brown (15.4.54)	0	7	0	4
296	**29**	8 c. blk. & blue (15.4.54)	0	9	0	5
297	**30**	12 c. turq.-blue & brn.-olive (*shades*) (15.4.54)	1	0	0	7
298	**31**	24 c. rose-red and black (2.3.56)	1	8	1	3
299	**32**	48 c. deep violet (2.3.56) ..	3	3	3	0
300	**33**	60 c. blue-grn. & brn.-pur. (*shades*) (3.4.56) ..	4	6	4	6
301	**34**	$1.20, carmine & bronze-green (3.4.56) ..	8	0	9	0
302	**35**	$2.40 black (1.2.57) ..	16	0	18	0

1958 (23 Apr.). *Inauguration of British Caribbean Federation. As Nos.* 135/7 *of Antigua.*

No.	Description	Unused s.	d.	Used s.	d.
303	3 c. deep green	0	8	0	8
304	6 c. blue	0	10	0	10
305	12 c. scarlet	1	3	1	9

38. Deep Water Harbour, Bridgetown.

(Recess. Bradbury, Wilkinson.)

1961 (6 May). *Opening of Deep Water Harbour, Bridgetown. W* **w.12.** *P* 11 × 12.

No.	Type	Description	Unused s.	d.	Used s.	d.
306	**38**	4 c. black and red-orange	0	9	0	10
307	,,	8 c. black and blue ..	1	3	1	6
308	,,	24 c. carm.-red and black	2	6	3	0

39. Scout Badge and Map of Barbados.

(Recess. Bradbury, Wilkinson.)

1962 (9 Mar.). *Golden Jubilee of Barbados Boy Scout Association. W* **w.12.** *P* 11½ × 11.

No.	Type	Description	Unused s.	d.	Used s.	d.
309	**39**	4 c. black and orange ..	0	10	0	10
310	,,	12 c. blue & olive-brown ..	1	9	2	0
311	,,	$1.20, carmine & olive-grn.	14	0	17	6

1964 (14 Jan.)–**65.** *As Nos.* 290, *etc., but wmk.* w.**12.**

No.	Type	Description	Unused s.	d.	Used s.	d.
312	**24**	1 c. indigo (6.10.64) ..	0	3	0	3
313	**27**	4 c. black and orange ..	0	5	0	7
314	**29**	8 c. blk. & blue (29.6.65)	1	6	1	9
315	**30**	12 c. turquoise-blue and brown-olive (29.6.65)	2	0	2	6
316	**31**	24 c. rose-red and black (6.10.64)	1	8	1	2
317	**32**	48 c. deep violet	3	3	4	6
318	**33**	60 c. blue-green & brown-purple (6.10.64) ..	4	6	4	6
319	**35**	$2.40, black (29.6.65) ..	40	0	50	0

1965 (17 May). *I.T.U. Centenary. As Nos.* 166/7 *of Antigua.*

320	2 c. lilac and red	0	6	0	8
321	48 c. yellow and grey-brown	4	0	4	6

40. Deep Sea Coral.

41. Lobster.

42. Sea Horse.

43. Sea Urchin.

44. Staghorn Coral.

45. Butterfly Fish.

46. File Shell.

47. Balloon Fish.

48. Angel Fish.

49. Brain Coral.

50. Brittie Star.

51. Flying Fish.

52. Queen Conch Shell.

53. Fiddler Crab.

(Des. V. Whiteley, from drawings by Mrs. J. Walker. Photo. Harrison.)

1965 (15 JULY). *W* w.**12**. *P* 14×13½.

322 **40** 1 c. black, pink and blue 0 3 0 4
323 **41** 2 c. olive-brown, yellow and magenta .. 0 3 0 4
324 **42** 3 c. olive-brn. & orange 0 4 0 5
325 **43** 4 c. dp. blue & olive-green 0 5 0 6
326 **44** 5 c. sepia, rose and lilac .. 0 5 0 6
327 **45** 6 c. multicoloured .. 0 6 0 7
328 **46** 8 c. multicoloured .. 0 7 0 8
329 **47** 12 c. multicoloured .. 0 10 0 11
330 **48** 15 c. black, greenish yellow and red 1 1 1 2
331 **49** 25 c. ulramine and yellow-ochre 1 10 2 3
332 **50** 35 c. brown-red & dp. grn. 2 0 2 3
333 **51** 50 c. bright blue and apple-green 3 4 4 0
334 **52** $1 multicoloured .. 5 6 7 0
335 **53** $2.50, multicoloured .. 13 6 15 0

For new printings with sideways wmk., see Addenda.

1966 (24 JAN.). *Churchill Commemoration. As Nos.* 170/3 *of Antigua.*

336 1 c. new blue 0 3 0 4
337 4 c. deep green 0 5 0 7
338 25 c. brown 1 10 2 3
339 35 c. bluish violet 2 6 3 0

1966 (4 FEB.). *Royal Visit. As Nos.* 174/5 *of Antigua.*

340 3 c. black and ultramarine .. 0 5 0 6
341 35 c. black and magenta .. 2 6 3 0

POSTAGE DUE STAMPS.

D 1

(Typo. De La Rue.)

1934–47. *Wmk. Mult. Script CA. P* 14.

D1 D **1** ½d. green (10.2.35) .. 1 6 0 10
D2 ,, 1d. black (2.1.34) .. 6 0 1 0
a. Bisected (½d.) (on piece) .. — £20
D3 ,, 3d. carmine (13.3.47) .. 40 0 10 0

The use of the bisected 1d. stamp was officially authorised March 1934 pending the arrival of supplies of the ½d. received 1935. Some specimens had the value "½d." written across the half stamp in red ink. (*Price on piece* £20).

1950 (8 DEC.)–**53**. *Values in cents. Wmk. Mult. Script CA. P* 14.

D4 D **1** 1 c. green, O 4 6 4 0
a. *Deep green*, C (29.11.51) .. 0 3 0 8
b. Error. Crown missing, W9a, C £18
c. Error. St. Edward's Crown, W9b, C £15
D5 ,, 2 c. black, O 4 6 6 0
a. Chalky paper (20.1.53) .. 0 4 0 8
c. Error. St. Edward's Crown, W9b, C £16
D6 ,, 6 c. carmine, O 10 0 12 6
a. Chalky paper (20.1.53) .. 0 8 0 9
b. Error. Crown missing, W9a, C £18
c. Error. St. Edward's Crown, W9b, C £16

The 1 c. stamps have no dot below "c".

1965 (3 AUG.). *As Nos.* D4/6 *but wmk.* w.**12**. *Chalky paper.*

D7 D **1** 1 c. deep green (*shades*) .. 0 2 0 3
D8 ,, 2 c. black 0 3 0 5
D9 ,, 6 c. carmine 0 6 0 9

The 1 c. has no dot below "c".

BARBUDA.

BARBUDA

(1)

1922 (13 JULY). *Stamps of Leeward Islands optd. with T* **1**. *All are Die II.*

(*a*) *Wmk. Mult. Script CA.*

1 **11** ½d. deep green, O .. 4 6 6 0
2 ,, 1d. bright scarlet, O .. 4 6 6 0
3 **10** 2d. slate-grey, O 5 0 12 6
4 **11** 2½d. bright blue, O .. 6 0 7 0
5 ,, 6d. dull and brt. purple, C 15 0 17 6
6 **10** 2s. purple & blue/*blue*, C 40 0 47 6
7 ,, 3s. bright green & violet, C 75 0 85 0
8 ,, 4s. black and red, C (R.) 85 0 90 0

(*b*) *Wmk. Mult. Crown CA.*

9 **10** 3d. dull pur./*pale yellow*, C 6 0 10 0
10 **12** 1s. black/*emerald*, C (R.) 15 0 20 0
11 ,, 5s. grn. & red/*pale yellow*, C £8 £9

Postage stamps of Antigua are now used in Barbuda.

BASUTOLAND.

1. King George V, Crocodile and Mountains.

2. King George VI, Crocodile and Mountains.

(Recess. Waterlow.)

1933 (1 Dec.). *Wmk. Mult. Script CA. P 12½.*

1 **1**	½d. emerald	.. ..	0 6	0 8
2 ,,	1d. scarlet	.. ..	0 8	0 10
3 ,,	2d. bright purple	.. ..	1 9	2 6
4 ,,	3d. bright blue	.. ..	2 6	4 0
5 ,,	4d. grey	.. ..	6 6	7 6
6 ,,	6d. orange-yellow	.. ..	8 6	12 6
7 ,,	1s. red-orange	.. ..	15 0	20 0
8 ,,	2s. 6d. sepia	.. ..	35 0	40 0
9 ,,	5s. violet	.. ..	55 0	65 0
10 ,,	10s. olive-green	.. ..	£8	£9

1935 (4 May). *Silver Jubilee. As Nos. 91/4 of Antigua. P 13½×14.*

11	1d. deep blue and carmine	..	1 0	1 3
12	2d. ultramarine and grey	..	3 0	4 0
13	3d. brown and deep blue	..	4 0	5 0
14	6d. slate and purple	..	6 0	8 6

1937 (12 May). *Coronation. As Nos. 13/15 of Aden. P 14.*

15	1d. scarlet	.. ..	0 5	0 6
16	2d. bright purple	.. ..	0 11	1 2
17	3d. bright blue	.. ..	1 6	1 9

(Recess. Waterlow.)

1938 (1 Apr.). *Wmk. Mult. Script CA. P 12½.*

18 **2**	½d. green	.. ..	0 6	0 6
19 ,,	1d. scarlet	.. ..	0 6	0 4
20 ,,	1½d. light blue	.. ..	0 6	0 6
21 ,,	2d. bright purple	.. ..	0 8	0 8
22 ,,	3d. bright blue	.. ..	1 0	1 3
23 ,,	4d. grey	.. ..	1 3	1 6
24 ,,	6d. orange-yellow	.. ..	1 6	2 0
25 ,,	1s. red-orange	.. ..	2 6	2 6
26 ,,	2s. 6d. sepia	.. ..	6 0	8 6
27 ,,	5s. violet	.. ..	10 0	12 6
28 ,,	10s. olive-green	.. ..	25 0	27 6

Basutoland
(3)

1945 (3 Dec.). *Victory. Stamps of South Africa, optd. with T* **3**. *inscr. alternately in English and Afrikaans.*

		Un. pair	*Used pair*	*Used single*
29 **55**	1d. brown & carmine	0 6	1 0	0 3
30 **56**	2d. slate-bl. & violet	0 10	1 6	0 6
31 **57**	3d. deep blue & blue	1 3	2 6	0 9

4. King George VI.

5. King George VI and Queen Elizabeth.

6. Queen Elizabeth II as Princess, and Princess Margaret.

7. The Royal Family.

(Recess. Waterlow.)

1947 (17 Feb.). *Royal Visit. Wmk. Mult. Script CA. P 12½.*

32 **4**	1d. scarlet	.. .. ..	0 3	0 5
33 **5**	2d. green	.. .. ..	0 4	0 6
34 **6**	3d. ultramarine	.. ..	0 8	0 10
35 **7**	1s. mauve	.. .. ..	2 0	2 6

1948 (1 Dec.). *Royal Silver Wedding. As Nos. 30/1 of Aden.*

36	1½d. ultramarine	.. ..	0 6	0 6
37	10s. grey-olive	.. ..	20 0	22 6

1949 (10 Oct.). *75th Anniv. of Universal Postal Union. As Nos. 114/7 of Antigua.*

38	1½d. blue	.. .. ..	0 6	0 8
39	3d. deep blue	.. .. ..	1 0	1 3
40	6d. orange	.. .. ..	1 9	2 0
41	1s. red-brown	.. .. ..	3 6	4 0

1953 (3 June). *Coronation. As No. 47 of Aden.*

42	2d. black and reddish purple ..	1 3	1 6

8. Qiloane.

9. Orange River.

10. Mosuto Horseman.

11. Basuto Household.

12. Maletsunyane Falls.

13. Herd-boy with Lesiba.

14. Pastoral Scene.

15. Aeroplane over Lancers' Gap.

16. Old Fort Leribe.

17. Mission Cave House.

18. Mohair (Shearing Goats).

(Recess. De La Rue & Co.)

1954 (18 Oct.). *Wmk. Mult. Script CA. P* 13½ *or* 11½ (10s.).

No.	Type		s.	d.	s.	d.
43	**8**	½d. grey-black and sepia ..	0	3	0	3
44	**9**	1d. grey-blk. & bluish grn.	0	4	0	4
45	**10**	2d. dp. brt. blue & orange	0	5	0	5
46	**11**	3d. yellow-green and deep rose-red (*shades*) ..	0	8	0	8
47	**12**	4½d. indigo & dp. ultram...	1	0	3	0
48	**13**	6d. chestnut & dp. grey-grn.	1	0	1	0
49	**14**	1s. bronze-green & purple	2	3	2	6
50	**15**	1s. 3d. brn. & turq.-green	2	9	3	0
51	**16**	2s. 6d. deep ultramarine and crimson (*shades*) ..	6	0	7	0
52	**17**	5s. black & carmine-red ..	12	0	14	0
53	**18**	10s. black and maroon ..	22	6	27	6

½d. ▬

(19)

1959 (1 Aug.). *No.* 45 *surch. with Type* **19** *by South African Govt. Ptr., Pretoria.*

No.	Type		s.	d.	s.	d.
54	**10**	½d. on 2d. deep bright blue and orange	1	0	1	3

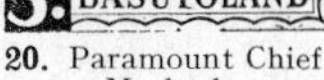

20. Paramount Chief Moshesh.

21. Council House.

22. Mosuto Horseman.

(Des. from drawings by James Walton. Recess. Waterlow & Sons.)

1959 (15 Dec.). *Inauguration of National Council. W* w.**12**. *P* 13×13½.

55	**20**	3d. blk. and yellow-olive ..	1	3	1	3
56	**21**	1s. carm. and yell.-green ..	3	0	3	6
57	**22**	1s. 3d. ultram. & red-orge.	5	0	5	0

Currency changed. 100 cents = 1 rand.

½c. (23) 1c. (24) 2c (25)

2½c (I) 2½c (II) 3½c (I) 3½c (II)

5c (I) 5c (II) 10c (I) 10c (II)

12½c (I) 12½c (II) 50c (I) 50c (II)

25c (I) 25c (II) 25c (III)

R1 (I) R1 (II) R1 (III)

(Surch. by South African Govt. Printer, Pretoria.)

1961. (14 Feb.). *T***8** to **18** *surch.* as *T* **23** *to* **25.**

58	**23**	½ c. on ½d.	0	3	0	6
		a. Surch. double				
59	**24**	1 c. on 1d.	0	3	0	6
60	**25**	2 c. on 2d.	0	8	0	8
		a. Surch. inverted	£75			
61	,,	2½ c. on 3d. (Type I) ..	2	0	2	6
		a. Type II	1	3	1	6
		b. Type II inverted				
62	,,	3½ c. on 4½d. (Type I) ..	1	3	1	6
		a. Type II	60	0	80	0
63	,,	5 c. on 6d. (Type I) ..	1	3	1	6
		a. Type II	1	9	2	0
64	,,	10 c. on 1s. (Type I) ..	2	6	3	0
		a. Type II	£20		£20	
65	,,	12½ c. on 1s. 3d. (Type I) ..	8	6	10	0
		a. Type II	5	0	6	0
66	,,	25 c. on 2s. 6d. (Type I) ..	8	6	8	6
		a. Type II	£12		£15	
		b. Type III	8	6	8	6
67	,,	50 c. on 5s. (Type I) ..	35	0	35	0
		a. Type II	12	6	12	6
68	,,	1 r. on 10s. (Type I) ..	£12		£10	
		a. Type II	£12		£12	
		b. Type III	20	0	25	0

There were two printings of the 2½ c. Type II, differing in the position of the surcharge on the stamps.

26. Basuto Household.

(Recess. De La Rue.)

1961–63. *Value in cents. Wmk. Mult. Script CA. P* 13½ *or* 11½ (1 *r.*).

69	**8**	½ c. grey-black and sepia (25.9.62)	0	2	0	2
70	**9**	1 c. grey-black and bluish green (25.9.62) ..	0	6	0	6
71	**10**	2 c. deep bright blue and orange (17.12.62) ..	0	5	0	4
72	**26**	2½ c. yellow-grn. & dp. rose-red (*shades*) (14.2.61) ..	0	10	1	0
73	**12**	3½ c. indigo and deep ultramarine (25.9.62) ..	0	7	0	8
74	**13**	5 c. chestnut & deep grey-green (10.8.62) ..	1	6	1	9
75	**14**	10 c. bronze-green & purple (22.10.62)	1	5	1	8
76	**15**	12½ c. brown and turquoise-green (17.12.62) ..	3	0	3	6
77	**16**	25 c. deep ultramarine and crimson (25.9.62) ..	3	6	4	0
78	**17**	50 c. black and carmine-red (22.10.62) ..	8	0	9	0
79	**18**	1 r. black and maroon (*shades*) (4.2.63) ..	13	3	15	0

1963 (4 June). *Freedom from Hunger. As No.* 63 *of Aden.*

80	12½ c. reddish violet	2	3	2	6

1963 (2 Sept.). *Red Cross Centenary. As Nos.* 147/8 *of Antigua.*

81	2½ c. red and black	0	9	0	9
82	12½ c. red and blue	2	3	2	6

1964. *As Nos.* 69, *etc., but wmk.* w.**12.**

84	**9**	1 c. grey-black and bluish green (11.8.64) ..	0	3	0	4
86	**26**	2½ c. pale yellow-green and rose-red (10.3.64) ..	0	6	0	6
88	**13**	5 c. chestnut and deep grey-green (10.11.64)	0	10	1	0
90	**15**	12½ c. brown and turquoise-green (10.11.64) ..	1	9	2	0
92	**17**	50 c. black and carmine-red (29.9.64)	6	9	7	6

27. Mosotho Woman and Child.

28. Maseru Border Post.

29. Mountain Scene.

30. Legislative Buildings.

(Des. V. Whiteley. Photo. Harrison.)

1965 (10 May). *New Constitution. W* w.**12**. *P* 14×13½.

94	**27**	2½ c. multicoloured ..	..	0 7	0 9
95	**28**	3½ c. multicoloured ..	..	0 9	1 0
96	**29**	5 c. multicoloured ..	..	1 0	1 3
97	**30**	12½ c. multicoloured ..	..	2 3	2 6

1965 (17 May). *I.T.U. Centenary. As Nos.* 166/7 *of Antigua.*

98	1 c. orange-red & brt. purple	0 6	0 8
99	20 c. lt. blue & orange-brown	3 9	4 6

1965 (25 Oct.). *International Co-operation Year. As Nos.* 168/9 *of Antigua.*

100	½ c. reddish purple and turquoise-green	0 4	0 6
101	12½ c. deep bluish green and lavender	2 9	3 6

1966 (24 Jan.). *Churchill Commemoration. As Nos.* 170/3 *of Antigua.*

102	1 c. new blue	0 4	0 6
103	2½ c. deep green	0 7	0 9
104	10 c. brown	1 8	2 3
105	22½ c. bluish violet	4 0	4 6

OFFICIAL STAMPS.

1934 (4 May). *Optd.* "OFFICIAL"

O 1	**1**	½d. emerald	£130	£150
O 2	,,	1d. scarlet	£70	£80
O 3	,,	2d. bright purple	£60	£50
O 4	,,	6d. orange-yellow	—	£60

Collectors are advised to buy these stamps only from reliable sources. They were not sold to the public.

POSTAGE DUE STAMPS.

D 1

D 2

(Typo. De La Rue.)

1933 (1 Dec.)–**1952**. *Wmk. Mult. Script CA. P* 14.

D1	**D 1**	1d. carmine, O	5 0	6 0
		a. Scarlet, O ('38)	25 0	30 0
		b. Deep carmine, C (24.10.51)	1 6	2 6
		c. Error. Crown missing, C ..	£16	
		d. Error. St. Edward's Crn., C	£16	
D2	,,	2d. violet, O	10 0	12 6
		a. Chalky paper (6.11.52) ..	1 0	2 6
		b. Error. Crown missing, C ..	£18	
		c. Error. St. Edward's Crn., C	£12	

(Typo. De La Rue & Co.)

1956 (1 Dec.). *Wmk. Mult. Script CA. P* **14.**

D3	**D 2**	1d. carmine	1 6	2 6
D4	,,	2d. deep reddish violet ..	1 6	2 6

5c 5c
(I) (II)

1961 (14 Feb.). *Surch. as T* **24**, *but without stop.*

D5	**D 2**	1 c. on 1d. carmine ..	0 6	0 8
D6	,,	1 c. on 2d. dp. reddish vio.	0 6	0 8
D7	,,	5 c. on 2d. dp. reddish vio. (Type I) ..	1 6	2 0
		a. Type II	£15	

1961 (June). *No.* D2a *surch. as T* **24** (*without stop*).

D8	**D 1**	5 c. on 2d. violet ..	40 0	50 0
		a. Error. Missing Crown, W9a	£250	
		b. Error. St. Ed. Crown, W9b	£100	

1964. *As No.* D3/4 *but values in cents. Chalky paper. W* w.**12** (*sideways on* 1 *c.*). *P* 14.

D 9	**D 2**	1 c. carmine	0 3	0 5
D10	,,	5 c. deep reddish violet	0 10	1 6

POSTAL FISCAL

In July 1961 the 10s. stamp, T **18**, surcharged "R1 Revenue", was used for postage at at least one post office, but such usage was officially unauthorized.

BATUM.

(BRITISH OCCUPATION.)

1

БАТУМ. ОБ.

Руб **10** Руб
(2)

1919. *Litho. Imperf.*

1	**1**	5 k. green	1 0	2 0
2	,,	10 k. ultramarine	1 0	2 0
3	,,	50 k. yellow	1 6	2 6
4	,,	1 r. chocolate	1 6	2 6
5	,,	3 r. violet	5 6	7 6
6	,,	5 r. brown	7 6	9 0

Russian stamps. Arms types, surch. with T **2.**

7	10 r. on 1 k. orange (*imperf.*)	35 0	35 0
8	10 r. on 3 k. red (*imperf.*) ..	17 6	20 0
9	10 r. on 5 k. dull pur. (*perf.*)	£10	£10
10	10 r. on 10 on 7 k. d. bl. (*perf.*)	£9	£9

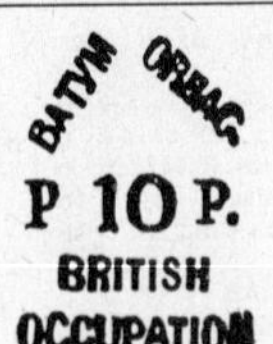

(3)

БАТУМЪ
BRITISH
P. 15 P.
OCCUPATION
ОБЛ.

(4)

1919. *Russian stamps, Arms types, surch. with T* **3** *or* **4.** *Imperf.*

11	10 rbls. on 3 k. red	15	0	17	6
12	15 rbls. on 1 k. orange ..	35	0	35	0
	a. Surcharge in red. . ..	35	0	35	0
	b. Surcharge in violet ..	35	0	35	0

BRITISH
OCCUPATION

(5)

БАТУМ.ОБЛ
P.50P.
BRITISH
OCCUPATION

(6)

1919. *T* **1**, *new colours etc., optd. with T* **5.**

13	5 k. yellow-green	3	0	3	6
14	10 k. bright blue	3	0	3	6
15	25 k. orange-yellow	3	0	3	6
16	1 rbl. pale blue	1	9	2	6
17	2 rbls. pink	1	6	2	0
18	3 rbls. bright violet	1	9	2	6
19	5 rbls. brown	2	6	4	0
	a. Error. "CCUPATION" ..	£5		£6	
20	7 rbls. brownish red	4	6	5	0

1920. *Russian Arms stamps, surch. as T* **6.**

(*a*) *Perf.*

21	25 r. on 5 k. dull purple ..	22	6	25	0
22	25 r. on 5 k. dull purple (B.) ..	20	0	25	0
23	25 r. on 10 on 7 k. blue ..	30	0	30	0
24	25 r. on 10 on 7 k. blue (B.) ..	30	0	30	0
25	25 r. on 20 on 14 k. red and blue	35	0	35	0
26	25 r. on 20 on 14 k. red and blue (B.)	35	0	35	0
27	25 r. on 25 k. pur. & green (B.)	35	0	35	0
28	25 r. on 25 k. pur. & green ..	35	0	35	0
29	25 r. on 50 k. green & purple	17	6	17	6
30	25 r. on 50 k. grn. & pur. (B.)	30	0	30	0
31	50 r. on 2 k. green	45	0	45	0
32	50 r. on 3 k. red	45	0	45	0
33	50 r. on 4 k. rose	45	0	45	0
34	50 r. on 5 k. dull purple ..	40	0	40	0

(*b*) *Imperf.*

35	50 r. on 2 k. green	£6	£6
36	50 r. on 3 k. red	£8	£8
37	50 r. on 5 k. dull purple ..	£14	£14

Romanov issue, as T **25** *of Russia, surch. with T* **6.**

38	50 r. on 4 k. rose-carmine (B.)	50	0	50	0

Russian Arms stamps surch. as T **3.** (*a*) *Imperf.*

39	50 r. on 1 k. orange	£8	£8
40	50 r. on 2 k. green	£14	£14

(*b*) *Perf.*

41	50 r. on 2 k. green	£18	£18
42	50 r. on 3 k. red	£18	£18
43	50 r. on 4 k. rose	£14	£14
44	50 r. on 5 k. dull purple ..	£10	£10
44*a*	50 r. on 10 k. deep blue (C.) ..	£22	£22
45	50 r. on 15 k. ultram. & purple	£12	£12

РУБ 25 ЛЕЙ
25 РУБ. 25

(7)

R. 50 R.
BRITISH
OCCUPATION
РУБ.

(8)

1920. *Nos.* 13 *and* 15 *surch. with T* **7.**

46	25 r. on 5 k. yellow-green ..	20	0	20	0
47	25 r. on 5 k. yellow-green (B.)	22	6	22	6
48	25 r. on 25 k. orange-yellow ..	17	6	20	0
49	25 r. on 25 k. orange-yell. (B.)	45	0	45	0

1920. *No.* 3 *surch. with T* **8.**

50	50 r. on 50 k. yellow	17	6	17	6
51	50 r. on 50 k. yellow (B.) ..	35	0	35	0

1920 (June). *T* **1** (*new colours etc.*) *optd. with T* **5**, *in black. Imperf.*

A. *Normal.* B. *Error* "BPITISH."

		A.				B.			
52	1 r. chestnut ..	0	4	0	6	12	6	20	0
53	2 r. pale blue ..	0	4	0	6	12	6	20	0
54	3 r. pink	0	4	0	6	12	6	20	0
55	5 r. black-brown	0	4	0	6	12	6	20	0
56	7 r. yellow ..	0	6	0	9	12	6	20	0
57	10 r. myrtle-green	1	0	1	6	25	0	30	0
58	15 r. violet ..	1	6	2	0	25	0	30	0
59	25 r. scarlet ..	2	6	3	0	40	0	45	0
60	50 r. deep blue ..	3	6	5	0	45	0	55	0

BECHUANALAND.

(A) BRITISH BECHUANALAND.

British
Bechuanaland

(1)

BRITISH
BECHUANALAND

(2)

1885 (Dec.)–**86.** *Stamps of Cape of Good Hope ("Hope" seated) optd. with T* **1.**

1	**6**	½d. slate (R.) (wmk. CA) ..	15	0	15	0
		a. Opt. double, in red and in black	£14			
2	,,	3d. claret (wmk. CA) ..	20	0	25	0
3	,,	4d. blue (wmk. CC)	45	0	40	0

Wmk. Anchor (*Cape, T* **13**).

4	**6**	½d. grey-black	7	6	6	0
		a. Error "ritish"	£14		£14	
5	,,	1d. pale rose-red	10	0	8	6
		a. Error "ritish"	£38		£45	
		b. Overprint double	—		£45	
6	,,	2d. bistre	30	0	15	0
		a. Error "ritish"	£45		£35	
7	**4**	6d. purple	40	0	45	0
8	,,	1s. green	£15		£8	
		a. Error "ritish"	£180			

Overprints with stop after "Bechuanaland" are forged.

1887 (Oct.). *Stamp of Gt. Britain optd. with T* **2.**

9	**71**	½d. vermilion	1	6	2	0
		a. Overprint double				

3

4

5

(Typo. De La Rue.)

1887. *P* 13½, 14.

(*a*) *Wmk. Orb.* (G.B. *T* **48**).

10 **3** 1d. lilac and black 12 6 6 0
11 ,, 2d. lilac and black 18 6 6 0
a. Pale dull lilac and black .. 25 0 25 0
12 ,, 3d. lilac and black 5 0 7 6
a. Pale reddish lilac and black .. 22 6 25 0
13 ,, 4d. lilac and black 35 0 10 0
14 ,, 6d. lilac and black 30 0 10 0

(*b*) *Wmk. Script* "V R" *sideways, reading up.*

15 **4** 1s. green and black .. 22 6 12 6
16 ,, 2s. green and black .. 45 0 25 0
17 ,, 2s. 6d. green and black .. 50 0 30 0
18 ,, 5s. green and black .. 90 0 95 0
19 ,, 10s. green and black .. £10 £12

(*c*) *Wmk. two orbs, sideways.*

20 **5** £1 lilac and black .. £50 £55
21 ,, £5 lilac and black (S. £25) .. £150 £80

Several values of the above series are known on blued paper. No. 11*a* is the first printing of the 2d. (on safety paper?) and has a faded appearance.

1d. (6) 1s. (7)

1888 (7 Aug.). *Surch. as T* **6** *or* **7**.

22 **3** 1d. on 1d. lilac and black .. 8 6 8 6
a. Surcharge double .. ..
23 ,, 2d. on 2d. lilac and blk. (R.) 12 6 10 0
a. Pale dull lilac and black .. 50 0 35 0
b. Curved foot to "2" £14 £14
24 ,, 2d. on 2d. lilac and blk. (G.) — £40
25 ,, 4d. on 4d. lilac and blk. (R.) £6 £5
26 ,, 6d. on 6d. lilac and black .. 80 0 45 0
27 ,, 6d. on 6d. lilac and blk. (B.) — £85
28 **4** 1s. on 1s. grn. and black .. £6 75 0

One Half-Penny (8) British Bechuanaland. (9) British Bechuanaland. (10)

1888 (Dec.). *No.* 12*a* *surch. with T* **8**.

29 **3** ½d. on 3d. pale reddish lilac and black £5 £5

1889. *T* **6** *of Cape of Good Hope* (*wmk. Anchor*) *optd. with T* **9**.

30 ½d. slate (G.) 12 6 17 6
a. Opt. double £16
b. Opt. double, one inverted .. £16
c. Opt. double, one vertical .. £16
d. As Var. c, se-tenant with stamp without opt. £50
e. "British" omitted .. ..

1891 (Nov.). *T* **6** *of Cape of Good Hope* (*wmk. Anchor*), *optd. with T* **10**, *reading upwards.*

31 1d. rose-red 25 0 25 0
a. No dots to "i" of "British" .. £7 £7
b. "British" omitted .. .. — £8
32 2d. bistre 4 6 5 0
a. No stop after "Bechuanaland" £8

See also Nos. 38 and 39.

BRITISH BECHUANALAND (11) BRITISH BECHUANALAND (12)

1891 (Dec.)–**1894.** *Stamps of Great Britain optd. with T* **11**.

33 **57** 1d. lilac 2 6 1 6
34 **73** 2d. green and carmine .. 3 6 3 0
35 **76** 4d. green and purple-brown 4 6 4 0
a. Bisected (on cover) .. † £85
36 **79** 6d. purple/*rose-red* .. 6 0 6 0
37 **82** 1s. green (July, 1894) .. 12 6 20 0

1893–95. *As Nos.* 31 *and* 32, *but T* **10** *reads downwards.*

38 1d. rose-red (1893) 3 6 3 6
a. "British" omitted .. £9
b. No dots to "i" of "British" .. 80 0 85 0
39 2d. bistre (1895) 5 0 4 0
a. Opt. double £40 £36
b. "British" omitted £12 £12
c. No dots to "i" of "British" £5 £6

1897. *T* **6** *of Cape of Good Hope* (*wmk. Anchor*), *optd. as T* **12**. (*First figure is distance between lines of overprint: second the length of* "BECHUANALAND.")

40 ½d. yell.-grn. (13 mm./16 mm.) 2 6 5 0
41 ½d. yell.-grn. (10½ mm./15 mm.) 8 6 10 0
42 ½d. yell.-grn. (13½ mm./15 mm.) 17 6 20 0

The Colony of British Bechuanaland was annexed to Cape of Good Hope on 16 Nov., 1895. British Bechuanaland stamps continued in use in the Protectorate until replaced by the Protectorate issue of 1897 (Nos. 59–65).

(B) BECHUANALAND PROTECTORATE.

Protectorate (13) Protectorate (14)

Protectorate (15)

1888 (Aug.). *No.* 9 *optd.*

43 **13** ½d. vermilion 4 0 6 0
a. "Protectorate" double .. £8
44 **14** ½d. vermilion 65 0 65 0
a. "Protectorate" inverted .. 45 0 45 0
b. "Portectorate" for "Protectorate" inverted ..
c. "Protectorate" double .. 85 0
d. "Protectorate" double and inverted £24 £18
45 **15** ½d. vermilion 65 0 80 0
a. "Protectorate" double .. £18
b. "Protectorrte" for "Protectorate" .. ..

Protectorate 1d (16)

1888 (Aug.). *Nos.* 10/19 *surch. or optd.* " Protectorate " *only as T* **16.**

46 **3** 1d. on 1d. lilac and black .. 4 0 5 0
a. Small figure "1" £14 £14
47 ,, 2d. on 2d. lilac and black .. 17 6 15 0
b. Curved foot to "2" .. £12 £12
48 ,, 3d. on 3d. pale reddish lilac and black 85 0 90 0
49 ,, 4d. on 4d. lilac and black .. £5 £5
50 ,, 6d. on 6d. lilac and black .. 40 0 30 0
51 **4** 1s. green and black .. 70 0 40 0
a. First "o" omitted .. £25 £25
52 ,, 2s. green and black .. £18 £20
a. First "o" omitted .. £75
53 ,, 2s. 6d. green and black .. £22 £22
a. First "o" omitted .. £85
54 ,, 5s. green and black .. £50 £60
a. First "o" omitted .. £100
55 ,, 10s. green and black .. £100 £110
a. First "o" omitted .. £250

No. 25 (*red* " 4d.") *optd. with T* **13.**

56 **3** 4d. on 4d. lilac and black .. 60 0 35 0

Bechuanaland

Protectorate

Protectorate.

Fourpence

(17) (18)

1889. *T* **6** *of Cape of Good Hope* (*wmk. Anchor*), *optd. with T* **17.**

57 ½d. slate (G.) 4 6 10 0
a. Opt. double £10 £12
b. "Bechuanaland" omitted .. £25

No. 9 *surch. with T* **18.**

58 4d. on ½d. vermilion 10 0 10 0
a. Surch. (T 18) inverted .. — £275

Nos. 43 to 58 were issued by the British Bechuanaland administration for use in the Protectorate. From 1890 to 1897 the stamps of British Bechuanaland were used.

BECHUANALAND
PROTECTORATE
(19)

BECHUANALAND PROTECTORATE
(20)

1897 (Oct.)–**1902.** *Stamps of Great Britain* (*Queen Victoria*) *optd. with T* **19.**

59 **71** ½d. vermilion 2 0 2 6
60 ,, ½d. blue-green (25.2.02) .. 2 6 2 6
61 **57** 1d. lilac 2 0 2 6
62 **73** 2d. green and carmine .. 4 0 5 0
63 **75** 3d. purple/*yellow* (12.97) .. 8 0 10 0
64 **76** 4d. green and purple-brown 12 6 15 0
65 **79** 6d. purple/*rose-red* .. 17 6 20 0

1904–**13.** *Stamps of Great Britain* (*King Edward VII*) *optd. with T* **20.**

66 **83** ½d. blue-green (3.06) .. 3 6 4 0
67 ,, ½d. yellow-green (11.08) .. 3 6 4 0
68 ,, 1d. scarlet (4.05) 3 6 4 0
69 **86** 2½d. ultramarine (29.11.04) 12 6 15 0
a. Stop after "P" in "PROTECTORATE" £45
70 **93** 1s. grn. & scarlet (1912) .. 27 6 40 0
71 ,, 1s. grn. & carmine (1913) 27 6 35 0

Nos. 70 and 71 are the Somerset House printings.

1912 (Sept.). *T* **102** *of Great Britain* (*King George V, wmk. Crown*) *optd. with T* **20.**

72 **102** 1d. scarlet 3 0 3 6
a. No cross on crown .. — £7

BECHUANALAND
PROTECTORATE
(21)

1914–**24.** *Stamps of Great Britain* (*King George V*) *optd.*

(*a*) *With T* **20** (*wmk. Script Cypher, T* **100**).

73 **105** ½d. green 1 6 1 6
74 **104** 1d. scarlet 1 6 1 6
75 **105** 1½d. red-brown 3 0 3 6
76 **106** 2d. red-brown (Die I) .. 4 6 3 6
77 ,, 2d. orange (Die II) (1924) 25 0 20 0
78 **104** 2½d. ultramarine 4 6 6 0
79 **106** 3d. blue-violet 12 6 15 0
80 ,, 4d. slate-green 10 0 15 0
81 **107** 6d. dull purple, C .. 10 0 15 0
82 **108** 1s. bistre-brown .. 12 6 17 6

(*b*) *With T* **21.** (*Wmk. T* **110.**)

(i) *Waterlow printings.* (1914.)

83 **109** 2s. 6d. deep sepia-brown 65 0 50 0
a. Re-entry £30 £40
b. Opt. double, one albino .. £8
84 ,, 5s. rose-carmine 60 0 70 0
a. Opt. double, one albino .. £25

(ii) *De La Rue printings.* (1916–20.)

85 **109** 2s. 6d. grey-brown (1916) 30 0 37 6
a. Re-entry £36
86 ,, 2s. 6d. deep brown (1920) 45 0 55 0
a. Opt. treble, two albino ..
87 ,, 5s. bright carmine (1920) £7 £8
a. Opt. double, one albino ..

(iii) *Bradbury, Wilkinson printings.* (1920–23.)

88 **109** 2s. 6d. chocolate-brown 27 6 35 0
a. Major Re-entry .. ..
89 ,, 5s. rose-red 45 0 55 0
90 ,, 5s. deep carmine .. 50 0 60 0

A 1d., King George V, Type **2** of South Africa, overprinted " Bechuanaland Protectorate ", was issued for a short period in 1922 as a Revenue stamp.

1925–**27.** *As* 1914–24, *but W* **111** (*block letters*).

91 **105** ½d. green 2 6 3 0
92 **104** 1d. scarlet 2 6 3 0
93 **106** 2d. orange (Die II) .. 5 0 5 0
94 ,, 3d. violet 6 0 8 6
95 ,, 4d. grey-green 7 6 10 0
96 **107** 6d. purple, C 15 0 20 0
97 ,, 6d. purple, O 10 0 15 0
98 **108** 1s. bistre-brown 17 6 20 0

22. King George V, Baobab Tree and Cattle drinking.

23. King George VI Baobab Tree and Cattle drinking.

(Des. from photo by Resident Commissioner, Ngamiland. Recess. Waterlow.)

1932 (12 Dec.). *Wmk. Mult. Script CA. P* 12½.

99 **22** ½d. green 0 9 1 0
100 ,, 1d. scarlet 0 9 1 0
101 ,, 2d. brown 2 0 2 0

102 **22** 3d. ultramarine 2 6 3 0
103 ,, 4d. orange 3 6 5 0
104 ,, 6d. purple 4 0 6 0
105 ,, 1s. black and olive-green 7 6 8 6
106 ,, 2s. black and orange .. 30 0 35 0
107 ,, 2s. 6d. black and scarlet 30 0 40 0
108 ,, 3s. black and purple .. 42 6 55 0
109 ,, 5s. black and ultramarine 55 0 70 0
110 ,, 10s. black and brown .. £7 £9

Extra flagstaff variety.

1935 (4 May). *Silver Jubilee. As Nos.* 91/4 *of Antigua but ptd. by B. W. & Co. P* 11 × 12.

111 1d. deep blue and scarlet .. 0 6 0 8
a. Extra flagstaff 50 0
112 2d. ultramarine & grey-black 2 0 2 6
a. Extra flagstaff 40 0
113 3d. brown and deep blue .. 3 0 3 6
a. Extra flagstaff 60 0
114 6d. slate and purple 3 6 4 6
a. Extra flagstaff 70 0

1937 (12 May). *Coronation. As Nos.* 13/15 *of Aden. P* 14.

115 1d. scarlet 0 5 0 6
116 2d. yellow-brown 1 0 1 2
117 3d. bright blue 1 6 1 9

(Recess. Waterlow.)

1938 (1 Apr.)–**1943.** *Wmk. Mult. Script CA. P* 12½.

118 **23** ½d. green 0 4 0 4
a. Light yellow-green ('42) .. 2 6 2 6
119 ,, 1d. scarlet 0 6 0 3
120 ,, 1½d. dull blue 3 0 1 6
a. Bright blue ('43) .. 0 6 0 6
121 ,, 2d. brown 0 8 0 8
122 ,, 3d. ultramarine 0 9 1 0
123 ,, 4d. orange 1 6 2 0
124 ,, 6d. deep reddish purple .. 17 6 10 0
a. Purple ('43) 2 0 2 6
125 ,, 1s. black and olive-green 3 0 3 6
126 ,, 2s. 6d. black and scarlet 6 0 8 6
127 ,, 5s. black and ultramarine 12 6 15 0
128 ,, 10s. black and brown .. 25 0 30 0

Bechuanaland
(24)

1945 (3 Dec.). *Victory. Stamps of South Africa, optd. with T* **24.** *Inscr. alternately in English and Afrikaans.*

			Un. pair	*Used pair*	*Used single*
129	**55**	1d. brown & carm.	1 0	1 6	0 6
130	**56**	2d. slate-blue & vio.	1 6	2 6	0 10
131	**57**	3d. deep blue & bl.	2 6	3 6	1 3
		a. Opt. omitted (in vert. pr. with normal)	£550	†	†

1947 (17 Feb.). *Royal Visit. As Nos.* 32/5 *of Basutoland.*

		Un.	*Us.*
132	1d. scarlet	0 3	0 3
133	2d. green	0 4	0 4
134	3d. ultramarine	0 8	0 10
135	1s. mauve	2 0	2 6

1948 (1 Dec.). *Royal Silver Wedding. As Nos.* 30/1 *of Aden.*

136 1½d. ultramarine 0 6 0 8
137 10s. black 20 0 22 6

1949 (10 Oct.). 75*th Anniv. of Universal Postal Union. As Nos.* 114/7 *of Antigua.*

138 1½d. blue 0 10 1 0
139 3d. deep blue 1 0 1 3
140 6d. magenta 1 6 2 6
141 1s. olive 3 6 4 0

1953 (3 June). *Coronation. As No.* 47 *of Aden.*

142 2d. black and brown .. 1 0 1 3

25. Queen Elizabeth II, Baobab Tree and Cattle drinking.

(Des. from photo by Resident Commissioner, Ngamiland. Recess. Waterlow.)

1955 (3 Jan.)–**58.** *Wmk. Mult. Script. CA. P* 13½ × 14.

143 **25** ½d. green 0 3 0 3
144 ,, 1d. rose-red 0 4 0 4
145 ,, 2d. red-brown 0 5 0 5
146 ,, 3d. ultramarine (*shades*) 0 8 0 8
146*a* ,, 4d. red-orange (1.12.58) .. 0 9 0 9
147 ,, 4½d. blackish blue 1 0 3 0
148 ,, 6d. purple 1 0 1 0
149 ,, 1s. black & brown-olive 2 0 2 0
150 ,, 1s. 3d. black and lilac .. 3 0 3 9
151 ,, 2s. 6d. black and rose-red 6 0 7 0
152 ,, 5s. black and violet-blue 12 6 15 0
153 ,, 10s. black and red-brown 25 0 30 0

26. Queen Victoria, Queen Elizabeth II and Landscape.

(Photo. Harrison & Sons.)

1960 (21 Jan.). *Seventy-fifth Anniv. of Bechuanaland Protectorate. W* w.**12.** *P* 14½ × 14.

154 **26** 1d. sepia and black .. 1 0 1 0
155 ,, 3d. magenta and black .. 1 6 1 6
156 ,, 6d. bright blue and black .. 2 3 2 6

Currency changed. 100 cents = 1 rand.

1c (27) **1c** (I) **1c** (II) **5c** (I) **5c** (II)

3 (I) **3** (II) **3** (III) (3½ c. on 4d.) **R1** (I) **R1** (II)

(Surch. by South African Govt. Printer, Pretoria.)

1961 (14 Feb.). *T* **25** *surch. as T* **27.**

No.	Type	Description	Unused	Used
157	**27**	1 c. on 1d. (Type I)	0 9	0 9
		a. Type II	1 0	1 3
158	,,	2 c. on 2d.	0 6	0 8
159	,,	2½ c. on 2d. (*two types*)	1 0	1 0
		a. Surch. omitted (in pair with normal)	£225	
160	,,	2½ c. on 3d.	10 0	10 0
161	,,	3½ c. on 4d. (Type I)	5 0	6 0
		a. Type II	15 0	15 0
		b. Wide surch. (I)	£7	£8
		c. Wide surch. (II)	£20	
		d. Type III	1 3	1 6
162	,,	5 c. on 6d. (Type I)	6 0	6 0
		a. Type II	1 6	1 9
163	,,	10 c. on 1s.	2 6	3 0
164	,,	12½ c. on 1s. 3d.	3 6	4 0
165	,,	25 c. on 2s. 6d.	6 0	7 6
166	,,	50 c. on 5s.	12 6	12 6
167	,,	1 r. on 10s. (Type I)	£150	£85
		a. Type II (1st Ptg.)	£5	£6
		b. Type II (2nd Ptg.)	25 0	30 0

No. 161—3½c. on 4d. Types I and II of "3" were mixed in the sheet of 60 stamps—38 of Type I, 22 of Type II. The "wide surcharge" measures 9½ mm. overall (with "C" spaced 1½ mm. from "½") and comes on 8 of the 10 stamps in the last vertical row (5 × Type I, 3 × Type II). The surcharge on the remainder of the sheet varies between 8½ and 9¼ mm.

Type III was a later printing.

Nos. 167a/b—1 rand (Type II). The First Printing (No. 167a) had the surcharge at bottom left; in the Second Printing (No. 167b) it was placed towards the bottom of the stamp, either centrally or towards the right.

Later printings of the 2½ c. on 2d. and 12½ c. on 1s. 3d. were from fresh settings of type, but insufficiently different for separate listing here. Later printings of the 10 c. and 25 c. were identical with the originals.

28. Golden Oriole.

29. African Hoopoe.

30. Scarlet-chested Sunbird.

31. Cape Widow-bird.

32. Swallow-tailed Bee-eater.

33. Grey Hornbill.

34. Red-headed Weaver.

35. Brown-hooded Kingfisher.

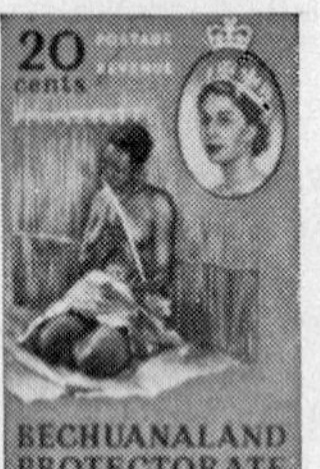

36. Woman Musician.

38. Woman Grinding Maize.

37. Baobab Tree.

39. Bechuana Ox.

40. Lion.

41. Police Camel Patrol.

(Des. P. Jones. Photo. Harrison & Sons.)

1961 (2 Oct.). *W* w.**12**. *P* 14×14½ (*vert.*) *or* 14½×14 (*horiz.*).

168	**28**	1 c. yell., red, blk. & lilac	0	3	0	3
169	**29**	2 c. orge., blk. & yell.-ol.	0	5	0	4
170	**30**	2½ c. carmine, green, black and bistre ..	0	6	0	5
171	**31**	3½ c. yell., blk., sep. & pink	0	7	0	8
172	**32**	5 c. yell., bl., blk. & buff	0	10	1	0
173	**33**	7½ c. brown, red, black and apple-green	1	1	1	3
174	**34**	10 c. red, yellow, sepia and turquoise-green	1	5	1	8
175	**35**	12½ c. buff, blue, red and grey-black ..	1	9	2	0
176	**36**	20 c. yellow-brown & drab	2	9	3	3
177	**37**	25 c. dp. brown and lemon	3	6	4	0
178	**38**	35 c. deep blue & orange	4	8	5	0
179	**39**	50 c. sepia and olive ..	6	9	7	6
180	**40**	1 r. black and cinnamon	13	3	15	0
181	**41**	2 r. brown & turq.-blue	25	0	30	0

1963 (4 June). *Freedom from Hunger. As No.* 63 *of Aden.*

182	12½ c. bluish green	2	6	2	9

1963 (2 Sept.). *Red Cross Centenary. As Nos.* 147/8 *of Antigua.*

183	2½ c. red and black ..	0	10	1	3
184	12½ c. red and blue	2	6	2	9

1964 (23 April). 400*th Anniv. of Birth of William Shakespeare. As No.* 164 *of Antigua.*

185	12½ c. light brown	3	3	3	6

(C) BECHUANALAND.

SELF GOVERNMENT.

42. Map and Gaberones Dam.

(Des. V. Whiteley. Photo. Harrison & Sons.)

1965 (1 Mar.). *New Constitution. W* w.**12**. *P* 14½×14.

186	**42**	2½ c. red and gold ..	1	0	1	0
187	,,	5 c. ultramarine & gold	1	6	1	9
188	,,	12½ c. brown and gold ..	2	9	3	0
189	,,	25 c. green and gold ..	5	0	5	6

1965 (17 May). *I.T.U. Centenary. As Nos.* 166/7 *of Antigua.*

190	2½ c. red and bistre-yellow ..	0	6	0	8
191	12½ c. mauve and brown ..	3	0	3	6

1965 (25 Oct.). *International Co-operation Year. As Nos.* 168/9 *of Antigua.*

192	1 c. reddish purple and turquoise-green	0	4	0	6
193	12½ c. dp. bluish green & lav.	2	9	3	3

1966 (24 Jan.). *Churchill Commemoration. As Nos.* 170/3 *of Antigua.*

194	1 c. new blue	0	4	0	6
195	2½ c. deep green	0	7	0	9
196	12½ c. brown	2	3	2	9
197	20 c. bluish violet	3	3	4	0

POSTAGE DUE STAMPS.

BECHUANALAND PROTECTORATE

(D 1)

BECHUANALAND
PROTECTORATE

(D 2)

1926. *Type* D **1** *of Great Britain, optd. with Types* D **1** or D **2** (2*d.*).

D1	½d. emerald (No. D 10*b*) ..	1	6	2	0
D2	1d. carmine (No. D 10*a*) ..	2	6	3	6
D3	2d. agate (No. D 13) ..	4	0	6	0

D 3

1c 1c

I. (Small.) II. (Large.)

(Typo. De La Rue & Co.)

1932 (12 Dec.)–**58**. *Wmk. Mult. Script CA. P* 14.

D4	D **3**	½d. sage-green	4	6	6	0
D5	,,	1d. carmine, O ..	4	6	6	0
		a. Chalky paper (27.11.58) ..	1	0	1	6
D6	,,	2d. violet, O	10	0	12	6
		a. Chalky paper (27.11.58) ..	1	9	3	0

1961 (14 Feb.). *Surch. as T* **27**.

D7	D **3**	1 c. on 1d., C (Type I) ..	1	6	2	0
		a. Type II (chalky paper) ..	0	9	1	6
		aa. Double surch. (Type II) ..	£40			
		b. Type II (ordinary paper) ..	£10			
D8	,,	2 c. on 2d., C (Type I) ..	1	6	2	0
		a. Type II (chalky paper)	2	0	2	6
		b. Type II (ordinary paper) ..	£12			
D9	,,	5 c. on ½d.	2	6	3	6

1961 (15 Nov.). *As Type* D **3** *but values in cents. Chalky paper. Wmk. Mult. Script CA. P* 14.

D10	1 c. carmine	0	3	0	6
D11	2 c. violet	0	5	0	8
D12	5 c. green	0	10	1	3

POSTAL FISCAL.

Bechuanaland

Protectorate

(F 1)

1910. *Stamp of Transvaal* (*King Edward VII wmk. Mult. Crown CA*), *optd. with Type* F **1**.

F1	6d. black and orange, C (B.)	£10	£12

This provisional was issued for fiscal purposes, but a few were allowed to be used for postage.

BERMUDA.

O 1

O 2

1848–61. *Postmasters' Stamps. Adhesives prepared and issued by the postmasters at Hamilton and St. Georges.*

(a) By W. B. Perot at Hamilton.

No.	Type	Description	Unused	Used
O1	**O 1**	1d. black (1848, 1849) ..	—	£3750
O2	,,	1d. red/*white* (1853) ..	—	£4500
O3	,,	1d. red/*blue* (1854, 1856)	—	£4500

(b) By W. B. Perot at Hamilton.

No.	Type	Description	Unused	Used
O4	**O 2**	(1d.) red/*greyish blue* (1861)	—	£1750

(c) By J. H. Thies at St. Georges.
As Type **O 2** *but inscr.* " ST. GEORGES ".

No.	Type	Description	Unused	Used
O5	–	(1d.) red (1860)	—	£4250

Stamps of Type **O 1** bear manuscript value and signature, and the dates given are those inscribed on the known copies existing. Although the franking value is believed to have been 1d., it was not given on Nos. O4/5.

1

2

3

4

5

(Typo. De La Rue.)

1865–1903. *Wmk. Crown CC.*

(a) P 14.

No.	Type	Description	Unused	Used
1	**1**	1d. rose-red (25.9.65) ..	27 6	5 0
2	,,	1d. pale rose	35 0	7 6
3	**2**	2d. dull blue (14.3.66) ..	50 0	22 6
4	,,	2d. bright blue ..	80 0	25 0
5	**3**	3d. yellow-buff (10.3.73) ..	£18	60 0
5*a*	,,	3d. orange	£18	60 0
6	**4**	6d. dull purple (25.9.65) ..	£14	£5
7	,,	6d. dull mauve	12 6	15 0
8	**5**	1s. green (25.9.65)	60 0	40 0
		(b) Imperf.		
9	**1**	1d. rose-red	£300	£250
		(c) P 14 × 12½.		
10	**3**	3d. yellow-buff (1882) ..	£10	55 0
10*a*	**4**	6d. bright mauve (1903) ..	7 6	8 6
11	**5**	1s. green (1894)	15 0	35 0
		a. Vert. strip of 3, two stamps imperf. horiz.	£350	
		b. Imperf. at right		

Though manufactured early in 1880, stamps p. 14 × 12½ were not issued until the dates given above. No. 11 does not exist with wing margins, and the error, No. 11b, has the right-hand sheet margin attached.

THREE PENCE (6) THREE PENCE (6*a*)

THREE PENCE (7)

1874 (12 MAR.–19 MAY). *Nos.* 1 *and* 8 *surch. diagonally.* (*a*) *With T* **6.** (" P " *and* " R " *different type.*)

No.	Description	Unused	Used
12	3d. on 1d. rose-red	£325	
13	3d. on 1s. green	£55	£35
	(*b*) *With T* **6*a*.** (" P " *same type as* " R ".)		
13*b*	3d. on 1s. green	£80	£70
	(*c*) *With T* **7.** (19 May.)		
14	3d. on 1s. green	£55	£35

The 3d. on 1d. was not regularly issued, though a few specimens were used later. Nos. 13, 13*b* and 14, being handstamped, are found with double or partial double surcharges.

One
Penny.
(8)

1875 (MARCH–MAY). *Surch. with T* **8.**

No.	Type	Description	Unused	Used
15	**2**	1d. on 2d. (No. 4) (23 Apr.) ..	£35	£20
		a. No stop after " Penny " ..		
16	**3**	1d. on 3d. (No. 5) (8 May) ..	£22	£24
17	**5**	1d. on 1s. (No. 8) (11 Mar.) ..	£8	£8
		a. Surch. inverted	—	£325
		b. No stop after " Penny " ..		

8

10

(Typo. De La Rue.)

1880 (23 MAR.). *Wmk. Crown CC. P* 14.
19 **9** ½d. stone 3 6 4 6
20 **10** 4d. orange-red 6 0 4 6

ONE FARTHING

11 (12)
(Typo. De La Rue.)

1883–96. *Wmk. Crown CA. P* 14.
21 **9** ½d. dull grn. (Oct., '92).. 2 6 2 6
21*a* „ ½d. dp. grey-green (1893) 1 6 2 6
22 **1** 1d. dull rose (Dec., '83) .. 70 0 10 0
23 „ 1d. rose-red 50 0 6 0
24 „ 1d. carmine-rose (1886) .. 20 0 2 6
24*a* „ 1d. aniline carmine (1889) 5 0 0 9
25 **2** 2d. blue (Dec., '86) .. 25 0 8 0
26 „ 2d. aniline pur. (July, '93) 15 0 10 0
26*a* „ 2d. brown-purple (1898) 6 6 6 0
27 **11** 2½d. dp. ultram. (10.11.84) 10 0 2 0
27*a* „ 2½d. pale ultramarine .. 6 0 2 0
28 **3** 3d. grey (Jan., '86) .. 8 6 7 6
29 **5** 1s. yellow-brown (1893) 30 0 27 6
29*a* „ 1s. olive-brown 20 0 25 0

1901. *As Nos.* 29/*a but colour changed, surch. with T* **12.**
30 **5** ¼d. on 1s. dull grey .. 0 9 1 0
30*a* „ ¼d. on 1s. bluish grey .. 0 6 1 0

13. Dock.
(Typo. De La Rue.)

1902–3. *Wmk. Crown CA. P* 14.
31 **13** ½d. black and green (1903) 10 0 4 0
32 „ 1d. brown and carmine .. 5 0 1 0
33 „ 3d. magenta & sage-green 6 0 8 6

1904. *Wmk. Crown CA. P* 14.
34 **10** 4d. orange-brown.. .. 30 0 37 6

1906–9. *Wmk. Mult. Crown CA. P* 14.
34*a* **13** ¼d. brown & violet (1908) 2 6 3 0
35 „ ½d. black and green .. 6 0 5 0
36 „ 1d. brown and carmine .. 7 6 1 0
37 „ 2d. grey and orange (1907) 8 0 10 0
38 „ 2½d. brown & ultramarine 15 0 15 0
39 „ 4d. blue & chocolate (1909) 10 0 7 6

1908–10. *Wmk. Mult. Crown CA. P* 14.
41 **13** ½d. green (1909) 7 6 6 0
42 „ 1d. red 4 0 2 0
43 „ 2½d. blue (1910) .. 15 0 15 0

14  15
(Recess. De La Rue.)

1910–25. *Wmk. Mult. Crown CA. P* 14.
44 **14** ¼d. brown (26.3.12) .. 0 9 2 0
a. Pale brown 4 0 4 6
45 „ ½d. green (1910) 2 0 0 10
a. Deep green 7 6 3 6
46 „ 1d. red (1910) 2 0 0 3
a. Rose-red 10 0 0 6
b. Carmine 17 6 7 6
47 „ 2d. grey (Jan., '13) .. 3 6 7 6
48 „ 2½d. blue (27.3.12) 3 0 5 0
49 „ 3d. purple/*yellow* (Jan., '13) 7 6 7 6
49*a* „ 4d. red/*yellow* (1.9.19) .. 7 6 7 6
50 „ 6d. purple (26.3.12) .. 17 6 25 0
a. Pale claret (2.6.24) .. 10 0 15 0
51 „ 1s. black/*green* (26.3.12) .. 15 0 15 0
a. Jet-black/olive (1925) .. 12 6 12 6

Nos. 44 to 51*a* are comb-perf. 13.8 × 14. No. 45 exists also line-perf. 13.75.

(Typo. De La Rue.)

1918 (30 MAR.)–**20.** *Wmk. Mult. Crown CA. P* 14.
51*b* **15** 2s. purple & blue/*blue*, C (19.6.20) 18 6 27 6
52 „ 2s. 6d. black & red/*blue*, C 30 0 40 0
52*a* „ 4s. black & carmine, C (19.6.20) 35 0 50 0
53 „ 5s. green and red/*yellow*, C 35 0 40 0
54 „ 10s. green & red/*green*, C £10 £12
55 „ £1 purple and black/*red*, C £20 £22

Beware of cleaned copies of the 10s. with faked postmarks.

WAR TAX (16) WAR TAX (17)

1918 (4 MAY). *Nos.* 46 *and* 46a *optd. locally with T* **16.**
56 **14** 1d. red 1 0 1 3
a. Rose-red 0 3 0 10

1920 (MAR.). *No.* 46*b optd. with T* **17.**
58 **14** 1d. carmine 1 0 1 6

Tercentenary of Representative Institutions. 1st Issue.

18

(Des. by the Governor (Gen. Sir James Willcocks). Typo. De La Rue.)

1920–21. *P* 14.
(*a*) *Wmk. Mult. Crown CA (sideways)* (19.1.21).
59 **18** ¼d. brown, O 1 6 3 0
60 „ ½d. green, O 2 6 5 0
61 „ 2d. grey, O 8 6 17 6
62 „ 3d. dull and deep purple/*pale yellow*, C 12 6 20 0
63 „ 4d. black and red/*pale yellow*, C 20 0 27 6
64 „ 1s. black/*blue-green*, C .. 35 0 45 0
(*b*) *Wmk. Mult. Script CA (sideways).*
65 **18** 1d. carmine, O (11.11.20) 3 6 3 6
66 „ 2½d. brt. blue, O (11.11.20) 10 0 16 0
67 „ 6d. dull and bright purple, C (19.1.21) 17 6 20 0

2nd Issue.

19

(Des. H. J. Dale. Recess. De La Rue.)

1921 (12 May). *P* 14.

(*a*) *Wmk. Mult. Crown CA* (*sideways*).

68	**19**	2d. slate-grey	12	6	15	0
69	,,	2½d. bright ultramarine ..	12	6	12	6
70	,,	3d. purple/*pale yellow* ..	12	6	17	6
71	,,	4d. red/*pale yellow* ..	12	6	18	6
72	,,	6d. purple	22	6	27	6
73	,,	1s. black/*green*	35	0	45	0

(*b*) *Wmk. Mult. Script CA* (*sideways*).

74	**19**	¼d. brown	1	9	3	6
75	,,	½d. green	3	6	4	0
76	,,	1d. deep carmine	3	0	2	0

Type I

Type II

Type I Type II

1922–25. *Wmk. Mult. Script CA. P* 14.

76*a*	**14**	¼d. brown (July, '28) ..	0	8	1	6
77	,,	½d. green (Nov. '22) ..	0	4	0	3
78	,,	1d. scarlet (I) (Nov. '22)	3	6	0	3
78*a*	,,	1d. carmine (I) (Nov. '22)	6	6	1	0
79	,,	1d. carmine (II) (Oct. '28)	2	0	0	9
79*a*	,,	1d. carmine-lake (II) ('34)	2	6	0	6
79*b*	,,	1½d. red-brown (27.3.34)..	3	6	1	6
80	,,	2d. grey (Dec., '23) ..	2	0	3	0
81	,,	2½d. palesage-grn. (Dec.'22)	27	6	35	0
81*a*	,,	2½d. deep sage-green ('24)	7	6	8	6
82	,,	2½d. ultram. (I) (1.12.26)..	8	6	3	6
82*a*	,,	2½d. ultram. (II) (Mar. '32)	3	0	3	0
83	,,	3d. ultram. (Dec., '24) ..	25	0	45	0
84	,,	3d. pur./*yell.* (Oct. '26) ..	3	0	4	6
85	,,	4d. red/*yellow* (Aug. '24)	3	0	3	6
86	,,	6d. purple (Aug. '24) ..	5	0	6	0
87	,,	1s. blk./*emer.* (Oct., '27)	27	6	25	0
87*a*	,,	1s. brownish black/*yellow-green* ('34) ..	60	0	65	0
88	**15**	2s. purple & bright blue/*blue*, C (Sept., '27) ..	25	0	30	0
89	,,	2s. 6d. black and red/*blue*, C (April '27) ..	40	0	50	0
89*a*	,,	2s. 6d. black & orge.-ver./*blue*, C ('30).. ..	£18		£20	
89*b*	,,	2s. 6d. blk. & verm./*blue*, C ('30)	45	0	50	0
92	,,	10s. green & red/*emer.*, C (Dec. '24)	£12		£14	
93	,,	12s. 6d. grey and orange, C O (Aug. '32) ..	£20		£24	

1d. In Type II a strong line completes the scroll at top left which in Type I is very weak. There are two plates of Type I differing slightly in the shape of "1d" both having rounded corners and in the spacing of marginal jubilee lines. Type II is without jubilee lines and "1d" has square corners.

2½d. Type I: Short, thick figures, especially the "1"; small "d". Type II: Figures taller and thinner; "d" larger.

Nos. 76*a* to 87 exist both line-perf. 13.75 and comb-perf. 13.8 × 14 except Nos. 79*b*, 82*a* and 87*a* which are line-perf. only.

No. 89*a*, which is from an early printing, is a much paler vermilion than the vermilion shades of subsequent printings.

No. 93 on ordinary paper would seem to be an error. Our prices are for the chalky paper.

1935 (6 May) *Silver Jubilee. As T* **13** *of Antigua. Recess. W'low. & Sons. Wmk. Mult. Script CA. P* 11 × 12.

94	1d. deep blue and scarlet ..	0	10	1	0
95	1½d. ultramarine and grey ..	1	3	1	6
96	2½d. brown and deep blue ..	6	6	7	0
97	1s. slate and purple ..	12	6	15	0

20. Hamilton Harbour.

21 South Shore near Spanish Rock.

22. The *Lucie.*

23. Grape Bay, Paget Parish.

24. Point House, Warwick Parish.

25. House at Par-la-Ville, Hamilton.

(Recess. Bradbury, Wilkinson.)

1936 (14 Apr.). *Wmk. Mult. Script CA (sideways on horiz. designs). P* 12.

98	**20**	½d. bright green	0 4	0 4
99	**21**	1d. black and scarlet ..	0 9	0 6
100	"	1½d. black and chocolate ..	1 0	1 0
101	**22**	2d. black and pale blue ..	4 6	5 0
102	**23**	2½d. light and deep blue ..	2 6	3 0
103	**24**	3d. black and scarlet ..	6 6	8 0
104	**25**	6d. carmine-rose & violet	1 0	0 8
105	**23**	1s. green	8 0	10 0
106	**20**	1s. 6d. brown	2 6	1 6

All are line-perf. 11.9, except printings of the 6d., from July 1951 onwards, which are comb. perf. 11.9 × 11.75.

1937 (14 May). *Coronation Issue. As T* **2** *of Aden. Recess. D. L. R. & Co. Wmk. Mult. Script CA. P* 14.

107	1d. scarlet	0 6	0 6
108	1½d. yellow-brown	0 10	1 0
109	2½d. bright blue	1 6	2 0

26. Ships in Hamilton Harbour.

27. St. David's Lighthouse.

28. Longtail, Arms of Bermuda and Native Flower.

(Des. Miss Higginbotham (T **28**). Recess. Bradbury, Wilkinson.)

1938 (20 Jan.)–**1952.** *T* **22**, *T* **23** *but with portrait of King George VI) and T* **26** *to* **28.** *Wmk. Mult. Script CA. P* 12.

110	**26**	1d. black and rose-red	22 6	5 0
		a. Black and dull red ..	0 6	0 6
111	,,	1½d. blue and chocolate	0 6	0 3
112	**22**	2d. light blue and sepia	27 6	25 0
112*a*		2d. ultram. and scar. (12.11.40)	1 6	2 0
113	**23**	2½d. light and deep blue	3 6	3 0
113*a*	,,	2½d. light blue and sepia (18.12.41)	0 8	0 9
		b. Brt. blue & sepia (23.9.52)	1 3	1 3
114	**27**	3d. black and rose-red	8 6	7 6
114*a*	,,	3d. black and deep blue (16.7.41)	1 0	0 8
114*b*	**28**	7½d. blk., blue & yellow-green (18.12.41) ..	3 6	4 0
115	**23**	1s. green	3 0	2 6

The 1d. (110), 2d. (112), 2½d. (113/3*a*), 3d. (114) and 7½d. are line-perf. 11.9. The others exist line-perf. 11.9 (early printings) and comb-perf. 11.9 × 11.75 (printings from July 1950)

29. King George VI.

(Typo. De La Rue.)

1938 (20 Jan.)–**1953.** *T* **29.** *P* 14.

(*a*) *Wmk. Mult. Script CA.*

116	2s. deep pur. & ultram./*grey-blue*, C	30 0	17 6
	a. Purple & blue/deep bl., O ('42)	15 0	12 6
	b. Purple & deep blue/pale blue, O ('43)	8 6	7 6
	c. Perf. 13. *Dull purple & blue/pale blue*, O (15.2.50) ..	7 6	8 6
117	2s. 6d. blk. & red/*grey-blue*, C	25 0	20 0
	a. Black & red/p. blue, O ('42) ..	10 0	10 0
	b. Perf. 13. *Black & orge-red/pale blue*, O (10.10.50) ..	10 0	17 6
	c. Perf. 13. *Black & red/pale blue*, O (18.6.52)	12 6	15 0
118	5s. green and red/*yellow*, C	37 6	25 0
	a. Pale grn. & red/pale yell., O ('43)	10 6	10 6
	b. Perf. 13. *P. grn. & red/p. yell.*, OC (15.2.50)	8 0	10 6
119	10s. green & dp. lake/*grn.*, C	£15	£12
	a. Green & red/green, O ('39) ..	30 0	50 0
	b. Perf. 13. *Green & verm./grn.*, O (21.9.51)	50 0	75 0
	ba. Perf. 13. *Green & dull red/grn.*, O (16.4.53)	30 0	35 0
120	12s. 6d. grey and brownish orange, C	75 0	80 0
	a. Grey & orange, OC ('43) ..	30 0	40 0
	*b. Grey & yellow**, O (?'47) ..	£28	£30
	c. Perf. 13. *Grey & orange*, C (10.10.50)	35 0	47 6

(*b*) *Wmk. Mult. Crown CA.*

121	£1 purple and black/*red*, C	£8	£5
	a. Brn.-purple & blk./salmon, C ('42)	40 0	40 0
	b. Perf. 13. *Violet and black/scarlet*, C (?Dec. '51) ..	40 0	50 0

In No. 116*a* the coloured surfacing of the paper is mottled with white specks sometimes accompanied by very close horizontal lines.

In Nos. 116*b*, 117*a* and 118*a* the surfacing is the same colour as the back, sometimes applied in widely spaced horizontal lines giving the appearance of laid paper.

In No. 119 the surfacing is bright yellowish green and in No. 119*a* bluish green.

Early printings of the 2s., 2s. 6d., 5s. and 10s. exist perf. 14.2 line in addition to the normal perforation which is 13.9 × 13.8 comb. These are comparatively rare.

*No. 120*b* is the so-called "lemon" shade.

HALF
PENNY

X **X**

(30)

1940 (20 Dec.). *No.* 110 *surch. with T* **30.**
122 **26** ½d. on 1d. black and red (*shades*) 1 6 3 0

The spacing between "PENNY" and "X" varies from 12½ mm. to 14 mm.

1946 (6 Nov.). *Victory. As Nos.* 28/9 *of Aden.*
123 1½d. brown 0 4 0 6
124 3d. blue 0 10 1 0

1948 (1 Dec.). *Royal Silver Wedding. As Nos.* 30/1 *of Aden.*
125 1½d. red-brown 0 6 0 6
126 £1 carmine 40 0 45 0

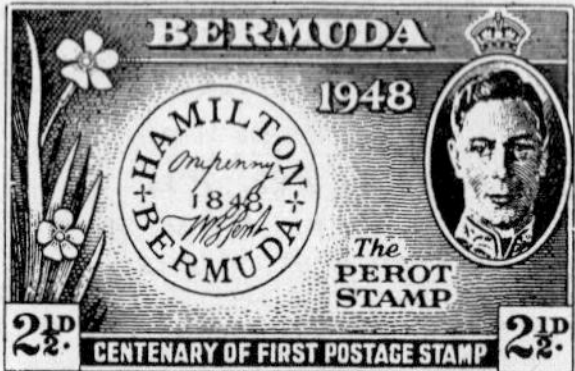

31. Postmaster Perot's Stamp.

(Recess. Bradbury, Wilkinson.)

1949 (11 Apr.). *100th Anniv. of Postmaster Perot's Stamp. Wmk. Mult. Script CA. P* 13½.
127 **31** 2½d. blue and brown .. 1 0 1 3
128 ,, 3d. black and blue .. 1 6 1 9
129 ,, 6d. violet and green .. 2 6 3 0

1949 (10 Oct.). *75th Anniv. of Universal Postal Union. As Nos.* 114/7 *of Antigua.*
130 2½d. blue-black 1 0 1 3
131 3d. deep blue 1 9 2 0
132 6d. purple 2 0 2 6
133 1s. blue-green 4 0 4 6

1953 (4 June). *Coronation. As No.* 47 *of Aden, but ptd. by B. W. & Co.*
134 1½d. black and blue 1 0 1 3

32. Easter Lilies.

33. Postmaster Perot's Stamp.

34. Easter Lily.

42. Warwick Fort.

35. Bermuda Racing Dinghy.

36. Sir George Somers and *Sea Venture.*

37. Map of Bermuda.

Die I. "Sandy's". Die II. "Sandys".

38. *Sea Venture,* Inter-island Boat, Coin and Perot Stamp.

39. Longtail, or Boatswain Boat.

40. Early Bermudan Coinage.

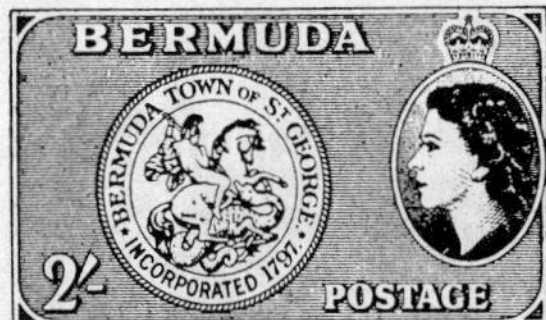

41. Arms of St. George's.

43. Hog Coin.

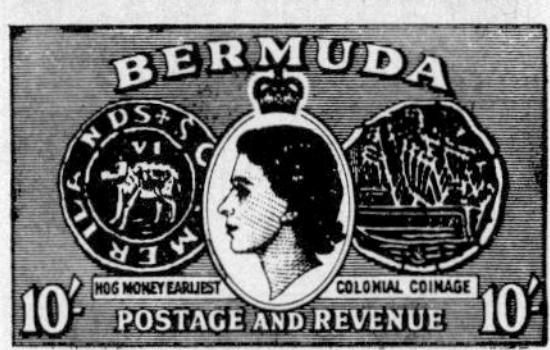

44. Obverse and Reverse of Hog Coin.

45. Arms of Bermuda.

(Des. C. Deakins (T **32, 37, 43**), J. Berry (T **33, 34, 36, 40**), B. Brown (T **35, 39**), D. Haig (T **38**), Pamela Braley-Smith (T **42**) and E. C. Leslie (T **44**). Recess (except £1, centre typo.), Bradbury, Wilkinson & Co.)

1953 (9 Nov.)–**62.** *Wmk. Mult. Script CA.* *P* 13½.

No.	Type	Description				
135	**32**	½d. olive-green (*shades*)	0	4	0	4
136	**33**	1d. black & red (*shades*)	0	4	0	4
137	**34**	1½d. green	0	4	0	3
138	**35**	2d. ultram. & brown-red	0	5	0	4
139	**36**	2½d. rose-red	0	6	0	5
140	**37**	3d. deep purple (I) ..	2	0	2	6
140*a*	,,	3d. dp. pur. (II) (2.1.57)	0	7	0	7
141	**33**	4d. black & bright blue	1	0	1	6
142	**38**	4½d. emerald	1	3	2	0
143	**39**	6d. black & deep turq.	1	3	1	3
143*a*	,,	8d. black & red (16.5.55)	1	6	2	0
143*b*	**38**	9d. violet (6.1.58) ..	2	0	2	6
144	**40**	1s. orange	1	9	1	3
145	**37**	1s. 3d. blue (I) (*shades*)	3	6	3	6
145*b*	,,	1s. 3d. blue (II) (2.1.57)	2	6	2	0
		c. Bright blue (II) (14.8.62)	2	6	2	0
146	**41**	2s. brown	3	9	3	0
147	**42**	2s. 6d. scarlet	5	0	3	6
148	**43**	5s. carmine	8	0	7	6
149	**44**	10s. dp. ultram. (*shades*)	17	6	18	6
150	**45**	£1 brown, blue, red, green & bronze-green	35	0	37	6

1953 (26 Nov.). *Royal Visit. As No.* 143 *but inscr.* "ROYAL VISIT 1953" *in top left corner.*

No.	Type	Description				
151	**39**	6d. blk. & deep turquoise	1	6	1	6

Three Power Talks
December, 1953.
(**46**)

50TH ANNIVERSARY
U S – BERMUDA
OCEAN RACE 1956
(**47**)

1953 (8 Dec.). *Three Power Talks. Nos.* 140 *and* 145 *optd. with T* **46.**

No.	Type	Description				
152	**37**	3d. deep purple (B.) ..	1	6	1	6
153	,,	1s. 3d. blue (R.) ..	3	0	3	3

There are two settings of T **46.**

1956 (22 June). *50th Anniv. United States-Bermuda Yacht Race. Nos.* 143*a and* 145 *optd. with T* **47** *by The Bermuda Press.*

No.	Type	Description				
154	**39**	8d. black and red (Bk.) ..	2	0	2	0
155	**37**	1s. 3d. greenish blue (R.) ..	2	6	3	6

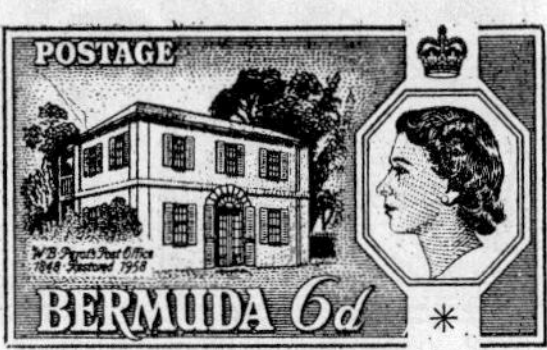

48. Perot's Post Office.

(Des. W. H. Harrington. Recess. Bradbury Wilkinson & Co.)

1959 (1 Jan.). *Wmk. Mult. Script CA.* *P* 13½.

No.	Type	Description				
156	**48**	6d. black & deep mauve ..	1	0	1	0

49. Arms of King James I and Queen Elizabeth II.

(Des. W. Harrington. Recess; arms litho. De La Rue & Co.)

1959 (29 July). *350th Anniv. of Settlement. Arms, red, yellow and blue; frame colours below. W* w.**12.** *P* 13.

No.	Type	Description				
157	**49**	1½d. grey-blue	1	0	1	0
158	,,	3d. drab-grey	1	3	1	3
159	,,	4d. reddish purple ..	1	3	1	3
160	,,	8d. slate-violet	2	3	2	6
161	,,	9d. olive-green	2	9	3	6
162	,,	1s. 3d. brown	3	6	5	0

50. The Old Rectory, St. George's, *c*.1730.

51. Church of St. Peter, St. George's.

52. Government House, 1892.

53. The Cathedral, Hamilton, 1894.

54. H.M. Dockyard, 1811.

55. Perot's Post Office, 1848.

56. G.P.O., Hamilton, 1869.

57. Library, Par-la-Ville.

58. Christ Church, Warwick, 1719.

59. City Hall, Hamilton, 1960.

60. Bermuda Cottage, *c.* 1705.

61. Town of St. George.

62. Bermuda House, *c.* 1710.

63. Bermuda House, early 18th century.

64. Colonial Secretariat, 1833.

65. Old Post Office, Somerset, 1890.

66. The House of Assembly, 1815.

(Des. D. A. Harrington. Photo. Harrison & Sons.)

1962 (26 Oct.)–**65.** *W* w.**12.** *P* 12½.

No.	Type	Description	Unused	Used
163	**50**	1d. reddish purple, black and orange	0 3	0 3
164	**51**	2d. lilac, ind., yell. & grn.	0 4	0 4
165	**52**	3d. yell.-brown & lt. blue	0 6	0 6
166	**53**	4d. red-brn. & magenta	0 7	0 6
167	**54**	5d. grey-blue and rose ..	0 9	0 9
168	**55**	6d. grey-bl. emer. & lt. bl.	0 10	0 9
169	**56**	8d. bright blue, bright green and orange ..	1 0	1 0
170	**57**	9d. light blue and brown	1 1	1 2
170*a*	**60**	10d. violet & ochre (8.2.65)	1 3	1 9
171	**58**	1s. black, emerald, bright blue and orange ..	1 5	1 3
172	**59**	1s. 3d. lake, grey & bistre	1 9	1 0
173	**60**	1s. 6d. violet and ochre..	3 0	2 9
174	**61**	2s. red-brown and orange	2 9	2 6
175	**62**	2s. 3d. bistre-brown and yellow-green ..	3 2	3 0
176	**63**	2s. 6d. bistre-brown, bl'sh green & olive-yellow	3 6	3 0
177	**64**	5s. brn,-pur. & bl.-green	6 9	6 6
178	**65**	10s. magenta, deep bluish green and buff ..	13 3	14 0
179	**66**	£1 black, yellow-olive and yellow-orange ..	25 0	28 0

1963 (4 June). *Freedom from Hunger. As No.* 63 *of Aden.*

No.	Description	Unused	Used
180	1s. 3d. sepia	2 3	2 6

1963 (2 Sept.). *Red Cross Centenary. As Nos.* 147/8 *of Antigua.*

No.	Description	Unused	Used
181	3d. red and black	0 7	0 8
182	1s. 3d. red and blue.. ..	2 3	2 6

67. Finn Boat.

(Des. V. Whiteley. Photo. De La Rue.)

1964 (28 Sept.). *Olympic Games, Tokio. W* w.**12.** *P* 14 × 13½.

No.	Type	Description	Unused	Used
183	**67**	3d. red, violet and blue ..	1 6	2 0

1965 (17 May). *I.T.U. Centenary. As Nos.* 166/7 *of Antigua.*

No.	Description	Unused	Used
184	3d. light blue and emerald ..	0 10	1 0
185	2s. yellow and ultramarine..	4 0	4 6

68. Scout Badge and St. Edward's Crown.

(Des. W. Harrington. Photo. Harrison.)

1965 (24 JULY). *50th Anniv. of Bermuda Boy Scouts Association. W* w.**12**. *P* 12½.

186 **68** 2s. multicoloured 6 0 7 6

1965 (25 OCT.). *International Co-operation Year. As Nos.* 168/9 *of Antigua.*

187 4d. reddish purple and turquoise-green 1 0 1 3

188 2s. 6d. deep bluish green and lavender 5 6 6 6

1966 (24 JAN.). *Churchill Commemoration. As Nos.* 170/3 *of Antigua.*

189 3d. new blue 0 7 0 9

190 6d. deep green 1 0 1 3

191 10d. brown 1 6 2 0

192 1s. 3d. bluish violet .. 2 3 2 9

BRITISH ANTARCTIC TERRITORY.

1. M.V. *Kista Dan.*

2. Manhauling.

3. Muskeg (tractor).

4. Skiing.

5. Beaver (aircraft).

6. R.R.S. *John Biscoe.*

7. Camp Scene.

8. H.M.S. *Protector.*

9. Sledging.

10. Otter (aircraft.)

11. Huskies.

12. Helicopter.

13. Snocat (tractor).

14. R.R.S. *Shackleton.*

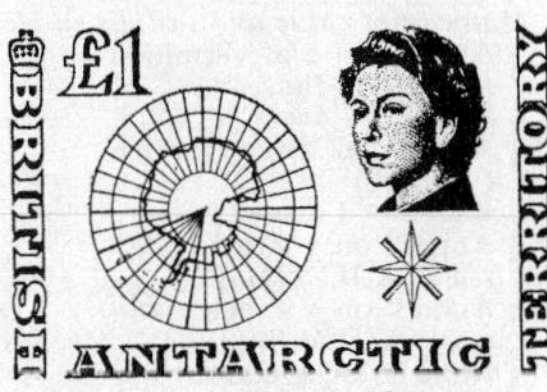

15. Antarctic Map.

(Des. M. Goaman. Recess. Bradbury, Wilkinson.)

1963 (1 Feb.). *W* w.**12.** *P* 11×11½.

1	**1**	½d. deep blue	0 2	0 3
2	**2**	1d. brown	0 3	0 3
3	**3**	1½d. red and brown-purple	0 4	0 4
4	**4**	2d. purple	0 4	0 4
5	**5**	2½d. myrtle-green	0 5	0 5
6	**6**	3d. greenish blue	0 6	0 7
7	**7**	4d. sepia	0 7	0 8
8	**8**	6d. olive & deep ultram.	0 10	1 0
9	**9**	9d. olive-green	1 1	1 3
10	**10**	1s. dp. turquoise-blue ..	1 5	1 6
11	**11**	2s. deep violet and bistre	2 9	3 0
12	**12**	2s. 6d. blue	3 6	3 9
13	**13**	5s. orange and rose-red ..	6 9	7 6
14	**14**	10s. ultram. and emerald..	13 3	15 0
15	**15**	£1 black and light blue ..	25 0	30 0

1966 (24 Jan.). *Churchill Commemoration. As Nos.* 170/3 *of Antigua.*

16	½d. new blue	0 3	0 5
17	1d. deep green..	0 4	0 6
18	1s. brown	1 8	2 3
19	2s. bluish violet	3 3	4 6

BRITISH CENTRAL AFRICA.

See NYASALAND PROTECTORATE.

BRITISH COLUMBIA & VANCOUVER ISLAND.

1

(Typo. De La Rue & Co.)

1860. *No wmk. Imperf.*

1	**1**	2½d. pale dull red	£175

1860. *No wmk. P* 14.

2	**1**	2½d. deep reddish rose ..	£25	£18
3	"	2½d. pale reddish rose ..	£25	£18

From June 20, 1864, to Nov. 1, 1865, the 2½d. was sold for 3d., and did duty as a 3d. provisional No. 1 was never actually issued.

VANCOUVER ISLAND.

2

3

(Typo. De La Rue.)

1865 (19 Sept.). *Wmk. Crown CC.* (*a*) *Imperf.*

11	**2**	5 c. rose	£1800	£550
12	**3**	10 c. blue	£120	£100

Medium or poor copies of Nos. 11 and 12 can be supplied at much lower prices, when in stock.

(*b*) *P* 14.

13	**2**	5 c. rose	£20	£18
14	**3**	10 c. blue	£20	£18

BRITISH COLUMBIA.

4

(Typo. De La Rue.)

1865 (1 Nov.)–**67.** *Wmk. Crown CC. P* 14.

21	**4**	3d. deep blue	£5	90 0
22	,,	3d. pale blue (1867) ..	£5	90 0

On 19 Nov., 1866, British Columbia and Vancouver Island were consolidated as one territory, called British Columbia, after which date the current stamps of each colony were distributed and used throughout the combined territory.

Though bearing the names of both colonies the 2½d. of 1860 was mainly used for inland postage in British Columbia.

TWO CENTS (5) **5.CENTS.5** (6)

1868–71. T **4** *in various colours. Wmk. Crown CC. Surch. as T* **5** *or* **6.**

(*a*) *P* 12½ (March, 1869).

23	5 c. red (Bk.)	£40	£40
24	10 c. lake (B.)	£35	£25
25	25 c. yellow (V.)	£25	£22
26	50 c. mauve (R.)	£25	£20
27	1 dol. green (G.)	£65	£60

(*b*) *P* 14.

28	2 c. brown (Bk.) (Jan., '68) ..	£5	80 0
29	5 c. pale red (Bk.) (May, '69)	£8	£5
30	10 c. lake (B.)	£50	
31	25 c. yellow (V.) (July, '69) ..	£9	£6
32	50 c. mauve (R.) (Feb. '71) ..	£28	
33	1 dol. green (G.)	£75	

Nos. 30 and 33 were not issued.

The stamps of British Columbia were withdrawn from use on July 20, 1871, when the Colony joined the Dominion of Canada.

BRITISH EAST AFRICA.

I. Company's Administration.

BRITISH EAST AFRICA COMPANY HALF ANNA (1)

BRITISH EAST AFRICA COMPANY 1 ANNA (2)

(Surch. De La Rue.)

1890 (May). *Stamps of Great Britain (Queen Victoria). Surch. as T* **1** *or* **2** (1 *a. and* 4 *a.*).

1	**57**	½ a. on 1d. dull purple ..	£7	£6
		a. "hALF" *for* "hALF"	£55	
2	**73**	1 a. on 2d. green and carm.	£22	£10
3	**78**	4 a. on 5d. dull pur. & blue	£14	£10

3

4

(Litho. Bradbury, Wilkinson & Co.)

1890 (Oct.)–**1894.** *P* 14.

4	**3**	½ a. deep brown	3 0	3 6
		a. Pale brown	1 6	2 0
		b. Imperf.	40 0	30 0
		c. Imperf. between (pair) ..	£10	£10
5	"	1 a. blue-green	3 0	4 0
		a. Deep blue-green	2 0	4 0
		b. Imperf.	60 0	50 0
6	"	2 a. vermilion	4 0	6 0
		a. Imperf.	50 0	45 0
7	"	2½ a. black/*buff*	12 6	12 6
		a. Black/yellow	6 0	6 0
		b. Imperf.	50 0	50 0
		c. Imperf. between (pair) ..	£10	£10
8	"	3 a. black/*dull red*	12 6	15 0
		a. Black/bright red	4 0	6 0
		b. Imperf.	50 0	50 0
		c. Imperf. between (pair) ..	£10	£10
9	,,	4 a. yellow-brown	5 0	8 0
		a. Imperf.	60 0	70 0
10	"	4 a. grey (*imperf.*)	£15	£20
11	"	4½ a. dull violet	20 0	20 0
		a. Purple	5 0	
		b. Imperf.	60 0	70 0
		c. Imperf. between (pair) ..	£10	£10
12	"	8 a. bright blue	5 0	6 0
		a. Imperf.	£5	£6
13	"	8 a. grey	£5	£6
14	"	1 r. carmine	6 0	10 0
		a. Imperf.	£15	£7
15	"	1 r. grey	70 0	70 0
16	**4**	2 r. brick-red	15 0	20 0
17	"	3 r. slate-purple	17 6	20 0
18	"	4 r. ultramarine	22 6	30 0
19	"	5 r. grey-green	22 6	35 0

Note.—For the 5 a. and 7½ a. in *T* **3**, see Nos. 29 and 30.

The paper on Nos. 7, 7*a*, 8 and 8*a* is coloured on the surface only.

The entire sheet of each value of the above is watermarked "PURE LINEN WOVE BANK" and "W. C. S. & Co." in a monogram, the trademark of the makers Messrs. William Collins Sons & Co., but the ½ a., 1 a., 2½ a., 3 a. and 4½ a. were also printed on paper without watermark. Single specimens cannot always be distinguished.

1891. *Provisionals.* (*a*) *New value handstamped in dull violet, and manuscript initials in black.*

20	**3**	"½ Anna" on 2 a. vermilion ("A.D.") (Jan.) ..	£60	£20
		a. "½ Anna" double	—	£35
21	"	"1 Anna" on 4 a. brown ("A.B.") (Feb.) ..	£150	£45

(*b*) *Manuscript value and initials in black.*

22	**3**	"½ Anna" on 2 a. vermilion ("A.B.") (Jan.)	—	£24
		a. Error. "½ Annas" ("A.B.")	—	£35
23	"	"½ Anna" on 2 a. vermilion ("A.D.")	—	£24
		a. Error. "½ Annas"	—	£30
24	"	"½ Anna" on 3 a. black/*dull red* ("A.B.") (May) ..	£60	£35
25	"	"1 Anna" on 3 a. black/*dull red* ("V.H.M.") (June) ..	—	£32
26	"	"1 Anna" on 4 a. brown ("A.B.") (March) ..	£50	£20

A.D. = Andrew Dick, representative of the Company in Mombasa.

A.B. = Archibald Brown, cashier of the Company.

V.H.M. = Victor H. Mackenzie, bank manager in Mombasa.

5
ANNAS.
(5)

(Surch. Bradbury, Wilkinson.)

1894 (1 Nov.). *Surch. as T* **5**.
27 **3** 5 a. on 8 a. bright blue .. 65 0 70 0
28 ,, 7½ a. on 1 r. carmine .. 65 0 70 0

1894 (Dec.). *No wmk. P* 14.
29 **3** 5 a. black/*grey-blue* .. 2 0 17 6
30 ,, 7½ a. black 3 0 22 6

These two stamps have "LD" after "COMPANY" in the inscription.

The paper on No. 29 is coloured on the surface only.

1895 (22 Feb.). *Surch. with manuscript value and initials* ("T.E.C.R.").
31 **3** "½ anna" on 3 a. blk./*dull red* 60 0 45 0
32 ,, "1 anna" on 3 a. blk./*dull red* £40 £40

T.E.C.R. = T. E. C. Remington, postmaster.

II. Imperial Administration.

British
East
Africa
(6)

(Handstamped at Mombasa.)

1895 (1 July). *Optd. with T* **6**.
33 **3** ½ a. dull brown 40 0 25 0
a. Deep brown 40 0 25 0
34 " 1 a. blue-green 65 0 70 0
a. Deep blue-green 65 0 70 0
b. Opt. double £8
35 " 2 a. vermilion £5 £5
a. Opt. double .. ..
36 " 2½ a. black/*yellow* £5 50 0
a. Opt. double .. .. — £10
37 " 3 a. black/*dull red* 45 0 40 0
38 " 4 a. yellow-brown 30 0 40 0
a. Opt. double .. .. — £8
39 " 4½ a. dull violet £7 £5
a. Purple £12 £10
b. Opt. double .. ..
40 " 5 a. black/*grey-blue* £12 £10
a. Opt. double .. ..
41 " 7½ a. black 85 0 85 0
a. Opt. double £12 £12
42 " 8 a. bright blue 70 0 70 0
a. Opt. double £15
b. Opt. inverted £50
43 " 1 r. carmine 50 0 50 0
a. Opt. double £15
44 **4** 2 r. brick-red £10 £12
45 " 3 r. deep purple £7 £8
a. Opt. double .. ..
46 " 4 r. ultramarine £7 £8
a. Opt. double £20
47 " 5 r. grey-green £15 £18
a. Opt. double £28

2½
(7)

British
East
Africa
(8)

British
East
Africa
(9)

(Surcharged locally.)

1895 (Oct.). *No. 39 surch. with T* **7**.
48 **3** 2½ on 4½ a. dull violet (R.) .. £6 £5

(Overprinted at the offices of a Zanzibar newspaper.)

1895 (Nov.). *Stamps of India* (*Queen Victoria*) *optd. with T* **8** *or* **9** (*2 r. to 5 r.*).
49 **23** ½ a. deep green 4 6 3 0
a. "Britlsh" for "British" .. £35
b. "Brltish" for "British" .. 60 0
c. "Afrlca" for "Africa" .. 75 0
50 **25** 1 a. plum 6 0 5 0
a. "Britlsh" for "British" .. £38
b. "Brltish" for "British" .. 60 0
c. "Afrlca" for "Africa" .. £5
51 **26** 1½ a. sepia 6 0 6 0
a. "Brltish" for "British" .. 75 0
b. "Afrlca" for "Africa" .. £5
52 **27** 2 a. ultramarine 5 0 6 0
a. "Britlsh" for "British" .. £38
b. "Brltish" for "British" .. 75 0
c. "Afrlca" for "Africa" .. 75 0 75 0
53 **36** 2½ a. green 6 0 6 0
a. "Blitish" for "British" .. £60
b. "Bpitish" for "British" £60
c. "Britlsh" for "British" .. — £45
d. "Eas" for "East" .. £18
e. "Brltish" for "British" . 90 0 90 0
f. "Afrlca" for "Africa" .. 75 0
54 **28** 3 a. brown-orange .. 12 6 15 0
a. "Brltish" for "British" .. 75 0 75 0
b. "Afrlca" for "Africa" .. £5
55 **29** 4 a. olive-green 17 6 17 6
a. Slate-green 15 0 15 0
b. "Brltish" for "British" .. 75 0 75 0
c. "Afrlca" for "Africa" .. £5
56 **21** 6 a. pale brown 15 0 15 0
a. "Brltish" for "British" £10
b. "Afrlca" for "Africa" .. £6
57 **31** 8 a. dull mauve 35 0 35 0
a. "Brltish" for "British" £6
b. "Afrlca" for "Africa" .. £10
c. Magenta 25 0 30 0
ca. "Ease" for "East" .. — £50
58 **32** 12 a. purple/*red* 25 0 30 0
a. "Brltish" for "British" .. £6 £6
b. "Afrlca" for "Africa" .. £10
59 **33** 1 r. slate 45 0 50 0
60 **37** 1 r. green and carmine .. 32 6 37 6
a. "Ease" for "East" .. £60
b. "Brltish" for "British" .. £8
c. "Afrlca" for "Africa" .. £9
d. Opt. double, one sideways £6
61 **38** 2 r. carmine and yell.-brn. 70 0 80 0
62 " 3 r. brown and green .. 85 0 85 0
63 " 5 r. ultramarine & violet .. £5 £6
a. Opt. double £60

The relative positions of the three lines of the overprint vary considerably.

There are many less important varieties, such as inverted "s" in "British", wide and narrow "B", and inverted "V" for "A" in "Africa".

The 2, 3, and 5 r., normally overprinted in larger type than the lower values, are also known with the smaller overprint, but were not issued thus for postal purposes.

2½
(10)

11

(Surcharged locally.)

1895 (Dec.). *No.* 51 *surch. with T* **10** *in bright red.*

64	**26**	2½ on 1½ a. sepia ..	45 0	35 0
		a. Inverted "1" in fraction ..	£12	

No. 51 also exists surcharged with *T* **12, 13** and **14** in *brown-red*. These stamps were sent to the Postal Union authorities at Berne, but were never issued to the public.

(Recess. De La Rue & Co.)

1896 (19 May)–**19 01.** *Wmk. Crown CA.*

65	**11**	½ a. yellow-green ..	0 9	0 9
66	"	1 a. carmine-red	1 9	0 9
		a. Bright rose-red	1 6	0 6
		b. Rosine (1901)	25 0	6 0
67	"	2 a. chocolate	3 6	3 6
68	"	2½ a. deep blue	5 0	3 0
		a. Violet-blue	5 0	2 6
69	"	3 a. grey ..	5 0	6 0
70	"	4 a. deep green	8 6	4 0
71	"	4½ a. orange-yellow	8 6	10 0
72	"	5 a. yellow-bistre ..	10 0	12 6
73	"	7½ a. mauve..	15 0	15 0
74	"	8 a. grey-olive	8 6	12 6
75	"	1 r. pale dull blue	35 0	35 0
		a Ultramarine	32 6	32 6
76	"	2 r. orange..	45 0	45 0
77	"	3 r. deep violet	45 0	45 0
78	"	4 r. carmine-lake ..	55 0	55 0
79	"	5 r. sepia ..	60 0	70 0

1897 (Jan.). *Stamps of Zanzibar* (1896 *issue*) *optd. with T* **8.** *Wmk. Single Rosette.*

80	**13**	½ a. green and red	40 0	45 0
81	,,	1 a. indigo and red	55 0	55 0
82	,,	2 a. red-brown and red	40 0	40 0
83	,,	4½ a. orange and red	50 0	50 0
84	,,	5 a. bistre and red	50 0	50 0
85	,,	7½ a. mauve and red	75 0	75 0

An overprint similar to *T* **8**, but with stop after "Africa." is known in *red* on the 1 a. and in *black* on the other values. These were made for purposes of official record, but not issued to the public.

Stamps of Zanzibar, wmk. "Multiple Rosettes" and overprinted with *T* **8** are forgeries.

2½ (12) **2½** (13) **2½** (14)

(Surcharged locally.)

1897 (Jan.). *Nos.* 157 *and* 162 *of Zanzibar optd. with T* **8** *and further surch. as shown, in red.*

86	**12**	2½ on 1 a. indigo and red ..	60 0	50 0
		a. "2" over "1" for "½" ..	£30	
		b. Opt. T 8 double ..	£125	
87	**13**	2½ on 1 a. indigo and red ..	85 0	70 0
88	**14**	2½ on 1 a. indigo and red ..	65 0	55 0
89	**12**	2½ on 3 a. grey and red ..	55 0	45 0
		a. "2" over "1" for "½" ..		
90	**13**	2½ on 3 a. grey and red ..	60 0	50 0
91	**14**	2½ on 3 a. grey and red ..	70 0	60 0

Both the notes after No. 85 also apply here.

15

(Recess. De La Rue.)

1897 (Nov.). *Wmk. Crown CC. P* 14.

92	**15**	1 r. dull blue	35 0	30 0
		a. Bright ultramarine	40 0	30 0
93	,,	2 r. orange ..	65 0	70 0
94	,,	3 r. deep violet	85 0	95 0
95	,,	4 r. carmine	£8	£10
96	,,	5 r. deep sepia	£8	£10
97	,,	10 r. yellow-bistre ..	£22	£22
98	,,	20 r. pale green (S. £10)	£65	£70
99	,,	50 r. mauve (S. £25)	£200	£225

In 1903 stamps of British E. Africa were superseded by those of East Africa and Uganda Protectorate. (*See* Kenya, Uganda and Tanganyika.)

BRITISH GUIANA.

For GREAT BRITAIN **stamps used in British Guiana, see page** 65.

— SIMPLIFICATION (see Introduction**) —**

Nos. 1 to 115.

1, 8, 4, 6. 9, 10. 11, 20, 21. 24, 26. 29, 40, 41, 51, 58, 60, 62, 47, 49, 64. 85, 88, 90, 94, 74, 95, 99, 103, 105.

Nos. 116 to 125.

Take cheapest stamp of each value, ignoring types.

1

(Set up and printed at the office of the *Royal Gazette*, Georgetown, British Guiana.)

1850 (1 July)–**51.** *T* **1.** *Type-set. Black impression. Medium wove paper.*

Prices are for—(I) *Cut square,* (II) *Cut round.*

		I Used.	II Used.
1	2 c. *rose* (1851) ..	—	£6000
2	4 c. *orange*	£2000	£400
3	4 c. *lemon-yellow*	£2200	£500
4	8 c. *green*	£1250	£250
5	12 c. *blue* ..	£500	£200
6	12 c. *indigo*	£900	£200
7	12 c. *pale blue*	£1000	£250
	a. "2" of "12" with straight foot		
	b. "1" of "12" omitted ..	†	£2500
	Pelure paper.		
8	4 c. *pale yellow*	£1750	£400

These stamps were initialled by the postmaster, or the Post Office clerks, before they were issued. The initials are—E. T. E. D(alton), E. D. W(ight), J. B. S(mith), H. A. K(illikelley), and W. H. L(ortimer). There are several types of each value.

2

(Litho. Waterlow & Sons.)

1852 (Jan.). *Surface-coloured paper.*

No.	Type	Description	*Un.*	*Used*
9	**2**	1 c. black/*magenta*	£800	£400
10	,,	4 c. black/*deep blue*	£900	£450

There are two types of each value.

Reprints, on thicker paper and perf. 12½, were made in 1865. (*Price £5 either value.*)

Reprints with the perforations removed are sometimes offered as genuine originals.

***NOTE.**—*Prices for Nos. 9 and 10 are for fine copies. Poor to medium specimens can be supplied when in stock at from one-tenth of above prices.*

3

(Dies eng. and stamps litho. Waterlow & Sons.)

1853. *Imperf.*

No.	Type	Description	*Un.*	*Used*
11	**3**	1 c. vermilion	£110	£75

This 1 c. in *reddish brown* is probably a proof.

ONE CENT — A

ONE CENT — B

ONE CENT — C

ONE CENT — D

A. "o" large and 1 mm. from left corner.
B. "o" small and ¾ mm. from left corner.
C. "o" small and ¾ mm. from left corner. "NT" widely spaced.
D. "ONE" close together, "o" 1¼ mm. from left corner.

1858–59. *Fresh lithographic transfers with varying labels of value. White line above value. Imperf.*

No.	Type	Description	*Un.*	*Used*
12	**3**	1 c. dull red (A)	—	£80
13	,,	1 c. brownish red (A) ..	—	£80
14	,,	1 c. dull red (B)	£175	£90
15	,,	1 c. brownish red (B) ..	—	£90
16	,,	1 c. dull red (C)	£150	£90
17	,,	1 c. dull red (D)		

NOTE.—*These prices are for fine copies with four margins. Medium specimens can be supplied at much lower rates.*

4

5

1853–59. *Imperf.*

No.	Type	Description	*Un.*	*Used*
18	**4**	4 c. deep blue (1853)	£100	£60
		a. Retouched	£150	£90
19	,,	4 c. blue (1855)	£90	£60
20	,,	4 c. pale blue (1859) ..	£75	£45
		a. Retouched	£125	£60

NOTE *after* No. 17 *also applies here.*

These stamps are generally found with a white line or traces of it above the label of value and lower corner figures. In some stamps on the sheet this line is missing, owing to having been retouched, and in these cases a line of colour usually appears in its place.

The 1 c. and 4 c. stamps were reprinted in 1865 from fresh transfers of five varieties. These are on *thin* paper and perf. 12½.

1860. *Figures in corners framed. Imperf.*

No.	Type	Description	*Un.*	*Used*
21	**5**	4 c. blue	£110	£50

6

(Type-set and printed at the *Official Gazette* by Baum and Dallas, Georgetown.)

1856 (Feb.). *Surface-coloured paper.*

No.	Type	Description	*Un.*	*Used*
23	**6**	1 c. black/*magenta* ..		
24	,,	4 c. black/*magenta*	—	£750
25	,,	4 c. black/*rose-carmine* ..	—	£1000
26	,,	4 c. black/*blue*	—	£2000

1856 (Aug.). *Paper coloured through.*

No.	Type	Description	*Un.*	*Used*
27	**6**	4 c. black/*deep blue* ..	—	£3500

These stamps, like those of the first issue, were initialled before being issued; the initials are—E.T.E.D., E.D.W., C.A. W(atson), and W.H.L.

The 4 c. is known in eight types differing in the position of the inscriptions.

7

A B C D E F

(Dies eng. and litho. Waterlow.)

1860. *T* **7.** *Tablets of value as illustrated. Thick paper. P* 12.

No.	Description	*Un.*	*Used*
29	1 c. pale rose	£65	£15
30	2 c. deep orange	£5	60 0
31	2 c. pale orange	£5	60 0
32	4 c. deep blue	£15	75 0

No.	Type	Description	Unused	Used
33		4 c. blue	£12	70 0
34		8 c. brownish rose	£16	90 0
35		8 c. pink	£14	80 0
36		12 c. lilac	£25	65 0
37		12 c. grey-lilac	£20	65 0
38		24 c. deep green	£70	£7
39		24 c. green	£60	£7

The 1 c. was reprinted in 1865 on *thin* paper, P 12½–13, and in a different shade. *Price* 7s. 6d.

The 12 c. in both shades is frequently found surcharged with a large " 5d." in *red*; this is to denote the proportion of postage repayable by the colony to Great Britain for oversea letters.

1861. *T* **7.** *Colour changed.*

No.	Type	Description	Unused	Used
40		1 c. reddish brown	£15	£7

1862. *T* **7.** *Thin paper. P* 12.

No.	Type	Description	Unused	Used
41		1 c. brown	£23	£17
42		1 c. black	70 0	40 0
43		2 c. orange	65 0	35 0
44		4 c. blue	£5	40 0
45		4 c. pale blue	70 0	35 0
46		8 c. pink	£5	60 0
47		12 c. dull purple	£5	35 0
48		12 c. purple	£5	40 0
49		12 c. lilac	£7	45 0
50		24 c. green	£35	£5

1863. *T* **7.** *Thin paper. P* 12½–13.

No.	Type	Description	Unused	Used
51		1 c. black	17 6	27 6
52		2 c. orange	60 0	35 0
53		4 c. blue	65 0	35 0
54		8 c. pink	£7	90 0
55		12 c. brownish lilac	£25	95 0
56		24 c. green	£30	95 0

Specimens are found on *pelure* paper.

1863. *T* **7.** *Medium paper. P* 12½–13.

No.	Type	Description	Unused	Used
57		1 c. black	37 6	30 0
58		2 c. deep orange	35 0	30 0
59		2 c. orange	42 6	32 6
60		4 c. greyish blue	50 0	32 6
61		4 c. blue	60 0	40 0
62		8 c. pink	£8	55 0
63		12 c. brownish lliac	£15	£5
64		24 c. green	£8	70 0
65		24 c. deep green	£15	75 0

1866. *T* **7.** *P* 10.

No.	Type	Description	Unused	Used
65*a*		12 c. grey-lilac	£15	80 0

8

9

G

H

I

K

New transfers for the 1 c., 2 c., 8 c., and 12 c., with the spaces between values and the word " CENTS " about 1 mm.

1863–64. *Medium paper. P* 12½–13.

No.	Type	Description	Unused	Used
66	**8**	1 c. black	25 0	30 0
67	,,	2 c. orange-red	35 0	12 6
68	,,	2 c. orange	30 0	10 0
69	**9**	6 c. blue	75 0	60 0
70	,,	6 c. greenish blue	75 0	60 0
71	,,	6 c. deep blue	65 0	60 0
72	,,	6 c. milky blue	£5	60 0
73	**8**	8 c. pink	£5	30 0
74	,,	8 c. carmine	£5	30 0
75	,,	12 c. grey-lilac	£17	25 0
76	,,	12 c. brownish purple	£22	40 0
77	**9**	24 c. green (*perf.* 12)	£12	35 0
78	,,	24 c. yellow-green (*perf.* 12)	£5	22 6
79	,,	24 c. yellow-grn. (*p.* 12½–13)	£6	22 6
80	,,	24 c. green (*perf.* 12½–13)	£6	25 0
81	,,	24 c. blue-green (*p.* 12½–13)	£9	40 0
82	,,	48 c. pale red	£7	60 0
83	,,	48 c. deep red	£7	65 0
84	,,	48 c. carmine-rose	£12	60 0

The 4 c. corresponding to this issue can only be distinguished from that of the previous issue by minor plating flaws.

There is a variety of the 6 c. with stop before " VICISSIM ".

Varieties of most of the values of issues of 1863-64 and 1866 are to be found on both very thin and thick papers.

1866. *P* 10.

No.	Type	Description	Unused	Used
85	**8**	1 c. black	15 0	8 6
86	,,	1 c. grey-black	17 6	12 6
87	,,	2 c. orange	30 0	12 6
88	,,	2 c. reddish orange	22 6	12 6
89	,,	4 c. slate-blue	65 0	22 6
90	,,	4 c. blue	65 0	20 0
		a. Bisected (on cover)	†	£100
		b. Do. Imperf. (on cover)	†	—
91	,,	4 c. pale blue	70 0	25 0
92	**9**	6 c. milky blue	£7	50 0
93	,,	6 c. ultramarine	£7	60 0
94	,,	6 c. dull blue	£7	50 0
95	**8**	8 c. pink	£6	30 0
96	,,	8 c. brownish pink	£7	30 0
96*a*	,,	8 c. carmine	£7	35 0
97	,,	12 c. pale lilac	£12	35 0
98	,,	12 c. grey-lilac	£7	30 0
99	,,	12 c. brownish grey	£6	30 0
100	,,	12 c. lilac	£6	25 0
101	**9**	24 c. dark green	£12	27 6
102	,,	24 c. bluish green	—	22 6
103	,,	24 c. yellow-green	£7	20 0
104	,,	48 c. crimson	£16	60 0
105	,,	48 c. red	£14	60 0

1875. *P* 15.

No.	Type	Description	Unused	Used
106	**8**	1 c. black	20 0	15 0
107	,,	2 c. orange-red	£6	27 6
108	,,	2 c. orange	£5	27 6
109	,,	4 c. bright blue	£16	£6
111	**9**	6 c. ultramarine	£16	£5
112	**8**	8 c. deep rose	£8	80 0
113	,,	12 c. lilac	£20	75 0
114	**9**	24 c. yellow-green	£25	75 0
115	,,	24 c. deep green	£25	75 0

There is a variety of the 48 c. *with* stop after " P " in " PETIMUSQUE ".

The 6 c., 24 c. and 48 c. are known *imperf.* but in this state are probably proofs.

1862 (OCT.). *Type-set and printed by Mr. George Melville at the office of the " Royal Gazette," Georgetown. Black on coloured paper. Roul.* 6.

10

NOTE.

Prices for stamps of this 1862 issue are for good average copies. Superb copies with roulettes on all sides are worth considerably more.

No.	Type	Description	Unused	Used
116	**10**	1 c. *rose* (12 *in sheet*)	£50	£25
		a. Unsigned	£12	
		b. " 1 " for " I " in " BRITISH "	—	£35
		c. Wrong ornament on left	—	£35
117	,,	2 c. *yellow* (12 *in sheet*)	£50	£25
		a. Unsigned	£12	
		b. " 1 " for " I " in " BRITISH "	—	£33
		c. Wrong ornament on left	—	£25

11  12

118 **11** 1 c. *rose* (8 *in sheet*) .. £65 £25
- a. Unsigned £12
- b. "1" for "I" in "BRITISH" — £35
- c. "1" for "I" in "GUIANA" — £35
- d. Italic "S" in "POSTAGE" — £30
- e. Narrow "T" in "CENTS" — £30
- f. Wrong ornament in top frame .. .. — £30
- g. Wrong ornament in left frame .. .. — £30

119 ,, 2 c. *yellow* (8 *in sheet*) .. £75 £28
- a. Unsigned.. .. .. £12
- b. "1" for "I" in "BRITISH" — £35
- c. "1" for "I" in "GUIANA" — £35
- d. Italic "S" in "POSTAGE" — £35
- e. "O" for "O" in "TWO" and narrow "T" in "CENTS" .. .. — £35
- f. Wrong ornament in top frame .. .. .. — £30
- g. Italic "T" in "TWO" .. — £30

120 **12** 1 c. *rose* (4 *in sheet*) .. £100 £45
- a. Unsigned.. .. £30
- b. "1" for "I" in "GUIANA" — £45
- c. "C" for "O" in "POSTAGE" .. .. — £45

121 ,, 2 c. *yellow* (4 *in sheet*) .. £125 £40
- a. Unsigned.. ..
- b. "1" for "I" in "GUIANA" — £45
- c. "C" for "O" in "POSTAGE" .. .. — £45

13  14

122 **13** 4 c. *blue* (10 *in sheet*) .. £40 £25
- a. Unsigned.. .. ..
- b. Ornament omitted on right — £35

123 **14** 4 c. *blue* (6 *in sheet*) .. £60 £30
- a. Unsigned.. .. .. £25

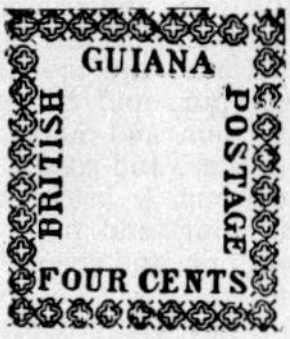

15

124 **15** 4 c. *blue* (6 *in sheet*) .. £65 £35
- a. Unsigned £25
- b. "1" for "I" in "BRITISH" — £45

As T **15**, *but with four thin inner lines.*

125 – 4 c. *blue* (2 *in sheet*) .. £185 £135
- a. Unsigned.. .. ..

There are in all 24 varieties of type of each value. The stamps were initialled in the centre before use by the Acting Receiver-General of the colony—Robert Mather.

16

(17)

(Typo. De La Rue.)

1876 (1 July). *Wmk. Crown CC.* (*a*) *P* 14.

126 **16**	1 c. slate	7 6	1 6
127 ,,	2 c. orange	30 0	2 6
128 ,,	4 c. blue	70 0	20 0
129 ,,	6 c. brown	50 0	20 0
130 ,,	8 c. rose	55 0	10 0
131 ,,	12 c. pale violet ..	60 0	15 0
132 ,,	24 c. emerald-green ..	65 0	20 0
133 ,,	48 c. red-brown ..	75 0	35 0
134 ,,	96 c. olive-bistre	£28	£16

(*b*) *P* 12½.

135 ,, 4 c. blue £50 £25

(*c*) *Perf. compound of* 14 × 12½.

136 ,, 1 c. slate .. .. — £25

1878. *Various stamps with bars ruled in ink, in black. Bars vary in depth of colour.*

A. *On ordinary issues.*
With two horizontal bars.

137 (1 c.) on 6 c. brown (No. 129) 40 0 55 0

6 Nov. *With horizontal and vertical bars, T* **17.**

138 (1 c.) on 6 c. ultram. (No. 93) £7 60 0
139 (1 c.) on 6 c. brown (No. 129) £8 75 0

B. Nov. *On stamps overprinted* "OFFICIAL". *Horizontal bars across* "OFFICIAL".

140 1 c. black (No. O1) 85 0 75 0
141 1 c. slate (No. O6) 80 0 50 0
142 2 c. orange (No. O7) .. £6 70 0

With two horizontal bars and one vertical.

144 (1 c.) on 4 c. blue (No. O8) .. 75 0 70 0
145 (1 c.) on 6 c. brown (No. O9) £6 75 0
146 (2 c.) on 8 c. rose (No. O3) .. £6 £5

23 Nov. *With one horizontal bar and one vertical.*

148 (2 c.) on 8 c. rose (No. O10) £8 85 0

1 (18) 1 (19) 2 (20) 2 (21)

1881 (Dec.). *Various stamps with bar ruled in ink obliterating original value, and surch. with figure.*

A. *On ordinary issues.*

149 **18** 1 on 48 c. red (No. 105) .. 27 6 17 6
150 **19** 1 on 96 c. ol.-bis. (No. 134) 6 0 10 0

The obliterating bar is found 1, 2½, or 4 mm. wide.

151 **20** 2 on 96 c. ol.-bis. (No. 134) 10 0 20 0
152 **21** 2 on 96 c. ol.-bis. (No. 134) 25 0 35 0

The obliterating bar is found 1 or 3 mm. wide.

B. *On stamps overprinted* "OFFICIAL".

1
OFFICIAL
(22)

153 **22** 1 on 22 c. brownish purple (No. O4) 50 0 45 0
154 ,, 1 on 48 c. red-brown (*as* No. 133) 60 0 70 0

2
OFFICIAL
(23)

2
OFFICIAL
(24)

Nos. 131 *and* 132 *surch. with T* **23** *or* **24.**

155 **23** 2 on 12 c. pale violet .. £6 £6
156 **24** 2 on 12 c. pale violet .. 50 0 50 0
 a. Surch. double £40 £40
157 **23** 2 on 24 c. emerald-green .. £6 £6
158 **24** 2 on 24 c. emerald-green 70 0 50 0
 a. Surch. double £50

2
OFFICIAL
(25)

Surch. as T **25.**

161 2 on 24 c. green (No. O5) .. £6 £6

The obliterating bar is 1, 2, or 3 mm. wide.

26 27

(Printed by Baldwin & Co., Georgetown.)

1882. *Black impression. P* 12. *Perforated with the word* "SPECIMEN" *diagonally.*

162 **26** 1 c. *magenta* 35 0 30 0
 a. Imperf. between (pair) ..
 b. Without "SPECIMEN" .. £6 £5
 c. "1" with foot 80 0 70 0
163 „ 2 c. *yellow* 45 0 30 0
 a. Without "SPECIMEN" .. £5 £5
 b. Small "2" 40 0 40 0
164 **27** 1 c. *magenta* 40 0 40 0
 a. Without "SPECIMEN" .. £6 £5
165 „ 2 c. *yellow* 45 0 45 0
 a. Bisected diagonally (1 c.) ..
 b. Without "SPECIMEN" .. £6 £6
 c. Small "2" £5 £5

These stamps were perforated "SPECIMEN" as a precaution against fraud. Stamps are known with "SPECIMEN" double.

These were printed in sheets of twelve in two settings using the same clichés:—

1st setting. Four rows of three, T **26** being Nos. 5, 6, 7, 8, 11 and 12, and T **27** the remainder.

2nd setting. Six rows of two, T **26** being Nos. 3, 7, 8, 9, 11 and 12, and T **27** the remainder.

Se-tenant pairs are worth about 20% more.

Varieties: The "1" with foot (T **26** only) is No. 9 in the first setting and No. 7 in the second. The small "2" in T **26** occurs on Nos. 7, 8 and 12 in the first setting and Nos. 9, 11 and 12 in the second setting; in T **27** it is No. 9 in the first setting and No. 10 in the second.

(Typo. De La Rue.)

1882 (MAY). *Wmk. Crown CA. P* 14.

170 **16** 1 c. slate 7 6 1 6
171 „ 2 c. orange 17 6 2 0
 a. Value doubly printed ..
172 „ 4 c. blue 45 0 20 0
173 „ 6 c. brown 15 0 17 6
174 „ 8 c. rose 50 0 5 0

INLAND
2 CENTS
REVENUE
(28)

4 CENTS
(*a*)

4 CENTS
(*b*)

1888–89. *T* **16** (*without value in lower label*) *optd.* "INLAND REVENUE", *and surch. with value as T* **28.** *Two types of* "4", *as* (*a*) *and* (*b*). *Wmk. Crown CA. P* 14.

175 1 c. dull purple 2 0 2 6
176 2 c. dull purple 2 6 2 6
177 3 c. dull purple 2 0 2 0
178 4 c. dull purple (*a*) .. 2 6 3 0
 a. Larger fig. "4" (*b*) .. 15 0 12 6
179 6 c. dull purple 4 6 4 0
180 8 c. dull purple 2 6 3 6
181 10 c. dull purple 8 6 7 6
182 20 c. dull purple 15 0 17 6
183 40 c. dull purple 25 0 22 6
184 72 c. dull purple 22 6 27 6
185 1 dol. green £18 £18
186 2 dol. green £10 £10
187 3 dol. green £5 £5
188 4 dol. green (*a*) £14 £16
 a. Larger fig. "4" (*b*) .. £35 £35
189 5 dol. green £6 £6

2
(29)

1889 (5 JUNE). *No.* 176 *surch. locally as T* **29.**

192 "2" on 2 c. dull purple (R.) 2 6 2 6

The varieties with figure "2" *inverted* or *double-printed* were made privately by a postal employee in Demerara.

30

INLAND
One
Cent
~~1 DOLLAR~~
REVENUE
(31)

(Typo. De La Rue.)

1889 (SEPT.). *Wmk. Crown CA. P* 14.

193 **30** 1 c. dull pur. & slate-grey 2 6 1 6
194 „ 2 c. dull pur. and orange 2 0 1 0
195 „ 4 c. dull pur. and ultram. 7 6 5 0
196 „ 4 c. dull pur. and cobalt 15 0 7 6
197 „ 6 c. dull pur. and brown 22 6 17 6
198 „ 6 c. dull pur. and maroon 10 0 7 6
199 „ 8 c. dull pur. and rose .. 10 0 6 0
200 „ 12 c. dull pur. & brt. pur. 10 0 5 0
200*a* „ 12 c. dull pur. and mauve 10 0 6 0
201 „ 24 c. dull pur. and green .. 10 0 10 0
202 „ 48 c. dull pur. & orge.-red 27 6 20 0
203 „ 72 c. dull pur. and red-brn. 30 0 30 0
204 „ 72 c. dull pur. and yell.-brn. 40 0 50 0
205 „ 96 c. dull pur. and carmine 70 0 80 0
206 „ 96 c. dull pur. and rosine .. 90 0 95 0

1890 (15 JULY). *Stamps of* 1888-89 *surch. locally* "One Cent", *in red, as in T* **31.**

207 1 c. on 1 dol. (No. 185) .. 3 6 2 6
 a. Surch. double .. .. — £7
208 1 c. on 2 dol. (No. 186) .. 2 0 2 6
 a. Surch. double £12
209 1 c. on 3 dol. (No. 187) .. 3 6 3 0
 a. Surch. double £7

210 1 c. on 4 dol. (No. 188) .. 7 0 12 6
a. Surch. double £10
b. Larger fig. "4" (*b*) 30 0 35 0

1890 (Dec.)–**1891.** *Wmk. Crown CA. P* 14.
213 **30** 1 c. sea-green (1891) .. 1 0 0 6
214 ,, 5 c. ultramarine (1891) .. 6 0 2 0
215 ,, 8 c. dull purple & greenish black 12 6 15 0

32. Mount Roraima.

33. Kaieteur Falls.

(Recess. De La Rue and Co.)

1898. *Jubilee. Wmk. Crown CC. P* 14.
216 **32** 1 c. blue-blk. & carmine 5 0 2 6
217 **33** 2 c. brown and indigo .. 6 6 3 6
a. Imperf. between (pair) ..
218 ,, 2 c. brown and blue .. 12 6 3 0
219 **32** 5 c. green and sepia .. 15 0 15 0
a. Imperf. between (pair) ..
220 **33** 10 c. blue-blk. & orge.-red 20 0 30 0
221 **32** 15 c. red-brown and blue 35 0 40 0

The 1 c. was later retouched, the lines of shading on the mountains in the background being strengthened, and along the ridge distinct from each other, whereas, in the original, they are more or less blurred. In the retouched die the shading of the sky is less pronounced.

TWO CENTS.
(34)

1899. *Surch. with T* **34.**
222 **32** 2 c. on 5 c. (No. 219) .. 3 0 3 6
a. No stop after "CENTS" .. 45 0 55 0
223 **33** 2 c. on 10 c. (No. 220) .. 3 6 4 0
a. No stop after "CENTS" .. 40 0 45 0
b. "GENTS" for "CENTS" .. 55 0 65 0
c. Surch. inverted £24 £30
224 **32** 2 c. on 15 c. (No. 221) .. 4 6 4 6
a. No stop after "CENTS" .. 40 0 50 0
b. Surch. double £40
c. Surch. double one without stop .. .. ..
d. Surch. inverted £30 £32

The "no stop" variety occurs on the 53rd stamp in sheets of No. 222*a* and of the first setting of No. 223*a* and on the 21st stamp in the second setting of No. 223*a*.

The "GENTS" error is on the 55th stamp in the sheet.

Of No. 224*c* only one specimen exists.

1900–7. *T* **30.** *Wmk. Crown CA. P* 14.
233 1 c. grey-green ('07) 3 0 0 10
234 2 c. dull purple and carmine 4 0 1 6
235 2 c. dull purple & black/*red* 1 0 0 3
236 6 c. grey-blk. & ultram. ('02) 20 0 10 0
237 48 c. grey & purple-brn. ('01) 55 0 65 0
238 48 c. brownish grey & brn. ('07) 45 0 60 0
239 60 c. green and rosine ('03) .. £6 £7

No. 233 is a reissue of No. 213 in non-fugitive ink.

1905–7. *T* **30.** *Wmk. Multiple Crown CA. P* 14.
240 1 c. grey-green 2 6 0 6
241 2 c. purple & black/*red*, OC 1 3 0 6
242 4 c. dull pur. & ultram., OC 20 0 17 6
243 5 c. dull pur. & blue/*blue*, OC 12 6 10 0
244 6 c. grey-blk. & ultram., OC 32 6 37 6
245 12 c. dull & bright pur., OC .. 42 6 32 6
246 24 c. dull pur. & grn., OC ('06) 10 0 12 6
247 48 c. grey & pur.-brown, OC 30 0 40 0
248 60 c. green and rosine, OC .. 35 0 40 0
249 72 c. pur. & orge.-brn., C ('07) 75 0 75 0
250 96 c. blk. & verm./*yell.*, C ('06) 55 0 70 0

35

1905. *Optd.* "POSTAGE AND REVENUE". *Wmk. Multiple Crown CA. P* 14.
251 **35** $2.40, green and violet, C £20 £24

1907–10. *Colours changed. Wmk. Mult. Crown CA. P* 14.
252 **30** 1 c. blue-green, O ('10) .. 2 0 0 9
253 ,, 2 c. rose-red, O 8 6 0 6
254 ,, 4 c. brown and purple, O 6 0 4 0
255 ,, 5 c. ultramarine, O .. 3 6 2 6
256 ,, 6 c. grey and black, O .. 17 6 12 6
257 ,, 12 c. orange and mauve, O 8 6 8 6

1910. *Redrawn. Wmk. Mult. Crown CA. P* 14.
258 **30** 2 c. rose-red, O 1 6 0 6

In this redrawn type the flag at the main truck is close to the mast, whereas in the former type it appears to be flying loose from halyards. There are two background lines above the value "2 CENTS" instead of three and the "S" is farther away from the end of the tablet.

37

War Tax
(38)

(Typo. De La Rue & Co.)

1913–21. *Wmk. Mult. Crown CA. P* 14.
259 **37** 1 c. yellow-green, O .. 2 6 1 0
259*a* ,, 1 c. blue-green, O (1917) 2 0 0 6
260 ,, 2 c. carmine, O .. 1 6 0 6
260*a* ,, 2 c. scarlet, O (1916) .. 1 9 0 6
261 ,, 4 c. brn. & brt. pur., C 5 0 2 6
261*a* ,, 4 c. dp. brn. & pur., C 7 6 1 9
262 ,, 5 c. bright blue, O .. 3 6 2 6
263 ,, 6 c. grey & blk., O .. 4 0 3 0
264 ,, 12 c. orge. & violet, C .. 7 6 3 0
265 ,, 24 c. dull pur. & grn., O 8 0 7 0
266 ,, 48 c. grey & pur.-brn., C 17 6 20 0
267 ,, 60 c. grn. & rosine, C .. 40 0 40 0
268 ,, 72 c. pur. & orge.-brn., C 45 0 45 0

269 **37** 96 c. blk. & ver./*yell.*, C (1915) 40 0 45 0
- *a. White back* (1913) .. 35 0 40 0
- *b. On lemon* (1916) .. 45 0 50 0
- *c. On pale yellow* (1921) .. 35 0 50 0

1918 (4 JAN.). *No. 260a optd. with T* **38.**

271 **37** 2 c. scarlet 0 6 0 8

The relative positions of the words "WAR" and "TAX" vary considerably in the sheet.

1921–27. *Wmk. Mult. Script CA. P* 14.

272 **37** 1 c. green, O 0 10 0 4
273 ,, 2 c. rose-carmine, O .. 1 3 0 4
274 ,, 4 c. brown & brt. pur., O 1 0 0 6
275 ,, 12 c. orange and violet, O 5 0 4 0
276 ,, 24 c. dull pur. & green, C 8 0 8 0
277 ,, 48 c. black & pur., C ('26) 22 6 17 6
278 ,, 60 c. grn. & rosine, C ('26) 35 0 37 6
279 ,, 72 c. dull purple & orange-brown, C 35 0 37 6
280 ,, 96 c. blk. & red/*yell.*, C ('27) 40 0 45 0

1922–23. *Colours changed. Wmk. Mult. Script CA. P* 14.

281 **37** 2 c. bright violet, O .. 1 6 0 6
282 ,, 6 c. bright blue, O .. 3 6 2 6

39. Ploughing a Rice Field.

40. Indian shooting Fish. **41.** Kaieteur Falls.

42. Public Buildings, Georgetown.

(Recess. Waterlow.)

1931 (21 JULY). *Centenary of County Union. Wmk. Mult. Script CA. P* 12½.

283 **39** 1 c. emerald-green 1 9 2 0
284 **40** 2 c. brown 3 6 2 0
285 **41** 4 c. carmine 8 6 4 0
286 **42** 6 c. blue 15 0 12 6
287 **41** $1 violet 65 0 70 0

43. Ploughing a Rice Field.

44. Gold Mining.

45. Shooting Logs over Falls.

46. Stabroek Market.

47. Sugar Canes in Punts.

48. Forest Road.

49. Victoria Regia Lilies.

50. Mount Roraima. **51.** Sir Walter Raleigh and his son. **52.** Botanical Gardens.

(Recess. Waterlow & Sons, Ltd.)

1934–51. *Types as* **40** (*2 c.*) *and* **41** (*4 c. and 50 c.*) *but without dates at top of frame* and T* **43** *to* **52.** *Wmk. Mult. Script CA (sideways on horiz. designs). P 12½.*

288 **43** 1 c. green 0 6 0 4
289 **40*** 2 c. red-brown 1 0 0 6
290 **44** 3 c. scarlet 0 6 0 6
aa. Wmk. error. Crown missing
a. Perf. 12½ × 13½ (30.12.43) 4 6 2 0
b. Perf. 13 × 14 (28.4.49) .. 0 8 0 8
291 **41*** 4 c. slate-violet 2 0 0 8
a. Imperf. between (vert. pair)
292 **45** 6 c. deep ultramarine .. 3 6 3 0
293 **46** 12 c. red-orange 1 0 0 8
a. Perf. 14 × 13 (16.4.51) .. 1 0 0 8
294 **47** 24 c. purple 10 0 7 6
295 **48** 48 c. black 30 0 35 0
296 **41*** 50 c. green 30 0 35 0
297 **49** 60 c. red-brown 75 0 65 0
298 **50** 72 c. purple 7 6 7 6
299 **51** 96 c. black 70 0 75 0
300 **52** $1 bright violet 65 0 65 0

1935 (6 May). *Silver Jubilee. As T* **13** *of Antigua. Recess. D. L. R. & Co. Wmk. Mult. Script CA. P 13½ × 14.*

301 2 c. ultramarine and grey .. 0 10 0 8
302 6 c. brown and deep blue .. 3 6 3 0
303 12 c. green and indigo .. 6 6 6 6
304 24 c. slate and purple .. 8 0 9 0

1937 (12 May). *Coronation. As T* **2** *of Aden. Recess. D. L. R. & Co. Wmk. Mult. Script CA. P 14.*

305 2 c. yellow-brown 0 6 0 4
306 4 c. grey-black 1 0 1 0
307 6 c. bright blue 1 6 1 3

53. South America.

54. Victoria Regia Lilies.

(Recess. Waterlow & Sons, Ltd.)

1938 (1 Feb.)–**1952.** *As earlier types but portrait of King George VI in place of King George V. Wmk. Mult. Script CA. P 12½.*

308 **43** 1 c. yellow-green 3 6 1 0
aa. Green ('44) 0 6 0 3
a. Perf. 14 × 13 ('49) .. 0 6 0 4
309 **41** 2 c. slate-violet 0 6 0 3
a. Perf. 13 × 14 (28.4.49) .. 0 6 0 3
310 **53** 4 c. scarlet and black .. 0 10 0 3
a. Imperf between (vert. pair) £145 £120
b. Perf. 13 × 14 ('52) .. 0 10 0 9
311 **40** 6 c. deep ultramarine .. 0 9 0 6
a. Perf. 13 × 14 (24.10.49) .. 1 0 0 4
312 **47** 24 c. blue-green 45 0 15 0
a. Wmk. sideways .. 3 6 3 0
313 **41** 36 c. bright violet (7.3.38) 4 0 2 0
a. Perf. 13 × 14 (13.12.51) .. 2 6 2 0
314 **48** 48 c. orange .. 5 0 2 6
a. Perf. 14 × 13 (14.6.51) .. 4 0 7 6
315 **45** 60 c. red-brown 5 0 3 6
316 **51** 96 c. purple 15 0 6 0
a. Perf. 12½ × 13½ ('44) .. 12 6 7 6
b. Perf. 13 × 14 (8.2.51) .. 8 6 7 6
317 **52** $1 bright violet 8 0 4 6
a. Perf. 14 × 13 ('51) .. £28 £22
318 **50** $2 purple (11.6.45) .. 15 0 17 6
a. Perf. 14 × 13 (9.8.50) .. 17 6 17 6
319 **54** $3 red-brown (2.7.45) .. 27 6 30 0
a. Bright red-brn. (Dec. '46) 65 0 40 0
b. Perf. 14 × 13. *Red-brown* (29.10.52) .. 25 0 30 0

1946 (21 Oct.). *Victory. As Nos. 28/9 of Aden.*

320 3 c. carmine 0 4 0 6
321 6 c. blue 0 6 0 9

1948 (20 Dec.). *Royal Silver Wedding. As Nos. 30/1 of Aden; (recess $3).*

322 3 c. scarlet 0 4 0 4
323 $3 red-brown 20 0 22 6

1949 (10 Oct.). *75th Anniv. of Universal Postal Union. As Nos. 114/7 of Antigua.*

324 4 c. carmine 1 6 1 6
325 6 c. deep blue 2 6 2 6
326 12 c. orange 3 0 3 6
327 24 c. blue-green 5 0 6 0

1951 (16 Feb.). *University Coll. of B.W.I. As Nos. 118/9 of Antigua.*

328 3 c. black and carmine .. 0 10 0 10
329 6 c. black and blue 1 3 1 3

1953 (2 June). *Coronation. As No. 47 of Aden.*

330 4 c. black and scarlet .. 1 0 0 9

55. G.P.O. Georgetown.

56. Botanical Gardens.

57. Victoria Regia Lilies.

58. Amerindian Shooting Fish.

62. Felling Greenheart.

59. Map of Caribbean.

60. Rice Combine-harvester.

61. Sugar Cane Entering Factory.

63. Mining for Bauxite.

64. Mount Roraima.

65. Kaieteur Falls.

66. Arapaima.

67. Toucan.

68. Dredging Gold.

69. Arms of British Guiana.

(Centre litho., frame recess ($1); recess (others). Waterlow (until 1961), then De La Rue.)

1954 (1 Dec.)–**62.** *Wmk. Mult. Script CA. P* 12½ × 13 (*horiz.*) *or* 13 (*vert.*).

331	**55**	1 c. black	0	2	0	2
332	**56**	2 c. myrtle-green ..	0	3	0	2
333	**57**	3 c. brn.-olive & red-brn.	0	4	0	4
334	**58**	4 c. violet..	1	0	1	0
		a. De La Rue ptg. (*shades*) (5.12.61)	0	4	0	4
335	**59**	5 c. scarlet and black ..	0	8	0	8
336	**60**	6 c. yellow-green (*shades*)	0	6	0	6
337	**61**	8 c. ultramarine	0	7	0	6
338	**62**	12 c. black and reddish brown (*shades*) ..	1	6	0	8
339	**63**	24 c. black and brownish orange (*shades*) ..	2	6	1	6
340	**64**	36 c. rose-carmine & black	3	6	3	0
341	**65**	48 c. ultramarine & brown-lake (*shades*) ..	6	0	6	0
		ab. De La Rue ptg. *Brt. ultram. & pale brown-lake* (19.9.61)	5	0	5	0
342	**66**	72 c. carmine & emerald ..	8	0	9	0
		a. De La Rue ptg. (17.7.62)	6	6	7	0
343	**67**	$1 pink, yell., grn. & blk.	10	0	10	0
344	**68**	$2 deep mauve (*shades*)	15	0	16	0
345	**69**	$5 ultramarine & black	45	0	47	6
		a. De La Rue ptg. (19.9.61)..	26	0	27	6

The separately listed De La Rue printings are identifiable as singles by the single wide-tooth perfs. at each side at the *bottom* of the stamps. In the Waterlow these wide teeth are at the *top*.

70

(Photo. Harrison.)

1961 (23 Oct.). *History and Culture Week. W* w.**12.** *P* 14½ × 14.

346	**70**	5 c. sepia and orange-red	0	9	0	9
347	,,	6 c. sepia and blue-green	0	9	0	10
348	,,	30 c. sepia & yellow-orange	2	9	3	6

1963 (14 July). *Freedom from Hunger. As No.* 63 *of Aden.*

349	20 c. reddish violet	2	9	3	3

1963 (2 Sept.). *Red Cross Centenary. As Nos.* 147/8 *of Antigua.*

350	5 c. red and black	0	6	0	9
351	20 c. red and blue	2	6	2	6

1963–64. *As Nos.* 335/44, *but wmk.* w.**12.**

356	**59**	5 c. scarlet & blk. (28.5.64)	0	5	0	5
359	**62**	12 c. black and yellowish brown (6.10.64) ..	0	10	0	8
360	**63**	24 c. black and bright orange (10.12.63) ..	1	5	2	0
361	**64**	36 c. rose-carmine & black (10.12.63)	2	0	2	6
362	**65**	48 c. brt. ultram. & Venetian red (25.11.63) ..	2	9	3	6
363	**66**	72 c. carmine and emerald (25.11.63)	4	0	4	6
364	**67**	$1 pink, yellow, green and black (10.12.63)	5	6	6	9
365	**68**	$2 reddish mauve (10.12.63)	11	0	13	0

71. Weightlifting.

(Photo. De La Rue.)

1964 (1 Oct.). *Olympic Games, Tokio. W* w.**12.** *P* 13 × 13½.

367	**71**	5 c. orange	0	8	0	10
368	,,	8 c. blue	1	0	1	3
369	,,	25 c. magenta	3	6	4	0

1965 (17 May). *I.T.U. Centenary. As Nos.* 166/7 *of Antigua.*

370	5 c. emerald & yellow-olive..	0	8	0	10
371	25 c. light blue and magenta..	2	6	3	0

1965 (25 Oct.). *International Co-operation Year. As Nos.* 168/9 *of Antigua.*

372	5 c. reddish pur. & turq.-grn.	0	8	0	10
373	25 c. dp. bluish green & lav...	2	6	3	0

72. St. George's Cathedral, Georgetown.

(Des. Jennifer Toombs. Photo. Harrison.)

1966 (24 Jan.). *Churchill Commemoration. W* w.**12.** *P* 14 × 14½.

374	**72**	5 c. black, crimson & gold	0	6	0	8
375	,,	25 c. black, blue and gold	1	10	2	3

1966 (3 Feb.). *Royal Visit. As Nos.* 174/5 *of Antigua.*

376	3 c. black and ultramarine ..	0	5	0	6
377	25 c. black and magenta ..	1	10	2	3

POSTAGE DUE STAMPS.

D 1

(Typo. De La Rue.)

1940 (Mar.)–**55.** *Wmk. Mult. Script CA. P* 14.

D1 **D 1** 1 c. green, O 5 0 6 0
a. *Deep green*, C (30.4.52) .. 0 2 0 6
b. W9a (Crown missing), C £16
c. W9b (St. Ed. Crown), C. . £12
D2 ,, 2 c. black, O 6 0 3 6
aa. Chalky paper (30.4.52) .. 0 3 0 4
a. W9a (Crown missing), C. . £15
b. W9b (St. Ed. Crown), C. . £8
D3 ,, 4 c. brt. blue, C (1.5.52) 0 4 0 6
a. W9a (Crown missing), C. . £12
b. W9b (St. Ed. Crown), C. . £8
D4 ,, 12 c. scarlet, O 10 0 12 6
a. Chalky paper (19.7.55) .. 0 10 1 0

OFFICIAL STAMPS.

OFFICIAL (O 1) **OFFICIAL** (O 2)

1875. *Optd. with Type* O **1** (1 c.) *or* O **2** (*others*). *P* 10.

O1 **8** 1 c. black (R.) 30 0 30 0
a. Imperf. between (pair) ..
O2 ,, 2 c. orange £7 30 0
O3 ,, 8 c. rose £14 £7
O4 **7** 12 c. brownish purple .. £40 £20
O5 **9** 24 c. green £25 £10

Two types of the word "OFFICIAL" are found on each value. On the 1 c. the word is either 16 or 17 mm. long. On the other values the chief difference is in the shape and position of the letter "O" in "OFFICIAL". In one case the "O" is upright, in the other it slants to the left.

1877. *Optd. with Type* O **2.** *Word Crown CC. P* 14.

O 6 **16** 1 c. slate £12 £6
a. Imperf. betwn. (vert. pr.)
O 7 ,, 2 c. orange 80 0 25 0
O 8 ,, 4 c. blue £6 60 0
O 9 ,, 6 c. brown £120 £25
O10 ,, 8 c. rose £120 £22

Prepared for use, but not issued.

O11 **16** 12 c. pale violet .. £60
O12 ,, 24 c. green £80

The "OFFICIAL" overprints have been extensively forged.

The use of Official stamps was discontinued in 1878.

BRITISH HONDURAS.

For GREAT BRITAIN stamps used in British Honduras, see page 65.

1

(Typo. De La Rue & Co.)

1866 (Jan.). *No wmk. P* 14.

1 **1** 1d. pale blue 50 0 60 0
a. Imperf. between (pair) ..
2 ,, 1d. blue 50 0 60 0
3 ,, 6d. rose £8 £7
4 ,, 1s. green £10 £5

1872–79. *Wmk. Crown CC.* (*a*) *P* 12½.

5 **1** 1d. pale blue 80 0 35 0
6 ,, 1d. deep blue 50 0 27 6
7 ,, 3d. red-brown 90 0 65 0
8 ,, 3d. chocolate £6 90 0
9 ,, 6d. rose £12 40 0
9*a* ,, 6d. bright rose-carmine .. £22 50 0
10 ,, 1s. green £16 40 0
10*a* ,, 1s. deep green £20 40 0
b. Imperf. between (pair) ..

(*b*) *P* 14.

11 **1** 1d. pale blue 65 0 35 0
12 ,, 1d. blue 55 0 30 0
a. Imperf. between (pair) £80
13 ,, 3d. chestnut £5 35 0
14 ,, 4d. mauve (1879) £8 30 0
15 ,, 6d. rose £20 £18
16 ,, 1s. green £8 30 0
a. Imperf. between (pair) ..

1882–87. *Wmk. Crown CA. P* 14.

17 **1** 1d. blue (1884) 55 0 60 0
18 ,, 1d. rose (1884) 35 0 27 6
a. Bisected (½d.) (on cover) ..
19 ,, 1d. carmine 50 0 30 0
20 ,, 4d. mauve (1882) £5 17 6
21 ,, 6d. yellow (1885) £15 £12
22 ,, 1s. grey (1887) £22 £12

2
CENTS
(2)

1888 (1 Jan.)–**1889.** *Stamps of* 1872–87 *surch. as T* **2.**

(*a*) *P* 12½. *Wmk. Crown CC.*

23 **1** 2 c. on 6d. rose £10 £10
24 ,, 3 c. on 3d. chocolate .. £500 £200

There are very dangerous forgeries of these surcharges.

(*b*) *P* 14.

25 **1** 2 c. on 1d. rose (CA) .. 15 0 27 6
a. Surch. inverted £110 £100
b. Surch. double £100 £100
c. Bisected (1 c.) (on cover) .. — £8
26 ,, 2 c. on 6d. rose (CC) .. £6 £6
a. Surch. double £100
b. Bisected (1 c.) (on cover) .. — £16
c. Slanting "2" with curved foot £40

27	1	3 c. on 3d. red-brown (CC)	£6	90 0
28	,,	10 c. on 4d. mauve (CA) ..	55 0	20 0
29	,,	20 c. on 6d. yellow (CA) ..	20 0	50 0
30	,,	50 c. on 1s. grey (CA) ..	£40	£45
		a. Error. 5 c. on 1s. ..	£425	

TWO

(3)

No. 30 surch. with T **3**.

35	"TWO" on 50 c. on 1s. grey (R.)	70 0	75 0
	a. Bisected (1c.) (on cover)	—	£10
	b. Surch. in black ..	£800	£700
	c. Surch. double (R. + Bk.)	£700	£650

2

CENTS

(4)

Wmk. Crown CA. Surch. as T **4**. *P* 14.

37	1	2 c. on 1d. carmine ..	1 0	4 0
		a. Bisected (1 c.) (on cover) ..	—	£5
38	,,	3 c. on 3d. red-brown ..	2 6	3 6
39	,,	10 c. on 4d. mauve	7 6	3 6
		a. Surcharge double		
40	,,	20 c. on 6d. yellow (1889) ..	15 0	25 0
41	,,	50 c. on 1s. grey	50 0	65 0

6

~~10~~

CENTS

(5)

1891. *No. 39 surch. with new value, as in T* **5**.

43	6 c. on 10 c. on 4d. mauve (R.)	3 6	6 0
	a. "6" and bar inverted ..	£30	£30
	b. "6" only inverted	—	£250
44	6 c. on 10 c. on 4d. mauve (Bk.)	3 6	8 6
	a. "6" and bar inverted ..	£275	£75
	b. "6" only inverted	—	£250

Of variety (*b*) only six copies of each can exist, as one of each of these errors came in the first six sheets, and the mistake was then corrected. Of variety (*a*) more copies exist.

1891. *Surch. as T* **4**. *Wmk. Crown CA. P* 14.

47	1	6 c. on 3d. ultramarine ..	5 0	12 6

1

CENT

(6)

1891. *Surch. with T* **6**. *Wmk. Crown CA. P* 14.

48	1	1 c. on 1d. dull green ..	2 0	2 0

FIVE (7) **15** (7*a*)

1891. *No. 38 surch. with T 7 and 47 with T 7a.*

49	1	5 c. on 3 c. on 3d. red-brn.	4 0	10 0
		a. Wide space between "I" and "V"	35 0	45 0
		b. "FIVE" and bar double ..	£16	
50	,,	15 c. on 6 c. on 3d. ultram.	10 0	20 0
		a. Surch. double ..		

8

9

10

11

(Typo. De La Rue & Co.)

1891–98. *Wmk. Crown CA. P* 14.

51	8	1 c. dull green	2 6	2 0
52	,,	2 c. carmine-rose	2 6	1 6
53	,,	3 c. brown	5 0	7 6
54	,,	5 c. ultramarine (1895) ..	20 0	3 6
55	,,	6 c. ultramarine	5 0	4 6
56	9	10 c. mauve & green (1895)	18 6	20 0
57	,,	12 c. pale mauve and green	8 6	17 6
58	,,	12 c. violet and green ..	20 0	27 6
59	,,	24 c. yellow and blue ..	10 0	27 6
60	,,	24 c. orange and blue ..	37 6	50 0
61	,,	25 c. red-brn. & grn. (1898)	45 0	50 0
62	10	50 c. green and carmine ..	30 0	40 0
63	11	$1 green and carmine ..	50 0	60 0
64	,,	$2 green and ultramarine	£7	£8
65	,,	$5 green and black ..	£24	£27

1899. *Optd.* "REVENUE". A. *Overprint* 12 *mm. long.* B. *Overprint* 11 *mm. long.*

			A.		B.	
66	5 c. (No. 54) ..		5 0	5 0	7 0	10 0
	a. "BEVENUE" ..		60 0	70 0	†	
67	10 c. (No. 56) ..		10 0	12 6	17 6	20 0
	a. "BEVENUE" ..		£17	—	†	
	b. "REVENU" ..		†		£35	£18
68	25 c. (No. 61) ..		8 0	12 6	8 0	10 0
	a. "BEVENUE" ..		£6	£7	†	
69	50 c. (No. 41) ..		£10	£10	£9	£9
	a. "BEVENUE" ..		£225	—	†	

Two minor varieties, a small "U" and a tall, narrow "U" are found in the word "REVENUE".

1900–1. *Wmk. Crown CA. P* 14.

78	11	5 c. grey-black and ultramarine/*blue*	3 6	5 0
79	10	10 c. dull pur. & grn. (1901)	6 0	20 0

14

15

(Typo. De La Rue & Co.)

1902–4. *Wmk. Crown CA. P* 14.

80	14	1 c. grey-grn. & grn. (1904)	12 6	25 0
81	,,	2 c. purple and black/*red*	3 0	1 6
82	,,	5 c. grey-black & blue/*blue*	5 0	5 0
83	15	20 c. dull & bright pur. (1904)	17 6	40 0

1905–07. *Wmk. Mult. Crown CA. P* 14.
84 **14** 1 c. grey-green & grn., OC 2 6 2 6
85 ,, 2 c. purple & black/*red*, OC 2 6 1 9
86 ,, 5 c. grey-blk. & blue/*blue*, C 3 6 5 0
87 **15** 10 c. dull pur. & emer.-grn., C 5 0 15 0
89 ,, 25 c. dull pur. & orge., C .. 20 0 22 6
90 ,, 50 c. grey-grn. & carm., C 30 0 37 6
91 **14** $1 grey-grn. & carm., C 65 0 75 0
92 ,, $2 grey-green & blue, C £8 £10
93 ,, $5 grey-green & black, C £27 £30

Dates of issue:—1905, 1 c. to 5 c.; 1907, remainder.

1908–10. *Colours changed. Wmk. Mult. Crown CA. P* 14.
95 **14** 1 c. blue-green, O .. 3 6 2 6
96 ,, 2 c. carmine, O (1908) .. 2 6 2 0
97 ,, 5 c. ultramarine, O .. 6 0 4 0
100 **15** 25 c. black/*green*, C .. 20 0 50 0

16

17

(Typo. De La Rue.)

1913–21. *Wmk. Mult. Crown CA. P* 14.
101 **16** 1 c. blue-green, O .. 0 8 0 8
101*a* ,, 1 c. yellow-green, O .. 0 9 1 0
102 ,, 2 c. red, O 2 0 1 9
102*a* ,, 2 c. bright scar., O ('16) 1 6 2 0
102*b* ,, 2 c. scarlet, O (1917) .. 1 3 1 3
102*c* ,, **2 c. red/*bluish*** 10 0 12 6
103 ,, 3 c. orange O (1917) .. 1 0 1 0
104 ,, 5 c. bright blue, O .. 5 0 3 0
105 **17** 10 c. dull purple and yellow-green, C .. 8 6 7 6
105*a* ,, 10 c. dull purple & bright green, C 7 6 12 6
106 ,, 25 c. black/*green*, C .. 6 0 8 0
a. On blue-green, olive back (1917) 15 0 30 0
b. On emerald back (1921) 12 6 30 0
107 ,, 50 c. pur. & blue/*blue*, C 12 6 20 0
108 **16** $1 black and carm., C 25 0 40 0
109 ,, $2 purple and green, C 90 0 £5
110 ,, $5 pur. & black/*red*, C £20 £22

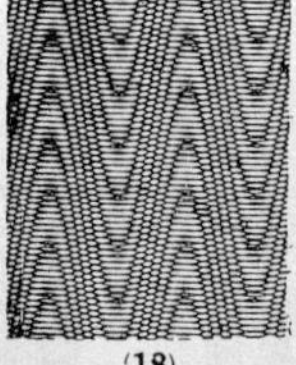
(18)

1915. *Optd. with T* **18** *in violet.*
111 **16** 1 c. green 6 0 17 6
111*a* ,, 1 c. yellow-green .. 3 6 10 0
112 ,, 2 c. scarlet 3 6 4 0
113 ,, 5 c. bright blue 3 0 12 6

These stamps were shipped early in the 1914–18 war, and were thus overprinted, so that if seized by the enemy, they could be distinguished and rendered invalid.

WAR
(19)

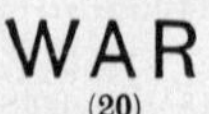

(20)

1916. *No.* 111. *Optd. locally with T* **19.**
114 **16** 1 c. green 0 4 0 8
a. Overprint inverted .. £7 £8

1917. *Optd. with T* **19.**
116 **16** 1 c. yellow-green .. 0 9 1 6
117 ,, 1 c. blue-green 0 6 1 6
118 ,, 3 c. orange 1 3 2 6
a. Overprint double .. £17

1918. *Optd. with T* **20.**
119 **16** 1 c. blue-green/*bluish* .. 0 6 0 6
119*a* ,, 1 c. yellow-green .. 2 0 1 6
120 ,, 3 c. orange 0 6 1 0

21

(Recess. De La Rue.)

1921. *Peace Commemoration. Wmk. Mult. Crown CA (sideways). P* 14.
121 **21** 2 c. rose-red 8 6 6 0

1921. *As T* **21** *but with words* "PEACE" *omitted. Wmk. Mult. Script CA (sideways). P* 14.
122 4 c. slate 15 0 6 0

1922. *Wmk. Mult. Script CA. P* 14.
123 **16** 1 c. green, O 4 0 3 0

22

BELIZE
RELIEF FUND
PLUS
3 CENTS
(23)

(Typo. De La Rue.)

1922–33. *P* 14. (*a*) *Wmk. Mult. Crown CA.*
124 **22** 25 c. black/*emerald*, C .. 25 0 40 0
125 ,, $5 purple & black/*red*, C £18 £20

(*b*) *Wmk. Mult. Script CA.*
126 **22** 1 c. green, O (1929) .. 0 8 0 6
127 ,, 2 c. brown, O 0 6 0 6
128 ,, 2 c. rose-carmine, O (1927) 1 0 0 8
128*a* ,, 3 c. orange, O (1933) .. 2 6 1 6
129 ,, 4 c. grey, O (1929) .. 1 6 1 6
130 ,, 5 c. ultramarine, O (1922) 2 6 1 6
131 ,, 5 c. milky blue, O (1923) 5 0 7 6
132 ,, 10 c. dull pur. & sage-grn., C 4 0 2 6
133 ,, 25 c. black/*emerald*, C .. 5 0 7 6
134 ,, 50 c. pur. & blue/*blue*, C .. 17 6 22 6
136 ,, $1 black and scarlet, C 25 0 30 0
137 ,, $2 yell.-grn. & brt. pur. C 65 0 70 0

1932. *Belize Relief Fund. Surch. as T* **23.** *Wmk. Mult. Script CA. P* 14.
138 **22** 1 c. + 1 c. green, O .. 1 6 8 0
139 ,, 2 c. + 2 c. rose-carmine, O 2 6 8 0
140 ,, 3 c. + 3 c. orange, O .. 4 0 10 0
141 ,, 4 c. + 4 c grey O (R.) .. 10 0 17 6
142 ,, 5 c. + 5 c. ultramarine, O 17 6 30 0

1935 (6 MAY). *Silver Jubilee. As Nos.* 91/4 *of Antigua, but ptd. by B.W. & Co. P* 11 × 12.
143 3 c. ultramarine & grey-black 1 0 1 6
a. Extra flagstaff 70 0

144	4 c. green and indigo ..	2 0	2 6
	a. Extra flagstaff	£10	
145	5 c. brown and deep blue ..	3 0	4 0
146	25 c. slate and purple ..	6 6	10 0
	a. Extra flagstaff	£14	

For illustration of "extra flagstaff" variety, see Bechuanaland.

1937 (12 May). *Coronation. As Nos.* 13/15 *of Aden. P* 14.

147	3 c. orange	0 4	0 8
148	4 c. grey-black	0 9	1 3
149	5 c. bright blue	1 0	1 6

24. Maya figures.

25. Chicle tapping.

26. Cobune palm.

27. Local Products.

28. Grapefruit.

29. Mahogany logs in river.

30. Sergeant's Cay.

31. Dorey.

32. Chicle industry.

33. Court House, Belize.

34. Mahogany felling.

35. Arms of Colony.

(Recess. Bradbury, Wilkinson.)

1938–47?. *Wmk. Mult. Script CA (sideways on horizontal stamps). P* 11½ × 11 *(horiz. designs) or* 11 × 11½ *(vert. designs.).*

150	**24**	1 c. bright magenta & grn.	0 6	0 6
151	**25**	2 c. black and scarlet ..	0 6	0 8
		a. Perf. 12	6 0	8 6

152	**26**	3 c. purple and brown ..	0	9	0	10
153	**27**	4 c. black and green ..	1	0	1	0
154	**28**	5 c. mauve and dull blue	1	0	1	0
155	**29**	10 c. green & reddish brown	1	0	0	8
156	**30**	15 c. brown and light blue	2	6	1	6
157	**31**	25 c. blue and green ..	3	0	2	6
158	**32**	50 c. black and purple ..	7	0	7	0
159	**33**	$1 scarlet and olive ..	12	6	15	0
160	**34**	$2 deep blue and maroon	25	0	27	6
161	**35**	$5 scarlet and brown ..	60	0	65	0

Dates of issue. 10.1.38, 3 c., 4 c. and 5 c.; 14.2.38, 1 c., 2 c. (p. 11 × 11½), 10 c., 15 c., 25 c. and 50 c. 28.2.38, $1, $2, and $5; 1947 ? 2 c. (p. 12).

1946 (9 Sept.). *Victory. As Nos.* 28/9 *of Aden.*

162	3 c. brown	0	4	0	6
163	5 c. blue	0	6	1	0

1948 (1 Oct.). *Royal Silver Wedding. As Nos.* 30/1 *of Aden.*

164	4 c. green	0	10	1	0
165	$5 brown	90	0		£6

36. Island of St. George's Cay.

37. H M. Sloop, *Merlin.*

(Recess. Waterlow.)

1949 (10 Jan.). *150th Anniv. of Battle of St. George's Cay. Wmk. Mult. Script CA. P* 12½.

166	**36**	1 c. ultra marine & green	0	6	0	10
167	,,	3 c. blue & yellow-brown	0	8	1	0
168	,,	4 c. olive and violet ..	0	9	1	3
169	**37**	5 c. brown and deep blue	1	3	1	6
170	,,	10 c. green and red-brown	1	9	2	6
171	,,	15 c. emerald and ultram.	3	6	5	0

1949 (10 Oct.). *75th Anniv. of U.P.U. As Nos.* 114/7 *of Antigua.*

172	4 c. blue-green	1	6	1	6
173	5 c. deep blue	2	6	3	0
174	10 c. red-brown	4	6	5	0
175	25 c. blue	10	0	12	6

1951 (16 Feb.). *Inauguration of B.W.I. University College. As Nos.* 118/9 *of Antigua.*

176	3 c. reddish violet & brown	0	10	0	10
177	10 c. green and brown ..	1	9	1	9

1953 (2 June). *Coronation. As No.* 47 *of Aden.*

178	4 c. black and green	1	0	1	6

38. Arms of British Honduras.

39. Mountain Cow.

40. Mace and Legislative Council Chamber.

41. Pine Industry.

42. Spiny Lobster.

43. Stanley Field Airport.

44. Maya Frieze.

45. Blue Butterfly.

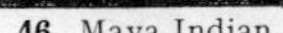
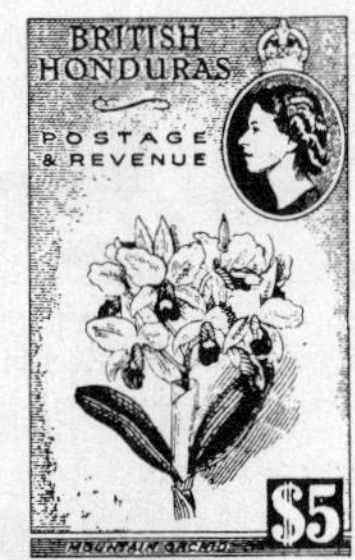

46. Maya Indian. **49.** Mountain Orchid.

47. Armadillo.

48. Hawkesworth Bridge.

(Recess. Waterlow (until 1961), then De La Rue.)

1953 (1 Sept.)–**57.** *Wmk. Mult. Script CA. P* 13½.

179	**38**	1 c. green and black ..	0	3	0	4
180	**39**	2 c. yellow-brn. & black	0	6	0	8
		a. Perf. 14 (18.9.57) ..	1	0	1	3
181	**40**	3 c. reddish violet and bright purple (*shades*)	0	9	0	9
		a. Perf. 14 (18.9.57) ..	0	9	0	9
182	**41**	4 c. brown and green ..	0	6	0	6
183	**42**	5 c. deep olive-green and scarlet	2	6	2	6
		a. Perf. 14 (15.5.57) ..	0	9	1	0
184	**43**	10 c. slate & bright blue ..	1	0	0	10
185	**44**	15 c. green and violet ..	1	6	1	6
186	**45**	25 c. brt. blue & yell.-brn.	2	0	2	0
187	**46**	50 c. yellow-brown and reddish purple (*shades*)	4	6	5	0
188	**47**	$1 slate-blue & red-brn.	9	0	9	0
189	**48**	$2 scarlet and grey ..	17	6	17	6
190	**49**	$5 purple and slate ..	40	0	40	0

50. Belize from Fort George, 1842.

51. Public Seals, 1860 and 1960.

52. Tamarind Tree, Newtown Barracks.

(Recess. Bradbury, Wilkinson.)

1960 (1 July). *Post Office Centenary. W* w.**12.** *P* 11½ × 11.

191	**50**	2 c. green	0	8	0	8
192	**51**	10 c. deep carmine ..	1	9	1	9
193	**52**	15 c. blue	3	6	3	6

NEW CONSTITUTION 1960 (**53**)

HURRICANE HATTIE (**54**)

1961 (1 Mar.). *New Constitution. Nos.* 180*a*, 181*a and* 184/5 *optd. with T* **53** *by Waterlow and Sons.*

194	**39**	2 c. yellow-brown & black	1	0	1	3
195	**40**	3 c. red'sh vio. & brt. pur.	1	3	1	9
196	**43**	10 c. slate and brt. blue ..	2	9	3	3
197	**44**	15 c. green and violet ..	4	6	5	0

1962 (15 Jan.). *Hurricane Hattie Relief Fund. Optd. with T* **54** *by De La Rue.*

198	**38**	1 c. green and black ..	0	10	1	2
199	**43**	10 c. slate and bright blue	1	9	2	3
200	**45**	25 c. brt. blue & yell.-brown	3	9	4	0
201	**46**	50 c. yellow-brown & reddish purple	6	6	8	0

55. Great Curassow.

56. Red-legged Honeycreeper.

57. American Jacana.

58. Great Kiskadee.

59. Scarlet-rumped Tanager.

60. Scarlet Macaw.

61. Massena Trogon.

62. Red-footed Booby.

63. Keel-billed Toucan.

64. Magnificent Frigate Bird.

65. Rufous-tailed Jacamar.

66. Montezuma Oropendola.

(Des. D. R. Eckelberry. Photo. Harrison.)

1962 (2 Apr.). *W* w.**12**. *P* 14 × 14½.

202	**55**	1 c. multicoloured	..	0	2	0	2
203	**56**	2 c. multicoloured	..	0	3	0	3
204	**57**	3 c. multicoloured	..	0	4	0	4
		a. Blue-green (legs) missing		£50			
205	**58**	4 c. multicoloured	..	0	5	0	5
206	**59**	5 c. multicoloured	..	0	6	0	6
207	**60**	10 c. multicoloured	..	0	10	0	10
208	**61**	15 c. multicoloured	..	1	1	1	4
209	**62**	25 c. multicoloured	..	1	9	2	0
210	**63**	50 c. multicoloured	..	3	6	4	6
211	**64**	$1 multicoloured	..	6	9	7	6
212	**65**	$2 multicoloured	..	13	3	15	0
213	**66**	$5 multicoloured	..	31	3	35	0

1963 (4 June). *Freedom from Hunger. As No. 63 of Aden.*

214		22 c. bluish green ..	..	2	9	3	0

1963 (2 Sept.). *Red Cross Centenary. As Nos. 147/8 of Antigua.*

215		4 c. red and black ..	..	0	6	0	9
216		22 c. red and blue ..	..	2	9	3	0

SELF GOVERNMENT 1964

(67)

1964. *New Constitution. Nos.* 202, 204/5, 207 *and* 209 *optd. with T* **67**.

217	**55**	1 c. multicoloured (20.4)		0	5	0	5
218	**57**	3 c. multicoloured (20.4)		0	7	0	8
219	**58**	4 c. multicoloured (3.2)	..	0	9	0	10
220	**60**	10 c. multicoloured (20.4)		1	3	1	6
221	**62**	25 c. multicoloured (3.2)	..	2	9	3	3

1965 (17 MAY). *I.T.U. Centenary. As Nos. 166/7 of Antigua.*
222 2 c. orange-red & lt. green 0 6 0 9
223 50 c. yellow & light purple 5 6 6 6

1965 (25 OCT.). *International Co-operation Year. As Nos. 168/9 of Antigua.*
224 1 c. reddish pur. & turq.-grn. 0 4 0 6
225 22 c. dp. bluish grn. & lavender 2 6 3 0

1966 (24 JAN.). *Churchill Commemoration. As Nos. 170/3 of Antigua.*
226 1 c. new blue 0 3 0 5
227 4 c. deep green 0 7 0 9
228 22 c. brown 2 0 2 6
229 25 c. bluish violet 2 3 3 0

POSTAGE DUE STAMPS.

D 1

(Typo. De La Rue & Co.)

1923–64. *Wmk. Mult. Script CA. P* 14.
D1 **D 1** 1 c. black, O 4 6 5 0
a. Chalky paper (25.9.56) .. 0 6 0 6
b. White uncoated paper (9.4.64) 0 2 0 6
D2 ,, 2 c. black, O 4 6 4 0
a. Chalky paper (25.9.56) .. 0 3 0 6
D3 ,, 4 c. black, O 10 0 10 0
a. Chalky paper (25.9.56) .. 0 6 0 10

The early ordinary paper printings were yellowish and quite distinct from No. D1b.

1965 (3 AUG.). As No. D3*a but wmk.* w.**12.**
D6 **D 1** 4 c. black 0 5 0 7

BRITISH LEVANT.

80 PARAS (1) 4 PIASTRES (2)

12 PIASTRES (3)

Stamps of Great Britain (Queen Victoria) surch. as T **1** *to* **3**.

1885 (1 APRIL).
1 **64** 40 par. on 2½d. lilac .. 12 6 5 0
2 **62** 80 par. on 5d. green .. 70 0 10 0
3 **58** 12 pi. on 2s. 6d. lilac/*bluish* .. £10 £6
a. On paper deeply blued .. £16 £10
b. On white paper 25 0 12 6

1887–96.
4 **74** 40 par. on 2½d. purple/*blue* .. 2 0 0 6
a. Surch. double £50 £50
5 **78** 80 par. on 5d. purple & blue 8 6 1 6
a. Small "0" in "80" .. 65 0 45 0
6 **81** 4 pi. on 10d. purple and carmine (1896) 8 6 10 0
a. Large, wide "4" 35 0 35 0

1893 (25 FEB.). *Roughly handstamped at Constantinople, as T* **1**.
7 **71** 40 par. on ½d. vermilion .. £10 £5

This provisional was in use five days only. As fraudulent copies were made with the original handstamp, this stamp should only be purchased from undoubted sources. (Price of genuine stamp, used on envelope, from £12.)

1902–5. *Stamps of King Edward VII surch. as T* **1** *to* **3**.
8 **86** 40 par. on 2½d. bright blue, O (6.2.02) .. 4 6 1 0
9 **89** 80 par. on 5d. purple and blue, O (5.6.02) .. 4 6 4 0
a. Small "0" in "80" .. 85 0 45 0
10 **92** 4 pi. on 10d. purple and carmine, O (6.9.02) .. 6 0 4 0
a. No cross on crown .. 80 0 80 0
b. Chalky paper 6 0 6 0
ba. Chalky. No cross on crown £5 £5
11 **94** 12 pi. on 2s. 6d. dull purple, O (29.8.03) 25 0 30 0
a. Reddish purple, C 25 0 30 0
12 **95** 24 pi. on 5s. car., O (1905) 40 0 50 0

LEVANT (4)

1905. *Stamps of King Edward VII optd. with T* **4**.
13 **83** ½d. pale yellow-green, O 1 6 0 9
14 ,, 1d. scarlet, O .. 2 0 1 6
15 **84** 1½d. dull pur. & yell.-grn., O 7 6 6 0
a. Chalky paper 6 0 6 0
16 **85** 2d. grey-green & carm., O 6 0 6 0
a. Green and carmine, C .. 3 6 5 0
17 **86** 2½d. bright blue, O .. 17 6 20 0
18 **87** 3d. purple/*yellow*, O .. 15 0 17 6
19 **88** 4d. green & choc.-brn., O 17 6 20 0
20 **89** 5d. purple and blue, O .. 25 0 27 6
21 **83** 6d. dull purple, O .. 20 0 22 6
22 **93** 1s. green and carmine, O 20 0 22 6
a. Chalky paper 20 0 20 0

1 PIASTRE (5)

1906. *Surch. in* "PIASTRES" *instead of* "PARAS" *as T* **5** *and* **2**.
23 **86** 1 pi. on 2½d. bright blue, O 2 6 1 0
24 **89** 2 pi. on 5d. pur. & blue, O 5 0 4 0
a. Chalky paper 5 0 4 0

1 Piastre (6)

1906 (2 JULY). *Issued at Beirut. No.* 16 *surch. with T* **6**.
25 **85** 1 pi. on 2d. grn. & carm., O £40 £26

1 PIASTRE 10 PARAS (7)

1909 (NOV.–DEC.). *Stamps of King Edward VII surch. as T* **1** (30 *par.*), **7**, *and* **2** (5 *pi.*).
26 **84** 30 par. on 1½d. dull purple and green, C .. 4 0 4 0
27 **87** 1 pi. 10 par. on 3d. purple/*yellow*, C .. 17 6 25 0
28 **88** 1 pi. 30 par. on 4d. green & chocolate-brown, C 17 6 25 0
29 ,, 1 pi. 30 par. on 4d. orange, O (16.12.09) .. 22 6 25 0
30 **83** 2 pi. 20 par. on 6d. reddish purple, C .. 35 0 32 6
31 **93** 5 pi. on 1s. grn. & carm., C 10 6 10 6

1¾ PIASTRE (8) 4 Normal "4". 4 Pointed "4".

1910 (FEB.). *Stamps of King Edward VII surch. as T* **8**.
32 **87** 1¼ pi. on 3d. purple/*yell.*, C 2 0 2 6
33 **88** 1¾ pi. on 4d. orange, O .. 3 0 3 0
a. Thin, pointed "4" in fraction 15 0 25 0
34 **83** 2½ pi. on 6d. reddish pur., C 5 0 6 0

1 PIASTRE (9) **1 PIASTRE** (10)

1911. *Stamps of King Edward VII, Harrison or Somerset House ptgs., surch. or optd.*

(a) Surch. with T **5.**

35 **86** 1 pi. on 2½d. brt. blue (*p.* 14) 3 0 3 0
36 „ 1 pi. on 2½d. brt. blue (*perf.* 15×14) 5 0 3 0

(b) Surch. with T **9.**

37 **86** 1 pi. on 2½d. brt. blue (*perf.* 15×14) 6 6 1 6

(c) Surch. with T **10.**

38 **86** 1 pi. on 2½d. brt. blue (*perf.* 15×14) 3 6 1 6

Type differences. In T **5** the letters are tall and narrow and the space enclosed by the upper part of the "A" is small.

In T **9** the opening of the "A" is similar, but the letters are shorter and broader, the "P" and the "E" being particularly noticeable.

In T **10** the letters are short and broad, but the "A" is thin and open.

(d) Surch. as T **1** *to* **3.**

39 **84** 30 par. on 1½d. dull reddish purple & yellow-green 3 0 2 0
a. Slate-purple and green .. 2 6 2 6
40 **89** 2 pi. on 5d. pur. & brt. blue 2 6 2 6
41 **92** 4 pi. on 10d. dull purple and scarlet 30 0 17 6
a. Dull purple and carmine .. 10 0 15 0
42 **93** 5 pi. on 1s. grn. & carmine 10 0 10 0
43 **94** 12 pi. on 2s. 6d. deep reddish purple 45 0 50 0
a. Dull purple (greyish) .. 22 6 20 0
b. Pale reddish purple .. 22 6 25 0
44 **95** 24 pi. on 5s. carmine .. 45 0 50 0

(e) Optd. with T **4.**

45 **83** ½d. yellow-green (*perf.* 14) 3 6 7 6

Stamps of King George V optd. with T **4.**

(a) **1911** (Sept.). *Dies A. Wmk. Crown.*

46 **98** ½d. yellow-green (No. 322) 1 6 2 6
47 **99** 1d. deep rose-red (No. 327) 1 6 2 6
a. No cross on crown ..

(b) **1912** (Mar.). *Redrawn types. Wmk. Crown.*

48 **101** ½d. green (No. 339) .. 0 6 0 6
49 **102** 1d. scarlet (No. 342) .. 1 0 0 10

(c) **1913** (July). *New types. Wmk. Royal Cypher.*

50 **105** ½d. green (No. 351) .. 1 0 0 8
51 **104** 1d. scarlet (No. 358) .. 1 0 2 0

These two stamps were reissued in 1919.

For other values of this series with "LEVANT" overprint see Nos. 68 to 74.

1913–14. *Stamps of King George V, wmk. Royal Cypher. surch. as T* **1** *(30 par.),* **10** *(1 pi.),* **8** *or* **2** *(4 and 5 pi.).*

52 **105** 30 par. on 1½d. red-brown 2 0 4 6
53 **104** 1 pi. on 2½d. bright blue 1 6 1 6
54 **106** 1¼ pi. on 3d. violet .. 3 0 5 0
55 „ 1¾ pi. on 4d. grey-green .. 4 6 8 6
a. Thin, pointed "4" in fraction 60 0 60 0
56 **108** 4 pi. on 10d. turq.-blue 10 0 17 6
57 „ 5 pi. on 1s. bistre-brown 15 0 25 0

1½ PIASTRES (11) **15 PIASTRES** (12)

1921. *Stamps of King George V, wmk. Royal Cypher, surch. as T* **1** *(30 par.),* **11** *and* **12** *(15 and 18¾ pi.).*

58 **105** 30 par. on ½d. green .. 0 6 0 8
59 **104** 1½ pi. on 1d. scarlet .. 0 6 0 6
60 „ 3¾ pi. on 2½d. blue .. 1 0 0 10
61 **106** 4½ pi. on 3d. blue-violet .. 1 0 1 6
62 **107** 7½ pi. on 5d. yellow-brown 1 6 1 0
63 **108** 15 pi. on 10d. turq.-blue 2 6 2 6
64 „ 18¾ pi. on 1s. bistre-brown 3 0 3 0

45 PIASTRES (13)

1921. *Stamps of King George V (Bradbury, Wilkinson printing) surch. as T* **13.**

65 **109** 45 pi. on 2s. 6d. chocolate brown 10 0 12 6
66 „ 90 pi on 5s. rose-red .. 25 0 12 6
67 „ 180 pi. on 10s. dull grey-blue 40 0 15 0

1921. *Stamps of King George V optd. as T* **4.**

68 **106** 2d. red-orange (Die I) .. 1 6 2 0
69 „ 3d. blue-violet 3 0 2 0
70 „ 4d. grey-green 4 0 4 6
71 **107** 5d. yellow-brown .. 5 0 6 0
72 „ 6d. reddish purple. C .. 6 6 7 0
73 **108** 1s. bistre-brown .. 7 6 5 0
74 **109** 2s. 6d. chocolate-brown .. 25 0 30 0

On No. 74 the letters of the overprint are shorter, being only 3 mm. high.

The British P.O.'s in the Turkish Empire were closed in 1914. The 1921 issues were in use during the British Occupation after the War.

SPECIAL ISSUE FOR SALONICA.

Levant (S 1)

1916 (End of Feb. *to* 9 March). *Stamps of Gt. Britain, optd. with Type* S **1.**

S 1 **105** ½d. green 60 0 80 0
a. Overprint double £45 £45
b. Overprint omitted (in vertical pair with normal) .. £35 £40
S 2 **104** 1d. scarlet 60 0 80 0
a. Overprint double £50 £50
S 3 **106** 2d. red-orange (Die I) .. £12 £18
S 4 „ 3d. blue-violet £7 £9
a. Overprint double .. ..
S 5 „ 4d. grey-green £12 £18
S 6 **107** 6d. reddish purple .. £7 £9
a. Overprint omitted (in vertical pair with normal) .. £35 £40
S 7 **108** 9d. agate £30 £40
a. Overprint double .. £175 £175
S 8 „ 1s. bistre-brown .. £30 £35

There are numerous forgeries of this overprint.

BRITISH NEW GUINEA.

See **PAPUA.**

BRITISH OCCUPATION OF FORMER ITALIAN COLONIES.

MIDDLE EAST FORCES.

For use in territory occupied by British Forces in Eritrea (1942), Italian Somaliland (1942), Cyrenaica (1943), Tripolitania (1943), and some of the Dodecanese Islands (1945).

PRICES. Our prices for used stamps with "M.E.F." overprints are for specimens with identifiable postmarks of the territories in which they were issued. These stamps were also used in the United Kingdom, with official sanction, from the summer of 1950 onwards, and with U.K. postmarks are worth about 25 per cent less.

M.E.F. (M 1)

1942 (2 Mar.). *Stamps of Great Britain optd. in London and Cairo with Type* M **1,** *in black.* W **127.** *P* 15×14.

M1 **128** 1d. scarlet (No. 463) .. 0 6 0 8

No.	Type	Description	s.	d.	s.	d.
M2	**128**	2d. orange (No. 465) ..	0	10	1	0
M3	,,	2½d. ultram. (No. 466) ..	0	10	1	0
M4	,,	3d. violet (No. 467) ..	1	0	1	6
		a. Opt. double ..				
M5	**129**	5d. brown	1	6	2	0

There are two printings in the above issue.

I. By Harrison & Sons. Ltd., London. Opt.: 14 mm. Sharp lettering with upright oblong stops.

II. By Army Printing Services, Cairo. Opt. 13½ mm. The setting comprises three rows with sharp lettering and square stops, and seven rows with thick rough lettering and rounded stops.

Both printings were issued simultaneously.

1943 (1 Jan.)–**1947.** *Stamps of Great Britain optd. in London as Type* M **1.**

(*a*) *In blue-black.* *W* **127.** *P* 15 × 14

No.	Type	Description	s.	d.	s.	d.
M 6	**128**	1d. pale scarlet (No. 486)	0	4	0	6
M 7	,,	2d. pale orange (No. 488)	0	6	0	8
M 8	,,	2½d. lt. ultram. (No. 489)	0	8	0	10
M 9	,,	3d. pale violet (No. 490)	0	10	1	3
M10	**129**	5d. brown	1	0	1	3
M11	,,	6d. purple	1	3	1	6
M12	**130**	9d. deep olive-green ..	4	0	4	0
M13	,,	1s. bistre-brown ..	2	6	3	0

(*b*) *In black.* *W* **133.** *P* 14.

No.	Type	Description	s.	d.	s.	d.
M14	**131**	2s. 6d. yellow-green ..	7	6	8	6
M15	,,	5s. red ('47)	12	6	17	6
M16	**132**	10s. ultramarine ('47) ..	20	0	22	0

On Nos. M6 to M13 the overprint measures 13½ mm. and the letters are sharp with square stops. The 5d. is best distinguished by the shade of the opt. which is black in the Cairo printing and blue-black in No. M10.

POSTAGE DUE STAMPS.

M.E.F.

(MD 1)

1942. *Postage Due Stamps of Great Britain optd. with Type* MD **1**, *in blue.* *W* **127** (*sideways*). *P* 14 × 15.

No.	Type	Description	s.	d.	s.	d.
MD1	D **1**	½d. emerald	0	6	1	0
MD2	,,	1d. carmine	0	8	1	0
MD3	,,	2d. agate	1	9	2	0
MD4	,,	3d. violet	1	3	3	0
MD5	,,	1s. deep blue	3	6	6	0

ERITREA.

British Military Administration.

B. M. A.
ERITREA

10
CENTS

(E 1)

B. M. A.
ERITREA

5 SHILLINGS

(E 2)

1948–9. *Stamps of Great Britain surch. as Types* E **1** *or* E **2.**

No.	Type	Description	s.	d.	s.	d.
E 1	**128**	5 c. on ½d. pale green ..	0	8	1	6
E 2	,,	10 c on 1d. pale scarlet ..	0	8	1	6
E 3	,,	20 c. on 2d. pale orange ..	0	8	1	9
E 4	,,	25 c. on 2½d. lt. ultram.	0	10	2	0
E 5	,,	30 c on 3d. pale violet ..	1	0	2	0
E 6	**129**	40 c. on 5d. brown ..	1	3	2	0
E 7	,,	50 c. on 6d. purple ..	1	6	2	0
E 7*a*	**130**	65 c. on 8d. bright carm. (1.2.49)	2	6	5	0
E 8	,,	75 c. on 9d. dp. ol.-grn.	2	0	2	6
E 9	,,	1s. on 1s. bistre-brown	2	6	3	0
E10	**131**	2s. 50 c. on 2s. 6d. yellow-green ..	15	0	17	6
E11	,,	5s. on 5s. red ..	17	6	22	6
E12	**132**	10s. on 10s. ultramarine	18	5	25	0

British Administration.

1950 (6 Feb.). *As Nos.* E1/E12, *but surch.* " B.A. ERITREA " *and new values instead of* " B.M.A. " *etc.*

No.	Type	Description	s.	d.	s.	d.
E13	**128**	5 c. on ½d. pale green ..	0	6	0	10
E14	,,	10 c. on 1d. pale scarlet ..	0	8	0	10
E15	,,	20 c. on 2d. pale orange	0	10	1	9
E16	,,	25 c. on 2½d. light ultram.	1	0	1	3
E17	,,	30 c. on 3d. pale violet ..	1	3	1	9
E18	**129**	40 c. on 5d. brown ..	1	3	1	0
E19	,,	50 c. on 6d. purple ..	1	3	1	0
E20	**130**	65 c. on 8d. brt. carmine	1	6	2	0
E21	,,	75 c. on 9d. dp. olive-grn.	2	0	2	0
E22	,,	1 s. on 1s. bistre-brown	2	0	2	0
E23	**131**	2 s. 50 c. on 2s. 6d. yellow-green	12	6	12	6
E24	,,	5 s. on 5s. red	17	6	20	0
E25	**132**	10 s. on 10s. ultramarine	50	0	40	0

1951 (3 May). *Nos.* 503/4, 506/7 *and* 509/11 *of Great Britain surch.* " B.A. ERITREA " *and new values.*

No.	Type	Description	s.	d.	s.	d.
E26	**128**	5 c. on ½d. pale orange ..	0	8	1	6
E27	,,	10 c. on 1d. light ultram.	0	8	1	6
E28	,,	20 c. on 2d. pale red-brn.	1	0	1	0
E29	,,	25 c. on 2½d. pale scarlet	1	3	1	3
E30	**147**	2 s. 50 c. on 2s. 6d. yellow-green ..	17	6	20	0
E31	**148**	5 s. on 5s. red ..	32	6	35	0
E32	**149**	10 s. on 10s. ultramarine	50	0	50	0

POSTAGE DUE STAMPS.

B. M. A.
ERITREA

10 CENTS

(ED 1)

1948. *Postage Due stamps of Great Britain surch. as Type* ED **1.**

No.	Type	Description	s.	d.	s.	d.
ED1	D **1**	5 c. on ½d. emerald ..	7	6	10	0
ED2	,,	10 c. on 1d. carmine ..	7	6	10	0
ED3	,,	20 c. on 2d. agate ..	6	0	12	6
ED4	,,	30 c. on 3d. violet ..	8	6	12	6
ED5	,,	1 s. on 1s. deep blue ..	10	6	17	6

1950 (6 Feb.). *As Nos.* ED1/5, *but surch.* " B.A. ERITREA " *and new values instead of* " B.M.A." *etc.*

No.	Type	Description	s.	d.	s.	d.
ED 6	D **1**	5 c. on ½d. emerald ..	10	0	12	6
ED 7	,,	10 c. on 1d. carmine ..	8	6	10	0
		a. "C" of "CENTS" omitted	£150			
ED 8	,,	20 c. on 2d. agate ..	7	6	10	0
ED 9	,,	30 c. on 3d. violet ..	12	6	15	0
ED10	,,	1 s. on 1s. deep blue	15	0	20	0

Stamps of Ethiopia were used in Eritrea after Sept. 15, 1952 following federation with Ethiopia.

SOMALIA.

British Occupation.

E.A.F.

(S **1.** " East Africa Forces ").

1943 (15 Jan.)–**46.** *Stamps of Great Britain optd. with Type* S **1**, *in blue.*

No.	Type	Description	s.	d.	s.	d.
S1	**128**	1d. pale scarlet ..	0	6	1	0
S2	,,	2d. pale orange	0	8	0	10
S3	,,	2½d. light ultramarine ..	0	10	1	3
S4	,,	3d. pale violet	1	0	1	3
S5	**129**	5d. brown	1	3	1	3
S6	,,	6d. purple	1	6	1	6
S7	**130**	9d. deep olive-green ..	1	9	4	0
S8	,,	1s. bistre-brown ..	2	6	2	0
S9	**131**	2s. 6d. yellow-green ('46)	7	6	10	0

The note *re* used prices above Type M **1** of Middle East Forces also applies to the above issue.

BRITISH MILITARY ADMINISTRATION.

1948 (27 MAY). *Stamps of Great Britain surch.* "B.M.A./SOMALIA" *and new values, as Types* E **1** *and* E **2** *of Eritrea.*

S10	**128**	5 c. on ½d. pale green ..	0	9	1	3
S11	„	15 c. on 1½d. pale red-brn.	4	0	6	0
S12	„	20 c. on 2d. pale orange ..	1	3	3	6
S13	„	25 c. on 2½d. lt. ultram...	1	0	1	6
S14	„	30 c. on 3d. pale violet ..	4	0	7	6
S15	**129**	40 c. on 5d. brown ..	1	6	4	0
S16	„	50 c. on 6d. purple ..	2	0	5	0
S17	**130**	75 c. on 9d. dp. ol.-green	6	0	10	0
S18	„	1 s. on 1s. bistre-brown	3	0	3	6
S19	**131**	2 s. 50 c. on 2s. 6d. yell.-green	15	0	22	6
S20	„	5 s. on 5s. red	25	0	35	0

BRITISH ADMINISTRATION.

1950 (2 JAN.) *As Nos.* S10/20, *but surch.* "B.A./SOMALIA" *and new values, instead of* "B.M.A." *etc.*

S21	**128**	5 c. on ½d. pale green ..	1	0	1	9
S22	„	15 c. on 1½d. pale red-brn.	3	6	6	0
S23	„	20 c. on 2d. pale orange ..	3	6	5	0
S24	„	25 c. on 2½d. lt. ultram...	1	6	2	6
S25	„	30 c. on 3d. pale violet ..	4	0	5	0
S26	**129**	40 c. on 5d. brown ..	3	0	4	0
S27	„	50 c. on 6d. purple ..	2	6	4	0
S28	**130**	75 c. on 9d. dp. ol.-green	5	0	7	6
S29	„	1 s. on 1s. bistre-brown	3	0	5	0
S30	**131**	2 s. 50 c. on 2s. 6d. yellow-green	25	0	30	0
S31	„	5 s. on 5s. red	30	0	40	0

Somalia reverted to Italian Administration on Dec. 2, 1950, later becoming independent. For subsequent issues, see Part II, under Italian Colonies, and Part III.

TRIPOLITANIA.

BRITISH MILITARY ADMINISTRATION.

1948 (1 JULY). *Stamps of Great Britain surch.* "B.M.A./TRIPOLITANIA" *and new values, as Types* E **1** *and* E **2** *of Eritrea, but expressed in M(ilitary) A(dministration) L(ire).*

T 1	**128**	1 l. on ½d. pale green ..	1	3	2	6
T 2	„	2 l. on 1d. pale scarlet	0	9	1	6
T 3	„	3 l. on 1½d. pale red-brown	1	0	2	0
T 4	„	4 l. on 2d. pale orange	1	0	1	6
T 5	„	5 l. on 2½d. lt. ultram.	1	0	2	0
T 6	„	6 l. on 3d. pale violet ..	1	0	2	6
T 7	**129**	10 l. on 5d. brown ..	1	0	1	6
T 8	„	12 l. on 6d. purple ..	1	6	1	6
T 9	**130**	18 l. on 9d. dp. ol.-green	3	0	6	0
T10	„	24 l. on 1s. bistre-brown	4	0	6	6
T11	**131**	60 l. on 2s. 6d. yell.-grn.	12	6	17	6
T12	„	120 l. on 5s. red ..	27	6	40	0
T13	**132**	240 l. on 10s. ultramarine	37	6	47	6

BRITISH ADMINISTRATION

1950 (6 FEB.). *As Nos.* T1/13, *but surch.* "B.A. TRIPOLITANIA" *and new values, instead of* "B.M.A." *etc.*

T14	**128**	1 l. on ½d. pale green ..	1	3	2	6
T15	„	2 l. on 1d. pale scarlet	0	9	1	6
T16	„	3 l. on 1½d. pale red-brown ..	1	6	3	6
T17	„	4 l. on 2d. pale orange	1	0	2	0
T18	„	5 l. on 2½d. lt. ultram.	1	0	2	0
T19	„	6 l. on 3d. pale violet ..	1	0	2	0
T20	**129**	10 l. on 5d. brown ..	1	3	1	6
T21	„	12 l. on 6d. purple ..	1	6	1	3
T22	**130**	18 l. on 9d. dp. ol.-green	2	0	4	0
T23	„	24 l. on 1s. bistre-brown	3	0	4	0
T24	**131**	60 l. on 2s. 6d. yell.-grn.	17	6	20	0
T25	„	120 l. on 5s. red	35	0	45	0
T26	**132**	240 l. on 10s. ultramarine	50	0	60	0

1951 (3 MAY). *Nos.* 503/7 *and* 509/11 *of Great Britain surch.* "B.A. TRIPOLITANIA" *and new values.*

T27	**128**	1 l. on ½d. pale orange	1	0	2	6
T28	„	l. on 1d. light ultram.	1	0	2	0
T29	**128**	3 l. on 1½d. pale green	1	9	3	0
T30	„	4 l. on 2d. pale red-brn.	1	6	3	0
T31	„	5 l. on 2½d. pale scar.	1	0	1	6
T32	**147**	60 l. on 2s. 6d. yell.-grn.	20	0	27	6
T33	**148**	120 l. on 5s. red	30	0	40	0
T34	**149**	240 l. on 10s. ultramarine	60	0	65	0

POSTAGE DUE STAMPS.

1948. *Postage Due stamps of Great Britain surch.* "B.M.A./TRIPOLITANIA" *and new values, as Type* ED **1** *of Eritrea, but expressed in M(ilitary) A(dministration) L(ire).*

TD1	D **1**	1 l. on ½d. emerald ..	2	0	3	0
TD2	„	2 l. on 1d. carmine ..	2	6	4	0
TD3	„	4 l. on 2d. agate ..	6	0	10	0
TD4	„	6 l. on 3d. violet ..	7	6	12	6
TD5	„	24 l. on 1s. deep blue ..	12	6	20	0

1950 (6 FEB.). *As Nos.* TD1/5, *but surch.* "B.A. TRIPOLITANIA" *and new values, instead of* "B.M.A." *etc.*

TD 6	D **1**	1 l. on ½d. emerald ..	3	0	5	0
TD 7	„	2 l. on 1d. carmine ..	5	0	7	6
TD 8	„	4 l. on 2d. agate ..	6	0	10	0
TD 9	„	6 l. on 3d. violet ..	6	0	10	0
TD10	„	24 l. on 1s. deep blue ..	22	6	30	0

Tripolitania is now part of the Independent Kingdom of Libya.

BRITISH P.O's IN CRETE.

BRITISH SPHERE OF ADMINISTRATION.
(CANDIA.)

During the provisional Joint Administration by France, Great Britain, Italy, and Russia.

1

2

1898 (25 NOV.). *Handstruck locally. Imperf.*

1	**1**	20 par. bright violet ..	£14	£12

1898 (3 DEC.). *Litho. by M. Grundmann, Athens. P* 11½.

2	**2**	10 par. blue	8	6	15	0
		a. Imperf. (pair)	£6			
3	„	20 par. green	8	6	15	0
		a. Imperf. (pair)	£6			

1899. *P* 11½.

4	**2**	10 par. brown	15	0	25	0
		a. Imperf. (pair)	£6			
5	„	20 par. rose	25	0	25	0
		a. Imperf. (pair)				

BRITISH SOLOMON IS. PROTECTORATE.

1

(Des. C. M. Woodford. Litho. W. E. Smith & Co., Sydney.)

1907 (14 Feb.). *No wmk.* *P* 11.

No.	Type	Description	Unused	Used
1	1	½d. ultramarine	10 0	17 6
2	,,	1d. rose-carmine	20 0	22 6
3	,,	2d. indigo	22 6	30 0
		a. Imperf. betw. (horiz. pair)		
4	,,	2½d. orange-yellow	27 6	27 6
		a. Imperf. betw. (vert. pair)	£100	
		b. Imperf. betw. (horiz. pair)	£85	£90
5	,,	5d. emerald-green	50 0	55 0
6	,,	6d. chocolate	60 0	70 0
		a. Imperf. betw. (vert. pair)	£75	
7	,,	1s. bright purple	65 0	75 0

Three types exist of the ½d. and 2½d., and six each of the other values, differing in minor details.

2

(Recess. De La Rue & Co.)

1908 (1 Nov.)–**1911**. *Wmk. Mult. Crown CA sideways.* *P* 14.

No.	Type	Description	Unused	Used
8	2	½d. green	1 6	3 6
9	,,	1d. red	3 0	4 0
10	,,	2d. greyish slate	4 6	7 6
11	,,	2½d. ultramarine	6 6	12 6
11a	,,	4d. red/*yell.* (Mar., 1911)	10 0	15 0
12	,,	5d. olive	12 6	15 0
13	,,	6d. claret	15 0	17 6
14	,,	1s. black/*green*	22 6	27 6
15	,,	2s. purple/*blue* (Mar., 1910)	45 0	70 0
16	,,	2s. 6d. red/*blue* (Mar., 1910)	75 0	80 0
17	,,	5s. green/*yell.* (Mar., 1910)	£7	£8

The ½d. and 1d. were issued in 1913 on rather thinner paper and with brownish gum.

3

4

(T **3** and **4**. Typo. De La Rue & Co.)

1913. *Inscribed* "POSTAGE" "POSTAGE". *Wmk. Mult. Crown CA.* *P* 14.

No.	Type	Description	Unused	Used
18	3	½d. green (1 April)	2 0	3 6
19	,,	1d. red (1 April)	5 0	15 0
20	,,	3d. purple/*yell.* (27 Feb.)	6 0	12 6
		a. *On orange-buff*	8 6	17 6
21	,,	11d. dull pur. & scar. (27 Feb.)	12 6	25 0

1914–23. *Inscribed* "POSTAGE" "REVENUE" *Wmk. Mult. Crown CA.* *P* 14.

No.	Type	Description	Unused	Used
22	4	½d. green, O	1 0	3 0
23	,,	½d. yellow-green, O (1917)	1 0	3 0
24	,,	1d. carmine-red, O	1 0	2 0
25	,,	1d. scarlet, O (1917)	2 6	4 6
26	,,	2d. grey, O	4 0	10 0
27	,,	2½d. ultramarine, O	2 6	7 6
28	,,	3d. pur./*p. yell.*, C (Jan., '23)	32 6	50 0
29	,,	4d. black & red/*yellow*, C	15 0	7 6
30	,,	5d. dull pur. & olive-grn., C	10 0	15 0
31	,,	5d. brn.-pur. & olive-grn., C	10 0	15 0
32	,,	6d. dull & bright purple, C	7 6	12 6
33	,,	1s. black/*green*, C	12 6	25 0
		a. *On blue-green, olive back*	12 6	20 0
34	,,	2s. purple & blue/*blue*, C	15 0	20 0
35	,,	2s. 6d. black & red/*blue*, C	17 6	25 0
36	,,	5s. green & red/*yellow*, C	50 0	50 0
		a. *On orange-buff* (1920)	50 0	75 0
37	,,	10s. green and red/*green*, C	£8	£10
38	,,	£1 purple and black/*red*, C	£20	£20

Variations in the coloured papers are mostly due to climate and do not indicate separate printings.

1922–31. *Wmk. Mult. Script CA.* *P* 14.

No.	Type	Description	Unused	Used
39	4	½d. green, O (Oct., 1922)	0 9	2 0
40	,,	1d. scarlet, O (Aug., 1923)	17 6	15 0
41	,,	1d. dull violet, O (1927)	2 0	3 0
42	3	1½d. bright scar., O (1924)	1 6	2 0
43	4	2d. slate-grey, O (Apr., '23)	2 0	5 0
44	,,	3d. pale ultram., O (Nov.'23)	2 0	7 6
45	,,	4d. blk. & red/*yell.*, C ('27)	3 0	7 6
45a	,,	4½d. red-brown, O ('31)	6 0	12 6
46	,,	5d. dull pur. & olive-grn., C	6 0	12 6
47	,,	6d. dull & bright purple, C	6 0	12 6
48	,,	1s. black/*emerald*, C	8 6	15 0
49	,,	2s. pur. & blue/*blue*, C ('27)	12 6	25 0
50	,,	2s. 6d. black & red/*blue*, C	17 6	30 0
51	,,	5s. grn. & red/*pale yell.*, C	27 6	35 0
52	,,	10s. grn. & red/*emer.*, C ('25)	£20	£22

1935 (6 May). *Silver Jubilee. As Nos.* 91/4 *of Antigua.* *P* 13½ × 14.

No.	Description	Unused	Used
53	1½d. deep blue and carmine	1 3	2 0
54	3d. brown and deep blue	7 6	8 6
55	6d. light blue and olive-green	8 6	20 0
56	1s. slate and purple	12 6	12 6

1937 (13 May). *Coronation Issue. As Nos.* 13/15 *of Aden but ptd. by B.W. & Co.* *P* 11 × 11½.

No.	Description	Unused	Used
57	1d. violet	0 8	0 10
58	1½d. carmine	1 0	1 2
59	3d. blue	1 3	1 9

5. Spears and Shield.

6. Native Constable and Chief.

7. Artificial Island, Malaita.

8. Canoe House.

9. Roviana Canoe.

10. Roviana Canoes.

11. Native House, Reef Islands.

12. Coco-nut Plantation.

13. Breadfruit.

14. Tinakula Volcano.

15. Megapodes.

16. Malaita Canoe.

(Recess. De La Rue (2d., 3d., 2s. and 2s. 6d.). Waterlow (others).)

1939 (1 Feb.)–**1951**. *Wmk. Mult. Script CA. P* 13½ *(2d., 3d., 2s. and 2s. 6d.) or* 12½ *(others).*

No.	Type	Description	s.	d.	s.	d.
60	**5**	½d. blue and blue-green ..	0	4	0	8
61	**6**	1d. brown and deep violet	0	6	0	8
62	**7**	1½d. blue-green and carmine	0	8	0	10
63	**8**	2d. orange-brown and black	0	10	1	3
		a. Perf. 12 (7.11.51)	1	0	2	0
64	**9**	2½d. magenta & sage-green	1	0	1	3
		a. Imperf. between (vert. pair)	£350			
65	**10**	3d. black and ultramarine	1	6	2	0
		a. Perf. 12 (29.11.51).. ..	1	3	1	0
66	**11**	4½d. green and chocolate ..	17	6	25	0
67	**12**	6d. deep vio. & reddish pur.	1	3	2	0
68	**13**	1s. green and black ..	2	3	3	0
69	**14**	2s. black and orange ..	4	0	6	0
70	**15**	2s. 6d. black and violet ..	30	0	30	0
71	**16**	5s. emerald-green & scarlet	10	0	12	6
72	**11**	10s. sage-green & magenta (27.4.42)	20	0	25	0

1946 (15 Oct.). *Victory. As Nos.* 28/9 *of Aden.*

No.	Description	s.	d.	s.	d.
73	1½d. carmine	0	6	0	9
74	3d. blue	0	10	1	3

1949 (14 Mar.). *Royal Silver Wedding. As Nos.* 30/1 *of Aden.*

No.	Description	s.	d.	s.	d.
75	2d. black	0	8	0	8
76	10s. magenta	15	0	17	6

1949 (10 Oct.). *75th Anniv. of Universal Postal Union. As Nos.* 114/7 *of Antigua.*

No.	Description	s.	d.	s.	d.
77	2d. red-brown	1	0	1	0
78	3d. deep blue	1	0	1	0
79	5d. deep blue-green	2	6	2	0
80	1s. blue-black	4	0	4	0

1953 (2 June). *Coronation. As No.* 47 *of Aden.*

No.	Description	s.	d.	s.	d.
81	2d. black and grey-black ..	1	0	2	0

17. Ysabel Canoe.

18. Roviana Canoes.

19. Artificial Island, Malaita.

20. Canoe House.

21. Roviana Canoe.

22. Malaita Canoe.

23. Map.

24. Trading Schooner.

25. Henderson Airfield, Guadalcanal.

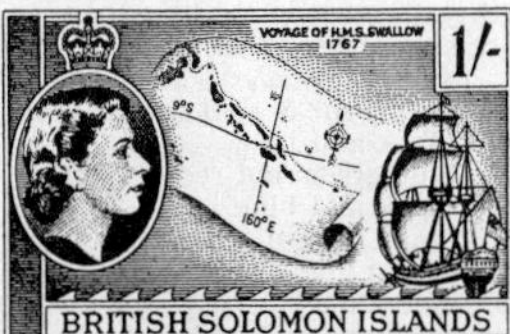

26. Voyage of H.M.S. *Swallow*, 1767.

27. Tinakula Volcano.

28. Native House, Reef Islands.

30. Native Constable and Chief.

29. Mendaña and Ship.

31. Arms of the Protectorate.

(Des. Miss I. R. Stinson (½d.), R. Bailey (2½d.), R. A. Sweet (5d., 1s.), Capt. J. Brett Hilder (6d., 8d., 5s.). Recess. Bradbury, Wilkinson (½d., 2½d., 5d., 6d., 8d., 1s., 5s.), De La Rue & Co. (1d., 2d., 2s.), Waterlow & Sons, (1½d., 3d., 2s. 6d., 10s., £1).)

1956 (1 Mar.)–**60.** *Wmk. Mult. Script CA. P* 12 (*1d., 2d., 2s.*), 13 (*1½d., 3d., 2s. 6d., 10s., £1*) *or* 11½ (*others*).

82 **17** ½d. orange and purple .. 0 3 0 3

83	**18**	1d. yell.-grn. & red-brown	0	4	0	6
84	**19**	1½d. slate-green and carmine-red (*shades*) ..	0	6	0	7
85	**20**	2d. deep brn. & dull green	0	6	0	8
86	**21**	2½d. black and blue ..	0	5	0	7
87	**22**	3d. blue-green and red ..	0	8	0	10
88	**23**	5d. black and blue ..	2	0	2	6
89	**24**	6d. black & turq.-green ..	1	0	1	3
90	**25**	8d. bright blue and black ..	2	0	2	6
90*a*	,,	9d. emerald & blk. (28.1.60)	2	0	2	6
91	**26**	1s. slate and yellow-brown (*shades*)	1	10	2	3
91*a*	**23**	1s. 3d. black and blue (*shades*) (28.1.60) ..	2	0	2	6
92	**27**	2s. black and carmine ..	3	0	4	0
93	**28**	2s. 6d. emerald and bright purple (*shades*) ..	5	0	6	0
94	**29**	5s. red-brown	6	6	8	6
95	**30**	10s. sepia	12	9	19	0
96	**31**	£1 black and blue (5.11.58)	24	0	30	0

32. Frigate Bird.

(Litho. J. Enschedé & Sons.)

1961 (19 JAN.). *New Constitution, 1960.* *W* w.**12.** (*sideways*). *P* 13×12½.

97	**32**	2d. black and turq.-green ..	0	8	0	8
98	,,	3d. black and rose-carmine	0	10	0	11
99	,,	9d. black and reddish purple	1	9	2	0

Nos. 97/9 exist with wmk. showing Crown to right or left of " CA ". *Prices same either way.*

1963 (4 JUNE). *Freedom from Hunger. As No.* 63 *of Aden.*

100	1s. 3d. ultramarine	2	0	2	6

1963 (2 SEPT.). *Red Cross Centenary. As Nos.* 147/8 *of Antigua.*

101	2d. red and black	0	6	0	9
102	9d. red and blue	1	6	1	9

1963–64. *As Nos.* 83, *etc., but wmk.* w.**12.**

103	**18**	1d. yellow-green and red-brown (9.7.64) ..	0	4	0	4
104	**19**	1½d. slate-green and red (9.7.64)	0	4	0	5
105	**20**	2d. deep brown and dull green (9.7.64) ..	0	5	0	6
106	**22**	3d. light blue-green and scarlet (26.11.63) ..	0	6	0	7
107	**24**	6d. black & turq. (7.7.64)	3	6	4	6
108	**25**	9d. emer. & black (7.7.64)	1	1	1	2
109	**23**	1s. 3d. blk. & blue (7.7.64)	5	0	7	6
110	**27**	2s. blk. & carm. (9.7.64)	5	0	10	0
111	**28**	2s. 6d. emerald and reddish purple (9.7.64) ..	10	0	12	6

33. Makira Food Bowl.

34. *Dendrobium veratrifolium* (orchid).

35. Scorpion Shell.

36. Hornbill.

37. Ysabel Shield.

38. Rennellese Club.

39. Moorish Idol.

40. Frigate Bird.

41. *Dendrobium macrophyllum* (orchid).

42. *Dendrobium spectabilis* (orchid).

43. Sanford's Eagle.

44. Malaita Belt.

45. *Ornithoptera victoreae.*

46. White Cockatoo.

47. Western Canoe Figurehead.

(Des. M. C. Farrar Bell. Litho. De La Rue.)

1965 (24 MAY). *W* w.**12**. *P* 13 × 12½.

No.	Type	Description	Unused		Used	
112	**33**	½d. black, deep slate-blue and light blue ..	0	3	0	4
113	**34**	1d. black, orange & yellow	0	5	0	7
114	**35**	1½d. black, blue and yellow-green	0	6	0	7
115	**36**	2d. black, ultramarine and light blue	0	6	0	8
116	**37**	2½d. black, lt. brown and pale yellow-brown ..	0	7	0	9
117	**38**	3d. black, green and light green	0	10	1	0
118	**39**	6d. black, magenta and yellow-orange ..	1	0	1	3
119	**40**	9d. brn'sh blk., dp. bluish green and pale yellow	1	6	1	9
120	**41**	1s. black, chocolate and magenta	2	0	2	6
121	**42**	1s. 3d. black & rose-red	2	6	3	0
122	**43**	2s. black, bright purple and lilac	3	6	4	0
123	**44**	2s. 6d. black, olive-brown and light brown ..	5	0	6	0
124	**45**	5s. black, ultramarine and violet	10	0	12	6
125	**46**	10s. black, olive-green and yellow	17	6	20	0
126	**47**	£1 black, deep reddish violet and pink ..	27	6	30	0

1965 (28 JUNE). *I.T.U. Centenary. As Nos.* 166/7 *of Antigua.*

No.	Description	Unused		Used	
127	2d. orge.-red and turq.-blue	0	6	0	8
128	3d. turq.-blue and olive-brown	0	9	1	0

1965 (25 OCT.). *International Co-operation Year. As Nos.* 168/9 *of Antigua.*

No.	Description	Unused		Used	
129	1d. reddish purple and turquoise-green	0	4	0	6
130	2s. 6d. deep bluish green and lavender	3	9	4	6

1966 (24 JAN.). *Churchill Commemoration. As Nos.* 170/3 *of Antigua.*

No.	Description	Unused		Used	
131	2d. new blue	0	5	0	7
132	9d. deep green	1	1	1	6
133	1s. 3d. brown	1	8	2	3
134	2s. 6d. bluish violet ..	3	3	4	0

(100 cents = $1 Australian.)

≡2c

(48)

1966 (14 Feb.). *Decimal currency. Nos.* 112/26 *variously surch. as T* **48**.

135	1 c. on ½d.	0	2	0	3
136	2 c. on 1d.	0	4	0	5
137	3 c. on 1½d.	0	6	0	8
138	4 c. on 2d.	0	7	0	9
139	5 c. on 6d.	0	9	0	10
140	6 c. on 2½d.	0	10	1	0
141	7 c. on 3d.	0	11	1	2
142	8 c. on 9d.	1	0	1	3
143	10 c. on 1s.	1	3	1	6
144	13 c. on 1s. 3d.	1	6	1	9
145	20 c. on 2s.	2	3	2	9
146	25 c. on 2s. 6d.	2	9	3	3
147	50 c. on 5s. (R.)	5	4	6	0
148	$1 on 10s.	10	6	12	0
149	$2 on £1	21	0	25	0

POSTAGE DUE STAMPS.

D 1

(Typo. Bradbury, Wilkinson.)

1940. *Wmk. Mult. Script CA. P* 12.

D 1	**D 1**	1d. emerald-green ..	0	9	2	0
D 2	,,	2d. scarlet	1	0	2	0
D 3	,,	3d. brown	1	6	2	6
D 4	,,	4d. blue	2	0	3	0
D 5	,,	5d. grey-green ..	2	6	3	6
D 6	,,	6d. purple	3	6	5	0
D 7	,,	1s. violet	6	0	7	6
D 8	,,	1s. 6d. turquoise-green ..	12	6	17	6

BRITISH SOMALILAND.

See SOMALILAND PROTECTORATE

BRITISH SOUTH AFRICA COMPANY.

See RHODESIA.

BRUNEI.

BRUNEI.

BRUNEI.
(1)

TWO CENTS.
(2)

BRUNEI.

25 CENTS.

(3)

1906. *Stamps of Labuan, T* **42** (*Nos.* 116*a, etc.*), *optd. with T* **1**, *or surch. as T* **2** (*the* 25 *c. T* **3**), *in red.*

1	1	c. black and purple	27	6	40	0
		a. Error. Opt. in black ..	£65		£70	
2	2	c. on 3 c. black and sepia ..	8	6	12	6
		a. "BRUNEI" double	£140			
3	2	c. on 8 c. black & vermilion	30	0	45	0
		a. "TWO CENTS" double ..	£225			
		b. "TWO CENTS" omitted in vert. pr. with normal	£225			
4	3	c. black and sepia	30	0	40	0
5	4	c. on 12 c. black and yellow	6	0	12	6
6	5	c. on 16 c. green and brown	25	0	40	0
7	8	c. black and vermilion ..	15	0	25	0
8	10	c. on 16 c. green and brown	10	0	17	6
9	25	c. on 16 c. green and brown	£6		£10	
10	30	c. on 16 c. green and brown	80	0	£5	
11	50	c. on 16 c. green and brown	80	0	£5	
12	1	dol. on 8 c. black & verm. ..	80	0	£6	

PRINTERS
All Brunei stamps from Nos. 14 to 99 were recess-printed by De La Rue & Co. Ltd.

4. View on Brunei River.

1907. *Wmk. Mult. Crown CA. P* 14.

14	**4**	1 c. grey-blk. & pale green	2	6	3	6
15	,,	2 c. grey-black and scarlet	3	6	4	0
16	,,	3 c. grey-blk. and chocolate	5	6	7	6
17	,,	4 c. grey-black and mauve	6	0	7	6
		a. Grey-black and reddish purple	40	0	40	0
18	,,	5 c. grey-black and blue ..	27	6	30	0
19	,,	8 c. grey-black and orange	10	6	20	0
20	,,	10 c. grey-blk. and deep grn.	12	6	10	0
21	,,	25 c. pale blue and ochre-brn.	17	6	25	0
22	,,	30 c. violet and black ..	15	0	20	0
23	,,	50 c. green and deep brown	12	6	25	0
24	,,	$1 red and grey	50	0	55	0

I

II

I. *Double plate.* Lowest line of shading on water is dotted.

II. *Single plate.* Dotted line of shading removed.

Stamps printed in two colours are as I.

1908–12. *Colours changed. Double or single plates Wmk. Mult. Crown CA. P 14.*

24a	4	1 c. green (I)	3 6	4 0
25	,,	1 c. green (II)	1 6	1 0
26	,,	2 c. black and brown (1911)	1 3	1 9
27	,,	3 c. scarlet (I)	2 0	1 9
27a	,,	3 c. scarlet (II)	16 0	17 6
28	,,	4 c. claret (II) (1912)	1 6	1 6
29	,,	5 c. black and orange	3 0	5 0
31	,,	8 c. blue and indigo-blue	4 0	6 0
33	,,	10 c. purple/*yell.* (II) (1912)	4 0	4 0
		a. *On pale yellow*	3 6	4 0
34	,,	25 c. deep lilac (II) (1912)	3 6	4 0
35	,,	30 c. pur. & orge.-yell. (1912)	4 6	7 6
36	,,	50 c. black/*green* (II) (1912)	27 6	50 0
		a. *On blue-green*	15 0	17 6
37	,,	$1 black & red/*blue* (1912)	15 0	20 0
38	,,	$5 carmine/*green* (I)	£5	£6
39	,,	$25 black/*red* (I)	£26	£40

Retouch. Normal.

MALAYA—BORNEO EXHIBITION. 1922.

(5)

Retouches. We list the very distinctive 5 c. Retouch (top left value tablet, 1st row, 8th stamp) but there are others of interest, notably in the clouds.

1916. *Colours changed. Single plates. Wmk. Mult. Crown CA. P 14.*

40	4	5 c. orange	4 6	4 6
		a. "5 c." retouch	£10	£10
41	,,	8 c. ultramarine	6 0	10 0

1922. *Optd. with T* **5**, *in black.*

42	4	1 c. green (II)	5 0	15 0
43	,,	2 c. black and brown	6 0	15 0
44	,,	3 c. scarlet (II)	6 0	30 0
45	,,	4 c. claret (II)	6 0	40 0
46	,,	5 c. orange (II)	10 0	50 0
		a. "5 c." retouch	£20	£30
47	,,	10 c. purple/*yellow* (II)	15 0	60 0
48	,,	25 c. purple (II)	20 0	70 0
49	,,	50 c. black/*blue-green* (II)	60 0	£8
50	,,	$1 black and red/*blue*	60 0	£8

6. Native houses, Brunei Town.

1924–37. *Printed from single plates as Type II, except 30 c. and $1 as Type I. Wmk. Mult. Script CA. P 14.*

51	4	1 c. black ('26)	0 9	0 9
52	,,	2 c. brown	2 3	3 6
52a	,,	2 c. green ('33)	1 0	1 0
53	,,	3 c. green	5 0	5 0
54	,,	4 c. maroon	6 6	4 6
55	,,	4 c. orange ('29)	2 0	2 0
56	,,	5 c. orange-yellow*	3 6	3 6
		a. "5 c." retouch	£15	£15
57	,,	5 c. grey ('31)	6 0	7 6
		a. "5 c." retouch	£35	£35
57b	,,	5 c. chocolate ('33)	1 9	1 9
		c. "5 c." retouch	£8	£8
58	6	6 c. intense black**	5 0	6 0
59	,,	6 c. scarlet ('31)	10 0	15 0
60	4	8 c. ultramarine ('27)	7 6	7 6
60a	4	8 c. grey-black ('33)	3 6	2 6
60b	,,	10 c. purple/*yellow* ('37)	20 0	10 0
61	6	12 c. blue	12 6	12 6
		a. *Pale greenish blue*	£10	£12
62	4	25 c. slate-purple ('31)	7 6	8 6
63	,,	30 c. pur. & orge.-yell. ('31)	10 0	12 0
64	,,	50 c. black/*emer.* ('31)	20 0	25 0
65	,,	$1 blk. & red/*blue* ('31)	35 0	35 0

* For 5 c. orange, see No. 69.

** For 6 c. black, see No. 69*d*. Apart from the difference in shade there is a variation in size, No. 58 being 37¾ mm. long and No. 69*d* 39 mm.

1947 (2 Jan.)–**1951.** *Colours changed and new values. Wmk. Mult. Script CA. P 14.*

66	4	1 c. chocolate	0 3	0 4
67	,,	2 c. grey	0 6	0 6
		a. Perf. 14½ × 13½ (25.9.50)	1 6	2 0
		ab. *Black* (27.6.51)	0 6	2 0
68	6	3 c. green	0 8	0 8
69	4	5 c. orange	0 6	0 6
		a. "5 c." retouch	80 0	80 0
		b. Perf. 14½ × 13½ (25.9.50)	3 0	5 0
		c. Ditto, "5 c." retouch	80 0	80 0
69d	6	6 c. black*	0 6	1 3
70	4	8 c. scarlet	0 9	0 9
		a. Perf. 13 (25.1.51)	1 3	2 6
71	,,	10 c. violet	0 10	0 10
		a. Perf. 14½ × 13½ (25.9.50)	1 3	2 6
72	,,	15 c. ultramarine	1 0	1 0
73	,,	25 c. purple	1 3	1 9
		a. Perf. 14½ × 13½ (25.1.51)	1 9	3 0
74	,,	30 c. black and orange	1 3	1 9
		a. Perf. 14½ × 13½ (25.1.51)	2 6	5 0
75	,,	50 c. black	2 0	3 0
		a. Perf. 13 (25.9.50)	4 0	10 0
76	,,	$1 black and scarlet	4 0	4 6
77	,,	$5 grn. & red-orge. (2.2.48)	20 0	25 0
78	,,	$10 black & purple (2.2.48)	40 0	45 0

* See also No. 58.

7. Sultan Ahmed Tajudin and Brunei Town.

1949 (22 Sept.). *Sultan's Silver Jubilee. Wmk. Mult. Script CA. P 13.*

79	7	8 c. black and carmine	2 6	2 6
80	,,	25 c. purple and red-orange	3 0	3 0
81	,,	50 c. black and blue	4 0	4 6

1949 (10 Oct.). *75th Anniv. of Universal Postal Union. As Nos. 114/7 of Antigua.*

82	8 c. carmine	0 10	0 10
83	15 c. deep blue	1 3	1 3
84	25 c. magenta	1 9	2 0
85	50 c. blue-black	3 6	4 0

8. Sultan Omar Ali Saifuddin.

9. Native houses, Brunei Town.

1952 (1 Mar.). *Wmk. Mult. Script CA.* *P* 13.

No.	Type		s.	d.	s.	d.
86	8	1 c. black	0	2	0	6
87	,,	2 c. black & orange ..	0	3	0	6
88	,,	3 c. black & lake-brown	0	4	0	6
89	,,	4 c. black & green ..	0	4	0	4
90	,,	6 c. black & grey ..	0	5	0	8
91	,,	8 c. blk. & crim. (*shades*)	0	6	0	9
92	,,	10 c. black & sepia ..	0	7	0	10
93	,,	12 c. black & violet ..	0	7	0	10
94	,,	15 c. black & pale blue ..	0	9	0	10
95	,,	25 c. black & pur. (*shades*)	1	1	1	2
96	,,	50 c. blk. & ultram. (*shades*)	2	0	2	3
97	9	$1 blk. & green (*shades*)	3	4	3	6
98	,,	$2 black & scarlet ..	6	6	7	6
99	,,	$5 black & mar. (*shades*)	15	6	16	0

10. Brunei Mosque and Sultan Omar.

(Recess. Bradbury, Wilkinson & Co.)

1958 (24 Sept.). *Opening of Brunei Mosque.* *W* w.**12.** *P* 13½.

No.	Type		s.	d.	s.	d.
100	10	8 c. black & myrtle-grn.	0	10	1	0
101	,,	15 c. black and carmine ..	1	6	1	9
102	,,	35 c. black and deep lilac	3	0	3	6

11. " Protein Foods ".

(Des. M. Goaman. Photo. Harrison.)

1963 (4 June). *Freedom from Hunger.* *W* w.**12.** *P* 14 × 14½.

No.	Type		s.	d.	s.	d.
103	11	12 c. sepia	1	6	1	9

1964. *As Nos.* 86, *etc. but wmk.* w.**12.**

No.	Type		s.	d.	s.	d.
104	8	1 c. black (17.3) ..	0	1	0	2
105	,,	2 c. black & orange (17.3)	0	2	0	2
106	,,	3 c. black and lake brown (10.11)	0	3	0	3
107	,,	4 c. black & green (12.5) ..	0	3	0	3
108	,,	6 c. black & grey (12.5) ..	0	4	0	5
109	,,	8 c. black & crimson-lake (12.5)	0	5	0	6
110	8	10 c. black and sepia (12.5)	0	6	0	7
111	,,	12 c. black & violet (12.5) ..	0	6	0	8
112	,,	15 c. black & p. blue (12.5)	0	7	0	8
113	,,	25 c. black & purple (12.5)	0	11	1	0
114	,,	50 c. blk. & ultram. (10.11)	1	8	1	10

12. I.T.U. Emblem.

(Des. M. Goaman. Litho. Enschedé.)

1965 (17 May). *I.T.U. Centenary.* *W* w.**12.** *P* 11 × 11½.

No.		s.	d.	s.	d.
118	4 c. mauve & orange-brown	0	6	0	8
119	75 c. orge.-yell. & lt. emerald	3	9	4	6

13. I.C.Y. Emblem.

(Des. V. Whiteley. Litho. Harrison.)

1965 (25 Oct.). *International Co-operation Year.* *W* w.**12.** *P* 14.

No.	Type		s.	d.	s.	d.
120	13	4 c. reddish purple and turquoise-green ..	0	6	0	8
121	,,	15 c. deep bluish green and lavender	1	0	1	3

14. Sir Winston Churchill and St. Paul's Cathedral in Wartime.

(Des. Jennifer Toombs. Photo. Harrison.)

1966 (24 Jan.). *Churchill Commemoration.* *W* w.**12.** *P* 14.

No.	Type		s.	d.	s.	d.
122	14	3 c. black, cerise, gold and new blue	0	4	0	6
123	,,	10 c. black, cerise, gold and deep green	0	7	0	9
124	,,	15 c. black, cerise, gold and brown	0	9	1	0
125	,,	75 c. black, cerise, gold and bluish violet	3	0	3	6

JAPANESE OCCUPATION OF BRUNEI.

Stamps listed under this heading were valid in Brunei, Labuan, North Borneo and Sarawak.

府政國帝本日大

("Imperial Japanese Government")

(1)

1942–45. *Stamps of Brunei handstamped with T* **1** *in violet to blue. Wmk. Mult. Script CA (except Nos.* J16/17, *Mult. Crown CA).* P 14.

No.	Type	Description	Unused		Used	
J 1	**4**	1 c. black..	5	0	7	6
J 2	,,	2 c. green..	75	0		£6
J 3	,,	2 c. orange ('45).. ..	4	6	6	0
J 4	,,	3 c. green..	50	0	80	0
J 5	,,	4 c. orange	6	0	7	6
J 6	,,	5 c. chocolate	5	0	7	6
		aa. "5 c." retouch	£22			
J 6*a*	**6**	6 c. greenish grey (*p.* 14×11½)	90	0		£5
J 6*b*	,,	6 c. scarlet	£30		£40	
J 7	**4**	8 c. grey-black	£25		£30	
J 8	**6**	8 c. red	3	6	4	6
J 9	**4**	10 c. purple/*yellow* ..	7	6	8	6
J10	**6**	12 c. blue	7	6	8	6
J11	,,	15 c. ultramarine ('45) ..	7	6	10	0
J12	**4**	25 c. slate-purple	25	0	30	0
J13	,,	30 c. purple & orge.-yell.	£8		£10	
J14	,,	50 c. black/*emerald* ..	27	6	30	0
J15	,,	$1 black & red/*blue* ..	32	6	35	0
J16	,,	$5 carmine/*green* ..	£22			
J17	,,	$25 black/*red*	£40			

The overprint varies in shade from violet to blue, and, being handstamped, exists double and treble.

Nos. 3, 8 and 11 were not issued without the overprint.

便郵國帝

(2)

1944. *No.* 51 *of Brunei surch. with T* 2 (*"Imperial Japanese Post* $3") *in orange-red.*

No.	Type	Description	Unused
J18	**4**	$3 on 1 c. black	£60

BURMA.
(BRITISH DOMINION.)

BURMA (1) BURMA (1*a*)

1937 (1 April). *Stamps of India (King George V inscr.* "INDIA POSTAGE") *optd. with T* **1** *or* **1***a* (*rupee values*). *W* **69.** *P* 14.

No.	Description	Unused		Used	
1	3 p. slate	0	6	0	6
2	½ a. green	0	6	0	6
3	9 p. deep green	1	0	0	9
4	1 a. chocolate	1	0	0	4
5	2 a. vermilion (*small die*) ..	1	0	0	6
6	2½ a. orange	1	6	0	8
7	3 a. carmine	3	0	2	6
8	3½ a. deep blue	3	0	2	6
	a. Dull blue	22	6	25	0
9	4 a. sage-green	3	6	1	0
10	6 a. bistre	3	0	2	0
11	8 a. reddish purple	3	6	2	0
12	12 a. claret	4	0	5	0
13	1 r. chocolate and green ..	6	0	3	0
14	2 r. carmine and orange ..	15	0	5	0
15	5 r. ultramarine and purple	35	0	25	0
16	10 r. green and scarlet ..	50	0	35	0
17	15 r. blue and olive	£10			£6
18	25 r. orange and blue ..	£15			£12

The opt. is at top on all values except the 3 a.

2. King George VI and "Chinthes".

3. King George VI and "Nagas".

4. Royal Barge.

5. Burma Teak.

6. Burma Rice.

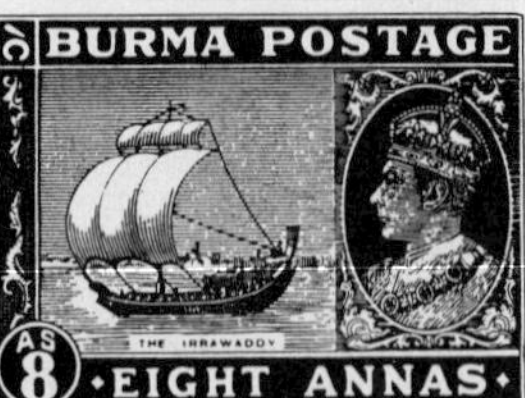

7. R. Irrawaddy.

8. King George VI and Peacock.

9. King George VI and " Nats ".

10. Elephants' Heads.

(Des. Maung Kyi (*T* **4**), Maung Hline (*T* **5**), Maung Ohn Pe (*T* **6**) and N. K. D. Naigamwalla (*T* **7**). Offset-litho. Security Ptg. Press, Nasik.)

1938 (15 Nov.)–**40.** *W* **10.** *P* 14 (*vert.*) *or* 13½ × 13 (*horiz.*).

No.	Type	Description	Unused	Used
18*a*	**2**	1 p. red-orange (1.8.40) ..	0 4	3 0
19	,,	3 p. bright violet	0 10	0 6
20	,,	6 p. bright blue	1 0	0 4
21	,,	9 p. yellow-green	2 0	3 0
22	**3**	1 a. purple-brown.. ..	1 0	0 6
23	,,	1½ a. turquoise-green ..	1 9	1 3
24	,,	2 a. carmine	2 0	0 9
25	**4**	2 a. 6 p. claret	3 0	2 6
26	**5**	3 a. dull violet	5 0	4 0
27	**6**	3 a. 6 p. light blue and blue	10 0	15 0
28	**3**	4 a. greenish blue	3 6	2 6
29	**7**	8 a. myrtle-green	5 0	4 0
30	**8**	1 r. purple and blue ..	10 6	5 0
31	,,	2 r. brown and purple ..	20 0	8 6
32	**9**	5 r. violet and scarlet ..	70 0	45 0
33	,,	10 r. brown and myrtle ..	£7	£6

The 1 a. exists offset-lithographed and typographed, the latter having a " Jubilee " line in the sheet margin.

COMMEMORATION
POSTAGE STAMP
6th MAY 1840

(11)

1940 (6 May.). *Centenary of First Adhesive Postage Stamps. No.* 25 *surch. with T* **11.**

No.	Type	Description	Unused	Used
34	**4**	1 a. on 2 a. 6 p. claret ..	12 6	10 0

British Military Administration.

MILY ADMN (**12**) MILY ADMN (**13**)

1945. *Nos.* 18*a to* 33, *optd. with T* **12** (*small stamps*) *or* **13** (*others*).

No.	Type	Description	Unused	Used
35	**2**	1 p. red-orange	0 3	0 3
36	,,	3 p. bright violet	0 3	0 3
37	,,	6 p. bright blue	0 3	0 4
38	,,	9 p. yellow-green	0 3	0 5
39	**3**	1 a. purple-brown	0 3	0 4
40	,,	1½ a. turquoise-green ..	0 4	0 6
41	,,	2 a. carmine	0 5	0 6
42	**4**	2 a. 6 p. claret	0 6	0 8
43	**5**	3 a. dull violet	0 6	1 0
44	**6**	3 a. 6 p. light blue and blue	1 0	1 0
45	**3**	4 a. greenish blue	1 0	1 3
46	**7**	8 a. myrtle-green	1 3	1 6
47	**8**	1 r. purple and blue ..	2 0	2 6
48	,,	2 r. brown and purple ..	4 0	5 0
49	**9**	5 r. violet and scarlet ..	10 0	10 6
50	,,	10 r. brown and myrtle ..	19 6	20 0

Civil Administration.

1946 (1 Jan.). *Colours changed.*

No.	Type	Description	Unused	Used
51	**2**	3 p. brown	0 3	0 3
52	,,	6 p. deep violet	0 3	0 3
53	,,	9 p. green	0 3	0 3
54	**3**	1 a. blue	0 6	0 6
55	,,	1½ a. orange	0 4	0 3
56	,,	2 a. claret	0 5	0 4
57	**4**	2 a. 6 p. greenish blue ..	0 6	0 6
57*a*	**5**	3 a. blue-violet	1 0	1 0
57*b*	**6**	3 a. 6 p. black and ultram.	1 0	1 0
58	**3**	4 a. purple..	0 9	1 0
59	**7**	8 a. maroon	1 6	2 0
60	**8**	1 r. violet and maroon ..	2 6	1 6
61	,,	2 r. brown and orange ..	5 0	4 6
62	**9**	5 r. green and brown ..	15 0	12 6
63	,,	10 r. claret and violet ..	25 0	27 6

14. Burman.

15. Burmese Woman.

16. Chinthe.

17. Elephant.

(Des. A. G. I. McGeogh. Offset-litho, Nasik.)

1946 (2 May). *Victory. P* 13. *W* **10** *sideways.*

No.	Type	Description				
64	**14**	9 p. turquoise-green.	0	6	0	9
65	**15**	1½ a. violet	0	8	0	10
66	**16**	2 a. carmine	0	10	1	0
67	**17**	3 a. 6 p. ultramarine	1	0	1	6

Interim Burmese Government.

ကြားဖြတ်
အစိုးရ။

(**18.** *Trans.* "Interim Government.")

1947 (1 Oct.). *Stamps of* 1946 *optd. with T* **18** (*small stamps*) *or larger opt.* (*others*).

No.	Type	Description				
68	**2**	3 p. brown	0	3	0	3
69	,,	6 p. deep violet	0	3	0	3
70	,,	9 p. green	0	3	0	3
		a. Overprint inverted	60	0	60	0
71	**3**	1 a. blue	0	4	0	4
72	,,	1½ a. orange	0	4	0	4
73	,,	2 a. claret	0	5	0	4
74	**4**	2 a. 6 p. greenish blue	0	8	0	6
75	**5**	3 a. blue-violet	0	8	0	6
76	**6**	3 a. 6 p. black and ultram.	0	10	0	8
77	**3**	4 a. purple	0	8	0	6
78	**7**	8 a. maroon	1	3	1	6
79	**8**	1 r. violet and maroon	2	6	2	0
80	,,	2 r. brown and orange	5	0	4	0
81	**9**	5 r. green and brown	12	6	10	0
82	,,	10 r. claret and violet	20	0	20	0

OFFICIAL STAMPS.

BURMA

SERVICE

(O 1)

BURMA

SERVICE

(O 1*a*)

1937 (Apr.–June). *Stamps of India* (*King George V inscr.* "india postage") *optd. with Type* O **1** *or* O **1a** (*rupee values*). *W* **69.** *P* 14.

O 1	3 p. slate	0	4	0	3
O 2	½ a. green	2	6	0	3
O 3	9 p. deep green	1	6	0	6
O 4	1 a. chocolate	1	6	0	3
O 5	2 a. vermilion (*small die*)	1	6	0	6
O 6	2½ a. orange	2	0	2	0
O 7	4 a. sage-green	2	0	0	8
O 8	6 a. bistre	6	0	4	0
O 9	8 a. reddish purple (1.4.37)	3	6	2	0
O10	12 a. claret (1.4.37)	6	0	5	0
O11	1 r. choc. and green (1.4.37)	6	0	4	0
O12	2 r. carmine and orange	15	0	12	6
O13	5 r. ultramarine and purple	40	0	35	0
O14	10 r. green and scarlet	75	0	70	0

The bulk of the above issue was overprinted "burma" and "service" by offset-lithography at one operation; but a certain quantity of some values was overprinted at two operations.

SERVICE

(O 2)

SERVICE

(O 3)

1939. *Nos.* 19 *to* 24 *and* 28 *optd. with Type* O **2** (*typo.*) *and Nos.* 25 *and* 29 *to* 33 *optd. with Type* O **3** (*offset-litho.*).

No.	Type	Description				
O15	**2**	3 p. bright violet	0	6	0	3
O16	,,	6 p. bright blue	0	9	0	3
O17	,,	9 p. yellow-green	1	0	0	6
O18	**3**	1 a. purple-brown	1	0	0	3
O19	,,	1½ a. turquoise-green	2	0	0	6
O20	,,	2 a. carmine	1	6	0	3
O21	**4**	2 a. 6 p. claret	6	0	4	0
O22	**3**	4 a. greenish blue	5	0	0	10
O23	**7**	8 a. myrtle-green	7	6	5	0
O24	**8**	1 r. purple and blue	10	0	6	0
O25	,,	2 r. brown and purple	20	0	12	6
O26	**9**	5 r. violet and scarlet	40	0	25	0
O27	,,	10 r. brown and myrtle	80	0	65	0

Civil Administration.

1946. *Civil Administration. Nos.* 51 *to* 56 *and* 58 *optd. with Type* O **2** (*typo.*) *and Nos.* 57 *and* 59 *to* 63 *optd. with Type* O **3** (*offset-litho.*).

No.	Type	Description				
O28	**2**	3 p. brown	0	3	0	6
O29	,,	6 p. deep violet	0	3	0	3
O30	,,	9 p. green	0	3	0	6
O31	**3**	1 a. blue	0	3	0	3
O32	,,	1½ a. orange	0	4	0	4
O33	,,	2 a. claret	0	5	0	4
O34	**4**	2 a. 6 p. greenish blue	0	8	1	3
O35	**3**	4 a. purple	0	8	0	8
O36	**7**	8 a. maroon	1	3	1	6
O37	**8**	1 r. violet and maroon	2	0	1	6
O38	,,	2 r. brown and orange	4	0	5	6
O39	**9**	5 r. green and brown	10	0	17	6
O40	,,	10 r. claret and violet	20	0	27	6

Interim Burmese Government.

1947. *Interim Government. Nos.* O28 *to* O40 *optd. with T* **18** (*small stamps*) *or larger opt.* (*others*).

No.	Type	Description				
O41	**2**	3 p. brown	0	3	0	4
O42	,,	6 p. deep violet	0	3	0	4
O43	,,	9 p. green	0	4	0	6
O44	**3**	1 a. blue	0	10	0	3
O45	,,	1½ a. orange	1	0	0	3
O46	,,	2 a. claret	1	0	0	3
O47	**4**	2 a. 6 p. greenish blue	1	3	1	6
O48	**3**	4 a. purple	1	6	0	10
O49	**7**	8 a. maroon	2	0	1	0
O50	**8**	1 r. violet and maroon	4	0	3	6
O51	,,	2 r. brown and orange	7	0	6	0
O52	**9**	5 r. green and brown	12	6	17	6
O53	,,	10 r. claret and violet	25	0	27	6

For stamps of the independent Republic of Burma, see Part III of this Catalogue.

JAPANESE OCCUPATION OF BURMA.

(MARCH 1942 to MARCH 1945.)

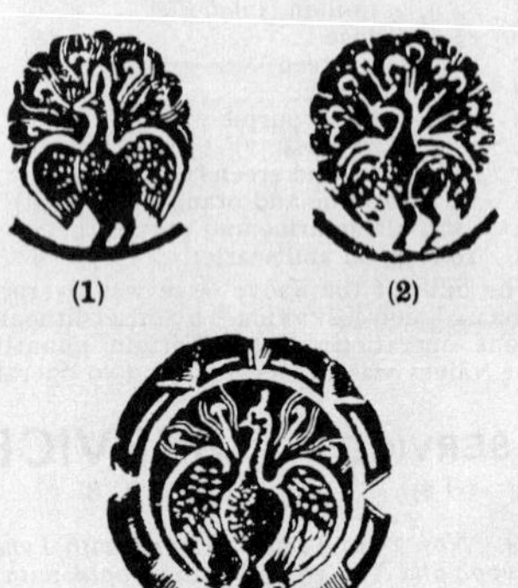

(1) (2) (3)

(For notes on overprint types see after No. J44.)

1942 (MAY). *Stamps of Burma overprinted with the national device of a Peacock.*

I. *Overprinted at Myaungmya.*

A. *With Type* **1** *in black.*

On Postage Stamps of King George V.

J 1		9 p. deep green (No. 3) ..	£6	
J 2		3½ a. deep blue (No. 8) ..	60 0	

On Official Stamp of King George V.

J 3		6 a. bistre (No. O8)	£6	

On Postage Stamps of King George VI.

J 4	**2**	9 p. yellow-green ..	£15	
J 5	**3**	1 a. purple-brown ..	£40	
J 6	,,	4 a. greenish blue (opt. black on red) ..	£10	
		a. Triple opt., black on double red	£35	

On Official Stamps of King George VI.

J 7	**2**	3 p. bright violet ..	30 0	60 0
J 8	,,	6 p. bright blue	10 0	30 0
J 9	**3**	1 a. purple-brown ..	10 0	30 0
J 9*a*	,,	1½ a. turquoise green ..	£40	
J10	,,	2 a. carmine	35 0	
J11	,,	4 a. greenish blue ..	25 0	35 0

The overprint on No. J6 was apparently first done in red, in error, and was then corrected by the application of the overprint in black. Some stamps have the black overprint so accurately superimposed that the red hardly shows. These are rare.

Nos. J5 and J9 exist with the Peacock overprint on both the typographed and the offset printings of the original stamps.

B. *With Types* **2** *or* **3** (*rupee values*), *in black.*

On Postage Stamps of King George VI.

J12	**2**	3 p. bright violet	20 0	80 0
J13	,,	6 p. bright blue	40 0	
J14	,,	9 p. yellow-green ..	20 0	60 0
J15	**3**	1 a. purple-brown.. ..	10 0	25 0
J16	,,	2 a. carmine	15 0	30 0
J17	,,	4 a. greenish blue ..	25 0	
		a. Opt. double		
		b. Opt. inverted	£30	
		c. Opt. double, one inverted..	£30	
		d. Opt. double, both inverted	£30	
J18	**8**	1 r. purple and blue ..	£24	
J19	,,	2 r. brown and purple ..	£16	

4

II. *Overprinted* (*at Pyapon?*) *with T* **4**, *in black* (*so-called experimental type*).

On Postage Stamps of King George VI.

J19*a*	**3**	1 a. purple-brown ..	£20	
J20	,,	2 a. carmine	£12	
		a. Opt. double		
J21	,,	4 a. greenish blue ..	£40	
		a. Opt. double		

Unused specimens of these stamps are usually in poor condition.

(5) (6)

III. *Overprinted at Henzada with T* **5** *in blue, or blue-black.*

On Postage Stamps of King George V.

J22		3 p. slate (No. 1)	4 0	10 0
		a. Opt. double..	25 0	40 0
J23		9 p. deep green (No. 3) ..	30 0	60 0
		a. Opt. double..	£5	
J24		2 a. vermilion (No. 5) ..	£9	£15

On Postage Stamps of King George VI.

J25	**2**	1 p. red-orange	£12	£20
J26	,,	3 p. bright violet ..	60 0	£6
J27	,,	6 p. bright blue	30 0	£5
		a. Opt. double	£8	
		b. Clear opt., on back and front	£25	
J28	,,	9 p. yellow-green ..	£35	
J29	**3**	1 a. purple-brown ..	15 0	30 0
		a. Opt. inverted	£10	
J30	,,	1½ a. turquoise-green ..	25 0	60 0
J31	,,	2 a. carmine	25 0	50 0
J32	,,	4 a. greenish blue ..	80 0	£6
		a. Opt. double	£10	
		b. Opt. inverted		

On Official Stamps of King George VI.

J33	**2**	3 p. bright violet ..	£7	£12
J34	,,	6 p. bright blue	£5	£10
J35	**3**	1½ a. turquoise-green ..	£9	£15
J35*a*	,,	2 a. carmine	£25	£25
J36	,,	4 a. greenish blue ..	£40	

Type **6** was officially applied only to postal stationery. However, the handstamp remained in the possession of a postal official who used it on postage stamps after the war. These stamps are no longer listed.

(6*a*)

(" Yon Thon " = " Office use ".)

IV. *Official Stamp of King George VI optd. at Myaungmya with Type* **6a** *in black.*

J44 **7** 8 a. myrtle-green £10

No. J44 was probably for official use.

There are two types of T **6a**, one with base of peacock 8 mm. long and the other with base about 5 mm. long. The neck and other details also vary. The two types are found *se tenant* in the sheet.

The Peacock overprints were applied to Burmese stamps by authority of the Japanese Army and the Burma Independence Army, and were on sale at post offices in the Delta area. Stocks were withdrawn about the middle of August, 1942.

Postage and Official stamps, thus overprinted, were used indiscriminately for ordinary postal purposes, with the probable exception of No. J44.

The Myaungmya overprints are usually clearly printed, and, with the exception of the 4 a. No. J6, always in black.

The Henzada overprints (except Type **6**) are usually in blue or blue-black, the blue sometimes having a violet tone. They generally show the details of the Peacock much less clearly and, due to heavy inking, or careless impression, sometimes appear as almost solid colour.

DISTINGUISHING FEATURES. Type **1**. Body and head of Peacock always clearly outlined by broad uncoloured band.

Type **2**. Peacock with slender neck and more delicately detailed tail. Clear spur on leg at right. Heavy fist-shaped blob of ink below and parallel to beak and neck.

Type **4**. No basic curve. Each feather separately outlined. Straight, short legs.

Type **5**. Much fine detail in wings and tail in clearly printed overprints. Thin, long legs ending in claws which, with the basic arc, enclose clear white spaces in well-printed copies. Blob of colour below beak shows shaded detail and never has the heavy fist-like appearance of this portion in Type **2**.

Two sub-types may be distinguished in T pe **5**, the basic arc of one having a chord of 14–15 mm. and the other 12½–13 mm.

Type **6**. Similar to Type **5**, but with arc deeply curved and reaching nearly to the top of the wings. Single diagonal line parallel to neck below beak.

Collectors are warned against forgeries of these overprints, often in the wrong colours or on the wrong values.

7

1942 (1 JUNE). *Impressed by hand.* P 12 × 11. *No gum.*

J45 **7** (No value) red £6 £9

This device was the personal seal of S. Yano, the Japanese official in charge of postal affairs. Some stamps show part of the papermaker's watermark, either " ABSORBO DUPLICATOR " or " ELEPHANT BRAND ", each with an elephant

8. Farmer.

(Typo. Rangoon.)

1942 (15 JUNE). *Value in annas.* P 11 × 11½. *Laid bâtonné paper. No gum.*

J46 **8** 1 a. scarlet 70 0 80 0

(**9**) (**10**)

1942 (22 SEPT.). *Contemporary Japanese stamps (Cat. Nos. in brackets) surch. as T* **9/10**.

J47 **9** ¼ a. on 1 s. chestnut (382) 50 0 70 0
a. Surch. inverted £15 £15
J48 ,, ½ a. on 2 s. scarlet (383) .. 50 0 80 0
a. Surch. inverted £8
b. Surch. double, inverted .. £20
J49 ,, ¾ a. on 3 s. green (384) .. 80 0
a. Surch. inverted £15 £15
b. Surch. double, one inverted — £20
J50 ,, 1 a. on 5 s. claret (409) .. 80 0 £6
a. Surch. inverted £12 £12
b. Surch. double, one inverted — £16
c. Surch. omitted (in pair with normal) .. .. — £15
J51 ,, 3 a. on 7 s. green ((388) .. £5 £6
a. Surch. inverted £12
J52 ,, 4 a. on 4 s. green (385) .. £5 £6
a. Surch. inv rted £15
J53 ,, 8 a. on 8 s. violet (389) .. £20 £25
a. Surch. inverted £25 £30
b. Surch. double, one inverted £50
c. Surch. in red £30 £35
d. Red surch. inverted .. £60
J54 **10** 1 r. on 10 s. lake (390) .. 60 0 70 0
a. Surch. inverted .. .. — £10
b. Surch. double .. ..
c. Surch. double (black and red) £18
d. Surch. omitted (in pair with normal) .. .. — £20
J55 ,, 2 r. on 20 s. ultram. (393) £6 £6
a. Surch. inverted £12 £15
b. Surch. double, inverted .. £12
c. Surch. omitted (in pair with normal black surch.). . £15 £15
d. Surch. in red £6 £6
e. Red surch. inverted .. £12
f. Red surch. double .. £25
g. Surch. omitted (in pair with normal red surch.) .. — £15
J56 ,, 5 r. on 30 s. blue-grn. (395) 40 0 45 0
a. Surch. inverted £40
b. Surch. double .. ..
c. Surch. in red 70 0 80 0
d. Red surch. inverted .. £12 £10
J56a and J56c se-tenant .. — £45
f. Surch. omitted (in pair with normal red surch.) .. — £15

Japanese stamp with vertical red opt. commemorating the fall of Singapore, similarly surcharged.

J56g **9** 4 a. on 4+2 s. green (C125) £10 £12
h. Surch. omitted (in pair with normal) £100

Currency changed. 100 cents=1 rupee.

15 C. 15 C.

(11) (12)

1942 (15 Oct.). *Previous issues, with "anna" surcharges obliterated, and handstamped with new value in cents, as T* **11** *and* **12** (*No.* J 57 *handstamped with new value only.*)

(*a*) *T* **8** (Farmer).

J57 **5 c. on 1 a. scarlet 45 0 60 0**

(*b*) *Contemporary Japanese issues.*

J58 1 c. on ½ a. on 1 s. (J47) .. £6 £6
a. "1 c." omitted in pair with normal .. ..
J59 2 c. on ½ a. on 2 s. (J48) .. £6 £6
J60 3 c. on ¾ a. on 3 s. (J49) .. £6 £6
a. Surch. in blue .. ..
J61 5 c. on 1 a. on 5 s. (J50) .. £6
J62 10 c. on 3 a. on 7 s. (J51) .. £8 £8
J63 15 c. on 4 a. on 4 s. (J52) .. 60 0 70 0
J64 20 c. on 8 a. on 8 s. (J53) .. £12 £15
a. 20 c. on 8 a. (R.) on 8 s. (J 53a) — £25

The "anna" surcharges were obliterated by any means available, in some cases by a bar or bars, and in others by the butt of a pencil dipped in ink. In the case of the fractional surcharges, the letter "A" and one figure of the fraction, were sometimes barred out, leaving the remainder of the fraction to represent the new value, e.g. the "1" of "½" deleted to create the 2 c. surcharge or the "4" of "¾" to create the 3 c. surcharge.

15 C.

(13)

1942. *Contemporary stamps of Japan* (*Cat. Nos. in brackets*) *surcharged in cents only, as T* **13**.

J65 1 c. on 1 s. chestnut (382) 50 0 60 0
a. Surch. inverted £6 £6
J66 2 c. on 2 s. scarlet (383) .. 60 0 70 0
J67 3 c. on 3 s. green (384) .. £5 £6
a. Surch. in blue £20 £25
b. Surch. in blue (inverted) .. £40 £50
J68 5 c. on 5 s. claret (409) .. £5 £6
a. Surch. in violet £25
b. Surch. in violet (inverted) — £15
J69 10 c. on 7 s. green (388) .. £5 £6
J70 15 c. on 4 s. green (385) 60 0 65 0
a. Surch. inverted £10 £12
J71 20 c. on 8 s. violet (389) £12 £12

Nos. J67*a* and J68*a* were issued for use in the Shan States

14. Burma State Crest.

1943 (15 Feb.). *P* 11. *No gum.*

J72 **14** 5 c. scarlet 50 0 80 0
a. Imperf.. .. .. 50 0 70 0
b. Printed both sides .. £20

This stamp was usually sold affixed to envelopes, particularly those with the embossed 1 a. King George VI stamp, which it covered. Unused specimens off cover are rarely met with and blocks are very rare.

15. Farmer.

1943. *P* 11½. *No gum.*

J73 **15** 1 c. orange (22 Mar.) 2 6 6 0
a. Brown-orange .. 4 0 8 0
J74 ,, 2 c. yellow-grn. (24 Mar.) 2 6 5 0
a. Blue-green .. 12 6
J75 ,, 3 c. light blue (25 Mar.) 2 6
a. On laid paper .. 40 0 60 0
J76 ,, 5 c. carmine (small "c") (17 Mar.) 20 0 30 0
J77 ,, 5 c. carmine (large "C") 1 9 3 0
a. Imperf. (pair) ..
J78 ,, 10 c. grey-brown (25 Mar.) 6 0 10 0
a. Imperf. (pair) .. £9
J79 ,, 15 c. magenta (26 Mar.) 0 3 6 0
a. On laid paper .. 40 0 60 0
b. Reversed "C" in value £20 £30
J80 ,, 20 c. grey-lilac (29 Mar.) 0 3 6 6
J81 ,, 30 c. deep blue-green (29 Mar.) 0 3 7 6

The 1 c., 2 c. and 3 c. have large "C" in value as illustrated. The 10 c. and higher values have small "c". Owing to hurried printing and the method of make-up (the different values being plugged in individually to the same basic plate) numerous varieties may be found in the values, e.g. missing stops and different types of figure or "c".

There are marked varieties of shade in this issue.

Imperf. stamps come from a proof sheet.

16. Soldier carving word "Independence". **17.** Rejoicing peasant.

18. Boy with national flag.

Des. Mg. Ba Thit (**16**), Mg. Ohn Maung (**17**), and Mg. Sol. Yi (**18**). Typo. Govt. Press, Rangoon.)

1943 (1 Aug.). *Independence Day*. (*a*) *Perf*. 11.

J82	**16**	1 c. orange	.. ..	10	0	20	0
J83	**17**	3 c. light blue	.. ..	20	0	25	0
J84	**18**	5 c. carmine	.. ..	20	0	25	0

(*b*) *Rouletted*.

J82*a*	**16**	1 c. orange	.. ..	5	0	8	6
J83*a*	**17**	3 c. light blue	.. ..	5	0	8	6
J84*a*	**18**	5 c. carmine	.. ..	5	0	8	6
		aa. Horiz. roulette omitted (vert. pair)	..				

(*c*) *Perf.* × *rouletted*.

J82*b*	**16**	1 c. orange	.. ..
J83*b*	**17**	3 c. light blue	.. ..
J84*b*	**18**	5 c. carmine	.. ..

(*d*) *Imperf*. (*pairs*).

J82*c*	**16**	1 c. orange	.. ..	£20	£25
J83*c*	**17**	3 c. light blue	.. ..	£20	£25
J84*c*	**18**	5 c. carmine	.. ..	£20	£25

The stamps perf. × rouletted may have one, two, or three sides perforated. They are scarce.

The rouletted stamps often appear to be roughly perforated owing to failure to make clean cuts. These apparent perforations are very small and quite unlike the large, clean holes of the stamps perforated 11.

A few imperforate sets, mounted on a special card folder and cancelled with the commemorative postmark were presented to officials. These are rare.

19. Burmese woman. **20.** Elephant carrying log.

21. Watch Tower, Mandalay.

(Typo. G. Kolff & Co., Batavia.)

1943 (1 Oct.). *P* 12½.

J85	**19**	1 c. red-orange ..	.. ..	8	0	15	0
J86	,,	2 c. yellow-green	.. ..	0	3	5	0
J87	,,	3 c. deep violet ..	.. ..	1	9	2	0
		a. Bright violet	.. ..	2	6	3	6
J88	**20**	5 c. carmine	.. ..	0	3	2	0
J89	,,	10 c. blue	.. ..	1	6	2	0
J90	,,	15 c. red-orange	.. ..	0	3	2	0
J91	,,	20 c. yellow-green	.. ..	0	4	5	0
J92	,,	30 c. olive-brown	.. ..	0	4	5	0
J93	**21**	1 r. red-orange ..	.. ..	0	8	6	6
J94	,,	2 r. bright violet	.. ..	1	0	7	6

22. Bullock Cart. **23.** Shan Woman.

1943. *P* 12½.

J 95	**22**	1 c. olive-brown	..	6	6
J 96	,,	2 c. yellow-green	..	6	6
J 97	,,	3 c. bright violet	..	11	0
J 98	,,	5 c. ultramarine	..	2	6
J 99	**23**	10 c. blue	..	4	6
J100	,,	20 c. carmine	..	4	6
J101	,,	30 c. olive-brown	..	5	0

The above series was for use in the Shan States. These states came under the administration of the Burmese Government on 24th December, 1943, and the stamps were later overprinted as below for use throughout Burma.

ဗမာနိုင်ငံတော်

၂၀ ဆင့်

(**24.** " Burma State " and value.)

1944 (1 Nov.). *Optd. as T* **24** (*the lower characters differ for each value*).

J102	**22**	1 c. olive-brown	..	4	0	6	6
J103	,,	2 c. yellow-green	..	0	4	4	0
		a. Opt. inverted ..	..	£50			
J104	,,	3 c. bright violet	..	3	0	6	6
J105	,,	5 c. ultramarine	..	1	6	2	6
J106	**23**	10 c. blue ..	..	3	0	5	0
J107	,,	20 c. carmine	..	0	4	6	0
J108	,,	30 c. olive-brown	..	0	4	6	0

BUSHIRE.
(BRITISH OCCUPATION.)

BUSHIRE
Under British Occupation.
(1)

1915 (15 Aug.). *Nos.* 503 *etc. of Persia* (*portrait*) *optd. with T* **1**.

1	1 ch. orange and green	..	20	0	17	6
	a. No stop ..	..	60	0	60	0
2	2 ch. sepia and carmine	..	20	0	17	6
	a. No stop	..	60	0	60	0
3	3 ch. green and grey	..	20	0	17	6
	a. No stop	..	65	0	65	0
4	5 ch. carmine and brown	..	£10		£8	
5	6 ch. lake and green ..	..	30	0	25	0
	a. No stop ..	..	70	0	60	0
6	9 ch. indigo-lilac and brown		30	0	25	0
	a. No stop	..	60	0	50	0
	b. Opt. double					
7	10 ch. brown and carmine	..	35	0	30	0
	a. No stop ..	..	70	0	60	0
8	12 ch. blue and green	..	45	0	40	0
	a. No stop ..	..	90	0	80	0
9	24 ch. green and purple	..	45	0	40	0
	a. No stop ..	..	90	0	80	0
10	1 kr. carmine and blue	..	45	0	40	0
	a. Double overprint ..	..				
	b. No stop ..	..	90	0	80	0
11	2 kr. claret and green	..	£6		£5	
	a. No stop	..	£10			

12 3 kr. black and lilac £6 £5
a. No stop £10
13 5 kr. blue and red 90 0 75 0
a. No stop £8
14 10 kr. rose and sepia 80 0 70 0
a. No stop £6

1915 (SEPT.). *Coronation issue of Persia, Nos. 566 etc., optd. with T* **1**.
15 1 ch. deep blue and carmine .. £22 £20
16 2 ch. carmine and deep blue .. £250 £225
17 3 ch. deep green £26 £24
18 5 ch. vermilion £250 £225
19 6 ch. carmine and green .. £175 £160
20 9 ch. deep violet and brown .. £26 £24
21 10 ch. brown and deep green .. £35 £32
22 12 ch. ultramarine £35 £32
23 24 ch. sepia and brown .. £24 £20
24 1 kr. black, brown and silver £24 £20
25 2 kr. carmine, slate and silver £24 £20
26 3 kr. sepia, dull lilac, and silver £26 £24
27 5 kr. slate, sepia and silver .. £24 £22
a. Overprint inverted .. ..
28 1 t. black, violet and gold .. £20 £18
29 3 t. red, crimson and gold .. £110 £100

1915. *No.* 552 *of Persia optd. with* **1**.
30 1 ch. on 5 ch. carm. & brown £145

Bushire, a seaport town of Persia, was occupied by the British on 8th August, 1915. The Persian postal authorities resumed control on 16th October, 1915.

CAMEROONS.
(BRITISH OCCUPATION.)

(A) (B)

The above are the types of German Colonial stamps that have been surcharged.

C.E.F. 1d. (1) C.E.F. 1s. (2)

1915. *German Colonial issues of Cameroons, Type* A *surch. as T* **1** *and Type* B *as T* **2**, *in black or blue.*
1 A ½d. on 3 pf. (No. 7) (B.) .. 9 0 9 0
2 ,, ½d. on 5 pf. (No. 21) (B.) .. 4 6 5 0
a. Surch. double £40 £20
b. Surch. in black 7 0 7 6
3 ,, 1d. on 10 pf. (No. 22) (B.) 4 0 4 6
a. Thin serif and foot to "1" .. 60 0 70 0
b. Surch. double £10
c. Surch. double with thin serif and foot to "1" .. ..
d. "1d." double, but "C.E.F." not double £175
e. Surch. in black 25 0 30 0
f. Surch. in black with thin serif and foot to "1" .. £6
g. "C.E.F." omitted £225
4 ,, 2d. on 20 pf. (No. 23) .. 4 0 8 0
5 ,, 2½d. on 25 pf. (No. 11) .. 8 0 12 0
a. Surch. double £275
6 ,, 3d. on 30 pf. (No. 12) .. 8 0 12 0
7 ,, 4d. on 40 pf. (No. 13) .. 8 0 12 0
a. Shorter "4" .. ..
8 A 6d. on 50 pf. (No. 14) .. 8 0 12 0
9 ,, 8d. on 80 pf. (No. 15) .. 8 0 12 0
10 B 1s. on 1 m. (No. 16) .. £10 £12
a. "s" inverted £40 £50
11 ,, 2s. on 2 m. (No. 17) .. £10 £12
a. "s" inverted £40 £50
12 ,, 3s. on 3 m. (No. 18) .. £10 £12
a. "s" inverted £40 £50
b. Surch. double £200
c. Surch. double and "s" inverted
13 ,, 5s. on 5 m. (No. 25a) .. £12 £15
a. "s" inverted £40 £50

The letters "C. E. F." signify "Cameroons Expeditionary Force." The above stamps were replaced by the then current issue of NIGERIA.

CANADA.

CANADIAN PROVINCES. The following Provinces issued their own stamps before joining the Confederation of Canada, whilst the former Dominion of Newfoundland became part of Canada in 1949. Their issues are listed in alphabetical order in this Catalogue:

BRITISH COLUMBIA and VANCOUVER IS.
NEW BRUNSWICK
NEWFOUNDLAND
NOVA SCOTIA
PRINCE EDWARD ISLAND

POSTMASTER'S PROVISIONAL

NEW CARLISLE, GASPÉ.

ENVELOPE

(1)

1851 (7 APRIL).
1 **1** 3d. black .. .. .. † —

Only one example is known, with the impression cancelled by the signature of the postmaster, R. W. Kelly.

COLONY OF CANADA.

— **SIMPLIFICATION** (see INTRODUCTION) —

Nos. 1 to 45.
1a, 2, 4.
23, 6, 12, 14, 22, 20c: 25, 26, 27a.
29, 44, 31, 33, 34, 38, 39, 42.

Nos. 46 to 76 and 113-114.
53, 55, 76, 56, 57, 58, 70, 59, 60, 61, 63a (113), 64 (114), 67.

Nos. 77 to 112 and 117 to 120.
101, 77, 80, 82, 83, 105, 106, 87, 107, 88, 109, 117, 118, 120, 89, 112.

1. Beaver.

(Designed by Sir Sandford Fleming.)

2. Prince Albert.

3

Major re-entry : Line through "EE PEN".

(Eng. and recess. Rawdon, Wright, Hatch and Edson, New York.)

1851. *Imperf. Laid paper.*

1	1	3d. red (23 April) ..	.. £750	£50
1*a*	,,	3d. orange-vermilion	.. £750	£50
		b. Major re-entry ..	.. —	£80
2	2	6d. slate-violet (15 May) ..	£500	£85
3	,,	6d. brown-purple ..	.. £700	£95
		a. Bisected (3d.) on cover		
4	3	12d. black (14 June)	£3500	£2750

There are several re-entries on the plate of the 3d. in addition to the major re-entry listed. All re-entries occur in this stamp on all papers.

1852–57. *Imperf.*

A. *Thin wove paper.*

6	1	3d. red	£60	£20
7	,,	3d. deep red	£60	£22
7*a*	,,	3d. scarlet-vermilion ..	£85	£30
		b. Major re-entry	—	£60
8	2	6d. slate-violet	£500	£150
9	,,	6d. greenish grey	£550	£175
9*a*	3	12d. black	—	£3000

B. *Medium hard wove paper.*

10	1	3d. red	£45	£25
11	,,	3d. deep red	£45	£25
11*a*	,,	3d. brown-red	£60	£30
		b. Major re-entry	—	£50
12	2	6d. slate-violet	£525	£70
		a. Bisected (3d.), on cover ..	—	£500
13	,,	6d. greenish grey	£500	£85
14	,,	6d. brownish grey	£550	£80
14*a*	3	12d. black	—	£3000

C. *Thick hard wove paper.*

15	1	3d. red	£80	£45
		a. Bisected, on cover		
16	2	6d. grey-lilac	£900	£175

D. *Very thick soft wove paper.*

17	2	6d. purple (reddish) ..	£500	£150
		a. Bisected (3d.), on cover ..		

1857. E. *Thin soft ribbed paper.*

18	1	3d. red	£100	£60

F. *Thin brittle wove paper*

19	1	3d. red	£100	£55

4. Jacques Cartier.

(Eng. and recess. Rawdon, Wright, Hatch and Edson, New York.)

1855 (JAN.). *Imperf.*

A. *Thin wove paper.*

20	4	10d. bright blue	£400	£80
20*a*	,,	10d. dull blue	£400	£80
		aa. Major re-entry*	—	£175

B. *Medium wove paper, semi-transparent.*

20*b*	4	10d. bright blue	£425	£85
20*c*	,,	10d. Prussian blue	£450	£70
		d. Major re-entry*	—	£175

1857. C. *Stout hard wove paper.*

21	4	10d. blue	£500	£90
		a. Major re-entry*	—	£175

These stamps may be divided into "wide" and "narrow," due to the shrinkage of the paper, which was wetted before printing, and which contracted unevenly when drying. The width varies from 17 mm. to 18 mm., the narrower being the commoner.

* The 10d. Major Re-entry listed shows strong doubling of top frame line and left-hand "8d. stg.", and line through lower parts of "ANAD" and "ENCE". There are other, lesser re-entries.

5

6

1857 (2 JUNE). *Imperf.*

22	5	7½d. pale yell.-grn. ..	£500	£300
22*a*	,,	7½d. deep yell.-grn. ..	£550	£250

There are several re-entries in these stamps.

The same remarks apply to this stamp as to the 10d. blue. The width varies less, being generally 18 to 18½ mm.

1857 (1 AUG.). *Imperf.*

A. *Stout hard wove paper.*

23	6	½d. deep rose	£70	£30

B. *Thin soft ribbed paper.*

24	6	½d. deep rose (*horiz.*) ..	£150	£100
24*a*	,,	½d. deep rose (*vert.*) ..	£300	£175

1858–59. *P* 11¾. A. *Stout wove paper.*

25	6	½d. deep rose	£45	£28
25*a*	,,	½d. lilac-rose	—	£40
26	1	3d. red	£60	£35
27	2	6d. brownish grey	£400	£200
27*a*	,,	6d. slate-violet	£500	£150

B. *Thin ribbed paper.*

27*b*	6	½d. deep rose-red	—	£250
28	1	3d. red	—	£100

C. *Thick hard paper.*

28*a*	1	3d. red	—	£100

The 3d. is known perf. 14, and also *percé en scie* 13, both being unofficial, but used at the period of issue.

7

8. Beaver.

9. Prince Albert.

10

11. Jacques Cartier.

(Recess. American Bank Note Co.)

(On 1st May, 1858, Messrs. Rawdon, Wright, Hatch, and Edson altered the name of their firm to "The American Bank Note Co.," and the "imprint" on sheets of the following stamps has the new title of the firm with "New York" added.)

1859 (1 July). *P* 12.

No.	Type	Description	Unused	Used
29	**7**	1 c. pale rose (to rose-red)	95 0	50 0
30	,,	1 c. dp. rose (to carm.-rose)	£8	65 0
		a. Imperf. (pair)	£150	
		b. Imperf. × perf.		
		c. Laid paper	—	£750
31	**8**	5 c. pale red	£8	35 0
32	,,	5 c. deep red	£8	35 0
		a. Re-entry*	—	£50
		b. Imperf. (pair)	£200	
		c. Bisected (2½ c.), on cover		£125
33	**9**	10 c black-brown	£300	£80
		a. Bisected (5 c.), on cover	—	£350
33*b*	,,	10 c. deep red-purple	£250	£60
		ba. Bisected (5 c.) on cover	—	£250
34	,,	10 c. purple (*shades*)	£35	£5
		a. Bisected (5 c.), on cover	—	£175
35	,,	10 c. brownish purple	£35	£5
36	,,	10 c. brown (to pale)	£40	£5
37	,,	10 c. dull violet	£30	95 0
38	,,	10 c. bright red-purple	£30	£5
		a. Imperf. (pair)	£200	
39	**10**	12½ c. deep yellow-green	£25	80 0
40	,,	12½ c. pale yellow-green	£25	70 0
41	,,	12½ c. blue-green	£30	75 0
		a. Imperf. (pair)	£200	
		b. Imperf. between (vert. pair)		
42	**11**	17 c. deep blue	£25	97 6
		a. Imperf. (pair)	£200	
43	,,	17 c. slate-blue	£50	£12
43*a*	,,	17 c. indigo	£30	£8
		b. Imperf. (pair)	£250	

* The price of No. 32*a* is for the very marked re-entry, showing oval frame line doubled above "CANADA". Slighter re-entries are worth from 50s. upwards in used condition.

As there were numerous P.O. Dept. orders for the 10 c., 12½ c. and 17 c. and some of these were executed by more than one separate printing, with no special care to ensure uniformity of colour, there is a wide range of shade, especially in the 10 c. and some shades recur at intervals after periods during which other shades predominated. The colour-names given in the above list therefore represent groups only.

It has been proved by leading Canadian specialists that the perforations may be an aid to the approximate dating a of a particular stamp, the gauge used measuring 11¾ × 11¾ from mid-July, 1859, to late 1862, 12 × 11¾ from early 1863 to mid-1865 and 12 × 12 from April, 1865 to 1868. Exceptionally in the 5 c. value many sheets were perforated 12 × 12 between May and October, 1862, whilst the last printings of the 12½ c. and 17 c. perf. 11¾ × 11¾ were in July 1863, the perf. 12 × 11¾ starting towards the end of 1863.

12

(Recess. American Bank Note Co.)

1864 (1 Aug.). *P* 12.

No.	Type	Description	Unused	Used
44	**12**	2 c. rose-red	£22	£12
45	,,	2 c. bright rose	£22	£12
		a. Imperf. (pair)	£80	

DOMINION OF CANADA.

13. *Large types.* **14.**

On 1 July, 1867, Canada, Nova Scotia, and New Brunswick were united, the combined territory being termed "The Dominion of Canada". Under the Act of Union provision was made for the admission of Newfoundland, Prince Edward Island, British Columbia, Rupert's Land, and the North-Western Territory.

(Recess. British American Bank Note Co., at Montreal or Ottawa.)

T **13** *and* **14** (*various frames*). *Montreal printings.*

1868 (March). (A) *Thin rather transparent crisp paper. P* 12.

No.	Type	Description	Unused	Used
46	**13**	½ c. black	95 0	65 0
47	**14**	1 c. red-brown	£18	95 0
48	,,	2 c. grass-green	£10	60 0
49	,,	3 c. red-brown	£22	60 0
50	,,	6 c. blackish brown	£100	£40
51	,,	12½ c. bright blue	£60	£30
52	,,	15 c. deep reddish purple	£95	£25

In these first printings the impression is generally blurred and the lines of the background are less clearly defined than in later printings.

1868–88. (B) *Medium to stout wove paper. P* 12.

No.	Type	Description	Unused	Used
53	**13**	½ c. black	45 0	45 0
54	,,	½ c. grey-black	40 0	40 0
		a. Imperf. between (pair)		
		b. Watermarked	—	£250
55	**14**	1 c. red-brown	£5	45 0
		a. Laid paper	£200	£75
		b. Watermarked (1868)	£70	£18
56	,,	2 c. deep green	£7	45 0
57	,,	2 c. pale emer.-green (1871)	£7	50 0
		a. Laid paper		
57*b*	,,	2 c. bluish green	£10	75 0
		c. Watermarked (1868)	£65	£28
58	,,	3 c. brown-red	£7	30 0
		a. Laid paper	£175	£17
		b. Watermarked (1868)	£90	£10
59	,,	6 c. blkish. brown (to choc.)	£15	50 0
		a. Watermarked (1868)	—	£65

60 **14** 6 c. yellow-brown (1870) .. £15 50 0
 a. Bisected (3 c.), on cover ..
61 ,, 12½ c. bright blue £12 50 0
 a. Watermarked (1868) .. £55 £25
62 ,, 12½ c. pale dull blue (milky) .. £12 75 0
63 ,, 15 c. deep reddish purple .. £30 85 0
63*a* ,, 15 c. pale reddish purple .. £25 85 0
 b. Watermarked (1868) .. — £45
64 ,, 15 c. dull violet-grey .. £12 70 0
 a. Watermarked (1868) .. — £40
65 ,, 15 c. dull grey-purple .. £15 75 0
66 ,, 15 c. clear dp. vio. (1880–81) £55 £30
67 ,, 15 c. deep slate (1881–88) .. £7 50 0
68 ,, 15 c. slaty blue £9 60 0

The watermark on the stout paper stamps consists of the words "E & G BOTHWELL CLUTHA MILLS," in large double-lined capitals. Portions of one or two letters only may be found on these stamps, which occur in the early printings of 1868.

The papers may, in most cases, be easily divided if the stamps are laid face downwards and carefully compared. The thin hard paper is more or less transparent and shows the design through the stamp; the thicker paper is softer to the feel and more opaque.

The paper of this issue may be still further subdivided in several values into sets on—(a) *Medium to stout wove.* (b) *Thin, soft very white:* and (c) *Thinner and poorer quality, sometimes greyish or yellowish* (*from* 1878 *to end of issue*).

Of the 2 c. laid paper No. 57*a* two examples only are known.

20

1873–78. (C) *Medium to stout wove paper.* *P* 11½ × 12.

69 **13** ½ c. black 70 0 65 0
70 **20** 5 c. olive-grn. (1 Oct., '75) £18 75 0
71 **14** 15 c. dull grey-purple (Dec., '74) £45 £15
72 ,, 15 c. lilac-grey (Mar., '77) £55 £15
 a. Script Wmk.* £175 £100
73 ,, 15 c. slaty blue £50 £20

*The watermark on No. 72*a* is part of the words "Alexr. Pirie & Sons" in script lettering, a very small quantity of paper thus watermarked having been used for printing this stamp.

1869. (D) *Colour changed. Stout wove paper.* *P* 12.

74 **14** 1 c. deep orge. (Jan., '69) £25 £7
75 ,, 1 c. orge.-yell. (May(?), '69) £25 £5
76 ,, 1 c. pale orange-yellow .. £28 75 0
 a. Imperf. .. .. ..

21 *Small types.* 27

(Nos. 77 114 and 117–120. Recess. British American Bank Note Co., at Montreal or Ottawa.)

1870–88. *T* **21** (*various frames*). *P* 12 (*or slightly under*).

Montreal printings.

Papers. (*a*) 1870–80. *Medium to stout wove.*
(*b*) 1870–72. *Thin, soft, very white.*
(*c*) 1878–97. *Thinner and poorer quality.*

77 **21** 1 c. bright orange (*a*, *b*) (1870–73) £6 45 0
78 ,, 1 c. orange-yellow (*a*) (1876–79) 45 0 5 0
79 ,, 1 c. pale dull yellow (*a*) (1877–79) 30 0 1 0
80 ,, 1 c. bright yellow (*a*, *c*) (1878–97) 15 0 0 4
 a. Imperf. (pair) (*c*) £12
 b. Bisected (½ c.) (on "Railway News") .. † £100
 c. Printed both sides .. £75
81 ,, 2 c. deep green (*a*, *b*) (1872–73 and 1876–78) .. 85 0 1 9
82 ,, 2 c. grass-grn. (*c*) (1878–88) 40 0 0 6
 a. Imperf. (pair) (1891-93?) .. £16
 b. Bisected (1 c.) on cover .. † £35
83 ,, 3 c. Indian red (*a*) (Jan., '70) £55 £8
 a. Perf. 12½ .. .. — £100
83*b* ,, 3 c. pale rose-red (*a*) (Sept. '70) £15 30 0
84 ,, 3 c. deep rose-red (*a*, *b*) (1870–73) £12 32 6
85 ,, 3 c. dull red (*a*) (1876–88) 70 0 2 6
86 ,, 3 c. orange-red (*a*, *c*) (1876–88) (*shades*) 40 0 1 6
87 ,, 5 c. olive-grey (*a*, *c*) (February, 1876–88) .. 60 0 4 0
88 ,, 6 c. yellowish brown (*a*, *b*, *c*) (1872–73 & 1876–90) .. 70 0 15 0
 a. Bisected (3 c.) on cover, .. † £90
89 ,, 10 c. pale lilac-magenta (*a*) (1876-?) £15 65 0
90 ,, 10 c. deep lilac-magenta (*a*, *c*) (March 1876–88) .. £12 65 0

1873–77. *P* 11½ × 12. *Medium to stout wove paper.*

90*a* **21** 1 c. bright orange .. £15 55 0
91 ,, 1 c. orge.-yellow (1873–79) £12 25 0
92 ,, 1 c. p. dull yell. (1877–79) £8 40 0
93 ,, 2 c. deep green (1873–78) £12 25 0
94 ,, 3 c. dull red (1875–79) .. £8 17 6
95 ,, 3 c. orange-red (1873–79) £6 10 6
96 ,, 5 c. olive-grey (1876–79) £7 25 0
97 ,, 6 c. yellowish brn. (1876–79) £7 22 6
98 ,, 10 c. very pale lilac-magenta (1874–79) .. £55 £15
99 ,, 10 c. deep lilac-magenta (1876–79) £28 £5

1882–97. *P* 12. *Thinnish paper often toned.*

101 **27** ½ c. black (July, 1882–97) 4 0 3 6
102 ,, ½ c. grey-black 7 0 3 6
 a. Imperf. (pr.) (1891-93?) .. £15
 b. Imperf. between (pair) .. £45

Ottawa printings.

1888–97. *As T* **14** *and* **21** (*various frames*). *P* 12. *Thinnish paper of poor quality, often toned grey or yellowish.*

103 **21** 2 c. dull sea-green (Jan., 1888) 55 0 2 0
104 ,, 2 c. blue-green (July, 1889–91) 72 6 2 6
105 ,, 3 c. rose-carmine (Oct., 1888-April, '89) .. £26 40 0
106 ,, 3 c. bright vermilion (Apr., 1889–97) 15 0 0 3
 a. Imperf. (pair) (1891-93?) .. £15
107 ,, 5 c. brownish grey (May, '88) 27 6 0 10
 a. Imperf. (pair) (1891-93) .. £15
108 ,, 6 c. deep chestnut (Oct., '90) 60 0 25 0
 a. "5 c." re-entry* .. ..

109	21	6 c. pale chestnut ..	55 0	22 6
		a. Imperf. (pair) (1891-93?) ..	£28	
110	,,	10 c. lilac-pink (Mar., '88)	£8	60 0
110a	,,	10 c. salmon-pink ..	£22	£12
111	,,	10 c. carm.-pink (1891?) ..	95 0	25 0
		a. Imperf. (pair) (1891-93?) ..	£22	
112	,,	10 c. brownish red (1894?)	80 0	25 0
		a. Imperf. (pair)	£18	
113	14	15 c. slate-pur. (July, '88)	75 0	40 0
114	,,	15 c. slate-vio. (May, '90)	90 0	40 0
		a. Imperf. (brn.-pur.)(pair) ..	£35	

NOTE.—The 1 c. showed no change in the Ottawa printings, so is not included. The 2 c. reverted to its previous grass-green shade in 1891, About 1895 remainders of the 15 c. were used concurrently with the 1888 and 1890 shades. They vary from grey and slate to a nearly true blue.

* No. 108a shows traces of the 5 c. value 2½ mm. lower than the 6 c. design.

28

29

(Recess. British American Bank Note Co.)

1893 (17 FEB.). *P* 12.

115	28	20 c. vermilion	£5	25 0
		a. Imperf. (pair)	£20	
116	,,	50 c. blue	£5	25 0
		a. Imperf. (Prussian blue) (pair) ..	£26	

1893 (1 AUG.). *P* 12.

117	29	8 c. pale bluish grey ..	70 0	6 0
		a. Imperf. (pair)	£12	
118	,,	8 c. bluish slate	70 0	5 0
119	,,	8 c. slate-purple	65 0	7 6
120	,,	8 c. blackish purple ..	65 0	8 6

PRINTERS. The following stamps to No. 287 were recess-printed by the American Bank Note Co., Ottawa, which in 1923 became the Canadian Bank Note Co.

30

(Des. L. Pereira and F. Brownell.)

1897 (19 JUNE). *Jubilee issue. P* 12.

121	30	½ c. black	16 0	20 0
122	,,	1 c. orange	3 0	2 6
123	,,	1 c. orange-yellow ..	2 6	2 0
		a. Bisected (½ c.) on cover		
124	,,	2 c. green	3 0	3 0
125	,,	2 c. deep green	5 0	3 0
126	,,	3 c. carmine	3 0	1 0
127	,,	5 c. slate-blue	20 0	15 0
128	,,	5 c. deep blue	15 0	15 0
129	,,	6 c. brown	45 0	50 0
130	,,	8 c. slate-violet	20 0	27 6
131	,,	10 c. purple	25 0	32 6
132	30	15 c. slate..	50 0	60 0
133	,,	20 c. vermilion	55 0	60 0
134	,,	50 c. pale ultramarine ..	70 0	65 0
135	,,	50 c. bright ultramarine	80 0	75 0
136	,,	$1 lake	£22	£20
137	,,	$2 deep violet	£30	£26
138	,,	$3 bistre	£40	£30
139	,,	$4 violet	£45	£30
140	,,	$5 olive-green	£45	£38

31

32

(From photograph by W. & D. Downey, London.)

1897–98. *P* 12.

141	31	½ c. grey-blk. (9 Nov. 1897)	1 9	2 6
142	,,	½ c. black	1 9	1 9
		a. Imperf. (pair)	£12	
143	,,	1 c. blue-grn. (Dec., 1897)	4 0	0 6
		a. Imperf. (pair)	£12	
144	,,	2 c. violet (Dec., 1897) ..	6 0	0 6
		a. Imperf. (pair) ..	£12	
145	,,	3 c. carmine (Jan., 1898)	7 0	0 6
		a. Imperf. (pair)	£12	
146	,,	5 c. dp. blue/*bluish* (Dec., 1897) ..	15 0	3 0
		a. Imperf. (pair)	£12	
147	,,	6 c. brown (Dec., 1897)..	17 6	22 6
		a. Imperf. (pair)	£12	
148	,,	8 c. orange (Dec., 1897)..	22 6	12 6
		a. Imperf. (pair)	£12	
149	,,	10 c. brownish purple (Jan., 1898) ..	65 0	65 0
		a. Imperf. (pair)	£12	

1898–1902. *P* 12.

150	32	½ c. black (Sept., 1898)..	1 0	0 6
		a. Imperf. (pair) ..	£12	
151	,,	1 c. blue-grn. (June, 1898)	3 0	0 3
152	,,	1 c. dp. grn./*toned paper* ..	17 6	3 6
		a. Imperf. (pair)	£12	
153	,,	2 c. purple (Sept., 1898)..	8 6	1 0
154	,,	2 c. violet	4 0	0 6
155	,,	2 c. rose-carm. (20.8.99)..	5 0	0 3
		a. Imperf. (pair) ..	£12	
156	,,	3 c. rose-carm. (June, 1898)	6 0	0 4
157	,,	5 c. slate-blue/*bluish* ..	30 0	1 9
		a. Imperf. (pair) ..	£12	
158	,,	5 c. Prussian blue/*bluish*	35 0	2 6
159	,,	6 c. brown (Sept., 1898)..	37 6	40 0
		a. Imperf. (pair)	£12	
160	,,	7 c. greenish yellow (23.12.02)	35 0	27 6
161	,,	8 c. orange-yellow (Oct., 1898)	65 0	40 0
162	,,	8 c. brownish orange ..	70 0	40 0
		a. Imperf. (pair)	£12	
163	,,	10 c. pale brownish purple (Nov., 1898) ..	65 0	15 0
164	,,	10 c. deep brownish purple	65 0	15 0
		a. Imperf. (pair)	£12	
165	,,	20 c. olive green (29.12.00)	£7	50 0

The 7 c. and 20 c. also exist imperf. but unlike the values listed in this condition, they have no gum. (*Price*, 7 c. £25, 20 c. £50 *pair, un.*)

33

(Des. Postmaster-General Mulock; frame, recess; colours, typo.)

1898 (7 Dec.). *Imperial Penny Postage. Design in black. British possessions in red. Oceans in colours given. P* 12.

166 **33** 2 c. lavender 12 6 3 6
167 " 2 c. greenish blue 15 0 5 0
168 " 2 c. blue 30 0 12 6
a. Imperf. (pair) £40

1899 (5 Jan.). *Provisionals used at Port Hood. No.* 156 *divided vertically and surch.*

169 **32** "1" in blue, on ⅓ of 3 c... — £475
170 " "2" in violet, on ⅔ of 3 c. — £425
a. Surch. double .. ..

2 CENTS
(34)

35. King Edward VII.

1899. *Surch. with T* **34** *by Public Printing Office.*

171 **31** 2 c. on 3 c. carm. (8 Aug.) 5 0 3 6
a. Surcharge inverted .. £38
172 **32** 2 c. on 3 c. rose-carmine (28 July) 4 0 1 9
a. Surcharge inverted .. £35

(Des. King George V when Prince of Wales and J. A. Tilleard.)

1903–12. *P* 12.

173 **35** 1 c. pale grn. (1.7.03) .. 7 6 0 4
174 " 1 c. deep green 9 6 0 3
175 " 1 c. green 4 6 0 3
176 " 2 c. rose-car. (1.7.03) .. 1 6 0 3
177 " 2 c. pale rose-carmine .. 1 3 0 3
a. Imperf. (pair) 22 6 22 6
178 " 5 c. blue/*bluish* (1.7.03) .. 22 6 0 8
179 " 5 c. indigo/*bluish*.. .. 30 0 1 3
a. Imperf. (pair) (-.7.1907).. £30 £35
180 " 7 c. yellow-olive (1.7.03) 35 0 6 0
181 " 7 c. greenish bistre (-.6.12) 90 0 25 0
182 " 10 c. brown-lilac (1.7.03).. 60 0 12 6
183 " 10 c. pale dull purple .. 60 0 17 6
184 " 10 c. dull purple .. 60 0 15 0
185 " 20 c. pale ol.-grn. (27.9.04) £7 35 0
186 " 20 c. deep olive-green .. £7 30 0
187 " 50 c. deep violet (19.11.08) £20 £6

36. King George V and Queen Mary when Prince and Princess of Wales.

37. Jacques Cartier and Samuel Champlain.

38. King Edward VII and Queen Alexandra.

39. Champlain's House in Quebec.

40. Generals Montcalm and Wolfe.

41. Quebec in 1700.

42. Champlain's Departure for the West.

43. Cartier's Arrival before Quebec.

(Des. Machado).

1908 (16 JULY). *Quebec Tercentenary.* *P* 12.

188	**36**	½ c. sepia	4	0	5	0
		a. Imperf. (pair)	£16			
189	**37**	1 c. blue-green	5	0	5	0
		a. Imperf. (pair)	£16			
190	**38**	2 c. carmine	5	0	1	0
		a. Imperf. (pair)	£16			
191	**39**	5 c. indigo	27	6	22	6
		a. Imperf. (pair)	£16			
192	**40**	7 c. olive-green	40	0	40	0
		a. Imperf. (pair)	£16			
193	**41**	10 c. violet	55	0	50	0
		a. Imperf. (pair)	£16			
194	**42**	15 c. brown-orange ..	80	0	80	0
		a. Imperf. (pair)	£16			
195	**43**	20 c. dull brown	£6		£7	
		a. Imperf. (pair)	£20			

Some values exist on both *toned* and *white* papers.

44

1912–18. *P* 12.

196	**44**	1 c. yellow-green	3	0	0	6
		a. With fine horizontal lines across stamp	60	0	60	0
197	,,	1 c. bluish green ..	6	0	0	4
198	,,	1 c. deep bluish green ..	5	0	0	3
199	,,	1 c. deep yellow-green ..	5	0	0	8
200	,,	2 c. rose-red	3	0	0	3
201	,,	2 c. deep rose-red ..	3	0	0	3
202	,,	2 c. pale rose-red ..	4	6	0	6
		a. With fine horizontal lines across stamp	55	0	35	0
203	,,	2 c. carmine	4	0	0	6
204	,,	3 c. brown (1918) ..	4	6	0	3
205	,,	3 c. deep brown ..	2	0	0	3
205*a*	,,	5 c. deep blue	18	0	1	3
206	,,	5 c. indigo	20	0	1	3
206*a*	,,	5 c. grey-blue	25	0	1	3
207	,,	7 c. pale sage-green ..	£6		60	0
208	,,	7 c. olive-yellow ..	22	6	5	0
209	,,	7 c. yellow-ochre (1916)	15	0	4	0
210	,,	10 c. brownish purple ..	25	0	4	0
211	,,	10 c. reddish purple ..	40	0	6	0
212	,,	20 c. olive-green ..	17	6	1	6
213	,,	20 c. olive	17	6	2	6
214	,,	50 c. sepia	30	0	12	6
215	,,	50 c. grey-black	£5		17	6

1912 (Nov.)–**1921.** *For use in coil-machines.*

(*a*) *P* 12 × *imperf.*

216	**44**	1 c. yellow-green ..	3	0	6	0
217	,,	1 c. blue-green	22	6	15	0
218	,,	2 c. deep rose-red ..	20	0	17	6
218*a*	,,	3 c. brown (1921) ..	8	0	10	0

(*b*) *Imperf.* × *perf.* 8.

219	**44**	1 c. yellow-green ..	6	0	2	0
220	,,	1 c. blue-green ..	12	6	5	0
221	,,	2 c. carmine	12	6	1	6
222	,,	2 c. rose-red	17	6	2	0
223	,,	2 c. scarlet	27	6	12	6
224	,,	3 c. brown (1918) ..	6	0	3	0

(*c*) *P* 8 × *imperf.*

224*a*	**44**	1 c. blue-green	80	0	45	0
224*b*	,,	2 c. carmine	80	0	45	0

The stamps impert. × perf. 8 were sold in coils over the counter; those perf. 8 × imperf. were on sale in automatic machines. Varieties showing perf. 12 on 2 or 3 adjacent sides and 1 or 2 sides imperf. are from booklets, or the margins of sheets.

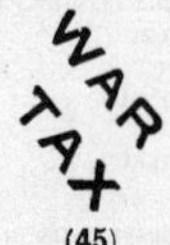

(45)

1915 (12 FEB.). *Optd. with T* **45.**

225	**44**	5 c. blue (Bk.)	65	0	85	0
226	,,	20 c. olive-green (Bk.) ..	40	0	55	0
227	,,	50 c. sepia (R.) ..	50	0	65	0

These stamps were intended for tax purposes, but owing to ambiguity in an official circular, dated 16 April, 1915, it was for a time believed that their use for postal purposes was authorised.

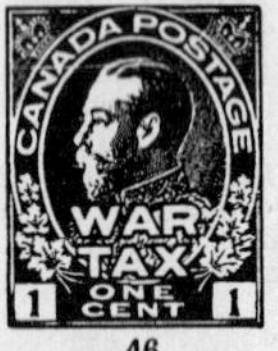

46

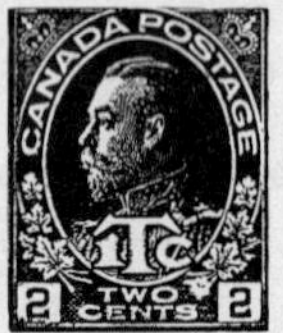

47

1915. *P* 12.

228	**46**	1 c. yellow-green ..	1	3	0	3
229	,,	2 c. carmine-red ..	2	6	1	3
230	,,	2 c. rose-carmine ..	6	6	7	0

Die I.

Die II.

In Die I there is a long horizontal coloured line under the foot of the "T", and a solid bar of colour runs upwards from the "1" to the "T". In Die II this solid bar of colour is absent, and there is a short horizontal line under the left side of the "T", with two short vertical dashes and a number of dots under the right-hand side.

1916 (JAN.). *P* 12.

231	**47**	2 c.+1 c. rose-red (Die I)	16	6	2	0
232	,,	2 c.+1 c. brt. carm. (Die I)	18	6	3	0
233	,,	2 c.+1 c. scarlet (Die I) ..	20	0	2	6

1916 (SEPT.). *P* 12.

234	**47**	2 c.+1 c. carm.-red (Die II)	£8		10	0

1916. *Imperf.* × *perf.* 8 (*coils*).

235	**47**	2 c.+1 c. rose-red (Die I)	35	0	4	6

1916. *P* 12 × 8.

236	**47**	2 c.+1 c. carm.-red (Die I)	12	6	35	0
237	,,	2 c.+1 c. brt. rose-red (Die I)	20	0	30	0

1916 (Sept.). *Colour changed.* *P* 12.

No.	Type	Description	Unused	Used
238	**47**	2 c.+1 c. brown (Die I) ..	£14	35 0
239	„	2 c.+1 c. yell.-brn. (Die II)	3 6	0 3
240	„	2 c.+1 c. deep brn. (Die II)	15 0	0 3

Imperf.×perf. 8.

No.	Type	Description	Unused	Used
241	**47**	2 c.+1 c brown (Die I) ..	50 0	10 0
243	„	2 c.+1 c. deep brn. (Die II)	12 6	6 0

48. Quebec Conference, 1864, from painting, "The Fathers of Confederation", by Robert Harris.

1917 (Sept.). 50*th Anniv. of Confederation.* *P* 12.

No.	Type	Description	Unused	Used
244	**48**	3 c. bistre-brown	8 0	1 9
		a. Imperf. (pair) (ungummed)	£20	
245	„	3 c. dark brown	7 6	1 0

1922–31. *As T* **44.** (*a*) *P* 12.

No.	Type	Description	Unused	Used
246	**44**	1 c. chrome-yellow ..	1 6	0 3
247	„	2 c. deep yellow-green	2 0	0 3
248	„	2 c. deep green ..	6 0	0 3
		a. Thin experimental paper (1924) ..	10 0	16 0
249	„	3 c. carmine (1923) ..	2 0	0 3
250	„	4 c. olive-yellow ..	10 0	4 0
251	„	4 c. yellow ochre ..	6 0	3 6
252	„	5 c. violet ..	7 6	3 0
		a. Thin experimental paper (1924)	17 6	18 6
253	„	5 c. reddish violet ..	12 6	6 0
254	„	7 c. red-brown	6 0	6 0
254*a*	„	8 c. blue (1925) ..	7 6	6 0
255	„	10 c. blue	8 6	2 0
255*a*	„	10 c. bistre-brown (1925)	8 0	2 6
255*b*	„	10 c. yellow-brown ..	17 6	6 0
256	„	$1 brown-orange (1923)	37 6	12 6

The **$1** differs from T **44** in that the value tablets are oval.

(*b*) *Imperf.×perf.* 8.

No.	Type	Description	Unused	Used
257	**44**	1 c. chrome-yell. (horiz. pr.)	3 6	3 0
		a. Imperf. between (vert. pair)	17 6	17 6
		b. Thick soft paper (pair)* ..	£10	
258	„	2 c. yellow-green (horiz. pr.)	6 0	1 3
		a. Imperf. between (vert. pr.)	17 6	20 0
		b. Thick soft paper (pair)* ..	£12	
259	„	3 c. carmine (horiz. pr.) ..	27 6	12 6
		a. Thick soft paper (vert. pr.)*	£18	

Used prices are for singles.

Nos. 257, 258, and 259 are the regular coils, which come in horizontal pairs or strips only.

* Nos. 257*b*, 258*b*, and 259*a* are the first printing in sheets (22 sheets in all), on thick soft paper which can be had in pairs, blocks, etc. Nos. 257*a* and 258*a* are a later sheet printing, on the normal paper. The colours differ slightly from those of 257*b* and 258*b* and the lettering of the inscription is sharply embossed as seen from the back of the stamps, whereas in the rare printing there is no embossed effect.

(*c*) *Imperf.* (1924.)

No.	Type	Description	Unused	Used
260	**44**	1 c. chrome-yellow ..	30 0	35 0
261	„	2 c. deep green	40 0	55 0
262	„	3 c. carmine	20 0	25 0

(*d*) *P* 12×*imperf.*

No.	Type	Description	Unused	Used
263	**44**	2 c. deep green	80 0	95 0

(*e*) *P* 12×8.

No.	Type	Description	Unused	Used
263*a*	**44**	3 c. carmine (24.6.31) ..	3 6	5 0

Nos. 260 to 262 were on sale only at the Philatelic Branch P.O. Dept., Ottawa.

2 CENTS (49) **2 CENTS** (50)

1926. *No.* 249 *surch.*

(*a*) *With T* **49**, *by the Govt. Printing Bureau.*

No.	Type	Description	Unused	Used
264	**44**	2 c. on 3 c. carm. (12.10.26)	35 0	40 0

(*b*) *With T* **50**, *by the Canadian Bank Note Co.*

No.	Type	Description	Unused	Used
265	**44**	2 c. on 3 c. carm. (10.11.26)	15 0	25 0
		a. Surch. double (partly treble)	£20	

51. Sir J. A. Macdonald.

54. Sir W. Laurier.

52. "The Fathers of Confederation".

53. Parliament Buildings, Ottawa.

55. Canada, Map 1867–1927.

1927 (29 June). 60*th Anniv. of Confederation.* *P* 12. I. *Commemorative Issue. Inscr.* "1867–1927. CANADA CONFEDERATION".

No.	Type	Description	Unused	Used
266	**51**	1 c. orange	2 6	0 4
267	**52**	2 c. green	1 3	0 4
268	**53**	3 c. carmine	3 6	2 0
269	**54**	5 c. violet	6 0	2 0
270	**55**	12 c. blue	8 6	6 0

56. Darcy McGee.

57. Sir W. Laurier and Sir J. A. Macdonald.

58. R. Baldwin and L. H. Lafontaine.

II. *Historical Issue.*

271	**56**	5 c. violet..	2	6	1	9
272	**57**	12 c. green	5	0	5	0
273	**58**	20 c. carmine	10	0	6	0

59

1928 (21 Sept.). *Air stamp.* *P* 12.

274	**59**	5 c. olive-brown	7	0	3	6
		a. Imperf.	£15			
		b. Imperf. between (vert. pair)	£30			
		c. Imperf. between (horiz. pr.)	£30			

60. King George V.

61. Mt. Hurd and Indian Totem Poles.

62. Quebec Bridge.

63. Harvesting with Horses.

64. Fishing smack *Bluenose.*

65. Parliament Buildings, Ottawa.

1928–29. (*a*) *P* 12.

275	**60**	1 c. orange (29.10.28) ..	1	0	0
276	"	2 c. green (17.10.28) ..	0	8	0
277	"	3 c. lake (12.12.28) ..	7	6	7
278	"	4 c. olive-bistre (1929) ..	5	0	6
279	"	5 c. violet (12.12.28) ..	2	0	3
280	"	8 c. blue (21.12.28) ..	3	6	3
281	**61**	10 c. green (5.11.28) ..	3	6	2
282	**62**	12 c. grey-black (8.1.29) ..	6	0	6
283	**63**	20 c. lake (8.1.29) ..	10	0	7
284	**64**	50 c. blue (8.1.29) ..	60	0	35
285	**65**	$1 olive-green (8.1.29) ..	£6		65

(*b*) *Imperf.* × *perf.* 8.

286	**60**	1 c. orange (1929) ..	12	6	12	6
287	,,	2 c. green	4	0	1	3

Slight differences in the size of many Canadian stamps, due to paper shrinkage, are to be found.

PRINTERS. The following stamps to No. 334 were recess-printed by the British American Bank Note Co.

66

67. Parliamentary Library, Ottawa.

68. The Old Citadel, Quebec.

69. Harvesting with Tractor.

70. Acadian Memorial Church and Statue of "Evangeline" Grand Pre, Nova Scotia.

71. Mt. Edith Cavell, Canadian Rockies.

Die I. 1 c. Die II.

Die I. 2 c. Die II.

1 c. Die. I. Three thick coloured lines and one thin between "P" and ornament, at right. Curved line in ball-ornament short.

Die II. Four thick lines. Curved line longer.

2 c. Die I. Three thick coloured lines between "P" and ornament, at left. Short line in ball.

Die II. Four thick lines. Curved line longer.

1930–31. (*a*) *P* 11.

288	**66**	1 c. orange (I) (17.7.30) ..	0	10	1	0
289	,,	2 c. green (I) (6.6.30) ..	0	8	0	6
290	,,	4 c. yell.-bistre (5.11.30)	2	6	2	0
291	,,	5 c. violet (18.6.30) ..	2	6	3	6
292	,,	8 c. blue (13.8.30) ..	7	6	12	6
293	**67**	10 c. olive-green (15.9.30)	5	0	1	9
294	**68**	12 c. grey-black (4.12.30)	5	0	5	0
295	**69**	20 c. red (4.12.30)	6	0	1	9
296	**70**	50 c. blue (4.12.30) ..	80	0	12	6
297	**71**	$1 olive-green (4.12.30)	75	0	25	0

(*b*) *Imperf.* × *perf.* 8½.

298	**66**	1 c. orange (I)	7	6	8	6
299	,,	2 c. green (I)	6	0	3	0

Colours changed and new value.

(*a*) *P* 11.

300	**66**	1 c. green (I) (6.12.30) ..	1	9	1	3
300*a*	,,	1 c. green (II)	2	6	0	6
301	,,	2 c. scarlet (I) (17.11.30)	1	6	0	4
301*a*	,,	2 c. scarlet (II)	2	0	0	4
302	,,	2 c. deep brn. (I) (4.7.31)	10	0	12	6
302*a*	,,	2 c. deep brown (II) ..	1	3	0	3
303	,,	3 c. scarlet (13.7.31) ..	1	0	0	3
304	,,	5 c. blue (13.11.30) ..	2	6	1	6
305	,,	8 c. red-orange (5.11.30)	3	6	4	6

(*b*) *Imperf.* × *perf.* 8½.

306	**66**	1 c. green (I)	2	6	1	0
307	,,	2 c. scarlet (I)	3	6	2	6
308	,,	2 c. deep brn. (I) (4.7.31)	4	0	2	6
309	,,	3 c. scarlet (13.7.31) ..	7	6	2	0

Some low values in the above and subsequent issues have been printed by both Rotary and "Flat plate" processes. The former can be distinguished by the gum, which has a striped appearance.

For 13 c. bright violet, *T* **68**, see No. 325.

72. Mercury and Western Hemisphere.

1930 (4 Dec.). *Air.* *P* 11.

310	**72**	5 c. deep brown	40	0	40	0

73. Sir Georges Etienne Cartier.

1931 (30 SEPT.). *P* 11.

312 **73** 10 c. olive-green 4 0 0 6

(74)

1932 (22 FEB.). *Air. No.* 274 *surch. with T* **74.**

313 **59** 6 c. on 5 c. olive-brown .. 7 0 4 0
- a. Surch. inverted (vert. pair) £22
- b. Triple surcharge £20
- c. Double surcharge.. .. £25

Collectors are warned against forged errors of No. 313, some of which bear unauthorized markings which purport to be the guarantee of Stanley Gibbons Ltd.

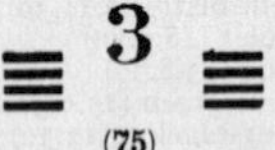

(75)

1932 (21 JUNE). *Nos.* 301/1*a surch. with T* **75.**

314 **66** 3 c. on 2 c. scarlet (I) .. 6 0 5 0

314*a* ,, 3 c. on 2 c. scarlet (II) .. 1 3 0 4

76. King George V.

77. Duke of Windsor when Prince of Wales.

78. Allegory of British Empire.

6 6

OTTAWA CONFERENCE
1932

(79)

1932 (12 JULY). *Ottawa Conference P* 11

(*a*) *Postage stamps.*

315 **76** 3 c. scarlet 0 8 0 3

316 **77** 5 c. blue 3 0 1 9

317 **78** 13 c. green 7 6 4 6

(*b*) *Air. No.* 310 *surch. with T* **79.**

318 **72** 6 c. on 5 c. deep brown (B.) 15 0 16 0

80. King George V.

Die I.

Die II.

1932 (1 DEC.)–**1933.** (*a*) *P* 11.

319 **80** 1 c. green 0 4 0 3

320 ,, 2 c. sepia 1 3 0 3

321 ,, 3 c. scarlet (Die I) .. 4 0 1 6

321*a* ,, 3 c. scarlet (Die II) .. 1 9 0 3

322 ,, 4 c. yellow-bistre .. 20 0 6 0

323 ,, 5 c. blue 3 0 0 3

324 ,, 8 c. red-orange 10 0 5 0

325 **68** 13 c. bright violet.. .. 15 0 2 0

(*b*) *Imperf.* × *perf.* 8½ ('33).

326 **80** 1 c. green 5 0 2 0

327 ,, 2 c. sepia 6 0 1 0

328 ,, 3 c. scarlet (Die II) .. 4 0 0 4

3 c. Die I: Pointed top of rt.-hand "3" level with white horizontal line above CENTS. Die II: point higher than line.

81. Parliament Buildings, Ottawa.

1933 (18 MAY). *U.P.U. Congress Preliminary Meeting. P* 11.

329 **81** 5 c. blue 6 6 3 6

WORLD'S
GRAIN EXHIBITION &
CONFERENCE

REGINA 1933
(82)

1933 (24 JULY). *World's Grain Exhibition and Conference, Regina. Optd. with T* **82.** *P* 11.

330 **69** 20 c. red (B.) 17 6 8 6

83. S.S. *Royal William* (after S. Skillett).

1933 (17 AUG.). *Centenary of First Trans-Atlanti Steamboat Crossing. P* 11.

331 **83** 5 c. blue 7 6 5

84. Jacques Cartier approaching land.

1934 (1 July). *Fourth Centenary of Discovery of Canada. P* 11.

332	**84**	3 c. blue	5	0	3	6

85. U.E.L. Statue, Hamilton.

1934 (1 July). 150*th Anniv. of Arrival of United Empire Loyalists. P* 11.

333	**85**	10 c. olive-green ..	20	0	8	6

86. Seal of New Brunswick.

1934 (16 Aug.). 150*th Anniv. of Province of New Brunswick. P* 11.

334	**86**	2 c. red-brown	5	0	5	0

PRINTERS. The following stamps were recess-printed by the Canadian Bank Note Co., Ottawa, *unless otherwise stated.*

87. Queen Elizabeth II when Princess.

88. King George VI when Duke of York.

89. King George V and Queen Mary.

90. Duke of Windsor when Prince of Wales.

91. Windsor Castle.

92. *Britannia.*

1935 (4 May). *Silver Jubilee. P* 12.

335	**87**	1 c. green	0	6	0	6
336	**88**	2 c. brown	0	6	0	3
337	**89**	3 c. carmine-red	0	8	0	3
338	**90**	5 c. blue	5	0	3	6
339	**91**	10 c. green	5	0	3	0
340	**92**	13 c. blue	12	6	8	6

93. King George V.

94. Royal Canadian Mounted Policeman.

95. Confederation, Charlottetown, 1864.

96. Niagara Falls.

97. Parliament Buildings, Victoria, B.C.

98. Champlain Monument, Quebec.

99. Daedalus.

1935 (1 June–5 Nov.). (*a*) *Postage*. (i) *P* 12.

341	**93**	1 c. green	0	8	0	3
342	,,	2 c. brown	0	10	0	3
343	,,	3 c. scarlet	1	0	0	3
344	,,	4 c. yellow	3	6	2	0
345	,,	5 c. blue	3	6	0	3
		a. Imperf. betwn. (horiz. pr.)	£25			
346	,,	8 c. orange	5	0	3	0
347	**94**	10 c. carmine	5	0	0	3
348	**95**	13 c. purple	6	0	3	0
349	**96**	20 c. olive-green	8	6	1	6
350	**97**	50 c. deep violet	16	0	7	6
351	**98**	$1 bright blue	30	0	17	6

(ii) *Coil stamps. Imperf.* × *perf.* 8.

352	**93**	1 c. green (5.11.35)	3	0	1	3
353	,,	2 c. brown (14.10.35)	3	6	0	6
354	,,	3 c. scarlet (20.7.35)	10	0	0	6

(*b*) *Air. P* 12.

355	**99**	6 c. red-brown	3	6	1	9

100. King George VI and Queen Elizabeth.

1937 (10 May). *Coronation. P* 12.

356	**100**	3 c. carmine	0	6	0	3

101. King George VI.

102. Memorial Chamber Parliament Buildings, Ottawa.

103. Entrance to Halifax Harbour.

104. Fort Garry Gate, Winnipeg.

105. Entrance, Vancouver Harbour.

106. Château de Ramezay, Montreal.

107. Seaplane over S.S. *Distributor* on R. Mackenzie.

(T **101.** Photograph by Bertram Park.)

1937–38. (*a*) *Postage.* (i) *P* 12.

No.	Type	Description		Unused	Used
357	**101**	1 c. green (1.4.37)	..	0 6	0 3
358	,,	2 c. brown (1.4.37)	..	0 8	0 3
359	,,	3 c. scarlet (1.4.37)	..	0 8	0 3
360	,,	4 c. yellow (10.5.37)	..	6 0	2 6
361	,,	5 c. blue (10.5.37)	..	1 6	0 3
362	,,	8 c. orange (10.5.37)	..	5 0	4 6
363	**102**	10 c. rose-carm. (15.6.38)		5 0	0 8
		a. Red	..	6 0	0 3
364	**103**	13 c. blue (15.11.38)	..	12 6	4 6
365	**104**	20 c. red-brown (15.6.38)		10 0	0 9
366	**105**	50 c. green (15.6.38)	..	32 6	10 0
367	**106**	$1 violet (15.6.38)	..	40 0	10 0

The 1 c., 2 c. and 3 c. exist in booklet panes of 4 or 6 stamps with three outer edges of the panes imperf.

(ii) *Coil stamps. Imperf.* × *perf.* 8.

No.	Type	Description		Unused	Used
368	**101**	1 c. green (15.6.37)	..	1 0	1 3
369	,,	2 c. brown (18.6.37)	..	1 6	1 3
370	,,	3 c. scarlet (15.4.37)	..	1 6	0 8

(*b*) *Air. P* 12.

No.	Type	Description		Unused	Used
371	**107**	6 c. blue (15.6.38)	..	3 0	1 0

108. Queen Elizabeth II when Princess and Princess Margaret.

109. National War Memorial, Ottawa.

110. King George VI and Queen Elizabeth.

1939 (15 May). *Royal Visit. P* 12.

No.	Type	Description		Unused	Used
372	**108**	1 c. black and green	..	1 6	0 6
373	**109**	2 c. black and brown	..	1 3	0 4
374	**110**	3 c. black and carmine	..	1 6	0 3

111. King George VI in Naval uniform.

112. King George VI in Military uniform.

113. King George VI in Air Force uniform.

114. Grain Elevator.

115. Farm Scene.

116. Parliament Buildings.

117. Ram Tank.

118. Corvette.

119. Munitions Factory.

120. Destroyer.

121. Air Training Camp.

1942 (1 July)–**1948.** *War Effort.*

(*a*) *Postage.* (i) *P* 12.

No.	Type	Description	Unused s.	d.	Used s.	d.
375	**111**	1 c. green	0	9	0	3
376	**112**	2 c. brown	1	0	0	3
377	**113**	3 c. carmine-lake	2	0	0	3
378	,,	3 c. purple (30.6.43)	1	0	0	3
379	**114**	4 c. slate	6	0	7	6
380	**112**	4 c. carmine-lake (1.4.43)	1	6	0	3
381	**111**	5 c. blue	2	0	0	3
382	**115**	8 c. red-brown	3	0	1	6
383	**116**	10 c. brown	5	0	0	3
384	**117**	13 c. dull green	10	0	8	6
385	,,	14 c. dull green (1.4.43)	6	0	1	9
386	**118**	20 c. chocolate	10	0	1	0
387	**119**	50 c. violet	20	0	5	0
388	**120**	$1 blue	60	0	15	0

The 1 c., 2 c., 3 c. carm. and 3 c. purple exist in blooklet panes of 4 stamps; the 1 c., 2 c., 3 c. purple and 4 c. carm. in booklet panes of 6 stamps producing single stamps with one or two adjacent sides imperf.

(ii) *Coil stamps. Imperf.*×*perf.* 8.

No.	Type	Description	Unused s.	d.	Used s.	d.
389	**111**	1 c. green	1	0	1	0
390	**112**	2 c. brown	1	6	1	6
391	**113**	3 c. carmine-lake	3	0	2	6
392	,,	3 c. purple	2	0	1	3
393	**112**	4 c. carmine-lake	2	6	1	0

(iii) *Booklet stamps. Imperf.*×*perf.* 12.

No.	Type	Description	Unused s.	d.	Used s.	d.
394	**111**	1 c. green	3	6	3	0
395	**113**	3 c. purple	4	6	3	0
396	**112**	4 c. carmine-lake	6	0	4	0

Nos. 394/6 are from booklets in which the stamps are in strips of three, imperforate at top and bottom and right-hand end.

(iv) *Coil stamps. Imperf.*×*perf.* $9\frac{1}{2}$ (1948).

No.	Type	Description	Unused s.	d.	Used s.	d.
397	**111**	1 c. green	3	6	3	0
397*a*	**112**	2 c. brown	10	0	8	6
398	**113**	3 c. purple	4	0	3	0
398*a*	**112**	4 c. carmine-lake	4	0	3	6

(*b*) *Air. P* 12.

No.	Type	Description	Unused s.	d.	Used s.	d.
399	**121**	6 c. blue	10	0	2	6
400	,,	7 c. blue (1.4.43)	3	0	0	9

122. Ontario Farm Scene.

123. Great Bear Lake.

124. St. Maurice River Power Station.

125. Combine Harvester.

126. Lumbering in British Columbia.

127. Train Ferry, Prince Edward Is.

128. Canada Geese in flight.

1946 (16 Sept.). *Peace Re-conversion. P* 12.

(*a*) *Postage.*

401	**122**	8 c. brown	2 0	2 6
402	**123**	10 c. olive-green	2 6	0 3
403	**124**	14 c. sepia	4 0	1 0
404	**125**	20 c. slate	5 0	0 4
405	**126**	50 c. green	20 0	3 0
406	**127**	$1 purple	32 6	6 0

(*b*) *Air.*

407	**128**	7 c. blue..	3 0	0 10

No. 407 exists in booklet panes of 4 stamps each, with one or two adjacent sides imperf.

129. Alexander Graham Bell and " Fame ".

130. " Canadian Citizenship ".

1947 (3 Mar.). 100*th Anniv. of Birth of Bell* (*inventor of telephone*). *P* 12.

408	**129**	4 c. blue	1 10	0 8

1947 (1 July). *Advent of Canadian Citizenship and Eightieth Anniv. of Confederation. P* 12.

409	**130**	4 c. blue	0 10	0 8

131. Queen Elizabeth II when Princess.

(From photograph by Dorothy Wilding.)

948 (16 Feb.). *Princess Elizabeth's Marriage. P* 12.

10	**131**	4 c. blue	0 10	0 4

132. Queen Victoria, Parliament Building, Ottawa, and King George VI.

1948 (1 Oct.). *One Hundred Years of Responsible Government. P* 12.

411	**132**	4 c. grey	0 10	0 4

133. Cabot's Ship *Matthew.*

1949 (1 Apr.). *Entry of Newfoundland into Canadian Confederation. P* 12.

412	**133**	4 c. green	1 0	0 8

134. " Founding of Halifax, 1749 ", after C. W. Jeffries, R.C.A., LL.D.

1949 (21 June). 200*th Anniv. of Halifax, Nova Scotia. P* 12.

413	**134**	4 c. violet..	1 0	0 8

135.

136. **137.**

138. King George VI. **139.**

(From photographs by Dorothy Wilding.)

1949 (15 Nov.)–**51.** (i). *P* 12.

414	**135**	1 c. green	0 4	0 3
415	**136**	2 c. sepia	0 10	0 6
415*a*	,,	2 c. olive-green (11.8.51)	0 4	0 3
416	**137**	3 c. purple	0 8	0 3
417	**138**	4 c. carmine-lake ..	0 10	0 3
417*a*	,,	4 c. vermilion (11.8.51)	0 8	0 3
418	**139**	5 c. blue..	1 0	0 3

(ii) *Imperf.×perf.* 9½ (*coil stamps*).

419	**135**	1 c. green	0	6	0	9
420	**136**	2 c. sepia	1	6	1	9
420*a*	,,	2 c. olive-green ('51) ..	0	8	0	6
421	**137**	3 c. purple	1	6	2	0
422	**138**	4 c. carmine-lake ..	4	6	4	0
422*a*	,,	4 c. vermilion ('51) ..	1	0	1	3

(iii) *Imperf.×perf.* 12 (*booklets*).

422*b*	**135**	1 c. green ('51)	0	4	0	8
423	**137**	3 c. purple ('50) ..	0	9	1	9
423*a*	**138**	4 c. carmine-lake ('51) ..	2	0	2	6
423*b*	,,	4 c. vermilion ('51) ..	3	0	3	6

The booklet stamps listed above are in strips of three, imperforate at top and bottom and right-hand end.

The 3 c. exists also in booklet panes of four stamps and the 4 c., both colours exists in panes of six stamps, producing single stamps with one side or two adjacent sides imperf.

140. King George VI.

(From photograph by Dorothy Wilding.)

1950 (19 Jan.). *As T* **135/9** *but without* " POSTES POSTAGE ", *as T* **140.** (i) *P* 12.

424	1 c. green	0	3	0	3
425	2 c. sepia	1	0	1	0
426	3 c. purple	0	9	0	4
427	4 c. carmine-lake	0	10	0	3
428	5 c. blue	1	3	1	3

(ii) *Imperf.×perf.* 9½ (*coil stamps*).

429	1 c. green	0	6	0	6
430	3 c. purple	0	8	0	9

141. Oil Wells in Alberta.

1950 (1 Mar.). *P* 12.

431	**141**	50 c. green	15	0	5	6

142. Drying Furs.

1950 (2 Oct.). *P* 12.

432	**142**	10 c. brown-purple ..	2	3	0	2

143. Fisherman.

1951 (1 Feb.). *P* 12.

433	**143**	$1 ultramarine	50	0	10	0

144. Sir R. L. Borden. **145.** W. L. Mackenzie King.

1951 (25 June). *Prime Ministers* (1*st issue*). *P* 12.

434	**144**	3 c. blue-green	0	9	0	6
435	**145**	4 c. rose-carmine ..	0	10	0	4

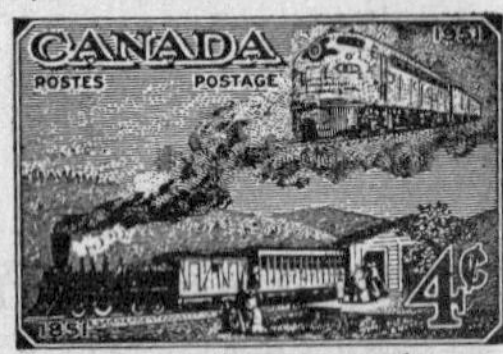

146. Mail Trains, 1851 and 1951.

147. SS. *City of Toronto* and SS. *Prince George.*

148. Mail Coach and Aeroplane.

149. Reproduction of 3d., 1851.

1951 (24 Sept.). *Canadian Stamp Centenary* *P* 12.

436	**146**	4 c. black	1	9	1	
437	**147**	5 c. violet	5	0	5	
438	**148**	7 c. blue	2	6	2	
439	**149**	15 c. scarlet	3	6	0	1

150. Queen Elizabeth II when Princess and Duk of Edinburgh.

1951 (26 Oct.). *Royal Visit.* *P* 12.
440 **150** 4 c. violet 0 9 0 4

151. Forestry Products.

(Des. A. L. Pollock.)

1952 (1 Apr.). *P* 12.
441 **151** 20 c. grey 4 6 0 6

152. Red Cross Emblem.

1952 (26 July). *Eighteenth International Red Cross Conference, Toronto. Design recess.; cross litho.* *P* 12.
442 **152** 4 c. scarlet and blue .. 0 9 0 4

153. Canada Goose.

(Des. E. Hahn.)

1952 (3 Nov.). *P* 12.
443 **153** 7 c. blue 1 0 0 8

1952 (3 Nov.). *Prime Ministers* (*2nd issue*). *Various portraits as T* **144**. *P* 12.
444 3 c. reddish purple 0 8 0 3
445 4 c. orange-red 0 9 0 3

Portraits:—3 c. Sir John J. C. Abbott; 4 c. A. Mackenzie.

54. Pacific Coast Indian House and Totem Pole.

(Des. E. Hahn.)

953 (2 Feb.). *P* 12.
46 **154** $1 black 10 0 6 0

155. Polar Bear.

156. Moose.

157. Bighorn Sheep.

(Des. J. Crosby (2 c.), E. Hahn (others).)

1953. (1 Apr.). *National Wild Life Week.* *P* 12.
447 **155** 2 c. blue 0 8 0 8
448 **156** 3 c. sepia 0 8 0 6
449 **157** 4 c. slate 1 0 0 8

158. Queen Elizabeth II. **159.**

(From photograph by Karsh, Ottawa.)

1953 (1 May). (i) *P* 12.
450 **158** 1 c. purple-brown .. 0 3 0 3
451 " 2 c. green 0 4 0 3
452 " 3 c. carmine 0 8 0 3
453 " 4 c. violet 0 10 0 4
454 " 5 c. ultramarine .. 0 10 0 5

(ii) *Imperf.* × *perf.* 9½ (*coil stamps*).
455 **158** 2 c. green 1 0 1 0
456 " 3 c. carmine 1 6 1 9
457 " 4 c. violet 2 0 2 0

(iii) *Imperf.* × *perf.* 12 (*booklets*).
458 **158** 1 c. purple-brown .. 0 8 0 8
459 " 3 c. carmine 1 0 1 0
460 " 4 c. violet 1 9 1 9

The booklet stamps listed above are in strips of three, imperforate at top and bottom and right-hand end. The 3 c. exists also in booklet panes of four stamps and the 4 c. exists in panes of six stamps, producing single stamps with one side or two adjacent sides imperf.

(Des. E. Hahn.)

1953 (1 June). *Coronation.* *P* 12.
461 **159** 4 c. violet 0 8 0 6

160. Textile Industry.

(Des. A. L. Pollock.)

1953 (2 Nov.). *P* 12.
462 **160** 50 c. deep bluish green .. 4 6 4 0

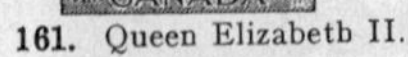

161. Queen Elizabeth II. **162.** Walrus.

163. Beaver. **164.** Gannet.

(From photograph by Dorothy Wilding.)

1954–62. (i) *P* 12.
463 **161** 1 c. purple-brn. (10 June) 0 3 0 2
a. Booklet pane. Five stamps plus one printed label ('56) 1 6
p. Two phosphor bands (13.1.62) 0 5 0 2
464 " 2 c. green (10.6.54) .. 0 4 0 2
p. Two phosphor bands (13.1.62) 0 5 0 2
465 " 3 c. carmine (10.6.54) .. 0 5 0 2
a. Imperf. btwn. (horiz. pr.)
p. Two phosphor bands (13.1.62) 0 10 0 2
466 " 4 c. violet (10.6.54) .. 0 6 0 2
a. Booklet pane. Five stamps plus one printed label ('56) 3 0
p. One phosphor band (13.1.62) 1 0 0 2
467 " 5 c. bright blue (1.4.54) .. 0 8 0 2
a. Booklet pane. Five stamps plus one printed label (8.54) 4 0
p. Two phosphor bands (13.1.62) 1 0 0 2
468 " 6 c. red-orange (10.6.54) .. 1 3 1 0
(ii) *Imperf.* × *perf.* 9½ (*coil stamps*).
469 **161** 2 c. green (9.9.54) .. 0 4 0 4
470 " 4 c. violet (23.8.54) .. 0 6 0 10
471 " 5 c. bright blue (6.7.54) .. 0 10 0 10

Stamps from the booklet panes have one side or two adjacent sides imperf. The 4 c. also exists in booklet panes of 6.

The 2 c. exists in blocks of 25 (5×5) and the 5 c. in blocks of 20 (5 × 4) with outer edges imperf. These come from "One Dollar Plastic Packages" sold at post offices. Prices (per pack): 2 c. (2 blocks of 25) 9*s.*; 5 c. (1 block of 20) 9*s.*

(Des. E. Hahn.)

1954 (1 Apr.). *National Wild Life Week.* *P* 12.
472 **162** 4 c. slate-black 0 8 0 6
473 **163** 5 c. ultramarine 0 10 0 6
a. Booklet pane. Five stamps plus one printed label .. 15 0

Stamps from the booklet pane have one side or two adjacent sides imperf.

(Des. L. Hyde.)

1954 (1 Apr.). *P* 12.
474 **164** 15 c. black 1 6 0 8

1954 (1 Nov.). *Prime Ministers* (3*rd issue*). *Various portraits as T* **144**. *P* 12.
475 4 c. violet 1 0 0 4
476 5 c. bright blue 1 0 0 4

Portraits:—4 c. Sir John Thompson; 5 c. Sir Mackenzie Bowell.

165. Eskimo Hunter.

(Des. H. Beament.)

1955 (21 Feb.). *P* 12.
477 **165** 10 c. purple-brown .. 1 1 0 4

166. Musk-ox.

167. Whooping Cranes.

(Des. E. Hahn (4 c.), Dr. W. Rowan (5 c.).)

1955 (4 Apr.). *National Wild Life Week.* *P* 12.
478 **166** 4 c. violet 1 0 0 6
479 **167** 5 c. ultramarine 1 6 0 10

168. Dove and Torch.

(Des. W. Lohse.)

1955 (1 June). *Tenth Anniv. of International Civil Aviation Organisation.* *P* 12.
480 **168** 5 c. ultramarine 2 6 0 6

169. Pioneer Settlers.

(Des. L. Hyde.)

1955 (30 JUNE). *50th Anniv. of Alberta and Saskatchewan Provinces.* *P* 12.
481 **169** 5 c. ultramarine 1 3 0 6

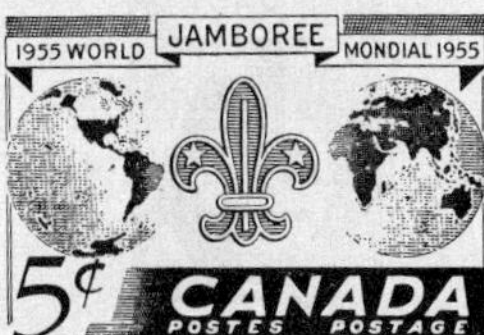

170. Scout Badge and Globe.

(Des. L. Hyde.)

1955 (20 AUG.). *Eighth World Scout Jamboree, Niagara-on-the-Lake.* *P* 12.
482 **170** 5 c. orange-brn. & green 1 6 0 8

1955 (8 NOV.). *Prime Ministers* (*4th Issue*). *Various portraits as T* **144.** *P* 12.
483 4 c. violet 0 10 0 4
484 5 c. bright blue 1 0 0 4

Portraits:—4 c. R. B. Bennett; 5 c. Sir Charles Tupper.

173. Ice-hockey Players.

(Des. J. Simpkins.)

1956 (23 JAN.). *Ice-hockey Commemoration.* *P* 12.
485 **173** 5 c. ultramarine 1 0 0 4

174. Caribou.

175. Mountain Goat.

(Des. E. Hahn.)

1956 (12 APR.). *National Wild Life Week.* *P* 12.
486 **174** 4 c. violet 0 9 0 3
487 **175** 5 c. bright blue 1 0 0 4

176. Pulp and Paper Industry.

177. Chemical Industry.

178

(Des. A. J. Casson (20 c.), A. L. Pollock (25 c.).)

1956 (7 JUNE). *P* 12.
488 **176** 20 c. green 1 10 0 6
489 **177** 25 c. red 2 4 0 6

(Des. A. Price.)

1956 (9 OCT.). *Fire Prevention Week.* *P* 12
490 **178** 5 c. red and black .. 0 10 0 4

179. Fishing.

180. Swimming.

181. Hunting.

182. Ski-ing.

(Des. L. Hyde.)

1957 (7 MAR.). *Outdoor Recreation.* *P* 12.
491 **179** 5 c. ultramarine 1 9 0 6
492 **180** 5 c. ultramarine 1 9 0 6
493 **181** 5 c. ultramarine 1 9 0 6
494 **182** 5 c. ultramarine 1 9 0 6

Block of 4, *se-tenant*, 12*s*. 6*d*. *un*.; 15*s*. *us*.

No. 491/4 are printed together in sheets of 50 (5×10). In the first, second, fourth and fifth verticlal rows the four different designs are arranged in *se-tenant* blocks, whilst the central row is made up as follows (reading downwards):—Nos. 491/4, 491/2 (or 493/4) 491/4.

183. Common Loon.

184. Thompson with Sextant, and North American Map.

(Des. L. Hyde.)

1957 (10 Apr.). *National Wild Life Week.* *P* 12.
495 **183** 5 c. black 0 9 0 4

(Des. G. A. Gundersen.)

1957 (5 June). *Centenary of Death of David Thompson (explorer).* *P* 12.
496 **184** 5 c. ultramarine 0 9 0 4

185. Parliament Buildings, Ottawa.

186. Globe within Posthorn.

(Des. Carl Mangold.)

1957 (14 Aug.). *14th U.P.U. Congress, Ottawa.* *P* 12.
497 **185** 5 c. grey-blue 1 0 0 6
498 **186** 15 c blackish blue .. 6 0 5 0

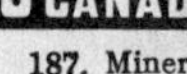

187. Miner.

188. Queen Elizabeth II and Duke of Edinburgh.

(Des. A. J. Casson.)

1957 (5 Sept.). *Mining Industry.* *P* 12.
499 **187** 5 c. black 0 10 0 4

(From photographs by Karsh, Ottawa.)

1957 (10 Oct.). *Royal Visit* *P* 12.
500 **188** 5 c. black 0 8 0 4

189. " A Free Press ".

(Des. A. L. Pollock.)

1958 (22 Jan.). *The Canadian Press.* *P* 12.
501 **189** 5 c. black 1 0 0 4

190. Microscope.

(Des. A. L. Pollock.)

1958 (5 Mar.). *International Geophysical Year.* *P* 12.
502 **190** 5 c. blue 0 9 0 4

191. Miner Panning for Gold.

(Des. J. Harman.)

1958 (8 May.) *Centenary of British Columbia.* *P* 12.
503 **191** 5 c. deep turquoise-green 0 9 0 4

192. La Verendrye (statue).

(Des. G. Trottier.)

1958 (4 June). *La Verendrye (explorer) Commemoration.* *P* 12.
504 **192** 5 c. ultramarine 0 9 0 4

193. Samuel de Champlain and the Heights of Quebec.

(Des. G. Trottier.)

1958 (26 June). *350th Anniv. of Founding of Quebec.* *P* 12.
505 **193** 5 c. brown-ochre & dp. grn. 0 9 0 4

194. Nurse.

(Des. G. Trottier.)

1958 (30 July). *National Health.* *P* 12.
506 **194** 5 c. reddish purple .. 0 9 0 4

195. " Petroleum 1858–1958 ".
(Des. A. L. Pollock.)

1958 (10 SEPT.). *Centenary of Canadian Oil Industry. P 12.*
507 **195** 5 c. scarlet and olive .. 0 9 0 4

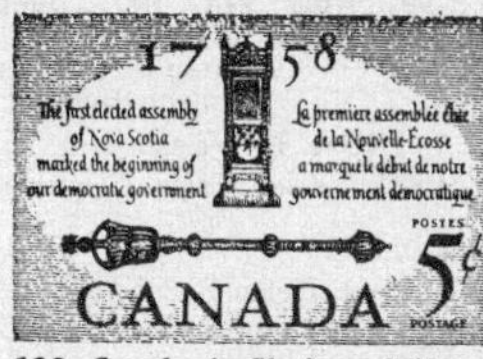

196. Speaker's Chair and Mace.
(Des. G. Trottier and C. Dair.)

1958 (2 OCT.). *Bicentenary of First Elected Assembly. P 12.*
508 **196** 5 c. deep slate 0 9 0 4

197. The " Silver Dart ".

1959 (23 FEB.). *50th Anniv. of First Flight of the " Silver Dart " in Canada. P 12.*
509 **197** 5 c. black and ultramarine 0 8 0 4

198. Globe showing N.A.T.O. Countries.
(Des. P. Weiss.)

1959 (2 APR.). *Tenth Anniv. of North Atlantic Treaty Organization. P 12.*
510 **198** 5 c. ultramarine.. .. 0 9 0 4

199 **200.** Queen Elizabeth II.
(Des. Helen Fitzgerald.)

1959 (13 MAY). *" Associated Country Women of the World " Commemoration. P 12.*
511 **199** 5 c. black & yellow-olive 0 9 0 4
(Des. after painting by Annigoni.)

1959 (18 JUNE). *Royal Visit. P 12.*
512 **200** 5 c. lake-red .. 0 9 0 4

ST. LAWRENCE SEAWAY · VOIE MARITIME DU ST-LAURENT
POSTAGE POSTES 5¢
CANADA

201. Maple Leaf linked with American Eagle.
(Des. A. L. Pollock, G. Trottier (of Canada); W. H. Buckley, A. J. Copeland, E. Metzl (of the United States).)

1959 (26 JUNE). *Opening of St. Lawrence Seaway. P 12.*
513 **201** 5 c. ultramarine and red 0 9 0 4
a. Centre inverted ..

202. Maple Leaves.
(Des. P. Weiss.)

1959 (10 SEPT.). *Bicentenary of Battle of Plains of Abraham (Quebec). P 12.*
514 **202** 5 c. deep green and red .. 0 9 0 4

1910 GIRL GUIDES ASSOCIATION DES GUIDES 1960
BE PREPARED · SOIS PRÊTE
CANADA
POSTAGE 5c POSTES

203

CANADA POSTES 5c
DOLLARD DES ORMEAUX
POSTAGE
1660

204. Dollard des Ormeaux.
(Des. Helen Fitzgerald.)

1960 (20 APR.). *Golden Jubilee of Canadian Girl Guides Movement. P 12.*
515 **203** 5 c. ultram. & orge.-brn. 0 9 0 4
(Des. P. Weiss.)

1960 (19 MAY). *Tercentenary of Battle of the Long Sault. P 12.*
516 **204** 5 c. ultram. & lt. brown .. 0 9 0 4

205. Surveyor, Bulldozer and Compass Rose.

206. E. Pauline Johnson.

(Des. B. J. Reddie.)

1961 (8 Feb.). *Northern Development. P* 12.

517 **205** 5 c. emerald and red .. 0 9 0 4

(Des. B. J. Reddie.)

1961 (10 Mar.). *Centenary of Birth of E. Pauline Johnson (Mohawk poetess). P* 12.

518 **206** 5 c. green and red .. 0 9 0 4

207. Arthur Meighen (statesman).

1961 (19 Apr.). *Arthur Meighen Commemoration. P* 12.

519 **207** 5 c. ultramarine 0 9 0 4

208. Engineers and Dam.

(Des. B. J. Reddie.)

1961 (28 June). *Tenth Anniv. of Colombo Plan. P* 12.

520 **208** 5 c. blue and brown .. 0 9 0 4

209. "Resources for Tomorrow". **210.** "Education".

(Des. A. L. Pollock.)

1961 (12 Oct.). *Natural Resources. P* 12.

521 **209** 5 c. blue-green and brown 0 9 0 4

(Des. Helen Fitzgerald.)

1962 (28 Feb.). *Education Year. P* 12.

522 **210** 5 c. black and orge.-brown 0 9 0 4

RED RIVER SETTLEMENT · 1812

LA COLONIE DE LA RIVIÈRE ROUGE · 1812

211. Lord Selkirk and Farmer.

(Des. Phillips-Gutkin Ltd.)

1962 (3 May). *150th Anniv. of Red River Settlement. P* 12.

523 **211** 5 c. chocolate and green .. 0 8 0 3

212. Talon bestowing gifts on married couple.

213. Br. Columbia & Vancouver Is. 2½d. stamp of 1860, and Parliament Buildings, B.C.

(Des. P. Weiss.)

1962 (13 June). *Jean Talon Commemoration. P* 12.

524 **212** 5 c. blue 0 8 0 3

(Des. Helen Bacon.)

1962 (22 Aug.). *Centenary of Victoria, B.C. P* 12.

525 **213** 5 c. red and black .. 0 8 0 3

CANADA POSTAGE POSTES **5c**

214. Highway (map version) and Provincial Arms.

(Des. A. L. Pollock.)

1962 (31 Aug.). *Opening of Trans-Canada Highway. P* 12.

526 **214** 5 c. black & orange-brn. 0 8 0 3

215. Queen Elizabeth II (from drawing by Ernst Roch).

1962-64. *T* **215** *and similar horiz. designs with different symbols at top left.* (*i*) *P* 12.

527 1 c. chocolate (4.2.63) .. 0 3 0 2
 a. Booklet pane. Five stamps plus one ptd. label (15.5.63) .. 1 0
 p. Two phosphor bands (15.5.63) .. 0 3 0 2

528 2 c. green (2.5.63) 0 4 0 2
 p. Two phosphor bands (15.5.63) .. 0 4 0 2

529 3 c. reddish violet (2.5.63) .. 0 5 0 2
 p. Two phosphor bands (15.5.63) .. 0 5 0 2

530 4 c. carmine-red (4.2.63) .. 0 6 0 2
 a. Booklet pane. Five stamps plus one ptd. label (15.5.63) .. 2 3
 p. One phosphor band* (15.5.63) .. 0 6 0

531 5 c. ultramarine (3.10.62) .. 0 8 0
 a. Booklet pane. Five stamps plus one ptd. label ('63) .. 3 0
 p. One phosphor band (31.1.63?) .. 0 8 0

(*ii*) *P* 9½ × *imperf.* (*coil stamps*).

532 2 c. green ('63) 0 4 0

532*a* 3 c. reddish violet ('64) .. 0 5 0

533 4 c. carmine-red (15.5.63) .. 0 6 0

534 5 c. ultramarine (15.5.63) .. 0 8 0

Symbols :—1 c. Crystals (Mining) ; 2 c. Tre (Forestry) ; 3 c. Fish (Fisheries) ; 4 c. Electricit pylon (Industrial power) ; 5 c. Wheat (Agricu ture).

Stamps from the booklet panes have one side or two adjacent sides imperf.

The 2 c. and 4 c. exist in blocks of 25 (5 × 5) and the 5 c. in blocks of 20 (4 × 5) with outer edges imperf. These come from "One Dollar Plastic Packages" sold at post offices. Prices (per pack): 2 c. (2 blocks of 25) 9s.; 4 c. (1 block of 25) 9s.; 5 c. (1 block of 20) 9s.

*No. 530p exists in three forms. The first printings had a single 4 mm. phosphor band down the centre of the stamp. In later printings an 8 mm. band was applied to each alternate vertical gutter, thus producing a 4 mm. band at left or right of the stamps.

216. Sir Casimir Gzowski.

(Des. P. Weiss.)

1963 (5 MAR.). *150th Birth Anniv. of Gzowski (engineer). P 12.*

535 **216** 5 c. reddish purple .. 0 8 0 3

217. "Export Trade".

(Des. A. L. Pollock.)

1963 (14 JUNE). *P 12.*

536 **217** $1 carmine 9 0 5 0

218. Frobisher and barque *Gabriel.*

(Des. P. Weiss.)

1963 (21 AUG.). *Sir Martin Frobisher Commemoration. P 12.*

537 **218** 5 c. ultramarine .. 0 8 0 3

219. Horseman and Map.

(Des. B. J. Reddie.)

1963 (25 SEPT.). *Bicentenary of Quebec-Trois Rivieres-Montreal Postal Service. P 12.*

538 **219** 5 c. red-brown & dp. grn. 0 8 0 3

220. Canada Geese. **221.** Jet Airliner (composite) and Uplands Airport, Ottawa.

(Des. A. Shortt and P. Arthur.)

1963 (30 OCT.). *P 12.*

539 **220** 15 c. blue 1 6 0 6

1964. *P 12.*

540	**221**	7 c. blue (11 Mar.)	..	0 10	1 3
540*a*	,,	8 c. blue (18 Nov.)	..	0 11	1 0

222. "Peace on Earth".

1964 (8 APR.). *"Peace". Litho. and recess. P 12.*

541 **222** 5 c. ochre, blue and turquoise-blue 0 8 0 9

223. Maple Leaves.

1964 (14 MAY). *"Canadian Unity". P 12.*

542 **223** 5 c. lake-red & light blue 0 8 0 9

224. White Trillium and Arms of Ontario.

225. White Garden Lily and Arms of Quebec.

226. Purple Violet and Arms of New Brunswick.

227. Mayflower and Arms of Nova Scotia.

228. Dogwood and Arms of British Columbia.

229. Prairie Crocus and Arms of Manitoba.

230. Lady's Slipper and Arms of Prince Edward Island.

231. Wild Rose and Arms of Alberta.

232. Prairie Lily and Arms of Saskatchewan.

233. Pitcher Plant and Arms of Newfoundland.

1964–66. *Provincial Emblems. Litho. and recess. P* 12.

543	**224**	5 c. green, brown & orange (30.6.64)	0 8	0 9
544	**225**	5 c. green, orange-brown and yellow (30.6.64)	0 8	0 9
545	**226**	5 c. carmine-red, green & bluish violet (3.2.65)	0 8	0 9
546	**227**	5 c. bl., red & grn. (3.2.65)	0 8	0 9
547	**228**	5 c. purple, green and yellow-brown (28.4.65)	0 8	0 9
548	**229**	5 c. red-brown, dp. bluish grn. & mauve (28.4.65)	0 8	0 9
549	**230**	5 c. slate-lilac, grn. & lt. reddish pur. (21.7.65)	0 8	0 9
550	**231**	5 c. green, yellow and rose-red (19.1.66) ..	0 8	0 9
551	**232**	5 c. sepia, orange and green (19.1.66) ..	0 8	0 9
552	**233**	5 c. black, green and red (23.2.66)	0 8	0 9

(237)

238. Fathers of the Confederation Memorial, Charlottetown.

1964 (15 JULY). *No.* 540 *surch. with T* **237.**

556	**221**	8 c. on 7 c. blue	0 11	1 6

(Des. P. Weiss.)

1964 (29 JULY). *Centenary of Charlottetown Conference. P* 12.

557	**238**	5 c. black	0 8	0

239. Maple Leaf and Hand with Quill Pen.

(Des. P. Weiss.)

1964 (9 SEPT.). *Centenary of Quebec Conference. P* 12.

558	**239**	5 c. light red & chocolate	0 8	0

240. Queen Elizabeth II. **241.** " Canadian Family ".

(Portrait by Anthony Buckley.)

1964 (5 Oct.). *Royal Visit.* *P* 12.

559 **240** 5 c. reddish purple .. 0 8 0 9

1964 (14 Oct.). *Christmas.* *P* 12.

560 **241** 3 c. scarlet 0 5 0 6
p. Two phosphor bands .. 0 5 0 6
561 ,, 5 c. ultramarine 0 8 0 9
p. Two phosphor bands .. 0 8 0 9

The 3 c. both ordinary and phosphor exist in blocks of 25 (5×5) with outer edges imperf. These come from " $1.50 Plastic Packages " sold at post offices. Price per pack (ordinary or phosphor) 13s. 6d.

242. " Co-operation ".

1965 (3 Mar.). *International Co-operation Year.* *P* 12.

562 **242** 5 c. grey-green 0 8 0 9

243. Sir W. Grenfell.

1965 (9 June). *Birth Centenary of Sir Wilfred Grenfell (missionary).* *P* 12.

563 **243** 5 c. deep bluish green .. 0 8 0 9

244. National Flag.

1965 (30 June). *Inauguration of National Flag.* *P* 12.

564 **244** 5 c. red and blue .. 0 8 0 9

245. Sir Winston Churchill. **246.** Peace Tower, Parliament Buildings, Ottawa.

(Des. P. Weiss from photo by Karsh. Litho.)

1965 (12 Aug.). *Churchill Commemoration.* *P* 12.

565 **245** 5 c. purple-brown .. 0 8 0 9

(Des. Philips-Gutkin.)

1965 (8 Sept.). *Inter-Parliamentary Union Conference, Ottawa.* *P* 12.

566 **246** 5 c. deep green 0 8 0 9

247. Parliament Buildings, Ottawa, 1865.

(Des. G. Trottier.)

1965 (8 Sept.). *Centenary of Proclamation of Ottawa as Capital.* *P* 12.

567 **247** 5 c. brown 0 8 0 9

248. " Gold, Frankincense and Myrrh ". **249.** " Alouette 2 " over Canada.

(Des. Helen Fitzgerald.)

1965 (13 Oct.). *Christmas.* *P* 12.

568 **248** 3 c. olive-green 0 5 0 6
569 ,, 5 c. ultramarine 0 8 0 9

The 3 c. exists in blocks of 25 (5×5) with outer edges imperf. These come from " $1.50 Plastic Packages " sold at post offices. Price per pack (two blocks of 25), 14s. 3d.

1966 (5 Jan.). *Launching of Canadian Satellite, " Alouette 2 ".* *P* 12.

570 **249** 5 c. ultramarine 0 8 0 9

REGISTRATION STAMPS.

R 1

Eng. & ptd. British-American Bank Note Co., Montreal and Ottawa.)

1875 (15 Nov.)–**92.** *White wove paper.* (*a*) *P* 12.

R 1	**R 1**	2 c. orange ..	.. 17	6	2	0
R 2	,,	2 c. orange-red ..	.. 42	6	17	6
R 3	,,	2 c. vermilion ..	.. 40	0	15	0
		a. Imperf. (pair)	—		£120	
R 4	,,	2 c. rose-carmine (1888)	90	0	45	0
R 5	,,	5 c. yellow-green	.. 35	0	3	6
R 6	,,	5 c. dark green ..	.. 25	0	1	6
		a. Imperf. (pair)	£12			
R 7	,,	5 c. blue-green (1888)	.. 45	0	3	0
R 7*a*	,,	5 c. dull sea-green (1892)	90	0	17	6
R 8	,,	8 c. bright blue ..	.. £10		£10	
R 9	,,	8 c. dull blue ..	.. £10		£10	

(*b*) *P* 12×11½.

R10	**R 1**	2 c. orange	—	£5
R11	,,	5 c. green (*shades*) ..	—	£20

Perfs. of Nos. R10/11 must measure exactly 12×11½.

SPECIAL DELIVERY STAMPS.

PRINTERS. The following Special Delivery and Postage Due stamps were recess-printed by the American Bank Note Co. (to 1928), the British American Bank Note Co. (to 1934), and the Canadian Bank Note Co. (1935 onwards).

S 1

1898 (28 June)–**1920.** *P* 12.

S 1	**S 1**	10 c. yellow-green	.. 50	0	25	0
S 2	,,	10 c. deep green (Dec. '13)	35	0	6	6
S 3	,,	10 c. blue-green (Aug. '20)	35	0	12	6

The differences between Types I and II (figures "10" with and without shading) formerly illustrated were due to wear of the plate. There was only one die.

S 2

1922 (Sept.). *P* 12.

S 4	**S 2**	20 c. carmine-red ..	.. 45	9	15	0

S **3.** Mail-carrying, 1867 and 1927.

1927. *60th Anniv. of Confederation.* *P* 12.

S 5	**S 3**	20 c. orange ..	.. 17	6	25	0

S 4

1930 (2 Sept.). *P* 11.

S 6	**S 4**	20 c. brown-red ..	.. 35	0	20	0

1933. *Type as* S **4**, *but inscr.* "CENTS" *in place of* "TWENTY CENTS". *P* 11.

S 7		20 c. brown-red ..	.. 30	0	20	0

S **5.** Allegory of Progress.

1935 (1 June). *P* 12.

S 8	**S 5**	20 c. scarlet ..	.. 10	0	12	6

S **6.** Canadian Coat of Arms.

1938–39. *P* 12.

S 9	**S 6**	10 c. green (1.4.39)	.. 10	6	5	0
S10	,,	20 c. scarlet (15.6.38)	.. 27	6	27	6

10

(S 7)

1939 (1 Mar.). *Surch. with Type* S **7.**

S11	**S 6**	10 on 20 c. scarlet	.. 10	0	10	

S 8. Coat of Arms and Flags.

S 9. Trans-Canada Plane.

1942 (1 July)–**1943.** *War Effort.* *P* 12.

(a) Postage.

S12	**S 8**	10 c. green	6 0	2 6

(b) Air.

S13	**S 9**	16 c. ultramarine ..	5 6	5 6
S14	,,	17 c. ultramarine (1.4.43)	6 0	6 0

S 10. Arms of Canada and Peace Symbols.

S 11. Transatlantic plane over Quebec.

1946 (16 Sept.)–**1947.** *P* 12.

(a) Postage.

S15	**S 10**	10 c. green	4 0	2 6

(b) Air. (i) *Circumflex accent in* " EXPRÊS ".

S16	**S 11**	17 c. ultramarine ..	10 0	16 6

(ii) *Grave accent in* " EXPRÈS ".

S17	**S 11**	17 c. ultramarine ('47) ..	8 0	8 0

POSTAGE DUE STAMPS.

PRINTERS. See note under " Special Delivery Stamps ".

D 1

D 2

1906 (1 July)–**1928.** *P* 12.

D1	**D 1**	1 c. dull violet	1 3	0 8
D2	,,	1 c. red-violet	1 0	0 8
		a. Thin paper (1924) ..	15 0	20 0
D3	,,	2 c. dull violet	2 6	0 8
D4	,,	2 c. red-violet	3 0	1 0
		a. Thin paper (1924) ..	10 0	12 6
D5	,,	4 c. violet ('28)	30 0	25 0
D6	,,	5 c. dull violet	3 0	1 9
D7	,,	5 c. red-violet	2 6	1 6
		a. Thin paper (1924) ..	7 6	10 0
D8	,,	10 c. violet ('28)	14 0	10 0

1930–32. *P* 11.

D 9	**D 2**	1 c. bright vio. (14.7.30)	1 9	1 9
D10	,,	2 c. bright vio. (21.8.30)	1 0	0 6
D11	,,	4 c. bright vio. (14.10.30)	4 6	4 6
D12	,,	5 c. bright vio. (12.12.31)	4 0	4 0
D13	,,	10 c. bright vio. (24.8.32)	40 0	10 0

D 3

D 4

1933–34. *P* 11.

D14	**D 3**	1 c. violet (5.5.34) ..	3 6	3 6
D15	,,	2 c. violet (20.12.33) ..	1 6	1 6
D16	,,	4 c. violet (12.12.33) ..	2 0	2 6
D18	,,	10 c. violet (20.12.33) ..	5 0	3 6

1935–65. *P* 12.

D19	**D 4**	1 c. violet (14.10.35) ..	0 3	0 3
D20	,,	2 c. violet (9.9.35) ..	0 4	0 3
D20*a*	,,	3 c. violet (4.65) ..	0 5	0 3
D21	,,	4 c. violet (2.7.35) ..	0 6	0 3
D22	,,	5 c. violet (Dec. '48) ..	0 8	0 6
D22*a*	,,	6 c. violet ('57) ..	0 9	0 10
D23	,,	10 c. violet (16.9.35) ..	1 1	0 4

OFFICIAL STAMPS.

We do not list stamps perforated " O.H.M.S. ".

O.H.M.S.

(O 1)

1949. *Optd. with Type* O **1** (1 *c. to* 4 *c.*) *or larger opt.*, 15 × 2 *mm.* (*others*).

(a) Postage.

O 1	**111**	1 c. green	1 3	0 8
O 2	**112**	2 c. brown	12 6	10 0
O 3	**113**	3 c. purple	1 3	0 6
O 4	**112**	4 c. carmine-lake ..	1 6	0 6
O 5	**123**	10 c. olive-green	4 0	2 6
O 6	**124**	14 c. sepia	6 0	1 0
O 7	**125**	20 c. slate	15 0	1 3
O 8	**126**	50 c. green	£12	£12
O 9	**127**	$1 purple	80 0	65 0

(b) Air.

O10	**128**	7 c. blue	10 0	10 0

A variety without stop after " S " is known on Nos. O5 to O10.

1949–50. *Optd. with Type* O **1** (1 *c. to* 5 *c.*) *or larger.*

O11	**135**	1 c. green	0 9	0 9
O12	**136**	2 c. sepia	1 6	1 0
O13	**137**	3 c. purple	1 6	0 8
O14	**138**	4 c. carmine-lake ..	1 6	0 8
O15	**139**	5 c. blue ('49)	2 0	1 0
O16	**141**	50 c. green ('50)	30 0	30 0

G (O **2**) **G** (O **3**) **G** (O **4**)

Type O **4** differs from Type O **3** in having a thinner appearance and an upward sloping left serif to the lower arm. It results from a new plate introduced about 1962 but so far used copies are only known with 1963 dates. Variations in thickness are known in Type O **2** but these are due to wear and subsequent cleaning of the plate.

1950 (2 Oct.)–**52.** *Optd. with Type* O **2** (1 *c. to* 5 *c.*) *or* O **3** (*others*).

(*a*) *Postage.*

O17	**135**	1 c. green	0 3	0 4
O18	**136**	2 c. sepia	1 3	1 0
O18*a*	,,	2 c. olive-grn. (Nov. '51)	0 8	0 6
O19	**137**	3 c. purple	0 8	0 4
O20	**138**	4 c. carmine-lake ..	1 6	0 9
O20*a*	,,	4 c. vermilion (1.5.52) ..	1 0	0 6
O21	**139**	5 c. blue	1 3	1 3
O22	**123**	10 c. olive-green	3 0	1 6
O23	**124**	14 c. sepia	7 6	3 6
O24	**125**	20 c. slate	15 0	1 9
O25	**141**	50 c. green	15 0	15 0
O26	**127**	$1 purple	£7	£9

(*b*) *Air.*

O27	**128**	7 c. blue	12 6	12 6

1950–51. *Optd. with Type* O **3.**

O28	**142**	10 c. brown-purple ..	3 6	1 0
		a. Opt. omitted in pair with normal	£75	£60
O29	**143**	$1 ultramarine (1.2.51)	£8	£9

1952–53. *Optd. with Type* O **3.**

O30	**153**	7 c. blue (3.11.52) ..	5 0	1 6
O31	**151**	20 c. grey (1.4.52) ..	3 6	1 6
O32	**154**	$1 black (2.2.53) ..	15 0	15 0

1953 (1 Sept.)–**63.** *Optd. with Type* O **2** (1 *c. to* 5 *c.*) *or* O **3** (50 *c.*).

O33	**158**	1 c. purple-brown ..	0 4	0 2
O34	,,	2 c. green	0 4	0 3
O35	,,	3 c. carmine	0 6	0 5
O36	,,	4 c. violet	0 9	0 6
O37	,,	5 c. ultramarine ..	1 0	0 8
O38	**160**	50 c. deep bluish green (2.11.53)	6 6	7 6
		a. Opt. Type O 4 ('63) ..	25 0	

1955–56. *Optd. with Type* O **2.** *P* 12.

O39	**161**	1 c. pur.-brn. (12.11.56)	0 4	0 6
O40	,,	2 c. green (19.1.56) ..	0 5	0 4
O42	,,	4 c. violet (23.7.56) ..	0 8	0 6
O43	,,	5 c. bright-blue (11.1.55)	0 10	0 8

1955–63. *Optd. with Type* O **3.**

O45	**165**	10 c. pur.-brn. (21.2.55)	1 9	1 0
		a. Opt. Type O 4 ('63) ..	12 6	
O46	**176**	20 c. green (4.12.56) ..	3 0	2 0
		a. Opt. Type O 4 ('63) ..	45 0	

1963 (15 May). *Optd. as Type* O **2.** *P* 12.

O47	**215**	1 c. chocolate	2 0	2 6
O48	"	2 c. green	2 6	3 0
O50	"	4 c. carmine-red ..	2 6	3 0
O51	"	5 c. ultramarine ..	3 0	3 6

The use of official stamps was discontinued on 31st December, 1963.

OFFICIAL SPECIAL DELIVERY STAMPS.

1950. *Optd. as Type* O **1**, *but larger.*

OS1	S **10**	10 c. green	20 0	25 0

1950 (2 Oct.). *Optd. as Type* O **2**, *but larger.*

OS2	S **10**	10 c. green	30 0	30 0

CAPE OF GOOD HOPE.

— SIMPLIFICATION (see Introduction) **—**

Nos. 1 to 22.

3, 4 : 5a, 5b, 6a, 7, 7b, 8, 8a.
13, 14.
18, 18a, 19, 19a, 20, 21.

3. Hope.

2

(Des. by Charles Bell, Surveyor-General; die eng. W. Humphrys; recess. Perkins Bacon.)

1853 (1 Sept.). *W* **2.** *Imperf.*

(*a*) *Paper deeply blued.*

1	**1**	1d. pale brick-red	£135	£25
		a. Deep brick-red	£160	£40
2	,,	4d. deep blue	£80	£15

(*b*) *Paper slightly blued* (*blueing not so pronounced at back*).

3	**1**	1d. brick red	£90	£22
		a. Brown-red	£120	£28
4	,,	4d. deep blue	£70	£6
		a. Pale blue	£100	£25

Both values are known with wmk. sideways.

1855–58. *White paper. W* **2.** *Imperf.*

5	**1**	1d. brick-red (1857)	—	£35
		a. Pale rose (1858)	£32	£25
		b. Deep rose-red	£40	£30
6	,,	4d. deep blue (1855)	£25	£5
		a. Blue	£25	£5
7	,,	6d. slate-lilac (18.2.58) ..	£70	£30
		a. Blued paper.	£85	£35
		b. Pale rose-lilac	£60	£30
		c. Deep rose-lilac	£110	£35
		d. Slate-purple. Blued paper ..	—	£50
8	,,	1s. bright yell.-grn. (18.2.58)	£70	£28
		a. Deep dark green	£30	£40

The method adopted for producing the plates of the 4d., 6d., and 1s. stamps involved the use of two dies, so that there are two types of each of these values, differing slightly in detail, but produced in equal numbers.

All values of this issue are known with watermark sideways. The 6d. is known bisected and used with 1d. for 4d. rate.

The 4d. is known in black, and it was at one time suggested that a small supply of stamps in this colour was issued on the occasion of the death of the Prince Consort, but there is no confirmation of this in the official records.

Varieties. Unofficially rouletted.

No.	Type	Description	Unused	Used
9	1	1d. brick-red		
10	,,	4d. blue	—	£225
11	,,	6d. rose-lilac	—	£275
12	,,	1s. bright yellow-green ..	—	£550

3. Hope.

(Local provisional (so-called "wood-block") issue. Engraved on steel by C. J. Roberts. Printed from stereotyped plates by Saul Solomon & Co., Cape Town.)

1861 (Feb.—April). *Laid paper. Imperf.*

No.	Type	Description	Unused	Used
13	3	1d. vermilion (27 Feb.) ..	£550	£250
		a. Carmine (7 March)	£550	£350
		b. Brick-red (10 April)	£975	£400
14	,,	4d. pale milky blue (23 Feb.)	£325	£250
		a. Pale grey-blue (Mar.?) ..	£450	£225
		b. Pale bright blue (Mar.?) ..	£450	£225
		c. Deep bright blue (12 April) ..	—	£650
		d. Blue	£500	£275

Errors of colour.

No.	Type	Description	Unused	Used
15	3	1d. pale milky blue	—	£1400
		a. Pale bright blue		£1600
16	,,	4d. vermilion		£1850
		a. Carmine	—	£2200

Variety. Retouch or repair to right-hand lower corner of stereo.

No.	Type	Description	Unused	Used
17	3	4d. pale milky blue ..	—	£550
		a. Pale bright blue	—	£650

Both values were officially reprinted in March, 1883, on wove paper. The 1d. is in deep red, and the 4d. in a deeper blue than that of the deepest shade of the issued stamp.

Specimens of the reprints have done postal duty, but their use thus was not intended. There are no reprints of the errors or of the retouched 4d.

Further reprints were made privately, but with official permission, in 1940/41, in colours much deeper than those of any of the original printings, and on thick carton paper.

Early in 1863, Perkins Bacon & Co. handed over the four plates used for printing the triangular Cape of Good Hope stamps to De La Rue & Co., who made all the subsequent printings.

(Printed from the Perkins Bacon plates by De La Rue & Co.)

1863–64. *W 2. Imperf.*

No.	Type	Description	Unused	Used
18	1	1d. deep carmine-red ..	£18	£20
		a. Deep brown-red	£20	£22
		b. Brownish red	£17	£20
19	,,	4d. dark blue	£16	£10
		a. Pale blue	£17	£15
		b. Slate-blue	£55	£45
		c. Steel-blue	£125	£40
20	,,	6d. bright mauve	£20	£32
21	,,	1s. bright emerald-green ..	£45	£60
		a. Pale emerald-green	£60	

All values of this issue are known with watermark lying sideways.

With the exception of the 4d., these stamps may be easily distinguished from those printed by Perkins Bacon & Co. by their colours, which are quite distinct.

The De La Rue stamps of all values are less clearly printed, the figure of Hope and the lettering of the inscriptions standing out less boldly, while the fine lines of the background appear blurred and broken when examined under a glass. The background as a whole often shows irregularity in the apparent depth of colour, due to wear of the plates.

For note regarding the two dies of the 4d., 6d., and 1s. *values, see after* No. 8.

Variety. Wmk. Crown CC (sideways).

No.	Type	Description	Unused	Used
22	1	1d. deep carmine-red ..	£1250	

This was a trial printing, and is only known unused.

All the triangular stamps were demonetised as from 1st October, 1900.

4. "Hope" seated, with vine and ram. (With outer frame-line.)

Four Pence.

(5)

(Designed by Charles Bell, Surveyor-General. Die engraved on steel and stamps typo. by De La Rue & Co.)

1864–77. *With outer frame-line surrounding the design. Wmk. Crown CC. P 14.*

No.	Type	Description	Unused	Used
23	4	1d. carmine-red (May, 1865)	55 0	20 0
		a. Rose-red	55 0	22 6
24	,,	4d. pale blue (Aug., 1865) ..	75 0	6 0
		a. Blue	80 0	5 0
		b. Ultramarine	£14	£5
		c. Deep blue (1872)	£6	6 0
25	,,	6d. pale lilac (before 21.3.64)	75 0	40 0
		a. Deep lilac	£10	22 6
		b. Violet (to bright) (1877) ..	85 0	6 0
26	,,	1s. deep green (Jan., 1864) ..	£16	40 0
		a. Green	70 0	10 0
		b. Blue-green	85 0	12 6

The 1d. rose-red, 6d. lilac, and 1s. blue-green are known imperf., probably from proof sheets.

The 1d. and 4d. stamps of this issue may be found with side and/or top outer frame-lines missing, due to wear of the plates.

(Surcharged by Saul Solomon & Co., Cape Town.)

1868 (17 Nov.). *No. 25a surcharged with T 5.*

No.	Type	Description	Unused	Used
27	4	4d. on 6d. deep lilac (R.) ..	£6	32 6
		a. "Peuce" for "Pence" ..		
		b. "Fonr" for "Four" ..	—	£30

Specimens may also be found with bars omitted or at the top of the stamp, due to misplacement of the sheet.

The space between the words and bars varies from 12½ to 16 mm., stamps with spacing 15½ and 16 mm. being rare. There were two printings, one of 120,000 in November, 1868, and another of 1,000,000 in December. Stamps showing widest spacings are probably from the earlier printing.

6. (No outer frame-line.)

(Die re-engraved. Typo. De La Rue.)

1871–76. *Outer frame-line removed. Wmk. Crown CC. P* 14.
28 **6** ½d. pale grey-blk. (Dec. '75) 8 0 10 0
  a. Deep grey-black 7 6 9 0
29 ,, 1d. pale car.-red (Feb. '72) .. 14 0 1 6
  a. Deep carmine-red 17 6 1 6
30 ,, 4d. dull blue (Dec. '76) .. 70 0 3 0
  a. Deep blue 70 0 3 6
  b. Ultramarine £10 80 0
31 ,, 5s. yellow-orange (25.8.71) .. £8 30 0

The ½d., 1d. and 5s. are known imperf., probably from proof sheets.

For the 3d. of this issue see Nos. 36 and 39.

ONE PENNY (7) **THREE PENCE** (8)

(Surcharged by Saul Solomon & Co., Cape Town.)

1874–76. *Nos. 25a and 26a surch. with T* **7.**
32 **4** 1d. on 6d. deep lilac (R) (1.9.74) £12 70 0
  a. "E" of "PENNY" omitted .. — £15
33 ,, 1d. on 1s. green (Nov. '76) 45 0 45 0

These provisionals are found with the bar only, either across the centre of the stamp or at top, with value only; or with value and bar close together, either at top or foot. Such varieties are due to misplacement of sheets during surcharging.

1879 (1 Nov.). *No. 30 surch. with T* **8.**
34 **6** 3d. on 4d. blue (R.) 80 0 15 0
  a. "PENCB" for "PENCE" £80 £20
  b. "THE.EE" for "THREE" £100 £25
  c. Surch. double .. .. — £95
  d. Variety b. double ..

The double surcharge must also have existed showing variety a. but only variety b. is known.

There are numerous minor varieties, including letters broken or out of alignment, due to defective printing and use of poor type.

The spacing between the bar and the words varies from 16½ to 18 mm.

THREEPENCE
(9)

(Surcharged by De La Rue & Co.)

1880 (Feb.). *Special printing of the 4d. in new colour, surch. with T* 9. *Wmk. Crown CC.*
35 **6** 3d. on 4d. pale dull rose .. 50 0 10 6

A minor constant variety exists with foot of "P" in "PENCE" broken off, making the letter appear shorter.

1880 (1 July). *Wmk. Crown CC. P* 14.
36 **6** 3d. pale dull rose £10 27 6

3 (10) **3** (11)

(Surch. by Saul Solomon & Co., Cape Town.)

1880 (Aug.). *No. 36 surcharged.*
37 **10** "3" on 3d. pale dull rose.. 47 6 7 6
  a. Surch. inverted £30 70 0
38 **11** "3" on 3d. pale dull rose.. £7 20 0
  a. Surch. inverted .. .. — £75

The "3" (T **10**) is sometimes found broken. Vertical pairs are known showing the two types of surcharge *se-tenant*, and vertical strips of three exist, the top stamp having surcharge T **10**, the middle stamp being without surcharge, and the lower stamp having surcharge T **11.**

1881 (Jan.). *Wmk. Crown CC. P* 14.
39 **6** 3d. pale claret 75 0 8 6
  a. Deep claret 60 0 7 6

This was a definite colour change made at the request of the Postmaster-General owing to the similarity between the colours of the 1d. stamp and the 3d. in pale dull rose. Imperf. copies are probably from proof sheets.

Proofs of this value were printed in brown, on unwatermarked wove paper and imperf., but the colour was rejected as unsuitable.

1882 (July). *Wmk. Crown CA. P* 14.
40 **6** 3d. pale claret 8 0 4 0
  a. Deep claret 10 0 3 6

One Half-penny.

(12)

(Surch. by Saul Solomon & Co., Cape Town.)

1882 (July). *Nos. 39a and 40a surch. with T* **12.**
41 **6** ½d. on 3d. dp. clar. (Wmk. CC) £100 £12
  a. Hyphen omitted .. ..
42 ,, ½d. on 3d. dp. clar. (Wmk. CA) 15 0 12 6
  a. "p" in "penny" omitted .. £60 £50
  b. "y" in "penny" omitted .. £60
  c. Hyphen omitted £28 £22

Varieties also exist with broken and defective letters, and with the obliterating bar omitted or at the top of the stamp.

1882–83. *Wmk. Crown CA. P* 14.
43 **6** ½d. black (1.9.82) 14 0 2 0
  a. Grey-black 6 0 1 6
44 ,, 1d. rose-red (July '82) .. 24 0 0 6
  a. Deep rose-red 20 0 0 6
45 ,, 2d. pale bistre (1.9.82) .. 45 0 1 3
  a. Deep bistre 65 0 0 9
46 **4** 6d. mauve (to brt.) (Aug. '82) 50 0 6 0
47 **6** 5s. orange (Aug. '83) .. £70 £7

Imperf. pairs of the ½d., 1d., and 2d. are known, probably from proof sheets.

For the 3d. stamp with this watermark see No. 40.

13. "Cabled Anchor".

1884–1890. *W* **13.** *P* 14.

No.	Type	Description	Unused		Used	
48	**6**	½d. black (Jan. '86)	1	6	0	3
		a. Grey-black	1	6	0	3
49	,,	1d. rose-red (Dec. '85)	1	9	0	4
		a. Carmine-red	1	6	0	3
50	,,	2d. pale bistre (Dec. '84) ..	6	0	0	6
		a. Deep bistre	2	9	0	6
51	,,	4d. blue (June '90)	5	0	1	3
		a. Deep blue	5	0	1	3
52	**4**	6d. reddish pur. (Dec. '84) ..	45	0	12	6
		a. Purple (shades)	6	0	1	6
		b. Bright mauve	20	0	1	9
53	,,	1s. yellow-green (Dec. '85) ..	75	0	12	6
		a. Blue-green (1889)	47	6	2	6
54	**6**	5s. orange (July '87)	65	0	10	0

All the above stamps are known in imperf. pairs, probably from proof sheets.

For later shade and colour changes, etc., see Nos. 59, *etc.*

2½d

(14)

(Surcharged by De La Rue & Co.)

1891 (Mar.). *Special printing of the 3d. in new colour, surch. with T* **14.**

No.	Type	Description	Unused		Used	
55	**6**	2½d. on 3d. pale magenta ..	10	0	3	6
		a. Deep magenta	3	6	2	6
		b. Fig. "1" with horiz. serif ..	70	0	50	0

Variety b occurs on two stamps (Nos. 8 and 49) of the pane of 60.

Two types of "d" are found in the surcharge, one with square end to serif at top, and the other with pointed serif.

15

ONE PENNY.

(16)

1892 (June). *W* **13.** *P* 14.

No.	Type	Description	Unused		Used	
56	**15**	2½d. sage-green	4	0	1	6
		a. Olive-green	12	6	2	0

(Surch. by W. A. Richards & Sons, Cape Town.)

1893 (March). *Nos.* 50/*a surch. with T* **16.**

No.	Type	Description	Unused		Used	
57	**6**	1d. on 2d. pale bistre	6	0	1	0
		a. Deep bistre	2	0	1	0
		b. No stop after "PENNY" ..	42	6	27	6
		c. Surcharge double	—		£26	

Variety b occurs on stamp No. 42 of the upper left-hand pane, and on No. 6 of the lower right-hand pane.

Minor varieties exist showing broken letters and letters out of alignment or widely spaced. Also with obliterating bar omitted, due to misplacement of the sheet during surcharging.

17. "Hope" standing. Table Bay in background.

18. Table Mountain and Bay with Arms of the Colony.

(Des. Mr. Mountford. Typo. De La Rue & Co.)

1893 (Oct.). *W* **13.** *P* 14.

No.	Type	Description	Unused		Used	
58	**17**	1d. rose-red	0	10	0	3
		a. Carmine	0	4	0	3

The above stamp is known in imperf. pairs, probably from proof sheets.

1893–98. *New colours, etc. W* **13.** *P* 14.

No.	Type	Description	Unused		Used	
59	**6**	½d. pale yell.-grn. (Dec. '96)	0	10	0	9
		a. Green	8	6	0	4
60	"	2d. choc.-brown (Mar. '97)	2	0	1	0
61	**15**	2½d. pale ultram. (May '96)	3	0	0	8
		a. Ultramarine	2	0	0	8
62	**6**	3d. brt. magenta (Sept. '98)	4	6	2	6
63	"	4d. sage-green (Mar. '97) ..	7	6	2	6
64	"	1s. blue-green (Dec. '93) ..	27	6	3	6
		a. Deep blue-green	75	0	15	0
65	"	1s. yellow-ochre (May '96)	10	0	2	0
66	"	5s. brn.-orange (June '96)	45	0	10	0

1898–1902. *W* **13.** *P* 14.

No.	Type	Description	Unused		Used	
67	**17**	½d. green (Oct. '98)	0	6	0	3
68	"	3d. magenta (Mar. '02) ..	6	0	4	6

(Des. E. Sturman. Typo. De La Rue & Co.)

1900 (Jan.). *W* **13.** *P* 14.

No.	Type	Description	Unused		Used	
69	**18**	1d. carmine	0	3	0	3

19

20

21

22

23

24

25

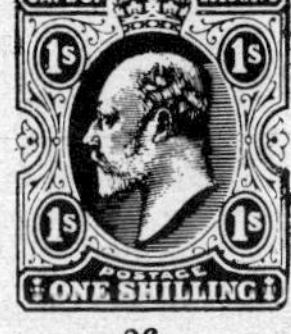

26

27

(Typo. De La Rue & Co.)

1902 (Dec.)–**04.** *W* **13.** *P* 14.

70	**19**	½d. green	0	9	0	3
71	**20**	1d. carmine	0	4	0	3
72	**21**	2d. brown (Oct. '04) ..	3	0	1	0
73	**22**	2½d. ultramarine (Mar. '04)	6	0	15	0
74	**23**	3d. magenta (Apr. '03) ..	3	6	0	6
75	**24**	4d. olive-green (Feb. '03)..	6	0	1	9
76	**25**	6d. bright mauve (Mar. '03)	7	6	1	6
77	**26**	1s. yellow-ochre	12	6	2	0
78	**27**	5s. brn.-orange (Feb. '03)	42	6	22	6

All values exist in imperf. pairs, from proof sheets.

When the Union of South Africa came into being in 1910 the stamps of the Cape of Good Hope (except the already demonetised triangulars) became available for postal use throughout the Union, until December 31st, 1937, from which date the stamps of the four provinces of the Union were demonetised. For Union issues see under South Africa.

MAFEKING SIEGE STAMPS.

There are numerous forgeries of the Mafeking overprints, many of which were brought home by soldiers returning from the Boer War.

24 March to 17 May, 1900.

MAFEKING,
3d.
BESIEGED.
(1)

MAFEKING
3d.
BESIEGED.
(2)

I. *Surcharged in fancy type as T* **1.**

(A) *On Cape of Good Hope stamps.*

1	**6**	1d. on ½d. green	85 0	55 0
2	**17**	1d. on ½d. green	£6	65 0
3	,,	3d. on 1d. carmine	£5	60 0
4	**6**	6d. on 3d. magenta	—	£18
5	,,	1s. on 4d. sage-green ..	£60	£18

A variety in the setting of each value exists without comma after "mafeking".

(B) *On Bechuanaland Prot. stamps of* 1897–1902.

6	1d. on ½d. vermilion	£5	55 0
	a. Surch. inverted	—	£250
7	3d. on 1d. lilac	£30	£7
	a. Surch. double..		
8	6d. on 2d. green and carmine	£30	£8
9	6d. on 3d. purple/*yellow* ..	£55	£10
	a. Surch. inverted		
	b. Surch. double..		

(C) *On British Bechuanaland stamps.*

10	6d. on 3d. lilac & blk. (No. 12)	£14	£6
11	1s. on 4d. (No. 35)	£40	£6
	a. Surch. double..	—	£275
	b. Surch. treble	—	£400
	c. Surch. double, one inverted ..	—	£400

II. *Surcharged in thin block letters as T* **2.**

(A) *On Bechuanaland Protectorate stamps.*

12	3d. on 1d. lilac (No. 61) ..	£20	£6
	a. Surch. double.. ..	—	£350
13	6d. on 2d. grn. & car. (No. 62)	£28	£7
14	1s. on 6d. pur./*r.-red* (No. 65)	£45	£8

(B) *On British Bechuanaland stamps.*

15	1s. on 6d. purple/*r.-red* (No. 36)	£75	£50
16	2s. on 1s. green (No. 37) ..	£50	£24

In the stamps overprinted "bechuanaland protectorate" and "british bechuanaland" the local surcharge is so adjusted as not to overlap the original overprint.

3 — Cadet Sergt.-major Goodyear. (Des. Dr. W. A. Hayes.)

4 — General Baden-Powell. (Des. Capt. Greener.)

III. *Produced by photographic process by Mr. D. Taylor. Horizontally laid paper. P* 12.

(*a*) 18½ mm. *wide.* (*b*) 21 mm. *wide.*

17	**3**	1d. pale blue/*blue*	£60	£35
18	,,	1d. deep blue/*blue*	£60	£40
		a. Imperf. (pair)	£360	
19	**4**	3d. pale blue/*blue* (*a*) ..	£70	£45
20	,,	3d. deep blue/*blue* (*a*) ..	£75	£50
		a. Imperf. between (horiz. pair)..	—	£600
		b. Double print	—	£600
21	,,	3d. pale blue/*blue* (*b*) ..	£175	£75
22	,,	3d. deep blue/*blue* (*b*) ..	£175	£75

Variety. Reversed design.

23	**4**	3d. blue/*blue* (*a*)	£700	£600

These stamps vary a great deal in colour from deep blue to pale grey.

VRYBURG.

TEMPORARY BOER OCCUPATION.

½ PENCE

Z.A.R.
(1)

1899 (Nov.). *Cape stamps surch. as T* **1.** A. *Surch.* 10 *mm. high.* B. *Surch.* 12 *mm. high.*

			A.		B.	
1	**6**	½ pence, green..	£6	£6	—	£25
2	**17**	1 pence, rose ..	£6	£6	—	£30
3	**4**	2 pence on 6d. mauve ..		†	—	£30
4	**15**	2½ pence, blue ..	—	£22	—	—

Nos. 1A, 2A, 4A, and 3B are known with italic "Z" in the surcharge.

BRITISH REOCCUPATION.

(2)

1900 (May). *Provisionals issued by the Military Authorities. Stamps of Transvaal* (*T* **33**) *optd. with T* **2.**

11	½d. green	—	£15
12	1d. carmine and green ..	£20	£18
13	2d. deep brown and green ..		
14	2½d. blue and green		

CAYMAN ISLANDS.

1

(T **1** to **13** typo. by De La Rue & Co.)

1901 (19 Feb.). *Wmk. Crown CA. P* 14.

No.	Type	Description	Unused	Used
1	**1**	½d. deep green	4 6	10 0
		a. Pale green	3 6	7 6
2	„	1d. rose-carmine	4 6	3 6
		a. Pale carmine	17 6	10 0

2

3

1901 (20 Dec.)–**1902**. *Wmk. Crown CA. P* 14.

No.	Type	Description	Unused	Used
3	**2**	½d. green (1902)	4 0	6 0
4	,,	1d. carmine (1902)	10 0	10 0
5	,,	2½d. bright blue	22 6	35 0
6	,,	6d. brown	45 0	50 0
7	**3**	1s. orange	£6	£7

1905–6. *Wmk. Mult. Crown CA. P* 14.

No.	Type	Description	Unused	Used
8	**2**	½d. green	3 6	6 0
9	,,	1d. carmine (1906)	22 6	27 6
10	,,	2½d. bright blue	15 0	22 6
11	,,	6d. brown	50 0	55 0
12	**3**	1s. orange	£6	£7

1907 (Mar.–April). *Wmk. Mult. Crown CA. P* 14.

No.	Type	Description	Unused	Used
13	**3**	4d. brown and blue	70 0	80 0
14	**2**	6d. olive and rose	70 0	80 0
15	**3**	1s. violet and green	£7	£8
16	,,	5s. salmon and green	£20	£22

One
Halfpenny.
(4)

1907 (Sept.). *No.* 9 *surch. with T* **4**.

No.	Type	Description	Unused	Used
17	**2**	½d. on 1d. carmine	£5	£6

½D (5) **1D** (6) **2½D** (7)

1907 (Nov.). *No.* 16 *surch. with T* **5** *or* **6**.

No.	Description	Unused	Used
18	½d. on 5s. salmon and green	£20	£28
	a. Surch. inverted		
	b. Surch. double	£80	£85
	c. Surch. double, one inverted		
	d. Surch. omitted (in pair with normal)		
19	1d. on 5s. salmon and green	£20	£28
	a. Surch. double	£95	

The ½d. on 5s. may be found with the figures "1" or "2" omitted, owing to defective printing.

1908 (Feb.). *No.* 13 *surch. with T* **7**.

No.	Description	Unused	Used
24	2½d. on 4d. brown and blue	£150	£175
	a. Surch. double		

The 1d. on 4d. is a revenue stamp and was never authorised for postal use.

8

9

1907–9. *Wmk. Mult. Crown CA. P* 14.

No.	Type	Description	Unused	Used
25	**8**	½d. green, O (1907)	1 6	2 6
26	,,	1d. carmine, O (1907)	2 6	3 6
27	,,	2½d. ultramarine, O	7 6	10 0
28	**9**	3d. purple/*yellow*, C	8 0	10 0
29	,,	4d. black & red/*yellow*, C	£10	£12
30	**8**	6d. dull & bright purple, C	10 0	25 0
30*a*	,,	6d. dull pur. & vio.-pur., C	12 6	22 6
31	**9**	1s. black/*green*, C (1909)	15 0	22 6
32	,,	5s. green and red/*yellow*, C	£6	£7

1908. *Wmk. Crown CA. P* 14.

No.	Type	Description	Unused	Used
35	**9**	1s. black/*green*, C	55 0	65 0
36	**8**	10s. green and red/*green*, C	£24	£28

11

1908–9. *Wmk. Mult. Crown CA. P* 14.

No.	Type	Description	Unused	Used
38	**11**	¼d. brown, O	1 0	2 0
39	„	¼d. grey-brown, O (1909)	1 0	1 6

12

13

1912–20. *Wmk. Mult. Crown CA. P* 14.

No.	Type	Description	Unused	Used
40	**13**	¼d. brown, O	0 8	1 0
41	**12**	½d. green, O	0 10	1 6
42	,,	1d. red, O (1913)	2 6	3 6
43	**13**	2d. pale grey, O	2 0	3 6
44	**12**	2½d. bright blue, O (1914)	9 0	14 0
44*a*	,,	2½d. deep bright blue, O	8 0	13 6
45	**13**	3d. purple/*yellow*, C (1920)	8 6	13 6
		a. White back (1913)	7 6	8 6
		b. On lemon (1915)	8 0	12 6
		c. On orange-buff (1920)	7 0	16 0
		d. On pale yellow (1920)	8 6	16 0
46	,,	4d. blk. & red/*yell.*, C ('13)	5 0	8 6
47	**12**	6d. dull & brt. pur., C ('13)	10 0	15 0
48	**13**	1s. black/*green*, C (1916)	10 0	16 0
		a. White back (1913)	10 0	15 0
49	,,	2s. pur. & brt. blue/*blue*, C	22 6	25 0
50	,,	3s. green and violet, C	25 0	32 6
51	,,	5s. grn. & red/*yell.*, C ('14)	£5	£6
52	**12**	10s. deep green and red/*green*, C (1915)	£8	£10
		a. White back (1913)	£7	£8
		b. On blue-grn. olive back ('20)	£7	£8

WAR STAMP. 1½d (14)

WAR STAMP. 1½d (15)

1917 (26 Feb.). *T* **12**, *surch. with T* **14** *or* **15**.

No.	Type	Description	Unused	Used
53	**14**	1½d. on 2½d. deep blue	4 0	7 6
		a. No fraction bar	65 0	75 0
54	**15**	1½d. on 2½d. deep blue	2 6	4 0
		a. No fraction bar	30 0	40 0

In No. 53 the spacing between the word "STAMP" and the top of the figure "1" varies between 1½ mm. and 5 mm.

WAR STAMP 1½d (16)

WAR STAMP 1½d (17)

WAR STAMP 1½d. (18)

1917 (4 Sept.). *T* **12** *surch. with T* **16** *or* **17**.

No.	Description	Unused	Used
55	1½d. on 2½d. deep blue (T **16**)	£40	£50
56	1½d. on 2½d. deep blue (T **17**)	0 9	1 0

1919–20. *T* **12** *and* **13** (*2½d. special printing*), *optd. only, or surch. in addition.*

No.	Type	Description	Unused	Used
57	**16**	½d. green (4.2.19)	0 8	1 0
58	**18**	1½d. on 2d. grey (10.3.20)	1 0	2 3
59	**17**	1½d. on 2½d. orge. (4.2.19)	1 0	1 3

In T **16** the "R" of "WAR" has a curved foot and the other letters vary slightly from T **17**. "1½d." is in thin type. In T **17** the "R" has straight foot, and the "1½d." differs.

The ½d. stamps on *buff* paper, and later consignments of the 2d. T **13** on *pinkish*, apparently derived their colour from the paper in which they were packed for despatch from England.

19

(Recess. De La Rue & Co.)

1921–26. *P* 14.

(a) Wmk. Mult. Crown CA.

No.	Type	Description	Unused	Used
60	**19**	3d. purple/*orange-buff*	5 0	7 6
61	"	3d. purple/*pale yellow*	60 0	65 0
62	"	4d. red/*yellow*	3 6	6 0
63	"	1s. black/*green*	7 0	7 6
64	"	5s. yellow-green/*pale yellow*	37 6	42 6
65	"	5s. blue-green/*pale yellow*	65 0	85 0
66	"	5s. deep green/*orange-buff*	65 0	75 0
67	"	10s. carmine/*green*	£8	£10

(b) Wmk. Mult. Script CA.

No.	Type	Description	Unused	Used
69	**19**	¼d. yellow-brown	0 6	0 6
70	"	½d. pale grey-green	0 6	0 8
71	"	1d. deep carmine-red	0 8	0 10
72	"	1½d. orange-brown	1 3	1 3
73	"	2d. slate-grey	1 9	2 0
74	"	2½d. bright blue	2 0	2 0
75	"	3d. purple/*yell.* (June, 1923)	2 6	3 0
76	"	4½d. sage-green (June, 1923)	7 6	10 0
77	"	6d. claret	9 0	8 6
78	"	6d. deep claret	35 0	42 6
79	"	1s. black/*green*	10 0	20 0
80	**19**	2s. violet/*blue*	22 6	25 0
81	"	3s. violet	25 0	32 6
82	"	5s. green/*yellow*	45 0	50 0
83	"	10s. carmine/*green* (15.9.26)	£8	£10

20. King William IV and King George V.

(Recess. Waterlow & Sons.)

1932 (5 Dec.). *Centenary of the "Assembly of Justices and Vestry". Wmk. Mult. Script CA. P* 12½.

No.	Type	Description	Unused	Used
84	**20**	¼d. brown	1 0	1 6
85	,,	½d. green	1 6	2 3
86	,,	1d. scarlet	2 6	3 6
87	,,	1½d. red-orange	3 0	4 0
88	,,	2d. grey	3 0	4 0
89	,,	2½d. ultramarine	3 6	4 0
90	,,	3d. olive-green	6 0	8 6
91	,,	6d. purple	20 0	27 6
92	,,	1s. black and brown	27 6	35 0
93	,,	2s. black and ultramarine	70 0	75 0
94	,,	5s. black and green	£9	£10
95	,,	10s. black and scarlet	£28	£30

1935 (6 May). *Silver Jubilee. As Nos.* 91/4 *of Antigua. P* 13½ × 14.

No.	Description	Unused	Used
96	½d. black and green	0 9	1 0
97	2½d. brown and deep blue	3 0	3 9
98	6d. light blue and olive-green	6 6	8 6
99	1s. slate and purple	7 6	13 6

21. Cayman Islands.

22. Cat Boat.

23. Booby Birds.

24. Conch Shells and Coconut Palms.

25. Hawksbill Turtles.

(Recess. Waterlow & Sons.)

1935. *Wmk. Mult. Script CA. P* 12½.

100	**21**	¼d. black and brown ..	0	6	0	9
101	**22**	½d. ultram. & yell.-green	0	9	1	0
102	**23**	1d. ultramarine and scarlet	4	6	4	6
103	**24**	1½d. black and orange ..	1	6	1	6
104	**22**	2d. ultramarine & purple	2	0	2	0
105	**25**	2½d. blue and black ..	5	0	6	0
106	**21**	3d. black and olive-green	3	9	3	6
107	**25**	6d. bright purple & black	7	6	10	0
108	**22**	1s. ultramarine & orange	10	6	12	6
109	**23**	2s. ultramarine & black	60	0	65	0
110	**25**	5s. green and black ..	85	0	90	0
111	**24**	10s. black and scarlet ..	£7		£8	

1937 (13 May). *Coronation Issue. As Nos.* 13/15 *of Aden but ptd. by B.W. & Co. P* 11 × 11½.

112	½d. green	0	5	0	7
113	1d. carmine	0	8	0	10
114	2½d. blue	1	6	2	0

26. Beach View.

27. Dolphin fish (*Coryphaena hippurus*).

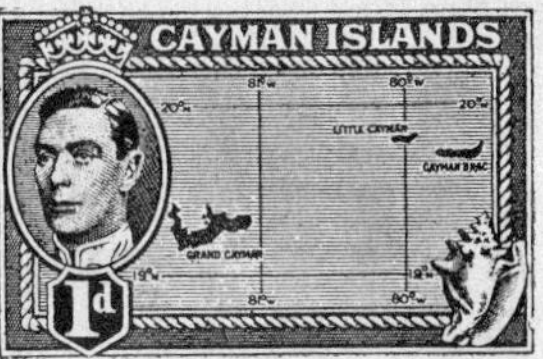

28. Cayman Islands.

29. Cayman Schooner.

30. Hawksbill Turtles.

(Recess. De La Rue (*T* **27** and **30**), Waterlow (others).)

1938 (5 May)–**1947.** *Wmk. Mult. Script CA (sideways on T* **26** *and* **28/9**). *Various perfs.*

115	**26**	¼d. red-orange (*p.* 12½) ..	0	3	0	3
		a. Perf. 13½ × 12½ ('43) ..	0	3	0	3
116	**27**	½d. green (*p.* 13 × 12) ..	0	6	0	6
		a. Perf. 14 ('43)	0	3	0	3
117	**28**	1d. scarlet (*p.* 12½) ..	0	10	0	10
118	**26**	1½d. black (*p.* 12½) ..	0	10	0	10
119	**30**	2d. violet (*p.* 12 × 13) ..	1	9	1	9
		a. Perf. 14 ('43)	0	10	1	0
120	**29**	2½d. bright blue (*p.* 12½) ..	0	6	0	10
120*a*	,,	2½d. orange (*p.* 12½) ('47)	1	3	1	3
121	**28**	3d. orange (*p.* 12½) ..	1	0	1	0
121*a*	,,	3d. brt. blue (*p.* 12½) ('47)	1	6	1	6
122	**30**	6d. olive-grn. (*p.* 12 × 13)	9	6	11	0
		a. Perf. 14 ('43)	3	0	3	0
		b. *Brownish olive, p.* 12 × 13 ('47)	4	0	5	0
123	**27**	1s. red-brn. (*p.* 13 × 12)	5	0	6	0
		a. Perf. 14 ('43)	6	0	6	0
124	**26**	2s. yellow-green (*shades*) (*p.* 12½)	27	6	30	0
		a. *Deep green* (July '43) ..	22	6	22	6
125	**29**	5s. crimson (*p.* 12½) ..	11	6	12	6
126	**30**	10s. chocolate (*p.* 12 × 13)	25	0	25	0
		a. Perf. 14 ('43)	25	0	25	0

1946 (26 Aug.). *Victory. As Nos.* 28/9 *of Aden.*

127	1½d. black	0	4	0	4
128	3d. orange-yellow	0	6	0	8

1948 (29 Nov.). *Royal Silver Wedding. As Nos.* 30/1 *of Aden.*

129	½d. green	0	3	0	3
130	10s. violet-blue	17	6	20	0

1949 (10 Oct.). *75th Anniv. of Universal Postal Union. As Nos.* 114/7 *of Antigua.*

131	2½d. orange	0	10	1	0

132	3d. deep blue..	1	3	1	6
133	6d. olive	2	0	2	6
134	1s. red-brown	3	6	4	6

31. Cat Boat.

32. Coconut Grove, Cayman Brac.

33. Green Turtle.

34. Thatch Rope Industry.

35. Cayman Seamen.

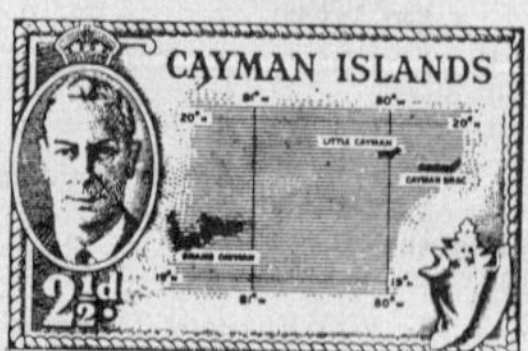

36. Map.

37. Parrot Fish.

38. Bluff, Cayman Brac.

39. Georgetown Harbour.

40. Turtle in "Crawl".

41. Cayman Schooner.

42. Boat-building.

43. Government Offices, Grand Cayman.

(Recess. Bradbury, Wilkinson & Co.)

1950 (2 Oct.). *Wmk. Mult. Script CA. P* 11½×11.

No.	Type	Description				
135	**31**	¼d. bt. blue & pale scarlet	0	6	0	8
136	**32**	½d. reddish violet and emerald-green ..	0	10	0	8
137	**33**	1d. olive-grn. & deep blue	1	9	2	0
138	**34**	1½d. green and brown ..	0	10	0	10
139	**35**	2d. reddish violet and rose-carmine ..	0	10	1	0
140	**36**	2½d. turquoise and black ..	1	0	1	3
141	**37**	3d. bt. green & light blue	2	6	3	0
142	**38**	6d. red-brown and blue ..	2	0	2	0
143	**39**	9d. scarlet & grey-green ..	3	0	3	6
144	**40**	1s. brown and orange ..	5	0	6	0
145	**41**	2s. violet & reddish purple	8	6	11	0
146	**42**	5s. olive-green & violet ..	15	0	18	0
147	**43**	10s. black and scarlet ..	32	6	36	0

44. Lighthouse, South Sound, Grand Cayman.

45. Queen Elizabeth II.

(Recess. Bradbury, Wilkinson & Co.)

1953–59. *As T* **31/43** (*but with portrait of Queen Elizabeth II in place of King George VI*) *and T* **44/5**. *Wmk. Mult. Script CA. P* 11½×11 *or* 11×11½ (*T* **44/5**).

No.	Type	Description				
148	**31**	¼d. deep bright blue and rose-red (*shades*) ..	0	3	0	3
149	**32**	½d. purple & bluish green	0	3	0	3
150	**33**	1d. brown-olive & indigo	0	4	0	4
151	**34**	1½d. dp. green & red-brown	0	5	0	5
152	**35**	2d. reddish violet & cerise	0	5	0	5
153	**36**	2½d. turquoise-blue & black	0	6	0	7
154	**37**	3d. bright green and blue	0	9	0	10
155	**44**	4d. blk. & dp. blue (*shades*)	0	8	1	0
156	**38**	6d. lake-brown & deep blue	1	0	1	0
157	**39**	9d. scarlet & bluish green	1	4	1	4
158	**40**	1s. brown and red-orange	1	9	1	9
159	**41**	2s. slate-vio. & reddish pur.	3	6	4	0
160	**42**	5s. olive-green & slate-vio.	7	6	8	0
161	**43**	10s. black and rose-red ..	17	6	20	0
161*a*	**45**	£1 blue	35	0	40	0

Dates of issue:—2.3.53, 4d.; 2.6.54, 2d., 2½d., 9d.; 7.7.54, ½d., 1d., 1½d., 6d.; 6.1.59, £1; 21.2.55, others.

1953 (2 June). *Coronation. As No.* 47 *of Aden but ptd. by B. W. & Co.*

162	1d. black and emerald ..	1	0	1	6

46. Arms of the Cayman Islands.

(Photo. De La Rue & Co.)

1959 (4 July). *New Constitution. Wmk. Mult. Script CA. P* 12.

No.	Type	Description				
163	**46**	2½d. black and light blue ..	3	6	4	0
164	,,	1s. black and orange ..	3	6	4	6

47. Cayman Parrot.

55. Angler with Kingfish.

48. Cat Boat.

49. *Schomburgkia thomsoniana* (orchid).

50. Cayman Islands (map).

51. Fisherman casting Net.

52. West Bay Beach.

53. Green Turtle.

54. Cayman Schooner.

56. Iguana.

57. Swimming Pool, Cayman Brac.

58. Water Sports.

59. Fort George.

60. Arms.

61. Queen Elizabeth II.

(Recess. Bradbury, Wilkinson.)

1962 (28 Nov.). *W* w.**12.** *P* 11 × 11½ (*vert.*) *or* 11½ × 11 (*horiz.*).

No.	Type	Description				
165	**47**	¼d. emerald & red (*shades*)	0	1	0	1
166	**48**	1d. blk. and yellow-olive	0	3	0	3
167	**49**	1½d. yellow and purple ..	0	4	0	4
168	**50**	2d. blue and deep brown	0	4	0	4
169	**51**	2½d. violet & bluish green	0	5	0	6
170	**52**	3d. brt. blue and carmine	0	6	0	7
171	**53**	4d. deep green and purple	0	7	0	8
172	**54**	6d. bluish green and sepia	0	10	0	10
173	**55**	9d. ultramarine & purple	1	1	1	3
174	**56**	1s. sepia and rose-red ..	1	5	1	6
175	**57**	1s. 3d. bluish green and orange-brown ..	1	9	2	3
176	**58**	1s. 9d. dp. turq. & violet	2	5	3	0
177	**59**	5s. plum and deep green	6	9	7	6
178	**60**	10s. olive and blue ..	13	3	15	0
179	**61**	£1 carmine and black ..	25	0	30	0

1963 (4 June). *Freedom from Hunger. As No. 63 of Aden.*

180	1s. 9d. carmine	4	0	4	6

1963 (2 Sept.). *Red Cross Centenary. As Nos. 147/8 of Antigua.*

181	1d. red and black	0	6	0	9
182	1s. 9d. red and blue.. ..	4	0	4	6

1964 (23 April). *400th Anniv. of Birth of William Shakespeare. As No. 164 of Antigua.*

183	6d. magenta	1	6	2	0

1965 (17 May). *I.T.U. Centenary. As Nos. 166/7 of Antigua.*

184	1d. blue and light purple ..	0	6	0	9
185	1s. 3d. bright purple & green	2	6	3	3

1965 (25 Oct.). *International Co-operation Year. As Nos. 168/9 of Antigua.*

186	1d. reddish pur. & turq.-grn.	0	6	0	9
187	1s. dp. bluish green & lav.	2	0	2	9

1966 (24 Jan.). *Churchill Commemoration. As Nos. 170/3 of Antigua.*

188 ¼d. new blue 0 2 0 3
189 1d. deep green 0 4 0 6
190 1s. brown 1 8 2 3
191 1s. 9d. bluish violet .. 3 0 4 0

1966 (4 Feb.). *Royal Visit. As Nos. 174/5 of Antigua.*

192 1d. black and ultramarine .. 0 4 0 6
193 1s. 9d. black and magenta .. 3 0 4 0

CEYLON.

—SIMPLIFICATION (see Introduction)—

Nos. 1 to 67.
4. 5, 7, 9, 10, 11, 12, 13, 14, 15, 16, 17, 19. 42, 33, 44, 27, 48a, 50, 51, 53, 67, 54, 55. 65, 58, 59, 61, 62, 63.

Nos. 68 to 117.
71, 72, 75, 78, 96, 98, 100, 83, 102, 103, 105, 106, 108, 109, 110, 111a, 113, 114, 116.

NOTE.—*The prices of the imperf. stamps of Ceylon vary greatly according to condition. The following prices are for fine copies with four margins.*

Poor to medium specimens can be supplied at much lower prices.

Crown Colony.

1 2

(Recess. Perkins Bacon.)

1857 (1 April). *Blued paper. Wmk. Star* T w. **1**. *Imperf.*

1 **1** 6d. purple-brown £450 £50

(Typo. De La Rue.)

1857 (Oct.)–**58**. *No wmk. Imperf.*
(*a*) *Blue glazed paper.*
3 **2** ½d. lilac £150 £45
(*b*) *White glazed paper.*
4 **2** ½d. lilac (1858) £18 £12

3 4

(Recess. Perkins Bacon.)

NOTE.—Beware of stamps of Type **3** which are often offered with corners added.

1857–59. *White paper. Wmk. Star,* T w. **1**. *Imperf.*

5 **1** 1d. blue (24.8.57) £12 65 0
6 ,, 1d. deep blue £15 65 0
a. Blued paper .. .. — £8
7 **1** 2d. deep green (24.8.57) .. £15 £6
8 ,, 2d. yellow-green £12 £6
9 **3** 4d. dull rose (23.4.59) £4500 £500
10 **1** 5d. chestnut (2.7.57) .. £50 £20
11 ,, 6d. purple-brown £85 £15
12 ,, 6d. brown £275 £45
12*a* ,, 6d. deep brown £400 £100
13 **3** 8d. brown (23.4.59) .. £450 £185
14 ,, 9d. pur.-brn. (23.4.59) .. £1000 £90
15 **4** 10d. orange-verm. (2.7.57) £50 £30
16 ,, 1s. dull violet (2.7.57) .. £60 £25
17 **3** 1s. 9d. green (23.4.59) .. £50 £50
18 ,, 1s. 9d. pale yellow-green £120 £100
19 ,, 2s. blue (23.4.59) £350 £160

Varieties. Rouletted.

20 **2** ½d. lilac (*No wmk.*) .. ..
21 **1** 1d. blue (*Wmk. Star*) ..
22 ,, 2d. dp. green (*Wmk. Star*) .. £150 £125

These rouletted stamps are believed to have been made by some Ceylon firm for their own convenience.

(Recess. Perkins Bacon.)

1861. *Wmk. Star,* T w. **1**.
(*a*) *Clean-cut perf.* 14 *to* 15½.
23 **1** 1d. deep blue £10 60 0
24 ,, 1d. pale blue £18 £5
25 ,, 2d. green £25 95 0
27 ,, 5d. chestnut £10 60 0
29 **4** 1s. dull violet £10 90 0
30 **3** 2s. deep full blue £55 £35

(*b*) *Intermediate perf.* 14 *to* 15½.
31 **1** 1d. deep blue £9 60 0
32 ,, 1d. blue £10 70 0
33 ,, 2d. green £10 £8
34 **3** 4d. dull rose £75 £40
34*a* **1** 5d. chestnut £35 £20
35 ,, 6d. brown £50 £12
36 ,, 6d. yellowish brown .. — £18
36*a* ,, 6d. olive-brown .. .. — £12
37 **3** 8d. brown £100 £25
38 ,, 9d. dull purple-brown .. £200 £25
40 **4** 1s. bright violet £6 95 0
41 ,, 1s. dull violet £6 85 0

(*c*) *Rough perf.* 14 *to* 15½.
42 **1** 1d. blue £5 35 0
43 ,, 1d. blue (*bleuté paper*) .. £20 75 0
44 **3** 4d. rose-red £12 £7
45 ,, 4d. deep rose-red £12 £8
47 **1** 6d. yellowish brown .. £75 £20
48 ,, 6d. blackish brown .. £30 £10
48*a* ,, 6d. olive-brown £45 £8
49 **3** 8d. brown £100 £30
50 ,, 8d. yellow-brown £75 £30
51 ,, 9d. olive-brown £38 95 0
52 ,, 9d. yellowish brown .. £40 £8
53 ,, 9d. deep brown £6 £5
53*a* **4** 10d. orange-vermilion .. £15 95 0
b. Imperf. between (pair) ..
54 ,, 1s. dull violet £10 60 0
55 **3** 2s. blue £18 £10
56 ,, 2s. deep blue £20 £12

Variety. Prepared for use, but not issued.
57 **3** 1s. 9d. green £30

(Recess. or Typo. (T **2**). De La Rue.)

1862. *Smooth paper. No wmk.* P 13.
58 **1** 1d. blue £5 40 0
59 ,, 5d. deep red-brown £65 £20
60 ,, 6d. reddish brown £6 95 0
61 ,, 6d. deep brown £8 95 0
62 **3** 9d. brown £38 £10
63 **4** 1s. cold violet £50 £12

The 1s. is known imperf., but not used. The "no wmk." stamps were printed on paper having the papermaker's name and date, "T H SAUNDERS 1862" across the sheets, and one or more of these letters or figures are often found on the stamps.

No wmk. P 11½, 12.
64 **1** 1d. blue £25 £8

1864. *Glazed paper. No wmk. P* 12½.
65 **2** ½d. pale lilac £12 £12

(Ptd. by Perkins Bacon & Co., perforated by De La Rue & Co.)

1864 (Sept.). *T* **4**. *Wmk. Star. Type* w. **1**. *P* 12½.
66 10d. vermilion £25 65 0
67 10d. orange-red £20 75 0

5

6

(Recess. or Typo. (T **2**). De La Rue.)

1863–66. *Paper medium thin and slightly soft. Printed on paper with the watermarks arranged in four panes, each of* 60, *with the words* "CROWN COLONIES" *between the panes. Portions of these letters often appear on the stamps. Wmk. T* **5**. *The wmk. is* 22½ *mm. high and the Crown and CC are closer together, vertically, than in T* **6**, *and the CC's are oval.*

(*a*) *P* 11½, 12.
68 **1** 1d. blue £20 £5

(*b*) *P* 13.
69 **1** 6d. brown £100 £8
70 **3** 9d. brown £150 £25

(*c*) *P* 12½.
71 **2** ½d. mauve 40 0 35 0
72 ,, ½d. lilac 50 0 32 6
73 ,, ½d. deep lilac 50 0 40 0
74 **1** 1d. dark blue 65 0 25 0
75 ,, 1d. blue 65 0 27 6
76 ,, 2d. yellow-green £450 £40
77 ,, 2d. deep bottle-green .. — £500
78 ,, 2d. grey-green £6 40 0
79 ,, 2d. emerald-green £12 £15
80 ,, 2d. maize £25 £7
81 **3** 4d. lake-rose £20 95 0
82 ,, 4d. rose £10 70 0
83 **1** 5d. reddish brown £18 £10
84 ,, 5d. deep sage-green .. £120 £30
84*a* ,, 5d. olive-green £8 90 0
85 ,, 6d. brown 90 0 50 0
86 ,, 6d. reddish brown .. 95 0 55 0
87 ,, 6d. deep brown 80 0 35 0
88 **3** 8d. light carm.-brown .. 95 0 75 0
89 ,, 8d. dark carm.-brown .. 95 0 75 0
90 ,, 9d. brown £15 90 0
91 **4** 10d. vermilion £45 80 0
91*a* ,, 10d. orange £20 95 0
92 **3** 2s. dark blue £18 75 0

The ½d. lilac; 1d. blue; 2d. grey-green; 2d. maize; and 5d. deep sage-green and olive-green, are known imperf.

1867. *Paper hand-made. Prepared and used only for these Ceylon stamps. Watermarks arranged in one pane of* 240 *in* 20 *rows of* 12, *with the words* "CROWN COLONIES" *twice in each side margin. Wmk. T* **6**. *The wmk. is* 21 *mm. high and the* "CC's" *are nearly round. P* 12½.
93 **1** 1d. pale blue 70 0 27 6
94 ,, 1d. Prussian blue .. 60 0 32 6
95 ,, 2d. maize 95 0 40 0
96 ,, 2d. olive-yellow 75 0 35 0
97 ,, 2d. greenish-yellow .. £16 £8
98 ,, 2d. orange-yellow .. 70 0 30 0
99 **3** 4d. pale rose 90 0 65 0
100 ,, 4d. rose 60 0 32 6
101 **1** 5d. pale sage-green .. 82 6 45 0
102 ,, 5d. deep olive-green .. £5 42 6
103 ,, 5d. deep myrtle-green .. 65 0 50 0
104 ,, 6d. deep brown 70 0 30 0
105 ,, 6d. blackish brown .. 85 0 37 6
106 ,, 6d. red-brown 65 0 30 0
107 **3** 8d. pale carm.-brown .. £5 95 0
108 ,, 8d. deep carm.-brown .. 80 0 60 0
109 ,, 9d. bistre-brown £12 60 0
110 ,, 9d. deep brown 50 0 40 0
111 **4** 10d. vermilion £60 £20
111*a* ,, 10d. red-orange 95 0 32 6
112 ,, 10d. orange 95 0 35 0
113 ,, 1s. lilac £25 70 0
114 ,, 1s. violet £6 35 0
115 **3** 2s. pale blue £8 65 0
116 ,, 2s. blue £5 45 0
117 ,, 2s. Prussian blue .. £5 45 0

The 1d. pale blue, 6d. deep brown, 9d. deep brown and 10d. orange are known imperf. but only unused.

PRINTERS. All stamps from No. 118 to 367 were typo. by De La Rue & Co.

7

8

1866. *Wmk. Crown CC. P* 12½.
118 **7** 3d. rose £12 £6

1867–68. *Wmk. Crown CC. P* 14.
119 **8** 1d. blue 30 0 20 0
120 **7** 3d. pale rose (1867) .. 85 0 55 0
120*a* ,, 3d. deep rose 85 0 55 0

9

10

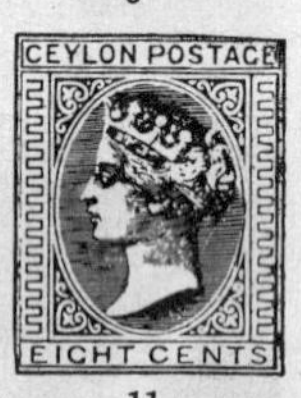

11

12

13

14

15

16

17

18

19

1872–80. *Wmk. Crown CC.* (*a*) *P* 14.

121	**9**	2 c. pale brown (*shades*) ..	7 0	1 9
122	**10**	4 c. grey	20 0	2 0
123	"	4 c. rosy mauve (1880) ..	35 0	4 0
124	**11**	8 c. orange-yellow ..	30 0	16 0
125	"	8 c. yellow	30 0	17 6
126	**12**	16 c. pale violet	50 0	15 0
127	**13**	24 c. green	42 6	15 0
128	**14**	32 c. slate (1877)	80 0	20 0
129	**15**	36 c. blue	80 0	25 0
130	**16**	48 c. rose	75 0	20 0
131	**17**	64 c. red-brown (1877) ..	£8	90 0
132	**18**	96 c. drab	95 0	40 0

(*b*) *P* 14 × 12½.

133	**9**	2 c. brown	£10	40 0
134	**10**	4 c. grey	£10	27 6
135	**11**	8 c. orange-yellow ..	£8	55 0

(*c*) *P* 12½.

136	**9**	2 c. brown	£55	75 0
137	**10**	4 c. grey	£35	£7

(*d*) *P* 12½ × 14.

138	**19**	2 r. 50 c. dull-rose ..	£28	£14

Prepared for use and sent out to Ceylon, but not issued unsurcharged.

139	**14**	32 c. slate (*perf.* 14 × 12½)	£45
140	**17**	64 c. red-brn. (*perf.* 14 × 12½)	£80
141	**19**	2 r. 50 c. dull rose (*perf.* 12½)	£70

SIXTEEN

16

CENTS

(20)

1882. *Nos.* 127 *and* 131 *surch. as T* **20.**

142	**13**	16 c. on 24 c. green ..	55 0	30 0
143	**17**	20 c. on 64 c. red-brown ..	35 0	15 0
		a. Surch. double	—	£60

1883–98. *Wmk. Crown CA. P* 14.

146	**9**	2 c. pale brown ..	35 0	4 0
147	,,	2 c. dull green (1884) ..	1 0	0 9
148	**10**	4 c. rosy mauve ..	3 6	1 0
149	,,	4 c. rose (1884)	10 0	25 0
150	**11**	8 c. orange	17 6	22 6
150*a*	,,	8 c. yellow (1898) ..	10 0	15 0
151	**12**	16 c. pale violet	£40	£14

Trial perforation. P 12.

151*a*	**9**	2 c. dull green	£70
151*b*	**10**	4 c. rose	£200
151*c*	**13**	24 c. brown-purple ..	£110

Prepared for use and sent out to Ceylon, but not issued unsurcharged. P 14.

152	**13**	24 c. brown-purple ..	£50

Postage &

FIVE CENTS

Revenue

(21)

TEN CENTS

(22)

Twenty Cents

(23)

1885. *T* **10/19** *surch. locally as T* **21/24.**

I. *Wmk. Crown CC.*

(*a*) *P* 14.

152*a*	**21**	5 c. on 16 c. pale violet	£80	
153	,,	5 c. on 24 c. green ..	£80	£6
154	,,	5 c. on 32 c. slate ..	45 0	30 0
		a. Surch. inverted ..	—	£35
		b. Dark grey	45 0	30 0
155	,,	5 c. on 36 c. blue ..	55 0	12 6
		a. Surch. inverted ..	—	£22
156	,,	5 c. on 48 c. rose ..	£12	55 0
157	,,	5 c. on 64 c. red-brown	50 0	12 6
		a. Surch. double ..	—	£18
158	,,	5 c. on 96 c. drab ..	£10	75 0
161	**22**	10 c. on 16 c. pale violet	£45	£40
162	,,	10 c. on 24 c. green ..	£22	£6
163	,,	10 c. on 36 c. blue ..	£14	£10
164	,,	10 c. on 64 c. red-brown	£6	90 0
165	,,	20 c. on 24 c. green ..	70 0	45 0
166	**23**	20 c. on 32 c. slate ..	55 0	50 0
		a. Dark grey ..	55 0	47 6
167	,,	25 c. on 32 c. slate ..	30 0	27 6
		a. Dark grey	30 0	22 6
168	,,	28 c. on 48 c. rose ..	42 6	20 0
		a. Surch. double ..	—	£35
169	**22**	30 c. on 36 c. blue ..	30 0	32 6
		a. Surch. inverted ..	£12	£6
170	,,	56 c. on 96 c. drab ..	55 0	45 0

(*b*) *P* 14 × 12½.

172	**21**	5 c. on 32 c. slate ..	£5	45 0
173	,,	5 c. on 64 c. red-brown ..	£6	50 0
174	**22**	10 c. on 64 c. red-brown	75 0	75 0
		a. Imperf. betwn. (vert. pair)	£80	

One Rupee Twelve Cents

(24)

175	**24**	1 r. 12 c. on 2 r. 50 c. dull rose (*p.* 12½) ..	£14	65 0
176	,,	1 r. 12 c. on 2 r. 50 c. dull rose (*p.* 12½ × 14) ..	55 0	50 0

II. *Wmk. Crown CA. P* 14.

177	**21**	5 c. on 4 c. rosy mauve	£22	
178	,,	5 c. on 4 c. rose	15 0	2 6
		a. Surch. inverted	£25	£20

179 **21** 5 c. on 8 c. orange-yellow 32 6 10 0
  a. Surch. double .. .. — £12
  b. Surch. inverted .. .. — £35
180 ,, 5 c. on 16 c. pale violet .. 45 0 22 6
  a. Surch. inverted .. .. — £65
181 ,, 5 c. on 24 c. green ..
182 ,, 5 c. on 24 c. brown-purple £24 £9
184 **22** 10 c. on 16 c. pale violet .. — £40
185 ,, 10 c. on 25 c. brn.-purple 35 0 25 0
186 ,, 15 c. on 16 c. pale violet .. 35 0 30 0

REVENUE AND POSTAGE

10 CENTS

(26)

5 CENTS

(25)

1 R. 12 C.

(27)

1885–87. *T* **11** *to* **15, 18** *and* **19** *surch. by De La Rue, as T* **25** *to* **27**. *P* 14.

I. *Wmk. Crown CA.*

187 **25** 5 c. on 8 c. lilac 12 6 2 0
188 **26** 10 c. on 24 c. brn.-purple 32 6 17 6
189 ,, 15 c. on 16 c. orange-yellow 35 0 25 0
190 ,, 28 c. on 32 c. slate .. 32 6 10 0
191 ,, 30 c. on 36 c. olive-green .. 47 6 40 0
192 ,, 56 c. on 96 c. drab .. 37 6 25 0

II. *Wmk. Crown CC (sideways).*

193 **27** 1 r. 12 c. on 2 r. 50 c. dull rose 55 0 60 0

28

29

1886. *Wmk. Crown CA. P* 14.

Type (*a*) has thicker lines in the background and masses of solid colour under the chin, in front of the throat, at the back of the neck, and at the base. Type (*b*) has thinner lines in the background, and coil and pendent curl clearer.

194 **28** 5 c. dull purple (*a*) .. 8 0 0 8
195 ,, 5 c. dull purple (*b*) .. 0 6 0 4
196 **29** 15 c. sage-green 3 6 3 6
197 ,, 15 c. olive-green 3 6 1 6
198 ,, 25 c. yellow-brown .. 4 0 7 6
  a. Value in yellow 95 0 80 0
199 ,, 28 c. slate 8 6 6 0

30

1887. *Wmk. Crown CC. P* 14.

201 **30** 1 r. 12 c. dull rose .. 25 0 15 0

This stamp comes on both white and bluish paper with wmk. sideways, and, in a different shade, with upright wmk.

TWO CENTS (31)

TWO (32)

2 Cents (33)

Two Cents (34)

2 Cents (35)

1888–90. *Nos.* 148/9 *surch. with T* **31/5**.

202 **31** 2 c. on 4 c. rosy mauve .. 1 6 1 6
  a. Surch. inverted 15 0 15 0
  b. Surch. double, one inverted — 65 0
203 ,, 2 c. on 4 c. rose 2 0 2 0
  a. Surch. inverted 22 6 20 0
  b. Surch. double .. .. — 50 0
204 **32** 2 (c.) on 4 c. rosy mauve .. 2 0 1 9
  a. Surch. inverted 42 6 40 0
  b. Surch. double 60 0 60 0
  c. Surch. double, one inverted 35 0 30 0
205 ,, 2 (c.) on 4 c. rose 3 6 1 6
  a. Surch. inverted £6
  b. Surch. double 65 0 62 6
  c. Surch. double, one inverted 65 0 67 6
206 **33** 2 c. on 4 c. rosy mauve .. 50 0 50 0
  a. Surch. inverted .. .. — 62 6
  b. Surch. double, one inverted 85 0
207 ,, 2 c. on 4 c. rose 4 0 6 6
  a. Surch. inverted 22 6 30 0
  b. Surch. double .. ..
  c. Surch. double, one inverted 20 0 25 0
208 **34** 2 c. on 4 c. rosy mauve .. 40 0 35 0
  a. Surch. inverted 80 0 50 0
209 ,, 2 c. on 4 c. rose 3 0 2 0
  a. Surch. inverted 20 0 25 0
  b. Surch. double 50 0 55 0
  c. Surch. double, one inverted 20 0 22 6
210 **35** 2 c. on 4 c. rosy mauve .. 40 0 42 6
  a. Surch. inverted 80 0 85 0
  b. Surch. double, one inverted 80 0 85 0
  c. Surch. double .. .. — 70 0
  d. "s" of "Cents" inverted..
  e. As d. Whole surch. inverted
211 ,, 2 c. on 4 c. rose 8 6 3 0
  a. Surch. inverted 15 0 17 6
  b. Surch. double 80 0 75 0
  c. Surch. double, one inverted 35 0 35 0
  d. "s" of "Cents" inverted — £5

The 4 c. *rose* and the 4 c. *rosy mauve* are found surcharged "Postal Commission 3 (or 'Three') Cents". They denote the extra commission charged by the Post Office on postal orders which had not been cashed within three months of the date of issue. For a short time the Post Office did not object to the use of these stamps on letters.

POSTAGE

Five Cents

REVENUE

(36)

1890. *No.* 197 *surcharged with T* **36**.

233 5 c. on 15 c. olive-green .. 3 6 4 0
  a. Surcharge inverted 30 0 32 6
  b. Surcharge double £10 £7
  c. "Flve" for "Five" £8
  d. Variety. As c., inverted ..
  e. "REVENUE" omitted .. £10 £8
  f. Inverted "s" in "Cents" .. 30 0 35 0
  g. Variety. As f., and whole surcharge inverted £30
  h. "REVENUE" omitted and inverted "s" in "Cents" .. £20
  i. "POSTAGE" spaced between "T" and "A" £5

FIFTEEN CENTS
(37)

3 Cents
(38)

1891. *Nos.* 198 *and* 199 *surcharged with T* **37.**

239 15 c. on 25 c. yellow-brown .. 20 0 22 6
240 15 c. on 28 c. slate 15 0 17 6

1892. *Stamps of* 1883–84 *and* 1886 *surcharged with T* **38,** *in black.*

241 3 c. on 4 c. rosy mauve .. 2 0 2 6
242 3 c. on 4 c. rose 3 6 8 6
243 3 c. on 28 c. slate 2 6 4 0
a. Surcharge double £5

39

1893. *Wmk. Crown CA. P* 14.

245 **39** 3 c. ter.-cotta & blue-grn. 2 0 2 0
246 **29** 30 c. bt. mve. & chestnut.. 6 0 5 0
247 ,, 30 c. bt. vio. & chestnut .. 6 0 6 0

1898. *Wmk. Crown CA. P* 14.

248 **10** 4 c. carmine-rose .. 7 6 12 6

1899. *Wmk. Crown CA. P* 14.

249 **19** 2 r. 50 c. purple/*red* .. 55 0 60 0

Six Cents
(40)

2 R. 25 C.
(41)

1899. *No.* 196 *surch. with T* **40.**

250 6 c. on 15 c. sage-green .. 1 6 3 0

1899. *As No.* 138 *but colour changed and perf.* 14, *surch. as T* **41.**

254 1 r. 50 c. on 2 r. 50 c. slate 35 0 40 0
255 2 r. 25 c. on 2 r. 50 c. yellow 60 0 85 0

43

1899–1900. *Wmk. Crown CA* (1 *r.* 50 *c. and* 2 *r.* 25 *c. wmk. Crown CC*). *P* 14.

256 **9** 2 c. pale orange-brown 1 6 1 0
257 **39** 3 c. deep green 1 0 1 3
258 **10** 4 c. yellow 1 6 3 0
259 **29** 6 c. rose and black .. 1 0 0 6
260 **39** 12 c. sage-green and rose 4 0 6 0
261 **29** 15 c. blue 5 0 3 6
262 **39** 75 c. black and red-brown 7 6 8 6
263 **43** 1 r. 50 c. rose 42 6 35 0
264 ,, 2 r. 25 c. dull blue .. 50 0 40 0

44

45

46

47

48

1903–5. *Wmk. Crown CA. P* 14.

265 **44** 2 c. red-brown 2 6 1 0
266 **45** 3 c. green 2 6 1 6
267 ,, 4 c. orange-yellow & blue 3 6 2 6
268 **46** 5 c. dull purple .. 2 0 0 9
269 **47** 6 c. carmine 3 0 2 0
270 **45** 12 c. sage-green & rosine 9 0 8 0
271 **48** 15 c. blue 12 6 3 0
272 ,, 25 c. bistre .. 10 0 9 0
273 ,, 30 c. dull violet and green 8 0 4 0
274 **45** 75 c. dull blue & orge. ('05) 15 0 20 0
275 **48** 1 r. 50c. greyish slate ('04) £5 £5
276 ,, 2 r. 25 c. brn. & grn. ('04) £5 £5

1904–5. *Wmk. Mult. Crown CA. P* 14.

277 **44** 2 c. red-brown, O .. 0 6 0 4
278 **45** 3 c. green, O 1 6 0 6
279 ,, 4 c. orange & ultram., O 1 6 2 0
280 **46** 5 c. dull purple, OC .. 3 6 0 3
281 **47** 6 c. carmine, O .. 1 3 0 6
282 **45** 12 c. sage-grn. & rosine, O 4 0 2 0
283 **48** 15 c. blue, O 3 0 1 0
284 ,, 25 c. bistre, O ('05) .. 10 0 6 0
285 ,, 30 c. violet & grn., O ('05) 8 0 2 0
286 **45** 75 c. dull blue and orange, O ('05) 12 6 12 6
287 **48** 1 r. 50 c. grey, O ('05) .. 25 0 25 0
288 ,, 2 r. 25 c. brn. & green, O 30 0 35 0

50

51

1908. *Wmk. Mult. Crown CA. P* 14.

289 **50** 5 c. deep purple, O .. 2 0 0 4
290 ,, 5 c. dull purple, O .. 4 0 0 4
291 **51** 6 c. carmine, O .. 1 0 0 4

1910–11. *Wmk. Mult. Crown CA. P* 14.

No.	Type	Description	Unused	Used
292	**44**	2 c. brn.-orange, O (1911)	0 6	0 3
293	**48**	3 c. green, O (1911) ..	2 6	0 4
294	,,	10 c. sage-grn. & marone, O	3 6	1 6
295	,,	25 c. grey, O	4 0	3 0
296	,,	50 c. chocolate, O ..	10 0	10 0
297	,,	1 r. purple/*yellow*, O ..	12 6	12 6
298	,,	2 r. red/*yellow*, O ..	27 6	30 0
299	,,	5 r. black/*green*, O ..	£5	£5
300	,,	10 r. black/*red*, O ..	£15	£12

52

53

(A)

(B)

Stamps of Type **52** are normally printed in two operations, but the 1 c. and 5 c., together with later issues of the 3 c. and 6 c., were printed from special plates at one operation. These plates are distinguished by a large " C " in the value tablet as illustration B. Except for the 5 c. (which is Die I), the frames also differ slightly from Dies I and II, described in the Introduction, but the 3 c. is similar to Die I and the 1 c. and 6 c. similar to Die II, except that inner top corners of side panels are square and not curved as in Die II.

All stamps with wmk. Mult. Crown CA are Die I unless otherwise stated.

1912–25. *T* **52** *and* **53** (50 *r. to* 1000 *r.*). *Wmk. Mult. Crown CA. P* 14.

No.	Description	Unused	Used
301	1 c. brown, O	0 3	0 3
302	2 c. brown-orange, O ..	0 6	0 3
303	2 c. deep org.-brn., O ..	0 4	0 3
304	3 c. yellow-green, O (A)	3 6	2 0
305	3 c. deep green, O (A) ..	3 6	1 9
306	3 c. blue-green, O (B) ..	1 0	0 8
307	5 c. purple, O	2 6	0 6
308	5 c. bright magenta, O..	0 6	0 3
309	6 c. scarlet, O (A) ..	4 0	0 8
310	6 c. bright scarlet, O (A)	2 0	0 6
311	6 c. pale scarlet, O (B) ..	3 0	0 6
312	6 c. carmine, O (B) ..	8 6	0 6
313	10 c. sage-green, O ..	3 6	2 0
314	10 c. deep sage-green, O..	4 0	1 9
315	15 c. ultramarine, O ..	4 6	2 3
316	15 c. deep bright blue, O	6 0	2 9
317	25 c. yellow and blue, O..	4 0	2 3
318	25 c. orange and blue, O	5 0	2 9
319	30 c. blue-green & violet, C	5 0	3 0
320	30 c. yellow-grn. & violet, C	7 6	5 0
321	50 c. black and scarlet, C..	5 0	3 0
322	1 r. purple/*yellow*, C ..	7 6	8 6
	a. White back (1914) ..	7 6	8 6
	b. On lemon (1916) ..	20 0	12 6
	c. On orange-buff	25 0	27 6
	d. On pale yellow	22 6	17 6
323	2 r. black & red/*yellow*, C	10 0	20 0
	a. White back	12 6	17 6
	b. On lemon	47 6	42 6
	c. On orange-buff	40 0	42 6
	d. On pale yellow	42 6	40 0
324	5 r. black/*green*, C ..	25 0	30 0
	a. White back	30 0	35 0
	b. On blue-grn., olive back (1921)	35 0	40 0
	c. On emerald back (Die II)..	£10	£10
325	10 r. purple & blk./*red*, C	80 0	80 0
	a. Die II	£5	
326	20 r. black and red/*blue*, C	£12	£10
327	50 r. dull purple, C ..	£85	
328	100 r. grey-black, C ..	£300	
329	500 r. dull green, C ..	£1250	
329*a*	1000 r. purple/*red*, C (1925)	£3500	

The 5 c., 6 c. (B) and 30 c. are known with watermark sideways. (6 c., 3s. 6d. un.; 30 c., 7s. 6d. un.).

WAR STAMP

(54)

WAR STAMP ONE CENT

(55)

1918 (18 Nov.). (*a*) *T* **52** *optd. with T* **54**.

No.	Description	Unused	Used
330	2 c. brown-orange	0 3	0 3
	a. Overprint inverted	60 0	60 0
	b. Overprint double	60 0	60 0
331	3 c. green (A)	0 3	0 4
	a. Overprint double	£8	£8
332	3 c. green (B)	0 6	0 4
333	5 c. purple	0 3	0 4
	a. Overprint double	65 0	65 0
334	5 c. bright magenta	1 0	1 0
	a. Overprint inverted	60 0	60 0
	b. Overprint double	40 0	40 0

(*b*) *T* **52** *surch. with T* **55**.

No.	Description	Unused	Used
335	1 c. on 5 c. purple	0 3	0 4
336	1 c. on 5 c. bright magenta	0 3	0 6

Collectors are warned against forgeries of the errors in the " WAR STAMP " overprints.

1918. T **52** *surch. as T* **55**, *but without* " WAR STAMP ".

No.	Description	Unused	Used
337	1 c. on 5 c. purple	0 3	0 3
338	1 c. on 5 c. bright magenta	0 6	0 8

1921–27. *Wmk. Mult. Script CA. P* 14.

No.	Type	Description	Unused	Used
339	**52**	1 c. brown, O (1927) ..	0 3	0 3
340	,,	2 c. brn.-orge., O (Die II)	0 8	0 3
341	,,	3 c. green, O (B) ..	4 0	0 6
342	,,	5 c. bright magenta, O..	0 10	0 3
343	,,	6 c. carmine-red, O (B)..	2 0	0 4
344	,,	10 c. sage-grn., O (Die I)	4 0	1 0
		a. Die II	3 0	1 0
345	,,	15 c. ultramarine, O (Die I)	8 0	8 0
346	,,	25 c. yell. & blue, O (Die I)	6 0	3 6
		a. Die II	7 6	5 0
347	,,	30 c. yellow-green & violet, C (Die I)	6 0	6 0
		a. Die II	6 0	3 6
348	,,	50 c. blk. & scar.., C (Die I)	75 0	50 0
		a. Die II	10 0	2 0
349	,,	1 r. pur./*paleyell.*, C (Die I)	40 0	25 0
		a. Die II	20 0	17 6
350	,,	2 r. black & red/*pale yellow* C (Die II)	15 0	12 6
351	,,	5 r. blk./*emer.*, C (Die II)	40 0	35 0
352	,,	20 r. black & red/*blue*, C (Die II)	£15	£18
353	**53**	50 r. dull purple, C ..	£85	
354	,,	100 r. grey-black, C ..	£325	

1922–27. *New colours and values. Wmk. Mult. Script CA. P* 14.

No.	Type	Description	Unused	Used
355	**52**	3 c. slate-grey, O (B) ..	0 8	0 3
356	,,	6 c. bright violet, O (B)	0 8	0 3
357	,,	9 c. red/*yell.*, O (Die II)	1 0	0 6
358	,,	12 c. rose-scar., O (Die I)	9 0	10 0
		a. Die II	5 0	7 6
359	,,	15 c. green/*pale yellow*, O (Die I)	4 0	2 6
		a. Die II	2 6	2 6
360	,,	20 c. bright blue, O (Die I)	6 6	3 6
		a. Die II	3 0	2 0
360*b*	**53**	100 r. dull pur. & bl. C ..	£375	

The 3 c. (No. 355) is known with watermark sideways.

2 Cents.

(56)

(Surch. at Ceylon Govt. Printing Works.)

1926 (27 Nov.). *Nos.* 355 *and* 356 *surch. as T* **56.**

361 **52** 2 c. on 3 c. slate-grey .. 1 6 1 6
 a. Surch. double £6
 b. Bar omitted .. 90 0
362 „ 5 c. on 6 c. bright violet .. 1 0 1 3

57

1927 (27 Nov.)–**29.** *T* **57.** *Wmk. Mult. Script CA. P* 14.

363 1 r. dull and bright purple, C ('28) 9 0 6 0
364 2 r. green. & carm., C ('29) .. 10 0 8 6
365 5 r. green and dull purple, C ('28) 50 0 35 0
366 10 r. green & brn. orange, C 90 0 75 0
367 20 r. dull purple and blue, C £11 £8

No. 364. Collectors are warned against faked 2 r. stamps, showing what purports to be a double centre.

1935 (6 May). *Silver Jubilee. As Nos.* 91/4 *of Antigua. P* $13\frac{1}{2} \times 14$.

368 6 c. ultramarine and grey .. 0 6 0 4
369 9 c. green and indigo .. 2 3 1 6
370 20 c. brown and deep blue .. 3 6 3 0
371 50 c. slate and purple .. 7 6 6 6

58. Tapping Rubber. **59.** Colombo Harbour.

60. Adam's Peak.

61. Plucking Tea. **62.** Coconut Palms.

63. Hill Paddy (rice),

64. River Scene.

65. Temple of the Tooth, Kandy.

66. Ancient Irrigation Tank.

67. Wild Elephants.

68. Trincomalee.

(Recess. De La Rue (2 c., 3 c., 20 c. and 50 c.), Bradbury, Wilkinson (others).)

1935–36. *Wmk. Mult. Script CA (sideways on 10 c., 15 c., 25 c., 30 c. and 1 r.). Various perfs.*

No.	Type	Description				
372	**58**	2 c. black and carmine (*perf.* 12×13) ..	0	3	0	3
		a. Perf. 14..	8	0	1	6
373	**60**	3 c. black and olive-green (*perf.* 13×12) ..	0	4	0	3
		a. Perf. 14..	6	0	1	6
374	**59**	6 c. black and blue (*perf.* 11×11½)	0	6	0	2
375	**61**	9 c. green and orange (*perf.* 11×11½) ..	1	0	1	0
376	**63**	10 c. black and purple (*perf.* 11½×11) ...	1	0	0	8
377	**64**	15 c. red-brown and green (*perf.* 11½×11) ..	3	6	2	0
378	**62**	20 c. black and grey-blue (*perf.* 12×13) ..	5	0	2	0
379	**65**	25 c. deep blue & chocolate (*perf.* 11½×11) ..	3	6	2	0
380	**66**	30 c. carmine and green (*perf.* 11½×11) ..	6	0	4	6
381	**67**	50 c. black and mauve (*perf.* 14)	20	0	6	0
382	**68**	1 r. violet-blue & choc. (*perf.* 11½×11) ..	25	0	17	6

Dates of issue:—1935. May 1, 2 c., 15 c. and 25 c. June 1, 10 c. July 1, 1 r. Aug. 1, 30 c. Oct. 1, 3 c. 1936. Jan. 1, 6 c., 9 c., 20 c. and 50 c.

1937 (12 MAY.). *Coronation. As Nos. 13/15 of Aden but ptd. by B.W. & Co. P* 11×11½.

383	6 c. carmine	0	4	0	4
384	9 c. green	0	8	0	10
385	20 c. blue	1	0	1	0

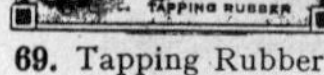

69. Tapping Rubber. **71.** Ancient Guard-stone, Anuradhapura.

70. Sigiriya (Lion Rock).

(Recess. Bradbury, Wilkinson:—stamps perf. 11×11½ or 11½×11. De La Rue:—all stamps with other perfs.).

1938–49. *T* **69** *to* **71** *and types as* 1935–36, *but with portrait of King George VI instead of King George V and "* POSTAGE & REVENUE *" omitted. Wmk. Mult. Script CA (sideways on 10 c., 15 c., 25 c., 30c. and 1 r.). Various perfs.*

No.	Type	Description				
386	**69**	2 c. black and carmine (*p.* 12×13)	10	0	0	8
		a. Perf. 13½×13	30	0	0	8
		b. Perf. 13½	1	0	0	3
		c. Perf. 11×11½ ('44) ..	0	3	0	3
		d. Perf. 12 (22.4.49) ..	0	3	0	4
387	**60**	3 c. black and deep blue-green (*p.* 13×12) ..	12	6	0	10
		a. Perf. 13×13½	£15		3	0
		b. Perf. 13½	1	0	0	3
		c. Perf. 14 ('41)	30	0	2	6
		d. Perf. 11½×11 ('42) ..	0	6	0	6
		da. Perf. 12 (14.1.46) ..	0	3	0	3
387*e*	**62**	5 c. sage-green & orange (*p.* 13½)	0	4	0	6
		f. Perf. 12 ('47)	0	3	0	3
388	**59**	6 c. black and blue (*p.* 11×11½)	0	3	0	3
389	**70**	10 c. black and light blue (*p.* 11½×11)	0	8	0	4
		a. Wmk. upright ('44) ..	0	4	0	3
390	**64**	15 c. green and red-brown (*p.* 11½×11)	0	10	0	3
		a. Wmk. upright ('45) ..	0	9	0	4
391	**61**	20 c. black and grey-blue (*p.* 11×11½)	0	7	0	3
392	**65**	25 c. deep blue and choc. (*p.* 11½×11)	1	3	0	6
		a. Wmk. upright ('44) ..	0	8	0	6
393	**66**	30 c. carmine and green (*p.* 11½×11)	3	6	2	6
		a. Wmk. upright ('45) ..	2	6	1	3
394	**67**	50 c. black and mauve (*p.* 13×12)	£6		27	6
		a. Perf. 13×13½	£8		12	6
		b. Perf. 13½	8	6	1	6
		c. Perf. 14 ('42)	35	0	12	6
		d. Perf. 11½×11 ('42) ..	2	0	1	0
		e. Perf. 12 (14.1.46) ..	1	6	1	0
395	**68**	1 r. blue-violet and choc. (*p.* 11½×11)	5	0	2	6
		a. Wmk. upright ('44) ..	6	0	2	6
396	**71**	2 r. black and carmine (*p.* 11×11½)	7	6	7	6
396*a*	,,	2 r. black and violet (*p.* 11×11½)	7	6	3	6

Dates of issue:—1938. Jan. 1, 6 c. and 15 c. Jan. 15, 20 c. and 25 c. Feb. 1, 10 c., 30 c., 1 r. and 2 r. No. 396. Mar. 21, 3 c. No. 387. Apr. 25, 2 c. No. 386 and 50 c. No. 394; 1943, Jan. 1, 5 c. No. 387*e*; 1947, Mar. 15, 2 r. No. 396*a*; others as indicated.

72. King George VI.

(Typo. De La Rue.)

1938–43. *Wmk. Mult. Script CA. P* 14.

No.	Type	Description				
397	**72**	5 r. grn. & pur. (*shades*), C	17	6	8	6
		a. Green and pale pur., O ('43)	12	6	7	6

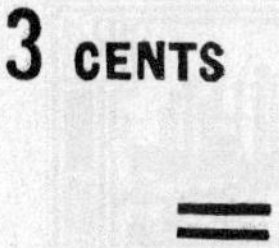

3 CENTS (73)

3 CENTS (74)

1940–41. *Nos.* 388 *and* 391 *surch.*

398 **73** 3 c. on 6 c. (10.5.41) .. 0 3 0 4
399 **74** 3 c. on 20 c. (5.11.40) .. 1 3 1 3

1946 (10 Dec.). *Victory. As Nos.* 28/9 *of Aden.*

400 6 c. blue 0 4 0 4
401 15 c. brown 0 8 0 9

75. Parliament Building.

76. Adam's Peak. **77.** Anuradhapura.

78. Temple of the Tooth.

(Des. R. Tenison and M. S. V. Rodrigo. Recess. Bradbury, Wilkinson.)

1947 (25 Nov.). *Inauguration of New Constitution. Wmk. Mult. Script CA. P* 11 × 12 (*horiz.*) *or* 12 × 11 (*vert.*).

402 **75** 6 c. black and blue .. 0 4 0 4
403 **76** 10 c. blk., orange & carm. 0 6 0 6
404 **78** 15 c. green and purple .. 0 8 0 8
405 **77** 25 c. ochre & emer.-green 1 0 1 6

Dominion of Ceylon.

79. Lion Flag of Dominion. **80.** D. S. Senanayake.

81. Lotus Flowers and Sinhalese Letters " Sri ".

(Recess. (flag typo.). Bradbury, Wilkinson.)

1949. *First Anniv. of Independence* (*a*) (4 Feb.). *Wmk. Mult. Script CA* (*sideways on* 4 *c.*). *P* 12½ × 12 (4 *c.*) *or* 12 × 12½ (5 *c.*).

406 **79** 4 c. yell., carm., & brown 0 10 0 6
407 **80** 5 c. brown and green .. 0 10 0 6

(*b*) (5 Apr.). *W* **81** (*sideways on* 15 *c.*). *P* 13 × 12½ (15 *c.*) *or* 12 × 12½ (25 *c.*).

408 **79** 15 c. yell., carm. & verm. 1 3 0 6
409 **80** 25 c. brown and blue .. 2 0 0 10

The 15 c. is larger, measuring 28 × 22 mm.

82. Globe and Forms of Transport.

83

84

(Recess. De La Rue & Co.)

1949 (10 Oct.). *75th Anniv. of Universal Postal Union.* *W* **81.** *P* 13 (25 *c.*) *or* 12 (*others*).

410	**82**	5 c. brown and bluish green	0	6	0	6
411	**83**	15 c. black and carmine ..	1	3	1	8
412	**84**	25 c. black and ultramarine	2	0	2	0

85. Kandyan Dancer.

86. Kiri Vehera, Polonnaruwa.

87. Vesak Orchid.

88. Sigiriya (Lion Rock).

89. Octagon Library, Temple of the Tooth.

90. Ruins at Madirigiriya.

(Recess. Bradbury, Wilkinson & Co.)

1950 (4 Feb.). *W* **81.** *P* 11×11½ (75 *c.*), 11½×11 (1 *r.*), 12×12½ (*others*).

413	**85**	4 c. purple and scarlet ..	0	3	0	3
414	**86**	5 c. green	0	3	0	3
415	**87**	15 c. blue-green & violet ..	1	6	0	6
416	**88**	30 c. carmine and yellow ..	1	0	0	3
417	**89**	75 c. ultram. and orange ..	2	0	0	9
418	**90**	1 r. deep blue and brown	3	0	1	6

91. Ruhuna National Park.

92. Ancient Guard-stone, Anuradhapura.

93. Harvesting Rice.

94. Coconut Trees.

95. Sigiriya Fresco.

96. Star Orchid.

97. Rubber Plantation.

98. Outrigger Canoe.

99. Tea Plantation.

100. River Gal Dam.

101. Bas-relief, Anuradhapura.

102. Harvesting Rice.

(Photo. Courvoisier.)

1951–54. *No wmk. P* 11½.

419	**91**	2 c. brown and blue-green	0	6	0	3
420	**92**	3 c. black and slate-violet	0	3	0	3
421	**93**	6 c. brn.-blk. & yell.-grn.	0	4	0	3
422	**94**	10 c. green and blue-grey ..	0	8	0	3
423	**95**	25 c. orge.-brn. & brt. blue	0	10	0	4
424	**96**	35 c. red and deep green (I)	3	6	0	6
		a. Type II	2	6	0	9
425	**97**	40 c. deep brown	1	3	0	8
426	**98**	50 c. indigo and slate-grey	1	6	0	4
427	**99**	85 c. blk. & dp. blue-grn.	2	6	1	3
428	**100**	2 r. blue and deep brown	6	0	2	6
429	**101**	5 r. brown and orange ..	17	6	6	6
430	**102**	10 r. red-brown & buff ..	32	6	18	6

No. 424a. In Type II of the 35 c. value, a dot has been added above the third Tamil character in the second line of the inscription at the top right corner.

Dates of issue :—1.8.51, 10 c. ; 1.2.52, 35 c. (I) ; '54, 35 c. (II) ; 15.3.54, 25 c., 50 c., 5 r., 10 r. ; 15.5.54, 2 c., 3 c., 6 c., 40 c., 85 c. and 2 r.

103. Ceylon Mace and Symbols of Progress.

(Photo. Harrison.)

1952 (23 Feb.). *Colombo Plan Exhibition. Chalk-surfaced paper. W* **81** *(sideways). P* 14½ × 14.

431	**103**	5 c. green	0	10	0	10
432	,,	15 c. ultramarine ..	1	6	1	3

104. Queen Elizabeth II.

(Recess. Bradbury, Wilkinson.)

1953 (2 June). *Coronation. W* **81.** *P* 12 × 13.

433	**104**	5 c. green	0	6	0	6

105. Ceremonial Procession.

(Recess. De La Rue.)

1954 (10 Apr.). *Royal Visit. W* **81** *(sideways). P* 13 × 12½.

434	**105**	10 c. deep blue	0	8	0	6

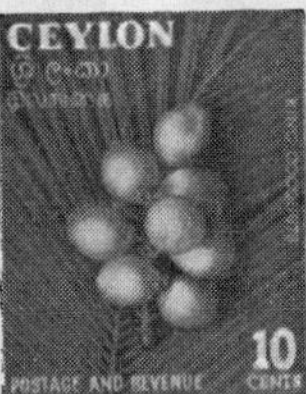

106. King Coconuts.

(Photo. Courvoisier.)

1954 (1 Dec.). *No wmk. P* 11½.

435	**106**	10 c. orange, bistre-brown and buff	0	6	0	3

107. Farm Produce.

(Photo. Harrison & Sons.)

1955 (10 Dec.). *Royal Agricultural and Food Exhibition. W* **81** *(sideways). P* 14 × 14½.

436 **107** 10 c. brown and orange .. 0 6 0 5

108. Sir John Kotelawala and House of Representatives.

(Photo. Courvoisier.)

1956 (26 Mar.). *Prime Minister's* 25 *years of Public Service. P* 11½.

437 **108** 10 c. deep bluish green .. 0 6 0 5

109. Arrival of Vijaya in Ceylon.

110. Lampstand and Dharmachakra.

111. Hand of Peace and Dharmachakra.

112. Dharmachakra encircling the Globe.

(Photo. Courvoisier.)

1956. *Buddha Jayanti. P* 11½.

438 **109** 3 c. blue & brownish grey (23 May) 0 4 0 3

439 **110** 4 c. + 2 c. greenish yellow & deep blue (10 May) 1 0 0 9

440 **111** 10 c. + 5 c. carm., yell. & grey (10 May) .. 1 6 1 10

441 **112** 15 c. bright blue (23 May) 1 3 0 8

113. Mail Transport. **114.** Stamp of 1857.

(Photo. J. Enschedé & Sons (4 c., 10 c.), Courvoisier (others).).

1957 (1 Apr.). *Centenary of First Ceylon Postage Stamp. P* 12½ × 13 *(4 c., 10 c.) or* 11½ *(others)*.

442 **113** 4 c. orange-red & deep bluish green .. 0 4 0 4

443 ,, 10 c. vermilion and blue 0 6 0 4

444 **114** 35 c. brown, yellow & blue 1 3 0 10

445 ,, 85 c. brn., yell. & grey-grn. 2 3 2 3

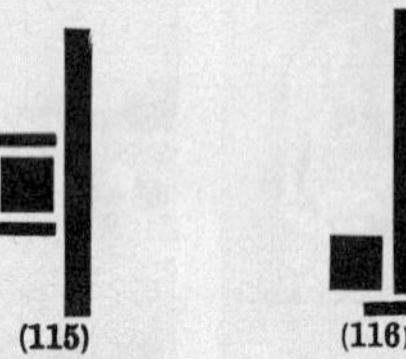

(115) **(116)**

1958 (15 Jan.). *Nos.* 439/40 ***with premium obliterated as T*** **115** *(4 c.)* ***or T*** **116** *(10 c.)*.

446 **110** 4 c. greenish yellow and deep blue 0 4 0 3

a. Opt. inverted .. ..

b. Opt. double .. ..

447 **111** 10 c. carmine, yell. & grey 0 8 0 4

a. Opt. inverted £16

The 4 c. exists with opt. misplaced to right so that some stamps show the vertical bar on the left (*Price £10 un.*).

117. Kandyan Dancer.

(Recess. Bradbury, Wilkinson (4 c., 5 c., 15 c., 30 c., 75 c., 1 r.). Photo. Courvoisier (others).)

1958 (14 May)–**59.** *As earlier types, but inscriptions redrawn as in T* **117.** *W* **81**; *P* 11 × 11½ *(75 c.),* 11½ × 11 *(1 r.) or* 12 × 12½ *(4 c., 5 c., 15 c., 30 c.). No wmk.; P* 11½ *(others).*

448 **91** 2 c. brown & blue-green 0 1 0 2

449 **92** 3 c. black & slate-violet 0 2 0 2

450 **117** 4 c. purple and scarlet .. 0 2 0 2

451 **86** 5 c. grn. (*shades*) (1.10.58) 0 4 0 4

452	**93**	6 c. brown-black & yellow-green	0	3	0	2
453	**106**	10 c. orange, bistre-brown and buff (1.10.58) ..	0	8	0	3
454	**87**	15 c. blue-green & violet (1.10.58)	0	5	0	3
455	**95**	25 c. orange-brown & brt. blue	0	8	0	4
456	**88**	30 c. carm. & yell. (1.5.59)	0	9	0	4
457	**96**	35 c. red and deep green (II) (15.7.58) ..	0	10	0	3
459	**98**	50 c. indigo and slate-grey (15.7.58)	1	1	0	4
460	**89**	75 c. ultramarine & orange (*shades*) (1.5.59) ..	1	8	1	0
461	**99**	85 c. black & deep blue-green (1.5.59) ..	1	9	1	3
462	**90**	1 r. deep blue & brown (1.10.58)	2	6	1	3
463	**100**	2 r. blue & deep brown	4	0	2	6
464	**101**	5 r. brown and orange ..	10	0	4	0
465	**102**	10 r. red-brown and buff	19	6	10	0

118. " Human Rights ".

(Photo. J. Enschedé & Sons, Haarlem.)

1958 (10 Dec.). *Tenth Anniv. of Declaration of Human Rights.* P 13 × 12½.

466	**118**	10 c. vermilion & dull pur.	0	6	0	4
467	,,	85 c. verm. & dp. blue-grn.	3	0	3	0

119. Portraits of Founders and University Buildings.

(Photo. J. Enschedé & Sons, Haarlem.)

1959 (31 Dec.). *Institution of Pirivena Universities.* P 13 × 12½.

468	**119**	10 c. red-orge. & ultram.	0	6	0	3

120. Uprooted Tree. **121.** S. W. R. D. Bandaranaike.

(Des. W. A. Ariyasena. Photo. Courvoisier.)

1960 (7 Apr.). *World Refugee Year.* P 11½.

469	**120**	4 c. red-brown & gold	0	6	0	4
470	,,	25 c. blackish vio. & gold	1	0	0	8

(Photo. Courvoisier.)

1961 (8 Jan.). *Prime Minister Bandaranaike Commemoration.* P 11½.

471	**121**	10 c. dp. blue & greenish blue	0	7	0	4
		a. Portrait redrawn ('61) ..	3	0	2	0

No. 471a can be identified by Mr. Bandaranaike's dark hair at temples.

122. Ceylon Scout Badge. **123.** Campaign Emblem.

(Des. W. A. Ariyasena. Photo. Courvoisier). (Photo. Harrison & Sons.)

1962 (26 Feb.). *Golden Jubilee of Ceylon Boy Scouts Association.* P 11½.

472	**122**	35 c. buff and blue ..	1	0	1	0

1962 (7 Apr.). *Malaria Eradication.* W **81.** P 14½ × 14.

473	**123**	25 c. red-orange and sepia	1	0	0	8

124. Moth and Comet Aircraft.

(Photo. Courvoisier.)

1963 (28 Feb.). *25th Anniv. of Airmail.* P 11½.

474	**124**	50 c. black and light blue	1	6	1	9

125. " Produce " and Campaign Emblem.

(Photo. Courvoisier.)

1963 (21 Mar.). *Freedom from Hunger.* P 11½.

475	**125**	5 c. vermilion and blue	0	4	0	4
476	,,	25 c. brown & yellow-olive	0	10	0	8

ශත

2

சதம்

(**126**)

1963 (1 June). *No.* 450 *surch. with T* **126.**

477 **117**	2 c. on 4 c. pur. & scarlet	0 2	0 2
	a. Surch. inverted ..	..	
	b. Surch double ..	..	

127. " Rural Life ".

(Photo. Harrison & Sons.)

1963 (5 July). *Golden Jubilee of Ceylon Co-operative Movement. W* **81.** *P* 14 × 14½.

478 **127** 60 c. rose-red and black .. 2 0 2 0

128. S. W. R. D. Bandaranaike.

(Recess. Courvoisier.)

1963 (26 Sept.). *P* 11½.

479 **128** 10 c. light blue 0 9 0 6

129. Terrain, Elephant and Tree.

(Photo. Harrison & Sons.)

1963 (2 Dec.). *National Conservation Week. W* **81.** *P* 14 × 14½.

480 **129** 5 c. sepia and blue .. 0 4 0 4

130. S. W. R. D. Bandaranaike.

131. Anagarika Dharmapala (Buddhist missionary).

(T **130/1.** Photo. Courvoisier.)

1964 (1 July). *P* 11½.

481 **130** 10 c. deep violet-blue and greenish grey .. 0 4 0 4

1964 (16 Sept.). *Birth Centenary of Anagarika Dharmapala (founder of Maha Bodhi Society). P* 11½.

482 **131** 25 c. sepia & olive-yellow 1 0 0 11

134. Grackle.

137. Peacock.

138. Ruins at Madirigiriya.

143. Jungle Fowl.

144. Oriole.

146. Tea Plantation

(Photo. Courvoisier (20 c.), Harrison (60 c., 1 r.), De La Rue (others).)

1964–66. *No wmk.* (20 *c.*), *W* **81** (*others*). *P* 11½ (20 *c.*), 14½ × 14 (60 *c.*) *or* 14 (*others*).

485 **134** 5 c. multicoloured .. 0 3 0 2

488 **137** 15 c. multicoloured .. 0 5 0 2

489 **138** 20 c. brown-purple & buff 0 6 0 3
494 **143** 60 c. multicoloured .. 1 4 0 8
495 **144** 75 c. multicoloured .. 1 8 0 8
497 **146** 1 r. brown & bluish grn. 2 0 0 8
MS500*a* 148 × 174 mm. 5 c., 15 c., 60 c., 75. Imperf. .. 4 0

Dates of issue: 1.10.64, 20 c., 1 r.; 5.2.66, others.

150. Exhibition Buildings and Cogwheels.

(Photo. State Ptg. Wks., Budapest.)

1964 (1 Dec.). *Industrial Exhibition. T* **150** *and similar horiz. design. No wmk. P* 11.
501 – 5 c. multicoloured .. 0 4 0 6
502 **150** 5 c. multicoloured .. 0 4 0 6

No. 501 is inscribed "INDUSTRIAL EXHIBITION" in Sinhala and Tamil, No. 502 in Sinhala and English. The stamps were issued together *se-tenant* in alternate vertical rows, producing horizontal pairs.

151. Trains of 1864 and 1964.

(Photo. Harrison & Sons.)

1964 (21 Dec.). *Centenary of Ceylon Railways. T* **151** *and similar horiz. design. W* **81.** *P* 14 × 14½.
503 – 60 c. blue, reddish purple and yellow-green .. 1 8 1 9
504 **151** 60 c. blue, reddish purple and yellow-green .. 1 8 1 9

No. 503 is inscribed "RAILWAY CENTENARY" in Sinhala and Tamil, No. 504 in Sinhala and English. The stamps were issued together *se-tenant* in alternate horizontal rows, producing vertical pairs.

152. I.T.U. Emblem and Symbols.

(Photo. Harrison & Sons.)

1965 (16 May). *I.T.U. Centenary. W* **81.** *P* 14½.
505 **152** 2 c. bright blue and red 0 2 0 2
506 ,, 30 c. brown and red .. 0 11 1 0

153. I.C.Y. Emblem.

(Photo. Courvoisier.)

1965 (26 June). *International Co-operation Year. T* **153** *and similar horiz. design. P* 11½.
507 3 c. dp. blue & rose-carmine 0 3 0 3
508 50 c. black, rose-carm. & gold 1 4 1 5

No. 508 is similar to T **153** but has the multi-lingual inscription "CEYLON" rearranged.

5 ■

154. Town Hall, Colombo. **(155)**

(Photo. Courvoisier.)

1965 (29 Oct.). *Centenary of Colombo Municipal Council. P* 11 × 11½.
509 **154** 25 c. myrtle-green & sepia 0 8 0 9

1965 (18 Dec.). *No.* 481 *surch. with T* **155.**
510 **130** 5 c. on 10 c. deep violet-blue & greenish grey 0 3 0 3

156. D. S. Senanayake. (24 × 30 *mm.*).

(Photo. Courvoisier.)

1966 (22 Mar.). *Senanayake Commemoration. P* 11½.
511 **156** 10 c. myrtle-green .. 0 4 0 3

For illustration see *Addenda*.

OFFICIAL STAMPS.

1869. *Issues of* 1863–68 *overprinted* " SERVICE " *in block letters.*

Although these stamps were prepared for use and sent out to the colony, they were never issued.

Prices :

		Narrow " SERVICE "			Wide " SERVICE "	
No. 98.	2d.	..	30 0		1d. blue	20 0
,, 104.	6d.	..	35 0		3d. rose	45 0
,, 108.	8d.	..	70 0			
,, 113.	1s.	..	80 0			
,, 116.	2s.	..	80 0			
,, 116.	2s. *imp.*		£10			

On

Service

(O 3)

Contemporary issues overprinted with Type O **3.**

1895–96.

O1 **9** 2 c. green 5 0 0 6
O2 **39** 3 c. terra-cotta & bl.-grn. 3 0 3 0
O3 **28** 5 c. dull purple (*b*) .. 1 0 0 3
O4 **29** 15 c. sage-green 5 0 1 3
O5 ,, 25 c. yellow-brown .. 6 0 2 0
O6 ,, 30 c. bright mauve & brown 2 6 1 0
O7 **30** 1 r. 12 c. dull rose .. 45 0 32 6

The varieties of the 1 r. 12 c. mentioned in note after No. 201 all exist with the " On Service " overprint.

1899–1900.

O 8 **9** 2 c. pale orange-brown .. 2 6 0 4
O 9 **39** 3 c. deep green 4 6 2 6
O10 **29** 15 c. blue 6 0 1 9
O11 **39** 75 c. black and red-brown (R.) ('99) 6 0 4 0

1903. *King Edward VII.*

O12 **44** 2 c. orange-brown .. 7 0 4 0
O13 **45** 3 c. green 4 0 5 0
O14 **46** 5 c. dull purple .. 6 0 2 6
O15 **48** 15 c. blue 10 0 4 0
O16 ,, 25 c. bistre 30 0 30 0
O17 ,, 30 c. dull violet & green .. 12 6 6 6

About half a dozen sheets of the 15 c. were overprinted with a space of 3 mm. instead of 4 mm. between the words " On " and "Service".

POSTAL FISCAL.

1952 (1 Dec.). *As T* **72** *but inscr.* " REVENUE " *at sides.*

F1 10 r. dull grn. & yell.-orge., C 50 0 37 6

This revenue stamp was on sale for postal use from December 1st, 1952, until March 14th, 1954.

CHANNEL ISLANDS.

I. Stamps issued under British authority during the German Occupation.

GUERNSEY

BISECTS. On December 24th, 1940, authority was given, by Post Office notice, that prepayment of penny postage could be effected by using half a British 2d. stamp, diagonally bisected. Such stamps were first used on December 27th, 1940.

The 2d. stamps generally available were those of the Postal Centenary issue, 1940 (S.G. 482) and the first colour of the King George VI issue (S.G. 465). A number of the 2d. King George V, 1912–22, and of the King George V photogravure stamp (S.G. 442) which were in the hands of philatelists, were also bisected and used. *Price* S.G. 482 *bisected and used on cover or piece* 35*s.*, S.G. 465 *ditto*, £10.

1

(Des. E. W. Vaudin. Typo. Guernsey Press Co. Ltd.)

1941–44. *Rouletted.* (*a*) *White paper. No wmk.*

G1 **1** ½d. green (*shades*) (7.4.41) .. 1 6 1 6
a. Olive-green 3 0 2 6
b. Blue-green 7 6 5 0
c. Imperf. between (horiz. pair) £75
d. Imperf. between (vert. pair) £100
G2 ,, 1d. scarlet (18 Feb., '41) .. 1 0 0 9
a. Imperf. (pair) £12 £12
b. Vermilion 7 6 1 6
c. Imperf. between (horiz. pair) £75
d. Imperf. between (vert. pair) £100
G3 ,, 2½d. ultram. (12 Apr., '44) .. 7 6 7 6

(*b*) *Bluish French bank-note paper. Wmk. loops.*

G4 **1** ½d. bright grn. (11 Mar., '42) 10 0 22 6
G5 ,, 1d. scarlet (7 Apr., '42) .. 10 0 22 6

JERSEY.

1

(Des. Major N. V. L. Rybot. Typo. *Evening Post*, Jersey.)

1941–42. *White paper. No wmk. P* 11.

J1 **1** ½d. bright grn. (29.1.42) .. 2 0 2 6
a. Imperf. between (vert. pair) .. £100
b. Imperf. between (horiz. pair) .. £75
c. Imperf. (pair) £12
d. On greyish paper 2 6 5 0
J2 ,, 1d. scarlet (1.4.41) 1 9 2 6
a. Imperf. between (vert. pair) ..
b. Imperf. between (horiz. pair) .. £75
c. On chalk-surfaced paper .. 35 0 40 0
d. On greyish paper 2 6 2 6

2. Old Jersey Farm.

3. Portelet Bay.

4. Corbière Lighthouse.

5. Elizabeth Castle.

6. Mont Orgueil Castle.

7. Gathering Vraic (seaweed).

(Des. E. Blampied. Eng. H. Cortot. Typo. French Govt. Works, Paris.)

1943. *No wmk. P* 13½.

J3	**2**	½d. green (1 June)	2	6	2	0
J4	**3**	1d. scarlet (1 June) ..	1	6	1	6
		a. On newsprint	2	6	5	0
J5	**4**	1½d. brown (8 June) ..	2	6	5	0
J6	**5**	2d. orange-yellow (8 June)	2	6	3	0
J7	**6**	2½d. blue (29 June)	3	6	4	0
		a. On newsprint	5	0	8	6
J8	**7**	3d. violet (29 June) ..	5	0	7	6

II. GENERAL ISSUE.

C **1.** Gathering Vraic.

C **2.** Islanders gathering Vraic.

(Des. 1d. J. R. R. Stobie. 2½d. from drawing by E. Blampied. Photo. Harrison & Sons, Ltd.)

1948 (10 May). *Third Anniv. of Liberation. W* **127** *of Great Britain. P* 15 × 14.

C1	C **1**	1d. scarlet	0	4	0	4
C2	C **2**	2½d. ultramarine	0	6	0	6

For Guernsey and Jersey Regional issues, see *Great Britain*.

CHINA.

BRITISH POST OFFICES.

See after **HONG KONG.**

CHRISTMAS ISLAND.

Formerly a part of the Colony of Singapore: now an Australian territory.

1. Queen Elizabeth II.

(Recess; name and value typo. in black. Note Printing Branch, Commonwealth Bank, Melbourne.)

1958 (15 Oct.). *No wmk. P* 14½.

1	**1**	2 c. yellow-orange ..	0	4	0	6
2	,,	4 c. brown	0	5	0	7
3	,,	5 c. deep mauve	0	6	0	8
4	,,	6 c. grey-blue	0	6	0	9
5	,,	8 c. black-brown	0	7	0	9
6	,,	10 c. violet	0	9	1	0
7	,,	12 c. carmine	0	10	1	2
8	,,	20 c. blue	1	2	1	6
9	,,	50 c. yellow-green	2	3	2	9
10	,,	$1 deep bluish green ..	4	6	5	0

2. Map.

3. Moonflower.

4. Robber Crab.

5. Island Scene.

8. Flying Fish Cove.

6. Phosphate Train.

7. Raising Phosphate.

9. Loading Cantilever.

10. Frigate Bird.

11. Golden Bo'sun Bird.

(Recess. Note Ptg. Branch, Reserve Bank of Australia, Melbourne.)

1963 (28 Aug.). *P* 14½ × 14 ($1) *or* 14½ (*others*).

11	**2**	2 c. orange . .	0 2	0 2
12	**3**	4 c. red-brown	0 3	0 3
13	**4**	5 c. purple	0 4	0 4
14	**5**	6 c. indigo . .	0 4	0 5
15	**6**	8 c. black . .	0 5	0 6
16	**7**	10 c. violet	0 6	0 8
17	**8**	12 c. brown-red	0 6	0 8
18	**9**	20 c. blue . .	0 10	1 0
19	**10**	50 c. green . .	1 8	2 0
20	**11**	$1 yellow	3 4	4 0

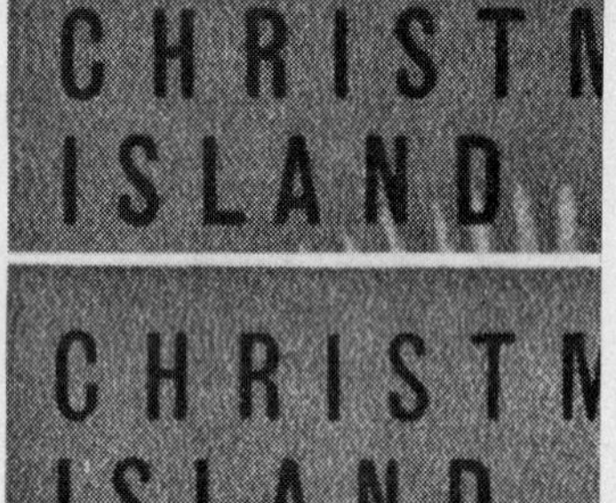

I Thick lettering.
II Thinner lettering.

1965. 50*th Anniv. of Gallipoli Landing. As T* **181** *of Australia, but slightly larger* (22 × 34½ *mm.*). *Photo.*

21	10 c. sepia, black & emerald (I) (14.4) . .	0 9	1 6
	a. Black-brown, black and light emerald (II)	0 7	0 9

COCOS (KEELING) IS.

Formerly incorporated with Singapore: an Australian territory since 1955.

1. Copra Industry.

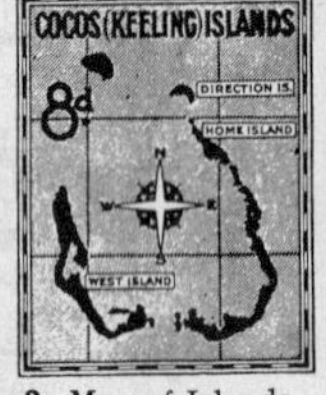

3. Map of Islands.

2. Super Constellation Airliner.

4. Palms.

5. Dukong (sailboat).

6. White Tern.

(Recess. Note Ptg. Branch, Reserve Bank of Australia, Melbourne.)

1963 (11 June). *P* 14½×14 (5*d.*, 2*s.* 3*d.*) *or* 14½ (*others*).

1	**1**	3d. chocolate	0	6	0	7
2	**2**	5d. ultramarine	0	9	0	11
3	**3**	8d. scarlet	1	1	1	5
4	**4**	1s. green	1	5	1	10
5	**5**	2s. deep purple	2	9	3	9
6	**6**	2s. 3d. deep green	3	0	5	6

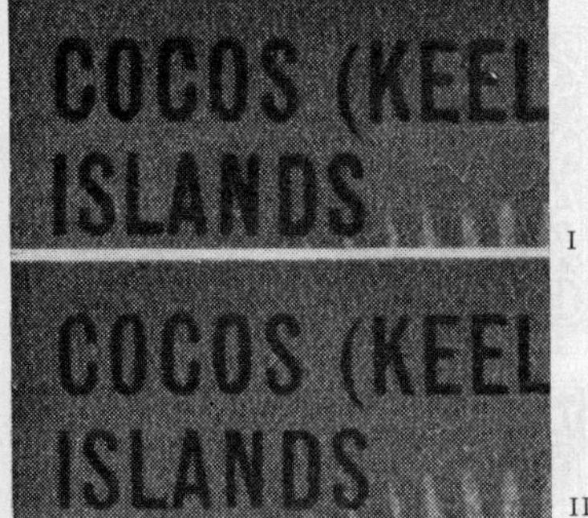

I

II

I Thick lettering.
II Thinner lettering.

1965. 50*th Anniv. of Gallipoli Landing. As T* **181** *of Australia, but slightly larger* (22×34½ *mm.*). *Photo.*

7	5d. sepia, black and emerald (I) (1.44)	0	9	1	3
	a. Black-brown, black and light emerald (II) (24.4)	0	8	0	10

With the introduction of decimal currency on 14th February, 1966, Australian stamps were used in Cocos Islands.

COOK ISLANDS.

(RAROTONGA.)

These are also known as the Hervey Islands. The islands of Manikiki, Rakahanga, and Pukapuka were annexed to the group in October, 1890, and use the same stamps.

1

(Des. F. Moss. Typo. Govt. Printing Office Wellington.)

1892 (7 May). *No wmk. P* 12½.
A. *Toned paper.* B. *White paper.*

			A.				B.			
1	**1**	1d. black ..	20	0	25	0	17	6	25	0
		a. Imp. betwn. (vert. pr.) ..	£70							
2	”	1½d. mauve	27	6	32	6	20	0	30	0
3	”	2½d. blue	40	0	50	0	25	0	35	0
4	”	10d. carmine ..	80	0	£5		80	0	£5	

2. Queen Makea Takau.

3. Torea or Wry-bill.

(Eng. A. E. Cousins. Typo. Govt. Printing Office, Wellington.)

1893–1900. *W* **12***a of New Zealand* (N Z *and Star wide apart*).

		(*a*) *P* 12×11½. (7.8.93–'94.)				
5	**2**	1d. brown	15	0	30	0
6	”	1d. blue (2.94)	10	0	7	0
7	”	1½d. mauve	5	0	10	0
8	”	2½d. rose	12	6	27	6
		a. Rose-carmine	40	0	50	0
9	”	5d. olive-black	10	0	17	6
10	”	10d. green	22	6	40	0
		(*b*) *P* 11. (July, 1896–1900.)				
11	**3**	½d. blue (9.99)	5	0	10	0
12	**2**	1d. blue	3	6	12	6
13	”	1d. brown (4.99)	10	0	30	0
14	”	1½d. deep lilac	5	6	10	0
		a. Deep mauve	3	0	10	0
15	**3**	2d. brown (6.98)	5	6	10	0
		a. Deep brown (2.1900) ..	5	6	10	0
16	**2**	2½d. pale rose	35	0	50	0
		a. Deep rose	5	6	12	6
17	”	5d. olive-black	15	0	25	0
18	**3**	6d. purple (6.98)	20	0	30	0
		a. Bright purple (2.1900) ..	20	0	30	0
19	**2**	10d. green	20	0	27	6
20	**3**	1s. red (6.98)	35	0	50	0
		a. Deep carmine (2.1900) ..	35	0	50	0

The above are on white paper except the 2d., 6d. and 1s. which are on toned and No. 13 which is on cream paper.

ONE
HALF
PENNY
(4) (5)

1899 (24 Apr.). *No. 12 surch. with T* **4**.

21 **2** ½d. on 1d. blue 17 6 30 0
a. Surch. inverted £25 £30
b. Surch. double £30 £35

1901 (Oct.). *No. 13 optd. with T* **5**.

22 **2** 1d. brown £8 £5
a. Crown inverted £38 £40
b. Crown sideways £50 £60
c. Optd. with crown twice .. £60 £75

1902. *No wmk. P* 11.

(*a*) *Medium white Cowan paper.* (Feb.).

23 **3** ½d. blue-green 3 6 10 0
24 **2** 1d. dull rose 12 6 17 6

(*b*) *Thick white Pirie paper.* (May).

25 **3** ½d. yellow-green 3 6 6 6
a. Imp. betwn. (horiz. pr.) .. £30
26 **2** 1d. rose-red 6 6 12 6
a. Rose-lake 4 0 8 0
27 " 2½d. dull blue 6 0 12 6

1902 (Sept.). *W* **41** *of New Zealand (single-lined NZ and Star, close together; sideways on T* **2**).

28 **3** ½d. yellow-green 2 6 6 0
a. Grey-green 12 6 17 6
29 **2** 1d. rose-pink 3 6 10 0
30 " 1½d. deep mauve 5 0 10 0
31 **3** 2d. deep brown 5 0 10 0
a. No figures of value .. £60 £70
32 **2** 2½d. deep blue 3 6 7 6
33 " 5d. olive-black 15 0 20 0
34 **3** 6d. purple 17 6 25 0
35 **2** 10d. green 17 6 25 0
36 **3** 1s. carmine 15 0 20 0

1909–11. *W* **41** *of New Zealand.*

37 **3** ½d. green (*p.* 14½ × 14) ('11) .. 5 6 8 6
38 **2** 1d. deep red (*perf.* 14) .. 12 6 15 0

1913–19. *W* **41** *of New Zealand. Chalk-surfaced paper.*

39 **3** ½d. deep green (*p.* 14) ('15) 3 0 6 6
40 **2** 1d. red (*perf.* 14) (7.13) .. 3 6 8 6
41 " 1d. red (*p.* 14 × 14½) ('14) .. 8 6 10 0
42 " 1½d. dp. mauve (*p.* 14) ('15) 35 0 15 0
43 " 1½d. dp. mve. (*p.* 14 × 15) ('16) 5 0 8 6
44 **3** 2d. dp. brn. (*p.* 15 × 14) ('19) 10 0 30 0
45 **2** 10d. green (*p.* 14 × 15) ('18) .. 25 0 60 0
46 **3** 1s. carmine (*p.* 15 × 14) ('19) 25 0 60 0

RAROTONGA

APA PENE
(8)

RAROTONGA
(9)

1919. *Contemporary stamps of New Zealand surch. as T* **8**, *in red* (R.) *or blue* (B.).

T **60***b and* **51** (1d.) *surface-printed.*
P 14 × 15.

50 ½d. green (R.) 0 8 3 0
51 1d. carmine (B.) 0 9 2 6
52 1½d. orange-brown (R.) .. 1 0 5 0
53 2d. yellow (R.) 2 0 5 0
54 3d. chocolate (B.) 2 6 6 6

T **60**, *engraved.*
(*a*) *P* 14 × 14½. (*b*) *P* 14 × 13½.

55 2½d. blue (R.) (*a*) 2 6 6 0
56 2½d. blue (R.) (*b*) 2 6 10 0
a. Vert. pair (55/56) 22 6 30 0
57 3d. chocolate (B.) (*a*) .. 5 0 15 0
58 3d. chocolate (B.) (*b*) .. 7 6 17 6
a. Vert. pair (57/58) 35 0 45 0
59 4d. violet (B.) (*a*) 3 0 10 0
60 4d. violet (B.) (*b*) 3 0 15 0
a. Vert. pair (59/60) 25 0 35 0
61 4½d. deep green (B.) (*a*) .. 2 6 8 0
62 4½d. deep green (B.) (*b*) .. 3 0 12 6
a. Vert. pair (61/62) 25 0 35 0
63 6d. carmine (B.) (*a*) 5 0 15 0
64 6d. carmine (B.) (*b*) 5 0 12 6
a. Vert. pair (63/64) 40 0 55 0
65 7½d. red-brown (B.) (*b*) .. 6 0 17 6
66 9d. sage-green (R.) (*a*) .. 4 0 15 0
67 9d. sage-green (R.) (*b*) .. 4 6 15 0
a. Vert. pair (66/67) 40 0 65 0
68 1s. vermilion (B.) (*a*) .. 7 6 22 6
69 1s. vermilion (B.) (*b*) .. 10 0 22 6
a. Vert. pair (68/69) 50 0 75 0

1921. *Type* F **4** *of New Zealand optd. with T* **9**. *P* 14½ × 14.

70 2s. blue (No. F 166) (R.) .. 30 0 60 0
71 2s. 6d. brown (No. F 167) (B.) 20 0 50 0
72 5s. yell.-grn. (No. F 170) (R.) 55 0 80 0
73 10s. claret (No. F 174) (B.) .. £5 £6
74 £1 rose (No. F 176) (B.) .. £10 £12

See also Nos. 87/*d*.

10. Capt. Cook landing.

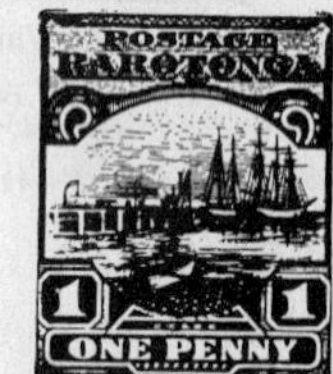

11. Wharf at Avarua.

12. Capt. Cook.

13. Palm Tree.

14. Huts at Arorangi.

15. Avarua Harbour.

(Designed, engraved and recess-printed by Perkins Bacon & Co.)

1920. *No wmk. P* 14.

75 **10** ½d. black and green .. 5 0 5 0
76 **11** 1d. black and carmine-red 5 0 6 0
77 **12** 1½d. black & dull blue .. 8 6 12 6
78 **13** 3d. black and chocolate .. 10 0 15 0
79 **14** 6d. brown & yellow-orange 10 0 17 6
80 **15** 1s. black and violet .. 15 0 25 0

1925. *Wmk. T* **41** *of New Zealand. P* 14.

81 **10** ½d. black and green .. 5 0 6 6
82 **11** 1d. black & deep carmine 5 0 5 0

1926. *As Nos.* 70/4, *but white paper and gum, and overprint in carmine.*

87 2s. blue £25 £32
87*a* 2s. 6d. brown 35 0 60 0

87*b* 5s. yellow-green 90 0 £6
87*c* 10s. claret £8 £10
87*d* £1 rose £15 £20

1926. *T* **72** (*"Admiral" Type*) *of New Zealand, overprinted with T* **9.** (*a*) *"Jones" chalk-surfaced paper.*

88 **2s. deep blue (R.)** 15 6 35 0

(*b*) *"Cowan" thick chalk-surfaced paper.*

89 **2s. light blue (R.)** 12 6 32 6
90 **3s. bright mauve (R.)** .. 16 0 35 0

16. Native Chief.

17. Rarotonga Harbour

1927. *Wmk. T* **41** *of New Zealand. P* 14.

91 **16** 2½d. red-brown & steel-blue 8 6 12 6
92 **17** 4d. green and violet .. 6 0 12 6

TWO PENCE

(**18**)

1931. *Surch. with T* **18.** *P* 14. (*a*) *No wmk.*

93 **12** 2d. on 1½d. black & blue (R). 5 0 8 6

(*b*) *W* **41** *of New Zealand.*

94 **12** 2d. on 1½d. blk. & blue (R.) 5 0 10 0

1931. *T* **73a** *of New Zealand (various frames) optd. with T* **9.** *W* **41** *of New Zealand. P* 14.

95 2s. 6d. brown (B.) 20 0 30 0
96 5s. green (R.) 50 0 65 0
97 10s. carmine (B.) £6 £8
98 £1 pink (B.) £10 £12

19. Capt. Cook landing.

20. Capt. Cook.

21. Double Maori canoe.

22. Natives working cargo.

23. Port of Avarua.

24. R.M.S. *Monowai.*

25. King George V.

(Des. L. C. Mitchell. Recess. Perkins, Bacon.)

1932 (16 MAR.). *No wmk. P* 13.

99 **19** ½d. black & deep green 1 6 3 0
a. Perf. 14 .. .. 15 0 22 6
100 **20** 1d. black and lake .. 3 6 6 0
a. Centre inverted.. .. £125 £150
b. Perf. 14 .. .. 17 6 25 0
101 **21** 2d. black and brown .. 5 0 7 6
a. Perf. 14 .. .. 17 6 25 0
102 **22** 2½d. black & deep blue .. 17 6 25 0
a. Perf. 14 .. .. 15 0 17 6
103 **23** 4d. black & bright blue 17 6 25 0
a. Perf. 14 .. .. 15 0 25 0
b. Perf. 14×13 .. .. 27 6 40 0
104 **24** 6d. black and orange .. 27 6 40 0
a. Perf. 14 .. .. 10 0 22 6
105 **25** 1s. blk. & violet(*perf.* 14) 16 0 30 0

(Recess-printed from Perkins, Bacon's plates at the Government Printing Office, Wellington, N.Z.)

1933–36. *Wmk. T* **41** *of New Zealand.* (*Single* N Z *and Star*). *P* 14.

106 **19** ½d. black & deep green 0 6 0 8
107 **20** 1d. black & scarlet ('35) 0 8 0 10
108 **21** 2d. black & brown ('36) 0 8 1 0
109 **22** 2½d. black & deep blue .. 1 0 1 6
110 **23** 4d. black & bright blue 2 0 2 6
111 **24** 6d. blk. & orge.-yell. ('36) 3 9 3 0
112 **25** 1s. black & violet ('36) .. 20 0 35 0

SILVER JUBILEE OF KING GEORGE V. 1910-1935.

(**26**)

Normal letters.

B K E N

B K E N

Narrow letters.

1935 (7 MAY). *Silver Jubilee. Optd. with T* **26** (*wider vertical spacing on* 6d.). *Colours changed. W* **41** *of New Zealand. P* 14.

113 **20** 1d. red-brown & lake .. 1 0 1 6
a. Narrow "K" in "KING" 5 0
b. Narrow "B" in "JUBILEE" 6 0
114 **22** 2½d. dull & deep blue (R.) 2 6 5 0
a. Narrow first "E" in "GEORGE" 12 6 15 0
115 **24** 6d. green and orange .. 10 6 15 0
a. Narrow "N" in "KING" 37 6

COOK ISLANDS.

(**27**)

COOK IS'DS.

(**28**)

1932–36. *Stamps of New Zealand optd. with T* **27.** *W* **41** *of New Zealand. P* 14.

(*a*) *T* **72** (*"Admiral" Type*).

116 2s. blue (Bk.) (15.7.36) .. 15 0 30 0
117 3s. mauve (Bk.) (15.7.36) .. 22 6 37 6

(*b*) *As T* **73a** (*"Arms" Type*).

118 2s. 6d. brown (Bk.) (15.7.36) 12 6 30 0
119 5s. green (R.) (15.7.36) .. 45 0 60 0
120 10s. carm.-lake (Bk.) (15.7.36) 85 0 £5
121 £1 pink (Bk.) (15.7.36) .. £7 £9
122 £3 green (R.) ('32) .. £15 £20
123 £5 blue (R.) ('32) £35 £40

1937 (1 June) *Coronation. Nos.* 599/601 *of New Zealand optd. with T* **28.**

124 **106** 1d. carmine 0 6 0 10
125 „ 2½d. Prussian blue .. 1 0 1 6
126 „ 6d. red-orange 2 0 3 0

29. King George VI.

30. Native Village.

31. Native Canoe.

32. Tropical Landscape.

(Des. J. Berry (2s., 3s., and frame of 1s.). Eng. Bradbury, Wilkinson, London. Recess. Govt. Ptg. Office, Wellington, N.Z.)

1938 (2 May). *W* **41** *of New Zealand. P* 14.

127 **29** 1s. black and violet • .. 5 0 6 0
128 **30** 2s. black and red-brown .. 7 6 10 0
129 **31** 3s. lt. blue & emerald-grn. 12 6 15 0

(Recess. Bradbury, Wilkinson.)

1940 (2 Sept.). *Surch. as in T* **32.** *W* **98** *of New Zealand. P* 13½ × 14.

130 **32** 3d. on 1½d. black & purple 0 9 0 9

Type **32** was not issued without surcharge.

(Recess. Govt. Ptg. Office, Wellington.)

1944–46. *W* **98** *of New Zealand* (*sideways on* ½*d.,* 1*d.,* 1*s. and* 2*s.*). *P* 14.

131 **19** ½d. black and deep green 0 6 0 8
132 **20** 1d. black and scarlet ('45) 0 6 0 8
133 **21** 2d. blk. & brn. (Feb. '46) 0 8 1 0
134 **22** 2½d. black & deep blue ('45) 1 0 1 6
135 **23** 4d. black and blue .. 1 6 2 0
136 **24** 6d. black and orange .. 2 0 2 6
137 **29** 1s. black and violet ('44) 3 0 5 0
138 **30** 2s. black & red-brn. ('45) 6 0 10 0
139 **31** 3s. light blue & emerald-green ('45) 10 0 15 0

1944–53. *As T* **73***a* (" *Arms* ") *of New Zealand, but optd. with T* **27.** *Wmk. T* **98** *of New Zealand. P* 14.

140 2s. 6d. brown ('48) 7 6 12 6
141 5s. green (R.) 12 6 17 6
142 10s. carmine-lake (10.48) .. 17 6 25 0
143 £1 pink (11.47) 35 0 45 0
144 £3 green (R.)(28.5.53) .. £5 £6
145 £5 blue (R.) (25.10.50) .. £8 £10

COOK
ISLANDS
(**33**)

1946 (1 June). *Peace. Stamps of New Zealand optd. with T* **33** (*reading up and down at sides on* 2*d.*).

146 **132** 1d. green 0 4 0 6
147 **134** 2d. purple (B.) 0 6 0 10
148 **138** 6d. chocolate and verm. 1 0 1 6
149 **139** 8d. black & carm. (B.) .. 1 6 2 0

34. Ngatangiia Channel, Rarotonga.

35. Capt. Cook and Map of Hervey Islands.

36. Rarotonga and Rev. John Williams.

37. Aitutaki and Palm Trees.

38. Rarotonga Airfield.

39. Penrhyn Village.

40. Native Hut.

41. Map and Statue of Capt. Cook.

42. Native Hut and Palms.

43. M.V. *Matua.*

(Des. J. Berry. Recess. Waterlow.)

1949 (1 Aug.)–**61**. *W* **98** *of New Zealand* (*sideways on shilling values*). *P* 13½×13 (*horiz.*) *or* 13×13½ (*vert.*).

150	**34**	½d. violet and brown ..	0	4	0	6
151	**35**	1d. chestnut and green ..	0	6	0	8
152	**36**	2d. reddish brown & scarlet	0	7	0	9
153	**37**	3d. green and ultramarine	1	0	1	3
		a. Wmk. sideways (white opaque paper (22.5.61)	5	0	7	6
154	**38**	5d. emerald-green & violet	7	6	10	0
155	**39**	6d. black and carmine ..	1	6	2	0
156	**40**	8d. olive-green and orange	1	9	2	6
157	**41**	1s. light blue and chocolate	2	6	3	0
158	**42**	2s. yellow-brown & carmine	5	0	6	6
159	**43**	3s. light blue & bluish grn.	7	6	10	0

See note on white opaque paper below No. 736 of New Zealand.

1953 (25 May). *Coronation. As designs of New Zealand, but inscr.* "COOK ISLANDS".

160	**164**	3d. brown	1	0	1	3
161	**166**	6d. slate-grey	1	6	1	9

1/6

● ●

(44)

1960 (1 Apr.). *No.* 154 *surch. with T* **44**.

162	**38**	1s. 6d. on 5d. emer.-green and violet	5	0	6	0

45. Tiare Maori.

47. Frangipani.

48. Love Tern.

46. Fishing God.

49. Hibiscus.

51. Oranges.

50. Bonito.

52. Queen Elizabeth II.

53. Island Scene.

54. Administration Centre, Mangaia.

55. Rarotonga.

(Des. J. Berry. Recess. (1s. 6d.), litho. (others). Bradbury, Wilkinson.)

1963 (4 June). *Wmk. T* **98** *of New Zealand (sideways). P* 13½×13 (*1d., 2d., 8d.*), 13×13½ (*3d., 5d., 6d., 1s.*) *or* 13½ (*others*).

No.	Type	Description	Un. s.	Un. d.	Used s.	Used d.
163	**45**	1d. emer.-green & yellow ..	0	3	0	3
164	**46**	2d. brown-red and yellow	0	4	0	4
165	**47**	3d. yellow, yellow-green & reddish violet	0	6	0	6
166	**48**	5d. blue and black ..	0	9	0	10
167	**49**	6d. red, yellow and green ..	0	10	1	0
168	**50**	8d. black and blue ..	1	0	1	3
169	**51**	1s. orange-yellow and yellow-green	1	5	1	8
170	**52**	1s. 6d. bluish violet ..	2	0	2	8
171	**53**	2s. bistre-brn. & grey-blue	2	9	3	8
172	**54**	3s. black and yellow-green	4	0	5	3
173	**55**	5s. bistre-brown and blue	6	9	8	0

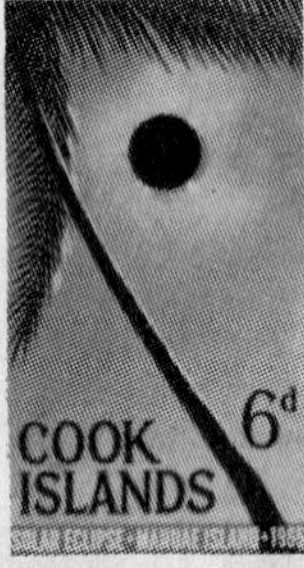

56. Eclipse and Palm.

(Des. L. C. Mitchell. Litho. Bradbury Wilkinson.)

1965 (31 May). *Solar Eclipse Observation, Manuae Island. W* **98** *of New Zealand. P* 13½.

No.	Type	Description	Un. s.	Un. d.	Used s.	Used d.
174	**56**	6d. black, yellow & lt. blue	0	10	1	3

57. N.Z. Ensign and Map.

58. London Missionary Society Church.

59. Proclamation of Cession, 1900.

60. Nikao School.

(Des. R. M. Conly (4d.), L. C. Mitchell (10d., 1s.), J. Berry (1s. 9d.). Litho. Bradbury, Wilkinson.)

1965 (16 Sept.). *Internal Self-Government. W* **98** *of New Zealand (sideways). P* 13½.

No.	Type	Description	Un. s.	Un. d.	Used s.	Used d.
175	**57**	4d. red and blue ..	1	0	1	6
176	**58**	10d. multicoloured ..	2	0	2	6
177	**59**	1s. multicoloured ..	2	9	3	0
178	**60**	1s. 9d. multicoloured ..	5	0	6	6

In Memoriam
Sir Winston Churchill
1874 - 1965

(61)

1966 (24 Jan.). *Churchill Commemoration. Nos.* 171/3 *and* 175/7 *optd. with T* **61**, *in red.*

No.	Type	Description	Un. s.	Un. d.	Used s.	Used d.
179	**57**	4d. red and blue ..	2	0	3	0
180	**58**	10d. multicoloured ..	3	6	5	0
		a. Opt. inverted	£200			
181	**59**	1s. multicoloured ..	5	0	6	6
182	**53**	2s. bistre-brn. & grey-blue	8	0	10	0
183	**54**	3s. black & yellow-green	12	0	15	0
184	**55**	5s. bistre-brown and blue	20	0	25	0

CYPRUS.

CROWN COLONY.

For GREAT BRITAIN stamps used in Cyprus, see page 59.

(Stamps of Great Britain overprinted by De La Rue & Co.)

CYPRUS (1) CYPRUS (2)

Note.—All Cyprus stamps are perf. 14 unless otherwise stated.

1880.

No.	Type	Description	Un. s.	Un. d.	Used s.	Used d.
1	**1**	½d. rose	70	0	75	0
		a. Opt. double (Pl. 15)	—		£85	

Plate No.	*Un. s. d.*	*Used. s. d.*	*Plate. No.*	*Un. s. d.*	*Used. s. d.*
12. ..	£5	£6	19. ..	£60	£14
15. ..	70 0	75 0			

2 2 1d. red 10 0 12 6
a. Opt. double (Pl. 208) £125
aa. Opt. double (Pl. 218) £80
b. Pair, one without opt. (Pl. 208) £175

Plate No.	Un. s. d.	Used... s. d...	Plate No.	Un. s. d.	Used. s. d.
174.	.. £35	£30	208.	.. 70 0	12 6
181.	.. 80 0	60 0	215.	.. 12 6	12 6
184.	.. £60	£50	216.	.. 10 0	15 0
193.	.. £65	—	217.	.. 10 0	15 0
196.	.. £65	—	218.	.. 15 0	20 0
201.	.. 12 6	15 0	220.	.. £25	£9
205.	.. 25 0	40 0			

3 2 2½d. rosy mauve 3 6 6 0
a. Large thin "c" (Plate 14) .. 15 0 20 0
b. Large thin "c" (Plate 15) .. 20 0 25 0

14.	.. 3 6	6 0	15.	.. 5 0	20 0

4 2 4d. sage-green (Plate 16) .. £5 £6
5 ,, 6d. grey (Plate 16) £12 £12
6 ,, 1s. green (Plate 13) £40 £28

HALF-PENNY (3) 18 mm.

HALF-PENNY (4) 16 or 16½ mm.

HALF-PENNY (5) 13 mm.

30 PARAS (6)

1881. *No. 2 surch.*

7 3 ½d. on 1d. red 40 0 45 0
a. "HALFPENN" *(all plates) from* £25 £25

Plate No.	Un. s. d.	Used. s. d.	Plate No.	Un. s. d.	Used. s. d.
174.	.. 70 0	£10	215.	.. £10	£15
181.	.. 70 0	70 0	216.	.. 40 0	50 0
201.	.. 40 0	45 0	217.	.. £20	£20
205.	.. 40 0	45 0	218.	.. £15	£15
208.	.. 80 0	90 0	220.	.. £8	£8

8 4 ½d. on 1d. red 90 0 90 0
a. Surch. double (Pl. 201) .. £55

201.	.. 90 0	90 0	218.	.. —	—
216.	.. £9	£12			

9 5 ½d. on 1d. red 35 0 40 0
a. Surch. double (Pl. 201) ..
aa. Surch. double (Pl. 205) .. £20
ab. Surch. double (Pl. 215) .. £12 £12
b. Surch. treble (Pl. 205) ..
ba. Surch. treble (Pl. 215) .. £20
bb. Surch. treble (Pl. 217) ..
bc. Surch. treble (Pl. 218) ..
c. Surch. quadruple (Pl. 205) .. £65
ca. Surch. quadruple (Pl. 215) .. £55
d. "CYPRUS" double (Pl. 218) .. £110

201.	.. —	—	217.	.. 50 0	60 0
205.	.. £6		218.	.. 40 0	45 0
215.	.. 35 0	40 0			

10 6 30 paras on 1d. red £5 80 0
a. Surch. double, one invtd. (Pl. 216) £70
aa. Surch. double, one invtd. (Pl. 220) £40 £50

201.	.. £7	80 0	217.	.. £7	80 0
216.	.. £5	85 0	220.	.. £7	£8

CYPRUS / ONE PIASTRE

7

(Typo. De La Rue & Co.)

1881 (July). *Die I. Wmk. Crown CC.*

16 7 ½ pias. emerald-green .. £6 45 0
17 ,, 1 pias. rose £8 45 0
18 ,, 2 pias. blue £8 30 0
19 7 4 pias. pale olive-green .. £20 £7
20 ,, 6 pias. olive-grey £25 £20

Stamps of Queen Victoria initialled "J. A. B." or overprinted "POSTAL SURCHARGE" with or without the same initials were employed for accounting purposes between the Chief Post Office and sub-offices. The initials are those of the then Postmaster, Mr. J. A. Bulmer.

½ (8) ½ ½ (9) ½ 30 PARAS (10)

1882. *T 7, surch.*

Varieties of T **9**: *(a) Figures "½" 8½ mm. apart, (b) 6 to 7 mm. apart.*

21 8 ½ pias. emerald-green .. £8 45 0
22 9 ½ pias. emerald-green *(a)* .. £110 £15
22a ,, ½ pias. emerald-green *(b)* .. £140
23 10 30 paras on 1 pias. rose .. £35 £7

(i.) *Small "1" on right.*

24 9 ½ pias. emerald-green *(a)* .. £225 £110

(ii.) *Large "1" on left.*

24a 9 ½ pias. emerald-green *(a)* .. — £55

Type **8** was made locally, Type **9** in London. Type **9** may be found with the figure "2" of slightly different size.

1882–86. *Wmk. Crown CA. T* **7** *surch. Die I.**

25 8 ½ pias. emerald-green .. 40 0 30 0
a. Surch. double .. — £40
26 9 ½ pias. emerald-green *(a)* .. £8 15 0
a. Large "1" on left £60 £15
b. Small "1" on right .. £85 £20
27 ,, ½ pias. emerald-green *(b)* .. £8 80 0

T **7** *unsurcharged. Die I.*

28 7 ½ pias. emerald-green .. £70 £18
28a ,, ½ pias. dull green 6 0 1 6
29 ,, 30 paras pale mauve .. 30 0 15 0
30 ,, 1 pias. carmine 30 0 3 6
31 ,, 2 pias. dull blue 40 0 3 6
32 ,, 4 pias. pale olive-green .. £6 20 0
32a ,, 4 pias. deep olive-green .. £10 20 0
33 ,, 6 pias. olive-grey .. 30 0 20 0
34 ,, 12 pias. orange-brown .. £6 55 0

Die II.

35 7 ½ pias. dull green 6 0 1 6
36 ,, 30 paras mauve 6 0 6 0
37 ,, 1 pias. carmine 17 6 6 0
38 ,, 2 pias. ultramarine .. 12 6 2 6
38a ,, 4 pias. pale olive-green .. 25 0 10 0
39 ,, 4 pias. olive-green .. 60 0 17 6
40 ,, 6 pias. olive-grey .. 50 0 £12
41 ,, 12 pias. orange-brown .. 60 0 £6

* For description and illustration of differences between Die I and Die II see Introduction.

1894–96. *T 7. Die II. Wmk. Crown CA.*

42 7 ½ pi. green and carmine .. 1 3 0 6
43 ,, 30 pa. brt. mauve and green 2 6 1 3
44 ,, 1 pi. carmine and blue .. 6 0 1 0
45 ,, 2 pi. blue and purple .. 3 6 2 0
46 ,, 4 pi. sage-green & purple .. 12 6 8 0
47 ,, 6 pi. sepia and green .. 15 0 10 6
48 ,, 9 pi. brown and carmine .. 20 0 12 6
49 ,, 12 pi. orange-brown & black 20 0 35 0
50 ,, 18 pi. greyish slate & brown 47 6 30 0
51 ,, 45 pi. grey-purple and blue .. 80 0 90 0

11

(Typo. De La Rue & Co.)

1903. *Wmk. Crown CA.*

No.	Type	Stamp	Unused	Used
52	**11**	½ pi. green and carmine ..	2 6	0 6
53	,,	30 pa. violet and green ..	1 9	2 0
54	,,	1 pi. carmine and blue ..	12 6	2 0
55	,,	2 pi. blue and purple ..	22 6	10 0
56	,,	4 pi. olive-green & purple	60 0	27 6
57	,,	6 pi. sepia and green ..	£8	£9
58	,,	9 pi. brown and carmine ..	£15	£18
59	,,	12 pi. chestnut and black ..	30 0	35 0
60	,,	18 pi. black and brown ..	£12	£14
61	,,	45 pi. dull pur. & ultram.	£20	£35

1904–10. *Wmk. Multiple Crown CA.*

No.	Type	Stamp	Unused	Used
61*a*	**11**	5 pa. bistre & black ('07)	1 6	1 0
61*b*	,,	10 pa. orange & green ('07)	1 6	0 9
61*c*	,,	10 pa. yellow and green ..	55 0	20 0
62	,,	½ pi. green and carmine ..	1 6	0 6
63	,,	30 pa. purple and green ..	10 0	2 0
63*a*	,,	30 pa. violet & green ('10)	7 6	2 6
64	,,	1 pi. carmine and blue ..	4 0	1 3
65	,,	2 pi. blue and purple ..	5 0	1 6
66	,,	4 pi. olive-green & purple	17 6	12 6
67	,,	6 pi. sepia and green ..	25 0	12 6
68	,,	9 pi. brown and carmine	12 6	12 6
69	,,	12 pi. chestnut & blk. ('06)	60 0	30 0
70	,,	18 pi. black and brown ..	65 0	22 6
71	,,	45 pi. dull purple & ultram.	£7	80 0

12

(Typo. De La Rue & Co.)

1912. *Wmk. Mult. Crown CA.*

No.	Type	Stamp	Unused	Used
73	**12**	10 pa. orange and green ..	1 6	1 0
73*a*	,,	10 pa. orge.-yell. & brt. grn.	3 0	2 0
74	,,	½ pi. green and carmine ..	0 9	0 6
74*a*	,,	½ pi. yellow-green & carm.	3 0	0 9
75	,,	30 pa. violet and green ..	1 6	0 6
76	,,	1 pi. rose-red and blue ..	6 0	2 6
77	,,	1 pi. carmine and blue ..	15 0	2 0
78	,,	2 pi. blue and purple ..	6 6	1 6
79	,,	4 pi. olive-green & purple	10 0	4 6
80	,,	6 pi. sepia and green ..	10 0	8 6
81	,,	9 pi. brown and carmine	40 0	22 6
81*a*	,,	9 pi. pale brn. & carmine	55 0	40 0
82	,,	12 pi. chestnut and black ..	17 6	17 6
83	,,	18 pi. black and brown ..	32 6	17 6
84	,,	45 pi. dull purple & ultram.	£6	£6

1921–23. *Wmk. Mult. Script CA.*

No.	Type	Stamp	Unused	Used
85	**12**	10 pa. orange and green ..	1 0	3 0
86	,,	30 pa. violet and green ..	1 6	0 9
87	,,	1 pi. carmine and blue ..	15 0	17 6
88	,,	2 pi. blue and purple ..	10 0	10 0
89	,,	4 pi. olive-green & purple	10 0	12 6
90	,,	6 pi. sepia and green ..	17 6	25 0
91	,,	9 pi. brown and carmine ..	22 6	40 0
92	,,	18 pi. black and brown ..	£8	£10
93	,,	45 pi. dull purple & ultram.	£15	£15

1922–23. *Colours changed and new values.*

(*a*) *Wmk. Mult. Script CA.*

No.	Type	Stamp	Unused	Used
94	**12**	10 pa. grey and yellow ..	5 0	7 6
95	,,	30 pa. green	2 6	2 0
96	,,	1 pi. violet and red ..	5 0	6 0
97	,,	1½ pi. yellow and black ..	5 0	6 0
98	,,	2 pi. carmine and blue ..	17 6	20 0
99	,,	2¾ pi. blue and purple ..	17 6	20 0

(*b*) *Wmk. Mult. Crown CA.*

No.	Type	Stamp	Unused	Used
100	**12**	10s. green & red/*pale yellow*	£40	£45
101	,,	£1 purple and black/*red* ..	£150	£165

13

1924–28. *Chalk-surfaced paper.*

(*a*) *Wmk. Mult Crown CA.*

No.	Type	Stamp	Unused	Used
102	**13**	£1 purple and black/*red*	£15	£18

(*b*) *Wmk. Mult. Script CA.*

No.	Type	Stamp	Unused	Used
103	**13**	¼ pi. grey and chestnut ..	1 0	1 3
104	,,	½ pi. black	1 3	2 0
105	,,	¾ pi. green	1 3	1 0
106	,,	1 pi. purple and chestnut	2 0	1 0
107	,,	1½ pi. orange and black ..	2 6	4 6
108	,,	2 pi. carmine and green ..	4 6	7 6
109	,,	2¾ pi. bright blue & purple	5 0	7 0
110	,,	4 pi. sage-green & purple	6 0	7 0
111	,,	4½ pi. black & orge./*emerald*	7 0	10 0
112	,,	6 pi. olive-brown & green	10 0	12 6
113	,,	9 pi. brown and purple ..	15 0	15 0
114	,,	12 pi. chestnut and black ..	15 0	40 0
115	,,	18 pi. black and orange ..	30 0	20 0
116	,,	45 pi. purple and blue ..	65 0	65 0
117	,,	90 pi. green and red/*yellow*	£8	£10
117*a*	,,	£5 black/*yellow* ('28) ..	£350	£425

1925. *Wmk. Mult. Script CA.*

No.	Type	Stamp	Unused	Used
118	**13**	½ pi. green, C	1 0	1 3
119	,,	¾ pi. black, C	0 9	0 6
120	,,	1½ pi. scarlet, O	2 6	3 6
121	,,	2 pi. yellow and black, C	5 0	7 6
122	,,	2½ pi. bright blue, O ..	6 6	1 6

In the above set the fraction bar in the value is horizontal. In Nos. 97, 99, 107 and 109 it is diagonal.

14. Silver coin of Amathus.

15. Philosopher Zeno.

16. Map of Cyprus.

17. Discovery of Body of St. Barnabas.

18. Cloister, Abbey of Bella Paise.

19. Badge of Cyprus.

20. Tekke of Umm Haram.

21. Statue of Richard I, London.

22. St. Nicholas, Famagusta.

23. King George V.

(Recess. Bradbury, Wilkinson.)

1928 (1 Feb.). *50th Anniv. of British Rule. Wmk. Mult. Script CA. P 12.*

123	**14**	¾ pi. deep dull purple ..	1	6	1	6
124	**15**	1 pi. black & greenish blue	5	0	6	0
125	**16**	1½ pi. scarlet	4	0	5	0
126	**17**	2½ pi. light blue	5	0	8	0
127	**18**	4 pi. deep brown.. ..	12	6	15	0
128	**19**	6 pi. blue	14	0	22	6
129	**20**	9 pi. maroon ..	18	6	25	0
130	**21**	18 pi. black and brown ..	30	0	45	0
131	**22**	45 pi. violet and blue ..	50	0	60	0
132	**23**	£1 blue & bistre-brown	£15		£16	

24. Vouni Palace.

25. Salamis.

26. Peristerona Church.

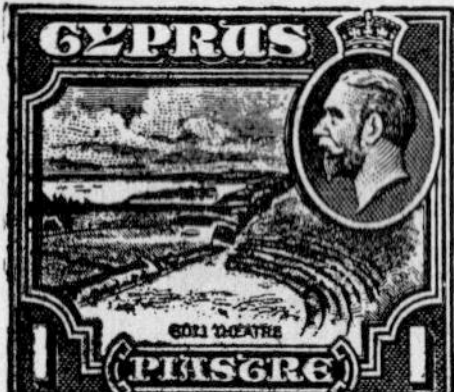

27. Soli Theatre.

28. Kyrenia Harbour.

29. Kolossi Castle.

30. St. Sophia, Nicosia.

31. Bairakdar Mosque.

32. Queen's Window, St. Hilarion Castle.

33. Buyuk Khan, Nicosia.

34. Forest Scene.

(Recess. Waterlow & Sons.)

1934 (1 Dec.). *Wmk. Mult. Script CA (sideways on ½ p., 1½ p., 2½ p., 4½ p., 6 p., 9 p. and 18 p.).*

No.	Type	Description	Unused	Used
133	**24**	¼ p. ultram. & orge.-brn.	0 6	0 6
		a. Imp. between (vert. pair.)	£300	
134	**25**	½ p. green	0 8	0 6
		a. Imp. between (vert. pair)	£250	
135	**26**	¾ p. black and violet ..	0 9	0 6
		a. Imp. between (pair) ..	£300	
136	**27**	1 p. black and red-brown	1 6	1 0
		a. Imp. between (pair) ..	£250	
137	**28**	1½ p. carmine	1 9	1 6
138	**29**	2½ p. ultramarine	2 6	2 6
139	**30**	4½ p. black and crimson ..	6 0	7 6
140	**31**	6 p. black and blue ..	8 6	9 0
141	**32**	9 p. sepia and violet ..	15 0	17 6
142	**33**	18 p. black & olive-green	22 6	30 0
143	**34**	45 p. green and black ..	70 0	80 0

1935 (6 May). *Silver Jubilee. As Nos. 91/4 of Antigua, but ptd. by W'low & Sons. P* 11 × 12.

No.	Description	Unused	Used
144	¾ p. ultramarine and grey ..	0 9	0 9
145	1½ p. deep blue and scarlet ..	2 6	3 0
146	2½ p. brown and deep blue ..	5 0	6 0
147	9 p. slate and purple.. ..	15 0	17 6

1937 (12 May.). *Coronation. As Nos. 13/5 of Aden, but ptd. by B.W. & Co. P* 11 × 11½.

No.	Description	Unused	Used
148	¾ p. grey	0 9	0 9
149	1½ p. carmine	1 0	1 6
150	2½ p. blue	2 0	2 6

35. Vouni Palace.

36. Map of Cyprus.

37. " Citadel " (Othello's Tower), Famagusta.

38. King George VI.

(Recess. Waterlow & Sons, Ltd.)

1938 (12 MAY)–**1951.** *T* **35** *to* **38** *and other designs as* 1934, *but with portrait of King George VI. Wmk. Mult. Script CA. P* 12½.

151	**35**	½ p. ultram. & orge.-brn.	0	4	0	6
152	**25**	½ p. green	0	4	0	4
152*a*	,,	½ p. violet (2.7.51) ..	0	10	0	6
153	**26**	¾ p. black and violet ..	2	6	0	8
154	**27**	1 p. orange	0	6	0	3
		a. Perf. 13½ × 12½ ..	£15		15	0
155	**28**	1½ p. carmine	2	0	2	0
155*a*	,,	1½ p. violet (15.3.43) ..	0	8	0	4
155*ab*	,,	1½ p. green (2.7.51) ..	1	0	0	6
155*b*	**26**	2 p. blk. & car. (30.1.42)	0	6	0	6
		c. Perf. 12½ × 13½ ('44) ..	2	6	1	3
156	**29**	2½ p. ultramarine ..	10	0	10	0
156*a*	,,	3 p. ultram. (30.1.42) ..	0	10	0	8
156*b*	,,	4 p. ultram. (2.7.51) ..	1	0	0	8
157	**36**	4½ p. grey	1	0	0	8
158	**31**	6 p. black and blue ..	2	6	3	0
159	**37**	9 p. black and purple ..	2	0	1	3
160	**33**	18 p. black & olive-green	15	0	6	0
		a. Black and sage-green ('47)	6	6	4	0
161	**34**	45 p. green and black ..	10	0	6	0
162	**38**	90 p. mauve and black ..	45	0	30	0
163	,,	£1 scarlet and indigo ..	65	0	65	0

1946 (21 OCT.). *Victory. As Nos.* 28/9 *of Aden.*

164	1½ p. deep violet	0	4	0	6
165	3 p. blue	0	8	1	0

1948 (20 DEC.). *Royal Silver Wedding. As Nos.* 30/1 *of Aden.*

166	1½ p. violet	0	4	0	4
167	£1 indigo	45	0	50	0

1949 (10 OCT.). *75th Anniv. of Universal Postal Union. As Nos.* 114/7 *of Antigua but inscr.* " CYPRUS " (*recess*).

168	1½ p. violet	1	0	1	0
169	2 p. carmine-red	1	3	1	3
170	3 p. deep blue	2	0	2	0
171	9 p. purple	4	0	5	0

1953 (2 JUNE). *Coronation. As No.* 47 *of Aden, but ptd. by B. W. & Co.*

172	1½ p. black and emerald ..	0	9	1	0

(New currency. 1,000 mils. = £1)

39. Carobs.

40. Grapes.

41. Oranges.

42. Copper Pyrites Mine.

43. Troodos Forest.

44. Beach of Aphrodite.

45. Ancient Coin of Paphos.

46. Kyrenia.

47. Harvest in Mesaoria.

48. Famagusta Harbour.

49. St. Hilarion Castle.

50. Hala Sultan Tekke.

51. Kanakaria Church.

52. Coins of Salamis, Paphos, Citium and Idalium.

53. Arms of Byzantium, Lusignan, Ottoman Empire and Venice.

(Recess. Bradbury, Wilkinson & Co. Ltd.)

1955 (1 Aug.)–**60.** *Wmk. Mult. Script CA. P* 13½. (*Nos.* 183/5) *or* 11½ (*others*).

173	**39**	2 m.	blackish brown ..	0	3	1	0
174	**40**	3 m.	blue-violet ..	0	3	1	0
175	**41**	5 m.	brn.-orange (*shades*)	0	4	0	4
176	**42**	10 m.	dp. brn. & dp. grn.	0	6	0	6
177	**43**	15 m.	olive-green and ind.	1	0	1	0
			aa. Yellow-olive & indigo (17.9.58)	25	0	12	6
			a. Bistre & indigo (14.6.60)	45	0	22	6
178	**44**	20 m.	brn. & dp. brt. blue	0	10	0	10
179	**45**	25 m.	dp. turq.-bl. (*shades*)	2	0	2	0
180	**46**	30 m.	black & carm.-lake	1	0	1	3
181	**47**	35 m.	orange-brown & dp. turquoise-blue ..	1	6	1	9
182	**48**	40 m.	deep green & sepia	2	0	2	0
183	**49**	50 m.	turquoise-blue and reddish brown ..	2	6	2	0
184	**50**	100 m.	mauve & bluish grn.	4	6	5	0
185	**51**	250 m.	dp. grey-blue & brn.	12	6	14	0
186	**52**	500 m.	slate and purple ..	27	6	27	6
187	**53**	£1	brown-lake & slate	55	0	60	0

REPUBLIC.

ΚΥΠΡΙΑΚΗ
ΔΗΜΟΚΡΑΤΙΑ
KIBRIS
CUMHURIYETI

(**54.** " Cyprus Republic ".) **55.** Map of Cyprus.

1960 (16 Aug.). *T* **39** *to* **53** *optd. as T* **54**, *in blue. Opt. larger on Nos.* 191/7 *and in two lines on Nos.* 198/202.

No.	Type	Description	Unused	Used
188	**39**	2 m. blackish brown ..	1 0	2 9
189	**40**	3 m. blue-violet ..	1 0	2 9
190	**41**	5 m. brn.-orange (*shades*)	1 0	0 8
191	**42**	10 m. dp. brown & dp. grn.	1 6	1 0
192	**43**	15 m. yellow bistre and indigo (*shades*) ..	2 0	1 9
		a. *Olive-green & indigo* ..	£30	
193	**44**	20 m. brn. & dp. brt. blue	2 3	2 3
		a. Opt. double	†	£350
194	**4**	25 m. dp. turquoise-blue (*shades*)	2 9	2 9
195	**46**	30 m. blk. & carm.-lake ..	3 6	2 6
		a. Opt. double	†	£350
196	**47**	35 m. orange-brown and dp. turquoise-blue	3 6	2 9
197	**48**	40 m. dp. green and sepia	4 6	3 9
198	**49**	50 m. turquoise-blue and reddish brown ..	6 0	4 6
199	**50**	100 m. mauve & bluish grn.	11 0	9 0
200	**51**	250 m. dp. grey-blue & brn.	27 6	25 0
201	**52**	500 m. slate and purple ..	70 0	85 0
202	**53**	£1 brown-lake & slate	£6	£7

Only one used copy of each of Nos. 193*a* and 195*a* is known.

(Recess. Bradbury, Wilkinson.)

1960 (16 Aug.). *Constitution of Republic. W* w.**12.** *P* 11½.

No.	Type	Description	Unused	Used
203	**55**	10 m. sepia & deep green	1 0	1 0
204	,,	30 m. ultram. & dp. brown	3 6	3 6
205	,,	100 m. purple & deep slate	7 6	10 0

PRINTERS. All the following were lithographed by Aspioti-Elka, Athens, *unless otherwise stated.*

56. Doves.

(Des. T. Kurpershoek.)

1962 (19 Mar.). *Europa. P* 14×13.

No.	Type	Description	Unused	Used
206	**56**	10 m. purple and mauve	0 6	0 9
207	,,	40 m. ultram. & cobalt ..	1 6	1 9
208	,,	100 m. emerald & pale grn.	3 6	4 0

57. Campaign Emblem.

1962 (14 May). *Malaria Eradication. P* 14×13½.

No.	Type	Description	Unused	Used
209	**57**	10 m. black & olive-green	0 8	0 10
210	,,	30 m. black and brown ..	1 9	2 0

WATERMARK VARIETIES. The issues printed by Aspioti-Elka with *W* **58** are known with the vertical stamps having the watermark normal or inverted and the horizontal stamps with the watermark reading upwards or downwards.

58. Mult. K C K Δ and Map.

59. Iron Age Jug.

60. Grapes.

61. Bronze Head of Apollo.

62. St. Sophia Church. **65.** Head of Aphrodite.

63. St. Barnabas' Church.

64. Temple of Apollo Hylates.

66. Skiing at Troodos.

67. Salamis Gymnasium.

68. Hala Sultan Tekke.

70. Cyprus Moufflon.

69. Bellapais Abbey.

71. St. Hilarion Castle.

1962 (17 SEPT.). *W* **58.** *P* 13½ × 14 (*vert.*) *or* 14 × 13½ (*horiz.*).

211	**59**	3 m. dp. brn. & orge.-brn.	0	2	0	2
212	**60**	5 m. purple and grey-grn.	0	3	0	3
213	**61**	10 m. black & yell.-grn.	0	5	0	6
214	**62**	15 m. blk. & reddish pur.	0	6	0	6
215	**63**	25 m. dp. brn. & chestnut	0	10	0	10
216	**64**	30 m. dp. blue & lt. blue	0	11	1	0
217	**65**	35 m. lt. green and blue	1	1	1	2
218	**66**	40 m. black & violet-blue	1	2	1	3
219	**67**	50 m. bronze-grn. & bistre	1	5	1	6
220	**68**	100 m. dp. brn. & yell.-brn.	2	9	3	0
221	**69**	250 m. black & cinnamon	6	9	7	0
222	**70**	500 m. dp. brn. & lt. grn.	13	3	13	6
223	**71**	£1 bronze-grn. & grey	25	0	27	6

72. Europa " Tree ".

(Des. Lex Weyer.)

1963 (28 JAN.). *Europa.* *W* **58** (*sideways*). P 14 × 13½.

224	**72**	10 m. brt. blue and black	0	8	0	10
225	,,	40 m. carm.-red & black	1	6	1	9
226	,,	150 m. emerald-grn. & blk.	6	0	7	6

73. Harvester.

74. Demeter, Goddess of Corn.

1963 (21 MAR.). *Freedom from Hunger.* *W* **58.** *P* 13½ × 14.

227	**73**	25 m. ochre, sepia & brt. bl.	1	0	1	0
228	**74**	75 m. grey, black and lake	2	6	2	6

75. Wolf Cub in Camp.

76. Sea Scout.

77. Scout with Moufflon.

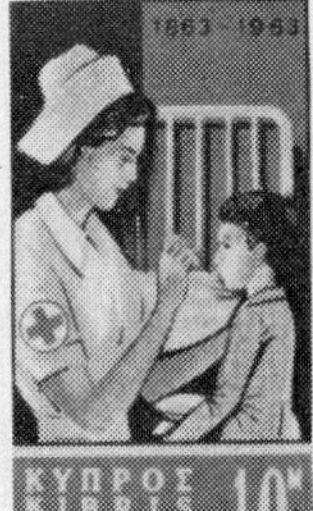

78. Nurse tending Child.

79. Children's Home, Kyrenia.

1963 (21 Aug.). *50th Anniv. of Cyprus Scout Movement. W* **58**. *P* 13½ × 14.

229 **75** 3 m. brown, black, dull green and turquoise 0 6 0 7
230 **76** 20 m. bluish violet, brown, black & light blue . . 1 3 1 3
231 **77** 150 m. brn., blk., olive & bl. 7 0 8 0
MS231*a* 110 × 90 mm. Nos. 229/31 (sold at 250 m.). Imperf. 60 0

1963 (9 Sept.). *Centenary of Red Cross. W* **58** *(sideways on* 100 *m.). P* 13½ × 14 *(*10 *m.) or* 14 × 13½ *(*100 *m.).*

232 **78** 10 m. red, blue, grey-blue, chestnut and black 0 9 1 0
233 **79** 100 m. red, grn., blk. & bl. 4 3 5 0

80. " Co-operation " (emblem).

(Des. A. Holm.)

1963 (4 Nov.). *Europa. W* **58** *(sideways). P* 14 × 13½.

234 **80** 20 m. buff, blue & violet 0 9 0 10
235 " 30 m. grey, yellow & blue 1 6 1 9
236 " 150 m. buff, blue & orange-brown 4 6 5 0

(81)

1964 (5 May). *U.N. Security Council's Cyprus Resolutions, March,* 1964. *Nos.* 213, 216, 218/20 *optd. with T* **81** *in blue.*

237 **61** 10 m. black & yellow-grn. 1 0 1 2
238 **64** 30 m. dp. blue & lt. blue 2 6 3 0
239 **66** 40 m. black & violet-blue 3 0 3 6
240 **67** 50 m. bronze-grn. & bistre 3 6 4 0
241 **68** 100 m. dp. brn. & yell.-brn. 7 0 8 6

82. Soli Theatre.

83. Curium Theatre.

84. Salamis Theatre.

85. Othello Tower, and scene from Shakespeare's *Othello*.

1964 (15 June). *400th Anniv. of Shakespeare's Birth. W* **58**. *P* 13½ × 13.

242 **82** 15 m. ochre, grey-green, violet-blue & black 0 7 0 11
243 **83** 35 m. yell.-brn., brn., blk., lt. blue & dp. blue 1 4 1 6
244 **84** 50 m. drab, dull green, blue and black . . 1 8 1 10
245 **85** 100 m. brn.-purple, olive, lt. brown & black . . 3 3 3 9

86. Running.

89. Europa " Flower ".

87. Boxing.

88. Charioteers.

1964 (6 July). *Olympic Games, Tokio.* *W* **58** (*sideways, 25 m., 75 m.*). *P* 13½ × 14 (10 *m.*) *or* 14 × 13½ (*others*).

246 **86** 10 m. brn., blk. & yellow 0 6 0 10
247 **87** 25 m. brn., blue & blue-grey 1 0 1 2
248 **88** 75 m. brown, black and orange-red 2 6 2 9

MS248*a* 110 × 90 mm. Nos. 246/8 (sold at 250 m.). Imperf. .. 10 0

(Des. G. Bétemps.)

1964 (14 Sept.). *Europa.* *W* **58.** *P* 13½ × 14.

249 **89** 20 m. chestnut & lt. ochre 0 10 1 0
250 ,, 30 m. ultram. & lt. blue 1 1 1 6
251 ,, 150 m. olive and light blue-green 4 9 5 6

90. Dionysus and Acme.

91. Silenus (satyr.)

92. Commandaria Wine.

93. Wine Factory.

1964 (26 Oct.). *Cyprus Wines.* *W* **58** (*sideways, 10 m., 100 m.*). *P* 14 × 13½ (*horiz.*) *or* 13½ × 14 (*vert.*).

252 **90** 10 m. multicoloured .. 0 6 0 9
253 **91** 40 m. multicoloured .. 1 6 1 9
254 **92** 50 m. multicoloured .. 2 0 2 3
255 **93** 100 m. multicoloured .. 3 9 4 6

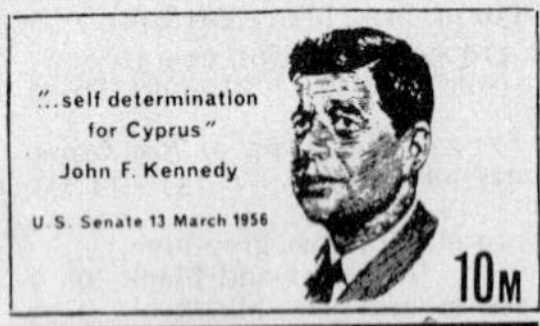

94. President Kennedy.

1965 (15 Feb.). *President Kennedy Commemoration.* *W* **58** (*sideways*). *P* 14 × 13½.

256 **94** 10 m. ultramarine .. 0 6 0 1
257 ,, 40 m. green 1 5 1
258 ,, 100 m. carmine-lake .. 3 3 4

MS258*a* 110 × 90 mm. Nos. 256/8 (sold at 250 m.). Imperf... 12 0

95. " Old Age ".

96. " Accident ".

97. " Maternity ".

1965 (12 Apr.). *Social Insurance Law.* *W* **58.** *P* 13½ × 12 (75 *m.*) *or* 13½ × 14 (*others*).

259 **95** 30 m. drab and dull green 1 1 1 6
260 **96** 45 m. light grey-green, blue and deep ultramarine 1 8 1 10
261 **97** 75 m. red-brown and flesh 2 6 2 9

98. I.T.U. Emblem and Symbols.

1965 (17 May). *I.T.U. Centenary.* *W* **58** (*sideways*). *P* 14 × 13½.

262 **98** 15 m. blk., brn. & yellow 0 7 0 10
263 ,, 60 m. blk., grn. & lt. grn. 2 3 2 9
264 ,, 75 m. blk., indigo & lt. bl. 2 6 3 6

99. I.C.Y. Emblem.

1965 (17 May). *International Co-operation Year.* *W* **58** (*sideways*). *P* 14 × 13½.

265 **99** 50 m. brown, deep green and lt. yellow-brn. 1 6 2 3
266 ,, 100 m. purple, deep green and light purple .. 3 3 4 6

100. Europa " Sprig ".
(Des. H. Karlsson.)

1965 (27 Sept.). *Europa.* *W* **58** (*sideways*). *P* 14 × 13½.

267 **100** 5 m. black, orange-brn. and orange .. 0 3 0 5
268 ,, 45 m. black, orange-brn. and lt. emerald .. 1 4 2 0
269 ,, 150 m. black, orange-brn. and light grey .. 4 0 5 0

U. N.
Resolution
on Cyprus
18 Dec. 1965
(**101**)

1966 (31 Jan.). *U.N. General Assembly's Cyprus Resolution,* 18 *December* 1965. *Nos.* 211, 213, 216 *and* 221 *optd. with T* **101**, *in blue.*

270 **59** 3 m. dp. brn. & orge.-brn. 0 6 0 8
271 **61** 10 m. black & yellow-grn. 0 8 0 10
272 **64** 30 m. dp. blue & lt. blue 1 6 1 9
273 **69** 250 m. black and cinnamon 8 6 10 0

DOMINICA.

For GREAT BRITAIN stamps used in Dominica, see page 65.

1 ½ (**2**) **1/2** (**3**) Half Penny (**4**)

(Typo. De La Rue & Co.)

1874 (4 May). *T* **1.** *Wmk. Crown CC.* *P* 12½.

1 1d. lilac 60 0 45 0
2 6d. green £12 85 0
3 1s. dull magenta £8 55 0

1877–79. *T* **1.** *Wmk. Crown CC.* *P* 14.

4 ½d. olive-yellow (1879) 35 0 42 6
5 1d. lilac 17 6 10 0
a. Bisected vert. or diag. (½d.) .. — £10
6 2½d. red-brown (1879) £8 60 0
7 4d. blue (1879) £7 27 6
a. Malformed " CE " in " PENCE " .. £42 £20
8 6d. green £9 65 0
9 1s. magenta £7 85 0

No. 5 *bisected and surcharged.*

1882 (25 Nov.).

10 **2** ½(d.), in *black,* on half 1d. .. £8 80 0
a. Surch. inverted £60 £50
b. Surcharges tête-bêche (pair) £100
11 **3** ½(d.), in *red* on half 1d. .. 35 0 35 0
a. Surch. inverted £50 £30
c. Surch. double .. ..

1883 (Mar.).

14 **4** ½d. in *black,* on half 1d. .. 60 0 50 0
a. Unsevered pair £8 £10

Type **4** is found reading up or down.

1883–84. *Wmk. Crown CA.* *P* 14.

15 **1** ½d. olive-yellow 12 6 25 0
16 ,, 2½d. red-brown (1884) .. £6 35 0

Half Penny
(5)

One Penny
(6)

1886 (Mar.). *Nos.* 8 *and* 9 *surch.*

No.	Type	Description	Unused	Used
17	5	½d. on 6d. green	30 0	50 0
18	6	1d. on 6d. green	£2250	£1500
19	,,	1d. on 1s. magenta	30 0	30 0
		a. Surch. double	—	£250

There are variations in the spacing of the letters of "One Penny" in the surcharge of No. 19.

1886. *Wmk. Crown CA. P* 14.

No.	Type	Description	Unused	Used
20	1	½d. dull green	3 6	15 0
21	,,	1d. lilac	25 0	30 0
		a. Bisected (½d.) (on cover) ..	—	£16
22	,,	4d. grey	10 0	12 6
		a. Malformed "CE" in "PENCE"	£6	£5

1887–88. *Wmk. Crown CA. P* 14.

No.	Type	Description	Unused	Used
23	1	1d. rose	15 0	17 6
23*a*	,,	1d. deep carmine ..	3 0	5 0
		b. Bisected (½d.) (on cover) ..	—	£25
24	,,	2½d. ultramarine	10 0	10 6
25	,,	6d. orange	45 0	70 0
26	,,	1s. dull magenta ..	£15	£22

The stamps of Dominica were superseded by the general issue for "Leeward Islands" on 31st October, 1890, but the sets following were in concurrent use with the stamps inscribed "LEEWARD ISLANDS" until 31st December, 1939, when the island came under the administration of the Windward Is.

WATERMARKS. Nos. 27/91 all have the watermark *sideways* except Nos. 36, 46, and 54.

9. View of Dominica from the sea.

10

(T **9** to **11** typo. De La Rue & Co.)

1903. *T* **9** *and* **10** (5*s*.). *Wmk. Crown CC. P* 14.

No.	Description	Unused	Used
27	½d. green and grey-green, OC	3 6	3 0
28	1d. grey and red, OC ..	3 0	2 0
29	2d. green and brown, OC ..	12 6	17 6
30	2½d. grey and bright blue, OC	12 6	22 6
31	3d. dull pur. & grey-blk., OC	17 6	20 0
32	6d. grey and chestnut, O ..	30 0	42 6
33	1s. magenta & grey-green, OC	32 6	35 0
34	2s. grey-black and purple, O	35 0	40 0
35	2s. 6d. grey-green & maize, O	50 0	55 0
36	5s. black and brown, O ..	£20	£22

1907–8. *T* **9** *and* **10** (5*s*.). *Wmk. Multiple Crown CA. P* 14.

No.	Description	Unused	Used
37	½d. green, OC	1 9	1 6
38	1d. grey and red, C	4 6	3 6
39	2d. green and brown, C ..	12 6	17 6
40	2½d. grey and bright blue, C ..	20 0	25 0
41	3d. dull pur. & grey-black, C	20 0	22 6
42	6d. black & chestnut, C ('08)	£10	£12
43	1s. magenta & grey-green, C	42 6	50 0
44	2s. grey-black & pur., C ('08)	55 0	65 0
45	2s. 6d. grey-green and maize, C ('08)	75 0	85 0
46	5s. black and brown, C ('08)	£10	£8

1908–19. *T* **9**. *Wmk. Mult. Crown CA. P* 14.

No.	Description	Unused	Used
47	½d. blue-green, O	1 0	1 3
47*a*	½d. deep green, O (1918) ..	1 0	1 0
48	1d. carmine-red, O ..	1 6	0 9
48*a*	1d. scarlet, O	1 6	1 3
49	2d. grey, O ('09)	6 0	15 0
49*a*	2d. slate, O	7 6	15 0
50	2½d. blue, O	6 0	10 0
50*a*	2½d. bright blue, O	6 0	7 6
51	3d. purple/*yellow*, OC ('09)	6 0	10 0
	a. On pale yellow	6 0	6 0
52	6d. dull & brt. purple, C ('09)	8 6	10 0
52*a*	6d. dull purple, O	10 0	20 0
53	1s. black/*green*, OC ('10) ..	12 6	15 0
53*a*	2s. purple and deep blue/*blue*, C (1919)	25 0	37 6

11

1914. *Wmk. Mult. Crown CA. P* 14.

No.	Type	Description	Unused	Used
54	11	5s. red and green/*yellow*, C	£8	£10

WAR TAX
ONE HALFPENNY
(12)

WAR TAX
(13)

1916. *No.* 47 *surch. with T* **12**.

No.	Description	Unused	Used
55	½d. on ½d. blue-green (R.) ..	0 8	1 3
	a. Small "o" in "ONE"	10 0	12 6
	b. "ONE HALFPENNY" albino	£10	

1918 (18 March). *No.* 47 *optd. locally with T* **13**.

No.	Description	Unused	Used
56	½d. blue-green	2 0	3 0

WAR TAX
(14)

WAR TAX
=1½D.=
(15)

1918 (June). *Nos.* 47 *and* 51 *optd. in London with T* **14**.

No.	Description	Unused	Used
57	½d. blue-green	0 6	0 9
58	3d. purple/*yellow* (R.) ..	1 0	1 9

1919. *Special printing of T* **9**, *surch. with T* **15**

No.	Description	Unused	Used
59	1½d. on 2½d. orange (R.) ..	0 9	1 3

1920. *As No.* 59, *but without* "WAR TAX".

No.	Description	Unused	Used
60	1½d. on 2½d. orange (Bk.) ..	1 6	2 [illegible]

1921. *Wmk. Mult. Crown CA. P* 14.

No.	Type	Description	Unused	Used
61	9	2s. 6d. black & red/*blue*, C	25 0	40 [illegible]

1921. *Wmk. Mult. Crown CA.* *P* 14.

No.	Type	Description	Unused	Used
62	**9**	½d. blue-green	2 0	7 6
63	,,	1d. carmine-red	2 0	1 9
64	,,	1½d. orange	7 6	10 0
65	,,	2d. grey	9 0	10 0
66	,,	2½d. bright blue	10 0	15 0
67	,,	6d. purple, C	12 6	17 6
69	,,	2s. purple and blue/*blue*	55 0	70 0
70	,,	2s. 6d. black and red/*blue*	£5	£7

The 1½d. has figures of value, in the lower corners, and no ornamentation below words of value.

16

(Typo. De La Rue & Co.)

1923 (Feb.)–**1927.** *Chalk-surfaced paper.* *P* 14.

(*a*) *Wmk. Mult. Script CA.*

No.	Type	Description	Unused	Used
71	**16**	½d. black and green	0 9	1 0
72	,,	1d. black and bright violet	3 6	3 6
73	,,	1½d. black and scarlet	2 0	1 6
74	,,	2d. black and grey	2 6	2 6
75	,,	2½d. black & orange-yellow	3 0	6 0
76	,,	3d. black and ultramarine	3 0	6 0
77	,,	4d. black and brown	5 0	8 6
78	,,	6d. black & bright magenta	6 0	10 0
79	,,	1s. black/*emerald*	10 0	15 0
80	,,	2s. black and blue/*blue*	17 6	25 0
81	,,	2s. 6d. black & red/*blue*	22 6	27 6
82	,,	3s. blk. & pur./*yell.* (1927)	22 6	30 0
83	,,	4s. black and red/*emerald*	30 0	35 0
84	,,	5s. blk. & grn./*yell.* (1927)	30 0	35 0

(*b*) *Wmk. Mult. Crown CA.*

No.	Type	Description	Unused	Used
85	**16**	3s. black & purple/*yellow*	32 6	45 0
86	,,	5s. black and green/*yellow*	42 6	50 0
87	,,	£1 black and purple/*red*	£23	£26

1927–33. *Colours changed. Chalk-surfaced paper. Wmk. Mult. Script CA.* *P* 14.

No.	Type	Description	Unused	Used
88	**16**	1d. black and scarlet	1 6	1 0
89	,,	1½d. black and red-brown	1 6	1 3
90	,,	2½d. black and ultramarine	3 0	4 0
91	,,	3d. black and red/*yellow*	3 6	3 0

1935 (6 May). *Silver Jubilee. As Nos.* 91/4 *of Antigua.* *P* 13½ × 14.

No.	Description	Unused	Used
92	1d. deep blue and carmine	0 8	1 3
93	1½d. ultramarine and grey	1 0	1 6
94	2½d. brown and deep blue	5 0	6 0
95	1s. slate and purple	12 6	15 0

1937 (12 May). *Coronation. As Nos.* 13/15 *of Aden, but printed by B. W. & Co.* *P* 11 × 11½.

No.	Description	Unused	Used
96	1d. carmine	0 6	0 8
97	1½d. yellow-brown	0 8	0 10
98	2½d. blue	1 6	2 0

17. Fresh Water Lake.

18. Layou River.

19. Picking Limes.

20. Boiling Lake.

21. King George VI.

(Recess. Waterlow & Sons.)

1938 (15 Aug.)–**47.** *Wmk. Mult. Script CA.* *P* 12½.

No.	Type	Description	Unused	Used
99	**17**	½d. brown and green	0 3	0 3
100	**18**	1d. grey and scarlet	0 6	0 6
101	**19**	1½d. green and purple	0 8	0 6
102	**20**	2d. carmine & grey-black	0 8	0 8
103	**19**	2½d. purple & bright blue	8 6	6 0
		a. *Purple & brt. ultram.* ('42)	0 9	0 9
104	**18**	3d. olive-green & brown	1 0	1 0
104*a*	**19**	3½d. ultram. and purple (15.10.47)	1 0	1 0
105	**17**	6d. emerald-green & vio.	1 9	1 9
105*a*	,,	7d. green & yell.-brown (15.10.47)	1 9	2 6
106	**20**	1s. violet & olive-green	3 0	3 0
106*a*	**18**	2s. slate and purple (15.10.47)	7 0	10 0
107	**17**	2s. 6d. black & verm.	7 0	12 6
108	**18**	5s. light blue and sepia	12 6	15 0
108*a*	**20**	10s. black and brown-orange (15.10.47)	25 0	32 6

(Photo. Harrison & Sons.)

1940 (15 Apr.). *Wmk. Mult. Script CA.* *P* 15 × 14.

No.	Type	Description	Unused	Used
109	**21**	¼d. chocolate, CO	0 3	0 3

1946 (14 Oct.). *Victory. As Nos.* 28/9 *of Aden.*

No.	Description	Unused	Used
110	1d. carmine	0 3	0 6
111	3½d. blue	0 8	1 0

1948 (1 Dec.). *Royal Silver Wedding. As Nos.* 30/1 *of Aden.*

No.	Description	Unused	Used
112	1d. scarlet	0 4	0 4
113	10s. red-brown	20 0	25 0

1949 (10 Oct.). *75th Anniv. of Universal Postal Union. As Nos.* 114/7 *of Antigua.*

No.	Description	Unused	Used
114	5 c. blue	0 8	1 0
115	6 c. brown	1 0	1 3
116	12 c. purple	2 0	2 6
117	24 c. olive	4 0	5 0

1951 (16 Feb.). *Inauguration of B.W.I. University College. As Nos.* 118/9 *of Antigua.*

118	3 c. yellow-green and reddish violet	1	3	1	3
119	12 c. deep green and carmine	3	6	3	6

22. King George VI.

23. Drying Cocoa.

24. Making Carib Baskets.

25. Lime Plantation.

26. Picking Oranges.

27. Bananas.

28. Botanical Gardens.

29. Drying Vanilla Beans.

30. Fresh Water Lake.

31. Layou River.

32. Boiling Lake.

33. Picking Oranges.

(Photo. Harrison & Sons, Ltd. (½ c.). Recess Bradbury, Wilkinson & Co., Ltd. (others).)

1951 (1 July). *Wmk. Mult. Script CA. P* 15 × 1[illegible] (½ *c.*), 13½ × 13 ($2.40), 13 × 13½ (*others*).

No.	Type	Description				
120	**22**	½ c. chocolate	0	4	0	[illegible]
121	**23**	1 c. black and vermilion	0	8	0	1[illegible]
122	**24**	2 c. red-brn. & dp. green	0	6	0	[illegible]
123	**25**	3 c. grn. & reddish violet	0	6	0	1[illegible]
124	**26**	4 c. brown-orge. & sepia	1	0	1	[illegible]
125	**27**	5 c. black and carmine ..	1	0	1	[illegible]
126	**28**	6 c. olive and chestnut ..	1	0	1	[illegible]
127	**29**	8 c. blue-green and blue..	1	9	2	[illegible]

128	**30**	12 c. black & bright green	2	3	2	3
129	**31**	14 c. blue and violet ..	2	0	2	0
130	**32**	24 c. reddish violet and rose-carmine	3	6	4	0
131	**25**	48 c. brt. grn. & red-orge.	8	0	12	6
132	**24**	60 c. carmine and black ..	10	0	12	6
133	**30**	$1.20 emerald and black ..	15	0	25	0
134	**33**	$2.40 orange and black ..	27	6	37	6

NEW
CONSTITUTION
1951
(**34**)

1951 (15 Oct.). *New Constitution. Optd. with T* **34** *by Bradbury, Wilkinson & Co.*

135	**25**	3 c. green & reddish violet	0	10	1	3
136	**27**	5 c. black and carmine ..	1	3	1	9
137	**29**	8 c. blue-grn. & blue (R.)	1	3	2	0
138	**31**	14 c. blue and violet (R.) ..	2	0	3	6

1953 (2 June). *Coronation. As No.* 47 *of Aden.*

139		2 c. black and deep green ..	1	0	1	6

35. Queen Elizabeth II.

36. Picking Oranges.

(Photo. Harrison (½ c.). Recess. Bradbury, Wilkinson (others).)

1954 (1 Oct.). *As T* **22/33** (*but with portrait of Queen Elizabeth II in place of King George VI, as in T* **35/6**). *Wmk. Mult. Script CA. P* 15 × 14 (½ *c.*), 13½ × 13 ($2.40), 13 × 13½ (*others*).

140	**35**	½ c. brown	0	3	0	3
141	**23**	1 c. black and vermilion	0	3	0	3
142	**24**	2 c. chocolate and myrtle-green (*shades*) ..	0	6	0	8
143	**25**	3 c. green and purple ..	1	6	2	0
144	**36**	4 c. brown-orange & sepia	0	4	0	6
145	**27**	5 c. black & carmine-red	2	3	2	6
146	**28**	6 c. bronze-grn. & red-brn.	0	6	0	8
147	**29**	8 c. dp. green & dp. blue	0	8	0	8
148	**30**	12 c. black and emerald ..	1	0	1	0
149	**31**	14 c. blue and purple ..	1	3	1	6
150	**32**	24 c. purple and carmine ..	2	0	2	0
151	**25**	48 c. green & red-orange ..	55	0	65	0
152	**24**	60 c. rose-red and black ..	5	0	6	0
153	**30**	$1.20 emerald and black	8	6	10	0
154	**33**	$2.40 yellow-orge. & blk.	18	6	20	0

37. Mat Making.

38. Canoe Making.

39. Bananas.

(Recess. Bradbury, Wilkinson & Co.)

1957 (15 Oct.). *Wmk. Mult. Script CA. P* 13 × 13½.

155	**37**	3 c. black and carmine ..	0	6	0	6
156	**38**	5 c. light blue and sepia-brown (*shades*) ..	0	6	0	8
157	**39**	10 c. grn. and brn. (*shades*)	1	0	1	0
158	**37**	48 c. deep brown & violet	25	0	30	0

1958 (22 Apr.). *Inauguration of British Caribbean Federation. As Nos.* 135/7 *of Antigua.*

159		3 c. deep green	0	10	0	10
160		6 c. blue	1	3	1	6
161		12 c. scarlet	1	9	2	3

40. Seashore at Rosalie.

41. Queen Elizabeth II.

42. Sailing Canoe.

43. Sulphur Springs.

44. Road Making.

45. Dug-out Canoe.

46. Crapaud.

47. Scotts Head.

48. Traditional Costume.

50. Sisserou Parrot.

Two types of 14 c.

I. Eyes of model looking straight ahead.
II. Eyes looking to her right.

49. Bananas.

51. Goodwill.

52. Cocoa Tree.

53. Coat of Arms.

54. Trafalgar Falls. **55.** Coconut Palm.

(Des. S. Scott. Photo. Harrison.)

1963 (16 May)–**65.** *W* w.**12.** *P* 14 × 14½ (*vert.*), 14½ × 14 (*horiz.*).

162	**40**	1 c. green, blue and sepia	0	2	0	2
163	**41**	2 c. bright blue	0	3	0	3
164	**42**	3 c. blackish brown & blue	0	4	0	4
165	**43**	4 c. grn., sepia & slate-vio.	0	4	0	5
166	**41**	5 c. magenta	0	5	0	6
167	**44**	6 c. grn., bistre & violet	0	6	0	7
168	**45**	8 c. green, sepia & black	0	7	0	8
169	**46**	10 c. sepia and pink ..	0	9	0	10
170	**47**	12 c. green, blue & blackish brown	0	10	0	10
171	**48**	14 c. multicoloured (I) ..	2	0	2	6
171*a*	,,	14 c. mult. (II) (1.4.65) ..	0	11	1	0
172	**49**	15 c. yellow, grn. & brown	0	11	1	0
173	**50**	24 c. multicoloured ..	1	5	1	8
174	**51**	48 c. green, blue and black	2	9	3	6
175	**52**	60 c. orange, green & black	3	6	4	6
176	**53**	$1.20, multicoloured ..	6	9	8	0
177	**54**	$2.40, blue, turq. & brn.	13	3	15	0
178	**55**	$4.80, grn., blue & brown	25	0	30	0

1963 (4 June). *Freedom from Hunger. As No.* 63 *of Aden.*

179 15 c. reddish violet 2 0 2 3

1963 (2 Sept.). *Red Cross Centenary. As Nos.* 147/8 *of Antigua.*

180 5 c. red and black 0 8 0 11
181 15 c. red and blue 1 6 1 9

1964 (23 April). 400*th Anniv. of Birth of William Shakespeare. As No.* 164 *of Antigua.*

182 15 c. bright purple 1 9 2 0

1965 (17 May). *I.T.U. Centenary. As Nos.* 166/7 *of Antigua.*

183 2 c. light emerald and blue 0 6 0 8
184 48 c. turquoise-blue and grey 5 0 6 0

1965 (25 Oct.). *International Co-operation Year. As Nos.* 168/9 *of Antigua.*

185 1 c. reddish purple and turquoise-green 0 4 0 6
186 15 c. dp. bluish green & lav. 1 6 2 0

1966 (24 Jan.). *Churchill Commemoration. As Nos.* 170/3 *of Antigua.*

187 1 c. new blue 0 3 0 4
188 5 c. deep green 0 6 0 8
189 15 c. brown 1 2 1 6
190 24 c. bluish violet 1 8 2 3

1966 (4 Feb.). *Royal Visit. As Nos.* 174/5 *of Antigua.*

191 5 c. black and ultramarine 0 6 0 8
192 15 c. black and magenta .. 1 2 1 6

POSTAL FISCALS.

REVENUE (R **1**) Revenue (R **2**)

1879–86. *Optd. with Type* R **1.**

(*a*) *Wmk. Crown CC.*

R 1 **1** 1d. lilac 12 6 10 0
a. Bisected vert. (½d.) on cover

R 2 **1** 6d. green 3 6 10 0
R 3 ,, 1s. magenta 12 6 30 0

(*b*) *Wmk. Crown CA.*

R 4 **1** 1d. lilac (1886) 1 6 3 6

1888. *Optd. with Type* R **2.** *Wmk. Crown CA.*

R 6 **1** 1d. carmine 60 0 55 0

EAST AFRICA.

The following stamps were issued by the East African Postal Administration for use in Uganda, Kenya and Tanganyika (or later, Tanzania, excluding Zanzibar).

1. Chrysanthemum Emblem. **2.**

3. East African " Flags ".

(Des. V. Whiteley. Photo. Harrison & Sons.)

1964 (21 Oct.). *Olympic Games, Tokio. P* 14½.

1 **1** 30 c. yellow and reddish violet 0 9 0 10
2 **2** 50 c. dp. reddish violet & yell. 1 0 1 3
3 **3** 1s. 30, orange-yellow, deep green and light blue .. 2 3 2 6
4 ,, 2s. 50, magenta, deep violet-blue and light blue .. 4 6 6 0

4. Rally Badge. **5.** Cars *en route.*

(Photo. Harrison & Sons.)

1965 (15 Apr.). *13th East African Safari Rally.* *P* 14.

No.	Type	Description	Unused	Used
5	**4**	30 c. black, yellow and turquoise	0 9	1 0
6	,,	50 c. black, yellow and brown	1 2	1 5
7	**5**	1s. 30, dp. bluish green, yellow-ochre and blue ..	2 9	3 3
8	,,	2s. 50, dp. bluish green, brown-red and light blue	5 6	6 0

6. I.T.U. Emblem and Symbols.

(Photo. Harrison & Sons.)

1965 (17 May). *I.T.U. Centenary.* *P* 14½.

No.	Type	Description	Unused	Used
9	**6**	30 c. gold, choc. & magenta	0 9	0 10
10	,,	50 c. gold, chocolate and grey	1 0	1 3
11	,,	1s. 30, gold, choc. and blue	2 3	2 6
12	,,	2s. 50, gold, chocolate and turquoise-green ..	4 6	6 0

7. I.C.Y. Emblem.

(Photo. Harrison & Sons.)

1965 (4 Aug.). *International Co-operation Year.* *P* 14½ × 14.

No.	Type	Description	Unused	Used
13	**7**	30 c. dp. bluish grn. & gold	0 7	0 9
14	,,	50 c. black and gold.. ..	1 0	1 2
15	,,	1s. 30, ultramarine & gold	2 3	2 6
16	,,	2s. 50, carmine-red & gold	4 6	4 9

8. Game Park Lodge, Tanzania.

9. Murchison Falls, Uganda.

10. Flamingoes, Lake Nakuru, Kenya.

11. Deep Sea Fishing, Tanzania.

(Des. Mrs. R. M. Fennessy. Photo. Harrison.)

1966 (4 Apr.). *Tourism.* *P* 14½.

No.	Type	Description	Unused	Used
17	**8**	30 c. multicoloured ..	0 7	0 9
18	**9**	50 c. multicoloured ..	1 0	1 2
19	**10**	1s. 30, multicoloured ..	2 3	2 6
20	**11**	2s. 50, multicoloured ..	4 6	4 9

EAST AFRICA AND UGANDA PROTECTORATES.

See **KENYA, UGANDA AND TANGANYIKA.**

EAST AFRICA (G.E.A.).

See **TANGANYIKA.**

EGYPT.

For all issues see Part III of the Stanley Gibbons Catalogue.

FALKLAND ISLANDS.

— SIMPLIFICATION (see Introduction)—
Nos. 1 to 40.

1, 2, 3, 4.
8, 9, 12, 16, 17, 18, 20, 21, 22, 24, 25, 27, 29
31, 33.
35, 36. 10*a*, 35*a*. 38, 39.

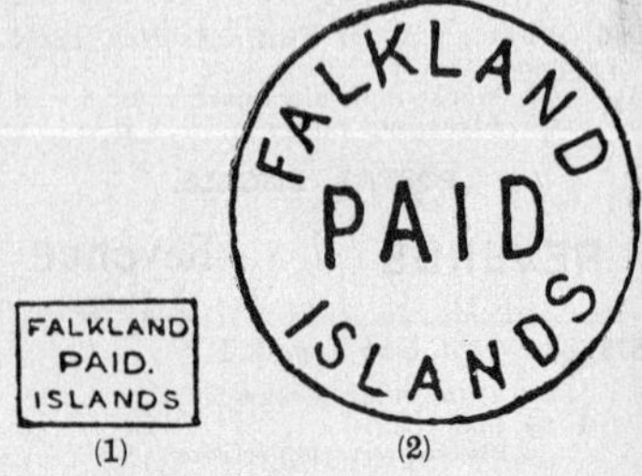

(1) (2)

1861–77. *The Franks.*

FR1 **1** In black, *on cover* £300
FR2 **2** In red, *on cover* (1877) £450

On *piece*, FR1 on white or coloured papers £5; FR2 on white £15. The use of these franks ceased when the first stamps were issued.

3

(Recess. Bradbury, Wilkinson.)

NOTE.—Nos. 1, 2, 3, 4, 10, 26, 35 and 37 exist with one or two sides imperf. from the margin of the sheets.

1878–79. *No wmk.* *P* 14, 14½.

1 **3** 1d. claret (19.6.78) £10 £12
2 ,, 4d. grey-black (Sept. 1879) .. £30 £12
a. On wmkd. paper £40 £15
3 ,, 6d. blue-green (19.6.78) .. 75 0 85 0
4 ,, 1s. bistre-brown (1878) .. 45 0 70 0

No. 2*a* shows portions of the papermaker's watermark—" R. TURNER, CHAFFORD MILLS "—in double-lined capitals.

1883–1902. *Wmk. Crown CA* (*upright*). *P* 14, 14½.

In the ½d., 2d., 2½d. and 9d. the figures of value in the lower corners are replaced by small rosettes and the words of value are in colour.

5 **3** ½d. blue-green (Dec. 1891) .. 25 0 45 0
6 ,, ½d. green (1892) 32 6 40 0
7 ,, ½d. deep yellow-green (1894) 27 6 40 0
8 ,, ½d. yellow-green (1895) .. 2 6 5 0
9 ,, 1d. dull claret (1883) .. £20 £10
a. Imperf. between (horiz. pr.) .. £650
10 ,, 1d. red-brown (April 1891) 80 0 90 0
a. Bisected (on cover) (1891) .. † £45
11 ,, 1d. orge. red-brn. (Dec. '91) 75 0 80 0
12 ,, 1d. brown (1892) 50 0 50 0
13 ,, 1d. russet brown (1892) .. 80 0 80 0
14 ,, 1d. orange-brown (1894) .. 40 0 40 0
15 ,, 1d. bright claret (1894) .. 60 0 70 0
16 ,, 1d. Venetian red (1895) .. 12 6 10 0
17 ,, 1d. pale red (1899) .. 7 6 7 6
18 ,, 1d. orange-red (1902) .. 10 0 10 0
19 ,, 2d. reddish purple (1895) .. 12 6 20 0
20 ,, 2d. pale purple (1898) .. 10 0 17 6
21 ,, 2½d. pale chalky ultram. ('91) 35 0 35 0
22 ,, 2½d. blue (1892) 42 6 37 6
23 ,, 2½d. Prussian blue (1894) .. £16 £12
24 ,, 2½d. ultramarine (bright *to* deep) (1894) 8 0 12 6
25 ,, 4d. grey-black (1883) .. 65 0 60 0
26 ,, 4d. olive grey-black (1890) 45 0 40 0
27 ,, 4d. pure grey-black (1894) .. £26 £30
28 ,, 4d. olive-black (1895) .. 15 0 25 0
29 ,, 6d. orange-yellow (1892) .. 25 0 32 6
30 ,, 6d. yellow (1896) 32 6 37 6
31 ,, 9d. orange-vermilion (1895) 17 6 42 6
32 ,, 9d. pale vermilion (1896) .. 30 0 45 0
33 ,, 1s. grey-brown (1895) .. 22 0 32 6
34 ,, 1s. yellow-brown (1896) .. 15 0 32 6

NOTES.—The plates used for these stamps lid not fit the paper, and therefore the wmk. ıppears in all sorts of positions, a well-centred Crown CA being scarce.

1d. No. 9 can be distinguished from No. 15 apart from the shade difference), in that the ormer has crinkly gum and watermark normal or occasionally inverted and reversed), whilst No. 15 has smooth gum, and watermark normally *eversed.*

4d. No. 27 always has the watermark reversed.

1885–91. *Wmk. Crown CA sideways* (*to right or left*). *P* 14, 14½.

35 **3** 1d. claret (1885) 60 0 40 0
a. Bisected (on cover) (1891) .. † £35
36 ,, 4d. pale grey-black (1885) .. £6 45 0
37 ,, 4d. grey-black (1887) .. £6 45 0

In 1891 the postage to the United Kingdom and Colonies was reduced from 4d. to 2½d. per ½ oz. As no ½d. or 2½d. stamps were yet available, the 1d. was allowed to be bisected (see Nos. 10*a* and 35*a*) and used for half its value until the following provisionals appeared.

½d.

(4)

1891. *Stamps bisected diagonally and each half surch. diagonally with T* **4.**

38 **3** ½d. on half of 1d. claret (No. 35) £30 £30
a. Unsevered pair £70 £85
b. Unsevered pair se-tenant with unsurcharged whole stamp ... £425
c. Surch. double £60
d. Surch. inverted £70 £70
e. Surch. sideways .. .. — £50
39 ,, ½d. on half of 1d. red-brown (No. 10) £20 £15
a. Unsevered pair .. .. — £45
b. Surch. double £65
40 ,, ½d. on half of 1d. orange red-brown (No. 11) (Dec. 1891) £35 £38
a. Unsevered pair £80
b. Surch. inverted £80

Bisected stamps were authorised by decree dated 1 Jan., 1891, and were used until 11 Jan., 1892.

5

6

(Recess. Bradbury, Wilkinson & Co.)

1898 (June). *Wmk. Crown CC.* *P* 14, 14½.

41 **5** 2s. 6d. deep blue £11 £12
42 **6** 5s. red £9 £10

7

8

(Recess. De La Rue & Co.)

1904–12. *Wmk. Mult. Crown CA.* *P* 14.

43 **7** ½d. yellow-green (1904) .. 3 0 5 0
44 ,, ½d. pale yellow-green on thick paper (1907) .. 6 0 15 0
45 ,, ½d. deep yellow-green (1911) 3 6 4 6
46 ,, 1d. vermilion (1904) .. 4 0 2 0

47 **7** 1d. verm., thick paper (1907) 2 6 1 6
48 ,, 1d. dull coppery red (1907) £7 £5
49 ,, 1d. orange-vermilion (1911) 4 0 2 0
50 ,, 2d. purple (1904) 8 0 15 0
51 ,, 2d. reddish purple (1912) .. £25 £30
52 ,, 2½d. ultramarine 17 6 35 0
a. *Pale ultramarine* £12 £12
53 ,, 2½d. deep blue (1912) .. £22 £26
54 ,, 6d. orange (1904) 22 6 27 6
55 ,, 1s. brown (1904) 20 0 32 6
56 **8** 3s. green (1904) 70 0 75 0
57 ,, 3s. deep green (1906) .. 50 0 60 0
58 ,, 5s. red (1904) £7 £6

1906. *Wmk. Mult. Crown CA., sideways. P* 14.
59 **7** 1d. vermilion 2 6 5 0

SOUTH GEORGIA "UNDERPRINT". From late 1909 a small handstamp inscribed "South Georgia" was used on mail from that place, the intention being that it should be applied below the stamps, although it sometimes appears across them. It is found in conjunction with all contemporary King Edward VII issues, and some values of the Victorian issue, until its use finally ceased in June, 1912. Examples are scarce, particularly with the Falkland Is. date-stamp.

9

10

(Recess. De La Rue & Co.)

1912–20. *Wmk. Mult. Crown CA. P* 14.
60 **9** ½d. yellow-green (1912) .. 2 0 5 0
61 ,, ½d. dp. yellow-green (1914) 15 0 20 0
62 ,, ½d. pale green (1918) .. 6 6 8 6
63 ,, ½d. green (1919) 3 6 5 0
64 ,, ½d. green on thick greyish paper (1920) 6 0 15 0
65 ,, 1d. vermilion (1912) .. 4 0 3 6
66 ,, 1d. orange-verm. (1914) .. 12 6 8 6
67 ,, 1d. scarlet (1919) 2 0 2 6
68 ,, 1d. scarlet on thick greyish paper (1920) 10 0 2 6
69 ,, 2d. deep purple (1912) .. 5 0 11 6
70 ,, 2d. pale purple (1919) .. 6 6 12 6
71 ,, 2½d. dark blue (1912) .. 13 6 22 6
72 ,, 2½d. bright blue (1914) .. 11 0 13 6
73 ,, 2½d. milky blue (1916) .. £7 £8
74 ,, 2½d. blue (1919) 6 0 15 0
75 ,, 6d. yellow-orange (1912) .. 10 0 20 0
76 ,, 6d. brown-orange (1919) .. 10 0 12 6
77 ,, 1s. yellow-brown (1912) .. 32 6 37 6
78 ,, 1s. bistre brown (1919) .. 35 0 37 6
79 ,, 1s. brown on greyish paper (1920) 25 0 50 0
80 ,, 1s. deep brown on greyish paper 35 0 60 0
81 **10** 3s. deep green (1912) .. 35 0 55 0
82 ,, 5s. red (1912) 60 0 75 0
83 ,, 5s. purple (1914) 45 0 55 0
84 ,, 10s. red/*green* (1913) .. £9 £11
85 ,, £1 black/*red* (1913) .. £28 £32

The 2½d. No. 74 was bisected and used as 1d. stamp in S. Georgia in 1923. This procedure was not authorised from Port Stanley.

PORT FOSTER OVERPRINT. The ½d. and 1d. stamps of the above issue, and the 1d. King Edward VII, exist used with a "PORT FOSTER" handstamped opt., applied at Port Foster, Deception Island, during the 1912–13 whaling season. Unused stamps and higher values bearing the opt. were "made to order".

WAR STAMP

(11)

1918–20. *Optd. locally with T* **11.**
86 **9** ½d. yellow-green 3 6 10 0
87 ,, ½d. pale green 0 6 3 6
a. Albino opt. £55
88 ,, ½d. green 0 6 3 6
89 ,, ½d. green on thick greyish paper 6 0 25 0
90 ,, 1d. bright orange-vermilion 5 0 7 6
91 ,, 1d. pale scarlet 1 0 4 0
a. Opt. double £60
b. Opt. double, one albino .. £32
92 ,, 1d. scarlet 1 0 1 6
93 ,, 1d. scarlet on thick greyish paper 60 0 £6
94 ,, 1s. yellow-brown 55 0 90 0
95 ,, 1s. pale bistre-brown .. 6 0 8 6
a. Opt. double, one albino .. £55 £60
96 ,, 1s. brown on thick greyish paper 15 0 17 6
a. Opt. double, one albino .. £60 £70
97 ,, 1s. deep brown on thick greyish paper 20 0 50 0

1921–29. *Wmk. Mult. Script CA. P* 14.
98 **9** ½d. bright yellow-green .. 1 6 3 6
99 ,, ½d. green (1925) 2 6 7 6
100 ,, 1d. scarlet-verm. (1924) .. 1 3 1 3
101 ,, 1d. scarlet (1925) .. 7 6 3 0
102 ,, 1d. deep scarlet (1928) .. 6 0 6 0
103 ,, 2d. reddish purple (1923) 6 6 8 6
104 ,, 2d. purple (1927) .. 1 0 6 0
105 ,, 2½d. indigo 6 0 15 0
106 ,, 2½d. dp. pur./*lemon* (1923) 4 6 6 6
107 ,, 2½d. pale pur./*yellow* (1925) 7 6 15 0
108 ,, 2½d. dark blue (1927) .. 10 0 25 0
109 ,, 2½d. steel-blue (Jan. '28) .. 5 0 22 6
110 ,, 2½d. Prussian blue (1929) £18 £22
111 ,, 6d. orange (1925) .. 7 6 10 0
112 ,, 6d. pale orange 50 0 60 0
113 ,, 1s. bistre-brown .. 30 0 35 0
114 **10** 3s. green (1923) 45 0 60 0

2½D

(12)

1928. *No.* 104 *surch. with T* **12.**
115 **9** 2½d. on 2d. purple £75 £85
a. Surcharge double

13. Whale and Penguins. **14.**

(Recess. Perkins, Bacon & Co.)

1929 (2 SEPT.)–**1936.** *P* 14.
(*a*) *Wmk. Mult. Script CA.*
116 **13** ½d. green 0 8 1 9
117 ,, 1d. scarlet 0 10 0 9
a. Deep red 10 0 22 6
118 ,, 2d. grey 1 3 2 6
119 ,, 2½d. blue 1 9 5 0
120 **14** 4d. orange ('31) 3 6 10 0
a. Deep orange 12 6 15 0
121 **13** 6d. purple 7 6 8 6
a. Reddish purple ('36) .. 17 6 15 0
122 ,, 1s. black/*emerald* .. 8 0 10 0
a. On bright emerald ('36) .. 15 0 25 0

123	**13**	2s. 6d. carmine/*blue*	.. 22	6	27	6
124	,,	5s. green/*yellow* ..	.. 37	6	50	0
125	,,	10s. carmine/*emerald*	..	£5		£6

(*b*) *Wmk. Mult. Crown CA.*

126	**13**	£1 black/*red*	..	.. £20	£24

Two kinds of perforation exist:

A. Comb perf. 13.9:—original values of 1929.

B. Line perf. 13.9, 14.2 or compound:—4d. and 1936 printings of ½d., 1d., 6d. and 1s.

15. Romney Marsh Ram.

16. Iceberg.

17. Whale-catcher *Bransfield.*

18. Port Louis.

19. Map of Falkland Islands.

20. South Georgia.

21. Whale.

22. Govt. House, Stanley.

23. Battle Memorial.

24. King Penguin.

25. Coat of Arms.

26. King George V.

(Des. (except 6d.) by G. Roberts. Eng. and recess. Bradbury, Wilkinson.)

1933 (2 Jan.). *Centenary of British Occupation. Wmk. Mult. Script CA. P* 12.

127	**15**	½d. black and green ..	3 6	5 0
128	**16**	1d. black and scarlet ..	2 6	3 6
129	**17**	1½d. black and blue ..	3 6	7 0
130	**18**	2d. black and brown ..	7 6	9 6
131	**19**	3d. black and violet ..	12 6	16 6
132	**20**	4d. black and orange ..	20 0	27 6
133	**21**	6d. black and slate ..	60 0	60 0
134	**22**	1s. black and olive-green	40 0	50 0
135	**23**	2s. 6d. black and violet..	75 0	£5
136	**24**	5s. black and yellow ..	£45	£45
		a. Black and yellow-orange ..	£125	£60
137	**25**	10s. black and chestnut..	£35	£40
138	**26**	20s. black and carmine ..	£125	£140

1935 (7 May). *Silver Jubilee. As Nos.* 91/4 *of Antigua, but printed by B. W. & Co. P* 11 × 12.

139	1d. deep blue and scarlet ..	0 6	0 10
140	2½d. brown and deep blue ..	2 0	3 0
141	4d. green and indigo ..	3 6	4 6
142	1s. slate and purple.. ..	8 6	10 0
	a. Extra flagstaff	£90	

For illustration of "extra flagstaff" variety see Bechuanaland.

1937 (12 May). *Coronation. As Nos.* 13/15 *of Aden, but printed by B. W. & Co. P* 11 × 11½.

143	½d. green	0 6	0 8
144	1d. carmine	0 8	1 0
145	2½d. blue	1 6	2 0

27. Whales' Jaw Bones.

28. Black-necked Swan.

29. Battle Memorial.

30. Flock of Sheep.

31. Upland Goose.

32. R.R.S. *Discovery II.*

33. R.R.S. *William Scoresby.*

34. Mount Sugar Top.

34*a*. Turkey Vultures.

35. Gentoo Penguins.

36. Sea Lion.

37. Deception Island.

38. Arms of the Falkland Islands.

(Des. G. Roberts (except 6d. and 9d.). Recess Bradbury, Wilkinson.)

1938 (3 Jan.)–**1949.** *Wmk. Mult. Script CA. P* 12.

No.	Type	Description				
146	**27**	½d. black and green ..	0	4	0	6
147	**28**	1d. black and carmine ..	30	0	22	6
		a. Black and scarlet ('40) ..	5	0	5	0
148	**29**	1d. black & vio. (14.7.41)	0	8	0	8
149	"	2d. black & deep violet..	2	6	4	0
150	**28**	2d. blk. & car.-red (14.7.41)	0	8	1	0
151	**30**	2½d. black and bright blue	3	6	4	0
152	**31**	2½d. black & blue (15.6.49)	3	6	4	0
153	**30**	3d. black & blue (14.7.41)	1	6	1	6
154	**31**	4d. black and purple ..	2	3	2	9
155	**32**	6d. black and brown ..	14	0	18	0
156	"	6d. black (15.6.49) ..	2	0	3	0
157	**33**	9d. black and grey-blue..	2	0	2	3
158	**34**	1s. pale blue	45	0	50	0
		a. Deep blue ('42)	3	0	4	0
159	**34a**	1s. 3d., black & carmine-red (10.12.46) ..	4	0	4	9
160	**35**	2s. 6d. slate	30	0	35	0
161	**36**	5s. brt. blue and chestnut	22	6	27	6
		a. Indigo and yellow-brown ..	£30		£12	
162	**37**	10s. black and orange ..	27	6	35	0
163	**38**	£1 black and violet ..	55	0	62	6

1946 (7 Oct.). *Victory. As Nos.* 28/9 *of Aden.*

164	1d. dull violet	0	4	0	6
165	3d. blue	0	8	1	0

1948 (1 Nov.). *Royal Silver Wedding. As Nos.* 30/1 *of Aden.*

166	2½d. ultramarine	0	8	1	0
167	£1 mauve	£6		£8	

1949 (10 Oct.). *75th Anniv. of Universal Postal Union. As Nos.* 114/7 *of Antigua.*

168	1d. violet	1	0	1	0
169	3d. deep blue..	1	6	1	9
170	1s. 3d. deep blue-green ..	6	0	7	6
171	2s. blue	10	0	12	6

39. Sheep.

40. R.M.S. *Fitzroy*.

41. Upland Goose.

42. Map of Falkland Is.

43. Arms of the Colony.

47. Gentoo Penguins.

44. Auster Aircraft.

45. M.S.S. *John Biscoe.*

46. View of the Two Sisters.

48. Kelp Goose and Gander.

49. Sheep Shearing.

50. Battle Memorial.

51. Sea-lion and Female (Clapmatch).

52. Hulk of *Great Britain.*

(Recess. Waterlow & Sons.)

1952 (2 Jan.). *Wmk. Mult. Script CA. P* 13 × 13½ (*vert.*) *or* 13½ × 13 (*horiz.*).

No.	Type	Description		Unused	Used
172	**39**	½d. green	.. ..	0 8	0 10
173	**40**	1d. scarlet	.. ..	0 6	0 6
174	**41**	2d. violet	.. ..	1 6	2 0
175	**42**	2½d. black & light ultram.		0 9	1 0
176	**43**	3d. deep ultramarine	..	1 0	1 0
177	**44**	4d. reddish purple	..	1 0	1 3
178	**45**	6d. bistre-brown	..	1 9	2 0
179	**46**	9d. orange-yellow	..	2 6	3 6
180	**47**	1s. black	.. ..	8 6	8 6
181	**48**	1s. 3d. orange	.. ..	3 0	5 0
182	**49**	2s. 6d. olive-green	..	6 0	7 6
183	**50**	5s. purple	.. ..	10 0	11 6
184	**51**	10s. grey ..	.. ..	20 0	22 6
185	**52**	£1 black	.. ..	40 0	45 0

1953 (4 June). *Coronation. As No.* 47 *of Aden.*

No.	Description		Unused	Used
186	1d. black and scarlet	..	1 0	1 6

53. M.S.S. *John Biscoe.*

(Recess. Waterlow & Sons, Ltd.)

1955–57. *As T* **39/47** (*but with portrait of Queen Elizabeth II in place of King George VI as in T* **53**). *Wmk. Mult. Script CA. P* 13 × 13½ (*vert.*) *or* 13½ × 13 (*horiz.*).

No.	Type	Description		Unused	Used
187	**39**	½d. green (2.9.57) ..	..	0 10	1 3
188	**40**	1d. scarlet (2.9.57)	..	1 3	1 3
189	**41**	2d. violet (3.9.56)	..	2 6	2 6
190	**53**	6d. dp. yellow-brn. (1.6.55)		4 0	4 0
191	**46**	9d. orange-yellow (2.9.57)		5 0	6 0
192	**47**	1s. black (15.7.55)	..	7 0	7 6

54. Falkland Islands Thrush.

55. Dominican Gull.

56. Gentoo Penguins.

57. Falkland Islands Marsh Starling.

58. Upland Geese.

59. Steamer Ducks.

60. Rock-hopper Penguin.

61. Black-browed Albatross.

62. Silver Grebe.

63. Pied Oystercatchers.

64. Yellow-billed Teal.

65. Kelp Geese.

66. King Cormorants.

67. Carancho.

68. Black-necked Swan.

(Recess. Waterlow (until 1962), then De La Rue.)

1960 (10 Feb.). *W* w. **12**. *P* 13½.

193	**54**	½d. black and myrtle-green (*shades*) ..	0	2	0	2
194	**55**	1d. black & scar. (*shades*)	0	3	0	3
195	**56**	2d. black and blue ..	0	4	0	4
196	**57**	2½d. black & yellow-brown	0	5	0	5
197	**58**	3d. black and olive ..	0	6	0	7
198	**59**	4d. black and carmine ..	0	7	0	10
199	**60**	5½d. black and violet ..	0	10	1	0
200	**61**	6d. black and sepia ..	0	10	1	0
201	**62**	9d. black & orange-red ..	1	1	1	4
202	**63**	1s. black & maroon ..	1	5	1	9
203	**64**	1s. 3d. black & ultram.	1	9	2	6
204	**65**	2s. black and brown-red	3	0	4	6
205	**66**	5s. black and turquoise	7	6	10	0
206	**67**	10s. black and purple ..	17	6	22	6
207	**68**	£1 black & orange-yellow	30	0	35	0

69. Morse Key. **70.** One-valve Receiver.

71. Rotary Spark Transmitter.

(Des. M. Goaman. Photo. J. Enschedé & Sons.)

1962 (5 Oct.). *50th Anniv. of Establishment of Radio Communications.* *W* w.**12.** *P* 11½×11.

208 **69** 6d. carm.-lake and orange 2 9 3 3
209 **70** 1s. deep bluish green and yellow-olive 4 6 5 6
210 **71** 2s. deep violet & ultram. 8 6 9 6

1963 (4 June). *Freedom from Hunger. As No.* 63 *of Aden.*

211 1s. ultramarine 2 3 2 6

1963 (2 Sept). *Red Cross Centenary. As Nos.* 147/8 *of Antigua.*

212 1d. red and black 0 6 0 8
213 1s. red and blue 2 6 3 0

1964 (23 April). 400*th Anniv. of Birth of William Shakespeare. As No.* 164 *of Antigua.*

214 6d. black 1 6 2 0

72. H.M.S. *Glasgow.*

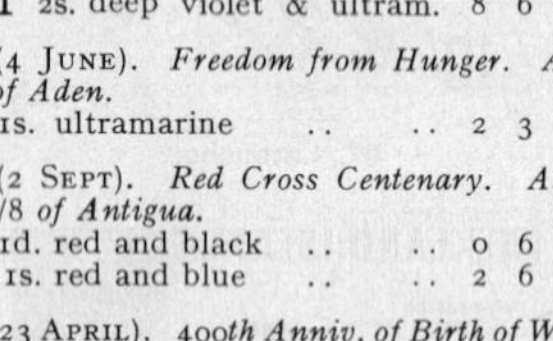

73. H.M.S. *Kent.*

74. H.M.S. *Invincible.*

75. Battle Memorial.

(Recess. De La Rue.)

1964 (8 Dec.). 50*th Anniv. of the Battle of the Falkland Islands.* *W* w.**12.** *P* 13×14 (2s.) *or* 13 (*others*).

215 **72** 2½d. black and red .. 1 3 1 3
216 **73** 6d. black and light blue.. 2 3 2 3
217 **74** 1s. black and carmine-red 3 6 3 6
218 **75** 2s. black and blue .. 6 0 6 0

1965 (26 May). *I.T.U. Centenary. As Nos.* 166/7 *of Antigua.*

219 1d. light blue and deep blue 0 6 0 8
220 2s. lilac and bistre-yellow .. 4 0 5 6

1965 (25 Oct.). *International Co-operation Year. As No.* 168/9 *of Antigua.*

221 1d. reddish pur. & turq.-grn. 0 6 0 8
222 1s. dp. bluish green & lav. 2 0 2 9

1966 (24 Jan.). *Churchill Commemoration. As Nos.* 170/3 *of Antigua.*

223 ½d. new blue 0 3 0 4
224 1d. deep green 0 4 0 6
225 1s. brown 1 8 2 6
226 2s. bluish violet 3 3 4 6

FALKLAND ISLANDS DEPENDENCIES.

A. GRAHAM LAND.

GRAHAM LAND

DEPENDENCY OF

(1)

1944 (12 Feb.)–**45.** *Stamps of Falkland Is. optd. with T* **1**, *in red.*

A 1 **27** ½d. black and green .. 0 3 0 4
A 2 **29** 1d. black and violet .. 0 4 0 6
A 3 **28** 2d. black & carmine-red 0 8 0 8
A 4 **30** 3d. black and blue .. 0 10 1 0
A 5 **31** 4d. black and purple .. 1 0 1 3
A 6 **32** 6d. black and brown .. 5 0 5 0
a. Blue-black and brown ('45) .. 15 0
A 7 **33** 9d. black and grey-blue .. 2 6 3 0
A 8 **34** 1s. deep blue 3 0 4 6

B. SOUTH GEORGIA.

1944 (3 Apr.)–**45.** *Stamps of Falkland Is. optd.* "SOUTH GEORGIA/DEPENDENCY OF", *in red, as T* **1** *of Graham Land.*

No.	Type	Description	Unused	Used
B 1	27	½d. black and green	0 3	0 4
B 2	29	1d. black and violet	0 4	0 10
B 3	28	2d. black & carmine-red	0 10	1 0
B 4	30	3d. black and blue	1 6	1 9
B 5	31	4d. black and purple	1 0	1 3
B 6	32	6d. black and brown	5 0	5 0
		a. Blue-black and brown ('45)	15 0	
B 7	33	9d. black and grey-blue	2 0	3 0
B 8	34	1s. deep blue	2 6	4 6

For later issues, see under South Georgia.

C. SOUTH ORKNEYS.

1944 (21 Feb.)–**45.** *Stamps of Falkland Is. optd.* "SOUTH ORKNEYS/DEPENDENCY OF", *in red, as T* **1** *of Graham Land.*

No.	Type	Description	Unused	Used
C 1	27	½d. black and green	0 3	0 6
C 2	29	1d. black and violet	0 4	0 6
C 3	28	2d. black & carmine-red	0 6	0 9
C 4	30	3d. black and blue	0 10	1 6
C 5	31	4d. black and purple	1 0	1 6
C 6	32	6d. black and brown	5 0	5 0
		a. Blue-black and brown ('45)	15 0	
C 7	33	9d. black and grey-blue	2 0	3 6
C 8	34	1s. deep blue	2 6	4 6

D. SOUTH SHETLANDS.

1944–45. *Stamps of Falkland Is. optd.* "SOUTH SHETLANDS/DEPENDENCY OF", *in red, as T* **1** *of Graham Land.*

No.	Type	Description	Unused	Used
D 1	27	½d. black and green	0 3	0 6
D 2	29	1d. black and violet	0 4	0 6
D 3	28	2d. black & carmine-red	0 6	0 8
D 4	30	3d. black and blue	0 10	1 0
D 5	31	4d. black and purple	1 0	1 3
D 6	32	6d. black and brown	5 0	5 0
		a. Blue-black and brown ('45)	15 0	
D 7	33	9d. black and grey-blue	2 0	3 0
D 8	34	1s. deep blue	2 6	4 6

E. GENERAL ISSUES.

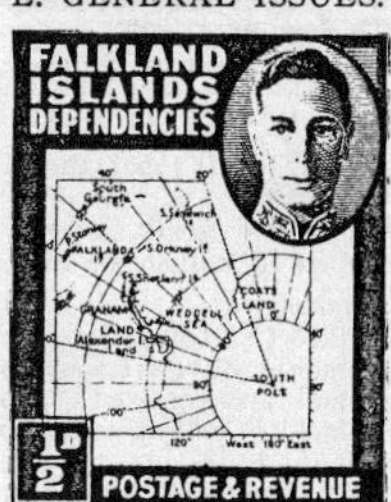

2

(Map litho., frame recess. De La Rue.)

1946 (1 Feb)—**49.** *Wmk. Mult. Script CA. sideways. P* 12.

(a) Map thick and coarse.

No.	Type	Description	Unused	Used
G 1	2	½d. black and green	0 3	0 8
G 2	,,	1d. black and violet	0 4	0 10
G 3	,,	2d. black and carmine	0 8	1 0
G 4	,,	3d. black and blue	0 8	1 0
G 5	,,	4d. black and claret	0 9	1 6
G 6	,,	6d. black and orange	1 6	2 6
		a. Black and ochre	15 0	25 0
G 7	,,	9d. black and brown	1 9	3 0
G 8	,,	1s. black and purple	2 6	3 6

(b) Map thin and clear (16.2.48).

No.	Type	Description	Unused	Used
G 9	2	½d. black and green	0 6	0 10
G10	,,	1d. black and violet	0 10	1 3
G11	,,	2d. black & carmine	1 0	1 9
G11*a*	,,	2½d. black & deep blue (6.3.49)	1 3	1 6
G12	,,	3d. black and blue	1 6	2 0
G13	,,	4d. black and claret	1 9	2 0
G14	2	6d. black and orange	2 0	3 0
G15	,,	9d. black and brown	2 6	3 6
G16	,,	1s. black and purple	3 6	4 6

In Nos. G1 to 8 a variety with a gap in the 80th parallel occurs six times in each sheet of all values in positions 4, 9, 24, 29, 44, and 49.

In Nos. G9 to 16 the map is redrawn; the "0°" meridian does not touch the "s" of "COATS", the "n" of "Alexander" is not joined to the "L" of "Land" below, and the loops of letters "s" and "t" are generally more open.

1946 (4 Oct.). *Victory. As Nos.* 28/9 *of Aden.*

No.	Description	Unused	Used
G17	1d. deep violet	0 6	0 6
G18	3d. blue	0 10	1 4

1948 (6 Dec.). *Royal Silver Wedding. As Nos.* 30/1 *of Aden but inscr.* "FALKLAND ISLANDS DEPENDENCIES" *(recess* 1s.).

No.	Description	Unused	Used
G19	2½d. ultramarine	0 9	1 0
G20	1s. violet-blue	3 0	3 6

1949 (10 Oct.). *75th Anniv. of U.P.U. As Nos.* 114/7 *of Antigua.*

No.	Description	Unused	Used
G21	1d. violet	1 0	1 6
G22	2d. carmine-red	1 6	1 9
G23	3d. deep blue	2 6	3 0
G24	6d. red-orange	4 6	5 6

1953 (4 June). *Coronation. As No.* 47 *of Aden.*

No.	Description	Unused	Used
G25	1d. black and violet	1 6	1 6

3. *John Biscoe*, 1947–52.

10. *Discovery*, 1925–27.

4. *Trepassey*, 1945–47.

5. *Wyatt Earp*, 1934–36.

6. *Eagle*, 1944–45.

7. *Penola*, 1934–37.

8. *Discovery II*, 1929–37.

9. *William Scoresby*, 1926–46.

11. *Endurance*, 1914–16.

14. *Français* 1903–05.

12. *Deutschland*, 1910–12.

13. *Pourquoi-Pas?* 1908–10.

15. *Scotia*, 1902–04.

17. *Belgica*, 1897–99.

16. *Antarctic*, 1901–03.

(Recess. Waterlow (until 1962), then De La Rue.)

1954 (1 FEB.). *Wmk. Mult. Script CA. P* 12½.

No.	Type	Description	Unused	Used
G26	**3**	½d. black & bluish green (*shades*)	1 0	1 3
G27	**4**	1d. blk. & sep.-brn. (*shades*	1 0	1 3
G28	**5**	1½d. black & olive (*shades*)	0 10	1 0
G29	**6**	2d. black and rose-red ..	0 9	0 9
G30	**7**	2½d. black & yellow-ochre	0 9	0 9
G31	**8**	3d. black & dp. brt. blue	0 10	0 11
G32	**9**	4d. blk. & brt. reddish pur	1 4	1 7
G33	**10**	6d. black and deep lilac ..	1 8	2 0
G34	**11**	9d. black	2 3	3 3
G35	**12**	1s. black and brown ..	2 6	2 9
G36	**13**	2s. black and carmine	5 0	6 0
G37	**14**	2s. 6d. black & pale turq.	6 0	7 0
G38	**15**	5s. black and violet ..	11 6	16 0
G39	**16**	10s. black and blue ..	24 0	26 0
G40	**17**	£1 black	50 0	60 0

TRANS-ANTARCTIC EXPEDITION 1955-1958

(18)

1956 (30 JAN.). *Trans-Antarctic Expedition. Nos.* G27, G30/1 *and* G33 *optd. with T* **18**.

No.	Type	Description	Unused	Used
G41	**4**	1d. black & sepia-brown	0 8	0 10
G42	**7**	2½d. black & yellow-ochre	1 3	1 9
G43	**8**	3d. black & dp. brt. blue	1 3	1 9
G44	**10**	6d. black and deep lilac	2 3	2 9

The stamps of Falkland Islands Dependencies were withdrawn on July 16th, 1963. They were superseded by issues for BRITISH ANTARCTIC TERRITORY and SOUTH GEORGIA.

FIJI.

—SIMPLIFICATION (see INTRODUCTION) —

Nos. 1 to 90.

5, 6, 7, 8, 9.
11, 12, 14. 17, 18, 19.
20, 21, 22: 39, 40, 41.
46, 46a: 55, 55a. 64, 69.
82, 73, 90, 86.

Nos. 91 to 183.

If desired this group can be reduced to about 20 stamps by the omission of shades and perfs.

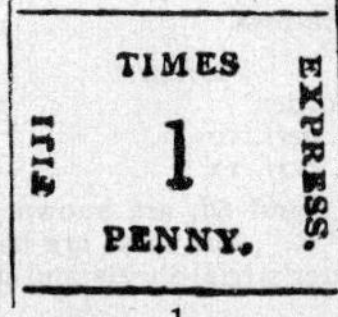

1

(Type-set and printed at the office of *The Fiji Times*, Levuka, Ovalau, Fiji, in sheets of twenty-four stamps arranged in four rows of six stamps of each value in the following order: 6d., 1s., 1d., 3d.)

T **1.** *Rouletted in the printing.*

(*a*) **1870** (1 Nov.). *Quadrillé paper.*

1 1d. black/*rose* £35 £45
2 3d. black/*rose* £40 £50
3 6d. black/*rose* £60 £70
4 1s. black/*rose* £35 £40

(*b*) **1871.** *Laid bâtonné paper.*

5 1d. black/*rose* £20 £18
6 3d. black/*rose* £20 £25
7 6d. black/*rose* £24 £35
8 9d. black/*rose* £24 £35
9 1s. black/*rose* £24 £35

The stamps of the last group were printed from the same plate as the first, but the values of the last three stamps in the bottom row of the sheet were altered to "9d." by inserting figures "9" in place of the figures "3".

There are no reprints of these stamps, but the 1d., 3d., 6d., and 1s. are known in the correct type on *yellow wove* paper; these are probably *proofs*. There are also two different sets of imitations made by the proprietors of *The Fiji Times* to meet the demands of collectors. The first of these were made in 1876 and are on *vertically laid* paper, *imperf.* and *pin-perf.*; these are smaller than the originals. The others were made later and are on thick *wove* paper of a deep *rosy mauve* colour.

KING CAKOBAU, JUNE, 1871, TO OCT., 1874.

2

3

(Eng. and electrotyped by A. L. Jackson. Typo. Govt. Printing Office, Sydney.)

1871 (Nov.). *Wove paper. Wmk.* "FIJI POSTAGE" *in small sans-serif capitals across the middle row of stamps in the sheet. P* 12½.

10 **2** 1d. pale blue 32 6 32 6
11 ,, 1d. deep blue 32 6 37 6
12 ,, 3d. yellow-green 45 0 60 0
13 **2** 3d. deep yellow-green .. 50 0 60 0
14 **3** 6d. dull rose 55 0 65 0
15 ,, 6d. carmine-rose 60 0 65 0

The 3d. differs from T **2** in having a white circle containing coloured pearls surrounding the centre.

All three values are known *imperf.*, but were not issued in that condition.

Two

Cents

(4)

1872 (13 JAN.). *Surch. as T* **4.**

16 **2** 2 c. on 1d. pale blue .. 22 6 25 0
17 ,, 2 c. on 1d. deep blue .. 22 6 27 6
18 ,, 6 c. on 3d. yellow-green .. 27 6 35 0
19 **3** 12 c. on 6d. carmine-rose .. 55 0 55 0

FIJI ISLANDS CEDED TO GREAT BRITAIN, 10 OCT., 1874.

V.R.

(5)

1874 (10 OCT.). *Nos.* 16 *to* 19 *optd. at the* "*Polynesian Gazette*" *Office, Levuka.*

(*a*) "V.R." *Gothic* (*T* **5**).

20 1d. (2 c.) blue £18 £8
21 3d. (6 c.) green £25 £20
22 6d. (12 c.) rose £18 £8

Varieties.

(i.) *No stop after* "R" (*No.* 13 *on sheet*).

23 1d. (2 c.) blue .. .. ..

V.R. V.R.

(**5***a*) (*enlarged*) (**5***b*)

(ii.) *Cross pattée stop after* "R" (*T* **5***a*) (*No.* 26 *on sheet*).

26 1d. (2 c.) blue .. ..
27 3d. (6 c.) green .. ..
28 6d. (12 c.) rose .. .. — £30

(iii.) *Round raised stop after* "V" (*No.* 28 *on sheet*).

29 1d. (2 c.) blue .. .. — £75
30 3d. (6 c.) green .. ..
31 6d. (12 c.) rose .. ..

(iv.) *Round raised stops after* "V" *and* "R" (*No.* 29 *on sheet*).

32 1d. (2 c.) blue .. ..
33 3d. (6 c.) green .. ..
34 6d. (12 c.) rose .. ..

(v.) *Inverted* "A" *used for* "V" (*T* **5***b*) (*No.* 30 *on sheet*).

35 1d. (2 c.) blue .. .. — £65
36 3d. (6 c.) green £125
37 6d. (12 c.) rose .. .. — £75

(vi.) *Overprint inverted.*

38 6d. (12 c.) rose .. ..

V.R.

(6)

(*b*) "V.R." *Roman* (*T* **6**).

39 1d. (2 c.) blue £16 £8
40 3d. (6 c.) green £35 £28
41 6d. (12 c.) rose £12 £10

Varieties. (i) *No stop after* "R".
(*No.* 43 on sheet.)

42 1d. (2 c.) blue £65 £70
43 3d. (6 c.) green £95
44 6d. (12 c.) rose .. .. — £70

(ii.) *Overprint inverted*

45 6d. (12 c.) rose £115

The stamps issued during the reign of Queen Victoria are fully described in *The Postage Stamps of the Fiji Islands* by Charles J. Phillips.

2d.
(7)

1875 (May ?). *Stamps of 1874 surch. in Levuka with T* **7**, *in red.*

No.	Type	Description	Unused	Used
46	**5**	2d. on 3d. (6 c.) green ..	£14	£7
46*a*	**6**	2d. on 3d. (6 c.) green ..	£16	£10
		Varieties.		
47	**5**	No stop after "R" ..	£45	£25
48	,,	Cross pattée stop after "R"	£65	£30
49	,,	Round raised stop after "V"	£45	£18
50	,,	Round raised stops after "V" and "R" ..	£70	£32
51	,,	Inverted "A" for "V" ..	£70	£32
52	**6**	No stop after "R" ..	£65	£32
53	**5**	No stop after "2d" ..	£55	£28
54	**6**	Stop between "2" & "d" (2.d)		

1875 (30 Sept.). *Stamps of 1874 surch. with T* **7** *in black.*

No.	Type	Description	Unused	Used
55	**5**	2d. on 3d. (6 c.) green ..	£22	£14
55*a*	**6**	2d. on 3d. (6 c.) green ..	£28	£22
		Varieties.		
56	**5**	No stop after "R" ..	£110	£45
57	,,	Cross pattée stop after "R"	£95	£45
58	,,	Round raised stop after "V"	£85	£38
59	,,	Round raised stops after "V" and "R"	£110	£48
60	,,	Inverted "A" for "V" ..	£95	£42
61	**6**	No stop after "R" ..	£95	£48
62	**5**	No stop after "2d" ..	£95	£42
63	**6**	Stop between "2" and "d" (2.d)		
63*a*	,,	"V.R." double ..	—	£85

1875 (20 Nov.). *Stamps of 12 c. on 6d. rose, of 1872, surch. in Levuka, "2d." (T 7) and "V.R." at one operation.*

(*a*) "V.R." *Gothic* (*T* **5**).

No.	Description	Unused	Used
64	2d. on 6d. (12 c.) rose ..	£42	£18
	Varieties.		
65	Surcharge double	—	£85
66	Inverted "A" for "V" ..	£38	£30
67	Inverted "A" for "V" and round raised stop after "V"	£48	£32
68	Inverted "A" for "V" and round raised stops after "V" and "R"	£48	£30

(*b*) "V.R." *Roman* (*T* **6**).

No.	Description	Unused	Used
69	2d. on 6d. (12 c.) rose ..	£32	£20
	Variety.		
70	Surcharge double	—	£75

(8)

Two Pence
(9)

Typo. Government Printing Office, Sydney, from the plates of 1871, on sheets of paper previously lithographed "V.R." (*T* **8**); *the 3d. surch. with T* **9**.

1876 (31 Jan.). *Wove paper. P* 12½.

No.	Description	Unused	Used
71	1d. grey-blue	27 6	27 6
72	1d. dull blue	27 6	27 6
73	2d. on 3d. pale green ..	27 6	27 6
74	2d. on 3d. deep green ..	27 6	27 6
75	6d. pale rose	42 6	32 6
76	6d. dull rose	37 6	27 6
77	6d. carmine-rose	37 6	27 6
	Varieties.		
78	1d. doubly printed		
79	1d. void corner		
80	6d. doubly printed		

Most of the above stamps are known *imperf.* and also on laid paper; these are from the printer's trial or waste sheets, and they were never issued. (For list see *Fiji Handbook.*)

The 3d. *green*, is also known without the surcharge "Two Pence"; this variety was not issued.

1877 (5 Jan.). *As last but laid paper. P* 12½.

No.	Description	Unused	Used
81	1d. blue	15 0	18 6
	a. Imperf. between (pair) ..	£16	
82	1d. deep blue	15 0	18 6
83	2d. on 3d. yellow-green ..	45 0	35 0
84	2d. on 3d. deep yellow-green	45 0	42 6
85	6d. rose	17 6	22 6
86	6d. carmine-rose	17 6	22 6
	Varieties.		
87	1d. void corner	75 0	65 0
88	2d. on 3d. *perf.* 10		
89	2d. on 3d. *perf.* 11		

The 1d., 3d., and 6d. are known without the monogram "V.R.", but these are believed to be only from printer's trial sheets and never issued.

1877 (12 Oct.). *Optd. with T* **8** *and surch. as T* **9**. *Laid paper. P* 12½.

No.	Type	Description	Unused	Used
90	**2**	4d. on 3d. mauve	18 6	16 0
		a. Imperf. between (pair) ..	£22	

10

11

A. Four Pence
B. Four Pence

Type A: Length 12½ mm.
Type B: Length 14 mm.

Note also the different shape of the two "e"s.

Printed from new plates made from the original dies of 1871, but "C.R." altered to "V.R." The 2d. and 4d. were made from the old 3d die. Manufactured at the Government Printing Office, Sydney Paper-maker's name "T. H. SAUNDERS" *or* "SANDERSON" *in double-lined capitals extending over seven stamps in each full sheet.*

1878–1900. *T* **10** *and* **11** (6*d.*); *the surcharges on 1d., 2d., and 3d. as T* **9** *or on 4d. as Types* A *or* B *in black. Wove paper.*

(*a*) P 12½ (1878–80).

No.	Description	Unused	Used
91	1d. pale ultramarine	6 0	6 0
91*a*	1d. ultramarine	10 6	7 6
92	2d. on 3d. green	6 0	7 0
93	2d. yellow-green	12 6	7 0
94	2d. blue-green	12 6	7 0
95	6d. rose	50 0	12 6
	Error of colour.		
95*a*	2d. ultramarine		

(*b*) *P* 10 (1881–90).

No.	Description	Unused	Used
96	1d. dull blue	22 6	5 0
97	1d. ultramarine	9 0	3 6
97*a*	1d. Cambridge blue (12.7.83)	15 0	3 0
98	2d. yellow-green	5 0	3 0
99	2d. blue-green	5 0	3 0
100	4d. on 2d. pale mauve (A) ..	17 6	8 6
101	4d. on 2d. dull purple (A) ..	17 6	8 6

101a 4d. on 2d. dull purple (B) .. — £7
102 4d. on 1d. mauve 9 0 9 0
102a 4d. mauve 32 6
103 4d. deep purple 32 6 32 6
104 6d. pale rose 37 6 12 6
105 6d. bright rose 15 0 15 0

(c) P 10×12½ (1882).

106 1d. ultramarine 22 6 20 0
107 2d. green £5 20 0
108 6d. rose £10 30 0

(d) P 12½×10 (1890).

109 1d. ultramarine .. ..

(e) P 12×10 *or* 10×12 (1885).

110 1d. ultramarine 25 0 10 0
110a 1d. dull blue .. .. ..
111 2d. yellow-green 22 6 12 6
111a 6d. rose .. .. ..

(f) P 11×10 (1893).

112 1d. ultramarine 2 6 3 0
113 4d. pale mauve 6 0 7 6
114 6d. pale rose 6 0 7 6
115 6d. rose 7 6 7 6

(g) P 11 (1897–99).

116 4d. mauve 6 6 7 6
117 6d. dull rose 12 6 12 6
118 6d. bright rose 22 6 15 0

Variety. Printed on both sides (Dec., 1899).

119 6d. dull rose £17 £10

(h) P 11×*nearly* 12 (1900).

Under this heading are included all the stamps formerly catalogued as *perfs.* 12×11; 11×12; 11×11½; or 11½×11. They are all compounds of *perf.* 11 with that of the machine gauging *nearly* 12, which has sometimes been measured as 11½ and sometimes as 12.

120 4d. deep purple 15 0
121 4d. bright purple 5 0 6 0
122 6d. rose 25 0
123 6d. bright rose 7 6 5 0

(i) *Imperf.* (1883–90).

124 1d. ultramarine .. ..
125 2d. yellow-green .. ..
126 4d. on 2d. pale mauve ..
127 6d. rose .. .. ..

12

13

1881–1900. *Electrotyped and printed at Government Printing Office, Sydney. Wmk. paper-maker's name as in* 1878–1900 *issue.*

(a) P 10 (19 Oct., 1881).

128 **12** 1s. pale brown 20 0 12 6
129 ,, 1s. deep brown 22 6 15 0

(b) P 11×10 (1894).

130 **12** 1s. pale brown 17 6 15 0

(c) P 11 (1898).

131 **12** 1s. pale brown 27 6 17 6

(d) P 11×*nearly* 12 (1900).

132 **12** 1s. pale brown 17 6 15 0
133 ,, 1s. brown 17 6 15 0
134 ,, 1s. deep brown 35 0 35 0

1882 (23 May). *Lithographed in Sydney, on toned paper watermarked with paper-maker's name* "Cowan" *in old English outline type once in each sheet. Centre in first colour.* P 10.

135 **13** 5s. dull red and black .. 85 0 95 0

In July, 1900, an electrotyped plate of a 5s. stamp was made and stamps were printed from it with pale orange-red centre and grey-black frame; these are known *perf.* 10, *perf. nearly* 12, and *imperf.* These stamps were sold as remainders with a special obliteration dated "15 Dec., 00," but were not issued for postal use. The design differs in many particulars from the issued stamp.

2½d. (14) 2½d. (15)

Stamps printed in Sydney and surch. at Govt. Ptg. Office, Suva.

1891 (1 Jan.). *Surch.* P 10.
(a) *Fraction* 1 *mm. from* "2" (T **14**).
(b) *Fraction* 2 *mm. from* "2" (T **15**).

136 **10** 2½d. on 2d. green (a) .. 17 6 20 0
137 ,, 2½d. on 2d. green (b) .. 85 0 80 0

½d. (16) 5d (17)

1892 (1 Mar.). *Surch. with T* **17**. P 10.

138 **10** ½d. on 1d. dull blue .. 35 0 35 0
139 ,, ½d. on 1d. ultramarine .. 22 0 10 6

1892 (25 July). *Surch. with T* **17**. P 10.

140 **10** 5d. on 4d. deep purple .. 50 0 47 6
141 ,, 5d. on 4d. dull purple .. 45 0 50 0

FIVE PENCE (**18**) 2 mm. spacing. FIVE PENCE (**19**) 3 mm. spacing.

1892 (30 Nov.). *Surch. with T* **18**. P 10.

142 **11** 5d. on 6d. brownish rose .. 50 0 50 0
143 ,, 5d. on 6d. bright rose .. 35 0 37 6
a. Perf. 12×12½ .. ..

1892 (31 Dec.). *Surch. with T* **19**. P 10.

145 **11** 5d. on 6d. rose 65 0
146 ,, 5d. on 6d. deep rose .. 42 6
147 ,, 5d. on 6d. brownish rose 35 0

20

21. Native Canoe.

22

(Printed in Sydney from electrotyped plates.)

1891–1902. *Wove paper watermarked in the sheets, either* "SANDERSON" *or* "NEW SOUTH WALES GOVERNMENT" *in outline capitals.*

(a) P 10 (1891–93).

148 **20** ½d. slate-grey 2 6 2 0
149 **21** 1d. black 2 6 2 0

150	**21**	2d. pale green	35 0	5 0
151	**22**	2½d. chocolate	12 6	10 0
152	**21**	5d. ultramarine	12 6	10 0

(*b*) *P* 11 × 10 (1893–97).

153	**20**	½d. slate-grey	7 6	7 6
154	**21**	1d. black	3 6	1 6
155	,,	2d. green	3 0	1 6
156	**22**	2½d. brown	5 0	5 0
157	,,	2½d. chocolate	12 6	7 6
158	,,	2½d. yellowish brown ..		
159	**21**	5d. ultramarine..	6 0	7 6

(*c*) *P* 11 (1893–98).

160	**20**	½d. slate-grey	2 0	3 6
161	,,	½d. greenish slate ..	6 6	4 0
162	**21**	1d. black	2 0	1 6
163	,,	1d. pale mauve ..	2 0	0 9
164	,,	1d. rosy mauve.. ..	2 0	0 9
165	,,	2d. dull green ..	2 6	1 6
166	,,	2d. emerald-green ..	2 0	1 0
167	**22**	2½d. brown	5 0	4 0
168	,,	2½d. yellowish brown ..	10 6	12 6
169	**21**	5d. ultramarine.. ..		

(*d*) *P* 10 × 12 (1894–98).

170	**20**	½d. pale grey		
171	**21**	1d. black	3 0	2 6
172	,,	2d. dull green	—	£9

(*e*) *Perf. nearly* 12 (1895–97).

173	**20**	½d. grey	17 6	
174	,,	½d. greenish slate ..	5 0	5 0
175	**21**	1d. black	£5	7 6
176	,,	1d. rosy mauve.. ..	2 0	2 6
177	,,	2d. dull green	42 6	15 0

(*f*) *P* 11 *and nearly* 12, *compound* (1897–1902).

178	**20**	½d. greenish slate ..	2 0	2 6
178*a*	**21**	1d. black	£5	
179	,,	1d. pale rosy mauve ..	1 6	2 0
180	,,	1d. rosy mauve.. ..	1 6	1 0
181	,,	2d. dull green	10 0	4 0
182	**22**	2½d. brown	8 6	8 6
183	,,	2½d. yellow-brown ..	6 0	6 0

The 2½d. brown is known *doubly printed*, but only occurs in the remainders and with the special obliteration. It was never issued for postal use.

23

24

(Typo. De La Rue.)

1903 (1 Feb.). *T* **23** *and* **24** (*2d., 4d., 6d. and 5s.*). *Wmk. Crown CA. P* 14.

184	½d. green and pale green ..	1 0	1 9
185	1d. dull purple and black/*red*	6 0	1 6
186	2d. dull purple and orange ..	2 6	2 6
187	2½d. dull purple and blue/*blue*	15 0	15 0
188	3d. dull purple and purple ..	5 0	6 0
189	4d. dull purple and black ..	6 0	7 6
190	5d. dull purple and green ..	7 6	8 6
191	6d. dull purple and carmine	7 6	8 6
192	1s. green and carmine ..	25 0	30 0
193	5s. green and black	65 0	80 0
194	£1 grey-black and ultram..	£24	£26

1904–9. *T* **23.** *Wmk. Mult. Crown CA. P* 14.

195	½d. green and pale green, O	2 6	1 3
196	1d. purple and black/*red*, O	2 6	1 0
197	1s. green & carm., C (1909)	30 0	35 0

1906–12. *T* **23** *and* **24.** *Wmk. Mult. Crown CA. P* 14.

198	½d. green, O (1908)	1 6	0 9
199	1d. red, O (1906)	1 6	0 6
200	2½d. bright blue, O (1910) ..	5 0	6 0
201	6d. dull purple, C (1910) ..	6 0	7 6
202	1s. black/*green*, C (1911) ..	8 6	12 6
203	5s. green & red/*yell.*. C (1911)	75 0	85 0
204	£1 pur. & blk./*red*, C (1912)	£30	£35

25

26

(Typo. De La Rue.)

1912–23. *Wmk. Mult. Crown CA. P* 14.

205	**26**	½d. brown, O (1916) ..	0 6	0 8
206	,,	½d. deep brown, O (1916)	0 4	0 10
207	**25**	½d. green, O	1 0	1 0
208	,,	½d. yellow-green, O (1915)	6 6	6 0
209	,,	½d. blue-green, O (1917)	2 0	1 0
210	,,	1d. carmine, O	2 3	0 10
211	,,	1d. brt. scarlet, O (1916)..	2 0	0 6
212	,,	1d. deep rose, O (1919) ..	2 3	0 3
213	**26**	2d. greyish slate, O ..	1 6	1 3
		a. Wmk. sideways		
214	**25**	2½d. bright blue, O ..	7 6	10 0
215	,,	3d. purple/*yellow*, O ..	7 0	8 6
		a. On lemon (1915)	7 0	13 6
		aa. Wmk. sideways	£25	
		b. On pale yellow (Die I) ..	7 0	9 6
		c. On pale yellow (Die II) ..	6 0	9 6
216	**26**	4d. black and red/*yell.*, O	12 6	15 0
		a. On lemon	8 6	12 6
		b. On orange-buff	40 0	47 6
		c. On pale yellow (Die I) (1921)	15 0	17 6
		d. On pale yell. (Die II) (1923)	12 6	17 6
217	**25**	5d. dull pur. & ol.-grn., C	7 6	8 6
218	**26**	6d. dull & brt. purple, C ..	6 0	7 6
219	**25**	1s. black/*green*, C ..	12 6	17 6
		a. White back	7 6	12 6
		b. On blue-green, olive back (1917)	12 6	15 0
		c. On emerald back (Die I) (1921)	10 0	15 0
		d. On emerald back (Die II) (1923)	12 6	7 6
220	**26**	2s. 6d. black & red/*blue*, C (1916)	17 6	15 0
221	,,	5s. green & red/yellow, C	30 0	35 0
222	**25**	£1 pur. & blk./*red*, C (Die I)	£15	£20
		a. Die II	£15	£20

WAR STAMP

(**27**)

1916–19. *Optd. locally with T* **27.**

223	**25**	½d. green	0 6	1 0
224	,,	½d. yellow-green (1916) ..	1 0	2 0
		a. Overprint double ..		
		b. Overprint inverted ..	£12	
225	,,	1d. carmine	17 6	20 0
226	,,	1d. bright scarlet ..	2 0	2 6
		a. Opt. omitted (strip of 12, one stamp without opt.) ..	£125	
		b. Opt. inverted	£12	
227	,,	1d. deep rose (1919) ..	2 0	2 6

No. 226*a* occurred on one sheet only, the overprint being so misplaced that all the stamps of the last vertical row of the second pane escaped the overprint entirely.

1922–27. *Wmk. Mult. Script CA. P* 14.

228	**26**	½d. deep brown, O ..	1 0	10 0
229	**25**	½d. green, O	0 3	0 4

No.	Type	Description		s.	d.	s.	d.
230	**25**	1d. carmine-red, O	..	3	6	3	0
231	,,	1d. violet, O	.. ..	0	8	0	8
232	**26**	1½d. scarlet, O	.. ..	1	9	1	6
233	,,	2d. grey, O	.. ..	0	9	0	6
234	**25**	3d. bright blue, O	..	1	6	2	0
235	**26**	4d. black & red/*yellow*, O		5	0	5	0
236	**25**	5d. dull pur. & sage-grn., O		2	6	3	0
237	**26**	6d. dull & brt. purple, O		2	6	2	6
238	**25**	1s. black/*emerald*, C	..	10	0	10	0
239	**26**	2s. purple & blue/*blue*, C		17	6	25	0
240	,,	2s. 6d. blk. & red/*blue*, C		20	0	25	0
241	,,	5s. green & red/*yellow*, C		50	0	55	0

1935 (6 May). *Silver Jubilee. As Nos.* 91/4 *of Antigua. P* 13½ × 14.

No.	Description		s.	d.	s.	d.
242	1½d. deep blue and carmine	..	1	0	1	6
243	2d. ultramarine and grey	..	2	0	3	0
244	3d. brown and deep blue	..	4	6	5	0
245	1s. slate and purple	..	7	6	12	6

1937 (12 May). *Coronation. As Nos.* 13/15 *of Aden, but ptd. by B. W. & Co. P* 11 × 11½.

No.	Description		s.	d.	s.	d.
246	1d. purple	.. .. ..	0	4	0	6
247	2d. grey-black	.. ..	0	9	1	0
248	3d. Prussian blue	.. ..	1	3	2	0

28. Natives Sailing Canoe.

29. Native Village.

30. Native Canoe.

Die I. **30.** Die II.
Empty Canoe. Native in Canoe.

31. Map of Fiji Islands.

Die I. **31.** Die II.
Without "180°" With "180°"

32. Government Offices.

33. Canoe and Arms of Fiji.

34. Sugar Cane.

35. Spearing Fish by Torchlight.

36. Arms of Fiji.

37. Suva Harbour.

38. River Scene.

39. Chief's Hut

40. Paw-Paw Tree. **41.** Police Bugler.

(Des. V. E. Ousey (T **28**, **35** and **38**), C. D. Lovejoy (T **29**, **30** and **34**), I. Stinton (T **28** and **39**) and A. V. Guy (T **31** and **37**). Recess. De La Rue (T **28**, **30**, **31**, **32** and **36**), Waterlow (others).)

1938 (5 Apr.)–**1955.** *Wmk. Mult. Script CA. Various perfs.*

No.	Type	Description	Unused	Used
249	**28**	½d. green (*p* 13½) ..	0 3	0 4
		a. Perf. 14	8 0	10 0
		b. Perf. 12 . ..	0 4	0 6
250	**29**	1d. brn. & blue (*p* 12½) ..	0 6	0 4
251	**30**	1½d. car. (Die I) (*p* 13½) ..	8 0	8 0
252	,,	1½d. car. (Die II) (*p* 13½)	1 0	1 6
		a. *Dark carmine*	10 0	12 6
		b. Perf. 14	16 0	18 6
		c. Perf. 12	0 6	0 8
253	**31**	2d. brown & green (Die I) (*p* 13½)	15 0	2 6
254	,,	2d. brown & green (Die II) (*p* 13½)	5 0	4 6
255	**32**	2d. grn. & mgnta. (*p* 13½)	0 8	0 8
		a. Perf. 12	0 10	0 8
256	**31**	2½d. brn & green (Die II) (*p* 14)	1 3	1 6
		a. Perf. 13½	0 10	0 6
		b. Perf. 12	0 8	0 6
257	**33**	3d. blue (*p* 12½) ..	1 0	1 0
258	**34**	5d. blue & scar. (*p* 12½) ..	30 0	35 0
259	,,	5d. yellow-green & scarlet (*p* 12½)	1 3	1 6
260	**31**	6d. blk. (Die I) (*p* 13×12)	40 0	45 0
261	,,	6d. blk. (Die II) (*p* 13½)	1 3	1 6
		a. *Violet-black*	20 0	20 0
		b. Perf. 12. *Black*	1 6	1 3
261*c*	**36**	8d. carmine (*p* 14) ..	3 0	4 0
		d. Perf. 13	1 9	2 6
262	**35**	1s. blk. & yell. (*p* 12½)	3 6	2 6
263	**36**	1s. 5d. blk. & carm. (*p* 14)	2 6	2 9
263*a*	,,	1s. 6d. ultramarine (*p* 14)	3 6	4 6
		b. Perf. 13	2 6	3 6
264	**37**	2s. vio. & orge. (*p* 12½)	3 6	3 0
265	**38**	2s. 6d. grn. & brn. (*p* 12½)	5 0	5 0
266	**39**	5s. grn. & pur. (*p* 12½) ..	10 0	9 0
266*a*	**40**	10s. orge. & emer. (*p* 12½)	25 0	27 6
266*b*	**41**	£1 ultram. & car. (*p* 12½)	35 0	42 6

Dates of issue:—1940, 1½d. (No. 252), 2d. (No. 254); 1.10.40, 5d. (No. 259), 6d. (No. 261); 13.6.40, 1s. 5d.; 1941, ½d. (No. 249*a*); 1942, 1½d. (No. 252*b*); 19.5.42, 2d. (No. 255); 6.2.42, 2½d. (Nos. 256/6*a*); 1.44, 6d. (No. 261*a*); 1946, 2d. (No. 255*a*); 1947, 6d. (No. 261*b*); 1948, ½d. (No. 249*b*), 2½d. (No. 256*b*); 15.11.48, 8d. (No. 261*c*); 21.7.49, 1½d. (No. 252*c*); 13.3.50, 10s. and £1; 7.6.50, 8d. (No. 261*d*); 1.8.50, 1s. 6d. (No. 263*a*); 16.2.55, 1s. 6d. (No. 263*b*). Others, 5.4.38.

2½d.

(42)

1941 (10 Feb.). *No.* 254 *surch. with T* **42.**

No.	Type	Description	Unused	Used
267	**31**	2½d. on 2d. brown & green	0 6	0 6

1946 (17 Aug.). *Victory. As Nos.* 28/9 *of Aden.*

No.	Description	Unused	Used
268	2½d. green	0 6	0 7
269	3d. blue	0 7	0 10

1948 (17 Dec.). *Royal Silver Wedding. As Nos.* 30/1 *of Aden.*

No.	Description	Unused	Used
270	2½d. green	0 6	0 8
271	5s. violet-blue	12 6	12 6

1949 (10 Oct.). *75th Anniv. of U.P.U. As Nos.* 114/7 *of Antigua.*

No.	Description	Unused	Used
272	2d. bright reddish purple ..	0 6	0 8
273	3d. deep blue	0 8	1 0
274	8d. carmine-red	1 9	2 6
275	1s. 6d. blue	4 0	5 0

43. Children Bathing.

44. Rugby Footballer.

(Recess. Bradbury, Wilkinson & Co.)

1951 (17 Sept.). *Health Stamps. Wmk. Mult. Script CA. P* 13½.

276	**43**	1d.+1d. brown	1	0	2	0
277	**44**	2d.+1d. green	1	6	2	6

1953 (2 June). *Coronation. As No.* 47 *of Aden.*

278	2½d. black and green ..	1	4	1	8

45. Arms of Fiji.

(Recess. De La Rue & Co.)

1953 (16 Dec.). *Royal Visit. Wmk. Mult. Script CA. P* 13.

279	**45**	8d. deep carmine-red ..	1	9	2	0

46. Queen Elizabeth II (after Annigoni).

47. Government Offices.

48. Loading Copra.

49. Sugar Cane Train.

50. Preparing Bananas for Export.

51. Gold Industry.

(Des. V. E. Ousey (½d., 1s., 2s. 6d.), A. V. Guy (6d.). Recess. (De La Rue ½d., 2d., 6d., 8d.), Waterlow (1s., 2s. 6d., 10s., £1) and Bradbury, Wilkinson (others).)

1954–56. *T* **46/51** *and designs as T* **28/41** *(but with portrait of Queen Elizabeth II in place of King George VI, as in T* **47**). *Wmk. Mult. Script CA. P* 12 (2*d*.), 13 (8*d*.), 12½ (1*s*., 2*s*. 6*d*., 10*s*., £1), 11½×11 (3*d*., 1*s*. 6*d*., 2*s*., 5*s*.) *or* 11½ (½*d*., *and T* **46**).

280	**28**	½d. myrtle-green	0	3	0	3
281	**46**	1d. turquoise-blue ..	0	5	0	6
282	,,	1½d. sepia	0	5	0	6
283	**47**	2d. green and magenta ..	0	6	0	6
284	**46**	2½d. blue-violet	0	6	0	6
285	**48**	3d. brown and reddish violet (*shades*) ..	0	8	0	10
287	**31**	6d. black	1	0	1	0
288	**36**	8d. dp. carm.-red (*shades*)	1	6	1	6
289	**35**	1s. black and yellow ..	1	9	2	0
290	**49**	1s. 6d. bl. & myrtle-grn.	2	6	3	0
291	**50**	2s. black and carmine ..	3	6	4	0
292	**38**	2s. 6d. bluish green and brown (*shades*) ..	4	6	4	6
293	**51**	5s. ochre and blue ..	7	6	8	0
294	**40**	10s. orange and emerald ..	50	0	55	0
295	**41**	£1 ultramarine and carm.	40	0	45	0

Dates of issue: 1954—1 Feb. (2d., 1s., 2s. 6d.). 1 July (½d., 6d., 8d., 10s., £1). 1956—1 June (1d.), 1 Oct. (others).

52. River Scene.

53. Cross of Lorraine.

(Recess. Bradbury, Wilkinson.)

1954 (1 Apr.). *Health Stamps. Wmk. Mult. Script CA. P* 11 × 11½.

No.	Type	Value	Description				
296	**52**	1½d. + ½d.	bistre-brn. & grn.	1	3	1	6
297	**53**	2½d. + ½d.	orange and black	1	6	2	0

54. Queen Elizabeth II (after Annigoni).

56. Hibiscus.

55. Fijian beating Lali.

57. Yaqona Ceremony.

58. Location Map.

59. Nadi Airport.

60. Kandavu Parrot.

61. Cutting Sugar-cane.

62. Arms of Fiji.

(Des. M. Goaman: Photo. Harrison (8d., 4s.). Recess. Bradbury, Wilkinson (others).)

1959–63. *Wmk. Mult. Script CA. P* 11½ (*T* **4**[illegible] *and* **54**), 11½ × 11 (*6d.*, *10d.*, *1s.*, *2s. 6d.*, *10s.* *£1*), 14½ × 14 (*8d*) *or* 14 × 14½ (*4s.*).

No.	Type	Value	Description				
298	**46**	½d.	emer.-green (14.11.61)	0	2	0	[illegible]
299	**54**	1d.	deep ultram. (3.12.62)	0	6	0	[illegible]
300	,,	1½d.	sepia (3.12.62) ..	0	4	0	[illegible]
301	**46**	2d.	rose-red (14.11.61) ..	0	5	0	[illegible]
302	,,	2½d.	orange-brown (3.12.62)	0	5	0	[illegible]
303	**55**	6d.	carm. & blk. (14.11.61)	1	6	1	[illegible]
304	**56**	8d.	scarlet, yellow, green and black (1.8.61) ..	2	6	3	[illegible]
305	**57**	10d.	brown & carm. (1.4.63)	5	0	6	[illegible]
306	**58**	1s.	lt. bl. & bl. (14.11.61)	1	4	1	[illegible]
307	**59**	2s.	6d. black and purple (14.11.61)	4	0	4	[illegible]
308	**60**	4s.	red, green, blue and slate-green (13.7.59) ..	10	0	12	[illegible]
309	**61**	10s.	emerald and deep sepia (14.11.61) ..	25	0	30	[illegible]
310	**62**	£1	blk. & orge. (14.11.61)	40	0	42	[illegible]

Nos. 299 and 312 have turtles on either sid[illegible] of "Fiji" instead of shells.

63. Queen Elizabeth II.

65. White Orchid.

64. International Dateline.

66. Orange Dove.

(Des. M. Goaman: Photo. Harrison (3d., 9d., 1s. 6d., 2s., 4s., 5s.). Recess. Bradbury, Wilkinson (others).)

1962 (3 Dec.)–**66.** *W* w.**12.** *P* 11½ (1*d.*, 2*d.*), 12½ (3*d.*), 11½ × 11 (6*d.*, 10*d.*, 2*s.* 6*d.*, 10*s.*, £1), 14½ × 14 (9*d.*, 2*s.*) *or* 14 × 14½ (1*s.* 6*d.*, 4*s.*, 5*s.*).

312	**54**	1d. deep ultram. (14.1.64)	0	3	0	4
314	**46**	2d. rose-red (3.8.65) ..	0	4	0	4
316	**63**	3d. multicoloured ..	0	5	0	6
317	**55**	6d. carm. & blk. (9.6.64)	0	9	0	11
318	**56**	9d. scarlet, yellow, green & ultramarine (1.4.63)	1	0	1	2
319	**57**	10d. brn. & carm. (14.1.64)	1	1	1	6
321	**64**	1s. 6d. red, yellow, gold, black and blue ..	1	11	2	6
322	**65**	2s. yellow-green, green and copper	2	6	3	0
323	**59**	2s. 6d. black and purple (3.8.65)	3	2	3	6
324	**60**	4s. red, yellow-green, blue and green (1.4.64) ..	6	0	7	6
324*a*	,,	4s. red, green, blue and slate-green (1.3.66) ..	4	9	5	0
325	**66**	5s. red, yellow and grey ..	6	0	7	6
326	**61**	10s. emerald and deep sepia (14.1.64)	12	0	14	0
327	**62**	£1 black & orge. (9.6.64)	24	0	27	6

ROYAL VISIT

1963

(**67**)

ROYAL VISIT 1963

(**68**)

1963 (1 Feb.). *Royal Visit. Nos.* 316 *and* 306 *optd.*

328	**67**	3d. multicoloured	1	3	1	9
329	**68**	1s. light blue and blue ..	4	0	4	6

1963 (4 June). *Freedom from Hunger. As No.* 63 *of Aden.*

330	2s. ultramarine	4	6	6	0

69. Running.

70. Throwing the Discus. **71.** Hockey.

72. High-jumping.

(Des. M. Goaman. Photo. Harrison.)

1963 (17 July). *First South Pacific Games, Suva. W* w.**12.** *P* 14½.

331	**69**	3d. red-brn., yell. & black	1	6	1	9
332	**70**	9d. red-brn., vio. & black	3	3	3	9
333	**71**	1s. red-brn., green & black	3	9	4	6
334	**72**	2s. 6d. red-brown, lt. blue and black	10	6	12	6

1963 (2 Sept). *Red Cross Centenary. As Nos.* 147/8 *of Antigua.*

335	2d. red and black	0	8	0	10
336	2s. red and blue	4	6	6	0

(**73.** Cable-laying ship, *Retriever*.)

1963 (3 Dec.). *Opening of COMPAC (Trans-Pacific Telephone Cable). As No.* 306 (*but W* w.12) *optd. with T* **73.**

337	**58**	1s. light blue and blue ..	4	6	6	6

74. Jamborette Emblem.

75. Scouts of Three Races.

(Des. V. Whiteley assisted by Norman L. Joe, Asst. D.C., Fiji Scouts for Jamboree emblem. Photo. Harrison.)

1964 (3 Aug.). *50th Anniv. of Fijian Scout Movement. W* w.**12.** *P* 12½.

338 **74** 3d. red, gold, ultramarine and deep green .. 1 0 1 6
339 **75** 1s. violet & yellow-brown 4 6 6 0

76. Flying-boat " Aotearoa ".

77. Fiji Airways " Heron ".

78. " Aotearoa " and Map.

(Des. V. Whiteley. Photo. Harrison.)

1964 (24 Oct.). *25th Anniv. of First Fiji-Tonga Airmail Service. W* w.**12.** *P* 14½×14 (1s.) *or* 12½ (*others*).

340 **76** 3d. black and vermilion .. 1 0 1 6
341 **77** 6d. vermilion & brt. blue 2 0 2 6
342 **78** 1s. black & turquoise-blue 5 0 6 0

1965 (17 May). *I.T.U. Centenary. As Nos.* 166/7 *of Antigua.*

343 3d. blue and rose-carmine .. 0 10 1 0
344 2s. orange-yellow and bistre 4 0 5 0

1965 (15 Oct.). *International Co-operation Year. As Nos.* 168/9 *of Antigua.*

345 2d. reddish pur. & turq.-grn. 0 6 0 8
346 2s. 6d. dp. bluish grn. & lav. 4 6 5 6

1966 (24 Jan.). *Churchill Commemoration. As Nos.* 170/3 *of Antigua.*

347 3d. new blue 0 6 0 9
348 9d. deep green 1 2 1 6
349 1s. brown 1 8 2 0
350 2s. 6d. bluish violet 4 0 5 0

POSTAGE DUE STAMPS.

D 1

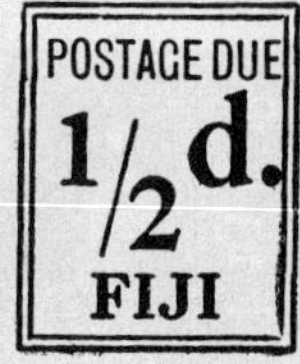

D 2

1917 (Jan.). *Type* D **1.** *Printed locally, on thick yellowish white laid paper. P* 11.

D 1 ½d. black £28 £23
D 2 1d. black £10 £6
D 3 2d. black £10 80 0
D 4 3d. black £12 £7
D 5 4d. black £30 £25

1917 (April). *Narrower setting, value in ½d. as Type* D **2.**

D 5*a* ½d. black £30 £15
D 5*b* 1d. black £10 80 0
D 5*c* 2d. black .. .. ..

1d. and 2d. stamps must have wide margins (3½ to 4 mm.) on the vertical sides to be Nos. D2 or D3. Stamps with narrow margins of approximately the same width on all four sides are Nos. D5*b* or D5*c*.

D 3

D 4

(Typo. De La Rue & Co.)

1918 (1 June). *Wmk. Mult. Crown CA. P* 14.

D 6 D **3** ½d. black 2 6 3 0
D 7 ,, 1d. black 2 6 3 0
D 8 ,, 2d. black 4 0 4 6
D 9 ,, 3d. black 5 0 6 0
D 10 ,, 4d. black 8 6 10 0

(Typo. Waterlow & Co.)

1940. *Wmk. Mult. Script CA. P* 12½.

D 11 D **4** 1d. emerald-green .. 1 0 2 0
D 12 ,, 2d. emerald-green ... 1 3 2 0
D 13 ,, 3d. emerald-green .. 1 6 2 6
D 14 ,, 4d. emerald-green .. 2 6 3 6
D 15 ,, 5d. emerald-green .. 3 6 5 0
D 16 ,, 6d. emerald-green .. 5 0 7 6
D 17 ,, 1s. carmine-lake .. 7 6 12 6
D 18 ,, 1s. 6d. carmine-lake .. 17 6 25 0

GAMBIA.

1

(Typo. and embossed by De La Rue & Co.)

1869 (Mar.). *No wmk. Imperf.*

1	1	4d. brown	£45	£22
2	,,	4d. pale brown	£38	£25
3	,,	6d. deep blue	£38	£22
3a	,,	6d. blue	£38	£22
4	,,	6d. pale blue	£150	£125

Our prices for the 6d., pale blue, No. 4, are for stamps which are pale by comparison with specimens of the "deep blue" and "blue" colour groups listed under Nos. 3 and 3a. An exceptionally pale shade is recognized by specialists and this is rare.

1874 (Aug.). *Wmk. Crown CC. Imperf.*

5	1	4d. brown	£38	£25
6	,,	4d. pale brown	£38	£25
7	,,	6d. deep blue	£35	£28
8	,,	6d. blue	£32	£25

NOTE—The prices of Nos. 1 to 8 are for fine copies, with good margins and embossing. Brilliant or poor copies can be supplied at prices consistent with their condition.

1880 (June). *Wmk. Crown CC. P 14 (comb).*

10	1	½d. deep orange	12 6	15 0
11	,,	½d. dull orange	12 6	12 6
		a. Twice embossed	£100	
		b. Twice embossed, one inverted	—	£120
12	,,	1d. maroon	12 6	10 0
		a. Twice embossed	£90	
		b. Twice embossed, one inverted	—	£125
13	,,	2d. rose	27 6	20 0
14	,,	3d. pale dull ultramarine	40 0	37 6
		a. Twice embossed	—	£90
14b	,,	3d. bright ultramarine	50 0	30 0
15	,,	4d. brown	£20	35 0
16	,,	4d. pale brown	£20	40 0
17	,,	6d. deep blue	95 0	80 0
18	,,	6d. blue	97 6	80 0
19	,,	1s. green	£20	£14
20	,,	1s. deep green	£20	£14

The watermark in this issue is found sideways as well as upright. These stamps also exist in line perf. 14, believed to have come from the first delivery to the Colony. Some of them are rare.

1886 (Jan.)–**87.** *Wmk. Crown CA, sideways. P 14.*

21	1	½d. myrtle-green (1887)	2 6	2 6
22	,,	½d. grey-green (1887)	2 6	4 0
		a. Twice embossed (*shades*)	£60	
22b	,,	1d. maroon		
23	,,	1d. crimson (1887)	4 0	7 0
23a	,,	1d. aniline crimson (1887)	27 6	25 0
23b	,,	1d. pale carmine (1887)	15 0	17 6
		c. Twice embossed	£70	
24	,,	2d. orange (1887)	15 0	10 0
		a. Twice embossed	£90	
25	,,	2d. deep orange (1887)	12 6	10 6
		a. Twice embossed	£100	
25b	,,	2d. yellow-buff (1887)	£60	
25c	,,	2d. yellow	£70	
26	,,	2½d. ultramarine	17 6	15 0
27	,,	2½d. deep bright blue	15 0	8 6
		a. Twice embossed	£90	
28	,,	3d. slate-grey	10 0	12 6
		a. Twice embossed	—	£100
29	1	3d. grey	8 6	17 6
29a	,,	3d. pearl-grey	12 6	17 6
30	,,	4d. brown	12 6	12 6
31	,,	4d. deep brown	10 0	10 0
32	,,	6d. yellowish olive-green	£6	60 0
32a	,,	6d. olive-green	95 0	75 0
33	,,	6d. bronze-green	25 0	35 0
33a	,,	6d. deep bronze-green	35 0	42 6
34	,,	6d. slate-green	30 0	35 0
35	,,	1s. violet	17 6	25 0
		a. Twice embossed, one inverted	£160	
36	,,	1s. deep violet	22 6	40 0
36a	,,	1s. aniline violet	£60	

The ½d., 2d., 3d., 4d., 6d. (No. 32) and 1s. with watermark Crown CA are known imperf.

NOTE.—The majority of the stamps of T1 with so-called "double embossing" are merely specimens in which the printing and embossing do not register accurately, and have no special value.

2

(Typo. De La Rue.)

1898 (Jan.)–**1902.** *Wmk. Crown CA. P 14.*

37	2	½d. dull green	3 0	3 6
38	,,	1d. carmine	6 0	3 6
39	,,	2d. orange and mauve	8 6	12 6
40	,,	2½d. ultramarine	6 0	12 6
41	,,	3d. reddish pur. and blue	15 0	20 0
41a	,,	3d. dp. pur. & ultram. ('02)	75 0	70 0
42	,,	4d. brown and blue	10 0	25 0
43	,,	6d. olive-green and carmine	20 0	37 6
44	,,	1s. violet and green	35 0	50 0

3

4

(Typo. De La Rue.)

1902–5. *Wmk. Crown CA. P 14.*

45	3	½d. green	1 3	3 0
46	,,	1d. carmine	3 0	1 9
47	,,	2d. orange and mauve	6 0	10 0
48	,,	2½d. ultramarine	15 0	17 6
49	,,	3d. purple and ultramarine	12 6	10 0
50	,,	4d. brown and ultramarine	12 6	25 0
51	,,	6d. pale sage-grn. & carmine	12 6	22 6
52	,,	1s. violet and green	65 0	75 0
53	4	1s.6d. grn. & carm./*yell.* ('05)	35 0	50 0
54	,,	2s. deep slate and orange	40 0	60 0
55	,,	2s. 6d. pur. & brn./*yell.* ('05)	50 0	60 0
56	,,	3s. carm. & grn./*yell.* ('05)	50 0	60 0

1904–6. *Wmk. Mult. Crown CA. P 14.*

57	3	½d. green	1 6	1 9
58	,,	1d. carmine ('04)	3 0	1 3
59	,,	2d. orange and mauve ('06)	17 6	20 0
60	,,	2½d. bright blue	8 6	8 6
60a	,,	2½d. bright blue & ultram.	20 0	25 0
61	,,	3d. purple & ultramarine	15 0	20 0
62	,,	4d. brown & ultram. ('06)	20 0	35 0
63	4	5d. grey and black	17 6	22 6
64	3	6d. olive-grn. & carmine ('06)	17 6	22 6
65	4	7½d. green and carmine	20 0	30 0
66	,,	10d. olive and carmine	45 0	50 0

No.	Type	Description	Unused	Used
67	3	1s. violet and green ..	65 0	70 0
68	4	2s. deep slate & orange ..	£8	£10

HALF PENNY

(5)

ONE PENNY

(6)

1906 (April). *Nos.* 55 *and* 56 *surch. with T* **5** *and* **6** *respectively.*

No.	Type	Description	Unused	Used
69		½d. on 2s. 6d. pur. & brn./*yell.*	£5	£7
70		1d. on 3s. carm. & green/*yell.*	£7	£9
		a. Surch. double	£225	

The spacing between the words and bars on No. 69 varies from 4 mm. to 5 mm.

A constant variety with broken " E " is found in the surcharge of No. 69.

1909. *Colours changed. Wmk. Mult. Crown CA. P* 14.

No.	Type	Description	Unused	Used
72	3	½d. blue-green	3 0	3 0
73	,,	1d. red	2 6	0 10
74	,,	2d. greyish slate	6 0	5 0
75	,,	3d. purple/*yellow*	10 0	8 0
75*a*	,,	3d. purple/*lemon-yellow* ..	12 6	12 6
76	,,	4d. black & red/*yellow* ..	7 6	8 0
77	4	5d. orange & purple ..	7 0	10 0
78	3	6d. dull & bright purple ..	8 6	8 6
79	4	7½d. brown & blue ..	10 0	10 6
80	,,	10d. pale sage-grn. & carm.	10 0	12 6
81	3	1s. black/*green*	12 6	15 0
82	4	1s. 6d. violet and green ..	35 0	40 0
83	,,	2s. purple & brt. blue/*blue*	40 0	45 0
84	,,	2s. 6d. black and red/*blue*	50 0	60 0
85	,,	3s. yellow and green ..	60 0	70 0

GAMBIA POSTAGE POSTAGE ½d

7

GAMBIA POSTAGE POSTAGE 1½d

8

(Typo. De La Rue & Co.)

1912–22. *Wmk. Mult. Crown CA. P* 14.

No.	Type	Description	Unused	Used
86	7	½d. pale green, O ..	1 6	2 3
87	,,	½d. green, O	1 6	2 3
88	,,	½d. deep green, O ..	1 0	1 6
89	,,	1d. red, O	1 6	1 0
89*a*	,,	1d. rose-red, O	2 0	1 3
90	,,	1d. scarlet, O (1916) ..	3 6	1 6
91	8	1½d. ol.-grn. & bl.-grn., O	4 0	7 6
92	7	2d. greyish slate, O ..	2 6	3 6
93	,,	2½d. deep bright blue, O	10 0	11 0
94	,,	2½d. bright blue, O ..	6 0	6 0
95	,,	3d. purple/*yellow*, O ..	3 6	4 0
		a. On lemon (1917)	35 0	50 0
		b. On orange-buff (1920) ..	4 0	10 0
		c. On pale yellow ..	4 0	6 6
96	,,	4d. black & red/*yellow*, O	10 0	17 6
		a. On lemon	5 0	17 6
		b. On orange-buff ..	7 6	12 6
		c. On pale yellow	10 0	17 6
97	8	5d. orange & purple, O ..	5 0	6 0
98	7	6d. dull & brt. pur., O ..	6 0	6 6
99	8	7½d. brown and blue, O ..	7 0	7 6
100	,,	10d. p. sage-grn. & car., O	15 0	12 6
101	,,	10d. dp. sage grn. & car., O	15 0	12 6
102	7	1s. black/*green*, O ..	6 0	7 6
		a. On emerald back	10 0	17 6
103	8	1s. 6d. violet & green, O	15 0	17 6
104	,,	2s. purple & blue/*blue*, O	17 6	20 0
105	,,	2s. 6d. blk. & red/*blue*, O	20 0	35 0
106	,,	3s. yellow and green, O	22 6	35 0
107	,,	5s. green & red/*pale yellow*, C ('22)	70 0	£5

1921–22. *Wmk. Mult. Script CA. P* 14.

No.	Type	Description	Unused	Used
108	7	½d. dull green, O	1 0	3 0
109	,,	1d. carmine-red, O ..	1 0	1 0
110	8	1½d. ol.-grn. & blue-grn., O	10 0	12 6
111	7	2d. grey, O	4 0	8 6
112	,,	2½d. bright blue, O ..	5 0	7 6
113	8	5d. orange & purple, O ..	6 0	20 0
114	7	6d. dull & brt. purple, O	6 0	12 6
115	8	7½d. brown & blue, O	8 0	10 6
116	,,	10d. pale sage-grn. & car., O	9 0	17 6
117	,,	4s. black & red, C (1922)	60 0	90 0

POSTAGE & REVENUE GAMBIA HALF PENNY ½d

9

POSTAGE REVENUE GAMBIA 2/6 TWO SHILLINGS & SIX PENCE 2/6

10

(Recess. De La Rue & Co.)

1922–27. *Portrait and shield in black. P* 14.

(*a*) *Wmk. Mult. Crown CA.*

No.	Type	Description	Unused	Used
118	9	4d. red/*yellow*	3 0	5 0
119	,,	7½d. purple/*yellow*	7 6	15 0
120	10	1s. purple/*yellow*	15 0	35 0
121	,,	5s. green/*yellow* ..	£6	£7

(*b*) *Wmk. Mult. Script CA.*

No.	Type	Description	Unused	Used
122	9	½d. green	0 6	1 0
123	,,	½d. deep green	1 3	2 6
124	,,	1d. brown	0 8	0 10
125	,,	1½d. bright rose-scarlet ..	1 0	1 3
126	,,	2d. grey	2 6	3 6
127	,,	2½d. orange-yellow ..	2 6	7 6
128	,,	3d. bright blue ..	3 0	4 0
129	,,	4d. red/*yellow*	5 0	8 6
130	,,	5d. sage-green	10 0	17 6
131	,,	6d. claret	6 0	8 6
132	,,	7½d. purple/*yellow*	15 0	20 0
133	,,	10d. blue	12 6	15 0
134	10	1s. purple/*yellow*	10 0	12 6
135	,,	1s. 6d. blue	15 0	20 0
136	,,	2s. purple/*blue*	15 0	17 6
137	,,	2s. 6d. deep green ..	20 0	25 0
138	,,	3s. bright aniline violet ..	35 0	40 0
139	,,	3s. slate-purple ..	£35	£38
140	,,	4s. brown	32 6	40 0
141	,,	5s. green/*yellow*	50 0	60 0
142	,,	10s. sage-green	£6	£7

No. 139 has been faked, but note that this stamp is comb. perf. 13.9 × 13.8 whereas No. 138 is line perf. 14 exactly.

1935 (6 May). *Silver Jubilee. As T* **13** *of Antigua. Recess. B.W. & Co. Wmk. Mult. Script CA. P* 11 × 12.

No.	Description	Unused	Used
143	1½d. deep blue and scarlet ..	0 8	1 0
	a. Extra flagstaff	80 0	
144	3d. brown and deep blue ..	3 0	4 6
	a. Extra flagstaff	£8	
145	6d. light blue and olive-green	4 0	4 6
	a. Extra flagstaff	£8	
146	1s. slate and purple ..	6 6	8 0
	a. Extra flagstaff	£14	

For illustration of " extra flagstaff " variety see Bechuanaland.

1937 (12 May). *Coronation. As T* **2** *of Aden Recess. B.W. & Co. Wmk. Mult. Script CA P* 11 × 11½.

No.	Description	Unused	Used
147	1d. yellow-brown	0 4	0 [illegible]
148	1½d. carmine	0 9	0 [illegible]
149	3d. blue	1 6	2 [illegible]

11. Elephant.

(Recess. Bradbury, Wilkinson & Co.)

1938 (1 Apr.)–**1946.** *Wmk. Mult. Script CA. P* 12.

150	**11**	½d. black & emer.-green	0	3	0	3
151	"	1d. purple and brown ..	0	6	0	3
152	"	1½d. lake and carmine ..	25	0	17	6
		a. Lake and scarlet ('42) ..	1	0	1	3
152*b*	"	1½d. blue & black (2.1.45)	0	8	0	6
153	"	2d. blue and black ..	1	6	3	0
153*a*	"	2d. lake & scarlet ('43)	0	8	0	10
154	"	3d. light blue & grey-blue	1	0	0	8
154*a*	"	5d. sage-green & purple-brown (13.3.41) ..	1	6	2	0
155	"	6d. olive-green & claret	1	9	1	0
156	"	1s. slate-blue & violet ..	3	0	1	3
156*a*	"	1s. 3d. chocolate & light blue (28.11.46)	3	0	3	6
157	"	2s. carmine and blue ..	5	0	6	0
158	"	2s. 6d. sepia & dull green	7	0	8	0
159	"	4s. vermilion and purple	10	0	12	6
160	"	5s. blue and vermilion ..	12	6	15	0
161	"	10s. orange and black ..	25	0	27	6

1946 (6 Aug.). *Victory. As Nos.* 28/9 *of Aden.*

162	1½d. black	0	4	0	6
163	3d. blue	0	6	1	0

1948 (24 Dec.). *Royal Silver Wedding. As Nos.* 30/1 *of Aden.*

164	1½d. black	0	6	0	6
165	£1 mauve	30	0	35	0

1949 (10 Oct.). *75th Anniv. of Universal Postal Union. As Nos.* 114/7 *of Antigua.*

166	1½d. blue-black	1	0	1	0
167	3d. deep blue..	1	3	1	3
168	6d. magenta	2	6	3	0
169	1s. violet	4	6	5	0

1953 (2 June). *Coronation. As No.* 47 *of Aden. but ptd. by B. W. & Co.*

170	1½d. black & dp. bright blue	1	0	1	6

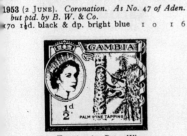

12. Tapping for Palm Wine.

13. Cutter.

14. Wollof Woman.

15. Barra Canoe.

16. S.S. *Lady Wright.*

17. James Island.

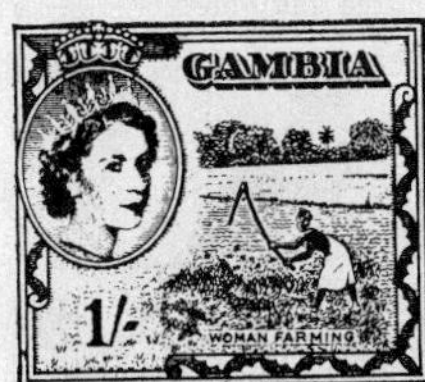

18. Woman Hoeing.

19. Elephant and Palm.

(Des. Mrs. O. W. Meronti. Recess. De La Rue.)

1953 (2 Nov.). *Wmk. Mult. Script. CA. P* 13½.

171	**12**	½d. carmine-red and bluish green (*shades*) ..	0	3	0	3
172	**13**	1d. deep ultramarine and deep brown (*shades*)..	0	4	0	3
173	**14**	1½d. dp. brn. & grey-black	0	5	0	4
174	**15**	2½d. black and carmine-red	0	6	0	6
175	**16**	3d. deep blue & slate-lilac	0	7	0	10
176	**17**	4d. black and deep blue..	1	0	1	6
177	**12**	6d. brn. & reddish purple	1	0	1	0
178	**18**	1s. yell.-brn. & yell.-green	1	8	1	9
179	**13**	1s. 3d. ultramarine and pale blue (*shades*) ..	2	3	2	0
180	**15**	2s. indigo and carmine ..	3	6	4	0
181	**18**	2s. 6d. deep bluish green and sepia	5	0	6	0
182	**17**	4s. grey-blue & Indian red	7	0	8	0
183	**14**	5s. chocolate & brt. blue	9	0	10	0
184	**16**	10s. dp. bl. & myrtle-green	17	6	20	0
185	**19**	£1 green and black ..	35	0	40	0

20. Queen Elizabeth II and Palm. **21.** Queen Elizabeth II and West African Map.

(Des. J. R. F. Ithier (T **20**), A. W. Morley (T **21**). Recess. Bradbury, Wilkinson.)

1961 (2 Dec.). *Royal Visit. W* w.**12**. *P* 11½.

186	**20**	2d. green and purple ..	0	8	0	10
187	**21**	3d. turq.-blue and sepia ..	1	0	1	0
188	,,	6d. blue and cerise ..	1	6	1	9
189	**20**	1s. 3d. violet & myrt.-grn.	3	6	4	0

1963 (4 June). *Freedom from Hunger. As No.* 63 *of Aden.*

190	1s. 3d. carmine	2	6	3	0

1963 (2 Sept.). *Red Cross Centenary. As Nos.* 147/8 *of Antigua.*

191	2d. red and black	0	6	0	8
192	1s. 3d. red and blue.. ..	2	6	3	0

22. Beautiful Long-tailed Sunbird.

23. Yellow-mantled Whidah.

24. Cattle Egret.

25. Yellow-bellied Parrot.

26. Long-tailed Parakeet.

27. Amethyst Starling.

28. Village Weaver.

29. Rufous-crowned Roller.

30. Red-eyed Turtle Dove.

31. Bush Fowl.

32. Palm-nut Vulture.

33. Orange-cheeked Waxbill.

34. Emerald Cuckoo.

(Des. V. Whiteley. Photo. Harrison.)

963 (4 Nov.). *W.* w.**12.** *P* 12½ × 13.

93	**22**	½d. multicoloured	..	0 3		0 3
94	**23**	1d. multicoloured	..	0 4		0 3
95	**24**	1½d. multicoloured	..	0 5		0 5
96	**25**	2d. multicoloured	..	0 6		0 5
97	**26**	3d. multicoloured	..	0 7		0 6
198	**27**	4d. multicoloured	..	0 9		0 9
199	**28**	6d. multicoloured	..	1 0		1 3
200	**29**	1s. multicoloured	..	1 9		2 3
201	**30**	1s. 3d. multicoloured	..	2 3		2 6
202	**31**	2s. 6d. multicoloured	..	4 0		4 9
203	**32**	5s. multicoloured	..	10 0		11 0
204	**33**	10s. multicoloured	..	17 6		20 0
205	**34**	£1 multicoloured	..	33 0		40 0

SELF GOVERNMENT
1963

(35)

1963 (7 Nov.). *New Constitution. Nos.* 194, 197, 200/1 *optd. with T* **35.**

206	**23**	1d. multicoloured	..	0 9	0 10
207	**26**	3d. multicoloured	..	1 0	1 3
208	**29**	1s. multicoloured	..	3 6	4 0
209	**30**	1s. 3d. multicoloured	..	4 9	3 6

1964 (23 April). 400*th Anniv. of Birth of William Shakespeare. As No.* 164 *of Antigua.*

210 6d. greenish blue 1 6 1 8

INDEPENDENT
within the Commonwealth.

36. Gambia Flag and River. **37.** Arms.

(Des. V. Whiteley. Photo. Harrison.)

1965 (18 Feb.). *Independence. P* 14½.

211	**36**	½d. multicoloured	..	0 3	0 4
212	**37**	2d. multicoloured	..	0 5	0 7
213	**36**	7½d. multicoloured	..	1 3	1 9
214	**37**	1s. 6d. multicoloured	..	2 6	4 6

INDEPENDENCE
1965

(38)

1965 (18 Feb.). *Nos.* 193/205 *optd. with T* **38** *or with date centred* (1*d.*, 2*d.*, 3*d.*, 4*d.*, 1*s.*, 5*s.*, 10*s.*, £1).

215	**22**	½d. multicoloured	..	0 3	0 4
216	**23**	1d. multicoloured	..	0 4	0 5
217	**24**	1½d. multicoloured	..	0 5	0 5
218	**25**	2d. multicoloured	..	0 5	0 6
219	**26**	3d. multicoloured	..	0 7	0 9
220	**27**	4d. multicoloured	..	0 9	0 11
221	**28**	6d. multicoloured	..	1 0	1 2
222	**29**	1s. multicoloured	..	1 8	2 6
223	**30**	1s. 3d. multicoloured	..	2 3	2 9
224	**31**	2s. 6d. multicoloured	..	4 6	4 9
225	**32**	5s. multicoloured	..	8 0	9 0
226	**33**	10s. multicoloured	..	16 0	18 0
227	**34**	£1 multicoloured	..	30 0	35 0

39. I.T.U. Emblem and Symbols.

(Des. V. Whiteley. Photo. Harrison.)

1965 (17 May). *I.T.U. Centenary.* *P* 14½.

228	**39**	1d. silver and Prussian blue	0	4	0	5
229	,,	1s. 6d. gold & bluish violet	2	6	3	0

40. Sir Winston Churchill and Houses o Parliament.

(Des. Jennifer Toombs. Photo. Harrison.)

1966 (24 Jan.). *Churchill Commemoration* *P* 14 × 14½.

230	**40**	1d. multicoloured ..	0	4	0	
231	,,	6d. multicoloured ..	1	0	1	
232	,,	1s. 6d. multicoloured ..	2	6	3	

41. Cordon Bleu.

42. Whistling Teal.

43. Red-throated Bee-eate

44. Pied Kingfisher.

45. Napoleon Bishop.

46. River Eagle.

47. Yellow-bellied Fruit Pigeon.

48. Blue-bellied Roller.

49. Pigmy Kingfisher.

50. Spur-winged Goose.

51. Little Woodpecker.

52. Violet Plantain-eate

53. Pintailed Whydah.

(Des. V. Whiteley. Photo. Harrison.)

1966 (18 Feb.). *P* 14 × 14½ (£1) *or* 12 × 13 (*others*).

No.	Type	Value		Unused s.	d.	Used s.	d.
233	**41**	½d. multicoloured	..	0	2	0	3
234	**42**	1d. multicoloured	..	0	3	0	4
235	**43**	1½d. multicoloured	..	0	4	0	4
236	**44**	2d. multicoloured	..	0	4	0	5
237	**45**	3d. multicoloured	..	0	6	0	7
238	**46**	4d. multicoloured	..	0	7	0	9
239	**47**	6d. multicoloured	..	0	10	1	0
240	**48**	1s. multicoloured	..	1	5	2	0
241	**49**	1s. 6d. multicoloured	..	2	0	2	6
242	**50**	2s. 6d. multicoloured	..	3	6	4	0
243	**51**	5s. multicoloured	..	6	9	7	6
244	**52**	10s. multicoloured	..	13	3	15	0
245	**53**	£1 multicoloured	..	25	0	30	0

GHANA.

DOMINION.

NOTE. CANCELLED REMAINDERS.

We quote no price in the used column of those stamps (marked instead with an asterisk) which appeared in 1961 as cancelled-to-order remainders often indistinguishable from genuinely used.

29. Dr. Kwame Nkrumah, Fish Eagle and Map of Africa.

(Photo. Harrison & Sons, Ltd.)

1957 (6 Mar.). *Independence. Wmk. Mult. Script CA. P* 14 × 14½.

No.	Type	Value		Unused s.	d.	Used
166	**29**	2d. scarlet	.. ..	0	4	*
167	,,	2½d. green ..	.. ..	0	6	*
168	,,	4d. brown	.. ..	0	8	*
169	,,	1s. 3d. deep blue..	..	1	9	*

GHANA
INDEPENDENCE
6TH MARCH,
1957.

(**30**)

1957 (6 Mar.). *Nos.* 153/5, 158, 160/4 *of Gold Coast optd. as T* **30.**

No.	Type	Value		Unused s.	d.	Used
170	**20**	½d. bis.-brn. & scar. (*shades*)		0	6	*
171	**17**	1d. deep blue (R.)	..	0	6	*
172	**18**	1½d. emerald-green	..	0	8	*
173	**21**	3d. magenta	.. ..	0	8	*
174	**23**	6d. black and orange (R.)		1	3	*
175	**24**	1s. black and orange-red		2	0	*
176	**25**	2s. brn.-olive and carmine		3	6	*
177	**26**	5s. purple and black	..	8	0	*
178	**27**	10s. black and olive-green		20	0	*

The 6d. (No. 174) exists with double overprint.

For the 2d., 2½d., and 4d. see Nos. 190/2.

31. Viking Ship.

32. Galleon.

33. M.V. *Volta River.*

(Des. W. W. Wind. Recess. E. A. Wright Bank Note Co., Philadelphia.)

1957 (27 Dec.). *Inauguration of Black Star Shipping Line. No wmk. P* 12.

No.	Type	Value		Unused s.	d.	Used s.	d.
179	**31**	2½d. emerald-green	..	1	6	2	0
		a. Imperf. between (vert. pair)		£200			
180	**32**	1s. 3d. deep blue	..	5	0	6	0
181	**33**	5s. bright purple	..	20	0	30	0

PRINTERS. The following stamps were printed in photogravure by Harrison & Sons *except where otherwise stated.*

34. Ambassador Hotel, Accra.

35. State Opening of Parliament.

36. National Monument.

37. Ghana Coat-of-Arms.

1958 (6 Mar.). *First Anniv. of Independence. Wmk. Mult. Script CA. P* 14½ × 14 (2s.) *or* 14 × 14½ (*others*).

No.	Type	Description	Unused	Used
182	**34**	½d. black, red, yellow, green and carmine	0 6	0 6
183	**35**	2½d. black, red, green and yellow	0 8	0 9
184	**36**	1s. 3d. black, red, yellow, green and blue	6 0	8 6
185	**37**	2s. red, yellow, blue, green, brown & black	8 6	11 6

38. Map showing the Independent African States.

39. Map of Africa and Flaming Torch.

(Des. R. Milton.)

1958 (15 Apr.). *First Conference of Independent Africa States, Accra. Wmk. Mult. Script CA. P* 13½ × 14½ (2½*d.*, 3*d.*) *or* 14½ × 13½ (*others*).

No.	Type	Description	Unused	Used
186	**38**	2½d. black, bistre and bright carmine-red	0 6	0 8
187	,,	3d. black, bistre, brown and bright green	0 8	0 10
188	**39**	1s. black, yellow, red and dull blue	2 0	2 6
189	,,	2s. 6d black, yellow, red and dull violet	6 0	8 6

1958 (26 May). *Nos.* 156/7, 159 *of Gold Coast optd. as T* **30.**

No.	Type	Description	Unused	Used
190	**19**	2d. chocolate	0 4	0 6
191	**28**	2½d. scarlet	1 6	1 9
192	**22**	4d. blue	4 6	7 6

Nos. 190/2 were officially issued on May 26th, 1958 although, in error, small quantities were sold at certain post offices when Nos. 170/8 appeared.

40. Eagle over Globe.

41. " Britannia " Airliner.

42. " Stratocruiser " and Albatross.

PRIME MINISTER'S VISIT, U.S.A. AND CANADA

43. Fish Eagle and Jet Aircraft. (**44**)

(Des. M. Goaman (2½d., 2s. 6d.), R. Milton (1s. 3d.), W. Wind (2s.).)

1958 (15 JULY). *Inauguration of Ghana Airways. Wmk. Mult. Script CA. P* 15×14. (2*s.* 6*d.*) *or* 14×15 (*others*).

193 **40** 2½d. black, yellow-bistre and rose-carmine .. 0 6 0 6
194 **41** 1s. 3d. blue, blk., brn.-red, yell., grn. & lgt. blue 2 0 2 6
195 **42** 2s. blk., bl., brn.-red, yell., green and pale blue .. 3 6 4 0
196 **43** 2s. 6d. black and bistre .. 5 0 6 0

1958 (18 JULY). *Prime Minister's Visit to the United States and Canada. Nos.* 166/9 *optd. with T* **44.**

197 **29** 2d. scarlet 0 5 0 5
198 ,, 2½d. green 0 6 0 7
199 ,, 4d. brown 0 10 1 0
200 ,, 1s. 3d. deep blue .. 2 6 3 0

45

(Des. W. Wind.)

1958 (24 OCT.). *United Nations Day. Wmk. Mult. Script CA. P* 14×14½.

201 **45** 2½d. purple-brown, green and black 0 5 0 6
202 ,, 1s. 3d. purple-brown, blue and black .. 2 0 2 6
203 ,, 2s. 6d. purple-brown, violet and black .. 4 0 5 0

46. Dr. Nkrumah and Lincoln Statue. Washington.

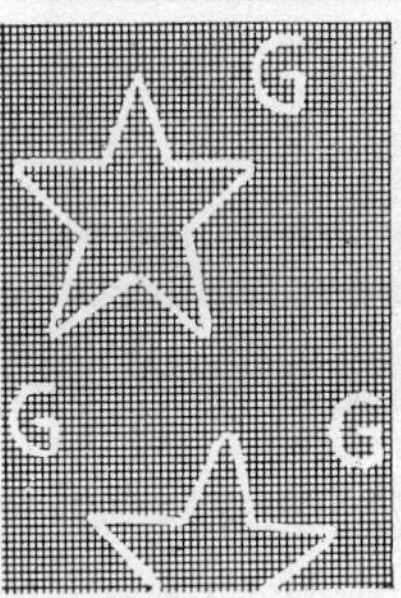

47

(Des. M. Goaman.)

1959 (12 FEB.). *150th Anniv. of Birth of Abraham Lincoln. W* **47.** *P* 14×14½.

204 **46** 2½d. pink and deep purple 0 5 0 6
205 ,, 1s. 3d. light blue & blue 1 9 2 6
206 ,, 2s. 6d. orange-yellow and deep olive-green .. 3 6 5 0

MS206*a* 102×77 mm. Nos. 204/6. Imperf. 35 0

48. Kente Cloth and Traditional Symbols.

49. Talking Drums and Elephant-horn Blower.

50. "Symbol of Greeting".

51. Map of Africa, Ghana Flag and Palms.

(Des. Mrs. T. Sutherland (½d.), M. Karoly (2½d.), K. Antubam (1s. 3d.), A. M. Medina (2s.).)

1959 (6 Mar.). *Second Anniv. of Independence.* *W* **47.** *P* 14½×14 (2*s.*) *or* 14×14½ (*others*).

207	**48**	½d. multicoloured	..	0	6	0	6
208	**49**	2½d. multicoloured	..	0	6	0	6
209	**50**	1s. 3d. multicoloured	..	2	0	2	6
210	**51**	2s. multicoloured	..	3	6	4	0

52. Globe and Flags.

(Des. Mrs. H. Potter.)

1959 (15 Apr.). *Africa Freedom Day.* *W* **47.** *P* 14½×14.

211	**52**	2½d. multicoloured	..	0	6	0	6
212	,,	8½d. multicoloured	..	1	6	1	9

53. " God's Omnipotence ".

54. Nkrumah Statue, Accra.

55. Ghana Timber.

56. Volta River.

57. Cocoa Bean.

58. "God's Omnipotence".

59. Diamond and Mine.

60. Fire-crowned Bishop.

61. Golden Spider Lily. **62.** Shell Ginger.

63. Giant Plantain Eater.

64. Tiger Orchid. **67.** Crowned Cranes.

65. Tropical African Cichlid.

65*a*. Leaping Antelope.

66. Pennant-winged Nightjar.

(Des. Mrs. T. Sutherland (½d., 3d.), Ghana Information Bureau (source of 1d. and 2d.), O. Haulkland (1½d.), M. Medina (2½d., 4d.). M. Goaman (6d., 1s. 3d., 2s. 6d.), W. Wind (11d., 1s., 2s., 5s.), W. H. Brown (10s.), M. Shamir (£1).)

1959 (5 Oct.)–**61.** *W* **47.** *P* 11½ × 12 (*½d.*), 12 × 11½ (*1d.*), 14 × 14½ (*1½d., 11d., 1s., 2s. and 5s.*), 14 × 15 (*10s.*) *or* 14½ × 14 (*others*).

(*a*) *Postage.*

213	**53**	½d. multicoloured (I) ..	0	4	0	6
213*a*	,,	½d. multicoloured (II) (29.4.61)	0	3	0	3
214	**54**	1d. multicoloured ..	0	4	0	4
215	**55**	1½d. multicoloured ..	0	5	0	4
216	**56**	2d. multicoloured ..	0	5	0	5
217	**57**	2½d. multicoloured ..	0	6	0	6
218	**58**	3d. multicoloured (I) ..	0	10	0	10
218*a*	,,	3d. multicoloured (II) (29.4.61)	0	7	0	7
219	**59**	4d. multicoloured ..	0	9	0	7
220	**60**	6d. multicoloured ..	1	0	0	10
221	**61**	11d. multicoloured ..	1	7	1	6
222	**62**	1s. multicoloured ..	1	8	1	2
223	**63**	2s. 6d. multicoloured ..	4	6	4	9
224	**64**	5s. multicoloured ..	8	0	7	9
225	**65**	10s. multicoloured ..	16	0	15	0
225*a*	**65*a***	£1 multicoloured (29.4.61)	35	0	35	0

(*b*) *Air.*

226	**66**	1s. 3d. multicoloured ..	2	3	1	10
227	**67**	2s. multicoloured ..	3	3	3	9

Nos. 213/*a* and 218/*a*. I. inscr. "GOD'S OMNIPOTENCE"; II. inscr. "GYE NYAME".

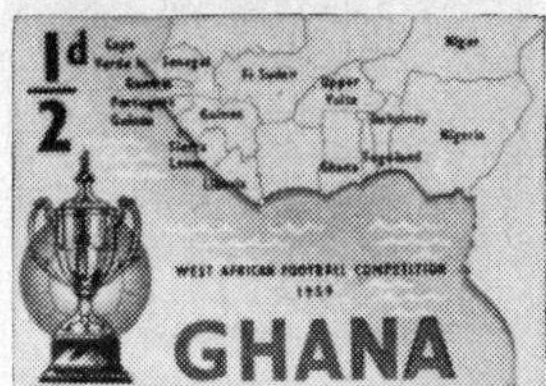

68. Gold Cup and West African Map.

69. Footballers. **72.** "Kwame Nkrumah" Gold Cup.

70. Goalkeeper saving ball.

71. Forward attacking goal.

(Des. R. Lehmann (½d., 3d.), M. & G. Shamir (1d.), W. Wind (8d.), and K. Antubam (2s. 6d.).)

1959 (15 Oct.). *West African Football Competition*, 1959. *W* **47.** *P* 14×14½ (1*d.*, 2*s.* 6*d.*) *or* 14½×14 (*others*).

228 **68** ½d. multicoloured .. 0 6 *
229 **69** 1d. multicoloured .. 0 9 *
230 **70** 3d. multicoloured .. 2 0 *
231 **71** 8d. multicoloured .. 3 0 *
232 **72** 2s. 6d. multicoloured .. 9 0 *

73. The Duke of Edinburgh and Arms of Ghana.

(Des. A. S. B. New.)

1959 (24 Nov.). *Visit of the Duke of Edinburgh to Ghana*. *W* **47.** *P* 15×14.

233 **73** 3d. black and magenta .. 0 9 *

74. Ghana Flag and Talking Drums.

75. Ghana Flag and U.N. Emblem. **76.**

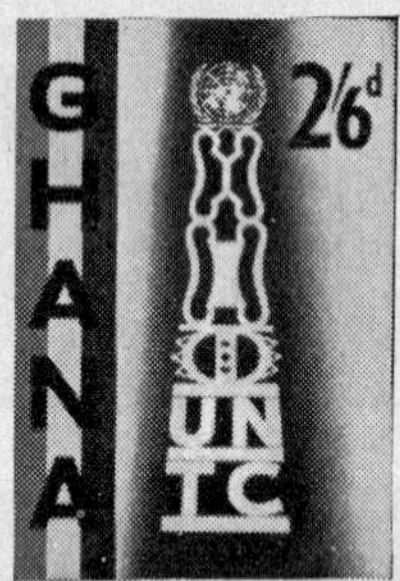

77. " Totem Pole ".

(Des. M. Medina (T 74/6), K. Antubam (T 77).)

1959 (10 Dec.). *United Nations Trusteeship Council*. *W* **47.** *P* 14½×14 (3*d.*) *or* 14×14½ (*others*.)

234 **74** 3d multicoloured .. 0 8 *
235 **75** 6d. multicoloured .. 1 0 *
236 **76** 1s. 3d. multicoloured .. 2 6 *
237 **77** 2s. 6d. multicoloured .. 4 6 *

78. Eagles in Flight. **79.** Fireworks.

80. "Third Anniversary". **81.** "Ship of State".

(Des. M. Medina (½d.), M. Goaman (3d.), W. Wind (1s. 3d., 2s.).)

1960 (6 MAR.). *Third Anniv. of Independence. W* **47**. *P* 14 × 14½.

238	**78**	½d. multicoloured	..	0 3	*
239	**79**	3d. multicoloured	..	0 8	*
240	**80**	1s. 3d. multicoloured	..	2 0	*
241	**81**	2s. multicoloured	..	4 0	*

82

83

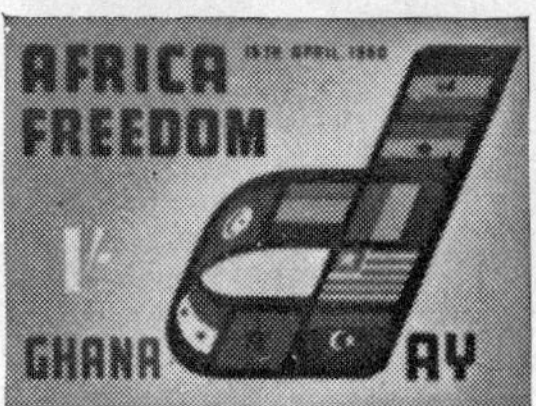

84

(Des. W. Wind.)

.960 (15 APR.). *Africa Freedom Day.* *W* **47**. *P* 14½ × 14.

42	**82**	3d. multicoloured	..	0 8	*
43	**83**	6d. multicoloured	..	1 0	*
44	**84**	1s. multicoloured	..	2 0	*

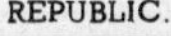

85. President Nkrumah.

86. Ghana Flag. **87.** Torch of Freedom.

88. Arms of Ghana.

(Des. M. Medina (3d., 10s.), W. Wind (1s. 3d., 2s.).)

1960 (1 JULY). *Republic Day. W* **47**. *P* 14½ × 14 (10s.) *or* 14 × 14½ (*others*).

245	**85**	3d. multicoloured	..	1 0	1 0
246	**86**	1s. 3d. multicoloured	..	3 6	4 0
247	**87**	2s. multicoloured	..	5 0	6 0
248	**88**	10s. multicoloured	..	20 0	22 6

MS248*a* 102 × 77 mm. Nos. 145/8 Imperf. 25 0

89. Olympic Torch.

90. Athlete.

(Des. A. Medina (T **89**), W. Wind (T **90**).)

1960 (15 Aug.). *Olympic Games.* *W* **47.** *P* 14 × 14½ (*T* **89**) *or* 14½ × 14 (*T* **90**).

No.	Type	Description		Unused		Used	
249	**89**	3d. multicoloured	..	0	8	0	8
250	,,	6d. multicoloured	..	2	0	2	0
251	**90**	1s. 3d. multicoloured	..	2	6	3	0
252	,,	2s. 6d. multicoloured	..	4	6	5	0

91. Pres. Nkrumah.

92. Pres. Nkrumah. **93.**

(Des. M. Goaman (3d., 6d.), W. Wind (1s. 3d.).)

1960 (21 Sept.). *Founder's Day.* *W* **47.** *P* 14½ × 14 (3*d*.) *or* 14 × 14½ (*others*).

No.	Type	Description		Unused		Used	
253	**91**	3d. multicoloured	..	0	6	0	6
254	**92**	6d. multicoloured	..	1	6	1	6
255	**93**	1s. 3d. multicoloured	..	3	0	3	6

94. U.N. Emblem and Ghana Flag. **95.** U.N. Emblem and Torch.

96. U.N. Emblem within Laurel.

(Des. M. Goaman (3d., 1s. 3d.), W. Wind (6d.).)

1960 (10 Dec.). *Human Rights Day.* *W* **47.** *P* 14 × 14½.

No.	Type	Description		Unused		Used	
256	**94**	3d. multicoloured	..	0	6	0	6
257	**95**	6d. yellow, black & blue	..	1	0	1	0
258	**96**	1s. 3d. multicoloured	..	3	0	3	0

97. Talking Drums. **98.** Map of Africa.

99. Flags and Map.

(Des. M. Goaman (T **97**), A. S. B. New (T **98**), W. Wind (T **99**).)

1961 (15 Apr.). *Africa Freedom Day.* *W* **47.** *P* 14½ × 14 (2*s*.) *or* 14 × 14½ (*others*).

No.	Type	Description		Unused		Used	
259	**97**	3d. multicoloured	..	0	6	0	6
260	**98**	6d. red, blk. and green	..	1	6	1	6
261	**99**	2s. multicoloured	..	4	6	4	6

100. Eagle on Column. **101.** " Flower ".

102. Ghana Flags. **103.** Dove with Olive Branch.

104. World Map, Chain and Olive Branch.

105. Rostrum, Conference Room.

(Des. A. S. B. New (3d.), M. Shamir (1s. 3d.), W. Wind (2s.).)

1961 (1 July). *First Anniv. of Republic.* W **47.** *P* 14 × 14½.

262	**100**	3d. multicoloured ..	0	8	0	8
263	**101**	1s. 3d. multicoloured ..	2	6	3	0
264	**102**	2s. multicoloured ..	4	6	5	0

(Des. V. Whiteley.)

1961 (1 Sept.). *Belgrade Conference.* W **47.** *P* 14 × 14½ (*3d.*) *or* 14½ × 14 (*others*).

265	**103**	3d. yellow-green	1	0	1	0
266	**104**	1s. 3d. deep blue ..	3	6	4	0
267	**105**	5s. brt. reddish purple ..	17	6	20	0

106. Pres. Nkrumah and Globe.

107. President and Kente Cloth. **108.** President in National Costume.

(Des. M. Medina (3d.), M. Goaman (1s. 3d.), Miriam Karoly (5s.).)

1961 (21 Sept.). *Founder's Day.* W **47.** *P* 14½ × 14 (*3d.*) *or* 14 × 14½ (*others*).

268	**106**	3d. multicoloured ..	1	0	1	0
269	**107**	1s. 3d. multicoloured ..	3	6	4	0
270	**108**	5s. multicoloured ..	17	6	20	0

MS270*a*. Three sheets 106 × 86 mm. (3d.) or 86 × 106 mm. (others) each with Nos. 268/70 in block of four. Imperf.

Price or three sheets un. 60s.

109. Queen Elizabeth II and African Map.

1961 (9 Nov.). *Royal Visit.* W **47.** *P* 14½ × 14.

271	**109**	3d. black, red, yell., grn., gold & brown-purple	1	0	1	0

272 **109** 1s. 3d. black, red, yellow, grn., gold & turq.-blue 3 6 4 0
273 ,, 5s. black, red, yell., grn., gold and ultramarine 17 6 22 6
MS273*a* 106 × 84 mm. No. 273 in block of four. Imperf. .. 60 0

110. Ships in Tema Harbour.

111. Aircraft and Ships at Tema.

(Des. C. Bottiau. Litho. Enschedé & Sons.)

1962 (10 Feb.). *Opening of Tema Harbour. No wmk. P* 14 × 13. *(a) Postage.*
274 **110** 3d. red, blue, yellow, green and black 1 0 1 3

(*b*) *Air.*

275 **111** 1s. 3d. orange, blue, red, yellow, green & black 5 0 7 6
276 ,, 2s. 6d. yellow, grey-blue, red, green and black .. 7 6 9 6

112. Africa and Peace Dove. **113.** Compass over Africa.

(Des. R. Hegeman. Litho. Enschedé.)

1962 (6 Mar.). *First Anniv. of Casablanca Conference. No wmk. P* 13 × 14. *(a) Postage.*
277 **112** 3d. red, blue, yellow, green and black 1 0 1 0

(*b*) *Air.*

278 **112** 1s. 3d. red, yellow, green and black 5 0 6 0
279 **112** 2s. 6d. black, red, yellow and green 7 6 8 6

(Des. R. Hegeman.)

1962 (24 Apr.). *Africa Freedom Day. W* **47.** *P* 14 × 14½.
280 **113** 3d. sepia, blue-green and reddish purple .. 0 6 0 6
281 ,, 6d. sepia, blue-green and orange-brown .. 1 0 1 0
282 ,, 1s. 3d. sepia, blue-green and red 2 6 2 6

114. Ghana Star and "Five Continents". **115.** Atomic Bomb-burst "Skull".

116. Dove of Peace.

(Des. M. Goaman (3d.), M. Shamir (6d.), W. Wind (1s. 3d.).)

1962 (21 June.) *Accra Assembly. W* **47.** *P*14 × 14½.
283 **114** 3d. black and lake-red .. 1 0 1 0
284 **115** 6d. black and scarlet .. 5 0 6 0
285 **116** 1s. 3d. turquoise .. 7 6 8 6

117. Patrice Lumumba.

(Des. A. S. B. New.)

1962 (30 June). *First Death Anniv. of Lumumba W* **47.** *P* 14½ × 14.
286 **117** 3d. blk. & orange-yellow 0 9 0
287 ,, 6d. black, green & lake 1 6 1
288 ,, 1s. 3d. black, pink and black-green 3 3 3

118. Star over Two Columns.

119. Flaming Torch.

120. Eagle trailing Flag.

Des. A. S. B. New (3d.), A. Medina (6d.), M. Goaman (1s. 3d.). Litho. Enschedé.)

1962 (1 July). *2nd Anniv. of Republic.* *P* 14 × 13½ (1s. 3d.) *or* 13½ × 14 (*others*).

289	**118**	3d.	violet, black, red, yellow and green ..	0	9	0	9
290	**119**	6d.	red, yellow, green, black and violet ..	1	6	1	6
291	**120**	1s.	3d. red, yellow, green and indigo	3	3	3	3

President Nkrumah.

122. Nkrumah Medallion.

123. Pres. Nkrumah and Ghana Star.

124. Laying " Ghana " brick.

(Litho. Enschedé.)

1962 (21 Sept.). *Founder's Day.* *P* 13 × 14½.

292	**121**	1d.	black, red, green and yellow	0	3	0	4
293	**122**	3d.	orange, black, red, green, yellow & cream	0	6	0	6
294	**123**	1s.	3d. black and brt. blue	2	3	2	6
295	**124**	2s.	black, red, olive-green and yellow	3	0	3	0

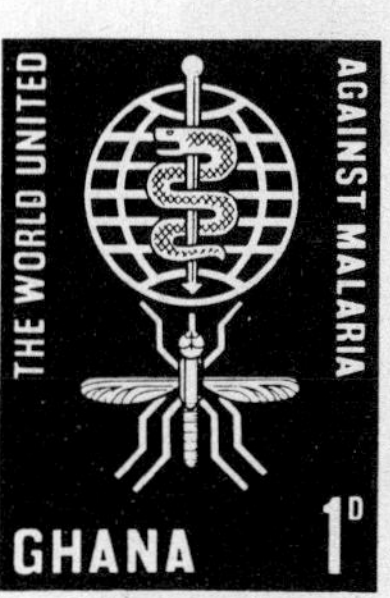

125. Campaign Emblem.

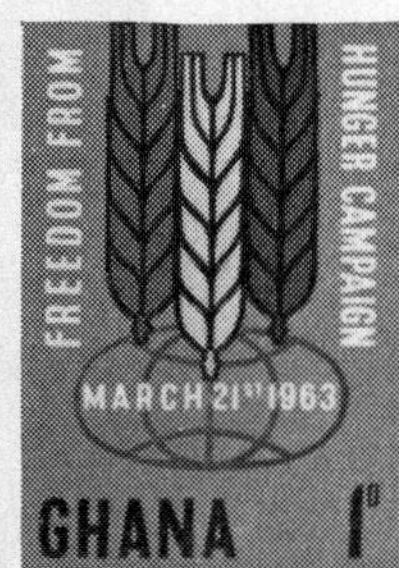

126. Campaign Emblem.

127. Emblem in Hands.

128. World Map and Emblem.

1962 (3 Dec.). *Malaria Eradication.* *W* **47.** *P* 14 × 14½.

296 **125** 1d. cerise 0 3 0 4
297 ,, 4d. yellow-green 0 10 1 0
298 ,, 6d. bistre 1 0 1 0
299 ,, 1s. 3d. bluish violet .. 2 3 2 6
MS299*a* 90 × 115 mm. Nos. 296/9. Imperf. 7 6

1963 (21 Mar.). *Freedom from Hunger.* *W* **47.** *P* 14 × 14½ (1*d.*) *or* 14½ × 14 (*others*).

300 **126** 1d. yellow, red, green, black and light blue 0 5 0 5
301 **127** 4d. sepia, yellow & orange 0 9 0 9
302 **128** 1s. 3d. ochre, black & grn. 2 6 3 0

129. Map of Africa.

130. Carved Stool.

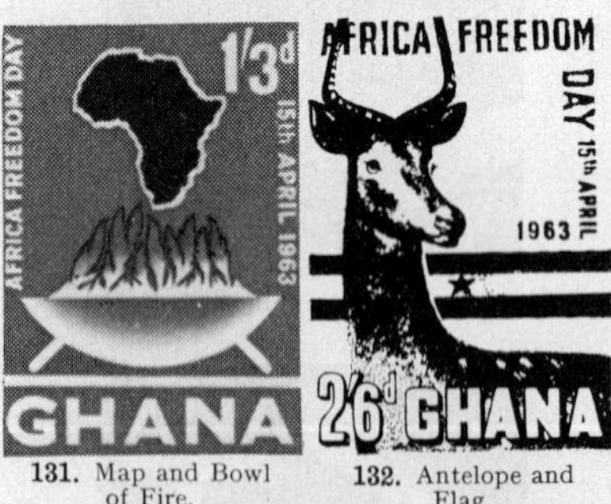

131. Map and Bowl of Fire. **132.** Antelope and Flag.

1963 (15 Apr.). *Africa Freedom Day.* *W* **47.** *P* 14½ × 14 (4*d.*) *or* 14 × 14½ (*others*).

303 **129** 1d. gold and red .. 0 3 0 3
304 **130** 4d. red, black and yellow 0 7 0 8
305 **131** 1s. 3d. black, red, yellow and green 2 3 2 6
306 **132** 2s. 6d. multicoloured .. 4 6 4 6

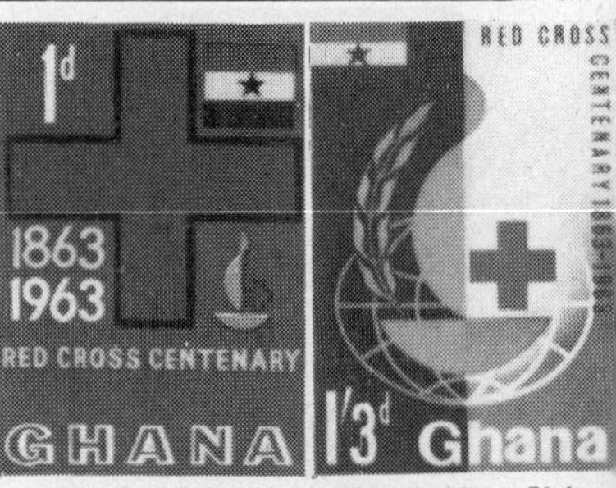

133. Red Cross. **136.** Emblem, Globe Laurel.

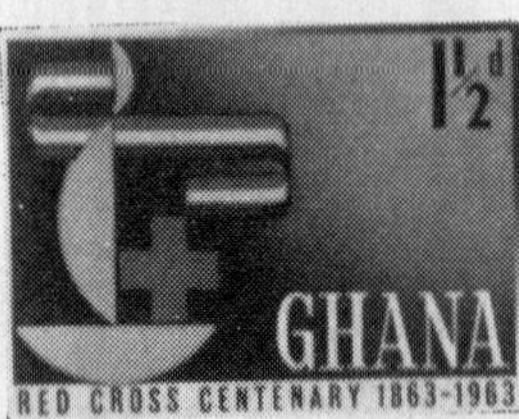

134. Centenary Emblem.

135. Nurses and Child.

(Des. R. Hegeman (4d.), M. Shamir (others).)

1963 (8 May). *Red Cross Centenary.* *W* **47.** *P* 14 × 14½ (1*d.*, 1*s.* 3*d.*), *or* 14 × 14½ (*others*)

307 **133** 1d. multicoloured .. 0 3 0 3
308 **134** 1½d. multicoloured .. 0 4 0 4
309 **135** 4d. multicoloured .. 0 8 0 10
310 **136** 1s. 3d. multicoloured .. 2 6 2 6
MS310*a* 102 × 127 mm. Nos. 307/10. Imperf. 6 0

137. "3rd Anniversary".

138. Three Ghanaian Flags.

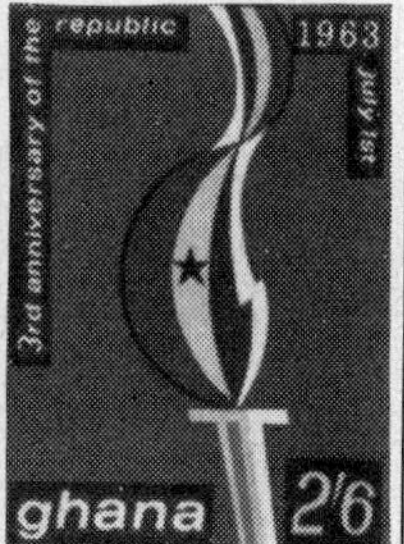

139. Map, Flag and Star. **140.** Flag and Torch.

(Des. M. Goaman (1d., 4d.), R. Hegeman (others).)

1963 (1 July). *3rd Anniv. of Republic.* *W* **47.** *P* 14½ × 14 (*horiz.*) *or* 14 × 14½ (*vert.*).

311	**137**	1d. red, yellow, green, black and sepia ..	0	3	0	3
312	**138**	4d. red, yellow, green, black and blue ..	0	8	0	10
313	**139**	1s. 3d. green, black, red and yellow	2	6	2	6
314	**140**	2s. 6d. red, yellow, green, black & dp. violet-bl.	4	0	4	0

141. Pres. Nkrumah and Ghanaian Flag. **142.**

143. Pres. Nkrumah and Fireworks.

144. Native Symbol of Wisdom.

(Des. R. Hegeman (1d., 4d.), M. Shamir (1s. 3d.), G. Rose (5s.).)

1963 (21 Sept.). *Founder's Day. W* **47.** *P* 14 × 14½ (*vert.*) *or* 14½ × 14 (*horiz.*).

315	**141**	1d. blk., red, yell. & grn.	0	3	0	4
316	**142**	4d. red, yell., grn. & blk.	0	8	1	0
317	**143**	1s. 3d. red, yellow, green and brown	2	6	2	6
318	**144**	5s. yellow & bright reddish purple	7	6	8	6

145. Rameses II, Abu Simbel. **148.** Sphinx, Sebua.

146. Rock Paintings.

147. Queen Nefertari.

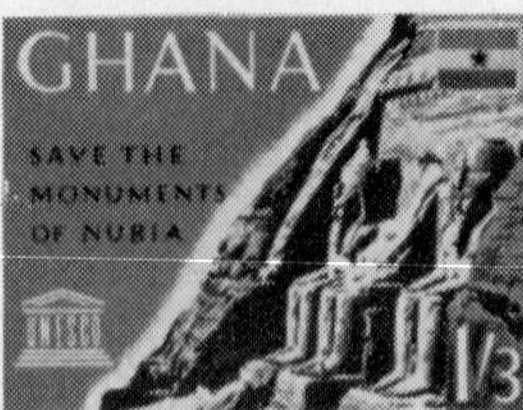

149. Rock Temple, Abu Simbel.

(Des. M. C. Farrar-Bell and R. Hegeman. Litho. (1½d., 2d.) or photo. (others). Enschedé.)

1963 (1 Nov.). *Nubian Monument Preservation. No wmk. P* 11½ × 11 (*vert.*) *or* 11 × 11½ (*horiz.*).

319	**145**	1d. multicoloured	..	0	4	0	3
320	**146**	1½d. multicoloured	..	0	6	0	6
321	**147**	2d. multicoloured	..	0	6	0	6
322	**148**	4d. multicoloured	..	0	8	1	0
323	**149**	1s. 3d. multicoloured	..	2	6	2	6

150. Steam and Diesel Locomotives.

(Des. H. L. W. Stevens.)

1963 (1 Dec.). *60th Anniv. of Ghana Railway. W* **47**. *P* 14½ × 14.

324	**150**	1d. multicoloured	..	0	6	0	6
325	"	6d. multicoloured	..	1	3	1	3
326	"	1s. 3d. multicoloured	..	2	6	2	6
327	"	2s. 6d. multicoloured	..	4	0	4	0

151. Eleanor Roosevelt and " Flame of Freedom ".

152. Eleanor Roosevelt.

153. Eleanor Roosevelt and Emblems.

(Des. R. Hegeman and F. H. Savage. Photo. Enschedé.)

1963 (10 Dec.). *15th Anniv. of Declaration of Human Rights. No wmk. P* 11 × 11½ (1s. 3*d.*) *or* 11½ × 11 (*others*).

328	**151**	1d. multicoloured	..	0	3	0	3
329	"	4d. multicoloured	..	0	8	1	0
330	**152**	6d. multicoloured	..	1	3	1	3
331	**153**	1s. 3d. multicoloured	..	2	6	2	6

No. 329 differs slightly from No. 328 in the arrangement of the trailing " flame " and of the background within the circular emblem.

154. Sun and Globe Emblem.

1964 (15 June). *International Quiet Sun Years. W* **47**. *P* 14½.

332	**154**	3d. multicoloured	..	0	6	0	6
333	,,	6d. multicoloured	..	1	0	1	0
334	,,	1s. 3d. multicoloured	..	2	6	3	0
MS334*a*		90 × 90 mm. No. 334 in block of four. Imperf.	..	12	6		

155. Harvesting Corn on State Farm.

156. Oil Refinery, Tema.

157. " Communal Labour ".

158. Procession headed by Flag.

(Des. M. Shamir. Photo. Govt. Ptg. Press, Tel Aviv.)

1964 (1 July). *4th Anniv. of Republic. P* 13 × 14.

335 **155** 3d. olive, brown and yellow-olive 0 8 0 8
336 **156** 6d. bluish green, brown and turquoise-green .. 1 0 1 0
337 **157** 1s. 3d. brown-red, brown and salmon-red .. 2 3 2 3
338 **158** 5s. red, green, brown and light violet-blue .. 7 6 9 0
MS338*a* 126 × 100 mm. Nos. 335/8. Imperf. 15 0

159. Globe and Dove.

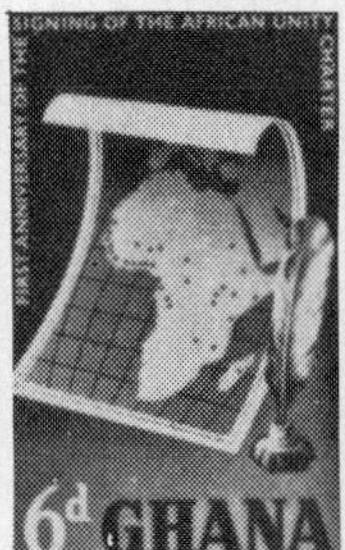

160. Map of Africa and Quill Pen. **162.** Planting Flower.

161. Hitched Rope on Map of Africa.

Des. M. Shamir. Litho. Lewin-Epstein, Ltd., Bat Yam, Israel.)

964 (15 July). *1st Anniv. of African Unity Charter. P* 14.

39 **159** 3d. multicoloured .. 0 8 0 8
40 **160** 6d. dp. bronze-grn. & red 1 0 1 0
41 **161** 1s. 3d. multicoloured .. 2 3 2 3
42 **162** 5s. multicoloured .. 7 6 9 0

163. Pres. Nkrumah and Hibiscus Flowers.

1964 (21 Sept.). *Founder's Day. W* **47**. *P* 14 × 14½.

343 **163** 3d. sepia, red, deep green and light blue .. 0 8 0 8
344 ,, 6d. sepia, red, deep green and yellow 1 0 1 0
345 ,, 1s. 3d. sepia, red, deep green and grey .. 2 3 2 3
346 ,, 2s. 6d. sepia, red, deep green and lt. emerald 4 3 5 0

164. Hurdling.

165. Running.

166. Boxing.

167. Long-jumping.

168. Football.

169. Athlete holding Olympic Torch.

170. Olympic " Rings " and Flags.

1964 (25 Oct.). *Olympic Games, Tokio.* *W* **47.** *P* 14½ × 14 (*horiz.*) *or* 14 × 14½ (*vert.*).

No.	Type	Description	Unused		Used	
347	**164**	1d. multicoloured ..	0	4	0	4
348	**165**	2½d. multicoloured ..	0	7	0	7
349	**166**	3d. multicoloured ..	0	8	0	8
350	**167**	4d. multicoloured ..	0	9	0	11
351	**168**	6d. multicoloured ..	1	0	1	3
352	**169**	1s. 3d. multicoloured ..	2	3	2	3
353	**170**	5s. multicoloured ..	7	6	9	0
MS353*a*		128 × 102 mm. Nos. 351/3 Imperf.	25	0		

171. G. Washington Carver (botanist) and Plant.

172. Albert Einstein (scientist) and Atomic Symbol.

(Des. M. Shamir.)

1964 (7 Dec.). *UNESCO Week.* *W* **47.** *P* 14½.

No.	Type	Description	Unused		Used	
354	**171**	6d. deep blue and green ..	1	0	1	2
355	**172**	1s. 3d. reddish purple and greenish blue ..	2	3	2	9
356	**171**	5s. sepia and orange-red	8	0	9	0
MS356*a*		127½ × 77 mm. Nos. 354/6 Imperf.	15	0		

173. African Elephant.

174. Secretary Bird.

175. Purple Wreath.

176. Grey Parrot.

177. Mousebird.

178. African Tulip Tree.

179. Amethyst Starling.

180. Hippopotamus.

(Photo. Enschedé.)

1964 (DEC.). *P* 11½×11 (*vert.*) *or* 11×11½ (*horiz.*).

357	**173**	1d. multicoloured ..	0 4	0 4
358	**174**	1½d. multicoloured ..	0 5	0 5
359	**175**	2½d. multicoloured ..	0 6	0 6
360	**176**	3d. multicoloured ..	0 8	0 9
361	**177**	4d. multicoloured ..	0 9	0 11
362	**178**	6d. multicoloured ..	1 0	1 3
363	**179**	1s. 3d. multicoloured ..	2 3	2 9
364	**180**	2s. 6d. multicoloured ..	4 3	5 0

MS364*a* 150×86 mm. Nos. 357/8 and 150×110 mm. Nos. 360/4. Both imperf.
Price per two sheets un. 25*s.*

181. I.C.Y. Emblem.

(Litho. Enschedé.)

1965 (22 FEB.). *International Co-operation Year. P* 14×12½.

365	**181**	1d. multicoloured ..	0 4	0 5
366	,,	4d. multicoloured ..	0 9	0 11
367	,,	6d. multicoloured ..	1 0	1 2
368	,,	1s. 3d. multicoloured ..	2 3	2 9

MS368*a* 100×100 mm. No. 368 in block of four. Imperf. .. 15 0

182. I.T.U. Emblem and Symbols.

(Litho. Enschedé.)

1965 (12 APR.). *I.T.U. Centenary. P* 13½.

369	**182**	1d. black, red, green and olive-yellow	0 4	0 5
370	,,	6d. black, red, green and chestnut	1 0	1 2
371	,,	1s. 3d. black, red, green and light blue ..	2 3	2 9
372	,,	5s. black, red, green and bistre	8 0	9 0

MS372*a* 132×115 mm. Nos. 369/72. Imperf. 15 0

183. Lincoln's Home.

184. Lincoln's Inaugural Address.

185. Abraham Lincoln.

186. Adaption of U.S. 90 c. Lincoln Stamp of 1869.

(Des. M. C. Farrar Bell (6d.), A. S. B. New (1s. 3d., 5s.), R. Hegeman (2s.).)

1965 (17 MAY). *Death Centenary of Abraham Lincoln. W* **47.** *P* 12½.

373	**183**	6d. red-brown, greenish yellow, red and green	1	0	1	2
374	**184**	1s. 3d. blk., red and blue	2	3	2	9
375	**185**	2s. black, orange-brown and greenish yellow..	3	3	4	6
376	**186**	5s. black and red ..	8	0	9	0

MS376*a* 115 × 115 mm. Nos. 373/6 Imperf. 20 0

(New currency. 100 pesawas = 1 cedi.)

187. Obverse (Pres. Nkrumah) and Reverse of 5 p. Coin.

(Photo. Enschedé).

1965 (19 JULY). *Introduction of Decimal Currency. T* **187** *and similar horiz. designs. Multicoloured. P* 11 × 13 (5 *p.*, 10 *p.*), 13 × 12½ (25 *p.*) *or* 13½ × 14 (50 *p.*).

377	5 p.	Type **187**	0	11	1	0
378	10 p.	As Type **187**	1	6	1	10
379	25 p.	Size 63 × 39 mm. ..	3	6	4	0
380	50 p.	Size 71 × 43½ mm. ..	6	9	7	6

The coins in Nos. 378/80 are all circular and express the same denominations as on the stamps.

₵2·40

Ghana New Currency
19th July, 1965.

(188)

1965 (19 JULY). *Stamps of* 1959–61 *surch. as T* **188** *diagonally upwards* (D) *or horizontally,* (H). *Multicoloured.* (*a*) *Postage.*

381	**26**	1 p. on 1d. (R.) (D) ..	0	3	0	5
382	**28**	2 p. on 2d. (B.) (H) ..	0	5	0	7
383	**30**	3 p. on 3d. (Br.) (H) ..	3	0	4	6
384	**31**	4 p. on 4d. (B.) (H) ..	0	7	0	9
385	**32**	6 p. on 6d. (Bk.) (H) ..	0	10	1	0
386	**33**	11 p. on 11d. (White) (D)	1	4	1	8
387	**34**	12 p. on 1s. (B.) (D) ..	1	9	2	3
388	**35**	30 p. on 2s. 6d. (B.) (H) ..	4	6	5	6
389	**36**	60 p. on 5s. (B.) (D) ..	6	9	7	6
390	**37**	₵1.20 on 10s. (B.) (D) ..	13	3	16	0
391	**38**	₵2.40 on £1 (B.) (D) ..	25	0	30	0
		(*b*) *Air.*				
392	**39**	15 p. on 1s. 3d. (White) (H)	1	9	2	3
393	**40**	24 p. on 2s. (G.) (D) ..	2	0	2	9

On the diagonal surcharges the values are horiz.

The 30 p. was not released in Ghana until 30th July and the 3 p. sometime later.

189. " OAU " and Flag.

190. "OAU", Heads and Flag.

191. O.A.U. Emblem and Flag.

(T **189/91.** *Illustrations reduced: actual size* 60 × 30 *mm.*)

192. African Map and Flag.

193. "Sunburst" and Flag.

194. "OAU" on Map, and Flag.

1965 (21 Oct.). *O.A.U. Summit Conference, Accra. W* **47.** *P* 14 (*T* **189/91**) *or* 14½ × 14 (*others*).

394	**189**	1 p. multicoloured	..	0	3	0	5
395	**190**	2 p. multicoloured	..	0	4	0	7
396	**191**	5 p. multicoloured	..	0	9	1	0
397	**192**	6 p. multicoloured	..	0	10	1	2
398	**193**	15 p. multicoloured	..	1	9	2	3
399	**194**	24 p. multicoloured	..	2	9	3	6

195. Goalkeeper saving Ball.

196. Player with Ball.

197. Player, Ball and Soccer Cup.

(Photo. Enschedé.)

1965 (15 Nov.). *African Soccer Cup Competition. P* 13 × 14 (15 *p.*) *or* 14 × 13 (*others*).

400	**195**	6 p. multicoloured	..	1	0	1	5
401	**196**	15 p. multicoloured	..	2	3	2	9
402	**197**	24 p. multicoloured	..	3	3	4	6

198. Pres. Kennedy and Grave Memorial.

199. Pres. Kennedy and Eternal Flame.

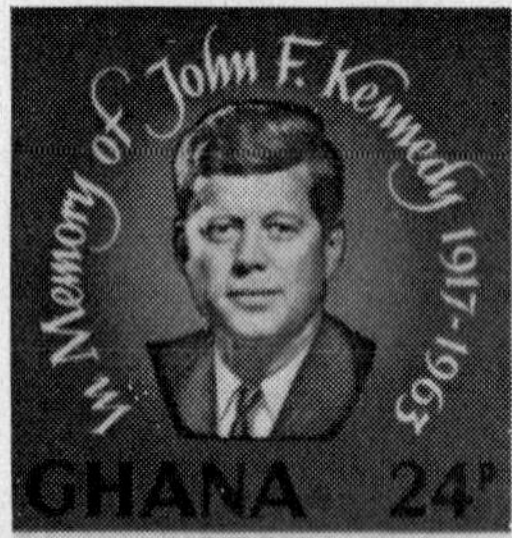

200. Pres. Kennedy and Memorial Inscription.

201. President Kennedy.

1965 (15 Dec.). *2nd Anniv. of President Kennedy's Death.* *W* **47.** *P* 12½.

403	**198**	6 p. multicoloured ..	0	10	1	2
404	**199**	15 p. violet, red & green	1	9	2	3
405	**200**	24 p. black & reddish vio.	2	9	3	6
406	**201**	30 p. dull purple & black	3	6	4	6

202. Section of Dam and Generators.

203. Dam and Lake Volta.

204. Word " GHANA " as Dam.

205. " Fertility ".

(Photo. Enschedé.)

1966 (22 Jan.). *Volta River Project.* *P* 11×11½.

408	**202**	6 p. multicoloured ..	0	10	1	2
409	**203**	15 p. multicoloured ..	1	9	2	3
410	**204**	24 p. multicoloured ..	2	9	3	6
411	**205**	30 p. black and new blue	3	6	4	6

1966 (7 Feb.). " *Black Stars* " *Victory in African Soccer Cup Competition. Nos.* 400/2 *optd.* " Black Stars Retain African Cup 21st Nov., 1965 ".

412	**195**	6 p. multicoloured ..	0	10	1	2
413	**196**	15 p. multicoloured ..	1	9	2	3
414	**197**	24 p. multicoloured ..	2	9	3	6

POSTAGE DUE STAMPS.

GHANA

(D 2)

D 3

1958 (25 June). *Postage Due stamps of Gold Coast. Chalk-surfaced paper. Optd. with Type* D **2**, *in red.*

D 9	D **1**	1d. black	0	6	0	8
D10	,,	2d. black	0	6	0	8
D11	,,	3d. black	0	9	1	0
D12	,,	6d. black	1	3	1	6
D13	,,	1s. black	3	0	3	6

(Typo. De La Rue & Co.)

1958 (1 Dec.). *Type* D **3**. *Chalk-surfaced paper. Wmk. Mult. Script CA.* P 14.

D14	D **3**	1d. carmine	0 4	0 6
D15	,,	2d. green	0 6	0 8
D16	,,	3d. orange	0 8	1 0
D17	,,	6d. ultramarine	1 0	1 6
D18	,,	1s. reddish violet	1 9	2 6

3p.
Ghana New Currency
19th July. 1965.

(D **4**)

1965. *Nos.* D14/8 *surch. as Type* D **4** *diagonally upwards* (D) *or horizontally* (H).

D19	D **3**	1 p. on 1d. (D)	0 3	0 5
D20	,,	2 p. on 2d. (B.) (H)	0 4	0 6
D21	,,	3 p. on 3d. (B.) (H)	0 6	0 9
D22	,,	6 p. on 6d. (R.) (H)	0 10	1 0
D23	,,	12 p. on 1s. (B.) (D)	1 9	2 3

On the diagonal surcharges the figures of value are horizontal.

GIBRALTAR.

For GREAT BRITAIN stamps used in Gibraltar, see page 58.

GIBRALTAR

(1)

1886 (1 Jan.). *Contemporary types of Bermuda optd. with T* **1** *by De La Rue & Co. Wmk. Crown CA.* P 14.

1	**9**	½d. dull green	7 6	8 6
2	**1**	1d. rose-red	25 0	11 6
3	**2**	2d. purple-brown	85 0	45 0
4	**11**	2½d. ultramarine	95 0	7 6
		a. Optd. in blue-black	£12	75 0
5	**10**	4d. orange-red	£8	£5
6	**4**	6d. deep lilac	£16	£10
7	**5**	1s. yellow-brown	£30	£30

PRINTER. All Gibraltar stamps to No. 109 were typographed by De La Rue & Co., Ltd.

2

3

4

5

1886 (Dec.). *Wmk. Crown CA.* P 14.

8	**2**	½d. dull green	5 0	6 0
9	**3**	1d. rose	9 6	5 0
10	**4**	2d. brown-purple	27 6	30 0
11	**5**	2½d. blue	22 6	7 6
12	**4**	4d. orange-brown	55 0	67 6
13	,,	6d. lilac	£6	£6
14	,,	1s. bistre	£15	£12

See also Nos. 39 to 45.

5 CENTIMOS

(**6**)

1889 (July). *Surcharged as T* **6**.

15	**2**	5 c. on ½d. green	6 0	8 6
16	**3**	10 c. on 1d. rose	7 0	9 6
17	**4**	25 c. on 2d. brown-purple	7 6	9 6
		a. Small "I" in "CENTIMOS"	£6	£6
		b. Broken "N" in "CENTIMOS"	£6	£6
18	**5**	25 c. on 2½d. bright blue	10 6	7 6
		a. Small "I" in "CENTIMOS"	£8	£6
		b. Broken "N" in "CENTIMOS"	£8	£6
19	**4**	40 c. on 4d. orange-brown	25 0	37 6
20	,,	50 c. on 6d. bright lilac	25 0	37 6
		a. Bisect diag. (25 c.) (on cover)		
21	,,	75 c. on 1s. bistre	50 0	50 0

The small "i" is No. 32 and the broken "N" No. 59 on the pane. Two varieties of the figure "5" of the 5 c., 25 c., 50 c., and 75 c. may also be found.

7

1889 (Nov.). *T* **7**. *Issue in Spanish currency. Wmk. Crown CA.* P 14.

26	5 c. green	1 3	1 3
27	10 c. carmine	1 6	2 0
	a. Bisect diag. (5 c.) (on cover)	†	£50
28	25 c. ultramarine	3 6	0 8
29	25 c. deep ultramarine	12 6	1 0
30	40 c. orange-brown	3 0	5 0
	a. Bisect diag. (20 c.) (on cover)	†	£60
31	50 c. bright lilac	4 0	9 6
32	75 c. olive-green	22 6	25 0
33	1 p. bistre	25 0	25 0
34	5 p. slate-grey	30 0	40 0
	Error. value omitted.		
35	No value, carmine	£575	

1895. *Wmk. Crown CA.* P 14.

35*a*	**7**	20 c. olive-green	6 0	12 6
36	,,	20 c. olive-green & brown	5 0	12 6
37	,,	1 p. bistre & ultramarine	5 0	7 6
38	,,	2 p. black and carmine	10 0	12 6

1898. *Reissue in English currency. Wmk. Crown CA.* P 14.

39	**2**	½d. grey-green	1 3	1 6
40	**3**	1d. carmine	2 0	0 6
41	**4**	2d. brown-purple & ultram.	5 0	10 0
42	**5**	2½d. bright ultramarine	6 0	4 0
43	**4**	4d. orange-brown & green	9 0	12 6
44	,,	6d. violet and red	10 0	12 6
45	,,	1s. bistre and carmine	12 6	17 6

No. 39 is greyer than No. 8, No. 40 brighter and deeper than No. 9, and No. 42 much brighter than No. 11.

8

9

1903. *Wmk. Crown CA. P* 14.
46 **8** ½d. grey-green and green .. 4 6 4 6
47 ,, 1d. dull purple/*red* 5 0 1 6
48 ,, 2d. grey-green and carmine 8 0 10 6
49 ,, 2½d. dull purple & black/*blue* 7 0 6 6
50 ,, 6d. dull purple and violet .. 15 0 18 0
51 ,, 1s. black and carmine .. 15 0 18 0
52 **9** 2s. green and blue £5 £6
53 ,, 4s. dull purple and green .. £5 £8
54 ,, 8s. dull purple & black/*blue* £7 £8
55 ,, £1 dull purple & black/*red* £75 £85

1904–7. *Wmk. Mult. Crown CA. P* 14.
56 **8** ½d. dull & bright green OC 3 0 1 0
57 ,, 1d. dull purple/*red*, OC .. 1 6 1 0
a. Bisected (½d.) (on cover) .. † £45
58 ,, 2d. grey-grn. & carm., OC 6 0 6 0
59 ,, 2½d. pur. & blk./*blue*, C ('07) 35 0 40 0
60 ,, 6d. d. pur. & vio., OC ('06) 6 6 9 0
61 ,, 1s. black & carm., OC ('05) 10 0 12 6
62 **9** 2s. green & blue, OC (1905) 55 0 55 0
63 ,, 4s. deep purple & green, C £10 £12
64 ,, £1 dp. pur. & black/*red*, C £75 £85

1907–11. *Wmk. Mult. Crown CA. P* 14.
66 **8** ½d. blue-green, O 1 0 0 10
67 ,, 1d. carmine, O 1 3 0 3
68 ,, 2d. greyish slate, O (1910) 5 0 7 6
69 ,, 2½d. ultramarine, O .. 5 0 4 0
70 ,, 6d. dull & bright purple, C £15 £25
71 ,, 1s. black/*green*, C (1910) .. 18 6 20 0
72 **9** 2s. purple & bright blue/*blue*, C (1910) 80 0 90 0
73 ,, 4s. black & carm., C (1910) 90 0 £5
74 ,, 8s. purple & grn., C (1911) £32 £35

10

11

1912-24. *T* **10** (*to* 1s.) *and* **11.** *Wmk. Mult. Crown CA. P.* 14.
76 ½d. blue-green, O 0 6 0 4
76*a* ½d. yellow-green, O (1917) .. 0 6 0 8
77 1d. carmine-red, O 1 0 1 0
77*a* 1d. scarlet, O (1916) .. 3 0 0 9
78 2d. greyish slate, O 4 0 3 0
79 2½d. deep bright blue, O .. 5 0 5 0
79*a* 2½d. pale ultramarine, O .. 5 0 6 0
80 6d. dull purple and mauve, C 4 0 7 6
81 1s. black/*green*, OC 8 6 10 0
a. On blue-green, olive back (1919) 10 0 15 0
b. On emerald surface (1923) .. 10 0 25 0
c. On emerald back (1924) C 10 0 25 0
82 2s. dull purple & blue/*blue*, C 10 0 10 0
83 4s. black and carmine, C .. 30 0 40 0
84 8s. dull purple and green, C 60 0 80 0
85 £1 dull purple & black/*red*, C £12 £15

WAR TAX
(12)

1918 (15 April). *T* **10** *optd. locally with T* **12.**
86 ½d. green 0 4 0 8

Two printings of this overprint exist, the second being in slightly heavier type.

3 PENCE (I) THREE PENCE (II)

1921-27. *T* **10** *and* **11.** *Wmk. Mult. Script CA. P* 14.
89 ½d. green, O (1927) .. 0 4 0 3
90 1d. carmine-red, O (1921) 1 3 0 6
91 1½d. chestnut, O (1922) .. 3 6 1 0
92 1½d. pale chestnut, O (1924) 3 0 0 9
93 2d. grey, O (1921) 1 9 2 6
94 2½d. bright blue, O (1921) .. 7 6 12 6
95 3d. bright blue, O (I) (1921) 3 6 3 0
96 3d. ultramarine, O (I) .. 4 0 5 0
97 6d. dull pur. & mve., C ('23) 6 0 8 0
97*a* 6d. bright pur. & magenta, C (1926) 6 0 9 0
98 1s. black/*emerald*, C (1924) 12 6 15 0
99 2s. grey-purple & blue/*blue*, C (1924) 20 0 30 0
99*a* 2s. reddish purple & blue/*blue*, C (1925) 10 0 20 0
100 4s. blk. & carmine, C (1924) 70 0 90 0
101 8s. dull pur. & grn., C (1924) £24 £26

1925-32. *T* **10** (1s.) *and* **11.** *New values, etc. Wmk. Mult. Script CA. P* 14.
102 1s. sage-grn. & blk., C (1929) 15 0 20 0
102*a* 1s. olive & black, C (1932) 15 0 20 0
103 2s. red-brn. & blk., C (1929) 22 6 27 6
104 2s. 6d. green & black, C .. 25 0 32 6
105 5s. carmine and black, C .. 42 6 50 0
106 10s. deep ultram. & black, C 65 0 75 0
107 £1 red-orange & black, C (1927) £18 £22
a. Yellow and black, C £100
b. Pale orange and black, C .. £120
108 £5 violet and black, C .. £185 £200

1930. *T* **10** *inscribed* "THREE PENCE" *Wmk. Mult. Script CA. P* 14.
109 3d. ultramarine (II) .. 10 0 6 0

13. The Rock of Gibraltar.

(Des. Capt. H. St. C. Garrood. Recess. De La Rue.)

1931–33. *T* **13** *(and similar type). Wmk. Mult. Script CA.* A. *P* 14. B. 13½×14.

		A.		B.	
110	1d. scar. (1.7.31)	1 3	1 9	7 6	2 0
111	1½d. red-brown (1.7.31) ..	2 6	1 9	4 6	1 9
112	2d. pale grey ('32)	3 6	2 0	7 6	2 0
113	3d. blue (1.6.33)	7 6	10 0	15 0	17 6

Figures of value take the place of both corner ornaments at the base of the 2d. and 3d.

1935 (6 May). *Silver Jubilee. As Nos.* 91/4 *of Antigua, but ptd. by B. W. & Co. P* 11×12.

114	2d. ultramarine & grey-black	1 6	1 9
	a. Extra flagstaff	60 0	
115	3d. brown and deep blue ..	3 0	4 6
	a. Extra flagstaff	£20	
116	6d. green and indigo ..	5 0	6 6
	a. Extra flagstaff	£10	
117	1s. slate and purple ..	8 6	8 6
	a. Extra flagstaff	£14	

For illustration of "extra flagstaff" variety see Bechuanaland.

1937 (12 May). *Coronation. As Nos.* 13/5 *of Aden, but ptd. by B. W. & Co. P* 11×11½.

118	½d. green	0 3	0 2
119	2d. grey-black	1 0	1 0
120	3d. blue	1 6	1 9

14. King George VI

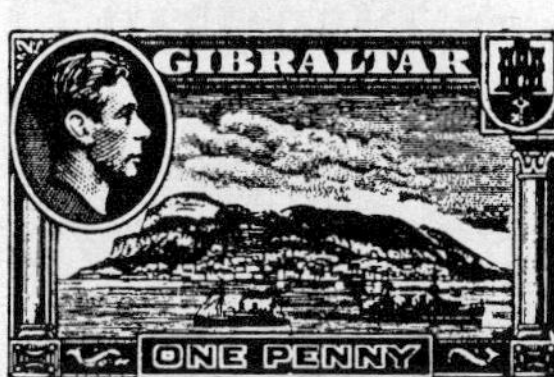

15. Rock of Gibraltar.

16. The Rock (North Side).

17. Europa Point.

18. Moorish Castle.

19. Southport Gate.

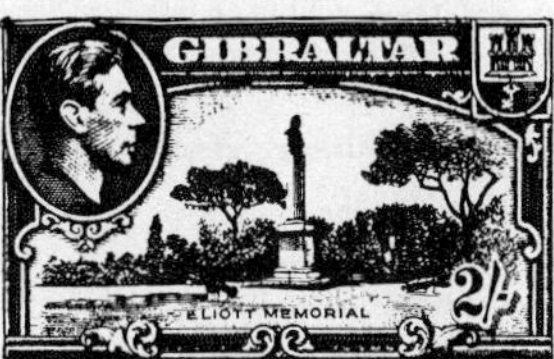

20. Eliott Memorial.

21. Government House.

22. Catalan Bay.

(Recess. De La Rue & Co.)

1938–51. *Wmk. Mult. Script CA.*

121	**14**	½d. deep grn. (*p.* 13½×14)	0 3	0 3
122	**15**	1d. yellow-brown (*p.* 14)	1 3	1 9
		a. Perf. 13½	1 0	1 3
		ab. Perf. 13½. Wmk. sideways	1 0	2 6
		b. Perf. 13. Wmk. sideways. *Red-brown* ('42) ..	0 6	0 8
		c. Perf. 13. Wmk. sideways. *Deep brown* ('44) ..	2 6	3 6
		d. Perf. 13. *Red-brown* ('49) ..	0 8	1 6
123	**15**	1½d. carmine (*p.* 14) ..	1 6	2 0
		a. Perf. 13½	£8	42 6
123*b*	,,	1½d. slate-vio. (*p.* 13) ('43)	0 8	1 0

No.	Type	Description	s.	d.	s.	d.
124	**16**	2d. grey (*p.* 14)	10	0	2	6
		a. Perf. 13½	2	0	2	0
		ab. Perf. 13½. Wmk. sideways	£45		25	0
		b. Perf. 13. Wmk. sideways ('42)	1	0	1	3
124*c*	,,	2d. carmine (*p.* 13) (*wmk. sideways*) ('44) ..	0	8	1	0
125	**17**	3d. light blue (*p.* 13½) ..	1	6	1	0
		a. Perf. 14	65	0	25	0
		b. Perf. 13 ('42)	1	3	0	8
		ba. Greenish blue (Feb. '51) ..	1	3	0	10
125*c*	,,	5d. red-orge. (*p.* 13) ('47)	1	6	3	0
126	**18**	6d. carmine & grey-violet (*p.* 13½)	15	0	6	6
		a. Perf. 14	75	0	10	0
		b. Perf. 13 ('42)	2	6	1	3
		c. Perf. 13. *Scarlet and grey-violet* ('45)	5	0	3	6
127	**19**	1s. black & green (*p.* 14)	25	0	20	0
		a. Perf. 13½	30	0	10	0
		b. Perf. 13 ('42)	3	0	3	6
128	**20**	2s. black & brn. (*p.* 14) ..	60	0	60	0
		a. Perf. 13½	60	0	35	0
		b. Perf. 13 ('42)	6	0	7	6
129	**21**	5s. black & carm. (*p.* 14)	90	0	90	0
		a. Perf. 13½	42	6	30	0
		b. Perf. 13 ('44)	17	6	15	0
130	**22**	10s. black & blue (*p.* 14) ..	60	0	65	0
		a. Perf. 13 ('43)	25	0	30	0
131	**14**	£1 orange (*p.* 13½ × 14) ..	60	0	70	0

1946 (12 Oct.). *Victory. As Nos.* 28/9 *of Aden.*

No.	Description	s.	d.	s.	d.
132	½d. green	0	4	0	6
133	3d. ultramarine	0	10	1	0

1948 (1 Dec.). *Royal Silver Wedding. As Nos.* 30/1 *of Aden.*

No.	Description	s.	d.	s.	d.
134	½d. green	0	6	0	6
135	£1 brown-orange	40	0	45	0

1949 (10 Oct.). *75th Anniv. of Universal Postal Union. As Nos.* 114/7 *of Antigua.*

No.	Description	s.	d.	s.	d.
136	2d. carmine	2	0	2	6
137	3d. deep blue	2	6	2	6
138	6d. purple	4	0	5	0
139	1s. blue-green	7	6	8	6

NEW
CONSTITUTION
1950

(**23**)

1950 (1 Aug.). *Inauguration of Legislative Council. Nos.* 124*c*, 125*b*, 126*b and* 127*b optd. as T* **23**.

No.	Type	Description	s.	d.	s.	d.
140	**16**	2d. carmine	1	6	1	6
141	**17**	3d. light blue	2	0	2	6
142	**18**	6d. carmine & grey-violet	3	6	4	6
143	**19**	1s. black and green (R.) ..	5	0	6	6

The 6d. exists with overprint double, but on stamps from the lower part of the sheet the two impressions are almost co-incident.

1953 (2 June). *Coronation. As No.* 47 *of Aden.*

No.	Description	s.	d.	s.	d.
144	½d. black and bronze-green ..	0	9	0	8

24. Cargo and Passenger Wharves.

25. South View from Straits.

26. Tunny-Fishing Industry.

27. Southport Gate.

28. Sailing in the Bay.

29. Ocean-going Liner.

30. Coaling Wharf.

31. Airport.

32. Europa Point.

33. Straits from Buena Vista.

34. Rosia Bay and Straits.

35. Main Entrance, Government House.

36. Tower of Homage, Moorish Castle.

37. Arms of Gibraltar.

(Recess. (except £1, centre litho.) De La Rue.)

1953 (19 Oct.). *Wmk. Mult. Script CA. P* 13.

			s.	d.	s.	d.
145	**24**	½d. indigo and grey-green	0	3	0	4
146	**25**	1d. bluish green (*shades*)	0	5	0	3
147	**26**	1½d. black	0	6	0	6
148	**27**	2d. dp. olive-brn. (*shades*)	0	8	0	9
149	**28**	2½d. carmine (*shades*) ..	0	8	0	9
150	**29**	3d. light blue (*shades*) ..	0	8	0	6
151	**30**	4d. ultramarine (*shades*) ..	1	0	1	3
152	**31**	5d. maroon (*shades*) ..	1	0	1	6
153	**32**	6d. blk. & p. blue (*shades*)	1	3	1	0
154	**33**	1s. pale blue & red-brown (*shades*)	2	0	1	9
155	**34**	2s. orange and reddish violet (*shades*) ..	5	0	4	6
156	**35**	5s. deep brown	10	0	9	6
157	**36**	10s. reddish brn. & ultram.	22	6	22	6
158	**37**	£1 scarlet & orge.-yellow	40	0	40	0

1954 (10 May). *Royal Visit. As No.* 150 *but inscr.* " ROYAL VISIT 1954 " *at top.*

159	3d. greenish blue	1	0	1	3

38. Gibraltar Candytuft.

41. The Keys.

39. Moorish Castle.

40. St. George's Hall.

42. The Rock by Moonlight.

43. Catalan Bay.

44. Map of Gibraltar.

45. Air Terminal.

46. American War Memorial.

50. Rock Lily. (*Narcissus niveus*).

47. Rock Ape.

48. Barbary Partridge.

49. Blue Rock Thrush.

51. Rock and Badge of Gibraltar Regiment

Des. J. Celecia (½d., 2d., 2½d., 2s., 10s.), N. A. Langdon (1d., 3d., 6d., 7d., 9d., 1s.), M. Bonilla (4d.), L. J. Gomez (5s.), Sgt. T. A. Griffiths (£1). Recess (£1) or photo. (others) De La Rue.)

1960 (29 Oct.). *W* w. **12**. *P* 14 (£1) *or* 13 (*others*.

160	**38**	½d. brt. pur. & emer.-grn.	0	2	0	
161	**39**	1d. black and yell.-green	0	3	0	
162	**40**	2d. indigo & orange-brn.	0	4	0	
163	**41**	2½d. black and blue (*shades*)	0	5	0	
164	**42**	3d. dp. blue & red-orange	0	6	0	
165	**43**	4d. dp. red-brn. & turq.	0	7	0	
166	**44**	6d. sepia and emerald ..	0	10	0	
167	**45**	7d. indigo & carmine-red	0	11	0	
168	**46**	9d. grey-blue & greenish bl.	1	1	1	
169	**47**	1s. sepia and bluish green	1	5	1	
170	**48**	2s. chocolate & ultram...	2	9	2	
171	**49**	5s. turq.-blue & olive-brn.	6	9	6	
172	**50**	10s. yellow and blue ..	13	3	12	
173	**51**	£1 black & brown-orange	25	0	25	

1963 (4 JUNE). *Freedom from Hunger. As No. 63 of Aden.*
174 9d. sepia 2 0 2 3

1963 (2 SEPT.). *Red Cross Centenary. As Nos. 147/8 of Antigua.*
175 1d. red and black 0 9 1 0
176 9d. red and blue 2 6 2 9

1964 (23 APRIL). *400th Anniv. of Birth of William Shakespeare. As No. 164 of Antigua.*
177 7d. bistre-brown 2 0 2 3

NEW CONSTITUTION 1964.

(52)

1964 (16 OCT.). *New Constitution. Nos. 164 and 166 optd. with T* **52.**
178 **42** 3d. dp. blue and red-orange 1 3 1 6
179 **44** 6d. sepia and emerald .. 2 0 2 3
a. No stop after "1964" .. £7

1965 (17 MAY). *I.T.U. Centenary. As Nos. 166/7 of Antigua.*
180 4d. light emerald and yellow 1 0 1 6
181 2s. apple-green and deep blue 4 6 5 6

1965 (25 OCT.). *International Co-operation Year. As Nos. 168/9 of Antigua.*
182 ½d. dp. bluish green & lav. 0 4 0 4
183 4d. reddish pur. & turq.-grn. 1 0 1 6

The value of the ½d. stamp is shown as "1/2".

1966 (24 JAN.). *Churchill Commemoration. As Nos. 170/3 of Antigua.*
184 ½d. new blue 0 3 0 4
185 1d. deep green 0 4 0 6
186 4d. brown 0 9 0 11
187 9d. bluish violet 1 4 1 9

POSTAGE DUE STAMPS.

D 1

(Typo. De La Rue & Co.)

1956 (1 DEC.). *Chalky paper. Wmk. Mult. Script CA. P 14.*
D1 **D 1** 1d. green 0 3 0 6
D2 ,, 2d. sepia 0 4 0 8
D3 ,, 4d. blue 0 7 1 0

GILBERT AND ELLICE ISLANDS.

GILBERT & ELLICE

PROTECTORATE

(1)

911. *Stamps of Fiji optd. with T* **1.** *Wmk. Mult. Crown CA.*
23 ½d. green, O 25 0 37 6
,, 1d. red, O 55 0 60 0
24 2d. grey, O 10 0 25 0
4 **3** 2½d. ultramarine, O .. 10 0 30 0
5 ,, 5d. pur. and olive-green, C 30 0 42 6
6 **24** 6d. dull & bright purple, C 30 0 45 0
7 **23** 1s. black/*green*, (R.) C .. 25 0 55 0

2. Pandanus Pine.

3

(T **2** recess, T **3** typo. De La Rue.)

1911. *Wmk. Mult. Crown CA. P 14.*
8 **2** ½d. green 4 0 7 6
9 ,, 1d. carmine 5 0 6 0
10 ,, 2d. grey 5 0 10 0
11 ,, 2½d. blue 5 0 10 0

1912–24. *Wmk. Mult. Crown CA. P 14.*
12 **3** ½d. green, O 0 9 1 6
12a ,, ½d. yellow-green, O (1916) 1 0 3 0
13 ,, 1d. carmine, O 1 6 2 6
13a ,, 1d. scarlet, O 7 6 8 6
14 ,, 2d. greyish slate, O (1916) 16 0 12 6
15 ,, 2½d. bright blue, O (1916) 7 0 8 6
15a ,, 3d. purple/*yellow*, C (1919) 2 6 5 0
16 ,, 4d. black & red/*yellow*, C 3 6 7 6
17 ,, 5d. dull pur. & sage-grn., C 15 0 20 0
18 ,, 6d. dull & bright purple, C 5 0 15 0
19 ,, 1s. black/*green*, C .. 20 0 17 6
20 ,, 2s. purple and blue/*blue*, C 25 0 35 0
21 ,, 2s. 6d. black & red/*blue*, C 30 0 40 0
22 ,, 5s. green & red/*yellow*, C.. 42 6 60 0
23 ,, £1 purple and black/*red*, C (Die II), ('24) £22 £40

WAR TAX

(5)

1918 (SEPT.). *T* **3** *optd. with T* **5.**
26 1d. red 0 6 2 0

1922–27. *Wmk. Mult. Script CA. P 14.*
27 **3** ½d. green, O 0 6 1 0
27a ,, 1d. violet, O 1 0 1 6
28 ,, 1½d. scarlet, O 3 0 4 0
30 ,, 2d. slate-grey, O 6 0 8 6
35 ,, 10s. green & red/*emer.*, C .. £7 £9

1935 (6 MAY). *Silver Jubilee. As Nos. 91/4 of Antigua, but ptd. by B.W. & Co. P 11×12.*
36 1d. ultramarine & grey-black 4 0 7 6
37 1½d. deep blue and scarlet . 3 6 5 0
38 3d. brown and deep blue .. 20 0 25 0
39 1s. slate and purple.. .. 45 0 50 0

1937 (12 MAY). *Coronation. As Nos. 13/5 of Aden.*
40 1d. violet 0 6 0 10
41 1½d. scarlet 1 0 1 6
42 3d. bright blue 2 0 2 6

6. Frigate Bird.

7. Pandanus Pine.

8. Canoe crossing Reef.

9. Canoe and Boat-house.

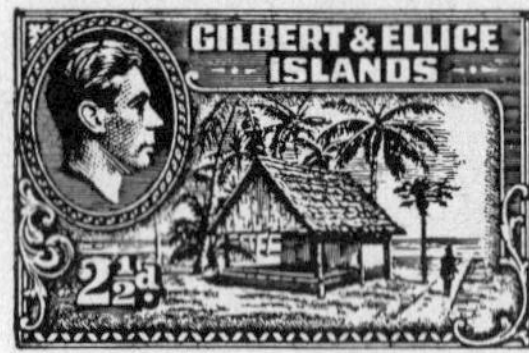

10. Native House.

11. Seascape.

12. Ellice Is. Canoe.

13. Coconut Palms.

14. Cantilever Jetty, Ocean Is.

15. H.M.C.S. *Nimanoa.*

16. Gilbert Is. Canoe.

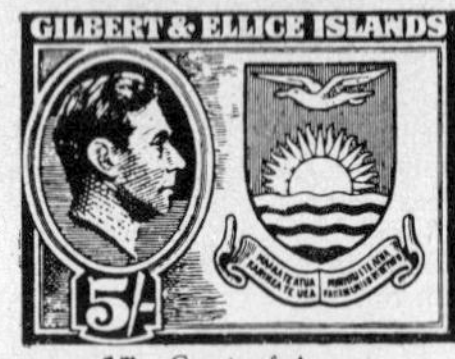

17. Coat of Arms.

(Recess. Bradbury, Wilkinson (½d., 2d., 2s. 6d.) Waterlow (1d., 5d., 6d., 2s., 5s.), De La Ru (1½d., 2½d., 3d., 1s.).)

1939 (14 Jan.)–**55.** *Wmk. Mult. Script CA (side ways on ½d., 2d. and 2s. 6d.).*

43	**6**	½d. slate-blue & blue-green (*p.* 11½ × 11)	0	6	0	
44	**7**	1d. emerald-green & purple (*p.* 12½)	0	8	0	1
45	**8**	1½d. blk. & carm. (*p.* 13½)	0	9	1	
46	**9**	2d. red-brown and black (*p.* 11½ × 11)	1	0	1	
47	**10**	2½d. blk. & ol.-grn. (*p.* 13½)	1	3	1	
48	**11**	3d. blk. & ultram. (*p.* 13½)	1	3	1	
		a. Perf. 12. *Black and bright blue* (24.8.55)	1	0	1	
49	**12**	5d. brt. bl. & sepia (*p.* 12½)	1	6	2	
50	**13**	6d. ol.-grn. & vio. (*p.* 12½)	1	9	2	

51 **14** 1s. blk. & turq.-bl. (*p.* 13½) 4 0 6 0
a. Perf. 12 (8.5.51) 2 6 4 0
52 **15** 2s. brt. bl. & verm. (*p.* 12½) 6 0 8 6
53 **16** 2s. 6d. blue and emerald-green (*p.* 11½ × 11) .. 7 6 10 0
54 **17** 5s. scar. & brt. bl. (*p.* 12½) 12 6 15 0

1946 (16 Dec.). *Victory. As Nos.* 28/9 *of Aden.*
55 1d. purple 0 4 0 6
56 3d. blue 0 8 1 0

1949 (29 Aug.). *Royal Silver Wedding. As Nos.* 30/1 *of Aden.*
57 1d. violet 0 6 1 0
58 £1 scarlet 27 6 30 0

1949 (10 Oct.). *75th Anniv. of U.P.U. As Nos.* 114/7 *of Antigua.*
59 1d. purple 0 6 0 8
60 2d. grey-black 1 0 1 3
61 3d. deep blue 1 6 2 0
62 1s. blue 4 0 5 0

1953 (2 June). *Coronation. As No.* 47 *of Aden.*
63 2d. black and grey-black .. 1 0 1 6

18. Frigate Bird.

(Recess. Bradbury, Wilkinson (½d., 2d., 2s. 6d.), Waterlow (1d., 5d., 6d., 2s., 5s.), De La Rue (2½d., 3d., 1s., 10s.) and after 1962, 1d., 5d.)

1956 (1 Aug.). *As T* **6/17** (*but Queen portrait as in T* **18**). *Wmk. Mult. Script CA. P* 11½ × 11 (*½d., 2d.,* 2s. *6d.*), 12½ (*1d., 5d., 6d.,* 2s., 5s.) *or* 12 (*2½d., 3d.,* 1s., 10s.).
64 **18** ½d. black & dp. brt. blue .. 0 3 0 3
65 **7** 1d. brn.-olive & dp. violet 0 4 0 4
66 **9** 2d. bluish green and deep purple (*shades*) .. 0 6 0 6
67 **10** 2½d. black & myrtle-green 0 5 0 6
68 **11** 3d. black and carmine-red 0 6 0 7
69 **12** 5d. ultramarine and red-orange (*shades*) .. 0 9 0 11
70 **13** 6d. chestnut & black-brown 0 11 1 0
71 **14** 1s. black and bronze-green 1 5 2 3
72 **15** 2s. dp. bright blue & sepia 2 9 3 9
73 **16** 2s. 6d. scarlet & deep blue 3 3 4 9
74 **17** 5s. grnish. bl. & bluish grn. 6 6 8 6
75 **8** 10s. black and turquoise .. 12 9 19 6

19. Loading Phosphate from Cantilever.

20. Phosphate Rock.

21. Phosphate-mining.

(Des. R. Turrell (2d.), M. Thoma (2½d.), M. A. W. Hook and A. Larkin (1s.). Photo. De La Rue & Co.)

1960 (1 May). *Diamond Jubilee of Phosphate Discovery at Ocean Island. W* w. **12.** *P* 12.
76 **19** 2d. green & carmine-rose 1 0 1 3
77 **20** 2½d. black and olive-green .. 1 3 1 6
78 **21** 1s. black & dp. turquoise 4 0 4 6

1963 (1 Aug.). *Freedom from Hunger. As No.* 63 *of Aden.*
79 10d. ultramarine 2 0 2 6

1963 (5 Oct). *Red Cross Centenary. As Nos.* 147/8 *of Antigua.*
80 2d. red and black 0 8 0 10
81 10d. red and blue 2 6 3 0

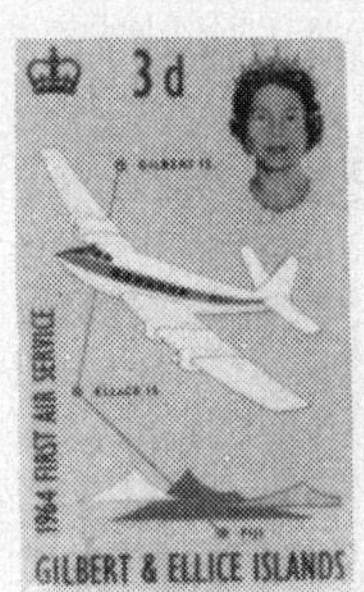

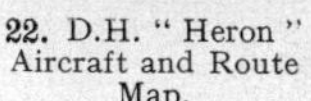

22. D.H. " Heron " Aircraft and Route Map.

24. D.H. " Heron " Aircraft over Tarawa Lagoon.

23. Heron in Flight.

(Des. Mrs. D. R. Barwick. Litho. Enschedé.)

1964 (20 July). *First Air Service. W* w.**12** (*sideways, 3d.,* 3s. *7d.*). *P* 11 × 11½ (1s.) *or* 11½ × 11 (*others*).
82 **22** 3d. blue, black and lt. blue 0 9 0 10
83 **23** 1s. lt. blue, black & dp. blue 2 0 2 3
84 **24** 3s. 7d. deep green, black and light emerald 5 6 6 0

Nos. 82/4 exist with watermark showing Crown to right or left of " CA ". *Prices same either way.*

(Recess. Bradbury, Wilkinson (2d.), De La Rue (6d.).)

1964–65. *As Nos.* 66 *and* 70 *but wmk.* w.**12.**

85 **9** 2d. bluish green and purple (30.10.64) 0 8 0 10
86 **13** 6d. chestnut and black-brown (4.5.65) 2 0 2 6

1965 (4 June). *I.T.U. Centenary. As Nos.* 166/7 *of Antigua.*

87 3d. red-orange and deep bluish green 0 8 0 10
88 2s. 6d. turquoise-blue and light purple 5 0 6 0

25. Mancaba and Gilbertese Man blowing Bu Shell.

26. Ellice Islanders Reef-fishing by Flare.

27. Gilbertese Girl weaving Head-garland.

28. Gilbertese Woman performing Ruoia.

29. Gilbertese Man performing Kamei.

30. Gilbertese Girl drawing Water.

31. Ellice Islander performing a Fatele.

32. Ellice Youths performing Spear Dance.

33. Gilbertese Girl tending Ikaroa Babai plant.

34. Ellice Islanders dancing a Fatele.

35. Ellice Islanders pounding Pulaka.

36. Gilbertese Women's Dance.

37. Gilbertese Boys playing a Stick Game.

38. Ellice Youths beating the Box for the Fatele.

39. Coat-of-Arms.

(Des. V. Whiteley, from drawings by Mrs. D. R. Barwick. Litho. Bradbury, Wilkinson.)

1965 (16 Aug.). *Centres multicoloured.* *W* w.**12.** *P* 12 × 11 (*vert.*) *or* 11 × 12 (*horiz.*).

No.	Type	Description	Unused	Used
89	**25**	½d. turquoise-green	0 3	0 3
90	**26**	1d. deep violet-blue	0 4	0 5
91	**27**	2d. bistre	0 5	0 6
92	**28**	3d. rose-red	0 6	0 7
93	**29**	4d. purple	0 7	0 9
94	**30**	5d. cerise	0 9	0 11
95	**31**	6d. turquoise-blue	0 11	1 1
96	**32**	7d. bistre-brown	1 0	1 4
97	**33**	1s. bluish violet	1 5	1 10
98	**34**	1s. 6d. lemon	2 3	2 9
99	**35**	2s. yellow-olive	2 9	3 3
00	**36**	3s. 7d. new blue	4 9	6 0
01	**37**	5s. light yellow-olive	6 6	7 9
02	**38**	10s. dull green	12 6	16 6
03	**39**	£1 light turquoise-blue	24 0	30 0

965 (25 Oct.). *International Co-operation Year. As Nos.* 168/9 *of Antigua.*

No.	Description	Unused	Used
04	½d. reddish pur. & turq.-grn.	0 6	0 8
05	3s. 7d. dp. bluish grn. & lav.	4 9	5 6

966 (24 Jan.). *Churchill Commemoration. As Nos.* 170/3 *of Antigua.*

No.	Description	Unused	Used
06	½d. new blue	0 3	0 6
07	3d. deep green	0 6	0 9
08	3s. brown	4 6	5 6
09	3s. 7d. bluish violet	5 0	6 0

(New currency. 100 cents = $1 Australian.)

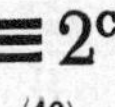

(40)

1966 (14 Feb.). *Decimal currency. Nos.* 89/103 *surch. as T* **40.**

No.	Type	Description	Unused	Used
110	**26**	1 c. on 1d. dp. violet-blue	0 2	0 3
111	**27**	2 c. on 2d. bistre	0 4	0 6
112	**28**	3 c. on 3d. rose-red	0 6	0 7
113	**25**	4 c. on ½d. turquoise-grn.	0 7	0 8
114	**31**	5 c. on 6d. turquoise-blue	0 9	0 11
115	**29**	6 c. on 4d. purple	0 10	1 0
116	**30**	8 c. on 5d. cerise	1 0	1 2
117	**33**	10 c. on 1s. bluish violet	1 3	1 6
118	**32**	15 c. on 7d. bistre-brown	1 8	2 3
119	**34**	20 c. on 1s. 6d. lemon	2 3	3 0
120	**35**	25 c. on 2s. yellow-olive	2 9	3 6
121	**36**	35 c. on 3s. 7d. new blue	3 9	4 6
122	**37**	50 c. on 5s. lt. yellow-olive	5 4	6 6
123	**38**	$1 on 10s. dull green	10 6	12 6
124	**39**	$2 on £1 lt. turq.-blue	21 0	25 0

POSTAGE DUE STAMPS.

GILBERT & ELLICE ISLANDS
1d
POSTAGE DUE

(D 1)

(Typo. Bradbury, Wilkinson.)

1940. *Wmk. Mult. Script CA. P* 12.

No.	Type	Description	Unused	Used
D1	**D 1**	1d. emerald-green	0 6	1 0
D2	,,	2d. scarlet	0 6	1 3
D3	,,	3d. brown	0 8	1 6
D4	,,	4d. blue	1 6	2 6
D5	,,	5d. grey-green	1 9	3 0
D6	,,	6d. purple	2 6	3 9
D7	,,	1s. violet	5 0	7 6
D8	,,	1s. 6d. turquoise-green	12 6	20 0

GOLD COAST.

POSTAGE
GOLD COAST
ONE PENNY

1

(Typo. De La Rue.)

1875 (July). *Wmk. Crown CC. P* 12½.

No.	Type	Description	Unused	Used
1	**1**	1d. blue	£24	95 0
2	,,	4d. magenta	£26	£5
3	,,	6d. orange	£32	95 0

1876–79. *Wmk. Crown CC. P* 14.

No.	Type	Description	Unused	Used
4	**1**	½d. olive-yellow (1879)	45 0	60 0
5	,,	1d. blue	20 0	17 6
		a. Bisected diag. (½d.) (on cover)	†	£40
6	,,	2d. green (1879)	55 0	45 0
		a. Bisected diag. (1d.) (on cover)	†	£45
7	,,	4d. magenta	£6	22 6
		a. Quartered (1d.) (on cover)	†	£80
8	,,	6d. orange	£6	42 6

1883 (May). *No.* 7 *surch. locally.*

No.	Type	Description	Unused	Used
8*a*	**1**	"1d." on 4d. magenta		

1883. *Wmk. Crown CA. P* 14.

No.	Type	Description	Unused	Used
9	**1**	½d. olive-yellow (Jan.)	£12	80 0
10	,,	1d. blue (May)	£45	£5

1884–89. *Wmk. Crown CA. P* 14.

No.	Type	Description	Unused	Used
10*a*	**1**	½d. green (Aug. '84)	2 0	2 0
11	,,	½d. dull green	2 0	3 6
12	,,	1d. rose-carmine (Aug. '84)	2 6	2 6

No.	Type	Description	Unused	Used
12a	1	1d. carmine	2 0	1 9
		b. Bisected diag. (½d.)(on cover)		
13	,,	2d. grey (Aug. '84) ..	4 0	7 0
		a. Value omitted		
13b	,,	2d. slate	3 0	3 0
14	,,	3d. olive-yellow (Sept. '89)	15 0	15 0
14a	,,	3d. olive	10 0	15 0
15	,,	4d. deep mauve (Mar. '85)	5 0	3 6
15a	,,	4d. rosy mauve	10 0	7 6
16	,,	6d. orange (Jan. '89) ..	10 0	8 0
16a	,,	6d. orange-brown ..	8 6	7 6
17	,,	1s. violet (1888)	45 0	37 6
17a	,,	1s. bright mauve	10 0	8 6
18	,,	2s. yellow-brown (1888) ..	£5	70 0
19	,,	2s. deep brown	35 0	35 0

ONE
PENNY.

(2)

1889 (Mar.). *No.* 16 *surch. with T* **2.**

No.	Type	Description	Unused	Used
20	1	1d. on 6d. orange	£10	90 0

In some sheets specimens may be found with the bar and "penny" spaced 8 mm., the normal spacing being 7 mm.

1891 (13 Mar.). *Value in second colour. Wmk. Crown CA. P* 14.

No.	Type	Description	Unused	Used
21	1	2½d. ultramarine and orange	3 6	2 6

3

4

1889 (Sept.)–**94.** *Wmk. Crown CA. P* 14.

No.	Type	Description	Unused	Used
22	3	5s. dull mauve and blue ..	65 0	40 0
23	,,	10s. dull mauve and red ..	£6	55 0
23a	,,	10s. dull mauve & carmine	£10	£5
24	,,	20s. green and red	£325	
25	,,	20s. dull mauve and black/*red* ('94)	£12	80 0

1898–1902. *Wmk. Crown CA. P* 14.

No.	Type	Description	Unused	Used
26	3	½d. dull mauve & green ..	0 10	0 9
27	,,	1d. dull mauve & rose ..	2 0	1 0
27a	4	2d. dull mauve & orange-red ('02)	22 6	35 0
28	3	2½d. dull mauve & ultram.	12 6	25 0
29	4	3d. dull mauve & orange..	6 0	7 6
30	,,	6d. dull mauve & violet ..	7 0	7 0
31	3	1s. green & black ..	22 6	27 6
32	,,	2s. green & carmine ..	45 0	40 0
33	,,	5s. green & mauve (1900)	80 0	50 0
34	,,	10s. green & brown (1900)	£8	70 0

1901 (6 Oct.). *Nos.* 28 *and* 30 *surch. with T* **2.**

No.	Type	Description	Unused	Used
35		1d. on 2½d. dull mve. & ultram.	3 6	10 0
36		1d. on 6d. dull mve. & violet	3 6	10 0
		a. "one" omitted	£30	

6

7

1902. *Wmk. Crown CA. P* 14.

No.	Type	Description	Unused	Used
38	6	½d. dull purple & green ..	1 0	1 3
39	,,	1d. dull purple & carmine..	0 10	0 6
40	7	2d. dull purple & orge.-red	7 0	5 0
41	6	2½d. dull purple & ultram..	10 0	15 0
42	7	3d. dull purple & orange ..	6 0	5 0
43	,,	6d. dull purple & violet ..	7 0	8 0
44	6	1s. green & black	10 0	15 0
45	,,	2s. green & carmine ..	40 0	45 0
46	,,	5s. green & mauve.. ..	40 0	60 0
47	,,	10s. green & brown	£7	£5
48	,,	20s. purple & black/*red* ..	£20	£15

1904–7. *Wmk. Mult. Crown CA. P* 14.

No.	Type	Description	Unused	Used
49	6	½d. dull purple & green, O (1907)	3 6	2 6
50	,,	1d. dull purple and carmine, OC ('04)	4 6	1 0
51	7	2d. dull purple & orange-red, OC ('04) ..	4 6	3 6
52	6	2½d. dull purple & ultramarine, O (10.06) ..	50 0	45 0
53	7	3d. dull purple & orange, OC (10.05)	12 6	7 6
54	,,	6d. dull purple and violet, OC (5.07)	20 0	15 0
57	,,	2s. 6d. grn. & yell., C (3.06)	85 0	£7

1907–13. *Wmk. Mult. Crown CA. P* 14.

No.	Type	Description	Unused	Used
59	6	½d. dull green, O	0 8	1 3
59a	,,	½d. blue-green, O.. ..	1 0	1 0
60	,,	1d. red, O	2 0	0 6
61	7	2d. greyish slate, O (1909)	6 0	4 0
62	6	2½d. blue, O	6 0	3 6
63	7	3d. purple/*yellow*, C (1909)	7 6	4 0
64	,,	6d. dull & dp. pur., C ('08)	17 6	8 6
64a	,,	6d. dull & brt. pur., C ('11)	8 0	10 0
65	6	1s. black/*green*, C (1909)..	12 6	8 6
66	,,	2s. purple and blue/*blue*, OC ('10)	22 6	35 0
67	7	2s. 6d. bl. & red/*bl.*, C ('11)	60 0	65 0
68	6	5s. grn. & red/*yell.*, C ('13)	£7	£9

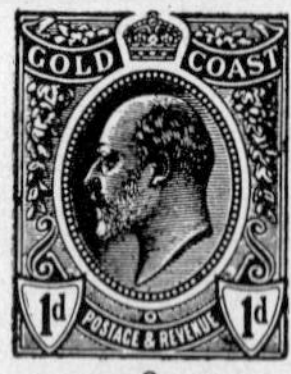
8

(Typo. De La Rue.)

1908 (Nov.). *Wmk. Mult. Crown CA. P* 14.

No.	Type	Description	Unused	Used
69	8	1d. red, O	1 6	0

9

10

11

(Typo. De La Rue.)

1913–23. *Wmk. Mult. Crown CA. P* 14.

70 **9** ½d. green, O 2 3 0 6
71 ,, ½d. yellow-green, O (1916) 4 0 1 3
72 **10** 1d. red, O 1 0 0 3
73 ,, 1d. scarlet, O 3 6 0 9
74 **11** 2d. grey, O 20 0 2 0
75 ,, 2d. slate-grey, O 17 6 2 0
76 **9** 2½d. bright blue, O 6 0 4 0
77 **11** 3d. purple/*yellow*, C ('15).. 6 0 1 6
a. *White back* (1913) .. 3 0 3 6
b. *On orange-buff* (1919) .. 27 6 10 0
c. *On pale yellow* (Die II), C 25 0 17 6
78 ,, 6d. dull & bright purple .. 10 0 10 0
79 **9** 1s. black/*green*, C .. 7 6 6 6
a. *On blue-green, olive back* .. 7 6 6 0
b. *On emerald back* (Die I) .. 17 6 12 6
c. *On emerald back* (Die II) .. 15 0 6 6
80 ,, 2s. purple and blue/*blue*, C (Die I) 25 0 15 0
a. Die II £18 £10
81 **11** 2s. 6d. black and red/*blue*, C (Die I) 27 6 20 0
a. Die II 95 0 95 0
82 **9** 5s. grn. & red/*yell.*, C ('15) 70 0 70 0
a. *White back* 32 6 60 0
b. *On orange-buff* 70 0 77 6
c. *On pale yellow* (Die I) .. 95 0 95 0
d. Die II 85 0 £7
83 ,, 10s. grn. & red/*grn.*, C ('16) 80 0 £6
a. *On bl.-grn., olive back* (1919) 70 0 £5
b. *On emerald back* £5 £6
84 ,, 20s. pur. & blk./*red*, C ('16) £15 £12

WAR TAX

ONE PENNY

(12)

1918 (June). *Surch. with T* **12.**

85 **10** 1d. on 1d. red 0 9 0 9

1921–25. *Wmk. Mult. Script CA. P* 14.

86 **9** ½d. green, O 1 0 0 6
87 **10** 1d. choc.-brown, O (1922) 0 8 0 3
88 **11** 1½d. red, O (1922) .. 2 0 0 8
89 ,, 2d. grey, O 3 0 1 3
90 **9** 2½d. yell.-orange, O (1922) 2 6 10 0
91 **11** 3d. bright blue, O (1922) 2 6 4 0
94 ,, 6d. dull & brt. purple, C 6 0 7 6
95 **9** 1s. blk./*emerald*, C (1925) 8 6 12 6
96 ,, 2s. purple & blue/*blue*, C (1923) 20 0 25 0
97 **11** 2s. 6d. black & red/*blue*, C (1925) 27 6 32 6
98 **9** 5s. green and red/*pale yellow*, C (1024) .. 42 6 55 0
00 **11** 15s. dull purple & green, C (Die I) £20 £22
a. Die II (1924) £15 £17
02 ,, £2 green & orange, C (Die I) £55 £60

In Nos. 88, 100 and 102 the words "GOLD OAST" are in distinctly larger letters.

13.
King George V and Christiansborg Castle.

(Photo. Harrison & Sons.)

1928 (1 Aug.). *Wmk. Mult. Script CA. P* 13½×15.

103 **13** ½d. green 0 6 0 6
104 ,, 1d. red-brown 0 8 0 3
105 ,, 1½d. scarlet 3 0 3 6
106 ,, 2d. slate 1 9 1 0
107 ,, 2½d. orange-yellow .. 6 0 12 6
108 ,, 3d. blue 4 0 2 6
109 ,, 6d. black and purple .. 6 0 3 6
110 ,, 1s. black and vermilion.. 12 6 12 6
111 ,, 2s. black and violet .. 25 0 22 6
112 ,, 5s. carmine & olive-green 65 0 70 0

1935 (6 May). *Silver Jubilee. As Nos.* 91/4 *of Antigua, but ptd. by B. W. & Co. P* 11×12.

113 1d. ultramarine & grey-black 0 6 0 8
a. Extra flagstaff £6
114 3d. brown and deep blue .. 5 0 5 0
a. Extra flagstsff 80 0
115 6d. green and indigo .. 8 6 8 0
a. Extra flagstaff 80 0
116 1s. slate and purple .. 10 6 15 0
a. Extra flagstaff 80 0

For illustration of "extra flagstaff" variety see Bechuanaland.

1937 (12 May). *Coronation. As Nos.* 13/5 *of Aden, but ptd. by B.W. & Co. P* 11×11½.

117 1d. buff 0 4 0 6
118 2d. slate 0 10 1 3
119 3d. blue 1 9 1 9

14

15. King George VI and Christiansborg Castle, Accra.

(Recess. Bradbury, Wilkinson & Co.)

1938 (1 Apr.)–**41.** *Wmk. Mult. Script CA. P* 11½×12.

120 **14** ½d. green 0 3 0 3
121 ,, 1d. red-brown 0 4 0 3
122 ,, 1½d. scarlet 0 5 0 4
123 ,, 2d. slate 0 5 0 3
124 ,, 3d. blue 0 8 0 8
125 ,, 4d. magenta 1 0 1 3
126 ,, 6d. purple 0 10 0 8
127 ,, 9d. orange 1 6 3 0
128 **15** 1s. black and olive-green 2 0 1 9
129 ,, 1s. 3d. brown & turquoise-brown (12.4.41) .. 2 0 3 0
130 ,, 2s. blue and violet .. 7 6 4 0
131 ,, 5s. olive-green & carmine 15 0 12 6
132 ,, 10s. black & violet (1940) 25 0 30 0

Nos. 120 to 132, except 1s. 3d. and 10s., exist in two perforations: (*a*) Line-perf. 12, from early printings; (*b*) Comb-perf. 12 × 11.7 (vertical design) or 11.7 × 12 (horiz. design), from later printings. The 1s. 3d. and 10s. exist only comb-perf. 11.7 × 12.

1946 (14 Oct.). *Victory. As Nos.* 28/9 *of Aden. P* 13 × 14.

133	2d. slate-violet	1	0	0	9
	a. Perf. 13½	0	5	1	0
134	4d. claret	2	0	1	9
	a. Perf. 13½	0	8	1	9

16. Northern Territories Mounted Constabulary.

19. Talking Drums.

17. Christiansborg Castle.

18. Emblem of Joint Provincial Council.

20. Map showing position of Gold Coast.

21. Manganese Mine.

22. Lake Bosumtwi.

23. Cocoa Farmer.

27. Forest.

24. Breaking Cocoa Pods.

25. Trooping the Colour.

26. Surfboats.

(Recess. Bradbury, Wilkinson.)

1948 (1 July). *Wmk. Mult. Script CA. P* 12 × 11 (*vert.*) *or* 11½ × 12 (*horiz.*).

135	**16**	½d. emerald-green ..	0	3	0
136	**17**	1d. blue	0	6	0
137	**18**	1½d. scarlet	0	6	0
138	**19**	2d. purple-brown ..	0	6	0
139	**20**	2½d. yellow-brn. & scarlet	1	3	1
140	**21**	3d. light blue	0	8	0
141	**22**	4d. magenta	2	0	2
142	**23**	6d. black and orange ..	1	0	0
143	**24**	1s. black and vermilion ..	2	0	1
144	**25**	2s. sage-green & magenta	4	0	2
145	**26**	5s. purple and black ..	15	0	8
146	**27**	10s. black and sage-green	20	0	16

1948 (20 Dec.). *Royal Silver Wedding. As Nos.* 30/1 *of Aden.*

147	1½d. scarlet	0	4	0	6
148	10s. grey-olive	17	6	20	0

1949 (10 Oct.). *75th Anniv. of U.P.U. As Nos.* 114/7 *of Antigua.*

149	2d. red-brown	1	0	1	6
150	2½d. orange	2	0	3	0
151	3d. deep blue	5	0	7	6
152	1s. blue-green	10	0	12	6

28. Northern Territories Mounted Constabulary.

(Recess. Bradbury, Wilkinson & Co.)

1952–54. *As T* **16/27** *(but with portrait of Queen Elizabeth II in place of King George VI, as in T* **28**). *Portrait faces left on* ½d., 4d., 6d., 1s., 2s., *and* 5s. *Wmk. Mult. Script CA. P* 12×11½ *(vert.) or* 11½×12 *(horiz.).*

153	**20**	½d. yellow-brown & scarlet (*shades*)	0	6	0	6
154	**17**	1d. deep blue	0	4	0	3
155	**18**	1½d. emerald-green ..	0	4	1	0
156	**19**	2d. chocolate	0	6	0	3
157	**28**	2½d. scarlet	0	8	1	3
158	**21**	3d. magenta	0	10	0	6
159	**22**	4d. blue	1	0	1	0
160	**23**	6d. black and orange	1	3	0	6
161	**24**	1s. black and orange-red	2	6	0	8
162	**25**	2s. brown-olive and carm.	5	0	2	6
163	**26**	5s. purple and black ..	25	0	7	6
164	**27**	10s. black and olive-green	35	0	12	6

Dates of issue: 1952—19 Dec., 2½d. 1953—1 April, ½d., 1½d., 3d., 4d. 1954—1 Mar., other values.

1953 (2 June). *Coronation. As No.* 47 *of Aden, but ptd. by B. W. & Co.*

165	2d. black and sepia	1	3	0	4

POSTAGE DUE STAMPS.

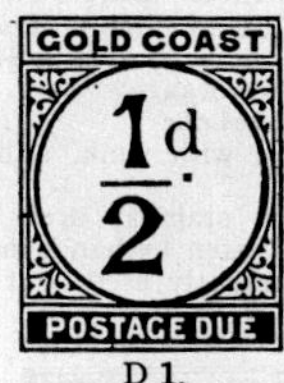

D 1.

(Typo. De La Rue & Co.)

1923. *Yellowish toned paper. Wmk. Mult. Script CA. P* 14.

D1	**D 1**	½d. black	30	0	25	0
D2	,,	1d. black	1	6	2	6
D3	,,	2d. black	5	0	5	0
D4	,,	3d. black	7	6	7	0

1951–52. *Type* D 1. *Chalk-surfaced paper. Wmk. Mult. Script CA. P* 14.

D5	2d. black (13.12.51)	0 8	1 6
	a. Error. Crown missing, W9a ..	£25	
	b. Error. St. Edward's Crown, W9b	£15	
D6	3d. black (13.12.51)	1 3	3 0
	a. Error. Crown missing, W9a ..	£20	
	b. Error. St Edward's Crown, W9b	£15	
D7	6d. black (1.10.52)	2 6	4 0
	a. Error. Crown missing, W9a ..	£20	
	b. Error. St. Edward's Crown, W9b	£15	
D8	1s. black (1.10.52)	5 0	7 6
	b. Error. St. Edward's Crown, W9b	£15	

On March 6th, 1957 Gold Coast became the Dominion of Ghana (*q.v.*).

GRENADA

For GREAT BRITAIN stamps used in Grenada, see page 66.

—SIMPLIFICATION (see Introduction)**—**
Nos. 1 to 29.

2, 3. 4, 6, 9. 10, 17. 14, 12.
21, 22, 23, 13. 24, 26. 27, 29.

PRINTERS. Types **1** and **5** recess-printed by Perkins, Bacon and Co.

1

1861–62. *No wmk.* A. *Rough perf.* 14–16.

1	**1**	1d. bluish green	£180	£25
2	,,	1d. green (May 1862) ..	£6	£6
		a. Imperf. between (horiz. pair)		
3	,,	6d. rose (*shades*)	£50	£12
		B. *Wove paper. Perf.* 11–12.		
3*a*	**1**	6d. lake-red	£80	

No. 3*a* is only known unused, but has also been seen on laid paper.

2. Small Star.

Wmk. s = Wmk. sideways (two points of Star downwards)

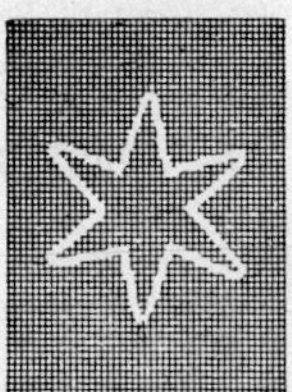

3. Large Star.

4. Broad-pointed Star.

1863–71. *W* **2** (*Small Star*). *Rough perf.* 14–16.

No.	Type	Description	Unused	Used
4	**1**	1d. green (1864)	60 0	35 0
5	,,	1d. yellowish green	£5	60 0
6	,,	6d. rose (*shades*) (Feb. 63)	£25	40 0
7	,,	6d. orange-red (*shades*) ..	£40	40 0
8	,,	6d. dull rose-red (wmk. s) ..	—	£20
9	,,	6d. vermilion	£25	65 0
		a. Double impression	—	£150

The sideways wmk. is an identifying aid to the rare shade, No. 8. Normally in this issue the wmk. is upright, but it also exists sideways.

1873. *W* **2** (*Small Star sideways*). *Clean-cut perf.* 15.

No.	Type	Description	Unused	Used
10	**1**	1d. deep green	£5	55 0
		a. Bisected diag. (on cover) ..	†	£80

1873-74. *W* **3** (*Large Star*). *Intermediate perf.* 15.

No.	Type	Description	Unused	Used
11	**1**	1d. blue-grn. (wmk. s) (1874)	£8	65 0
		a. Double impression ..		
		b. Imperf. between (pair) ..	—	£250
12	,,	6d. orange-vermilion (upright wmk.)	£25	60 0

5

POSTAGE

ONE SHILLING

(6)

NOTE. The early ½d., 2½d., 4d. and 1s. postage stamps were made by surcharging the undenominated Type **5** design.

The surcharges were from two founts of type—one about 1½ mm. high, the other 2 mm. high—so there are short and tall letters on the same stamp; also the spacing varies considerably, so that the length of the words varies.

1875 (JULY). *Blue surch.* (*T* **6**). *W* **3** (*Large Star*). *P* 14.

No.	Type	Description	Unused	Used
13	**5**	1s. deep mauve	£12	35 0
		a. Error. "SHLLIING" ..	—	£70
		b. Error. "NE SHILLING"	—	£90
		c. Error. Inverted "S" in "POSTAGE" ..	£60	£35
		d. Error. "OSTAGE" ..		

1875 (DEC.). *W* **3** (*Large Star, upright*).

No.	Type	Description	Unused	Used
14	**1**	1d. grn. *to* yell.-grn. (p. 14)	80 0	35 0
		a. Bisected diag. (on cover) ..	†	£80
15	,,	1d. green (perf. 15) ..	—	£150

No. 14 was perforated at Somerset House. 40 sheets of No. 15 were perforated by Perkins, Bacon to replace spoilages and to complete the order.

1878. *W* **2** (*Small Star, sideways*). *Intermediate perf.* 15.

No.	Type	Description	Unused	Used
16	**1**	1d. green	£22	80 0
17	,,	6d. deep vermilion ..	£35	80 0
		a. Double impression ..	—	£150

1879. *W* **2** (*Small Star, upright*). *Rough perf.* 15.

No.	Type	Description	Unused	Used
18	**1**	1d. pale green (thin paper)	£20	40 0
		a. Double impression ..		

1881 (APRIL). *W* **2** (*Small Star, sideways*). *Rough perf.* 14½.

No.	Type	Description	Unused	Used
19	**1**	1d. green	£10	45 0
		a. Bisected diag. (on cover) ..	†	£80

POSTAGE — HALF-PENNY (7)

POSTAGE — TWO PENCE HALF-PENNY. (8)

POSTAGE — FOUR PENCE (9)

1881 (APRIL). *Black surcharges* (*T* **7** *to* **9**). *P* 14½.

A. *Wmk. Large star, T* **3**.

No.	Type	Description	Unused	Used
20	**5**	½d. pale mauve	50 0	35 0
21	,,	½d. deep mauve	20 0	35 0
		a. Imperf. (pair)	£35	
		b. Surcharge double	£20	
		c. Error. "OSTAGE" ..	£12	£10
		d. Error. No hyphen ..	£10	80 0
		e. Wmk. upright	—	£35
		f. Ditto. "OSTAGE". ..	—	£110
22	,,	2½d. rose-lake	90 0	40 0
		a. Imperf. (pair)	£40	
		b. Imperf. between (horiz. pair)	£90	
		c. Error. "PENNY" (no stop)	£15	95 0
		d. Error. "PENCF" ..	£28	£12
23	,,	4d. blue	£5	50 0

The watermark is normally *sideways* on the ½d.

B. *Wmk. Broad-pointed Star, T* **4**.

No.	Type	Description	Unused	Used
24	**5**	2½d. rose-lake	£20	80 0
		a. Error. "PENNY" (no stop)	£50	£14
		b. Error. "PENCF" ..	£60	£28
25	,,	2½d. claret	£60	£20
		a. Error. "PENNY" (no stop)	£90	£50
		b. Error. "PENCF" ..	£150	£110
26	,,	4d. blue	£20	£20

ONE PENNY

(10)

POSTAGE.

(11)

POSTAGE POSTAGE

(12)

1883 (JAN.). *Revenue stamps* (*T* **5** *with green surcharge as in T* **10**) *optd. for postage. W* **2** (*Small Star*). *P* 14½.

A. *Optd. horizontally with T* **11**.

No.	Type	Description	Unused	Used
27	**5**	1d. orange	£15	90 0
		a. "POSTAGE" inverted ..	£135	£90
		b. "POSTAGE" double ..	£85	£90
		c. Invtd. "S" in "POSTAGE"	£55	£45
		d. Bisected diag. (on piece) ..	†	£225

B. *Optd. diagonally with T* **11** *twice on each stamp, the stamps being cut and each half used as* ½*d.*

No.	Type	Description	Unused	Used
28	**5**	Half of 1d. orange ..	£55	£22
		a. Unsevered pair	£225	£110
		b. "POSTAGE" inverted ..		

C. *Optd. with T* **12**, *the stamp divided diagonally and each half used as* ½*d.*

No.	Type	Description	Unused	Used
29	**5**	Half of 1d. orange ..	£17	£10
		a. Unsevered pair	£60	£35

Nos. 27/9 exist with wmk. either upright or sideways.

1d. Revenue stamps are known with "POSTAGE" written by hand, in red or black. These were apparently used, but not officially authorised.

13

(Typo. De La Rue.)

1883. *Wmk. Crown CA. P* 14.

30 **13** ½d. dull green (Feb.) .. 2 0 2 0
a. Tête-bêche (pr.) 6 0 10 0

31 ,, 1d. carmine (Feb.) .. 35 0 15 0
a. Tête-bêche (pr.) £12 £20

32 ,, 2½d. ultramarine (May) .. 5 0 3 6
a. Tête-bêche (pr.) 20 0 25 0

33 ,, 4d. greyish slate (May) .. 10 0 10 0
a. Tête-bêche (pr.) 25 0 32 6

34 ,, 6d. mauve (May) .. 10 0 15 0
a. Tête-bêche (pr.) 27 6 30 0

35 ,, 8d. grey-brown (Feb.) .. 10 0 20 0
a. Tête-bêche (pr.) 30 0 50 0

36 ,, 1s. pale violet (April) .. £8 £6
a. Tête-bêche (pr.) £50

Types **13** and **15** were printed in rows tête-bêche in the sheets.

d.
1
POSTAGE.
(**14**)

1886. *Revenue stamps* (*T* **5** *with green surch. as T* **10**), *surch. with T* **14**. *P* 14.

A. *Wmk. Large Star, T* **3**.

37 **5** 1d. on 1½d. orange (Oct.) .. 50 0 45 0
a. Type 14 inverted £18 £18
b. Type 14 double £25 £20
c. Error. "THRFE" .. £25 £20
d. Error. "PFNCE £25 £15
e. Error. "HALH" .. £25 £20
f. Bisected diag. (on cover) .. † £30

38 ,, 1d. on 1s. orange (Dec.) .. 60 0 60 0
a. Error. "POSTAGE" (no stop)
b. Error. "SHILLNG" .. £35 £40
c. Error. Wide space (3½ mm.) betwn. "ONE" & "SHILLING" £28 £18
d. Bisected diag. (on cover) .. † £25

B. *Wmk. Small Star, T* **2**.

39 **5** 1d. on 4d. orange (Nov.) .. £6 90 0

GRENADA
POSTAGE & REVENUE
ONE PENNY
15

1887 (Jan.). *Wmk. Crown CA. P* 14.

40 **15** 1d. carmine 1 6 1 6
a. Tête-bêche (pr.) 4 0 7 0

4*d.*
POSTAGE
(**16**)

HALF
PENNY
POSTAGE
(**17**)

1888–91. *Revenue stamps* (*T* **5** *with green surch. as T* **10**) *surcharged. Wmk. Small Star, W* **2**. *P* 14½.

A. **1888** (31 Mar.). *Surch. with T* **16**.

I. 4 *mm. between value and* "POSTAGE".

41 **5** 4d. on 2s. orange .. 40 0 45 0
a. Upright "d" .. £25 £25
b. Wide space (2¼ mm.) between "TWO" & "SHILLINGS" £6 £6
c. First "S" in "SHILLINGS" inverted £26 £26

II. 5 *mm. between value and* "POSTAGE".

42 **5** 4d. on 2s. orange .. 70 0 75 0
a. Wide spacing (as 41b) .. £18 £20
b. "S" inverted (as 41c) .. £45 £45

B. **1889** (Dec.). *Surch. as T* **17**.

43 **5** ½d. on 2s. orange 30 0 35 0
a. Type 17 double £22 £25
b. Wide spacing (as 41b) .. 90 0 95 0
c. "S" inverted (as 41c) .. £26 £26

POSTAGE
d.
1
AND
REVENUE
(**18**)

POSTAGE
AND
REVENUE
1d.
(**19**)

C. **1890** (Dec.). *Surch. with T* **18**.

44 **5** 1d. on 2s. orange £7 £8
a. Surcharge inverted .. £30
b. Wide spacing (as 41b) .. £18 £18
c. "S" inverted (as 41c) .. £38

D. **1891** (Jan.). *Surch. with T* **19**.

45 **5** 1d. on 2s. orange .. 50 0 60 0
a. No stop after "1d" .. £18
b. Wide spacing (as 41b) .. £15
c. "S" inverted (as 41c)

1891 (Jan.). *Surch. with T* **19**.

46 **13** 1d. on 8d. grey-brown .. 30 0 25 0
a. Tête-bêche (pair) .. 70 0
b. Surcharge inverted .. £20 £20
c. No stop after "1d" .. £12 £16

2½d.
(**20**)

1891 (Dec.). *Surch. with T* **20**.

47 **13** 2½d. on 8d. grey-brown .. 30 0 30 0
a. Tête-bêche (pair) .. 90 0
b. Inverted surcharge ..
c. Double surcharge .. £15 £40
d. Double surch., one inverted — £25
e. Treble surch. .. .. — £40

There are two types of fraction; in one the "1" has horizontal serif and the "2" commences in a ball; in the other the "1" has sloping serif and the "2" is without ball. Each type occurs 30 times in the pane of 60.

GRENADA
POSTAGE
& REVENUE
1d
21

GRENADA
POSTAGE
& REVENUE
8d
22

(Typo. De La Rue & Co.)

1895–99. *Wmk. Crown CA. P* 14.

48 **22** ½d. mauve & green (1899) 1 9 2 0
49 **21** 1d. mauve & carm. (1896) 1 6 0 9
50 ,, 2d. mauve & brn. (1899).. 45 0 65 0
51 ,, 2½d. mauve & ultramarine 6 0 5 0
52 **22** 3d. mauve and orange .. 15 0 20 0
53 **21** 6d. mauve and green .. 15 0 27 6
54 **22** 8d. mauve and black .. 32 6 45 0
55 ,, 1s. green and orange .. 30 0 47 6

23. Flagship of Columbus.

(Recess. De La Rue & Co.)

1898 (15 Aug.). *400th Anniv. of Discovery of Grenada by Columbus. Wmk. Crown CC. P* 14.

56 **23** 2½d. ultramarine 22 6 30 0
a. Bluish paper 65 0 75 0

24 25

(Typo. De La Rue.)

1902. *Wmk. Crown CA. P* 14.

57 **24** ½d. dull purple and green.. 1 9 2 0
58 **25** 1d. dull purple & carmine 1 6 1 0
59 ,, 2d. dull purple and brown 8 6 25 0
60 ,, 2½d. dull purple & ultram. 12 6 25 0
61 **24** 3d. dull purple & orange.. 6 7 7 6
62 **25** 6d. dull purple and green.. 12 6 17 6
63 **24** 1s. green and orange .. 22 6 35 0
64 ,, 2s. green and ultramarine 45 0 50 0
65 **25** 5s. green and carmine .. 75 0 85 0
66 **24** 10s. green and purple .. £18 £20

1904–6. *Wmk. Mult. Crown CA. P* 14.

67 **24** ½d. pur. & green, O ('05) .. 27 6 30 0
68 **25** 1d. pur. & carm., O ('04) .. 12 6 10 0
69 ,, 2d. pur. & brown, O ('05) 50 0 55 0
70 ,, 2½d. pur. & ultram., O ('05) 50 0 55 0
71 **24** 3d. pur. & orge., OC ('05) 10 0 17 6
72 **25** 6d. pur. & grn., OC ('06).. 12 6 20 0
73 **24** 1s. green & orge., O ('05) 20 0 22 6
74 ,, 2s. grn. & ultram., OC ('06) 75 0 85 0
75 **25** 5s. grn. & carm., O ('06).. £7 £8
76 **24** 10s. grn. & purple, O ('06) £24 £26

26. Badge of the Colony. **27.**

(Recess. De La Rue & Co.)

1906. *Wmk. Mult. Crown CA. P* 14.

77 **26** ½d. green 1 6 1 9
78 ,, 1d. carmine 1 9 1 0
79 ,, 2d. orange 8 0 10 0
80 ,, 2½d. blue 12 6 12 6
81 ,, 2½d. ultramarine 17 6 17 6

(Typo. De La Rue & Co.)

1908. *Wmk. Crown CA. P* 14.

82 **27** 1s black/*green*, C .. 32 6 55 0
83 ,, 10s. green & red/*green*, C £14 £16

1908–11. *Wmk. Mult. Crown CA. P* 14.

84 **27** 3d. dull purple/*yellow*, C 6 0 12 6
85 ,, 6d. dull pur & purple, C 25 0 32 6
86 ,, 1s black/*green*, C (1911) 12 6 20 0
87 ,, 2s. blue & purple/*blue*, C 40 0 47 6
88 ,, 5s. green & red/*yellow*, C 90 0 95 0

28

WAR TAX
(29)

WAR TAX
(30)

(Typo. De La Rue & Co.)

1913 (Jan.)–**1921.** *Wmk. Mult. Crown CA. P* 14.

89 **28** ½d. yellow-green, O .. 1 3 1 6
90 ,, ½d. green, O 0 9 1 3
91 ,, 1d. red, O 0 10 0 6
92 ,, 1d. scarlet, O (1916) .. 1 0 0 10
93 ,, 2d. orange, O 1 9 5 0
94 ,, 2½d. bright blue, O .. 3 6 8 6
95 ,, 2½d. dull blue, O .. 6 0 12 6
96 ,, 3d. purple/*yellow*, C .. 3 0 7 6
a. *White back* 4 0 15 0
b. *On lemon* 8 6 15 0
c. *On pale yellow* 8 6 15 0
97 ,, 6d. dull & bright pur., C 5 0 10 0
98 ,, 1s. black/*green*, C .. 7 6 17 6
a. *White back* 10 0 17 6
b. *On blue-green, olive back* .. £5 £5
c. *On emerald surface* .. 10 0 22 6
d. *On emerald back* 8 6 20 0
99 ,, 2s. pur. & blue/*blue*, C.. 17 6 27 6
100 ,, 5s. grn. & red/*yell.*, C .. 30 0 45 0
a. *On pale yellow* 60 0 70 0
101 ,, 10s. grn. & red/*green*, C.. £5 £7
a. *On emerald back* £5 £7

1916 (1 June)–**1918.** *Optd. locally with T* **29.**

109 **28** 1d. carmine 7 6 17 6
a. Opt. inverted £32
110 ,, 1d. red 22 6 27 6
a. "T Δ X" 75 0 85 0

A small "A" in "WAR", 2 mm. high, is found on Nos. 29, 38 and 48 of the pane and a very small "A" in "TAX", 1½ mm. high, on No. 11. Value about twice normal. The normal "A" is 2¼ mm. high.

No. 110*a* is on No. 56 of the left-hand pane.

Optd. with T **30** *in London.*

(*a*) *On white paper.*

111 **28** 1d. scarlet (Sept., '16) .. 0 6 1 0

(*b*) *On bluish paper.*

112 **28** 1d. carmine-red (May, '18) 1 0 3 6

1921–31. *Wmk. Mult. Script CA. P* 14.

113 **28** ½d. green, O 0 9 0 9
114 ,, 1d. carmine-red, O .. 1 0 0 6
115 ,, 2d. orange, O 2 0 2 0
116 ,, 2½d. deep dull blue, O .. 60 0 65 0
116*a* ,, 2½d. bright blue, O (1926) 3 0 5 0
116*b* ,, 2½d. brt. ultram., O ('31) 4 0 6 0
117 ,, 6d. dull & brt. purple, C 8 0 17 6
118 ,, 1s. black/*emerald*, C .. 10 0 25 0
119 ,, 2s. pur. & blue/*blue*, C.. 17 6 30 0
120 ,, 5s. grn. & red/*pale yell.*, C 32 6 45 0
121 ,, 10s. grn. & red/*emerald*, C 70 0 80 0

1921–23. *Colours changed and new values. Wmk. Mult. Script CA. P* 14.

122 **28** 1d. brown, O 1 3 0 6
123 ,, 1½d. rose-red, O 1 9 1 6
124 ,, 2½d. grey, O 3 6 12 6
125 ,, 3d. bright blue, O .. 4 6 12 6
126 ,, 5d. dull pur. & sage-grn., C 6 0 17 6
127 ,, 9d. dull purple & black, C 8 6 17 6
128 ,, 3s. green and violet, C 27 6 42 6

1926–29. *New values and colours. Wmk. Mult. Script CA. P* 14.

129 **28** 2d. grey, O 3 0 4 0
130 ,, 3d. purple/*yellow*, C .. 3 0 8 6

No.	Type	Description	Unused	Used
131	28	4d. black and red/*yellow*, C	3 0	12 6
132	,,	6d. black and carmine, C	6 0	14 0
133	,,	1s. chestnut, C	15 0	20 0
134	,,	2s. 6d. black and carmine/*blue*, C ('29)	37 6	42 6

31. Grand Anse Beach.

32. Badge of the Colony.

33. Grand Etang.

34. St. George's.

(Recess. Waterlow & Sons.)

1934 (23 Oct.)–**1936.** *Wmk. Mult. Script CA.* (*sideways on T* **32**). *P* 12½.

No.	Type	Description	Unused	Used
135	31	½d. green	0 4	0 4
		a. Perf. 12½ × 13½ ('36) ..	10 0	30 0
136	32	1d. black and sepia ..	1 3	1 3
		a. Perf. 13½ × 12½ ('36) ..	7 6	8 6
137	33	1½d. black and scarlet ..	2 3	1 6
		a. Perf. 12½ × 13½ ('36) ..	10 0	10 0
138	32	2d. black and orange ..	2 0	3 0
139	34	2½d. blue	1 9	2 0
140	32	3d. black & olive-green ..	2 6	3 6
141	,,	6d. black and purple ..	3 6	6 0
142	,,	1s. black and brown ..	10 0	12 6
143	,,	2s. 6d. black & ultram.	30 0	37 6
144	,,	5s. black and violet ..	47 6	55 0

1935 (6 May). *Silver Jubilee. As T* **13** *of Antigua but ptd. by Waterlow. P* 11 × 12.

No.	Description	Unused	Used
145	½d. black and green	0 6	0 8
146	1d. ultramarine and grey ..	1 0	1 0
147	1½d. deep blue and scarlet ..	2 0	2 6
148	1s. slate and purple ..	12 6	15 0

1937 (12 May). *Coronation. As T* **2** *of Aden but ptd. by B. W. & Co. P* 11 × 11½.

No.	Description	Unused	Used
149	1d. violet	0 3	0 4
150	1½d. carmine	0 6	0 8
151	2½d. blue	1 6	2 0

35. King George VI.

(Photo. Harrison & Sons.)

1937 (12 July). *Wmk. Mult. Script CA. P* 15 × 14.

No.	Type	Description	Unused	Used
152	35	¼d. brown, CO	0 3	0 3
		a. Chocolate, CO	1 0	0 4

The ordinary paper is thick, smooth and opaque.

36. Grand Anse Beach.

40. Badge of the Colony.

(Recess. De La Rue (10s.), Waterlow (others).)

1938 (16 Mar.)–**50.** As *T* **31/4** (*but portrait of King George VI as in T* **36**) *and T* **40.** *Wmk. Mult. Script CA* (*sideways on T* **32**). *P* 12½ *or* 12 × 13 (10s.).

No.	Type	Description	Unused	Used
153	36	½d. yellow-green	1 3	1 0
		a. Perf. 12½ × 13½ ('38) ..	5 0	4 0
		b. Perf. 12½. *Blue-green* ('43)	0 3	0 4
		ba. Perf. 12½ × 13½. *Blue-green*	7 6	12 6
154	32	1d. black and sepia ..	0 6	0 4
		a. Perf. 13½ × 12½ (1938) ..	0 8	0 8
155	33	1½d. black and scarlet ..	0 5	0 4
		a. Perf. 12½ × 13½ (1938) ..	15 0	3 0
156	32	2d. black and orange ..	0 8	0 8
		a. Perf. 13½ × 12½ (1938) ..	0 10	0 6
157	34	2½d. bright blue	0 6	0 6
		a. Perf. 12½ × 13½ (?Mar. '50)	£220	£14
158	32	3d. black and olive-green	12 6	10 0
		a. Perf. 13½ × 12½ ('41) ..	4 6	3 0
		ab. Perf. 13½ × 12½. *Black and brown-olive* ('42)	1 3	1 6
		b. Perf. 12½. *Black and brown-olive* (16.8.50)	1 3	1 6
159	,,	6d. black and purple ..	1 3	1 6
		a. Perf. 13½ × 12½ ('42) ..	1 6	1 3
160	,,	1s. black and brown ..	3 0	3 0
		a. Perf. 13½ × 12½ ('41) ..	2 6	3 0
161	,,	2s. black & ultramarine ..	5 0	6 0
		a. Perf. 13½ × 12½ ('41) ..	8 6	6 0
162	,,	5s. black and violet ..	10 0	10 0
		a. Perf. 13½ × 12½ ('47) ..	27 6	35 0
163	40	10s. slate-blue and carmine (*narrow*) (p. 12 × 13)	50 0	45 0
		a. Perf. 14. *Pale blue and carmine-rose* (*narrow*) ..	£6	£6
		b. Perf. 14. *Slate-blue and carmine* (*narrow*) ('43) ..	25 0	27 6
		c. Perf. 12. *Slate-blue and carmine* (*narrow*) ('43) ..	£25	£26
		d. Perf. 14. *Slate-blue and claret* (*wide*) ('44) ..	75 0	85 0
		e. Perf. 14. *Blue-black and carmine* (*wide*) ('47) ..	20 0	25 0

In the earlier printings of the 10s. the paper was dampened before printing and the subsequent shrinkage produced narrow frames 23½ to 23¾ mm. wide. Later printings were made on dry paper producing wide frames 24¼ mm. wide.

No. 163*a* is one of the earlier printings line perf. 13.8 × 14.1.

No. 163*b* is line-perf. 14.1.

Nos. 163*a* and 163*b* may be found with gum more or less yellow due to local climatic conditions.

1946 (25 Sept.). *Victory. As Nos. 28/9 of Aden.*

No.	Description	Unused	Used
164	1½d. carmine	0 6	0 8
165	3½d. blue	0 10	1 3

1948 (27 Oct.). *Royal Silver Wedding. As Nos. 30/1 of Aden.*

No.	Description	Unused	Used
166	1½d. scarlet	0 6	0 9
167	10s. slate-green	22 6	25 0

1949 (10 Oct.). *75th Anniv. of Universal Postal Union. As Nos. 114/7 of Antigua.*

No.	Description	Unused	Used
168	5 c. ultramarine	0 6	0 8
169	6 c olive	1 0	1 3
170	12 c. magenta	1 6	3 0
171	24 c. red-brown	2 6	4 6

41. King George VI. **42.** Badge of the Colony.

43. Badge of the Colony.

(Recess. Bradbury, Wilkinson (*T* 39), De La Rue (others).)

1951 (8 Jan.). *Wmk. Mult. Script CA. P* 11½ (*T* **41**), 11½ × 12½ (*T* **42**), *and* 11½ × 13 (*T* **43**).

No.	Type	Description	Unused	Used
172	**41**	½ c. black and red-brown	0 3	1 0
173	,,	1 c. black & emerald-grn.	0 4	0 3
174	,,	2 c. black and brown ..	0 6	0 6
175	,,	3 c. black & rose-carmine	0 9	0 6
176	,,	4 c. black and orange ..	1 0	1 6
177	,,	5 c. black and violet ..	0 9	0 9
178	,,	6 c. black and olive ..	1 0	0 10
179	,,	7 c. black and light blue	1 0	0 10
180	,,	12 c. black and purple ..	6 0	5 0
181	**42**	25 c. black and sepia ..	2 6	2 6
182	,,	50 c. black and blue ..	4 0	4 6
183	,,	$1.50 black & yell.-orange	17 6	30 0
184	**43**	$2.50 slate-blue & carmine	20 0	25 0

1951 (16 Feb.). *Inauguration of B.W.I. University College. As Nos. 118/9 of Antigua.*

No.	Description	Unused	Used
185	3 c. black and carmine	1 0	1 0
186	6 c. black and olive	1 6	1 6

NEW CONSTITUTION

1951
(44)

1951 (21 Sept.). *New Constitution. Optd. with T* **44** *by Bradbury, Wilkinson & Co.*

No.	Type	Description	Unused	Used
187	**41**	3 c. black & rose-carmine	0 8	0 8
188	,,	4 c. black and orange ..	0 10	1 0
189	,,	5 c. black and violet (R.)	1 0	1 6
190	,,	12 c. black and purple ..	1 9	2 6

1953 (3 June). *Coronation. As No. 47 of Aden.*

No.	Description	Unused	Used
191	3 c. black and carmine-red ..	1 0	1 3

45. Queen Elizabeth II. **46.** Badge of the Colony.

47. Badge of the Colony.

(Recess. B.W. & Co. (T **45**), D.L.R. & Co. (T **46/7**).)

1953–59. *Wmk. Mult. Script CA. P* 11½ (*T* **45**), 11½ × 12½ (*T* **46**), *or* 11½ × 13 (*T* **47**).

No.	Type	Description	Unused	Used
192	**45**	½ c. black and brown ..	0 2	0 3
193	,,	1 c. black & dp. emerald	0 3	0 3
194	,,	2 c. black and sepia ..	0 6	0 6
195	,,	3 c. black & carmine-red	0 6	0 6
196	,,	4 c. black & brown-orange	0 6	0 6
197	,,	5 c. black & deep violet..	0 8	0 8
198	,,	6 c. black & olive-green..	0 7	0 7
199	,,	7 c. black and blue ..	0 7	0 9
200	,,	12 c. black & reddish pur.	1 3	1 6
201	**46**	25 c. black and sepia ..	2 0	2 3
202	,,	50 c. black and deep blue..	3 4	3 9
203	,,	$1.50, black & brown-orange	10 0	10 6
204	**47**	$2.50, slate-blue & carmine	16 9	21 0

Dates of issue: 1953—15 June, 1 c., 12 c.; 15 Sept., 2 c.; 28 Dec., ½ c., 6 c. 1954—22 Feb., 3 c., 4 c., 5 c. 1955—10 Jan., 25 c.; 6 June, 7 c.; 2 Dec., 50 c., $1.50. 1959—16 Nov., $2.50.

1958 (22 Apr.). *Inauguration of British Caribbean Federation. As Nos. 135/7 of Antigua.*

No.	Description	Unused	Used
205	3 c. deep green	0 9	1 0
206	6 c. blue	1 3	1 6
207	12 c. scarlet	2 9	3 3

48. Queen Victoria, Queen Elizabeth II, Mail Van and Post Office, St. George's.

49. Queen Victoria, Queen Elizabeth II and *La Concepcion.*

50. Queen Victoria, Queen Elizabeth II, R.M.S.P. *Solent* and Dakota aircraft.

(Photo. Harrison & Sons.)

1961 (1 June). *Stamp Centenary.* *W* w.**12**. *P* 14½ × 14.

208	**48**	3 c. crimson and black ..	1 3	1 6
209	**49**	8 c. brt. blue and orange	2 9	3 3
210	**50**	25 c. lake and blue ..	4 9	5 6

1963 (4 June). *Freedom from Hunger. As No.* 63 *of Aden.*

11	8 c. bluish green	1 6	1 6

963 (2 Sept.). *Red Cross Centenary. As Nos.* 147/8 *of Antigua.*

12	3 c. red and black	0 8	1 0
13	25 c. red and blue	2 6	3 0

964 (12 May). *As Nos.* 194/7, 200/1, *but wmk.* w.**12**.

14	**45**	2 c. black and sepia ..	0 4	0 4
15	,,	3 c. black & carmine-red	0 5	0 5
16	,,	4 c. black & brown-orange	0 5	0 5
17	,,	5 c. black and deep violet	0 6	0 5
18	,,	12 c. black & reddish pur.	1 0	1 0
19	**46**	25 c. black and sepia ..	1 10	1 10

965 (17 May). *I.T.U. Centenary. As Nos.* 166/7 *of Antigua.*

20	2 c. red-orange and yellow-olive	0 6	0 8
21	50 c. lemon and light red ..	4 6	5 6

965 (25 Oct.). *International Co-operation Year. As Nos.* 168/9 *of Antigua.*

22	1 c. reddish pur. & turq.-grn.	0 4	0 6
23	25 c. dp. bluish green & lav.	2 0	2 6

966 (24 Jan.). *Churchill Commemoration. As Nos.* 170/3 *of Antigua.*

24	1 c. new blue	0 3	0 4
25	3 c. deep green	0 5	0 6
26	25 c. brown	1 10	2 3
27	35 c. bluish violet	2 6	3 0

966 (4 Feb.). *Royal Visit. As Nos.* 174/5 *of Antigua.*

28	3 c. black and ultramarine	0 5	0 7
29	35 c. black and magenta ..	2 6	3 0

On 23rd December, 1965 No. 203 was issued urcharged "2" but this was intended for fiscal nd revenue purposes and it was not authorised o be used postally, although some are known to ave passed through the mail.

52. Hillsborough, Carriacou.

53. Bougainvillea.

54. Flamboyant Plant.

55. Levera Beach.

56. Careenage, St. George's. (*Inscr.* "CARENAGE".)

57. Annandale Falls.

58. Cocoa Pods.

59. Inner Harbour.

60. Nutmeg.

61. St. George's.

62. Grand Anse Beach.

63. Bananas.

64. Badge of the Colony.

65. Queen Elizabeth II.

66. Map of Grenada.

(Des. V. Whiteley. Photo. Harrison.)

1966 (1 Apr.). *W* w.**12**. *P* 14½ ($1, $2, $3) *or* 14½ × 13½ (*others*).

No.	Type	Value	Colour		Unused		Used	
231	**52**	1 c.	multicoloured	..	0	2	0	2
232	**53**	2 c.	multicoloured	..	0	3	0	3
233	**54**	3 c.	multicoloured	..	0	4	0	4
234	**55**	5 c.	multicoloured	..	0	4	0	4
235	**56**	6 c.	multicoloured	..	0	6	0	6
236	**57**	8 c.	multicoloured	..	0	7	0	7
237	**58**	10 c.	multicoloured	..	0	9	0	9
238	**59**	12 c.	multicoloured	..	0	10	0	10
239	**60**	15 c.	multicoloured	..	0	11	1	[illegible]
240	**61**	25 c.	multicoloured	..	1	6	1	[illegible]
241	**62**	35 c.	multicoloured	..	2	0	2	[illegible]
242	**63**	50 c.	multicoloured	..	2	10	3	[illegible]
243	**64**	$1	multicoloured	..	5	6	6	[illegible]
244	**65**	$2	multicoloured	..	11	0	12	[illegible]
245	**66**	$3	multicoloured	..	16	6	18	[illegible]

POSTAGE DUE STAMPS.

D 1

1d.

SURCHARGE
POSTAGE

(D 2)

(Typo. De La Rue & Co.)

1892. (*a*) *Type* D **1**. *Wmk. Crown CA*. *P* 1[illegible]

No.	Type	Description		Unused		Used
D1	D **1**	1d. blue-black	.. ..	15	0	7
D2	,,	2d. blue-black	.. ..	27	6	12
D3	,,	3d. blue-black	.. ..	35	0	15

(*b*) *Nos.* 34 *and* 35 *surch. locally as Type* D [illegible]

No.	Type	Description		Unused		Used
D4	**13**	1d. on 6d. mauve	.. ..	30	0	12
		a. Tête-bêche (pr.)	.. ..	75	0	
		b. Surch. double	.. ..	—		75

D5	13	1d. on 8d. grey-brown	£10	20 0
		a. Tête-bêche (pr.)	£25	
D6	,,	2d. on 6d. mauve	40 0	17 6
		a. Tête-bêche (pr.)	£7	
D7	,,	2d. on 8d. grey-brown	£22	60 0
		a. Tête-bêche (pr.)	£60	

1906. *Wmk. Mult. Crown CA. P 14.*

D 8	D 1	1d. blue-black	1 6	2 6
D 9	,,	2d. blue-black	2 6	2 6
D10	,,	3d. blue-black	5 0	7 6

1921–22. *As Type* D 1, *but inscr.* " POSTAGE DUE ". *Wmk. Mult. Script CA. P 14.*

D11	1d. black	1 6	2 0
D12	1½d. black	2 6	4 0
D13	2d. black	3 6	3 6
D14	3d. black	6 0	4 0

1952 (1 Mar.). *As Type* D 1, *but inscr.* " POSTAGE DUE ". *Value in cents. Chalk-surfaced paper. Wmk. Mult. Script CA. P 14.*

D15	2 c. black	0 2	0 4
	a. Error. Crown missing. W9a	£20	
	b. Error. St. Edward Crown, W9b	£9	
D16	4 c. black	0 4	0 8
	a. Error. Crown missing. W9a	£10	
	b. Error. St. Edward Crown, W9b	£10	
D17	6 c. black	0 6	1 0
	a. Error. Crown missing, W9a	£20	
	b. Error. St. Edward Crown, W9b	£30	
D18	8 c. black	0 7	1 6
	a. Error. Crown missing, W9a	£25	
	b. Error. St. Edward Crown, W9b	£25	

GRIQUALAND WEST.

Stamps of the Cape of Good Hope, T 4 *(4d., 6d. and 1s.) and* 6 *(½d., 1d., 4d. and 5s.), wmk. Crown CC, perf. 14, with various opts.*

1874 (Sept.). *With manuscript surcharge.*

1	1d. in red on 4d. blue (T 4)	£25	£20

1877 (Mar.). *Overprinted* " G.W.", *in black.*

2	1d. carmine-red	£15	£5
	a. Overprint double	†	—

Overprinted " G.W." *in red.*

3	4d. blue (T 6)	£10	80 0

G (1) G (2) G (3) G (4) G (5) G (6)

G (7) G (8) G (9) G (10) G (11)

G (12) G (13) G (14)

A. *Overprinted with large capital letter.*

1877 (April). I. *First printing, in black on the* 1d. *and in red on the other values. SEVEN principal varieties of type* (T 1, 2, 3, 4, 5, 6 *and* 8).

4	1	½d. grey-black	17 6	17 6
5	2	½d. grey-black	40 0	50 0
6	3	½d. grey-black	15 0	25 0
7	4	½d. grey-black	35 0	35 0
8	5	½d. grey-black	40 0	45 0
9	6	½d. grey-black	17 6	15 0
10	8	½d. grey-black		
11	1	1d. carmine-red	15 0	12 6
12	2	1d. carmine-red	55 0	50 0
13	3	1d. carmine-red	22 6	20 0
14	4	1d. carmine-red	30 0	30 0
15	5	1d. carmine-red	65 0	45 0
16	6	1d. carmine-red	17 6	15 0
17	1	4d. blue (T 4)	£7	25 0
18	2	4d. blue (T 4)	£20	£5
19	3	4d. blue (T 4)	£18	60 0
20	4	4d. blue (T 4)	£22	£10
21	5	4d. blue (T 4)	£22	£12
22	6	4d. blue (T 4)	£12	60 0
23	8	4d. blue (T 4)		
24	1	4d. blue (T 6)	£6	22 6
25	2	4d. blue (T 6)	—	£5
26	3	4d. blue (T 6)	£9	35 0
27	4	4d. blue (T 6)	£9	35 0
28	5	4d. blue (T 6)	£14	£5
29	6	4d. blue (T 6)	£7	32 6
30	8	4d. blue (T 6)	£75	
31	1	6d. dull violet	75 0	35 0
32	2	6d. dull violet	£10	75 0
33	3	6d. dull violet	£6	27 6
34	4	6d. dull violet	£12	£5
35	5	6d. dull violet	£10	£5
36	6	6d. dull violet	£5	30 0
37	8	6d. dull violet		
38	1	1s. green	95 0	17 6
		a. Opt. inverted	—	£22
39	2	1s. green	£10	60 0
		a. Opt. inverted		
40	3	1s. green	65 0	25 0
41	4	1s. green	£10	27 6
		a. Opt. inverted		
42	5	1s. green	£10	40 0
43	6	1s. green	95 0	20 0
		a. Opt. inverted		
44	8	1s. green		
45	1	5s. orange	£20	17 6
46	2	5s. orange	—	45 0
47	3	5s. orange	£22	20 6
48	4	5s. orange	—	32 6
49	5	5s. orange	£32	40 0
50	6	5s. orange	£22	15 0
51	8	5s. orange	£110	

The setting of the above was in two panes of 60. Sub-types of Types 1 and 2 are found. The 1d., Type 8, of this setting can only be distinguished when *se-tenant* with Type 3.

1878. II. *Second printing, in black for all values. NINE principal varieties of type* (T 6 *to* 14).

52	7	1d. carmine-red	17 6	17 6
53	8	1d. carmine-red	25 0	25 0
54	9	1d. carmine-red	40 0	37 6
55	10	1d. carmine-red	£7	
56	11	1d. carmine-red	35 0	35 0
57	12	1d. carmine-red	£7	£7
58	13	1d. carmine-red	£6	90 0
59	14	1d. carmine-red	£22	£22
60	6	4d. blue (T 6)	£14	80 0
61	7	4d. blue (T 6)	£5	30 0
62	8	4d. blue (T 6)	£14	75 0
63	9	4d. blue (T 6)	£7	35 0
64	10	4d. blue (T 6)	£24	£12
65	11	4d. blue (T 6)	£14	75 0
66	12	4d. blue (T 6)	£17	£6
67	13	4d. blue (T 6)	£22	£14
68	14	4d. blue (T 6)	—	£9
69	6	6d. dull violet	£24	£7
70	7	6d. dull violet	£12	90 0
		a. Opt. double		
71	8	6d. dull violet	£24	£5
72	9	6d. dull violet	£14	£6
		a. Opt. double		
73	10	6d. dull violet	£22	
74	11	6d. dull violet	£55	£22
75	12	6d. dull violet	£28	£12
76	13	6d. dull violet	£30	£18
77	14	6d. dull violet	£55	£24

The 1d., T 6, of this printing can only be distinguished from the same variety of the first printing when it is *se-tenant* with another type.

The type without horizontal or vertical serifs, previously illustrated as T 10, is a broken " G " of the type now shown under that number.

Minor varieties may be found of T 7 and 12.

The 4d., 1s. and 5s. overprinted with Type 7 in red, previously listed, are now not believed to exist.

G (15) G (16) G (17)

B. *Overprinted with small capital letter.*

1878 (July). I. *First printing, in red or in black.*

(*a*) *Red overprint.*

78 **15** ½d. grey-black 10 0 12 6
 a. Opt. inverted 12 6 15 0
 b. Opt. double 75 0
 c. Opt. double, both inverted .. £5
79 **16** ½d. grey-black 12 6 15 0
 a. Opt. inverted 15 0 17 6
 b. Opt. double £5 £5
 c. Opt. double, both inverted ..
80 **15** 4d. blue (T **6**) £17 £7
 a. Opt. inverted £14 £5
81 **16** 4d. blue (T **6**) .. .. — £6
 a. Opt. inverted £20 £6

(*b*) *Black overprint.*

82 **15** ½d. grey-black £14 £9
 a. Opt. inverted £14
 b. Black opt. normal, with additional red opt. T 15 invert. £17
 c. Ditto, but red opt. is T 16 .. £8
83 **16** ½d. grey-black 65 0 65 0
 a. Optd. inverted 65 0 65 0
 b. Black opt. normal, with additional red opt. T 15 inverted £12
84 **15** 1d. carmine-red 15 0 7 6
 a. Opt. inverted 15 0 12 6
 b. Ditto, with additional red opt. T 15 inverted 45 0 55 0
 c. Ditto, with additional red opt. T 16 inverted .. ..
 d. Opt. double £12 85 0
 e. Opt. double, both inverted .. £12 95 0
85 **16** 1d. carmine-red 12 6 12 6
 a. Opt. inverted £5 45 0
 b. Ditto. with additional red opt. T 16 inverted £5 £5
 c. Opt. double .. .. — £7
 d. Opt. double, both inverted .. — £9
86 **15** 4d. blue (T **4**) .. .. — £10
87 **16** 4d. blue (T **4**) .. .. — £12
88 **15** 4d. blue (T **6**) £5 30 0
 a. Opt. inverted £12 £6
 b. Opt. double .. .. — £12
 c. Opt. double, both inverted ..
89 **16** 4d. blue (T **6**) £10 17 6
 a. Opt. inverted £18 45 0
 b. Opt. double .. .. — £16
 c. Opt. double, both inverted ..
90 **15** 6d. dull violet 90 0 55 0
91 **16** 6d. dull violet .. .. — 55 0

1879 (?). II. *Second printing, in black only.*

92 **17** ½d. grey-black 12 6 10 0
 a. Opt. double £16 £16
93 ,, 1d. carmine-red 12 6 7 6
 a. Opt. inverted .. .. — £6
 b. Opt. double .. .. — £10
 c. Opt. treble .. ..
94 ,, 4d. blue (T **6**) 15 0 7 6
 b. Opt. double .. .. — £10
95 ,, 6d. mauve £5 12 6
 a. Opt. inverted .. .. — 60 0
 b. Opt. double £22 £12
96 ,, 1s. green 70 0 7 6
 a. Opt. double £14 £10
97 ,, 5s. orange £14 12 6
 a. Opt. double £18 £5
 b. Opt. treble .. .. — £12

Besides the type shown above, which is the normal, there are in this printing three or four minor varieties differing in the shape and size of the body of the letter. In this setting are also found at least two varieties very like the upright "antique" of the first printing in small capitals.

The stamps of Griqualand West became obsolete in October, 1880, when the stock on hand of Cape stamps overprinted with small "G" was returned from Kimberley to Cape Town and redistributed among various post offices in Cape Colony, where they were used as ordinary Cape stamps.

HELIGOLAND.

Collectors should be on their guard against reprints of Heligoland stamps, which are very numerous and of little value.

1

2

(Die eng. Herr Schilling. Typo. Printing Works, Berlin.)

1867. *T* **1.** *Head embossed in colourless relief. Rouletted.*

1 ½ sch. green and rose (Die I) .. £22 £30
2 ½ sch. green and rose (Die II) .. £38 £50
3 1 sch. rose and blue-green .. £12 £12
4 2 sch. rose and grass-green .. 45 0 £7
5 6 sch. green and rose 45 0 £17

In Nos. 1 to 9, the second colour is that of the spandrels in the ½ and 1 sch., and of the central background also in the 2 and 6 sch. In Die I the small curl below the chignon is solid and projects downwards, while in Die II it is in the shape of a hook opening to the left.

1869–72. *T* **1.** *P* 13½×14½.

6 ½ sch. yellow-green and rose .. £5 £8
7 ½ sch. blue-green and rose .. £5 £8
8 1 sch. rose & pale blue-green .. 95 0 £10
9 1 sch. rose and yellow-green .. £5 £10

1873. *T* **1.** *P* 13½×14½.

10 ¼ sch. rose and green .. 40 0 £70
11 ¼ sch. deep rose & pale green 45 0 £70
12 ¾ sch. green and rose .. 40 0 £70
13 1½ sch. green and rose .. 55 0 £14

Error, colours reversed.

14 ¼ sch. green and deep rose .. £5 £95

In Nos. 10, 11, 13, and 14 the second colour is that of the central background.

In No. 12 the second colour is also that of the side labels and side marginal lines.

1875. *T* **2.** *Head embossed in colourless relief. P* 13½×14½.

15 1 pf. (¼d.) deep green & rose .. 27 6 £35
16 2 pf. (½d.) deep rose & green .. 27 6 £55
17 5 pf. (¾d.) deep yell.-grn. & rose 30 0 32 6
18 5 pf. (¾d.) deep green & rose .. 40 0 75 0
19 10 pf. (1½d.) deep rose and deep green 35 0 42 6
20 10 pf. (1½d.) scarlet and pale blue-green 32 6 37 6
21 10 pf. (1½d.) rose aniline and pale yellow-green .. 50 0 55 0
22 25 pf. (3d.) deep green & rose .. 35 0 50 0
23 50 pf. (6d.) deep rose & green .. 50 0 65 0

The first colour given above is that of the central background, the second that of the frame.

3

(Die eng. A. Schiffner. Typo. Imperial Printing Works, Berlin.)

1876. *T* **3.** *P* 13½ × 14½.

24 3 pf. (⅜d.) green, red & yellow-orange £6 £22

24*a* 3 pf. (⅜d.) pale grn. red & yell. £6

25 20 pf. (2½d.) rose, grn. & yellow 40 0 35 0

26 20 pf. (2½d.) rose-carmine, deep green and orange .. £6 65 0

27 20 pf. (2½d.) dull red, pale green and lemon 40 0 45 0

28 20 pf. (2½d.) vermilion aniline, bright green and lemon 40 0 45 0

Colours. 3 pf. (1) Frame and top band of shield. (2) Centre band of shield. (3) Border of shield.

20 pf. (1) Frame and centre band. (2) Upper band. (3) Border of shield.

4

5

(Die eng. A. Schiffner. Typo. Imperial Printing Works, Berlin.)

1879. *T* **4** *and* **5.** (*a*) *P* 13½ × 14½.

29 1 m. (1s.) dp. grn., scar. & blk. 85 0 £10

30 1 m. (1s.) dp. grn., rose aniline and black £6 £12

31 5 m. (5s.) dp. grn., rose aniline and black 90 0 £38

(*b*) *P* 11½.

32 1 m. (1s.) deep green, scarlet and black £22

33 5 m. (5s.) deep green, scarlet and black £22

a. Imperf. between (pair) .. £175

The stamps perf. 11½ are given above on the ground that specimens exist on the original envelopes and are known to have been genuinely postally used.

Numerous reprints of the ¼ sch. (including the *error*), ½ sch. (Die II), ¾ sch., 1 sch., 1½ sch., 2 sch., 6 sch., 1 pf., 2 pf. and 3 pf. were made between 1875 and 1895. It is impossible to describe them all here. Collectors should exercise caution in purchasing stamps of which reprints exist.

Heligoland was ceded to Germany, 9 Aug., 1890.

HONG KONG.

PRINTERS. All stamps of Hong Kong were typographed by De La Rue & Co. *unless otherwise stated.*

NOTE.—*Mint or fine used specimens of the earlier Hong Kong stamps are rarely met with and are worth considerably more than our prices which are for stamps in average condition. Inferior specimens can be supplied at much lower prices.*

1

2

3

1862 (8 Dec.). *No wmk.* *P* 14.

1 **1** 2 c. brown £6 60 0

a. Deep brown £7 80 0

2 ,, 8 c. yellow-buff £10 80 0

3 ,, 12 c. pale greenish blue .. £5 60 0

4 **3** 18 c. lilac £7 60 0

5 ,, 24 c. green £16 £6

6 ,, 48 c. rose £35 £10

7 ,, 96 c. brownish grey £35 £10

1863-74. *Wmk. Crown CC.* *P* 14.

8 **1** 2 c. deep brown (1865) .. 60 0 37 6

a. Brown 60 0 8 6

b. Pale yellowish brown .. 80 0 25 0

9 **2** 4 c. grey (1863) 25 0 17 6

a. Slate 22 6 7 6

b. Deep slate 85 0 12 6

c. Greenish grey 75 0 45 0

d. Bluish slate £6 27 6

e. Variety. Perf. 12½. (1870) .. £30 £12

10 ,, 6 c. lilac (1863) £6 17 6

a. Mauve £6 27 6

11 **1** 8 c. pale dull orange (1865) £6 15 0

a. Brownish orange .. 90 0 17 6

b. Bright orange £8 12 6

12 ,, 12 c. pale gr'nish blue ('64?) £10 40 0

a. Pale blue 12 6 12 6

b. Deep blue 95 0 15 0

13 **3** 18 c. lilac (1866) £50 £14

14 ,, 24 c. green (1865) 85 0 17 6

a. Pale green £8 35 0

b. Deep green £12 50 0

15 **2** 30 c. vermilion (1863) .. £12 27 6

a. Orange-vermilion .. £10 32 6

16 ,, 30 c. mauve (1871) 50 0 15 0

17 **3** 48 c. pale rose (1865) .. £7 60 0

a. Rose-carmine £9 35 0

b. Bright claret .. .. † —

18 ,, 96 c. olive-bistre (1865) .. £85 £18

19 ,, 96 c. brownish grey (1866) .. £8 37 6

a. Brownish black £10 35 0

There is a wide range of shades in this issue, of which we can only indicate the main groups.

No. 12 is the same shade as No. 3 without wmk., the impression having a waxy appearance.

16 cents. (4) *28 cents.* (5)

1877. *Nos.* 13 *and* 16 *surch. with T* **4** *or* **5.**

20 **3** 16 c. on 18 c. lilac £22 £7

a. Space between "n" and "t" of "cents" .. ..

21 **2** 28 c. on 30 c. mauve £12 65 0

1877 (Aug.). *Wmk. Crown CC.* *P* 14.

22 **3** 16 c. yellow £14 65 0

5 cents. (6) **10 cents.** (7)

1880 (Mar.). *Surch. with T* **6** *or* **7.**

23 **1** 5 c. on 8 c. brt. or. (No. 11*b*) £8 80 0

a. Surcharge inverted .. .. — £250

b. Surcharge double .. .. ..

24 **3** 5 c. on 18 c. lilac (No. 13) .. £6 60 0
25 **1** 10 c. on 12 c. p. bl. (No. 12*a*) £6 85 0
a. Blue £6 55 0
26 **3** 10 c. on 16 c. yellow (No. 22) £14 £6
a. Surcharge inverted.. .. — £250
27 ,, 10 c. on 24 c. green (No. 14) £7 70 0

1880. *Wmk. Crown CC. P* 14.
28 **1** 2 c. dull rose 27 6 17 6
a. Rose 32 6 17 6
29 **2** 5 c. blue 50 0 25 0
30 ,, 10 c. mauve 70 0 18 0
31 **3** 48 c. brown £8 70 0

1882–83. *Wmk. Crown CA. P* 14.
32 **1** 2 c. rose-lake 42 6 30 0
a. Rose-pink 80 0 57 6
b. Variety. Perf. 12 .. .. £140
33 ,, 2 c. carmine.. .. .. 3 0 1 3
a. Aniline carmine 6 0 0 10
34 **2** 5 c. pale blue 6 0 1 0
a. Blue 5 0 1 0
35 ,, 10 c. dull mauve £6 17 6
36 ,, 10 c. green (1883) 32 6 4 6
a. Deep blue-green £25 30 0

20 CENTS (8) **50 CENTS** (9) **1 DOLLAR** (10)

1885 (June). *Surch. with T* **8** *to* **10.** (*Wmk. Crown CA. P* 14).
37 **2** 20 c. on 30 c. orange-red .. 30 0 6 0
a. Double surcharge £35
38 **3** 50 c. on 48 c. yellowish brn. 50 0 22 6
39 ,, $1 on 96 c. grey-olive .. 55 0 47 6

1891 (1 Jan.). *Wmk. Crown CA. P* 14.
40 **2** 10 c. purple/*red* 3 0 0 9
41 ,, 30 c. yellowish green .. 65 0 50 0
a. Grey-green 17 6 15 0

Note.—No. 41, and the provisionals formed by surcharging this stamp, should not be confused with faded or washed copies of the grey-green, which turns to a very yellow-green shade when damped.

Surch. with T **8** *to* **10.** *Wmk. Crown CA. P* 14.
42 **2** 20 c. on 30 c. yellowish green (No. 41) 55 0 60 0
a. Grey-green (No. 41*a*) .. 30 0 40 0
43 **3** 50 c. on 48 c. dull purple .. 60 0 60 0
44 ,, $1 on 96 c. purple/*red* .. 85 0 85 0

弍 (11) (20 c.) 五十 (12) (50 c.) 五十 (12*a*) 壹員 (13) ($1)

1891. *Surch. with T* **8** *to* **10.** *As Nos.* 42 *to* 44, *but handstamped Chinese characters added at top of label at left.* (*T* **11** *to* **13.**)
45 **2** 20 c. on 30 c. yellowish grn. 25 0 7 6
a. Grey-green 7 6 5 0
b. Type 11 double £20
c. Type 11 double one inverted
d. Type 11 at each side .. £20
e. Type 11 omitted (pair with normal) £18 £20
f. Type 11 at each side and Type 12 (50 c.) twice at left £32
g. Type 11 large £10 80 0
h. "20 CENTS" double ..
46 **3** 50 c. on 48 c. dull purple .. 12 6 7 6
a. Type 12 double £20
b. Type 12 inverted .. £25
c. Type 12 double, one inverted £20
d. Type 12 at each side .. £18
e. Type 12 inverted at left, normal at right.. .. £22
f. Type 12 omitted (pair with normal) £16
g. Chinese characters larger (T 12*a*) 40 0 25 0
47 **3** $1 on 96 c. purple/*red* .. 65 0 15 0
a. Type 13 at each side .. £22 £22

1841 Hong Kong JUBILEE 1891 (14) **7 cents.** (15) **14 cents.** (16)

1891 (22 Jan.). *50th Anniv. of Colony. Optd. with T* **14.**
48 **1** 2 c. carmine (No. 33) .. 15 0 20 0
a. Short "J" in "JUBILEE".. 70 0 70 0
b. Short "U" in "JUBILEE" 55 0 55 0
c. Broken "1" in "1891" .. 75 0 75 0
d. Tall narrow "K" in "KONG" £14 £14
e. Overprint double £80 £90
f. Space between "O" and "N" of "HONG" £15 £15

This overprint was applied in a setting of 12, and other less marked varieties therefore exist.

1891. *Surch. with T* **15** *or* **16.**
49 **2** 7 c. on 10 c. green (No. 36) (Jan.) 20 0 12 6
a. Antique "t" in "cents." .. £12 £5
b. Surcharge double £40 £25
50 ,, 14 c. on 30 c. mauve (No. 16) (Apr.) 55 0 60 0
a. Antique "t" in "cents." .. £55 £20

The true antique "t" must not be confounded with a small "t" with short foot, which is sometimes mistaken for it. In the antique "t" the cross-bar is accurately bisected by the vertical stroke, the latter being thick at the top. The lower curve bends towards the right and does not turn upwards so far as in the normal.

Dangerous forgeries of these two surcharges exist.

1896 *Wmk. Crown CA. P* 14.
51 **2** 4 c. slate-grey 2 0 0 8

1898. *Surch. with T* **10**, *and hand-stamped Chinese characters as T* **13.** *Wmk. Crown CA. P* 14.
52 **3** $1 on 96 c. black 45 0 35 0
a. Grey-black 37 6 30 0
b. Type 13 double £12
c. Type 13 inverted £20
d. Type 13 double, one inverted £30
e. Type 13 at each side .. £20 £28
f. Type 13 inverted at left, normal at right £26
g. Type 13 normal at left, inverted at right £15 £18
h. Type 13 twice at left, once at right £15

Surch. with T **10** *only.*
53 **3** $1 on 96 c. black £6 £7
a. Grey-black £8

10 CENTS (17) 拾 (18) 拾 (19)

1898 (April). *Surch. with T* **17.**
54 **2** 10 c. on 30 c. grey-green (No. 41*a*) £6 £25
a. Figures "10" widely spaced (1½ mm.) ..

As No. 54, *but with Chinese character*, *T* **18**, *in addition.*

No.	Type	Description	Unused	Used
55	**2**	10 c. on 30 c. grey-green (No. 41*a*)	15 0	35 0
		a. Yellowish green	95 0	
		b. Figures "10" widely spaced (1½ mm.)	85 0	75 0
		c. Chinese character large (Type 19)	80 0	90 0
		d. Stamps with and without Chinese surch. *se-tenant* (pair)	£90	

1900–02. *Wmk. Crown CA. P* 14.

No.	Type	Description	Unused	Used
56	**1**	2 c. dull green	0 8	0 6
57	**2**	4 c. carmine	1 3	0 4
58	,,	5 c. yellow	5 0	6 0
59	,,	10 c. ultramarine	2 0	1 6
60	**1**	12 c. blue (1902)	8 0	25 0
61	**2**	30 c. brown (1901)	7 6	12 6

1903. *Wmk. Crown CA. P* 14.

No.	Type	Description	Unused	Used
62	**20**	1 c. dull purple and brown	0 6	0 8
63	,,	2 c. dull green	1 0	1 3
64	**21**	4 c. purple/*red*	1 3	0 8
65	,,	5 c. dull grn. & brn.-orange	3 6	6 0
66	,,	8 c. slate and violet ..	3 6	1 9
67	**20**	10 c. purple and blue/*blue* ..	5 0	1 9
68	**23**	12 c. green & purple/*yellow*	3 6	3 0
69	,,	20 c. slate and chestnut ..	7 6	4 0
70	**22**	30 c. dull green and black ..	8 6	5 0
71	**23**	50 c. dull green & magenta	17 6	20 0
72	**20**	$1 purple and sage-green	22 6	17 6
73	**23**	$2 slate and scarlet ..	70 0	85 0
74	**22**	$3 slate and dull blue ..	75 0	80 0
75	**23**	$5 purple and blue-green	95 0	£5
76	**22**	$10 slate and orange/*blue* ..	£18	£12

1904–7. *Wmk. Mult. Crown CA. P* 14.

No.	Type	Description	Unused	Used
77	**20**	2 c. dull green, CO ..	1 0	0 8
78	**21**	4 c. purple/*red*, CO ..	1 0	0 6
79	,,	5 c. dull green and brown-orange, CO	2 6	1 6
80	**22**	6 c. or.-vm. & pur., C ('07)	2 6	3 0
81	**21**	8 c. slate & violet, C ('07)	4 0	1 9
82	**20**	10 c. purple & blue/*blue*, O	6 0	1 6
83	**23**	12 c. grn. & pur./*yell.*, C ('07)	7 0	5 0
84	,,	20 c. slate and chestnut, CO	5 0	2 0
85	**22**	30 c. dull grn. & blk., CO	7 0	4 0
86	**23**	50 c. grn. & magenta, CO	10 0	4 0
87	**20**	$1 pur. & sage-green, CO	25 0	10 0
88	**23**	$2 slate and scarlet, CO	60 0	52 6
89	**22**	$3 slate and dull blue, C	70 0	80 0
90	**23**	$5 purple & blue-green, C	£6	80 0
91	**22**	$10 slate & orge./*blue*, CO	£18	£18

1907–11. *Wmk. Mult. Crown CA. P* 14.

No.	Type	Description	Unused	Used
92	**20**	1 c. brown, O (1910) ..	0 6	0 8
93	,,	2 c. deep green, O ..	4 6	0 8
		a. Green	1 6	0 3
94	**21**	4 c. carmine-red, O ..	1 0	0 3
95	**20**	10 c. bright ultramarine, O	2 6	0 6
96	**23**	20 c. pur. & sage-grn., C ('11)	12 6	12 6
97	**22**	30 c. pur. & or.-yell., C ('11)	7 6	7 6
98	**23**	50 c. black/*green*, C (1911)	12 6	7 6
99	,,	$2 car.-red & blk., C ('10)	50 0	85 0

1912–21. *Wmk. Mult. Crown CA. P* 14.

No.	Type	Description	Unused	Used
100	**24**	1 c. brown, O	1 9	0 6
		a. Black-brown	2 6	0 8
		b. Crown broken at right ..	£5	£6
101	,,	2 c. deep green, O ..	1 3	0 4
		a. Green	2 0	0 4
102	**25**	4 c. carmine-red, O ..	2 0	0 4
		a. Scarlet	6 0	1 6
103	**26**	6 c. yellow-orange, O ..	6 0	5 0
		a. Brown-orange	1 9	1 9
104	**25**	8 c. grey, O	10 0	3 6
		a. Slate	18 6	2 6
105	**24**	10 c. ultramarine, O ..	12 6	2 0
		a. Deep bright ultramarine ..	7 0	0 6
106	**27**	12 c. purple/*yellow*, C ..	7 0	4 0
		a. White back	5 0	5 0
107	,,	20 c. purple & sage-grn., C	5 0	2 0
108	**28**	25 c. purple and magenta, C (1914) .. (A)*	10 0	10 0
109	,,	25 c. purple and magenta, C (1920) .. (B)*	22 6	35 0
110	**26**	30 c. pur. & orge.-yell., C	27 6	10 0
		a. Purple and orange ..	8 6	2 6
111	**27**	50 c. black/*blue-green*, C..	10 0	3 0
		a. White back ..	6 0	4 0
		b. On blue-green, olive back ..	70 0	10 0
		c. On emerald surface ..	20 0	12 6
		d. On emerald back.. ..	15 0	20 0
112	**24**	$1 purple & blue/*blue*, C	17 6	10 0
113	**27**	$2 car.-red & grey-blk., C	40 0	20 0

114 **26** $3 green and purple, C 47 6 37 6
115 **27** $5 green & red/*green*, C 85 0 70 0
a. White back 60 0 55 0
b. On blue-green, olive back .. £5 50 0
116 **26** $10 pur. & black/*red*, C.. 80 0 30 0

* In Type A of the 25 c. the upper Chinese character in the left-hand label has a short vertical stroke crossing it at the foot. In Type B this stroke is absent.

1921–37. *Wmk. Mult Script CA.* P 14.

117 **24** 1 c. brown, O 0 4 0 3
118 ,, 2 c. blue-green, O .. 0 8 0 4
a. Yellow-green 2 0 0 9
118*b* ,, 2 c. grey, O (Apr. '37).. 1 9 2 6
119 **25** 3 c. grey, O ('31) .. 1 3 0 6
120 ,, 4 c. carmine-rose, O .. 0 8 0 3
a. Carmine-red 0 6 0 3
b. Top of lower Chinese characters at right broken off 75 0 80 0
121 ,, 5 c. violet, O ('31) .. 0 8 0 4
122 ,, 8 c. grey, O 4 0 6 6
123 ,, 8 c. orange, O 1 9 1 9
124 **24** 10 c. bright ultram., O.. 0 8 0 3
124*a* **27** 12 c. purple/*yellow*, C ('33) 3 0 2 6
125 ,, 20 c. pur. & sage-grn., C 3 0 1 0
126 **28** 25 c. pur. & mag., C (B.) 2 0 2 6
127 **26** 30 c. pur.&chrome-yell., C 6 0 2 0
a. Purple & orange-yellow 17 6 7 6
128 **27** 50 c. black/*emerald*, C ('24) 5 0 2 0
129 **24** $1 pur. & blue/*blue*, C 10 0 4 0
130 **27** $2 carmine-red & grey-black, C 27 6 10 0
131 **26** $3 green & dull purple, C ('26) 65 0 20 0
132 **27** $5 green & red/*emerald*, C ('25) 65 0 35 0

1935 (6 May). *Silver Jubilee. As Nos.* 91/4 *of Antigua, but ptd. by B.W. & Co.* P 11 × 12.

133 3 c. ultramarine & grey-black 0 6 0 9
134 5 c. green and indigo .. 1 0 0 9
a. Extra flagstaff £10
135 10 c. brown and deep blue .. 3 0 3 6
136 20 c. slate and purple.. .. 4 0 5 0

For illustration of "extra flagstaff" variety see Bechuanaland.

1937 (12 May). *Coronation. As Nos.* 13/5 *of Aden, but ptd. by B.W. & Co.* P 11 × 11½.

137 4 c. green 0 3 0 5
138 15 c. carmine 0 9 1 0
139 25 c. blue 1 3 1 6

29. King George VI.

1938–52. *Wmk. Mult. Script CA.* P 14.

140 **29** 1 c. brown (24.5.38) .. 0 3 0 6
a. Pale brown (27.2.52) .. 0 6 1 0
141 ,, 2 c. grey (5.4.38) .. 0 6 0 6
a. Perf. 15 × 14 ('41) .. 2 6 2 6
142 ,, 4 c. orange (5.4.38) .. 0 8 0 6
a. Perf. 15 × 14 ('46) .. 0 4 0 8
143 ,, 5 c. green (24.5.38) .. 0 4 0 3
a. Perf. 15 × 14 ('41) .. 0 4 1 0
144 ,, 8 c. red-brown (1.11.41) 1 0 1 3
a. Error. Imperf. ..
145 ,, 10 c. bright violet (13.4.38) 5 0 3 0
a. Dull violet ('46) .. 0 10 0 3
b. Perf. 15 × 14 *Dull vio.*('41) 0 10 1 3
146 ,, 15 c. scarlet (13.4.38) .. 0 6 0 6
147 **29** 20 c. black (1.2.46) .. 1 0 1 0
148 ,, 20 c. scarlet ('48) .. 0 8 0 8
149 ,, 25 c. bright blue (5.4.38) 1 3 1 0
150 ,, 25 c. pale sage-grn. (9.4.46) 1 3 1 6
151 ,, 30 c. yell.-olive (13.4.38) 40 0 20 0
a. P 15 × 14. *Sage-grn.* ('41) 1 9 3 6
152 ,, 30 c. blue (9.4.46) .. 1 3 0 6
153 ,, 50 c. purple, O (13.4.38) 1 6 1 9
a. Bright purple, C ('47) .. 1 9 0 8
b. P 15 × 14. *Dull lilac* ('41) 2 0 2 6
154 ,, 80 c. carmine, C (2.2.48) 2 6 1 6
155 ,, $1 pale purple & blue, C 7 6 7 6
a. Pale reddish purple and blue, O ('41) 3 0 4 6
156 ,, $1 red-orge. & grn., OC ('46).. .. .. 2 6 1 0
157 ,, $2 red-orange and green, C (25.5.38).. .. 42 6 20 0
158 ,, $2 violet & scarlet, OC ('46).. .. .. 7 0 2 6
159 ,, $5 purple & scarlet, C (2.6.38) 20 0 12 6
160 ,, $5 grn. & violet, O ('46) 17 6 15 0
a. Yellow-grn. & vio. OC ('46) 17 6 5 0
161 ,, $10 green & violet, C (2.6.38) 60 0 45 0
162 ,, $10 vio. & blue, O ('46) 25 0 30 0
a. Reddish vio. & blue, C ('47) 25 0 6 0

The varieties perf. 15 × 14 with the exception of the 4 c. were printed and perforated by Bradbury, Wilkinson & Co., Ltd. from De La Rue plates and are on rough-surfaced paper. The 4 c. is smoother.

No. 144*a*. One imperforate sheet was found and most of the stamps were sold singly to the public at a branch P.O. and used for postage.

30. Street Scene.

34. The Hong Kong Bank.

31. Liner and Junk.

32. The University.

33. The Harbour.

35. China Clipper and Seaplane.

(Des. W. E. Jones. Recess. Bradbury, Wilkinson & Co.)

1941 (26 Feb.). *Centenary of British Occupation. Wmk. Mult. Script CA (sideways on horiz. designs). P* $13\frac{1}{2} \times 13$ *(2 c. and 25 c.) or* $13 \times 13\frac{1}{2}$ *(others).*

163 **30** 2 c. orange & chocolate .. 1 3 1 6
164 **31** 4 c. brt. purple & carmine 1 9 4 9
165 **32** 5 c. black and green .. 1 0 0 9
166 **33** 15 c. black and scarlet .. 2 9 3 9
167 **34** 25 c. chocolate and blue .. 6 0 7 0
168 **35** $1 blue and orange .. 9 0 11 6

36. King George VI and Phœnix.

(Des. W. E. Jones. Recess. De La Rue & Co.)

1946 (29 Aug.). *Victory. Wmk. Mult. Script CA. P* 13.

169 **36** 30 c. blue and red .. 1 6 2 0
170 ,, $1 brown and red .. 4 0 6 0

1948 (22 Dec.). *Royal Silver Wedding. As Nos.* 30/1 *of Aden.*

171 10 c. violet 0 6 0 6
172 $10 carmine 25 0 30 0

1949 (10 Oct.). 75*th Anniv. of Universal Postal Union. As Nos.* 114/7 *of Antigua.*

173 10 c. violet 0 6 0 6
174 20 c. carmine-red 1 0 1 0
175 30 c. deep blue 1 6 1 6
176 80 c. bright reddish purple .. 4 0 4 6

1953 (2 June). *Coronation. As Nos.* 47 *of Aden.*

177 10 c. black and slate-lilac .. 0 6 0 6

37. Queen Elizabeth II.

1954 (5 Jan.)–**60.** *Wmk. Mult. Script CA. P* 14.

178 **37** 5 c. orange 0 5 0 6
a. Imperf. (pair) £200
179 ,, 10 c. lilac (*shades*) .. 0 6 0 4
180 ,, 15 c. green (*shades*) .. 0 8 0 6
181 ,, 20 c. brown, C 0 8 0 3
182 ,, 25 c. scarlet (*shades*), C .. 0 10 0 6
183 ,, 30 c. grey (*shades*), C .. 1 6 0 6
184 ,, 40 c. bright blue (*shades*), C 1 6 1 0
185 ,, 50 c. reddish purple, C .. 1 6 0 6
186 ,, 65 c. grey, C (20.6.60) .. 1 9 1 6
187 ,, $1 orange and green, C 2 3 0 8
188 ,, $1.30, blue & red (*shades*), C (20.6.60) 3 0 1 6
189 ,, $2 reddish violet and scarlet (*shades*), C .. 5 0 2 0
190 ,, $5 grn. & pur. (*shades*), C 12 6 4 0
191 ,, $10 reddish violet and brt. blue (*shades*), C 25 0 8 6

No. 178a. One sheet was found: 90 stamps imperf., 10 perf. three sides only.

38. University Arms.

(Photo. Harrison & Sons.)

1961 (11 Sept.). *Golden Jubilee of Hong Kong University. W* w. **12.** *P* $11\frac{1}{2} \times 12$.

192 **38** $1 multicoloured .. 4 6 5 6
a. Gold ptg. omitted ..

39. Statue of Queen Victoria.

(Photo. Harrison & Sons.)

1962 (4 May). *Stamp Centenary. W* w.**12.** *P* $14\frac{1}{2}$.

193 **39** 10 c. black and magenta .. 0 10 0 10
194 ,, 20 c. black and light blue 1 6 1 9
195 ,, 50 c. black and bistre .. 2 9 3 3

40. Queen Elizabeth II (after Annigoni). **41.**

(Photo. Harrison & Sons.)

1962 (4 Oct.). *W* w.**12.** *P* 15×14 *(5 c. to $1) or* $14 \times 14\frac{1}{2}$ *(others).*

196 **40** 5 c. red-orange 0 3 0 2
197 ,, 10 c. reddish violet .. 0 4 0 2
198 ,, 15 c. emerald 0 5 0 2
199 ,, 20 c. red-brown 0 6 0 3
200 ,, 25 c. cerise 0 7 0 4

201 **40** 30 c. deep grey-blue 0 8 0 4
202 ,, 40 c. deep bluish green .. 0 10 0 5
203 ,, 50 c. scarlet 0 11 0 6
204 ,, 65 c. ultramarine 1 2 0 8
205 ,, $1 sepia 1 9 0 8
206 **41** $1.30, multicoloured .. 2 4 1 0
207 ,, $2 multicoloured .. 3 6 1 0
208 ,, $5 multicoloured .. 8 4 3 0
209 ,, $10 multicoloured .. 16 6 7 6
210 ,, $20 multicoloured .. 31 9 13 6

1963 (4 June). *Freedom from Hunger. As No. 63 of Aden, but additionally inscr. in Chinese characters.*
211 $1.30 bluish green 3 0 3 0

1963 (2 Sept.). *Red Cross Centenary. As Nos. 147/8 of Antigua, but additionally inscr. in Chinese characters.*
212 10 c. red and black .. 0 6 0 7
213 $1.30 red and blue .. 3 0 3 0

1965 (17 May). *I.T.U. Centenary. As Nos. 166/7 of Antigua.*
214 10 c. light purple and orange-yellow 0 6 0 8
215 $1. 30, olive-yellow and deep bluish green .. 3 0 3 6

1965 (25 Oct.). *International Co-operation Year. As Nos. 168/9 of Antigua.*
216 10 c. reddish pur. & turq.-grn. 0 6 0 7
217 $1.30, dp. bluish green & lav. 3 0 3 6

1966 (24 Jan.). *Churchill Commemoration. As Nos. 170/3 of Antigua but additionally inscr. in Chinese characters.*
218 10 c. new blue 0 5 0 6
219 50 c. deep green 1 1 1 3
220 $1. 30, brown 2 10 3 6
221 $2 bluish violet 4 6 5 6

POSTAGE DUE STAMPS.

D 1

1923 (Dec.)–**56**. *Wmk. Mult. Script CA (upright or sideways). P* 14.
D1 **D 1** 1 c. brown, O 0 6 0 8
a. Chalk-surfaced paper, wmk. sideways (21.3.56) 0 1 0 4
D2 ,, 2 c. green 0 6 1 6
D3 ,, 4 c. scarlet 1 6 2 6
D4 ,, 6 c. yellow 2 6 5 0
D5 ,, 10 c. bright ultramarine .. 3 6 2 6

1938 (Feb.)–**63**. *Wmk. Mult. Script CA (sideways). P* 14.
D 6 **D 1** 2 c. grey, O 0 6 0 8
a. Chalky paper (21.3.56) 0 1 0 4
D 7 ,, 4 c. orange, O .. 0 8 0 10
a. Chalky paper. *orange-yellow* (23.5.61) .. 0 6 0 8
D 8 ,, 6 c. scarlet 0 3 0 9
D 8*a* ,, 8 c. chestnut ('46) .. 0 3 0 9
D 9 ,, 10 c. violet, O 0 8 1 0
a. Chalky paper (17.9.63) 0 4 0 6
D11 ,, 20 c. black ('46) .. 0 6 1 3
D12 ,, 50 c. blue ('47) 0 11 2 0

1965 (15 Apr.). *As No. D7a but W* w.**12** *and colour changed.*
D15 **D 1** 4 c. yellow-orange, C.. 0 2 0 4

FISCALS, ETC., USED FOR POSTAGE.

I. Stamps inscribed "Stamp Duty."

NOTE—The dated circular "Hong Kong" cancellation with "Paid All" in lower segment normally indicates fiscal, not postal, use, but a few instances are known where it was applied *in red*, for postal purposes.

F 1

F 2

F 3

1874–1902. *Wmk. Crown CC.*

(*a*) *P* 15½×15.
F1 **F 1** $2 olive-green 40 0 10 0
a. Thin paper 70 0 25 0
F2 **F 2** $3 dull violet 15 0 8 0
a. Thin paper 27 6 20 0
b. Bluish paper .. ..
F3 **F 3** $10 rose-carmine £12 £7

(*b*) *P* 14.
F4 **F 1** $2 dull bluish grn. (1890) 20 0 25 0
F5 **F 2** $3 dull mauve (1902) .. 20 0 25 0
a. Bluish paper .. ..
F6 **F 3** $10 grey-green (? 1884) .. £7

12 CENTS (F 4)

5 DOLLARS (F 5)

1882. *No.* F3 *surch. with Type* F 4.
F7 **F 3** 12 c. on $10 rose-carmine 37 6 60

1891 (Jan.). *Surch. with Type* F 5. *Wmk. Crown CA. P* 14.
F8 **F 3** $5 on $10 purple/*red* .. 35 0 40

F 6

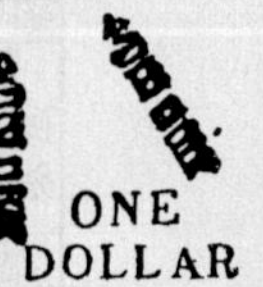

(F 7)

1890. *Wmk. Crown CA. P 14.*
F9 F **6** 2 c. dull purple 7 0 6 0

1897 (SEPT.). *Surch. with Type* F **7.**
F10 F **1** $1 on $2 olive-green (No. F1) 15 0 22 6
a. Chinese surcharge wholly omitted .. £16 £14
F11 ,, $1 on $2 dull bluish green (No. F4) 25 0 37 6
a. Chinese surcharge wholly omitted 75 0 60 0
b. Diag. portion of Chinese surcharge omitted ..

F 8

1938 (11 JAN.). *Wmk. Mult. Script CA. P 14.*
F12 F **8** 5 c. green 70 0 10 0

Authorised for postal use from Jan. 11th to 21st, 1938.

II. Stamps specially surcharged for use on Postcards.

3 CENTS (P 1) **THREE** (P 2)

1879. *Wmk. Crown CC. P 14. Surch. as Type* P **1.**
P1 **3** 3 c. on 16 c. yellow (No. 22) 55 0 55 0
P2 ,, 5 c. on 18 c. lilac (No. 13) .. 45 0 45 0
No. P 2 surch. with Type P **2.**
P3 **3** 3 on 5 c. on 18 c. lilac .. £32

III. Stamps overprinted "S.O." (Stamp Office), or "S.D." (Stamp Duty).

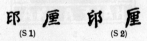

S. O. 印 厘 (S 1) **S. D.** 印 厘 (S 2)

1891. *Optd. with Types* S **1** *or* S **2.**
S1 S **1** 2 c. carmine (No. 33) .. 45 0 45 0
S2 S **2** 2 c. carmine (No. 33) .. 25 0 30 0
S3 S **1** 10 c. purple/*red* (No. 40) .. 60 0 60 0

Other fiscal stamps are found apparently postally used, but there is no evidence that this use was authorised.

JAPANESE OCCUPATION OF HONG KONG.

壹圓五拾錢 暫定 香港總督部 (1) 叁圓 暫定 香港總督部 (2)

1945 (MAR.). *Stamps of Japan surch. with T* **1** *(No. J1) or as T* **2.**
J1 1.50 yen on 1 s. brown 2 6 10 0
J2 3 yen on 2 s. scarlet 2 6 10 0
J3 5 yen on 5 s. claret 65 0 30 0

No. J3 has four characters of value similarly arranged but differing from T **2.**

Designs ($18\frac{1}{2} \times 22$ mm.):—1 s. Girl Worker; 2 s. Gen. Nogi; 5 s. Admiral Togo.

CHINA.

BRITISH POST OFFICES.

CHINA

(1)

1917–21. *Stamps of Hong Kong, 1912–21 (wmk. Mult. Crown CA), optd. with T* **1.**
1 1 c. brown, O 0 4 0 4
a. Crown broken at side .. £9
b. Black-brown, O 0 4 0 4
2 2 c. green, O 0 0 0 3
3 4 c. carmine-red, O 0 8 0 2
4 6 c. orange, O 1 6 0 8
5 8 c. slate, O 1 9 1 6
6 10 c. ultramarine, O 3 0 0 6
7 12 c. purple/*yellow*, C .. 3 6 2 0
8 20 c. purple & sage-green, C 4 6 1 0
9 25 c. purple & magenta, C (A) 6 0 10 0
11 30 c. pur. & orange-yellow, C 8 6 2 6
12 50 c. blk./*bl.-grn.*, C (*olive back*) 15 0 4 0
a. On emerald surface 10 6 7 6
b. On emerald back 9 0 6 0
13 $1 reddish purple and bright blue/*blue*, C 20 0 4 0
a. Grey-pur. & blue/blue, C .. 25 0 6 0
14 $2 car.-red & grey-black, C 50 0 27 6
15 $3 green and purple, C .. 60 0 50 0
16 $5 green and red/*blue-green*, C (*olive back*) 40 0 50 0
17 $10 purple & black/*red.*, C .. 75 0 90 0

1922–27. *As last, but wmk. Mult. Script CA.*
18 1 c. brown, O 0 4 1 3
19 2 c. green, O 0 4 1 8
20 4 c. carmine-rose, O 0 6 0 3
a. Lower Chinese character at right broken at top 70 0 80 0
21 6 c. orange-yellow, O .. 1 0 2 6
22 8 c. grey, O 1 3 1 6
23 10 c. bright ultramarine, O .. 1 9 2 0
24 20 c. purple and sage-green, C 1 9 2 6
25 25 c. purple & magenta, C (B) 4 0 7 6
26 50 c. black/*emerald*, C (1927) 5 0 17 6
27 $1 purple & blue/*blue*, C .. 12 6 18 6
28 $2 car.-red & grey-black, C 30 0 30 0

The use of these stamps was discontinued as from 1st Oct., 1930, on the closing of the British P.Os concerned.

INDIA.

— **SIMPLIFICATION (see** INTRODUCTION — **Nos. 1 to 34.** 1, 2, 14, 23, 32.

(1)

(Embossed. De La Rue & Co.)

1852 (1 July). "Scinde Dawk."
s.1 **1** ½ a. white £300 £120
s.2 " ½ a. blue £600 £200
s.3 " ½ a. scarlet .. .. .. — £600

These stamps were issued under the authority of Sir Bartle Frere, Commissioner in Scinde. They were suppressed in October, 1854.

GENERAL ISSUES.

Under the Honourable East India Company.

2 (much reduced in size).

3
(Actual size of ½ a. and 1 a. stamps.)

(The ½ a., 1 a. and 4 a. were lithographed in Calcutta at the office of the Surveyor-General on ungummed paper watermarked as T **2** (the "No. 4" paper) with the Arms of the East India Co. in the sheet. The watermark is sideways on the ½ a. and 1 a., and upright on the 4 a. where the paper was trimmed so that only the central portion showing the oval and the Arms was used.)

1854 (April). *T* **3.**
1 ½ a. vermilion £75

This stamp, with 9½ arches in the side border, was prepared for use and a supply was sent to Bombay, but was not officially issued.

4

1854 (1 Oct.). *Die I.*
2 **4** ½ a. blue 55 0 25 0
a. Printed on both sides — £350
3 ,, ½ a. pale blue £5 30 0
4 **4** ½ a. deep blue 75 0 30 0
5 ,, ½ a. indigo £5 45 0

We give the official date of issue, but copies are known which were put on sale as much as a fortnight earlier.

These stamps were printed between 5 May and 29 July, 1854. (Printing 30 millions).

4a.

Die II.
6 **4a** ½ a. blue £5 £10
7 ,, ½ a. indigo £5 £10

The bulk were printed between 1 and 12 August, 1854, with some extra sheets on or before 2 Nov. (Printing about 2 millions).

5

Die III.
8 **5** ½ a. pale blue £35 70 0
8a ,, ½ a. blue £30 60 0
9 ,, ½ a. greenish blue £35 £10
10 ,, ½ a. deep blue £40 95 0

These stamps were printed between 3 July and 25 August, 1855. (Printing about 4¾ millions).

The Three Dies of the ½ Anna.

Die I. *Chignon shading* mostly solid blobs of colour. *Corner ornaments*, solid blue stars with long points, always conspicuous. *Band below diadem* always heavily shaded. *Diadem and jewels.* The middle and right-hand jewels usually show a clearly defined cross. *Outer frame lines.* Stamps with white or faintly shaded chignons and weak frame lines are usually Die I (worn state).

Die II. *Chignon* normally shows much less shading. A strong line of colour separates hair and chignon. *Corner ornaments.* The right blue star is characteristic (see illustration) but tends to disappear. It never obliterates the white cross. *Band below diadem.* As Die but heavier, sometimes solid. *Diadem and jewels.* As Die I but usually fainter. *Outer frame lines.* Always strong and conspicuous.

DIE III. *Chignon shading* shows numerous fine lines, often blurred. *Corner ornaments* have a small hollow blue star with short points, which tends to disappear as in Die II. *Band below diadem,* shows light shading or hardly any shading. *Diadem and jewels.* Jewels usually marked with a solid squat star. The ornaments between the stars appear in the shape of a characteristic white " w ". *Frame lines* variable.

The above notes give the general characteristics of the three Dies, but there are a few exceptions due to retouching, etc.

6

(See note below No. 14.)

Die I.

:1	**6** 1 a. deep red	£15	80	0
:2	,, 1 a. red	£15	70	0

Printing of these stamps commenced on 6 July, 1854, and continued into August. Printing, see note below No. 14.)

7

ie II. With more lines in the chignon than in Die I, and with white curved line where chignon joins head.*

3	**7** 1 a. deep red	£8	75	0
	,, 1 a. dull red	75 0	75	0

* Very worn printings of Die II may be found ith chignon nearly as white as in Die I.

In stamps of Die I, however, the small blob red projecting from the hair into the chignon always visible.

These stamps were printed in August and September, 1854. (Total printing, Dies I and II together, about $7\frac{3}{4}$ millions.)

8

Die III. With pointed bust.

15	**8** 1 a. red	£55	£18
16	,, 1 a. dull red	£55	£18

These stamps were printed between 7 July and 25 August, 1855. (Printing, about $1\frac{1}{2}$ millions.)

9. (Actual size.)

NOTE. Our catalogue prices for Four Annas stamps are for cut-square specimens, with clear margins and in good condition. Cut-to-shape copies are worth from 3% to 20% of these prices according to condition.

Four Dies of the Head:—

I. II.

DIE I. Band of diadem and chignon strongly shaded.

DIE II. Lines in band of diadem worn. Few lines in the upper part of the chignon, which, however, shows a strongly drawn comma-like mark.

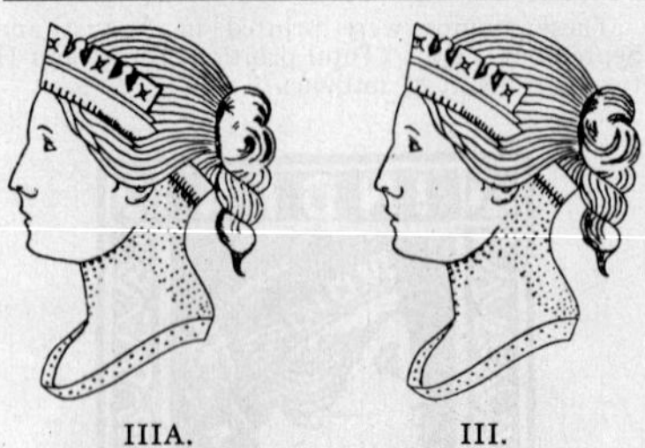

IIIA. III.

Die IIIA. Upper part of chignon partly redrawn, showing two short, curved vertical lines in the NE corner. "Comma" has disappeared.

Die III. Upper part of chignon completely redrawn, but band of diadem shows only a few short lines.

Two Dies of the Frame:—

DIE I. Outer frame lines weak. Very small dots of colour, or none at all, in the "R" and "A's" The white lines to the right of "INDIA" are separated, by a line of colour, from the inner white circle.

DIE II. Outer frame lines strengthened. Dots in the "R" and "A's" strong. White lines to right of "INDIA" break into inner white circle.

1854 (15 OCT.). *T* **9**. *W* **2** *upright, central portion only. Imperf.*

1st Printing. Head Die I. Frame Die I. Stamps widely spaced and separated by blue wavy line.

		Un.	*Used*	*Us. pr.*
17	4 a. indigo and red	£110	£32	£110
18	4 a. blue & pale red	£100	£32	£110
	a. Head inverted (*cut to shape*)	—	£400–£1400	—

This printing was made between 13 and 28 Oct., 1854. (Printing, 206,040.)

2nd Printing Head Die II. Frame Die I. Stamps widely spaced and separated by blue wavy line.

19	4 a. blue and red	£85	£26	£80
20	4 a. indigo & dp. red	£95	£30	£85

This printing was made between 1 and 13 Dec., 1854. (Printing, 393,960.)

3rd Printing. Head, Dies II, IIIA and III. Frame, Dies I and II. Stamps widely spaced and separated by blue wavy line.

21	4 a. bt. blue & bt. red (Head III, Frame I)	£300	£80	£200
	a. Head II, Frame I ..	—	£110	—
	b. Head IIIA, Frame I	—	£100	£275
	c. Head III, Frame II			

This printing was made between 10 March and 2 April, 1855. (Printing, 138,960.)

4th Printing. Head Die III.. Frame Die II. Stamps closely spaced 2 to 2½ mm. without separating line.

22	4 a. dp blue & red ..	£55	£24	£65
23	4 a. blue and red ..	£40	£22	£60
24	4 a. p. blue & p. red	£55	£24	£65

This printing was made between 3 April and 9 May, 1855. (Printing, 540,960.)

5th Printing. Head Die III. Frame Die II Stamps spaced 4 to 6 mm. without separating line.

25	4 a. blue & rose-red ..	£95	£32	£11
26	4 a. dp. blue & red ..	£80	£26	£10

This printing was made between 4 Oct. and 3 Nov., 1855. (Printing, 380,064.)

Serrated perf. about 18, or pin-perf.

27 ½ a. blue (Die I) .. ..
28 1 a. red (Die I) .. ..
29 1 a. red (Die II) .. ..
30 4 a. blue & red (Die II) ..

This is believed to be an unofficial perforation Most of the known specimens bear Madras circle postmarks (C122 to C126), but some are know with Bombay postmarks. Beware of fakes.

10

11

(Plate made at Mint, Calcutta. Typo., Stam Office.)

1854 (6 OCT.). *Sheet wmk. sideways, as W* **2** *b with* "No. 3" *at top left.* Imperf.*

31	**10**	2 a. pale green ..	.. 75 0	35	
32	„	2 a. deep green ..	.. 70 0	30	
33	„	2 a. dull green ..	.. 90 0	35	
34	„	2 a. emerald-green ..	.. £30	£	

* The 2 a. was also printed on paper wi sheet wmk. incorporating the words "STAM OFFICE. One Anna", etc. (Price £5 un. or us

There is a wide range of shade in the 2 a., the main groups being blue-green, yellow-green, and green, varying in brightness and depth.

Many stamps show traces of lines external to the design shown in our illustration. Stamps with this frame on all four sides are scarce.

Many reprints of the ½, 1, 2, and 4 a. exist.

PRINTERS. All Indian stamps from No. 35 to 200 were typographed by De La Rue & Co.

1855 (Oct.). *Blue glazed paper. No wmk. P* 14.

35 **11** 4 a. black £15 40 0
a. Imperf. (pair) .. .. — £15
b. Bisected (on cover) .. .. — £40
36 „ 8 a. carmine (Die I) £15 50 0
a. Imperf. (pair) £45
b. Bisected (on cover) .. .. — £40

The first supply of the 4 a. was on white paper, but it is difficult to distinguish from No. 45.

In the 8 a. the paper varies from deep blue to almost white.

For difference between Die I and Die II in the 8 a., see illustrations above No. 73.

1856–64. *No wmk. Paper yellowish to white. P* 14.

37 **11** ½ a. blue (Die I) 17 6 2 0
a. Imperf. (pair) £10 £20
38 „ ½ a. pale blue (Die I) .. 17 6 2 0
39 „ 1 a. brown 30 0 5 0
a. Imperf. between (vert. pair)
b. Imperf. (pair) £25
c. Bisected (on cover) ..
40 „ 1 a. deep brown 27 6 6 0
41 „ 2 a. dull pink £6 42 6
a. Imperf. (pair) £35
42 „ 2 a. yellow-buff 70 0 22 6
a. Imperf. (pair) £28 £30
43 „ 2 a. yellow 70 0 27 6
44 „ 2 a. orange £5 27 6
a. Imperf. (pair) £40 £45
45 „ 4 a. black 65 0 17 6
a. Bisected diagonally (2 a.) (on cover) .. .. — £40
b. Imperf. (pair) £35 £40
46 „ 4 a. grey-black 65 0 15 0
47 „ 4 a. green (1864) £15 57 6
48 „ 8 a. carmine (Die I) .. 65 0 32 6
49 „ 8 a. pale carmine (Die I) .. 60 0 32 6
a. Bisected (on cover) .. .. — £40

Prepared for use, but not officially issued.

50 **11** 2 a. yellow-green £10 £15
a. Imperf. (pair) £12

This stamp is known with trial obliterations, and a few are known postally used. It also exists *imperf.*, but is not known used thus.

For difference between Die I and Die II in the ½ a., see illustrations above No. 75.

UNDER THE CROWN

On the 1 November, 1858, Her Majesty Queen Victoria assumed the government of the territories in India "heretofore administered in trust by the Honourable East India Company".

12

13

1860 (9 May). *No wmk. P* 14.

51 **12** 8 p. purple/*bluish* .. £15 £12
52 „ 8 p. purple/*white* .. 32 6 22 6
a. Bisected diagonally (4 p.) (on cover) .. .. — £35
b. Imperf. (pair) £35 £45
53 „ 8 p. mauve 40 0 32 6

The bisected stamps of the issues of 1855–60 listed above were used exclusively in the Straits Settlements during shortage of stocks of certain values. Prices are for Singapore cancellations on original. Penang marks are considerably rarer.

1865. *Paper yellowish to white. W* **13.** *P* 14.

54 **11** ½ a. blue (Die I) 8 6 1 0
a. Imperf. .. .. .. — £17
55 „ ½ a. pale blue (Die I) .. 4 0 1 0
56 **12** 8 p. purple 16 0 15 0
57 „ 8 p. mauve 20 0 17 6
58 **11** 1 a. pale brown 10 0 1 0
59 „ 1 a. deep brown 4 0 1 0
60 „ 1 a. chocolate 8 6 1 0
61 „ 2 a. yellow 35 0 10 0
62 „ 2 a. orange 42 6 6 0
a. Imperf. .. .. .. — £40
63 „ 2 a. brown-orange 22 6 10 0
64 „ 4 a. green £6 55 0
65 „ 8 a. carmine (Die I) .. £15 £6

The 8 p. mauve, No. 57, is found variously surcharged "NINE" or "NINE PIE" by local postmasters, to indicate that it was being sold for 9 pies, as was the case at one period. Such surcharges were made without Government sanction.

The stamps of India, wmk. Elephant's Head, surcharged with a crown and value in "cents," were used in the Straits Settlements; q.v.

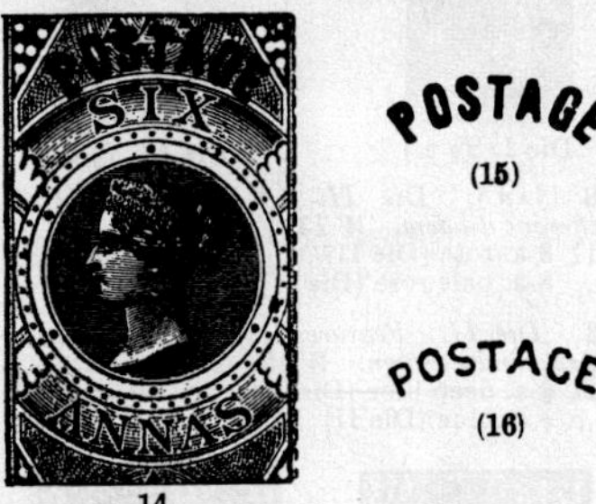

14 (15) (16)

1866 (28 June). *T* **14** *optd. P* 14 (*at sides only*).

(*a*) *As T* **15.**

66 6 a. purple (G.) £30 £10
a. Overprint inverted .. .. — £150

There are 20 different types of this overprint.

(*b*) *With T* **16.**

68 6 a. purple (G.) £50 £8

17 18

(4 annas.)

Die I Die II

Die I.—Mouth closed, line from corner of mouth downwards only. Pointed chin.

Die II.—Mouth slightly open; lips, chin, and throat defined by line of colour. Rounded chin.

1866 (Sept.)–**1867.** *W* **13.** *P* 14.

69 **17** 4 a. green (Die I) 22 6 2 6
70 ,, 4 a. deep green (Die I) .. 25 0 2 6
71 ,, 4 a. blue-green (Die II) .. 20 0 2 0
72 **18** 6 a. 8 p. slate 40 0 60 0
a. Imperf. (pair) £35

Die I. (8 a.)

Die II. (8 a.)

Die I. (½ a.)

Die II. (½ a.)

1868 (Jan.). *Die II. Profile redrawn and different diadem.* *W* **13.** *P* 14.

73 **11** 8 a. rose (Die II) 25 0 17 6
74 ,, 8 a. pale rose (Die II) .. 27 6 15 0

1873. *Die II. Features, especially the mouth, more firmly drawn.* *W* **13.** *P* 14.

75 **11** ½ a. deep blue (Die II) .. 6 0 1 0
76 ,, ½ a. blue (Die II) 6 0 1 0

19

20

1874. *W* **13.** *P* 14.

77 **19** 9 p. bright mauve 15 0 20 0
78 ,, 9 p. pale mauve 15 0 22 6
79 **20** 1 r. slate 32 6 30 0

21

22

1876 (Oct.). *W* **13.** *P* 14.

80 **21** 6 a. olive-bistre 10 0 7 6
81 ,, 6 a. pale brown 10 0 7 6
82 **22** 12 a. Venetian red 12 6 17 6

EMPIRE OF INDIA

Queen Victoria assumed the title of Empress of India in 1877, and the inscription on the stamps was altered from "EAST INDIA" to "INDIA."

23

24

25

26

27

28

29

30

31

32

33

34

1882–88. *W* **34.** *P* 14.

84 **23** ½ a. deep blue-green .. 0 8 0 4
85 ,, ½ a. blue-green 0 8 0 4
a. Double impression .. £9
86 **24** 9 p. rose 3 0 5
87 ,, 9 p. aniline carmine .. 2 0 3

88	25	1 a. brown-purple	1	6	0	4
89	,,	1 a. plum	1	6	0	4
90	26	1 a. 6 p. sepia	2	6	2	6
91	27	2 a. pale blue	2	0	0	6
92	,,	2 a. blue	5	0	0	6
		a. Double impression	£18		£15	
93	28	3 a. orange	27	6	10	0
94	,,	3 a. brown-orange	7	6	1	0
95	29	4 a. olive-green	10	0	1	3
96	,,	4 a. slate-green	8	6	1	3
97	30	4 a. 6 p. yellow-green	15	0	15	0
98	31	8 a. dull mauve	15	0	7	6
99	,,	8 a. magenta	15	0	6	0
100	32	12 a. purple/*red*	10	0	7	6
101	33	1 r. slate	10	0	10	0

No. 92a is from a sheet of 2 a. stamps with a very marked double impression issued in Karachi in 1896–97. Most of the stamps were used on telegrams.

2½ As.

(35)

1891 (1 Jan.). *No.* 97 *surcharged with T* **35**.

102	2½ a. on 4½ a. yellow-green	6	0	10	0

There are several varieties in this surcharge due to variations in the relative positions of the letters and figures.

36

37

1892 (Jan.)–**1897**. *W* **34**. *P* 14.

103	36	2½ a. yellow-green	2	6	2	0
104	,,	2½ a. pale blue-green (1897)	5	0	2	6
105	37	1 r. green and rose	25	0	15	0
106	,,	1 r. green & aniline carm.	10	6	10	0

38

(Head of Queen from portrait by von Angeli.)

1895. *T* **38**. *Wmk. Star, T* **34**. *P* 14.

107	2 r. carmine & yellow-brown	25	0	15	0
107*a*	2 r. carmine and brown	30	0	15	0
108	3 r. brown and green	40	0	20	0
109	5 r. ultramarine and violet	45	0	40	0

(39)

40

1898. *No.* 85 *surch. with T* **39**.

110	23	"¼" on ½ a. blue-green	0	4	0	4
		a. Surcharge double	£7			
		b. Stamp printed double	£10			

1899. *W* **34**. *P* 14.

111	40	3 p. aniline carmine	0	4	0	4

1900. *W* **34**. *P* 14.

112	40	3 p. grey	0	3	0	3
113	23	½ a. pale yellow-green	1	3	0	4
114	,,	½ a. yellow-green	0	10	0	4
115	25	1 a. carmine	0	10	0	4
116	27	2 a. pale violet	7	6	3	0
117	,,	2 a. mauve	6	6	2	6
118	36	2½ a. ultramarine	10	0	10	0

41

42

43

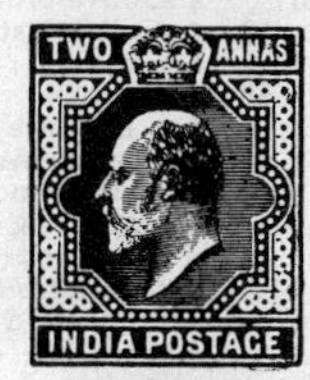

44

45

46

47

48

49

50

51  52

1902–11. *W* **34.** *P* 14.

No.	Type	Value	Description	Unused s.	d.	Used s.	d.
119	**41**	3 p.	grey	0	4	0	3
120	,,	3 p.	slate-grey (1904) ..	0	4	0	3
121	**42**	½ a.	yellow-green ..	1	6	0	8
122	,,	½ a.	green	1	3	0	3
123	**43**	1 a.	carmine	0	6	0	3
124	**44**	2 a.	violet	5	0	0	4
125	,,	2 a.	mauve	4	0	0	3
126	**45**	2½ a.	ultramarine	8	6	1	0
127	**46**	3 a.	orange-brown ..	8	6	1	3
128	**47**	4 a.	olive	7	6	1	6
129	,,	4 a.	pale olive	6	6	1	3
130	,,	4 a.	olive-brown	20	0	10	0
131	**48**	6 a.	olive-bistre	20	0	12	6
132	,,	6 a.	maize	17	6	10	0
133	**49**	8 a.	mauve	15	0	4	0
134	,,	8 a.	magenta (1910) ..	15	0	4	0
135	**50**	12 a.	purple/*red*	17	6	10	0
136	**51**	1 r.	green and carmine ..	10	0	3	6
137	,,	1 r.	green & scar. (1911)	30	0	5	0
138	**52**	2 r.	rose-red & yell.-brn.	25	0	10	0
139	,,	2 r.	carmine & yell.-brn.	22	6	10	0
140	,,	3 r.	brown & grn. (1904)	40	0	30	0
141	,,	3 r.	red-brn. & grn. (1911)	40	0	45	0
142	,,	5 r.	ultra. & violet (1904)	80	0	80	0
143	,,	5 r.	ultramarine & deep lilac (1911)	90	0	80	0
144	,,	10 r.	grn. & carm. (1909)	85	0	35	0
146	,,	15 r.	blue & ol.-brn. (1909)	£6		40	0
147	,,	25 r.	brownish orge. & blue	£26		£18	

1905. *No.* 122 *surch. with T* **39.**

No.	Type	Description	Unused s.	d.	Used s.	d.
148	**42**	"¼" on ½ a. green ..	0	3	0	3
		a. Surcharge inverted ..	—		£6	

It is doubtful if No. 148a exists unused with genuine surcharge.

53  54

1906. *W* **34.** *P* 14.

No.	Type	Value	Description	Unused s.	d.	Used s.	d.
149	**53**	½ a.	green	0	4	0	3
150	**54**	1 a.	carmine	0	6	0	3

55  56

57 58* 59 60 61 62 63 64 65 66 67

*T **58.** Two types of the 1½ a ; (A) As illustrated. (B) Inscribed "1½ As". "ONE AND HALF ANNAS".

1911 (Dec.)–**1922.** *W* **34.** *P* 14.

No.	Type	Description	Unused	Used
151	**55**	3 p. pale grey ..	1 0	0 4
152	,,	3 p. grey ..	0 4	0 3
153	,,	3 p. slate-grey ..	1 0	0 3
154	,,	3 p. blue-slate (1922) ..	1 0	0 6
155	**56**	½ a. yellow-green ..	0 3	0 3
		a. Double print ..	£6	
156	,,	½ a. pale blue-green ..	0 6	0 3
159	**57**	1 a. rose-carmine ..	1 0	0 3
160	,,	1 a. carmine ..	0 10	0 3
161	,,	1 a. aniline carmine ..	2 0	0 4
162	,,	1 a. pale rose-car., C ('18)	3 0	0 8
163	**58**	1½ a. choc. (Type A) ('19)	2 6	1 3
164	,,	1½ a. grey-brown (Type A)	7 6	4 0
165	,,	1½ a. choc. (Type B) ('21)	4 0	3 6
166	**59**	2 a. dull purple ..	2 6	0 10
167	,,	2 a. mauve ..	2 6	0 3
168	,,	2 a. violet ..	10 0	0 6
169	,,	2 a. brt. pur. (Jan. '19) ..	7 6	1 0
170	**60**	2½ a. ultramarine ..	8 6	10 0
171	**61**	2½ a. ultramarine (1913) ..	3 0	1 0
172	**62**	3 a. dull orange ..	5 0	1 0
173	,,	3 a. orange-brown ..	5 0	1 0
74	**63**	4 a. deep olive ..	7 6	0 8
75	,,	4 a. olive-green ..	6 0	0 8
76	**64**	6 a. bistre ..	8 6	2 6
77	,,	6 a. yellow-bistre ..	8 6	3 0
78	,,	6 a. deep bistre-brown ..	10 0	4 0
79	**65**	8 a. purple ..	10 0	2 6
80	,,	8 a. mauve ..	20 0	2 6
81	,,	8 a. deep lilac ..	15 0	2 6
82	,,	8 a. brt. aniline mauve ..	17 6	2 6
83	**66**	12 a. dull claret ..	17 6	4 6
84	,,	12 a. claret ..	17 6	4 6
85	**67**	1 r. brown and green ..	22 6	5 0
86	,,	1 r. red-brn. & blue-green	18 6	3 0
87	,,	2 r. carmine & brown ..	22 6	2 0
88	,,	5 r. ultram. and violet ..	55 0	10 6
89	,,	10 r. green and scarlet ..	75 0	17 6
90	,,	15 r. blue and olive ..	£10	40 0
91	,,	25 r. orange and blue ..	£12	60 0

A variety of the 3 pies exists with line joining P" and "S" of value at right, sometimes escribed as "3 Rs."

NINE

PIES

(68)

NOTE.—*Collectors are warned against forgeries of all the later surcharges of India, and particularly the errors.*

21. *T* **57** *surch. with T* **68.**

No.	Description	Unused	Used
2	9 p. on 1 a. rose-carmine ..	0 6	0 6
	a. Error. "NINE—NINE" ..	40 0	
	b. Error. "PIES—PIES" ..	40 0	
	c. Surch. double ..	£7	£8
3	9 p. on 1 a. carmine-pink ..	0 9	0 6
4	9 p. on 1 a. aniline carmine ..	1 0	1 0

22. *T* **56** *surch. with T* **39.**

No.	Description	Unused	Used
5	¼ on ½ a. yellow-green ..	0 3	0 3
	a. Surch. inverted ..	25 0	
6	¼ on ½ a. blue-green ..	0 8	0 6

22–26. *W* **34.** *P* 14.

No.	Type	Description	Unused	Used
7	**57**	1 a. chocolate ..	0 8	0 3
8	**58**	1½ a. rose-carm. (Type B)	2 6	0 8
9	**61**	2½ a. orange ..	7 6	4 0
o	**62**	3 a. ultramarine	22 6	3 0

69

70

71

PRINTERS. The following issues of postage and contemporary official stamps were all printed by the Security Printing Press, Nasik, *unless otherwise stated.*

1926–33. *Typo.* *W* **69.** *P* 14.

No.	Type	Description	Unused	Used
201	**55**	3 p. slate ..	0 4	0 3
202	**56**	½ a. green ..	0 4	0 3
203	**57**	1 a. chocolate ..	1 0	0 3
		a. Tête-bêche (pair) ..	4 0	6 0
204	**58**	1½ a. rose-carm. (Type B)	3 6	1 3
205	**59**	2 a. bright purple ..	5 0	3 0
206	**70**	2 a. purple ..	3 0	0 4
		a. Tête-bêche (pair) ..	15 0	15 0
207	**61**	2½ a. orange ..	2 6	0 3
208	**62**	3 a. ultramarine ..	7 6	3 0
209	,,	3 a. blue ('31) ..	7 6	1 6
210	**63**	4 a. pale sage-green ..	4 0	0 6
211	**71**	4 a. sage-green ..	10 0	0 6
212	**65**	8 a. reddish purple ..	12 6	0 8
213	**66**	12 a. claret ..	17 6	1 0
214	**67**	1 r. chocolate & green ..	8 6	0 6
215	,,	2 r. carmine & orange ..	12 6	2 0
216	,,	5 r. ultram. & purple ..	32 6	10 0
217	,,	10 r. green and scarlet ..	60 0	15 0
218	,,	15 r. blue and olive ..	55 0	50 0
219	,,	25 r. orange and blue ..	80 0	60 0

72

(Des. R. Grant. Offset-litho.)

1929 (22 Oct.). *Air.* *W* **69.** *P* 14.

No.	Type	Description	Unused	Used
220	**72**	2 a. deep blue-green ..	2 0	1 6
221	,,	3 a. blue ..	3 6	4 0
222	,,	4 a. olive-green ..	5 0	4 0
223	,,	6 a. bistre ..	7 6	4 0
224	,,	8 a. purple ..	10 0	10 0
225	,,	12 a. rose-red ..	15 0	25 0

73. Purana Qila.

74. War Memorial Arch.

75. Council House.

76. The Viceroy's House.

77. Government of India Secretariat.

78. Dominion Columns and the Secretariat.

(Des. H. W. Barr. Offset-litho.)

1931 (9 Feb.). *Inauguration of New Delhi.* *W* **69.** *P* 14.

226	**73**	¼ a. olive-grn. & orge.-brn.	0	10	3	0
227	**74**	½ a. violet and green ..	1	0	1	0
228	**75**	1 a. mauve and chocolate	1	0	0	8
229	**76**	2 a. green and blue ..	2	0	2	0
230	**77**	3 a. chocolate and carmine	4	0	4	6
231	**78**	1 r. violet and green ..	20	0	25	0

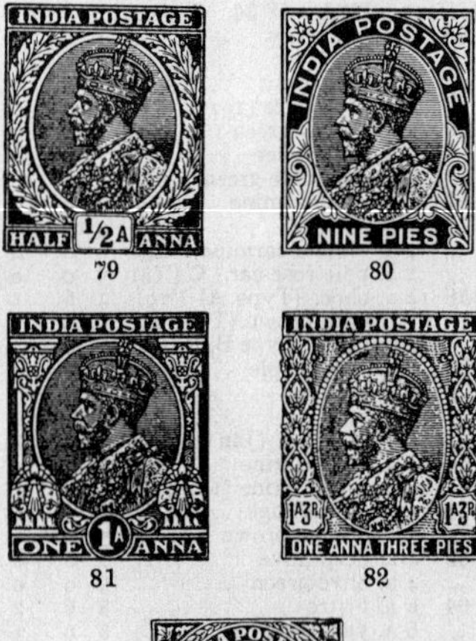

79 **80** **81** **82**

83

(1¼ a. and 3½ a. offset-litho, 9 p. both offse
litho. and typo. Other values typo.)

1932–36. *W* **69.** *P* 14.

232	**79**	½ a. green ('34)	0	6	0
233	**80**	9 p. deep grn. (22.4.32)	0	8	0
234	**81**	1 a. chocolate ('34) ..	1	0	0
235	**82**	1¼ a. mauve (22.4.32) ..	1	3	0
236	**70**	2 a. vermilion	37	6	20
236*a*	**59**	2 a. vermilion ('34) ..	12	6	1
236*b*	,,	2 a. ver. (*small die*) ('36)	6	0	2
237	**62**	3 a. carmine	3	6	1
238	**83**	3½ a. ultramarine (22.4.32)	7	6	1
239	**64**	6 a. bistre ('35) ..	40	0	20

No. 236*a* measures 19 × 22.6 mm. and No. 23
18.4 × 21.8 mm.

84. Gateway of India, Bombay.

85. Victoria Memorial, Calcutta.

86. Rameswaram Temple, Madras.

87. Jain Temple, Calcutta.

88. Taj Mahal, Agra.

89. Golden Temple, Amritsar.

90. Pagoda in Mandalay.

35. *Silver Jubilee. Offset-litho. W* **69.** *P* 14.

0	**84**	½ a. black & yellow-green	0	3	0	4
1	**85**	9 p. black and grey-green	0	6	0	6
2	**86**	1 a. black and brown ..	0	8	0	4
3	**87**	1¼ a. black & brt. violet ..	0	8	0	6
4	**88**	2½ a. black and orange ..	2	0	1	9
5	**89**	3½ a. black & dull ultram.	4	6	5	0
6	**90**	8 a. black and purple ..	10	0	8	6

91. King George VI.

92. Dak Runner.

93. Dak Bullock Cart.

94. Dak Tonga.

95. Dak Camel.

96. Mail Train.

97. Mail Steamer.

98. Mail lorry.

99. Mail Plane (small head).

100. King George VI.

1937 (23 Aug.–15 Dec.). *Typo.* *W* **69.** *P* 14.

No.	Type	Description				
247	**91**	3 p. slate	1	6	0	3
248	,,	½ a. red-brown	1	6	0	3
249	,,	9 p. green (23.8.37) ..	2	6	0	3
250	,,	1 a. carmine (23.8.37) ..	0	6	0	3
		a. Tête-bêche (Vert. pair)..	1	9	1	0
251	**92**	2 a. vermilion	3	6	0	3
252	**93**	2½ a. bright violet ..	1	0	0	4
253	**94**	3 a. yellow-green .	2	6	1	0
254	**95**	3½ a. bright blue ..	3	0	2	0
255	**96**	4 a. brown	3	0	0	8
256	**97**	6 a. turquoise-green ..	4	0	1	9
257	**98**	8 a. slate-violet ..	5	0	1	0
258	**99**	12 a. lake	7	6	3	0
259	**100**	1 r. grey and red-brown	3	6	0	6
260	,,	2 r. purple and brown..	8	6	0	9
261	,,	5 r. green and blue ..	16	0	1	6
262	,,	10 r. purple and claret ..	32	6	4	0
263	,,	15 r. brown and green ..	57	6	42	6
264	,,	25 r. slate-vio. & purple..	75	0	30	0

100*a*. King George VI.

101. King George VI. **102.**

103. Mail Plane (large head).

1940–43. *Typo.* *W* **69.** *P* 14.

No.	Type	Description			
265	**100*a***	3 p. slate	0	3	0
266	,,	½ a. purple (1.10.42) ..	0	3	0
267	,,	9 p. green	0	3	0
268	,,	1 a. carmine (1.4.43) ..	0	4	0
269	**101**	1 a. 3 p. bistre	2	0	0
269*a*	,,	1½ a. dull violet (9.42) ..	0	4	0
270	,,	2 a. vermilion	0	8	0
271	,,	3 a. bright violet ('42) ..	0	9	0
272	,,	3½ a. bright blue	1	0	0
273	**102**	4 a. brown	1	0	0
274	,,	6 a. turquoise-green ..	1	3	0
275	,,	8 a. slate-violet	1	9	0
276	,,	12 a. lake	3	6	1
277	**103**	14 a. purple (15.10.40) ..	3	6	1

The 1½ a. and 3 a. were at first printed b offset-lithography and were of finer executi and without Jubilee lines in the sheet margir

105. " Victory " and King George VI.

1946 (2 Jan.). *Victory.* *Offset-litho.* *W*
P 13.

No.	Type	Description			
278	**105**	9 p. yellow-grn. (8.2.46)	0	5	0
279	,,	1½ a. dull violet	0	8	0
280	,,	3½ a. bright blue.. ..	1	0	1
281	,,	12 a. claret (8.2.46) ..	2	6	3

3 PIES

(106)

1946. *Surch. with T* **106.**

282 **101** 3 p. on 1 a. 3 p. bistre .. 0 3 0 3

DOMINION OF INDIA.

301. Asokan Capital.

302. Indian National Flag.

303. Modern Aircraft.

47. *Independence. Offset-litho.* W **69.** *P* 14.

1	**301**	1½ a. grey-grn. (15 Dec.)	0	4	0	3
2	**302**	3½ a. orange-red, blue and green (21 Nov.) ..	0	8	0	6
3	**303**	12 a. ultram. (15 Dec.) ..	2	6	1	0

304. Modern Aircraft.

48. *Air. Inauguration of India-U. K. Air Service. Offset-litho.* W **69.** *P* 14.

4 **304** 12 a. black & ultramarine 2 6 3 0

305. Mahatma Gandhi. **306.**

(Photo. Courvoisier, La Chaux-de Fonds.)

1948 (15 Aug.). *First Anniv. Indian Independence. P* 11½.

305	**305**	1½ a. brown	0	6	0	6
306	,,	3½ a. violet	1	3	1	0
307	,,	12 a. grey-green	2	0	1	9
308	**306**	10 r. purple-brn. & lake ..	35	0	55	0

307. Ajanta Panel.

308. Konarak Horse.

309. Trimurti.

310. Bodhisattva.

311. Nataraja.

312. Sanchi Stupa, East Gate.

313. Bodh Gaya Temple.

314. Bhuvanesvara.

315. Gol Gumbad, Bijapur.

316. Kandarya Mahadeva Temple.

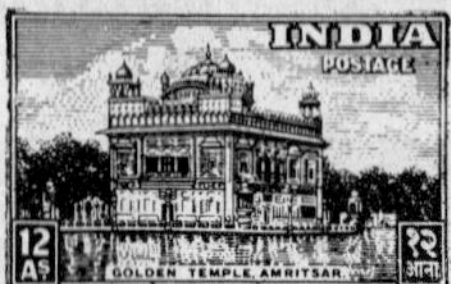

317. Golden Temple, Amritsar.

318. Victory Tower, Chittorgarh. 321. Qutb Minar, Delhi.

319. Red Fort, Delhi.

320. Taj Mahal, Agra.

322. Satrunjaya Temple. Palitana.

(Des. T. I. Archer and I. M. Das. Typo. (low values), offset-litho. (rupee values).)

1949 (15 Aug.). *W* **69**. *P* 14 (3 *p. to* 2 *a.*), 13½ (3 *a. to* 12 *a.*), 14×13½ (1 *r. and* 10 *r.*), 13½×14 (2 *r. and* 5 *r.*), 13 (15 *r.*).

309	**307**	3 p. slate-violet ..	0	3	0	
310	**308**	6 p. purple-brown ..	0	3	0	
311	**309**	9 p. yellow-green ..	0	3	0	
312	**310**	1 a. turquoise	0	6	0	
313	**311**	2 a. carmine	0	9	0	
314	**312**	3 a. brown-orange ..	0	9	0	
315	**313**	3½ a. bright blue ..	5	0	3	
316	**314**	4 a. lake	3	0	0	
317	**315**	6 a. violet	3	0	1	
318	**316**	8 a. turquoise-green ..	2	6	0	
319	**317**	12 a. dull blue	4	0	1	
320	**318**	1 r. dull violet & green	7	6	0	
321	**319**	2 r. claret and violet ..	7	6	1	
322	**320**	5 r. bl.-grn. & red.-brn.	25	0	3	
323	**321**	10 r. pur.-brn. & dp. blue	70	0	15	
		a. Purple-brown and blue ..	85	0	12	
324	**322**	15 r. brown and claret ..	70	0	25	

For T **310** with statue reversed, see No. 333

323. Globe and Asokan Capital.

1949 (Oct.). *75th Anniv. of U.P.U. Offset-lith* *W* **69**. *P* 13.

325	**323**	9 p. green	1	0	1	
326	,,	2 a. rose	2	0	2	
327	,,	3½ a. bright blue ..	2	6	2	
328	,,	12 a. brown-purple ..	4	0	4	

REPUBLIC OF INDIA.

324. Rejoicing Crowds.

325. Quill, Ink-well and Verse.

326. Ear of Corn and Plough.

327. Spinning-wheel and Cloth.

(Des. D. J. Keymer & Co. Offset-litho.)

1950 (26 JAN.). *Inauguration of Republic.* *W* **69.** *P* 13.

329	**324**	2 a. scarlet	1 0	0 4
330	**325**	3½ a. ultramarine ..	1 6	1 0
331	**326**	4 a. violet	1 9	1 0
332	**327**	12 a. marone	3 0	3 6

328. **As T 310, but statue reversed.**

1950 (15 JULY)–**51.** *Typo.* *W* **69.** *P* 14 (1 *a.*). 13½ (*others*).

333	**328**	1 a. turquoise	0 6	0 3
333*a*	**313**	2½ a. lake (30.4.51) ..	1 0	0 8
333*b*	**314**	4 a. brt. blue (30.4.51)	1 9	0 3

329. Stegodon Ganesa.

1951 (13 JAN.). *Centenary of Geological Survey of India. Offset-litho.* *W* **69.** *P* 13.

334	**329**	2 a. black and claret ..	2 0	2 0

330. Torch. **331.** Kabir.

1951 (4 MAR.). *First Asian Games, New Delhi. Offset-litho.* *W* **69.** *P* 14.

335	**330**	2 a. reddish purple and brown-orange ..	1 0	1 6
336	„	12 a. chocolate & lt. blue	3 6	3 6

PROCESS. All the following issues were printed by photogravure.

1952 (1 OCT.). *Indian Saints and Poets. As T* **331** (*Various portraits; similar frames*). *W* **69.** *P* 14.

337	9 p. bright emerald-green ..	0 6	0 6
338	1 a. carmine	1 6	1 0
339	2 a. orange-red	1 6	1 6
340	4 a. bright blue	2 0	1 0
341	4½ a. bright mauve	2 6	1 6
342	12 a. brown	5 0	3 6

Portraits:—1 a. Tulsidas; 2 a. Meera; 4 a. Surdas; 4½ a. Ghalib; 12 a. Tagore.

332. Locomotives in 1853 and 1953.

1953 (16 APR.). *Railway Centenary.* *W* **69.** *P* 14.

343	**332**	2 a. black	0 9	0 6

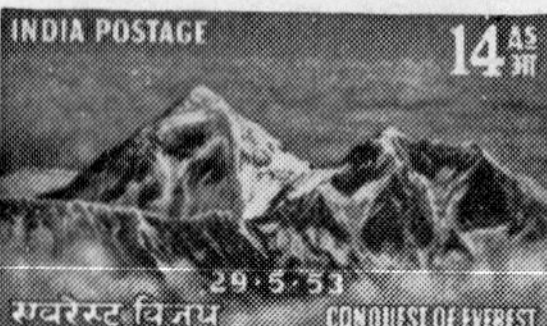

333. Mount Everest.

1953 (2 Oct.). *Conquest of Mount Everest.* *W* **69.** *P* 14½ × 14.

344	**333**	2 a. bright violet ..	0 8	0 8
345	,,	14 a. brown	3 6	4 0

334. Telegraph Poles of 1851 and 1951.

1953 (1 Nov.). *Centenary of Indian Telegraphs.* *W* **69.** *P* 14.

346	**334**	2 a. blue-green	0 8	0 8
347	,,	12 a. blue	4 0	3 0

335. Postal Transport, 1854.

336. " Airmail ".

337. Postal Transport, 1954.

1954 (1 Oct.). *Stamp Centenary.* *W* **69.** *P* 14.

348	**335**	1 a. reddish purple ..	0 4	0 6
349	**336**	2 a. cerise	0 9	1 0
350	**337**	4 a. orange-brown ..	1 0	1 0
351	**336**	14 a. blue	3 6	3 6

338. U.N. Emblem and Lotus.

1954 (24 Oct.). *United Nations Day.* *W* **69.** *P* 13.

352	**338**	2 a. turquoise-green ..	1 6	1 6

339. Forest Research Institute.

1954 (11 Dec.). *Fourth World Forestry Congress. Dehra Dun.* *W* **69.** *P* 14½ × 14.

353	**339**	2 a. ultramarine	0 8	0 8

340. Tractor.

341. Power Loom.

342. Bullock-driven Well.

343. Damodar Valley Dam.

344. Woman Spinning.

345. Woman Weaving with Hand Loom.

346. Bullocks.

348. Chittaranjan Locomotive Works.

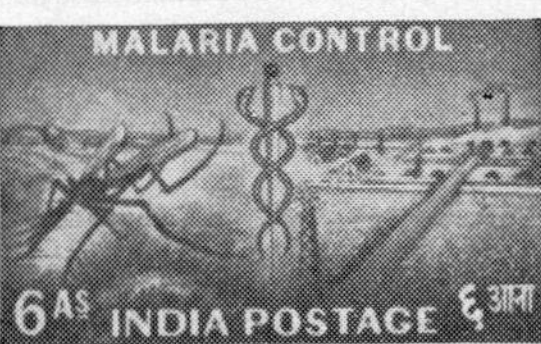

347. "Malaria Control" (Mosquito and Staff of Aesculapius).

349. Marine Drive, Bombay.

350. Hindustan Aircraft Factory, Bangalore.

352. Telephone Engineer.

351. Kashmir Landscape.

353. Cape Comorin.

354. Mt. Kangchenjunga.

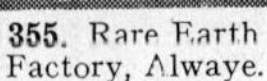

355. Rare Earth Factory, Alwaye.

356. Sindri Fertiliser Factory.

357. Steel Plant.

1955 (26 JAN.). *Five Year Plan.* *W* **69** (*sideways on small horiz. designs*). *P* 14×14½ (*small horiz.*) *or* 14½×14 (*others*).

354	**340**	3 p. bright purple	0	3	0	3
355	**341**	6 p. violet	0	6	0	3
356	**342**	9 p. orange-brown ..	0	6	0	3
357	**343**	1 a. blue-green	0	6	0	3
358	**344**	2 a. light blue	0	6	0	3
359	**345**	3 a. pale blue-green ..	0	8	0	2
360	**346**	4 a. rose-carmine ..	1	3	0	6
361	**347**	6 a. yellow-brown ..	1	3	0	6
362	**348**	8 a. blue	2	3	0	6
363	**349**	10 a. turquoise-green ..	2	3	2	0
364	**350**	12 a. bright blue ..	3	0	1	0
365	**351**	14 a. bright green ..	3	0	2	0
366	**352**	1 r. deep dull green ..	4	0	1	0
367	**353**	1 r. 2 a. grey	5	0	5	0
368	**354**	1 r. 8 a. reddish purple	7	6	6	0
369	**355**	2 r. cerise	7	6	2	0
370	**356**	5 r. brown	25	0	6	6
371	**357**	10 r. orange	50	0	15	0

For stamps as Nos. 366, 369/71 but W **374** see Nos. 417/22.

358. Bodhi Tree.

359. Round Parasol and Bodhi Tree.

(Des. C. R. Pakrashi (2 a.), R. D'Silva (14 a.).)

1956 (24 MAY). *Buddha Jayanti.* *W* **69.** *P* 13×13½ (2 *a.*) *or* 13½×13 (14 *a.*).

372	**358**	2 a. sepia	0	9	0	8
373	**359**	14 a. vermilion	6	0	4	6

360. Lokmanya Bal Gangadhar Tilak.

1956 (23 July). *Birth Centenary of Tilak (journalist). W* **69.** *P* 13×13½.

374	**360**	2 a. chestnut	0 8	0 6

Currency changed. 100 n(aye) p(aise) = 1 rupee.

361. Map of India.

1957 (1 Apr.)–**58.** *W* **69** *(sideways). P* 14×14½.

375	**361**	1 n.p. blue-green ..	0 3	0 3
376	"	2 n.p. light brown ..	0 3	0 3
377	"	3 n.p. deep brown ..	0 3	0 3
378	"	5 n.p. bright green ..	0 4	0 3
379	"	6 n.p. grey	0 6	0 4
379*a*	"	8 n.p. light blue-green (7.5.58)	2 0	0 6
380	"	10 n.p. deep dull green ..	0 6	0 3
381	"	13 n.p. bright carmine-red	0 6	0 4
381*a*	"	15 n.p. violet (16.1.58) ..	1 0	0 6
382	"	20 n.p. blue	1 0	0 4
383	"	25 n.p. ultramarine ..	1 3	0 4
384	"	50 n.p. orange	1 6	0 8
385	"	75 n.p. reddish purple ..	3 6	1 0
385*a*	"	90 n.p. brt. pur. (16.1.58)	4 0	1 6

The 8, 15 and 90 n.p. have their value expressed as "nP".

For similar stamps but W **374** see Nos. 399/411.

362. The Rani of Jhansi.

363. Shrine.

1957 (15 Aug.). *Indian Mutiny Centenary. W* **69.** *P* 14½×14 (15 *n.p.*) *or* 13×13½ (90 *n.p.*).

386	**362**	15 n.p. brown ..	0 10	0 10
387	**363**	90 n.p. reddish purple ..	6 0	2 6

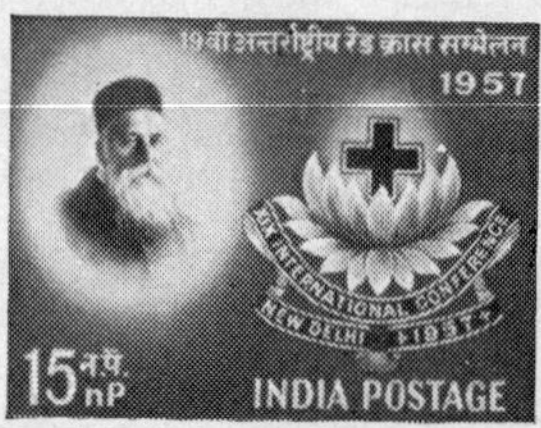

364. Henri Dunant and Conference Emblem.

1957 (28 Oct.). *19th International Red Cross Conference, New Delhi. W* **69.** *P* 13½×13.

388	**364**	15 n.p. deep grey & carm.	0 9	0 6

365. "Nutrition".

366. "Education".

367. "Recreation".

1957 (14 Nov.). *National Children's Day. W* **69.** *P* 14×13½ (90 *n.p.*) *or* 13½×14 *(others)*.

389	**365**	8 n.p. reddish purple ..	0 8	0 4
390	**366**	15 n.p. turquoise-green ..	0 8	0 6
391	**367**	90 n.p. orange-brown ..	2 6	2 6

368. Bombay University.

369. Calcutta University.

370. Madras University.

1957 (31 Dec.). *Centenary of Indian Universities.* *W* **69.** *P* 14 × 14½ (*No.* 392) *or* 13½ × 14 (*others*).

392 **368** 10 n.p. violet 0 8 0 8
393 **369** 10 n.p. grey 0 8 0 8
394 **370** 10 n.p. light brown .. 0 8 0 8

371. J. N. Tata (founder) and Steel Plant.

1958 (1 Mar.). 50*th Anniv. of Steel Industry.* *W* **69.** *P* 14½ × 14.

395 **371** 15 n.p. orange-red .. 0 8 0 6

372. Dr. D. K. Karve.

1958 (18 Apr.). *Centenary of Birth of Karve (educationist).* *W* **69.** *P* 14.

396 **372** 15 n.p. orange-brown .. 0 8 0 6

373. " Wapiti " and " Hunter " Aircraft.

1958 (30 Apr.). *Silver Jubilee of Indian Air Force* *W* **69.** *P* 14½ × 14.

397 **373** 15 n.p. blue 0 8 0 6
398 „ 90 n.p. ultramarine .. 5 0 3 0

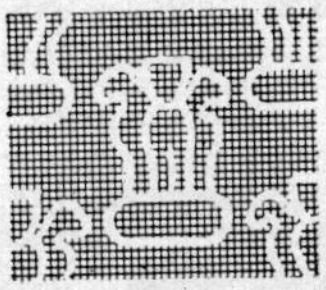

374. Asokan Capital.

1958–63. *As Nos.* 375/85*a but W* **374.**

399 **361** 1 n.p. blue-green .. 0 1 0 2
400 „ 2 n.p. light brown .. 0 1 0 2
401 „ 3 n.p. deep brown .. 0 2 0 2
402 „ 5 n.p. bright green .. 0 3 0 2
402*a* „ 6 n.p. grey 0 4 0 4
403 „ 8 n.p. light blue-green .. 0 4 0 2
404 „ 10 n.p. deep dull green .. 0 4 0 2
405 „ 13 n.p. brt. carmine-red .. 0 5 0 6
406 „ 15 n.p. violet 0 5 0 2
407 „ 20 n.p. blue 0 6 0 3
408 „ 25 n.p. ultramarine .. 0 8 0 4
409 „ 50 n.p. orange 1 1 0 8
410 „ 75 n.p. reddish purple .. 1 8 0 8
411 „ 90 n.p. bright purple .. 1 10 1 0

Dates of issue:—1958, 3, 8 n.p.; 27th Oct., 2, 5, 10, 20, 25 n.p. 1959 50 n.p., 75 n.p. 1960. 1 n.p., 90 n.p.; Oct., 15 n.p. 1963, 6 n.p., 13 n.p.

375. Bipin Chandra Pal.

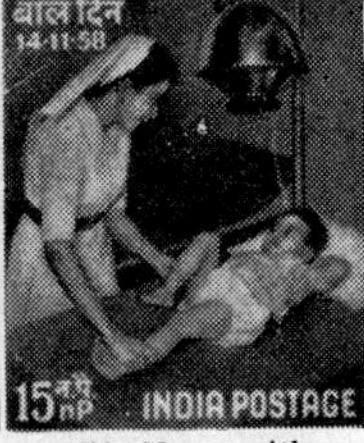

376. Nurse with Child Patient.

1958 (7 Nov.). *Birth Centenary of Pal (patriot). W* **374.** *P* 14×13½.
412 **375** 15 n.p. deep dull green .. 0 8 0 6

1958 (14 Nov.). *National Children's Day. W* **374.** *P* 14×13½.
413 **376** 15 n.p. violet 0 8 0 6

377. Jagadis Chandra Bose.

1958 (30 Nov.). *Centenary of Birth of Bose (botanist). W* **374.** *P* 14×13½.
414 **377** 15 n.p. dp. turq.-green .. 0 8 0 6

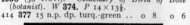

378. Exhibition Gate.

1958 (30 Dec.). *India* 1958 *Exhibition, New Delhi. W* **374** *(sideways). P* 14½×14.
415 **378** 15 n.p. reddish purple .. 0 8 0 6

379. Sir Jamsetjee Jejeebhoy.

1959 (15 Apr.). *Death Centenary of Jejeebhoy (philanthropist). W* **374.** *P* 14×13½.
416 **379** 15 n.p. brown 0 8 0 6

1959. *As Nos.* 366, 369/71, *but W* **374.**

417 **352**	1 r. deep dull green ..	2 0	0 8
420 **355**	2 r. cerise	4 0	1 6
421 **356**	5 r. brown	10 0	3 6
422 **357**	10 r. orange	19 6	12 6

380. " The Triumph of Labour " (after Chowdhury).

1959 (15 June). *40th Anniv. of International Labour Organization. W* **374** *(sideways). P* 14½×14.
423 **380** 15 n.p. dull green .. 0 8 0 6

381. Boys awaiting admission to Children's Home.

1959 (14 Nov.). *National Children's Day. W* **374.** *P* 14×14½.
424 **381** 15 n.p. deep dull green .. 0 8 0 6
a. Imperf. (pair) .. ..

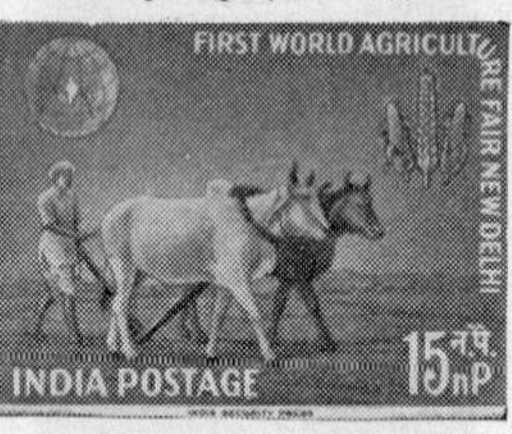

382. " Agriculture ".

1959 (30 Dec.). *First World Agriculture Fair, New Delhi. W* **374.** *P* 13½×13.
425 **382** 15 n.p. grey 0 8 0 6

383. Thiruvalluvar (poet).

1960 (15 Feb.). *Thiruvalluvar Commemoration. W* **374.** *P* 14×13½.
426 **383** 15 n.p. reddish purple .. 0 8 0 6

384. Yaksha pleading with the Cloud (from the " Meghaduta ").

385. Shakuntala writing a letter to Dushyanta (from the " Shakuntala ").

1960 (22 JUNE). *Kalidasa (poet) Commemoration.* *W* **374.** *P* 13.

427	**384**	15 n.p. grey	0 8	0 6
428	**385**	1 r. 3 n.p. pale yellow and brown	2 9	2 0

386. S. Bharati (poet). **387.** Dr. M. Visvesvaraya.

1960 (11 SEPT.). *Subramania Bharati Commemoration.* *W* **374.** *P* 14 × 13½.

429	**386**	15 n.p. blue	0 8	0 6

1960 (15 SEPT.). *Centenary of Birth of Dr. M. Visvesvaraya.* *W* **374.** *P* 13 × 13½.

430	**387**	15 n.p. brn. & brt. carm.	0 8	0 6

388. " Children's Health ".

1960 (14 NOV.). *Children's Day.* *W* **374.** *P* 13½ × 13.

431	**388**	15 n.p. dp. dull green ..	0 8	0 6

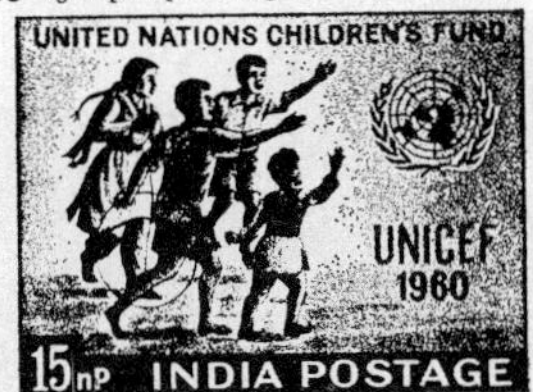

389. Children greeting U.N. Emblem.

1960 (11 DEC.). *U.N.I.C.E.F. Day.* *W* **374.** *P* 13½ × 13.

432	**389**	15 n.p. orange-brown and olive-brown ..	0 9	0 6

390. Tyagaraja (Indian saint).

1961 (6 JAN.). *Tyagaraja Commemoration.* *W* **374.** *P* 14 × 13½.

433	**390**	15 n.p. greenish blue ..	0 8	0 4

391. " First Aerial Post " cancellation.

392. " Air India " Boeing 707 jetliner and Humber-Sommer plane.

393. H. Pecquet flying Humber-Sommer plane, and " Aerial Post " cancellation.

1961 (18 FEB.). *50th Anniv. of First Official Airmail Flight, Allahabad-Naini.* *W* **374.** *P* 14 (5 *n.p.*) *or* 13 × 13½ (*others*).

434	**391**	5 n.p. olive-drab ..	1 0	1 0
435	**392**	15 n.p. dp. green & grey	1 0	1 0
436	**393**	1 r. purple and grey ..	5 0	5 0

394. Shivaji on horseback.

395. Motilal Nehru.

1961 (17 Apr.). *Shivaji Commemoration.* *W* **374.** *P* 13 × 13½.

437 **394** 15 n.p. brown and green 0 8 0 4

1961 (6 May). *Birth Centenary of Pandit Motilal Nehru.* *W* **374.** *P* 14.

438 **395** 15 n.p. olive-brown and brown-orange .. 0 8 0 4

396. Tagore.

1961 (7 May). *Birth Centenary of Rabindranath Tagore.* *W* **374.** *P* 13 × 13½.

439 **396** 15 n.p. yellow-orange and blue-green .. 1 6 1 0

397. All India Radio Emblem and Transmitting Aerials.

1961 (8 June). *Silver Jubilee of All India Radio.* *W* **374.** *P* 13½ × 13.

440 **397** 15 n.p. ultramarine .. 0 8 0 4

398. P. Chandra Ray.

399. V. N. Bhatkande.

1961 (2 Aug.). *Birth Centenary of Ray (scientist).* *W* **374.** *P* 14 × 13½.

441 **398** 15 n.p. grey 0 8 0 4

1961 (1 Sept.). *Birth Centenary of Bhatkande (musician).* *W* **374.** *P* 13 × 13½.

442 **399** 15 n.p. olive-brown .. 0 8 0 4

400. Child at lathe.

401. Fair Emblem and Main Gate.

1961 (14 Nov.). *Children's Day.* *W* **374.** *P* 14 × 13½.

443 **400** 15 n.p. brown 0 8 0 4

1961 (14 Nov.). *Indian Industries Fair, New Delhi.* *W* **374.** *P* 14 × 14½.

444 **401** 15 n.p. blue & carmine .. 0 8 0 4

402. Indian Forest.

403. Pitalkhora: Yaksha.

404. Kalibangan Seal.

1961 (21 Nov.). *Centenary of Scientific Forestry. W* **374.** *P* 13 × 13½.
445 **402** 15 n.p. green and brown 0 8 0 4

1961 (14 Dec.). *Centenary of Indian Archaeological Survey. W* **374.** *P* 14 × 13½ (15 *n.p.*) *or* 13½ × 14 (90 *n.p.*).
446 **403** 15 n.p. orange-brown .. 0 8 0 4
447 **404** 90 n.p. yellow-olive and light brown .. 2 6 2 0

405. M. M. Malaviya. **406.** Gauhati Refinery.

1961 (24 Dec.). *Birth Centenary of Malaviya (President of National Congress). W* **374.** *P* 14 × 13½.
448 **405** 15 n.p. deep slate .. 0 8 0 4

1962 (1 Jan.). *Inauguration of Gauhati Oil Refinery. W* **374.** *P* 13 × 13½.
449 **406** 15 n.p. blue 0 8 0 4

407. Bhikaiji Cama. **408.** Panchayati at work and Parliament Building.

1962 (26 Jan.). *Birth Centenary of Bhikaiji Cama (revolutionary). W* **374.** *P* 14.
450 **407** 15 n.p. reddish purple .. 0 8 0 4

1962 (26 Jan.). *Panchayati Raj Commemoration. W* **374.** *P* 13 × 13½.
451 **408** 15 n.p. bright purple .. 0 8 0 4

409. D. Saraswati (religious educator). **410.** G. S. Vidhyarthi (patriot).

1962 (4 Mar.). *Saraswati Commemoration. W* **374.** *P* 14.
452 **409** 15 n.p. orange-brown .. 0 8 0 4

1962 (25 Mar.). *Vidhyarthi Commemoration. W* **374.** *P* 14 × 13½.
453 **410** 15 n.p. red-brown .. 0 8 0 4

411. Malaria Eradication Emblem. **412.** Dr. R. Prasad (former President of India)

1962 (7 Apr.). *Malaria Eradication. W* **374.** *P* 13 × 13½.
454 **411** 15 n.p. yellow and claret 0 9 0 6

1962 (13 May). *Dr. Rajendra Prasad Commemoration. W* **374.** *P* 13.
455 **412** 15 n.p. brt. pur. (*shades*) 0 9 0 4

413. Calcutta High Court.

414. Madras High Court.

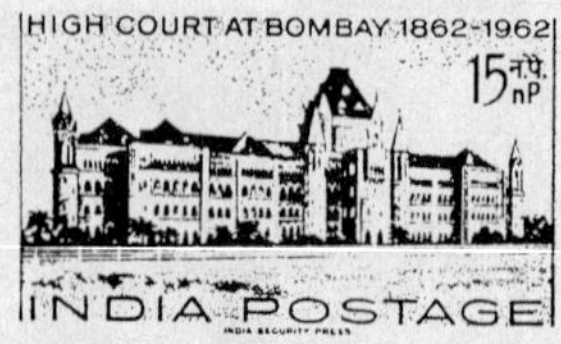

415. Bombay High Court.

1962. *Centenary of Indian High Courts.* *W* **374.** *P* 14.
456 **413** 15 n.p. dull green (1 July) 0 6 0 4
457 **414** 15 n.p. red-brown (6 Aug.) 0 6 0 4
458 **415** 15 n.p. slate (14 Aug.) .. 0 6 0 4

416. Ramabai Ranade.

1962 (15 Aug.). *Birth Centenary of Ramabai Ranade (social reformer).* *W* **374.** *P* 14 × 13½.
459 **416** 15 n.p. orange-brown .. 0 6 0 6

417. Indian One-horned Rhinoceros.

1962 (1 Oct.). *Wild Life Week.* *W* **374.** *P* 13½ × 14.
460 **417** 15 n.p. red-brown and deep turquoise .. 1 0 1 0

418. " Passing the Flag to Youth ".

1962 (14 Nov.). *Children's Day.* *W* **374.** *P* 13½ × 13.
461 **418** 15 n.p. orange-red and turquoise-green .. 0 6 0 6

419. Human Eye within Lotus Blossom.

1962 (3 Dec.). *19th International Ophthalmology Congress, New Delhi.* *W* **374.** *P* 13½ × 13.
462 **419** 15 n.p. deep olive-brown 0 6 0 6

420. S. Ramanujan.

421. S. Vivekananda.

1962 (22 Dec.). *75th Anniv. of Birth of Ramanujan (mathematician).* *W* **374.** *P* 13½ × 14.
463 **420** 15 n.p. deep olive-brown 0 6 0 6

1963 (17 Jan.). *Birth Centenary of Vivekananda (philosopher).* *W* **374.** *P* 14 × 14½.
464 **421** 15 n.p. orange-brown and yellow-olive .. 0 9 0 9

Re.1

(422)

1963 (2 Feb.). *No.* 428 *surch. with T* **422.**
465 **385** 1 r. on 1 r. 3 n.p. pale yellow and brown .. 2 6 2 0

423. Hands reaching for F.A.O. Emblem.

1963 (21 MAR.). *Freedom from Hunger*. *W* **374.** *P* 13.
466 **423** 15 n.p. grey-blue .. 0 6 0 6

424. Henri Dunant and Centenary Emblem.

1963 (8 MAY). *Red Cross Centenary*. *W* **374.** *P* 13.
467 **424** 15 n.p. red and grey .. 0 9 0 6
a. Red (cross) omitted . .

425. Artillery and Helicopter.

426. Sentry and Parachutists.

1963 (15 AUG.). *Defence Campaign*. *W* **374.** *P* 14.
468 **425** 15 n.p. grey-green .. 0 6 0 6
469 **426** 1 r. red-brown .. 2 6 1 9

427. D. Naoroji (patriot).

1963 (4 SEPT.). *Dadabhai Naoroji Commemoration*. *W* **374.** *P* 13.
470 **427** 15 n.p. grey 0 6 0 6

428. Mrs. Annie Besant (patriot and theosophist.)

1963 (1 OCT.). *Mrs. Annie Besant Commemoration*. *W* **374.** *P* 13½ × 14.
471 **428** 15 n.p. turquoise-green .. 0 6 0 6

429. Gaur.

430. Himalayan Panda.

431. Indian Elephant.

432. Tiger.

433. Indian Lion.

1963 (7 Oct.). *Wild Life Preservation.* *W* **374.** *P* 13½×14 (10 *n.p.*) *or* 13 (*others*).

472	**429**	10 n.p. blk. & yell.-orge.	o	6	o	4
473	**430**	15 n.p. orge.-brn. & green	o	9	o	6
474	**431**	30 n.p. slate & yell.-ochre	1	0	1	0
475	**432**	50 n.p. orange and deep grey-green ..	1	6	1	6
476	**433**	1 r. lt. brown and blue	2	6	2	9

434. " School Meals ".

1963 (14 Nov.). *Children's Day.* *W* **374.** *P* 14×13½.
477 **434** 15 n.p. bistre-brown .. o 6 o 6

435. Eleanor Roosevelt at spinning-wheel.

1963 (10 Dec.). *15th Anniv. of Declaration of Human Rights.* *W* **374.** *P* 13½×13.
478 **435** 15 n.p. reddish purple .. o 6 o 6

436. Dipalakshmi (bronze).

1964 (4 Jan.). *26th International Orientalists Congress, New Delhi.* *W* **374.** *P* 13×13½.
479 **436** 15 n.p. deep ultramarine o 6 o 6

437. Gopabandhu Das (patriot and socia reformer).

1964 (4 Jan.). *Gopabandhu Das Commemoration* *W* **374.** *P* 13×13½.
480 **437** 15 n.p. deep dull purple.. o 6 o 6

438. Purandaradasa.

1964 (14 Jan.). *400th Anniv. of Death of Puran daradasa (musician).* *W* **374.** *P* 13×13½.
481 **438** 15 n.p. light brown .. o 6 o

439. S. C. Bose and I.N.A. Badge.

440. Bose and Indian National Army.

1964 (23 JAN.). *67th Anniv. of Birth of Subhas Chandra Bose (nationalist).* *W* **374.** *P* 13.

482 **439** 15 n.p. yellow-bistre .. 0 6 0 6

483 **440** 55 n.p. black, orange and orange-red .. 1 9 1 9

441. Sarojini Naidu. **442.** Kasturba Gandhi.

1964 (13 FEB.). *85th Anniv. of Birth of Mrs. Sarojini Naidu (patriot).* *W* **374.** *P* 14.

484 **441** 15 n.p. deep grey-green and purple .. 0 6 0 6

1964 (22 FEB.). *20th Anniv. of Death of Kasturba Gandhi.* *W* **374.** *P* 14 × 13½.

485 **442** 15 n.p. orange-brown .. 0 6 0 6

443. Dr. W. M. Haffkine.

1964 (16 MAR.). *Haffkine Commemoration.* *W* **374.** *P* 13.

486 **443** 15 n.p. dp. purple-brown/*buff* .. 0 6 0 6

(Value expressed as paisa instead of naye paisa.)

444. Jawaharlal Nehru.

1964 (12 JUNE). *Nehru Mourning Issue. No wmk.* *P* 13½ × 13.

487 **444** 15 p. deep slate 0 6 0 6

445. Sir A. Mookerjee.

1964 (29 JUNE). *Birth Centenary of Sir Asutosh Mookerjee (education reformer).* *W* **374.** *P* 13½ × 13.

488 **445** 15 p. bistre-brown and yellow-olive .. 0 6 0 6

446. Sri Aurobindo.

1964 (15 AUG.). *92nd Birth Anniv. of Sri Aurobindo (religious leader).* *W* **374.** *P* 13 × 13½.

489 **446** 15 p. dull purple .. 0 6 0 6

447. Raja R. Roy.

1964 (27 SEPT.). *Raja Rammohun Roy Commemoration.* *W* **374.** *P* 13 × 13½.

490 **447** 15 n.p. brown 0 6 0 6

448. I.S.O. Emblem and Globe.

1964 (9 Nov.). *Sixth International Organisation for Standardisation General Assembly, Bombay. No wmk. P* 13 × 13½.
491 **448** 15 p. carmine 0 6 0 6

449. Jawaharlal Nehru (medallion).
450. St. Thomas (after statue, Ortona Cathedral, Italy).

1964 (14 Nov.). *Children's Day. No wmk. P* 14 × 13½.
492 **449** 15 p. slate 0 6 0 6

1964 (2 Dec.). *St. Thomas Commemoration. No wmk. P* 14 × 13½.
493 **450** 15 p. reddish purple .. 0 6 0 6

No. 493 was issued on the occasion of Pope Paul's visit to India.

451. Globe.

1964 (14 Dec.). *22nd International Geological Congress. W* **374**. *P* 14 × 13½.
494 **451** 15 p. blue-green 0 6 0 6

452. J. Tata (industrialist).

1965 (7 Jan.). *Jamsetji Tata Commemoration. No wmk. P* 13½ × 13.
495 **452** 15 p. dull purple & orange 0 6 0 6

453. Lala Lajpat Rai.

1965 (28 Jan.). *Birth Centenary of Lala Lajpat Rai (patriot). No wmk. P* 13 × 13½.
496 **453** 15 p. light brown .. 0 6 0 6

454. Globe and Congress Emblem.

1965 (8 Feb.). *20th International Chamber of Commerce Congress, New Delhi. No wmk. P* 13½ × 13.
497 **454** 15 p. grey-green & carm. 0 6 0 6

455. Freighter *Jalausha* and Visakhapatnam.

1965 (5 Apr.). *National Maritime Day. W* **374** *(sideways). P* 14½ × 14.
498 **455** 15 p. blue.. .. .. 0 6 0 6

456. Abraham Lincoln.

1965 (15 APR.). *Death Centenary of Abraham Lincoln. W* **374.** *P* 13.
499 **456** 15 p. brown & yell.-ochre o 6 o 6

457. I.T.U. Emblem and Symbols.

1965 (17 MAY). *I.T.U. Centenary. W* **374** (*sideways*). *P* 14½ × 14.
500 **457** 15 p. reddish purple .. o 6 o 6

458. " Everlasting Flame ".

1965 (27 MAY). *First Anniv. of Nehru's Death. W* **374.** *P* 13.
501 **458** 15 p. carmine and blue .. o 6 o 6

459. I.C.Y. Emblem.

1965 (26 JUNE). *International Co-operation Year. No wmk. P* 13½ × 13.
502 **459** 15 p. deep olive and yellow-brown .. .. o 6 o 6

460. Climbers on Summit.

469. Plucking Tea.

478. Atomic Reactor, Trombay.

1965 (15 AUG.). *Indian Mount Everest Expedition. No wmk. P* 13.
503 **460** 15 p. deep reddish purple o 6 o 6

1965. *W* **374** (*sideways on* 10 *r.*). *P* 14 × 14½ (15 *p.*) *or* 14½ × 14 (10 *r.*).
512 **469** 15 p. bronze-grn. (15.8.65) o 5 o 2
521 **478** 10 r. black and bronze-green (14.11.65) .. 19 6 12 6

Nos. 504/20 have been allocated to the definitive series.

479. G. B. Pant (statesman).

480. V. Patel.

1965 (10 SEPT.). *Govind Ballabh Pant Commemoration. W* **374.** *P* 13.
522 **479** 15 p. brown & dp. green o 6 o 7

1965 (31 OCT.). *90th Birth Anniv. of Vallabhbhai Patel (statesman). W* **374.** *P* 14 × 13½.
523 **480** 15 p. blackish brown .. o 5 o 6

481. C. Das.

482. Vidyapati (poet).

1965 (5 NOV.). *95th Birth Anniv. of Chittaranjan Das (lawyer and patriot). W* **374.** *P* 13.
524 **481** 15 p. yellow-brown .. o 6 o 6

1965 (17 NOV.). *Vidyapati Commemoration. W* **374.** *P* 14 × 14½.
525 **482** 15 p. yellow-brown .. o 5 o 6

483. Sikandra, Agra.

1966 (24 Jan.). *Pacific Area Travel Association Conference, New Delhi. No wmk. P* $13\frac{1}{2} \times 14$.
526 **483** 15 p. slate 0 5 0 6

484. Soldier, Fighters and Warship.

1966 (26 Jan.). *Indian Armed Forces. No wmk. P* 14.
527 **484** 15 p. violet 0 5 0 6

485. Lal Bahadur Shastri.

1966 (26 Jan.). *Shastri Mourning Issue. No wmk. P* $13 \times 13\frac{1}{2}$.
528 **485** 15 p. black 0 5 0 6

OFFICIAL STAMPS.

Stamps overprinted "POSTAL SERVICE" or "P. I. N." were not used as postage stamps, and are therefore omitted.

Service.

(O 1)

1866 (1 Aug.). *Optd. locally with Type* O **1.** *P* 14.

A. *No wmk.*

O1 **11** ½ a. blue .. .. .. — 85 0
O2 ,, ½ a. pale blue .. .. — 85 0
a. Inverted .. .. ..
O3 ,, 1 a. brown .. .. — £5
O4 ,, 1 a. deep brown .. .. — £5
O5 ,, 8 a. carmine 20 0 45 0

B. *Wmk. Elephant's Head, T* **13.**

O 6 **11** ½ a. blue £7 35 0
O 7 ,, ½ a. pale blue £7 45 0
a. Inverted .. .. ..
b. No dot on "i" (No. 50 on pane) .. .. ..
c. No stop (No. 77 on pane) ..
O 8 **11** 1 a. brown £6 45 0
O 9 ,, 1 a. deep brown £6 45 0
a. No dot on "i" .. ..
b. No stop .. .. ..
O10 ,, 2 a. orange 90 0 55 0
O11 ,, 2 a. yellow £5 60 0
a. Inverted .. .. ..
b. Imperf. .. .. ..
O12 ,, 4 a. green 60 0 80 0
a. Inverted £30 £25

Optd. with Type O **1.**

O13 **17** 4 a. green (Die I) £15 £8

A variety with wide and more open capital "S" occurs six times in sheets of all values. Price four times the normal.

Reprints exist of Nos. O6, O8 and O13; the latter is Die II instead of Die I.

1872 (Jan.). *Optd. with Type* O **1.** *Wmk. Elephant's Head, T* **13.**

O14 **12** 8 p. purple 40 0 65 0
a. No dot on "i" £15
b. No stop £15

Reprints of the overprint have been made, in a different setting, on the 8 pies, purple, no watermark.

O 2

O 3

O 4

1866. *Type* O **2.** *Thick blue glazed paper. Surch.* "SERVICE—TWO ANNAS". *P* 14 (*at sides only*).
O15 2 a. purple £35 £17

Types O **3,** O **4** *and similar type. Optd.* "SERVICE POSTAGE," *in two lines. P* 14 (*at sides only*).
O16 2 a. purple (G.) £35 £17
O17 4 a. purple (G.) £75 £45
O18 8 a. purple (G.) £300 £85

So-called reprints of Nos. O15 to O18 are known, but in these the surcharge differs entirely in the spacing, etc., of the words; they are more properly described as Government imitations. The imitations of No. O15 have surcharge in *black* or in *green*.

O 6

1867. *With semi-circular opt.* "SERVICE POSTAGE". *Wmk. Large Crown. P* 15½ × 15.

O19	O **6**	½ a. mauve/*lilac* (G.) ..	£25	£7
		a. Overprint double ..	£50	

This stamp exists with reprinted overprint which has a full stop after "POSTAGE.".

Service.

(O **7**)

1867–73. *Wmk. Elephant's Head, T* **13**. *P* 14. *Optd. by De La Rue & Co. with Type* O **7**.

O20	**11**	½ a. blue (Die I)	15 0	1 0
O21	,,	½ a. pale blue (Die I) ..	12 6	1 9
O22	,,	½ a. blue (Die II)	£10	60 0
O23	,,	1 a. brown	17 6	1 3
O24	,,	1 a. deep brown	16 0	1 0
O25	,,	1 a. chocolate	20 0	2 6
O26	,,	2 a. yellow	10 0	5 0
O27	,,	2 a. orange	6 0	1 0
O28	**17**	4 a. pale green (Die I) ..	4 6	1 6
O29	,,	4 a. green (Die I) ..	2 6	1 0
O30	**11**	8 a. rose (Die II) ..	4 6	1 3
O30*a*	,,	8 a. pale rose (Die II) ..	6 0	2 0

Prepared for use, but not issued.

O30*b*	**18**	6 a. 8 p. slate	£7	

On H. S. M. (O **8**)

On H. S. M. (O **9**)

1874–82. *Optd. with Type* O **8**.

O31	**11**	½ a. blue (Die II) ..	5 0	0 6
O32	,,	1 a. brown	5 0	0 6
O33	,,	2 a. yellow	35 0	15 0
O33*a*	,,	2 a. orange	30 0	15 0
O34	**17**	4 a. green (Die I) ..	8 6	3 0
O35	**11**	8 a. rose (Die II) ..	10 0	10 0

Overprinted in blue-black.

O36	**11**	½ a. blue (Die II) ..	£20	70 0
O37	,,	1 a. brown	£30	£5

1883–99. *Wmk. Star, T* **34**. *P* 14. *Optd. with Type* O **9**.

O37*a*	**40**	3 p. aniline carmine ..	0 6	0 6
O38	**23**	½ a. deep blue-green ..	1 6	0 3
		a. Overprint double ..	—	£8
O39	,,	½ a. blue-green ..	0 6	0 3
O40	**25**	1 a. brown-purple ..	0 8	0 3
		a. Overprint inverted ..	£6	£10
		b. Overprint double ..	—	£16
O41	,,	1 a. plum	0 4	0 3
O42	**27**	2 a. pale blue	4 0	0 3
O43	,,	2 a. blue	1 0	0 3
O44	**29**	4 a. olive-green	2 0	0 3
O44*a*	,,	4 a. slate-green	3 0	0 3
O45	**31**	8 a. dull mauve	10 0	2 0
O46	,,	8 a. magenta	4 0	1 0
O47	**37**	1 r. green and rose ..	8 0	3 0
O48	,,	1 r. green and carmine	8 6	3 0

1900. *Optd. with Type* O **9**.

O49	**23**	½ a. pale yellow-green ..	1 6	0 3
O49*a*	,,	½ a. yellow-green ..	1 9	0 3
O50	**25**	1 a. carmine	1 0	0 3
		a. Overprint inverted ..	—	£12
		b. Overprint double ..	—	£15
O51	**26**	2 a. pale violet	7 6	0 6
O52	,,	2 a. mauve	12 6	0 9

1902–5. *Stamps of King Edward VII optd. with Type* O **9**.

O54	3 p. grey	2 0	0 8
O55	3 p. slate-grey (1905) ..	0 6	0 4
O56	½ a. green (No. 122) ..	1 3	0 3
O57	1 a. carmine (No. 123) ..	0 4	0 3
O58	2 a. violet	2 6	0 6
O59	2 a. mauve	1 0	0 3
O60	4 a. olive	1 9	0 3
O61	4 a. pale olive	1 6	0 3
O62	6 a. olive-bistre	1 9	0 4
O63	8 a. mauve	3 6	0 9
O64	8 a. magenta	4 0	0 9
O65	1 r. green and carmine (1905)	3 6	0 8

1906. *Optd. with Type* O **9**.

O66	**53**	½ a. green (No. 149) ..	0 6	0 3
O67	**54**	1 a. carmine (No. 150) ..	0 6	0 3

On H. S. M.

(O **9*a***)

1909. *T* **52** *optd. with Type* O **9*a***.

O68	2	r. carmine & yellow-brown	12 6	2 0
O68*a*	2	r. rose-red & yellow-brown	7 6	2 0
O69	5	r. ultramarine and violet ..	17 6	5 0
O70	10	r. green and carmine ..	27 6	12 6
O70*a*	10	r. green and scarlet ..	40 0	12 6
O71	15	r. blue and olive-brown ..	40 0	40 0
O72	25	r. brownish orange & blue	57 6	70 0

SERVICE (O **10**)

SERVICE (O **11**)

1912. *Stamps of King George V (wmk. Single Star, T* **34**) *optd. with Type* O **10** (14 *mm.*) *or* O **11** (*rupee values,* 21½ *mm.*).

O73	**55**	3 p. grey	0 8	0 3
O74	,,	3 p. slate-grey	0 4	0 3
O75	,,	3 p. blue-slate	0 10	0 3
O76	**56**	½ a. yellow-green ..	0 3	0 3
		a. Overprint double ..	70 0	
O77	,,	½ a. pale blue-green ..	0 3	0 3
O80	**57**	1 a. rose-carmine ..	0 6	0 3
O81	,,	1 a. carmine	0 8	0 3
O82	,,	1 a. aniline carmine ..	0 8	0 3
		a. Overprint double ..	—	£12
O83	**59**	2 a. mauve	0 9	0 3
O84	,,	2 a. purple	0 9	0 3
O85	**63**	4 a. deep olive	1 9	0 3
O86	,,	4 a. olive-green ..	1 3	0 4
O87	**64**	6 a. yellow-bistre ..	4 6	2 0
O88	,,	6 a. deep bistre-brown ..	7 6	2 0
O89	**65**	8 a. purple	5 0	1 6
O89*a*	,,	8 a. mauve	2 6	1 0
O90	,,	8 a. bright aniline mauve	15 0	5 0
O91	**67**	1 r. red-brn. & blue-grn.	4 0	0 8
O92	,,	2 r. rose-carm. & brown	8 6	4 6
O93	,,	5 r. ultram. & violet ..	22 6	10 6
O94	,,	10 r. green and scarlet ..	45 0	30 0
O95	,,	15 r. blue and olive ..	60 0	70 0
O96	,,	25 r. orange and blue ..	85 0	£5

NINE

PIES

(O 12)

1921. *No.* O80 *surch. with Type* O **12.**
O97 9 p. on 1 a. rose-carmine .. 0 8 0 6

1922. *No.* 197 *optd. with Type* O **10.**
O98 1 a. chocolate 0 4 0 3

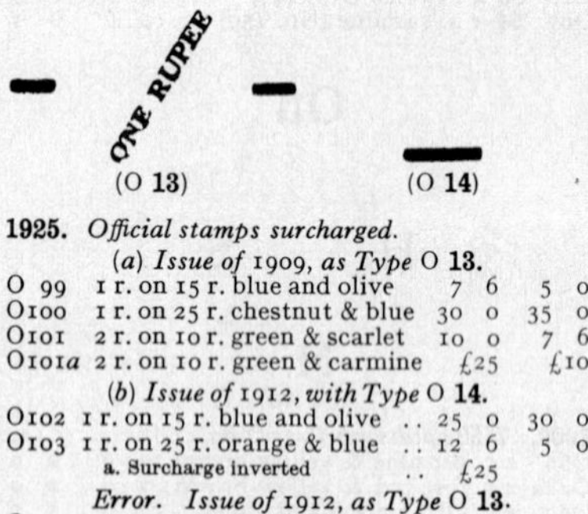

(O 13) (O 14)

1925. *Official stamps surcharged.*

(*a*) *Issue of* 1909, *as Type* O **13.**
O 99 1 r. on 15 r. blue and olive 7 6 5 0
O100 1 r. on 25 r. chestnut & blue 30 0 35 0
O101 2 r. on 10 r. green & scarlet 10 0 7 6
O101*a* 2 r. on 10 r. green & carmine £25 £10

(*b*) *Issue of* 1912, *with Type* O **14.**
O102 1 r. on 15 r. blue and olive .. 25 0 30 0
O103 1 r. on 25 r. orange & blue .. 12 6 5 0
a. Surcharge inverted .. £25

Error. *Issue of* 1912, *as Type* O **13.**
O104 2 r. on 10 r. green & scarlet £50

SERVICE

ONE ANNA

(O 15) (O 16)

1926. *No.* O62 *surch. with Type* O **15.**
O105 1 a. on 6 a. olive-bistre .. 1 6 1 9

1926. *Postage stamps of* 1911–22 (*wmk. Single Star*), *surch. as Type* O **16.**
O106 1 a. on 1½ a. (No. 163) .. 0 8 0 4
O107 1 a. on 1½ a. (No. 165) .. 1 9 1 3
a. Error. 1 a. on 1 a. (No. 197) £15
O108 1 a. on 2½ a. (No. 171) .. 2 0 2 0

The surcharge on No. O108 has no bars at top.

SERVICE **SERVICE**

(O 17) (O 18)

1926–31. *Stamps of King George V* (*wmk. Multiple Star, T* **69**) *optd. with Types* O **17** 13½ *mm.*) *or* O **18** (19½ *mm., rupee values*).
O109 **55** 3 p. slate (1.10.29) .. 0 3 0 3
O110 **56** ½ a. green ('31) .. 1 0 0 3
O111 **57** 1 a. chocolate 0 4 0 3
O112 **70** 2 a. purple 0 8 0 3
O113 **71** 4 a. sage-green .. 1 3 0 6
O115 **65** 8 a. reddish purple .. 2 6 0 4
O116 **66** 12 a. claret .. 2 0 0 10
O117 **67** 1 r. chocolate & grn. ('30) 6 0 0 8
O118 ,, 2 r. carmine & orge. ('30) 10 0 5 0
O120 ,, 10 r. green & scarlet ('31) 50 0 27 6

1930. *As No* O111, *but optd. as Type* O **10** (14 *mm.*).
O125 **57** 1 a. chocolate 37 6 12 6

1932–36. *Stamps of King George V* (*wmk. Mult. Star, T* **69**) *optd. with Type* O **17** (13½ *mm.*).
O126 **79** ½ a. green ('35) .. 0 3 0 3
O127 **80** 9 p. deep green .. 0 9 0 3
O127*a* **81** 1 a. chocolate ('36) .. 0 4 0 3
O128 **82** 1¼ a. mauve 0 6 0 3
O129 **70** 2 a. vermilion .. 3 6 0 3
O130 **59** 2 a. vermilion ('35) .. 1 3 2 6
O130*a* ,, 2 a. verm. ('36) (*small die*) 1 6 0 8
O131 **61** 2½ a. orange (22.4.32) .. 1 0 0 4
O132 **63** 4 a. sage-green ('35) .. 1 9 0 8
O133 **64** 6 a. bistre ('36) .. 3 6 5 0

1937–39. *Stamps of King George VI optd. as Types* O **17** or O **18** (*rupee values*).
O135 **91** ½ a. red-brown ('38) .. 1 0 0 3
O136 ,, 9 p. green ('37) .. 3 6 0 3
O137 ,, 1 a. carmine ('37) .. 0 6 0 3
O138 **100** 1 r. grey & red-brn. (5.38) 2 6 0 8
O139 ,, 2 r. pur. & brn. (5.38) 5 0 2 0
O140 ,, 5 r. green & blue (10.38) 12 6 7 6
O141 ,, 10 r. pur. & claret ('39) 22 6 12 6

(O 19)

1939 (MAY). *Stamp of King George V, surch. with Type* O **19.**
O142 **82** 1 a. on 1¼ a. mauve .. 0 6 0 3

O 20

1939 (1 JUNE)–**1943.** *Typo.* *W* **69.** *P* 14.
O143 O **20** 3 p. slate 0 2 0
O144 ,, ½ a. red-brown .. 0 6 0
O144*a* ,, ½ a. purple ('42) .. 0 3 0
O145 ,, 9 p. green 0 3 0
O146 ,, 1 a. carmine 0 4 0
O146*a* ,, 1 a. 3 p. bistre ('41) .. 0 6 0
O146*b* ,, 1½ a. dull violet ('43) .. 1 0 0
O147 ,, 2 a. vermilion 0 6 0
O148 ,, 2½ a. bright violet .. 0 8 0
O149 ,, 4 a. brown 0 9 0
O150 ,, 8 a. slate-violet .. 1 3 0

1948. (AUG.). *First Anniv. Indian Independence. Mahatma Gandhi postage stamps optd* "SERVICE", *as Type* O **17.**
O150*a* **305** 1½ a. brown 85 0 85
O150*b* ,, 3½ a. violet £50 £5
O150*c* ,, 12 a. grey-green .. £100
O150*d* **306** 10 r. purple-brn. & lake £300

O 21. Asokan Capital. O 22.

1950-51. *Typo.* (O **21**) *or litho.* (O **22**). *W* **69**. *P* 14.

O151 O **21** 3 p. slate-violet .. 0 2 0 3
O152 ,, 6 p. purple-brown .. 0 3 0 3
O153 ,, 9 p. green 0 6 0 3
O154 ,, 1 a. turquoise .. 0 6 0 3
O155 ,, 2 a. carmine 0 6 0 3
O156 ,, 3 a. red-orange .. 1 9 0 3
O157 ,, 4 a. lake 2 0 0 4
O157*a* ,, 4 a. ultramarine .. 1 9 0 4
O158 ,, 6 a. bright violet .. 2 0 0 6
O159 ,, 8 a. red-brown .. 1 6 0 6
O160 O **22** 1 r. violet 2 6 0 8
O161 ,, 2 r. rose-carmine .. 4 0 1 9
O162 ,, 5 r. blue-green .. 12 6 10 0
O163 ,, 10 r. reddish brown 22 6 15 0

Dates of issue: 2.1.50, rupee values; 1.7.50, other values, except 4 a. ultramarine ('51).

1957 (1 Apr.)–**58.** *Value in naye paise. Typo.* (*t.*) *or litho.* (*l.*) *W* **69**. *P* 14.

O164 O **21** 1 n.p. slate (*l.*) .. 0 4 0 5
a. Slate-black (l.) .. 0 4 0 6
b. Greenish slate (t.) .. 0 4 0 6
O165 ,, 2 n.p. blackish violet (*t.*) 0 4 0 4
O166 ,, 3 n.p. chocolate (*t.*) .. 0 3 0 3
O167 ,, 5 n.p. green (*l.*) .. 0 6 0 3
a. Deep emerald (t.) .. 0 4 0 4
O168 ,, 6 n.p. turquoise-blue (*t.*) 0 6 0 4
O170 ,, 13 n.p. scarlet (*t.*) .. 0 6 0 4
O170*a* ,, 15 n.p. reddish violet (*l.*) (–.6.58) 0 8 0 4
b. Reddish violet (t.) .. 1 0 1 0
O171 ,, 20 n.p. red (*l.*) .. 1 0 0 4
a. Vermilion (t.) .. 1 0 0 6
O172 ,, 25 n.p. violet-blue (*l.*) .. 1 3 0 8
a. Ultramarine (t.) .. 1 3 0 10
O173 ,, 50 n.p. red-brown (*l.*) .. 2 0 1 6
a. Reddish brown (t.) .. 2 0 1 6

1958–63. *As Nos.* O164/73 *and* O160/3 *but W* **374**. *Litho.* (*Nos.* O180, O185/8) *or typo.* (*others.*) *P* 14.

O175 O **21** 1 n.p. slate-blk. (–.1.59) 0 1 0 2
O176 ,, 2 n.p. blackish violet (–.1.59) 0 1 0 2
O177 ,, 3 n.p. choc. (–.11.58) 0 2 0 2
O178 ,, 5 n.p. deep emerald (–.11.58) .. 0 3 0 2
O179 ,, 6 n.p. turq.-bl. (–.5.59) 0 3 0 2
O180 ,, 10 n.p. dp. grey-grn. ('63) 0 4 0 5
O180*a* ,, 13 n.p. scarlet ('63) .. 0 5 0 6
O181 ,, 15 n.p. dp. vio. (–.11.58) 0 5 0 3
a. Lt. reddish violet ('61) 0 5 0 3
O182 ,, 20 n.p. verm. (–.5.59) .. 0 6 0 3
O183 ,, 25 n.p. ultram. (–.7.59) 0 8 0 4
O184 ,, 50 n.p. reddish brown (–.6.59) 1 1 0 8
O185 O **22** 1 r. reddish violet (–.2.59) 2 0 0 8
O186 ,, 2 r. rose-carmine ('60) 4 0 2 0
O187 ,, 5 r. bl.-grn. (–.7.59) 10 0 6 0
O188 ,, 10 r. reddish brown (–.7.59) 19 6 10 0

CHINA EXPEDITIONARY FORCE.

C. E. F.

(C)

Contemporary stamps of India overprinted with Type C, *in black.*

1900. *Stamps of Queen Victoria.*

C 1 **40** 3 pies, carmine 0 6 0 8
C 2 **23** ½ a. green 0 6 0 8
C 3 **25** 1 a. brown-purple .. 1 6 2 0
C 4 **27** 2 a. ultramarine .. 3 6 5 0
C 5 **36** 2½ a. green 5 0 7 6
C 6 **28** 3 a. orange 10 0 15 0
C 7 **29** 4 a. olive-green 4 0 6 0
C 8 **31** 8 a. magenta 4 0 6 0
C 9 **32** 12 a. purple/*red* 5 0 8 6
C10 **37** 1 r. green and carmine .. 10 0 12 6

Prepared, but not issued.

C10*a* **26** 1 a. 6 p. sepia £10

1904 (27 Feb.).

C11 **25** 1 a. carmine 15 0 12 6

1904. *Stamps of King Edward VII.*

C12 **41** 3 pies, pale grey .. 1 6 2 6
C12*a* ,, 3 pies, slate-grey .. 3 0 3 0
C13 **43** 1 a. carmine 5 0 5 6
C14 **44** 2 a. pale violet 6 0 2 6
C15 **45** 2½ a. ultramarine .. 5 0 9 0
C16 **46** 3 a. orange-brown .. 5 0 9 0
C17 **47** 4 a. olive-green .. 8 6 10 0
C18 **49** 8 a. magenta 8 6 10 0
C19 **50** 12 a. purple/*red* .. 10 0 17 6
C20 **51** 1 r. green and carmine 7 0 12 6

1909. "POSTAGE & REVENUE."

C21 **53** ½ a. green (No. 149) .. 2 6 3 0
C22 **54** 1 a. carmine (No. 150) 2 0 1 6

1913–21. *Stamps of King George V. Wmk. Star.*

C23 **55** 3 p. slate-grey (1913) .. 1 0 2 6
C24 **56** ½ a. green 1 6 2 9
C25 **57** 1 a. aniline carmine .. 2 0 4 0
C26 **58** 1½ a. chocolate (Type A) 6 0 8 6
C27 **59** 2 a. mauve 6 0 12 6
C28 **61** 2½ a. bright blue .. 7 6 12 6
C29 **62** 3 a. orange-brown .. 10 0 15 0
C30 **63** 4 a. olive-green .. 15 0 20 0
C32 **65** 8 a. mauve 15 0 25 0
C33 **66** 12 a. claret 12 6 30 0
C34 **67** 1 r. red-brn. & blue-grn. 50 0 85 0

INDIAN EXPEDITIONARY FORCES 1914-22.

I. E. F.

(E)

1914. *Stamps of India (King George V) overprinted with Type* E *in black.*

E 1 **55** 3 pies, slate-grey .. 0 3 0 3
a. No stop after "F" .. 15 0 10 0
b. No stop after "E" .. 25 0 20 0
c. Overprint double .. 25 0 20 0
E 2 **56** ½ a. yellow-green .. 0 3 0 3
a. No stop after "F" . 25 0 25 0
E 3 **57** 1 a. aniline carmine .. 0 3 0 4
a. No stop after "F" .. 32 6 17 6
E 4 ,, 1 a. carmine 1 0 1 0
E 5 **59** 2 a. mauve 0 8 0 10
a. No stop after "F" .. 50 0 50 0
b. No stop after "E" .. 60 0 60 0
E 6 **61** 2½ a. ultramarine .. 1 0 2 6
a. No stop after "F" .. 65 0 70 0
E 7 **62** 3 a. orange-brown .. 1 6 1 9
a. No stop after "F" .. 65 0 70 0
E 8 **63** 4 a. olive-green .. 1 9 2 6
a. No stop after "F" .. 70 0 80 0
E 9 **65** 8 a. purple 2 6 3 6
a. No stop after "F" .. 80 0 90 0
E10 ,, 8 a. mauve 10 6 17 6
E11 **66** 12 a. dull claret .. 12 6 12 6
a. No stop after "F" .. 90 0 £5
E12 ,, 12 a. claret 5 6 10 0
E13 **67** 1 r. red-brn. & blue-grn. 6 0 12 6

INDIAN CUSTODIAN FORCES IN KOREA.

भारतीय
संरक्षा कटक
कोरिया
(K 1)

1953. *Stamps of India optd. with Type* K **1**.

No.	Type	Description		
K 1	**307**	3 p. slate-violet ..	0 9	1 0
K 2	**308**	6 p. purple-brown ..	0 9	1 0
K 3	**309**	9 p. yellow-green ..	1 0	1 6
K 4	**328**	1 a. turquoise	1 6	2 0
K 5	**311**	2 a. carmine	2 6	3 0
K 6	**313**	2½ a. lake	3 0	3 6
K 7	**312**	3 a. brown-orange ..	4 0	4 6
K 8	**314**	4 a. bright blue ..	4 6	5 0
K 9	**315**	6 a. violet	6 6	7 6
K10	**316**	8 a. turquoise-green ..	7 6	9 0
K11	**317**	12 a. dull blue	12 6	15 0
K12	**318**	1 r. dull violet & green	17 6	20 0

INDIAN U.N. FORCE IN CONGO.

U.N. FORCE
(INDIA)
CONGO
(U 1)

1962 (15 JAN). *Stamps of India optd. with Type* U **1**. *W* **69** (13 *n.p.*) *or W* **374** (*others*).

No.	Type	Description		
U1	**361**	1 n.p. blue-green ..	0 1	0 8
U2	,,	2 n.p. light brown ..	0 1	1 3
U3	,,	5 n.p. bright green ..	0 3	1 6
U4	,,	8 n.p. light blue-green ..	0 4	2 0
U5	,,	13 n.p. bright carmine-red	0 5	5 0
U6	,,	50 n.p. orange	1 1	10 0

INDIAN U.N. FORCE IN GAZA (PALESTINE).

UNEF
(Z 1)

1965 (15 JAN.). *No.* 492 *of India optd. with Type* Z **1**.

No.	Type	Description		
Z1	**449**	15 p. slate (C.)	0 5	0 6

INTERNATIONAL COMMISSION IN INDO-CHINA.

अन्तर्राष्ट्रीय आयोग कम्बोज (N 1) — अन्तर्राष्ट्रीय आयोग लाओस (N 2) — अन्तर्राष्ट्रीय आयोग वियत नाम (N 3)

1954 (1 DEC.). *Stamps of India.* *W* **69**.

No.	Type	Description		
		(*a*) *Optd. as Type* N **1**, *for use in Cambodia.*		
N 1	**307**	3 p. slate-violet ..	0 9	1 0
N 2	**328**	1 a. turquoise	1 3	1 6
N 3	**311**	2 a. carmine	1 6	2 3
N 4	**316**	8 a. turquoise-green ..	5 6	6 6
N 5	**317**	12 a. dull blue	8 6	9 6
		(*b*) *Optd. as Type* N **2**, *for use in Laos.*		
N 6	**307**	3 p. slate-violet ..	0 9	1 0
N 7	**328**	1 a. turquoise	1 3	1 6
N 8	**311**	2 a. carmine	1 6	2 3
N 9	**316**	8 a. turquoise-green ..	5 6	6 6
N10	**317**	12 a. dull blue	8 6	9 6
		(*c*) *Optd. as Type* N **3**, *for use in Viet-Nam.*		
N11	**307**	3 p. slate-violet ..	0 9	1 0
N12	**328**	1 a. turquoise	1 3	1 6
N13	**311**	2 a. carmine	1 6	2 3
N14	**316**	8 a. turquoise-green ..	5 6	6 6
N15	**317**	12 a. dull blue	8 6	9 6

1957 (1 APR.). *Stamps of India.* *W* **69**.

No.	Type	Description		
		(*a*) *Optd. as Type* N **1** *for use in Cambodia.*		
N16	**361**	2 n.p. light brown ..	0 1	0 4
N17	,,	6 n.p. grey	0 3	1 0
N18	,,	13 n.p. bright carmine-red	0 5	2 0
N19	,,	50 n.p. orange	1 1	7 6
N20	,,	75 n.p. reddish purple	1 8	10 6
		(*b*) *Optd. as Type* N **2** *for use in Laos.*		
N21	**361**	2 n.p. light brown ..	0 3	1 0
N22	,,	6 n.p. grey	0 6	2 6
N23	,,	13 n.p. bright carmine-red	0 9	4 0
N24	,,	50 n.p. orange	1 9	15 0
N25	,,	75 n.p. reddish purple ..	2 6	22 6
		(*c*) *Optd. as Type* N **3** *for use in Viet-Nam.*		
N26	**361**	2 n.p. light brown ..	0 3	0 6
N27	,,	6 n.p. grey	0 6	1 6
N28	,,	13 n.p. bright carmine-red	0 9	3 0
N29	,,	50 n.p. orange	1 9	10 6
N30	,,	75 n.p. reddish purple ..	2 6	15 0

1962–65. *Stamps of India.* *W* **374**.

No.	Type	Description	
		(*a*) *Optd. as Type* N **1** *for use in Cambodia.*	
N32	**361**	2 n.p. light brown ..	32 6
		(*b*) *Optd. as Type* N **2**, *for use in Laos.*	
N38	**361**	2 n.p. light brown ..	32 6
N39	,,	3 n.p. dp. brown (1.8.63)	1 6
N40	,,	5 n.p. brt. green (1.8.63)	0 6
N41	,,	50 n.p. orange ('65) ..	2 6
N42	,,	75 n.p. reddish pur. ('65)	3 0
		(*c*) *Optd. as Type* N **3**, *for use in Viet-Nam.*	
N43	**361**	1 n.p. blue-green ..	3 6
N44	,,	2 n.p. light brown ..	32 6
N45	,,	3 n.p. deep brown ('63?)	1 6
N46	,,	5 n.p. bright green ('63)	0 6
N47	,,	50 n.p. orange ('65) ..	2 6
N48	,,	75 n.p. reddish pur. ('65)	3 0

ICC
(N 4)

1965 (15 JAN.). *No.* 492 *of India optd. with Type N* **4** *for use in Laos and Viet-Nam.*

No.	Type	Description	
N49	**449**	15 p. slate (C.)	1 0

JAPANESE OCCUPATION.

I. ANDAMAN AND NICOBAR ISLANDS.

The Andaman Islands in the Bay of Bengal were occupied on the 23rd March 1942 and the Nicobar Islands in July 1942. Civil administration was resumed in October 1945.

The following Indian stamps were surcharged with large figures preceded by a decimal point:—

Postage stamps—.3 on ½ a. (No. 248), .5 on 1 a. (No. 250), .10 on 2 a. (No. 236*b*), .30 on 6 a. (No. 274).

Official stamps—.10 on 1 a. 3 p. (No. O146*b*), .20 on 3 p. (No. O143) from booklet panes, .20 in red on 3 p. (No. O143).

II. IMPHAL.

The following are stated to have been used in the occupied areas of India during the drive on Imphal. Issued by the Indian National Army.

Typo. No gum. Perf. 11 or imperf. 1 p. violet, 1 p. maroon, 1 a. green.

INDIAN CONVENTION STATES.

(Stamps of Chamba, Gwalior, Jind, Nabha and Patiala ceased to be valid for postage on January 1st, 1951, when they were replaced by those of the Republic of India, valid from April 1st, 1950.)

Stamps of India overprinted.

The following are the types of Indian stamps overprinted for use in the six States of CHAMBA, FARIDKOT, GWALIOR, JIND, NABHA, and PATIALA (except where otherwise stated):—

Head of Queen Victoria: ½ a. (**23**), 1 a. (**25**), 1½ a. (**26**), 2 a. (**27**), 2½ a. (**36**), 3 a. (**28**), 4 a. (**29**), 6 a. (**21**), 8 a. (**31**), 12 a. (**32**), 1 r. (**33** and **37**), 2, 3, and 5 r. (**38**), 3 pies (**40**).

Head of King Edward VII: 3 pies (**41**), ½ a. (**42**), 1 a. (**43**), 2 a. (**44**), 2½ a. (**45**), 3 a. (**46**), 4 a. (**47**), 6 a. (**48**), 8 a. (**49**), 12 a. (**50**), 1 r. (**51**), 2, 3, and 5 r. (**52**).

Head of King George V: 3 pies (**55**), ½ a. (**56** and **79**), 9 pies (**80**), 1 a. (**57** and **81**), 1¼ a. (**82**), 1½ a. (**58** A and B), 2 a. (**59** and **70**), 2½ a. (**61**), 3 a. (**62**), 3½ a. (**83**), 4 a. (**63** and **71**), 6 a. (**64**), 8 a. (**65**), 12 a. (**66**), rupee values (**67**).

Stamps of King George VI: (*see type columns*).

These stamps had franking power throughout British India.

The minor varieties, such as smaller letters, etc., formerly given, being mostly due to broken letters and unequal inking when printing, are now omitted. Variations in the length of words due to unequal spacing when setting are also omitted.

CHAMBA.

CHAMBA STATE (1)

1886–95. *Queen Victoria. Optd. with T* **1**.

No.	Description	Unused	Used
1	½ a. deep green	0 4	0 6
	a. Error. "CHMABA"	£6	
	b. Error. "8TATE"	£15	
2	1 a. brown-purple	1 0	1 6
	a. Error. "CHMABA"	£15	
	b. Error. "8TATE"	£20	
3	1 a. plum	0 9	1 0
4	1½ a. sepia (1895)	3 6	5 0
5	2 a. dull blue	1 6	1 3
	a. Error. "CHAMBA" twice		
	b. Error. "CHMABA"	£30	
	c. Error. "8TATE"	£20	
6	2 a. ultramarine	1 6	2 0
7	2½ a. green (1895)	15 0	22 6
8	3 a. orange (1887)	7 6	9 6
	a. Error. "CHMABA"	£60	
9	3 a. brown-orange	2 0	2 3
10	4 a. olive-green	2 0	3 0
	a. Error. "CHMABA"	£30	
	b. Error. "8TATE"	£40	
11	4 a. slate-green	1 6	2 6
12	6 a. olive-bistre (1890)	5 0	7 6
13	6 a. bistre-brown	6 0	7 0
14	8 a. dull mauve (1887)	7 6	8 6
	a. Error. "CHMABA"	£50	
15	8 a. magenta	3 6	5 0
16	12 a. purple/*red* (1890)	3 6	6 0
	a. Error. "CHMABA"	£75	
	b. Error. "SLATE"	£80	
17	1 r. slate (1887)	40 0	60 0
	a. Error. "CHMABA"	£100	
18	1 r. green and carmine (1895)	5 0	7 6
19	2 r. carm. & yell.-brn. (1895)	55 0	
20	3 r. brown & green (1895)	55 0	
21	5 r. ultram. & violet (1895)	65 0	

1900–4. *Optd. with T* **1**.

No.	Description	Unused	Used
22	3 pies, carmine	0 4	0 6
23	3 pies, grey (1904)	0 8	0 10
	a. Overprint inverted	85 0	
24	½ a. pale green (1902)	0 10	1 0
25	½ a. green	0 4	0 10
26	1 a. carmine (1902)	0 4	0 6
27	2 a. pale violet (1903)	10 0	16 0

1903–5. *King Edward VII. Optd. with T* **1**.

No.	Description	Unused	Used
28	3 pies, pale grey	0 3	0 6
29	3 pies, slate-grey (1905)	0 3	0 4
30	½ a. green	0 6	0 6
31	1 a. carmine	0 6	0 8
32	2 a. pale violet (1904)	1 6	2 6
33	2 a. mauve	1 3	2 0
34	3 a. orange-brown (1905)	2 0	2 0
35	4 a. olive-green (1904)	2 0	2 6
36	6 a. olive-bistre (1905)	2 0	2 6
37	8 a. dull mauve (1904)	2 6	3 6
38	8 a. magenta	4 0	6 0
39	12 a. purple/*red* (1905)	4 0	5 0
40	1 r. green & carmine (1904)	4 6	6 0

1907. *Nos.* 149/50 *of India optd. with T* **1**.

No.	Type	Description	Unused	Used
41	**53**	½ a. green	0 3	0 3
42	**54**	1 a. carmine	1 3	1 6

1913. *King George V optd. with T* **1**.

No.	Type	Description	Unused	Used
43	**55**	3 p. slate-grey	0 3	0 3
44	**56**	½ a. green	0 4	0 8
45	**57**	1 a. rose-carmine	0 8	0 10
46	,,	1 a. aniline carmine	0 8	0 10
47	**59**	2 a. mauve	1 0	1 6
48	**62**	3 a. orange-brown	1 6	1 9
49	**63**	4 a. olive	1 0	1 6
50	**64**	6 a. olive-bistre	1 0	2 0
51	**65**	8 a. purple	1 9	2 6
52	**66**	12 a. dull claret	2 6	3 6
53	**67**	1 r. brown and green	5 0	6 0

CHAMBA (2)

1921. *No.* 192 *of India optd. with T* **2**.

No.	Type	Description	Unused	Used
54	**57**	9 p. on 1 a. rose-carmine	4 0	5 0

1922–27. *Optd. with T* **1**. *New values, etc.*

No.	Type	Description	Unused	Used
55	**57**	1 a. chocolate	0 5	0 8
56	**58**	1½ a. chocolate (Type A)	20 0	30 0
57	,,	1½ a. chocolate (Type B)	1 0	1 6
58	,,	1½ a. rose-carmine (Type B)	2 6	4 0
59	**61**	2½ a. ultramarine	2 6	4 0
60	,,	2½ a. orange	2 6	4 0
61	**62**	3 a. ultramarine	5 0	6 0

CHAMBA STATE (3) CHAMBA STATE (4)

1927–37. *King George V (Nasik printing, wmk. Mult. Star). Optd. at Nasik with T* **3** *or* **4** *(1 r.).*

No.	Type	Description	Unused	Used
62	**55**	3 p. slate	0 3	0 3
63	**56**	½ a. green	0 3	0 4
64	**80**	9 p. deep green	0 3	0 4
65	**57**	1 a. chocolate	0 6	0 6
66	**82**	1¼ a. mauve	0 9	1 0
67	**58**	1½ a. rose-carmine (Type B)	0 6	0 6
68	**70**	2 a. purple	1 0	1 0
69	**61**	2½ a. orange	1 0	1 0
70	**62**	3 a. bright blue	1 6	2 0
71	**71**	4 a. sage-green	1 0	1 3
72	**64**	6 a. bistre ('37)	50 0	
73	**65**	8 a. reddish purple	1 9	2 6
74	**66**	12 a. claret	3 6	6 0
75	**67**	1 r. chocolate & green	5 0	5 0

1935–36. *New types and colours. Optd. with T* **3**.

No.	Type	Description	Unused	Used
76	**79**	½ a. green	0 6	0 6
77	**81**	1 a. chocolate	0 4	0 6
78	**59**	2 a. vermilion (No. 236*a*)	0 10	0 10
79	,,	2 a. vermilion (*small die*, No. 236*b*)	30 0	
80	**62**	3 a. carmine	1 3	1 6
81	**63**	4 a. sage-green ('36)	2 0	1 9

CHAMBA STATE
(5)

CHAMBA **(6)** **CHAMBA** **(7)**

1938. *King George VI. Optd. with T* **3** (3 *p. to* 1 *a.*), *T* **5** (2 *a. to* 12 *a.*) *or T* **4** (*rupee values*).

No.	Type	Description				
82	**91**	3 p. slate	0	8	1	3
83	,,	½ a. red-brown	1	0	1	9
84	,,	9 p. green	1	9	2	3
85	,,	1 a. carmine	0	6	1	3
86	**92**	2 a. vermilion	0	9	1	9
87	**93**	2½ a. bright violet ..	1	0	2	3
88	**94**	3 a. yellow-green ..	6	0	8	6
89	**95**	3½ a. bright blue	1	3	3	6
90	**96**	4 a. brown	1	3	3	6
91	**97**	6 a. turquoise-green ..	12	6	20	0
92	**98**	8 a. slate-violet	2	6	7	6
93	**99**	12 a. lake	5	0	9	0
94	**100**	1 r. grey & red-brown ..	7	6	12	6
95	,,	2 r. purple and brown ..	15	0	17	6
96	,,	5 r. green and blue ..	32	6	40	0
97	,,	10 r. purple and claret ..	70	0	80	0
98	,,	15 r. brown and green ..	£7		£8	
99	,,	25 r. slate-violet & purple	£12		£14	

1943–48. *Optd. with T* **6** (*to* 12 *a.*), "CHAMBA" *only, as in T* **5** (14 *a.*) *or T* **7** (*rupee values*).

(*a*) *Stamps of* 1937.

No.	Type	Description				
100	**91**	½ a. red-brown	1	6	2	3
101	,,	1 a. carmine	1	9	1	9
102	**100**	1 r. grey and red-brown	15	0	17	6
103	,,	2 r. purple and brown ..	20	0	22	6
104	,,	5 r. green and blue ..	80	0	80	0
105	,,	10 r. purple and claret ..	£6		£6	
106	,,	15 r. brown and green ..	£7		£7	
107	,,	25 r. slate-violet & purple	£12		£12	

(*b*) *Stamps of* 1940–43.

No.	Type	Description				
108	**100*a***	3 p. slate	0	3	0	3
109	,,	½ a. purple	0	3	0	3
110	,,	9 p. green	0	6	0	6
111	,,	1 a. carmine	0	6	0	6
112	**101**	1½ a. dull violet	0	7	0	6
113	,,	2 a. vermilion	0	8	1	0
114	,,	3 a. bright violet	0	10	1	3
115	,,	3½ a. bright blue	0	10	1	6
116	**102**	4 a. brown	1	0	1	6
117	,,	6 a. turquoise-green ..	1	6	3	0
118	,,	8 a. slate-violet	2	6	4	0
119	,,	12 a. lake	3	6	5	0
120	**103**	14 a. purple ('48) ..	12	6	20	0

OFFICIAL STAMPS.

SERVICE

CHAMBA STATE
(O **1**)

1886–98. *Queen Victoria. Optd. with Type* O **1**.

O 1	½ a. deep green	0	6	0	3
	a. Error. "CHMABA" ..	90	0		
	b. Error. "SERV CE" ..	—		£8	
	c. Error. "STATE" ..	£10			
O 2	1 a. brown-purple	1	3	0	9
	a. Error. "CHMABA" ..	£10			
	b. Error. "SERV CE" ..	£15			
	c. Error. "8TATE" ..	£20			
O 3	1 a. plum	0	8	0	4
	a. Error. "SERVICE" double. .	£7		60	0
O 4	2 a. dull blue	1	3	1	9
	a. Error. "CHMABA" ..	£25			
O 5	2 a. ultramarine (1887) ..	1	0	1	6
O 6	3 a. orange (1890)	8	6	10	0
	a. Error. "CHMABA" ..	£35			
O 7	3 a. brown-orange	5	0	5	6
O 8	4 a. olive-green	1	9	1	6
	a. Error. "CHMABA" ..	£25			
	b. Error. "SERV CE" ..	£45			
	c. Error. "STATE" ..	£25			
O 9	4 a. slate-green	3	0	4	0
O10	6 a. olive-bistre (1890) ..	4	6	5	0
O11	6 a. bistre-brown	12	6	15	0
O12	8 a. dull mauve (1887) ..	5	0	6	0
	a. Error. "CHMABA" ..	£60			
O13	8 a. magenta	5	0	6	0
O14	12 a. purple/*red* (1890) ..	17	6	22	6
	a. Error. "CHMABA" ..	£60			
O15	1 r. slate (1890)	20	0	25	0
	a. Error. "CHMABA" ..	£70			
O16	1 r. green & carm. (1898) ..	12	6	17	6

1902–4. *Colours changed.*

O17	3 pies, grey (1904)	0	6	0	6
O18	½ a. pale green	0	7	0	7
O19	½ a. green	0	6	0	6
O20	1 a. carmine	0	9	1	0
O21	2 a. pale violet (1903) ..	6	6	8	6

1903–5. *King Edward VII. Optd. as Type* O **1**.

O22	3 pies, pale grey	2	0	0	8
O23	3 pies, slate-grey (1905) ..	0	2	0	2
O24	½ a. yellow-green	0	4	0	5
O25	1 a. carmine	0	7	0	8
O26	2 a. pale violet (1904) ..	2	0	1	9
O27	2 a. mauve	1	0	0	6
O28	4 a. olive-green (1905) ..	1	6	1	9
O29	8 a. dull mauve (1905) ..	3	0	3	6
O30	8 a. magenta	3	6	4	0
O31	1 r. green and carmine (1905)	3	6	4	0

The 2 a. mauve, King Edward VII, overprinted "On H.M.S.", was discovered in Calcutta, but was not sent to Chamba, and is an unissued variety. (Price 40s.)

1907. *Nos.* 149/50 *of India, optd. with Type* O **1**.

O32	½ a. green	1	6	1	0
	a. Inverted overprint ..	£45			
O33	1 a. carmine	3	6	2	6

The error, No. O32*a*, was due to an inverted cliché which was corrected after a few sheets had been printed.

1913–14. *King George V Service stamps* (*wmk. Single Star*) *optd. with T* **1**.

O34	3 p. slate-grey	0	3	0	3
O35	3 p. grey	0	3	0	3
O36	½ a. yellow-green	0	3	0	3
O37	½ a. pale blue-green	0	4	0	3
O38	1 a. aniline carmine	0	4	0	4
O39	1 a. rose-carmine	0	6	0	3
O40	2 a. mauve (1914)	0	8	1	
O41	4 a. olive	1	3	1	
O42	8 a. purple	2	0	3	
O43	1 r. brown and green (1914)	3	6	5	

1914. *King George V. Optd. with Type* O **1**.

No.	Type	Description				
O44	**59**	2 a. mauve	15	0	22	
O45	**63**	4 a. olive	30	0	40	

1921. *No.* O97 *of India optd. with T* **2** *at top.*

No.	Type	Description				
O46	**57**	9 p. on 1 a. rose-carmine	1	6	2	

1925. *As* 1913–14. *New colour.*

No.	Type	Description				
O47	**57**	1 a. chocolate	0	8	0	

CHAMBA STATE SERVICE
(O **2**)

CHAMBA STATE SERVICE
(O **3**)

1927-39. *King George V* (*Nasik printing, wmk Mult. Star*), *optd. at Nasik with Type* O **2** O **3** *rupee values*).

No.	Type	Description			
O48	**55**	3 p. slate	0	3	0
O49	**56**	½ a. green	0	3	0
O50	**80**	9 p. deep green	0	3	0
O51	**57**	1 a. chocolate	0	6	0
O52	**82**	1¼ a. mauve	0	4	0
O53	**70**	2 a. purple	0	10	1
O54	**71**	4 a. sage-green	0	9	1

O55	**65**	8 a. reddish purple ..	1 9	2 6
O56	**66**	12 a. claret	3 0	4 0
O57	**67**	1 r. chocolate & green ..	4 0	6 0
O58	,,	2 r. carmine & orge. ('39)	30 0	
O59	,,	5 r. ultram. & pur. ('39)	40 0	
O60	,,	10 r. grn. and scar. ('39)	60 0	

1935–39. *New types and colours. Optd. with Type* O **2.**

O61	**79**	½ a. green	0 3	0 3
O62	**81**	1 a. chocolate	0 3	0 4
O63	**59**	2 a. vermilion	0 8	0 10
O64	,,	2 a. verm. (*small die*) ('39)	0 8	0 10
O65	**63**	4 a. sage-green ('36) ..	0 9	1 0

1938–40. *King George VI. Optd. with Type* O **2** *or* O **3** (*rupee values*).

O66	**91**	9 p. green	2 6	3 6
O67	,,	1 a. carmine	1 0	1 6
O68	**100**	1 r. grey & red-brn. ('40?)	£24	£15
O69	,,	2 r. pur. & brown ('40)	12 6	15 0
O70	,,	5 r. green & blue ('40) ..	25 0	27 6
O71	,,	10 r. pur. & claret ('40)	60 0	60 0

CHAMBA
SERVICE
(O **4**)

1941–43. (*a*) *Official stamps optd. with T* **6.**

O72	O **20**	3 p. slate	0 6	0 6
O73	,,	½ a. red-brown	1 6	1 9
O74	,,	½ a. purple	0 6	0 6
O75	,,	9 p. green	0 6	0 8
O76	,,	1 a. carmine	0 8	0 6
O77	,,	1 a. 3 p. bistre ..	10 0	6 0
O78	,,	1½ a. dull violet ..	1 0	1 3
O79	,,	2 a. vermilion ..	1 6	1 6
O80	,,	2½ a. bright violet ..	1 6	1 9
O81	,,	4 a. brown	3 6	5 0
O82	,,	8 a. slate-violet ..	6 0	8 0

(*b*) *Postage stamps optd. with Type* O **4.**

O83	**100**	1 r. grey and red-brown	8 6	10 0
O84	,,	2 r. purple and brown ..	10 6	12 6
O85	,,	5 r. green and blue ..	30 0	32 6
O86	,,	10 r. purple and claret ..	50 0	55 0

FARIDKOT.

For earlier issues, see under INDIAN STATES.

FARIDKOT
STATE
(1)

1887 (1 JAN.)–**1900.** *Queen Victoria. Optd. with T* **1.**

1	½ a. deep green	1 3	1 3
2	1 a. brown-purple	2 0	2 0
3	1 a. plum	4 0	4 0
4	2 a. blue	5 0	5 0
5	2 a. deep blue	6 0	6 0
6	3 a. orange	5 0	6 0
7	3 a. brown-orange	6 6	6 6
8	4 a. olive-green	6 0	7 6
	a. Error "ARIDKOT," ..	£15	
9	4 a. slate-green	6 0	7 6
0	6 a. olive-bistre	12 6	12 6
	a. Error. "ARIDKOT" ..	£18	
1	6 a. bistre-brown	7 0	7 6
2	8 a. dull mauve	12 6	12 6
	a. Error. "ARIDKOT" ..	£20	
3	8 a. magenta	12 6	15 0
4	12 a. purple/*red* (1900) ..	37 6	40 0
5	1 r. slate	37 6	40 0
	a. Error. "ARIDKOT" ..		
6	1 r. green and carmine (1893)	27 6	32 6

The ½ a., 1 a., 2 a., 3 a., 4 a., 8 a. and 1 r. are nown with broken "O" (looking like a "C") "FARIDKOT".

1900. *Optd. with T* **1.**

17	3 p. carmine	2 6	4 0

OFFICIAL STAMPS.

SERVICE

FARIDKOT
STATE
(O 1)

1886–96. *Queen Victoria. Optd. with Type* O **1.**

O 1	½ a. deep green	1 3	1 6
	a. Error. "SERV CE" ..	£6	
O 2	1 a. brown-purple	1 6	1 9
O 3	1 a. plum	3 0	2 6
	a. Error. "SERV CE" ..	£12	
O 4	2 a. dull blue	6 0	5 0
	a. Error. "SERV CE" ..		
O 5	2 a. deep blue	5 0	6 0
O 6	3 a. orange	5 0	8 6
O 7	3 a. brown-orange	5 0	8 6
O 8	4 a. olive-green	7 6	8 0
	a. Error. "SERV CE" ..	£14	
O 9	4 a. slate-green	7 0	8 0
O10	6 a. olive-bistre	40 0	42 6
	a. Error. "ARIDKOT" ..	£18	
	b. Error. "SERVIC" ..	£12	
O11	6 a. bistre-brown	15 0	20 0
O12	8 a. dull mauve	6 6	8 6
	a. Error. "SERV CE" ..		
O13	8 a. magenta	12 6	15 0
O14	1 r. slate	27 6	32 6
O15	1 r. green & carmine (1896)	45 0	55 0

The ½ a., 1 a., 2 a., 3 a., 4 a. and 8 a. are known with the broken "O".

This State ceased to use overprinted stamps after March 31, 1901.

GWALIOR.

गवालियर

GWALIOR
(1)

1885 (MAY). *Queen Victoria. The* 4 *a. is India T* **17.** *Optd. with T* **1.**

(A) *Space between two lines of overprint* 13 *mm. Hindi inscription* 13 *to* 14 *mm. long.*

1	½ a. deep green	30 0	22 6
2	1 a. brown-purple	30 0	27 6
3	2 a. dull blue	27 6	12 6

A variety exists of the ½ a. in which the space between the two lines of overprint is only 9½ mm. but this is probably from a proof sheet.

(B) JUNE. *Space between two lines of overprint* 15 *mm. on* 6 *a. and* 16 *to* 17 *mm. on other values.*

(I) *Hindi inscription* 13 *to* 14 *mm. long.*

(II) *Hindi inscription* 15 *to* 15½ *mm. long.*

		I.		II.	
4	½ a. deep green ..	30 0	—	32 6	—
5	1 a. brown-purple	30 0	—	40 0	—
6	1½ a. sepia	35 0	—	57 6	—
7	2 a. dull blue ..	30 0	—	55 0	—
8	4 a. green ..	47 6	—	70 0	—
9	6 a. olive-bistre ..	57 6	—	75 0	—

10	8 a. dull mauve ..	75 0	—	75 0	—
11	1 r. slate	70 0	—	75 0	—

These two overprints are both found on the same sheet in the proportion of three of the former to one of the latter.

GWALIOR
गवालियर
(2)

Overprinted with T **2**.

A. **1885** (Sept.). *In red.*
(I) *Hindi inscription* 13 *to* 14 *mm. long.*
(II) *Hindi inscription* 15 *to* 15½ *mm. long.*

No.		I.		II.	
12	½ a. deep green ..	1 6	2 0	2 0	2 0
13	2 a. dull blue ..	10 6	12 6	30 0	30 0
14	4 a. green ..	18 6	22 6	65 0	65 0
15	1 r. slate	17 6	22 6	42 6	47 6

Reprints have been made of Nos. 12 to 15, but the majority of the specimens have the word "REPRINT" overprinted upon them.

(*The* 4 *a. below is T* **29**).

B. **1885–96.** *In black.*
(I) *Hindi inscription* 13 *to* 14 *mm. long.*
(II) *Hindi inscription* 15 *to* 15½ *mm. long.*

No.		I.		II.	
16	½ a. dp. green ('89)	1 3	1 3	0 4	0 3
	a. Overprint double	—	—	—	£8
	b. Error. "GWALICR"	†		85 0	
17	9 p. carmine ('91)	60 0	55 0	60 0	65 0
18	1 a. brown-purple	1 6	0 9	1 3	0 10
19	1 a. plum ..	—	—	1 0	0 6
20	1½ a. sepia	0 10	1 0	0 9	1 0
21	2 a. dull blue ..	4 6	4 6	2 0	1 0
22	2 a. deep blue ..	6 6	6 6	3 0	1 6
23	2½ a. green ('96) ..	†		6 0	9 6
	a. Error. "GWALICR"	†		£25	
24	3 a. orange ..	5 6	5 6	7 6	6 6
25	3 a. brown-orange	5 0	5 0	2 0	1 6
26	4 a. olive-grn. ('89)	7 6	6 0	3 0	3 0
27	4 a. slate-green ..	9 6	6 0	3 0	2 6
28	6 a. olive-bistre ..	6 6	7 6	6 0	6 0
29	6 a. bistre-brown	2 0	2 0	3 0	6 0
30	8 a. dull mauve ..	7 6	7 6	4 6	3 6
31	8 a. magenta ..	—	—	12 0	14 0
32	12 a. pur./*red* ('91)	17 6	18 6	4 6	2 0
33	1 r. slate ('89) ..	50 0		4 0	4 6
34	1 r. grn. & carmine ('96) ..	†		7 6	9 0
	a. Error. "GWALICR"	†		£25	
35	2 r. carm. & yellow-brown ('96) ..	†		12 6	17 6
36	3 r. brn. & grn. ('96)	†		20 0	22 6
37	5 r. ultram. & violet ('96)	†		25 0	27 6

The ½ a., 1 a., 2 a. and 3 a. exist with space between "1" and "o" of "GWALIOR".

1899–1908. *Optd. with T* **2** (II).

38	3 pies, carmine	0 3	0 3
	a. Opt. inverted	£10	£8
	b. Small "G"		
39	3 pies, grey (1904)	15 0	
40	½ a. pale green (1901) ..	0 6	0 6
41	1 a. carmine (1901) ..	0 8	0 6
42	2 a. pale violet (1901) ..	1 3	1 3
43	2½ a. ultramarine (1903) ..	1 9	2 0

"GWALIOR" 13 *mm. long. Opt. spaced* 2¾ *mm.* (1908).

44	3 r. brown and green ..	35 0	
45	5 r. ultramarine and violet ..	55 0	

1903–08. *King Edward VII. Optd. as T* **2**.
(I) "GWALIOR" 14 *mm. long. Overprint spaced* 1¾ *mm.*
(II) "GWALIOR" 13 *mm. long. Overprint spaced* 2¾ *mm.*

No.		I.		II.	
46	3 pies, pale grey	0 4	0 3	1 0	0 3
47	3 pies, slate-grey ..	0 3	0 3	0 3	0 3
48	½ a. green ..	0 5	0 4	†	
49	1 a. carmine ..	0 5	0 3	1 6	1 0
50	2 a. pale violet ..	1 6	1 6	†	
51	2 a. mauve ..	1 6	1 0	0 10	0 6
52	2½ a. ultramarine ..	22 6	—	2 6	3 6
53	3 a. orange-brown	1 6	1 6	1 6	1 3
54	4 a. olive-green ..	2 3	2 0	1 0	1 0
55	4 a. slate-green ..	4 0	4 6	†	
56	6 a. olive-bistre ..	3 0	3 6	3 0	2 9
57	8 a. dull mauve ..	4 6	5 6	5 0	5 0
58	8 a. magenta ..	2 6	2 6	5 0	5 0
59	12 a. purple/*red* ..	3 6	4 0	3 6	4 0
60	1 r. green & carm.	4 6	5 6	7 6	3 6
61	2 r. carmine and yellow-brown	90 0	£5	15 0	17 6
62	3 r. brown & green	†		50 0	55 0
63	5 r. ultram. & vio.	†		30 0	32 6

Dates of issue: Opt. I—1904, Nos. 50, 53; 1905, Nos. 47, 52, 54, 57, 59, 60; 1906, No. 56; Others 1903. Opt. II—1908.

1907. *Nos.* 149 *and* 150 *of India overprinted as T* **2**. "GWALIOR" 14 *mm. long. Overprint spaced* 1¾ *mm.*

64	½ a. green	0 4	0 3

"GWALIOR" 13 *mm. long. Overprint spaced* 2¾ *mm.*

65	½ a. green	0 4	0 3
66	1 a. carmine	0 6	0 3

1912–14. *King George V. Optd. as T* **2**.

67	**55**	3 pies, slate-grey	0 3	0 3
68	**56**	½ a. green	0 3	0 3
		a. Overprint inverted ..		
69	**57**	1 a. aniline carmine ..	0 6	0 3
		a. Overprint double ..	40 0	
70	**59**	2 a. mauve	0 10	0 3
71	**62**	3 a. orange-brown ..	1 0	0 3
72	**63**	4 a. olive (1913)	1 0	0 3
73	**64**	6 a. olive-bistre	1 6	0 8
74	**65**	8 a. purple (1913) ..	2 0	1 [illegible]
75	**66**	12 a. dull claret (1914) ..	3 0	1 [illegible]
76	**67**	1 r. brown and green ..	3 6	3 [illegible]
77	,,	2 r. carm.-rose & brown ..	7 6	5 [illegible]
78	,,	5 r. ultramarine and violet	20 0	20 [illegible]

GWALIOR
(3)

1922. *No.* 192 *of India optd. with T* **3**.

79	**57**	9 p. on 1 a. rose-carmine ..	0 6	0

1923–27. *Optd. T* **2**. *New colours and values.*

80	**57**	1 a. chocolate ('23) ..	0 4	0
81	**58**	1½ as. choc. (Type B) ('25)	1 3	1
82	,,	1½ as. rose-car. (Type B) ('27)	0 6	0
83	**61**	2½ a. ultramarine ('25) ..	2 0	2
84	,,	2½ a. orange ('27)	1 6	1
85	**62**	3 a. ultramarine ('24) ..	1 6	0

GWALIOR
गवालियर
(4)

GWALIOR
गवालियर
(5)

1928–36. *King George V* (*Nasik printing, wm. Mult. Star*), *optd. at Nasik with T* **4** *or* (*rupee values*).

86	**55**	3 p. slate ('32)	0 3	0
87	**56**	½ a. green ('30)	0 3	0
88	**80**	9 p. deep green ('33) ..	0 4	0
89	**57**	1 a. chocolate	0 6	0
90	**82**	1¼ a. mauve ('36) ..	0 4	0

91	**70**	2 a. purple	0 6	0 3
92	**62**	3 a. bright blue	1 0	0 8
93	**71**	4 a. sage-green	1 3	0 8
94	**65**	8 a. reddish purple ..	1 6	1 0
95	**66**	12 a. claret..	1 9	1 6
96	**67**	1 r. chocolate and green	3 0	3 0
97	,,	2 r. carmine and orange	5 6	2 6
98	,,	5 r. ultram. & purple ('29)	20 0	20 0
99	,,	10 r. green & scarlet ('30)..	40 0	40 0
100	,,	15 r. blue and olive ('30) ..	55 0	55 0
101	,,	25 r. orange and blue ('30)	85 0	90 0

1936. *New types and colours. Optd. with T* **4.**

102	**79**	½ a. green	0 3	0 4
103	**81**	1 a. chocolate	0 3	0 4
104	**59**	2 a. vermilion	0 6	0 6

1938–49. *King George VI. Optd. with T* **4** *or* **5** *(rupee values).*

105	**91**	3 p. slate ('40) ..	0 9	0 4
106	,,	½ a. red-brown ..	0 9	0 4
107	,,	9 p. green ('40) ..	40 0	17 6
108	,,	1 a. carmine ..	0 8	0 3
109	**94**	3 a. yellow-green ('39)	1 9	1 3
110	**96**	4 a. brown ..	7 6	7 6
111	**97**	6 a. turquoise-green ('39)	2 6	2 6
112	**100**	1 r. grey & red.-brn. ('45)	4 6	5 0
113	,,	2 r. purple & brown ('49)	8 0	10 0
114	,,	5 r. green and blue ('49)	22 6	25 0
115	,,	10 r. purple & claret ('49)	45 0	45 0
116	,,	15 r. brown & green ('49)	90 0	90 0
117	,,	25 r. slate-vio. & pur. ('49)	£6	£6

1944–48. *King George VI. Optd. with T* **4.**

118	**100a**	3 p. slate	0 3	0 3
119	,,	½ a. purple	0 3	0 3
120	,,	9 p. green	0 3	0 4
121	,,	1 a. carmine	0 4	0 4
122	**101**	1½ a. dull violet ..	0 6	0 6
123	,,	2 a. vermilion	0 6	0 6
124	,,	3 a. bright violet ..	0 10	0 10
125	**102**	4 a. brown	0 9	2 0
126	,,	6 a. turquoise-grn. ('48)	4 0	5 0
127	,,	8 a. slate-violet ('45) ..	2 6	3 6
128	,,	12 a. lake ('45)	3 0	4 6

GWALIOR

गवालियर

(6)

1949. *King George VI. Optd. with T* **6** *at the Gwalior Govt. Ptg. Wks.*

129	**100a**	3 p. slate	0 8	0 10
130	,,	½ a. purple	0 10	1 0
131	,,	1 a. carmine	1 0	1 0
132	**101**	2 a. vermilion ..	2 6	3 6
133	,,	3 a. bright violet ..	6 0	6 6
134	**102**	4 a. brown	3 6	5 0
135	,,	6 a. turquoise-green ..	20 0	25 0
136	,,	8 a. slate-violet ..	35 0	45 0
137	,,	12 a. lake	£5	£6

OFFICIAL STAMPS.

गवालियर

सरविस

(O 1)

1895–96. *Queen Victoria. Optd. with Type* O **1.**

O 1	½ a. deep green	0 4	0 3
O 2	1 a. brown-purple	1 6	0 3
O 3	1 a. plum	0 6	0 3
O 4	2 a. dull blue	2 6	0 8
O 5	2 a. deep blue	1 3	0 6
O 6	4 a. olive-green	5 0	5 0
O 7	4 a. slate-green	1 6	1 0
O 8	8 a. dull mauve	7 6	6 0
O 9	8 a. magenta..	4 0	3 6
O10	1 r. green & carmine (1896)	5 0	5 6

Varieties. (i.) *The last two characters of the lower word transposed, so that it reads* " Sersiv ".

O11	½ a. deep green	25 0	25 0
O12	1 a. plum	35 0	32 6
O13	2 a. deep blue	70 0	
O14	4 a. olive-green	£10	
O15	8 a. magenta	£36	
O16	1 r. green and carmine ..	£60	

(ii) *Fourth character in lower word omitted.*

O17	½ a. deep green	—	20 0
O18	1 a. plum	—	35 0
O19	2 a. deep blue	£5	80 0
O20	4 a. olive-green	—	£7
O21	8 a. magenta ..		

(iii.) *Overprint double.*

O22	½ a. deep green	—	£12

1901–4. *Optd. with Type* O **1.**

O23	3 pies, carmine (1902) ..	1 0	1 3
O24	3 pies, grey (1904)	1 0	0 9
O25	½ a. pale green	0 6	0 3
O26	½ a. green	0 4	0 3
O27	1 a. carmine	2 0	0 3
O28	2 a. pale violet (1903) ..	1 0	2 0

1903–5. *King Edward VII. Optd. as Type* O **1.**
Overprint spaced 10 *mm.*

O29	3 pies, pale grey	0 4	0 3
O30	3 pies, slate-grey (1905) ..	0 3	0 3
O31	½ a. green	0 6	0 3
O32	1 a. carmine	0 4	0 3
O33	2 a. pale violet (1905) ..	1 9	0 8
O34	2 a. mauve	1 9	0 8
O35	4 a. olive-green (1905) ..	6 0	5 0
O36	8 a. dull mauve (1905) ..	4 0	2 0
O37	8 a. magenta	3 6	3 6
O38	1 r. green & carmine (1905)	4 6	3 6

Overprint spaced 8 *mm.*

O39	3 pies, pale grey	2 6	0 8
O40	3 pies, slate-grey	2 6	0 6
O41	½ a. green	1 9	0 3
O42	1 a. carmine	0 6	0 2
O43	2 a. mauve	2 0	0 8
O44	4 a. olive-green	6 0	2 6
O45	8 a. dull mauve	10 0	5 0
O46	1 r. green and carmine ..	10 0	12 6

1907. *Nos.* 149 *and* 150 *of India optd. as Type* O **1.**
Overprint spaced 10 *mm.*

O47	½ a. green	0 6	0 3
O48	1 a. carmine	1 3	0 3

Overprint spaced 8 *mm.*

O49	½ a. green	0 6	0 3
O50	1 a. carmine	22 6	6 6

1913. *King George V. Optd with Type* O **1.**

O51	**55**	3 pies, slate-grey	0 3	0 3
O52	**56**	½ a. green	0 3	0 3
O53	**57**	1 a. rose-carmine ..	0 6	0 3
O54	,,	1 a. aniline carmine ..	0 4	0 3
		a. Overprint double ..	40 0	
O55	**59**	2 a. mauve	0 8	0 3
O56	**63**	4 a. olive	1 0	0 4
O57	**65**	8 a. purple	1 9	1 0
O58	**67**	1 r. brown and green ..	5 0	2 6

1922. *No.* O97 *of India optd. with T* **3.**

O59	**57**	9 p. on 1 a. rose-carmine	0 8	0 6

1923. *Overprint Type* O **1.** *New colour.*

O60	**57**	1 a. chocolate	0 6	0 3

गवालियर

सरविस

(O 2)

1927–35. *King George V (Nasik printing, wmk. Mult. Star), optd. at Nasik as Type* O **1.** *(but top line of overprint measures* 13 *mm. instead of* 14 *mm.) or with Type* O **2** *(rupee values).*

No.	Type	Value	Unused	Used
O61	**55**	3 pies, slate	0 3	0 3
O62	**56**	½ a. green	0 3	0 4
O63	**80**	9 p. deep green ('35) ..	0 3	0 4
O64	**57**	1 a. chocolate	0 4	0 3
O65	**82**	1¼ a. mauve ('33)	0 4	0 4
O66	**70**	2 a. purple	0 6	0 3
O67	**71**	4 a. sage-green	1 0	0 6
O68	**65**	8 a. reddish purple ('28)	1 3	0 8
O69	**67**	1 r. chocolate & green ..	2 6	1 3
O70	,,	2 r. car. & orange ('35)	4 6	6 0
O71	,,	5 r. ultram. & pur. ('32)	20 0	20 0
O72	,,	10 r. green & scar. ('32) ..	40 0	50 0

1936–37. *New types. Optd. as Type* O **1** *(*13 *mm.).*

No.	Type	Value	Unused	Used
O73	**79**	½ a. green	0 3	0 4
O74	**81**	1 a. chocolate	0 4	0 5
O75	**59**	2 a. vermilion	0 6	0 8
O76	,,	2 a. vermilion (*small die*)	0 6	0 3
O77	**63**	4 a. sage-green ('37) ..	0 8	0 6

1938. *King George VI. Optd. as Type* O **1** *(*13 *mm.).*

No.	Type	Value	Unused	Used
O78	**91**	½ a. red-brown	5 0	0 4
O79	,,	1 a. carmine	5 0	0 4

गवालियर

(O 3)

1940–48. *Official stamps optd. with Type* O **3.**

No.	Type	Value	Unused	Used
O80	O **20**	3 pies, slate	0 6	0 6
O81	,,	½ a. red-brown ..	3 0	2 0
O82	,,	½ a. purple	0 5	0 6
O83	,,	9 p. green	0 5	0 6
O84	,,	1 a. carmine	0 6	0 6
O85	,,	1 a. 3 p. bistre ..	2 0	2 0
O86	,,	1½ a. dull violet ..	1 0	0 8
O87	,,	2 a. vermilion	1 0	1 0
O88	,,	4 a. brown	0 9	1 3
O89	,,	8 a. slate-violet ..	2 0	3 0

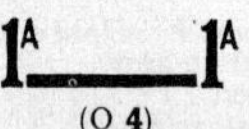

(O 4)

1942. *Stamp of* 1932 *(King George V) optd. with Type* O **1** *and surch. with Type* O **4.**

No.	Type	Value	Unused	Used
O90	**82**	1 a. on 1¼ a. mauve ..	7 6	4 0

1944–48. *King George VI. Optd. with Type* O **2.**

No.	Type	Value	Unused	Used
O91	**100**	1 r. grey and red-brown	3 6	4 0
O92	,,	2 r. purple and brown ..	7 6	10 0
O93	,,	5 r. green and blue ..	25 0	30 0
O94	,,	10 r. purple & claret ('48)	50 0	60 0

JIND.

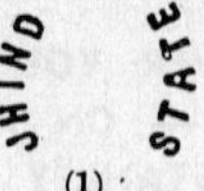

(1)

1885. *Queen Victoria. Optd. with T* **1.** *The* 4 *a. is India T* **17.**

No.	Value	Unused	Used
1	½ a. deep green	4 0	3 6
	a. Opt. inverted	95 0	97 6
2	1 a. brown-purple	17 6	20 0
	a. Opt. inverted	—	£7
3	2 a. dull blue	12 6	12 6
	a. Opt. inverted	£12	
4	4 a. green	30 0	32 6
5	8 a. dull mauve	£7	
	a. Opt. inverted	£50	
6	1 r. slate	£7	
	a. Opt. inverted		

All six values exist with reprinted overprint. In these, words "JHIND" and "STATE" are 8 and 9 mm. in length respectively, whereas in the originals the words are 9 and 9½ mm.

JEEND STATE (2) **JHIND STATE** (3)

1885. *Optd. with T* **2.**

No.	Value	Unused	Used
7	½ a. deep green (R.)	37 6	
8	1 a. brown-purple	37 6	
9	2 a. dull blue (R.)	37 6	
10	4 a. green (R.)	42 6	
11	8 a. dull mauve	42 6	
12	1 r. slate (R.)	57 6	

1886. *Optd. with T* **3,** *in red.*

No.	Value	Unused	Used
13	½ a. green	25 0	
	a. "JEIND" for "JHIND" ..	£8	
14	2 a. dull blue	32 6	
	a. "JEIND" for "JHIND" ..	£10	
15	4 a. green	50 0	
16	1 r. slate	55 0	
	a. "JEIND" for "JHIND" ..	£45	

1886–98. *Optd. with T* **3.** *The* 4 *a. is India T* **2**

No.	Value	Unused	Used
17	½ a. deep green (1888) ..	0 4	0
	a. Opt. inverted	£8	
18	1 a. brown-purple	1 3	1
	a. "JEIND" for "JHIND" ..	£8	
19	1 a. plum	1 0	1
20	1½ a. sepia (1897)	3 6	3
21	2 a. dull blue (1891) ..	2 0	1
22	2 a. ultramarine	2 6	1
23	3 a. brown-orange	1 9	1
24	4 a. olive-green (1891) ..	3 0	2
25	4 a. slate-green	3 6	2
26	6 a. olive-bistre (1891) ..	6 0	8
27	6 a. bistre-brown	5 0	7
28	8 a. dull mauve	6 0	8
	a. "JEIND" for "JHIND" ..	£40	
29	8 a. magenta	5 0	7
30	12 a. purple/*red* (1897) ..	5 0	7
31	1 r. slate (1891)	8 6	12
32	1 r. green & carmine (1898)	10 6	17
33	2 r. carmine & yell.-brn. ('97)	£5	
34	3 r. brown and green ..	£6	
35	5 r. ultram & violet (1897) ..	£8	

Varieties exist in which the word "JHIND measures 10½ mm. and 9¾ mm. instead of 10 mı Such varieties are to be found on Nos. 17, 18, 2 24, 28 and 31.

1900–4. *Optd. with T* **3.**

No.	Value	Unused	Used
36	3 pies, carmine	0 4	0
37	3 pies, grey (1904)	0 3	0
38	½ a. pale green (1902) ..	1 6	2
39	½ a. green	5 0	6
40	1 a. carmine (1902)	1 6	2

1903–9. *King Edward VII. Optd. with T* **3.**

No.	Value	Unused	Used
41	3 pies, pale grey	0 6	0
42	3 pies, slate-grey (1905) ..	0 4	0
43	½ a. green	0 8	0
44	1 a. carmine	0 6	0
45	2 a. pale violet	1 6	1
46	2 a. mauve (1906)	1 3	1
47	2½ a. ultramarine (1909) ..	1 6	2

48 **3** a. orange-brown 1 0 1 3
a. Opt. double 95 0
49 4 a. olive-green 1 9 2 6
50 4 a. slate-green 2 0 3 0
51 6 a. bistre (1905) 2 6 3 6
52 8 a. dull mauve 2 0 3 6
53 8 a. magenta 2 0 3 6
54 12 a. purple/*red* (1905) .. 3 0 5 0
55 1 r. green and carmine (1905) 4 0 5 0

1907–9. *Nos.* 149/50 *of India optd. with T* **3**.
56 **53** ½ a. green 0 3 0 3
57 **54** 1 a. carmine (1909) .. 0 4 0 3

1913. *King George V. Optd. with T* **3**.
58 **55** 3 pies, slate-grey 0 6 0 10
59 **56** ½ a. green 0 6 0 10
60 **57** 1 a. aniline carmine .. 0 9 1 3
61 **59** 2 a. mauve 2 0 3 6
62 **62** 3 a. orange-brown .. 7 6 10 0
63 **64** 6 a. olive-bistre 12 6 17 6

JIND
STATE
(4)

1914–27. *King George V. Optd. with T* **4**.
64 **55** 3 pies, slate-grey 0 3 0 3
65 **56** ½ a. green 0 4 0 4
66 **57** 1 a. aniline carmine .. 0 4 0 4
67 **58** 1½ a. choc. (Type A) (1922) 2 0 3 0
68 ,, 1½ a. choc. (Type B) (1924) 2 6 3 6
69 **59** 2 a. mauve.. .. .. 0 7 0 3
70 **61** 2½ a. ultramarine (1922) .. 2 6 4 6
71 **62** 3 a. orange-brown .. 1 0 2 0
72 **63** 4 a. olive 1 6 2 0
73 **64** 6 a. olive-bistre 1 9 2 6
74 **65** 8 a. purple 1 9 3 0
75 **66** 12 a. dull claret 2 6 3 3
76 **67** 1 r. brown and green .. 4 0 6 6
7 ,, 2 r. carmine & yell.-brown 10 0 16 0
8 ,, 5 r. ultramarine and violet 45 0 57 6

922. *No.* 192 *of India optd.* " JIND " *in block capitals.*
9 **57** 9 p. on 1 a. rose-carmine .. 5 0 8 6

924–27. *Optd. with T* **4**. *New colours.*
0 **57** 1 a. chocolate 0 8 1 0
1 **58** 1½ a. rose-carmine (Type B) 1 3 2 3
2 **61** 2½ a. orange.. .. .. 1 3 2 3
3 **62** 3 a. bright blue 1 6 2 9

JIND STATE
(5)

JIND STATE
(6)

927–37. *King George V (Nasik printing, wmk. Mult. Star), optd. at Nasik with T* **5** *or* **6** *(rupee values).*
4 **55** 3 pies, slate 0 3 0 3
5 **56** ½ a. green 0 4 0 4
6 **80** 9 p. deep green 0 3 0 4
7 **57** 1 a. chocolate 0 5 0 4
8 **82** 1¼ a. mauve 0 6 0 3
9 **58** 1½ a. rose-carm. (Type B) 0 8 0 6
0 **70** 2 a. purple 0 8 0 6
1 **61** 2½ a. orange 0 10 1 0
2 **62** 3 a. bright blue 1 3 1 6
3 **83** 3½ a. ultramarine ('37) .. 0 10 1 3
4 **71** 4 a. sage-green 1 3 1 6
5 **64** 6 a. bistre ('37) 1 3 1 9
6 **65** 8 a. reddish purple .. 2 6 3 0
7 **66** 12 a. claret 3 6 4 0
8 **67** 1 r. chocolate and green 4 0 5 0
9 ,, 2 r. carmine and orange.. 7 6 8 6
0 ,, 5 r. ultramarine & purple 20 0 22 6
1 ,, 10 r. green and carmine 37 6 45 0
2 ,, 15 r. blue and olive .. 65 0 72 6
3 ,, 25 r. orange and blue .. 85 0 £6

34. *New types and colours. Optd. with T* **5**.
79 ½ a. green.. .. .. 0 3 0 3
81 1 a. chocolate 0 6 0 4

106 **59** 2 a. vermilion 0 8 0 6
107 **62** 3 a. carmine 0 10 0 8
108 **63** 4 a. sage-green 1 0 1 3

1937–38. *King George VI. Optd. with T* **5** *or T* **6** *(rupee values).*
109 **91** 3 p. slate 1 0 1 0
110 ,, ½ a. red-brown 1 3 2 6
111 ,, 9 p. green (23.8.37) .. 1 6 2 6
112 ,, 1 a. carmine (23.8.37) 0 6 0 9
113 **92** 2 a. vermilion 0 6 2 0
114 **93** 2½ a. bright violet .. 0 9 2 0
115 **94** 3 a. yellow-green .. 1 0 2 6
116 **95** 3½ a. bright blue 1 6 3 0
117 **96** 4 a. brown 1 6 3 0
118 **97** 6 a. turquoise-green .. 2 0 4 0
119 **98** 8 a. slate-violet.. .. 2 6 4 0
120 **99** 12 a. lake 4 0 7 6
121 **100** 1 r. grey and red-brown 5 0 7 6
122 ,, 2 r. purple and brown .. 8 6 12 6
123 ,, 5 r. green and blue .. 25 0 30 0
124 ,, 10 r. purple and claret .. 50 0 60 0
125 ,, 15 r. brown and green .. £6 £7
126 ,, 25 r. slate-violet & purple £11 £12

JIND
(7)

1942–43. *King George VI. Optd. with T* **7**.

(a) Stamps of 1937.
127 **91** 3 p. slate 3 0 4 0
128 ,, ½ a. red-brown 2 0 2 0
129 ,, 9 p. green 3 6 5 0
130 ,, 1 a. carmine 2 0 3 6
131 **100** 1 r. grey and red-brown 4 6 6 6
132 ,, 2 r. purple and brown .. 7 6 10 6
133 ,, 5 r. green and blue .. 22 6 27 6
134 ,, 10 r. purple and claret .. 50 0 60 0
135 ,, 15 r. brown and green .. 70 0 90 0
136 ,, 25 r. slate-vio. and purple £6 £7

(b) Stamps of 1940–43.
137 **100a** 3 p. slate 0 3 0 6
138 ,, ½ a. purple 0 3 0 6
139 ,, 9 p. green 0 6 0 8
140 ,, 1 a. carmine 0 6 0 8
141 **101** 1 a. 3 p. bistre 0 8 1 0
142 ,, 1½ a. dull violet 2 6 2 6
143 ,, 2 a. vermilion 0 8 1 0
144 ,, 3 a. bright violet .. 1 0 1 6
145 ,, 3½ a. bright blue .. 1 3 2 0
146 **102** 4 a. brown 1 3 2 6
147 ,, 6 a. turquoise-green .. 1 6 2 9
148 ,, 8 a. slate-violet .. 2 0 3 0
149 ,, 12 a. lake 3 6 6 6

OFFICIAL STAMPS.

JHIND STATE
SERVICE
(O 15)

SERVICE
JHIND
STATE
(O 16)

1885. *Queen Victoria. Optd. with Type* O **15**.
O1 ½ a. deep green 0 9 0 9
O2 1 a. brown-purple 0 6 0 4
O3 2 a. dull blue 17 6 17 6

Optd. as Type O **15**, *but* " JHIND STATE " *inverted.*
O4 ½ a. deep green 55 0 37 6
O5 1 a. brown-purple 10 0 10 0
O6 2 a. dull blue £22

The three values have had the overprint reprinted in the same way as the ordinary stamps of 1885. See note after No. 6.

1885. *Optd. with T* **2** *and* " SERVICE ".
O7 ½ a. deep green (R.) 40 0
O8 1 a. brown-purple 40 0
O9 2 a. dull blue (R.) 45 0

1886. *Optd. with Type* O **16**, *in red.*
O10 ½ a. deep green 30 0
a. "ERVICE" for "SERVICE"
b. "JEIND" for "JHIND" .. £10
O11 2 a. dull blue 40 0
a. "ERVICE" for "SERVICE"
b. "JEIND" for "JHIND" .. £14

1886–97. *Optd. with Type* O **16.**
O12 ½ a. deep green (1888) .. 0 6 0 3
O13 1 a. brown-purple 27 6
a. "ERVICE" for "SERVICE"
b. "JEIND" for "JHIND" .. £12
O14 1 a. plum 1 6 0 9
O15 2 a. dull blue (1893) .. 2 0 1 0
O16 2 a. ultramarine 1 6 1 0
O17 4 a. olive-green (1892) .. 3 0 1 6
O18 4 a. slate-green 3 6 3 6
O19 8 a. dull mauve (1892) .. 6 0 6 0
O20 8 a. magenta 8 6 12 6
O21 1 r. grn. & carmine (1897) .. 15 0 17 6

Varieties mentioned in note after No. 35 exist on Nos. O12, O15, O17 and O20.

Varieties with "SERVICE" measuring 11½ mm. are to be found in the case of Nos. O12, O16, O18, O20 and O21.

1902. *Optd. with Type* O **16.**
O22 ½ a. yellow-green 1 0 0 6

1903–6. *King Edward VII. Optd. with Type* O **16.**
O23 3 pies, pale grey 1 0 0 4
O24 3 pies, slate-grey (1906) .. 0 8 0 4
O25 ½ a. green 1 6 0 4
a. "HIND" .. .. .. — £10
O26 1 a. carmine 3 6 0 3
a. "HIND" .. .. .. — £10
O27 2 a. pale violet 2 6 1 0
O28 2 a. mauve 1 3 0 3
O29 4 a. olive-green 3 0 2 0
O30 8 a. dull mauve 6 6 6 6
O31 8 a. magenta 5 0 5 0
O32 1 r. green & carmine (1906) 7 6 8 6

1907. *Nos.* 149/50 *of India optd. with Type* O **16.**
O33 ½ a. green 0 8 0 3
O34 1 a. carmine 1 3 0 3

1914–27. *King George V. Service stamps of India overprinted with T* **4.**
O35 **55** 3 pies, slate-grey 0 3 0 3
O36 **56** ½ a. green 0 3 0 3
O37 **57** 1 a. aniline carmine .. 0 4 0 3
O38 ,, 1 a. pale rose-carmine .. 0 8 0 3
O39 **59** 2 a. mauve 0 5 0 3
O40 **63** 4 a. olive 0 8 0 4
O41 **64** 6 a. yellow-bistre 1 6 2 6
O42 **65** 8 a. purple 1 3 1 6
O43 **67** 1 r. brown and green .. 3 0 2 0
O44 ,, 2 r. carmine & yellow-brn. 8 6 10 6
O45 ,, 5 r. ultramarine & violet 30 0 35 0

1924. *As* 1914–27. *New colour.*
O46 **57** 1 a. chocolate 0 6 0 2

JIND STATE
SERVICE
(O 17)

JIND STATE
SERVICE
(O 18)

1927–37. *King George V (Nasik printing, wmk. Mult. Star), optd. with Types* O **17** *or* O **18** *(rupee values).*
O47 **55** 3 pies, slate 0 2 0 3
O48 **56** ½ a. green 0 3 0 4
O49 **80** 9 p. deep green .. 0 3 0 3
O50 **57** 1 a. chocolate 0 4 0 3
O51 **82** 1½ a. mauve 0 4 0 3
O52 **70** 2 a. purple 0 9 0 6
O53 **61** 2½ a. orange ('37) 0 7 0 6
O54 **71** 4 a. sage-green 0 9 0 4
O55 **64** 6 a. bistre ('37) 1 3 1 9
O56 **65** 8 a. reddish purple .. 1 9 2 6
O57 **66** 12 a. claret 2 3 3 6
O58 **67** 1 r. chocolate & green .. 3 0 4 0
O59 ,, 2 r. carmine & orange .. 6 0 7 6
O60 ,, 5 r. ultram. & purple .. 15 0 18 6
O61 ,, 10 r. green & carmine .. 30 0 35 0

1934. *Optd. with Type* O **17.**
O62 **79** ½ a. green 0 3 0 3
O63 **81** 1 a. chocolate 0 4 0 3
O64 **59** 2 a. vermilion 0 6 0 6
O65 **63** 4 a. sage-green 0 10 0 10

1937–42 (?). *King George VI. Optd. with Types* O **17** *or* O **18** *(rupee values).*
O66 **91** ½ a. red-brown ('42?) .. 5 0 1 0
O67 ,, 9 p. green 1 6 1 0
O68 ,, 1 a. carmine 1 0 1 3
O69 **100** 1 r. grey & red-brn. ('40) 7 6 8 6
O70 ,, 2 r. purple & brn. ('40) 12 6 12 6
O71 ,, 5 r. green & blue ('40) .. 32 6 37 6
O72 ,, 10 r. purple & claret ('40) 50 0 62 6

JIND
SERVICE
(O 19)

1940–43? (*a*) *Official stamps optd. with T* **7.**
O73 O **20** 3 p. slate 0 3 0 6
O74 ,, ½ a. red-brown .. 3 0 3 6
O75 ,, ½ a. purple ('43?) .. 0 6 0
O76 ,, 9 p. green 0 4 0
O77 ,, 1 a. carmine 0 6 0
O78 ,, 1½ a. dull violet .. 2 0 1
O79 ,, 2 a. vermilion 0 6 0
O80 ,, 2½ a. bright violet .. 0 8 1
O81 ,, 4 a. brown 1 3 0 1
O82 ,, 8 a. slate-violet .. 2 6 2

(*b*) *Postage stamps optd. with Type* O **19.**
O83 **100** 1 r. grey and red-brown 6 0 8
O84 ,, 2 r. purple and brown .. 8 6 10
O85 ,, 5 r. green and blue .. 22 6 27
O86 ,, 10 r. purple and claret .. 42 6 47

NABHA.

NABHA STATE
(1)

NABHA
STATE
(2)

1885 (MAY). *Queen Victoria. The* 4 *a. is Ind… T* **17.** *Optd. with T* **1.**
1 ½ a. deep green 3 0 3
2 1 a. brown-purple 17 6 22
3 2 a. dull blue 15 0 17
4 4 a. green 30 0
5 8 a. dull mauve £6
6 1 r. slate £6

All six values have had the overprint reprinte… On the reprints the words "NABHA" a… "STATE" both measure 9¼ mm. in lengt… whereas on the originals these words measu… 11 and 10 mm. respectively. The varieties w… overprint double formerly catalogued are n… known to be reprints.

1885. (NOV.). *Optd. with T* **2**, *in red.*
10 ½ a. deep green 1 9 1
11 2 a. dull blue 2 6 3
12 4 a. green 16 0 17
13 1 r. slate 45 0 50

1887–97. *Optd. with T* **2**, *in black. The* 4 *a.… India T* **29.**
14 ½ a. deep green 0 9 0
15 9 p. carmine (1892) .. 2 0 2
16 1 a. brown-purple 2 6 1
17 1 a. plum 0 8 0

No.	Description	Unused	Used
18	1½ a. sepia (1891)	1 9	2 0
	a. "ABHA" for "NABHA"	£8	
19	2 a. dull blue	2 6	1 6
20	2 a. ultramarine	2 6	1 6
21	3 a. orange (1889)	7 6	7 6
22	3 a. brown-orange	2 6	2 0
23	4 a. olive-green	2 6	1 9
24	4 a. slate-green	3 0	2 6
25	6 a. olive-bistre (1889)	6 6	6 6
26	6 a. bistre-brown	6 0	7 6
27	8 a. dull mauve	4 0	4 6
28	12 a. purple/*red* (1889)	4 6	4 6
29	1 r. slate	10 0	12 6
30	1 r. green & carmine (1893)	5 0	5 0
	a. "N BHA" for "NABHA"		
31	2 r. carmine & yell.-brn. ('97)	60 0	70 0
32	3 r. brown & green (1897)	65 0	75 0
33	5 r. ultramarine & vio. (1897)	70 0	80 0

Nos. 10, 11, 12, 13, and 27 have had the overprint reprinted, but in nearly every case the reprints have had the word "SPECIMEN" overprinted upon them.

1900 (Nov.). *Overprinted with T* **2**.

No.	Description	Unused	Used
36	3 pies, carmine	0 3	0 3

1903–10. *King Edward VII. Optd. with T* **2**.

No.	Description	Unused	Used
37	3 pies, pale grey	0 6	0 6
37*a*	3 pies, slate-grey (1906)	0 4	0 3
38	½ a. green	0 10	0 6
	a. Error. "NABH"	£5	
39	1 a. carmine	1 3	1 3
40	2 a. pale violet	3 0	3 0
40*a*	2 a. mauve	1 0	1 0
40*b*	2½ a. ultramarine (1910)	40 0	
41	3 a. orange-brown	1 6	1 3
42	4 a. olive-green	1 9	1 9
43	6 a. olive-bistre	2 6	3 0
44	8 a. dull mauve	3 6	3 6
44*a*	8 a. magenta	3 6	3 6
45	12 a. purple/*red*	4 6	5 0
46	1 r. green and carmine	4 6	6 0

1907. *Nos.* 149 *and* 150 *of India optd. with T* **2**.

No.	Description	Unused	Used
47	½ a. green	0 8	0 8
48	1 a. carmine	1 3	1 3

1913. *Head of King George V. Overprinted with T* **2**.

No.	Description	Unused	Used
49	3 pies, slate	0 3	0 3
50	½ a. green	0 4	0 3
51	1 a. aniline carmine	0 6	0 6
52	2 a. mauve	0 8	0 8
53	3 a. orange-brown	0 10	0 10
54	4 a. olive	1 0	1 0
55	6 a. olive-bistre	1 3	1 6
56	8 a. purple	1 9	2 0
57	12 a. dull claret	2 6	2 9
58	1 r. brown and green	3 0	3 0

1924. *As* 1913. *New colour.*

No.	Description	Unused	Used
59	1 a. chocolate	0 6	0 6

NABHA STATE (3) NABHA STATE (4)

1928–37. *Head of King George V (Nasik printing, wmk. Mult. Star), optd. as T* **3** *or* **4** *(rupee values).*

No.	Type	Description	Unused	Used
60	**55**	3 p. slate ('32)	0 4	0 3
61	**56**	½ a. green	0 4	0 3
61*a*	**80**	9 p. deep green ('37)	0 3	0 4
62	**57**	1 a. chocolate	0 3	0 3
63	**82**	1¼ a. mauve ('37)	0 4	0 6
64	**70**	2 a. purple ('32)	0 8	0 9
65	**61**	2½ a. orange ('32)	0 10	1 0
66	**62**	3 a. bright blue ('30)	1 0	1 0
67	**71**	4 a. sage-green ('32)	1 3	1 6
71	**67**	2 r. carm. & orange ('32)	10 0	12 6
72	,,	5 r. ultram. & purple ('32)	22 6	25 0

1936–37. *New types and colours. Optd. as T* **3**.

No.	Type	Description	Unused	Used
73	**79**	½ a. green	0 3	0 4
74	**81**	1 a. chocolate	0 4	0 6
75	**62**	3 a. carmine ('37)	1 0	1 3
76	**63**	4 a. sage-green ('37)	1 3	1 6

NABHA STATE (5)

1938–39. *Head of King George VI. Optd. as T* **3** *(3 p. to 1 a.), T* **5** *(2 a. to 12 a.) or T* **4** *(rupee values).*

No.	Type	Description	Unused	Used
77	**91**	3 p. slate	4 0	3 6
78	,,	½ a. red-brown	2 6	3 0
79	,,	9 p. green	12 6	10 0
80	,,	1 a. carmine	0 6	0 8
81	**92**	2 a. vermilion	0 10	1 9
82	**93**	2½ a. bright violet	1 0	2 0
83	**94**	3 a. yellow-green	1 6	3 0
84	**95**	3½ a. bright blue	2 6	4 6
85	**96**	4 a. brown	1 9	4 6
86	**97**	6 a. turquoise-green	3 0	6 0
87	**98**	8 a. slate-violet	3 3	7 6
88	**99**	12 a. lake	6 0	8 6
89	**100**	1 r. grey and red-brown	4 0	7 6
90	,,	2 r. purple and brown	7 6	10 0
91	,,	5 r. green and blue	25 0	30 0
92	,,	10 r. purple & claret ('39)	60 0	70 0
93	,,	15 r. brn. and green ('39)	£6	£7
94	,,	25 r. slate-vio. & pur. ('39)	£9	£10

NABHA (6)

1942–45. *Head of King George VI. Optd. with T* **6**.

(a) Stamps of 1937.

No.	Type	Description	Unused	Used
95	**91**	3 p. slate	8 0	6 0
96	,,	½ a. red-brown	17 6	20 0
97	,,	9 p. green	5 0	6 0
98	,,	1 a. carmine	3 6	5 0

(b) Stamps of 1940–43.

No.	Type	Description	Unused	Used
105	**100*a***	3 p. slate	0 3	0 3
106	,,	½ a. purple	0 3	0 6
107	,,	9 p. green	0 6	0 9
108	,,	1 a. carmine	0 4	0 9
109	**101**	1 a. 3 p. bistre	0 4	0 9
110	,,	1½ a. dull violet	0 6	1 0
111	,,	2 a. vermilion	0 9	1 0
112	,,	3 a. bright violet	1 3	1 0
113	,,	3½ a. bright blue	1 6	2 0
114	**102**	4 a. brown	1 6	2 0
115	,,	6 a. turquoise-green	1 9	3 0
116	,,	8 a. slate-violet	2 6	4 0
117	,,	12 a. lake	3 6	6 0

OFFICIAL STAMPS.

NABHA STATE SERVICE (O 8)

SERVICE NABHA STATE (O 9)

1885 (May). *Head of Queen Victoria. Optd. with Type* O **8**.

No.	Description	Unused	Used
O1	½ a. deep green	3 6	3 0
O2	1 a. brown-purple	1 0	1 3
O3	2 a. dull blue	45 0	45 0

The three values have had the overprint reprinted in the same way as the ordinary stamps of 1885.

1885 (Nov.). *Optd. with Type* O **9**.

No.	Description	Unused	Used
O4	½ a. deep green (R.)	5 0	5 0
O5	2 a. deep blue (R.)	2 6	2 6

1888–97. *Optd. with Type* O **9**. *The* 4 *a. is India T* **29**.

No.	Description	Unused	Used
O 6	½ a. deep green	0 6	0 3
O 7	1 a. brown-purple (1892)	1 6	1 0
O 8	1 a. plum	2 0	1 0

O 9	2 a. dull blue	2 0	2 6
O10	2 a. ultramarine	2 9	3 3
O11	3 a. orange (1891)	7 6	8 6
O12	3 a. brown-orange	7 6	8 6
O13	4 a. olive-green	2 0	2 0
O14	4 a. slate-green	2 6	2 6
O15	6 a. olive-bistre (1889) ..	6 6	7 6
O16	6 a. bistre-brown	95 0	
O17	8 a. dull mauve (1889) ..	5 0	6 0
O18	12 a. purple/*red* (1889) ..	15 0	17 6
O19	1 r. slate (1889)	32 6	42 6
O20	1 r. green & carmine (1897)	15 0	20 0

Varieties. (i.) " SERVICE." *with stop.*

O21	½ a. deep green	17 6	3 0
O22	1 a. plum	5 0	1 6

(ii.) " NABHA STATE " *double.*

O23	1 a. plum	£6	

(iii.) " S ATE " *for* " STATE."

O23*a*	½ a. deep green		

Nos. O4, O5 and O7 exist with reprinted overprint, but in nearly every case the stamps bear the words " SPECIMEN."

1903–06. *Head of King Edward VII. Optd. with Type* O **9.**

O24	3 pies, pale grey (1906) ..	3 6	3 6
O25	3 pies, slate-grey (1906) ..	1 6	1 6
O26	½ a. green	0 8	0 9
O27	1 a. carmine	0 10	0 9
O28	2 a. pale violet	3 0	3 0
O29	2 a. mauve	2 3	2 3
O30	4 a. olive-green	1 9	1 3
O32	8 a. dull mauve	3 0	4 0
O33	8 a. magenta	4 0	5 0
O34	1 r. green and carmine ..	5 0	6 0

1907. *Nos.* 149 *and* 150 *of India optd. with Type* O **9.**

O35	½ a. green	0 6	0 6
O36	1 a. carmine	0 8	0 10

1913. *Head of King George V. Optd. with Type* O **9.**

O37	4 a. olive	40 0	
O38	1 r. brown and green ..	£6	

1913. *Official stamps of India overprinted with T* **2.**

O39	3 pies, slate-grey	0 4	0 8
O39*a*	3 pies, bluish slate	0 3	0 6
O40	½ a. green	0 3	0 3
O41	1 a. aniline carmine	0 4	0 3
O42	2 a. mauve	0 6	0 6
O43	4 a. olive	0 10	1 3
O44	8 a. dull mauve	1 6	1 9
O46	1 r. brown and green ..	3 0	3 6

NABHA STATE
SERVICE
(O 10)

1932–45. *Head of King George V (Nasik printing, wmk. Mult. Star), optd. at Nasik with Type* O **10.**

O47	**55**	3 p. slate	0 3	0 6
O50	**81**	1 a. chocolate ('35) ..	0 6	0 8
O50*a*	**63**	4 a. sage-green ('45) ..	3 0	1 6
O51	**65**	8 a. reddish purple ('37)	4 6	5 0

1938. *Head of King George VI. Optd. as Type* O **10.**

O54	**91**	9 p. green	5 0	7 6
O55	,,	1 a. carmine	1 0	1 6

NABHA
SERVICE
(O 11)

1943–44. (*a*) *Official stamps optd. with T* **6.**

O56	O **20**	3 p. slate	0 3	0 3
O57	,,	½ a. red-brown	0 9	0 9
O57*a*	,,	½ a. purple ('44) ..	0 3	0 3
O58	,,	9 p. green	0 8	0 8
O59	O **20**	1 a. carmine	0 6	0 4
O61	,,	1½ a. dull violet	0 6	0 9
O62	,,	2 a. vermilion	0 9	1 0
O64	,,	4 a. brown	1 0	1 3
O65	,,	8 a. slate-violet ..	1 9	3 0

(*b*) *Postage stamps optd. with Type* O **11**

O66	**100**	1 r. grey and red-brown	3 6	6 0
O67	,,	2 r. purple and brown ..	7 6	10 0
O68	,,	5 r. green and blue ..	30 0	35 0

PATIALA.

PUTTIALLA STATE
(1)

PUTTIALLA
STATE
(2)

1884. *Queen Victoria. Optd. with T* **1,** *in red. The* 4 *a. is India T* **17.**

1	½ a. deep green	4 0	4
	a. Opt. double	£12	£1
2	1 a. brown-purple	32 6	30
	a. Opt. double		
	b. Optd. in red and in black ..	£8	
3	2 a. dull blue	12 6	17
4	4 a. green	15 0	12
5	8 a. dull mauve	£7	£
	a. Opt. inverted		
	b. Optd. in red and in black ..	42 6	
6	1 r. slate	60 0	70

1885. *Overprinted with T* **2.** (*a*) *In red.*

7	½ a. deep green	1 0	1
	a. Error. " AUTTIALLA " ..	6 0	
	b. Error. " STATE " only ..		
8	2 a. dull blue	3 0	2
	a. Error. " AUTTIALLA " ..	15 0	
9	4 a. green	5 0	5
	a. Opt. in red and in black ..	£6	
10	1 r. slate	12 6	15
	a. Error. " AUTTIALLA " ..	£10	

(*b*) *In black.*

11	1 a. brown-purple	0 6	0
	a. Opt. in red and in black ..	10 0	
	b. Error. " AUTTIALLA " ..	35 0	
	ba. Error. Opt. in red and in black	£10	£
12	8 a. dull mauve	4 0	6
	a. Error " AUTTIALLA " ..	£10	

The ½, 2, and 4 a. (T **29**), and 1 r. (all ove printed in black), are proofs.

All six values exist with reprinted overprin and the error " AUTTIALLA STAT. " has be reprinted in complete sheets on all values and addition in black on the ½, 2, 4 a., and 1 Nearly all these however, are found with t word " REPRINT " overprinted upon them.

The error " PUTTILLA " formerly catalogued considered doubtful.

PATIALA
STATE
(3)

1891–96. *Optd. with T* **3.** *The* 4 *a. is India T*

13	½ a. deep green	0 4	0
14	9 p. carmine	1 0	1
15	1 a. brown-purple	0 9	0
16	1 a. plum	1 6	0
	a. Error. " PATIALA " omitted	£6	
17	1½ a. sepia	1 6	2
18	2 a. dull blue (1896)	2 0	0
19	2 a. ultramarine	2 6	0
20	3 a. brown-orange	1 9	2
21	4 a. olive-green (1896) ..	2 0	1
	a. Error. " PATIALA " omitted ..	£8	
22	4 a. slate-green	1 3	1

23	6 a. bistre-brown	2	6	1	9
24	6 a. olive-bistre	6	0		
25	8 a. dull mauve				
26	8 a. magenta (1896)	2	6	2	6
27	12 a. purple/*red*	2	6	3	0
28	1 r. green and carmine (1896)	7	6	10	0
29	2 r. carm. & yellow-brn. ('95)	85	0		
30	3 r. brown and green (1895) ..	£6			
31	5 r. ultramarine & violet (1895)	£8			

1899–1902. *Optd. with T* **3.**

32	3 pies, carmine (1899) ..	0	3	0	3
33	½ a. pale green	0	8	0	9
34	1 a. carmine	1	0	0	10

1903–06. *Head of King Edward VII. Optd. with T* **3.**

35	3 pies, pale grey ..	0	6	0	3
36	3 pies, slate-grey (1906) ..	0	4	0	3
37	½ a. green	0	4	0	3
38	1 a. carmine	0	6	0	3
39	2 a. pale violet	0	6	0	4
.0	3 a. orange-brown ..	0	10	0	6
.1	4 a. olive-green (1905) ..	1	6	0	8
.2	6 a. olive-bistre (1905) ..	2	6	1	9
3	8 a. dull mauve (1906) ..	3	0	2	6
4	12 a. purple/*red* (1906) ..	4	0	5	0
5	1 r. green and carmine (1905)	4	6	5	6

912. *Nos.* 149 *and* 150 *of India optd. with T* **3.**

6	½ a. green	0	3	0	4
7	1 a. carmine	0	4	0	6

912–26. *Head of King George V. Optd. with T* **3.**

8	**55**	3 pies, slate-grey	0	3	0	3
	56	½ a. green	0	3	0	3
	57	1 a. aniline carmine ..	0	5	0	3
	58	1½ a. chocolate (Type A) ..	1	6	2	6
	59	2 a. mauve	0	8	0	6
	62	3 a. orange-brown ..	1	3	0	10
	63	4 a. olive	1	0	0	8
	64	6 a. yellow-brown ..	1	3	1	3
		a. Yellow-bistre ..	4	0	4	0
	65	8 a. purple	1	9	2	0
	66	12 a. dull claret ..	2	0	2	0
	67	1 r. brown and green ..	3	6	3	0
	,,	2 r. carmine & yellow-brn.	7	6	8	6
	,,	5 r. ultramarine & violet ..	22	6	25	0

23–26. *As* 1912–26. *New colours.*

57	1 a. chocolate	0	6	0	4
62	3 a. ultramarine ('26) ..	1	0	1	6

PATIALA STATE (4) **PATIALA STATE** (5)

28–34. *King George V (Nasik printing, wmk. Mult. Star) optd. at Nasik with T* **4** *or* **5** *(rupee values).*

55	3 p. slate	0	3	0	3
56	½ a. green	0	3	0	3
80	9 p. deep green	0	3	0	3
57	1 a. chocolate	0	4	0	3
82	1¼ a. mauve	0	4	0	3
70	2 a. purple	0	8	0	6
61	2½ a. orange	0	8	0	8
62	3 a. bright blue	0	8	0	6
71	4 a. sage-green	1	3	0	8
65	8 a. reddish purple ..	2	6	2	0
67	1 r. chocolate and green ..	4	0	3	0
,,	2 r. carmine and orange ..	7	6	8	6

he 9 p. exists printed both by offset-lithography and typography.

5–37. *Optd. with T* **4.**

79	½ a. blue-green ('37) ..	0	2	0	3
31	1 a. chocolate ('36) ..	0	4	0	3
59	2 a. vermilion ('36) ..	0	6	0	6
32	3 a. carmine ('37) ..	0	9	1	3
33	4 a. sage-green	0	8	1	0

PATIALA STATE
(6)

1937–38. *King George VI. Optd. with T* **4** *(3 p. to 1 a.), T* **6** *(2 a. to 12 a.), or T* **5** *(rupee values).*

80	**91**	3 p. slate	15	0	10	0
81	,,	½ a. red-brown	3	0	2	0
82	,,	9 p. green ('37)	3	0	2	0
83	,,	1 a. carmine ('37) ..	0	9	0	6
84	**92**	2 a. vermilion	0	10	1	6
85	**93**	2½ a. bright violet	1	0	2	0
86	**94**	3 a. yellow-green	1	0	2	6
87	**95**	3½ a. bright blue	2	0	2	6
88	**96**	4 a. brown	1	3	3	0
89	**97**	6 a. turquoise-green ..	1	9	3	0
90	**98**	8 a. slate-violet	2	6	4	0
91	**99**	12 a. lake	6	0	7	6
92	**100**	1 r. grey and red-brown	7	6	10	0
93	,,	2 r. purple and brown ..	10	0	12	6
94	,,	5 r. green and blue ..	20	0	27	6
95	,,	10 r. purple and claret ..	45	0	55	0
96	,,	15 r. brown and green ..	80	0	90	0
97	,,	25 r. slate-vio. and purple	£6		£7	

PATIALA (7) **PATIALA** (8)

1943–47. *King George VI. Optd. with T* **7** *or* **8** *(rupee value).*

(a) Stamps of 1937.

98	**91**	3 p. slate	3	6	3	0
99	,,	½ a. red-brown	4	0	4	0
100	,,	9 p. green	7	6	4	0
101	,,	1 a. carmine	3	6	3	6
102	**100**	1 r. grey & red-brn. ('47)	4	6	6	0

(b) Stamps of 1940–43.

103	**100a**	3 p. slate	0	3	0	3
104	,,	½ a. purple	0	4	0	3
105	,,	9 p. green	0	3	0	4
		a. Opt. omitted (vert. pr. with normal)	£175			
106	,,	1 a. carmine	0	4	0	6
107	**101**	1 a. 3 p. bistre	1	0	1	6
108	,,	1½ a. violet	0	6	0	4
109	,,	2 a. vermilion	0	6	0	4
110	,,	3 a. bright violet ..	1	0	1	0
111	,,	3½ a. bright blue ..	1	3	2	6
112	**102**	4 a. brown	1	3	2	0
113	,,	6 a. turquoise-green ..	1	6	2	6
114	,,	8 a. slate-violet ..	2	0	3	0
115	,,	12 a. lake	3	6	6	0

OFFICIAL STAMPS.

PUTTIALLA SERVICE STATE
(O 1)

1884. *Queen Victoria. Optd. with Type* O 1, "SERVICE" *in black, the rest in red.*

O1	½ a. deep green	2	6	1	0
O2	1 a. brown-purple	0	6	0	6
	a. Red opt. inverted	£8		£5	
	b. Red opt. double	—		80	0
	c. "SERVICE" double ..	£7		£5	
	d. "SERVICE" inverted ..	—		£20	
O3	2 a. dull blue	£7		20	0

SERVICE PUTTIALLA STATE (O 2) **SERVICE PUTTIALLA STATE** (O 3)

1885–90. *(a) Optd. with Type* O **2**, "SERVICE" *in black, the rest in red.*

O4 ½ a. deep green 1 3 0 6
 a. "SERVICE" double .. — 75 0
 b. "AUTTIALLA" for "PUTTIALLA" 40 0 12 6

(b) Optd. with Type O **2**, *all in black.*

O5 1 a. brown-purple 0 6 0 4
 a. "SERVICE" double.. .. £10 £10
 b. Opt. double, one inverted .. — £20
 c. "AUTTIALLA" for "PUTTIALLA" £5

(c) Optd. with Type O **3**.

O6 ½ a. deep green (Bk.) (1890).. 0 6 0 4
O7 2 a. dull blue (R.) 1 0 0 9
 a. Opt. double, one inverted .. — £22
 b. "PUTTILLA" for "PUTTIALLA"

There are reprints of Nos. O4, O5 and O7. The first has the word "SERVICE" in the large type in *red* instead of the small type in *black*, and the second has the word in the large type in *black* in place of the small type. The 2 a. with Type O **3**, in *black*, is a proof. The ½ a. "AUTTIALLA" has also been reprinted, but nearly all the above have been overprinted "REPRINT". No. O7b is probably from an essay sheet.

SERVICE

PATIALA
STATE
(O **4**)

1891–1903. *Optd. with Type* O **4**, *in black.*

O 8 ½ a. deep green (1895) .. 0 4 0 3
 a. "SERVICE" inverted .. 40 0
 b. "I" of "SERVICE" omitted £6
O 9 1 a. plum (1900) 0 9 0 4
 a. "SERVICE" inverted 40 0
O10 2 a. dull blue (1898) .. 2 6 1 3
 a. "SERVICE" inverted .. 40 0
O11 2 a. deep blue 3 6 3 6
O12 3 a. brown-orange 1 3 1 0
 a. "I" of "SERVICE" omitted
O13 4 a. olive-green 1 0 1 0
 a. "I" of "SERVICE" omitted
O14 4 a. slate-green 0 10 1 0
O15 6 a. bistre-brown 2 0 2 0
O16 8 a. dull mauve 2 0 2 0
 a. "I" of "SERVICE" omitted
O17 8 a. magenta (1898) .. 2 0 2 0
O18 12 a. purple/*red* 2 0 2 0
 a. "I" of "SERVICE" omitted
O19 1 r. slate 2 6 1 9
 a. "I" of "SERVICE" omitted
O20 1 r. green & carmine (1903) 15 0 17 6

The errors with "SERVICE" inverted are genuine, but it is believed they were never issued.

Varieties are known in which the letters of the word "SERVICE" are irregularly spaced, making the length about 11½ mm. instead of the usual 10½ mm.

1902. *Colour changed.*

O21 1 a. carmine 0 9 0 3

1903–10. *King Edward VII. Optd. with Type* O **4**.

O22 3 pies, pale grey 0 6 0 6
O23 3 pies, slate-grey (1909) .. 0 4 0 4
O24 ½ a. green 0 3 0 3
O25 1 a. carmine 0 4 0 3
O26 2 a. pale violet (1905) .. 0 6 0 4
O27 2 a. mauve 0 6 0 4
O28 3 a. orange-brown 2 6 3 0
O29 4 a. olive-green (1905) .. 0 9 0 4
O30 8 a. dull mauve 1 6 1 0
O31 8 a. magenta (1910) .. 1 9 2 0
O32 1 r. green & carmine (1906) 3 0 2 6

1907. *Nos.* 149/50 *of India optd. with Type* O **4**.

O33 **53** ½ a. green 0 3 0 3
O34 **54** 1 a. carmine 0 6 0 3

1913–26. *King George V. Official stamps of India optd. with T* **3**.

O35 **55** 3 pies, slate-grey 0 3 0 3
O36 ,, 3 pies, bluish slate .. 0 3 0 3
O37 **56** ½ a. green 0 3 0 3
O38 **57** 1 a. carmine 0 4 0 3
O39 **59** 2 a. mauve 0 6 0 3
O40 **63** 4 a. olive 0 10 0 4
O41 **64** 6 a. yellow-bistre.. .. 1 0 0 8
O42 **65** 8 a. purple.. .. .. 1 3 0 9
O43 **67** 1 r. brown and green .. 3 6 4 0
O44 ,, 2 r. carmine & yellow-brn. 10 0 15 0
O45 ,, 5 r. ultramarine & violet 20 0 27 6

1925. *As* 1913–26. *New colour.*

O46 **57** 1 a. brown 0 8 0 4

PATIALA STATE
SERVICE
(O **5**)

PATIALA STATE
SERVICE
(O **6**)

1927–36. *King George V (Nasik printing, wmk. Mult. Star), optd. at Nasik with Type* O **5** *or Type* O **6** *(rupee values).*

O47 **55** 3 p. slate 0 3 0
 a. Blue opt. 0 6 0
O48 **56** ½ a. green 0 3 0
O49 **57** 1 a. chocolate 0 3 0
O50 **82** 1¼ a. mauve 0 4 0
O51 **70** 2 a. purple 0 8 0
O52 ,, 2 a. vermilion 0 6 0
O53 **61** 2½ a. orange 0 6 0
O54 **71** 4 a. sage-green 0 9 0
O55 **65** 8 a. reddish purple .. 1 6 0
O56 **67** 1 r. chocolate & green .. 3 6 1
O57 ,, 2 r. carm. & orge. ('36).. 6 0 7

1935–39. *New types. Optd. with Type* O

O58 **79** ½ a. green ('36) 0 2 0
O59 **81** 1 a. chocolate ('36) .. 0 3 0
O60 **59** 2 a. vermilion 0 4 0
O61 ,, 2 a. verm. (*small die*) ('39) 0 6 0
O62 **63** 4 a. sage-green ('36) .. 0 8 0

1938–43. *King George VI. Optd. with Types* O *or* O **6** *(rupee values).*

O63 **91** ½ a. red-brown ('39) .. 2 0 0
O64 ,, 9 p. green ('43) 25 0 35
O65 ,, 1 a. carmine .. 2 6 0
O66 **100** 1 r. grey & red-brn. ('39) 5 0 6
O67 ,, 2 r. pur. & brown ('39).. 8 0 10
O68 ,, 5 r. green & blue ('39) .. 20 0 20

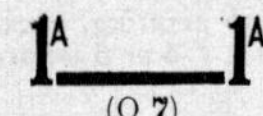
(O **7**)

(O **8**)

1939–40. *Stamp of* 1932 *(King George V).*

(a) Optd. with Types O **5** *and* O **7**.

O69 **82** 1 a. on 1¼ a. mauve .. 2 0

(b) Optd. with T **4** *and* O **8**.

O70 **82** 1 a. on 1¼ a. mauve ('40).. 1 6

"SERVICE" measures 9¼ mm. on No. O69 only 8¾ mm. on O70.

PATIALA
SERVICE
(O **9**)

1940–45. *(a) Official stamps optd. with T* **7**.

O71 **O 20** 3 p. slate ('41) 0 3
O72 ,, ½ a. red-brown .. 0 3
O73 ,, ½ a. purple ('44) .. 0 3
O74 ,, 9 p. green 0 4

O75	O **20**	1 a. carmine ..	0 6	0 3
O76	,,	1 a. 3 p. bistre ..	0 9	0 9
O77	,,	1½ a. dull violet ..	0 6	0 6
O78	,,	2 a. vermilion ('41) ..	0 6	0 6
O79	,,	2½ a. bright violet ('41) ..	0 6	1 0
O80	,,	4 a. brown ('45) ..	1 0	1 0
O81	,,	8 a. slate-violet ('45) ..	1 6	2 6

(*b*) *Postage stamps optd. with Type* O **9.**

O82	**100**	1 r. grey and red-brown	2 6	3 6
O83	,,	2 r. purple and brown ..	8 6	10 6
O84	,,	5 r. green and blue ('45)	15 0	10 6

INDIAN STATES.

Postage stamps of the Indian States, current at that date, were replaced by those of the REPUBLIC OF INDIA on Apr. 1, 1950.

Unless otherwise stated, all became obsolete on May 1, 1950 (with the exception of the "Anchal" stamps of Travancore-Cochin, which remained current until July 1, 1951).

ALWAR.

1 (1 a.)

877. *Litho. Rouletted.*

1	**1**	¼ a. grey-blue	5 0	4 0
		a. Ultramarine	6 0	3 6
		b. Imperf. between (pr.)	—	£5
		c. Bright blue	35 0	20 0
	,,	1 a. brown	6 0	7 6
		a. Imperf. between (pr.) ..	£6	£6
		b. Red-brown	7 6	8 6
		c. Chocolate	15 0	8 6

899. *Redrawn. Stamps printed further apart, giving wide margins.* P 12.

	1	¼ a. slate-blue	15 0	12 6
		a. Imperf. between (pr.) ..	£8	£8
	,,	½ a. emerald-green	£50	

899–1901. *Narrow margins.* P 12.

	1	½ a. emerald-green ..	17 6	15 0
		a. Imperf. between (pr.) ..	£6	
		b. Imperf. (pair) ..	£6	
		c. Pale green	17 6	15 0

In Nos. 3 to 5*c* only the bottom outer frame-ne is thick, whereas Nos. 1 and 2 have the left-and frame-line also thick, as shown in T **1.**

The stamps of Alwar became obsolete in the atter part of 1902.

BAHAWALPUR.

See under PAKISTAN

BAMRA.

BAMRA postage — 1 (¼ a.)

BAMRA postage — 2 (½ a.)

BAMRA postage — 3 (1 a.)

BAMRA postage — 4 (2 a.)

BAMRA postage — 5 (4 a.)

BAMRA postage — 6 (8 a.)

(Typo. Jagannata Ballabh Press, Deogarh.)

1888. *Imperf.*

1	**1**	¼ a. black/*yellow*	£5	
2	**2**	½ a. black/*rose*	60 0	
3	**3**	1 a. black/*blue*	60 0	
4	**4**	2 a. black/*green*	60 0	
5	**5**	4 a. black/*yellow*	60 0	
6	**6**	8 a. black/*rose*	60 0	

The following varieties exist:—

(i) "g" of "postage" inverted: ¼ a., ½ a., 1 a.

(ii) "a" of "postage" omitted: 2 a., 4 a., 8 a.

(iii) Last native character inverted: ¼ a.

Prices of varieties from £14.

BAMRA postage

(7)

With last native character as in illustration.

7 **7** ¼ a. black/*yellow*

These stamps were all printed from the same plate of 96 stamps, 12×8, but for some values only part of the plate was used. We thus have 96 varieties of the ½, 4 and 8 a., 72 of the 1 a., 80 of the 2 a. and not less than 88 of the ¼ a.

One stamp in each sheet has the scroll ornament inverted.

There are two forms of the third native character. In the first five horizontal rows it is as in T **1** and in the last three rows as in T **4.**

These stamps have been reprinted: the ¼ a. and ½ a. in blocks of 8 varieties and all the values in blocks of 20 varieties. T **1** has the fourth character, in the native inscription, in the form which distinguishes the reprints.

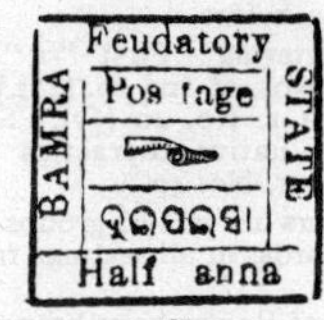

8

1890 (JULY)–1893. *Black on coloured paper.*

A. "Postage" *with capital* "P".

8	**8**	¼ a. on *mauve* ..	3 6	4 0
9	,,	¼ a. on *bright rose* (1891) ..	6 0	4 0
10	,,	¼ a. on *magenta* (1893)	3 6	5 0
11	,,	¼ a. on *blue-green* ..	6 0	6 0
12	,,	¼ a. on *green* (1891)	7 6	6 0
13	,,	1 a. on *yellow*	15 0	12 6
14	,,	1 a. on *orange*	40 0	40 0
15	,,	2 a. on *mauve*	20 0	15 0
16	,,	2 a. on *rose-red* ..	8 6	8 6
17	,,	2 a. on *bright-rose* ..	10 0	10 0
18	,,	4 a. on *mauve* ..	£5	£5
19	,,	4 a. on *rose-red* ..	17 6	17 6
20	,,	4 a. on *bright rose* ..	12 6	12 6
21	,,	8 a. on *mauve* ..	30 0	30 0
22	,,	8 a. on *rose-red* ..	15 0	12 6
23	,,	8 a. on *bright rose* ..	15 0	12 6
24	,,	1 r. on *mauve* ..	70 0	70 0
25	,,	1 r. on *bright rose* ..	50 0	50 0

The native characters are found in one group, or divided into two groups.

Various errors of lettering may be found :—" Eeudatory ". ¼ a. No. 8, ½ a. No. 11, 1 a. No. 13, 2 a. No. 15, 4 a. No. 18 and No. 19, 1 r. No. 24. (*Prices* 15*s. to* 90*s.*). " BAMBA ", 4 a. No. 19, 8 a. No. 21, 1 r. No. 24. (*Prices* 50*s. to* £6). " Foudatory " and " Postagc ". 8 a. No. 21. (£6). " Postagc ". 1 r. No. 24. (£6). " annas " for "anna ". 1 a. No. 14 (£7). Small " r " in "rupee ". 1 r. No. 25. (£8).

In the ¼ a. No. 8 there are also " Quatrer " for " Quarter " (15*s.*) and inverted " e " in " Postage " (15*s.*), and in the ¼ a. No. 10, first " a " in " anna " inverted (35*s.*), " AMRA " of " BAMRA " inverted, and " M " and second " A " of " BAMRA " inverted (35*s. each*).

B. " postage " *with small* " p." (1891–93).

No.	Type					
26	8	¼ a. on *bright rose* (1891)	6	0	4	0
27	"	¼ a. on *magenta* (1893)	3	6	4	0
28	"	½ a. on *blue-green*	6	0	8	6
29	"	½ a. on *green* (1893)	7	6	9	0
30	"	1 a. on *yellow*	7	0	10	0
31	"	1 a. on *orange*	70	0	70	0
32	"	2 a. on *rose-red*	6	0	8	0
33	"	2 a. on *bright rose*	7	6	8	0
34	"	4 a. on *rose-red* (1891)	12	6	15	0
35	"	4 a. on *bright rose*	15	0	17	6
36	"	8 a. on *mauve* (1891)	20	0	20	0
37	"	8 a. on *rose-red*	10	0	12	6
38	"	8 a. on *bright rose*	20	0	20	0
39	"	1 r. on *mauve* (1891)	90	0	90	0
40	"	1 r. on *bright rose*	60	0	60	0

There are 10 settings of Type **8.** The first setting (of 20 varieties) has capital " P " throughout. The remaining settings (of 16 varieties) have capital " P " and small " p " mixed.

There are 4 sizes of the central ornament, which represents an elephant's trunk holding a stick :—(*a*) 4 mm. long ; (*b*) 5 mm.; (*c*) 6½ mm.; (*d*) 11 mm.

These ornaments are also found inverted.

Ornaments (*a*) are found in all settings ; (*b*) in all settings from the 3rd to the 10th ; (*c*) in the 1st and 2nd settings ; and (*d*) only in the 1st setting.

The native characters are found in one or two groups, as before.

Errors of lettering : First " a " of " anna " inverted. ½ a. Nos. 28 and 29. (25*s.*). Small " r " in " rupee ". 1 r. No. 40 (£7). Small " r " in " rupee ". and native characters in the order 2, 3, 1, 4, 5. 1 r. No. 40.

The characters are in two groups in the values from 1 a. upwards, in all settings from the third to the tenth.

The stamps of Bamra have been obsolete since 1894.

BARWANI.

(All the stamps of Barwani are typographed.)

1. Rana Ranjitsingh.

1921. *Clear impression. Medium wove paper. Pin-perf.* 7 *all round.*

1	1	¼ a. deep blue-green	£7
2	"	½ a. dull blue	£7

The first ¼ a. stamp of Barwani was variously chronicled in India, on issue, as "deep blue-green ", " deep blue " and " blue-grey ". We did not chronicle the ¼ a. deep blue-green until January, 1925, and it became what has hitherto been our No. 12, but erroneously listed as on laid paper. From the evidence of flaws, etc., this ¼ a. may well be the first issue but we are not absolutely satisfied and should be glad to receive any further evidence, either for or against. The only ¼ a. blue-grey which we have seen is that now listed as No. 16*a* but we have no reason to believe that this was the first issue.

Whatever the period of issue, the two stamps listed above are obviously of the same group, as paper, perforation and impression are similar.

1921. *Blurred impression. Soft wove paper. Pin-perf.* 7 *on* two *or* three *sides.*

3	1	¼ a. green	40	0
4	"	½ a. blue (to pale)	40	0

NOTE. As the small sheets of Barwani stamps were often not perforated all round many of the earlier stamps are perforated on two or three sides only. Owing to the elementary method of printing the colours vary greatly in depth, even within a single sheet.

1921–22. *Blurred impression. Pin-perf.* 7.

(*a*) *Glazed paper.*

5	1	¼ a. dull ultramarine	£8	

(*b*) *Thickish wove paper.*

6	1	¼ a. blue (pale to deep)	20	0
7	"	½ a. green	65	0

Nos. 6 and 7 are sometimes perforated all round.

(*c*) *Vertically laid white paper. Imperf.*

8	1	¼ a. green (pale to bright)	35	0
9	"	½ a. green (pale to deep)	12	6
		a. Perf. 11 at top or bottom only	17	6
		b. On toned (vert. laid)	20	0

It is suggested that No. 8 may be an error due to printing from the wrong plate.

2. Rana Ranjitsingh. **3.**

1922–31. *Perf.* 11. (*a*) *Thick glazed paper.*

10	2	1 a. vermilion	8	6	30
		a. Imperf. between (pr.)	75	0	
11	"	1 a. rose-carmine (1931)	15	0	
12	"	2 a. purple	10	0	
		a. Doubly printed	80	0	
		b. Imperf. between (pr.)	80	0	
		c. *Violet*	35	0	

No. 11 is perforated all round.

(*b*) *Thin smooth unglazed wove paper.*

13	1	½ a. green (bright to deep)	8	6
		a. Imperf. between (pr.)		
14	2	1 a. vermilion	£35	

(*c*) *Thick toned wove paper.*

15	2	2 a. purple	35	0	50

1922 (?) *Thin wove paper. Pin-perf.* 8½.

16	1	¼ a. greyish ultramarine	8	6
		aa. Imperf. (pair)	75	0
		a. *Blue-grey/toned*	8	6
		b. Imperf. between (vert. pr.)	75	0

1923–26. *Various papers and perfs.*

17	1	¼ a. black/*toned* (wove, pin-perf. 7) ('23)	55	0

18 **1** ¼ a. rose (horiz. laid, p. 12) ('23) 6 0 7 6
a. Imperf. between (pr.) .. 50 0
b. Pin-perf. 7 .. .. 30 0
c. Perf. compound of 12 and 6 .. 25 0
19 ,, ¼ a. blue (vert. laid, p. 11) ('26) 7 6 8 6

The colours of Nos. 18 and 19 vary considerably. Both are perforated all round and have a papermaker's wmk. in the sheet.

1927. *Very defective impression. Thin, hard wove paper. Perf. 7 all round.*
20 **1** ¼ a. milky blue 25 0
21 ,, ½ a. bright yellow-green .. 40 0
a. Imperf. between (horiz. pr.) ..

In these two stamps the portrait is nearly invisible.

1927–31. (*a*) *Thick wove paper. Sewing machine perf.* 6.
22 **3** 4 a. yellow-brown 50 0
a. Pin-perf. 7 .. .. 90 0
(*b*) *Thin wove paper. Pin-perf.* 7.
23 **3** 4 a. orange-brown 40 0
(*c*) *Glazed paper. P* 11 *all round.*
24 **3** 4 a. salmon (to orange) .. 40 0
a. Imperf. between (horiz. pr.) ..

1928. *Thick glazed paper. Pin-perf.* 7, *all round.*
25 **1** ¼ a. deep bright blue .. 12 6
26 ,, ½ a. bright yellow-green .. 12 6

1928 (Nov.). *Thick glazed paper. P* 11 (*rough*).
27 **1** ¼ a. ultramarine 7 6
a. Tête-bêche (horiz. pr.) .. 22 6
28 ,, ½ a. apple-green 10 0
a. Tête-bêche (vert. pr.) .. 27 6

No. 27 was printed in sheets of 8 (4 × 2) with the two centre pairs *tête-bêche* while No. 28, in similar sheets, had the two horizontal rows *tête-bêche*.

1929 (Jan.). *Thick glazed paper. P* 11 (*clean-cut*) *all round.*
29 **1** ¼ a. deep blue 5 0 7 6
a. Imperf. between (pr.) .. 75 0
30 ,, ½ a. turquoise-green (to deep blue-green) .. 4 0 7 6
a. Imperf. between (pr.) .. 60 0

GUM. Nos. 1 to 30 are ungummed. The following stamps have gum.

4. Rana Devi Singh. **5.**

1932–48.
A. *Close setting* (2 *mm.*). *P* 11, 12 *or compound.*
B. *Wide setting* (3–4 *mm.*). *P* 11.

	A.		B.	
31 **4** ¼ a. slate ..	5 0	10 0	2 0	5 0
32 ,, ½ a. blue-green ..	5 0	10 0	2 6	5 0
33 ,, 1 a. brown ..	5 0	10 0	7 6	10 0
a. *Chocolate* P 8½ ('48)	†		20 0	—
34 ,, 2 a. purple ..	6 0	—	—	—
a. *Reddish purple*	†		20 0	—
35 ,, 4 a. olive-green	12 6	20 0	22 6	—

The measurements given in the heading indicate the horizontal spacing between impressions. There are eight settings of this interesting issue: four "Close" where the over-all stamp dimensions from centre to centre of perfs. vary in width from 21½ to 23 mm. and in height from 25 to 27½ mm.; and four "Wide", width 23–23½ mm. and height 29–30 mm.

1935–48. *P* 11. A. *Close setting* (3–4½ *mm.*). B. *Wide setting* (7–10 *mm.*).

	A.		B.	
36 **1** ¼ a. black ..	3 6	—	5 0	6 0
37 ,, ½ a. blue-green ('38?) ..	20 0	—	†	
a. *Dp. yell.-grn.*	10 0	—	3 0	7 6
38 **2** 1 a. brn. (*shades*)	6 0	7 6	15 0	—
a. Perf. 8½ (5 mm.) ('48) ..	†		10 0	—
39 ,, 2 a. bright purple ('47?) ..	†		75 0	95 0
40 ,, 2 a. rose-carmine ('48) ..	†		20 0	—
41 **3** 4 a. sage-green ..	40 0	40 0	15 0	—
a. *Pale sage-grn.*	†		6 0	12 6

There was one "Close" setting (over-all stamp size 25 × 29 mm.) and four "Wide" settings with over-all sizes 26½–31½ × 31–36½ mm. There was also one "Medium" setting (26½ × 31 mm.) but this was confined to the 1 a. perf. 8½, No. 38a.

1938. *P* 11.
42 **5** 1 a. brown 30 0

The stamps of Barwani became obsolete on July 1st, 1948.

BHOPAL.

The correct English inscription on these stamps is "H.H. NAWAB SHAH JAHAN BEGAM". As the stamps were printed from lithographic stones, on which each unit was drawn separately by hand, numerous errors of spelling occurred. These are constant in all sheets and are worth a premium.

EMBOSSING. Types **1/3** and **6** to **12*a*** all have the centre Hindi inscriptions embossed. Almost all varieties can be found with the embossing inverted or sideways, as well as upright.

Nawab Shah Jahan Begam, 1868–1901.

1 (¼ a.)

1876–77. *Double frame,* 20 *varieties of each value. Lithographed.*
1 **1** ¼ a. black £10 £10
2 ,, ½ a. red 20 0 20 0
Varieties: "BFGAM", "BEGAN" or "EGAM". ¼ a. (£8 *each*) and ½ a. (35*s. each*).

2 (½ a.)

Single frame, 20 *varieties of the* ½ *a.*
3 **2** ½ a. black .. .. .. — £35
4 ,, ½ a. red 8 6 12 0
Variety: "NWAB." ½ a. (32*s.* 6*d.*). Also occurs on ¼ a.

3 (½ a.)

40 *varieties* (2 *plates*), *all lettered* "EEGAM" *for* "BEGAM."

5 **3** ½ a. black 1 3 2 6

In Nos. 1 to 5 the value is expressed in two different forms at foot.

4 (½ a.)

5 (½ a.)

1878–79. *Value in parenthesis;* 32 *varieties.*

6 **4** ½ a. green (*imperf.*) 6 0 7 6
7 ,, ½ a. green (*perf.*) 6 0 7 6

Value not in parenthesis; 32 *varieties. Imperf.*

8 **5** ½ a. red 5 0 6 0
9 ,, ½ a. brown 35 0 45 0

Varieties: "JAHN", "NWAB" or "EEGAM". ½ a. red (20*s. each*). ½ a. brown (£5 *each*).

1880. *T* **5** *redrawn; value not in parenthesis;* 32 *varieties of each value. No errors on sheet of* ½ *a.*

(*a*) *Imperf.*

10 ¼ a. blue-green 7 6
11 ½ a. brown-red 8 6 8 6

(*b*) *Perf.*

12 ¼ a. blue-green 4 0
13 ½ a. brown-red 4 6

Varieties: "NAWA" and "CHAH". ¼ a. Imperf. (25*s. each*) or perf. (12*s.* 6*d. each*).

1884. *T* **5** *again redrawn;* 32 *varieties, some with value in parenthesis, others not. Perf.*

14 ¼ a. greenish blue 4 6

In this plate there is a slanting dash under and to left of the letters "JA" of "JAHAN," instead of a character like a large comma, as on all previous varieties of this design.

Variety: "ANAWAB" (35*s.*).

1895. *T* **5** *again redrawn;* 8 *varieties. Laid paper.*

15 ½ a. red (*imperf.*) 5 0 6 0
16 ½ a. red (*perf.*) .. .. — £8

In these cases where the same design has been redrawn several times, and each time in a number of varieties of type, it is not easy to distinguish the various issues. Nos. 6 and 7 may be distinguished from Nos. 10 and 12 by the presence or absence of the parenthesis marks (); 8 9 and 11 differ principally in colour; 8 and 15 are very much alike, but differ in the value as well as in paper.

6 (1 a.)

1881. 24 *varieties of each value. Imperf.*

17 **6** ¼ a. black 1 6
18 ,, ½ a. red 3 6 7 6
19 ,, 1 a. brown 3 6 7 6
20 ,, 2 a. blue 5 0
21 ,, 4 a. buff 10 0

Varieties: "NWAB". ¼ a., ½ a., 1 a., 2 a. (12*s.* 6*d. each*). 4 a. (25*s.*).

In this issue all values were produced from the same drawing, and therefore show exactly the same varieties of type. The value at foot in this and all the following issues is given in only one form.

7 (½ a.)

1886. *Similar to T* **6** *but normally lettered* "BEGAN"; *larger lettering;* 32 *varieties.*

(*a*) *Imperf.*

22 **7** ½ a. pale red 3 6 7 6

(*b*) *Perf.*

23 **7** ½ a. pale red £8

Varieties: "BEGAM" and "NWAB". ½ a. imperf. (15*s. each*). Also exist perf.

8 (4 a.)

1886. *T* **8.** *T* **6** *redrawn;* 24 *varieties. The* "M" *of* "BEGAM" *is an inverted* "W". *The width of the stamps is rather greater than the height.*

Wove paper. Imperf.

24 **8** 4 a. yellow 20 0

Laid paper.

25 **8** 4 a. yellow (*imperf.*) .. 10 0
26 ,, 4 a. yellow (*perf.*) .. 7 6 7 6

Variety: "EEGAM". No. 24 (27*s.* 6*d.*), 25 (15*s.*) and 26 (10*s.*).

1889. *T* **6** *again redrawn;* 32 *varieties, lettered* "BEGAN."

27 ¼ a. black (*perf.*) 4 0 5 0
28 ¼ a. black (*imperf.*) 5 0 6 0

Variety: "EEGAN". Perf. (10*s.*) or imperf. (15*s.*).

9 (¼ a.)

1889–90. *T* **9.** *T* **6** *again redrawn; 24 varieties of each value, all with " M " like an inverted " W." Wove paper. Imperf.*

29 **9** ¼ a. black 1 6 2 6
30 ,, 1 a. brown 3 6 4 6
31 ,, 2 a. blue 3 0 3 6
32 ,, 4 a. orange-yellow 4 0 7 6

Perf.

33 **9** ¼ a. black 3 0 3 6
34 ,, 1 a. brown 4 0 5 0
35 ,, 2 a. blue 2 6 3 0
36 ,, 4 a. orange-yellow 6 0 7 6

Nos. 32 and 36 are nearly square, in many cases rather larger in height than in width.

Varieties: " EEGAM " and " BBGAM ". 1 a. imperf. (15*s. each*) or perf. (17*s.* 6*d. each*). " BBEGAM " and " NAWAH ". 2 a. imperf. (27*s.* 6*d. each*) or perf. (25*s. each*).

1891. *As last, but 32 varieties.*

37 **9** ½ a. red (*imperf.*) 4 0 4 6
38 ,, ½ a. red (*perf.*) 3 6 4 0

1894–98. *T* **6** *again redrawn; 24 varieties, almost all showing a character inside the octagon below, as in T* **9.** *Wove paper.*

39 1 a. deep brown (*imperf.*) .. 4 0 4 6
40 1 a. red-brown (*imperf.*) .. 40 0
41 1 a. deep brown (*perf.*) .. 8 6 8 6

10 (1 a.)

As Nos. 39 to 41, but printed from a fresh transfer (?), showing the lines blurred and shaky. Wove paper. Imperf. (1898).

42 **10** 1 a. purple brown 10 0 12 6
43 ,, 1 a. purple-brown/*buff* .. 6 0 7 0

Variety: " NAWAH ". No. 42 (60*s.*), No. 43 (30*s.*). The above, including the varieties, are known without embossing.

11 (½ a.)

1895. *T* **11**; 8 *varieties, lettered " EEGAM ". White laid paper.*

44 **11** ½ a. black (*imperf.*) .. 7 6 7 6
45 ,, ½ a. black (*perf.*) .. 8 0 8 0

12 (½ a.)

Narrow label at bottom; 8 varieties, ettered " W W " for " H. H."

46 **12** ½ a. black (*imperf.*) .. 3 6 4 0

12*a*

T **12***a*; 8 *varieties.*

47 **12***a* ½ a. red (*imperf.*) 5 0 6 0

No. 47 is a combination of Types **1** and **6**, having the double outer frame to the octagon and the value in one form only.

13 (¼ a.) 14 (¼ a.)

1884. *32 varieties. Perf.*

48 **13** ¼ a. blue-green £5 £5

Varieties: " JAN " (£10); " BEGM ", " NWAB ", " SHAHAN ", " JAHA " and " JN " (£20 *each*).

1895. *T* **14**, *double-lined frame round each stamp; 6 varieties lettered " JAN." Laid paper.*

49 **14** ¼ a. bright green (*imperf.*) .. 9 0 10 0

15 (½ a.)

1884. *32 varieties of each value. Laid paper.*

50 **15** ¼ a. blue-green (*imperf.*) £5 £5
51 ,, ¼ a. blue-green (*perf.*) .. 0 9
52 ,, ½ a. black (*imperf.*) .. 2 0 2 6
53 ,, ½ a. black (*perf.*) 0 9

The ½ a. of this issue is in *blue-green*, or *greenish blue*. Both values were printed from the same stone, the value alone being altered. There are therefore the same varieties of each. These are the only stamps of this design on laid paper.
Varieties: "NWAB", "SAH" and "NAWA". ¼ a. imperf. (£15 *each*). ¼ a. perf. (6*s*. *each*). ½ a. imperf. (10*s*. *each*). ½ a. perf. (7*s*. 6*d*. *each*).

1886. *T* **15** *redrawn; 32 varieties of each value. "N" of "NAWAB" reversed. Wove paper.*

54 ¼ a. green (*imperf.*) 1 0 1 3
55 ¼ a. green (*perf.*) 1 0 1 9
56 ½ a. red (*imperf.*) 1 9 2 6

The ¼ a varies from *yellow-green* to *deep green*.
Varieties: ¼ a. green, imperf. or perf. "NAWA", "NWAB", "NWABA", "NAWAA", and "BEGAAM" as well as "NWABA" (on same stamp). (*From* 5*s*. *each*). ½ a. red, imperf. "SAH" and "NAWABA". (6*s*. *each*).

1888. *T* **15** *again redrawn; 32 varieties, letters in upper angles smaller. "N" of "NAWAB" correct. Wove paper.*

57 ¼ a. deep green (*imperf.*) .. 2 0 2 6
58 ¼ a. deep green (*perf.*) .. 2 6 2 6

Nos. 50 to 58 have the dash under the letters "JA." as in No. 14.
Varieties: "SAH" and "NAWA". Imperf. (10*s*. *each*) or perf. (15*s*. *each*).

1891. *T* **15** *again redrawn; 32 varieties, lettered "NWAB." Wove paper. (a) Imperf.*

59 ½ a. red.. .. .. .. 1 6 2 0

(*b*) *P* 3 *to* 4½, *or about* 7.

60 ½ a. red.. .. .. .. 3 0 3 6

Nos. 59 and 60 have the comma under "JA".
Variety "SAH". Imperf. (15*s*.) or perf. (30*s*.).

1894. *T* **15** *again redrawn; letters in corners larger than in 1888, value in very small characters; 32 varieties, all with "G" in left-hand lower corner. Wove paper.*

61 ¼ a. green (*imperf.*) 2 0 2 0
62 ¼ a. green (*perf.*) 2 6 2 6

Nos. 61 and 62 have neither the dash nor the comma under "JA".
Varieites: (*a*) "NAWAH" and (*b*) value in brackets (25*s*. *each*).

16 (¼ a.)

1896. *T* **16**; *oval narrower, stops after "H.H." space after "NAWAB". The line down the centre is under the first "H" of "SHAH" or between "HA" instead of being under the second "H" or between "AH". Wove paper. Imperf.*

63 **16** ¼ a. bright green 0 9 1 0
64 ,, ¼ a. pale green 1 6 1 9
65 ,, ¼ a. black 1 6 1 6

Variety: "SHAN". ¼ a. No. 63 (5*s*.), No. 64 (10*s*.) No. 65 (10*s*.).

1899. *T* **15**. *Printed apparently from a transfer from the stone of* 1891; *the first "A" of "NAWAB" always absent. Numerous defective and malformed letters. Wove paper. Imperf.*

66 ½ a. black (NWAB) 1 6 5 0

Varieties: "NWASBAHJANNI", "SBAH", "SBAN" "NWIB", "BEIAM" and "SHH". (12*s*. 6*d*. *each*).

17 (8 a.)

18 (¼ a.)

1890–91. *T* **17**; 10 *varieties. Single-line frame to each stamp. (a) Wove paper.*

67 **17** 8 a. slate-green (*imperf.*) .. 40 0 40 0
68 ,, 8 a. slate-green (*perf.*) .. 40 0 40 0

Varieties: "HAH" and "JABAN". Imperf. or perf. (70*s*. *each*).

(*b*) *Thin laid paper.*

69 **17** 8 a. green-black (*imperf.*) .. 35 0 35 0
70 ,, 8 a. green-black (*perf.*) .. 35 0 35 0

Varieties: "HAH" and "JABAN". Imperf. or perf. (70*s*. *each*).

1893. *T* **17** *redrawn. No frame to each stamp, but a frame to the sheet.* 10 *varieties. (a) Wove paper.*

71 8 a. green-black (*imperf.*) .. 35 0 35 0
72 8 a. green-black (*perf.*) .. 35 0 35 0

(*b*) *Thin laid paper. Imperf.*

73 8 a. green-black 60 0 60 0

1898. *Defective transfer from the stone of* 1893. *Lettering irregular. Wove paper. Imperf.*

74 8 a. green-black 30 0 40 0
75 8 a. black 30 0 40 0

Variety: Reversed "E" in "BEGAM". Nos 74 and 75 (70*s*. *each*).

1896–1901. *T* **18**. 32 *varieties. Imperf.*

76 **18** ¼ a. black 3 0 3 6

Printed from a fresh transfer (?), lines shaky Imperf. (1899).

77 ¼ a. black 7 6 7 6

The same, on thick wove paper (1901).

78 ¼ a. black £5 £5

Nawab Sultan Jahan Begam, 1901–1926.

19 (¼ a.)

1902. *T* **19**. *With the octagonal embossed devic of the previous issues.* 16 *varieties of* ¼ *a., varieties of each of the other values. Thi yellowish wove paper. Imperf.*

79 **19** ¼ a. rose 5 0 6
80 ,, ½ a. rose-red 5 0 6
81 ,, ½ a. black 5 0 6
a. Printed both sides
82 ,, 1 a. brown 7 6 6
83 ,, 1 a. red-brown 7 6 6
84 ,, 2 a. blue 12 6 8
85 ,, 4 a. orange £5
86 ,, 4 a. yellow 70 0 70
87 ,, 8 a. lilac 80 0 80
88 ,, 1 r. rose £5

1903. *With a circular embossed device. 32 varieties (two plates) of ¼ a., 8 fresh varieties of ½ a. and 2 a., 4 a., 8 a., and 1 r., as before.*

A. *Wove paper.* B. *Laid paper.*

			A.		B.	
89	**19**	¼ a. rose-red ..	2 0	2 0	4 0	—
90	,,	¼ a. red.. ..	2 6	3 0	2 0	—
91	,,	½ a. black ..	2 0	2 6	5 0	5 0
92	,,	1 a. brown ..	4 0	—	†	
93	,,	1 a. red-brown..	4 0	—	—	—
94	,,	2 a. blue ..	7 6	7 6	—	—
95	,,	4 a. orange ..	£5	£5	†	
96	,,	4 a. yellow ..	70 0	70 0	—	—
97	,,	8 a. lilac ..	80 0	80 0	—	—
98	,,	1 r. rose ..	£5	£5	—	—

No. 71 *optd. with initial of the new Begum in red.*

99 8 a. green-black 60 0 75 0
a. Opt. inverted £8 £8

Some of the previous stamps remained on sale and probably in use) after the issue of the series of 1902, and some of these were afterwards put on sale with the new form of embossing; fresh plates were made of some of the old designs, in imitation of the earlier issues, and impressions from these were also sold with the new embossed device. We no longer list these doubtful items.

20

(Recess. Perkins, Bacon & Co.)

908. *P* 13½.

00 **20** 1 a. green 5 0 1 6
a. Printed both sides .. £10

The ordinary postage stamps of Bhopal ecame obsolete on July 1, 1908.

OFFICIAL STAMPS.

SERVICE

(O 1)

SERVICE **SERVICE**

(O 2) (O 3)

RINTERS. 1908 issue recess-ptd. and optd. y Perkins, Bacon & Co. Type O 4 and subequent types and opts., ptd. at Indian Govt. 'tg. Wks., Nasik.

908 (1 July). *As T* **20**, *but inscribed* "H. H. BEGUM'S SERVICE" *at left. No wmk. P* 13 *to* 15. *Overprinted* (*a*) *with Type* O **1**.

01 ½ a. yellow-green 2 6 0 3
a. Pair, one without overprint .. £5
b. Opt. double, one inverted .. £5
c. Opt. inverted £5 £5
02 1 a. carmine-red 1 6 0 3
a. Opt. inverted £5 £5
03 2 a. ultramarine 7 6 0 3
04 4 a. brown 15 0 1 0

(*b*) *With Type* O **2**.

05 ½ a. yellow-green 2 6 1 0
06 1 a. carmine-red 10 0 7 6
07 2 a. ultramarine 5 0 2 0
a. Opt. inverted 60 0
08 4 a. brown 60 0 2 0
a. Overprint inverted 60 0 60 0

The two overprints differ in the shape of the etters, noticeably in the "R".

O 4

1930–31. Type O **4** (25½ × 30½ *mm.*) *optd. with Type* O **3**. *Litho. P* 14.

309 ½ a. sage-green (1931) .. 2 0 1 6
310 1 a. carmine-red (1.7.30) .. 2 6 0 10
311 2 a. ultramarine (1.7.30) .. 3 6 1 0
312 4 a. chocolate (1.7.30) .. 6 6 1 6

The ½ a., 2 a., and 4 a. are inscribed "POSTAGE" at left.

1932–33. *As Type* O **4** (21 × 25 *mm.*), *but inscr.* "POSTAGE" *at left. Optd. with Type* O **1**. *Litho.*

(*a*) "BHOPAL STATE" *at right. P* 13.

313 ¼ a. orange 7 6 1 0
a. Perf. 11½ 8 6 1 0
b. Perf. 14 .. .. .. 32 6 1 0
c. Perf. 13½ 20 0 20 0
ca. Pair, one without opt. .. £8

(*b*) "BHOPAL GOVT." *at right. P* 13½.

314 ½ a. yellow-green 1 0 0 6
315 1 a. carmine-red 1 6 0 6
316 2 a. ultramarine 2 0 1 6
317 4 a. chocolate 3 6 2 6

¼A THREE PIES ONE ANNA

(O 5) (O 6) (O 7)

1935–36. *Nos.* 314, 316 *and* 317 *surch. as Types* O **5** *to* O **7**.

318 O **5** ¼ a. on ½ a. yell.-grn. (R.) 20 0 10 0
319 O **6** 3 p. on ½ a. yell.-grn. (R.) 2 6 1 0
a. "THEEE PIES" £5 £5
b. "THRFE" for "THREE" £5 £5
320 O **5** ¼ a. on 2 a. ultram. (R.) 25 0 10 0
a. Surch. inverted £10 £6
321 O **6** 3 p. on 2 a. ultram. (R.).. 2 6 2 6
a. Surch. inverted £8 £8
b. "THEEE PIES" .. £5 £5
ba. Do. Surch. inverted
c. "THRFE for "THREE" £5 £5
ca. Do. Surch. inverted
322 O **5** ¼ a. on 4 a. chocolate (R.) £10 40 0
323 ,, ¼ a. on 4 a. chocolate (Bk.) (25.5.36) .. 80 0 60 0
324 O **6** 3 p. on 4 a. chocolate (R.) 80 0 40 0
a. "THEEE PIES" .. 80 0
b. "THRER" for "THREE" £25 £25
c. "THRFE" for "THREE" £25 £25
325 ,, 3 p. on 4 a. chocolate (Bk.) (25.5.36) 10 0 6 0
a. "THRER" for "THREE" £10 £10
b. "FHREE" for "THREE" £10 £10
c. "PISE" for "PIES" .. £15 £15
d. "PIFS" for "PIES" .. £15 £15
326 O **7** 1 a. on ½ a. yell.-grn. (V.) 2 6 2 6
a. Surch. inverted £8 £8
b. First "N" in "ANNA" inverted 60 0 60 0
ba. Do. Surch. inverted .. £20 £20

327 O **7** 1 a. on 2 a. ultram. (R.) 2 6 2 0
a. Surch. inverted .. £8 £8
b. First "N" in "ANNA" inverted 60 0 60 0
ba. Do. Surch. inverted .. £20 £20
c. Surch. in violet £10 £10
ca. Do. Surch. inverted .. £25 £25
cb. As c, first "N" in "ANNA" inverted .. £35 £35
cc. Do. Surch. inverted .. £50 £50
328 ,, 1 a. on 2 a. ultramarine (Bk.) (25.5.36) .. 4 0 2 0
329 ,, 1 a. on 4 a. chocolate (B.) 2 6 2 0
a. First "N" in "ANNA" inverted 60 0 60 0

Nos. 318 to 325 are arranged in composite sheets of 100 (10 × 10). The two upper horizontal rows of each value are surcharged as Type O **5** and the next five rows as Type O **6**. The remaining three rows are also surcharged as Type O **6** but in a slightly narrower setting.

The surcharge on No. 323 differs from Type O **5** in the shape of the figures and letter.

O **8**

1935–39. *As Type* O **8.**
(*a*) *Litho. Inscr.* "BHOPAL GOVT. POSTAGE". *Optd.* "SERVICE" (13½ *mm.*). *P* 13½.
330 1 a. 3 p. blue and claret .. 1 6 1 3
(*b*) *Typo. Inscr.* "BHOPAL STATE POSTAGE". *Optd.* "SERVICE" (11 *mm.*). *P* 12.
331 1 a. 6 p. blue and claret ('37) 1 6 1 6
a. Imperf. between (pair) .. £8 £8
b. Opt. omitted £10 £10
c. Opt. double, one inverted .. £10 £10
331*d* 1 a. 6 p. claret ('39) .. 1 9 1 9
e. Imperf. between (pair) .. £8 £8
f. Opt. omitted £10 £10
g. Opt. double, one inverted .. £10 £10

O **9**

1936 (JULY)–**1938.** *Optd.* "SERVICE". *Typo. P* 12.
332 O **9** ¼ a. orange (Br.) 0 8 0 8
a. Imperf. betwn. (vert. pr.) £5 £5
b. Opt. inverted .. £5 £5
c. Black opt. 40 0 40 0
ca. Do. Opt. inverted .. £15 £15
333 ,, ¼ a. yellow (Br.) ('38) .. 0 8 0 8
334 ,, 1 a. scarlet 1 3 0 8
a. Imperf. between (pair) .. 50 0 50 0

O **10.** The Moti Mahal.

1936–49. *As Type* O **10** (*various palaces*). *Typo. P* 12.
(*a*) *Optd.* "SERVICE" (13½ *mm.*).
335 ½ a. purple-brn. & yell.-grn. 0 8 0 3
a. Imperf. between (pair) .. — 80 0
335*b* ½ a. purple-brn. & grn. ('38) 0 8 0 4
(*b*) *Optd.* "SERVICE" (11 *mm.*).
336 2 a. brown and blue ('37) .. 0 10 0 10
a. Imperf. between (pair) .. 80 0 80 0
b. Opt. inverted £7
336*c* 2 a. green and violet ('38) .. 1 0 0 10
d. Imperf. between (vert. pair) 80 0 80 0
337 4 a. blue and brown ('37) .. 2 6 2 6
a. Imperf. between (pair) .. £10 £10
b. Opt. omitted £7 £7
c. Opt. double £7 £7
340 8 a. bright purple & blue ('38) 3 0 3 0
a. Imperf. between (pair) .. £12 £12
b. Opt. omitted £7 £7
c. Opt. double £7 £7
341 1 r. light blue and bright purple (Br.) ('38) .. 4 6 3 6
a. Opt. in black (1944) .. 40 0 40 0
(*c*) *Optd.* "SERVICE" (11½ *mm.*) *with serifs.*
341*c* 1 r. dull blue and bright purple (Bk.) ('49) .. 70 0 70 0
d. "SREVICE" for "SERVICE" .. £10 £10
(*d*) *Optd.* "SERVICE" (13½ *mm.*) *with serifs.*
341*e* 8 a. bright purple & blue ('49) 95 0 95 0
f. "SERAICE" for "SERVICE" £15 £15

The ½ a. is inscr. "BHOPAL GOVT." below the arms, other values have "BHOPAL STATE".

Designs:—(37½ × 22½ mm.) 2 a. (Nos. 336/6*a*) The Moti Masjid, 4 a. (Nos. 337/8) Taj Mahal and Be-Nazir Palaces. (39 × 24mm.)—8 a. Ahmadabad Palace. (45½ × 27½ mm.)—1 r. (Nos. 341/1*c*) Rait Ghat.

O **11.** Tiger.

1940. *As Type* O **11** (*animals*). *Typo. P* 12
342 ¼ a. bright blue 7 6 2 6
343 1 a. bright purple (Chital) .. 20 0 3 0

1941. *As Type* O **8** *but coloured centre inscr* "SERVICE"; *bottom frame inscr.* "BHOPAL STATE POSTAGE". *Typo. P* 12.
344 1 a. 3 p. emerald-green .. 0 10 0 10

O **13.** The Moti Mahal.

1944–47. *As Type* O **13** (*various palaces*). *Typo. P* 12 *or imperf.*

345 O **13** ½ a. green 0 6 0 6
346 – 2 a. violet 2 0 2 0
346*a* – 2 a. bright purple ('46) 2 0 2 0
346*b* – 2 a. mauve ('47) .. 4 6 3 6
347 – 4 a. chocolate .. 3 6 3 6

Design inscr. "BHOPAL STATE":—2 a. (Nos. 346/6*b*) The Moti Masjid; 4 a. Be-Nazir Palaces.

O **14.** Arms of Bhopal.

— —

2 As.

(O **15**)

1945–49. *Typo. P* 12.

348 O **14** 3 p. bright blue .. 0 6 0 3
349 ,, 9 p. chestnut (*shades* .. 4 6 0 8
a. Imperf. (pair) .. £5 £5
349*b* ,, 1 a. purple 1 0 0 8
349*c* ,, 1 a. violet ('46) .. 12 6 3 0
350 ,, 1½ a. claret 0 10 0 6
352 ,, 3 a. yellow 2 6 3 0
a. Imperf. (pair) .. £5 £5
352*b* ,, 3 a. orange-brown ('49) 35 0
c. Imperf. (pair) £7 £7
353 ,, 6 a. carmine 5 0 8 0
a. Imperf. (pair) .. — £7

1949 (July). *Surch. with Type* O **15.** *P* 12.

354 O **14** 2 a. on 1½ a. claret .. 2 6 5 0
a. Imperf. (pair) .. £12 £10

2 As.

(O **16**)

1949 (?). *Surch. with Type* O **16.** *Imperf. or P* 12.

355 O **14** 2 a. on 1½ a. claret .. £35

There are at least three types of the figure "2" in the surcharge.

BHOR.

1

2

1879. *Very thick to thin native paper. Imperf.*

1 **1** ½ a. carmine (*shades*) 10 0 12 6
2 **2** 1 a. carmine (*shades*) 10 0 12 6

3. Pant Sachiv Shankarro Chimnaji.

1901. *Typo. Wove paper. Imperf.*

3 **3** ½ a. red 15 0 £5

BIJAWAR.

1. Maharaja Sir Sarwant Singh Bahadur.

(Typo. Beerindra Kumar & Co.)

1935–36. I. *P* 11 (1.7.35). II. *Roul.* 7 (1936).

			I.		II.
1 **1**	3 p. brown	..	2 6		1 0
	a. Printed on gummed side..		†		40 0
2 ,,	6 p. carmine	..	2 0	4 0	2 0
3 ,,	9 violet	..	2 6		5 0
4 ,,	1 a. blue	..	3 0		7 0
5 ,,	2 a. deep green	..	3 6		8 6

All values exist in imperf. between pairs. (*Prices* 40s. and upwards per pair.)

2. Maharaja Sir Sarwant Singh Bahadur.

1937 (July). *Typo. P* 9.

6 **2** 4 a. orange 7 6 10 0
a. Imp. between (vert. pair) .. £8
7 ,, 6 a. lemon 9 0 10 0
a. Imp. between (vert. pair) .. £10
8 ,, 8 a. emerald-green 12 6 15 0
9 ,, 12 a. greenish blue 15 0 17 6
10 ,, 1 r. bright violet 40 0 50 0
a. "1 Rs" for "1 R" .. £6 £8

BUNDI.

In Nos. 1 to 17 characters denoting the value are below the dagger, except in Nos. 2*a*, 11 and 17.

All Bundi stamps until 1914, are imperf.

1

1894 (May). *Each stamp with a distinct frame and the stamps not connected by the framing lines. Laid or wove paper.*

1	**1**	½ a. slate-grey	£75	£50
		a. Last two letters of value below the rest		

2. (Block of four stamps).

1894 (Dec.). *T* **2.** *The stamps are all joined together, with no space between them. Thin wove paper.*

2	**2**	½ a. slate-grey	30 0	30 0
		a. Value at top, name below ..	£10	£10
		b. Right upper ornament omitted	£20	£20
		c. Last two letters of value below the rest	£20	£20

3

1896 (Nov.). *T* **3.** *Dagger shorter, lines thicker. Stamps separate, and only joined by the framing lines at the top and sides of the sheet. Laid paper.*

3	**3**	½ a. slate-grey	6 0	7 0
		a. Last two letters of value below the rest	£20	£20

4. (1 anna)

5. (2 annas)

6. (2 annas)

1897–1900. *No shading in centre of blade of dagger. The stamps have spaces between them, but are connected by the framing lines, both vertically and horizontally. Laid paper.*

1. *Blade of dagger comparatively narrow, and either triangular, as in T* **4** *and* **6**, *or with the left-hand corner not touching the bar behind it, as in T* **5** (1897–98).

4	**4**	1 a. brick-red	17 6	30 0
5	**5**	1 a. brick-red	17 6	30 0
6	,,	2 a. yellowish green ..	20 0	40 0
7	**6**	2 a. emerald-green	20 0	40 0
8	**5**	4 a. green	50 0	60 0
9	,,	8 a. brick-red	60 0	70 0
10	,,	1 r. yellow/*blue*	£7	£7

7

2. *Blade varying in shape, but as a rule not touching the bar; value above and name below the dagger, instead of the reverse* (Jan., 1898).

11	**7**	4 a. emerald-green	25 0	
		a. Yellow-green	30 0	

8. (½ anna)

9. (8 annas)

3. *Blade wider and (except on the ½ a.) almost diamond shaped; it nearly always touches the bar* (1898–1900).

12	**8**	½ a. slate-grey (5.2.98)	3	6	3	6
13	**9**	1 a. brick-red (–.7.98)	4	0	3	0
14	,,	2 a. pale green (9.11.98)	10	0	10	0
		a. First two characters of value (=two) omitted	£8		£8	
15	,,	8 a. brick-red (–.7.98)	20	0	20	0
16	,,	1 r. yellow/*blue* (–.7.98)	30	0	30	0
		a. On wove paper	40	0	50	0

10

1898 (9 Nov.).
4. *Inscriptions as on No. 11; point of dagger to left.*

17	**10**	4 a. green	25	0	30	0
		a. Yellow-green	25	0	30	0

All the above stamps are lithographed in larger sheets, containing as many varieties of type as there are stamps in the sheets.

11. Maharao Raja Sir Raghubir Singh.

12 13

Top tablet. 1st character of 2nd group differs.

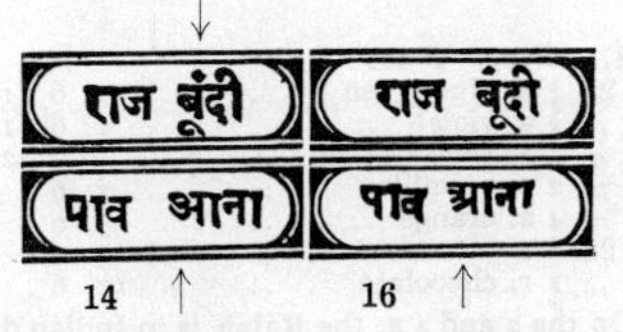

14 16

Top tablet. 1st character of 2nd group changed again. Loop at bottom of character in T **14** is sometimes attached.
Bottom tablet. In T **16** first character of 2nd group changed.

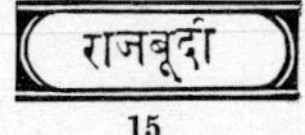

15

Top tablet. As T **14** but run together as one group.

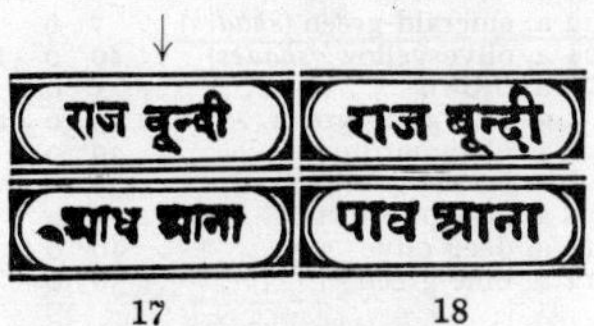

17 18

Top tablet. T **17** is as T **16** but 2nd group has four characters.
T **18** is as T **17** but both tablets have larger characters.

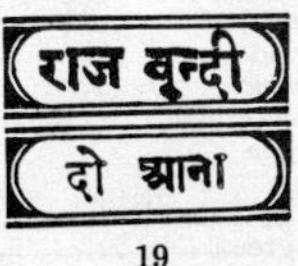

19

As T **18** but bottom tablet has smaller characters.

The denominations may be identified from the following illustrations. The ½ a., 3 a. and rupee values can be easily distinguished by their colours.

Bottom tablets:—

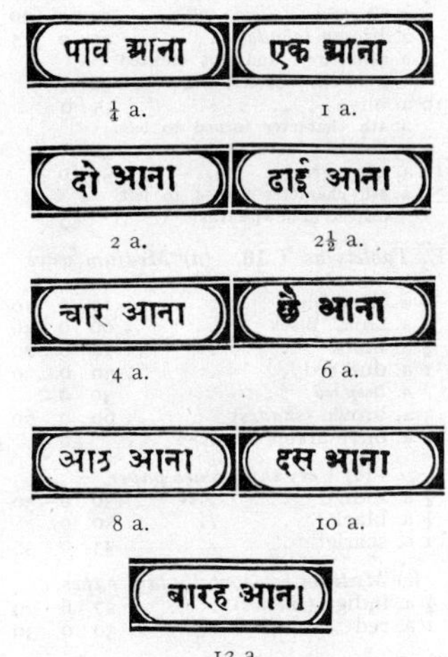

¼ a. 1 a. 2 a. 2½ a. 4 a. 6 a. 8 a. 10 a. 12 a.

1914–41. *T* **11.** *Typo. Ungummed paper.*
(i). *Rouletted in colour.*
A. *Top tablet as T* **12.**

18	½ a. black	10	0		
19	1 a. deep red	6	0		
20	2 a. emerald	6	0		
	a. Deep green (coarse ptg.)	7	6	10	0
21	2½ a. olive-yellow	10	0	12	6
22	3 a. brown	12	6		
23	4 a. yellow-green	80	0		
24	6 a. ultramarine	25	0		
25	1 r. violet	55	0		

B. *Top tablet as T* **13.**

26	¼ a. indigo (*shades*)	3	0	5	0
	a. Ultramarine	5	0		
27	½ a. black	5	0	5	0
28	1 a. vermilion	6	0		
	a. Carmine	6	0	7	6
	b. Brown-red	7	6		

29 2 a. emerald-green (*shades*) .. 7 6
30 2½ a. olive-yellow (*shades*) .. 10 0 12 6
31 3 a. brown 5 0
32 4 a. pale grass green 15 0 20 0
33 6 a. ultramarine 30 0
a. Indigo 30 0
34 8 a. orange-brown 25 0
35 10 a. deep olive 40 0
36 12 a. blue-green 50 0

C. *Tablets as T* **14.**

37 ¼ a. indigo 4 0 6 0
a. Deep blue 3 0
b. Ultramarine 10 0 10 0
38 ½ a. black 3 6 5 0
39 1 a. red-brown 6 0 7 6
a. Deep red 8 6 10 0
40 2 a. emerald 8 6 10 0
a. Sage-green 10 6
41 4 a. yellow-green 15 0 30 0
a. Pale green 20 0 40 0
42 8 a. orange 27 6 35 0
43 10 a. deep to pale olive .. 30 0 40 0
44 12 a. blue-green 35 0 40 0
45 1 r. lilac 50 0 70 0
46 2 r. brown and black .. £5
a. Red-brown and black .. £5
47 3 r. blue and brown .. £10 £12
48 4 r. green and red .. £30
49 5 r. red and green .. £30

D. *Top tablet as T* **15.**

50 2½ a. buff 15 0 20 0
a. Chestnut 20 0 30 0
51 3 a. brown (*shades*) .. 25 0 25 0
a. Semi-circle and dot omitted from 4th character 50 0
52 10 a. olive 35 0
a. 4th character turned to left instead of downwards .. 70 0
53 12 a. grey-green 50 0
a. 4th character turned to left instead of downwards .. £5

E. *Tablets as T* **16.** (*a*) *Medium wove paper.*

54 ¼ a. deep blue 10 0 10 0
a. Error. Black 60 0 40 0
55 ½ a. black 12 6 20 0
56 1 a. dull red 30 0 20 0
a. Deep red 30 0
57 3 a. brown (*shades*) .. 60 0 60 0
58 4 a. olive-green £8 £5

(*b*) *Very thick wove paper.*

59 ¼ a. indigo 30 0 30 0
60 ½ a. black 50 0
61 1 a. scarlet 35 0 35 0

(*c*) *Medium horizontally laid paper.*

62 ¼ a. indigo (*shades*) .. 27 6 20 0
63 1 a. red 30 0 30 0

F. *Tablets as T* **17.** *Medium wove paper* (*except* 1 *a.*).

64 ½ a. black 40 0 40 0
a. Vert. laid paper £18 £15
b. Horiz. laid paper £20 £20
65 1 a. red (*horiz. laid paper*) £20 £15
66 4 a. green £30 £30
a. Horiz. laid paper £5 60 0

G. *Tablets as T* **18.**

67 ¼ a. ultramarine 20 0 30 0
68 ½ a. black £25 £15
69 1 a. scarlet 50 0 50 0
70 4 a. green £6 £6
71 4 r. green and red .. £20
72 5 r. red and green .. £22

(ii). *P* 11. *Tablets as T* **18.**

73 ¼ a. ultramarine £5 £5
a. Turquoise-blue 20 0 40 0
74 ½ a. black £5 £5
75 1 a. scarlet £35 £25
a. Carmine 75 0 £5
76 2 a. green £5

H. *Tablets as T* **19.**

77 ½ a. black £30 £30
78 2 a. green £10 £10

20

1941-45. *Typo.* *P* 11.

79 **20** 3 p. bright blue 1 3 2 0
80 „ 6 p. dark blue 2 6 4 0
81 „ 1 a. orange-red 3 0 5 0
82 „ 2 a. brown 35 0 35 0
a. Deep brown ('45) 40 0 45 0
83 „ 4 a. bright green 32 6 40 0
84 „ 8 a. dull green 70 0 80 0
85 „ 1 r. deep blue 80 0

21. Maharao Rajah Bahadur Singh. **22.** Bundi.

1947. *Typo.* *P* 11.

86 **21** ¼ a. blue-green 1 6 10 0
87 „ ½ a. violet 1 6 15 0
88 „ 1 a. yellow-green 1 6 20 0
89 – 2 a. vermilion 2 6
90 – 4 a. orange 3 0
91 **22** 8 a. ultramarine 5 0
92 „ 1 r. chocolate 12 6

On the 2 and 4 a. the Rajah is in Indian dress.

OFFICIAL STAMPS.

BUNDI

BUNDI

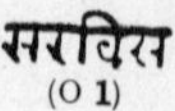

(O 1)

SERVICE

(O 2)

SERVICE

(O 3)

1918–41. *T* **11** *optd. as Types* O **1/3.** *Ungummed paper.*
A. *Optd. with Type* O **1**.
B. *Optd. as Type* O **2** *or in smaller, sans-serif type.*
C. *Optd. with Type* O **3**.

(i) *Rouletted in colour.*

No.	Description	A.		B.		C.	
	A. *Top tablet as T* **12**.						
O 1	2 a. emerald	15 0	—	†		†	
	a. Deep green (coarse ptg.)	30 0	—	50 0	—	£8	—
	b. Red opt.	40 0	—	60 0	—	†	
O 2	2½ a. olive-yellow	12 6	20 0	30 0	40 0	£10	—
	a. Red opt.	30 0	—	80 0	—	†	
O 3	3 a. brown	12 6	25 0	30 0	—	†	
	a. Green opt.	25 0	—	†		†	
O 4	6 a. ultramarine	35 0	—	60 0	—	£10	—
	a. Red opt.	£5	—	£7	—	£10	—
O 5	1 r. violet	60 0	—	£5	—	†	
	B. *Top tablet as T* **13**.						
O 6	¼ a. indigo	5 0	5 0	5 0	—	†	
	a. Red opt.	5 0	5 0	7 6	—	40 0	60 0
O 7	½ a. black	15 0	—	10 0	—	25 0	—
	a. Red opt.	15 0	—	40 0	—	£5	—
O 8	1 a. vermilion	10 0	—	12 6	—	50 0	—
	a. Carmine	7 6	—	15 0	—	†	
	b. Brown-red	†		25 0	—	†	
O 9	2 a. emerald-green (*shades*)	15 0	—	40 0	—	†	
O10	4 a. pale grass green	30 0	—	60 0	—	†	
O11	6 a. ultramarine	30 0	—	†		†	
	a. Indigo	30 0	—	40 0	—	†	
	b. Red opt.	30 0	—	50 0	—	†	
O12	8 a. orange-brown	60 0	—	£6	—	£12	—
O13	10 a. deep olive	70 0	—	£6	—	£12	—
	a. Red opt.	£6	—	£10	—	£15	—
O14	12 a. blue-green	£6	£6	£5	—	†	
	a. Red opt.	†		†		£15	
	C. *Tablets as T* **14**.						
O15	¼ a. deep blue	†		10 0	—	40 0	
	a. Red opt.	7 6	—	20 0	—	†	
	b. Green opt.	10 6	—	25 0	—	†	
	c. Ultramarine	£5	—	£5	—	£15	—
	d. Do. Red opt.	£8	—	£8	—	£20	—
O16	½ a. black	15 0	—	20 0	—	50 0	—
	a. Red opt.	5 0	—	40 0	—	£5	£5
	b. Green opt.	10 0	—	†		†	
O17	1 a. red-brown	7 6	—	†		†	
	a. Deep red	12 6	—	12 6	—	50 0	—
O18	2 a. emerald	25 0	—	30 0	—	†	
	a. Red opt.	†		£5	—	†	
	b. Sage-green	30 0	—	40 0	—	£5	£8
O19	4 a. yellow-green	35 0	—	60 0	—	†	
	a. Pale green	40 0	—	60 0	—	†	
O20	8 a. orange	50 0	—	£5	—	£10	—
O21	10 a. deep to pale olive	50 0	—	£5	—	£10	—
	a. Red opt.	£5	—	£10	—	£15	—
O22	12 a. blue-green	50 0	50 0	80 0	—	†	
	a. Red opt.	†		†		£15	—
O23	1 r. lilac	£7	—	†		†	
O24	2 r. brown and black	£18	—	£18	—	†	
	a. Red-brown and black	£15	£15	£15	£15	†	
	b. Red opt.	†		£20	—	†	
O25	3 r. blue and brown	£20	—	£20	—	†	
	a. Red opt.	£25	—	†		†	
O26	4 r. green and red	£50	—	£60	—	†	
O27	5 r. red and green	£50	—	£60	—	†	
	D. *Top tablet as T* **15**.						
O28	2½ a. buff	40 0	—	80 0	—	†	
	a. Chestnut	60 0	—	†		†	
	b. Red opt.	£6	—	†		†	
O29	3 a. brown (*shades*)	50 0	—	£5	—	†	
	a. Semi-circle and dot omitted from 4th character	£5	—	†		†	
	b. Red opt.	†		£8	—	†	
O30	10 a. olive	70 0	—	£5	—	£10	—
	a. 4th character turned to left instead of downwards	£7	—	†		†	
	b. Red opt.	£5	—	†		†	
O31	12 a. grey-green	80 0	—	£7	—	£12	—
	a. 4th character turned to left instead of downwards	£10	—	†		†	
	b. Red opt.	£8	—	£10	—	†	

No.	Description	A.		B.		C.	
	E. *Tablets as T* **16.** (*a*) *Medium wove paper.*						
O32	¼ a. deep blue	†		20 0	—	†	
	a. Red opt.	50 0	—	15 0	—	†	
	b. Error. Black	£5	—	£5	—	†	
	c. Do. Red opt.	£5	—	£5	—	†	
O33	½ a. black	£5	—	£5	—	†	
	a. Red opt.	£5	—	£5	—	†	
O34	1 a. deep red	£5	—	£5	—	£10	—
O35	3 a. brown (*shades*)	£8	—	£10	—	£20	—
	a. Red opt.	£15	—	£20	—	†	
	(*b*) *Very thick wove paper.*						
O36	¼ a. indigo	70 0	—	£5	—	†	
	a. Red opt.	70 0	—	£5	—	†	
	b. Green opt.	70 0	—	†		†	
O37	½ a. black	£5	—	£5	—	†	
O38	1 a. scarlet	55 0	—	75 0	—	†	
	(*c*) *Medium horizontally laid paper.*						
O39	¼ a. indigo (*shades*)	40 0	—	60 0	—	†	
	a. Red opt.	40 0	—	40 0	—	£5	—
O40	1 a. red	70 0	—	70 0	—	†	
	a. Red opt.	£10	—	£10	—	†	
	F. *Tablets as T* **17.** *Medium wove paper* (*except* 4 *a.*).						
O41	½ a. black	£18	—	£22	—	†	
	a. Vert. laid paper	£22	—	£25	—	†	
	b. Do. Red opt.	£22	—	£25	—	†	
	c. Horiz. laid paper (R.)	£25	—	£25	—	†	
O42	4 a. green (*horiz. laid paper*)	£15	—	†		†	
	a. Red opt.	£20	—	†		†	
	G. *Tablets as T* **18.**						
O43	¼ a. ultramarine	£22	—	£40	—	†	
	a. Red opt.	£22	—	£22	—	†	
O44	½ a. black	£60	—	£60	—	†	
	a. Red opt.	£60	—	†		£60	—
O45	1 a. scarlet	£25	—	£25	—	£50	—
O46	4 a. green	£30	—	£30	—	£50	—
	a. Red opt.	£40	—	†		£60	—
	(ii) *P* 11. *Tablets as T* **18.**						
O47	¼ a. ultramarine	£15	£20	£15	—	£20	—
	a. Red opt.	£20	—	£20	—	†	
	b. Turquoise-blue	£15	—	£22	—	£20	—
	c. Do. Red opt.	£25	—	†		†	
O48	½ a. black	£15	—	£20	£20	£30	—
	a. Red opt.	£20	—	£30	—	£20	—
O49	1 a. scarlet	£35	£35	£45	£45	£45	—
	a. Carmine	£25	—	£20	—	£20	—
O50	2 a. green	£15	—	£22	—	£8	—
	H. *Tablets as T* **19.**						
O51	½ a. black	£15	—	£20	—	£30	—
O52	2 a. green	£20	—	£22	—	†	

1941. *Nos.* 79 *to* 85 *optd.* "SERVICE".

No.	Type	Description	Unused	Used
O53	**20**	3 p. bright blue	2 6	5 0
O54	,,	6 p. dark blue	4 6	6 0
O55	,,	1 a. orange-red	7 6	10 0
O56	,,	2 a. brown	12 6	17 6
O57	,,	4 a. bright green	35 0	40 0
O58	,,	8 a. dull green	60 0	
O59	,,	1 r. deep blue	£5	

For later issues, see RAJASTHAN.

3

4

BUSSAHIR (BASHAHR).

1

2

5

6

7 8

(9)

1895 (20 JUNE). *Laid paper. Optd. with T* **9** *in pale greenish blue* (B.), *rose* (R.), *mauve* (M.) *or lake* (L.).

The initials are those of the Tika Raghunath Singh, son of the then Raja, who was the organiser and former director of the State Post Office.

(*a*) *Imperf.*

1	**1**	¼ a. pink (M.) (1.9.95)	40	0		
2	**2**	½ a. grey (R.M.)	17	6		
3	**3**	1 a. vermilion (M.)	17	6		
4	**4**	2 a. orange-yellow (R.M.L.)	20	0	£8	
5	**5**	4 a. slate-violet (R.M.L.)	30	0		
		a. Without monogram				
6	**6**	8 a. red-brown (B.M.)	25	0	25	0
		a. Without monogram	40	0		
		b. Thick paper	45	0		
7	**7**	12 a. green (L.)	40	0		
8	**8**	1 r. ultramarine (R.M.L.)	40	0		

(*b*) *Perf. with a sewing machine; gauge and size of holes varying between 7 and 11½.*

9	**1**	¼ a. pink (B.M.)	35	0	45	0
10	**2**	½ a. grey (R.)	17	6		
11	**3**	1 a. vermilion (M.)	17	6		
12	**4**	2 a. orange-yellow (B.M.)	20	0	£8	
13	**5**	4 a. slate-violet (B.R.M.)	40	0	£8	
		a. Without monogram				
14	**6**	8 a. red-brown (B.R.M.)	40	0	£12	
		a. Without monogram				
15	**7**	12 a. green (R.M.L.)	30	0		
		a. Without monogram				
16	**8**	1 r. ultramarine (R.M.)	30	0		
		a. Without monogram				

1899. *As* 1895, *but pin-perf. or rouletted.*

17	**3**	1 a. vermilion (M.)	45	0	£5	
18	**4**	2 a. orange-yellow (M.L.)	22	6	95	0
19	**5**	4 a. slate-violet (B.R.M.L.)	12	6		
20	**7**	12 a. green (R.)	35	0		
21	**8**	1 r. ultramarine (R.)	45	0		

Nos. 1 to 21 were in sheets of 24. They seem to have been overprinted and perforated as required. Those first issued for use were perforated, but they were subsequently supplied imperf., both to collectors and for use. Nos. 17 to 21 were some of the last supplies. No rule seems to have been observed as to the colour of the overprinted monogram; pale blue, rose and mauve were used from the first. The pale blue varies to greenish blue or blue-green, and appears quite green on the yellow stamps. The lake is possibly a mixture of the mauve and the rose—it is a quite distinct colour and apparently later than the others. Specimens without overprint are either remainders left in the Treasury or copies that have escaped accidentally; they have been found sticking to the backs of others that bore the overprint.

We no longer list separately the various colours of overprint but indicate against each basic stamp those we have seen.

Varieties may also be found doubly overprinted, in two different colours.

11 12 13 14 15 16

(Printed at the Bussahir Press by Maulvi Karam Bakhsh.)

Wove paper. Optd. with monogram " R.S.", *T* **9**, *in colours as* 1895 *issue.*

1896–98. *Printed* (*singly?*) *from plates or dies line-engraved. Pin perf. or rouletted.*

22	**11**	¼ a. deep violet (R.)	—	£8
23	**12**	½ a. bluish grey (R.)	£15	£8

1900–01. *Lithographed in sheets of various sizes.*

(*a*) *Imperf.*

24	**11**	¼ a. slate-violet (B.R.M.L.)	6	0		
25	**12**	½ a. blue (*shades*) (R.M.)	6	0	40	0
		a. Without monogram				
26	**13**	1 a. olive (*shades*) (R.L.)	20	0	30	0

(*b*) *Pin-perf. or rouletted.*

27	**11**	¼ a. slate-violet (R.M.L.)	7	0	20	0
28	**12**	½ a. blue (*shades*) (R.M.L.)	7	0	30	0
29	**13**	1 a. olive (*shades*) (R.M.L.)	12	6		
30	**14**	2 a. orange-yellow (B.)	£6		£8	

The ¼ a. and ½ a. are in sheets of 24, the 1 a. and 2 a. in blocks of 4.

Colours of ¼ a. and 1 *a. changed;* 2 *a. with dash before* " STATE " *and characters added in left lower label. Overprinted with monogram, T* **9**.

(*a*) *Imperf.*

31	**11**	¼ a. vermilion (B.M.)	5	0		
		a. Without monogram				
32	**13**	1 a. vermilion (B.M.)	7	6		
33	**15**	2 a. ochre (M.) (Sept., 1900)	17	6		
34	,,	2 a. yellow (M.) (Nov., 1900)	12	6		
35	,,	2 a. orange (B.M.) ('01)	15	0		
36	**16**	4 a. claret (B.R.M.)	40	0	£8	

(*b*) *Pin-perf. or rouletted.*

37	**11**	¼ a. vermilion (B.M.)	6	0		
38	**13**	1 a. vermilion (B.M.)	7	6	10	0
39	,,	1 a. brown-red (Mar., 1901)	—		£5	
40	**15**	2 a. ochre (B.M.) (Sept., '00)	17	6		
41	,,	2 a. yell. (B.R.M.) (Nov. '00)	12	6	20	0

42 **15** 2 a. orange (B.M.) ('01) .. 15 0 25 0
43 **16** 4 a. claret (B.R.M.) .. 40 0

The $\frac{1}{2}$ a. and 1 a. are in sheets of 24; the 2 a. in sheets of 50 differing throughout in the dash and the characters added at lower left; the 4 a. in sheets of 28.

(17)

The stamps of Bussahir have been obsolete since March 31, 1901. Numerous remainders were sold after this date, and all values were later reprinted in the colours of the originals, or in fancy colours, from the original stones, or from new ones. Printings were also made from new types, similar to those of the second issue of the 8 a., 12 a., and 1 r., values, in sheets of 8.

The stamps formerly catalogued with large overprint "R.N.S." (*T* **17**) are now believed never to have been issued for use.

Remainders are also found with overprint "P.S.", the initials of Padam Singh who succeeded Raghunath Singh in the direction of the Post Office, and with the original monogram "R.S." in a damaged state, giving it the appearance of a double-lined "R."

Reprints are frequently found on laid paper.

Collectors are warned against obliterated copies bearing the Rampur postmark with date "19 MA 1900." Many thousand remainders and reprints were thus obliterated for export after the closing of the State Post Office.

CHARKHARI.

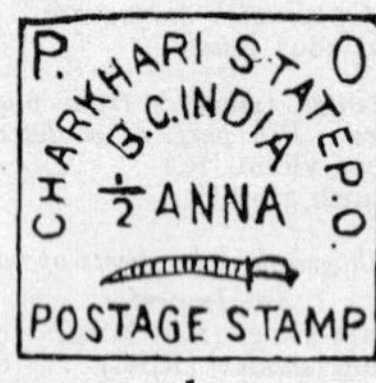

1

1894. *Value in the plural. Imperf.*

1 **1** 1 annas, dull green £38
2 ,, 2 annas, dull green £38
3 ,, 4 annas, dull green £38

1894–97. *Value in the singular. Imperf.*

6 **1** $\frac{1}{4}$ a. rose £18 £12
7 ,, $\frac{1}{4}$ a. magenta 12 6 10 0
8 ,, $\frac{1}{4}$ a. purple 7 6 6 0
9 ,, $\frac{1}{4}$ a. violet 7 6 7 6
11 ,, $\frac{1}{2}$ a. purple 6 0 10 0
12 ,, $\frac{1}{2}$ a. violet 10 0 12 6
13 ,, 1 a. emerald 10 0 12 6
14 ,, 1 a. green 12 6 15 0
15 ,, 1 a. deep green 12 6 15 0
16 ,, 2 a. emerald 20 0 20 0
17 ,, 2 a. green 20 0 20 0
17*a* ,, 2 a. deep green 20 0 20 0
18 ,, 4 a. emerald 20 0 25 0
19 ,, 4 a. green 20 0 25 0
20 ,, 4 a. deep green 20 0 25 0

Minor varieties may be found with the first "A" in "ANNA" not printed.

All the values are known upon various coloured papers, but these are proofs, or trial impressions of some kind.

1905–7. *Numerals changed; in the $\frac{1}{4}$ a. and $\frac{1}{2}$ a. the figures "4" and "2" are smaller than before; in the 1 a., 2 a., and 4 a. the figures are of quite different shape.*

32 **1** $\frac{1}{4}$ a. violet 20 0
33 ,, $\frac{1}{2}$ a. violet 30 0
34 ,, 1 a. green 40 0
35 ,, 2 a. green 50 0
36 ,, 4 a. green 60 0

2

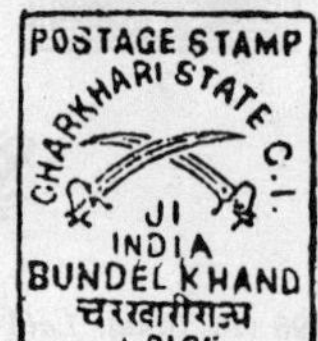

3

1909–11. *Litho. Wove paper. P* 11.

38 **2** 1 p. chestnut (Die I) .. £5 £5
39 ,, 1 p. turquoise-blue, (Die I) 1 6 3 0
39*a* ,, 1 p. gr'nish blue (Die I) ('11) 2 6 3 6
40 ,, $\frac{1}{2}$ a. scarlet .. 5 0
41 ,, 1 a. pale green .. 6 0
42 ,, 2 a. blue 10 0
43 ,, 4 a. deep green .. 10 0
44 ,, 8 a. brick red .. 12 6
45 ,, 1 r. chestnut .. 30 0

1912–19. Die II.

46 **2** 1 p. turquoise-blue .. 3 6 3 0
46*a* ,, $\frac{1}{2}$ a. red 4 6
46*b* ,, 1 a. olive-green (1919) 5 0

Die III.

Redrawn values under the crossed swords.

46*c* **2** 1 p. turquoise-blue.. .. 7 0 7 0
46*d* ,, 1 p. light brown .. 8 6

The native characters, denoting the value, vary in shape and size throughout the sheets, particularly in the 1 p. In Die II of this value these characters are notably larger and heavier, the first extending right over the "I" of "INDIA," which word is also larger than in Die I.

1919–24. *Imperf.*

49 **3** 1 p. violet 30 0 30 0
50 ,, 1 p. purple 32 6 32 6

4 (actual size 63×25 mm.)

1925. *Handstamped. (a) Wove paper. Imperf.*

51 **4** 1 a. violet 90 0 90 0

(b) Laid paper. P 11.

51*a* **4** 1 a. violet 90 0 £6

1930–43. *Typo. Imperf.*

52 **2** 1 p. deep blue 1 3
52*a* ,, 1 p. dull green ('43) .. 60 0
52*b* ,, 1 p. violet ('43) 25 0
53 ,, $\frac{1}{2}$ a. deep olive 2 6
53*a* ,, $\frac{1}{2}$ a. red-brown ('40) .. 8 0
53*b* ,, $\frac{1}{2}$ a. black ('43) 30 0
53*c* ,, $\frac{1}{2}$ a. red ('43) 25 0
53*d* ,, $\frac{1}{2}$ a. grey-brown £15
54 ,, 1 a. green 4 0
54*a* ,, 1 a. chocolate ('40) .. 5 0
54*b* ,, 1 a. red ('40) £8
55 ,, 2 a. light blue 4 0
a. Tête-bêche (pair) .. 30 0
55*b* ,, 2 a. greenish grey ('43) .. £10
56 ,, 4 a. carmine 20 0
a. Tête-bêche (pair) .. 45 0

5. Imlia Palace.

1931 (25 JUNE). *T* **5** *and similar designs. Typo. P* 11 *or* 12.

57	½ a. blue-green	0	6	0	6
58	1 a. blackish brown	0	4	0	6
	a. Imperf. btwn. (horiz. or vert. pr.)	30	0	30	0
59	2 a. violet	0	6	0	6
60	4 a. olive-green	0	6	0	8
61	8 a. magenta	0	8	0	10
62	1 r. green and rose	2	6	2	0
63	2 r. red and brown	4	0	2	0
64	3 r. chocolate and blue-green	7	6	2	0
	a. Imperf. between (horiz. pair) ..	40	0	40	0
65	5 r. turquoise and purple ..	8	6	3	6

Designs:—½ a. The Lake. 2 a. Industrial School. 4 a. Bird's-eye view of City. 8 a. The Fort. 1 r. Guest House. 2 r. Palace Gate. 3 r. Temples at Rainpur. 5 r. Goverdhan Temple.

This issue was the subject of speculative manipulation, large stocks being thrown on the market cancelled to order at very low prices and unused at less than face value. Numerous errors, probably produced clandestinely, exist. The issue was an authorized one but was eventually withdrawn by the State authorities.

½ As.

(6)

1940. *Nos.* 44/5 *surch. as T* **6**.

66	**2** ½ a. on 8 a. brick-red ..	35	0		
	a. No space between "½" and "As."	45	0		
	b. Surch. inverted	£25			
	c. "1" of "½" inverted ..	£25			
67	,, 1 a. on 1 r. chestnut ..	65	0		
	a. Surch. inverted	£25			
68	,, "1 ANNA" on 1 r. chestnut	£65			

COCHIN.

1

2

Dies by P. Orr & Sons, Madras; ptd. by Cochin Govt. at Ernakulam.)

1892 (1 APRIL). *No wmk., or wmk. large Umbrella in the sheet P* 12.

1	**1** ½ put. buff	10	0	6	0
	a. Orange-buff	10	0	6	0
	b. Yellow	12	6	7	6
	c. Imperf. (pair)	£15		£15	
	,, 1 put. purple	12	6	10	0
	a. Error. 1 p. deep violet (colour of 2 p.)	£15			
	2 2 put. deep violet	7	6	7	6

1896 (End of). *Similar to T* **1**, *but much larger. P* 12. (*a*) *Wmk. Arms and inscription in sheet.*

4	1 put. violet	40	0	50	0
	(*b*) *Wmk. Conch Shell to each stamp.*				
5	1 put. deep violet	25	0		

This stamp was originally printed for provisional use as a fiscal; afterwards it was authorized for postal use.

On laid paper.

6	½ put. orange-buff	£10	£5
	a. Orange	—	£5
	b. Yellow	—	£5

1897. *Wmk. a small Umbrella on each stamp. P* 12.

7	**1** ½ p. buff	10	0	7	6
	a. Orange	7	6	7	6
	ab. *Orange.* Imperf. (pair) ..				
	b. Yellow	7	0	7	6
8	,, 1 p. purple	10	0	10	0
	a. Deep violet	12	6	10	0
9	**2** 2 p. deep violet	20	0	15	0
	a. Imperf. (pair)	£7		£7	

The paper watermarked with a small umbrella is more transparent than that of the previous issue. The wmk. is not easy to distinguish.

3

4

5

6

1898. *Thin yellowish paper. Wmk. small Umbrella on each stamp. P* 12.

11	**3** 3 pies, blue	5	0	3	0
12	**4** ½ p. green	3	6	2	6
13	**5** 1 p. pink	6	0	4	0
	a. Tête-bêche (pair)	£30		£30	
	b. Laid paper	—		£20	
	ba. Laid paper. Tête-bêche (pair)				
13*c*	,, 1 p. red	7	6	2	6
13*d*	,, 1 p. carmine-red	7	6	2	6
14	**6** 2 p. deep violet	12	6	15	0
	a. Imperf. between (vert. pair)	£8		£8	

1903. *Thick white paper. Wmk. small Umbrella on each stamp. P* 12.

16	**3** 3 pies, blue	1	0	0	8
17	**4** ½ p. green	2	0	0	9
	a. Stamp sideways (in pair) ..	£25		£25	
18	**5** 1 p. pink	5	0	1	6
	a. Tête-bêche (pair)	£30			
19	**6** 2 p. deep violet	7	6	2	6
	a. Double impression	—		£10	

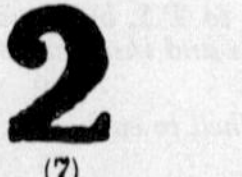

(7)

2

(7a)

1909. *T* **3** (*paper and perf. of* 1903), *surcharged with T* **7**, *in black.*

22	2 on 3 pies, rosy mauve	..	2 6	2 6
	a. Surch. T 7 inverted	..	£5	£5
	b. Surch. T 7 a. ..	..	£12	£12
	c. Tête-bêche (pair) ..	..	£7	£7

Varieties a and c were caused by the inversion of one stamp (No. 7) in the plate and the consequent inversion of the corresponding surcharge to correct the error.

8. Raja Sir Sri Rama Varma I. **8a.**

(Recess. Perkins, Bacon & Co.)

1911–23. *W* **8a.** *P* 14.

26	**8** 2 pies, brown	.. ..	1 3	0 9
	a. Imperf. (pair)	.. ..	—	£6
27	,, 3 pies, blue ..	.. ..	1 0	0 6
	a. Perf. 14×12½	.. ..	35 0	20 0
28	,, 4 pies, green	.. ..	2 0	0 6
28a	,, 4 pies, apple-green	..	7 6	2 6
29	,, 9 pies, carmine	.. ..	2 6	1 0
30	,, 1 a. brown-orange	..	3 0	0 8
31	,, 1½ a. purple ..	.. ..	12 6	1 6
32	,, 2 a. grey	.. ..	15 0	2 6
33	,, 3 a. vermilion	.. ..	£7	60 0

9. Maharaja Sir Sri Rama Varma II. **10.**

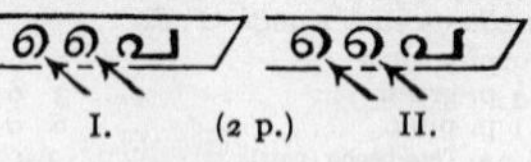

I. (2 p.) II.

I. (1 a.) II.

(Recess. Perkins, Bacon & Co.)

1918–22. *W* **8a.** *P* 14.

35	**10** 2 p. brown (Die I)	.. ..	10 0	1 0
	a. Die II ..	.. ..	0 6	0 2
36	,, 4 p. green (1919)	.. ..	2 6	0 3
37	,, 6 p. red-brown (1922)	..	3 6	0 3
38	,, 8 p. sepia (1922)	.. ..	4 0	0 8
39	,, 9 p. carmine	.. ..	15 0	1 0
40	,, 10 p. blue (1922)	.. ..	2 0	0 8
41	**9** 1 a. orange (Die I)	.. ..	15 9	0 0
	a. Die II ..	.. ..	1 6	0 4
42	**10** 1½ a. purple (1921)	.. ..	7 6	0 6
43	,, 2 a. grey ..	.. ..	12 6	1 0
44	,, 2¼ a. yellow-green (1922)	..	10 0	2 6
45	,, 3 a. vermilion	.. ..	25 0	2 6

2 2 2

Two pies (11) Two pies (12) Two pies (13)

2 2

Two Pies (14) Two Pies (15)

1922–29. *T* **8** (*P* 14), *surch. with T* **11/15.**

46	**11** 2 p. on 3 p. blue	..	2 6	0 10
	a. Surcharge double ..	..	£5	—
47	**12** 2 p. on 3 p. blue	..	10 0	1 0
	a. Capital "P" in "Pies"	..	30 0	30 0
	b. Surcharge double ..	..	£5	
	c. As a. Surcharge double	..		
48	**13** 2 p. on 3 p. blue (6.24)	..	3 0	1 3
	a. Capital "P" in "Pies"	..	35 0	35 0
	b. Perf. 14×12½	..	35 0	35 0
	c. As a. Perf. 14×12½	..	65 0	65 0
49	**14** 2 p. on 3 p. blue ('29)	..	2 6	1 6
	a. Surcharged with Type 15	..	£5	£5

There are four settings of these overprints. The first (July, 1922) consisted of 39 stamps with Type **11**, and 9 with Type **12**, and in Type **11** the centre of the "2" is above the "o" of "Two". In the second setting (May, 1924) there were 36 of Type **11** and 12 of Type **12**, and the centre of the figure is above the space between "Two" and "Pies". The third setting (June, 1924) consists of stamps with Type **13** only.

The fourth setting (1929) was also in sheets of 48 No. 49a being the first stamp in the fourth row

ONE ANNA

ഒരു അണ

Three Pies

൩ 3

ANCHAL & REVENUE

(16)

മൂന്നു പൈ

(17)

1928. *Surch. with T* **16.**

50	**10** 1 a. on 2¼ a. yellow-green	..	20 0	25
	a. "REVENUF" for "REVENUE"	..	£8	£
	b. Surch. double	..	£10	£1

1932–33. *Surch. as T* **17.** *W* **8a.** *P* 14.

51	**10** 3 p. on 4 p. green	..	7 6	2
52	,, 3 p. on 8 p. sepia ..	..	6 0	1
53	,, 9 p. on 10 p. blue	..	10 0	4

18. Maharaja Sir Sri Rama Varma III.

(Recess. Perkins, Bacon & Co.)

1933–38. *T* **18** (*but frame and inscription of* 1 *a. as T* **9**), *W* **8***a*. *P* 13×13½.

No.	Type	Description	Unused	Used
54	**18**	2 p. brown ('36)	2 6	0 2
55	,,	4 p. green	3 6	0 3
56	,,	6 p. red-brown	4 0	0 10
57	–	1 a. brown-orange ..	3 0	0 3
58	**18**	1 a. 8 p. carmine ..	12 6	7 6
59	,,	2 a. grey ('38)	5 0	0 4
60	,,	2¼ a. yellow-green ..	6 0	0 6
61	,,	3 a. vermilion ('38) ..	10 0	1 0
62	,,	3 a. 4 p. violet	4 0	0 10
63	,,	6 a. 8 p. sepia	9 0	5 0
64	,,	10 a. blue	12 6	7 6

For stamps in this design but lithographed, see Nos. 67–71.

1934. *Surcharged as T* **14**. *W* **8***a*. *P* 14.

No.	Type	Description	Unused	Used
65	**10**	6 p. on 8 p. sepia (R.) ..	5 0	3 0
66	,,	6 p. on 10 p. blue (R.) ..	10 0	5 0

(Lithographed in India.)

1938. *W* **8***a*. (I) *P* 11 *or* (II) *P* 13×13½.

No.	Type	Description	I. Unused	I. Used	II. Unused	II. Used
67	**18**	2 p. brown ..	4 0	0 4	15 0	2 0
68	,,	4 p. green ..	5 0	0 4	15 0	0 4
69	,,	6 p. red-brown	12 6	0 6	†	
70	,,	1 a. brown-orge.	50 0	50 0	60 0	£8
71	,,	2¼ a. sage-green	25 0	2 0	27 6	5 0

For No. 69 II, see No. O 51*a* II.

ANCHAL
(19)

THREE PIES
ANCHAL
(20)

SURCHARGED

ONE ANNA
THREE PIES
ANCHAL
(21)

NINE PIES
ANCHAL
(22)

NINE PIES
(23)

SURCHARGED
NINE PIES
(24)

ANCHAL
(25)

1939–44. *T* **18** *variously optd. or surch.*

I. *Recess-printed stamps, Nos.* 57/8.

No.	Description	Unused	Used
72	3 p. on 1 a. 8 p. carmine (*T* **20**)	£5	50 0
73	3 p. on 1 a. 8 p. carmine (*T* **21**)	10 0	5 0
74	6 p. on 1 a. 8 p. carmine (*T* **20**)	5 0	3 0
75	1 a. brown-orange (*T* **19**) ..	8 0	0 8
76	1 a. 3 p. on 1 a. 8 p. car. (*T* **21**)	5 0	1 6

II. *Lithographed stamps, Nos.* 68 *and* 70.
I. *P* 11. II. *P* 13×13½.

No.	Description	I. Unused	I. Used	II. Unused	II. Used
77	3 p. on 4 p. (*T* **21**) ..	25 0	3 0	50 0	6 0
78	6 p. on 1 a. (*T* **22**) ..	£15	£5	†	
79	6 p. on 1 a. (*T* **23**) ..	£15	£10	50 0	40 0
80	9 p. on 1 a. (*T* **22**) ..	80 0	80 0	†	
81	9 p. on 1 a. (*T* **23**) ..	†		£10	60 0
82	9 p. on 1 a. (*T* **24**) ..	†		40 0	1 6
83	1 a. (*T* **19**)	75 0	0 8	£5	80 0
84	1 a. (*T* **25**)	30 0	15 0	20 0	4 0

26. Maharaja Sri Kerala Varma I.

(**27**) *The actual measurement of this wmk. is* 6¼ × 3⅝ in.

1943. *Frame of* 1 *a. inscr.* " ANCHAL & REVENUE ". *Litho.* I. *P* 11. II. *P* 13×13½. (*a*) *W* **8***a*.

No.	Type	Description	I. Unused	I. Used	II. Unused	II. Used
85	**26**	2 p. grey-brown	†		3 0	1 0
85*a*	,,	4 p. green ..	†		£15	£12
85*b*	,,	1 a. brn.-orange	†		£15	£7
		(*b*) *W* **27**.				
86	**26**	2 p. grey-brown	—	—	15 0	0 4
87	,,	4 p. green ..	15 0	5 0	60 0	30 0
88	,,	6 p. red-brown	30 0	20 0	4 0	0 4
89	,,	9 p. ultramarine	40 0	10 0	†	
90	,,	1 a. brn.-orange	£6	80 0	£8	60 0
91	,,	2¼ a. yellow-grn.	75 0	25 0	12 6	1 0

Part of W **27** appears on many stamps in each sheet, while others are entirely without wmk.

1944. *T* **26** *variously optd. or surch.* I. *P* 11. II. *P* 13×13½. (*a*) *W* **8***a*.

No.	Description	I. Unused	I. Used	II. Unused	II. Used
92	3 p. on 4 p. (*T* **21**)	†		£8	20 0
92*a*	9 p. on 1 a. (*T* **23**)	†		30 0	7 6
92*b*	9 p. on 1 a. (*T* **24**)	†		1 0	0 8
92*c*	1 a. 3 p. on 1 a. (*T* **21**) ..	†		—	—
	(*b*) *W* **27**.				
93	2 p. on 6 p. (*T* **20**)	0 4	0 3	1 6	0 3
94	3 p. on 4 p. (*T* **20**)	3 6	0 6	†	
95	3 p. on 4 p. (*T* **21**)	†		2 6	0 4
96	3 p. on 6 p. (*T* **20**)	2 0	2 0	1 6	0 4
97	4 p. on 6 p. (*T* **20**)	†		3 6	1 6

28. Maharaja Sri Ravi Varma.

1944–48. *Litho.* *W* **27.** I. *P* 11. II. *P* 13×13½.

			I.				II.			
98	**28**	9 p. ultram. ..	35	0	7	6	10	0	1	6
99	,,	1 a. 3 p. mgnta.			†		22	6	1	6
100	,,	1 a. 9 p. ultram.			†		35	0	7	6

Dates of issue: 1946, 1 a. 9 p. 1948, 1 a. 3 p.

29. Maharaja Sri Ravi Varma.

1946–48. *Frame of* 1 *a. inscr.* "ANCHAL & REVENUE". *Litho.* *W* **27.** *P* 13.

101	**29**	2 p. chocolate	2	0	0	3
		a. Perf. 11	27	6	5	0
		b. Perf. 11×13	£15		£5	
102	,,	3 p. carmine	15	0	0	3
103	,,	4 p. grey-green	—		20	0
104	,,	6 p. red-brown ('47) ..	10	0	2	0
		a. Perf. 11	£7		0	6
105	,,	9 p. ultramarine	15	0	0	6
		a. Imperf. between (horiz. pair)				
106	,,	1 a. orange ('48) ..	20	0	15	0
		a. Perf. 11	£50			
107	,,	2 a. black	40	0	1	0
		a. Perf. 11	£7		3	6
108	,,	3 a. vermilion	60	0	3	0

30. Maharaja Sri Kerala Varma II.

1948–50. *Litho.* *W* **27.** *P* 11.

109	**30**	2 p. grey-brown ..	20	0	0	6
110	,,	3 p. carmine ..	10	0	0	6
111	,,	4 p. green.. ..	15	0	0	6
112	,,	6 p. chestnut	7	6	0	6
113	,,	9 p. ultramarine	7	6	1	0
114	,,	2 a. black.. ..	30	0	1	0
115	,,	3 a. orange-red ..	50	0	1	6
115a	,,	3 a. 4 p. violet ('50) ..	£5			

Nos. 109/12 and 115 exist in pairs imperf. between.

31. Chinese Nets.

32. Dutch Palace.

1949. *Litho.* *W* **27.** *P* 10½.

116	**31**	2 a. black	2	0	3	0
		a. Imperf. between (pair) ..				
117	**32**	2½ a. green	3	6	5	0

SIX PIES

ആറു പൈ

(33)

1949. *Surch. as T* **33.**

(i) *On* 1944–48 *issue. P* 13.

118	**28**	6 p. on 1 a. 3 p. mag. (Bk.)	4	6	1
119	,,	1 a. on 1 a. 9 p. ultram. (R.)	20	0	1

(ii) *On* 1946–48 *issue.*

120	**29**	3 p. on 9 p. ultram. (Bk.)	30	0	15
121	,,	6 p. on 1 a. 3 p. mag. (Bk.)	5	0	0
		a. Surch. double			
123	,,	1 a. on 1 a. 9 p. ultram. (R.)	30	0	0
		a. Surch. in black			

(iii) *On* 1948–50 *issue.*

124	**30**	3 p. on 9 p. ultram. (Bk.)	60	0	60
		a. Larger native characters, 20 mm. long	5	0	2
		b. Surch. double			
125	,,	3 p. on 9 p. ultram. (R.) ..	5	0	2
126	,,	6 p. on 9 p. ultram. (R.) ..	12	6	7

1949. *Surch. as T* **20.** *W* **27.** *P* 13.

126a	**29**	6 p. on 1 a. orange ..	£12	£1
127	,,	9 p. on 1 a. orange ..	£7	£

For later issues, see Travancore-Cochin.

OFFICIAL STAMPS.

On
C G
S

(O 1)

ON
C G
S

(O 2. Small "ON".)

1913. *Optd. with Type* O **1** (3 *p.*) *or* O **2** (*others*).
O 2 **8** 3 p. blue (R.) 35 0 0 8
a. Black opt.
O 3 ,, 4 p. green 12 6 0 4
a. Overprint inverted — £10
O 4 ,, 9 p. carmine 30 0 0 6
O 5 ,, 1½ a. purple 40 0 1 0
a. Overprint double £10
O 6 ,, 2 a. grey 25 0 0 8
O 7 ,, 3 a. vermilion 25 0 1 9
O 8 ,, 6 a. violet 40 0 8 0
O 9 ,, 12 a. ultramarine 60 0 12 6
O10 ,, 1½ r. deep green 50 0 40 0

No. O3 exists with watermark sideways only and No. O4 with watermark sideways as well as upright.

ON
C G
S
(O **3.** "G" without serif.)

8
Eight pies
(O **4**)

1919–33. *Optd. as Type* O **3.**
O11 **10** 4 p. green 10 0 0 4
a. Overprint double £10
O12 ,, 6 p. red-brown (1922) 10 0 0 4
a. Opt. double
O12*b* ,, 8 p. sepia 7 6 0 2
O13 ,, 9 p. carmine 20 0 0 10
O14 ,, 10 p. blue 20 0 0 10
O15 ,, 1½ a. purple (1921) .. 12 6 0 10
O15*a* ,, 2 a. grey 12 6 1 0
O16 ,, 2¼ a. yellow-green .. 10 0 1 0
a. Opt. double
O17 ,, 3 a. vermilion 30 0 4 0
a. Overprint inverted — £8
O19 ,, 6 a. violet (1924) .. 35 0 7 6
O19*a* ,, 12 a. ultramarine (1929) 37 6 12 6
O19*b* ,, 1½ r. deep green (1933) 50 0

1923. *T* **8** *and* **10** *surch. with Type* O **4.**
O20 8 p. on 9 p. carm. (No. O4) 65 0 1 3
a. Capital "P" in "Pies" — 20 0
O21 8 p. on 9 p. carm. (No. O 13) 65 0 1 3
a. Capital "P" in "Pies" — 10 0
b. "F" for "E" in "Eight" .. — 10 0

Varieties with smaller "i" or "t" in "Eight" and small "i" in "Pies" are also known.

1925 (April). *T* **10** *surch. as Type* O **4.**
O22 10 p. on 9 p. carm. (No. O 13) 45 0 0 4
a. Surch. inverted

1929. *T* **8** *surch. as Type* O **4.**
O23 10 p. on 9 p. carm. (No. O 4) 60 0 35 0

ON
C G
S
(O **5.** Straight back to "C".)

ON
C G
S
(O **6.** Circular "O"; "N" without serifs.)

1931. *Optd. with Type* O **5.**
O24 **10** 4 p. green 25 0 1 3
O25 ,, 6 p. red-brown 15 0 0 3
O26 ,, 8 p. sepia 10 0 0 6
O27 ,, 10 p. blue 10 0 0 6
O28 ,, 2 a. grey 12 6 0 6
O29 **10** 3 a. vermilion 20 0 1 3
O30 ,, 6 a. violet 80 0 1 0

1933. *Surch. in red as T* **14.**
O32 **10** 6 p. on 8 p. sepia (No. O26) 3 6 1 6
O33 ,, 6 p. on 10 p. blue (No. O27) 35 0 0 6

1933–44. *Recess-printed stamps of* 1933–38 *optd.*
(*a*) *With Type* O **5.**
O34 **18** 4 p. green 2 0 0 3
O35 ,, 6 p. red-brown 5 0 0 4
O36 ,, 1 a. brown-orange .. 15 0 0 4
O37 ,, 1 a. 8 p. carmine .. 10 0 0 6
O38 ,, 2 a. grey 22 6 0 4
O39 ,, 2¼ a. yellow-green .. 10 0 0 6
O40 ,, 3 a. vermilion 30 0 0 6
O41 ,, 3 a. 4 p. violet .. 20 0 1 0
O42 ,, 6 a. 8 p. sepia .. 20 0 1 6
O43 ,, 10 a. blue 20 0 2 0

(*b*) *With Type* O **6** (*typo.*).
O44 **18** 1 a. brown-orange £8 0 8
O45 ,, 2 a. grey-black 35 0 1 6
O46 ,, 3 a. vermilion 10 6 2 0

ON
C G
S
(O **7.** Curved back to "C".)

ON
C G
S
(O **8**)

ON
C G
S
(O **9.** Circular "O", "N" with serifs.)

ON
C G
S
(O **10.** Oval "O".)

ON
C G
S
(O **11**)

1938–44. *Lithographed stamps of* 1938, *W* **8a**, *optd.*
(*a*) *With Type* O **7** *or* O **8** (1 *a.*).

I. *P* 11. II. *P* 13×13½.
O47 **18** 4 p. green .. 25 0 15 0 30 0 1 6
O48 ,, 6 p. red-brown 12 6 0 10 †
O49 ,, 1 a. brn.-orge. £15 10 0 †
O50 ,, 2 a. grey-black 10 0 0 8 †
a. Opt. omitted — — †

(*b*) *With Type* O **9** (*litho.*) *or* O **10** (6 *p.*).
O51 **18** 6 p. red-brown † 3 6 0 6
O52 ,, 1 a. brn.-orge. 10 0 1 0 †
O53 ,, 3 a. vermilion 15 0 1 0 †

No. O51 II was not issued as a postage stamp in sheets without the overprint.

(*c*) *With Type* O **11.**
O53*a* **18** 6 p. red-brown £75 £45 †

1943. *Unissued stamps optd. with Type* O **10.** *Litho. W* **27.**

I. *P* 11. II. *P* 13×13½.
O54 **18** 4 p. green .. £12 50 0 2 6 1 6
O55 ,, 6 p. red-brown £15 40 0 £5 25 0
O56 ,, 1 a. brn.-orge. £5 2 6 10 0 12 6
O56*a* ,, 2 a. grey-black £12 1 6 †
O56*b* ,, 2¼ a. sage-green £18 70 0 †
O56*c* ,, 3 a. vermilion 70 0 20 0 †

1943. *Official stamps variously surch.* **20** *or* **21.**
(i) *On* 1½ *a. purple, of* 1919–33.
O57 **10** 9 p. on 1½ a. (*T* **20**) .. £8 7 6
(ii) *On recess-printed* 1 *a.* 8 *p. carmine of* 1933–44 (*opt. with Type* O **5**).
O58 3 p. on 1 a. 8 p. (*T* **21**) .. 1 6 0 8

O59 9 p. on 1 a. 8 p. (*T* **20**) .. £7 30 0
O60 1 a. 9 p. on 1 a. 8 p. (*T* **20**) 7 6 1 0
O61 1 a. 9 p. on 1 a. 8 p. (*T* **21**) 5 0 1 6

(iii) *On lithographed stamps of* 1938–44. *T* **18.**

(*a*) *W* **8a.**

		I. *P* 11.	II. *P* 13×13½.
O62	3 p. on 4 p. (*T* O **7** & **20**) ..	†	7 6 0 6
	a. Surch. double		— £15
O63	3 p. on 4 p. (*T* O **7** & **21**) ..	†	£12 60 0
O64	3 p. on 1 a. (*T* O **9** & **20**) ..	5 0 1 0	†
O65	9 p. on 1 a. (*T* O **9** & **20**) ..	£7 5 0	†
O66	1 a. 3 p. on 1 a. (*T* O **9** & **21**)	150 0 £5	†

(*b*) *W* **27.**

		I.	II.
O67	3 p. on 4 p. (*T* O **10** & **20**) ..	†	£18 £8
O67*a*	3 p. on 1 a. (*T* O **10** & **20**) ..	£6 £5	£12 80 0

1944. *Optd. with Type* O **10**, *W* **27.**

			I. *P* 11.	II. *P* 13×13½.
O68	**26**	4 p. green ..	£5 6 0	8 6 1 0
O69	,,	6 p. red-brn.	1 0 0 4	1 0 1 6
O70	,,	1 a. brn.-orge.	†	£50 £5
O71	,,	2 a. black ..	†	1 0 0 3
O72	,,	2¼ a. yell.-grn.	†	10 0 1 6
O73	,,	3 a. vermilion	7 6 3 6	10 0 2 6

1944. *Optd. with Type* O **10** *and variously surch. as Types* **20** *and* **21.** *W* **27.**

			I.	II.
O74	**26**	3 p. on 4 p. (*T* **20**) ..	25 0 3 0	5 0 0 3
O75	,,	3 p. on 4 p. (*T* **21**) ..	— —	40 0 5 0
O76	,,	3 p. on 1 a. (*T* **20**) ..	†	15 0 1 0
O77	,,	9 p. on 6 p. (*T* **20**)	†	12 6 0 4
O78	,,	9 p. on 6 p. (*T* **21**)	†	2 0 0 4
O79	,,	1 a. 3 p. on 1 a. (*T* **20**)	†	12 6 0 6
O80	,,	1 a. 3 p. on 1 a. (*T* **21**)	†	9 0 0 4

1944. *Stamps of* 1944–48 *optd. with Type* O **10.** *P* 13.

O81 **28** 9 p. ultramarine 2 0 0 6
O82 ,, 1 a. 3 p. magenta .. 2 0 0 8
a. Opt. double 40 0
O83 ,, 1 a. 9 p. ultramarine .. 2 6 2 0

1948. *Stamps of* 1946–48 *and unissued values optd. with Type* O **2.** *P* 13.

O84 **29** 3 p. carmine 0 4 0 2
O85 ,, 4 p. grey-green .. 40 0 5 0
O86 ,, 6 p. red-brown .. 2 6 0 9
O87 ,, 9 p. ultramarine .. 7 6 0 9
O88 ,, 1 a. 3 p. magenta .. 2 0 0 9
O89 ,, 1 a. 9 p. ultramarine .. 3 6 5 0
O90 ,, 2 a. black 2 6 0 6
O91 ,, 2¼ a. yellow-green .. 7 6 2 6

1949. *Stamps of* 1948–50 *and unissued values optd. with Type* O **8.**

O92 **30** 3 p. carmine 0 8 0 4
O93 ,, 4 p. green 1 0 0 4
a. Imp. between (pair) .. £25
O94 ,, 6 p. chestnut 1 0 0 6
a. Imp. between (vert. pair)
O95 ,, 9 p. ultramarine .. 1 3 0 6
O96 ,, 2 a. black 1 6 0 6
O97 ,, 2¼ a. yellow-green .. 3 0 1 0
O98 ,, 3 a. orange-red .. 3 0 1 0
O99 ,, 3 a. 4 p. violet .. 17 6 25 0

1949. *Official stamps surch. as T* **33.**

(i) *On* 1944–48 *issue.*

O100 **28** 1 a. on 1 a. 9 p. ult. (R.) 4 0 1 0

(ii) *On* 1946–48 *issue.*

O101 **29** 1 a. on 1 a. 9 p. ult. (R.) 27 6 10 0

(iii) *On* 1948–50 *issue.*

O103 **30** 6 p. on 3 p. carmine (Bk.) 1 0 1 0
a. Imp. between (vert. pair)
b. Surch. double ..
O104 ,, 9 p. on 4 p. green (Bk.) (18 mm. long) 2 6 1 6
a. Imp. between (hor. pair)
b. Larger native characters, 22 mm. long .. 2 6 3 0
ba. Ditto. Imp. between (horiz. pair) .. £10 £10

1949. *Stamp of* 1949 *optd.* "SERVICE".

O105 **30** 3 p. on 9 p. (No. 124*a*) .. 2 0 2 0

DHAR.

1

2

1897–1900. *Type-set. With oval handstamp. Imperf.*

1 **1** ½ pice, black/*red* 3 0 3 0
a. Handstamp omitted.. .. 30 0
b. Characters transposed (A) .. 25 0
c. Characters transposed (B) .. 30 0
d. Line below upper inscription.. £10 £10
e. Five characters at bottom left instead of four .. 3 0
2 ,, ¼ a. black/*orange* (1900) .. 5 0 6 6
a. Handstamp omitted.. .. £8
3 ,, ½ a. black/*magenta* .. 5 0 5 0
a. Line below upper inscription.. £10 £10
4 ,, 1 a. black/*green* .. 12 6 12 6
a. Line below upper inscription.. £10 £10
5 ,, 2 a. black/*yellow* (1900) .. 15 0 20 0
a. Ornament of top right corner transposed with one in top frame .. 30 0

In (A) the three characters forming the second word in the lower inscription are transposed (2), (3), (1); in (B) they are transposed (3), (2), (1).

1898–1900. *Typo. P* 11 *to* 12.

6 **2** ½ a. carmine 5 0 6
a. Imperf. .. ..
b. Deep rose 5 0
7 ,, 1 a. claret 4 6
8 ,, 1 a. reddish violet .. 10 0
a. Imperf. between (pair) 37 6
9 ,, 2 a. deep green .. 20 0

The stamps of Dhar have been obsolete since 31st March, 1901.

DUTTIA (DATIA).

1 (4 a.) Ganesh.

2 (½ a.)

1893. *Imperf.*

1 **1** ¼ a. black/*orange* £38
2 ,, ½ a. black/*blue-green* £40
3 **2** 1 a. red £45
4 **1** 2 a. black/*yellow* £38
5 ,, 4 a. black/*rose* £38

1897(?). *Imperf.*

6 **2** ½ a. black/*green* 20 0
a. Value in one group 40 0
7 ,, 1 a. black/*white* 30 0
a. Laid paper 15 0
8 ,, 2 a. black/*yellow* 25 0
9 ,, 2 a. black/*lemon* 40 0
10 ,, 4 a. black/*rose* 25 0

STATE DATIA POSTAGE

3 (½ a.)

STATE DATIA POSTAGE

4 (½ a.)

Name spelt "DATIA."

12 **3** ½ a. black/*green* £5
13 ,, 1 a. black/*white* £6
14 ,, 2 a. black/*yellow* £7
15 ,, 4 a. black/*rose* £7

1899–1906. (*a*) *Rouletted in colour or in black horizontally and at end of rows.*

16 **4** ½ a. vermilion 2 6
a. Rose-red 3 6
b. Pale rose 4 6
c. Lake 5 0
d. Carmine 6 6
e. Brownish red 6 6
ea. Tête-bêche (pair) £75
17 ,, ½ a. black/*blue-green* 4 0
a. On deep green 4 0
b. On yellow-green 3 6
c. On dull green (1906) 4 6
18 ,, 1 a. black/*white* 3 0
19 ,, 2 a. black/*lemon-yellow* 4 6
a. On orange-yellow 5 0
b. On buff-yellow 5 0
c. On pale yellow (1906) 4 0
20 ,, 4 a. black/*deep rose* 3 0
a. Tête-bêche (pair) .. ..

(*b*) *Rouletted in black between horizontal rows, but imperf. at top and bottom and at ends of rows.*

1 **4** 1 a. black/*white* .. ..

1904–5. *Without rouletting.*

2 **4** ½ a. red 2 6
3 ,, ½ a. black/*green* 10 0
4 ,, 1 a. black (1905) 4 0

1911. *P* 13½. *Stamps very wide apart.*

5 **4** ½ a. carmine 5 0
a. Stamps closer together .. 6 0
b. Imp. between. (horiz. pair) .. 80 0

1912(?). *Printed close together. Coloured roulette × imperf.*

5 **4** ½ a. black/*green* 5 0

Printed wide apart. P 13½ × *coloured roulette.*

7 **4** ½ a. carmine 4 6

P 13½ × *imperf.*

8 **4** ½ a. black/*dull green* .. 4 0

1916. *Colours changed. Imperf.*

9 **4** ½ a. deep blue 3 6 5 0
0 ,, ½ a. green 5 0 10 0
1 ,, 1 a. purple 7 6
a. Tête-bêche (pair) 40 0

32 **4** 2 a. brown 7 6
32*a* ,, 2 a. lilac 15 0

1918. *Colours changed. Imperf.*

33 **4** ½ a. blue 3 6
34 ,, 1 a. pink 5 0

P 11½.

35 **4** ½ a. black 12 6

1920. *Rouletted.*

36 **4** ½ a. blue 2 6 3 0
a. Roul. × perf. 7 .. .. 25 0 25 0
37 ,, ½ a. pink 2 6 3 0

1920(?). *Rough perf. about* 7.

38 **4** ½ a. dull red 7 6 7 6

All the stamps of Duttia were impressed with a circular handstamp (as a rule in *blue*) before issue.

This handstamp is an impression of the seal of Maharaja Sir Bhawani Singh, and has a figure of "Ganesh" in centre, surrounded by an inscription in Devanagari.

FARIDKOT.

N 1 (1 folus)

N 2 (1 paisa)

1879–86. *Rough, handstamped impressions. Imperf.*

(*a*) *Native thick laid paper.*

N1 **N 1** 1 f. ultramarine 40 0 20 0
N2 **N 2** 1 p. ultramarine 60 0 50 0

(*b*) *Ordinary laid paper.*

N3 **N 1** 1 f. ultramarine 10 0
N4 **N 2** 1 p. ultramarine .. .. — 20 0

(*c*) *Wove paper, thick to thinnish.*

N5 **N 1** 1 f. ultramarine 3 0 3 0
a. Tête-bêche (pair) .. 60 0
N6 **N 2** 1 p. ultramarine 7 6 7 6

(*d*) *Thin wove whity brown paper.*

N7 **N 2** 1 p. ultramarine 32 6 22 6

N 3

Wove paper. Imperf.

N8 **N 3** 1 p. ultramarine 4 6 7 6
a. Tête-bêche (pair) 60 0

It is doubtful whether stamps of Type **N 3** were ever used for postage.

These stamps became obsolete upon the introduction of the overprinted Indian stamps on 1st January, 1887. Impressions of these types in various colours, the ½ anna labels, and the later printings from re-engraved dies, were never in circulation at all.

HYDERABAD.

(DECCAN.)

1

2

(T 1 eng. Mr. Rapkin. Plates by Nissen & Parker, London. Recess.)

1869. *P* 11½.

1	**1**	1 a. olive-green	40	0	20	0
		a. Imperf. between (pair)	£5		£5	
		b. Imperf. (pair)				

Reprints in the colour of the issue, and also in fancy colours, were made in 1880 on white wove paper, perforated 12½.

1871 (JAN.). *Locally engraved; 240 varieties of each value; wove paper. Recess. P* 11½.

2	**2**	½ a. brown	12	6	12	6
3	,,	2 a. sage-green	60	0	50	0

Stamps exist showing traces of lines in the paper, but they do not appear to be printed on true laid paper.

Reprints of both values were made in 1880 on white wove paper, perforated 12½; the ½ a. is in orange-brown, and the 2 a. in bright green and in blue-green.

3

(Recess. Bradbury, Wilkinson & Co.)

A

Ordinary type.

B

Variety.

In A the coloured lines surrounding each of the four labels join a coloured circle round their inner edge, in B this circle is missing.

C D

C—is the normal.

D—has the character ʌ omitted.

1871–1909. (*a*) *Rough perf.* 11½.

6	**3**	½ a. red-brown	50	0	50	0
7	,,	1 a. purple-brown	£5		£5	
8	,,	2 a. green (A)				
9	,,	3 a. ochre-brown	80	0	90	0
10	,,	4 a. slate	£5		£5	
11	,,	8 a. deep brown				
12	,,	12 a. dull blue	£10		£10	

(*b*) *P* 12½.

13	**3**	½ a. red-brown	1	6	0	4
		a. Orange	5	0	3	0
		b. Orange-brown	0	8	0	4
		c. Brick-red	1	0	0	3
		ca. Imperf. between (pair) ..	£5		£5	
		cb. Pin-perf.				
		cc. Doubly printed	£5		£5	
		d. Rose-red	0	8	0	2
		e. Error. Magenta	£5		25	0
14	,,	1 a. purple-brown	5	0	7	6
		a. Drab	1	3	0	4
		aa. Imperf. (pair)	—		£5	
		ab. Pin-perf.				
		b. Grey-black	1	6	0	3
		c. Black (1909)	1	6	0	3
15	,,	2 a. green (A)	1	6	0	3
		a. Deep green (A)	1	6	0	3
		b. Blue-green (A)	2	0	0	6
		ba. Blue-green (B)				
		c. Pale green (A)	2	0	0	4
		ca. Pale green (B)	90	0	90	0
		d. Sage-green (A) (1909) ..	2	0	0	8
		da. Sage-green (B)	—		90	0
16	,,	3 a. ochre-brown	3	0	2	
		a. Chestnut	3	0	2	
		aa. Character omitted (D) ..	£10		£	
17	,,	4 a. slate	4	0	2	
		a. Imperf. between (pair) ..	£8		£	
		b. Greenish grey	3	6	2	
		c. Olive-green	12	6	12	
18	,,	8 a. deep brown	9	0	7	
		a. Imperf. between (pair) ..				
19	,,	12 a. pale ultramarine ..	12	6	12	
		a. Grey-green	10	0	10	

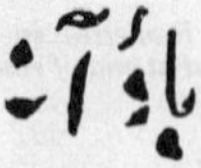

(4)

1900. *Surch. with T* 4. *P* 12½.

20	**3**	¼ a. on ½ a. orange-brown ..	0	8	0	
		a. Surch. inverted	70	0	50	

5

(Eng. Khusrat Ullah, Hyderabad.)

1902. *P* 12½.

21	**5**	¼ a. deep blue	10	0	7	
		a. Pale blue	10	0	7	

6

(6*a*)

(Recess. Allan G. Wyon, London.)

1905. *Wmk. T* 6a. *P* 12½.

22	**6**	¼ a. blue	1	6	0	
		a. Imperf.	30	0		
23	,,	½ a. orange	5	0	0	
		a. Vermilion	5	0	0	
		aa. Imperf.	30	0		
		b. Yellow	20	0	10	

1908–11. *T* **6.** *W* **6***a*. *Various perfs., also compound.*

A. *Perf.* 12½. B. *Perf.* 11½, 12. C. *Perf.* 11. D. *Perf.* 13½.

No.	Description	A.		B.		C.		D.	
24	¼ a. grey	3 6	0 4	6 0	0 6	20 0	10 0		
	a. Imp. betwn. (horiz. pr.)	£5	£5	†		†		†	
25	½ a. green	5 0	0 6	7 6	0 6	†		20 0	10 0
	a. Pale green	5 0	0 6	7 6	0 6	†		†	
	b. Blue-green	20 0	10 0	†		†		†	
26	1 a. carmine	20 0	1 0	2 6	0 6	15 0	10 0	†	
27	2 a. lilac	2 6	0 4	7 6	0 6	6 0	0 6	2 6	1 0
	a. Imperf. between (pair)	†		†		†		£5	£5
	b. Rose-lilac	†		†		†		6 0	0 6
28	3 a. brown-orange ('09)	5 0	0 6	10 0	1 0	5 0	1 6	2 6	0 6
29	4 a. olive-green ('09)	3 6	1 0	20 0	1 6	20 0	5 0	2 0	1 0
	a. Imp. betwn. (pr.)	†		†		£5	£5	†	
30	8 a. purple ('11)	15 0	2 6	20 0	10 0	5 0	1 0	4 0	0 6
31	12 a. blue-green ('11)	20 0	10 0	15 0	15 0	—	—	7 6	2 6

1912. *New plates eng. by Bradbury, Wilkinson & Co. Perfs. as before, or compound.*

No.	Description	A.		B.		C.		D.	
32	¼ a. grey-black	2 0	1 0	2 6	0 9	5 0	1 0	0 6	0 2
	a. Imp. betwn. (pr.)	£5	£5	†		†		†	
33	¼ a. purple	†		†		†		0 6	0 2
34	½ a. deep green	3 6	1 0	5 0	1 0	20 0	0 6	20 0	20 0
	a. Imp. betwn. (pr.)	†		†		†		60 0	60 0
	b. Imperf. (pair)	50 0	50 0	†		†		†	

In Wyon's ¼ a. stamp the fraction of value is closer to the end of the label than in the B. W. issue. In the Wyon ¼ a. and ½ a. the value in English and the label below are further apart than in the B.W.

Wyon's ¼ a. measures 19½×20 mm., and the ½ a. 19½×20½ mm.; both stamps from the Bradbury plates measure 19¾×21½ mm.

7. Symbols.

915. *T* **7.** *Inscr.* "Post & Receipt". *Various perfs. as above.*

No.	Description	A.		B.		C.		D.	
5	½ a. green	10 0	1 0	†		5 0	0 3	5 0	0 3
	a. Imperf. between (pair)	50 0	50 0	†		50 0	50 0	†	
	b. Imperf.	50 0	50 0						
6	1 a. carmine	20 0	1 0	†		5 0	0 3	5 0	0 3
	a. Imp. between (pr.)	70 0	70 0	†		†		†	
	b. Imperf.	50 0	50 0						
	c. Scarlet	†		†		†		10 0	2 0

For ½ a. claret, see No. 58.

8

927 (1 FEB.). *W* **6***a*. *P* 13½.

8	1 r. yellow	20 0	60 0

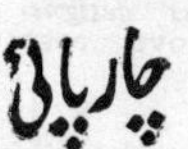

9. (4 pies.) **10.** (8 pies.)

30 (6 MAY). *Surch. as T* **9** *and* **10.** *Wmk. T* **6***a*. *P* 13½.

6	4 p. on ¼ a. grey-black (R.)	£5	25 0
	a. Perf. 11		
,,	4 p. on ¼ a. purple (R.)	0 8	0 3
7	8 p. on ½ a. green (R.)	0 6	0 3
	a. Imp. between (hor. pr.)	£12	£10
	b. Perf. 11	£12	£10

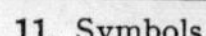

11. Symbols.

12. The Char Minar.

13. Bidar College.

14. Victory Tower, Daulatabad.

(Recess. Mint, Hyderabad.)

1931 (12 Nov.)–**47.** *T* **11** *to* **14** (*and similar types*). *W* **6a.** *Wove paper.* *P* 13½.

41	**11**	4 p. black ..	0	3	0	3
		a. Laid paper ('47) ..	20	0	15	0
		b. Imperf. (pair) ..	£10			
42	,,	8 p. green ..	0	4	0	3
		a. Imperf. between (vert. pr.)				
		b. Imperf. (pair) ..	£10			
		c. Laid paper ('47) ..	20	0	15	0
43	**12**	1 a. brown ..	0	6	0	3
44	–	2 a. violet ..	0	8	0	4
		a. Imperf. (pair) ..				
45	–	4 a. ultramarine ..	1	0	0	4
46	–	8 a. orange..	2	6	1	3
		a. Yellow-orange ('44) ..	£5		60	0
47	**13**	12 a. scarlet ..	5	0	2	6
48	**14**	1 r. yellow ..	7	6	12	6

Designs (*as T* **13/4**) :—2 a. High Court of Justice (horiz.). 4 a. Osman Sagar Reservoir (horiz.). 8 a. Entrance to Ajanta Caves (vert.).

15. Unani General Hospital.

16. Osmania General Hospital (37½ × 22½ mm.).

17. Osmania University (37½ × 22½ mm.).

18. Osmania Jubilee Hall.

(Offset. Indian Govt. Ptg. Wks., Nasik.)

1937 (13 Feb.). *T* **15/8** (*various designs inscr.* "H.E.H. THE NIZAM'S SILVER JUBILEE"). *P* 14.

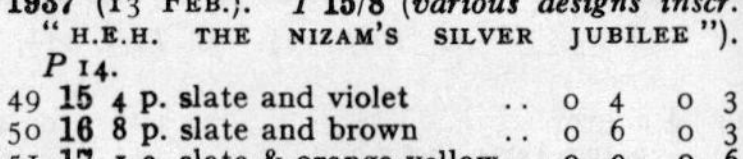

49	**15**	4 p. slate and violet ..	0	4	0	3
50	**16**	8 p. slate and brown ..	0	6	0	3
51	**17**	1 a. slate & orange-yellow..	0	9	0	6
52	**18**	2 a. slate and green ..	1	3	0	10

19. Family Reunion.

1946. *Victory Commemoration. Typo. Wove paper. P* 13½.

53	**19**	1 a. blue ..	0	8	0	8
		a. Imp. betwn. (vert. pr.) ..	£25			
		b. Laid paper ..	2	6	3	0

No. 53 exists with faint wmk. of native characters on each stamp and without wmk.

No. 53*b* has a large sheet wmk. reading "HYDERABAD GOVERNMENT", in circular frame, but parts of this do not appear on all stamps.

20. Town Hall.

(Litho. Government Press.)

1947 (17 Feb.). *Reformed Legislature. P* 13½.

54	**20**	1 a. black ..	0	6	0	
		a. Imperf. between (pair) ..				

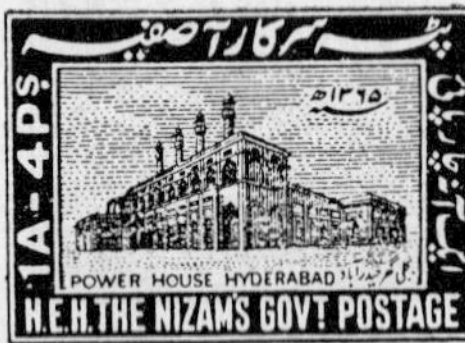

21. Power House, Hyderabad.

1947–49. *As T* **21** (*various designs insc* "H. E. H. THE NIZAM'S GOVT. POSTAGE" *Typo. W* **6a.** *P* 13½.

55	1 a. 4 p. green ..	0	4	0	
56	3 a. greenish blue ..	0	8	0	
57	6 a. sepia ..	4	0	4	
	a. Red-brown ('49) ..	£6			
	ab. Imperf. (pair) ..				

Designs :—3 a. Kaktyai Arch, Warangal For 6 a. Golkunda Fort.

1947. *As* 1915 *issue but colour changed. P* 13

58	**7**	½ a. claret ..	1	0	1	
		a. Imperf. between (hor. pr.) ..	—		£	

1948. *As T* **11** (" POSTAGE " *at foot*). *Recess. W* **6a**. *P* 13½.

59	6 p. claret	2 0	2 0

1949. *T* **11** (" POSTAGE " *at top*). *Litho. W* **6a**. *P* 13½.

60 **11**	2 p. bistre-brown	5 0	0 5
	a. Imperf. between (hor. pr.) ..		

OFFICIAL STAMPS.

(O 1)

1873–1909. *Optd. as Type* O **1**.

(A) *In red.* (B) *In black.*

No.		A.		B.	
O1 **1**	1 a. olive-green	—	22 6	—	—
O2 **2**	½ a. brown ..	—	52 6	—	22 6
O3 ,,	2 a. sage-green	—	75 0	—	32 6

Imitations of these overprints on genuine stamps and on reprints are found horizontally or vertically in various shades of red, in magenta and in black.

T **3** *optd. as Type* O **1**.

A. *In red.* B. *In black.*

(*a*) *Rough perf.* 11½.

No.		A.		B.	
O4	½ a. red-brown ..	—	—	—	—
O5	1 a. purple-brown	—	—	—	—
O6	2 a. green ..	—	—	—	—
O7	4 a. slate ..	—	—	—	—
O8	8 a. deep brown ..	—	—	—	—

(*b*) *P* 12½.

No.		A.		B.	
O 9	½ a. red-brown	15 0	15 0	8 6	6 0
O10	½ a. orge.-brn. ('09)	†		—	6 0
O11	1 a. purp.-brn.	20 0	15 0	—	7 6
O12	1 a. drab ..	15 0		6 0	6 0
	a. Opt. inverted	†		—	—
O13	1 a. black ('09) ..	†		2 0	0 2
O14	2 a. grn. (to dp.)	20 0		6 0	
	a. Opt. inverted	†		—	—
O15	2 a. sage-grn. (A) ('09) ..	†		—	1 6
	a. Type B ..	†		—	10 0
O16	3 a. ochre-brn.	—	—	6 0	5 0
O17	4 a. slate ..	30 0	17 6	10 6	8 0
O18	4 a. grnish. grey	†		20 0	
O19	8 a. deep brown	30 0		30 0	17 6
	a. Imperf. btn.(pr.)	£5			†
O20	12 a. blue ..	35 0		30 0	

The use of Official Stamps (Serkari) was discontinued in 1878, but was resumed in 1909, when the current stamps were optd. with the old dies.

1909–11. *T* **6** *optd. as Type* O **1**.

A. *Perf.* 12½. B. *Perf.* 11½, 12. C. *Perf.* 11.

No.		A.		B.		C.	
O21	½ a. orange	10 0	5 0	†		†	
	a. Vermilion	10 0	0 3	†		†	
	b. Opt. inverted	£5	£5	†		†	
O22	½ a. green (W.)	15 0	0 2	15 0	2 0	†	
	a. Pale green (W.)	15 0	0 2	15 0	2 0	†	
	b. Opt. inverted	†		£5	40 0	†	
	c. Imperf. between (pair)	£5	£5	†		†	
O23	1 a. carmine	15 0	0 2	20 0	3 0	—	20 0
	a. Opt. double	60 0		†		†	
O24	2 a. lilac	20 0	1 0	15 0	2 0	†	
O25	3 a. brown-orange	12 6	0 6	20 0	1 0	†	
	a. Opt. inverted	60 0	60 0	†		†	
O26	4 a. olive-green ('11)	10 0	2 6	10 0	2 6	†	
O27	8 a. purple ('11)	10 0	2 6	10 0	3 0	†	
O28	12 a. blue-green ('11)	10 0	2 6	10 0	3 0	†	

The Wyon and Bradbury, Wilkinson stamps are distinguished above and below by the use of the letters (W.) and (B.W.) respectively.

(O 2)

1911–12. *T* **6** *optd. with Type* O **2**.

A. *Perf.* 12½. B. *Perf.* 11½, 12. C. *Perf.* 11. D. *Perf.* 13½.

No.		A.		B.		C.		D.	
O29	¼ a. grey (W.)	20 0	2 6	—	0 6	†		†	
O30	¼ a. grey-black (B.W.) ..	0 6	0 2	2 6	0 4	1 0	0 2	2 6	0 2
	a. Opt. inverted	—	—	†		†		†	
	b. Pair, one without opt. ..	—	—	†		†		†	
O31	¼ a. lilac (B.W.)	†		†		†		2 0	3 0
	a. Imperf. between (pair) ..	†		†		†		£8	£5
O32	½ a. pale green (W.) ..	20 0	0 3	—	0 6	†		†	
O33	½ a. deep green (B.W.) ..	2 0	0 3	—	0 4	1 0	0 2	2 0	0 3
	a. Opt. inverted	60 0	40 0	†		£5	60 0	†	
	b. Imperf. between (pair) ..	†		†		£8	£5	£5	60 0
O34	1 a. carmine	2 0	0 3	10 0	0 4	1 3	0 4	—	—
	a. Opt. inverted	—	60 0	†		†		†	
O35	2 a. lilac	3 6	0 3	10 0	0 6	1 9	0 4	2 6	0 3
	a. Rose-lilac	†		†		†		20 0	1 0
O36	3 a. brown-orange	3 6	0 6	—	1 0	10 0	1 6	40 0	1 0
	a. Opt. inverted	—	£5	†		£8	£5	£8	£5
O37	4 a. olive-green	7 6	0 4	5 0	0 6	5 0	0 9	5 0	0 6
	a. Opt. inverted	£8	£5	†		†		£8	£5
O38	8 a. purple	12 6	1 6	—	—	15 0	2 0	7 6	0 6
O39	12 a. blue-green	17 6	2 6	—	—	20 0	5 0	10 0	2 6

1919. *T* **7** *optd. with Type* O **2**. *Various perfs. as above.*

No.		A.	B.	C.	D.
O40	½ a. green	— —	†	5 0 0 2	2 6 0 2
	a. Opt. inverted	†	†	— 40 0	— 40 0
	b. Pair, one without opt. ..	†	†	— —	†
	c. Imperf. between (pair) ..	†	†	†	£8 £5
O41	1 a. carmine	— —	†	5 0 0 2	2 6 0 3
	a. Opt. inverted	†	†	— 20 0	†
	b. Scarlet	†	†	†	5 0 1 0

1930–34. *T* **6** *and* **7** *optd. as Type* O **2** *and surch. at top of stamp, in red,* as *T* **9** *or* **10**.

O42	4 p. on ¼ a. grey-black (O30) ('34)	£10	50 0
O43	4 p. on ¼ a. lilac (O31) ..	2 6	0 3
	a. Red opt. superimposed on Type O 2		
	b. Imp. between (pair) ..	£10	£5
O44	8 p. on ½ a. green (O40) ..	2 6	0 3
	a. Red opt. superimposed on Type O 2	40 0	
	b. Imp. between (pair) ..	£10	£5
O45	8 p. on ½ a. green (O33) ..	£20	£10

In Nos. O43*a* and O44*a*, T **9** and **10** cover Type O **2** instead of being above it.

1934–44. *Nos.* 41/8 *optd. with Type* O **2**.

O46	4 p. black	0 3	0 3
	a. Imperf. (pair)		
	b. Imp. between (pair) ..	£20	£15
O47	8 p. green	0 3	0 3
	a. Opt. inverted		
	b. Imp. between (pair) ..	£20	£15
O48	1 a. brown	0 4	0 3
	a. Imp. between (pair) ..	£30	£20
O49	2 a. violet	0 6	0 3
	a. Imp. between (pair) ..	£40	£30
O50	4 a. ultramarine	0 10	0 8
O51	8 a. orange ('35)	2 6	1 6
	a. Yellow-orange ('44)	—	£5
O52	12 a. scarlet ('35)	3 0	2 0
O53	1 r. yellow ('35)	3 6	3 0

1947. *No.* 58 *optd. with Type* O **2**.

O54	**7** ½ a. claret	12 6	5 0

1949. *No.* 60 *optd. with Type* O **2**.

O55	**11** 2 p. bistre-brown	12 6	10 0

1950. *No.* 59 *optd. with Type* O **2**.

O56	6 p. claret	12 6	7 6

IDAR.

1. Maharaja Shri Himatsinhji. **2.**

(Typo. M. N. Kothari & Sons, Bombay.)

1939 (21 Feb.). *P* 11. (*a*) *White panels.*

1	**1** ½ a. green (*shades*)	7 6
	(*b*) *Coloured panels.*	
2	**1** ½ a. green (*shades*)	10 0

In No 2 the whole design is composed of half-tone dots. In No. 1 the dots are confined to the oval portrait.

(Typo. P. G. Mehta & Co., Himmatnagar.)

1944 (21 Oct.). *P* 12.

3	**2** ½ a. blue-green	1 6
	a. Yellow-green	6 0
	b. Imperf. between (pair) ..	40 0
4	**2** 1 a. violet	1 6
	a. Imperf. (pair)	
5	,, 2 a. blue	3 0
	a. Imperf. between (v. or h. pair) ..	£5
6	,, 4 a. vermilion	5 0

Nos. 1 to 6 are from booklet panes of 4 stamps, producing single stamps with one or two adjacent sides imperf.

A 1¼ a. is a clandestine production, and the 4 a. in violet is believed to be a colour trial.

INDORE

(HOLKAR.)

1. Maharaja Tukoji Rao II Holkar XI.

(Litho. Waterlow & Sons.)

1886. *P* 15. (*a*) *Thick white paper.*

1	**1** ½ a. bright mauve	15 0	15
	(*b*) *Thin white or yellowish paper.*		
2	**1** ½ a. pale mauve	8 0	10
3	,, ½ a. dull mauve	10 0	10

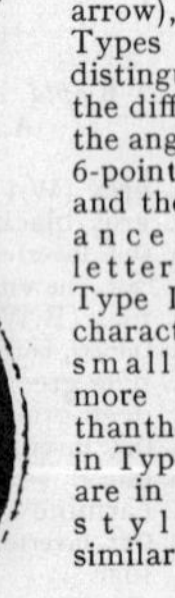

2. Type I.

2*a*. Type II.

NOTE.

In addition the differenc in the top line characte (marked b arrow), the tw Types can b distinguished b the difference the angles of th 6-pointed sta and the appea ance of th lettering. Type I the to characters a smaller an more crampe than the bottor in Type II bo are in the sar style an similarly space

1889. *Imperf.*

4	**2** ½ a. black/*pink*	20 0	20
4*a*	**2*a*** ½ a. black/*pink*	15 0	15

3. Maharaja Shivaji Rao Holkar XII.

(Recess. Waterlow & Sons, Ltd.)

1889–92. *Medium wove paper.* P 14 *to* 15.

5 **3** ¼ a. orange (9.2.92) .. 1 0 1 0
a. Imperf. between (pair) .. £5 £5
b. Very thick wove paper .. 5 0 3 0
6 ,, ½ a. dull violet 4 0 4 0
a. *Brown-purple* .. 2 0 1 6
b. Imperf. between (pair) .. £5 £5
7 ,, 1 a. green (7.2.92) 6 0 6 0
a. Imperf between (pair) .. £5 £5
8 ,, 2 a. vermilion (7.2.92) .. 12 6 7 6
a. Very thick wove paper .. 22 6 22 6

Maharaja Tukoji Rao III Holkar XIII. **5.**

(Recess. Perkins, Bacon & Co.)

904. P 13½, 14.

9 **4** ¼ a. orange 0 6 0 4
9a **5** ½ a. lake 45 0 0 10
b. Imperf. (pair) 60 0
,, 1 a. green 12 6 1 0
a. Imperf. (pair) .. ..
,, 2 a. brown 12 6 2 0
a. Imperf. (pair) .. ..
,, 3 a. violet 15 0 3 0
,, 4 a. ultramarine 20 0 5 0

पाव आना.

(6)

05. *No.* 6*a surch.* "QUARTER ANNA" *in Devanagari, as T* **6**.

½ a. on ½ a. brown-purple .. 17 6 17 6

OTE. From 1st March 1908 the use of Indore mps was restricted to official mail.

. Maharaja Yeshwant Rao II Holkar XIV.

(Recess. Perkins, Bacon & Co.)

8–38. P 13 *to* 14.

7 ½ a. orange 0 9 0 6
,, ½ a. claret 0 9 0 6
,, 1 a. green 0 9 0 6
,, 1¼ a. green ('33) 1 0 0 9
,, 2 a. sepia 7 6 5 0
,, 2 a. bluish green ('36) .. 2 6 2 0
,, 3 a. deep violet 3 6 4 6
,, 3½ a. violet ('34) 5 0 6 0

22 **7** 4 a. ultramarine 5 0 7 6
22*a* ,, 4 a. yellow-brown ('38) .. 10 0 7 6
23 ,, 8 a. slate-grey 20 0 20 0
23*a* ,, 8 a. red-orange ('38) .. 20 0 20 0
24 ,, 12 a. carmine ('34) .. 40 0 40 0

As T **7**, *but larger* (23×28 *mm.*).

25 1 r. black and light blue .. 20 0 20 0
26 2 r. black and carmine .. 30 0 30 0
27 5 r. black and brown-orange .. 70 0 70 0

(8)

9

1940 (1 Aug.). *Surch. as T* **8**.

28 QUARTER ANNA on 5 r. (No. 27) 2 0 1 6
29 HALF ANNA on 2 r. (No. 26) .. 4 6 2 6
30 ONE ANNA on 1¼ a. (No. 18) .. 5 0 2 0
a. Surch. inverted £20

(Typo. "*Times of India*" Press, Bombay.)

1941–47. P 11.

31 **9** ¼ a. red-orange 1 0 0 6
32 ,, ½ a. claret 1 0 0 6
33 ,, 1 a. green 1 6 0 8
34 ,, 1¼ a. yellow-green .. 3 0 2 0
35 ,, 2 a. turquoise-blue .. 25 0 15 0
35*a* ,, 4 a. yellow-brown ('47) .. 45 0 40 0

Larger size (23×28 *mm.*).

36 **9** 2 r. black & carmine ('43) .. 35 0 40 0
37 ,, 5 r. blk. & yell.-orge. ('43) .. 50 0 60 0

OFFICIAL STAMPS.

SERVICE **SERVICE**

(S 1) (S 2)

1904–6. *Optd. with Type* S **1**. P 13½, 14.

S1 **4** ¼ a. orange (1906) 0 4 0 6
S2 **5** ½ a. lake 0 4 0 3
a. Opt. inverted 35 0
b. Opt. double 20 0
c. Imperf. (pair) 60 0
d. *Brown-lake* 0 4 0 3
da. Opt. inverted 35 0
S3 ,, 1 a. green 0 6 0 4
S4 ,, 2 a. brown (1905) 1 0 1 0
a. Pair, one without opt. ..
S5 ,, 3 a. violet (1906) 5 0 5 0
a. Imperf. (pair) £8
S6 ,, 4 a. ultramarine (1905) .. 10 0 10 0

Optd. with Type S **2**. P 13½, 14.

S7 **5** ½ a. lake 0 4 0 6

Types S **1** and S **2** differ chiefly in the shape of the letter "R."

JAIPUR.

1. Chariot of the Sun. **2.**

1904. *T* **1.** *Value at sides in small letters and characters. 36 varieties (2 plates) of the ½ a. In Plate I the stamps are 2½ mm. apart horizontally; while in Plate II they are 4½ mm. apart. 12 varieties each of the 1 a. and 2 a. Roughly perf.* 14.

No.	Description	Unused	Used
1	½ a. pale blue (Plate I)	40 0	50 0
2	½ a. ultramarine (Plate I)	12 6	15 0
2a	½ a. grey-blue (Plate II)	—	£25
3	1 a. dull red	10 0	12 6
4	1 a. scarlet	15 0	
5	2 a. pale green	15 0	17 6
6	2 a. emerald-green	20 0	

Variety. Imperf. (Plate II).

No.	Description	Unused	Used
6a	½ a. blue (*shades*)	£25	

T **2**, *value in larger letters and characters.* 24 *varieties on one plate. Roughly perf.* 14.

No.	Description	Unused	Used
7	½ a. pale blue	15 0	15 0
8	½ a. deep blue	15 0	15 0
9	½ a. ultramarine	15 0	15 0
	a. Imperf.		

3. Chariot of the Sun-god, Surya.

(Recess. Perkins, Bacon & Co.)

1904. *T* **3.** *P* 12, 12½ *or compound.*

No.	Description	Unused	Used
10	½ a. blue	12 6	10 0
10a	1 a. brown-red	60 0	60 0
11	1 a. carmine	10 0	7 6
	a. Imperf. between (vert. pair)	£10	
12	2 a. deep green	12 6	12 6

1905–8. *T* **3.** *P* 13½.

No.	Description	Unused	Used
13	¼ a. olive-yellow (1906)	1 6	1 6
14	½ a. blue	2 0	1 6
14a	½ a. indigo	3 6	3 6
15	1 a. brown-red (1906)	25 0	25 0
15a	1 a. bright red (1908)	3 6	3 6
16	2 a. deep green	6 0	6 0
17	4 a. chestnut	12 6	12 6
18	8 a. bright violet	15 0	15 0
19	1 r. yellow	17 6	17 6
20	1 r. orange-yellow	25 0	
20a	1 r. yellow-ochre	20 0	20 0

4. Chariot of the Sun-god, Surya.

(Typo. Jail Press, Jaipur.)

1911. *Thin wove paper. Imperf. Six varieties of each value.*

No.	Type	Description	Unused	Used
21	**4**	¼ a. green	8 6	10 0
		a. Doubly printed		
		b. "¼" inv. at rt. upper corner	12 6	
		c. No stop after "STATE"	10 6	
22	,,	¼ a. greenish yellow	2 0	2 6
		a. "¼" inv. in rt. upper corner	5 0	
		b. No stop after "STATE"	4 6	
23	,,	½ a. ultramarine	2 0	2 6
		a. Doubly printed	12 6	
		b. No stop after "STATE"	3 0	
		c. Large "J" in "JAIPUR"	8 0	
		d. "⅓" for "½" at lower left	20 0	
24	**4**	½ a. grey-blue	2 6	2 6
		a. No stop after "STATE"	5 0	
		b. Large "J" in "JAIPUR"	10 6	
		c. "⅓" for "½" at lower left	20 0	
25	,,	1 a. rose-red	2 6	3 6
26	,,	2 a. greyish green	10 0	10 0
27	,,	2 a. deep green	10 0	10 0

One sheet of the ¼ a. is known in blue.

(Typo. as last.)

1913–18. *Paper-maker's wmk.* "DORLING & CO., LONDON," *in sheet. P* 11.

No.	Type	Description	Unused	Used
30	**3**	¼ a. olive-yellow	0 9	0 9
		a. Imperf. betw. (horiz. pair)		
31	,,	¼ a. olive	0 9	0 9
		a. Imperf. between (vert. or horiz. pair)	£5	£5
32	,,	½ a. ultramarine	0 9	1 0
		a. Imperf. between (pair)	£5	£5
33	,,	1 a. carmine (1918)	1 6	1 9
		a. Imperf. between (vert. pair)	£8	£8
33b	,,	1 a. rose-red	20 0	
33c	,,	1 a. scarlet	1 6	
		d. Imperf. between (vert. pair)	£8	£8
34	,,	2 a. green (1918)	3 0	3 0
35	,,	4 a. chocolate	5 0	
36	,,	4 a. pale brown	5 0	
		a. Imp. betwn. (horiz. pr.)	£10	

1928. *As* 1913–18. *Wmkd.* "OVERLAND BANK" *in sheet. P* 12.

No.	Type	Description	Unused	Used
36b	**3**	½ a. ultramarine	40 0	
37	,,	1 a. rose-red	50 0	
37a	,,	1 a. scarlet	50 0	
37b	,,	2 a. green	£5	
37c	,,	8 a. bright violet	£7	
37d	,,	1 r. orange-vermilion	£10	

३ आना

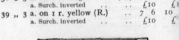

(5)

1926. *Surch. with T* **5.**

No.	Type	Description	Unused	Used
38	**3**	3 a. on 8 a. bright violet (R.)	7 6	10
		a. Surch. inverted	£10	£
39	,,	3 a. on 1 r. yellow (R.)	7 6	10
		a. Surch. inverted	£10	£

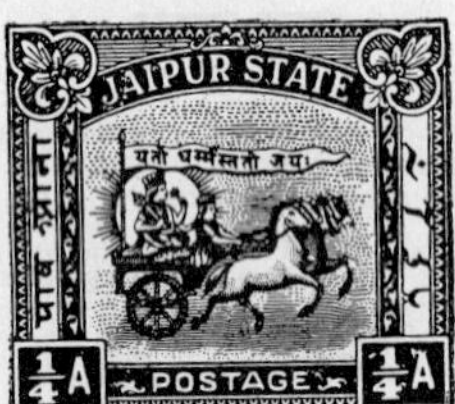

6. Chariot of the Sun.

7. Maharaja Sir Man Singh Bahadur.

8. Sowar in Armo

9. Maharajas Sawai Jai Singh and Sir Man Singh.

(Offset-litho. Security Printing Press, Nasik.)

1931 (14 Mar.). *Investiture of Maharaja. T* **6** *to* **9** (*various central designs*). *No wmk. P* 14.

40 **6** ¼ a. black and deep lake .. 0 9 0 6
41 **7** ½ a. black and violet .. 0 9 0 6
42 **8** 1 a. black and blue .. 7 6 3 0
43 ,, 2 a. black and buff 7 6 3 0
44 ,, 2½ a. black and carmine .. 50 0 30 0
45 **6** 3 a. black and myrtle .. 35 0 20 0
46 ,, 4 a. black and olive-green .. 20 0 15 0
47 ,, 6 a. black and deep blue .. 17 6 17 6
48 **8** 8 a. black and chocolate .. 20 0 20 0
49 **6** 1 r. black and pale olive .. 20 0 20 0
50 ,, 2 r. black and yellow-green 30 0 30 0
51 **9** 5 r. black and purple .. 50 0 60 0

Designs:—1 a. Elephant with State Banner. 2½ a. Dancing Peacock. (Inscribed "POSTAGE") 3 a. Bullock Carriage. 4 a. Elephant Carriage. ("POSTAGE & REVENUE".) 6 a. Albert Museum. 8 a. Sireh-Deorhi Gate. 1 r. Chandra Mahal ("POSTAGE & REVENUE".) 2 r. Amber Palace ("POSTAGE & REVENUE".)

Eighteen of these sets were issued for presentation purposes with a special surcharge "INVESTITURE—MARCH 14, 1931" in red.

10. Maharaja Sir Man Singh Bahadur.

One Rupee
(11)

पाव आना
(12)

(Offset-litho. Security Printing Press, Nasik.)

1932-46. *P* 14. (*a*) *Insc*r. "POSTAGE & REVENUE".

2 **10** 1 a. black and blue .. 1 0 0 9
3 ,, 2 a. black and buff .. 1 0 1 0
,, 4 a. black and grey-green 1 0 1 3
,, 8 a. black and chocolate .. 2 0 2 6
,, 1 r. black and yellow-bistre 10 0 12 6
,, 2 r. black and yellow-green 50 0 60 0

(*b*) *Inscr.* "POSTAGE".

7 ¼ a. black and brown-lake .. 0 8 0 3
,, ¾ a. black & brn.-red ('43?) 0 8 0 3
,, 1 a. black and blue ('43?) .. 0 9 0 6
,, 2 a. black and buff ('43?) .. 1 0 0 10
,, 2½ a. black and carmine .. 1 3 1 3
,, 3 a. black and green .. 1 6 1 6
,, 4 a. black & grey-grn. ('43?) 2 0 2 6
,, 6 a. black and deep blue .. 4 0 4 6
a. Black and pale blue ('46) .. 7 6 8 6
,, 8 a. black & chocolate('46) 5 0 6 0
,, 1 r. black & yell.-bistre ('46) 12 6 15 0

1936. *Nos.* 57 *and* 51 *surch. with T* **11.**

68 **10** 1 r. on 2 r. black and yellow-green (R.) 30 0 30 0
69 **9** 1 r. on 5 r. blk. & pur. (Bk.) 10 0 12 6

1938 (Dec.). *No.* 41 *surch.* "QUARTER ANNA" *in Devanagari, T* **12.**

70 **7** ¼ a. on ½ a. black & violet (R.) 20 0 25 0

13. Maharaja and Amber Palace.

(Recess. De La Rue & Co.)

1947 (Dec.)–**48.** *Silver Jubilee of Maharaja's Accession to Throne. Various designs as T* **13.** *P* 13½ × 14.

71 ¼ a. red-brown & green (5.48) 0 3 0 6
72 ½ a. green and violet 0 3 0 6
73 ¾ a. black and lake (5.48) .. 0 3 0 6
74 1 a. red-brown & ultramarine 0 6 0 9
75 2 a. violet and scarlet 0 8 1 0
76 3 a. green and black (5.48) .. 1 3 1 9
77 4 a. ultramarine and brown .. 1 9 3 0
78 8 a. vermilion and brown .. 2 6 4 0
79 1 r. purple and green (5.48) .. 6 0 8 6

Designs:—¼ a. Palace Gate; ¾ a. Map of Jaipur; 1 a. Observatory; 2 a. Wind Palace; 3 a. Coat of Arms; 4 a. Amber Fort Gate; 8 a. Chariot of the Sun; 1 r. Maharaja's portrait between State flags.

3 PIES
(14)

1947 (Dec.). *No.* 41 *surch. with T* **14.**

80 **7** 3 p. on ½ a. black & violet (R.) 3 0 3 6
a. "PIE" for "PIES" 35 0 35 0
b. Bars at left vertical 50 0 50 0
c. Surch. inverted 30 0 30 0
d. Surch. inverted and "PIE" for "PIES" £10 £10
e. Surch. double, one inverted .. £5 £5
f. As var. e, but inverted surch. showing "PIE" for "PIES" £10 £10

OFFICIAL STAMPS.

SERVICE
(O 1)

SERVICE
(O 2)

1929–30. *T* **3** *typographed. P* 11, 12, *or compound. Wmk.* "Overland Bank" (¼ a., ½ a., 1 a. and 2 a.) *or* "Dorling & Co. London" (4 a., 8 a. and 1 r.). (*a*) *Optd. with Type* O **1.**

O 1 ¼ a. olive 0 4 0 3
O 2 ½ a. ultramarine (Bk.) .. 1 0 0 6
a. Imperf. between (horiz. pair) 80 0 80 0
b. Opt. inverted £15 £15
c. Opt. double (R. and Bk.) .. £15 £15
O 3 ½ a. ultramarine (R.) ('30) .. 1 0 0 6
a. Imp. between. (horiz. pair) ..
O 3*b* 1 a. rose-red .. ..
c. Imperf. between (horiz. pair) £8 £8
O 4 1 a. scarlet 2 0 0 3
O 5 2 a. green 3 0 3 0

O 6 4 a. pale brown 6 0 7 6
a. Chocolate 6 0 7 6
O 7 8 a. bright violet (R.) .. 35 0 45 0
O 8 1 r. orange-vermilion .. 80 0 £5

(*b*) *Optd. with Type* O **2**.

O 9 ½ a. ultramarine (Bk.) .. £8 0 3
O10 ½ a. ultramarine (R.) .. £10 0 3
O11 8 a. bright violet £25 £25
O12 1 r. orange-vermilion .. £25 £25

आध आना SERVICE

(O 3) (O 4)

1932. *No.* O 5 *surch. with Type* O **3.**
O13 ½ a. on 2 a. green £20 2 0

1931–37. *Nos.* 41/3 *and* 46 *optd. at Nasik with Type* O **4**, *in red.*
O14 **7** ½ a. black and violet .. 0 3 0 3
O15 **8** 1 a. black and blue .. £30 0 3
O16 ,, 2 a. black and buff ('36) .. 0 6 0 4
O17 **6** 4 a. blk. & olive-grn. ('37) 1 0 0 8

1932–37. *Nos.* 52/6 *optd. at Nasik with Type* O **4**, *in red.*
O18 **10** 1 a. black and blue .. 0 4 0 3
O19 ,, 2 a. black and buff .. 0 8 0 3
O20 ,, 4 a. blk. & grey-grn. ('37) 6 0 6 0
O21 ,, 8 a. black and chocolate .. 2 6 3 c
O22 ,, 1 r. black & yellow-bistre 4 0 4 6

1932–46. *Stamps of* 1932–46, *inscr.* "POSTAGE".
(*a*) *Optd. at Nasik with Type* O **4**, *in red.*
O23 **7** ¼ a. blk. & brn.-lake ('36) 0 8 0 6
O24 ,, ¾ a. black & brn.-red ('44) 0 8 0 6
O25 ,, 1 a. black and blue ('41?) 1 9 0 10
O26 ,, 2 a. black and buff .. 2 0 2 0
O27 ,, 2½ a. black & carmine ('46) 2 6 3 0
O28 ,, 4 a. blk. & grey-grn. ('46) 2 6 3 0
O29 ,, 8 a. black & choc. ('46) .. 4 6 5 0

(*b*) *Optd. locally with Type* O **2**, *in black.*
O30 **7** ¼ a. black & red-brn. ('36) £7 £5

9 PIES

= =

(O 5)

1947. *No.* O25 *surch. with Type* O **5** *in red.*
O31 **7** 9 p. on 1 a. black and blue 1 3 1 3

1947 (Dec.). *No.* O14 *surch. as T* **14**, *but* "3 PIES" *placed higher.*
O32 **7** 3 p. on ½ a. blk. & vio. (R.) 30 0 35 0
a. Surch. double, one inverted 95 0 95 0
b. "PIE" for "PIES" .. £20 £20
c. Surch. inverted £40 £40

1949. *No.* O14 *surch.* "THREE-QUARTER ANNA" *in Devanagari, as T* **12**, *but with two bars on each side.*
O33 **7** ¾ a. on ½ a. blk. & vio. (R.) 15 0 15 0

There are three different types of surcharge in the setting of 30, which vary in one or other of the Hindi characters.

For later issues, see Rajasthan.

JAMMU AND KASHMIR.

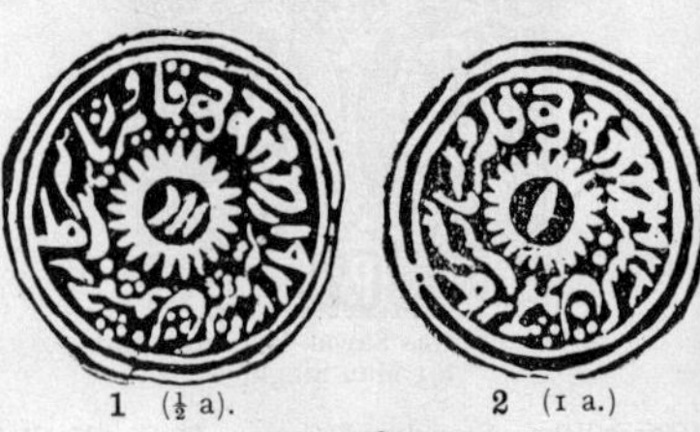

1 (½ a). **2** (1 a.)

3 (4 a.)

Characters denoting the value (on the circula stamps only) are approximately as shown in th central circle of the stamps illustrated above

Opinions are still divided as to whether *T* and *T* **3** are given their correct face values above The character in the centre of *T* **3** does represen 4 annas, whereas that in *T* **2** is meaningless in this notation. On the other hand other evid ence suggests that *T* **3** was the stamp used fo 1 anna.

The Circular Stamps. (Types **1** to **3**.)

(A) *Handstamped in water colours.*

1866 (Mar.)–**67.** *Native paper, thick to thi usually having the appearance of laid pap and tinted grey or brown. For Jammu an Kashmir.*

Cut □ *Cut* O
1 ½ a. grey-black .. 95 0 30 0 45 0 12
2 1 a. grey-black .. £10 — 65 0 —
3 4 a. grey-black .. £18 — 85 0 85
4 4 a. royal blue .. £35 £15 —
4*a* ½ a. ultramarine .. — — †
5 1 a. ultramarine .. £25 £10 £6 80
6 4 a. ultramarine .. £12 55 0 £7 30
7 1 a. indigo ('67) .. £25 — £12

1869–77. *Reissued for use in Jammu only.*
8 ½ a. red .. 55 0 — 22 6 -
9 1 a. red .. 25 0 60 0 12 0 -
10 4 a. red .. £5 — 40 0 -
11 ½ a. orange-red .. £6 — 55 0 -
12 1 a. orange-red .. 37 6 — 17 6 -
13 4 a. orange-red .. £5 — 40 0 -
13*a* 1 a. carm.-red ..
13*b* 1 a. orange ('72) ..

1874–76. *Special printings.*
14 ½ a. deep black .. 7 0 — 5 0 -
15 1 a. deep black .. 75 0 — 37 6 -
16 4 a. deep black .. £8 — 60 0 -
17 ½ a. bt. blue .. 37 6 — 17 6 -
18 1 a. bt. blue .. 35 0 — 12 6 -
19 4 a. bt. blue .. 25 0 — 10 0 -
20 ½ a. emld.-grn. .. 30 0 — 10 6 -
21 1 a. emld.-grn. .. 40 0 — 20 0 -
22 4 a. emld.-grn. .. 40 0 — 15 0 -
23 ½ a. yellow .. £10 — 47 6 -
24 1 a. yellow .. £8 — 47 6 -
25 4 a. yellow .. £7 — 50 0 -
25*a* 1 a. deep blue-black ('76)

These special printings were available for but little used.

(B) *Handstamped in oil colours. Heavy blurred prints.*

1877–78. (*a*) *Native paper.*

26	½ a. red	25 0	32 6	10 0	17 6
27	1 a. red	£8	£38	70 0	—
28	4 a. red	22 6	—	10 0	—
29	½ a. black	12 6	32 6	7 6	17 6
32	½ a. slate-blue	65 0	—	35 0	—
34	4 a. slate-blue	15 0	—	6 0	—
35	½ a. sage-green	£6	—	55 0	—
36	1 a. sage-green	£6	—	70 0	—
37	4 a. sage-green	£5	—	45 0	—
	(*b*) *European laid paper, medium to thick.*				
38	½ a. red	—	£20	—	£8
39	1 a. red	£6	—	45 0	—
41	½ a. black	8 6	50 0	5 0	20 0
44	½ a. slate-blue	10 0	—	6 0	—
45	1 a. slate-blue	£25	—	—	—
46	4 a. slate-blue	25 0	—	12 6	—
47	1 a. sage-green	£25	—	£15	—
48	1 a. yellow	85 0	—	60 0	—
	(*c*) *Thick yellowish wove paper.*				
48*a*	½ a. red ('78)	—	£20	—	£12

Forgeries exist of the ½ a. and 1 a. in types which were at one time supposed to be authentic.

Reprints and imitations (of which some of each were found in the official remainder stock, exist in a great variety of fancy colours, both on native paper, usually thinner and smoother than that of the originals, and on various thin European *wove* papers, on which the originals were never printed.

The imitations, which do not agree in type with the above illustrations, are also to be found on *laid* paper.

All the reprints, etc. are in oil colours or printer's ink. The originals in oil colour are usually blurred, particularly when on native paper. The reprints, etc. are usually clear.

(3*a*)

1877. *Provisional. Seal obliterator of Jammu handstamped in red water colour on pieces of native paper, and used as a ½ anna stamp.*

51*b*	**3*a*** (½ a.) rose-red	—	£20

THE RECTANGULAR STAMPS

I. FOR **JAMMU**.

½ a. ½ a.

1 a. **4** ½ a.

T **4** to **11** have a star at the top of the oval band; the characters denoting the value are in the upper part of the inner oval. All are dated 1923, corresponding with A.D. 1866.

T **4**. *Printed in blocks of four, three varieties of ½ anna and one of 1 anna.*

1867. *In water colour on native paper.*

52	½ a. grey-black	£10	£5
53	1 a. grey-black	£25	£25
54	½ a. indigo	£5	85 0
55	1 a. indigo	£10	£7
56	½ a. deep ultramarine	£5	85 0
57	1 a. deep ultramarine	£12	£8
58	½ a. deep violet-blue	£5	85 0
59	1 a. deep violet-blue	£15	£10
	1868–77. *In water colour on native paper.*		
60	½ a. red (*shades*)	10 6	10 0
61	1 a. red (*shades*)	20 0	17 6
62	½ a. orange-red	£7	47 6
63	1 a. orange-red	—	47 6
64	½ a. orange	£5	£5
65	1 a. orange		
	1874–76. *Special printings; in water colour on native paper.*		
66	½ a. bright blue	—	£5
67	1 a. bright blue	£6	£8
68	½ a. emerald-green	£30	£30
69	1 a. emerald-green	£30	£35
69*a*	½ a. jet-black	£6	£8
69*b*	1 a. jet-black	—	£35
	1877. *In oil colour.* (*a*) *Native paper.*		
70	½ a. red	35 0	30 0
71	1 a. red	60 0	45 0
72	½ a. brown-red	—	75 0
73	1 a. brown-red		
74	½ a. black	—	£20
75	1 a. black		
76	½ a. deep blue-black	—	£30
77	1 a. deep blue-black		
	(*b*) *Laid paper* (*medium or thick*).		
78	½ a. red	—	£25
	(*c*) *Thick wove paper.*		
79	½ a. red	—	£20
80	1 a. red		
	(*d*) *Thin laid, bâtonné paper.*		
84	½ a. red		
85	1 a. red		

The circular and rectangular stamps listed under the heading "Special Printings" did not supersede those in *red*, which was the normal colour for Jammu down to 1878. It is not known for what reason other colours were used during that period, but these stamps were printed in 1874 or 1875 and were certainly put into use. The rectangular stamps were again printed in *black* (jet-black, as against the greyish black of the 1867 printings) at that time, and impressions of the two periods can also be distinguished by the obliterations, which until 1868 were in *magenta* and after that in *black*.

There are reprints of these, in *oil* colour, *brown-red* and *bright blue*, on native paper; they are very clearly printed, which is not the case with the originals in *oil* colour.

II. FOR **KASHMIR**.

5

1866 (Sept.(?)). *Printed from a single die. Native laid paper.*

86 **5** ½ a. black £40 £18

Forgeries of this stamp are commonly met with, copied from an illustration in *Le Timbre-Poste.*

6 (½ a.) 7 (1 a.)

1866. *Native laid paper.*

87 **6** ½ a. black £27 £8
88 **7** 1 a. black £25 £17

The ½ a. was printed in a block of twenty varieties, and the 1 a. in a strip of five varieties.

8 (¼ a.)

9 (2 a.)

10 (4 a.)

11 (8 a.)

1867. *Native laid paper.*

90 **8** ¼ a. black 2 6 2 6
91 **6** ½ a. ultramarine 4 0 2 0
92 ,, ½ a. violet-blue 5 0 4 0
92*a* **7** 1 a. ultramarine £40 £25
94 ,, 1 a. orange.. .. .. 15 0 10 0
95 ,, 1 a. brown-orange .. 10 0 8 6
96 ,, 1 a. orange-vermilion .. 10 0 8 6
97 **9** 2 a. yellow 15 0 15 0
98 ,, 2 a. buff 17 6 17 6
99 **10** 4 a. green 20 0 17 6
100 ,, 4 a. sage-green £5 60 0
100*a* ,, 4 a. myrtle-green .. ..
101 **11** 8 a. red 22 6 22 6

Of the above, the ¼ a., 1 a., and 2 a. were printed in strips of five varieties, the ½ a. in a block of twenty varieties, and the 4 a. and 8 a. from single dies. Varieties at one time catalogued upon European papers were apparently never put into circulation, though some of them were printed while these stamps were still in use.

Nos. 86 to 101 are in *water* colour.

III. For **JAMMU AND KASHMIR.**

In the following issues there are 15 varieties on the sheets of the ⅛ a., ¼ a., and ½ a.; 20 varieties of the 1 a. and 2 a. and 8 varieties of the 4 a. and 8 a. The value is in the lower part of the central oval.

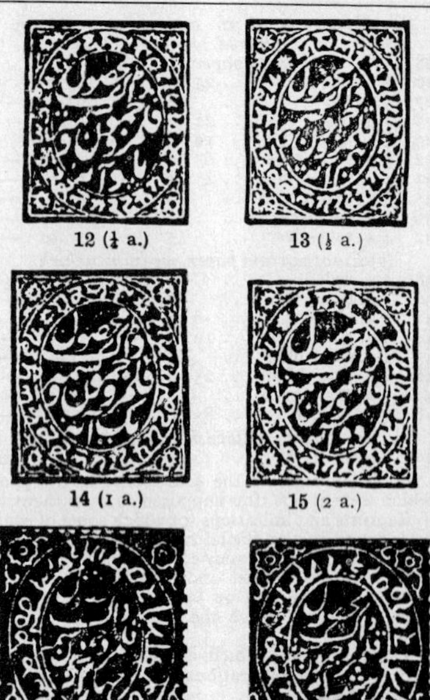

12 (¼ a.) 13 (½ a.) 14 (1 a.) 15 (2 a.) 16 (4 a.) 17 (8 a.)

1878–79. *Provisional printings.*

1. *Ordinary white laid paper, of varying thickness*

(*a*) *Rough perf.* 10 *to* 12 (i) *or* 13 *to* 16 (ii).

101*a* **12** ¼ a. red (i) .. ..
102 **13** ½ a. red (i) 6 0 7
103 **14** 1 a. red (ii) .. ..
104 **13** ½ a. slate-violet (i) .. 70 0 £
104*a* **14** 1 a. violet (ii) .. ..

(*b*) *Imperf.*

105 **13** ½ a. slate-violet (*shades*) 7 6 7
106 **14** 1 a. slate-purple 12 6 12
107 ,, 1 a. mauve 12 6 10
108 **15** 2 a. violet 12 6 12
109 ,, 2 a. bright mauve .. 12 6 12
110 ,, 2 a. slate-blue 15 0 15
111 ,, 2 a. dull blue 20 0 20
112 **12** ¼ a. red 20 0 30
113 **13** ½ a. red 7 6 7
114 **14** 1 a. red 8 6 10
115 **15** 2 a. red 55 0 35
116 **16** 4 a. red 45 0 35

2. *Medium wove paper.*

(*a*) *Rough perf.* 10 *to* 12.

117 **13** ½ a. red .. .. .. — 55

(*b*) *Imperf.*

117*b* **12** ¼ a. red .. .. ..
118 **13** ½ a. red 12 6 12
119 **14** 1 a. red 10 0 10
120 **15** 2 a. red 70 0 12

3. *Thick wove paper. Imperf.*

121 **13** ½ a. red 35 0
122 **14** 1 a. red 10 0 10
123 **15** 2 a. red 12 6 12

1879. *Definitive issue. Thin wove paper, fin to coarse.*

(*a*) *Rough perf.* 10 *to* 12.

124 **13** ½ a. red 80 0 55

(*b*) *Imperf.*

125 **12** ¼ a. red 2 0 2
126 **13** ½ a. red 1 6 1

127	**14**	1 a. red	2 0	3 0
128	**15**	2 a. red	3 0	3 0
129	**16**	4 a. red	5 0	6 0
130	**17**	8 a. red	6 0	7 6

1880 (March). *Provisional printing in water colour on thin bâtonné paper. Imperf.*

130*a*	**12**	¼ a. ultramarine	£15	£12

1881–83. *As Nos.* 124 *to* 130. *Colour changed.*

(*a*) *Rough perf.* 10 *to* 12.

130*b*	**13**	½ a. orange		

(*b*) *Imperf.*

131	**12**	¼ a. orange	10 0	7 6
132	**13**	½ a. orange	15 0	15 0
133	**14**	1 a. orange	10 0	10 0
134	**15**	2 a. orange	12 6	12 6
135	**16**	4 a. orange	15 0	
136	**17**	8 a. orange	22 6	

No. 127 was bisected diagonally at Leh in April, 1883, and each half used as a ½ a. Later, No. 133 was similarly bisected there. (*Used on cover* £5).

Nos. 125–130 and 132–136 were re-issued between 1890 and 1894 and used concurrently with the stamps which follow. Such re-issues can be identified by the "three-circle" cancellations, introduced in December, 1890.

18 (⅛ a.)

1883–94. *New colours. Thin wove papers, toned, coarse to fine, or fine white* (1889). *Imperf.*

38	**18**	⅛ a. yellow-brown	1 0	1 0
39	,,	⅛ a. yellow	1 0	1 0
40	**12**	¼ a. sepia	2 0	0 10
41	,,	¼ a. brown	1 0	0 10
		a. Double impression		
42	,,	¼ a. pale brown	1 0	0 10
		a. Error. ¼ a. green	75 0	
43	**13**	½ a. dull blue	8 6	
44	,,	½ a. bright blue	9 0	
45	,,	½ a. vermilion	5 0	1 6
46	,,	½ a. rose	5 0	1 0
47	,,	½ a. orange-red	4 0	1 0
48	**14**	1 a. greenish grey	1 6	1 6
49	,,	1 a. bright green	2 6	3 0
		a. Double impression		
50	,,	1 a. dull green	1 6	1 6
51	,,	1 a. blue-green	3 6	
52	**15**	2 a. red/*yellow*	2 0	1 9
53	,,	2 a. red/*yellow-green*	2 0	2 6
54	,,	2 a. red/*deep green*	5 0	5 0
55	**16**	4 a. deep green	4 0	4 0
56	,,	4 a. green	5 0	5 0
57	,,	4 a. pale green	6 0	6 0
58	,,	4 a. sage-green	5 0	
59	**17**	8 a. pale blue	8 0	8 0
59*a*	,,	8 a. deep blue	8 0	8 0
60	,,	8 a. bright blue	9 0	9 0
61	,,	8 a. indigo-blue	10 0	10 0
61*a*	,,	8 a. slate-lilac	12 6	12 6

Well-executed forgeries of the ⅛ a. to 8 a. have me from India, mostly postmarked; they may e detected by the type, which does not agree ith any variety on the genuine sheets, and also, the low values, by the margins being filled with colour, all but a thin white frame round e stamp. The forgeries of the 8 a. are in sheets eight like the originals.

Other forgeries of nearly all values also exist, showing all varieties of type. All values are on thin, coarse wove paper.

In February, 1890, a forgery, in water-colour, of the ½ a. orange, appeared, and many have been found genuinely used. (*Price* 20s.)

Nos. 143 and 144 were never issued.

1887–94. *Thin creamy laid paper. Imperf.*

162	**18**	⅛ a. yellow	30 0	27 6
163	**12**	¼ a. brown	10 0	12 6
164	**13**	½ a. brown-red (Mar. '87)	—	£5
165	,,	½ a. orange-red	17 6	10 0
166	**14**	1 a. grey-green	£10	£6
		Printed in water colour.		
168	**17**	8 blue	£7	£5

19

T **19** represents a ¼ a. stamp, which exists in sheets of twelve varieties, in *red* and *black*, on thin wove and laid papers, also in *red* on native paper, but which does not appear ever to have been issued for use. It was first seen in 1886.

The ¼ a. *brown*, and the 4 a. *green*, exist on ordinary white laid paper; the ½ a. *red* on native paper; the ¼ a. in *bright green*, on thin white wove (this may be an error in the colour of the 4 a.); and the 8 a. in *lilac* on thin white wove. None of these are known to have been in use.

OFFICIAL STAMPS.

1878. 1. *Ordinary white laid paper.*

(*a*) *Rough perf.* 10 *to* 12.

O 1	**13**	½ a. black		

(*b*) *Imperf.*

O 2	**13**	½ a. black	10 0	10 0
O 3	**14**	1 a. black	15 0	15 0
O 4	**15**	2 a. black	22 6	30 0

2. *Medium wove paper. Imperf.*

O 5	**14**	1 a. black		

1880–94. *Thin wove papers, toned, coarse to fine, or fine white* (1889). *Imperf.*

O 6	**12**	¼ a. black	0 10	0 10
		a. Double print	£6	
O 7	**13**	½ a. black	0 10	0 8
O 8	**14**	1 a. black	1 0	1 0
O 9	**15**	2 a. black	1 6	1 3
O10	**16**	4 a. black	2 0	2 0
O11	**17**	8 a. black	2 6	2 6

1887–94. *Thin creamy laid paper. Imperf.*

O12	**12**	¼ a. black	15 0	15 0
O13	**13**	½ a. black	15 0	15 0
O14	**14**	1 a. black	10 0	
O15	**15**	2 a. black	£8	
O16	**16**	4 a. black	75 0	50 0
O17	**17**	8 a. black	75 0	50 0

1889. *Stout white wove paper. Imperf.*

O18	**12**	¼ a. black		

The stamps of Kashmir have been obsolete since Nov. 1, 1894.

JASDAN

1. Sun.

(Typo. L. V. Indap & Co., Bombay.)

1942. *P* 8½—10½.

1	**1**	1 a. deep blue-green	6	0
		a. Bright green	5	0
		b. Yellow-green	5	0

A similar stamp in carmine is a fiscal.

JHALAWAR.

(Figure of an Apsara, "RHEMBA", a dancing nymph of the Hindu Paradise.)

• **1** (1 paisa) **2** (¼ anna)

1887–90. *Laid paper.*

1	**1**	1 p. yellow-green	15	0	20	0
		a. Blue-green	25	0	30	0
2	**2**	¼ a. green (*shades*)	7	6	10	0

The stamps formerly listed as on wove paper are from sheets on laid paper, with the laid lines almost invisible.

The stamps of Jhalawar have been obsolete since Nov. 1, 1900.

JIND.

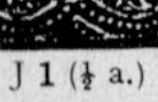

J **1** (½ a.)

J **2** (1 a.)

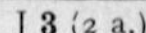

J **3** (2 a.)

J **4** (4 a.)

J **5** (8 a.)

(*The letter* " R " *on stamp is the initial of Raghbir Singh, at one time Rajah.*)

1874. *Thin yellowish paper. Imperf.*

J 1	J **1**	½ a. blue	20	0	10	0
		a. No frame to value. (Retouched all over) ..	£25		£20	
J 2	J **2**	1 a. rosy mauve	20	0	20	0
J 3	J **3**	2 a. yellow	5	0	15	0
J 4	,,	2 a. brown-buff	40	0	30	0
J 5	J **4**	4 a. green	60	0	15	0
J 6	J **5**	8 a. indigo-purple ..	£12		£5	
J 7	,,	8 a. slate-blue	£10		80	0

1876. *Bluish laid card-paper. Imperf.*

J 8	J **1**	½ a. blue	2	6	7	6
J 9	J **2**	1 a. purple	5	0	10	0
J10	J **3**	2 a. brown	6	0	10	0
J11	J **4**	4 a. green	7	6	12	6
J12	J **5**	8 a. slate-blue	15	0	22	6
J13	,,	8 a. purple	30	0	40	0

1885. *Bluish laid card-paper.* *P* 12.

J14	J **1**	½ a. blue	15	0	20	0

J **6** (¼ a.)

J **7** (½ a.)

J **8** (1 a.)

J **9** (2 a.)

J **10** (4 a.)

J **11** (8 a.)

1882–85. *Types J* **6** *to J* **11.** *25 varieties of eac value.* A. *Imperf.* (1882–4). B. *P* 12 (1885

(*a*) *Thin yellowish wove paper.*

		A.				B.		
J15	¼ a. buff (*shades*)	0	8	1	0	2	0	2
J16	¼ a. red-brown ..	1	0	1	6	4	6	—
	a. Doubly printed	45	0	—			†	
J17	½ a. lemon ..	1	9	3	0	1	3	1
J18	½ a. buff ..	4	0	4	0	1	3	1
J19	½ a. brown-buff	4	0	3	6	3	0	3
J20	1 a. brn. (*shades*)	3	6	4	0	3	6	5

		A.		B.	
J21	2 a. blue.. ..	3 0	3 6	4 6	—
J22	2 a. deep blue ..	4 0	4 6	6 0	7 6
J23	4 a. sage-green ..	3 6	4 0	8 6	10 0
J24	4 a. blue-green ..	6 0	8 0	10 0	—
	a. Imperf. betw. (pr.)	†		£8	—
J25	8 a. red ..	15 0	10 0	22 6	—
	(b) Laid paper.				
J26	¼ a. brown-buff..	6 0	—	35 0	-
J27	½ a. lemon ..	6 0	—	50 0	25 0
J28	1 a. brown ..	5 0	—	10 0	—
J29	2 a. blue.. ..	—	—	†	
J30	8 a. red ..	17 6	17 6	15 0	12 6
	(c) Thick white wove paper.				
J31	¼ a. brown-buff	60 0	—	†	
J32	1 a. brown ..	25 0	—	†	
J33	8 a. red ..	25 0	25 0	40 0	—

The perforated stamps ceased to be used for postal purposes in July, 1885, but are said to have been used later as fiscals. Other varieties exist, but they must either be fiscals or reprints, and it is not quite certain that all of those listed above were issued as early as 1885.

All the above stamps of Jind were lithographed by the Jind State Rajah's Press, Sungroor.

KISHANGARH.

1

1899. (a) Wove paper.			
1 1	1 a. green (*imperf.*)	60 0	£5
2 ,,	1 a. green (*pin-perf.*) ..	£5	
1900. Thin white wove paper. Imperf.			
3 1	1 a. blue	£20	

2 (½ a.)

3 (½ a.)

4 (1 a.)

Maharaja Sardul Singh.
5 (2 a.)

6 (4 a.)

7 (1 r.)

8 (2 r.)

9 (5 r.)

1899–1901. *T* **2** *to* **9.** *Thin white wove paper.* A. *Imperf.* B. *Pin-perf.*

		A.		B.	
4	¼ a. green ..	60 0	—	12 6	—
	a. Imperf. btwn. (pr.)	†		60 0	£5
5	¼ a. carmine.. ..	6 0	—	1 6	3 6
	a. Doubly printed	†		20 0	—
6	¼ a. pink ..	2 6	—	2 0	—
7	½ a. green ..	60 0	60 0	8 0	8 0
	a. Imperf. betwn. (pr.)	†		30 0	40 0
7*b*	½ a. yellow-green	60 0	70 0	30 0	40 0
8	½ a. red	40 0	25 0	†	
9	½ a. deep blue ..	8 0	10 0	6 0	5 0
10	½ a. blue	6 0	7 0	2 6	3 0
11	½ a. lilac ..	40 0	50 0	†	
12	½ a. slate-blue ..	8 0	10 0	†	
13	1 a. lilac	10 0	7 6	6 0	3 6
	a. Laid pp. *Red-lilac*	†		—	90 0
15	1 a. slate ..	10 0	8 0	6 0	7 6
15*a*	1 a. brown-lilac ..	10 0	8 0	†	
16	1 a. pink ..	£7	£8	35 0	—
17	2 a. dull orange ..	20 0	22 6	10 0	7 6
18	4 a. chocolate ..	10 0	—	8 0	8 0
	a. Thick laid paper	45 0	—	†	
19	1 r. dull green ..	30 0	—	20 0	35 0
	a. Thick laid paper	†		£15	—
19*b*	1 r. brown-lilac ..	£10	—	†	
20	2 r. red-brown ..	£8	—	75 0	—
	a. Thick laid paper	£15	—	£15	—
21	5 r. mauve ..	£5	—	80 0	—
	a. Thick laid paper	£15	—	£15	—

All varieties of this issue, both imperf. and pin.-perf., exist in *tête-bêche* vertical pairs from the centre of the sheet.

10 (½ a.)

10*a* (1 r.)

1901. *Toned wove paper. Pin-perf.*

45	**10**	½ a. dull pink	15 0	20 0
46	**4**	1 a. violet	80 0	£5
46*a*	**10*a***	1 r. dull green	60 0	£5

These were printed from plates: Nos. 45 and 46 in sheets of 24, No. 46a in sheets of 16. All the others, except Nos. 1, 2, and 3, were printed singly on paper with spaces ruled in pencil.

The 1 a. (No. 46) differs from T **4** in having an inscription in native characters below the words "ONE ANNA".

11 (½ a.)

12. Maharaja Sardul Singh.

1903. *Thick white wove glazed paper. Imperf.*

47	**11**	½ a. pink	25 0	20 0
47a	**12**	2 a. dull yellow	25 0	27 6

12a (8 a.)

1904. *T* **12a**. *Thin paper. Pin-perf.*

48		8 a. grey	30 0	
		a. Tête-bêche (pair)	60 0	

13. Maharaja Madan Singh. **14.**

(*T* **13.** Recess. Perkins Bacon & Co.)

1904–5. *P* 12½ (*all*) *and P* 13½ (¼ *a. to* 4 *a.*).

50	**13**	¼ a. carmine	2 6	2 0
51	,,	½ a. chestnut	2 0	2 0
52	,,	1 a. blue	2 6	2 6
53	,,	2 a. orange-yellow ..	25 0	25 0
54	,,	4 a. brown	15 0	15 0
54a	,,	8 a. violet (1905) ..	17 6	17 6
55	,,	1 r. green	20 0	20 0
56	,,	2 r. olive-yellow ..	40 0	45 0
57	,,	5 r. purple-brown ..	75 0	£5

1912. *Printed from half-tone blocks. No ornaments to left and right of value in English; large ornaments on either side of value in Hindi. Small stop after* "STATE".

(*a*) *Thin wove paper. Rouletted.*

58	**14**	2 a. deep violet ("TWO ANNA")	25 0	
		a. Tête-bêche (pair)	50 0	
		b. Imperf. (pair)		

No. 58 is printed in four rows, each inverted in respect to that above and below it.

(*b*) *Thick white chalk-surfaced paper. Rouletted in colour.* (*Medallion only in half-tone.*)

58c	**14**	¼ a. ultramarine	40 0	50 0

1913. *No ornaments on either side of value in English. Small ornaments in bottom label. No stop after* "STATE". *Thick white chalk-surfaced paper. Rouletted.*

58d	**14**	2 a. pur. ("TWO ANNAS")	30 0	80 0

15

(Typo. Diamond Soap Works, Kishangarh.)

1914. *Thick surfaced paper. Half-tone centre. Type-set inscriptions. Rouletted. Inscr.* "KISHANGARH".

59	**15**	¼ a. pale blue	1 0	1 0
		a. Imperf. (pair)	17 6	
		b. Error. "OUARTER" ..	20 0	
		c. Error. "KISHANGAHR"	20 0	
		d. Error. As last, imperf.		
60	,,	2 a. purple	25 0	40 0
		a. Error. "KISHANGAHR"	£5	£5

1913–16. *Stamps printed far apart, horizontally and vertically, otherwise as No.* 58*d*, *except as noted below.*

63	**14**	¼ a. blue ('13)	0 8	1 0
64	,,	½ a. green ('15)	0 8	1 0
		a. Printed both sides	£5	
		b. Emerald-green	3 0	
65	,,	1 a. red	2 0	2 6
66	,,	2 a. purple ("TWO ANNAS") ('15)	7 0	8 6
67	,,	4 a. bright blue	12 0	12 0
68	,,	8 a. brown	20 0	25 0
69	,,	1 r. mauve	40 0	50 0
70	,,	2 r. deep green	80 0	£5
71	,,	5 r. brown	£6	£

For this issue, ornaments were added on either side of the English value (except in the ¼ a.) and the inscription in the right label was re-set without stop.

16. Maharaja Yagyanarain Singhji. **17.**

1928–36. *Thick surfaced paper. Typo. Pin-perf.*

72	**16**	¼ a. light blue	0 9	1
73	,,	½ a. yellow-green	0 9	1
74	**17**	1 a. carmine	2 0	2
75	,,	2 a. purple	8 0	10
75a	,,	2 a. magenta ('36)	12 6	15
76	**16**	4 a. chestnut	5 0	6
77	,,	8 a. violet	6 0	8
78	,,	1 r. light green	15 0	17
79	,,	2 r. lemon-yellow ('29) ..	40 0	45
80	,,	5 r. claret ('29)	60 0	70
		a. Imperf. (pair)	£7	

The 4 a. to 5 r. are slightly larger than, bu otherwise similar to, the ¼ a. and ½ a. The 8 has a dotted background covering the who design.

1945–47. *As last, but thick, soft, unsurfaced paper. Poor impression. Typo. Pin-perf.*

No.	Type	Description	Unused	Used
81	**16**	¼ a. pale dull blue	3 0	5 0
82	,,	¼ a. greenish blue ('47) ..	5 0	7 0
83	,,	½ a. deep green	3 0	5 0
84	,,	½ a. yellow-green ('47) ..	6 0	7 6
85	**17**	1 a. carmine-red	8 0	9 0
86	,,	2 a. bright magenta ..	17 6	17 6
87	,,	2 a. maroon	£5	£5
88	**16**	4 a. brown	65 0	70 0
89	,,	8 a. violet	60 0	80 0
90	,,	1 r. green	£8	£10
91	,,	5 r. claret	£10	£15

Nos. 82 and 84 exist *imperf.* and No. 85 *imperf. between*, both horiz. and vert.

OFFICIAL STAMPS.

ON
K S
D

(31)

1918. *Overprint T* **31**, *in black, on* (i.) *Stamps of* 1899–1901. (*a*) *Imperf.*

No.	Description	Unused	Used
101	1 a. slate	—	7 6
	a. Inverted	12 6	
102	4 a. chocolate	—	65 0
	a. Inverted		
	(*b*) *Pin-perf.*		
102*b*	¼ a. green		
103	¼ a. pink	2 0	2 6
104	½ a. blue		
105	1 a. lilac	8 6	
	a. Inverted		
106	1 a. slate		
107	1 a. violet	12 6	
108	2 a. dull orange		
109	4 a. chocolate	45 0	45 0
110	1 r. dark green	£9	£9
111	2 r. red-brown	£15	£15
112	5 r. magenta	£20	£20
	(ii.) *Stamps of* 1903 *and* 1904.		
113	2 a. yellow	45 0	47 6
113*a*	8 a. grey	45 0	45 0
	(iii.) *Stamps of* 1904–5.		
114	¼ a. carmine	40 0	30 0
115	½ a. chestnut	1 0	1 3
116	1 a. blue	30 0	15 0
117	2 a. orange-yellow		
118	4 a. brown	40 0	40 0
119	8 a. violet	£8	£7
120	1 r. green	£25	£20
121	5 r. purple-brown		
	(iv.) *Stamps of* 1913–16.		
22	¼ a. blue	1 9	2 0
23	½ a. green	2 6	3 0
24	1 a. carmine	2 0	2 6
25	2 a. purple	4 0	4 0
26	4 a. bright blue	70 0	80 0
27	8 a. brown	90 0	95 0
28	1 r. lilac	£8	£8
29	2 r. deep green		
30	5 r. brown		
	(v.) *Stamps of* 1914.		
31	¼ a. pale blue	25 0	
32	2 a. purple	45 0	

All the above have been reported with overprint inverted, and many with overprint in red nd in all sorts of fancy positions. Some regularities took place at the sale of these tter, and it is doubtful if the varieties should e chronicled.

For later issues, see RAJASTHAN.

LAS BELA.

See under PAKISTAN.

MORVI.

1. Maharaja Sir Lakhdirji Waghji. **2.**

1931 (1 APRIL). *Typo. P* 12.
(*a*) *Printed in blocks of four. Stamps* 10 *mm. apart. Perf. on two or three sides.*

No.	Type	Description	Unused	Used
1	**1**	3 p. deep red	15 0	30 0
2	,,	½ a. blue	40 0	50 0

(*b*) *Printed in two blocks of four. Stamps* 5½ *mm. apart. Perf. on four sides.*

No.	Type	Description	Unused	Used
3	**1**	3 p. bright scarlet	4 0	7 6
		a. Error. Dull blue	15 0	
4	,,	½ a. dull blue	7 6	10 0
4*a*	,,	1 a. brown-red	10 0	12 6
4*b*	,,	2 a. yellow-brown	17 6	25 0

1932–33. *Horizontal background lines wider apart and portrait smaller than in T* **1**. *Typo. P* 11.

No.	Type	Description	Unused	Used
5	**2**	3 p. carmine-rose (*shades*) ..	2 0	5 0
6	,,	6 p. green	3 0	6 0
		a. Emerald-green	3 6	7 6
8	,,	1 a. ultramarine (to deep) ..	5 0	8 6
9	,,	2 a. bright violet ('33) ..	10 6	17 6
		a. Imperf. between (vert. pr.)		

3. Maharaja Sir Lakhdirji Waghji.

1934. *Typo. London ptg. P* 14.

No.	Type	Description	Unused	Used
10	**3**	3 p. carmine	1 3	2 6
11	,,	6 p. emerald-green	2 0	5 0
12	,,	1 a. purple brown	4 6	7 6
13	,,	2 a. bright violet	7 0	10 6

1935–48. *Typo. Morvi Press ptg. Rough perf.* 11.

No.	Type	Description	Unused	Used
14	**3**	3 p. scarlet (*shades*) ..	1 9	5 0
		a. Imperf. between. (horiz. pair)	£15	
15	,,	6 p. grey-green	2 0	6 0
		a. Emerald-green	10 0	
17	,,	1 a. brown	10 0	17 6
		a. Pale yellow-brown	22 6	40 0
		b. Chocolate	10 0	12 6
20	,,	2 a. dull violet (to deep) ..	6 0	20 0

Nos. 15*a*, 17*a* and 17*b* were issued between 1944 and 1948.

NANDGAON.

1

1892 (Feb.).

No.	Type	Description	Unused	Used
1	**1**	½ a. blue	15 0	£10
		a. Dull blue	25 0	
2	,,	2 a. rose	50 0	£25

Collectors are warned against copies of T **1** with faked postmarks. Genuinely used they are very rare.

(**2**)

3 (2 a.)

1893–94. *Optd. with T* **2** *in purple or grey.*

(i) *Printed wide apart on the sheet, no wavy lines between stamps.*

No.	Type	Description	Unused	Used
3	**3**	2 a. red	10 0	
		Without overprint.		
4	**3**	½ a. green	10 0	
5	,,	2 a. red	7 6	

(*ii*) *Printed closer together, wavy lines between stamps, the characters for* " half " *and* " two " *smaller than before.*

No.	Type	Description	Unused	Used
6	**3**	½ a. green	4 0	5 0
		a. Sage-green		
7	,,	1 a. rose (*laid paper*) ..	6 6	10 0
8	,,	1 a. rose (*wove paper*) ..	10 0	12 6
9	,,	2 a. dull carmine	10 0	12 6
		Without overprint.		
10	**3**	½ a. green	12 6	25 0
11	,,	1 a. rose (*laid paper*) ..	£5	
12	,,	1 a. rose (*wove paper*) ..	30 0	30 0

It has been stated that no stamps were regularly issued for postal use without the " control " mark, T **2**, but it is very doubtful if this is correct. The overprint probably indicates official use.

The 1 a. exists in *ultramarine* and in *brown*, but these appear to be reprints.

The stamps of Nandgaon have been obsolete since July, 1895.

NAWANAGAR.

1 (1 docra).

1877. *Laid paper.* (*a*) *Imperf.*

No.	Type	Description	Unused	Used
1	**1**	1 doc. blue (*shades*)	5 0	40 0
		a. Tête-bêche (pr.)	£50	
		(*b*) *Perf.* 12½ (*line*) *or* 11 (*harrow*).		
2	**1**	1 doc. slate-blue	£5	£8
		a. Tête-bêche (pr.) (*p.* 11) ..	£50	

2 (2 doc.)

3 (3 doc.)

1877. *T* **2** *and* **3**. *Black impression. Wove paper. Thick horizontal and vertical frame lines.*

(A) *Stamp* 14½–15 *mm. wide.*

(B) *Stamp* 16 *mm. wide.*

(C) *Stamp* 19 *mm. wide.*

No.	Description	A.	B.	C.
2*b*	1 doc. *deep mauve*	£15	£10	£10
2*c*	2 doc. *green*	†	†	£15
2*d*	3 doc. *yellow*	†	†	£25

Prices are for used. These stamps are not known unused.

1880. *As last, but thin frame lines, as illustrated.*

(D) *Stamp* 15 *to* 18 *mm. wide.*

(E) *Stamp* 14 *mm. wide.*

No.	Description	D. Unused	D. Used	E. Unused	E. Used
3	1 doc. *dp. mauve* ..	5 0	17 6	†	
	a. On rose ..	6 0	—	7 6	12 6
4	1 doc. *magenta* ..	†		3 6	—
5	2 doc. *yellow-green*	7 0	40 0	7 0	15 0
	a. On blue-green ..	8 6	—	15 0	—
6	3 doc. *orange-yellow*	12 6	—	†	
	a. On yellow ..	15 0	50 0	10 0	20 0
	ab. On yell. Laid pp.	80 0	—	50 0	—
	Error on sheet of one setting of the 3 *docra.*				
7	2 doc. *yellow* ..	£6		†	

There are several different settings of each value of this series.

4 (1 docra)

1893. (A) *P* 12. (B) *Imperf.* (*a*) *Thick wove paper.*

No.	Type	Description	A. Unused	A. Used	B. Unused	B. Used
8	**4**	1 doc. black ..	10 0	—	£10	—
9	,,	3 doc. orange ..	20 0	—	†	
		(*b*) *Thick laid paper.*				
10	**4**	1 doc. black ..	—	—	†	
		(*c*) *Thin wove paper.*				
11	**4**	1 doc. black (to grey) ..	2 6	3 6	80 0	—
		a. Imperf. between (pr.)	£10	—	†	
12	,,	2 doc. green ..	5 0	7 6	80 0	—
13	,,	3 doc. orge.-yell.	6 0	—	†	
		a. Imperf. between (pr.)	£10	—	†	
		b. Orange ..	7 6	10 0	50 0	—

(d) Thin, soft wove paper.

14 **4** 1 doc. black .. — — †
15 ,, 2 doc. dp. grn. 20 0 — †
16 ,, 3 doc. brn.-orge. 27 6 — †

The stamps of this State went out of use at the end of 1895.

NEPAL.

Nepal being an independent state, its stamps are now listed in Part III of the Stanley Gibbons Catalogue.

ORCHHA.

A set of four stamps, ½ a. red, 1 a. violet, 2 a. yellow and 4 a. deep blue-green, perforated, and in a design roughly similar to T **2**, was prepared about 1897 by a European jeweller, possibly with State authority. There is no evidence that they were issued and we therefore do not list them.

1

2

1913. *Background to arms unshaded. Very blurred impression. Wove paper. Imperf.*

1 ½ a. green 25 0
,, 1 a. red 30 0

1914–16. *Background shaded with short horizontal lines. Clearer impression. Wove paper. Imperf.*

2 ¼ a. brt. ultramarine (1915) .. 4 0
a. Grey-blue 1 3 2 0
b. Deep blue 3 6
,, ½ a. green 1 3 2 0
,, 1 a. scarlet 3 6 5 0
a. Orange-red 5 0 10 0
,, 2 a. red-brown (1916) .. 7 6 10 0
,, 4 a. ochre 10 0 12 6
a. Yellow-orange 15 0 17 6

There are two sizes of T **2** in the setting, one being the same as T **1** and the other as illustrated.

3. H.H. The Maharaja of Orchha. **4.**

(Offset. Indian Govt. Ptg. Wks., Nasik.)

939–42? *P* 13½ × 14 (*T* **3**) *or* 14 × 13½ (*T* **4**).

3 ¼ a. chocolate 0 9
,, ½ a. yellow-green 1 0
,, ¾ a. bright blue 1 0
,, 1 a. scarlet 1 6
,, 1½ a. blue 1 6

13 **3** 1½ a. mauve 1 6
14 ,, 2 a. vermilion 2 0
15 ,, 2½ a. turquoise-green .. 2 6
16 ,, 3 a. slate-violet 3 6
17 ,, 4 a. slate 5 0
18 ,, 8 a. magenta 10 0
19 **4** 1 r. grey-green 20 0
20 ,, 2 r. bright violet 60 0
21 ,, 5 r. yellow-orange .. £12
22 ,, 10 r. turquoise-green ('42?) £20

A series of 21 values, from ¼ a. to 25 r., bi-coloured and with a portrait of the Ruler in European dress, was introduced in 1935, but owing to lack of proper State control was offered in large quantities to dealers and collectors at less than face value. Eventually the authorities withdrew the issue and exchanged supplies for stamps of the 1939 issue. Though some of the values have been seen with what appears to be genuine postmarks, the circumstances of this issue were such that we feel we are serving the best interests of philately by continuing not to list it.

POONCH.

The stamps of Poonch are all *imperf.*, and printed in water-colours.

1

2

1876. *T* **1** (22 × 21 *mm.*). *Yellowish white, wove paper.*

1 6 p. red .. .. .. — £6

1877. *As T* **1** (19 × 17 *mm.*). *Same paper.*

1*a* ½ a. red .. .. — £50

1879. *T* **2** (21 × 19 *mm.*). *Same paper.*

2 ½ a. red .. .. — £22

3 (½ a.)

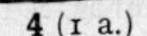

4 (1 a.)

5 (2 a.)

6 (4 a.)

1880. *Yellowish white, wove paper.*

3 **3** ½ a. red 50 0 30 0
4 **4** 1 a. red 60 0 40 0
5 **5** 2 a. red 70 0 70 0
6 **6** 4 a. red 70 0

1884. *T* **3** *to* **6.** *Toned wove bâtonné paper.*

7 ½ a. red 10 0 10 0
8 1 a. red 15 0
9 2 a. red 20 0 20 0
10 4 a. red 30 0

These are sometimes found gummed.

7. (1 pice)

1884–87. *T* **3** *to* **7.** *Various papers.*

(*a*) *White laid bâtonné or ribbed bâtonné.*

11 1 pice, red 17 6 20 0
12 ½ anna, red 2 6 3 0
13 1 anna, red 3 0
14 2 annas, red 5 0 6 0
15 4 annas, red 8 6

(*d*) *Thick white laid paper.*

22*a* 1 pice, red 50 0
23 ½ anna, red 12 6
24 1 anna, red 20 0
25 2 annas, red 40 0
26 4 annas, red 45 0

(*e*) *Yellow wove bâtonné.*

27 1 pice, red 12 6 15 0
28 ½ anna, red 15 0 12 6
29 1 anna, red 25 0
30 2 annas, red 12 6 17 6
31 4 annas, red 7 6 8 6

(*f*) *Orange-buff wove bâtonné.*

32 1 pice, red 2 6 2 6
33 ½ anna, red 20 0
34 2 annas, red 35 0
35 4 annas, red 15 0

(*g*) *Yellow laid paper.*

36 1 pice, red 5 0 6 0
37 ½ anna, red 10 0
38 1 anna, red 22 6
39 2 annas, red 25 0 25 0
40 4 annas, red 35 0

(*h*) *Yellow laid bâtonné.*

41 1 pice, red 30 0 12 6

(*i*) *Buff laid or ribbed bâtonné paper thicker than* (*f*).

42 1 anna, red 50 0
43 4 annas, red 70 0

(*j*) *Blue-green laid paper* (1887).

44 ½ anna, red 25 0
45 1 anna, red 20 0 20 0
46 2 annas, red 22 6
47 4 annas, red 25 0

(*k*) *Yellow-green laid paper.*

48 ½ anna, red .. .. ..

(*l*) *Blue-green wove bâtonné.*

49 1 pice, red 47 6 60 0
50 1 anna, red 3 6 5 0

(*m*) *Lavender wove bâtonné.*

51 1 anna, red 60 0
52 2 annas, red 3 0 6 0

(*n*) *Various coloured papers.*

53 1 p. red/*grey-blue laid* .. 17 6 20 0
54 1 p. red/*lilac laid* £6 £6
55 1 p. red/*blue wove bâtonné* .. 3 0 4 0

1888. *T* **3** *to* **7** *in aniline rose on various papers.*

56 1 p. on *blue wove bâtonné* .. 10 0
56*a* 1 p. on *buff laid* 15 0
57 ½ a. on *white laid* 27 6
58 1 a. on *green laid* 35 0 30 0
59 1 a. on *green wove bâtonné* .. 8 6 10 6
60 2 a. on *lavender wove bâtonné* 10 0 7 6
61 4 a. on *yellow laid* 30 0 25 0

OFFICIAL STAMPS

1888. *T* **3** *to* **7.** ***White laid bâtonné paper.***

101 1 pice, black 2 0 3 6
102 ½ anna, black 3 0 5 0
103 1 anna, black 4 0
104 2 annas, black 5 0 6 0
105 4 annas, black 6 0 6 0

White toned wove bâtonné paper.

106 1 pice, black 5 0
107 ½ anna, black 10 0 10 0
108 1 anna, black 25 0 25 0
109 2 annas, black 20 0 17 6
110 4 annas, black 25 0

The stamps of Poonch have been obsolete since 1894.

RAJASTHAN.

Rajasthan was formed in 1948 from a number of States in Rajputana; these included Bundi, Jaipur and Kishangarh, whose posts continued to function more or less separately until ordered by the Indian Government to close, on April 1st, 1950.

BUNDI.

(1)

1949. *Nos.* 86/92 *of Bundi handstamped with T* **1**.
A. *In black.* B. *In violet.* C. *In blue.*

		A.	B.	C.
1	¼ a. blue-green	2 6	10 0	50
	a. Machine-printed ..	—	†	†
2	½ a. violet	3 6	3 6	20
	a. Machine-printed ..	—	†	†
3	1 a. yellow-green ..	3 0	20 0	20
	a. Machine-printed ..	—	†	†
4	2 a. vermilion	3 6	20 0	—
	a. Machine-printed ..	3 6	†	†
5	4 a. orange	30 0	5 0	40
	a. Machine-printed ..	5 0	†	†
6	8 a. ultramarine	5 0	5 0	30
	a. Machine-printed ..	7 6	†	†
7	1 r. chocolate	—	—	40
	a. Machine-printed ..	10 0	†	†

The above prices are for unused copies.

JAIPUR.

राजस्थान

RAJASTHAN

(2)

1949. *T* **7** *of Jaipur optd. with T* **2**.

8 ¼ a. black & brown-lake (No. 58) (B.) 2 6
9 ½ a. blk. & vio. (No. 41) (R.) .. 2 6
10 ¾ a. black & brown-red (No. 59) (B.) 2 6
11 1 a. blk. & blue (No. 60) (R.) .. 2 6
12 2 a. blk. & buff (No. 61) (R.) .. 2 6
13 2½ a. blk. & carm. (No. 62) (B.) 3 0
14 3 a. blk. & green (No. 63) (R.) 3 6
15 4 a. black & grey-green (No. 64) (R.) 5 0
16 6 a. black & pale blue (No. 65*a*) (R.) 7 0

17 8 a. blk. & choc. (No. 66) (R.) 15 0
18 1 r. black & yellow-bistre (No. 67) (R.) 22 6

KISHANGARH.

1949. *Various stamps of Kishangarh handstamped with T* **1** *in red.*

19 ¼ a. blue (No. 63) 80 0 80 0
20 ¼ a. greenish blue (No. 82) .. 80 0 80 0
21 ½ a. deep blue (No. 9B) .. £5
22 ½ a. chestnut (No. 51) .. 60 0
23 ½ a. green (No. 64) 40 0 20 0
24 ½ a. yellow-green (No. 73) .. 40 0
25 ½ a. deep green (No. 83) ..
26 ½ a. yellow-green (No. 84) .. 10 0 5 0
27 1 a. lilac (No. 13B) 50 0
28 1 a. slate (No. 15a, perf.) .. 60 0
29 1 a. red (No. 65) 40 0 40 0
30 1 a. carmine-red (No. 85) .. 20 0 20 0
31 2 a. deep violet (No. 58) .. 30 0
32 2 a. purple (No. 58c) 50 0
33 2 a. purple (No. 66) 10 0 15 0
34 2 a. brt. magenta (No. 86) .. 60 0
35 2 a. maroon (No. 87) 60 0 40 0
36 4 a. brown (No. 54) 80 0
37 4 a. bright blue (No. 67) .. 80 0
38 4 a. chestnut (No. 76) .. 80 0
39 4 a. brown (No. 88) 15 0
40 8 a. grey (No. 48) £8
41 8 a. violet (No. 54a) 80 0
42 8 a. brown (No. 68) 25 0
43 8 a. violet (No. 77) 80 0
44 8 a. violet (No. 89) 25 0
45 1 r. green (No. 55) £7
46 1 r. mauve (No. 69) 40 0
47 1 r. light green (No. 78) .. £7
48 1 r. green (No. 90) 50 0
49 2 r. olive-yellow (No. 56) .. £8
50 2 r. deep green (No. 70) .. 30 0
51 2 r. lemon-yellow (No. 79) .. £8
52 2 r. yellow (1945–47) £12
53 5 r. purple-brown (No. 57) .. £10
54 5 r. brown (No. 71) 75 0
55 5 r. claret (No. 80) £10
56 5 r. red-brown (1945–47) .. £12

Nos. 52 and 56 were not issued without the Rajasthan overprint, and various values of the 1945–7 Kishangarh issue are known *imperf.* with the overprint.

RAJPIPLA.

1 (1 pice)

2 (2 a.)

3 (4 a.)

1880. *P* 11 (1 *p.*) *or* 12½.

1 1 p. blue 7 6 15 0
2 2 a. green 30 0 40 0
a. Imperf. between (pair) .. £25 £25
3 4 a. red 20 0 25 0

These stamps became obsolete in 1886.

SIRMOOR (SIRMUR).

1 (1 pice)

2

1879–80. *P* 11½.

1 **1** 1 p. pale green 15 0
2 ,, 1 p. blue (on *laid* paper) .. 10 0 £12
a. Imperf. between (pair) .. £20 £20
b. Imperf. (pair) .. ..

(Printed at Calcutta.)

1892. *Thick wove paper.* *P* 11½.

3 **2** 1 p. yellow-green 3 0 4 0
a. Imperf. between (pair) .. 70 0
b. Deep green 2 6 4 0
ba. Imperf. between (pair) .. £5 50 0
4 ,, 1 p. blue 5 0 5 0
a. Imperf. between (pair) .. 70 0
b. Imperf. (pair) .. ..

These were originally made as *reprints*, about 1891, to supply collectors, but there being very little demand for them they were put into use. The design was copied (including the perforations!) from an illustration in a dealer's catalogue.

3. Raja Sir Shamsher Parkash.
(Litho. Waterlow & Sons.)

1885–96. *T* **3.** *P* 14 *to* 15.

There were seven printings of the 3 and 6 pies, six of the 1 anna, and four of the 2 annas, the last being used optd. for official use (Nos. 99/102), all in sheets of seventy, made up of groups of transfers showing two or more minor varieties. There are two distinct varieties of the 3 p. and 6 p., as shown in Types A and B, C and D. Of these B and D are the types of the sixth printing of those values, and A and C those of all the other printings.

A B
C D

A and C have large white dots evenly placed between the ends of the upper and lower inscriptions; B has small white dots, and less space between the ends of the inscriptions; D has large spaces, and large white dots *not* in the centres of the spaces, especially at the left side.

The last printing of each value is only known with the Waterlow overprint, T **18**.

Roman figures denote printings.

No.	Type	Description	Unused	Used
7		3 p. chocolate (A) I, IV	1 6	1 3
8		3 p. brown (B) VI	0 9	0 9
9		3 p. orge. (A) II, III, IV, V	1 6	1 6
10		3 p. orange (B) VI	1 3	1 3
		a. Imperf.	£10	
11		6 p. blue-green (C) I	5 0	5 0
11a		6 p. bright green (C) III	40 0	40 0
12		6 p. green (C) II, IV	3 6	3 6
13		6 p. deep green (C) V	1 6	1 6
14		6 p. yellowish green (D) VI	2 6	2 6
15		1 a. bright blue, I	3 0	4 0
16		1 a. dull blue, III	20 0	20 0
16a		1 a. steel blue, IV	40 0	40 0
17		1 a. grey-blue, V	2 6	3 0
17a		1 a. slate-blue, VI	5 0	6 0
18		2 a. pink, I	12 6	12 6
18a		2 a. carmine, V	7 6	8 6
19		2 a. rose-red, VI	10 0	10 0

3 p. orange Printings III and IV are rare, being worth at least six times the value of other printings.

4

(Recess. Waterlow & Sons.)

1895–99. *P* 13 *to* 15.

No.	Type	Description	Unused	Used
20	4	3 p. orange-brown	5 0	2 0
21	,,	6 p. green	6 0	2 0
22	,,	1 a. blue	6 0	2 0
23	,,	2 a. rose	6 0	5 0
24	,,	3 a. yellow-green	8 6	15 0
25	,,	4 a. deep green	12 6	20 0
26	,,	8 a. deep blue	17 6	30 0
27	,,	1 r. vermilion	22 6	40 0

5. Raja Sir Surendar Bikram Parkash.

(Recess. Waterlow & Sons.)

1899. *P* 13 *to* 15.

No.	Type	Description	Unused	Used
28	5	3 a. yellow-green	10 0	25 0
29	,,	4 a. deep green	12 6	30 0
30	,,	8 a. deep blue	15 0	30 0
31	,,	1 r. vermilion	25 0	50 0

OFFICIAL STAMPS.

NOTE.—*The varieties occurring in the machine-printed* "On S.S.S." *overprints may, of course, also be found in the inverted and double overprints, and many of them are known thus.*

I. Machine-printed.

On

S. S.

S.

(11)

1890. *Optd. with T* **11.**

(*a*) *In black.*

No.	Type	Description	Unused	Used
50	3	6 p. green	£8	
		a. Stop before first "S"		
51	,,	2 a. rose-red	27 6	40 0
		a. Stop before first "S"	£6	

(*b*) *In red.*

No.	Type	Description	Unused	Used
52	3	6 p. green	10 0	6 0
		a. Stop before first "S"	50 0	
53	,,	1 a. blue	27 6	20 0
		a. Stop before first "S"	85 0	

(*c*) *Doubly optd. in red and in black.*

No.	Type	Description	Unused	Used
53b	3	6 p. green		
		c. Stop before first "S"		

On

S. S.

S.

(12)

On

S. S.

S.

(13)

1891. *Optd. with T* **12.**

(*a*) *In black.*

No.	Description	Unused	Used
54	3 p. orange	6 0	
	a. Opt. inverted		
55	6 p. green	7 0	7 6
	a. Opt. double		
	b. No stop after lower "S"		
	c. Raised stop before lower "S"		
56	1 a. blue		
57	2 a. rose-red	40 0	

(*b*) *In red.*

No.	Description	Unused	Used
58	6 p. green	37 6	20
	a. Opt. inverted	—	95
	b. Opt. double	—	90
59	1 a. blue	25 0	60
	a. Opt. inverted		
	b. Opt. double		
	c. No stop after lower "S"	30 0	

1892–97. *T* **3** *optd. with T* **13.**

(*a*) *In black.*

No.	Description	Unused	Used
60	3 p. orange	1 6	1
	a. Opt. inverted		
	b. First "S" inverted and stop raised	15 0	17
	c. No stop after lower "S"	10 0	12
	d. Raised stop after second "S"		
61	6 p. green	2 6	3
	a. First "S" inverted and stop raised	—	15
	b. Raised stop after second "S"		
62	1 a. blue	17 6	15
	a. Opt. double		
	b. First "S" inverted and stop raised	—	27
	c. No stop after lower "S"		
	d. Raised stop after second "S"		
63	2 a. rose-red	20 0	20
	a. Opt. inverted		
	b. First "S" inverted and stop raised		
	c. No stop after lower "S"		
	d. Raised stop after second "S"		

(*b*) *In red.*

No.	Description	Unused	Used
64	6 p. green	5 0	4
	a. Overprint inverted		
	b. First "S" inverted and stop raised	20 0	20
65	1 a. blue	17 6	5
	a. Overprint inverted		
	b. Overprint double		
	c. First "S" inverted and stop raised	20 0	20
	d. No stop after lower "S"	—	20

(*c*) *Doubly overprinted in black and red.*

No.	Description	Unused	Used
65e	6 p. green		

There are six settings of this overprint. T inverted "S" occurs in the 2nd and 5th setting and the missing stop in the 2nd setting of all values except the 6 p. In the 5th setting occurs the raised stop after 2nd "S".

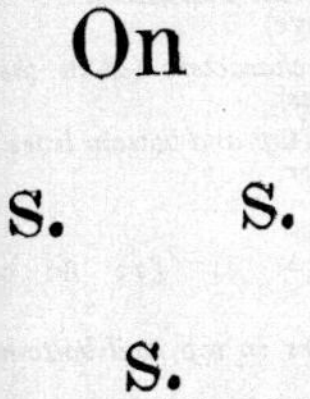

(14) 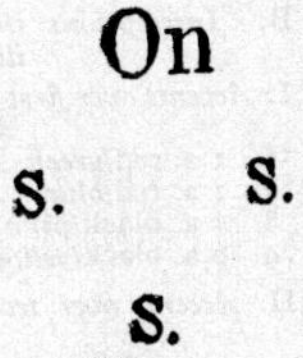 (15)

1896. *T* **3** *optd. as T* **14.**

66 3 p. orange 15 0 8 6
a. Comma after first "S" .. 30 0
b. Overprint inverted ..
67 6 p. green 10 0 5 0
a. Comma after first "S" .. — 20 0
b. Comma after lower "S" .. — 35 0
c. "S" at right inverted
68 1 a. blue 17 6 7 6
a. Comma after first "S" .. — 35 0
b. Comma after lower "S" ..
69 2 a. carmine 22 6 12 6
a. Comma after first "S"

There are four settings of this overprint; (1) 23 mm. high, includes the comma after lower "S"; (2) 25 mm. high, with variety, comma after first "S"; (3) and (4) 25 mm. high, with no important varieties.

1898 (Nov.). *T* **3** *optd. with T* **15.**

70 6 p. green .. .. .. — 10 0
a. Small "S" at right ..
b. Comma after lower "S" ..
c. Lower "S" inverted and stop raised .. .. ..
71 1 a. blue .. .. .. — 17 6
a. Small "S" at right ..
b. Small "S" without stop ..

There are two settings of this overprint. Nos. 70a and 71a/b occur in the first setting, and Nos. 70b/c in the second setting.

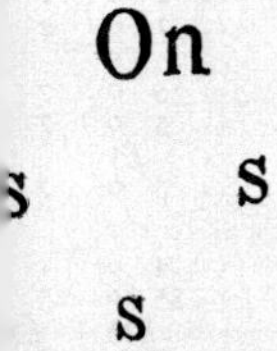

(16) 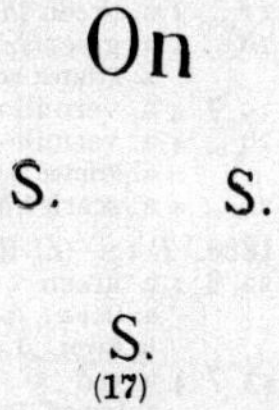 (17)

1899. *Overprinted as T* **16** *(but with stop after each "S"), in black.*

72 **3** 3 p. orange .. .. .. — 12 9
73 ,, 6 p. green .. .. .. — 8 9

1900. *Optd. as T* **17**, *in black.*

74 **3** 3 p. orange .. .. — 20 0
a. Raised stop after lower "S" — 60 0
75 ,, 6 p. green .. .. — 18 0
a. Raised stop after lower "S" — 65 0
b. Comma after first "S" .. — 80 0
76 ,, 1 a. blue .. .. — 25 0
a. Raised stop after lower "S" — 75 0
77 ,, 2 a. carmine .. ..
a. Raised stop after lower "S" — 35 0

There are two settings of this overprint: (1) 22 mm. high, with raised stop variety; (2) 23 mm. high, with "comma" variety in the 6 pies.

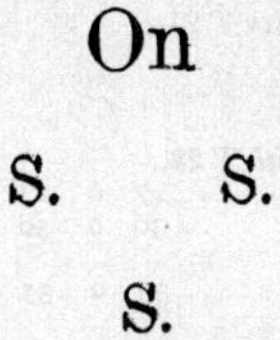

(18) 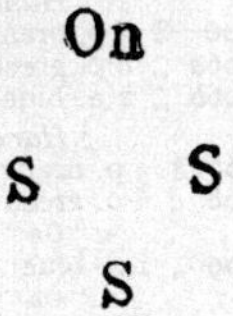 (19)

(Optd. by Waterlow & Sons.)

1900. *Optd. with T* **18**, *in black.*

78 **3** 3 p. orange 5 0 4 0
79 ,, 6 p. green 2 0 2 0
80 ,, 1 a. blue 1 6 1 6
81 ,, 2 a. carmine 10 0 12 6

II. HANDSTAMPED. The word "On" and each letter "S" struck separately.

1894. *Handstamped with T* **19.**

(*a*) *In black.*

94 **3** 3 p. orange 7 0 8 6
a. "On" sideways ..
95 ,, 6 p. green 15 0 12 0
a. "On" only ..
96 ,, 1 a. blue 17 6 17 6
97 ,, 2 a. rose-red 20 0 20 0
a. "On" only .. ..
b. "On" sideways .. ..

(*b*) *In red.*

98 **3** 6 p. green 40 0

1896. *Handstamped with letters similar to those of T* **13**, *with stops, but irregular.*

98a **3** 3 p. orange .. ..
98b ,, 6 p. green .. ..
c. "On" omitted ..
98d ,, 2 a. rose-red .. ..

1896. *Handstamped with letters similar to those of T* **14**, *with stops, but irregular.*

99 **3** 3 p. orange 15 0 17 6
a. "On" Double .. ..
100 ,, 6 p. green .. .. — 22 6
101 ,, 1 a. blue .. .. — 30 0
102 ,, 2 a. rose-red .. .. — 35 0

In No. 99a the second "On" is over the lower "S".

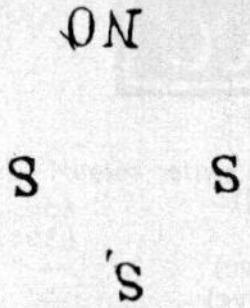

(20) 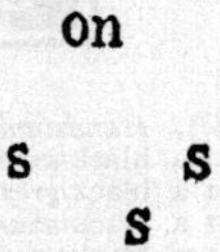 (21)

1896. *Handstamped with T* **20.**

103 **3** 3 p. orange 35 0 35 0
104 ,, 2 a. rose-red 70 0 70 0

Handstamped with T **21.**

104a **3** 3 p. orange 75 0 70 0
104b ,, 6 p. green .. ..
105 ,, 1 a. blue 70 0

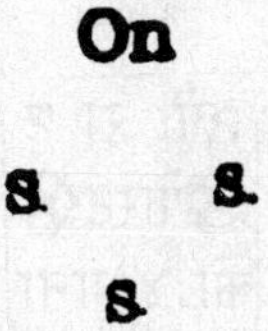

(21a) 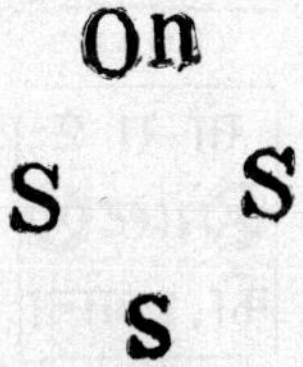 (22)

Handstamped with T **21a.**

No.	Type	Description	Unused	Used
106	**3**	3 p. orange		
106*a*	,,	6 p. green		
106*b*	,,	1 a. blue		

Handstamped with T **22.**

No.	Type	Description	Unused	Used
107	**3**	3 p. orange	27 6	27 6
108	,,	6 p. green	30 0	30 0
		a. " On " only		
109	,,	1 a. blue	35 0	35 0
		a. " On " only		
110	,,	2 a. rose-red	40 0	37 6

Mixed overprints.

(*a*) *Handstamped " On " as in T* **19**, *and press-printed opt. T* **13** *complete.*

No.	Type	Description	Unused	Used
111	**3**	6 p. green		

(*b*) *Handstamped opt. as T* **14**, *and press-printed overprint T* **13**, *complete.*

No.	Type	Description	Unused	Used
112	**3**	6 p. green		

Various other types of these handstamps are known to exist, but in the absence of evidence of their authenticity we do not list them. It is stated that stamps of T **4** were never officially overprinted.

The stamps of Sirmoor have been obsolete since 31 March, 1902.

SORUTH (JUNAGADH).

The name " Soruth " (or " Sorath ") was used for all the territory later known as Kathiawar (but referred to also as " Saurashtra "). Strictly speaking the name should have been applied only to a portion of Kathiawar including the state of Junagadh, which issued the stamps we list below (up to No. 57). As collectors have known these issues under the heading of " Soruth " for so long, we retain the name.

In Feb. 1948, under the new Constitution of India, the Union of Saurashtra was formed. This included, among other states, the former stamp-issuing units of Soruth, Jasdan, Morvi, Nawanagar and Wadhwan.

1

1864 (?). *Handstamped in water colour. Imperf.*

No.	Type	Description	Unused	Used
1	**1**	1 a. black/*azure* (laid) ..	£30	50 0
2	,,	1 a. black/*grey* (laid) ..	£30	50 0
3	,,	1 a. black/*azure* (wove) ..	—	£5
4	,,	1 a. black/*cream* (wove) ..	—	£5

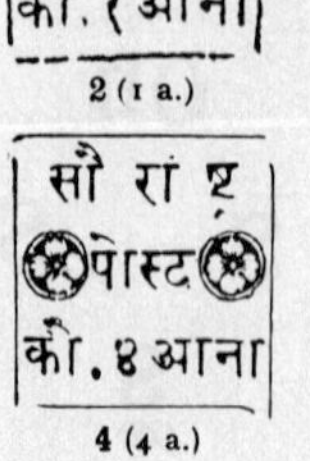

2 (1 a.) **3** (1 a.)

4 (4 a.) **5** (4 a.)

1868. *T* **2** *to* **5** (*two characters, Nagri and Gujrati, respectively for " 1 " and " 4 " as shown in the illustrations*). *Imperf.*

A. *Inscriptions in Gujrati characters.*

No.	Type	Description	Unused	Used
5		1 a. black/*yellowish* (wove) ..		

B. *Inscriptions in Nagri characters* (*as in the illustrations*).

I. *Accents over first letters in top and bottom lines. Wove paper.*

No.	Type	Description	Unused	Used
6		1 a. red/*green*		
7		1 a. red/*blue*		
8		1 a. black/*pink*	£12	80 0
9		2 a. black/*yellow*		

II. *Accents over second letters in top and bottom lines.*

(*a*) *Wove paper.*

No.	Type	Description	Unused	Used
10	**2**	1 a. black/*pink*	£8	50 0

(*b*) *Laid paper.*

No.	Type	Description	Unused	Used
11	**2**	1 a. black/*azure*	75 0	30 0
12	**3**	1 a. black/*azure*	£5	50 0
13	,,	1 a. red/*white*	60 0	75 0
14	**4**	4 a. black/*white*	£10	£12
15	**5**	4 a. black *white*	£12	£15

Official imitations, consisting of 1 a. carmine-red on white wove and white laid, 1 a. black on blue wove, 4 a. black on white wove, 4 a. black on blue wove, 4 a. red on white laid—all imperforate 1 a. carmine-red on white laid, 1 a. black on blue wove, 4 a. black on white laid and blue wove—all perforated 12, were made in 1890. Entire sheets of originals have 20 stamps. the imitations only 4 or 16.

6

7

1877. *Imperf.*

(*a*) *Medium laid paper, lines wide apart.*

(*b*) *Thick laid paper, lines wide apart.*

(*c*) *Thick laid paper, lines close together.*

No.	Type	Description	Unused	Used
16	**6**	1 a. green (*a*)	1 6	2
17	,,	1 a. green (*b*)	1 0	2
18	,,	1 a. green (*c*)	1 6	2
		a. Printed both sides	£5	
19	**7**	4 a. vermilion (*a*)	5 0	7
20	,,	4 a. vermilion/*toned* (*b*) ..	5 0	7
		a. Printed both sides	£5	
21	,,	4 a. scarlet/*bluish* (*b*) ..	5 0	7

1886. *P* 12. (*a*) *Wove paper.*

No.	Type	Description	Unused	Used
22	**6**	1 a. green	4 0	4
		a. Imperf. (pair)	35 0	25
		b. Error. 1 a. blue	£35	£3
23	**7**	4 a. red	5 0	6
		a. Imperf. (pair)	40 0	25

(*b*) *Toned laid paper.*

No.	Type	Description	Unused	Used
24	**6**	1 a. green	1 9	2
25	,,	1 a. emerald-green	3 6	5
		a. Error. 1 a. blue	£35	£3
26	**7**	4 a. red	2 6	3
27	,,	4 a. carmine	3 6	5

(*c*) *Bluish white laid paper.*

No.	Type	Description	Unused	Used
28	**6**	1 a. green	5 0	5
		a. Imperf. between (pair) ..	60 0	60
29	,,	4 a. scarlet	10 0	12

There is a very wide range of colours in bo values. The laid paper is found both vertical ar horizontal.

The 1 a. was first issued in sheets of 15 varietie and afterwards in sheets of 20; the 4 a. is horizontal strips of 5 varieties.

16 " Soruth " annas = 1 koree.

1 koree = 4 annas, Indian currency.

Three pies.
ત્રણ પાઇ.
(8)

One anna.
એક આનો.
(8*a*)

1913. *T* **6** *and* **7.** *P* 12. *Surch. in Indian currency with T* **8** *or* **8***a*.

(*a*) *On yellowish wove paper.*

34 3 p. on 1 a. emerald 0 10 1 0
a. Imperf. (pair) .. ..

(*b*) *On white wove paper.*

35 3 p. on 1 a. emerald 1 3 1 3
a. Imperf. between (pair) .. £5 £5
b. Surch. inverted 50 0 35 0
36 1 a. on 4 a. carmine 7 6 7 6
a. Imperf. (pair) .. ..
b. Surch. both sides .. ..
c. Capital "A" in "Anna" .. 9 0

(*c*) *On white laid paper.*

37 3 p. on 1 a. emerald .. ..
a. Imperf. (pair) .. .. — £6
38 1 a. on 4 a. red 10 0 10 0
a. Capital "A" in "Anna" ..
b. Inverted .. .. ..
c. Double .. .. ..
d. Double, one inverted .. ..

(*d*) *On toned wove paper.*

39 1 a. on 4 a. red 5 0 5 6
a. Imperf. (pair) .. ..
b. Capital "A" in "Anna" .. 12 6
c. Surch. inverted .. ..

1915. *T* **7** *and* **6.** *Wove or laid paper. P* 12.

40 3 p. bright green 2 0 2 0
a. Imperf. (pair) 3 0 4 0
41 1 a. red 2 0 3 0
a. Imperf. (pair) 10 0 12 0
b. Imperf. between (pair) ..
c. Laid paper 10 0 10 0

Nawab Sir Mahabat Khanji Rasulkhan.
9 10

(Typo. Junagadh State Press.)

.923. *Blurred impression. Laid paper. Pin-perf.* 12.

.2 **9** 1 a. red 7 6 7 6

Sheets of 16 stamps (8 × 2).

ત્રણ પાઇ
(11)

ત્રણ પાઈ
(12)

923. *Surch. with T* **11.**

3 **9** 3 p. on 1 a. red 7 6 7 6
a. Surch. with T 12 .. .. 10 0 10 0

Four stamps in the setting have surch. T **12** e. with top of last character curved to right.

924. *Pin-perf.* 12, *small holes. Wove paper.*

4 **10** 3 p. mauve 2 6 2 6
5 **9** 1 a. red 5 0 7 6
a. Imperf. (pair) 60 0 60 0

The 1 a. is from new and clearer clichés. Sheets f 16 stamps (4 × 4).

928–29. *P* 12, *large holes.*

6 **10** 3 p. mauve (*laid paper*) .. 1 9 1 9
a. Imperf. (pair) 12 6 12 6
b. Imperf. betwn. (horiz. pair)
c. Wove paper 7 6 7 6
7 **9** 1 a. red (*wove paper*) .. 15 0 15 0

No. 47 is as No. 45 except for perf. The laid paper shows wmk. State Arms in sheet. Both values are in sheets of 16 (4 × 4) or (3 p. only) in sheets of two panes of 16.

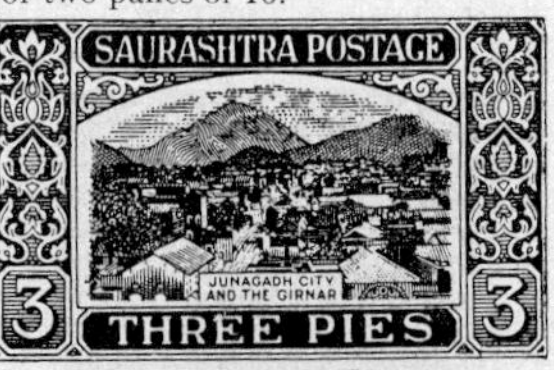

13. Junagadh City.

14. Gir Lion.

15. Nawab Sir Mahabat Khanji Rasulkhan

16. Kathi Horse.

(Printed at Nasik.)

1929 (1 OCT.). *P* 14. *Inscr.* "POSTAGE."

49 **13** 3 p. black and blackish green 3 0 2 0
50 **14** ½ a. black and deep blue .. 15 0 1 0
51 **15** 1 a. black and carmine .. 7 6 5 0
52 **16** 2 a. black and orange .. 25 0 1 0
53 **13** 3 a. black and carmine .. 5 0 3 0
54 **14** 4 a. black and purple .. 30 0 2 6
55 **16** 8 a. black and yellow-green 50 0 5 0
56 **15** 1 r. black and pale blue .. 12 6 10 0

1937. *As T* **15**, *but inscr.* "POSTAGE AND REVENUE". *P* 14.

57 **15** 1 a. black and carmine .. 3 6 4 0

Postage & Revenue

ONE ANNA
(**17**)

1949. (*a*) *No.* 50 *surch.* " POSTAGE & REVENUE/ ONE ANNA " *in seriffed capital letters, in red.*
58 **14** 1 a. on ½ a. black & dp. blue 10 0 12 0
a. Surch. double .. £15 £15
(*b*) *No.* 52 *surch. with T* **17**, *in green.*
59 **16** 1 a. on 2 a. black & orange 12 6 10 6

18

1949. *Court Fee stamp optd.* " U.S.S./REVENUE/ POSTAGE/SAURASHTRA ". *Typo. P* 11.
60 **18** 1 a. purple 10 0 10 0
a. " POSTAGE " omitted .. £12 £12
b. Opt. double £12 £12
c. " REVENUE POSTAGE " omitted £12 £12

1950 (MAR.). *No.* 49 *surch.* " POSTAGE & REVENUE/ONE ANNA ".
61 **13** 1 a. on 3 p. blk. & blksh. grn. 50 0 50 0
a. " P " of " POSTAGE " omitted £15 £15

OFFICIAL STAMPS.

SARKARI (O 1) SARKARI (O 2)

1929. *Optd. with Type* O **1** *in red.*
O1 **13** 3 p. black & blackish green 0 3 0 3
O2 **14** ½ a. black and deep blue .. 3 6 0 3
O3 **15** 1 a. black & carm. (No. 51) 0 4 0 3
O4 **16** 2 a. black and orange .. 3 6 0 6
O5 **13** 3 a. black and carmine .. 1 0 0 6
O6 **14** 4 a. black and purple .. 5 0 1 0
O7 **16** 8 a. black and yellow-green 7 6 2 0
O8 **15** 1 r. black and pale blue .. 7 6 7 6

1932-49. *Optd. with Type* O **2** *in red.*
O8*a* **13** 3 p. blk. & blk.-green ('49) £25 30 0
O8*b* **14** ½ a. black & dp. blue ('49) £25 25 0
O 9 **13** 3 a. black and carmine .. 40 0 30 0
O10 **14** 4 a. black and purple .. 55 0 45 0
O11 **16** 8 a. black & yellow-green 80 0 60 0
O12 **15** 1 r. black and pale blue.. £5 70 0

1938. *No.* 57 *optd. with Type* O **1**, *in red.*
O13 **15** 1 a. black and carmine .. 7 6 1 6

1949. *No.* 59 *optd. with Type* O **2**, *in red.*
O14 **16** 1 a. on 2 a. black & orange £5 60 0

1949. *Nos.* O4/O7 *surch.* " ONE ANNA " (2¼ *mm. high*).
O15 **16** 1 a. on 2 a. blk. & orge. (B.) £50 70 0
O16 **13** 1 a. on 3 a. blk. & car. (Bk.) £50 70 0
O17 **14** 1 a. on 4 a. blk. & pur. (Bk.) £50 70 0
a. " ANNE " for " ANNA " ..
b. " ANNN " for " ANNA " ..
O18 **16** 1 a. on 8 a. black and yellow-green (Bk.) .. £50 70 0
a. " ANNE " for " ANNA " ..
b. " ANNN " for " ANNA " ..

1949. *Surch.* " ONE ANNA " (4 *mm. high*).
O19 **15** 1 a. on 1 r. (No. O8) .. £12 60 0
O20 ,, 1 a. on 1 r. (No. O12) .. £17 80 0

TRAVANCORE.

1. Conch or Chank Shell.

2

1888. *T* **1** (*and similar types*). *Laid paper. P* 12.
1 1 ch. ultramarine 10 0 5 0
2 2 ch. red 12 6 10 0
3 4 ch. green 80 0 60 0

1889-94. *T* **1** (*and similar types*). *Wove paper. Wmk. T* **2**. *P* 12.
4 ½ ch. purple 0 9 0 2
4*a* ½ ch. lilac 0 8 0 2
5 1 ch. ultramarine 0 10 0 2
5*a* 1 ch. dull blue 1 3 0 2
6 2 ch. orange-red 5 0 1 0
6*a* 2 ch. carmine 4 0 1 0
7 2 ch. rose 4 0 1 0
a. Imperf. between (pair) .. £8
8 4 ch. green 6 0 2 6

Impressions of the 1, 2, and 4 chuckrams in various abnormal colours on *laid* paper have been met with. These are proofs.

3. Conch Shell.

1899-1901. *Types as* **1** *and* **3** (¾ chuckram). *W* **2**. *P* 12.
9 ½ ch. bright purple 1 0 0 4
a. Dull purple 0 8 0 4
10 ¾ ch. black 1 0 0 6
11 1 ch. violet-blue 10 0 1 6
12 2 ch. pale pink 7 6 1 3
13 4 ch. yellow-green 6 6 1 6

1903-39. *Types as* **1** *and* **3**, *new shades. W* **2**. *P* 12 *or* 12½.
14 ½ ch. deep violet 0 3 0 3
a. Violet 0 6 0 3
15 ¾ ch. mauve ('32) 0 4 0
16 ¾ ch. violet ('39) 0 4 0
17 1 ch. indigo 1 0 0
a. Pale blue 2 0 0
b. Deep blue 1 0 0
18 2 ch. scarlet 2 6 0
19 4 ch. blue-green 7 6 2
a. Dull green 10 0 2
20 4 ch. deep green (1911) .. 7 6 2

The above may also be found without wmk. but these are from watermarked sheets, th watermarks being more widely spaced on th sheet than the stamps.

(4)

1906. *Stamps as* **T 1** *surch. as* **T 4.**

21	½ ch. on ½ ch. bright purple	1	0	0	6
	a. Surch. inverted	80	0	30	0
	b. Dull purple	2	0	0	6
22	¼ ch. on ½ ch. violet	0	4	0	6
23	⅜ ch. on ½ ch. bright purple	1	6	0	6
	a. Dull purple	2	0	0	6
	ba. Ditto. surch. inverted				
24	⅜ ch. on ½ ch. violet	1	0	0	4
	a. Surch. inverted				

6

7

1908–11. **T 6, 1** *(modified) and* **7.** *W* **2.** *P* 12.

25	4 cash, pink (1908)	0	6	0	2
26	6 cash, red-brown (1910)	0	6	0	2
	a. Imperf. between (pair)	50	0		
27	3 ch. violet	3	6	0	2
	a. Imperf. between (pair)	£5			

9

10

11

1 C

(12)

1916–33. *W* **2.** *P* 12. *(***T 1** *modified.)*

No.	Type	Description				
28	**9**	10 cash, pink (1921)	0	6	0	3
		a. Imperf. between (pair)	50	0		
29	**1**	1¼ ch. claret (1920)	1	0	0	3
29a	,,	1¼ ch. rose ('33)	1	0	0	3
30	**10**	7 ch. purple	7	6	1	6
31	**11**	14 ch. orange	10	0	2	6
31a	,,	14 ch. yellow	7	6	5	0

1921–22. *Nos.* 25 *and* 17 *surch. as* **T 12.**

No.	Type	Description				
32	**6**	1 c. on 4 cash, pink	0	3	0	3
		a. Inverted	—		15	0
33	**3**	5 c. on 1 ch. indigo (R.)	0	4	0	2
		a. Inverted	40	0	10	0

1922–32. *W* **2.** *P* 12.

No.	Type	Description				
34	**9**	5 cash, olive-bistre	0	9	0	3
		a. Imperf. between (pair)	£5		£5	
35	,, **5**	5 cash, chocolate ('32)	0	6	0	3
		a. Imperf. between (pair)	75	0	75	0

13. Sri Padmanabha Shrine.

14. State Chariot.

15. Maharaja Sir Bala Rama Varma.

(Typo. Calcutta Chromotype Co.)

1931 (6 Nov.). *Coronation. Wmk. as* **T 2.** *P* 12.

No.	Type	Description				
36	**13**	6 cash, black and green	1	0	0	9
37	**14**	10 cash, black & ultram.	1	0	0	9
38	**15**	3 ch. black and purple	1	6	1	0

1932. *Wmk. as* **T 2.** *P* 12 *or* 12½.

(*a*) *No.* 29 *surch. as* **T 12** (*slightly smaller*).

No.	Type	Description				
39	**1**	1 c. on 1¼ ch. claret	0	3	0	3
		a. Surch. inverted	10	0		
		b. Surch. double	30	0	30	0
		c. "1" of surch. omitted	50	0	50	0
		d. Imperf. between (pair)	£5		£5	
40	,,	2 c. on 1¼ ch. claret	0	6	0	3
		a. Surch. inverted	10	0		
		b. Surch. double	30	0	30	0
		c. "2" of surch. omitted	50	0	50	0
		d. "C" of surch. omitted	50	0	50	0
		e. Imperf. between (pair)	£5		£5	

(*b*) **T 9** *surch. as* **T 12** (*wider spaced*).

41	1 c. on 5 cash, chocolate	1	0	0	4
	a. Surch. inverted	60	0		
	b. Pair, with and without surch.	£5			
42	1 c. on 5 cash, slate-purple	0	6	0	3
	a. "1" of surch. inverted	70	0		
	b. Imperf. between (horiz. pr.)	£5		£5	
43	2 c. on 10 cash, pink	0	4	0	4
	a. Surch. inverted	10	0		
	b. Surch. double	30	0	30	0
	c. Imperf. between (pair)	£5		£5	

16. Maharaja Sir Bala Rama Varma and Subramania Shrine.

(**T 16–18.** Typo. Travancore Mint.)

1937 (29 Mar.). *Temple Entry Proclamation.* **T 16** *and similar horiz. designs. Wmk. as* **T 2.** *P* 12 *or* 12½.

44	6 cash, carmine	0	6	0	4
	a. Imp. between (horiz. pair)	£18			
45	12 cash, bright blue	1	0	0	6
	a. Imp. between (vert. pair)	£18			
46	1½ ch. yellow-green	1	0	0	4
	a. Imp. between (horiz. pair)	£12			
47	3 ch. violet	2	6	1	6

Designs:—Maharaja's portrait and temples as follows: 12 cash Sri Padmanabha; 1½ ch. Mahadeva; 3 ch. Kanyakumari.

17. Lake Ashtamudi.

18. Maharaja Sir Bala Rama Varma.

1939 (9 Nov.). *Maharaja's 27th Birthday. As T* **17** *and* **18** *(various designs). Wmk. as T* **2** *(or portions). P* 11, 12, 12½ *or compound.*

48 1 ch. yellow-green 0 6 0 3
 a. Imperf. between (horiz. pair) 30 0 40 0
 b. Imperf. between (vert. pair).. 20 0 30 0
49 1½ ch. scarlet 2 0 1 6
 a. Imperf. between (pair) .. 30 0 40 0
 b. Double print .. ..
50 2 ch. orange 0 9 0 9
51 3 ch. brown 1 0 0 9
 a. Imperf. between (pair) .. 30 0 40 0
 b. Double print 35 0 35 0
52 4 ch. red 2 6 2 0
53 7 ch. light blue 5 0 3 6
54 14 ch. turquoise-green .. 10 0 7 6

Designs: As T **17**—Sri Padmanabha Shrine (4 ch.). Bust of Maharaja and Cape Comorin (7 ch.) and Pachipari Irrigation Reservoir (14 ch.). As T **18**—Bust of Maharaja in various frames (1½ ch. and 3 ch.).

19. Maharaja and Aruvikara Falls.

1941 (20 Oct.). *Maharaja's 29th Birthday. T* **19** *and similar type. Typo. Wmk. as T* **2** *(or portions). P* 11, 12. 12½ *or compound.*

55 6 cash, blackish violet .. 1 0 0 9
 a. Imperf. between (vert. pr.) 20 0
 b. Imperf. between (horiz. pair) 20 0
56 ¾ ch. brown 1 0 0 9
 a. Imperf. between (vert. pair).. 20 0
 b. Imperf. between (horiz. pair)

Design:—¾ ch. Maharaja and Marthanda Varma Bridge, Alwaye.

2 CASH

(20)

1943–44. *Nos.* 49, 55 *(colour changed) and* 56 *surch. as T* **20**. *P* 11, 12, 12½ *or compound.*

57 "2 CASH" on 1½ ch. scarlet .. 1 0 0 6
 a. Imperf. between (vert. pair) .. 50 0 50 0
58 "4 CASH" on ¾ ch. brown 1 0 0 6
59 "8 CASH" on 6 cash carmine 1 6 0 6
 a. Imperf. between (pair) .. 40 0 40 0

21. Maharaja Sir Bala Rama Varma. SPECIAL (22)

1946 (24 Oct.). *Maharaja's 34th Birthday. Typo. Conch shell wmk., as T* **2** *(or portions). P* 11, 12 *or* 12½.

60 **21** 8 cash, carmine 5 0 5 0
 a. Imperf. between (horiz. pair) .. 30 0

1946. *Service stamp No.* S49, *revalidated for ordinary postage with opt. T* **22**.

61 **19** 6 cash, blackish violet (O.) 60 0 10 0

SERVICE STAMPS.

On

S S

(S **1**) (Round "O")

1911 (16 Aug.)–**1930.** *Contemporary stamps overprinted as Type* S **1**.

S 1 4 cash, pink.. .. .. 0 3 0 3
 a. Opt. inverted .. .. — 5 0
S 2 5 cash, olive-bistre .. 0 6 0 3
 a Opt. inverted 6 0 4 0
S 2*b* 5 cash, chocolate 0 4 0 3
 c. Opt. inverted 4 0
S 3 6 cash, red-brown 0 6 0 3
 a. One "S" omitted ..
 b. Opt. inverted .. .. — 3 0
 c. Opt. double.. .. ..
S 4 10 cash, pink.. .. .. 0 8 0 3
 a. Opt. inverted .. .. — 3 0
 b. Opt. double .. ..
 c. First "S" inverted ..
 d. Imperf. between (pair) ..
 e. "S" at left omitted ..
 f. "Ou" for "On".. ..
S 4*g* 10 cash, scarlet .. ..
S 5 ½ ch. violet (R.) 0 4 0 3
 a. Opt. inverted .. .. — 2 6
 b. Imperf. between (pair) .. 30 0
S 6 1 ch. indigo (R.) 0 10 0 3
 a. Opt. inverted .. .. — 4 0
 b. Opt. double.. .. .. — 6 0
 c. "nO" for "On".. .. £5 £5
S 7 1¼ ch. claret 0 6 0 3
 a. Opt. inverted 10 0 4 0
 aa. Opt. double.. .. ..
 b. Stamp doubly printed ..
 c. Imperf. between (pair) ..
 d. "S" at right omitted ..
 e. "S" at right inverted ..
S 8 2 ch. scarlet.. .. .. 1 0 0 3
 a. Opt. inverted 4 0
S 9 3 ch. violet 0 10 0 3
 a. One "S" omitted ..
 b. Opt. inverted .. .. — 12 6
 c. Opt. double.. .. ..
 d. Imperf between (vert. pr.)..
S10 4 ch. deep green (No. 20) .. 2 6 0 3
 a. Opt. inverted 20 0
 b. Imperf between (pair) ..
S10*c* 7 ch. brown-purple .. 3 0 0 3
S10*d* 14 ch. orange 5 0 0 4
 e. Imperf between (pair) ..
 ea. "S" at right inverted .. 12 6
S10*f* 14 ch. yellow .. 5 0 0 6

In deep blue.

S11 4 cash, pink.. .. .. — 1
S12 6 cash, red-brown 15 0 2

No.	Type	Description	Unused	Used
S13		10 cash, pink	—	2 0
S14		1¼ ch. claret	—	2 6
S15		4 ch. deep green	—	5 0

On On 1 ch

S S S S 8 c

(S 2) (Oval "O") (S 3) (S 4)

1930–35. *Optd. as Type* S 2 *or smaller* (*s*), *or* S 3.

No.	Type	Description	Unused	Used
S16	6	4 cash, pink	20 0	10 0
S17	9	5 cash, chocolate	50 0	15 0
		a. Opt. inverted	£5	
S18	1	6 cash, red-brown	0 8	0 3
		a. "nO" for "On"	50 0	
S19	9	10 cash, pink	5 0	0 3
		a. Imperf. between (pair)	20 0	
		b. "S" at right inverted		
S20	1	½ ch. violet (Bk.)	0 4	0 3
S21	,,	½ ch. violet (R.)	0 6	0 3
S22	3	¾ ch. black (R.) (*s*)	1 3	0 3
S23	,,	¾ ch. black (R.) (S 3)	1 3	0 5
S24	,,	¾ ch. mauve	1 3	0 3
S25	1	1 ch. indigo (R.)	2 0	0 4
S26	,,	1½ ch. carmine-rose	5 0	2 6
S27	,,	1½ ch. carmine-rose (*s*)	3 0	1 0
S28	,,	1½ ch. rose	3 0	0 4
S29	7	3 ch. violet (Bk.)	3 9	0 3
S30	,,	3 ch. violet (R.)	4 0	0 3
		a. Opt. inverted		
		b. Imperf. between (vert. pair)		
S31	1	4 ch. green (R.)	4 6	1 0
S31*a*	,,	4 ch. green (R.) (S 3)	4 6	3 6
S32	,,	4 ch. green (Bk.)	10 0	2 0
S33	10	7 ch. brown-purple	6 6	1 0
		a. Imperf. between (pair)		
S34	11	14 ch. orange	10 0	4 0
		a. Imperf. between (pair)		

1932. *Official stamps surch. as* T 12 *or* S 4.

(*a*) *Overprint Type* S 1.

No.	Description	Unused	Used
S34*b*	6 c. on 5 cash, olive-bistre	5 0	0 6
	c. "S" at right inverted	—	10 0
	d. "S" at left inverted		
S35	6 c. on 5 cash, chocolate	0 8	0 3
	a. Surcharge inverted	6 6	
	b. "S" at right inverted		
	c. "S" at left inverted		
S36	12 c. on 10 cash, pink	1 3	0 3
	a. Surcharge inverted	6 0	
	b. "c" of "12 c." omitted	6 0	
	c. "Ou" for "On"		
	d. "S" at right inverted		
	e. "S" at left inverted	15 0	
	f. Service opt. and "12 c." inverted	10 0	10 0
S37	1 ch. 8 c. on 1¼ ch. claret	1 0	0 4
	a. "S" at right inverted		
	b. "S" at left inverted		

(*b*) *Overprint Type* S 2.

No.	Description	Unused	Used
S38	6 c. on 5 cash, chocolate	0 8	0 3
	a. "S" at right inverted		
	b. Surcharge inverted	6 0	
	c. Service opt. inverted		
S39	12 c. on 10 cash, pink	1 3	0 3
	a. Surcharge inverted	6 0	
	b. "c" of "12 c." omitted	6 0	
	c. "On" omitted		
	d. Service opt. inverted	15 0	15 0
S40	1 ch. 8 c. on 1¼ ch. claret	3 0	0 3
	a. Surcharge inverted		

SERVICE

(S 5)

1939–41. *Optd. with Type* S 5.

No.	Type	Description	Unused	Used
S40*b*	1	6 cash, red-brown ('41)	5 0	0 4
S41	3	¾ ch. violet	6 0	0 9
S41*a*	1	1½ ch. rose	5 0	3 0

1939 (9 Nov.). *Nos.* 48/54 *optd. with Type* S 5.

No.	Description	Unused	Used
S42	1 ch. yellow-green	0 3	0 3
	a. Imperf. between (vert. pair)	25 0	25 0
	b. Opt. inverted	35 0	35 0
	c. Opt. double	25 0	25 0
S43	1½ ch. scarlet	0 6	0 3
	a. Imperf. between (pair)	50 0	50 0
	b. "SESVICE" for "SERVICE"	30 0	30 0
S44	2 ch. orange	0 6	0 4
	a. "SESVICE" for "SERVICE"	30 0	30 0
S45	3 ch. brown	0 8	0 4
	a. "SESVICE" for "SERVICE"	30 0	30 0
	b. Imperf. between (vert. pair)	25 0	25 0
S46	4 ch. red	2 0	1 0
S47	7 ch. light blue	3 0	1 3
S48	14 ch. turquoise-green	5 0	3 0

1942. *Nos.* 55/6 *optd. with Type* S 5.

No.	Description	Unused	Used
S49	6 cash, blackish violet	1 0	0 3
S50	¾ ch. brown	1 0	0 3
	a. Imperf. between (vert. pair)		

1943–45. *Nos.* 57/9 *optd. with Type* S 5.

No.	Description	Unused	Used
S51	2 cash on 1½ ch. scarlet ('45)	0 8	0 2
	a. Pair, one with "2 CASH" omtd.	£5	£5
S52	4 cash on ¾ ch. brown ('45)	1 0	0 6
S53	8 cash on 6 cash, carmine	1 9	0 6
	a. Imperf. between (vert. pair)		

1947. *No.* 60 *optd. with Type* S 5.

No.	Type	Description	Unused	Used
S54	21	8 cash, carmine	10 0	7 6
		aa. Stamp doubly printed	60 0	
		a. No wmk.	45 0	

For later issues, see Travancore-Cochin.

TRAVANCORE COCHIN.

U. S. T. C. (1)   T.-C. (2)

1949. *No.* 106 *of Cochin optd.*

No.	Type	Description	Unused	Used
1	1	1 a. orange	20 0	
2	2	1 a. orange	17 6	

ONE ANNA

ഒരണ

(3)

1949 (July). *Stamps of Travancore surch. in* "PIES" *or* "ANNAS", *as* T 3; *No.* 3 *in red, others in black.* P 11, 12, 12½ *or* 13½.

No.	Type	Description	Unused	Used
3	19	2 p. on 6 cash, blackish violet	0 4	
4	21	4 p. on 8 cash, carmine	0 4	
		a. No wmk.		
5	17	½ a. on 1 ch. yellow-green	0 6	
		a. Surch. inverted	60 0	60 0
		b. "NANA" for "ANNA"	£5	£5
6	18	1 a. on 2 ch. orange	0 9	
7	–	2 a. on 4 ch. (No. 52)	1 6	
		a. Surch. inverted	£5	£5
8	–	3 a. on 7 ch. (No. 53)	4 6	
9	–	6 a. on 14 ch. (No. 54)	7 6	

Nos. 3 to 9 exist in pairs, imperf. between.

4. Conch or Chank Shell.

5. Palm Trees.

1950. *Offset-litho.* W **69** *of India.* P 14.

10 **4** 2 p. rose-carmine 5 0
11 **5** 4 p. ultramarine 6 0

T.-C.

SIX PIES

(**6**)

1950. *No.* 106 *of Cochin.* (*a*) *Surch. as T* **6**.

12 **29** 6 p. on 1 a. orange .. 7 6
13 ,, 9 p. on 1 a. orange .. 7 6

(*b*). *Optd. with T* **1** *and surch. below as in T* **6**.

14 **29** 6 p. on 1 a. orange 150 0

SERVICE STAMPS.

SERVICE (S **1**) SERVICE (S **2**)

1949–51. *Stamps of Travancore surch. with value as T* **3** *and* "SERVICE". *P* 11, 12, 12½ *or* 13½.

(*a*) "SERVICE" *in block capitals, Type* S **1**.

S 1 2 p. on 6 cash (No. 55) (R.) .. 0 2 0 2
a. Wmk. Cochin T 27 .. .. 0 4 0 3
S 2 4 p. on 8 cash (No. 60) .. 1 0 0 3
a. "FOUB" for "FOUR" .. £5 £5
b. No wmk. .. .. ..
S 3 ½ a. on 1 ch. (No. 48) .. 1 0 0 8
a. "NANA" for "ANNA" .. £5 £5
b. Pair, one without surch. .. 50 0 50 0
S 4 1 a. on 2 ch. (No. 50) .. 25 0 20 0
S 5 2 a. on 4 ch. (No. 52) .. 3 0 2 6
a. Pair, one without surch. .. £5 £5
b. Wmk. Cochin T 27 .. .. 1 6 2 6
S 6 3 a. on 7 ch. (No. 53) .. 3 6 3 6
a. No wmk. 95 0
S 7 6 a. on 14 ch. (No. 54) .. 10 0 6 0

(*b*) "SERVICE" *in seriffed capitals, Type* S **2**.

S 8 4 p. on 8 cash (No. 60) .. 0 4 0 3
a. "FOUB" for "FOUR" .. £5 £5
b. No wmk. £5 £5
S 9 ½ a. on 1 ch. (No. 48) .. 0 2 0 2
a. Wmk. Cochin T 27 .. .. 0 9 0 6
b. "AANA" for "ANNA" .. 75 0 75 0
c. Imperf. (pair) 20 0
S10 1 a. on 2 ch. (No. 50) .. 2 0 2 0
a. Wmk. Cochin T 27 .. .. 4 0 2 6
S11 2 a. on 4 ch. (No. 52) .. 4 0 4 0
S12 3 a. on 7 ch. (No. 53) .. 5 0 6 0
S13 6 a. on 14 ch. (No. 54) .. 7 6 6 0

The paper of stamps with W **27** of Cochin is much thicker than that with W **2** of Travancore. On the latter, at least a part of the Conch wmk. always appears; so that stamps without wmk. (other than Nos. S2*b* S6*a*, and S8*b*) must be from sheets normally with W **27** of Cochin. Nos. S2*b*, S6*a* and S8*b* are on thin paper entirely without wmk.

WADHWAN.

1

1888. *Thin toned wove paper.*

(*a*) *Irregular perf.* 12½ (*small holes*).

1 **1** ½ pice, black (II) 40 0
a. Imperf. between, pair .. ..

(*b*) *P* 12½ (*large holes*).

2 **1** ½ pice, black (I, III) 30 0

Medium toned wove paper.

3 **1** ½ pice, black (III) (*p.* 12½) .. 20 0
4 ,, ½ pice, black (V) (*p.* 12) .. 15 0

1892 (?). *Thick wove paper.* *P* 12.

5 **1** ½ pice, black/*toned* (VI, VII) .. 12 6
6 ,, ½ pice, black/*white* (IV) .. 12 6

The stamps were lithographed from seven stones (as indicated by Roman figures), in sheets of from 20 to 42 units, distinguishable by flaws.

Genuinely used copies are rare, but stamps cancelled-to-order are fairly common.

The stamps of Wadhwan have been obsolete for many years.

IONIAN ISLANDS.

For GREAT BRITAIN stamp used in Ionian Islands, see page 59.

1

(Recess. Perkins, Bacon & Co.)

1859 (15 May). *T* **1**. *Imperf.*

1 (½d.) orange (no wmk.) .. £10 £30
2 (1d.) blue (wmk. "**2**") .. 55 0 £26
3 (2d.) carmine (wmk. "**1**") .. 50 0 £26

On the 30th May, 1864, the islands were ceded to Greece, and these stamps became obsolete.

Great care should be exercised in buying used stamps, on or off cover, as forged postmarks are plentiful.

IRAQ.

For all issues, see Part III of the Stanley Gibbons Catalogue.

IRELAND (REPUBLIC).

All the issues of Ireland are listed together here, in this section of the Gibbons Catalogue, purely as a matter of convenience to collectors.

PROVISIONAL GOVERNMENT 16 JANUARY, 1922

Rialtas Sealadac na hÉireann 1922 (1)

Rialtas Sealadac na hÉireann 1922. (2)

Rialtas Sealadac na hÉireann 1922 (3)

("Provisional Government of Ireland, 1922."

1922 (17 Feb.). *T* **104** *to* **108** (*W* **100**) *and* **109** *of Great Britain overprinted in black.*

(*a*) *With* T **1**, *by Dollard Printing House, Ltd.*

1 ½d. green 0 4 0 6
 a. Overprint inverted £15 £12
2 1d. scarlet 0 6 0 6
 a. Overprint inverted £6
3 1d. carmine-red 3 0 0 8
4 2½d. bright ultramarine .. 3 0 6 0
5 3d. bluish violet 5 0 2 6
6 4d. grey-green 6 0 10 0
7 5d. yellow-brown 8 6 10 6
8 9d. agate 17 6 20 0
 a. Faint grey-black overprint .. 20 0 20 0
9 10d. turquoise-blue 8 0 17 6

The ½d. with red overprint is a trial or proof printing. (*Price* 75*s*.)

Bogus inverted T **1** overprints exist on the 2d., 4d., 9d. and 1s. values.

(*b*) *With* T **2**, *by Alex Thom* & Co.

10 1½d. chestnut 3 6 1 9
 a. Error, "PENCF" £10 £12
11 1½d. pale red-brown 1 6 1 6
12 2d. orange (Die I) 2 0 0 6
 a. Overprint inverted £8 £10
13 2d. orange (Die II) 1 6 0 6
 a. Overprint inverted £12 £12
14 6d. reddish purple, C.. .. 5 0 3 0
15 1s. bistre-brown 8 0 5 0

Varieties occur throughout the T **2** overprint in the relative positions of the lines of the overprint, the "R" of "Rialtas" being over either the "Se" or "S" of "Sealadac" or intermediately.

(*c*) *With* T **3** (*on Bradbury, Wilkinson printings, by Dollard, Ltd.*)

17 2s. 6d. chocolate-brown .. 35 0 47 6
18 2s. 6d. sepia-brown .. 45 0 50 0
19 5s. rose-red 35 0 75 0
21 10s. dull grey-blue 85 0 £6

1922 (1 April–July). *Optd. by Dollard Ltd. with T* **1**, *in red* (R.) *or carmine* (C.).

22 2½d. bright ultramarine (R.) .. 2 6 4 0
23 4d. grey-green (R.) .. 6 0 10 0
24 4d. grey-green (C.) (July) .. 22 6 27 6
25 9d. agate (R.) 12 6 12 6

1922 (June). *Optd. as T* **2**, *in black, by Harrison & Sons.*

26 ½d. green 1 6 2 3
27 1d. carmine-red 1 0 2 0
28 1½d. red-brown 6 0 7 6
29 2d. bright orange (Die I) .. 3 6 5 0
29*a* 2d. bright orange (Die II) .. 6 0 8 6

The Harrison overprint measures 15×17 mm. (maximum) against the 14½×16 mm. of *T* **2** (Thom printing) and is much bolder black than the latter, while the individual letters are taller, the "i" of "Rialtas" being specially outstanding. The "R" of "Rialtas" is always over the "Se" of "Sealadac". This special overprinting was made on stamps for issue in horizontal and vertical coils.

1922 (July). *Optd. as T* **2**, *but bolder, and in shiny blue-black ink by Alex Thom & Co., Ltd.*

30 1½d. bright chestnut 2 0 3 0
31 2d. orange (Die I) 22 6 0 10
32 2d. orange (Die II) 2 3 0 3
33 6d. reddish purple, C.. .. 6 0 3 0
34 1s. bistre-brown 16 0 8 0

These Thom printings are distinguishable from the Harrison printings by the size of the overprint, and from the previous Thom printings by the intensity and colour of the overprint, the latter being best seen when the stamp is looked through with a strong light behind it.

The 2d. stamp of this issue with inverted overprint was never issued.

1922 (July–Nov.). *Provisional printings by Alex. Thom & Co., Ltd.* (*a*) *Optd. as T* **2**, *in blue-black or red* (R.).

35 ½d. green 1 9 1 9
 a. Opt. in dull black 40 0 25 0
36 1d. scarlet 0 6 0 2
 a. Opt. in dull black 40 0
37 2½d. bright ultramarine (R.) .. 12 6 15 0
38 3d. bluish violet 3 0 3 0
 a. Opt. in dull black 35 0 30 0
39 4d. grey-green (R.) 2 6 6 0
40 5d. yellow-brown 5 0 12 6
41 9d. agate (R.) 7 6 8 6
42 9d. olive-green (R.) 7 6 10 0
43 10d. turquoise-blue 30 0 32 6
 a. Opt. in dull black £6

The varieties with overprint in dull black are said to be from proof sheets afterwards put into circulation. (See also No. 45*a*).

(*b*) *Optd. with T* **3** *in blue-black.*

44 2s. 6d. grey-brown £9 £10
45 5s. pale rose-red £10 £10
 a. Opt. in dull black £12
46 10s. dull grey-blue £15 £15

The overprint on Nos. 44 to 46 differs from that of Nos. 17 to 21 in being in blue-black instead of black, the "h" and "é" of "héireann" are closer together, while the impression is bolder and much more sharply defined, and the ink often glossy.

Rialtas
Sealadaċ
na
héireann
1922.

(4)

Saorstát
Éireann
1922

("Irish Free State 1922.")
(5. Wide date.)

1922 (Dec.). *Optd. by Thom with T* **4** (*wider setting*) *in blue-black.*

47 ½d. green 0 8 1 3
 a. Opt. in dull black .. .. — 85 0
48 1d. scarlet 2 0 1 6
49 1½d. red-brown 2 0 1 9
50 2d. orange (Die II) 7 6 4 0
51 1s. olive-bistre 17 6 27 6

The overprint T **4** measures 15¾×16 mm. (maximum).

Irish Free State, 6 December, 1922.

1922 (Dec.). *Optd. by Thom with T* **5**, *in shiny blue-black or in red* (R.).

52 ½d. green 0 3 0 3
 a. No accent in "Saorstat" .. £20
 b. Accent inserted by hand .. 80 0 70 0
 c. Opt. in dull black 35 0 30 0
53 1d. scarlet 0 3 0 6
 aa. No accent in "Saorstat"
 a. No accent and final "t" missing £95
 b. Accent inserted by hand .. £6 £5
 c. Accent and "t" inserted .. £8 £7
 d. Opt. in dull black 17 6 15 0
 e. "QNE" variety (G.B. 357a) ..
54 1½d. red-brown 0 8 1 3
 a. Opt. in dull black 15 0 12 6
55 2d. orange (Die II) 0 10 1 0
 a. Opt. in dull black 32 6 32 6
56 2½d. bright blue (R.) 2 0 4 0
 a. No accent £8 £6
57 3d. bluish violet 3 0 5 0
 a. No accent £6 £6
 b. Opt. in dull black 17 6 12 6
58 4d. grey-green (R.) 2 0 6 6
 a. No accent £6 £5
59 5d. yellow-brown 3 6 5 0
60 6d. reddish purple, C 2 6 3 0
 a. Accent inserted by hand .. £12 £10
 b. Opt. in dull black 30 0 25 0

61	9d. olive-green (R.)	6 0	10 0
	a. No accent	£12	£10
62	10d. turquoise-blue	3 0	15 0
63	1s. bistre-brown	6 0	10 0
	a. No accent	£80	
	b. Accent inserted by hand ..	£30	
64	2s. 6d. chocolate-brown ..	25 0	30 0
	a. No accent	£22	£22
	b. Accent reversed	£20	£20
	c. Opt. in dull black	60 0	
	d. Major Re-entry	£35	
65	5s. rose-red	47 6	60 0
	a. No accent	£26	£26
	b. Accent reversed	£24	£24
	c. Opt. in dull black	90 0	
66	10s. dull grey-blue	£6	£7
	a. No accent	£85	
	b. Accent reversed	£60	
	c. Opt. in dull black	£9	

The accents inserted by hand are in dull black. The reversed accents are grave (thus "à") instead of acute ("á"). A variety with "S" of "Saorstat" directly over "é" of "éireann," instead of to left, may be found in all values except the 2½d. and 4d. In the 2s. 6d., 5s., and 10s. it is very slightly to the left in the "S" over "é" variety, bringing the "á" of "Saorstat" directly above the last "n" of "éireann."

1923. *Overprinted by Messrs. Harrison with* **T 5** *in black, for use in horizontal and vertical coils.*

67	½d. green	1 6	2 0
	a. Long "1" in "1922" ..	17 6	20 0
68	1d. scarlet	5 0	6 0
	a. Long "1" in "1922" ..	22 6	25 0
69	1½d. red-brown	4 6	5 0
	a. Long "1" in "1922" ..	42 6	45 0
70	2d. orange (Die II)	3 0	4 0
	a. Long "1" in "1922" ..	22 6	25 0

In the Harrison overprint the characters are rather bolder than those of the Thom overprint, and the foot of the "1" of "1922" is usually rounded instead of square. The long "1" in "1922" has a serif at foot. The second "e" of "éireann" appears to be slightly raised.

6. "Sword of Light".

7. Map of Ireland.

8. Arms of Ireland.

9. Celtic Cross.

10

(Des. J. J. O'Reilly, *T* **6**; J. Ingram, *T* **7**; Miss M. Girling, *T* **8**; and Miss L. Williams, *T* **9**. Typo. Plates made by Royal Mint, London.)

PRINTERS. The following and all subsequent issues to No. 148 were printed at the Govt. Printing Works, Dublin, *unless otherwise stated.*

1922 (6 Dec.)–**35.** *W* **10.** *P* 15×14.

No.	Type	Description		
71	**6**	½d. bright green (20.4.23) ..	0 2	0 3
		a. Imperf. × perf. 14 (1934) ..	5 0	7 6
72	**7**	1d. carmine (23.2.23) ..	0 3	0 3
		a. P 15 × imp. (single perf.) ('33)	75 0	85 0
		b. Do. Wmk. sideways ..		
		c. P 15 × imperf. (1934) ..	7 6	7 6
73	,,	1½d. claret (2.2.23)	0 6	0 3
74	,,	2d. grey-green (6.12.22) ..	0 6	0 3
		a. Imperf. × perf. 14 (1934) ..	17 6	15 0
		b. Perf. 15 × imperf. (1935) ..	£90	£35
75	**8**	2½d. red-brown (7.9.23) ..	0 6	0 8
76	**9**	3d. ultramarine (17.3.23) ..	0 7	0 3
77	**8**	4d. slate-blue (28.9.23) ..	0 9	0 6
78	**6**	5d. bright violet (11.5.23) ..	2 6	1 6
79	,,	6d. claret (21.12.23) ..	1 0	0 4
80	**8**	9d. bright violet (26.10.23)	3 6	2 6
81	**9**	10d. brown (11.5.23) ..	3 0	3 0
82	**6**	1s. light blue (15.6.23) ..	12 6	3 0

No. 72*a* is imperf. vertically except for a single perf. at each top corner. It was issued for use in automatic machines.

Saorstát
Éireann
1922

(**11.** Narrow Date.)

1925–27. *Stamps of Great Britain.* **T 109** *Bradbury, Wilkinson printing) overprinted at the Government Printing Office.*

(*a*) *With T* **11** *in black or grey-black.*

83	2s. 6d. chocolate-brown ..	25 0	32 6
	a. Wide and narrow date (pr.) ('27)	75 0	
84	5s. rose-red	40 0	45 0
	a. Wide and narrow date (pr.) ('27)	£5	
85	10s. dull grey-blue ..	75 0	85 0
	a. Wide and narrow date (pr.) ('27)	£12	

The varieties with wide and narrow date *se-tenant* are from what is known as the "composite setting," in which some stamps showed the wide date, as T **5**, while in others the figures were close together, as in T **11**.

Single specimens of this printing with wide date may be distinguished from Nos. 64 to 66 by the colour of the ink, which is black or grey-black in the composite setting and blue-black in the Thom printing.

The type of the "composite" overprint usually shows distinct signs of wear.

(*b*) *As T* **5** (*wide date*) *in black.*

86	2s. 6d. chocolate	22 6	40 0
87	5s. rose-red	40 0	50 0
88	10s. dull grey-blue	£5	£6

This printing can be distinguished from the Thom overprints in dull black, by the clear, heavy impression (in deep black) which often shows in relief on the back of the stamp.

12. Daniel O'Connell.

(Des. Leo Whelan. Typo.)

1929 (22 JUNE). *Catholic Emancipation Centenary. T* **12.** *Wmk. T* **10.** *P* 15×14.

89	2d. grey-green	0	4	0	3
90	3d. blue	0	6	0	10
91	9d. bright violet	1	9	3	6

13. Shannon Barrage.

(Des. E. L. Lawrenson. Typo.)

1930 (15 OCT.). *Compl tion of Shannon Hydro-Electric Scheme. T* **13.** *Wmk. T* **10.** *P* 15×14.

92	2d. agate	0	4	0	3

14. Reaper. **15.** The Cross of Cong.

(T **14** and **15** des. G. Atkinson. Typo.)

1931 (12 JUNE). *200th Anniversary of the Royal Dublin Society. T* **14.** *Wmk. T* **10.** *P* 15×14.

93	2d. blue	0	4	0	3

1932 (12 MAY). *International Eucharistic Congress. T* **15.** *Wmk. T* **10.** *P* 15×14.

94	2d. grey-green	0	4	0	3
95	3d. blue	0	8	0	10

16. Adoration of the Cross. **17.** Hurler.

(T **16** to **19** des. R. J. King. Typo.)

1933 (18 SEPT.). "*Holy Year.*" *T* **16.** *Wmk. T* **10.** *P* 15×14.

96	2d. grey-green	0	4	0	3
97	3d. blue	0	8	0	8

1934 (27 JULY). *Golden Jubilee of the Gaelic Athletic Association. W* **10.** *P* 15×14.

98 **17**	2d. green	3	0	0	6

1935. *Stamps of Great Britain (Waterlow printings). Optd. as T* 5 (*wide date*).

99 **109**	2s. 6d. chocolate (No. 450)	40	0	45	0
100 ,,	5s. brt. rose-red (No. 451)	£5		£6	
101 ,,	10s. indigo (No. 452) ..	£18		£20	

18. St. Patrick.

1937 (8 SEPT.). *W* **10.** *P* 14×15.

102 **18**	2s. 6d. emerald-green ..	10	0	10	0
103 ,,	5s. marone	25	0	20	0
104 ,,	10s. blue	42	6	27	6

EIRE, 29 DECEMBER, 1937–17 APRIL, 1949.

19. Ireland and New Constitution.

1937 (29 DEC.). *Constitution Day. W* **10.** *P* 15×14.

105 **19**	2d. claret	0	4	0	3
106 ,,	3d. blue	1	6	2	0

For similar stamps see Nos. 176/7.

20. Father Mathew.

(Des. Sean Keating. Typo.)

1938 (1 JULY). *Centenary of Temperance Crusade. W* **10.** *P* 15×14.

107 **20**	2d. black	0	4	0	3
108 ,,	3d. blue	1	3	2	0

21. George Washington, American Eagle and Irish Harp.

(Des. G. Atkinson. Typo.)

1939 (1 MAR.). *150th Anniv. of U.S. Constitution and Installation of First U.S. President. W* **10.** *P* 15×14.

109 **21**	2d. scarlet	0	8	0	3
110 ,,	3d. blue	2	6	2	6

22

1940–49. *Typo.* W **22.** *P* 15 × 14 *or* 14 × 15 (*2s. 6d. to 10s.*).

111 **6** ½d. bright green (24.11.40) 0 2 0 2
112 **7** 1d. carmine (26.10.40) .. 0 3 0 1
a. From coils. P 14 × Imperf. ('41) 40 0 42 6
b. From coils. P 15 × Imperf. ('46) 22 6 8 6
113 ,, 1½d. claret (1.40) .. 0 6 0 1
114 ,, 2d. grey-green (1.40) .. 0 4 0 1
115 **8** 2½d. red-brown (3.41) .. 0 7 0 2
116 **9** 3d. blue (12.40) 0 6 0 2
117 **8** 4d. slate-blue (12.40) .. 0 7 0 2
118 **6** 5d. bright violet (7.40) 0 9 0 2
119 ,, 6d. claret ('42) 0 10 0 3
119*a* ,, 8d. scarlet (12.9.49) .. 1 0 0 6
120 **8** 9d. bright violet (7.40) .. 1 1 0 4
121 **9** 10d. brown (7.40) .. 1 3 0 10
121*a* ,, 11d. rose (12.9.49) .. 1 4 1 6
122 **6** 1s. light blue (6.40) .. 1 5 0 4
123 **18** 2s. 6d. emer.-grn. (10.2.43) 3 6 3 6
124 ,, 5s. maroon (15.12.42) .. 6 9 7 0
125 ,, 10s. blue (7.45) 13 3 17 6

1941
I gCuimne
Aiséirghe
1916

(**23.** *Trans.* "In memory of the rising of 1916".)

1941 (12 APR.). *25th Anniv. of Easter Rising* (1916). *Provisional issue.* T **7** *and* **9** (*2d. in new colour*), *optd. with T* **23.**

126 **7** 2d. orange (G.) 0 6 0 3
127 **9** 3d. blue (V.) 12 6 5 0

24. Volunteer and G.P.O., Dublin.

(Des. Victor Brown. Typo.)

1941 (27 OCT.). *25th Anniv. of Easter Rising* (1916). *Definitive issue.* W **22.** *P* 15 × 14.

128 **24** 2½d. blue-black 0 8 0 3

25. Dr. Douglas Hyde.

26. Sir William Rowan Hamilton.

(Des. Sean O'Sullivan. Typo.)

1943 (31 JULY). *50th Anniv. of Founding of Gaelic League.* W **22.** *P* 15 × 14.

129 **25** ½d. green 0 3 0 3
130 ,, 2½d. claret 0 8 0 3

(Des. Sean O'Sullivan from a bust by Hogan. Typo.)

1943 (13 NOV.). *Centenary of Announcement of Discovery of Quaternions.* W **22.** *P* 15 × 14.

131 **26** ½d. green 1 0 0 3
132 ,, 2½d. brown 2 6 0 6

27. Bro. Michael O'Clery.

(Des. R. J. King. Typo.)

1944 (30 JUNE). *Tercentenary of Death of Michael O'Clery.* (*Commemorating the "Annals of the Four Masters"*). W **22.** *P* 14 × 15.

133 **27** ½d. emerald-green .. 0 2 0 2
134 ,, 1s. red-brown 1 5 0 6

Although issued as commemoratives these two stamps were kept in use as part of the current issue.

28. Edmund Ignatius Rice.

29. "Youth Sowing Seeds of Freedom".

(Des. Sean O'Sullivan. Typo.)

1944 (29 AUG.). *Centenary of Irish Christian Brothers.* W **22.** *P* 15 × 14.

135 **28** 2½d. slate 0 8 0 3

(Des. R. J. King. Typo.)

1945 (15 SEPT.). *Centenary of Death of Thomas Davis* (*Founder of Young Ireland Movement*). W **22.** *P* 15 × 14.

136 **29** 2½d. blue 0 5 0
137 ,, 6d. claret 0 10 1

30. "Country and Homestead".

(Des. R. J. King. Typo.)

1946 (16 SEPT.). *Birth Centenaries of Davitt and Parnell* (*Land Reformers*). W **22.** *P* 15 × 14.

138 **30** 2½d. scarlet 0 6 0
139 ,, 3d. blue 1 0 0 1

31. Angel Victor over Rock of Cashel.

32. Over Lough Derg.

33. Over Croagh Patrick.

34. Over Glendalough.

)es. R. J. King. Recess. Waterlow & Sons.)

948 (7 APR.)–**65.** *Air.* *W* **22.** *P* 15 × 14.

40	**31**	1d. chocolate (4.4.49) ..	0	4	0	5
41	**32**	3d. blue	1	6	1	6
42	**33**	6d. magenta	0	10	1	0
42*a*	**32**	8d. lake-brown (13.12.54)	1	0	1	6
43	**34**	1s. green (4.4.49) ..	1	5	1	9
43*a*	**31**	1s. 3d. red-orge. (13.12.54)	1	9	2	0
43*b*	,,	1s. 5d. dp. ultram. (1.4.65)	1	11	2	3

35. Theobald Wolfe Tone.

(Des. K. Uhlemann. Typo.)

48 (19 Nov.). 150*th Anniv. of Insurrection.* *W* **22.** *P* 15 × 14.

4	**35**	2½d. reddish purple ..	0	6	0	3
5	,,	3d. violet	1	3	0	9

REPUBLIC, 18 APRIL, 1949.

36. Leinster House and Arms of Provinces.

(Des. Muriel Brandt. Typo.)

1949 (21 Nov.). *International Recognition of Republic.* *W* **22.** *P* 15 × 14.

146	**36**	2½d. reddish brown ..	0	6	0	3
147	,,	3d. bright blue	1	3	0	9

37. J. C. Mangan. **38.** Statue of St. Peter.

(Des. R. J. King. Typo.)

1949 (5 DEC.). 100*th Anniv. of Death of James Clarence Mangan (poet).* *W* **22.** *P* 15 × 14.

148	**37**	1d. green	2	6	0	6

(Recess. Waterlow & Sons.)

1950 (11 SEPT.). *Holy Year.* *W* **22.** *P* **12½.**

149	**38**	2½d. violet	0	6	0	3
150	,,	3d. blue	1	6	0	9
151	,,	9d. brown	5	0	3	0

PRINTERS. Nos. 152 to 200 were recess-printed by De La Rue & Co., Dublin, *unless otherwise stated.*

39. Thomas Moore. **40.** Irish Harp.

1952 (10 Nov.). *Centenary of Death of Moore (poet).* *W* **22.** *P* 13.

152	**39**	2½d. reddish purple ..	0	6	0	4
153	,,	3½d. deep olive-green ..	1	9	1	3

(Des. F. O'Ryan. Typo. Govt. Printing Works, Dublin.)

1953 (9 FEB.). "*An Tostal*" (*Ireland at Home*) *Festival.* *W* **22** (*sideways*). *P* 14 × 15.

154	**40**	2½d. emerald-green ..	0	8	0	3
155	,,	1s. 4d. blue	7	6	7	6

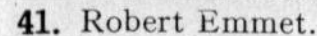

41. Robert Emmet. **42.** Madonna and Child (Della Robbia).

1953 (21 SEPT.). *150th Anniv. of Death of Emmet (patriot).* *W* **22.** *P* 13.
156 **41** 3d. deep bluish green .. 0 6 0 3
157 ,, 1s. 3d. carmine 5 0 3 0

1954 (24 MAY). *Marian Year.* *W* **22.** *P* 15.
158 **42** 3d. blue 4 0 0 6
159 ,, 5d. myrtle-green 8 6 2 6

43. Cardinal Newman. **44.** Statue of Commodore Barry.

(Des. L. Whelan. Typo. Govt. Printing Works, Dublin.)

1954 (19 JULY). *Centenary of Cardinal Newman's Rectorship of Catholic University of Ireland.* *W* **22.** *P* 15 × 14.
160 **43** 2d. bright purple 0 8 0 4
161 ,, 1s. 3d. blue 3 6 3 0

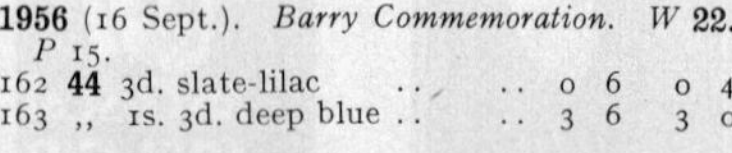

1956 (16 Sept.). *Barry Commemoration.* *W* **22.** *P* 15.
162 **44** 3d. slate-lilac 0 6 0 4
163 ,, 1s. 3d. deep blue 3 6 3 0

45. John Redmond. **46.** Thomas O'Crohan

1957 (11 JUNE). *Centenary of Birth of John Redmond (politician).* *W* **22.** *P* 14 × 15.
164 **45** 3d. deep blue 0 6 0 4
165 ,, 1s. 3d. brown-purple .. 3 0 2 6

1957 (1 JULY). *Centenary of Birth of Thomas O'Crohan (author).* *W* **22.** *P* 14 × 15.
166 **46** 2d. maroon 0 6 0 3
167 ,, 5d. violet 2 6 1 6

47. Admiral Brown. **48.** Father Luke Wadding (after painting by Ribera).

(Des. S. O'Sullivan. Typo. Govt. Printing Works, Dublin.)

1957 (23 SEPT.). *Centenary of Death of Admiral William Brown.* *W* **22.** *P* 15 × 14.
168 **47** 3d. blue 0 8 0 4
169 ,, 1s. 3d. carmine .. .. 3 6 3 c

1957 (25 NOV.). *300th Anniv. of Death of Father Luke Wadding (theologian).* *W* **22.** *P* 15.
170 **48** 3d. deep blue 0 8 0 4
171 ,, 1s. 3d. lake .. .. 3 6 3 c

49. Tom Clarke. **50.** Mother Mary Aikenhead.

1958 (28 JULY). *Centenary of Birth of Thomas J. ("Tom") Clarke (patriot).* *W* **22.** *P* 15.
172 **49** 3d. deep green 0 9 0
173 ,, 1s. 3d. red-brown .. 3 6 3

(Recess. Waterlow & Sons, Ltd.)

1958 (20 OCT.). *Centenary of Death of Mother Mary Aikenhead (foundress of Irish Sisters of Charity).* *W* **22.** *P* 15 × 14.
174 **50** 3d. Prussian blue 0 8 0
175 ,, 1s. 3d. rose-carmine .. 3 6 3

(Typo. Govt. Printing Works, Dublin.)

1958 (29 DEC.). *21st Anniv. of the Irish Constitution.* *Typo.* *W* **22.** *P* 15 × 14.
176 **19** 3d. brown 0 6 0
177 ,, 5d. emerald-green .. 1 9 1

51. Arthur Guinness.

1959 (20 JULY). *Bicentenary of Guinness Brewery.* *W* **22.** *P* 15.
178 **51** 3d. brown-purple .. 0 6 0
179 ,, 1s. 3d. blue 3 0 2

52. " The Flight of the Holy Family ".

(Des. K. Uhlemann.)

1960 (20 June). *World Refugee Year.* *W* **22.** *P* 15.
180 **52** 3d. purple 1 6 0 6
181 ,, 1s. 3d. sepia 5 0 4 0

53. Conference Emblem.

(Des. P. Rahikainen.)

1960 (19 Sept.). *Europa.* *W* **22.** *P* 15.
182 **53** 6d. light brown 15 0 4 0
183 ,, 1s. 3d. violet 27 6 17 6

54. Dublin Airport, De Haviland " Dragon " and Boeing "720" jet aircraft.

961 (26 June). *25th Anniv. of Aer Lingus.* *W* **22.** *P* 15.
84 **54** 6d. blue 2 6 2 0
85 ,, 1s. 3d. green 4 6 3 6

55. St. Patrick.

(Recess. Bradbury, Wilkinson & Co.)

961 (25 Sept.). *Fifteenth Death Centenary of St. Patrick.* *W* **22.** *P* 14½.
36 **55** 3d. blue 0 9 0 4
37 ,, 8d. purple 3 6 3 0
38 ,, 1s. 3d. green 6 0 3 6

56. J. O'Donovan and E. O'Curry.

(Recess. Bradbury, Wilkinson.)

1962 (26 Mar.). *Death Centenaries of O'Donovan and O'Curry (scholars).* *W* **22.** *P* 15.
189 **56** 3d. carmine 0 6 0 4
190 ,, 1s. 3d. purple 2 6 2 0

57. Europa " Tree ".

(Des. Lex Weyer.)

1962 (17 Sept.). *Europa.* *W* **22.** *P* 15.
191 **57** 6d. carmine-red 2 6 1 3
192 ,, 1s. 3d. turquoise 5 0 3 6

58. Campaign Emblem.

1963 (21 Mar.). *Freedom from Hunger.* *W* **22.** *P* 15.
193 **58** 4d. deep violet 0 9 0 6
194 ,, 1s. 3d. scarlet 2 3 2 6

59. " Co-operation ".

(Des. A. Holm.)

1963 (16 Sept.). *Europa.* *W* **22.** *P* 15.
195 **59** 6d. carmine 1 0 1 0
196 ,, 1s. 3d. blue 2 3 2 0

60. Centenary Emblem.

(Des. P. Wildbur. Photo. Harrison & Sons.)

1963 (2 Dec.). *Centenary of Red Cross.* *W* **22** *P* 14½ × 14.
197 **60** 4d. red and grey 0 8 0 10

198 **60** 1s. 3d. red, grey & light emerald 2 3 2 3

61. Wolfe Tone.

(Des. P. Wildbur.)

1964 (13 APR.). *Bicentenary of Birth of Wolfe Tone (revolutionary). W* **22.** *P* 15.

199 **61** 4d. black 0 8 0 8
200 ,, 1s. 3d. ultramarine .. 2 3 2 0

62. Irish Pavilion at Fair.

(Photo. Harrison & Sons.)

1964 (20 JULY). *New York World's Fair. W* **22.** *P* 14½ × 14.

201 **62** 5d. blue-grey, brown, violet and yellow-olive .. 0 10 1 0
202 ,, 1s. 5d. blue-grey, brown, turquoise-blue and light yellow-green 2 3 2 3

63. Europa " Flower ".

(Des. G. Bétemps. Photo. Harrison & Sons.)

1964 SEPT.). *Europa. W* **22** *(sideways). P* 14 × 14½.

203 **63** 8d. olive-green and blue .. 1 2 1 3
204 ,, 1s. 5d. red-brown & orange 2 3 2 3

64. " Waves of Communication ".

(Des. P. Wildbur. Photo. Harrison & Sons.)

1965 (17 MAY). *I.T.U. Centenary. W* **22.** *P* 14½ × 14.

205 **64** 3d. blue and green .. 0 7 0 10
206 ,, 8d. black and green .. 1 2 1 6

PRINTERS. Nos. 207 onwards were photogravure-printed by the Stamping Branch of the Revenue Commissioners, Dublin *unless otherwise stated.*

65. W. B. Yeats (poet).

(Des. R. Kyne, from drawing by S. O'Sullivan.)

1965 (14 JUNE). *Yeats' Birth Centenary. W* **22** *(sideways). P* 15.

207 **65** 5d. black, orange-brown and deep green .. 0 11 1 1
208 ,, 1s. 5d. black, grey-green and brown 2 3 3 0

66. I.C.Y. Emblem.

1965 (16 AUG.). *International Co-operation Year. W* **22.** *P* 15.

209 **66** 3d. ultram. and new blue 0 7 0 1
210 ,, 10d. deep brown & brown 1 6 1 1

67. Europa " Sprig ".

(Des. H. Karlsson.)

1965 (27 SEPT.). *Europa. W* **22.** *P* 15.

211 **67** 8d. black and brown-red .. 1 2 1
212 ,, 1s. 5d. purple and light turquoise-blue 2 3 3

POSTAGE DUE STAMPS.

D 1

(Typo. Govt. Printing Works, Dublin.)

1925. *W* **10.** *P* 14×15.

No.	Type	Value	Unused	Used
D 1	D 1	½d. emerald-green	1 0	1 3
D 2	,,	1d. carmine	1 0	1 6
D 3	,,	2d. deep green	1 3	1 6
		a. Wmk. sideways	5 0	
D 4	,,	6d. plum	3 0	1 9

1940–65. *W* **22.** *P* 14×15.

No.	Type	Value	Unused	Used
D 5	D 1	½d. emerald-green ('42)	0 3	0 4
D 6	,,	1d. carmine ('41)	0 3	0 3
D 7	,,	1½d. vermilion ('53)	0 4	0 6
D 8	,,	2d. deep green ('40)	0 4	0 3
D 9	,,	3d. blue ('53)	0 6	0 8
D10	,,	5d. blue-violet (3.3.43)	1 0	0 10
D11	,,	6d. plum (21.3.60)	0 10	0 8
D12	,,	8d. orange (30.10.62)	1 0	0 10
D13	,,	10d. brt. purple (27.1.65)	1 3	1 0

CONTROL LETTERS.

NOTE.—*Prices are for mint singles with control, but for further information see empanelled note under Great Britain at the beginning of the Control Letters.*

I. = Margin imperf. P. = Margin perf.

I. *Dollard printings.* (*a*) *In black.*

No.		Value	I.	P.
1	Q 21,	10d.	*	85 0
2	R 21,	½d.	10 0	2 0
3	,,	4d.	£8	*
4	S 21,	½d.	6 0	12 6
5	,,	1d.	6 6	30 0
6	,,	2½d.	35 0	12 6
7	,,	3d.	45 0	25 0
8	,,	4d.	15 0	£6
9	,,	5d.	27 6	32 6
10	,,	9d.	30 0	60 0
11	,,	10d.	60 0	30 0
12	S 22,	½d.	4 0	4 0
13	,,	1d.	2 0	3 0
13*a*	,,	2½d.	—	*
14	,,	3d.	15 0	45 0
15	,,	4d.	—	25 0
16	,,	5d.	22 6	*
16*a*	,,	9d.	*	£8
16*b*	,,	10d.	*	35 0
17	T 22,	1d.	90 0	40 0

(*b*) *In red or carmine* (C.).

No.		Value	I.	P.
18	R 21,	4d.	15 0	£8
19	S 21,	2½d.	20 0	£5
20	,,	4d.	50 0	*
21	,,	9d.	£6	32 6
22	S 22,	2½d.	12 6	12 6
23	,,	4d.	65 0	90 0
24	,,	4d. (C.)	50 0	85 0
25	,,	9d.	£8	35 0

II. *Thom printings.* *T* **2.**

(*a*) *In black or dull black* (½d. 1d., 3d. *and* 10d.).

No.		Value	I.	P.
26	Q 20,	1½d.	12 6	12 6
27	Q 21,	1½d.	15 0	10 0
28	R 21,	1s.	40 0	60 0
29	S 21,	2d. (Die I)	7 6	10 0
30	,,	6d.	17 6	*
31	,,	1s.	45 0	60 0
32	S 22,	2d. (Die I)	7 6	5 0
33	,,	2d. (,, II)	6 6	5 6
33*a*	,,	10d.	*	£10
34	,,	1s.	35 0	30 0
35	T 22,	½d.	£6	£6
35*a*	,,	1d.	£6	*
35*b*	,,	1½d.	*	75 0
C. 36	T 22,	2d. (Die I)	40 0	—
C. 37	,,	2d. (Die II)	32 6	*
C. 37*a*	,,	3d.	£6	£7
C. 38	,,	6d.	20 0	*

(*b*) *In red or carmine.*

No.		Value	I.	P.
C. 39	S 22,	4d. (C.)	*	£8
C. 40	,,	9d. agate	35 0	£7
C. 41	T 22,	2½d. (C.)	50 0	40 0
C. 42	,,	4d. (C.)	10 0	20 0
C. 43	,,	9d. olive	32 6	30 0

(*c*) *In blue-black.*

No.		Value	I.	P.
C. 44	S 22,	1d.	27 6	20 0
C. 45	,,	2d. (Die I.)	50 0	50 0
C. 46	,,	2d. (,, II.)	17 6	12 6
C. 48	,,	10d.	80 0	90 0
C. 49	,,	1s.	40 0	50 0
C. 50	T 22	½d.	10 0	7 6
C. 51	,,	1d.	4 0	3 0
C. 52	,,	1½d.	6 0	7 6
C. 53	,,	2d. (Die I.)	50 0	50 0
C. 54	,,	2d. (,, II.)	8 6	6 0
C. 55	,,	3d.	20 0	10 0
C. 56	,,	5d.	20 0	*
C. 57	,,	6d.	17 6	*
C. 58	,,	1s.	32 6	35 0
C. 59	U 22,	6d.	17 6	*

III. *Thom printings.* *T* **4** (*wide setting*) *in blue-black.*

No.		Value	I.	P.
C. 60	T 22,	1d.	30 0	*
C. 61	,,	1½d.	10 0	17 6
C. 62	,,	2d. (Die II.)	£5	50 0
C. 63	,,	1s.	45 0	60 0
C. 64	U 22,	½d.	3 0	3 0
C. 65	,,	1d.	17 6	10 0

IV. " SAORSTAT " *overprint.*

(*a*) *In blue-black or in red* (R.).

No.		Value	I.	P.
C. 66	T 22,	½d.	2 6	3 0
C. 67	,,	1d.	1 3	1 3
C. 68	,,	1½d.	£7	12 6
C. 69	,,	2d. (Die II.)	35 0	15 0
C. 70	,,	2½d. (R.)	7 6	£8
C. 71	,,	4d. (R.)	*	£8
C. 72	,,	5d.	12 6	10 0
C. 73	,,	9d. (R.)	15 0	17 6
C. 74	,,	10d.	80 0	22 6
C. 75	,,	1s.	25 0	*
C. 76	U 22,	6d.	8 6	*
C. 77	,,	½d.	1 6	1 3
C. 78	,,	1d.	2 6	2 0
C. 79	,,	1½d.	10 0	10 0
C. 80	,,	3d.	10 0	8 6
C. 81	,,	4d. (R.)	10 0	*
C. 82	,,	1s.	20 0	20 0
C. 83	U 23,	½d.	3 6	1 0
C. 84	,,	1d.	40 0	22 6
C. 85	,,	2½d. (R.)	12 6	10 0
C. 86	,,	4d. (R.)	12 6	*
C. 87	,,	5d.	12 0	*
C. 88	,,	9d. (R.)	17 6	20 0
C. 89	,,	1s.	20 0	17 6
C. 90	V 23,	6d.	8 6	—
C. 91	,,	4d. (R.)	*	10 0
C. 92	W 23,	6d.	12 6	

Only one specimen of C. 90 with perf. margin is known.

(*b*) *In dull black.*

No.		Value	I.	P.
C. 93	T 22,	½d.	60 0	*
C. 94	,,	1d.	50 0	—
C. 94*a*	,,	1½d.	*	—
C. 95	,,	2d. (Die II.)	65 0	—
C. 96	U 22,	6d.	60 0	*
C. 96*a*	,,	½d.	—	*
C. 97	,,	1½d.	*	—
C. 98	,,	3d.	70 0	*
C. 99	U 23,	½d.	*	60 0
C. 100	,,	1d.	*	80 0
C. 101	V 23,	6d.	60 0	*
C. 102	W 23,	6d.	60 0	*

NOTE.—The Harrison printings (Nos. 26/29*a* and 67/70), being issued in coils only, are not found with control attached.

JAMAICA.

For GREAT BRITAIN stamps used in Jamaica, see page 63.

PRINTERS.—*Until* 1923, *all the stamps of Jamaica were typographed by De La Rue & Co. unless otherwise stated.*

The official dates of issue are given, where known, but where definite information is not available the dates are those of earliest known use, etc.

1, 2, 3, 4, 5, 6, 7, A

PRICES.—The prices for the issue of 1860–63 are for good average copies. Fine well-centred copies are worth considerably more in most cases.

1860 (23 Nov.)–**1863.** *W* **7.** *P*14.

No.	Type	Description	Unused	Used
1	**1**	1d. pale blue	80 0	27 6
		a. Pale greenish blue	85 0	45 0
		b. Blue	65 0	17 6
		c. Deep blue	90 0	55 0
		d. Bisected (½d. Nov. '61) (on cover)	—	£30
2	**2**	2d. rose	£10	75 0
		a. Deep rose	£7	75 0
3	**3**	3d. green (10.9.63)	£6	50 0
4	**4**	4d. brown-orange	£14	60 0
		a. Red orange	£14	37 6
5	**5**	6d. dull lilac	£12	40 0
		a. Grey-purple	£15	65 0
		b. Deep purple	£50	90 0
6	**6**	1s. yellow-brown	£24	65 0
		a. Purple-brown	£16	55 0
		b. Dull brown	£14	65 0
A.		c. "$" for "S" in "SHILLING"	£90	£36

The diagonal bisection of the 1d. was authorized by a P.O. notice dated 20 Nov., 1861. Specimens are only of value when on original envelope or wrapper. The authority was withdrawn as from 1 Dec., 1872. Fakes are frequently met with. Other bisections were unauthorized.

The so-called "dollar variety" of the 1s. occurs once in each sheet of stamps in all shades and in later colours, etc., on the second stamp in the second row of the left upper pane. The prices quoted above are for the dull brown shade, the prices for the other shades being proportionate to their normal value.

All values except the 3d. are known imperf., mint only.

There are two types of watermark in the 3d. and 1s., one being short and squat and the other elongated.

8

9

10

1870–83. *Wmk. Crown CC.* (*a*) *P* 14.

No.	Type	Description	Unused	Used
7	**8**	½d. claret (29.10.72) ..	22 6	7
		a. Deep claret (1883)	17 6	6
8	**1**	1d. blue (20.8.73)	60 0	3
		a. Deep blue	70 0	3
9	**2**	2d. rose (April, '70)	60 0	1
		a. Deep rose	90 0	2
10	**3**	3d. green (1.3.70)	£7	12
11	**4**	4d. brown-orange (1872) ..	£7	20
		a. Red-orange	£14	12
12	**5**	6d. mauve (10.3.71)	55 0	17
13	**6**	1s. dull brn. (to deep) (23.2.73)	32 6	17
A.		a. "$" for "S" in "SHILLING"	£48	£2

(*b*) *P* 12½.

No.	Type	Description	Unused	Used
14	**9**	2s. Venetian red (27.8.75) ..	22 6	30
15	**10**	5s. lilac (27.8.75)	£6	£

The ½d., 1d., 4d., 2s. and 5s. are known imperforate.

1883–97. *Wmk. Crown CA. P* 14.

No.	Type	Description	Unused	Used
16	**8**	½d. yellow-green (1885) ..	3 0	1
		a. Green	0 10	0
17	**1**	1d. blue (1884)	£5	10
18	,,	1d. rose (to deep) (3.3.85) ..	27 6	4
		a. Carmine	25 0	4
19	**2**	2d. rose (to deep) (17.3.84) ..	£10	10
20	,,	2d. grey (1885)	75 0	1
		a. Slate	35 0	1
21	**3**	3d. sage-green (1886) ..	8 6	3
		a. Pale olive-green	7 6	4
22	**4**	4d. red-orange* (9.3.83) ..	£28	32
		a. Red-brown (shades)	10 0	1
23	**5**	6d. deep yellow (4.10.90) ..	25 0	27
		a. Orange-yellow	20 0	12

24 **6** 1s. brn. (to deep) (Mar. '97) 15 0 17 6
A. a. "$" for "S" in "SHILL-ING" £45 £26
b. *Chocolate* 40 0 37 6
25 **9** 2s. Venetian red (1897) .. 35 0 25 0
26 **10** 5s. lilac (1897) 65 0 85 0

* No. 22 is the same colour as No. 11*a*.

The 1d. carmine, 2d. slate, and 2s. are known imperf. All values to the 6d. inclusive are known perf. 12. These are proofs.

11

TWO PENCE
HALF-PENNY

(12)

1889–91. *Value tablet in second colour. Wmk. Crown CA. P* 14.

27 **11** 1d. purple & mve. (8.3.89) 1 3 0 8
28 ,, 2d. green (8.3.89) 15 0 8 6
a. Deep green (brown gum) .. 5 0 6 0
29 ,, 2½d. dull pur. & blue (25.2.91) 7 6 3 0

A very wide range of shades may be found in the 1d. The head-plate was printed in many shades of purple, and the duty-plate in various shades of mauve and purple and also in carmine, etc. The variations in the other values are not so numerous nor so pronounced.

(Surcharged by C. Vendryes, Kingston.)

1890 (4 (?) JUNE). *No. 22a surch. with T* **12**.

30 **4** 2½d. on 4d. red-brown .. 22 6 20 0
a. Spacing between lines of surcharge 1½ mm. .. 45 0 37 6
b. Surcharge double £12 £8
c. "PFNNY" for "PENNY" .. 85 0 85 0
d. "PFNNK" ("F" for "E" and broken "K" for "Y") .. £6 £5

This provisional was issued pending receipt of No. 29 which is listed above for convenience of reference.

Three settings exist. (1) Ten varieties arranged in a single vertical row and repeated six times in the pane. (2) Twelve varieties, in two horizontal rows of six, repeated five times, alternate rows show 1 m. and 1½ mm. spacing between lines of surcharge. (3) Three varieties, arranged horizontally and repeated twenty times. All these settings can be reconstructed by examination of the spacing and relative position of the words of the surcharge and of the broken letters, etc., which are numerous.

A variety reading "PFNNK", with the "K" unbroken, is a forgery.

Varieties c. and d. may be found in the double surcharge.

Surcharges misplaced either horizontally or vertically are met with, the normal position being central at the foot of the stamp with "HALF-PENNY" covering the old value.

13. Llandovery Falls, Jamaica (photo. by Dr. J. Johnston).

Recess. De La Rue.)

1900–1. *Wmk. Crown CC (sideways). P* 14.

31 **13** 1d. red (1.5.00) 3 0 0 10
32 ,, 1d. slate-blk. & red (25.9.01) 2 0 1 0
a. Blued paper 65 0 65 0
b. Imperf. between (pair) ..

Many shades exist of both centre and frame of the bi-coloured 1d. which was, of course, printed from two plates and the design shows minor differences from that of the 1d. red which was printed from a single plate.

14. Arms of Jamaica.

1903–4. *Wmk. Crown CA. P* 14.

33 **14** ½d. grey & dull grn (16.11.03 1 6 0 8
a. "SER.ET" for "SER-VIET" 50 0 47 6
34 ,, 1d. grey & carm. (24.2.04) .. 2 6 0 4
a. "SER.ET" for "SER-VIET" 27 6 22 6
35 ,, 2½d. grey & ultram. (16.11.03) 7 6 3 6
a. "SER.ET" for "SER-VIET" 65 0 70 0
36 ,, 5d. grey & yellow (1.3.04) .. 42 6 50 0
a. "SER.ET" for "SER-VIET" £90

The "SER.ET" variety occurs once in each sheet of stamps on the second stamp in the fourth row of the left upper pane.

The centres of the above and later bi-coloured stamps in the Arms type vary in colour from grey to grey-black.

1905–11. *Wmk. Mult. Crown CA. P* 14.

37 **14** ½d. grey and dull green, C (24.11.05) 2 6 0 6
a. "SER.ET" for "SER-VIET" 32 6 32 6
38 ,, 1d. grey & carm., C (20.11.05) 10 0 0 8
39 ,, 2½d. grey & ultramarine, C (12.11.07) 12 6 6 0
40 ,, 2½d. pale ultram., O (21.9.10) 4 6 4 0
a. Deep ultramarine, O .. 6 0 4 6
41 ,, 5d. grey & orange-yellow, C (24.4.07) 55 0 60 0
a. "SER.ET" for "SER-VIET" £90 £90
42 ,, 6d. dull & bright purple, C (18.8.11) 17 6 30 0
43 ,, 5s. grey & vio., C (Nov. '05) 70 0 50 0

See note above *re* grey centres.

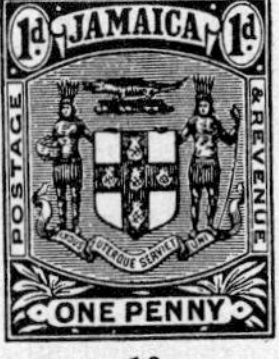

15 16

Arms type redrawn.

1906. *Wmk. Mult. Crown CA. P* 14.

44 **15** ½d. yellow-grn., O (8.11.06) 4 6 2 0
a. Dull green 1 0 0 6
b. Deep green 2 0 0 6
45 **16** 1d. carmine, O (1.10.06) .. 1 9 0 3

Queen Victoria types.

1905–11. *Wmk. Mult. Crown, CA. P* 14.

46 **3** 3d. olive-green, O (15.5.05) .. 7 6 1 9
a. Sage-green, O (1907) .. 12 6 1 9

47 **3** 3d. purple/*yell.*, O (10.3.10) 15 0 15 0
a. Pale pur./yell., C (11.7.10) .. 4 0 7 6
48 **4** 4d. red-brown, O (6.6.08) .. 60 0 60 0
49 „ 4d. black/*yellow*, C (21.9.10) 35 0 50 0
50 „ 4d. red/*yellow*, O (3.10.11) .. 3 6 10 0
51 **5** 6d. dull orange, O (27.6.06) 37 6 40 0
a. Golden yellow, O (Sept., '09) .. 30 0 32 6
52 „ 6d. lilac, O (19.11.09) .. 25 0 27 6
a. Purple, C (July, '10) .. 12 6 17 6
53 **6** 1s. brown, O (Nov. '06) .. 35 0 32 6
a. Deep brown, O 40 0 25 0
A. b. "$" for "S" in "SHILLING" £55 £45
54 **6** 1s. black/*green*, C (21.9.10).. 17 6 30 0
A. a. "$" for "S" in "SHILLING" £70 £70
55 **9** 2s. Venetian red, O (Nov. '08) £10 £8
56 „ 2s. purple/*blue*, C (21.9.10).. 20 0 12 6

17 **18**

King Edward VII.

1911 (3 Feb.). *Wmk. Mult. Crown CA. P* 14.
57 **17** 2d. grey, O 3 6 10 0

King George V.

1912-20. *Wmk. Mult. Crown CA. P* 14.
58 **18** 1d. carmine-red, O (5.12.12) 1 0 0 6
a. Scarlet, O (1916) 1 9 0 8
59 „ 1½d. brn.-orge., O (13.7.16) 4 0 1 0
a. Yellow-orange, O 12 6 1 6
60 „ 2d. grey, O (2.8.12) .. 3 0 8 6
a. Slate-grey, O 4 0 5 0
61 „ 2½d. blue, O (13.2.13) .. 3 0 1 6
a. Deep bright blue, O .. 2 6 1 9
62 „ 3d. purple/*yellow*, C (6.3.12) 5 0 1 6
a. White back, C (2.4.13) .. 3 6 1 9
b. On lemon, C (25.9.16) .. 12 6 5 0
63 „ 4d. blk. & red/*yell.*, C (4.4.13) 7 6 5 0
a. White back, C (7.5.14) .. 6 6 12 6
b. On lemon, C (1916) .. 65 0 50 0
c. On pale yellow, C (1919) .. 40 0 35 0
64 „ 6d. dull and bright purple, C (14.11.12) 12 6 17 6
a. Dull purple and bright mauve, C (1915) 10 0 8 6
b. Dull purple and bright magenta, C (1920) .. 8 6 5 0
65 „ 1s. black/*green*, C (2.8.12) 8 0 7 0
a. White back, C (4.1.15) .. 10 0 20 0
b. On blue-green, olive back, C ('20) 17 6 17 6
66 „ 2s. pur. & bright blue/*blue*, C (10.1.19) 37 6 42 6
67 „ 5s. grn. & red/*yellow*, C (5.9.19) 85 0 90 0
a. On pale yellow, C 80 0 85 0
b. On orange-buff, C £6 £6

For the ½d. in this design and the 6d. with Script wmk. see Nos. 107 and 90.

The paper of No. 67 is a bright yellow and the gum rough and dull. No. 67*a* is on practically the normal creamy "pale yellow" paper, and the gum is smooth and shiny. The paper of No 67*b* approaches the "coffee" colour of the true "orange-buff," and the colours of both head and frame are paler, the latter being of a carmine tone.

WAR STAMP. (19) WAR STAMP. (20) WAR STAMP. (21)

(Overprinted locally.)

1916 (1 April-Sept.). *Optd. with T* **19.**
68 **15** ½d. yellow-green 0 4 0 4
a. No stop after "STAMP" .. 10 0 10 0
b. Overprint double 90 0 85 0
c. Overprint inverted 70 0 65 0
d. Blue-green 0 6 0 4
da. No stop after "STAMP" .. 10 0 8 6
69 **18** 3d. purple/*yell.* (white back) 5 0 6 0
a. On lemon (June, '16) .. 3 0 6 0
aa. No stop after "STAMP" .. 20 0 20 0
b. On pale yellow (Sept., '16) .. 4 0 5 0

Minor varieties: ½d. (i) Small "P"; (ii) Space between "W" and "A"; (iii) "WARISTAMP" (raised quad between words); (iv) Two stops after "STAMP". 3d. "WARISTAMP".

Note.—The above and succeeding stamps with "WAR STAMP" overprint were issued for payment of a special war tax on letters and post cards or on parcels. Ordinary unoverprinted stamps could also be used for this purpose.

1916 (Sept.-Dec.). *Optd. with T* **20.**
70 **15** ½d. blue-green (*shades*) (2.10.16) 0 6 0
a. No stop after "STAMP" .. 15 0 12
b. Opt. omitted (in pair) .. £14 £1
c. "R" inserted by hand .. £10 £
71 **18** 1½d. orange (1.9.16) .. 0 10 0
aa. Wmk. sideways .. .. — £4
a. No stop after "STAMP" .. 10 0 8
b. "S" in "STAMP" omitd. 80 0 70
c. "S" inserted by hand .. £5
d. "R" in "WAR" omitted.. £12 £1
e. "R" inserted by hand .. £10 £
f. Inverted "d" for "P" .. 85 0 80
72 „ 3d. purple/*lemon* (2.10.16) 3 0 2
aa. Opt. inverted .. £14
a. No stop after "STAMP" .. 30 0 20
b. "S" in "STAMP" omitd. £8 £
c. "S" inserted by hand .. £6 £
d. "S" inserted inverted .. £12 £1
e. On yellow (Dec., '16) .. 17 6 17
ea. "S" in "STAMP" omitd. £12 £
eb. "S" inserted by hand .. £12 £
ec. "S" inserted inverted .. £14 £

Minor varieties, such as raised quads, small stop, double stop, spaced letters and letters of different sizes, also exist in this overprint.

1917 (March). *Optd. with T* **21.**
73 **15** ½d. blue-green (*shades*) (25.3.17) .. 0 4 0
a. No stop after "STAMP" .. 15 0 10
b. Stop inserted and "P" impressed a second time .. £12
c. Optd. on back only .. 90 0
d. Opt. inverted 22 6 20
74 **18** 1½d. orange (3.3.17) .. 0 3 0
aa. Wmk. sideways .. .. — £
a. No stop after "STAMP" .. 12 6 8
b. Stop inserted and "P" impressed a second time .. £14
c. Opt. double 80 0
d. Opt. inverted 95 0
75 „ 3d. purple/*yellow* (3.3.17) 1 6 1
a. No stop after "STAMP" .. 20 0 17
b. Stop inserted and "P" impressed a second time .. £12
c. Opt. inverted .. £8
d. Opt. sideways (reading up).. £20

There are numerous minor varieties in this overprint.

WAR STAMP
(22)

(Optd. by De La Rue & Co.)

1919 (4 Oct.). *Optd. with T* **22.**
76 **15** ½d. green (R.) 0 3 0
77 **18** 3d. purple/*yellow* (R.) .. 1 9 2
a. Pale purple/buff (R.) .. 1 6 2
b. Deep purple/buff (R.) .. 6 0 5

We list the most distinct variations in the 3d. The buff tone of the paper varies considerably in depth.

23. Jamaica Exhibition, 1891.

24. Arawak Woman Preparing Cassava.

26. King's House, Spanish Town.

25. War Contingent embarking.

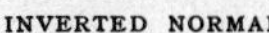

INVERTED NORMAL

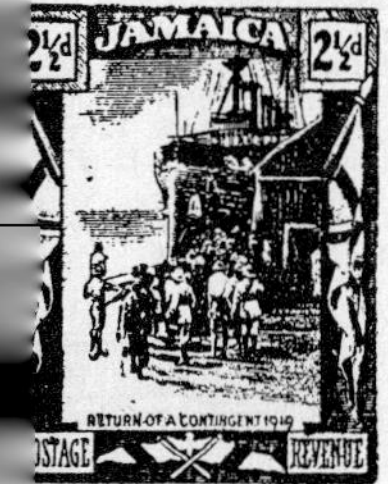

27. Return of War Contingent.

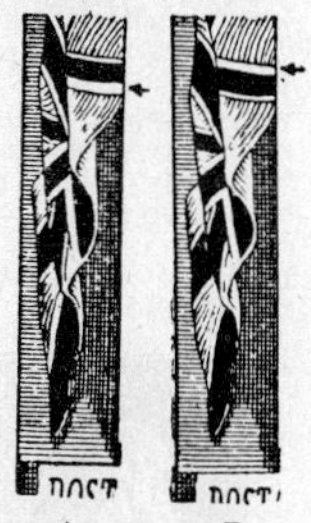

A B

28. Landing of Columbus.

29. Cathedral, Spanish Town.

30. Statue of Queen Victoria.

31. Admiral Rodney Memorial.

32. Sir Charles Metcalfe monument.

33. Jamaican scenery.

34

(Typo. (½d., 1d.), recess (others). De La Rue & Co.)

1919–21. *Wmk. Mult. Crown CA (sideways on 1d., 1½d. and 10s). P 14.*

No.	Type	Value	Description	Unused s.	d.	Used s.	d.
78	**23**	½d.	green and olive-green, C (12.11.20)	0	3	0	3
79	**24**	1d.	car. & orge., C (3.10.21)	1	6	0	3
80	**25**	1½d.	grn. (*shades*) (4.7.19) ..	1	0	0	3
81	**26**	2d.	indigo & grn. (18.2.21)	3	0	3	0
82	**27**	2½d.	dp. bl. & bl. (A) (18.2.21)	20	0	12	6
			a. *Blue-black and deep blue* (A)	4	0	4	0
83	**28**	3d.	myrtle-grn. & bl. (8.4.21)	3	0	0	6
84	**29**	4d.	brn. & dp. grn. (21.2.21)	12	6	12	6
85	**30**	1s.	orange-yellow and red-orange (10.12.20) ..	15	0	20	0
			a. Frame inverted	£1000		£800	
86	**31**	2s.	lt. bl. & brn. (10.12.20)	55	0	35	0
87	**32**	3s.	violet-blue and orange (10.12.20)	60	0	85	0
88	**33**	5s.	bl. & yell.-orge. (15.4.21)	85	0	85	0
			a. *Blue and pale dull orange* ..	85	0	85	0
89	**34**	10s.	myrtle-green (6.5.20) ..	£5		£5	

The 2½d. of the above series showed the Union Jack at left incorrectly as indicated in illustration A. In the issue on paper with Script wmk. the design was corrected (Illustration B).

A 6d. stamp illustrating the abolition of slavery was prepared and sent out in April, 1921, but for political reasons was not issued and the stock was destroyed. "SPECIMEN" copies are known on both the Mult. CA and Script CA papers, and are worth about £40 each.

1921 (21 Oct.). *Wmk. Mult. Script CA. P 14.*

No.	Type	Value	Description	Unused s.	d.	Used s.	d.
90	**18**	6d.	dull pur. & bt. mag., C	25	0	10	6

35. "POSTAGE & REVENUE" added.

36. Port Royal in 1853.

(Printing as before; the 6d. recess-printed.)

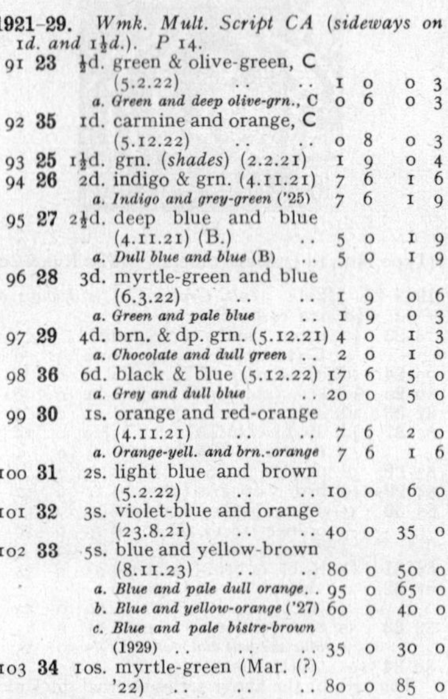

1921–29. *Wmk. Mult. Script CA (sideways on 1d. and 1½d.). P 14.*

No.	Type	Description	Unused	Used
91	**23**	½d. green & olive-green, C (5.2.22)	1 0	0 3
		a. Green and deep olive-grn., C	0 6	0 3
92	**35**	1d. carmine and orange, C (5.12.22)	0 8	0 3
93	**25**	1½d. grn. (*shades*) (2.2.21)	1 9	0 4
94	**26**	2d. indigo & grn. (4.11.21)	7 6	1 6
		a. Indigo and grey-green ('25)	7 6	1 9
95	**27**	2½d. deep blue and blue (4.11.21) (B.) ..	5 0	1 9
		a. Dull blue and blue (B)	5 0	1 9
96	**28**	3d. myrtle-green and blue (6.3.22)	1 9	0 6
		a. Green and pale blue ..	1 9	0 3
97	**29**	4d. brn. & dp. grn. (5.12.21)	4 0	1 3
		a. Chocolate and dull green ..	2 0	1 0
98	**36**	6d. black & blue (5.12.22)	17 6	5 0
		a. Grey and dull blue ..	20 0	5 0
99	**30**	1s. orange and red-orange (4.11.21)	7 6	2 0
		a. Orange-yell. and brn.-orange	7 6	1 6
100	**31**	2s. light blue and brown (5.2.22)	10 0	6 0
101	**32**	3s. violet-blue and orange (23.8.21)	40 0	35 0
102	**33**	5s. blue and yellow-brown (8.11.23)	80 0	50 0
		a. Blue and pale dull orange..	95 0	65 0
		b. Blue and yellow-orange ('27)	60 0	40 0
		c. Blue and pale bistre-brown (1929)	35 0	30 0
103	**34**	10s. myrtle-green (Mar. (?) '22)	80 0	85 0

The frame of No. 102*a* is the same colour as that of No. 88*a*.

The designs of all values of the pictorial series, with the exception of the 5s. and 10s. (which originated with the Governor, Sir Leslie Probyn), were selected by Mr. F. C. Cundall, F.S.A. The 1d. and 5s. were drawn by Miss Cundall, the 3d. by Mrs. Cundall, and the 10s. by De La Rue & Co. The 6d. is from a lithograph. The other designs are from photographs, the frames of all being the work of Miss Cundall and Miss Wood.

37

38

39

(Centres from photos by Miss V. F. Taylc Frames des. F. C. Cundall, F.S.A., and draw by Miss Cundall. Bradbury, Wilkinso Recess.)

1923 (1 Nov.). *Child Welfare. Wmk. Mu Script CA. P 12.*

No.	Type	Description	Unused	Used
104	**37**	½d.+½d. black and green	7 0	12
105	**38**	1d.+½d. black and scarlet	10 0	15
106	**39**	2½d.+½d. black and blue..	35 0	40

Sold at a premium of ½d. for the Child Welfa League, these stamps were on sale annually frc 1 November to 31 January, until 31 Januar 1927, when their sale ceased, the remainde being destroyed on 21 February, 1927.

Labels bearing a red cross and an aeroplar with or without the inscription "JAMAICA" "JAMAICA Half penny" were sold by Jamaica Patriotic Stamp League in aid various war-time funds. Their use on cor spondence was not forbidden and they frequently found postmarked, but they p formed no postal function.

1927 (Nov.). *Wmk. Mult. Script CA. P 14*

No.	Type	Description	Unused	Used
107	**18**	½d. green, O	0 2	0

40

41

42

Die I Die II

(Recess. De La Rue & Co.)

1929-32. *Wmk. Mult. Script CA. P* 14.

108 **40** 1d. scarlet (Die I) 0 9 0 6
a. Die II (1932) 0 6 0 3
109 **41** 1½d. chocolate 1 0 0 6
110 **42** 9d. maroon 12 6 6 0

In Die I the shading below JAMAICA is formed of thickened parallel lines, and in Die II of diagonal cross-hatching.

43. Coco Palms at Columbus Cove.

44. Wag Water River, St. Andrew.

45. Priestman's River, Portland.

(Dies eng. & recess. Waterlow & Sons.)

32. *Wmk. Mult. Script CA (sideways on* 2d. *and* 2½d.). *P* 12½.

1 **43** 2d. black and green .. 2 0 1 6
a. Imperf. between (vert. pair)
2 **44** 2½d. greenish blue & ultram. 2 6 2 6
a. Imperf. between (vert. pair)
3 **45** 6d. grey black & purple .. 8 6 6 0

35 (6 May). *Silver Jubilee. As Nos.* 91/4 *of Antigua, but ptd. by B.W. & Co. P* 11 × 12.

4 1d. deep blue and scarlet .. 0 6 0 3
5 1½d. ultramarine & grey-black 1 0 0 10
a. Extra flagstaff 50 0
6 6d. green and indigo .. 5 0 6 6
a. Extra flagstaff £7
7 1s. slate and purple .. 8 6 8 6
a. Extra flagstaff £14

For illustration of "extra flagstaff" variety Bechuanaland.

37 (12 May). *Coronation. As Nos.* 13/5 *of Aden.*

8 1d. scarlet 0 4 0 4
9 1½d. grey-black 0 10 1 0
0 2½d. bright blue 1 6 1 9

46. King George VI.

47. Coco Palms at Columbus Cove.

48. Bananas.

49. Citrus Grove.

50. Kingston Harbour.

51. Sugar Industry.

52. Bamboo Walk.

53. King George VI.

53*a*. Tobacco Growing and Cigar Making.

(Recess. De La Rue & Co. (T **46**, 5s. and 10s.), Waterlow & Sons (others).)

1938–52. *T* **46** *to* **53*a*** *and as T* **33**, **44** *and* **45** *but with inset portrait of King George VI, as in T* **47**. *Wmk. Mult. Script CA. P* 13½×14 (*½d.,* 1*d. and* 1½*d.*), 14 (5*s. and* 10*s.*) *or* 12½ (*others*).

No.	Type	Description				
121	**46**	½d. blue-green (10.10.38)	0	4	0	3
		a. Wmk. sideways	†		£80	
121*b*	,,	½d. orange (25.10.51) ..	0	4	0	4
122	,,	1d. scarlet (10.10.38) ..	0	4	0	3
122*a*	,,	1d. blue-green (25.10.51)	0	4	0	3
123	,,	1½d. brown (10.10.38) ..	0	5	0	3
		a. *Light red-brown*	£10		£5	
124	**47**	2d. grey and green ..	0	6	0	3
		a. Perf. 13×13½	0	8	0	4
		b. Perf. 12½×13 ('51) ..	0	6	0	4
125	**44**	2½d. greenish blue & ultram.	4	0	6	0
126	**48**	3d. ultramarine & green ..	0	8	0	6
126*a*	,,	3d. greenish blue and ultramarine (15.8.49)	3	6	2	0
126*b*	,,	3d. green & scar. (1.7.52)	0	8	0	8
127	**49**	4d. brown and green ..	0	10		10
128	**45**	6d. grey and purple ..	1	6	0	8
		a. Perf. 13½×13 (10.10.50) ..	1	3	0	6
129	**50**	9d. lake	1	6	1	0
130	**51**	1s. green & purple-brown	2	0	1	0
131	**52**	2s. blue and chocolate ..	5	0	2	0
132	**33**	5s. slate-blue & yellow-orange	15	0	12	6
		a. Perf. 13 (24.10.49) ..	35	0	40	0
		ab. *Bl. & orge.* (10.10.50)	10	0	10	0
133	**53**	10s. myrtle-green ..	20	0	22	6
		aa. Perf. 13 (10.10.50) ..	20	0	17	6
133*a*	**53*a***	£1 choc. & violet (15.8.49)	50	0	40	0

No. 123*a* should not be confused with intermediate shades of red-brown which are not scarce.

54. Courthouse, Falmouth.

55. King Charles II and King George VI.

56. Institute of Jamaica.

57. "Labour and Learning".

58. House of Assembly.

59. Scroll, Flag and King George VI.

(Recess. Waterlow & Sons.)

1945 (20 AUG.)–**1946.** *New Constitution. Wmk. Mult. Script CA. P* 12½.

No.	Type	Description				
134	**54**	1½d. sepia	0	4	0	3
		a. Perf. 12½ × 13 (1946)	0	8	0	6
135	**55**	2d. green	4	6	4	0
		a. Perf. 12½ × 13 (1945)	0	8	0	6
136	**56**	3d. ultramarine	0	10	1	6
		a. Perf. 13 (1946)	1	3	1	9
137	**58**	4½d. slate	1	3	1	6
		a. Perf. 13 (1946)	1	9	2	6
138	**57**	2s. red-brown	3	6	3	6
139	**59**	5s. indigo	7	6	15	0
140	**56**	10s. green	15	0	30	0

1946 (14 OCT.). *Victory. As Nos.* 28/9 *of Aden. P* 13½ × 14.

141	1½d. purple-brown	0	8	0	8
	a. Perf. 13½	0	6	0	8
142	3d. blue	1	3	1	9
	a. Perf. 13½	2	0	2	6

1948 (1 DEC.). *Royal Silver Wedding. As Nos.* 30/1 *of Aden.*

143	1½d. red-brown	0	6	0	6
144	£1 scarlet	37	6	40	0

1949 (10 OCT.). *75th Anniv. of Universal Postal Union. As Nos.* 114/7 *of Antigua.*

145	1½d. red-brown	0	8	0	8
146	2d. deep blue-green	0	10	1	0
147	3d. deep blue	1	0	1	6
48	6d. purple	2	6	2	6

951 (16 FEB.). *Inauguration of B.W.I. University College. As Nos.* 118/9 *of Antigua.*

49	2d. black and red-brown	0	8	0	8
50	6d. grey-black and purple	1	6	1	6

60. Scout Badge and Map of Caribbean.

61. Scout Badge and Map of Jamaica.

(Litho. Bradbury, Wilkinson & Co.)

52 (5 MAR.). *First Caribbean Scout Jamboree. Wmk. Mult. Script CA. P* 13½ × 13 (*2d.*) *or* 13 × 13½ (*6d.*)

No.	Type	Description				
1	**60**	2d. blue, apple-grn. & black	1	6	0	9
2	**61**	6d. yellow-green, carmine-red and black	2	6	3	0

53 (2 JUNE). *Coronation. As No.* 47 *of Aden.*

3	2d. black & dp. yellow-green	0	8	0	8

62. Coco Palms at Columbus Cove.

(Recess. Waterlow & Sons, Ltd.)

1953 (25 NOV.). *Royal Visit. Wmk. Mult. Script CA. P* 12½ × 13.

No.	Type	Description				
154	**62**	2d. grey-black and green	1	0	1	0

63. Man-o'-War at Port Royal.

64. Old Montego Bay.

65. Old Kingston.

66. Proclamation of Abolition of Slavery, 1838.

(Recess. De La Rue & Co.)

1955 (10 MAY). *Tercentenary Issue. Wmk. Mult. Script CA. P* 12½.

No.	Type	Description				
155	**63**	2d. black and olive-green	0	8	1	0
156	**64**	2½d. black & deep brt. blue	0	10	1	3
157	**65**	3d. black and claret	1	8	1	3
158	**66**	6d. black and carmine-red	2	9	3	8

67. Palms.

68. Sugar Cane.

69. Pineapples.

70. Bananas.

71. Mahoe.

72. Breadfruit.

73. Ackee.

74. Doctor Bird.

75. Blue Mountain Peak.

76. Royal Botanic Gardens, Hope.

77. Rafting on the Rio Grande.

78. Fort Charles.

79. Arms of Jamaica.

80. Arms of Jamaica.

(Recess. Bradbury, Wilkinson (T **79/80**), De Rue (others).)

1956. *Wmk. Mult. Script CA. P* 13 (*½d. to 6d*
13½ (*8d. to 2s.*) *or* 11½ (*3s. to £1*).

159	**67**	½d.	blk. & dp. orange-red	0	3	0
160	**68**	1d.	black and emerald ..	0	3	0
161	**69**	2d.	black & carmine-red	0	4	0
162	**70**	2½d.	blk. & dp. bright blue	0	6	0
163	**71**	3d.	emerald & red-brown	0	8	0
164	**72**	4d.	bronze-green and blue	0	10	0
165	**73**	5d.	scarlet & bronze-green	0	10	0
166	**74**	6d.	black & deep rose-red	1	0	0
167	**75**	8d.	ultram. & red-orange	1	6	1
168	**76**	1s.	yellow-green and blue	2	0	0
169	**77**	1s.	6d. ultramarine and reddish purple ..	3	0	1
170	**78**	2s.	blue and bronze-green (*shades*)	5	0	3
171	**79**	3s.	black and blue ..	7	0	5
172	,,	5s.	black & carmine-red	8	6	7
173	**80**	10s.	black and blue-green	17	6	18
174	,,	£1	black and purple ..	35	0	40

Dates of issue:—1 May, ½d., 1d.; 2 Au
2d.; 2½d., 3s.; 15 Aug., 5s., 10s., £1; 3 Se
6d.; 15 Nov., 8d., 1s., 1s. 6d., 2s.; 17 D
3d., 4d., 5d.

1958 (22 Apr.). *Inauguration of British Caribbean Federation. As Nos.* 135/7 *of Antigua.*

175	2d. deep green	0	8	0	8
176	5d. blue	1	3	1	3
177	6d. scarlet	2	3	2	3

81. *Britannia* flying over 1860 Packet-steamer.

82. Postal Mule-cart and Motor-van.

83. 1s. stamps of 1860 and 1956.

(Recess. Waterlow & Sons.)

960 (4 Jan.). *Stamp Centenary.* W w. **12.** *P* 13 × 13½ (1s.) *or* 13½ × 14 (*others*).

78	**81**	2d. blue and reddish purple	0	10	0	10
79	**82**	6d. carmine & olive-green	2	6	2	6
8o	**83**	1s. red-brown, yellow-green and blue	4	0	5	0

1
9
6
2
NDEPENDENCE
(84)

INDEPENDENCE
1962
(85)

62 (8 Aug.)–**63.** *Independence.* (*a*) *Optd. with T* **85** (3*d. to* 2*s*) *or as T* **84** (*others*). *Wmk. Mult. Script CA.*

1	**67**	½d. blk. & dp. orange-red	0	4	0	4
2	**68**	1d. black and emerald ..	0	5	0	4
3	**70**	2½d. blk. & dp. bright blue	0	8	0	6
4	**71**	3d. emerald & red-brown	0	8	0	6
5	**73**	5d. scarlet & bronze-green	1	0	0	11
6	**74**	6d. black and dp. rose-red	1	3	0	8
7	**75**	8d. ultram and red-orange (*opt. at upper left*) ..	1	6	1	3
		a. Opt. at lower left (17.9.63?)	20	0		
8	**76**	1s. yellow-green and blue	2	6	1	6
9	**78**	2s. blue and bronze-green (*shades*)	5	6	4	6
)	**79**	3s. black and blue ..	7	0	7	0
1	**80**	10s. black and blue-green	18	6	21	6
2	,,	£1 black and purple ..	37	6	42	6

86. Military Bugler and Map.

87. Gordon House and Banner.

88. Map, Factories and Fruit.

(Des. V. Whiteley. Photo. De La Rue.)

(*b*) *W* w.**12.** *P* 13.

193	**86**	2d. carmine, black, yellow and deep green ..	0	4	0	2
194	,,	4d. carm., blk., yell. & blue	0	8	0	6
195	**87**	1s. 6d. black and red ..	3	0	3	0
196	**88**	5s. bluish violet, yellow, green and light blue	10	0	11	6

89. Weightlifting, Boxing, Football and Cycling.

90. Diving, Sailing, Swimming and Water Polo.

91. Pole-vault, Javelin, Discus, Relay-racing and Hurdles.

92. Arms of Kingston and Athlete.

T **89/91** include the Seal of Kingston.
(Photo. Harrison & Sons.)

1962 (11 Aug.). *Ninth Central American and Caribbean Games, Kingston. W* w.**12.** *P* 14½ × 14.
197 **89** 1d. sepia and carmine-red 0 8 0 8
198 **90** 6d. sepia and greenish blue 1 6 1 3
199 **91** 8d. sepia and bistre .. 1 9 1 9
200 **92** 2s. sepia, yell., red & blue 4 6 5 0

An imperf. miniature sheet exists, but this was never available at face value or at any post office.

93. Farmer and Crops.

(Litho. De La Rue.)

1963 (4 June) *Freedom from Hunger. P* 12½.
201 **93** 1d. multicoloured .. 0 6 0 6
202 ,, 8d. multicoloured .. 1 9 1 9

1963 (Sept.). *Red Cross Centenary. As Nos.* 147/8 *of Antigua.*
203 2d. red and black 0 6 0 8
204 1s. 6d. red and blue.. .. 2 6 2 9

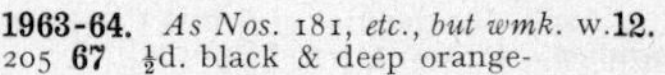

1963-64. *As Nos.* 181, *etc., but wmk.* w.**12.**
205 **67** ½d. black & deep orange-red (6.2.64) 0 3 0 4
206 **68** 1d. black & emer. (3.4.64) 0 6 0 6
207 **70** 2½d. black and deep bright blue (3.4.64) 0 8 0 10
208 **71** 3d. emerald & red-brown (12.63*) 1 0 1 3
209 **73** 5d. scarlet and bronze-green (3.4.64) .. 1 6 2 0
210 **75** 8d. ultramarine and red-orange (3.4.64) .. 2 6 3 0
211 **76** 1s. yellow-green and blue (21.12.63*) 4 0 4 0
212 **77** 2s. deep blue and deep bronze-green (3.4.64) 8 6 6 0
213 **79** 3s. black and blue (5.2.64) 10 0 8 6

The overprint on the 8d., 1s. and 2s. is at lower left, the others are as before.

* These are the earliest known dates recorded in Jamaica.

94. Carole Joan Crawford ("Miss World 1963").

(Photo. De La Rue.)

1964 (14 Feb.). *"Miss World* 1963*" Commemoration. P* 13.
214 **94** 3d. multicoloured .. 0 10 0
215 ,, 1s. multicoloured .. 2 0 2
216 ,, 1s. 6d. multicoloured .. 2 9 2
MS216*a* 153 × 101 mm. Nos. 214/6. Imperf. (25.5.64) .. 5 6

95. *Lignum vitae.*

96. Ackee.

97. Blue Mahoe.

98. Land Shells.

99. National Flag over Jamaica.

100. *Murex antillarum.*

101. *Papilio homerus.*

102. Doctor Bird.

103. Gypsum Industry.

104. National Stadium.

105. Palisadoes International Airport.

106. Bauxite Mining.

107 Blue Marlin (sport fishing).

108. Exploration of Sunken City, Port Royal.

109. Arms of Jamaica.

110. Queen Elizabeth II and National Flag.

111. Multiple " J " and Pineapple.

(Des. V. Whiteley. Photo. Harrison.)

[1]964 (4 May). *W* **111.** *P* 14½ (1*d.*, 2*d.*, 2½*d.*, 6*d.*, 8*d.*), 14 × 14½ (1½*d.*, 3*d.*, 4*d.*, 10*s.*), 14½ × 14 (9*d.*, 1*s.*, 3*s.*, 5*s.*, £1) *or* 13½ × 14½ (1*s.* 6*d.*, 2*s.*).

217	**95**	1d. violet-blue, deep grn. and light brown ..	0	3	0	2
218	**96**	1½d. multicoloured ..	0	4	0	3
219	**97**	2d. red, yell. & grey-grn.	0	4	0	2
220	**98**	2½d. multicoloured ..	0	5	0	4
221	**99**	3d. yellow, blk. & emer.	0	6	0	4
222	**100**	4d. ochre and violet ..	0	7	0	5
223	**101**	6d. multicoloured ..	0	10	0	4
224	**102**	8d. multicoloured ..	1	0	0	10
225	**103**	9d. blue & yellow-bistre	1	1	0	10
226	**104**	1s. black & light brown	1	5	0	10
		a. Light brown omitted ..				
227	**105**	1s. 6d. blk., lt. bl. & buff	2	0	1	6
228	**106**	2s. red-brn., blk. & lt. bl.	2	9	2	6
229	**107**	3s. blue and dull green ..	4	0	3	6
		a. Perf. 13½ × 14½	6	0	5	0
230	**108**	5s. black, ochre and blue	6	9	6	0
231	**109**	10s. multicoloured ..	13	3	15	0
232	**110**	£1 multicoloured ..	25	0	27	6

112. Scout Belt.

113. Globe, Scout Hat and Scarf.

114. Scout Badge and Alligator.
(*Reduced size illustration. Actual size* 61½ × 30½ *mm.*).

(Photo. Harrison.)

1964 (27 Aug.). *Sixth Inter-American Scout Conference, Kingston.* *W* **111.** *P* 14 (1s.) *or* 14½ × 14 (*others*).

233 **112** 3d. red, black and pink .. 0 9 0 9
234 **113** 8d. brt. blue, olive & blk. 1 6 1 9
235 **114** 1s. gold, dp. blue & lt. bl. 2 0 2 3

115. Gordon House, Kingston.

116. Headquarters House, Kingston.

117. House of Assembly, Spanish Town.

(Des. V. Whiteley. Photo. Harrison.)

1964 (16 Nov.). *Tenth Commonwealth Parliamentary Conference, Kingston.* *W* **111.** *P* 14½ × 14.

236 **115** 3d. black and yellow-green 0 9 1 0
237 **116** 6d. black & carmine-red 1 2 1 6
238 **117** 1s. 6d. black & brt. blue 2 9 3 9

118. Eleanor Roosevelt.

(Des. V. Whiteley. Photo. Harrison.)

1964 (10 Dec.). *16th Anniv. of Declaration o Human Rights.* *W* **111.** *P* 14½ × 14.

239 **118** 1s. black, red & lt. green 2 0 2

119. Guides Emblem on Map.

120. Guide Emblems.

(*Reduced size illustration. Actual size* 61½ × 3(*mm.*).

(Photo. Harrison.)

1965 (17 May). *Golden Jubilee of Jamaica G Guides Association.* *W* **111** (*sideways on 3d P* 14 × 14½ (*3d.*) *or* 14 (*1s.*).

240 **119** 3d. yellow, green and light blue 0 7 0
241 **120** 1s. yellow, black and apple-green 1 8 2

121. Uniform Cap.

122. Flag-bearer and Drummer.

(Photo. Harrison.)

965 (23 Aug.). *Salvation Army Centenary. W* **111.** *P* 14 × 14½ (*3d.*) *or* 14½ × 14 (*1s. 6d.*).

42	**121**	3d. multicoloured ..	0	9	1	0
43	**122**	1s. 6d. multicoloured ..	2	6	3	0

123. Paul Bogle, William Gordon and Morant Bay Court House.

(Photo. Enschedé.)

965 (29 Dec.). *Centenary of Morant Bay Rebellion. No wmk. P* 14 × 13.

44	**123**	3d. light brown, ultramarine and black ..	0	9	1	0
45	,,	1s. 6d. light brown, yellow-green and black	2	9	3	0
46	,,	3s. lt. brown, rose & black	5	0	5	9

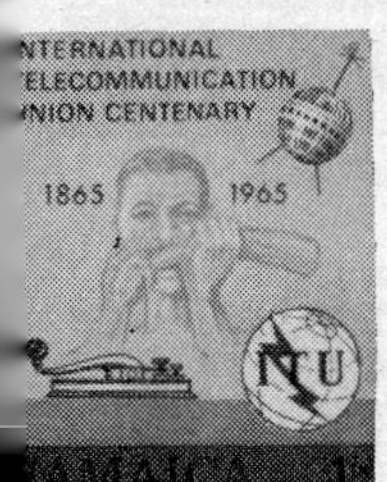

124. Abeng-blower, Telstar ", Morse Key ind I.T.U. Emblem.

(Photo. Harrison.)

ROYAL VISIT
MARCH 1966

(**125**)

1965 (29 Dec.). *I.T.U. Centenary. W* **111.** *P* 14 × 14½.

247	**124**	1s. black, grey-blue & red	1	9	2	0

1966 (3 Mar.). *Royal Visit. Nos.* 221, 223, 226/7 *optd. with T* **125.**

248	**99**	3d. yellow, blk. & emer.	0	7	0	10
249	**101**	6d. multicoloured . ..	1	0	1	2
250	**104**	1s. black and light brown	1	8	2	0
251	**105**	1s. 6d. blk., lt. bl. & buff	2	6	3	0

126. Sir Winston Churchill.

(Des. Jennifer Toombs. Photo. Harrison.)

1966 (18 April). *Churchill Commemoration. W* **111.** *P* 14.

252	**126**	6d. black and olive-green	1	0	1	2
253	,,	1s. bistre-brown and deep violet-blue	1	8	2	0

POSTAL FISCALS.

Revenue stamps were authorized for postal use by Post Office notice of 12 October, 1887.

F 1

(Typo. De La Rue & Co.)

1865-71 (Issued). *P* 14.

(*a*) *Wmk. Pineapple* (*T* **7**).

F1	**F 1**	1d. rose (1865)	80	0	80	0
		a. Imperf.				

(*b*) *Wmk. Crown CC.*

F2	**F 1**	1d. rose (1868)	20	0	22	6

(*c*) *Wmk. CA over Crown* (*T* w. **7** *sideways, covering two stamps*).

F3	**F 1**	1d. rose (1870 or 1871) ..	7	6	3	6
		a. Imperf.				

F 2

F 3

(Typo. De La Rue & Co.)

1855–74 (Issued). *Glazed paper.* *P* 14.

(*a*) *No wmk.*

F4	F 2	1½d. blue/*blue* (1857)	30	0	35	0
		a. Imperf. (1855)				
		b. Blue on white	60	0	60	0
F5	,,	3d. purple/*blue* (1857)	40	0	42	6
		a. Imperf. (1855)				
		b. Purple on lilac (1857)	25	0	25	0
		ba. Imperf. (1855)				
		c. Purple on white (1857)	30	0	30	0

(*b*) *Wmk. Crown CC.*

F6	F 2	3d. purple/*lilac* (1874)	4	0	6	0

All the above stamps *imperf.* are exceedingly rare postally used.

1858 (1 Jan.). (Issued). *No wmk.* *P* 15½×15.

F7	F 3	1s. rose/*bluish*	45	0	50	0
F8	,,	5s. lilac/*bluish*	£6		£8	
F9	,,	10s. green/*bluish*	£6		£8	

Telegraph stamps were also used postally, but no authority was given for such use.

OFFICIAL STAMPS.

OFFICIAL

(O 1)

(Overprinted by C. Vendryes, Kingston.)

1890 (1 April). *No.* 16 *overprinted with Type* O 1.

(*a*) "official" 17 *to* 17½ *mm. long.*

O1	8	½d. green	3	0	3	0
		a. "O" omitted				
		b. One "I" omitted				
		c. Both "I"s omitted	£20		£20	
		d. "L" omitted	—		£25	
		e. Overprint inverted	50	0	50	0
		f. Overprint double	50	0	50	0
		g. Overprint double, one inverted	£12		£12	
		h. Overprint double, one vert.	£35			
		j. Pair, overprints tête-bêche				

(*b*) "official" 15 *to* 16 *mm. long.*

O2	8	½d. green	20	0	20	0
		a. Overprint double	£22			

There were four (or possibly five) settings of this overprint, all but one being of the longer type. There are numerous minor varieties, due to broken type, etc. (*e.g.* a broken "E" used for "F").

Stamps with the 17–17½ mm. opt. were re-issued in 1894 during a temporary shortage of No. O3.

OFFICIAL

(O 2)

(Optd. by De La Rue & Co.)

1890–91. *Optd. with Type* O 2. *Wmk. Crown CA.* *P* 14.

O3	8	½d. green (1891)	1	6	0	9
O4	11	1d. rose (1.4.90)	1	6	0	9
O5	,,	2d. grey (1.4.90)	2	0	1	6

JORDAN.

(Formerly **TRANSJORDAN**)

For all issues, see Part III of the Stanley Gibbons Catalogue.

KENYA.

INDEPENDENT
within the Commonwealth.

46. Cattle Ranching.

47. Wood-carving.

48. Heavy Industry.

49. Timber Industry.

50. Jomo Kenyatta facing Mt. Kenya.

51. Fishing Industry.

52. Kenya Flag.

53. Pyrethrum Industry

54. National Assembly.

55. Tourism (Treetop Hotel).

56. Coffee Industry.

57. Tea Industry.

58. Mombasa Port.

59. Education (Royal College, Nairobi).

Des. V. Whiteley. Photo. Harrison & Sons.)

963 (12 DEC.). *Independence. P* 14 × 15 (*small designs*) *or* 14½ (*others*).

07	**46**	5 c. brown, deep blue, green and bistre ..	0	2	0	2
08	**47**	10 c. brown	0	3	0	2
09	**48**	15 c. magenta	0	4	0	2
10	**49**	20 c. black & yellow-green	0	5	0	5
11	**50**	30 c. black and yellow ..	0	6	0	4
12	**51**	40 c. brown and light blue	0	8	0	8
13	**52**	50 c. crimson, blk. & grn.	0	10	0	9
4	**53**	65 c. dp. turq.-grn. & yell.	1	0	1	6
5	**54**	1s. multicoloured ..	1	5	0	8
6	**55**	1s. 30, brown, black and yellow-green.. ..	1	10	1	0
7	**56**	2s. multicoloured ..	2	9	1	6
8	**57**	5s. brn., ult. & yell.-grn.	6	9	4	0
9	**58**	10s. brown and deep blue	13	3	10	0
0	**59**	20s. black and rose ..	25	0	20	0

REPUBLIC.

60. Cockerel.

61. Pres. Kenyatta.

62. African Lion.

63. Hartlaub's Touraco.

64. Nandi Flame.

(Des. M. Goaman. Photo. J. Enschedé & Sons.

1964 (12 Dec.). *Inauguration of Republic. P* 13×12½.

No.	Type	Description	Unused	Used
221	**60**	15 c. multicoloured ..	0 5	0 7
222	**61**	30 c. multicoloured ..	0 7	0 11
223	**62**	50 c. multicoloured ..	1 0	1 2
224	**63**	1 s. 30, multicoloured ..	2 3	2 9
225	**64**	2 s. 50, multicoloured ..	4 6	6 0

For commemorative issues inscribed "UGANDA KENYA TANGANYIKA & ZANZIBAR" (or "TANZANIA UGANDA KENYA") see under East Africa.

OFFICIAL STAMPS.

For use on official correspondence of the Kenya Government only.

OFFICIAL

(O **4**)

1964 (1 Oct.). *Optd. with Type* O **4**.

No.	Type	Description	Unused	Used
O21	**46**	5 c. brown, deep blue, green and bistre ..	0 3	0 3
O22	**47**	10 c. brown	0 4	0 5
O23	**48**	15 c. magenta	0 5	0 6
O24	**49**	20 c. black & yellow-green	0 6	0 7
O25	**50**	30 c. black and yellow ..	0 7	0 10
O26	**52**	50 c. crimson, black & grn.	1 0	1 2

KENYA, UGANDA AND TANGANYIKA.

For earlier issues see "British East Africa" and "Uganda."

For the issues of the Mandated Territory of Tanganyika and the war-time issues that preceded them see "Tanganyika."

PRINTERS. All the stamps issued between 1903 and 1927 were typographed by De La Rue & Co.

1

2

1903–4. *P* 14. (*a*) *Wmk. Crown CA.*

No.	Type	Description	Unused	Used
1	**1**	½ a. green	3 0	4 0
2	,,	1 a. grey and red	3 0	1 9
3	,,	2 a. dull & bright purple ..	8 0	12 6
4	,,	2½ a. blue	30 0	32 6
5	,,	3 a. brown-purple & green	30 0	45 0
6	,,	4 a. grey-green and black ..	25 0	27 6
7	,,	5 a. grey & orange-brown	55 0	65 0
8	,,	8 a. grey and pale blue ..	50 0	50 0
		(*b*) *Wmk. Crown CC.*		
9	**2**	1 r. green, OC	25 0	25 0
10	,,	2 r. dull & bright purple, O	60 0	65 0
11	,,	3 r. grey-green & black, O	75 0	80 0
12	,,	4 r. grey & emer.-green, O	80 0	85 0
13	,,	5 r. grey and red, O ..	£5	110 0
14	,,	10 r. grey and ultram., OC	£16	£18
15	,,	20 r. grey & stone, O (S. £15)	£80	£70
16	,,	50 r. grey & red-brown, O (S. £30)	£175	£200

1904–07. *Wmk. Mult. Crown CA. P* 14.

No.	Type	Description	Unused	Used
17	**1**	½ a. grey-green, OC ..	1 0	1 3
18	,,	1 a. grey and red, OC ..	0 9	0 6
19	,,	2 a. dull & brt. purple, OC	6 0	7 6
20	,,	2½ a. blue, O	25 0	27 6
20*a*	,,	2½ a. ultram. & blue, O ..	15 0	20 0
21	,,	3 a. brown-pur. & grn., OC	10 0	15 0
22	,,	4 a. grey-grn. & blk., OC	10 0	15 0
23	,,	5 a. grey & orge.-brn., OC	15 0	20 0
24	,,	8 a. grey & pale blue, OC	15 0	20 0
25	**2**	1 r. green, C ('07) ..	30 0	30
26	,,	2 r. dull and bright purple, C (1906)	45 0	37
27	,,	3 r. grey-grn. & blk., C ('07)	70 0	75
28	,,	4 r. grey & em.-grn., C ('07)	75 0	80
29	,,	5 r. grey & red, C ('07) ..	90 0	£
30	,,	10 r. grey & ultram., C ('07)	£18	£2
31	,,	20 r. grey and stone, C ('07) (S. £15)	£60	£6
32	,,	50 r. grey and red-brown, C ('07) (S. £30)	£185	£18

Currency changed. (100 cents=1 rupee).

1907–08. *Wmk. Mult. Crown CA. P* 14.

No.	Type	Description	Unused	Used
33	**1**	1 c. brown, O (1908) ..	0 9	0
34	,,	3 c. grey-green, O ..	1 0	1
34*a*	,,	3 c. blue-green, O ..	1 0	1
35	,,	6 c. red, O	3 6	0
36	,,	10 c. lilac & pale olive, C ..	5 0	7
37	,,	12 c. dull & bright purple, C	6 0	3
38	,,	15 c. bright blue, O ..	6 0	12
39	,,	25 c. grey-green & black, C	10 0	6
40	,,	50 c. grey-green & orange-brown, C	15 0	20
41	,,	75 c. grey & pale bl., C ('08)	22 6	30

Original

Redrawn

1910. *T* **1** *redrawn. Printed from a single pla Wmk. Mult. Crown CA. P* 14.

No.	Description	Unused	Used
42	6 c. red, O	3 6	1

In the redrawn type a fine white line has bee cut around the value tablets and above the nar tablet separating the latter from the leaves abov East Africa and Uganda is in shorter a thicker letters and Protectorates in tal letters than in No. 35.

3

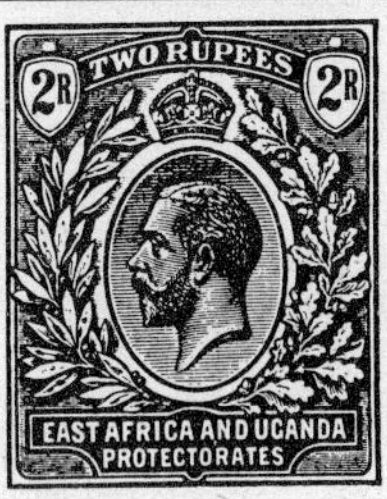

4

1912–22. *Wmk. Mult. Crown CA. P* 14.

No.	Type	Description	Unused	Used
43	3	1 c. black, O	0 4	0 6
44	,,	3 c. green, O	1 9	0 8
44*a*	,,	3 c. dp. bl.-grn., O (1917)	2 0	0 8
45	,,	6 c. red, O	1 0	0 8
45*a*	,,	6 c. scarlet, O (1917)	5 0	1 6
45*b*	,,	10 c. yellow-orange, O	12 6	1 3
46	,,	10 c. orange, O (1921)	6 0	1 6
47	,,	12 c. slate-grey, O	3 6	3 6
48	,,	15 c. bright blue, O	4 0	2 0
49	,,	25 c. black & red/*yellow*, C	5 0	2 6
		a. White back	5 0	6 6
		b. On lemon (1916)	25 0	20 0
		c. On orange-buff (1921)	45 0	7 6
		d. On pale yellow (1921)	22 6	6 0
50	,,	50 c. black and lilac, C	8 6	6 0
51	,,	75 c. black/*green*, C	12 6	16 0
		a. White back	10 0	20 0
		b. On blue-green, olive back	32 6	20 0
		c. On emerald, olive back	£10	£10
		d. On emerald back	22 6	20 0
52	4	1 r. black/*green*, C	15 0	15 0
		a. On emerald back	22 6	30 0
53	,,	2 r. red and black/*blue*, C	35 0	37 6
54	,,	3 r. violet and green, C	35 0	35 0
55	,,	4 r. red & green/*yellow*, C	55 0	50 0
		a. On pale yellow	80 0	80 0
56	,,	5 r. blue and dull purple, C	55 0	55 0
57	,,	10 r. red & green/*green*, C	85 0	85 0
58	,,	20 r. black & purple/*red* C	£18	£18
58*a*	,,	20 r. purple & bl./*bl.*, C ('18)	£18	£18
59	,,	50 r. carmine and green, C (S. £20)	£80	£85
60	,,	100 r. purple and black/*red*, C (S. £60)	£400	£425
61	,,	500 r. green and red/*green*, C (S. £125)	£2000	

4
cents
(5)

1919. *T* **3** *surcharged with T* **5.**

No.	Description	Unused	Used
62	4 c. on 6 c. scarlet	0 6	0 6
	a. Bars omitted	40 0	70 0
	b. Surcharge double	£8	£8
	c. Surcharge inverted	£6	£6
	d. Surcharge omitted (in pair)	£18	£18

1921–22. *Wmk. Mult. Script CA. P* 14.

No.	Type	Description	Unused	Used
63	3	1 c. black, O	0 9	0 9
64	,,	3 c. green, O	1 0	1 6
65	,,	3 c. blue-green, O	5 0	2 6
66	,,	6 c. carmine-red, O	3 0	1 6
67	,,	10 c. orange, O	3 0	0 6
68	,,	12 c. slate-grey, O	10 0	12 6
69	,,	15 c. bright blue, O	10 0	10 0
71	,,	50 c. black & dull purple, C	27 6	27 6
73	4	2 r. red and black/*blue*, C	42 6	45 0
74	,,	3 r. violet and green, C	60 0	65 0
75	,,	5 r. blue and dull purple, C	£5	£8
77	,,	50 r. carmine and green, C (S. £45)	£250	£275

Currency changed (100 cents=1 shilling).

6

7

1922. *Wmk. Mult. Script CA* (*sideways on T* **7**) *P* 14.

No.	Type	Description	Unused	Used
78	6	1 c. pale brown	0 9	0 9
79	,,	1 c. deep brown	2 0	2 0
80	,,	5 c. dull violet	1 3	0 4
81	,,	5 c. bright violet	2 0	1 3
82	,,	10 c. green	1 3	0 6
83	,,	12 c. jet-black	17 6	25 0
84	,,	12 c. grey-black	5 0	15 0
85	,,	15 c. rose-carmine	1 0	0 3
86	,,	20 c. dull orange-yellow	2 6	0 4
87	,,	20 c. bright orange	5 0	0 4
88	,,	30 c. ultramarine	2 6	0 9
89	,,	50 c. grey	6 0	0 9
90	,,	75 c. olive	10 0	15 0
91	7	1s. green, C	10 0	3 6
92	,,	2s. dull purple, C	10 0	8 6
93	,,	3s. brownish grey, C	25 0	15 0
93*a*	,,	3s. jet-black, C	37 6	40 0
94	,,	5s. carmine-red, C	35 0	35 0
95	,,	10s. bright blue, C	50 0	55 0
96	,,	£1 black and orange,	£20	£20
97	,,	£5 blk. & blue, C (S. £10)	£250	£160
98	,,	£10 blk. & grn., C (S. £25)	£850	
99	,,	£25 black & red, C (S. £50)	£2500	
100	,,	£50 blk. & brn., C (S. £50)	£3500	

1925–27. *Wmk. Mult. Script CA. P* 14.

No.	Type	Description	Unused	Used
100*a*	6	5 c. green	0 4	0 2
100*b*	,,	10 c. black	0 8	0 2
101	7	2s. 50 c. brown, C	35 0	50 0
102	,,	4s. grey, C	42 6	50 0
103	,,	7s. 50 c. orge.-yellow, C	90 0	£6
104	,,	£2 grn. & pur., C (S. £10)	£100	£100
105	,,	£3 pur. & yell., C (S. £10)	£175	£150
106	,,	£4 blk. & mag., C (S. £15)	£250	£275
107	,,	£20 red & grn., C (S. £50)	£2500	
108	,,	£75 purple and grey, C (S. £100)	£8500	
109	,,	£100 red & blk., C (S. £125)	£10000	

8. Kavirondo Cranes.

9. Dhow on Lake Victoria.

10. East African Lion.

12. Jinja Bridge by Ripon Falls.

11. Kilimanjaro.

13. Mt. Kenya.

14. Lake Naivasha.

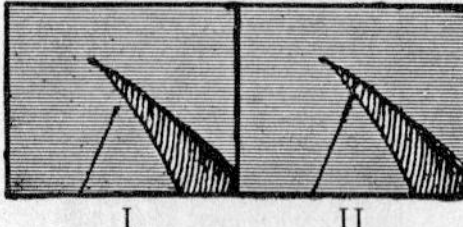

I II

(Des. 1 c., 20 c., 10s., R. C. Luck. 10 c., £1, A. Ross. 15 c., 2s., G. Gill Holmes. 30 c., 5s., R. N. Ambasana. 65 c., L. R. Cutts. T **10** typo., remainder recess. De La Rue & Co.)

1935 (1 May)–**1936.** *Wmk. Mult. Script CA. P* 12 × 13 (**10**), 14 (**9** *and* **14**) and 13 (*remainder*).

No.	Type	Description		
110	**8**	1 c. black and red-brown	0 6	0 6
111	**9**	5 c. black and green (I) ..	0 6	0 4
		a. Perf. 13 × 12 (I) ..	£25	£10
		b. Rope joined to sail (II) (perf. 14)	4 0	0 6
		c. Rope joined to sail (II) (perf. 13 × 12)	£30	£5
112	**10**	10 c. black and yellow, C	2 0	0 3
113	**11**	15 c. black and scarlet ..	0 10	0 3
114	**8**	20 c. black and orange ..	1 3	0 3
115	**12**	30 c. black and blue ..	2 0	1 0
116	**9**	50 c. brt. purple & blk. (I)	2 6	0 8
117	**13**	65 c. black and brown ..	7 6	8 6
118	**14**	1s. black and green ..	5 0	3 6
		a. Perf. 13 × 12 (1936) ..	£90	£6
119	**11**	2s. lake and purple ..	12 6	12 6
120	**14**	3s. blue and black ..	20 0	22 6
		a. Perf. 13 × 12	£160	
121	**12**	5s. black and carmine ..	35 0	32 6
122	**8**	10s. purple and blue ..	65 0	65 0
123	**10**	£1 black and red, C ..	£10	£7

1935 (7 May). *Silver Jubilee. As T* **13** *of Antigua. Recess. D.L.R. & Co. Wmk. Mult. Script CA. P* 13½ × 14.

124	20 c. light blue & olive-green	0 10	0 4
125	30 c. brown and deep blue ..	3 0	3 0
126	65 c. green and indigo ..	5 0	7 6
127	1s. slate and purple ..	8 0	7 6

1937 (12 May). *Coronation. As T* **2** *of Aden. Recess. D.L.R. & Co. Wmk. Mult. Script CA. P* 14.

128	5 c. green	0 3	0 3
129	20 c. orange	0 9	0 9
130	30 c. bright blue	1 6	1 9

15. Dhow on Lake Victoria.

10c
KENYA
TANGANYIKA
UGANDA
(**16**)

With dot. Dot removed.

In the 50 c., on Frame-plate 3, the dot was removed by retouching on all but five stamps (R 5/2, 6/1, 7/2, 7/4 and 9/1). In addition, other stamps show traces of the dot where the retouching was not completely effective.

(T **10** typo., others recess. De La Rue & Co.)

1938–54. *As T* **8** *to* **14** (*but with portrait of King George VI in place of King George V, as in T* **15**). *Wmk. Mult. Script CA.*

(*In this issue, to aid identification, the perforations are indicated to the nearest quarter.*)

No.	Type	Description		
131	**8**	1 c. black and red-brown (*perf.* 13¼)	0 3	0
		a. Perf. 13¼ × 13¾ ('46) ..	0 3	0
		ab. *Black and chocolate* p. 13¼ × 13¾ ('46) ..	1 6	1
132	**15**	5 c. black and green (II) (*perf.* 13 × 11¾) ..	0 4	0
133	,,	5 c. brown and orange (*perf.* 13 × 11¾) ('49)	1 0	1
		a. Perf. 13 × 12½ (14.6.50) ..	0 6	0
134	**14**	10 c. brn. & orange (*perf.* 13 × 11¾)	0 6	0
		a. Perf. 14 ('41)	25 0	4
135	,,	10 c. black & green (*perf.* 13 × 11¾) ('49) ..	0 4	0
		a. Perf. 13 × 12½ (14.6.50) ..	0 4	0
136	,,	10 c. brown and grey (*perf.* 13 × 12½) ('52) ..	0 4	0
137	**11**	15 c. black & scar. (*perf.* 13¼)	1 3	0
		a. Perf. 13¾ × 13¼ ('43) ..	0 6	0
138	,,	15 c. black and green (*perf.* 13¾ × 13¼) ('52) ..	0 5	0
139	**8**	20 c. black and orange (*perf.* 13¼)	2 0	0
		a. Perf. 14 ('41)	6 0	1
		b Perf. 13¼ × 13¾ ('42) ..	0 6	0

140 **15** 25 c. black and scarlet (*perf.* 13 × 12½) ('52) 2 0 2 6
141 **12** 30 c. blk. & bl. (*perf.* 13¼) 4 0 0 6
a. Perf. 14 ('41) 80 0 12 6
b. Perf. 13¼ × 13¾ ('42) .. 0 8 0 3
142 ,, 30 c. dull purple & brown (*perf.* 13¼ × 13¾) ('52) 0 8 0 4
143 **8** 40 c. black and blue (*perf.* 13¼ × 13¾) ('52) .. 1 0 1 0
144 **15** 50 c. brt. purple & black (II) (*perf.* 13 × 11¾) 1 6 0 4
a. Rope not joined to sail (I) £14 £7
b. Perf. 13 × 12½ ('49) .. 1 0 0 6
ba. Dot removed 2 6 0 9
bb. Ditto, in pair with normal 40 0
145 **14** 1s. black and brown (*perf.* 13 × 11¾) .. 2 6 0 6
a. Perf. 13 × 12½ ('49) .. 2 0 0 9
146 **11** 2s. lake & purple (*perf.* 13¼) 25 0 8 0
a. Perf. 14 ('42) 25 0 15 0
b. Perf. 13¾ × 13¼ ('44) .. 4 0 2 0
147 **14** 3s. blue and black (*perf.* 13 × 11¾) 7 6 4 0
a. Perf. 13 × 12½ (14.6.50) .. 6 0 5 0
148 **12** 5s. blk. & car. (*perf.* 13¼) 35 0 10 0
a. Perf. 14 ('41) 12 6 8 6
b. Perf. 13¼ × 13¾ ('44) .. 10 0 5 0
149 **8** 10s. purple and blue (*perf.* 13¼) 40 0 22 6
a. Perf. 14 ('41) 35 0 27 6
b. Perf. 13¼ × 13¾ ('44) .. 17 6 10 0
150 **10** £1 black and red (*perf.* 11¾ × 13), C £15 £5
a. Perf. 14, CO ('41) .. 45 0 35 0
b. Perf. 12½, C (21.1.54) .. 35 0 35 0

Dates of original issue:—11.4.38, 5 c.; 2.5.38, 1 c. to 10s.; and 12.10.38, £1. Others as indicated above.

1941 (1 July)–**1942.** *Pictorial Stamps of South Africa variously surch. as T* **16.** *Inscr. alternately in English and Afrikaans.*

		Un. pair	*Used pair*	*Used single*
151	5 c. on 1d. grey and car. (No. 56) ..	1 0	2 6	0 6
152	10 c. on 3d. ultram. (No. 59) ..	1 3	4 6	0 8
153	20 c. on 6d. green & verm. (No. 61*a*)	2 0	5 0	0 8
154	70 c. on 1s. brown & chalky blue (No. 62) (20.4.42) ..	4 0	6 0	1 0

1946 (11 Nov.). *Victory. As Nos.* 28/9 *of Aden.*

		Un.	*Used*
155	20 c. red-orange	0 6	0 9
156	30 c. blue	0 8	1 0

1948 (1 Dec.). *Royal Silver Wedding. As Nos.* 30/1 *of Aden.*

157	20 c. orange	0 6	0 6
158	£1 scarlet	32 6	32 6

1949 (10 Oct.). *75th Anniv. of Universal Postal Union. As Nos.* 114/7 *of Antigua.*

159	20 c. red-orange	0 8	0 6
160	30 c. deep blue	0 8	0 9
161	50 c. grey	2 0	1 9
162	1s. red-brown	3 6	3 6

17. Lake Naivasha.

(Recess. De La Rue & Co.)

1952 (1 Feb.). *Visit of Princess Elizabeth and Duke of Edinburgh. Wmk. Mult. Script CA. P* 13 × 12½.

163	**17**	10 c. black and green ..	0 10	0 10
164	,,	1s. black and brown ..	5 0	7 6

1953 (2 June). *Coronation. As No.* 47 *of Aden.*

165	20 c. black and red-orange ..	0 8	0 6

1954 (28 Apr.). *Royal Visit. As No.* 171 *but inscr.* "ROYAL VISIT 1954" *below portrait.*

166	30 c. black & dp. ultramarine	0 9	0 10

18. Owen Falls Dam.

19. Giraffe.

20. Lion.

24. Queen Elizabeth II.

21. Kilimanjaro.

22. Elephants.

23. Royal Lodge, Sagana.

(Des. O. C. Meronti (T **18** and **20**), G. Gill Holmes (T **19**), H. Grieme (T **22**), R. McLellan Sim (T **23**), De La Rue (others). Recess. De La Rue & Co.)

1954 (1 June)–**59.** *Wmk. Mult. Script CA. P* 13 (£1); *others*, 12½ × 13 (*vert.*) *or* 13 × 12½ (*horiz.*).

No.	Type	Description	Unused	Used
167	**18**	5 c. black & deep brown	0 3	0 3
		a. Vignette inverted ..		
168	**19**	10 c. carmine-red ..	0 5	0 3
169	**22**	15 c. black and light blue (28.3.58)	1 6	0 9
		a. Redrawn. Stop below "c" of "15 c." (29.4.59)	1 0	0 6
170	**20**	20 c. black and orange ..	0 8	0 3
		a. Imperf. (pair)	£275	
171	**18**	30 c. blk. & dp. ultram...	0 10	0 3
172	**20**	40 c. bistre-brn. (28.3.58)	1 3	0 6
173	**19**	50 c. reddish pur. (*shades*)	1 6	0 5
174	**21**	65 c. bluish green & brn.-purple (1.12.55) ..	4 6	3 0
175	**20**	1s. black and claret ..	1 9	0 6
176	**22**	1s. 30, orange and deep lilac (1.12.55) ..	3 6	0 9
177	**21**	2s. black & green (*shades*)	4 6	1 9
178	**22**	5s. black and orange ..	10 0	5 0
179	**23**	10s. blk. & deep ultram.	22 6	10 0
180	**24**	£1 brown-red and black (*shades*)	55 0	30 0

Only one used copy of No. 167*a* is known.

25. Map of E. Africa showing Lakes.

(Recess. Waterlow & Sons.)

1958 (30 July). *Centenary of Discovery of Lakes Tanganyika and Victoria by Burton and Speke. W* w. **12**. *P* 12½.

No.	Type	Description	Unused	Used
181	**25**	40 c. blue and deep green ..	1 9	2 3
182	,,	1s. 30 c. green and violet	4 0	4 0

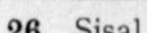

26. Sisal.

27. Cotton.

28. Coffee.

29. Gnu.

30. Ostrich.

31. Thomson's Gazelle.

32. Manta Ray.

33. Zebra.

34. Cheetah.

35. Mt. Kenya and Giant Plants.

36. Murchison Falls and Hippopotamus.

37. Mt. Kilimanjaro and Giraffe.

38. Candelabra Tree and Rhinoceros.

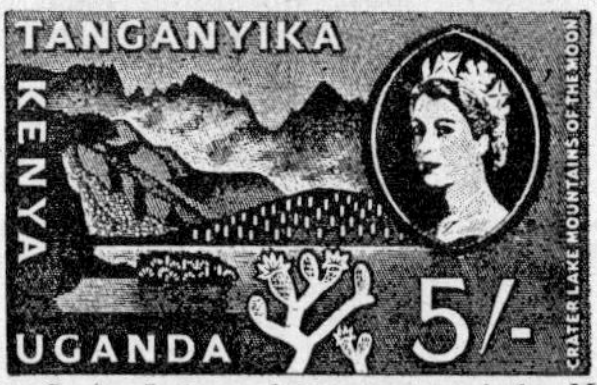

39. Crater Lake and Mountains of the Moon.

40. Ngorongoro Crater and Buffalo.

41. Queen Elizabeth II.

(Des. M. Goaman. Photo. (5 c. to 65 c.), recess (others). De La Rue.)

1960 (1 Oct.). *W* **9***c*. *P* 15 × 14 (5 *c. to* 65 *c.*), 13 (20*s.*) *or* 14 (*others*).

No.	Type	Description	Un. s.	d.	Used s.	d.
183	**26**	5 c. Prussian blue	0	3	0	3
184	**27**	10 c. yellow-green.. ..	0	4	0	3
185	**28**	15 c. dull purple	0	5	0	3
186	**29**	20 c. magenta	0	6	0	3
187	**30**	25 c. bronze-green ..	0	8	0	6
188	**31**	30 c. vermilion	0	7	0	3
189	**32**	40 c. greenish blue ..	1	0	0	4
190	**33**	50 c. slate-violet	1	0	0	9
191	**34**	65 c. yellow-olive	2	0	2	9
192	**35**	1s. dp. reddish violet and reddish purple ..	1	8	0	4
193	**36**	1s. 30, chocolate and brown-red	2	3	0	4
194	**37**	2s. deep grey-blue and greenish blue ..	3	3	1	2
195	**38**	2s. 50, olive-green and deep bluish green ..	5	6	4	6
196	**39**	5s. rose-red and purple	8	0	3	0
197	**40**	10s. blackish green and olive-green ..	17	6	7	6
198	**41**	20s. violet-blue and lake..	35	0	22	6

The 10 c. and 50 c. exist in coils with the designs slightly shorter in height, a wider horizontal gutter every eleven stamps and, in the case of the 10 c. only, printed with a coarser 200 screen instead of the normal 250. (*Price* 10 *c.*, 6*d. un.*). Plate 2 of 30 c. shows coarser 200 screen. (*Price* 8*d. un.*).

42. Land Tillage.

43. African with Corncob.

(Des. V. Whiteley. Photo. Harrison & Sons.)

1963 (21 Mar.). *Freedom from Hunger*. *P* 14½.

No.	Type	Description	Un. s.	d.	Used s.	d.
199	**42**	15 c. blue and yellow-olive	0	8	0	8
200	**43**	30 c. red-brown & yellow	1	3	1	3
201	**42**	50 c. blue & orange-brown	2	0	2	0
202	**43**	1s. 30, red-brn. & lt. blue	3	9	4	0

44. Scholars and Open Book.

(Photo. Harrison.)

1963 (28 June). *Founding of East African University*. *P* 14½.

No.	Type	Description	Un. s.	d.	Used s.	d.
203	**44**	30 c. lake, violet, black and greenish blue ..	0	10	0	8
204	,,	1s. 30, lake, blue, red and light yellow-brown..	2	6	2	6

45. Red Cross Emblem.

(Des. V. Whiteley. Photo. Harrison.)

1963 (2 Sept.). *Centenary of Red Cross. P* 14½.

No.	Type	Description	Unused	Used
205	**45**	30 c. red and blue ..	0 9	0 6
206	,,	50 c. red and yellow-brown	1 3	1 0

OFFICIAL STAMPS.

For use on official correspondence of the Tanganyika Government.

OFFICIAL
(O 1)

1959 (1 July). *Optd. as Type* O **1.**

No.	Type	Description	Unused	Used
O 1	**18**	5 c. black & deep brown	0 4	0 4
O 2	**19**	10 c. carmine-red ..	0 4	0 4
O 3	**22**	15 c. black and light blue (No. 169*a*)	0 6	0 4
O 4	**20**	20 c. black and orange ..	0 8	0 6
		a. Opt. double	—	£100
O 5	**18**	30 c. black & deep ultram.	1 0	0 9
O 6	**19**	50 c. reddish purple ..	1 3	1 0
O 7	**20**	1s. black and claret ..	1 8	1 6
O 8	**22**	1s. 30. orge. & dp. lilac	3 0	3 6
O 9	**21**	2s. black & bronze-green	3 9	4 0
O10	**22**	5s. black and orange ..	9 0	9 0
O11	**23**	10s. black & dp. ultram.	20 0	22 6
O12	**24**	£1 brown-red and black	40 0	45 0

The 1s. (O7) exists with overprint double, but with the two impressions almost co-incident.

OFFICIAL (O 2)   **OFFICIAL** (O 3)

1960 (18 Oct.). *Optd. with Type* O **2** (*cents values*) *or* O **3.**

No.	Type	Description	Unused	Used
O13	**26**	5 c. Prussian blue ..	0 4	0 5
O14	**27**	10 c. yellow-green ..	0 5	0 6
O15	**28**	15 c. dull purple ..	0 6	0 7
O16	**29**	20 c. magenta	0 8	0 9
O17	**31**	30 c. vermilion	0 10	0 10
O18	**33**	50 c. slate-violet ..	1 3	1 6
O19	**35**	1s. deep reddish violet and reddish purple ..	2 6	2 6
O20	**39**	5s. rose-red and purple	12 6	12 6

POSTAGE DUE STAMPS.

D 1

D 2

(Typo. Waterlow & Sons, Ltd.)

1928–33. *Wmk. Mult. Script CA. P* 15 × 14.

No.	Type	Description	Unused	Used
D1	D **1**	5 c. violet	1 3	1 6
D2	,,	10 c. vermilion	1 6	1 6
D3	,,	20 c. yellow-green ..	2 0	2 6
D4	,,	30 c. brown (1931) ..	3 0	5 0
D5	,,	40 c. dull blue	7 6	8 6
D6	,,	1s. grey-green ('33) ..	25 0	12 6

(Typo. De La Rue & Co.)

1935 (1 May)–**60.** *Wmk. Mult. Script CA. P* 14.

No.	Type	Description	Unused	Used
D 7	D **2**	5 c. violet	0 2	0 3
D 8	,,	10 c. scarlet	0 3	0 4
D 9	,,	20 c. green	0 5	0 6
D10	,,	30 c. brown	2 0	2 6
		a. *Bistre-brown* (19.7.60) ..	0 6	0 8
D11	,,	40 c. ultramarine ..	0 8	1 0
D12	,,	1s. grey	1 5	1 9

The stamps of "Kenya, Uganda and Tanganyika" (except for the Postage Due stamps) were withdrawn on 11th December, 1963. Separate issues are listed under Kenya, Tanganyika and Uganda respectively.

KUWAIT.

An independent Arab Shaikhdom, in special treaty relations with Great Britain until 1961.

KUWAIT (1)   KUWAIT (2)

1923 (1 Apr.)–**1924.** *Stamps of India* (*King George V*), *optd. with T* **1** *or* **2** (*rupee values,* 15½ *mm.*). *Star wmk. P* 14.

No.	Type	Description	Unused	Used
1	**56**	½ a. green	1 6	2 6
2	**57**	1 a. chocolate	1 6	2 6
3	**58**	1½ a. chocolate (A) ..	1 3	3 6
4	**59**	2 a. mauve..	2 0	1 6
5	**61**	2 a. 6 p. ultramarine ..	3 0	10 0
6	**62**	3 a. orange-brown ..	6 0	22 6
		a. Overprint inverted ..	75 0	
7	,,	3 a. ultramarine (1924) ..	15 0	2 0
8	**63**	4 a. olive-green	12 6	22 6
9	**64**	6 a. yellow-bistre	12 6	22 6
10	**65**	8 a. purple	20 0	22 6
11	**66**	12 a. claret	25 0	20 0
12	**67**	1 r. brown and green ..	15 0	10 0
13	,,	2 r. carm. & yell.-brn. ..	35 0	40 0
14	,,	5 r. ultramarine & violet..	£5	£6
15	,,	10 r. green and scarlet ..	£12	£14

Ordinary and Service stamps with overprint "KOWEIT" were prepared for use but were not issued. These sets are rare.

1929–37. *Stamps of India* (*King George V, Nasik printing*), *optd. as T* **1** *or* **2**, (*rupee values,* 19 *mm.*). *Mult. Star wmk. P* 14.

No.	Type	Description	Unused	Used
16	**56**	½ a. green	1 3	2 6
16*a*	**79**	½ a. green ('34)	6 0	1 3
17	**57**	1 a. chocolate	10 0	1 0
17*a*	**81**	1 a. chocolate ('34) ..	3 0	1 6
18	**70**	2 a. purple	1 6	1 9
19	,,	2 a. vermilion	40 0	45 0
19*a*	**59**	2 a. vermilion ('34) ..	6 0	7 6
19*b*	,,	2 a. verm. (*small die*) ('37)	1 6	1 0
20	**62**	3 a. bright blue	10 0	1 6
21	,,	3 a. carmine	12 6	12 6
22	**71**	4 a. sage-green	35 0	37 6
22*a*	**63**	4 a. sage-green ('34) ..	2 0	8 6
22*b*	**64**	6 a. bistre ('37)	3 0	12 6
23	**65**	8 a. reddish purple ..	15 0	15 0
24	**66**	12 a. claret	22 6	30 0
25	**67**	1 r. chocolate and green	15 0	22 6
26	,,	2 r. carmine and orange ..	30 0	35 0
27	,,	5 r. ultram. & pur. ('37)	65 0	75 0
28	,,	10 r. green & scarlet ('34)	£8	£9
29	,,	15 r. blue and olive ('37)	£15	£17

1933–34. *Air Stamps of India optd. as T* **2** (16½ *mm.*).

No.	Type	Description	Unused	Used
31	**72**	2 a. deep blue-green ..	10 6	15 0
32	,,	3 a. blue	4 0	6 0
33	,,	4 a. drab	£6	£6
34	,,	6 a. bistre ('34)	9 0	10 0

KUWAIT (3)   KUWAIT (4)

1939. *Stamps of India (King George VI) optd. with T* **3** *or* **4** *(rupee values).*

No.	Type	Description	Unused	Used
36	91	½ a. red-brown	1 3	1 3
38	„	1 a. carmine	2 0	2 0
39	92	2 a. vermilion	3 6	4 6
41	94	3 a. yellow-green	5 0	6 6
43	96	4 a. brown	7 6	10 0
44	97	6 a. turquoise-green	7 6	12 6
45	98	8 a. slate-violet	10 0	17 6
46	99	12 a. lake	22 6	30 0
47	100	1 r. grey and red-brown	6 6	7 6
48	„	2 r. purple and brown ..	10 0	12 6
49	„	5 r. green and blue ..	30 0	35 0
50	„	10 r. purple and claret ..	65 0	55 0
51	„	15 r. brown and green ..	90 0	£5

1945. *Stamps of India (King George VI on white background) optd. with T* **3.**

No.	Type	Description	Unused	Used
52	100a	3 p. slate	0 6	1 6
53	„	½ a. purple	0 3	1 3
54	„	9 p. green	0 3	2 6
55	„	1 a. carmine	0 8	1 3
56	101	1½ a. dull violet	0 6	2 0
57	„	2 a. vermilion	0 6	1 6
58	„	3 a. bright violet ..	0 9	1 6
59	„	3½ a. bright blue	1 0	3 6
60	102	4 a. brown	1 0	4 6
60a	„	6 a. turquoise-green ..	15 0	17 6
61	„	8 a. slate-violet	2 6	3 6
62	„	12 a. lake	3 6	6 0
63	103	14 a. purple	17 6	30 0

KUWAIT
1
ANNA
(5)

KUWAIT
5 RUPEES
(6)

NOTE. From 1948 onwards, for stamps with similar surcharges, but without name of country, see Muscat.

1948 (1 APR.)–**1949.** *Stamps of Great Britain (K.G. VI), surch. as T* **5** *or* **6** *(rupee values).*

No.	Type	Description	Unused	Used
64	128	½ a. on ½d. pale green ..	0 4	1 0
65	„	1 a. on 1d. pale scarlet ..	0 4	1 3
66	„	1½ a. on 1½d. pale red-brn.	0 6	1 0
67	„	2 a. on 2d. pale orange ..	0 6	0 10
68	„	2½ a. on 2½d. light ultram.	0 9	1 6
69	„	3 a. on 3d. pale violet ..	0 10	1 3
		a. Surch. omitted, in pair with normal		
70	129	6 a. on 6d. purple ..	1 3	1 6
71	130	1 r. on 1s. bistre-brown ..	3 6	4 6
72	131	2 r. on 2s. 6d. yell.-grn.	10 0	10 0
73	„	5 r. on 5s. red	18 6	18 6
73a	132	10 r. on 10s. ult. (4.7.49) ..	50 0	50 0

KUWAIT
2½
ANNAS
(7)

KUWAIT
15
RUPEES
(8)

1948. *Royal Silver Wedding. Nos.* 493/4 *of Great Britain surch. with T* **7** *or* **8.**

No.	Type	Description	Unused	Used
74	137	2½ a. on 2½d. ultramarine	1 0	1 0
75	138	15 r. on £1 blue	70 0	75 0

1948. *Olympic Games. Nos.* 495/8 *of Great Britain surch. as T* **7**, *but in one line* (6 *a.*) *or two lines (others).*

No.	Type	Description	Unused	Used
76	109	2½ a. on 2½d. ultramarine	1 3	2 0
77	140	3 a. on 3d. violet	1 3	2 0
78	141	6 a. on 6d. bright purple	3 0	4 0
79	142	1 r. on 1s. brown ..	6 0	8 6

1949 (10 OCT.). *75th Anniv. of Founding of Universal Postal Union. Nos.* 499/502 *of Great Britain surch.* "KUWAIT" *and new values.*

No.	Type	Description	Unused	Used
80	143	2½ a. on 2½d. ultramarine	1 3	1 6
81	144	3 a. on 3d. violet ..	2 0	2 6
82	145	6 a. on 6d. bright purple	4 0	4 0
83	146	1 r. on 1s. brown ..	6 0	7 6

1950–51. *Nos.* 503/11 *of Great Britain surch. as T* **5** *or* **6** *(rupee values).*

No.	Type	Description	Unused	Used
84	128	½ a. on ½d. pale orange ..	0 6	1 0
85	„	1 a. on 1d. light ultram.	0 6	0 10
86	„	1½ a. on 1½d. pale green ..	0 10	2 0
87	„	2 a. on 2d. pale red-brown	0 8	0 10
88	„	2½ a. on 2½d. pale scarlet	0 9	1 6
89	129	4 a. on 4d. light ultram.	1 6	1 6
90	147	2 r. on 2s. 6d. yell.-grn ..	7 6	8 0
91	148	5 r. on 5s. red	20 0	20 0
92	149	10 r. on 10s. ultramarine ..	32 6	35 0

Dates of issue:—2.10.50, 4 a.; 3.5.51, others.

1952–54. *Stamps of Great Britain (Queen Elizabeth II), Wmk. Tudor Crown surch. as T* **5.**

No.	Type	Description	Unused	Used
93	154	½ a. on ½d. orange-red ..	0 3	0 6
94	„	1 a. on 1d. ultramarine	0 4	0 8
95	„	1½ a. on 1½d green ..	0 6	0 8
96	„	2 a. on 2d. red-brown	0 9	1 0
97	155	2½ a. on 2½d. carmine-red	0 9	1 0
98	„	3 a. on 3d. deep lilac (B.)	0 10	1 0
99	156	4 a. on 4d. ultramarine	1 0	1 3
100	157	6 a. on 6d. reddish pur.	1 2	1 0
101	160	12 a. on 1s. 3d. green ..	3 0	3 0
102	159	1 r. on 1s. 6d. grey-blue	3 0	3 6

Dates of issue:—10.12.52, 1½ a., 2½ a.; 31.8.53, ½a., 1 a., 2 a.; 2.11.53, 4 a., 12 a., 1 r.; 18.1.54, 3 a., 6 a.

1953 (3 JUNE). *Coronation. Stamps of Great Britain surch.* "KUWAIT" *and new values.*

No.	Type	Description	Unused	Used
103	161	2½ a. on 2½d. carmine-red	2 0	2 6
104	162	4 a. on 4d. ultramarine ..	2 6	4 0
105	163	12 a. on 1s. 3d. deep yellow-green ..	7 6	12 6
106	164	1 r. on 1s. 6d. deep grey-blue	8 6	12 6

KUWAIT 2 RUPEES
I

KUWAIT 2 RUPEES
II
(9)

KUWAIT 5 RUPEES
I

KUWAIT 5 RUPEES
II
(10)

KUWAIT 10 RUPEES
I

KUWAIT 10 RUPEES
II
(11)

Type I (**9/11**). Type-set overprints. Bold (generally thicker) letters with sharp corners and straight edges. Bars close together and usually slightly longer than in Type II.

Type II (**9/11**). Plate-printed overprints. Thinner letters, rounder corners and rough edges. Bars wider part.

1955–57. *Nos.* 536/8 *of Great Britain surch.*

			I. (23.9.55)		II. (10.10.57)	
107	**166**	2 r. on 2s. 6d. blk.-brn.	7 6	8 0	£10	20 0
108	**167**	5 r. on 5s. rose-red	17 6	20 0	£18	35 0
109	**168**	10 r. on 10s. ultram.	40 0	45 0	£40	£12

1956. *Stamps of Great Britain (Queen Elizabeth II), Wmk. St. Edward's Crown, surch.* "KUWAIT" *and new value.*

110	**154**	½ a. on ½d. orange-red ..	0	3	0	8
111	,,	1 a. on 1d. ultramarine	0	8	1	3
112	,,	1½ a. on 1½d. green ..	0	8	1	6
113	,,	2 a. on 2d. red-brown ..	0	8	1	3
114	**155**	2½ a. on 2½d. carm.-red	1	3	2	6
116	**156**	4 a. on 4d. ultramarine	3	0	4	6
117	**157**	6 a. on 6d. reddish pur.	1	6	1	6
118	**160**	12 a. on 1s. 3d. green ..	5	0	6	0
119	**159**	1 r. on 1s. 6d. grey-blue	3	6	4	0

Currency changed. 100 n(aye) p(aise) = 1 rupee.

KUWAIT KUWAIT KUWAIT

NP 1 NP (12) NP 3 (13) NP 75 NP (14)

1957 (1 June)**-58.** *Stamps of Great Britain (Queen Elizabeth II. W* **165**, *St. Edward's Crown), surch. as T* **12** (1, 15, 25, 40. 50 *n.p.*) **14** (75). *n.p. or* **13** (*others*).

120	**157**	1 n.p. on 5d. brown ..	0	3	0	10
121	**154**	3 n.p. on ½d. orange-red	0	3	1	0
122	,,	6 n.p. on 1d. ultramarine	0	6	0	9
123	,,	9 n.p. on 1½d. green ..	0	6	0	9
124	,,	12 n.p. on 2d. lt. red-brn.	0	8	1	0
125	**155**	15 n.p. on 2½d. carmine-red (Type I) ..	1	3	1	3
		a. Type II (–.11.58) ..	£12		£8	
126	,,	20 n.p. on 3d. dp. lilac (B.)	1	6	1	0
127	**156**	25 n.p. on 4d. ultramarine	1	6	2	6
128	**157**	40 n.p. on 6d. reddish pur.	2	6	2	6
129	**158**	50 n.p. on 9d. bronze-grn.	4	0	4	6
130	**160**	75 n.p. on 1s. 3d. green ..	4	0	6	0

15. Shaikh Abdullah as-Salim as-Sabah.

16. Dhow.

17. Oil Pipe-lines.

18. Power Station.

19. Oil-Drilling Rig.

20. Single-masted Dhow.

21. Kuwait Mosque.

22. Main Square, Kuwait Town.

(Recess. De La Rue.)

1959 (1 Feb.). *P* 12½ (*Nos.* 131/6), 13½ × 13 (137/9) *or* 14 × 13½ (140/3).

131	**15**	5 n.p. bluish green ..	0	4	0	4
132	,,	10 n.p. brown-red (*shades*)	0	9	0	6
133	,,	15 n.p. brown	0	7	1	6
134	,,	20 n.p. slate-violet ..	0	8	0	8
135	,,	25 n.p. orange-red (*shades*)	1	0	1	[illegible]
136	,,	40 n.p. maroon	5	0	6	[illegible]
137	**16**	40 n.p. blue	1	3	1	[illegible]
138	**17**	50 n.p. scarlet	1	6	1	[illegible]
139	**18**	75 n.p. bronze-green ..	2	6	2	[illegible]
140	**19**	1 r. brown-purple ..	3	0	3	[illegible]
141	**20**	2 r. lt. blue & brown ..	7	6	6	[illegible]
142	**21**	5 r. blue-green	15	0	15	[illegible]
143	**22**	10 r. deep lilac	27	6	25	[illegible]

Nos. 131, 132 and 136 were issued on Februar[illegible] 1st, 1958, but were valid only for internal us[illegible] in Kuwait prior to February 1st, 1959.

23. Shaikh Abdullah and Flag.

(Recess. De La Rue.)

1960 (25 Feb.). *Tenth Anniv. of Shaikh's Accession. P* 14.

144	**23**	40 n.p. scarlet & olive-grn.	2	6	3	0
145	,,	60 n.p. scarlet and deep ultramarine ..	3	6	4	0

Currency changed. 1,000 fils = 1 dinar.

24. Shaikh Abdullah.

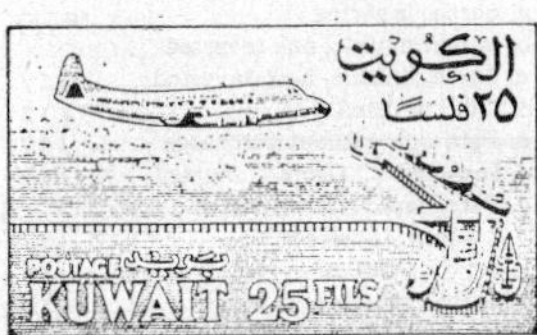

25. " Viscount " Airliner over South Pier, Mina al Ahmadi.

26. Shuwaikh Secondary School.

27. Wara Hill.

(Recess. De La Rue.)

1961 (1 Apr.–8 May). *Designs as T* **24, 21, 25, 20, 26, 16** (*larger size,* 32 × 22 *mm.*), *and* **27** *inscr. in new currency. P* 12½ (*T* **24**), 13½ (*T* **26**) *or* 14 × 13½ (*others*).

46	**24**	1 f. bluish green	0	3	0	2
47	,,	2 f. brown-red	0	3	0	3
48	,,	4 f. brown	0	4	0	6
49	,,	5 f. slate-violet	0	4	0	4
50	,,	8 f. orange-red	0	5	0	6
51	,,	15 f. maroon	0	7	0	7
52	**21**	20 f. blue-green	0	10	1	0
153	**25**	25 f. blue	1	0	1	3
154	**20**	30 f. light blue and brown	1	2	1	3
155	**26**	35 f. black and red (8.5.61)	1	4	1	6
156	**16**	40 f. blue	1	5	1	6
157	**27**	45 f. chocolate	1	7	1	9
158	**20**	75 f. sepia & emerald-green (27.4.61) ..	2	9	2	6
159	**26**	90 f. brown & deep ultramarine (27.4.61) ..	3	0	3	3
160	**25**	100 f. carmine-red ..	3	3	3	3
161	**16**	250 f. bronze-green ..	8	0	9	0
162	**27**	1 d. red-orange	30	0	25	0
163	**21**	3 d. red	90	0	95	0

Kuwait became completely independent on June 19th, 1961. Later stamp issues will be found in Part III of the Stanley Gibbons Catalogue.

OFFICIAL STAMPS.

KUWAIT

SERVICE

(O 1)

KUWAIT

SERVICE

(O 2)

1923–24. *Stamps of India* (*King George V*), *optd. with Types* O 1 *or* O 2 (*rupee values.* 15½–16 *mm.*). *Star wmk. P* 14.

O 1	**56**	½ a. green	0	9	3	0
O 2	**57**	1 a. chocolate	1	0	3	6
O 3	**58**	1½ a. chocolate (A) ..	3	6	6	0
O 4	**59**	2 a. mauve	2	6	6	0
O 5	**61**	2 a. 6 p. ultramarine ..	2	0	7	6
O 6	**62**	3 a. orange-brown ..	8	6	12	6
O 7	,,	3 a. ultramarine (1924) ..	4	0	8	6
O 8	**63**	4 a. olive-green	6	0	12	6
O 9	**65**	8 a. purple	6	0	17	6
O10	**67**	1 r. brown and green ..	10	0	25	0
O11	,,	2 r. carmine & yell.-brn.	12	6	30	0
O12	,,	5 r. ultramarine & violet	50	0	60	0
O13	,,	10 r. green and scarlet ..	90	0	95	0
O14	,,	15 r. blue and olive ..	£7		£9	

1929–33. *Stamps of India* (*Nasik printing*), *optd. as Types* O 1 (*spaced* 10 *mm.*) *or* O 2 (14½ *mm. between* × 19–20 *mm. wide*). *Mult. Star wmk. P* 14.

O16	**57**	1 a. chocolate	0	6	3	0
O17	**70**	2 a. purple	7	6	10	0
O19	**62**	3 a. blue	1	6	5	0
O20	**71**	4 a. sage-green	4	0	6	0
O21	**65**	8 a. reddish purple ..	3	6	7	6
O22	**66**	12 a. claret	10	0	17	6
O23	**67**	1 r. chocolate & green ..	10	0	20	0
O24	,,	2 r. carmine & orange ..	12	6	25	0
O25	,,	5 r. ultram. & purple ..	20	0	40	0
O26	,,	10 r. green and scarlet ..	40	0	65	0
O27	,,	15 r. blue and olive ..	£7		£9	

LABUAN.

1

(Recess. De La Rue & Co.)

1879 (May). *Wmk. CA over Crown, sideways. P* 14.

1	**1**	2 c. blue-green	£30	£28

2 1 6 c. orange-brown £9 £8
3 ,, 12 c. carmine £35 £24
4 ,, 16 c. blue 55 0 70 0

This watermark is always found sideways, and extends over two stamps, a single specimen showing only a portion of the Crown or the letters CA, which latter are tall and far apart. This paper was chiefly used for long fiscal stamps.

1880 (Jan.)–**1881.** *Wmk. Crown CC. P* 14.
5 **1** 2 c. yellow-green 20 0 25 0
6 ,, 6 c. orange-brown 65 0 60 0
7 ,, 10 c. brown 55 0 60 0
8 ,, 12 c. carmine £9 £9
9 ,, 16 c. blue (1881) 60 0 70 0

8 8 Eight Cents Eight Cents
(2) (3) (4) (5)

1880 (Aug.). *No.* 8 *surch. with numeral in centre, in black, and the original value obliterated, as T* **2**, *in red or black.*
11 8 c. on 12 c. carmine .. £28 £25
a. "8" inverted £28 £25
b. "12" not obliterated £32 £28
c. As b. with "8" inverted ..

No. 4 *surch. with two upright figures and No.* 8 *surch. with numeral in centre, and another across the original value as T* **3.**
12 6, in *red* on 16 c. blue .. £35 £30
a. With one "6" only ..
13 8, in *black*, on 12 c. carmine £28 £25
a. Both "8's" upright .. ..

1881 (Mar.). *No.* 8 *surch. as T* **4.**
14 8 c. on 12 c. carmine £7 £7

1881 (June). *No.* 8 *surch.* as *T* **5.**
15 8 c. on 12 c. carmine .. 50 0 50 0
a. Double £14
b. Inverted £35
c. Error "Eighr" £175

The error "Eighr" was No. 6 in the first printing, but this was soon corrected.

1882 (April). *Wmk. Crown CC. P* 14.
16 **1** 8 c. carmine 65 0 65 0

1883–86. *Wmk. Crown CA. P* 14.
17 **1** 2 c. green 17 6 20 0
a. Imperf. between (horiz. pr.) £45
18 ,, 8 c. carmine £6 95 0
19 ,, 10 c. yellow-brown 35 0 45 0
20 ,, 16 c. blue 70 0 80 0
21 ,, 40 c. amber 20 0 30 0

One Dollar A.S.H. 2 Cents 2 Cents
(6) (7) (8)

1883 (May). *No.* 9 *surch.* "*One Dollar A. S. H.*" *by hand, as T* **6.**
22 $1 on 16 c. blue (R.) £100 £85

The initials are those of the postmaster, Mr. A. S. Hamilton.

1885 (June). *Nos.* 18 *and* 9 *surch. as T* **7.**
23 2 c. on 8 c. carmine 60 0
a. Double .. .. ..
24 2 c. on 16 c. blue £35 £28

1885 (July). *No.* 20 *surch. as T* **8.**
25 2 c. on 16 c. blue £5 £6
a. Double .. .. ..

2 Cents 6 Cents
(9) (10)

1885 (Sept.). *No.* 18 *surch. diagonally, as T* **9.**
26 2 c. on 8 c. carmine 50 0 65 0

1885–6. *Wmk. Crown CA. P* 14.
27 **1** 2 c. rose-red (Sept. 1885) .. 3 6 6 0
28 ,, 2 c. pale rose-red 2 6 6 0
29 ,, 8 c. dp. violet (Sept., 1885) 20 0 15 0
30 ,, 8 c. mauve (1886) 17 6 17 6
32 ,, 10 c. sepia (May, 1886) .. 8 0 15 0
33 ,, 16 c. grey (May, 1886) .. 50 0 65 0

From Jan. 1st, 1890, while remaining a Crown Colony, the administration of Labuan was transferred to the British North Borneo Co., and the following stamps were issued by that Company.

1891 (Aug.). *T* **1** *surch. as T* **10.** *P* 14.
34 6 c. on 8 c. deep violet (No. 29) 45 0 45 0
a. Surch. inverted 60 0 60 0
b. Surch. double £10
c. Surch. double, one inverted .. £18
d. "Cents" omitted £18 £20
e. Imperf. between (pair) ..
35 6 c. on 8 c. mauve (No. 30) .. 6 0 8 6
a. Surch. inverted 40 0 40 0
b. Surch. double, one inverted ..
c. Surch. double, both inverted .. £17
d. "6" omitted £12
e. Pair, one without surcharge .. £17 £20
f. Inverted. "Cents" omitted .. £17
g. Pair, one without surch., one surch. inverted £22
36 6 c. on 8 c. mauve (R.) (No. 30) £18 £7
a. Surch. inverted £18 £8
37 6 c. on 16 c. blue, (No. 4) .. £80 £70
a. Surch. inverted £100
38 6 c. on 40 c. amber (No. 21) .. £100 £90
a. Surch. inverted £125 £125

(Recess. De La Rue & Co.)

1892. *No wmk. P* 14.
39 **1** 2 c. rose-lake 2 0 2 6
40 ,, 6 c. bright green 5 0 5 0
41 ,, 8 c. violet 5 0 6 0
42 ,, 8 c. pale violet 6 0 6 0
43 ,, 10 c. brown 6 0 6 0
44 ,, 10 c. sepia-brown 3 0 6 0
45 ,, 12 c. bright blue 6 0 7 6
46 ,, 16 c. grey 6 0 7 6
47 ,, 40 c. amber 17 6 20 0
48 ,, 40 c. brown-buff 25 0 25 0

The 6 c., 12 c., 16 c., and 40 c. are in sheets of 10, as are all the earlier issues. The other values are in sheets of 30.

Two Cents Six Cents
(11) (11*a*)

1892 (Dec.). *Nos.* 47 *and* 46 *surch. as T* **11** *or* **11a**.
49 2 c. on 40 c. amber ('92) .. 90 0 90
a. Inverted £10
50 6 c. on 16 c. grey (29 Dec., '92) £7 £
a. Surch. inverted .. .. £10 £
b. Surch. sideways £10 £1
c. "Six" omitted .. ..
d. "Cents" omitted .. ..

There are 10 types of each of these surcharges

(Litho. De La Rue & Co.)

1894 (APRIL.). *No wmk.* *P* 14.

51 **1** 2 c. carmine-pink 3 6 1 0
52 „ 6 c. bright green 7 6 3 0
53 „ 8 c. bright mauve 8 0 4 0
54 „ 10 c. brown 10 0 4 0
55 „ 12 c. pale blue 12 0 5 0
56 „ 16 c. grey 15 0 4 0
57 „ 40 c. orange-buff 25 0 6 0

The prices in the "used" column (No. 51 to 57) are for stamps "cancelled to order".

Collectors are warned against forgeries of this issue.

12

1894. *T* **24** *to* **32** *of North Borneo (colours changed), with* "LABUAN" *engraved on vignette plate as in T* **12**.

(*a*) *Name and central part of design in black.*

62 1 c. grey-mauve 3 0 3 6
a. Imperf. between (vert. pair) ..
63 2 c. blue 3 6 3 6
a. Imperf. (pair) £15
64 3 c. ochre 3 0 5 6
65 5 c. green 4 0 6 0
67 6 c. brown-lake 4 6 6 0
a. Imperf. (pair) £15
68 8 c. rose-red 3 6 6 6
69 8 c. pink 15 0 20 0
70 12 c. orange-vermilion 10 0 12 6
71 18 c. olive-brown 8 6 10 0
72 18 c. olive-bistre 10 0 17 6

(*b*) *Name and central part in blue.*

73 24 c. pale mauve 10 0 10 0
74 24 c. dull lilac 12 6 12 6

Nos. 62 to 74 can be supplied "cancelled to order" at prices considerably lower than those which are given above for postally used specimens.

LABUAN
40
CENTS
(22)

1895 (JUNE). *No.* 83 *of N. Borneo* ($1 *inscr.* "STATE OF NORTH BORNEO") *surch. as T* **22**.

75 4 c. on $1 scarlet 3 0 3 6
76 10 c. on $1 scarlet 4 0 5 0
77 20 c. on $1 scarlet 7 6 7 6
78 30 c. on $1 scarlet 7 6 7 6
79 40 c. on $1 scarlet 10 0 10 0

Nos. 75 to 79 can be supplied "cancelled to order" at half the prices quoted above for postally used stamps.

LABUAN
(23)

1846
JUBILEE
1896
(24)

T **32a** *to* **32c** *of North Borneo (as Nos.* 81 *to* 83, *but colours changed) optd. with T* **23**.

80 25 c. green (*canc.* 2s. 6d.) .. 25 0 30 0
a. Opt. omitted (*canc.* 8s.) .. 17 0
b. Imperf. Opt. omitted .. 35 0
81 50 c. marone (*canc.* 3s. 6d.) .. 27 6 20 0
a. Opt. omitted (*canc.* 8s.) .. 17 0
b. Imperf. Opt. omitted .. 35 0
82 $1 blue (*canc.* 4s. 6d.) .. 35 0 30 0
a. Opt. omitted (*canc.* 8s.) .. 18 0
b. Imperf. Opt. omitted .. 35 0

1896. *Jubilee of Cession of Labuan to Gt. Britain. Nos.* 62 *to* 68, *optd. with T* **24**.

83 1 c. black and grey-mauve .. 10 0 10 0
a. Error. "JEBILEE" .. — £12
b. Opt. double £6 £6
c. Opt. in orange £5 £6
84 2 c. black and blue 12 6 12 6
a. Impert. between (pair) .. £8
b. Error. "JEBILEE" .. £28
85 3 c. black and ochre 12 6 12 6
a. Error. "JEBILEE" .. — £55
b. Opt. double £5 60 0
c. Opt. treble £45
86 5 c. black and green 15 0 15 0
a. Opt. double £5 £5
87 6 c. black and brown-lake .. 15 0 12 6
a. Opt. double £8 £8
88 8 c. black and pink 12 6 10 0

1897 (APR.). *T* **34** *to* **45** *of North Borneo, inscribed* "LABUAN" *as in T* **12**. *Name and central part in black* (24 *c. in blue*).

89 1 c. greyish purple 5 0 4 0
89a 1 c. brown 3 6 3 6
90 2 c. blue (*canc.* 2d.) 6 0 4 0
a. Imperf. between (pair) ..
91 3 c. ochre 5 0 5 0
a. Imperf. between (pair) ..
92 5 c. green (*canc.* 4d.) 10 0 7 6
93 6 c. brown-lake 6 0 10 0
a. Imperf. between (pair) ..
94 8 c. rose-red 8 0 8 0
94a 8 c. vermilion 12 6 15 0
95 12 c. vermilion 12 6 10 0
96 18 c. olive-bistre 7 6 12 6
a. Imperf. between (pair) ..
97 24 c. grey-lilac 10 0 15 0

The 12, 18, and 24 c. above were errors; in the 12 c., "LABUAN" is over the value at the top; the 18 c. has "POSTAL REVENUE" instead of "POSTAGE AND REVENUE", and the 24 c. is without "POSTAGE AND REVENUE".

1897 (OCT.)–**1898.** *T* **42**, **46** *and* **47** *of North Borneo, inscribed* "LABUAN" *as in T* **12**.

98 12 c. black and vermilion .. 12 6 10 0
99 18 c. black and olive-bistre .. 20 0 25 0
100 24 c. blue and greyish mauve 10 0 15 0

In the 12 c. "LABUAN" is now correctly placed at foot of stamp. The 18 c. and 24 c. have the inscriptions on the stamps corrected, but the 18 c. still has "LABUAN" *over* the value at foot, and was further corrected as follows.

As No. 99, *but* "LABUAN" *at top.*

101 18 c. black and olive-bistre .. 10 0 12 6

Nos. 83 *to* 101 *(excluding the errors etc.) can be supplied "cancelled to order" at about one-third of the prices quoted above for postally used specimens.*

4
CENTS
(38)

1899. *Surch. with T* **38**.

102 4 c. on 5 c. (No. 92) .. 8 6 17 6
103 4 c. on 6 c. (No. 93) .. 8 6 17 6
104 4 c. on 8 c. (No. 94) .. 8 6 17 6

105 4 c. on 12 c. (No. 98) .. 10 0 20 0
106 4 c. on 18 c. (No. 101) .. 10 0 20 0
a. Surch. double £15 £10
107 4 c. on 24 c. (No. 100) .. 10 0 25 0
108 4 c. on 25 c. (No. 80) .. 10 0 30 0
109 4 c. on 50 c. (No. 81) .. 10 0 30 0
110 4 c. on $1 (No. 82) 10 0 30 0

1900. *T* **35, 37** *and* **38** *of North Borneo, inscribed* "LABUAN" *as in T* **12.**

111 2 c. black & grn. (*canc.* 6d.) .. 6 0 5 0
112 4 c. black & yellow-brown .. 7 6
a. Imperf. between (pair) .. £12
113 4 c. black & carm. (*canc.* 3d.) 6 0 3 6
114 5 c. blk. & pl. blue (*canc.* 6d.) 10 0 6 0

1902. *T* **41** *and* **43** *of North Borneo, inscribed* "LABUAN" *as in T* **12.**

115 10 c. brown and slate-lilac .. 10 0 12 6
116 16 c. green and chestnut .. 10 0 10 0

42

(Recess. Waterlow & Sons.)

1902–03. *T* **42.** *P* 13½ *to* 15 *etc.*

116*a* 1 c. black and purple .. 2 0 2 0
117 2 c. black and green 2 0 2 0
117*a* 3 c. black and sepia .. 1 6 2 6
118 4 c. black and carmine .. 1 6 1 3
119 8 c. black and vermilion .. 1 6 3 6
120 10 c. brown and slate-blue .. 2 0 2 6
a. Imperf. between (pair) .. £8
121 12 c. black and yellow .. 2 0 3 6
122 16 c. green and brown .. 2 6 3 6
123 18 c. black and pale brown .. 2 6 6 0
124 25 c. green and greenish blue 2 6 7 6
125 50 c. dull purple and lilac .. 3 0 12 6
126 $1 claret and orange .. 6 0 30 0

Error of colour. *Canc.*

126*a* 25 c. black & greenish blue — 85 0

Nos. 116*a to* 126 *can be supplied "cancelled to order" at about one quarter of the prices quoted above for postally used stamps.*

4
cents
(43)

1904. *Issues of* 1895 *and* 1897–8 *surcharged with T* **43,** *in black.*

127 4 c. on 5 c. (No. 92) .. 8 6
128 4 c. on 6 c. (No. 93) .. 8 6
129 4 c. on 8 c. (No. 94) .. 6 0
130 4 c. on 12 c. (No. 98) .. 6 0
131 4 c. on 18 c. (No. 101) .. 6 0
132 4 c. on 24 c. (No. 100) .. 6 0
133 4 c. on 25 c. (No. 80) .. 7 6
134 4 c. on 50 c. (No. 81) .. 7 6
135 4 c. on $1 (No. 82) 7 6

Varieties. (i) *Surcharge double.*

136 4 c. on 50 c. (No. 81) .. £9

(ii) *Surcharge triple.*

137 4 c. on 50 c. (No. 81) ..

LABUAN (44) **LABUAN** (45)

1905. *Nos.* 81, 83 (*in Labuan colour*), *and* 84 *to* 86 *of North Borneo overprinted locally with T* **44** (25 *c. and* $2) *or* **45**, *in black.*

139 25 c. indigo £45 £28
139*a* $1 blue .. .. .. — £20
140 $2 dull green £250 £70
141 $5 bright purple £250 £60
142 $10 brown .. .. .. — £150

The overprint on No. 140 is 12 mm. long.

POSTAGE DUE STAMPS.

POSTAGE DUE
(101)

1901. *Optd. with T* **101,** *vertically.*

201 2 c. black & grn. (No. 111) .. 10 0 3 6
a. Opt. double 75 0
202 3 c. black & ochre (No. 91) .. 4 0 7 6
203 4 c. black & carm. (No. 113) 10 0 10 0
a. Opt. double (*canc.*) .. .. — £6
204 5 c. blk. & pale bl. (No. 114) 7 6 10 0
205 6 c. blk. & brn.-lake (No. 93) 7 6 10 0
206 8 c. blk. & verm. (No. 94*a*) .. 10 0 12 6
a. Frame inverted (*canc.*) .. — £85
207 12 c. black & verm. (No. 98) .. 20 0 25 0
208 18 c. black & olive-bis. (No. 101) 5 0 10 0
209 24 c. blue & grey-mve. (No. 100) 5 0 10 0

Nos. 201 *to* 209 *can be supplied "cancelled to order" at prices considerably lower than those which are given above for postally used specimens.*

By Letters Patent dated 30 October, 1906, Labuan was incorporated with Straits Settlements and ceased issuing its own stamps. In 1946 it became part of the Colony of North Borneo.

LAGOS.

PRINTERS. All the stamps of Lagos were typographed by De La Rue & Co.

1

Type **1.**

1874 (10 JUNE)–**1875** (MAR.). *Wmk. Crown CC P* 12½.

The colour of the words of value (the second colour given below) frequently differs from that of the body of the stamp.

1 1d. lilac-mauve 65 0 70 0
2 2d. blue 60 0 50 0
3 3d. red-brown (1875) £7 70 0
4 3d. red-brn. & chestnut ('75) .. £6 70 0
5 4d. carmine 85 0 80 0
6 6d. blue-green £5 40 0
8 1s. orange (value 15½ mm.) ('75) £20 £14
9 1s. orange (value 16½ mm.) ('75) £18 £6

1876. *Wmk. Crown CC. P* 14.

10 1d. lilac-mauve 35 0 20 0
11 2d. blue 35 0 22 6
12 3d. red-brown £6 45 0
13 3d. chestnut £6 75 0
14 4d. carmine £9 20 0
a. Wmk. sideways .. .. — £2
15 6d. green .. .. .. 50 0 22 ·
16 1s. orange (value 16½ mm. long) £27 £·

1882 (JUNE)–**1885** (MAR.). *Wmk. Crown CA. P* 14.

17	1d. lilac-mauve	22 6	20 0
18	2d. blue	£6	22 6
19	3d. chestnut	20 0	20 0
20	4d. carmine	£6	25 0
21	1s. orange (1885)	10 0	20 0

1884 (DEC.)–**1886** (OCT.). *Wmk. Crown CA. P* 14.

22	½d. dull green (1886)	0 8	0 10
23	1d. rose-carmine	1 3	0 8
24	2d. grey	20 0	15 0
25	4d. pale violet	50 0	25 0
26	6d. olive-green	12 6	25 0
27	2s. 6d. olive-black (1886) ..	£40	£35
28	5s. blue (1886)	£70	£40
29	10s. purple-brown (1886) ..	£150	£85

We would warn collectors against clever forgeries of No. 27 to 29 on genuinely watermarked paper.

2½ PENNY A.

2½ PENNY B.

1887–1902. *Wmk. Crown CA. P* 14.

30	1	2d. dull mauve and blue ..	3 6	3 0
31	,,	2½d. ultramarine (A) ('91) ..	3 0	2 0
		a. Larger letters of value (B) ..	27 6	30 0
31*b*	,,	2½d. blue	£6	65 0
32	,,	3d. dull mauve & chestnut	6 0	6 0
33	,,	4d. dull mauve & black ..	5 0	5 0
34	,,	5d. dull mauve & grn. ('94)	6 0	17 6
35	,,	6d. dull mauve & mauve ..	6 0	10 0
35*a*	,,	6d. d. mve. & car. (Oct. '02)	12 6	15 0
36	,,	7½d. dull mve. & carm. ('94)	7 6	22 6
37	,,	10d. dull mve. & yell. ('94)	8 0	22 6
38	,,	1s. yellow-green & black ..	12 6	20 0
38*a*	,,	1s. blue-green & black ..	17 6	30 0
39	,,	2s. 6d. green and carmine	25 0	45 0
40	,,	5s. green and blue ..	45 0	65 0
41	,,	10s. green and brown ..	70 0	80 0

HALF PENNY

(2)

(3)

1893 (AUG.). *No.* 33 *surch. with T* **2**.

2	½d. on 4d. dull mauve & black	6 0	7 0
	a. Surch. double	90 0	90 0
	b. Surch. treble	£6	
	c. Error. ½d. on 2d. (No. 30) ..		

There were four settings of this surcharge, a carce setting in which "HALF PENNY" is 6½ mm. and three others in which the length is 6 mm.

904 (22 JAN.–NOV.). *Wmk. Crown CA. P* 14.

4	3	½d. dull green and green ..	5 0	8 6
5	,,	1d. purple and black/*red* ..	4 0	1 3
6	,,	2d. dull purple and blue ..	12 6	20 0
7	,,	2½d. dull pur. & blue/*blue* (B)	6 0	10 0
		a. Smaller letters of value as A	12 6	20 0
8	,,	3d. dull purple and brown ..	8 6	8 6
9	,,	6d. dull purple and mauve ..	45 0	20 0
0	,,	1s. green and black ..	42 6	45 0
1	,,	2s. 6d. green and carmine	£15	
2	,,	5s. green and blue ..	£14	£12
3	,,	10s. green and brown (Nov.)	£55	£55

1904 (22 OCT.)–**1905.** *T* **3.** *Wmk. Mult. Crown CA. P* 14.

54	½d. dull green & green, OC ..	1 3	1 0
55	1d. purple & black/*red*, OC ..	0 10	0 6
56	2d. dull pur. & blue, OC ('05)	3 6	4 0
57	2½d. dull purple and blue/*blue*, (B), C ('05)	7 6	10 0
	a. Smaller letters of value as A ..	47 6	47 6
58	3d. dull pur. & brn., OC ('05)	5 0	5 0
59	6d. dull pur. & mauve, OC	8 0	6 0
60	1s. green and black, OC ..	10 0	10 0
61	2s. 6d. green and carm., OC	20 0	27 6
62	5s. green and blue, OC (1905)	27 6	45 0
63	10s. green and brown, OC ..	90 0	90 0

By an Order in Council dated 16 February, 1906, the administration of the Southern Nigerian Protectorate was amalgamated with that of the colony of Lagos, and the combination was styled the Colony and Protectorate of Southern Nigeria.

LEEWARD ISLANDS.

Issues superseding the earlier issues, or in concurrent use with the later issues (from 1903), *of* Antigua, Dominica (*to* 31 Dec., 1939), Montserrat, Nevis, St. Christopher, St. Kitts-Nevis, and Virgin Islands.

PRINTERS. All the stamps of Leeward Islands were typographed by De La Rue & Co., *except where otherwise stated.*

1

2

1890. *Name and value in second colour. Wmk. Crown CA. P* 14.

1	1	½d. dull mauve and green ..	1 0	0 9
2	,,	1d. dull mauve and rose ..	1 0	0 6
3	,,	2½d. dull mauve and blue ..	4 0	3 0
4	,,	4d. dull mauve and orange	10 0	10 0
5	,,	6d. dull mauve and brown ..	8 6	17 6
6	,,	7d. dull mauve and slate ..	10 0	12 6
7	2	1s. green and carmine ..	30 0	45 0
8	,,	5s. green and blue	90 0	£7

(3)

One Penny

(4)

One Penny

(5)

1897. *Queen Victoria's Diamond Jubilee. T* **1** *and* **2** *optd. with T* **3**.

9	½d. dull mauve and green ..	8 6	12 6
	a. Opt. inverted		
	b. Opt. double	£15	
10	1d. dull mauve and rose ..	10 0	17 6
	a. Opt. double	£15	
	b. Opt. triple		
11	2½d. dull mauve and blue ..	10 0	17 6
	a. Opt. double	£15	
12	4d. dull mauve and orange ..	30 0	45 0
	a. Opt. double	£20	
13	6d. dull mauve and brown ..	50 0	65 0
	a. Opt. double	£60	
14	7d. dull mauve and slate ..	60 0	75 0
	a. Opt. double	£60	
15	1s. green and carmine ..	£12	£14

16 5s. green and blue £70 £70
a. Opt. double .. .. ..

1902. *Stamps of* 1890 *surcharged; the* 4d. *and* 6d. *with T* **4**, *and the* 7d. *with T* **5**.

17 1d. on 4d. dull mauve & orange 3 6 10 0
a. Pair, one with tall narrow "O" in "One" 20 0 30 0
b. Surch. double .. .. ..
18 1d. on 6d. dull mauve & brown 3 6 10 0
a. Pair, one with tall narrow "O" in "One" 25 0 30 0
19 1d. on 7d. dull mauve and slate 3 6 10 0

6

7

8

1902. *Wmk. Crown CA. P* 14.

22 **6** ½d. dull purple and green .. 1 6 1 3
23 ,, 1d. dull purple and carmine 1 0 0 10
24 **7** 2d. dull purple and ochre .. 5 0 7 6
25 **6** 2½d. dull purple & ultram. .. 5 0 7 6
26 **7** 3d. dull purple and black .. 8 0 10 0
27 **6** 6d. dull purple and brown 7 6 25 0
28 **8** 1s. green and carmine .. 12 6 22 6
29 **7** 2s. 6d. green and black .. 42 6 50 0
30 **8** 5s. green and blue .. 60 0 70 0

1905–8. *Wmk. Mult. Crown CA. P* 14.

31 **6** ½d. dull pur.&grn., OC ('06) 1 6 1 6
32 ,, 1d. dull purp. & carm., C .. 3 6 2 0
33 **7** 2d. dull pur. & ochre, C ('08) 8 0 22 6
34 **6** 2½d. dull pur. & ultram, C .. 32 6 37 6
35 **7** 3d. dull pur. & black, OC .. 12 6 22 6
36 **6** 6d. dull pur. & brn., C ('08) 25 0 40 0
37 **8** 1s. green & carmine, C ('08) 45 0 55 0

1907–11. *Wmk. Mult. Crown CA. P* 14.

39 **7** ½d. brown, O (1909) .. 0 6 0 9
40 **6** ½d. dull green, O .. 1 3 1 0
41 ,, 1d. bright red, O .. 4 0 0 10
41*a* ,, 1d. rose-carmine, O .. 12 6 1 6
41*b* **7** 2d. grey, O (1911) .. 5 0 12 6
42 **6** 2½d. bright blue, O .. 6 0 7 6
43 **7** 3d. pur./*yellow*, C (1910) 6 0 12 6
44 **6** 6d. dull & brt. pur., C ('11) 8 0 12 6
45 **8** 1s. black/*green*, C (1911) 12 6 17 6
46 **7** 2s. 6d. blk.& red/*bl.*, C ('11) 32 6 50 0
47 **8** 5s. grn. & red/*yell.*, C ('11) £5 £6

10

11

12

1912–22. *Wmk. Mult. Crown. CA. P* 14.

48 **10** ¼d. brown, O 0 4 0 4
49 ,, ¼d. pale brown, O .. 0 8 0 10
50 **11** ½d. yellow-green O ('13) 0 8 0 6
51 ,, ½d. deep green, O .. 0 6 0 8
52 ,, 1d. carmine-red, O .. 1 0 0 6
53 ,, 1d. bright scarlet, O ('15) 1 0 0 6
54 **10** 2d. slate-grey, O .. 3 0 5 0
55 **11** 2½d. bright blue, O .. 12 6 10 0
55*a* ,, 2½d. deep bright blue, O 10 0 4 0
56 **10** 3d. purple/*yellow*, C .. 3 6 4 6
a. White back 65 0 55 0
b. On lemon 8 6 15 0
c. On orange-buff 5 0 5 0
d. On pale yellow 40 0 45 0
57 ,, 4d. blk. & red/*pale yell.*, C (Die II) ('22) 3 6 8 6
58 **11** 6d. dull & bright purple, C 5 0 10 0
59 **12** 1s. black/*green*, C .. 7 6 12 6
a. White back 40 0 50 0
b. On blue-green, olive back .. 12 6 10 0
60 **10** 2s. purple & blue/*blue*, C (Die II) (1922) .. 10 0 22 6
61 ,, 2s. 6d. black & red/*blue*, C 25 0 32 6
62 **12** 5s. green & red/*yellow*, C 17 6 42 6
a. White back 35 0 37 6
b. On lemon (1916) 25 0 37 6

1921–32. *Wmk. Mult. Script CA. P* 14.

63 **10** ¼d. brown, O (Die II) .. 0 3 0 6
a. Die I ('32) 0 4 0 6
64 **11** ½d. blue-green, O (Die II) 0 4 0 4
a. Die I ('31) 1 6 6 0
65 ,, 1d. carmine-red, O (Die II) 1 3 1 6
66 **10** 2d. slate-grey, O 1 9 1 6
67 ,, 4d. blk. & red/*pale yellow*, C 2 6 5 0
68 ,, 5d. dull pur. & olive-grn., C 2 6 6 0
69 **11** 6d. dull and bright purple, C (Die II) 8 6 8 6
a. Die I ('32) 10 0 10 6
70 **12** 1s. black/*emer.*, C (Die II) 8 6 8 6
a. Die I ('32) 35 0 40 0
71 **10** 2s. purple & blue/*blue*, C .. 25 0 30 0
71*a* ,, 2s. red-pur. & blue/*blue*, C ('26) 20 0 27
72 ,, 2s. 6d. black & red/*blue*, C 27 6 35
73 ,, 3s. bright grn. & violet, C .. 25 0 35
74 ,, 4s. black and red, C .. 30 0 42
75 **12** 5s. grn. & red/*pale yellow*, C 50 0 60

1922–32. *Colours changed, etc. Wmk. Mult Script CA. P* 14.

76 **11** 1d. bright violet, O .. 0 6 0
77 ,, 1d. bright scarlet, O (Die II) ('29) 0 8 0
a. Die I ('32) 1 6 2
78 **10** 1½d. carmine-red, O .. 1 3 1
79 ,, 1½d. red-brn., O (Die II)('29) 1 0 1
a. Die I ('32) 2 6 3
80 **11** 2½d. orange-yellow, O .. 20 0 42
81 ,, 2½d. bright blue, O (Die II) 3 0 3
a. Die I ('32) 3 6 5
82 **10** 3d. ultramarine, O .. 15 0 17
a. Deep blue 12 6 20
83 ,, 3d. purple/*yellow*, C .. 3 0 8

13

1928. *P 14. Wmk. Mult. Script CA.*
84 **13** 10s. grn. & red/*green*, C .. £6 £7
Wmk. Mult. Crown CA.
85 **13** £1 purple & black/*red*, C .. £14 £16

1935 (6 May). *Silver Jubilee. As Nos. 91/4 of Antigua but printed by W'low & Sons. P* 11 × 12.
86 1d. deep blue and scarlet .. 0 8 0 10
87 1½d. ultramarine and grey .. 1 6 2 0
88 2½d. brown and deep blue .. 5 0 6 6
89 1s. slate and purple .. 10 6 12 6

1937 (12 May). *Coronation. As Nos.* 13/15 *of Aden. P* 14.
90 1d. scarlet 0 3 0 4
91 1½d. buff 0 10 1 0
92 2½d. bright blue 1 6 2 0

14 15

1d 1d
(Die A) (Die B)

1938 (25 Nov.)–**51.** *T* **14** (*and similar type, but with shaded value tablet,* ½*d.,* 1*d.,* 2½*d. and* 6*d.*) *and* **15** (10*s. and* £1). *P* 14.
(*a*) *Wmk. Mult. Script. CA.*
93 ½d. brown, O 0 3 0 3
a. Deep brown, C ('49) .. 0 6 0 6
94 ½d. blue-green 0 3 0 3
94*a* ½d. slate-grey, C ('49) .. 0 4 0 4
95 1d. scarlet (Die A) 4 0 4 0
95*a* 1d. scarlet (*shades*) (Die B) ('40) 0 4 0 4
95*b* 1d. carmine (Die B) ('42) .. 4 0 6 0
95*c* 1d. blue-green, C ('49) .. 0 9 0 9
96 1½d. red-brown 0 4 0 4
96*a* 1½d. orange & black, C ('49) 1 0 1 0
97 2d. slate-grey 0 6 0 6
97*a* 2d. scarlet, C ('49) 1 3 1 3
98 2½d. bright blue 0 6 0 6
98*a* 2½d. black & purple, C ('49) 1 0 1 0
99 3d. orange, C 7 0 5 0
a. Pale orange, O 0 8 0 6
99*b* 3d. bright blue, C ('49) .. 1 6 1 3
100 6d. dull and brt. purple, C O 1 0 1 3
101 1s. black/*emerald*, C O .. 2 6 2 6
a. Grey & black/emerald, O ('42) 32 6 25 0
b. Black & grey/emerald, O ('42) £5 30 0
102 2s. reddish purple & blue/*blue*, C O 7 6 7 6
a. Deep pur. and blue/blue, O ('47) 6 0 7 6
103 5s. green & red/*yellow*, C O 12 6 12 6
104 10s. green & red/*green*, C O .. 22 6 30 0
(*b*) *Wmk. Mult. Crown CA.*
105 £1 brn.-purple & blk./*red*, C £20 £18
a. Purple & blk./carm., C ('41) .. 50 0 70 0
b. Brn.-purple & blk./salmon, C ('43) 37 6 40 0
c. Perf. 13. *Violet & black/scarlet*, C (13.12.51) .. 35 0 45 0
ca. Wmk. sideways, p. 13 .. £250

In Die B the figure "1" has a broader top and more projecting serif.

1946 (1 Nov.). *Victory. As Nos.* 28/9 *of Aden.*
106 1½d. brown 0 6 0 8
107 3d. red-orange 0 9 1 3

1949 (2 Jan.). *Royal Silver Wedding. As Nos.* 30/1 *of Aden.*
108 2½d. ultramarine 0 10 1 0
109 5s. green 12 6 15 0

1949 (10 Oct.). *75th Anniv. of Universal Postal Union. As Nos.* 114/7 *of Antigua.*
110 2½d. blue-black 0 8 0 10
111 3d. deep blue.. .. .. 0 10 1 0
112 6d. magenta 3 0 3 0
113 1s. blue-green 4 0 4 0

1951 (16 Feb.). *Inauguration of B.W.I. University College. As Nos.* 118/9 *of Antigua.*
114 3 c. orange and black .. 0 10 0 10
115 12 c. rose-carmine & reddish violet 2 0 2 0

1953 (2 June). *Coronation. As No.* 47 *of Aden.*
116 3 c. black and green.. .. 1 0 1 6

16. Queen Elizabeth II. **17.**

1954 (22 Feb.). *Chalk-surfaced paper. Wmk. Mult. Script. CA. P* 14 (*T* **16**) *or* 13 (*T* **17**).
117 **16** ½ c. brown 0 3 0 3
118 „ 1 c. grey 0 6 0 6
119 „ 2 c. green.. .. .. 0 6 0 6
120 „ 3 c. yellow-orge. & black 0 8 0 8
121 „ 4 c. rose-red 0 8 0 8
122 „ 5 c. blk. & brown-purple 0 10 0 10
123 „ 6 c. yellow-orange .. 1 0 1 0
124 „ 8 c. ultramarine 1 3 1 3
125 „ 12 c. dull purple & reddish purple 1 6 1 6
126 „ 24 c. black and green .. 2 6 3 0
127 „ 48 c. dull pur. & ultram. 5 0 6 0
128 „ 60 c. brown and green .. 6 0 7 6
129 „ $1.20 yellow-green and rose-red 10 0 12 6
130 **17** $2.40 bluish green & red 20 0 22 6
131 „ $4.80 brn.-purple & blk. 35 0 40 0

The 3 c., 4 c., 6 c., 8 c., 24 c., 48 c., 60 c. and $1.20 have their value tablets unshaded.

The stamps of Leeward Islands were withdrawn and invalidated on 1st July, 1956.

LONG ISLAND.

(AEGEAN SEA)

1916 (7th to 26th May). *Turkish fiscal Stamps optd.* "G.R.I., Postage", *and new value. No wmk. P* 12.
1 ½d. in carmine, on 20 paras, green and buff £40

2 1d. in black, on 10 paras, carmine and buff £38

3 2½d. in magenta, on 1 pias., violet and buff £45

1

1916 (7TH TO 26TH MAY). *T 1. Imperf.*

(i) *Type-written in various colours or carbons, on pale green paper, ruled with horizontal grey lines. In sheets of sixteen, initialled by the Civil Administrator in red ink. No watermark.*

4 ½d. black £10
- a. Error. "7" for "&" ..

5 ½d. blue £12

6 ½d. mauve £24
- a. "G. R. I." twice .. ..

(ii) *Type-written in various colours or carbons on thin horizontally laid paper, watermarked in the sheets in double-lined capitals* " SILVER LINEN ". *In sheets of twenty, each stamp initialled in red ink.*

7 ½d. mauve £7
- a. Error. "7" for "&" .. £20

8 ½d. black £7
- a. Error. "postage" for "Postage" £26

9 ½d. blue £10

10 1d. mauve £6 £12
- a. Error. "ONR" for "ONE" .. £26
- b. Error. "Postegg" £22

11 1d. black £7
- a. Error. "7" for "&" and "RVEVUE" £26

12 1d. blue £7
- a. Error. "ONR" for "ONE" £18

13 1d. red £8 £12
- a. Error. "7" for "&" .. £26
- b. Error. "ONR" for "ONE" £20

14 2½d. black £17

15 2½d. blue £18 £26

15*a* 2½d. mauve £20

16 6d. mauve £9 £14

16*a* 6d. black £20

17 1s. mauve £7
- a. Error. "ISLANA" for "ISLAND" £26

18 1s. blue £8

19 1s. black £7
- a. Error. "ISLANA" for "ISLAND" £26
- b. Error. "Postge" for "Postage" £40
- c. Error. "Rebeuue" ..

(iii) *Type-written in various colours or carbons on thin wove paper. In sheets of twenty-four, each stamp initialled in pencil. No watermark.*

20 ½d. black £9

20*a* ½d. mauve £14

21 1d. black £8 £14

21*a* 1d. red £26 £26

22 2d. mauve £7

23 2d. black £8
- a. "ISLAD" £100
- b. Error. 1d. in the sheet of 2d.

24 2½d. black £8

24*a* 2½d. mauve £28 £14

25 6d. blue £6

26 6d. black £6
- a. Error. "Rvenne" for "Revenue" £24
- b. Error. 2d. in sheet of 6d. .. £28

Quantities issued : No. 1 (25) ; 2 (25) ; 3 (20) ; 4/6*a* (140 in all) ; 7/9 (280 in all) ; 10/13*b* (1,178 in all) ; 14/15*a* (80 in all) ; 16/16*a* (100 in all) ; 17/19*c* (532 in all) ; 20/20*a* (144 in all) ; 21/21*a* (144 in all) ; 22/23*b* (288 in all) ; 24/24*a* (144 in all) ; 25/26*b* (244 in all).

MADAGASCAR.

BRITISH CONSULAR MAIL.

USED STAMPS. Postmarks are not usually found on these issues. The unused have a gummed corner and when used either the gum is missing or the corner has been cut off.

1

(*Illustration reduced. Actual size* 38 × 63 *mm.*)

1884 (MAR.). *Rouletted vertically in colour With circular handstamp,* " BRITISH VICE CONSULATE ANTANANARIVO " *in black.*

(*a*) *Inscribed* " LETTER ".

1 **1** 6d. magenta £20 £2

- a. Handstamp in violet .. £35 £3

2 ,, 1s. magenta £10 £1

3 ,, 1s. 6d. magenta £10 £1

4 ,, 2s. magenta £14 £1

(*b*) *Inscribed* " POSTAL PACKET ".

5 **1** 1d. magenta (1 oz.) .. .. £8 £

- a. Without handstamp £60 £6

6 ,, 2d. magenta (2 oz.) £10 £1

7 ,, 3d. magenta (3 oz.) .. .. £8 £

8 ,, 4d. magenta (1 oz.) .. ..

- a. Handstamp in violet .. £30 £3
- b. Without handstamp £70 £7
- c. Altered by pen to "4 oz." .. £15 £1

Several of the values are known with the handstamp inverted and also double printed.

1886. *Provisionals. No.* 2 *with* " SHILLING *erased and* " PENNY " *written above in red ink and the same stamp with* " 1 OZ." *altered in red to* " 4½d." *and the Vice-Consul's initial* " W.C.P.", *added.*

9 **1** 1d. on 1s. magenta .. ..

10 ,, 4½d. on 1s. magenta .. ..

1886. *Colour changed.*

11	**1**	6d. rose-red	£12	£12

As T **1**, *but handstamp reading* " British Consular Mail—ANTANANARIVO."

12	4d. magenta (Bk.)	£40	£40
13	4d. magenta (V.)	£50	£50

Nos. 1 to 13 were printed in horizontal strips of four, two with the full stops normal and two with one of the full stops appearing as a small circle. This "hollow stop" appears after the "B" in the 1d., 4d., 6d. and 2s. and after the "M" in the 2d., 3d., 1s. and 1s. 6d.

2

Illustration reduced. Actual size 45×68 *mm.)*

1886. *T* **2.** *Rouletted vertically in colour.*
(*a*) *With period after* " POSTAGE " *and value.*
A. *Handstamp in black.* B. *In violet.*

		A.		B.	
14	1d. rose	85 0	85 0	£10	£10
15	1½d. rose	£15	£15	£16	£20
16	2d. rose	85 0	85 0	£10	£10
17	3d. rose	£15	£15	£10	£10
18	4½d. rose	£15	£15	£12	£12
19	8d. rose	£18	£18	£18	£18
20	9d. rose		†	£40	£40

(*b*) *Without period after* " POSTAGE " *and value. Handstamp in violet.*

21	1d. rose	£40	£40
22	1½d. rose	£50	£50
23	3d. rose	£40	£40
24	4½d. rose	£30	£30
25	6d. rose	£30	£30

(*c*) *Period after value.* " POSTAGE " *measures* 24½ *mm. in place of* 29½ *mm. Handstamp in violet.*

26	4d. rose	£20	£20
27	8d. rose	£16	£16
28	1s. 6d. rose	£65	£65
29	2s. rose	£50	£50

1886. *As T* **2**, *but handstamp reading* " BRITISH CONSULAR MAIL, ANTANANARIVO ". *Rouletted vertically in colour.*
(*a*) *With period after* " POSTAGE " *and the value.*
A. *Handstamp in black.* B. *In violet.*

		A		B	
30	1d. rose	70 0	70 0		†
31	1½d. rose	70 0	70 0		†
32	2d. rose	75 0	75 0		†
33	3d. rose	80 0	80 0		†
34	4½d. rose	80 0	80 0		†
35	8d. rose	85 0	85 0	£30	£30
36	9d. rose	85 0	85 0	£8	£8
	a. Without handstamp	£70	£70		

C. *Handstamp in red.*

37	3d. rose	—	£70
38	4½d. rose	—	£60

(*b*) *Without period after* " POSTAGE " *and the value.*
A. *Handstamp in black.* B. *In violet.*

		A		B	
39	1d. rose	70 0	70 0	80 0	80 0
	a. Without handstamp	£24	£24		
40	1½d. rose	70 0	70 0	85 0	85 0
	a. Without handstamp	£24	£24		
41	2d. rose	70 0	70 0	85 0	85 0
42	3d. rose	70 0	70 0	85 0	85 0
	a. Without handstamp	£45	£45		
43	4½d. rose	80 0	80 0	£5	£5
	a. Without handstamp	£45	£45		
44	6d. rose	80 0	80 0	£9	£9
	a. Without handstamp	£45	£45		

(*c*) *Period after value.* " POSTAGE " 24½ *mm. long in place of* 29½ *mm.*
A. *Handstamp in black.* B. *In violet.*

		A		B	
45	4d. rose	85 0	85 0	£9	£9
	a. Without handstamp	£45	£45		
46	8d. rose	£12	£12	£14	£14
	a. Without handstamp	£55	£55		
47	1s. rose	£8	£8	£30	£30
	a. Without handstamp	£50	£50		
48	1s. 6d. rose ..	£10	£10	£30	£30
	a. Without handstamp	£50	£50		
49	2s. rose	£15	£15	£30	£30
	a. Without handstamp	£55	£55		

These stamps were suppressed in 1887.

BRITISH INLAND MAIL.

4

5. Malagasy Runners.

1895 (JAN.). *Type-set at Antananarivo. Rouletted in black.*

(*a*) *Thick laid paper.*

50	**4**	4d. black	35 0	15 0
		a. " FUOR " for " FOUR " ..	—	£22

(*b*) *Wove paper.*

51	**4**	1d. blue-grey	40 0	17 6
52	,,	6d. pale yellow	40 0	25 0
53	,,	8d. salmon	40 0	25 0
54	,,	1s. fawn	55 0	25 0
55	,,	2s. bright rose	55 0	35 0
		a. Italic " 2 " at left	£8	£6
56	,,	4s. grey	60 0	35 0

There are six types of each value, printed in groups repeated four times on each sheet; the upper and lower groups are *tête-bêche*.

(Litho. John Haddon & Co., London.)

1895 (MAR.). *The inscription in the lower label varies for each value.* P 12.

57	**5**	2d. blue	10 0
		a. Imperf. between (pair) ..	
58	,,	4d. rose	10 0
		a. Imperf. between (pair) ..	£6
59	,,	6d. green	12 6
		a. Imperf. between (pair) ..	
60	,,	1s. slate-blue	17 6
		a. Imperf. between (pair) ..	
61	,,	2s. chocolate	22 6
		a. Imperf between (pair) ..	
62	,,	4s. bright purple	32 6
		a. Imperf. between (pair) ..	

This post was suppressed when the French entered Antananarivo at the end of September 1895.

MALAWI (NYASALAND)

44. Independence Monument.

45. Rising Sun.

46. National Flag.

47. Coat-of-Arms.

The portrait is of Dr. Hastings Banda (Prime Minister).

(Des. M. Goaman. Photo. Harrison.)

1964 (6 JULY). *Independence. P* 14½.

211	**44**	3d. yell.-olive & dp. sepia	0	7	0	9
212	**45**	6d. red, gold, blue, carmine and lake	1	0	1	2
213	**46**	1s. 3d. red, green, black and bluish violet ..	2	3	2	6
214	**47**	2s. 6d. multicoloured ..	5	0	6	0

48. Tung Tree.

(Des. V. Whiteley. Photo. Harrison.)

1964 (6 JULY)–**65.** *As Nos.* 199/210 *of Nyasaland but inscr.* " MALAWI ", *and new value and design* (9*d.*). *P* 14½.

215	**32**	½d. reddish violet ..	0	3	0	3
216	**33**	1d. black and green ..	0	4	0	5
217	**34**	2d. light red-brown ..	0	4	0	5
218	**35**	3d. red-brown, yellow-green and bistre-brown ..	0	6	0	7
219	**36**	4d. black and orange-yell.	0	7	0	9
220	**37**	6d. bluish violet, yellow-green and light blue ..	0	10	1	0
221	**48**	9d. bistre-brn., grn. & yell.	1	1	1	6
222	**38**	1s. brown, turquoise-blue and pale yellow ..	1	8	2	3
223	**39**	1s. 3d. bronze-green and chestnut	2	3	3	0
224	**40**	2s. 6d. brown and blue ..	4	6	4	9
225	**41**	5s. blue, grn., yell. & sep.	7	6	10	0
225*a*	,,	5s. blue, green, yellow and sepia (1.6.65)	6	9	7	6
226	**42**	10s. grn., orge.-brn. & blk.	13	3	15	0
227	**43**	£1 deep reddish purple and yellow	25	0	30	0

No. 225*a* is inscribed " LAKE MALAWI " instead of " LAKE NYASA ".

49. Christmas Star and Globe.

(Des. V. Whiteley. Photo. Harrison.)

1964 (1 DEC.). *Christmas. P* 14½.

228	**49**	3d. blue-green and gold ..	0	7	0	
229	,,	6d. magenta and gold ..	1	0	1	
230	,,	1s. 3d. reddish vio. & gold	2	3	2	
231	,,	2s. 6d. blue and gold ..	4	6	4	
MS231*a*		83 × 126 mm. Nos. 228/31. Imperf.	15	0		

50. Coins.

(Des. V. Whiteley. Photo. J. Enschedé & Sons

1965 (1 MAR.). *Malawi's First Coinage. Coi in black and silver. P* 13½.

232	**50**	3d. green	0	7	0	
233	,,	9d. magenta	1	4	1	
234	,,	1s. 6d. purple	2	6	2	
235	,,	3s. blue	4	9	5	

(51)

1965 (14 June). *Nos.* 223/4 *surch. as T* **51.**

236	**39**	1s. 6d. on 1s. 3d. bronze-green and chestnut ..	2	0	2	6
237	**40**	3s. on 2s. 6d. brown & blue	4	0	5	6

On No. 237 " 3/- " occurs below the bars.

52. Chilembwe leading Rebels.

(Des. M. Goaman. Photo. Harrison.)

1965 (20 Aug.). 50*th Anniv. of* 1915 *Rising.* *P* 14 × 14½.

238	**52**	3d. violet & lt. olive-green	0	7	0	11
239	,,	9d. olive-brn. & red-orge.	1	4	1	10
240	,,	1s. 6d. red-brn. & grey-bl.	2	6	3	0
241	,,	3s. turq.-grn. & slate-blue	4	9	6	0

53. " Learning and Scholarship ".

(Des. H. E. Baxter. Photo. Harrison.)

1965 (6 Oct.). *Opening of Malawi University.* *P* 14½.

242	**53**	3d. black and emerald ..	0	7	0	11
243	,,	9d. black and magenta ..	1	4	1	10
244	,,	1s. 6d. blk. & reddish violet	2	6	3	6
245	,,	3s. black and blue ..	4	9	6	6
MS246		127 × 84 mm. Nos. 242/6. Imperf.	8	6	10	6

54. *Papilio ophidicephalus mkuwadzi.*

55. *Papilio magdae.*

56. *Epamera handmani.*

57. *Amauris crawshayi.*

(Des. V. Whiteley. Photo. Enschedé.)

1966 (15 Feb.). *Malawi Butterflies.* *P* 13½.

247	**54**	4d. multicoloured ..	0	9	1	0
248	**55**	9d. multicoloured ..	1	4	1	10
249	**56**	1s. 6d. multicoloured ..	2	6	3	6
250	**57**	3s. multicoloured ..	4	9	6	6
MS251		130 × 100 mm. Nos. 247/50	12	0	12	0

MALAYA.

Under this heading we list for convenience of reference the various component stamp issuing units of the Federation of Malaya.

On 16th September, 1963, this Federation became part of Malaysia, which also incorporates North Borneo (Sabah), Sarawak and Singapore, until the latter became an independent state on 9th August, 1965.

We retain under Malaya the issues of Johore, Kedah, Kelantan, Malacca, Negri Sembilan, Pahang, Penang, Perak, Perlis and Trengganu, as they still use their own stamps.

There were no separate issues for Negri Sembilan, Pahang, Perak and Selangor between 1900 and 1935, during which time the general issues of the Federated Malay States were in use. In 1935 the formation of the Malayan Postal Union resulted in the reappearance of distinctive sets. Sungei Ujong ceased issuing stamps in 1895 when it was merged in Negri Sembilan.

PRINTERS. All Malayan postage stamps were typographed by De La Rue & Co., *unless otherwise stated.*

FEDERATED MALAY STATES

These issues were for use in the states of Negri Sembilan, Pahang, Perak and Selangor whose individual stamps they replaced.

FEDERATED MALAY STATES (1)

FEDERATED MALAY STATES (2)

1900. *Optd. with T* **1** (*cent values*) *or* **2** (*dollar values*).

(*a*) *Stamps of* Negri Sembilan (*T* **3**).

1	1 c. dull purple and green ..	3 0	4 0
2	2 c. dull purple and brown ..	25 0	25 0
3	3 c. dull purple and black ..	7 6	4 6
4	5 c. dull pur. & olive-yellow ..	55 0	65 0
5	10 c. dull purple and orange ..	6 0	12 6
6	20 c. green and olive	40 0	50 0
7	25 c. green and carmine ..	90 0	£5
8	50 c. green and black	45 0	55 0

(*b*) *Stamps of* Perak (*T* **31** *and* **32**).

9	5 c. dull purple & olive-yellow	25 0	35 0
10	10 c. dull purple and orange ..	50 0	55 0
	a. Bar omitted	£25	
11	$1 green and pale green ..	60 0	60 0
12	$2 green and carmine ..	55 0	60 0
12*a*	$5 green and ultramarine ..	£18	£16
12*b*	$25 green and orange (S. £35)	£550	

3

4

1900–1. *Perf.* 14. *T* **3.** *Wmk. Crown CA. sideways* (1901).

13	1 c. black and green.. ..	0 10	0 6
13*a*	1 c. grey and green ..	1 0	0 4
14	3 c. black and brown ..	2 0	0 10
14*a*	3 c. grey and brown.. ..	1 3	0 8
15	4 c. black and carmine ..	2 6	1 6
15*a*	4 c. grey and carmine ..	12 6	1 0
16	5 c. green & carm./*yellow* ..	4 0	5 0
17	8 c. black and ultramarine ..	15 0	4 0
17*a*	8 c. grey-brn. and ultram. ..	17 6	4 0
18	10 c. black and claret ..	12 6	3 0
18*a*	10 c. black and purple ..	17 6	2 6
19	20 c. mauve and black ..	22 6	4 6
20	50 c. black & orange-brown ..	42 6	17 6
20*a*	50 c. grey-brn. & oran.-brn...	55 0	25 0

Later printings in 1903–4 show the two upper lines of shading in the background at the corner nearest to the "s" of "STATE" blurred and running into one another, whereas in earlier printings these lines are distinct. Two plates were used for printing the central design of **T 3.** In Plate 1 the lines of background are regular throughout, but in Plate 2 they are lighter around the head and back of the tiger. The 5 c. was the only value with single wmk. to be printed from Plate 2. Stamps with multiple wmk. were printed for a short time from Plate 1, and show the two blurred lines of background near "s" of "STATE," but the majority of these stamps were printed from Plate 2 and later plates.

T **4.** *Wmk. Crown CC* (1900).

21	$1 green and pale green ..	75 0	55 0
22	$2 green and carmine ..	85 0	60 0
23	$5 green & brt. ultramarine..	£8	£6
23*a*	$5 green & pale ultramarine..	£10	£7
24	$25 green and orange (S. £25)	£150	£90

1904–10. *T* **3** *and* **4** (**$** *values*). *Wmk. Multiple Crown CA* (*sideways in T* **3**). *P* 14.

25	1 c. black & grn., O (10.04)	25 0	8 6
25*a*	1 c. grey-brown & green, O	3 0	2 6
26	3 c. grey & brown, OC (1.05)	10 0	2 6
26*a*	3 c. grey-brown & brown, C	7 6	0 3
27	4 c. black & scarlet, O (10.04)	7 6	1 6
27*a*	4 c. black and rose, OC ..	3 6	1 6
27*b*	4 c. black and deep rose, O (*aniline*) (1909)	—	2 6
28	5 c. green & carmine/*yellow*, OC (June '05) ..	3 6	2 6
28*a*	5 c. dp. grn. & carm./*yell.*, O	2 6	3 0
	b. On pale yellow	10 0	3 0
29	8 c. grey & ultram., OC (Mar. '05)	10 0	12 6
	a. Wmk. upright	10 0	6 0
30	10 c. black & claret, OC (10.04)	3 6	0 6
31	10 c. grey and purple, OC ..	7 6	1 6
31*a*	10 c. jet-black & brt. pur., O	5 6	0 8
32	20 c. mauve & black. OC (3.05)	3 0	0 8
33	50 c. blk. & orange-brown, OC (Mar. '05)	10 0	4 0
34	$1 green & pale grn., C ('07)	20 0	17 6
35	$2 green and carmine, C ..	40 0	32 6
36	$5 green and blue, C ..	£6	60 0
37	$25 grn. & orge., C ('10) (S. £8)	£70	£50

1906–18. *T* **3.** *Wmk. Mult. Crown CA, sideways. P* 14.

38	1 c. green, O (Die I) (1906)	1 9	0 3
38*a*	1 c. green, O (Die II) ..	1 0	0 4
38*b*	1 c. yellow-green, O (Die II)	6 0	0 4
38*c*	1 c. blue-green, O (Die II) ..	5 6	0 4
39	3 c. brown O (July '06) ..	2 0	0 3
40	3 c. carmine, O (Feb. '09) ..	2 0	0 3
40*a*	3 c. scarlet, O (1918) ..	2 6	0 [cut off]
41	8 c. ultramarine, O (Mar. '10)	12 6	2 [cut off]
41*a*	8 c. deep blue, O	7 6	3 [cut off]

Die I of the 1 c. was printed at two operation[s] from the old "head" and duty plates; Die I[I] from a new combination plate, in one operation[.] They can be distinguished as follows: Die I [has] thick line under "MALAY": serifs distinct. Th[e] "1 c" has short serifs to "1" and the "c" i[s] thinner than in Die II. Die II has thin lin[e] under "MALAY"; serifs are not distinct and "1 c" has longer serifs and a thicker "c". Other values from this date are all from doubl[e] plates, except 2 c., 3 c. and 4 c.

1919. *T* **3.** *Colours changed and new values.*

42	1 c. deep brown, O	3 0	3
43	2 c. green, O (July 1919) ..	1 0	1
43*a*	2 c. deep yellow-green, O ..	2 0	1
44	3 c. grey, O (18.12.19) ..	0 9	1
45	4 c. scar., O (Die I) (12.2.19)	1 3	1
45*a*	4 c. scarlet. O (Die II) ..	1 6	0
	b. Wmk. upright		
46	6 c. orange, O (12.2.19) ..	2 6	2
47	10 c. deep blue, O	4 6	2
48	10 c. bright blue, O	6 0	2
	a. Wmk. upright (inverted) ..		

1922–28. *T* **3** *and* **4** (**$** *values*). (*a*) *Wmk. Mul[t.] Script CA* (*sideways in T* **3**).

49	1 c. deep brown, O (Sept. '22)	3 0	1
50	3 c. grey, O (Feb.'23) ..	5 0	5
51	4 c. car.-red, O (Die II) (2.24)	0 9	0
52	5 c. mauve/*pale yell.*, O (3.22)	0 8	0
53	6 c. orange, O (Aug. 1922)..	1 9	1
54	10 c. bright blue, O (Mar. '23)	1 9	1
55	12 c. ultram., O (Sept. 1922)	3 6	0
56	20 c. dull purple and black, OC (Mar. '23)	4 0	0

57 50 c. black & orge., C (Apr. '24) 7 6 2 0
58 $1 pale green & grn., C ('26) 27 6 22 6
58a $1 grey-grn. & emer., C ('27) 17 6 22 6
58b $2 green & carm., C (1926) 25 0 30 0
59 $5 green & blue, C (1925).. £5 65 0
59a $25 grn. & orge., C ('28) (S.£8) £50 £35

(b) *Wmk. Mult. Crown CA, (sideways).*

60 35 c. scarlet/*pale yell.*, O (1922) 12 6 15 0

The 5 c. in mauve on white Script paper is the result of soaking early printings of No. 52 in water.

1923-34. *All T* **3.** *New values, colours and type changed. Wmk. Mult. Script CA (sideways).*

61 1 c. black, O (June 1923) .. 0 3 0 3
62 2 c. brown, O (1925) .. 3 0 2 0
63 2 c. green, O (1926).. .. 0 3 0 3
64 3 c. green, O (March 1924) 7 6 6 6
65 3 c. brown, O (1927) .. 0 9 0 3
66 4 c. orange, O (1926) .. 0 6 0 3
a. No wmk. £12
66b 5 c. brown, O (1932) .. 0 6 0 3
67 6 c. scarlet, O (1926) .. 0 10 0 3
68 10 c. blk. & blue, O (Oct. '23) 2 6 2 0
69 10 c. purple/*pale yellow*, C ('31) 4 6 1 6
70 25 c. pur. & brt. mag., C ('29) 6 0 2 6
71 30 c. pur. & orge.-yell., C ('29) 10 0 2 6
72 35 c. scarlet/*pale yell.*, O ('28) 17 6 12 6
72a 35 c. scarlet & purple, C ('31) 17 6 22 6
73 50 c. black/*green*, C ('31) .. 10 0 4 6
74 $1 black & red/*blue*, C ('31) 12 6 5 0
75 $2 green & red/*yell.*, C ('34) 20 0 25 0
76 $5 green & red/*grn.*, C ('34) £15 £7

POSTAGE DUE STAMPS.

D 1

(Typo. Waterlow & Sons, Ltd.)

1924 (1 JAN.)-**1926.** *Type* D **1.** *Wmk. Mult. Script CA (sideways). P* 15×14.

1 1 c. violet 2 6 0 8
2 2 c. black 0 4 0 6
2a 4 c. green (1926).. .. 0 9 0 8
3 8 c. red 2 0 5 0
4 10 c. orange 5 0 6 0
5 12 c. blue 5 0 7 6

JOHORE.

A State of the Federation of Malaya.

1876 (JULY). *T* **5** *of Straits optd. with Crescent and Star. Wmk. Crown CC.*

2 c. brown £175 £110
a. Opt. double .. ..

From Sept. 1878 to June 1884 no overprinted stamps were supplied to Johore.

5 of Straits (Wmk. Crown CA) optd. Name spelt "JOHORE".

JOHORE (1) JOHORE (2) JOHORE. (3)

1884 (JUNE).

2 **1** 2 c. rose £30

(*a*) "H" *and* "E" *wide, as shown.* (*b*) "H" *wide,* "E" *narrow.*

1884 (AUG.).

3 **2** 2 c. rose (*a*) (Opt. 16 mm. long) £12 £6
a. Opt. double .. ..
b. Opt. 16¾ mm. long £12 £6
ba. Opt. double .. ..
4 „ 2 c. rose (*b*) £14 £8
a. Opt. double .. ..

The triplet setting is made up of Nos. 3, 4 and 3b.

1885 (MARCH).

5 **3** 2 c. rose 60 0 75 0

JOHORE (4) JOHORE (5) JOHOR (6) Variety (*c*).

1886 (APRIL).

6 **4** 2 c. rose 40 0

1886 (?)

7 **5** 2 c. rose .. .. ..

As before, but name spelt "JOHOR".

(*c*) *All letters narrow.* (*d*) "H" *wide.*

1884 (AUG.)-**1885.**

8 **6** 2 c. rose (*c*) 7 6 9 0
9 „ 2 c. rose (*d*) (Feb. 1885) .. 30 0 35 0

There were several triplet settings of No. 8, the word varying in length from 12 to 15 mm. The "H" wide occurs as the first unit of one setting, with two units of No. 8.

JOHOR (7) JOHOR (8) JOHOR (9)

1884 (OCT.)-**1890.**

10 **7** 2 c. rose 8 6 10 0
a. Thin narrow "J" 35 0 35 0
11 „ 2 c. bright rose (1890) .. 17 6 17 6
a. Thin narrow "J" £5 £5

1886 (APRIL).

12 **8** 2 c. rose 20 0 17 6

1886 (MAY).

13 **9** 2 c. rose 25 0 20 0

1888. *Type similar to T* **7**, *but with stop.*

14 2 c. rose 40 0 40 0
a. Thin narrow "J" .. ..

JOHOR (10) JOHOR (11)

1890 (SEPT.).

15 **10** 2 c. bright rose 7 6 10 0

1891.

16 **11** 2 c. deep rose £40

The overprint on No. 16 is in much heavier type than that of No. 15.

Two CENTS (12) Two CENTS (13)

Two CENTS (14) *Two* CENTS (15)

1891 (MAY). *Optd. with name as T* **7** *and surch. as T* **12** *to* **15**.

17 **12** 2 c. on 24 c. green 35 0 35 0
18 **13** 2 c. on 24 c. green 20 0 20 0
19 **14** 2 c. on 24 c. green 45 0 45 0
20 **15** 2 c. on 24 c. green 17 6 20 0
a. Error. "CENST" (T 15) .. £14 £10

16. Sultan Aboubakar.

1891 (16 Nov.)–**1894**. *No wmk.* *P* 14.

21 **16** 1 c. dull pur. & mve. (7.94) 0 10 1 0
22 ,, 2 c. dull purple and yellow 1 6 3 0
23 ,, 3 c. dull pur. & carm. (7.94) 2 0 1 6
24 ,, 4 c. dull purple and black 6 0 4 6
25 ,, 5 c. dull purple and green 12 6 15 0
26 ,, 6 c. dull purple and blue .. 17 6 20 0
27 ,, $1 green and carmine .. 30 0 40 0

3 cents.

(17)

1894 (MARCH). *Surch. with T* **17**.

28 **16** 3 c. on 4 c. dull pur. & blk. 1 6 1 0
a. No stop 35 0 35 0
29 ,, 3 c. on 5 c. dull pur. & green 2 6 4 6
a. No stop 35 0 35 0
30 ,, 3 c. on 6 c. dull pur. & blue 1 6 2 6
a. No stop 35 0 35 0
31 ,, 3 c. on $1 green & carmine 17 6 25 0
a. No stop 75 0 80 0

KEMAHKOTAAN

(18)

1896 (MARCH). *Coronation of Sultan. Optd. with T* **18**.

32 **16** 1 c. dull purple & mauve .. 1 6 1 9
a. Error. "KETAHKOTAAN" .. 5 6 6 0
33 ,, 2 c. dull purple & yellow .. 1 3 1 3
a. Error. "KETAHKOTAAN" .. 5 6 6 0
34 ,, 3 c. dull purple and carmine 3 0 3 0
a. Error. "KETAHKOTAAN" .. 8 6 10 0
35 ,, 4 c. dull purple and black .. 3 0 3 0
a. Error. "KETAHKOTAAN" .. 4 0 6 6
36 ,, 5 c. dull purple and green .. 4 6 4 6
a. Error. "KETAHKOTAAN" .. 5 6 6 0
37 ,, 6 c. dull purple and blue .. 4 0 4 0
a. Error. "KETAHKOTAAN" .. 6 0 5 6
38 ,, $1 green and carmine .. 35 0 35 0
a. Error. "KETAHKOTAAN" .. 40 0 40 0

19. Sultan Ibrahim. **20.**

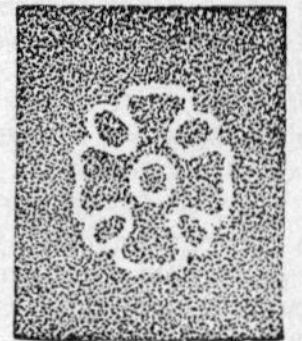

21 **22**

1896 (26 AUG.)–**1899**. *W* **22**. *P* 14.

39 **19** 1 c. green 1 0 0 8
40 ,, 2 c. green and blue .. 1 3 1 3
41 ,, 3 c. green and purple .. 3 0 0 10
42 ,, 4 c. green and carmine .. 1 9 1 3
43 ,, 4 c. yellow and red (1899) 1 9 1 3
44 ,, 5 c. green and brown .. 3 6 2 0
45 ,, 6 c. green and yellow .. 3 6 3 6
46 **20** 10 c. green and black .. 17 6 20 0
47 ,, 25 c. green and mauve .. 20 0 25 0
48 ,, 50 c. green and carmine .. 27 6 30 0
49 **19** $1 dull purple & green .. 30 0 30 0
50 **21** $2 dull purple & carmine 40 0 40 0
51 ,, $3 dull purple & blue .. 45 0 42 6
52 ,, $4 dull purple & brown .. 65 0 60 0
53 ,, $5 dull purple & yellow £7 70 0

Nos. 46 to 53 were issued in 1898.

3 cents. **10 cents.**

(23) **(24)**

1903 (APRIL). *Surch. with T* **23** *or* **24**.

54 **19** 3 c. on 4 c. yellow and red 1 0 0 1
a. Original value uncancelled 2 0 4
55 ,, 10 c. on 4 c. green & carmine 3 0 6
a. Tall "1" in "10" .. 60 0 60
b. Original value uncancelled .. 17 6 17
ba. As b with tall "1" in "10" £30

The bars on these stamps were ruled by han[d] with pen and ink.

50 Cents. **One Dollar**

(25) **(26)**

1903 (OCT.). *Surch. with T* **25** *or* **26**.

56 **21** 50 c. on $3 dull pur. & blue 30 0 35
57 ,, $1 on $2 dull pur. & carm. 40 0 45
a. Variety. "e" of "One" inverted £40

10 CENTS.

(27)

1904. *Surch. as T* **27**.

58 **19** 10 c. on 4 c. yell. & red (Apr.) 17 6 17
a. Surcharge double .. £40
59 ,, 10 c. on 4 c. grn. & car. (Aug.) 7 6 7
60 **21** 50 c. on $5 dull purple and yellow (May) 45 0 55

28 **29**

30. Sultan Sir Ibrahim.

1904 (Sept.). *W* **22.** *P* 14.

No.	Type	Description	Unused		Used	
61	**28**	1 c. dull pur. & grn., OC..	0	4	0	8
62	,,	2 c. dull pur. & orge., OC	1	3	2	6
63	,,	3 c. dull pur. & olive-blk., O	1	6	0	9
64	,,	4 c. dull pur. & carmine, O	4	0	2	0
65	,,	5 c. dull pur. & sage-grn., O	4	0	7	0
66	**30**	8 c. dull purple & blue, O	4	6	4	6
67	**29**	10 c. dull pur. & black, OC	4	6	10	0
68	,,	25 c. dull pur. & grn., O ..	6	6	10	0
69	,,	50 c. dull purple and red, O	7	6	8	6
70	**28**	$1 green and mauve, O..	22	6	20	0
71	**30**	$2 green and carmine, O	35	0	27	6
72	,,	$3 green and blue, O ..	40	0	30	0
73	,,	$4 green and brown, O..	40	0	42	6
74	,,	$5 green and orange, O	80	0	50	0
75	**29**	$10 green and black, O ..	£9		75	0
76	,,	$50 green and ultram., O (S. £20)	£175		£65	
77	,,	$100 green and scarlet., O (S. £35)	£400		£175	

1910 (Dec.)–**1919.** *Wmk. Mult. Rosettes (vertical). P* 14.

No.	Type	Description	Unused		Used	
78	**28**	1 c. dull purple & green, C	0	4	0	4
79	,,	2 c. dull pur. & orange, C	1	3	0	6
80	,,	3 c. dull pur. & olive-blk., C	1	9	0	2
		a. Wmk. horizontal (1910) ..	3	0	2	6
81	,,	4 c. dull pur. & carmine, C	1	6	0	6
		a. Wmk. horizontal (1910) ..	3	0	2	6
82	,,	5 c. dull pur. & sage-grn., C	1	0	0	8
83	**30**	8 c. dull purple & blue, C	3	6	5	0
84	**29**	10 c. dull purple & black, C	6	0	2	6
		a. Wmk. horizontal (1911) ..	10	0	7	0
85	,,	25 c. dull purple & green, C	6	6	10	0
86	,,	50 c. dull pur. & red, C ('19)	25	0	20	0
87	**28**	$1 grn. & mve., C (1918)	35	0	32	6

Nos. 78 to 85 were issued in 1912.

3 CENTS.

(31)

1912 (March). *No.* 66 *surch. with T* **31.**

No.	Type	Description	Unused		Used	
88		3 c. on 8 c. dull pur. & blue, O	5	0	4	0
		a. "T" of "CENTS" omitted				

1918–21. *Chalk-surfaced paper. Wmk. Mult. Crown CA. P* 14.

No.	Type	Description	Unused		Used	
89	**28**	2 c. dull pur. & grn. (1919)	0	9	0	6
90	,,	2 c. pur. & orange (1921)	0	9	1	0
91	,,	4 c. dull purple and red..	0	6	0	4
92	,,	5 c. dull purple and sage-green (1920) ..	1	0	1	9
93	**29**	10 c. dull purple and blue	1	9	1	9
94	,,	21 c. dull pur. & orge. (1919)	5	0	6	0
95	,,	25 c. dull pur. & grn. (1920)	8	6	10	0
96	,,	50 c. dull pur. & red (1920)	6	6	10	0
97	**28**	$1 green and mauve ..	17	6	17	6
98	**30**	$2 green and carmine ..	32	6	27	6
99	,,	$3 green and blue ..	35	0	35	0
00	,,	$4 green and brown ..	45	0	35	0
01	,,	$5 green and orange ..	65	0	55	0
02	**29**	$10 green and black ..	£8		£6	

922-40. *Chalk-surfaced paper. Wmk. Mult. Script CA. P* 14.

No.	Type	Description	Unused		Used	
03	**28**	1 c. dull purple and black	0	3	0	3
04	,,	2 c. purple & sepia (1924)	2	0	2	0
05	,,	2 c. green (1928)	0	6	0	6
106	**28**	3 c. green (1925)	1	9	3	0
107	,,	3 c. purple & sepia (1928)	1	6	1	6
108	,,	4 c. pur. & carmine (1924)	0	5	0	4
109	,,	5 c. dull pur. & sage-grn.	0	5	0	4
110		6 c. dull purple and claret	0	5	0	5
111	**29**	10 c. dull purple and blue	10	0	12	6
112	,,	10 c. dull pur. & yell. (1922)	0	8	0	4
113	**28**	12 c. dull purple and blue	7	6	1	6
114	,,	12 c. ultramarine (1940) ..	20	0	20	0
115	**29**	21 c. dull pur. & orge. ('28)	10	0	6	0
116	,,	25 c. dull purple & myrtle	1	6	1	6
117	**30**	30 c. dull pur. & orge. ('36)	2	0	3	0
118	,,	40 c. dull pur. & brn. ('36)	4	0	8	6
119	**29**	50 c. dull purple and red..	2	6	1	6
120	**28**	$1 green and mauve ..	7	6	3	6
121	**30**	$2 grn. & carmine (1923)	15	0	7	6
122	,,	$3 green and blue (1925)	35	0	35	0
123	,,	$4 green & brown (1926)	50	0	55	0
124	,,	$5 green and orange ..	65	0	40	0
125	**29**	$10 green & black (1924)	£7		£5	
126	,,	$50 grn. & ultram. (S. £20)	£100			
127	,,	$100 grn. & scarlet (S. £35)	£325			
128	,,	$500 blue & red ('26) (S. £75)	£2750			

32. Sultan Sir Ibrahim and Sultana.

(Recess. Waterlow & Sons.)

1935 (15 May). *Wmk. Mult. Script CA. (sideways). P* 12½.

No.	Type	Description	Unused		Used	
129	**32**	8 c. bright violet & slate	2	6	2	0

33. Sultan Sir Ibrahim. **34.**

(Recess. De La Rue & Co.)

1940 (Feb.). *Wmk. Mult. Script CA. P* 13½.

No.	Type	Description	Unused		Used	
130	**33**	8 c. black and pale blue ..	2	6	2	0

1948 (1 Dec.). *Royal Silver Wedding. As Nos.* 30/1 *of Aden.*

No.	Type	Description	Unused		Used	
131		10 c. violet	0	8	0	8
132		$5 green	35	0	40	0

1949 (2 May)–**1955.** *Wmk. Mult. Script CA. Chalk-surfaced paper. P* 17½ × 18.

No.	Type	Description	Unused		Used	
133	**34**	1 c. black	0	2	0	3
134	,,	2 c. orange	0	6	0	6
		a. Orange-yellow (22.1.52) ..	0	3	0	3
135	,,	3 c. green (*shades*) ..	0	10	1	0
136	,,	4 c. brown	0	4	0	6
136*a*	,,	5 c. bright purple (1.9.52)	0	6	0	3
137	,,	6 c. grey	0	6	0	6
		a. Pale grey (22.1.52) ..	1	0	1	3
		ac. Error. St. Ed. Crown W9b	£65			
138	,,	8 c. scarlet	1	3	1	6
138*a*	,,	8 c. green (1.9.52) ..	0	5	0	10
139	,,	10 c. magenta	0	8	0	3
		aa. Imperf. (pair)	£90			

No.	Type	Description	Unused	Used
139a	**34**	12 c. scarlet (1.9.52) ..	0 8	1 6
140	,,	15 c. ultramarine	1 9	1 3
141	,,	20 c. black and green ..	2 6	2 6
141a	,,	20 c. bright blue (1.9.52) ..	0 10	0 8
142	,,	25 c. purple and orange ..	1 9	0 8
142a	,,	30 c. scarlet & pur. (5.9.55)	3 0	1 6
142b	,,	35 c. scarlet & pur. (1.9.52)	2 6	2 0
143	,,	40 c. red and purple ..	4 0	7 0
144	,,	50 c. black and blue ..	2 0	0 10
145	,,	$1 blue and purple ..	4 0	3 0
146	,,	$2 green and scarlet ..	8 0	6 6
147	,,	$5 green and brown ..	17 6	10 0

1949 (10 Oct.). *75th Anniv. of U.P.U. As Nos.* 114/7 *of Antigua.*

No.	Description	Unused	Used
148	10 c. purple	0 8	0 8
149	15 c. deep blue	1 0	1 3
150	25 c. orange	2 0	2 0
151	50 c. blue-black	3 6	4 0

1953 (2 June). *Coronation. As No.* 47 *of Aden.*

No.	Description	Unused	Used
152	10 c. black and reddish purple	0 8	0 8

35. Sultan Sir Ibrahim.

(Recess. De La Rue & Co. Ltd.)

1955 (1 Nov.). *Diamond Jubilee of Sultan. Wmk. Mult. Script CA. P* 14.

No.	Type	Description	Unused	Used
153	**35**	10 c. carmine-red	0 6	0 6

36. Sultan Sir Ismail and Johore Coat-of-Arms.

(Photo. Courvoisier.)

1960 (10 Feb.). *Coronation of Sultan. No wmk. P* 11½.

No.	Type	Description	Unused	Used
154	**36**	10 c. multicoloured ..	0 6	0 6

1960. *As T* **10/19** *of Kedah, but with portrait of Sultan Ismail. $1 P* 13½, *others. P* 12½ × 13 *(vert.) or* 13 × 12½ *(horiz.).*

No.	Description	Unused	Used
155	1 c. black (7.10.60) ..	0 2	0 3
156	2 c. orange-red (7.10.60) ..	0 3	0 3
157	4 c. sepia (19.8.60) ..	0 4	0 4
158	5 c. carmine-lake (7.10.60)	0 5	0 4
159	8 c. myrtle-green (9.12.60)	0 6	0 7
160	10 c. deep maroon (10.6.60)	0 7	0 3
161	20 c. blue (9.12.60)	1 0	0 10
162	50 c. blk. & brt. blue (19.8.60)	2 0	1 2
163	$1 ultram. & reddish pur. (9.12.60)	4 2	3 0
164	$2 bronze-green and scar. (9.12.60)	7 9	6 0
165	$5 brown and bronze-green (7.10.60)	18 6	12 6

37. *Vanda hookeriana.*

38. *Arundina graminifolia.*

39. *Paphiopedilum niveum.*

40. *Spathoglottis plicata.*

41. *Arachnis flos-aeris.*

42. *Rhyncostylis retusa.*

43. *Phalaenopsis violacea.*
(Inset portrait of Sultan Ismail.)

(Des. A. Fraser-Brunner. Photo. Harrison.)

1965 (15 Nov.). *W* w. **13**. *P* 14½.

166	**37**	1 c. multicoloured	0	1	0	3
167	**38**	2 c. multicoloured	0	2	0	5
168	**39**	5 c. multicoloured	0	4	0	7
169	**40**	6 c. multicoloured	0	4	0	7
170	**41**	10 c. multicoloured	0	6	0	10
171	**42**	15 c. multicoloured	0	7	1	0
172	**43**	20 c. multicoloured	0	10	1	6

The higher values used in Johore are Nos. 20/27 of Malaysia.

POSTAGE DUE STAMPS.

D 1

(Typo. Waterlow.)

1938 (1 Jan.). *Wmk. Mult. Script CA. P* 12½.

D1	D **1**	1 c. carmine	3	0	4	6
D2	,,	4 c. green	3	6	5	0
D3	,,	8 c. orange	6	0	9	0
D4	,,	10 c. brown	6	6	10	0
D5	,,	12 c. purple	10	0	15	0

KEDAH.

A State of the Federation of Malaya.

1. Sheaf of rice.

2. Malay ploughing.

3. Council Chamber.

(Recess. De La Rue.)

1912 (July). *Wmk. Mult. Crown CA. P* 14.

1	**1**	1 c. black and green	0	6	0	4
2	,,	3 c. black and red	1	0	0	8
3	,,	4 c. rose and grey	3	0	1	0
4	,,	5 c. green and chestnut	3	6	4	6
5	,,	8 c. black and ultramarine	2	6	7	0
6	**2**	10 c. blue and sepia	3	6	2	0
7	,,	20 c. black and green	5	0	7	6
8	,,	30 c. black and rose	7	6	15	0
9	,,	40 c. black and purple	12	6	20	0
10	,,	50 c. brown and blue	12	6	25	0
11	**3**	$1 black and red/*yellow*	17	6	27	6
12	,,	$2 green and brown	25	0	37	6
13	,,	$3 black and blue/*blue*	60	0	65	0
14	,,	$5 black and red	85	0	90	0

1919–21. *New colours and values. Wmk. Mult. Crown CA. P* 14.

(i) Printed from separate plates for frame and centre, with dotted shading extending close to the central sheaf.

(ii) Printed from single plate, with white space around sheaf (as shown in T **1**).

15	**1**	1 c. brown (i)	0	4	0	8
18	,,	2 c. green (ii)	0	6	0	6
19	,,	3 c. deep purple (i)	0	10	4	0
20	,,	4 c. rose (i)	2	0	0	9
21	,,	4 c. red (ii)	1	3	0	8
22	**2**	21 c. purple	5	0	12	6
23	,,	25 c. blue and purple ('21)	7	6	15	0

ONE

DOLLAR

(4)

MALAYA-
BORNEO
EXHIBITION.

(5)

(Surch. by Ribeiro & Co., Penang.)

1919. *Surch. as T* **4**.

24	**3**	50 c. on $2 green and brown	60	0	75	0
		a. "C" of "CENTS" inserted by hand	£55		£55	
25	,,	$1 on $3 black & blue/*blue*	35	0	50	0

In 1919 1 c., 3 c. and 4 c. (both purple and scarlet) stamps of Straits Settlements were authorized for use in Kedah during a temporary shortage of Kedah stamps. Stamps so used can be identified by the postmark.

1921–24. *Wmk. Mult. Script CA. P* 14.

26	**1**	1 c. brown (ii)	0	6	0	3
27	,,	2 c. dull green (ii) (Die I)*	0	3	0	3
28	,,	3 c. deep purple (ii)	1	9	1	6
29	,,	4 c. deep carmine (ii)	1	0	0	3
30	**2**	10 c. blue and sepia	3	6	2	0
31	,,	20 c. black & yellow-green	5	0	2	6
32	,,	21 c. mauve and purple	10	0	15	0
33	,,	25 c. blue and purple	6	0	6	0
34	,,	30 c. black and rose	8	6	6	0
35	,,	40 c. black and purple	7	6	7	0
36	,,	50 c. brown and grey-blue	4	6	3	6
37	**3**	$1 black & red/*yellow*	15	0	9	0
38	,,	$2 myrtle and brown	25	0	35	0
39	,,	$3 black and blue/*blue*	50	0	60	0
40	,,	$5 black and deep carmine	60	0	65	0

*For 2 c., Die II, see No. 69.

1922. *Optd as T* **5**.

I. "BORNEO" 14 *mm. long.*

(*a*) *Wmk. Mult. Crown CA.*

41	**1**	2 c. green (ii)	4	6	5	0
42	**2**	21 c. mauve and purple	17	6	30	0
43	,,	25 c. blue and purple	22	6	35	0
		a. Overprint inverted	£70			
44	,,	50 c. brown and grey-blue	35	0	55	0

(*b*) *Wmk. Mult. Script CA.*

45	**1**	1 c. brown (ii)	3	6	6	0
46	,,	3 c. purple (ii)	5	0	10	0
47	,,	4 c. deep carmine (ii) ..	6	0	12	6
48	**2**	10 c. blue and sepia ..	8	6	15	0

There are setting variations in the size and shape of the letters, stop raised, stop omitted, etc., etc.

II. " BORNEO " 15–15½ *mm. long.*
Wmk. Mult. Crown CA.

49	**2**	21 c. mauve and purple ..	27	6
50	,,	25 c. blue and purple ..	32	6
51	,,	50 c. brown and grey-blue ..	50	0

1922–36. *New colours, etc. Wmk. Mult. Script CA. P* 14.

52	**1**	1 c. black (ii) (Die I)* ..	0	4	0	4
53	,,	3 c. green (ii)	1	3	0	8
54	,,	4 c. violet (ii) (1926) ..	0	10	0	4
55	,,	5 c. yellow (ii)	0	8	0	4
56	,,	6 c. carmine (ii) (1926) ..	0	8	0	8
57	,,	8 c. grey-black (Oct. '36)	8	6	3	6
58	**2**	12 c. black & indigo (1926) ..	6	0	8	6
59	,,	35 c. purple (1926)	20	0	30	0

*For 1 c., Die II, see No. 68a.

6. Sultan Abdul Hamid Halimshah.

(Recess. Waterlow & Sons, Ltd.)

1937 (30 JUNE). *Wmk. Mult. Script CA. P* 12½.

60	**6**	10 c. ultramarine & sepia ..	1	6	1	6
61	,,	12 c. black and violet ..	10	0	17	6
62	,,	25 c. ultramarine & purple ..	2	0	3	0
63	,,	30 c. green and scarlet ..	3	6	6	0
64	,,	40 c. black and purple ..	3	6	7	6
65	,,	50 c. brown and blue ..	4	0	4	6
66	,,	$1 black and green ..	6	0	8	6
67	,,	$2 green and brown ..	45	0	60	0
68	,,	$5 black and scarlet ..	25	0	40	0

I.

II.

I.

II.

1938–40. *As Nos.* 52 *and* 27, *but figures redrawn, as Dies* II.

68*a*	**1**	1 c. black ('38)	45	0	40	0
69	,,	2 c. bright green	£10		7	6

1 c. Die II. Figures " 1 " have square-cut corners instead of rounded, and larger top serif. Larger " C ". Line perf.

2 c. Die II. Figures " 2 " have circular instead of oval drops and the letters " c " are thin and tall instead of thick and rounded. Size of design : 19½ × 23 mm. instead of about 18½ × 22½ mm. Line perf.

1948 (1 DEC.). *Royal Silver Wedding. As Nos.* 30/1 *of Aden, but inscr.* " MALAYA KEDAH ".

70	10 c. violet	0	6	0	6
71	$5 carmine	35	0	40	0

1949 (10 OCT.). *75th Anniv. of U.P.U. As Nos.* 114/7 *of Antigua, but inscr.* " MALAYA KEDAH ".

72	10 c. purple	0	8	0	8
73	15 c. deep blue	1	0	1	3
74	25 c. orange	2	0	2	6
75	50 c. blue-black	4	6	4	6

7. Sheaf of Rice.

8. Sultan Tengku Badlishah.

1950 (1 JUNE)–**55.** *Wmk. Mult. Script CA. Chalk-surfaced paper. P* 17½ × 18.

76	**7**	1 c. black	0	3	0	8
77	,,	2 c. orange	0	2	0	3
78	,,	3 c. green	1	6	2	0
79	,,	4 c. brown	0	3	0	3
79*a*	,,	5 c. brt. pur. (*shades*) (1.9.52)	0	6	0	10
80	,,	6 c. grey	0	6	0	8
81	,,	8 c. scarlet	2	0	3	0
81*a*	,,	8 c. green (*shades*) (1.9.52)	1	6	2	6
82	,,	10 c. magenta	0	8	0	3
82*a*	,,	12 c. scarlet (1.9.52) ..	1	0	2	0
83	,,	15 c. ultramarine	4	0	1	6
84	,,	20 c. black and green ..	3	6	5	0
84*a*	,,	20 c. bright blue (1.9.52) ..	1	6	1	0
85	**8**	25 c. purple and orange ..	1	9	1	0
85*a*	,,	30 c. scar. & purple (5.9.55)	2	6	3	0
85*b*	,,	35 c. scar. & purple (1.9.52)	2	6	4	0
86	,,	40 c. red and purple ..	3	6	10	0
87	,,	50 c. black and blue ..	2	6	1	3
88	,,	$1 blue and purple ..	5	0	5	0
89	,,	$2 green and scarlet ..	12	6	15	0
90	,,	$5 green and brown ..	22	6	27	6

1953 (2 JUNE). *Coronation. As No.* 47 *of Aden.*

91	10 c. black & reddish purple ..	0	10	0	10

9. Copra.

10. Pineapples.

11. Ricefield.

12. Masjid Alwi Mosque, Kangar.

13. East Coast Railway.

14. Tiger.

15. Fishing Craft. 16. Aborigines with Blowpipes.

17. Government Offices.

18. Bersilat.

19. Weaving.

(Recess. De La Rue & Co.)

1957. *Inset portrait of Sultan Tengku Badlishah.* *W* w.**12.** *P* 13 × 12½ (1 *c. to* 8 *c.*), 12½ × 13 (10 *c.*, 20 *c.*), 12½ (50 *c.*, $2, $5) *or* 13½ ($1).

92	**9**	1 c. black	0	3	0	5
93	**10**	2 c. orange-red	0	5	0	5
94	**11**	4 c. sepia	0	6	0	6
95	**12**	5 c. carmine-lake ..	0	8	0	8
96	**13**	8 c. myrtle-green ..	1	6	2	6
97	**14**	10 c. deep brown	1	0	0	3
98	**15**	20 c. blue	1	0	1	3
99	**16**	50 c. black and blue ..	2	6	2	0
100	**17**	$1 ultramarine and reddish purple	5	0	6	0
101	**18**	$2 bronze-grn. & scarlet	15	0	17	6
102	**19**	$5 brown & bronze-grn.	27	6	45	0

Dates of issue:—26.6.57, 20 c., $5; 25.7.57, 2 c., 50 c., $1; 4.8.57, 10 c.; 21.8.57, others.

20. Sultan Tengku Adbul.

(Photo. Harrison & Sons.)

1959 (20 Feb.). *Installation of the Sultan.* *W* w.**12.** *P* 14 × 14½.

103	**20**	10 c. yellow, red, brown and bright blue ..	0	10	0	8

21. Sultan Tengku Abdul.

1959 (1 July)–**62.** *As Nos. 92/102 but with inset portrait of Sultan Tengku Abdul as in T* **21.**

No.	Type	Description	s.	d.	s.	d.
104	**21**	1 c. black	0	2	0	3
105	**10**	2 c. orange-red	0	3	0	3
106	**11**	4 c. sepia	0	4	0	4
107	**12**	5 c. carmine-lake ..	0	5	0	4
108	**13**	8 c. myrtle-green ..	0	6	0	10
109	**14**	10 c. deep brown ..	0	8	0	8
109*a*	,,	10 c. deep maroon (19.12.61)	0	7	0	3
110	**15**	20 c. blue	1	0	0	10
111	**16**	50 c. black and blue (*p.* 12½)	2	6	2	0
		a. Perf. 12½ × 13 (14.6.60) ..	2	0	1	6
112	**17**	$1 ultramarine & reddish purple	4	2	3	0
113	**18**	$2 bronze-grn. & scarlet	7	9	6	0
114	**19**	$5 brown & bronze-grn. (*p.* 12½)	20	0	15	0
		a. Perf. 13 × 12½ (26.11.62)	18	6	12	0

22. *Vanda hookeriana.*

1965 (15 Nov.). *As Nos. 166/72 of Johore but with inset portrait of Sultan Tengku Abdul as in T* **22.**

No.	Description	s.	d.	s.	d.
115	1 c. multicoloured	0	1	0	3
116	2 c. multicoloured	0	2	0	5
117	5 c. multicoloured	0	4	0	7
118	6 c. multicoloured	0	4	0	7
119	10 c. multicoloured	0	6	0	10
120	15 c. multicoloured	0	7	1	0
121	20 c. multicoloured	0	10	1	6

The higher values used in Kedah are Nos. 20/27 of Malaysia.

KELANTAN.

A State of the Federation of Malaya.

1

1911. *T* **1.** *Wmk. Mult. Crown CA. P* 14.

No.	Description	s.	d.	s.	d.
1	1 c. yellow-green, O ..	1	3	0	8
1*a*	1 c. blue-green, O	0	9	0	6
2	3 c. red, O	0	8	0	3
3	4 c. black and red, O ..	1	3	0	8
4	5 c. green & red/*yellow*, O ..	1	3	0	9
5	8 c. ultramarine, O ..	2	6	1	3
6	10 c. black and mauve, O ..	2	6	0	10
7	30 c. dull purple and red, C	5	0	2	0
7*a*	30 c. purple and carmine, C ..	17	6	17	6
8	50 c. black and orange, C	4	0	4	0
9	$1 green and emerald, C ..	35	0	35	0
10	$2 green and carmine, C ..	7	6	12	6
11	$5 green and blue, C ..	20	0	25	0
12	$25 green and orange, C ..	75	0	90	0

1915. *T* **1,** *colour changed. Wmk. Mult. Crown CA. P* 14.

No.	Description	s.	d.	s.	d.
13	$1 green and brown, C ..	17	6	12	6

1921–28. *T* **1.** *Wmk. Mult. Script CA. P* 14.

No.	Description	s.	d.	s.	d.
14	1 c. dull green, O	2	6	1	6
15	1 c. black, O	1	0	1	0
16	2 c. brown, O	4	0	5	0
16*a*	2 c. green, O (1926)	0	9	0	6
16*b*	3 c. brown, O (1927) ..	1	6	4	0
17	4 c. black and red, O ..	0	6	0	4
18	5 c. green & red/*pale yell.*, O	1	0	0	6
19	6 c. claret, O	5	0	4	6
19*a*	6 c. scarlet, O (1928) ..	6	0	5	0
20	10 c. black and mauve, O ..	3	0	1	0
21	30 c. purple & carm., C (1926)	5	0	7	6
22	50 c. black and orange, C ..	6	0	8	6
23	$1 green and brown, C ..	27	6	30	0

For the 4 c., 5 c. and 6 c. surcharged, see issues under "Japanese Occupation".

MALAYA

BORNEO

EXHIBITION

(2)

1922. *T* **1,** *overprinted with T* **2.**

(a) Wmk. Mult. Crown CA

No.	Description	s.	d.	s.	d.
30	4 c. black and red	6	0	10	0
31	5 c. green and red/*pale yellow*	5	0	10	0
32	30 c. dull purple and red ..	7	6	20	0
33	50 c. black and orange ..	9	0	22	6
34	$1 green and brown ..	20	0	45	0
35	$2 green and carmine ..	40	0	85	0
36	$5 green and blue	£7		£12	

(b) Wmk. Mult. Script CA.

No.	Description	s.	d.	s.	d.
37	1 c. green	3	6	6	0
38	10 c. black and mauve ..	7	6	20	0

3. Sultan Ismail. **4.**

(Recess. De La Rue & Co.)

1928–33. *T* **3.** *Wmk. Mult. Script CA.*

No.	Description	s.	d.	s.	d.
39	$1 blue (*perf.* 12)	22	6	30	
39*a*	$1 blue (*perf.* 14) ('33) ..	22	6	30	

(Recess. Bradbury, Wilkinson & Co.)

1937–40. *Wmk. Mult Script CA. P* 12.

No.	Type	Description	s.	d.	s.	d.
40	**4**	1 c. grey-olive and yellow ..	0	9	0	
41	,,	2 c. green	0	10	0	1
42	,,	4 c. scarlet	2	6	1	
43	,,	5 c. red-brown	1	9	1	
44	,,	6 c. lake	1	9	2	
45	,,	8 c. grey-olive	1	9	1	
46	,,	10 c. purple	2	6	2	
47	,,	12 c. blue	3	0	6	
48	,,	25 c. vermilion and violet ..	4	0	6	
49	,,	30 c. violet and scarlet ..	15	0	17	
50	,,	40 c. orange and blue-green	7	0	10	
51	,,	50 c. grey-olive and orange ..	17	6	17	
52	,,	$1 violet and blue-green ..	12	6	15	
53	,,	$2 red-brown and scarlet	£8		£	
54	,,	$5 vermilion and lake	£14		£	

Dates of issue: July, 1937 (all except the following)—Oct. '37, 6 c., 10 c., 30 c., 50 c. and $1. Mar. '40, $2 and $5.

For above issue surcharged see issues under " Japanese Occupation ".

1948 (1 Dec.). *Royal Silver Wedding. As Nos. 30/1 of Aden.*

55 10 c. violet 0 8 0 9
56 $5 carmine 35 0 40 0

1949 (10 Oct.). *75th Anniv. of Universal Postal Union. As Nos. 114/7 of Antigua.*

57 10 c. purple 0 9 2 0
58 15 c. deep blue 1 3 3 0
59 25 c. orange 2 6 6 0
60 50 c. blue-black 5 0 10 0

5. Sultan Tengku Ibrahim.

1951 (11 July)–**55.** *Chalk-surfaced paper. Wmk. Mult. Script CA. P* $17\frac{1}{2} \times 18$.

61 **5** 1 c. black 0 3 0 4
62 ,, 2 c. orange (*shades*) .. 0 3 0 4
63 ,, 3 c. green 1 0 1 6
64 ,, 4 c. brown 0 4 1 0
64a ,, 5 c. brt. pur. (*shades*) (1.9.52) 0 6 0 10
65 ,, 6 c. grey 0 6 1 0
66 ,, 8 c. scarlet 1 6 1 9
66a ,, 8 c. green (1.9.52) 1 0 1 6
67 ,, 10 c. magenta 0 8 0 3
67a ,, 12 c. scarlet (1.9.52) .. 1 3 1 6
68 ,, 15 c. ultramarine 2 0 2 6
69 ,, 20 c. black and green .. 3 0 3 6
69a ,, 20 c. bright blue (1.9.52) .. 2 0 1 9
70 ,, 25 c. purple and orange .. 2 6 1 6
70a ,, 30 c. scar. & purple (5.9.55) 3 0 2 6
70b ,, 35 c. scar. & purple (1.9.52) 3 0 5 0
71 ,, 40 c. red and purple .. 5 0 10 0
72 ,, 50 c. black and blue .. 2 6 3 6
73 ,, $1 blue and purple .. 4 6 5 0
74 ,, $2 green and scarlet .. 8 6 10 0
75 ,, $5 green & brown (*shades*) 27 6 35 0

1953 (2 June). *Coronation. As No. 47 of Aden.*

76 10 c. black and reddish purple 0 8 0 8

1957–63. *As Nos. 92/102 of Kedah but with inset portrait of Sultan Tengku Ibrahim.*

77 **9** 1 c. black 0 3 0 3
78 **10** 2 c. orange-red 0 3 0 4
  a. Red-orange (17.11.59) .. 1 0 0 9
79 **11** 4 c. sepia 0 4 0 4
80 **12** 5 c. carmine-lake 0 5 0 5
81 **13** 8 c. myrtle-green 0 6 1 0
82 **14** 10 c. deep brown 0 8 0 6
82a ,, 10 c. deep maroon (19.4.61) 0 8 3 6
83 **15** 20 c. blue 1 0 1 0
84 **16** 50 c. black and blue (*p.* $12\frac{1}{2}$) 2 6 2 0
  a. Perf. $12\frac{1}{2} \times 13$ (28.6.60) 2 0 1 6
85 **17** $1 ultramarine and reddish purple 4 2 4 2
86 **18** $2 bronze-green and scarlet (*p.* $12\frac{1}{2}$) 8 6 8 6
  a. Perf. $13 \times 12\frac{1}{2}$ (9.4.63) .. 7 9 7 9
87 **19** $5 brown & bronze-green (*p.* $12\frac{1}{2}$) 20 0 20 0
  a. Perf. $13 \times 12\frac{1}{2}$ (13.8.63) .. 18 6 18 6

Dates of issue:—26.6.57, 20 c., $5; 25.7.57, 2 c., 50 c., $1; 4.8.57, 10 c.; 21.8.57, others.

6. Sultan Yahya Petra and Crest of Kelantan.

(Photo. Harrison & Sons.)

1961 (17 July). *Installation of the Sultan. W* w.**12.** *P* 15×14.

88 **6** 10 c. multicoloured 0 8 0 8

7. Sultan Yahya Petra.

(Recess. De La Rue & Co.)

1961–62. *As Nos. 92/8 of Kedah but with inset portrait of Sultan Yahya Petra as in T* **7.** *W* w. **13.** *P* $12\frac{1}{2} \times 13$ (*vert.*) *or* $13 \times 12\frac{1}{2}$ (*horiz.*).

89 1 c. black (1.3.62) 0 2 0 3
90 2 c. orange-red (1.3.62) .. 0 3 0 3
91 4 c. sepia (1.3.62) 0 4 0 4
92 5 c. carmine-lake (1.3.62) .. 0 5 0 5
93 8 c. myrtle-grn. (*shades*) (1.3.62) 0 6 0 7
94 10 c. deep maroon (2.12.61) .. 0 7 0 7
95 20 c. blue (1.3.62) 1 0 0 10

8. *Vanda hookeriana.*

1965 (15 Nov.). *As Nos. 166/72 of Johore but with inset portraits of Sultan Yahya Petra as in T* **8.**

96 1 c. multicoloured 0 1 0 3
97 2 c. multicoloured 0 2 0 5
98 5 c. multicoloured 0 4 0 7
99 6 c. multicoloured 0 4 0 7
100 10 c. multicoloured 0 6 0 10
101 15 c. multicoloured 0 7 1 0
102 20 c. multicoloured 0 10 1 6

The higher values used in Kelantan are Nos. 20/27 of Malaysia.

MALACCA.

A former British Settlement, now part of the Federation of Malaya.

1948 (1 Dec.). *Royal Silver Wedding. As Nos. 30/1 of Aden, but inscr.* " MALAYA MALACCA ".

1 10 c. violet 0 8 0 8
2 $5 brown 35 0 40 0

1949 (1 Mar.)–**52.** *As T* **58** *of Straits Settlements, but inscr. " MALACCA " at foot. Wmk. Mult. Script CA. Chalk-surfaced paper. P* 17½ × 18.

3	1 c. black	0	3	0	6
4	2 c. orange	0	3	0	6
5	3 c. green	0	8	1	0
6	4 c. brown	0	4	0	6
6a	5 c. bright purple (1.9.52) ..	0	5	1	0
7	6 c. grey	0	6	1	0
8	8 c. scarlet	1	9	2	0
8a	8 c. green (1.9.52)	0	10	1	6
9	10 c. purple	0	9	0	3
9a	12 c. scarlet (1.9.52)	1	0	2	6
10	15 c. ultramarine	1	6	2	6
11	20 c. black and green.. ..	2	0	5	0
11a	20 c. bright blue (1.9.52) ..	1	6	1	6
12	25 c. purple and orange	2	0	1	0
12a	35 c. scarlet & purple (1.9.52)	2	0	6	0
13	40 c. red and purple	4	6	12	6
14	50 c. black and blue	3	0	2	0
15	$1 blue and purple ..	7	6	6	0
16	$2 green and scarlet	12	6	12	6
17	$5 green and brown ..	20	0	25	0

1949 (10 Oct.). *75th Anniv. of U.P.U. As Nos.* 114/7 *of Antigua.*

18	10 c. purple	0	10	0	10
19	15 c. deep blue	1	0	1	3
20	25 c. orange	2	0	2	6
21	50 c. blue-black	3	6	4	6

1953 (2 June). *Coronation. As No.* 47 *of Aden.*

22	10 c. black and reddish purple	0	10	1	0

1. Queen Elizabeth II.

1954–55. *Chalk-surfaced paper. Wmk. Mult. Script CA. P* 17½ × 18.

No.	Type	Description				
23	**1**	1 c. black	0	3	0	6
24	,,	2 c. yellow-orange ..	0	3	0	6
25	,,	4 c. brown (*shades*) ..	0	6	0	8
26	,,	5 c. bright purple	0	8	0	8
27	,,	6 c. grey	0	8	0	10
28	,,	8 c. green	2	0	2	6
29	,,	10 c. brown-purple (*shades*)	1	0	0	6
30	,,	12 c. rose-red	2	0	2	0
31	,,	20 c. bright blue	2	6	2	0
32	,,	25 c. brn.-purple & yell.-orge.	2	6	1	9
33	,,	30 c. rose-red & brown-purple	2	9	2	6
34	,,	35 c. rose-red & brown-purple	4	0	4	0
35	,,	50 c. black and bright blue..	5	0	2	6
36	,,	$1 brt. blue & brn.-purple	7	6	6	0
37	,,	$2 emerald and scarlet ..	22	6	20	0
38	,,	$5 emerald and brown ..	80	0	50	0

Dates of issue: 1954—9 June, 4 c., 6 c.; 1 July, 10 c.; 12 July, 5 c.; 8 Sept., 35 c., $1. 1955—5 Jan., 8 c., 12 c., 20 c., 50 c.; 27 Apr., 1 c., 2 c., 25 c., $2, $5; 5 Sept., 30 c.

1957. *As Nos.* 92/102 *of Kedah but with inset portrait of Queen Elizabeth II.*

No.	Type	Description				
39	**9**	1 c. black	0	3	0	3
40	**10**	2 c. orange-red	0	4	0	3
41	**11**	4 c. sepia	0	6	0	6
42	**12**	5 c. carmine-lake	0	7	0	5
43	**13**	8 c. myrtle-green	1	3	1	9
44	**14**	10 c. deep brown	1	3	0	2
45	**15**	20 c. blue	2	6	1	0
46	**16**	50 c. black and blue ..	4	0	1	9
47	**17**	$1 ultramarine and reddish purple	7	6	6	0
48	**18**	$2 bronze-grn. & scarlet	17	6	15	0
49	**19**	$5 brown & bronze-green	30	0	25	0

Dates of issue:—26.6.57, 20 c., $5; 25.7.57, 2 c., 50 c., $1; 4.8.57, 10 c.; 21.8.57, others.

2. Copra.

(Recess. De La Rue & Co.)

1960 (15 Mar.)-**62.** *As Nos.* 39/49, *but with inset picture of Melaka tree and Pelandok (mouse deer) as in T* **2.** *W* w. **12.** *P* 13 × 12½ (1 *c. to* 8 *c.*, $2, $5), 12½ × 13 (10 *c. to* 50 *c.*) *or* 13½ ($1).

50	1 c. black	0	2	0	3
51	2 c. orange-red	0	3	0	3
52	4 c. sepia	0	4	0	4
53	5 c. carmine-lake	0	5	0	4
54	8 c. myrtle-green	0	6	0	11
55	10 c. deep maroon	0	7	0	3
56	20 c. blue	1	0	0	11
57	50 c. black and blue ..	3	6	2	6
	a. Black & ultramarine (9.1.62)	2	0	1	6
58	$1 ultramarine & reddish purple	4	2	3	0
59	$2 bronze-green & scarlet	7	9	7	6
60	$5 brown & bronze-green..	18	6	18	0

3. *Vanda hookeriana.*

1965 (15 Nov.). *As Nos.* 166/72 *of Johore but wit[h] Arms of Malacca inset and inscr.* " MELAKA " *as in T* **3.**

61	1 c. multicoloured	0	1	0	
62	2 c. multicoloured	0	2	0	
63	5 c. multicoloured	0	4	0	
64	6 c. multicoloured	0	4	0	
65	10 c. multicoloured	0	6	0	1
66	15 c. multicoloured	0	7	1	
67	20 c. multicoloured	0	10	1	

The higher values used in Malacca are Nos 20/27 of Malaysia.

MALAYA (BRITISH MILITARY ADMINISTRATION).

For use throughout all Malay States and Singapore. From 1948 this general issue wa[s] gradually replaced by individual issues for eac[h] state.

BMA
MALAYA
(1)

1945–48. *T* **58** *of Straits Settlements optd. wi[th] T* **1.** *Values* 1 *c. to* 15 *c. from Die I (double-plate printing) or Die II (single-plate printing). Wmk. Mult. Script CA. P* 14 *or* 15 × 14 (*No.* 1

1	1 c. black, CO (I) (R.) ..	0	2	0	
2	2 c. orange, OC (II) ..	0	3	0	
3	2 c. orange, O (I) ('46) ..	3	0	3	
4	3 c. yellow-green, O (II) ..	0	4	0	
	a. Blue-green. OC (II) ('47) ..	0	3	0	
5	5 c. brown, C (II)	0	9	0	
6	6 c. grey, OC (II)	0	6	0	

No.	Value	Description	Unused s.	d.	Used s.	d.
7	8 c.	scarlet, O (II)	0	5	0	3
8	10 c.	slate-purple, C (I) ..	1	0	0	4
		a. Purple, OC (I) ('45)	1	0	0	3
		b. Magenta, C (I) ('48)	2	6	0	3
9	10 c.	purple, C (II) ('48) ..	0	6	0	6
10	12 c.	brt. ultramarine, C (I) ..	2	0	3	6
11	15 c.	brt. ultramarine, O (II)	7	6	10	0
12	15 c.	brt. ultram., OC (II) (R.)	0	10	0	8
		a. Blue, OC (II) (R.) ('47) ..	17	6	3	6
13	25 c.	dull purple & scarlet, OC	1	0	0	6
14	50 c.	black/*emerald,* CO (I) (R.) ('46)	1	8	0	4
15	$1	black and red, O ..	4	0	1	0
16	$2	green and scarlet, O ..	7	6	2	6
17	$5	green & red/*emerald,* C ..		£6		£7
18	$5	purple & orange, O ..	17	6	5	0

The 8 c. grey with "B M A" opt. was prepared but not officially issued.

Nos. 3 and 9 do not exist without the overprint.

Nos. 1, 2, 6, 7, 8*a* and 13 exist also on thin, rough ordinary paper.

No. 8*a* with reddish purple medallion and dull purple frame is from a printing with the head in fugitive ink which discolours with moisture.

MALAYAN FEDERATION.

Comprising the Settlements of Malacca and Penang and all the Malay States.

We list below the stamps intended for use throughout the Federation. See notes at the beginning of Malaya.

1. Tapping Rubber.

2. Federation Coat-of-Arms.

3. Tin Dredge.

4. Map of the Federation.

(Centre recess, frame litho. (6 c., 25 c.); centre litho, frame recess (12 c.); recess (30 c.), De La Rue & Co.)

1957 (5 May)–**61.** *W* w.**12.**

No.	Type	Description	Unused s.	d.	Used s.	d.
1	**1**	6 c. dp. blue, red, yellow & grey-blue (*shades*) (*p.* 13)	0	5	0	5
2	**2**	12 c. red, yellow, blue, black and scarlet (*p.* 13) ..	0	7	0	7
3	**3**	25 c. maroon, red, yellow and dull gr'nish blue (*p.* 13)	1	1	0	11
4	**4**	30 c. orange-red and lake (*p.* 13×12½)	3	0	1	3
		a. Perf. 13. *Orange-red & deep lake* (*shades*) (20.6.61) ..	1	4	1	0

5. Chief Minister Tengku Abdul Rahman and Populace greeting Independence.

(Des. A. B. Saman. Recess. Waterlow & Sons.)

1957 (31 Aug.). *Independence Day. Wmk. Mult. Script CA. P* 12½.

No.	Type	Description	Unused s.	d.	Used s.	d.
5	**5**	10 c. bistre-brown	0	10	0	6

6. United Nations Emblem.

7. United Nations Emblem.

(Recess. De La Rue & Co., Ltd.)

1958 (5 Mar.). *Economic Commission Asia and Far East Conference, Kuala Lumpur.* W w. **12.** P 13½ (12 c.) or 12½ (30 c).

6	**6**	12 c. carmine-red	1 3	1 3
7	**7**	30 c. maroon	1 9	1 6

8. Merdeka Stadium, Kuala Lumpur.

9. The Yang di Pertuan Agong (Abdul Rahman).

(Photo. Harrison & Sons.)

1958 (31 Aug.). *First Anniv. of Independence.* W w. **12.** P 13½ × 14½ (10 c.) or 14½ × 13½ (30 c.).

8	**8**	10 c. green, yellow, red & blue	0 6	0 6
9	**9**	30 c. red, yellow, violet-blue and green	1 9	1 3

10. "Human Rights".

12. Mace and Malayan Peoples.

11. Malayan with Torch of Freedom.

(Des. J. P. Hendroff. Litho. (10 c.), photo. (30 c.). De La Rue & Co.)

1958 (10 Dec.). *Tenth Anniv. of Declaration of Human Rights.* (a) W w. **12.** P 12½ × 13.

10	**10**	10 c. blue, blk., carm. & orge.	0 8	0 6

(b) *Wmk. Mult. Script CA.* P 13 × 12½.

11	**11**	30 c. deep green	1 9	1 3

(Photo. J. Enschedé & Sons, Haarlem.)

1959 (12 Sept.). *Inauguration of Parliament. No wmk.* P 13 × 14.

12	**12**	4 c. rose-red	0 6	0 6
13	,,	10 c. violet	0 8	0 8
14	,,	25 c. yellow-green	1 3	1 0

13

14

(Recess. De La Rue & Co.)

1960 (7 Apr.). *World Refugee Year.* W w. **12.** P 13 × 12½ (12 c.) or 12½ × 13 (30 c.).

15	**13**	12 c. purple	1 6	1 6
16	**14**	30 c. deep green	1 9	1 3

15. Seedling Rubber Tree and Map.

16. The Yang di-Pertuan Agong (Syed Putra).

(Photo. Japanese Govt. Ptg. Wks.)

1960 (19 Sept.). *Natural Rubber Research Conference and 15th International Rubber Study Group Meeting, Kuala Lumpur.* T **15** and *similar vert. design. No wmk.* P 13½ × 13

17	6 c. yellow-green, black, orange and red-brown	0 6	0
18	30 c. yellow-green, black, orange and bright blue	1 6	1

No. 18 is inscribed "INTERNATIONAL RUBBER STUDY GROUP 15TH MEETING KUALA LUMPUR" at foot.

(Photo. Harrison & Sons.)

1961 (4 Jan.). *Installation of Yang di-Pertuan Agong, Tuanku Syed Putra.* W w. **12** P 14 × 14½.

19	**16**	10 c. black and blue ..	0 8	0

17. Colombo Plan Emblem. **18.** Malaria Eradication Emblem.

(Photo. Japanese Govt. Ptg. Works.)

1961 (30 Oct.). *Colombo Plan Conference, Kuala Lumpur.* *P* 13½.

20 **17** 12 c. black and magenta .. 0 8 0 8
21 ,, 25 c. black & apple-green .. 1 3 1 0
22 ,, 30 c. black & turq.-blue .. 1 6 1 3

(Photo. Harrison & Sons.)

1962 (7 Apr.). *Malaria Eradication.* *W* w. **13.** *P* 14 × 14½.

23 **18** 25 c. orange-brown 1 3 1 0
24 ,, 30 c. deep lilac 1 6 1 3
25 ,, 50 c. ultramarine 2 6 2 0

19. Palmyra Palm Leaf.

(Photo. Harrison.)

1962 (21 July). *National Language Month.* *W* w.**13.** *P* 13½.

26 **19** 10 c. lt. brn. & dp. redsh. vio. 0 8 0 8
27 ,, 20 c. lt. brn. & dp. bl'sh grn. 1 0 1 0
28 ,, 50 c. lt. brown and magenta 2 6 2 6

20. " Shadows of the Future ".

(Photo. J. Enschedé & Sons.)

962 (1 Oct.). *Introduction of Free Primary Education.* *W* w.**13.** *P* 13½.

9 **20** 10 c. bright purple 0 8 0 8
0 ,, 25 c. ochre 1 3 1 0
1 ,, 30 c. emerald 1 6 1 3

21. Harvester and Fisherman.

(Photo. Courvoisier.)

1963 (21 Mar). *Freedom from Hunger.* *P* 11½.

32 **21** 25 c. carm. and apple-green 1 3 1 0
33 ,, 30 c. carmine and crimson 1 6 1 2
34 ,, 50 c. carmine & bright blue 2 6 1 9

22. Dam and Pylon.

(Photo. Harrison.)

1963 (26 June). *Cameron Highlands Hydro-Electric Scheme.* *Wmk.* w. **13.** *P* 14.

35 **22** 20 c. grn. & reddish violet 1 0 0 11
36 ,, 30 c. blue-green & ultram. 1 4 1 2

The definitive general issue for Malaysia and the low value sets for the individual states superseded the stamps of the Malayan Federation on 15th November, 1965.

MALAYAN POSTAL UNION

POSTAGE DUE STAMPS.

D 1

10

cents

(D 2)

(Typo. Waterlow until 1961, then De La Rue.)

1936–38. *Wmk. Mult. Script CA.* *P* 15 × 14.

D 1 D 1 1 c. slate-purple ('38) .. 1 0 1 6
D 2 ,, 4 c. green 1 6 2 6
D 3 ,, 8 c. scarlet 2 6 3 6
D 4 ,, 10 c. yellow-orange .. 2 6 1 0
D 5 ,, 12 c. pale ultramarine .. 6 0 7 6
D 6 ,, 50 c. black (Jan. '38) .. 6 0 8 6

For use in Negri Sembilan, Pahang, Perak, Selangor and Straits Settlements.

1945–49. *New values and colours.* *Wmk. Mult. Script CA.* *P* 15 × 14.

D 7 D 1 1 c. purple 2 0 3 0
D 8 ,, 3 c. green 7 6 7 6
D 9 ,, 5 c. scarlet 7 0 8 6
D10 ,, 8 c. yellow-orange ('49) 15 0 17 6
D11 ,, 9 c. yellow-orange .. 35 0 40 0
D12 ,, 15 c. pale ultramarine .. 55 0 55 0
D13 ,, 20 c. blue ('48) 10 0 12 6

1951 (8 Aug.)–**62.** *Wmk. Mult. Script CA.* *P* 14.

D14 **D 1** 1 c. violet (21.8.52) .. 0 3 0 4
D15 ,, 2 c. dp.slate-bl.(16.11.53) 0 6 0 8
 a. Perf. 12½ (15.11.60) .. 0 6 0 8
 b. P. 12½. Chalky paper (10.7.62) 0 5 0 6
 ba. Do. Imp. betwn. (vt. pr.)
D16 ,, 3 c. deep green (21.8.52) 3 6 4 6
D17 ,, 4 c. sepia (16.11.53) .. 1 0 1 6
 a. Perf. 12½ (15.11.60) .. 0 9 0 10
 b. P 12½. *Bistre-brown.* Chalky paper (10.7.62) 0 8 0 10
D18 ,, 5 c. vermilion 4 0 5 0
D19 ,, 8 c. yellow-orange .. 1 6 1 6
D20 ,, 12 c. brt. purple (1.2.54) 2 0 2 6
 a. P 12½. Chalky paper (10.7.62) 1 0 1 6
D21 ,, 20 c. blue.. .. .. 2 6 3 0
 a. P 12½. *Deep blue* (10.12.57) 1 6 1 9
 b. P 12½. *Deep blue.* Chalky paper (15.10.63) .. 5 0 6 0

Nos. D7 to D21b are or were for use in the Federation and Singapore, and from 1963 throughout Malaysia.

1964 (14 Apr.)–**65.** *Chalk-surfaced paper. Wmk. w.* **12** (*sideways on* 1 c.). *P* 12½.

D22 **D 1** 1 c. maroon 0 2 0 4
 a. P 12. Wmk. upright (4.5.65) 0 1 0 3
D23 ,, 2 c. deep slate-blue .. 0 6 0 8
 a. Perf. 12 (9.3.65) .. 0 2 0 4
D24 ,, 4 c. bistre-brown .. 0 8 0 10
 a. Perf. 12 (9.3.65) .. 0 3 0 6
D25 ,, 8 c. yellow-orge. (*p.* 12) (4.5.65) 0 5 0 7
D27 ,, 12 c. bright purple .. 0 8 1 0
 a. Perf. 12 (4.5.65) .. 0 6 0 8
D28 ,, 20 c. deep blue 1 0 1 3
 a. Perf. 12 (4.5.65) .. 0 10 1 0

1965 (Jan.). *As No.* D19 *surch. locally with Type* D **2**.

D29 **D 1** 10 c. on 8 c. yellow-orge. 10 0

This stamp differs from No. D19 in that it has been climatically affected.

NEGRI SEMBILAN.

A State of the Federation of Malaya.

Negri Sembilan

(1)

1891. *T* **5** *of Straits (wmk. Crown CA) optd. with T* **1.**

1 2 cents, rose 7 6 10 0

2 3

1891–94. *Wmk. Crown CA.* *P* 14.

2 **2** 1 c. green (1893) 3 6 2 0
3 ,, 2 c. rose 5 0 5 0
4 ,, 5 c. blue (1894) 17 6 20 0

1896–99. *Wmk. Crown CA.* *P* 14.

5 **3** 1 c. dull purp. & green (1899) 4 6 5 0
6 ,, 2 c. dull purple & brown .. 22 6 17 6
7 ,, 3 c. dull purple & carmine 4 0 2 0
8 ,, 5 c. dull purp. & orge.-yell. 6 0 10 0
9 ,, 8 c. dull purple & ultram. .. 15 0 17 6
10 **3** 10 c. dull purple & orange .. 32 6 27 6
11 ,, 15 c. green and violet .. 32 6 20 0
12 ,, 20 c. green and olive .. 45 0 45 0
13 ,, 25 c. green and carmine .. 55 0 55 0
14 ,, 50 c. green and black .. 75 0 80 0

Four cents.

(4)

Four cents.

(5)

1898 (Dec.)–**1899.** (*a*) *Surch. as T* **4.**

15 **3** 1 c. on 15 c. green & violet.. 85 0
 a. Inverted stop £14 £16
16 **2** 4 c. on 1 c. green 2 6 5 0
17 **3** 4 c. on 3 c. dull pur. & carm. 5 0 6 0
 a. Surcharge omitted (in pair with normal) £50 £45
 b. Surcharge double .. .. — £25
 c. "cents" repeated at left .. £8 £8
 d. "Four" repeated at right .. £8 £8
 e. Without bar
 f. Bar double .. .. .. † £50
18 **2** 4 c. on 5 c. blue 2 6 4 0

On Nos. 15 and 17 the bar is at the top of the stamp.

(*b*) *Surch. as T* **5.**

19 **3** 4 c. on 8 c. dull purple and ultram. (G.) (Dec. 1898) 3 6 4 0
 a. Surcharge omitted (in pair with normal) £65 £45
 b. Surcharge double in green .. £35
 c. Surcharge double, one red, one green £40 £40
20 ,, 4 c. on 8 c. dull purple and ultramarine (Bk.) .. £20 £20

6. Arms of Negri Sembilan. **7.**

1935–41. *Chalk-surfaced or ordinary paper* (O). *Wmk. Mult. Script CA.* *P* 14.

21 **6** 1 c. black 0 6 0 3
22 ,, 2 c. green 1 3 0 3
22*a* ,, 2 c. orange.. .. .. 2 0 6 0
22*b* ,, 3 c. green 2 0 4 0
23 ,, 4 c. orange.. .. .. 0 9 0 6
24 ,, 5 c. brown 0 9 0 3
24*a* ,, 6 c. scarlet 2 6 3 0
24*b* ,, 6 c. grey, O 6 0 25 0
25 ,, 8 c. grey 2 0 0 6
26 ,, 10 c. dull purple 1 6 1 6
27 ,, 12 c. bright ultramarine .. 1 6 2 6
27*a* ,, 15 c. ultramarine, O .. 5 0 17 6
28 ,, 25 c. dull purple & scarlet 3 0 4 0
29 ,, 30 c. dull purple & orange.. 3 0 7 6
30 ,, 40 c. scarlet and dull purple 3 6 8 6
31 ,, 50 c. black/*emerald*.. .. 6 0 4
32 ,, $1 black and red/*blue* .. 7 6 7
33 ,, $2 green and scarlet .. 20 0 25
34 ,, $5 green & red/*emerald* .. 35 0 45

An 8 c. scarlet was issued but only with opt during Japanese Occupation of Malaya. Unover printed specimens result from leakages.

On stamp No. 94 in sheets of the 6 c., Nos 24*a* and 24*b*, the stop is missing below the "c" of "6 c." at right.

Dates of issue:—2.12.35, 4 c., 8 c., 40 c. 5.12.35, 5 c.; 1.1.36, 1 c., 2 c. grn., 10 c., 12 c 30 c.; 1.2.36, 50 c.; 1.4.36, 25 c., $1; 16.5.36

$2, $5; 1.1.37, 6 c. scar.; --.8.41, 3 c.; 11.12.41, 2 c. orge.; 1941, 6 c. grey, 15 c.

1948 (1 DEC.). *Royal Silver Wedding. As Nos. 30/1 of Aden.*

No.		Description	Unused	Used
35		10 c. violet	0 8	0 8
36		$5 green	35 0	42 6

1949 (1 APR.)–**55.** *Chalk-surfaced paper. Wmk. Mult. Script CA. P* $17\frac{1}{2} \times 18$.

No.	Type	Description	Unused	Used
37	**7**	1 c. black	0 3	0 3
38	,,	2 c. orange	0 3	0 3
39	,,	3 c. green	1 0	1 9
40	,,	4 c. brown	0 6	0 6
40*a*	,,	5 c. brt. pur. (*shades*)(1.9.52)	0 6	0 8
41	,,	6 c. grey (*shades*)	0 6	0 8
42	,,	8 c. scarlet	1 3	3 0
42*a*	,,	8 c. green (1.9.52)	0 9	2 6
43	,,	10 c. purple	0 8	0 3
43*a*	,,	12 c. scarlet (1.9.52)	1 3	2 0
44	,,	15 c. ultramarine	1 9	2 0
45	,,	20 c. black and green	2 0	3 0
45*a*	,,	20 c. bright blue (1.9.52)	2 6	1 0
46	,,	25 c. purple and orange	1 6	1 0
46*a*	,,	30 c. scar. & purple (5.9.55)	2 6	2 0
46*b*	,,	35 c. scar. & purple (1.9.52)	3 0	3 6
47	,,	40 c. red and purple	3 6	7 6
48	,,	50 c. black and blue	3 6	2 0
49	,,	$1 blue and purple	6 0	2 6
50	,,	$2 green and scarlet	10 0	4 0
51	,,	$5 green and brown	22 6	17 6

1949 (10 OCT.). *75th Anniv. of U.P.U. As Nos. 114/7 of Antigua.*

No.		Description	Unused	Used
52		10 c. purple	0 8	0 8
53		15 c. deep blue	1 0	1 0
54		25 c. orange	2 6	2 6
55		50 c. blue-black	4 0	4 0

1953 (2 JUNE). *Coronation. As No. 47 of Aden.*

No.		Description	Unused	Used
56		10 c. black and reddish purple	0 8	0 8

1957–63. *As Nos. 92/102 of Kedah but with inset Arms of Negri Sembilan.*

No.	Type	Description	Unused	Used
57	**9**	1 c. black	0 2	0 3
58	**10**	2 c. orange-red	0 3	0 3
59	**11**	4 c. sepia	0 4	0 5
60	**12**	5 c. carmine-lake	0 5	0 5
61	**13**	8 c. myrtle-green	0 6	0 11
62	**14**	10 c. deep brown	0 8	0 6
62*a*	,,	10 c. deep maroon (10.1.61)	0 7	0 5
63	**15**	20 c. blue	1 0	1 2
64	**16**	50 c. black and blue (*p.* $12\frac{1}{2}$)	2 6	1 9
		a. Perf. $12\frac{1}{2} \times 13$ (19.7.60)	2 0	1 6
65	**17**	$1 ultram. & reddish pur.	4 2	4 6
66	**18**	$2 brze-grn. & scar. (*p.* $12\frac{1}{2}$)	9 0	10 0
		a. Perf. $13 \times 12\frac{1}{2}$ (15.1.63)	7 9	8 6
67	**19**	$5 brn. & brz.-grn.(*p.* $12\frac{1}{2}$)	20 0	22 6
		a. Perf. $13 \times 12\frac{1}{2}$ (6.3.62)	18 6	15 0
		b. P $13 \times 12\frac{1}{2}$. *Brown & yellow-olive* (13.11.62)	30 0	22 6

Dates of issue:—26.6.57, 20 c., $5; 25.7.57, c., 50 c., $1; 4.8.57, 10 c.; 21.8.57, others.

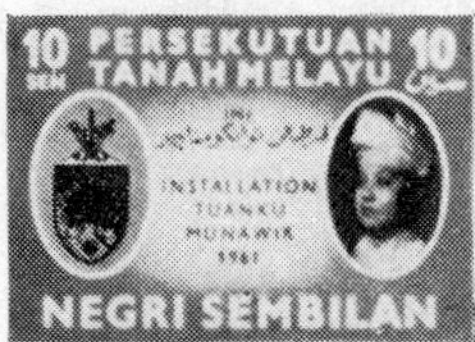

8. Tuanku Munawir.

(Photo. Enschedé & Sons.)

1961 (17 APR.). *Installation of Tuanku Munawir as Yang di-Pertuan Besar of Negri Sembilan. No wmk. P* 14×13.

No.	Type	Description	Unused	Used
68	**8**	10 c. multicoloured	0 8	0 8

9. *Vanda hookeriana.*

1965 (15 NOV.). *As Nos. 166/72 of Johore but with Arms of Negri Sembilan inset and inscr.* "NEGERI SEMBILAN" *as in T* **9**.

No.		Description	Unused	Used
69		1 c. multicoloured	0 1	0 3
70		2 c. multicoloured	0 2	0 5
71		5 c. multicoloured	0 4	0 7
72		6 c. multicoloured	0 4	0 7
73		10 c. multicoloured	0 6	0 10
74		15 c. multicoloured	0 7	1 0
75		20 c. multicoloured	0 10	1 6

The higher values used in Negri Sembilan are Nos. 20/27 of Malaysia.

PAHANG.

A State of the Federation of Malaya.

1889–90. *T* **5, 6, 19** *and* **7** *of Straits* (*wmk. Crown CA*) *optd. or surch.*

PAHANG (A) PAHANG (B)

1889 (JAN.).

No.	Type	Description	Unused	Used
1	A	2 c. rose	40 0	45 0
2	,,	8 c. orange	£20	£20
3	,,	10 c. slate	£5	£6

The 8 c. and 10 c. were overprinted in triplet form.

1889.

No.	Type	Description	Unused	Used
4	B	2 c. rose	8 6	10 0
		As No. 4, but in antique letters.		
4*a*		2 c. rose	£16	

The letters of the overprint on No. 4*a* are thinner and appear broader than those on No. 4.

PAHANG (C) PAHANG (D)

1890.

No.	Type	Description	Unused	Used
5	C	2 c. rose	£60	£40
6	D	2 c. rose	65 0	40 0

1891. *Optd. as No. 6 and surch. with new value with bar through old value.*

No.		Description	Unused	Used
7		Two CENTS on 24 c. green	£6	

No. 7 has the word "Two" as in No. 8 and "CENTS" as in No. 10, but in roman capitals.

PAHANG Two CENTS (E) PAHANG *Two* CENTS (F) PAHANG *Two* CENTS (G)

1891.

No.	Type	Description	Unused	Used
8	E	2 c. on 24 c. green	55 0	65 0
9	F	2 c. on 24 c. green	56 0	75 0
10	G	2 c. on 24 c. green	55 0	65 0

1

2

1891–95. *Wmk. Crown CA. P* 14.

No.	Type	Description	Unused		Used	
11	**1**	1 c. green (1895)	5	0	3	0
12	,,	2 c. rose	2	6	2	6
13	,,	5 c. blue (1893)	7	6	12	6

1895–99. *Wmk. Crown CA. P* 14.

No.	Type	Description	Unused		Used	
14	**2**	3 c. dull purple and carmine	2	6	2	0
14a	,,	4 c. dull pur. & carm. (1899)	3	0	4	0
15	,,	5 c. dull pur. & olive-yellow	17	6	20	0

1897. *No.* 13 *divided, and each half surcharged* "2 c." *or* "3 c." *in M.S., with initials.*

(i) *Diagonally.*

(a) *In red.* (*August*).

No.	Description	Unused	Used
16	2 c. on half of 5 c. blue ..	£25	£20
17	3 c. on half of 5 c. blue ..	£25	£20

(b) *In black.* (2 *Aug.*).

No.	Description	Unused	Used
17a	2 c. on half of 5 c. blue ..	—	£80
17b	3 c. on half of 5 c. blue ..	£100	£80

(ii) *Horizontally, in red.*

No.	Description	Unused	Used
17c	2 c. on half of 5 c. blue ..	—	£18
17d	3 c. on half of 5 c. blue ..	—	£18

The initials are "J. F. O.", standing for John Fortescue Owen, District Treasurer at Kuala Lipis, where the provisionals were made.

Pahang. (3) **Pahang.** (4)

1898. *T* **31** *of Perak optd. with T* **3.**

No.	Description	Unused		Used	
18	10 c. dull purple and orange ..	20	0	25	0
19	25 c. green and carmine ..	50	0	55	0
20	50 c. green and black	75	0	80	0
21	50 c. dull pur. & greenish blk.	£6		£6	

Nos. 72 *and* 75 *of Perak, optd. with T* **4.**

No.	Description	Unused	Used
22	$1 green and pale green ..	£5	£5
23	$5 green and ultramarine ..	£18	£18

Pahang Four cents (5) **Four cents.** (6)

1898. *T* **31** *of Perak surch. with T* **5.**

No.	Description	Unused		Used	
24	4 c. on 8 c. dull pur. & ultram.	6	0	10	0
	a. Surcharge inverted	£40		£25	
	b. Surcharge double	£10			

T **5** *on plain paper (no stamp), but issued for postage.*

No.	Description	Unused	Used
26	4 c. black	—	£22
26a	5 c. black	£15	

1899. *No.* 15 *surch. with T* **6.**

No.	Description	Unused		Used	
27	4 c. on 5 c. dull pur. & olive-yellow	15	0	15	0

7. Sultan Sir Abu Bakar.

8. Sultan Sir Abu Bakar.

1935–41. *Chalk-surfaced or ordinary paper* (O), *Wmk. Mult. Script CA. P* 14.

No.	Type	Description	Unused		Used	
28	**7**	1 c. black	0	4	0	4
29	,,	2 c. green	0	9	1	6
29a	,,	3 c. green (21.8.41), OC ..	1	0	3	0
30	,,	4 c. orange	0	9	0	4
31	,,	5 c. brown	0	9	0	4
32	,,	6 c. scarlet	3	0	3	6
33	,,	8 c. grey	2	0	0	9
33a	**7**	8 c. scarlet (11.12.41) ..	3	0	12	6
34	,,	10 c. dull purple	1	3	0	6
35	,,	12 c. bright ultramarine ..	1	9	6	0
35a	,,	15 c. ultram. (1.10.41) O ..	5	0	25	0
36	,,	25 c. dull purple & scarlet	2	6	4	0
37	,,	30 c. dull purple & orange ..	3	0	7	6
38	,,	40 c. scarlet & dull purple ..	4	6	10	0
39	,,	50 c. black/*emerald*	6	0	4	0
40	,,	$1 black and red/*blue* ..	12	6	15	0
41	,,	$2 green and scarlet ..	40	0	45	0
42	,,	$5 green & red/*emerald* ..	35	0	55	0

A 2 c. orange and a 6 c. grey were prepared but not officially issued.

Dates of issue as for Negri Sembilan.

1948 (1 Dec.). *Royal Silver Wedding. As Nos.* 30/1 *of Aden.*

No.	Description	Unused		Used	
43	10 c. violet	0	8	0	8
44	$5 green	35	0	40	0

1949 (10 Oct.). *75th Anniv. of Universal Postal Union. As Nos.* 114/7 *of Antigua.*

No.	Description	Unused		Used	
45	10 c. purple	0	8	0	8
46	15 c. deep blue	1	0	1	3
47	25 c. orange	2	0	2	0
48	50 c. blue-black	4	0	4	6

1950 (1 June)–**55.** *Wmk. Mult. Script CA. Chalk-surfaced paper. P* 17½ × 18.

No.	Type	Description	Unused		Used	
49	**8**	1 c. black	0	3	0	4
50	,,	2 c. orange	0	3	0	3
51	,,	3 c. green	1	6	2	0
52	,,	4 c. brown (*shades*) ..	0	6	0	6
52a	,,	5 c. brt. pur. (*shades*) (1.9.52)	0	6	1	0
53	,,	6 c. grey	0	9	1	3
54	,,	8 c. scarlet	1	3	2	0
54a	,,	8 c. green (1.9.52) ..	0	9	2	6
55	,,	10 c. magenta	0	10	0	3
55a	,,	12 c. scarlet (1.9.52) ..	1	6	2	6
56	,,	15 c. ultramarine	1	9	1	9
57	,,	20 c. black and green ..	2	6	6	0
57a	,,	20 c. bright blue (*shades*) (1.9.52) ..	2	0	1	0
58	,,	25 c. purple and orange ..	1	0	0	10
58a	,,	30 c. scarlet and brown-purple (*shades*) (5.9.55) ..	3	0	3	6
58b	,,	35 c. scar. & purple (1.9.52)	5	0	4	0
59	,,	40 c. red and purple ..	5	0	10	0
60	,,	50 c. black and blue ..	3	6	1	3
61	,,	$1 blue and purple ..	6	0	5	0
62	,,	$2 green and scarlet ..	10	0	15	0
63	,,	$5 green & brn. (*shades*)	25	0	22	6

1953 (2 June). *Coronation. As No.* 47 *of Aden.*

No.	Description	Unused		Used	
64	10 c. black and reddish purple	0	8	0	10

1957–62. *As Nos.* 92/102 *of Kedah but with inset portrait of Sultan Sir Abu Bakar.*

No.	Type	Description	Unused		Used	
65	**9**	1 c. black	0	2	0	[illegible]
66	**10**	2 c. orange-red	0	3	0	[illegible]
67	**11**	4 c. sepia	0	4	0	[illegible]
68	**12**	5 c. carmine-lake ..	0	5	0	[illegible]
69	**13**	8 c. myrtle-green	0	6	1	[illegible]
70	**14**	10 c. deep brown	1	0	0	[illegible]
70a	,,	10 c. dp. maroon (21.2.61)	0	7	0	[illegible]
71	**15**	20 c. blue	1	0	1	[illegible]
72	**16**	50 c. black and blue (*p.* 12½)	3	0	2	[illegible]
		a. Perf. 12½ × 13 (17.5.60) ..	2	0	1	[illegible]
73	**17**	$1 ultram. & reddish pur.	4	2	3	[illegible]
74	**18**	$2 brze.-grn. & scar. (*p.* 12½)	10	0	8	[illegible]
		a. Perf. 13 × 12½ (13.11.62) ..	7	9	7	
75	**19**	$5 brn. & brz.-grn. (*p.* 12½)	20	0	22	
		a. Perf. 13 × 12½ (17.5.60) ..	18	6	15	
		b. P 13 × 12½. *Brown & yell.-olive* (23.10.62)	25	0	20	

9. *Vanda hookeriana.*

1965 (15 Nov.). *As Nos.* 166/72 *of Johore but with inset portrait of Sultan Sir Abu Bakar as in T* **9**.

76 1 c. multicoloured 0 1 0 3
77 2 c. multicoloured 0 2 0 5
78 5 c. multicoloured 0 4 0 7
79 6 c. multicoloured 0 4 0 7
80 10 c. multicoloured 0 6 0 10
81 15 c. multicoloured 0 7 1 0
82 20 c. multicoloured 0 10 1 6

The higher values used in Pahang are Nos. 20/27 of Malaysia.

PENANG.

A former British Settlement, now part of the Federation of Malaya.

1948 (1 Dec.). *Royal Silver Wedding. As Nos.* 30/1 *of Aden.*

1 10 c. violet 0 6 0 6
2 $5 brown 35 0 40 0

1949 (21 Feb.)–**52.** *As T* **58** *of Straits Settlements, but inscr.* "PENANG" *at foot. Wmk. Mult. Script CA. Chalk-surfaced paper. P* 17½×18.

3 1 c. black 0 2 0 6
4 2 c. orange 0 3 0 3
5 3 c. green 0 9 1 0
6 4 c. brown 0 6 0 3
6a 5 c. bright purple (1.9.52) .. 0 8 0 6
7 6 c. grey 0 9 0 6
8 8 c. scarlet 1 3 2 0
8a 8 c. green (1.9.52) 1 0 2 6
9 10 c. purple 0 8 0 3
9a 12 c. scarlet (1.9.52) 1 0 2 0
10 15 c. ultramarine 1 6 0 10
11 20 c. black and green 2 0 1 6
11a 20 c. bright blue (1.9.52) .. 1 9 1 9
12 25 c. purple and orange .. 1 6 0 6
12a 35 c. scarlet & purple (1.9.52) 2 9 2 9
13 40 c. red and purple 3 0 7 0
14 50 c. black and blue 2 6 0 8
15 $1 blue and purple .. 5 0 1 0
16 $2 green and scarlet .. 8 6 2 0
17 $5 green and brown .. 20 0 4 0

1949 (10 Oct.). *75th Anniv. of Universal Postal Union. As Nos.* 114/7 *of Antigua.*

18 10 c. purple 0 8 0 8
19 15 c. deep blue 0 9 1 3
20 25 c. orange 1 9 2 0
21 50 c. blue-black 3 0 3 6

1953 (2 June). *Coronation. As No.* 47 *of Aden.*

22 10 c. black and reddish purple 0 10 0 8

1954–55. *As T* **1** *of Malacca* (*Queen Elizabeth II*) *but inscr.* "PENANG" *at foot. Chalk-surfaced paper. Wmk. Mult. Script CA. P* 17½×18.

23 1 c. black 0 3 0 4
24 2 c. yellow-orange 0 4 0 4
25 4 c. brown (*shades*) 0 8 0 6
26 5 c. bright purple (*shades*) .. 0 8 0 9
27 6 c. grey 1 6 1 3
28 8 c. green 1 6 2 0
29 10 c. brown-purple 1 6 0 4
30 12 c. rose-red 2 0 2 0
31 20 c. bright blue 2 6 1 0
32 25 c. brn.-purple & yell.-orange 2 6 1 0
33 30 c. rose-red & brown-purple 3 0 2 0
34 35 c. rose-red & brown-purple 3 6 3 6
35 50 c. black and bright blue .. 3 6 1 6
36 $1 brt. blue & brown-purple 6 0 3 0
37 $2 emerald and scarlet .. 12 6 6 0
38 $5 emerald and brown .. 40 0 20 0

Dates of issue: 1954—9 June, 6 c.; 1 Sept., c., 10 c., 20 c.; 8 Sept., 2 c., 35 c.; 1 Oct., 5 c., 1, $2; 1 Dec., 25 c., 50 c. 1955—5 Jan., 1 c., c., 12 c., $5; 5 Sept., 30 c.

1957. *As Nos.* 92/102 *of Kedah, but with inset portrait of Queen Elizabeth II.*

39 **9** 1 c. black 0 3 0 3
40 **10** 2 c. orange-red 0 4 0 3
41 **11** 4 c. sepia 0 6 0 5
42 **12** 5 c. carmine-lake 0 7 0 5
43 **13** 8 c. myrtle-green 1 6 1 6
44 **14** 10 c. deep brown 1 3 0 4
45 **15** 20 c. blue 3 0 1 3
46 **16** 50 c. black and blue .. 4 6 2 0
47 **17** $1 ultram. & reddish pur. 6 0 2 6
48 **18** $2 bronze-green & scarlet 12 6 7 6
49 **19** $5 brown & bronze-green 30 0 15 0

Dates of issue:—26.6.57, 20 c., $5; 25.7.57, 2 c., 50 c., $1; 4.8.57, 10 c.; 21.8.57, others.

1. Copra.

(Recess. De La Rue & Co.)

1960 (15 Mar.). *As Nos.* 39/49 *but with inse Arms of Penang as in T* **1**. *W w.* **12**. *P* 13×12½ (1 *c. to* 8 *c.*, $2, $5), 12½×13 (10 *c. to* 50 *c.*) *or* 13½ ($1).

50 1 c. black 0 2 0 3
51 2 c. orange-red 0 3 0 3
52 4 c. sepia 0 4 0 4
53 5 c. carmine-lake 0 5 0 4
54 8 c. myrtle-green 0 6 0 11
55 10 c. deep maroon 0 7 0 3
56 20 c. blue 1 0 0 10
57 50 c. black and blue 2 0 1 2
58 $1 ultram. & reddish purple 4 2 2 3
59 $2 bronze-green & scarlet .. 7 9 4 6
60 $5 brown and bronze-green 18 6 9 0

2. *Vanda hookeriana.*

1965 (15 Nov.). *As Nos.* 166/72 *of Johore but with Arms of Penang inset and inscr.* "PULAU PINANG" *as in T* **2**.

61 1 c. multicoloured 0 1 0 2
62 2 c. multicoloured 0 2 0 4
63 5 c. multicoloured 0 4 0 7
64 6 c. multicoloured 0 4 0 7
65 10 c. multicoloured 0 6 1 10
66 15 c. multicoloured 0 7 1 0
67 20 c. multicoloured 0 10 1 4

The higher values used in Penang are Nos. 20/27 of Malaysia.

PERAK.

A State of the Federation of Malaya.

1878. *T* **5** *of Straits Settlements optd. or surch.*

(A) *Wmk. Crown CC.*

Optd. with Crescent, Star and "*P*" *in an oval.*

1 2 c. brown £35 £25

PERAK
(1) Variety (*f*).

PERAK
(2)

1880–81. (*a*) *All letters wide.* (*b*) *All letters wide, but close together.* (*c*) " R " *narrow.* (*d*) " R " *and* " A " *narrow.* (*e*) " P " *and* " K " *wide.* (*f*) *All letters narrow.* (*g*) *All letters narrow, but close together.*

2 **1** 2 c. brown (*a*) .. .. — £8
3 ,, 2 c. brown (*b*) .. .. — £6
4 ,, 2 c. brown (*c*) 65 0 65 0
5 ,, 2 c. brown (*d*) 65 0 65 0
6 ,, 2 c. brown (*e*) £6 95 0
7 ,, 2 c. brown (*f*) 55 0 55 0
8 ,, 2 c. brown (*g*) £8 £6

Variety (*a*) is a single unit setting (1880). Triplet settings are as follows:—1880 (*b*)+(*b*)+(*b*); 1881 (*d*)+(*c*)+(*c*); 1881 (*c*)+(*c*)+(*e*). Variety (*g*) (1880) may be either a single unit or a triplet setting. Variety (*f*) (1881) is probably a triplet setting.

1881 .

9 **2** 2 c. brown 20 0 20 0

(B) *Wmk. Crown CA.*

1882–83." (*h*) " E " *wide.* (*k*) " A " *wide.*

10 **1** 2 c. brown (*f*) 12 6 15 0
11 ,, 2 c. rose (*f*) 10 0 12 6
12 ,, 2 c. rose (*h*) 10 0 12 6
13 ,, 2 c. rose (*k*) 10 0 12 6

Triplet settings are as follows·—1882, 2 c. brown (*f*)+(*f*)+(*f*). 1883, 2 c. rose (*f*)+(*k*)+(*h*); (*h*)+(*f*)+(*f*); (*h*)+(*f*)+(*k*).

2 CENTS PERAK (3)

2 CENTS PERAK (3*a*)

1883 (July). *Surch. vertically upwards.*
(*a*) " E " *of* " PERAK " *wide* (1¾ *mm.*).

14 **3** 2 c. on 4 c. rose £14 £12

(*b*) *All letters narrow* (" E " 1½ *mm. wide*).

15 **3** 2 c. on 4 c. rose £12 £10

Setting composed of two separate triplets, one for " 2 CENTS " and one for " PERAK ", the latter composed of two units of No. 15 and one of No. 14. This setting was employed on the lower nine rows of the sheet.

(*c*) *Unified surch.* (" 2 CENTS " *spaced* 19¾ × 3½ *mm. and* " PERAK " *set closer*).

15*a* **3*a*** 2 c. on 4 c. rose .. ..

It is believed that T **3*a*** was used only in the top row of the sheet.

PERAK (4)

PERAK (5)

PERAK (6)

PERAK (7)

1884–90.

16 **4** 2 c. rose (" E " wide) .. 2 0 2 0
a. " PERAK " double .. .. — £40
b. " PERAK " inverted .. £15
17 ,, 2 c. rose (" E " narrow) .. 17 6 20 0
a. " PERAK " inverted .. £12 £8

Triplet settings occur of:—1884. Nos. 17+16+16; Nos. 16+16+16. There is a setting of 30 (3×10) (1888) which contained two units of No. 17, also several settings of 60 (6×10) (1888–90) one of which contained three units of No. 17.

The variety " PERAK " inverted occurs in a triple setting and also in one setting of 60.

1886.

18 **5** 2 c. rose 0 6 2 0
a. Error. " FERAK " £6 £5

This error is usually found with the " F " altered in ink to " P ".

1886.

19 **6** 2 c. rose 3 6 6 0
20 **7** 2 c. rose 40 0 45 0

Nos. 19 and 20 are each triplet settings.

ONE CENT PERAK (8)

1 CENT PERAK (9)

1886. *Surch. vertically. No stop.*

21 **8** 1 c. on 2 c rose £25

As last, but stop after " PERAK ".

22 1 c. on 2 c. rose 15 0 20 0
a. Surch. double .. ..
23 1 c. on 2 c. (letters " N " wide) 15 0 20 0

A triplet setting composed of Nos. 22+23+22.

1886.

24 **9** 1 c. on 2 c. rose 30 0 30 0
a. Surch. double .. ..

A triplet setting.

One CENT PERAK (10)

ONE CENT PERAK (11)

1886.

25 **10** 1 c. on 2 c. rose 2 0 3 6
a. Error. " One " inverted .. £40
b. Surch. double £20

A triplet setting. The error occurred in the third unit on part of the printing only.

1887. *Surch. vertically.*

26 **11** 1 c. on 2 c. rose (B.) .. 20 0 20 0
27 ,, 1 c. on 2 c. rose (Bk.) .. £45 £35

1 CENT PERAK (12)

1 CENT PERAK (13)

1886.

28 **12** 1 c. on 2 c. rose £12 £12

The figure " 1 " in T **12** is a small roman character. A triplet setting.

1887.

29 **13** 1 c. on 2 c. rose £40

One CENT PERAK (14)

PERAK ONE CENT. (15)

One CENT PERAK (16)

1887-90.

30 **14** 1 c. on 2 c. rose .. 1 6 2

The first printings were in triplet form. Another printing was in a setting of 30 (3×10). In later printings it formed the upper five rows of settings of 60.

1889. *As No.* 30, *but with seriffed italic* " K ".

31 1 c. on 2 c. rose 55 0

1889. *Surch. as T* **14**, *but* " CENT " *in roman (upright) letters as in T* **17.**

32 1 c. on 2 c. rose £25 £2

1889.

33 **15** 1 c. on 2 c. rose 70 0 50
34 **16** 1 c. on 2 c. rose 45 0 50

One CENT PERAK (17) — One CENT PERAK (18) — One CENT PERAK. (19)

1889–90.

No.	Type	Description	Unused	Used
35	17	1 c. on 2 c. rose	10 0	12 6
		a. Error. "PREAK" ..	£12	£12
36	18	1 c. on 2 c. rose	7 6	7 6
37	19	1 c. on 2 c. rose	7 6	7 6

PERAK ONE CENT (20) — One CENT PERAK (21) — PERAK (22)

1890.

No.	Type	Description	Unused	Used
38	20	1 c. on 2 c. rose	—	£8
39	21	1 c. on 2 c. rose	12 6	10 0

1891.

No.	Type	Description	Unused	Used
40	22	2 c. rose	15 0	17 6

1891. *Optd.* "PERAK" *only, in bold roman letters* 2¾ *mm. high and* 13 *mm. long.*

No.	Type	Description	Unused	Used
41		2 c. rose		

PERAK One CENT (23) — PERAK Two CENTS (24) — PERAK One CENT (25)

PERAK One CENT (26) — PERAK One CENT (27) — PERAK One CENT (28)

PERAK One CENT (29)

1891. *Variously surch. with bar through original value.*

No.	Type	Description	Unused	Used
42	23	1 c. on 2 c. rose	2 0	3 0
		a. Narrow "O" in "One" ..	12 6	15 0
		b. Without bar	£10	
		c. No bar and narrow "O" ..		
43	25	1 c. on 2 c. rose	6 0	6 0
		a. Without bar	£30	
44	26	1 c. on 2 c. rose	2 0	3 0
		a. Without bar	£12	
45	27	1 c. on 2 c. rose	6 0	6 0
		a. Without bar	£30	
46	23	1 c. on 6 c. lilac	15 0	15 0
47	26	1 c. on 6 c. lilac	27 6	30 0
48	27	1 c. on 6 c. lilac	27 6	30 0
49	28	1 c. on 6 c. lilac	27 6	30 0
50	29	1 c. on 6 c. lilac	35 0	35 0
51	24	2 c. on 24 c. green	7 0	7 0
52	26	2 c. on 24 c. green	12 6	10 0
53	27	2 c. on 24 c. green	17 6	17 6
54	28	2 c. on 24 c. green	27 6	27 6
55	29	2 c. on 24 c. green	17 6	15 0

PERAK POSTAGE POSTAGE 1c

30

3 CENTS

(30*a*)

1892 (1 Jan.)–**1895.** *Wmk. Crown CA. P* 14.

No.	Type	Description	Unused	Used
57	30	1 c. green	2 6	0 6
58	,,	2 c. rose	2 6	0 6
59	,,	2 c. orange (9.9.95)	1 3	6 0
60	,,	5 c. blue	5 0	4 0

1895 (18 Apr.). *Surch. with T* **30a**.

No.	Type	Description	Unused	Used
61	30	3 c. on 5 c. rose	1 9	3 0

50c POSTAGE & REVENUE PERAK

31

$2 POSTAGE & REVENUE PERAK

32

1895–99. *P* 14. (*a*) *T* **31.** *Wmk. Crown CA.*

No.	Description	Unused	Used
62	1 c. dull purple and green ..	1 6	0 6
	a. "I G" for "I C" at left ..	17 6	
63	2 c. dull purple and brown ..	2 0	0 9
64	3 c. dull purple & carmine ..	1 6	0 6
65	4 c. dull purple & carm. (1899)	7 6	7 6
66	5 c. dull purple & olive-yellow	6 0	2 0
67	8 c. dull purple & ultram. ..	7 6	2 6
68	10 c. dull purple and orange ..	7 6	2 0
69	25 c. green and carmine ..	60 0	17 6
70	50 c. dull pur. & greenish black	35 0	25 0
71	50 c. green & black (1899) ..	65 0	37 6

(*b*) *T* **32.** *Wmk. Crown CC.*

No.	Description	Unused	Used
72	$1 green and pale green ..	80 0	60 0
73	$2 green and carmine ..	£10	£6
74	$3 green and ochre	£8	£5
75	$5 green and ultramarine ..	£25	£10
76	$25 green and orange (S. £15)	£200	£60

One Cent. (33) — ONE CENT. (34)

Three Cent. (35) — Three Cent. (36)

1900. *Stamps of* 1895–99 *surcharged.*

No.	Type	Description	Unused	Used
77	33	1 c. on 2 c. dull pur. & brn.	1 0	1 3
		a. Antique "e" in "One" ..	30 0	
		b. Antique "e" in "Cent" ..	20 0	
78	34	1 c. on 4 c. dull. pur. & carm.	1 0	2 0
79	33	1 c. on 5 c. dull purple and olive-yellow ..	1 6	2 0
		a. Antique "e" in "One" ..	30 0	
		b. Antique "e" in "Cent" ..	20 0	20 0
81	35	3 c. on 8 c. dull pur. & ult.	4 0	5 0
		a. Antique "e" in "Cent" ..	50 0	
		b. No stop after "Cent" ..	85 0	
		c. Surcharge double	£8	
82	,,	3 c. on 50 c. green & black	2 6	5 0
		a. Antique "e" in "Cent" ..	75 0	
		b. No stop after "Cent" ..	60 0	
83	36	3 c. on $1 grn. & pale grn.	22 6	27 6
		a. Small "t" in "Cent" ..	£6	£6
84	,,	3 c. on $2 green & carmine	12 6	17 6

37. Sultan Iskandar.

38. Sultan Iskandar.

1935–37. *Chalk-surfaced paper. Wmk. Mult. Script CA. P 14.*

95	37	1 c. black	0	5	0	5
96		2 c. green	0	6	0	5
97	,,	4 c. orange	1	0	1	0
98	,,	5 c. brown	0	9	0	4
99	,,	6 c. scarlet (1.1.37) ..	2	0	2	6
100	,,	8 c. grey	1	3	1	3
101	,,	10 c. dull purple ..	1	3	0	6
102	,,	12 c. bright ultramarine	2	6	3	6
103	,,	25 c. dull pur. & scarlet..	2	6	1	6
104	,,	30 c. dull pur. & orange..	3	0	4	0
105	,,	40 c. scarlet & dull purple	6	0	7	6
106	,,	50 c. black/*emerald* ..	5	0	2	6
107	,,	$1 black and red/*blue*	10	0	4	0
108	,,	$2 green and scarlet ..	20	0	8	0
109	,,	$5 green & red/*emerald*	40	0	32	6

Dates of issue as for Negri Sembilan.

1938–41. *Chalk-surfaced or ordinary paper* (O). *Wmk. Mult. Script CA. P 14*

110	38	1 c. black	1	0	0	6
111	,,	2 c. green	1	0	0	6
111*a*	,,	2 c. orange, OC ..	3	0	4	0
111*b*	,,	3 c. green, OC ..	3	6	3	0
112	,,	4 c. orange	2	0	1	0
113	,,	5 c. brown	1	3	0	6
114	,,	6 c. scarlet	10	0	1	3
115	,,	8 c. grey	2	6	1	0
115*a*	,,	8 c. scarlet ..	6	0	10	0
116	,,	10 c. dull purple ..	1	9	0	4
117	,,	12 c. bright ultramarine	3	6	3	0
117*a*	,,	15 c. bright ultram., O..	6	0	25	0
118	,,	25 c. dull pur. & scarlet..	15	0	7	6
119	,,	30 c. dull purple & orange	3	0	3	6
120	,,	40 c. scarlet & dull purple	3	6	3	0
121	,,	50 c. black/*emerald* ..	6	0	3	0
122	,,	$1 black and red/*blue*..	22	6	17	6
123	,,	$2 green and scarlet ..	60	0	60	0
124	,,	$5 green & red/*emerald*	£10		£12	

Dates of issue:—2.5.38, 40 c.; 17.10.38, 10 c., 12 c., 30 c. and 50 c.; 1.12.38, 8 c. grey; 13.1.39, 2 c. green; 1.2.39, 5 c.; –.4.39, 1 c.; –.5.39 4 c., –.–.39, 6 c. and 25 c.; –.–.40, $1; –.9.40, $2; –.1.41, $5; 30.10.41, 2 c. orge.; –.–.41, 3 c., 8 c. scarlet and 15 c.

1948 (1 Dec.). *Royal Silver Wedding. As Nos. 30/1 of Aden.*

125	10 c. violet	0	8	0	8
126	$5 green	35	0	40	0

1949 (10 Oct.). *75th Anniv. of Universal Postal Union. As Nos. 114/7 of Antigua.*

127	10 c. purple	0	8	0	8
128	15 c. deep blue	0	9	1	0
129	25 c. orange	1	9	2	0
130	50 c. blue-black	3	6	4	0

39. Sultan Yussuf 'Izzuddin Shah.

1950 (17 Aug.)–**55.** *Chalk-surfaced paper. Wmk. Mult. Script CA. P 17½ × 18.*

131	39	1 c. black	0	3	0	3
132	,,	2 c. orange	0	3	0	3
133	,,	3 c. green (*shades*) ..	2	6	2	6
134	,,	4 c. brown (*shades*) ..	0	4	0	4
134*a*	,,	5 c. brt. purple (*shades*) (1.9.52)	0	9	0	4
135	,,	6 c. grey	0	9	0	4
136	,,	8 c. scarlet	1	6	2	6
136*a*	,,	8 c. green (1.9.52) ..	2	0	2	0
137	,,	10 c. purple (*shades*) ..	0	8	0	3
137*a*	,,	12 c. scarlet (1.9.52) ..	2	6	2	6
138	,,	15 c. ultramarine ..	2	6	2	0
139	,,	20 c. black and green ..	3	0	3	0
139*a*	,,	20 c. bright blue (1.9.52)	2	6	0	9
140	,,	25 c. purple and orange..	1	6	0	9
140*a*	,,	30 c. scar. & pur. (5.9.55)	3	0	2	0
140*b*	,,	35 c. scar. & pur. (1.9.52)	3	0	2	0
141	,,	40 c. red and purple ..	3	0	6	6
142	,,	50 c. black and blue ..	2	6	1	0
143	,,	$1 blue and purple ..	6	0	2	6
144	,,	$2 green and scarlet ..	10	0	6	0
145	,,	$5 green and brown ..	25	0	17	6

1953 (2 June). *Coronation. As No. 47 of Aden.*

146	10 c. black & reddish purple	0	8	0	8

1957–61. *As Nos. 92/102 of Kedah but with inset portrait of Sultan Yussuf 'Izzuddin Shah.*

147	1 c. black	0	2	0	3
148	2 c. orange-red	0	3	0	3
	a. *Red-orange* (16.12.59) ..	1	0	1	0
149	4 c. sepia	0	4	0	4
150	5 c. carmine-lake	0	5	0	4
151	8 c. myrtle-green	0	6	0	11
152	10 c. deep brown	0	10	0	4
152*a*	10 c. dp. maroon (21.2.61) ..	0	7	0	3
153	20 c. blue	1	0	0	7
154	50 c. black and blue (*p.* 12½)	2	6	2	0
	a. Perf. 12½ × 13 (24.5.60) ..	2	0	1	2
155	$1 ultramarine & reddish purple	4	2	2	6
156	$2 brz.-grn. & scar. (*p.* 12½)	10	0	8	0
	a. Perf. 13 × 12½ (21.2.61) ..	7	9	5	6
157	$5 brn. & brz.-grn. (*p.* 12½)	25	0	20	0
	a. Perf. 13 × 12½ (24.5.60) ..	18	6	9	0

Dates of issue:—26.6.57, 20 c., $5; 25.7.57, 2 c., 50 c., $1; 4.8.57, 10 c.; 21.8.57, others.

40. *Vanda hookeriana.*

1965 (15 Nov.). *As Nos. 166/72 of Johore but with inset portrait of Sultan Idris as in T* **40.**

158	1 c. multicoloured	0	1	0	[illegible]
159	2 c. multicoloured	0	2	0	[illegible]
160	5 c. multicoloured	0	4	0	[illegible]
161	6 c. multicoloured	0	4	0	[illegible]
162	10 c. multicoloured	0	6	0	[illegible]
163	15 c. multicoloured	0	7	1	[illegible]
164	20 c. multicoloured	0	10	1	[illegible]

The higher values used in Perak are Nos. 20/2[illegible] of Malaysia.

OFFICIAL STAMPS.

P.G.S. (O 1) Service. (O 2)

1889 (1 Nov.). *Stamps of Straits Settlements optd with Type* O **1** *in black.*

O1	2 cents, CA, rose	8	0	8	[illegible]
	a. Overprint double	£35		£3[illegible]	
	b. No stop after "S"	60	0		
	c. Wide space between "G" & "S"	65	0		

O2 4 cents, CA, brown 17 6 17 6
a. No stop after "S" £6
b. Wide space between "G" & "S" 95 0
O3 6 cents, CA, lilac 50 0 50 0
a. Wide space between "G" & "S" £6
O4 8 cents, CA, orange 50 0 50 0
a. Wide space between "G" & "S" £6
O5 10 cents, CA, slate 80 0 80 0
a. Wide space between "G" & "S" £12 £12
O6 12 cents, CC, blue £8
a. Wide space between "G" & "S" £35
O7 12 cents, CA, brown-purple .. £12
a. Wide space between "G" & "S" £35
O8 24 cents, CC, green £25
a. Wide space between "G" & "S" £60
O9 24 cents, CA, green £7
a. Wide space between "G" & "S" £30

1894 (1 June). *No.* 60 *optd. with Type* O 2.
O10 5 c. blue 10 0 3 0
a. Overprint inverted £12 £10

1897. *No.* 66 *optd. with Type* O 2.
O11 5 c. dull purple & olive-yell. 3 0 1 0
a. Overprint double £7 £8

PERLIS.

A State of the Federation of Malaya.

1948 (1 Dec.). *Royal Silver Wedding. As Nos.* 30/1 *of Aden, but inscr.* "MALAYA PERLIS".
1 10 c. violet 0 8 0 10
2 $5 brown 40 0 45 0

1949 (10 Oct.). *75th Anniv. of U.P.U. As Nos.* 114/7 *of Antigua, but inscr.* "MALAYA PERLIS".
3 10 c. purple 0 8 1 0
4 15 c. deep blue 0 9 1 6
5 25 c. orange 1 9 2 6
6 50 c. blue-black 3 6 4 6

1. Raja Syed Putra.

951 (26 Mar.)–**55.** *Chalk-surfaced paper. Wmk. Mult. Script CA. P* 17½ × 18.
7 **1** 1 c. black 0 3 0 6
8 ,, 2 c. orange 0 3 0 10
9 ,, 3 c. green 3 0 4 0
0 ,, 4 c. brown 0 6 0 8
0a ,, 5 c. bright purple (1.9.52) 0 6 0 8
1 ,, 6 c. grey 0 9 1 0
2 ,, 8 c. scarlet 1 9 3 6
2a ,, 8 c. green (1.9.52) .. 1 6 2 0
3 ,, 10 c. purple 1 0 0 9
3a ,, 12 c. scarlet (1.9.52) .. 1 6 1 9
4 ,, 15 c. ultramarine 3 6 5 0
5 ,, 20 c. black and green .. 5 0 7 0
5a ,, 20 c. bright blue (1.9.52) 2 0 2 6
6 ,, 25 c. purple and orange .. 2 0 2 6
6a ,, 30 c. scar. & purple (5.9.55) 3 0 4 0
6b ,, 35 c. scar. & purple (1.9.52) 3 0 7 6
7 ,, 40 c. red and purple .. 7 6 10 0
8 ,, 50 c. black and blue .. 3 0 3 0
9 ,, $1 blue and purple .. 8 6 10 0
0 ,, $2 green and scarlet .. 12 6 17 6
1 ,, $5 green and brown .. 30 0 35 0

953 (2 June). *Coronation. As No.* 47 *of Aden.*
10 c. black & reddish purple .. 0 8 1 3

957–62. *As Nos.* 92/102 *of Kedah but with inset portrait of Raja Syea Putra.*
9 1 c. black 0 2 0 3
10 2 c. orange-red 0 3 0 3
11 4 c. sepia 0 4 0 5
12 5 c. carmine-lake 0 5 0 5
13 8 c. myrtle-green 0 6 1 0
28 **14** 10 c. deep brown 0 10 0 8
28a ,, 10 c. deep maroon (14.3.61) 0 7 0 7
29 **15** 20 c. blue 1 0 1 2
30 **16** 50 c. black and blue (*p.* 12½) 3 0 3 0
a. Perf. 12½ × 13 (8.5.62) .. 2 0 2 6
31 **17** $1 ultram. & reddish pur. 4 2 4 6
32 **18** $2 bronze-green & scarlet 7 9 9 0
33 **19** $5 brown & bronze-green 18 6 21 0

Dates of issue:—16.6.57, 20 c., $5; 25.7.57, 2 c., 50 c., $1; 4.8.57, 10 c.; 21.8.57, others.

2. *Vanda hookeriana.*

1965 (15 Nov.). *As Nos.* 166/72 *of Johore but with inset portrait of Tunku Bendahara Abu Bakar as in T* 2.
34 1 c. multicoloured 0 1 0 3
35 2 c. multicoloured 0 2 0 5
36 5 c. multicoloured 0 4 0 7
37 6 c. multicoloured 0 4 0 7
38 10 c. multicoloured 0 6 0 10
39 15 c. multicoloured 0 7 1 0
40 20 c. multicoloured 0 10 1 6

The higher values used in Perlis are Nos. 20/27 of Malaysia.

SELANGOR.

A State of the Federation of Malaya.

SELANGOR
(1)

1881–2. *T* **5** *of Straits, wmk. Crown CC, optd. as T* **1**.

Varieties. (*a*) *All letters narrow.* (*b*) "S" *wide.* (*c*) "S", "E", "A", *and* "N" *wide.* (*d*) "SELAN" *wide.* (*e*) "SEL" and "N" *wide.* (*f*) "EL" *wide.* (*g*) "E" *wide.* (*s*) "N" *wide.*

1 **1** 2 c. brown (*a*) 25 0 30 0
a. "S" inverted £8
2 ,, 2 c. brown (*b*) 30 0 32 6
3 ,, 2 c. brown (*c*) 75 0
4 ,, 2 c. brown (*d*) 75 0
5 ,, 2 c. brown (*e*) 75 0
6 ,, 2 c. brown (*s*) .. .. .. — £30

Overprinted in triplets composed of: 1881. (*a*)+(*b*)+(*a*); 1881. (*b*)+(*a*)+(*a*); 1882. (*c*)+(*e*)+(*d*). The setting containing (*s*) (1881) is not known.

1882. *Same type, wmk. Crown CA, optd. with capital* "S" *in black.*
7 2 c. brown .. .. .. — £60

1882–83. *T* **5** *of Straits, wmk. Crown CA, optd. as T* **1**.

Varieties. (*i*) "SEL", "N", *and* "G" *wide.* (*j*) "E" *and* "ANG" *wide.* (*k*) "ELANG" *wide.* (*l*) "SE" *and* "N" wide. (*m*) "S" *and* "N" *wide.* (*n*) "S" *and* "A" *wide.* (*o*) "S" *and* "L" *wide.*

8 **1** 2 c. brown (*a*) .. .. — 42 6
9 ,, 2 c. brown (*b*) 65 0 60 0
10 ,, 2 c. brown (*f*) .. .. — £5
11 ,, 2 c. brown (*g*) 70 0 70 0
12 ,, 2 c. brown (*i*) 70 0 70 0
13 ,, 2 c. brown (*j*) 70 0 70 0
14 ,, 2 c. brown (*k*) 70 0 70 0
15 ,, 2 c. brown (*l*) 37 6 42 6
16 ,, 2 c. brown (*m*) 37 6 42 6
17 ,, 2 c. brown (*n*) .. .. — £5
18 ,, 2 c. brown (*o*) .. .. — £22

Triplets are known of : 1882. (*i*)+(*j*)+(*k*); 1883. (*n*)+(*g*)+(*f*); 1883. (*l*)+(*b*)+(*m*). 1882. (*b*)+(*a*)+(?) are known in a pair; 1883. (*o*) is the first unit of a triplet but the second and third units are not yet known.

1883–85. *Wmk. Crown CA.*
Varieties. (*p*) " E " and " A " wide. (*q*) " A " *wide* (*r*) " L " *wide.* (*s*) " N " *wide.* (*t*) *all letters wide.* (*u*) " A " *narrow.* (*v*) " L " *narrow.*

19 **1** 2 c. rose (*b*) 20 0 22 6
20 ,, 2 c. rose (*f*) 15 0 15 0
21 ,, 2 c. rose (*g*) 15 0 20 0
22 ,, 2 c. rose (*o*) 27 6 30 0
23 ,, 2 c. rose (*p*) 20 0 25 0
24 ,, 2 c. rose (*q*) 42 6 35 0
25 ,, 2 c. rose (*r*) 47 6 45 0
26 ,, 2 c. rose (*s*) 25 0 30 0
27 ,, 2 c. rose (*t*) 42 6 35 0
28 ,, 2 c. rose (*u*) 22 6 27 6
29 ,, 2 c. rose (*v*) 17 6 17 6

Triplets are known of: 1883. (*o*)+(*g*)+(*g*); 1884. (*s*)+(*s*)+(*f*); 1884. (*b*)+(*p*)+(*f*); 1885. (*v*)+(*u*)+(*v*). The settings containing (1884) (*q*) and (*r*) and (1885) (*t*) are not known.

The 2 c. with all letters narrow, formerly listed, does not exist. Specimens with the wide " A " or wide " L " may be mistaken for this variety where these letters are defective, but may be detected by the spacing.

T **5** *of Straits, wmk. Crown CA, opt.* " SELANGOR ", *in various types.*

SELANGOR (2) SELANGOR (3) *Selangor* (4)

1885.
30 **2** 2 c. rose 4 0 6 0
31 **3** 2 c. rose (Oct.) 7 0 8 6
32 **4** 2 c. rose £20

SELANGOR (5) SELANGOR. (6)

1886 (MAY).
33 **5** 2 c. rose 12 6 12 6

1887.
34 **6** 2 c. rose (with stop) (Aug.).. 7 6 8 6
35 ,, 2 c. rose (without stop) .. 3 6 4 0

SELANGOR (7) *SELANGOR* (8)

SELANGOR (9)

1889. *Optd. vertically.*
36 **7** 2 c. rose £7 25 0
37 **8** 2 c. rose (Feb.) 60 0 50 0
38 **9** 2 c. rose (Feb.) 15 0 5 0

Opt. similar to T **8**, *but diagonal.*
39 2 c. rose £35

Opt. as T **9** *but horizontal.*
40 2 c. rose .. .. ..

1890. *Optd. with T* **6** *vertically. No stop.*
41 2 c. deep rose 12 6

SELANGOR (10) *SELANGOR* (11)

1890.
42 **10** 2 c. rose 60 0 4 0

1891.
43 **11** 2 c. deep rose £12 £6

SELANGOR Two CENTS (12) SELANGOR Two CENTS (13)

SELANGOR Two CENTS (14) SELANGOR *Two* CENTS (15) *SELANGOR* *Two* CENTS (16)

1891. *T* **7** *of Straits, surch. horizontally, with bar obliterating old value.*
44 **12** 2 c. on 24 c. green 35 0 45 0
45 **13** 2 c. on 24 c. green 20 0
a. Error. " SELANGCR " ..
46 **14** 2 c. on 24 c. green 35 0
47 **15** 2 c. on 24 c. green 30 0
48 **16** 2 c. on 24 c. green 10 0

The error, No. 45*a*, occurs in the first printing only and is No. 45 on the pane.

17

1891–95. *T* **17.** *Wmk. Crown CA. P* 14.
57 1 c. green 2 6 0
58 2 c. rose 3 6 1
59 2 c. orange (1895) 2 6 1
60 5 c. blue 5 0 3

1894. T **17**, *surch.* **3 CENTS**
61 3 c. on 5 c. rose 1 3 1

18

19

1895-98. *Wmk. Crown CA or Crown CC (dolla values). P* 14.
62 **18** 3 c. dull purple & carmine 2 6 0
63 ,, 5 c. dull pur. & olive-yell. 2 0 2
64 ,, 8 c. dull pur. and ultram. 35 0 8
65 ,, 10 c. dull purple and orange 4 0 1
66 ,, 25 c. green and carmine .. 50 0 30
67 ,, 50 c. green and black .. £10 55
67*a* ,, 50 c. dull pur. & grnsh. blk. 22 6 15
68 **19** $1 green & yellow-green 40 0 30
69 ,, $2 green and carmine .. 90 0 50
70 ,, $3 green and ochre .. £12 80
71 ,, $5 green and blue .. 60 0 60
72 ,, $10 green & purple (S. £6) £30 £
73 ,, $25 green & orange (S. £15) £100

One cent. (20) Three cents. (21)

1900. *Nos. 63 and 67 surch. with T* **20** *or* **21.**

No.		Description	Unused s.	d.	Used s.	d.
74		1 c. on 5 c. dull purple and olive-yellow	20	0	30	0
75		1 c. on 50 c. green & black ..	3	6	8	6
		a. " cent " repeated at left ..	£60			
76		3 c. on 50 c. green & black ..	6	0	8	6
		a. Antique " t " in " cents " ..	50	0	60	0

22. Mosque at Palace, Klang. **23.** Sultan Suleiman.

1935–41. *Chalk-surfaced or ordinary paper* (O). *Wmk. Mult. Script CA. P* 14 *or* 14×15 (*No.* 81*a*).

No.	Type	Description	Unused s.	d.	Used s.	d.
80	**22**	1 c. black	0	6	0	3
81	,,	2 c. green	0	9	0	3
81*a*	,,	2 c. orange, OC (21.8.41)	0	6	1	9
		ab. Perf. 14, O (Sept. '41) ..	27	6	12	6
81*b*	,,	3 c. green OC (21.8.41)..	0	6	2	6
82	,,	4 c. orange	0	9	0	3
83	,,	5 c. brown	0	9	0	2
84	,,	6 c. scarlet	1	3	1	6
85	,,	8 c. grey	1	3	0	10
86	,,	10 c. dull purple	1	6	0	9
87	,,	12 c. bright ultramarine ..	1	9	1	3
87*a*	,,	15 c. brt. ultram. O (1.10.41)	3	6	10	0
88	,,	25 c. dull purple & scarlet	3	0	2	6
89	,,	30 c. dull purple & orange	2	6	3	0
90	,,	40 c. scarlet and dull pur.	4	6	3	6
91	,,	50 c. black/*emerald* ..	5	0	3	0
92	**23**	$1 black and red/*blue* ..	8	6	5	0
93	,,	$2 green and scarlet ..	35	0	25	0
94	,,	$5 green & red/*emerald*	60	0	30	0

Dates of issue as for Negri Sembilan, except Nos. 81*a*/*ab*.

24. Sultan Hisamud-din Alam Shah. **25.**

941. *Wmk. Mult. Script CA. P* 14.

No.	Type	Description	Unused s.	d.	Used s.	d.
5	**24**	$1 blk. & red/*bl.*, C (15.4.41)	12	6	15	0
	,,	$2 grn. & scarlet, C (7.7.41)	17	6	30	0

A $5 green and red on emerald, T **24**, was sued overprinted during the Japanese occupaon of Malaya. Unoverprinted specimens are own, but were not issued thus.

48 (1 Dec.). *Royal Silver Wedding. As Nos.* 30/1 *of Aden.*

No.	Description	Unused s.	d.	Used s.	d.
	10 c. violet	0	8	0	8
	$5 green	35	0	40	0

49 (12 Sept.)–**55.** *Chalk-surfaced paper. Wmk. Mult. Script CA. P* $17\frac{1}{2}\times18$.

No.	Type	Description	Unused s.	d.	Used s.	d.
9	**25**	1 c. black	0	3	0	4
o	,,	2 c. orange	0	3	0	3
1	,,	3 c. green	0	9	1	6
2	,,	4 c. brown	0	4	0	3
2*a*	,,	5 c. bt. pur. (*shades*)(1.9.52)	0	10	0	6
3	,,	6 c. grey	0	9	0	6
4	,,	8 c. scarlet	1	6	3	0
4*a*	,,	8 c. green (1.9.52) ..	1	3	1	6
5	,,	10 c. purple	0	9	0	6
105*a*	**25**	12 c. scarlet (1.9.52) ..	1	6	1	3
106	,,	15 c. ultramarine	1	9	1	3
107	,,	20 c. black and green ..	3	6	2	6
107*a*	,,	20 c. bright blue (1.9.52)..	3	6	2	0
108	,,	25 c. purple and orange ..	1	6	0	6
108*a*	,,	30 c. scar. & purple (5.9.55)	3	0	1	9
108*b*	,,	35 c. scar. & purple (1.9.52)	3	6	2	0
109	,,	40 c. scarlet and purple ..	4	0	6	0
110	,,	50 c. black and blue ..	3	6	1	3
111	,,	$1 blue and purple ..	4	6	1	6
112	,,	$2 green and scarlet ..	10	0	4	0
113	,,	$5 green and brown ..	22	6	7	6

1949 (10 Oct.). *75th Anniv. of Universal Postal Union. As Nos.* 114/7 *of Antigua, but inscr.* "MALAYA SELANGOR".

No.	Description	Unused s.	d.	Used s.	d.
114	10 c. purple	0	8	0	8
115	15 c. deep blue	0	9	1	0
116	25 c. orange	1	9	2	6
117	50 c. blue-black	3	6	4	0

1953 (2 June). *Coronation. As No.* 47 *of Aden.*

No.	Description	Unused s.	d.	Used s.	d.
118	10 c. black & reddish purple	0	8	1	0

1957–61. *As. Nos.* 92/102 *of Kedah but with inset portrait of Sultan Hisamud-din Alam Shah.*

No.	Description	Unused s.	d.	Used s.	d.
119	1 c. black	0	4	0	6
120	2 c. orange-red (*shades*) ..	0	4	0	6
121	4 c. sepia	0	6	0	6
122	5 c. carmine-lake	0	6	0	3
123	8 c. myrtle-green	0	8	1	0
124	10 c. deep brown	0	8	0	3
124*a*	10 c. dp. maroon (9.5.61) ..	0	10	0	3
125	20 c. blue	1	3	0	6
126	50 c. black and blue (*p.* $12\frac{1}{2}$)	2	6	2	0
	a. Perf. $12\frac{1}{2}\times13$ (10.5.60) ..	2	0	0	11
127	$1 ultram. & reddish purple	4	2	1	10
128	$2 brz.-grn. & scar. (*p.* $12\frac{1}{2}$)	10	0	10	0
	a. Perf. $13\times12\frac{1}{2}$ (6.12.60) ..	7	9	7	6
129	$5 brn. & brz.-grn. (*p.* $12\frac{1}{2}$)	22	6	15	0
	a. Perf. $13\times12\frac{1}{2}$ (10.5.60) ..	18	6	12	0

Dates of issue :—26.6.57, 20 c., $5 ; 25.7.57, 2 c., 50 c., $1 ; 4.8.57, 10 c. ; 21.8.57, others.

26. Sultan Salahuddin Abdul Aziz Shah.

(Photo. Harrison & Sons.)

1961 (28 June). *Installation of the Sultan. W w.* **12.** *P* 15×14.

No.	Type	Description	Unused s.	d.	Used s.	d.
130	**26**	10 c. multicoloured ..	0	10	0	6
		a. Black ptg. misplaced ..	£85			

No. 130*a* is "The Double-headed Sultan" error, from one sheet where the majority of the stamps showed considerable black printing misplacement.

27. Sultan Salahuddin Abdul Aziz Shah.

1961–62. *As Nos.* 92/8 *of Kedah but with inset portrait of Sultan Salahuddin Abdul Aziz as in T* **27.** *W* w. **13.** *P* 12½×13 (*vert.*) *or* 13×12½ (*horiz.*).

131	1 c. black (1.3.62)	0	2	0	3
132	2 c. orange-red (1.3.62) ..	0	3	0	3
133	4 c. sepia (1.3.62) ..	0	4	0	5
134	5 c. carmine-lake (1.3.62) ..	0	5	0	5
135	8 c. myrtle-green (1.3.62) ..	0	6	0	7
136	10 c. deep maroon (1.11.61) ..	0	7	0	4
137	20 c. blue (1.3.62)	1	0	0	7

28. *Vanda hookeriana.*

1965 (15 Nov.). *As Nos.* 166/72 *of Johore but with inset portrait of Sultan Salahuddin Abdul Aziz Shah as in T* **28.**

138	1 c. multicoloured	0	1	0	2
139	2 c. multicoloured	0	2	0	4
140	5 c. multicoloured	0	4	0	7
141	6 c. multicoloured	0	4	0	7
142	10 c. multicoloured	0	6	0	10
143	15 c. multicoloured	0	7	1	0
144	20 c. multicoloured	0	10	1	4

The higher values used in Selangor are Nos. 20/27 of Malaysia.

STRAITS SETTLEMENTS.

Former Crown Colony comprising Singapore, Penang (with Province Wellesley and (until 1934) The Dindings), Malacca, Labuan, Cocos or Keeling Islands and Christmas Island.

THREE HALF CENTS
(1)

32 CENTS
(2)

1867 (1 Sept.). *Types* **11** *and* **17** *of India* (8 *a.* Die II, *others,* Die I), *wmk. Elephant's Head, surch. as T* **1** *and* **2** (24 *c. and* 32 *c.*) *in red* (R.), *blue* (B.), *black* (Bk.), *purple* (P.) *or green* (G.). *P* 14.

1	1½ c. on ½ a. blue (R.)	45	0	55	0
2	2 c. on 1 a. brown (R.) ..	60	0	50	0
3	3 c. on 1 a. brown (B.) ..	70	0	60	0
4	4 c. on 1 a. brown (Bk.) ..	£5		85	0
5	6 c. on 2 a. yellow (P.) ..	£12		£7	
6	8 c. on 2 a. yellow (G.) ..	£6		60	0
7	12 c. on 4 a. green (R.) ..	£16		£5	
	a. Surcharge double	£35			
8	24 c. on 8 a. rose (B.)	£10		£5	
9	32 c. on 2 a. yellow (Bk.) ..	£6		£5	

The 32 c. was re-issued for postal use in 1884. No. 7a is only known unused.

1869 (?). *No.* 1 *with* " THREE HALF " *deleted and* " 2 " *written above, in black manuscript.*

11	2 on 1½ c. on ½ a. blue ..	£65	£45

This stamp has been known from very early days and was apparently used in the Straits Settlements, but nothing is known of its history.

5

6

7

8

1867 (Dec.)–**1871.** *T* **5** *to* **8.** *Wmk. Crown CC. P* 14. (*The ornaments in the corners of the frames differ from each value*).

12	**5**	2 c. brown (June, 1868) ..	6 0	4	6
13	,,	2 c. yellow-brown ..	6 0	4	6
14	,,	2 c. deep brown	20 0	15	
15	,,	4 c. rose (July, 1868) ..	8 6	5	
15a	,,	4 c. deep rose	12 6	6	
16	,,	6 c. dull lilac (Jan., 1868)	25 0	22	
17	,,	6 c. bright lilac	37 6	15	
18	**6**	8 c. orange-yellow ..	40 0	15	
19	,,	8 c. orange	42 6	20	
20	,,	12 c. blue	40 0	10	
21	,,	12 c. ultramarine	42 6	25	
22	**7**	24 c. blue-green	40 0	12	
23	,,	24 c. yellow-green	55 0	30	
24	**8**	32 c. pale red	£5	47	
25	,,	96 c. grey	£5	47	
		a. Variety. Perf. 12½ (June 1871)	£25	£	

9

1872. *Wmk. Crown CC. P* 14.

27	**9**	30 c. claret	65 0	20

Stamps of 1867–71, *surcharged.*

Five Cents.
(10)

Seven Cents.
(11)

1879 (May). *With T* **10** *and* **11.**

28	**6**	5 c. on 8 c. orange	70 0	70
		a. No stop after " Cents " ..	£15	£
		b. " F i " spaced	£18	£
29	**8**	7 c. on 32 c. pale red ..	70 0	70
		a. No stop after " Cents " ..	£20	£

10 cents.
(12)

10 (a) 10 (b) 10 (c) 10 (d)
10 (e) 10 (f) 10 (g) 10 (h)
10 (i) 10 (j) 10 (k) 10 (l)

1880 (Mar.). *With T* **12** (*ten varieties of figures* "10").

(*a*) "1" thin curved serif and thin foot; "0" narrow. (*b*) "1" thick curved serif and thick foot; "0" broad. Both numerals heavy. (*c*) "1" as (*a*); "0" as (*b*). (*d*) "1" as (*a*) but thicker; "0" as (*a*). (*e*) As (*a*) but sides of "0" thicker. (*f*) "1" as (*d*); "0" as (*e*). (*g*) As (*a*) but "0" narrower. (*h*) "1" thin, curved serif and thick foot; "0" as (*g*). (*i*) "1" as (*b*); "0" as (*a*). (*j*) "1" as (*d*); "0" as (*g*). Numerals much closer than (*g*). (*k*) "1" as (*a*) but shorter, and with shorter serif and thicker foot; "0" as (*d*). (*l*) "1" straight serif; "0" as (*d*).

30	10 c. on 30 c. claret (*a*) ..	£5	85 0
31	10 c. on 30 c. claret (*b*) ..	£5	75 0
32	10 c. on 30 c. claret (*c*) ..	£25	
33	10 c. on 30 c. claret (*d*) ..	£25	£15
34	10 c. on 30 c. claret (*e*) ..	£60	£20
35	10 c. on 30 c. claret (*f*) ..	£60	
36	10 c. on 30 c. claret (*g*) ..	£28	£25
37	10 c. on 30 c. claret (*h*) ..	£60	
38	10 c. on 30 c. claret (*i*) ..	£60	£20
39	10 c. on 30 c. claret (*j*) ..	£40	

No. 31 is known with large stop after "cents" and also with stop low.

1880 (April). *As T* **12** *but without "cents."* (*eight varieties of figures* "10").

40	10 on 30 c. claret (*a*) ..	55 0	55 0
41	10 on 30 c. claret (*b*) ..	55 0	55 0
42	10 on 30 c. claret (*c*) ..	£15	£8
43	10 on 30 c. claret (*g*) ..	£40	£22
44	10 on 30 c. claret (*i*) ..	£65	£30
45	10 on 30 c. claret (*k*) ..	£65	
46	10 on 30 c. claret (*l*) ..	£65	£30
46*a*	10 on 30 c. claret (*m*) ..		

Variety (*m*) has the "1" as (*b*) and the "0" as (*g*).

5 cents. (13) 5 cents. (14) 5 cents. (15)

1880 (Aug.). *With T* **13** *to* **15**.

47	**13**	5 c. on 8 c. orange ..	75 0	80 0
48	**14**	5 c. on 8 c. orange ..	70 0	80 0
49	**15**	5 c. on 8 c. orange ..	£10	£10

In this setting, the first four rows of the pane have surcharge T **13**; the next five, T **14**; and the last, T **15**.

10 cents. (16) 5 cents. (17)

1880–81. *With T* **16**.

	10 c. on 6 c. lilac (11.81) ..	32 6	15 0
	10 c. on 12 c. ultram. (1.81) ..	35 0	20 0
	10 c. on 12 c. blue ..	30 0	20 0
	10 c. on 30 c. claret (12.80) ..	£7	50 0

A second printing of the 10 c. on 6 c. has the surcharge heavier and the "10" usually more to the left or right of "cents."

1882 (Jan.). *With T* **17**.

	5 c. on 4 c. rose	£12	£8

18

19

1882 (Jan.). *Wmk. Crown CC. P* 14.

55	**18**	5 c. purple-brown ..	37 6	40 0
56	**19**	10 c. slate	85 0	27 6

1882. *Wmk. Crown CA. P* 14.

57	**5**	2 c. brown (Aug.) ..	60 0	15 0
58	,,	4 c. rose (April) ..	45 0	12 6
59	**6**	8 c. orange (Sept.) ..	6 0	1 6
60	**19**	10 c. slate (Oct.) ..	3 0	1 3

TWO CENTS

(20)

1883 (April). *Nos.* 59 *and* 24 *surcharged with T* **20** *vertically upwards.*

(*a*) "cents" in narrow letters. (*b*) With wide "e." (*c*) Wide "en" and "s." (*d*) Wide "n." (*e*) Wide "s." (*f*) Wide "e" and "s."

61	**6**	2 c. on 8 c. orange (*a*) ..	60 0	60 0
		a. Surcharge double ..	£60	£40
62	,,	2 c. on 8 c. orange (*c*) ..	£6	£5
63	,,	2 c. on 8 c. orange (*d*) ..	45 0	45 0
64	,,	2 c. on 8 c. orange (*e*) ..	50 0	45 0
65	,,	2 c. on 8 c. orange (*f*) ..	50 0	42 6
66	**8**	2 c. on 32 c. pale red (*b*) ..	£12	£5
		a. Surcharge double ..		
67	,,	2 c. on 32 c. pale red (*e*) ..	£12	£5

Nos. 61 to 67 were surcharged in triplets as follows:—

2 *c. on* 8 *c.* (*e*)+(*f*)+(*d*) with (*a*) as a single unit for the top row only. Also (*a*)+(*a*)+(*a*) with (*c*) as the single unit.

2 *c. on* 32 *c.* (*e*)+(*b*)+(*e*) with (*b*) as the single unit.

Cents.

(21)

1883 (July). *Nos.* 58 *and* 20 *surch. with T* **21.**

68	2 c. on 4 c. rose (*CA*) ..	25 0	37 6
	a. "s" of "Cents" inverted ..	£35	£20
69	2 c. on 12 c. blue (*CC*) ..	£8	£5
	a. "s" of "Cents" inverted ..	£50	

1883 (July)–**1891.** *Wmk. Crown CA. P* 14.

70	**5**	2 c. pale rose ..	8 6	1 6
71	,,	2 c. bright rose ..	0 8	0 6
72	,,	4 c. pale brown ..	4 6	3 0
73	,,	4 c. deep brown ..	12 6	7 6
74	**18**	5 c. blue (8.83) ..	2 6	1 0
75	**5**	6 c. lilac (11.84) ..	30 0	17 6
76	,,	6 c. violet ..	7 6	5 0
77	**6**	12 c. dull purple ..	17 6	10 0
78	**7**	24 c. yellow-green (2.84) ..	42 6	5 0
79	,,	24 c. blue-green ..	8 6	6 0
80	**9**	30 c. claret (9.91) ..	15 0	7 6
81	**8**	32 c. orange-verm. (1.87) ..	7 6	6 0
82	,,	96 c. olive-grey (8.88) ..	32 6	32 6

4 Cents (22) 8 Cents (23)

1884 (Feb.–Aug.). *Surcharged with T* **22** *or* **23**, *in black or red* (R.). (*The* 12 *c. blue, wmk. Crown CC.*)

83	**18**	4 c. on 5 c. blue (Aug.) ..	£80	£95

84 **18** 4 c. on 5 c. blue (R.) (Aug.) 75 0 75 0
85 **6** 8 c. on 12 c. blue (Feb.) .. £9 £5
86 „ 8 c. on 12 c. dull pur. (Aug.) £8 £5

1884 (Aug.). *Surcharged with* T **20** *vertically upwards.*
87 **18** 2 c. on 5 c. blue (*a*) .. 45 0 75 0
88 „ 2 c. on 5 c. blue (*b*) .. 45 0 75 0
89 „ 2 c. on 5 c. blue (*c*) .. 45 0 75 0
a. Surcharge omitted, pair ..
b. Surcharge double .. ..

Nos. 87 to 89 were surcharged in a triplet composed of (*c*)+(*a*)+(*b*).

In Type (*a*) the letters "TS" are below the line of the word.

8

(24)

1884 (Sept.) *Nos.* 84 *ana* 86 *surcharged with large numeral, as* T **24**, *in addition, in red.*
90 " 4 " on 4 c. in *red* on 5 c. blue — £650
91 " 8 " on 8 c. in *black* on 12 c. dull purple £8 £8
a. T **24** double £150
92 " 8 " on 8 c. in *blue* on 12 c. dull purple £120

Nos. 86 and 91 are known with "s" of "Cents" low.

3 CENTS (25) THREE CENTS (26)

1885. *No.* 74 *and* T **8** *in new colour, wmk. Crown CA, surcharged with* T **25** *and* **26.**
93 **25** 3 c. on 5 c. blue (Sept.) £5 £6
a. Surch. double £60
94 **26** 3 c. on 32 c. pale magenta (Dec.) 2 6 6 0
95 „ 3 c. on 32 c. deep magenta .. 2 6 3 0

3 cents (27) 2 Cents (28)

1886 (April). *No.* 55 *surcharged with* T **27.**
96 **18** 3 c. on 5 c. purple-brown .. £10 £10

1887 (July). *No.* 74 *surcharged with* T **28.**
97 **18** 2 c. on 5 c. blue 20 0 35 0
a. "C" of "Cents" omitted .. — £60
b. Surcharge double £35

Nos. 93, 96 and 97 were surcharged in triplet settings.

10 CENTS (29) THIRTY CENTS (30)

1891 (Nov.). *Nos.* 78 *and* 81 *surch. with* T **29** *and* **30.**
98 **7** 10 c. on 24 c. yellow-green .. 4 0 3 6
a. Narrow "0" in "10" .. 30 0 40 0
99 **8** 30 c. on 32 c orange-verm... 12 6 12 6

The "R" of "THIRTY" and "N" of "CENTS" are found wide or narrow and in all possible combinations.

ONE CENT

(31)

1892. *Stamps of* 1882–91 (*wmk. Crown CA*) *surch. with* T **31.**
100 1 c. on 2 c. rose (March) .. 1 0 2 0
101 1 c. on 4 c. brown (May) .. 3 6 4 6
a. Surch. double £20
102 1 c. on 6 c. lilac (Feb.) .. 3 0 4 6
a. Surch. double, one inverted .. £24 £18
103 1 c. on 8 c. orange (Jan.) .. 1 6 2 6
104 1 c. on 12 c. dull purple (Mar.) 2 0 30 0

The following varieties may be found in T 31:—(1) narrow "N" on "ONE" and "CENT"; (2) wide "N" in "ONE" and "CENT"; (3) narrow "N" in "ONE", wide "N" in "CENT"; (4) wide "N" in "ONE", narrow "N" in "CENT"; (5) narrow "O" in "ONE"; (6) antique "E" in "CENT".

ONE CENT

(32)

1892–94. *Colours changed. Wmk. Crown CA. P* 14. *Surch. with* T **32** *and* **26.**
105 **6** 1 c. on 8c. green (Mar. '92) 0 6 1 6
106 **8** 3 c. on 32 c. carmine-rose (June, 1894) 1 0 1 6
a. Error. Surch. omitted .. £90

33

34

1892 (Mar.)–**1898.** *Wmk. Crown CA. P* 14.
107 **33** 1 c. green (Sept., 1892) .. 0 6 0
108 „ 3 c. carmine-rose (2.95) .. 1 0 0
109 „ 25 c. purple-brown & grn. 10 6 8
110 „ 25 c. dull purple & green 10 6 6
111 „ 50 c. olive-grn. & carmine 8 6 7
112 **34** $5 oran. & carm. (10.98) £12 £1

1894. *New colours. Wmk. Crown CA. P* 14.
113 **18** 5 c. brown (June) .. 4 0 2
114 **6** 8 c. ultramarine (June) .. 4 0 0
115 „ 8 c. bright blue 7 0 0
116 „ 12 c. brown-purple (Mar.) 8 6 10

4 cents. (35) FOUR CENTS (36)

1899. T **18** *and* **6** *surch. with* T **35.**
117 4 c. on 5 c. brn. (No. 113) (Jan.) 2 0 5
118 4 c. on 5 c. blue (No. 74) (Jan.) 2 0 6
119 4 c. on 8 c. ultram. (No. 114) (Jan.) 3 0 8
a. Surch. double .. .. £35 £
120 4 c. on 8 c. brt. blue (No. 115) 2 6 2

Nos. 118 and 119 exist with stop spaced 1½ m from the "s".

1899 (MAR.). *T* **18** (*wmk. Crown CA. P* 14), *surch. with T* **36.**

121		4 c. on 5 c. carmine	0	9	0	6
		a. Error. Surch. omitted ..	£425			

No. 121*a* is only known unused.

1899. *Colours changed. Wmk. Crown CA. P* 14.

123	**33**	3 c. brown (March) ..	2	0	0	10
124	„	3 c. yellow-brown	1	6	1	0
125	**5**	4 c. deep carmine (July) ..	2	6	1	0
126	**18**	5 c. magenta (July) ..	6	0	4	0

37 38

1902. *Wmk. Crown CA. P* 14.

127	**37**	1 c. grey-green	0	10	0	8
128	„	1 c. pale green	2	0	0	8
129	„	3 c. dull purple & orange	1	0	0	8
130	„	4 c. purple/*red*	1	9	1	0
131	**38**	5 c. dull purple	1	9	1	0
132	„	8 c. purple/*blue*	2	6	1	0
133	„	10 c. purple & black/*yell.*	5	0	1	0
134	**37**	25 c. dull purple and green	5	0	6	0
135	**38**	30 c. grey and carmine	12	6	12	6
136	**37**	50 c. deep green & carmine	12	6	12	6
137	„	50 c. dull green & carmine	22	6	27	6
138	**38**	$1 dull green and black	20	0	25	0
139	**37**	$2 dull purple & black ..	35	0	45	0
140	**38**	$5 dull grn. & brn.-orge.	£7		45	0
141	**37**	$100 purple & green/*yellow* (S. £30)	£750			

39 40

41 42

903–4. *Wmk. Crown CA. P* 14.

42	**39**	1 c. grey-green	1	3	1	9
43	**40**	3 c. dull purple	2	9	2	0
44	**41**	4 c. purple/*red*	3	0	0	4
45	**42**	8 c. purple/*blue*	6	6	1	6

904–6. *Wmk. Multiple Crown CA. P* 14.

46	**39**	1 c. deep green, OC ..	0	6	0	2
47	**40**	3 c. dull purple, OC ..	1	0	0	4
48	„	3 c. plum, O	1	6	0	8
49	**41**	4 c. purple/*red*, OC ..	1	6	0	3
50	**38**	5 c. dull purple, OC ('06)	3	6	6	0
51	**42**	8 c. purple/*blue*, OC ..	6	0	0	10
52	**38**	10 c. pur. & blk./*yell.*, OC	4	0	1	3

153	**37**	25 c. dull. pur. & grn., OC	5	0	5	0
154	**38**	30 c. grey & carmine, OC	6	0	6	0
155	**37**	50 c. dull grn. & car., OC	15	0	9	0
156	**38**	$1 dull grn. & black, OC	20	0	12	6
157	**37**	$2 dull pur. & blk., C ..	60	0	45	0
158	**38**	$5 dull grn. and brown-orange, OC ..	85	0	70	0
159	„	$25 grey-grn. & black, C	£200			
160	**37**	$100 pur. & grn./*yell.*, C ..	£800			

STRAITS SETTLEMENTS.
(43)

Straits Settlements.
(44)

STRAITS SETTLEMENTS.

FOUR CENTS.
(45)

1907. *T* **42** *of Labuan* (*Nos.* 116*a, etc.*) *optd. with T* **43** (*the* 10 *c. with T* **44**), *or surch. with T* **45** *in brownish red or black* (Bk.).

161	1 c. black and purple ..	25	0	30	0
162	2 c. black and green	60	0	55	0
163	3 c. black and sepia	10	0	15	0
164	4 c. on 12 c. black & yellow ..	2	6	3	6
	a. No stop after "CENTS" ..	85	0		
165	4 c. on 16 c. grn. & brn. (Bk.)	2	0	6	0
166	4 c. on 18 c. blk. & pale brown	2	0	5	0
	a. No stop after "CENTS" ..	85	0		
167	8 c. black and vermilion ..	3	0	6	0
168	10 c. brown and slate ..	2	6	6	0
	a. No stop after "SETTLEMENTS" ..	55	0		
169	25 c. green & greenish blue ..	7	6	11	6
170	50 c. dull purple & lilac ..	8	6	17	6
171	$1 claret and orange ..	20	0	25	0

Varieties. (i) "STRAITS SETTLEMENTS" *in both black and red.*

172 4 c. on 16 c. green & brown .. £24 £24

(ii) "FOUR CENTS" *and bar* 1½ *mm. below level of the rest of the row.*

173 4 c. on 18 c. black & pale brn. £10

This variety only occurs in a few sheets of the first printing and should be collected in horiz. pair with normal.

(iii) "FOUR CENTS" *and bar double.*

174 4 c. on 18 c. black & pale brn. £190

46 47

1906–11. *Wmk. Mult. Crown CA. P* 14.

175	**39**	1 c. blue-green, O (1910)	0	6	0	3
176	**40**	3 c. red, O (1908) ..	0	6	0	3
177	**41**	4 c. red, O (1907) ..	1	6	2	0
178	„	4 c. dull purple, OC ('08)	0	8	0	6
179	„	4 c. claret, O (1911) ..	3	6	2	0
180	**38**	5 c. orange, O (1909) ..	2	6	0	8
181	**42**	8 c. blue, O (1906) ..	1	0	0	4
182	**38**	10 c. purple/*yell.*, OC ('08)	1	9	0	8

183 **37** 25 c. dull & brt. pur., C ('09) 5 0 6 0
184 **38** 30 c. pur. and orange-yell., C ('09) .. 6 0 3 0
185 **37** 50 c. black/*green*, C ('10) .. 5 0 4 0
186 **38** $1 blk. & red/*bl.*, C ('11) 10 0 8 6
187 **37** $2 grn. & red/*yellow.*, C ('09) 20 0 17 6
188 **38** $5 green and red/*green*, C ('10) 65 0 45 0
189 **46** $25 purple and blue/*blue*, C ('11) (S. £25) .. £150 £45
189*a* ,, $500 purple and orange, C ('10) (S. £150) £10000

Beware of dangerous forgeries of No. 189*a*.

1910. *Chalk-surfaced paper. Wmk. Mult. Crown CA. P* 14.

190 **47** 21 c. dull purple & claret 10 6 30 0
191 ,, 45 c. black/*green* 10 0 12 6

48

49

50

51

52

53

54

RED CROSS

2c.

(55)

1912–22. $25, $100 *and* $500 *as T* **46**, *but with head of King George V. Wmk. Mult. Crown CA. P* 14.

192 **48** 1 c. green, O 0 6 0 4
193 ,, 1 c. blue-green, O (1917) 0 8 0 4
194 **49** 3 c. red, O 0 10 0 3
195 ,, 3 c. scarlet, O (1917) .. 0 8 0 3
196 **50** 4 c. dull purple, C .. 0 10 0 3
a. Wmk. sideways .. ..
197 **51** 5 c. orange, O 1 0 0 4
198 ,, 5 c. yellow-orange, O .. 1 3 0 6
199 **52** 8 c. ultramarine, O .. 1 6 0 6
200 **51** 10 c. pur./*yellow*, C (1913) 2 0 0 4
a. White back 2 6 1 3
b. On lemon 17 6 2 0
201 **53** 21 c. dull & brt. purple, C 7 6 10 0
202 **54** 25 c. dull purple & mauve, C ('14) 6 0 4 0
203 ,, 25 c. dull purple & vio., C 12 6 2 6
204 **51** 30 c. dull pur. & orge., C (1914) 5 0 3 6
205 **53** 45 c. black/*green*, C (white back) (1914) .. 5 0 10 0
a. On blue-green, olive back .. 7 6 8 6
b. On emerald back .. 7 6 12 6
206 **54** 50 c. black/*green*, C (1914) 7 6 6 0
a. On blue-green, olive back .. 15 0 7 6
b. On emerald back .. 10 0 7 6
c. On emerald back (Die II) 10 0 6 6
207 **51** $1 blk. & red/***blue***, C ('14) 12 6 8 6
208 **54** $2 green & red/*yellow*, C ('15) 25 0 20 0
a. White back (1914) .. 15 0 10 6
b. On orange-buff 60 0 42 6
c. On pale yellow 45 0
209 **51** $5 grn. & red/*grn.*, C ('14) 45 0 20 0
a. White back (1913) .. 42 6 27 6
b. On blue-green, olive-back .. 80 0 22 6
c. On emerald back .. £5 65 0
d. Die II 45 0 37 6
210 – $25 purple and blue/*blue*, C (S. £8) £100 £50
211 – $100 carmine and black/*blue*, C (S. £25) .. £350
212 – $500 purple and orange-brown, C (S. £50) .. £2500

1917. *Surcharged with T* **55** *in black.*

213 **49** 2 c. on 3 c. scarlet .. 2 6 7 6
a. No stop £5
214 **50** 2 c. on 4 c. dull purple .. 3 6 10 0
a. No stop £8 £8

1919–20. *Colours changed and new values. Wmk Mult. Crown CA. P* 14.

215 **48** 1 c. black, O 0 6 0 4
216 **52** 2 c. green, O 0 8 0
217 **50** 4 c. rose-scarlet, O .. 1 0 0
218 ,, 4 c. carmine, O 1 0 0
219 **52** 6 c. dull claret, O .. 1 9 1
220 ,, 6 c. deep claret, O .. 7 6 6
221 **51** 10 c. bright blue, O .. 4 0 0
222 ,, 10 c. deep bright blue, O 4 0 0

The 6 c. is similar to T **52**, but the head is in a beaded oval as in T **53**. The 2 c., 6 c. (and 12 c. below) have figures of value on a circular ground while in the 8 c. this is of oval shape.

1921–33. *Wmk. Mult. Script CA. P* 14.

25c 25c

Type I. Type II.

Two types of duty plate in the 25 c. In Type I the solid shading forming the back of the figure extends to the top of the curve; the upturned end of the foot of the 2 is short; two background lines above figure 5; c close to 5; STRAITS SETTLEMENTS in taller letters.

223 **48** 1 c. black, O 0 4 0
224 **52** 2 c. green, O 0 4 0
224*a* ,, 2 c. brown, O 2 6 2
225 **49** 3 c. green, O 1 6 1
226 **50** 4 c. carmine-red, O .. 2 0 1
226*a* ,, 4 c. brt. violet, O (1925) 0 9 0
226*b* ,, 4 c. orange, O (1929) .. 0 9 0
227 **51** 5 c. orange, O(Die II)('21) 1 9 0
a. Die I ('22) 4 0 0
227*b* ,, 5 c. brn., O (Die II) ('32) 3 0 0
c. Die I ('33) 1 6 0
228 **52** 6 c. dull claret, O .. 2 6 0
228*a* ,, 6 c. rose-pink, O (1925) 17 6 6

228*b* **52** 6 c. scarlet, O (1927) .. 1 3 0 4
229 **51** 10 c. bright blue, O (Die I) 5 0 0 4
229*a* ,, 10 c. purple/*yellow*, C (Die I) ('25) 8 6 8 0
b. Die II. *On pale yell.* ('27) 4 6 0 3
c. Die I. *On pale yell.* ('33) 2 6 0 6
230 **52** 12 c. bright blue, O .. 3 0 0 8
231 **53** 21 c. dull & brt. pur., C 20 0 30 0
232 **54** 25 c. dull purple & mauve, C (Die I. Type I) ('22) 17 6 20 0
a. Die II. Type I ('23) .. 35 0 7 6
b. Die II. Type II ('27) .. 12 6 1 0
233 **51** 30 c. dull pur. & orge., C (Die I) 35 0 20 0
a. Die II ('22) 10 0 0 9
234 **53** 35 c. dull purple & orange-yellow, C 15 0 6 0
a. Dull purple and orange .. 8 6 6 0
235 ,, 35 c. scar. & pur., C ('31) 5 0 6 0
235*a* **54** 50 c. black/*emerald*, C .. 6 6 1 3
236 **51** $1 black & red/*blue*, C 15 0 2 0
237 **54** $2 green and red/*pale yellow*, C 25 0 15 0
238 **51** $5 grn. & red/*green*, C 55 0 30 0
239 – $25 purple and blue/*blue*, C (S. £8) .. £60 £15
240 – $100 carmine and black/*blue*, C (S. £25) .. £375
240*a* – $500 purple and orange-brown, C (S. £50) .. £2000

An 8 c. in carmine was prepared but not issued.
The paper of No. 229*c* is the normal *pale ellow* at the back, but with a bright yellow urface. No. 229*a* is on paper of a *pale lemon* int and the impression is smudgy.

MALAYA-
BORNEO
EXHIBITION.
(56)

922. *T* **48** *and* **50** *to* **54**, *overprinted with T* **56**.
(*a*) *Wmk. Mult. Crown CA.*
41 2 c. green 17 6 15 0
42 4 c. scarlet 8 6 10 0
43 5 c. orange 10 6 12 6
44 8 c. ultramarine 2 6 5 0
45 25 c. dull pur. & mve. (No. 202) 7 6 10 0
46 45 c. black/*blue-grn., olive back* 6 6 12 6
47 $1 black and red/*blue* .. £8 £8
48 $2 green & red/*orange-buff* 22 6 32 6
a. On pale yellow 70 0 85 0
49 $5 green and red/*blue-green, olive back* £10 £12
(*b*) *Wmk. Mult. Script CA.*
50 1 c. black 0 9 1 6
51 2 c. green 1 0 2 0
52 4 c. carmine-red 2 0 4 0
53 5 c. orange (Die II) 3 6 6 0
54 10 c. bright blue (Die I) .. 2 6 6 0
5 $1 black & red/*blue* (Die II) 20 0 25 0

The following varieties may be found in most lues: (a) Small second "A" in "MALAYA." No stop. (c) No hyphen. (d) Oval last " in "BORNEO." (e) "EXHIBITION."

35 (6 MAY). *Silver Jubilee. As Nos.* 91/4 *of Antigua but ptd. by W'low & Sons. P* 11 × 12.
6 5 c. ultramarine and grey .. 0 8 0 6
7 8 c. green and indigo .. 2 0 2 6
8 12 c. brown and deep blue .. 2 6 3 0
9 25 c. slate and purple .. 4 0 4 0

HAVE YOU READ THE NOTES AT THE BEGINNING OF THIS CATALOGUE?

These often provide answers to the enquiries we receive.

57

58

1936–37. *Chalk-surfaced paper. Wmk. Mult. Script CA. P* 14.
260 **57** 1 c. black (1.1.37) 0 4 0 3
261 ,, 2 c. green 0 6 0 3
262 ,, 4 c. orange 0 8 0 6
263 ,, 5 c. brown 0 10 0 4
264 ,, 6 c. scarlet 1 0 1 3
265 ,, 8 c. grey 1 0 0 10
266 ,, 10 c. dull purple 2 0 0 8
267 ,, 12 c. bright ultramarine .. 7 6 1 0
268 ,, 25 c. dull purple & scarlet 4 6 0 9
269 ,, 30 c. dull purple & orange 7 0 3 0
270 ,, 40 c. scarlet & dull purple 7 6 6 0
271 ,, 50 c. black/*emerald* .. 8 6 5 0
272 ,, $1 black and red/*blue* .. 12 6 8 6
273 ,, $2 green and scarlet .. 22 6 17 6
274 ,, $5 green & red/*emerald* (1.1.37) 65 0 50 0

1937 (12 MAY). *Coronation. As Nos.* 13/15 *of Aden. P* 14.
275 4 c. orange 0 4 0 6
276 8 c. grey-black 1 0 1 3
277 12 c. bright blue 1 3 1 6

1937–41. *Chalk surfaced or ordinary paper* (O). *Wmk. Mult. Script CA. P* 14 *or* 15 × 14 (15 *c.*),
(*a*) *Die I* (*printed at two operations.*)
278 **58** 1 c. black 0 6 0 3
279 ,, 2 c. green 0 8 0 4
280 ,, 4 c. orange 2 0 0 9
281 ,, 5 c. brown 1 3 0 4
282 ,, 6 c. scarlet 1 6 0 6
283 ,, 8 c. grey 1 3 0 8
284 ,, 10 c. dull purple 1 3 0 3
285 ,, 12 c. ultramarine 1 9 0 6
286 ,, 25 c. dull purple & scarlet 12 6 1 9
287 ,, 30 c. dull purple & orange 8 0 4 0
288 ,, 40 c. scarlet & dull purple 10 0 7 6
289 ,, 50 c. black/*emerald* .. 7 6 1 6
290 ,, $1 black and red/*blue* .. 7 6 2 0
291 ,, $2 green and scarlet .. 15 0 6 0
292 ,, $5 green & red/*emerald*.. 60 0 10 0
(*b*) *Die II* (*printed at one operation.*)
293 **58** 2 c. green 10 0 0 8
294 ,, 2 c. orange 0 6 3 6
295 ,, 3 c. green, O 1 3 2 6
296 ,, 4 c. orange 22 6 0 6
297 ,, 5 c. brown 5 0 0 6
298 ,, 15 c. ultramarine, O .. 7 6 8 6

Dates of issue:—

	Nos.		Nos.		Nos.
8.11.37	284	1.1.38	278	29.10.38	296
19.11.37	281	1.1.38	280	28.12.38	293
1.12.37	287	10.1.38	282	18.2.39	297
6.12.37	279	10.1.38	285	5.9.41	295
11.12.37	286	26.1.38	283	6.10.41	294
20.12.37	288	26.1.38	289/92	6.10.41	298

Die I. Lines of background outside central oval touch the oval and the foliage of the palm tree is usually joined to the oval frame. The downward-pointing palm frond, opposite the King's eye, has two points.

Die II. Lines of background are separated from the oval by a white line and the foliage of the palm trees does not touch the outer frame. The palm frond has only one point.

The 6 c. grey, 8 c. scarlet and $5 purple and orange were issued only with the BMA overprint, but the 8 c. without opt. is known although in this state it was never issued.

The above issues ceased with the Japanese Occupation in 1942. After World War II, stamps of MALAYA (BRITISH MILITARY ADMINISTRATION) were issued.

POSTAGE DUE STAMPS.

D 1

1924–26. *Wmk. Mult. Script CA. P* 14.

D1	**D 1**	1 c. violet	1	0	0	8
D2	„	2 c. black	0	6	0	6
D2*a*	„	4 c. green ('26)	0	8	0	6
D3	„	8 c. scarlet	1	0	1	6
D4	„	10 c. orange	2	0	1	0
D5	„	12 c. bright blue	2	6	1	0

For later issues of Postage Due stamps, see MALAYAN POSTAL UNION.

SUNGEI UJONG.

Incorporated in Negri Sembilan in 1895. Now part of the Federation of Malaya.

(1)

SUNGEI
UJONG
(2)

SUNGEI
UJONG
(3)

T **5** *of Straits Settlements, wmk. Crown CC.*

1878. *Optd. with T* **1**.

1 **1** 2 c. brown £80 £75

The 2 c. brown, Wmk. Crown CC, optd. with letters "S. U." is a trial, not an issued stamp.

1881–82. *Optd. as T* **2**.

Varieties. (a) "S" *wide. (b) All letters narrow. (c) Letters* "N" *wide. (d)* "N," "E" *of* "SUNGEI," *and* "U" "NG" *of* "UJONG" *wide. (e)* "G," "J" *and* "O" *narrow. (f)* "G E" *and* "J O" *narrow. (h)* "S" *and* "E" *wide (i)* "N" of "UJONG" *wide.*

2	**2**	2 c. brown (*a*)	40	0		
		a. "S" inverted				
3	„	2 c. brown (*b*)	40	0		
4	„	2 c. brown (*d*)	50	0		
5	„	2 c. brown (*e*)	50	0		
6	„	2 c. brown (*f*)	50	0		
7	„	4 c. rose (*a*)	£40			
8	„	4 c. rose (*b*)	£25			
9	„	4 c. rose (*h*)				

On the 2 c. brown, the word "SUNGEI" was printed as a triplet and "UJONG" as a single unit. Triplets are known of: 1881. (*a*)+(*b*)+(*b*) 1881. (*d*)+(*e*)+(*f*).

On the 4 c. rose, "SUNGEI" and "UJONG" were printed as separate triplets. 1882. (*b*)+(*a*)+(*b*) for "SUNGEI" *and* (*b*)+(*b*)+(*b*) for "UJONG". The setting of (*h*) is not known.

1881. *Optd. as T* **3**.

10	**3**	2 c. brown (*a*)	£15		
11	„	2 c. brown (*b*)	50	0	
12	„	2 c. brown (*c*)	£25		£25
13	„	2 c. brown (*i*)	£50		

In the above settings, "SUNGEI" was printed as a triplet and "UJONG" as a single unit. A known triplet consists of: 1881. (*b*)+(*b*)+(*a*). Varieties (*i*) and (*c*) form the first and third units of another setting. A third setting appears to consist of three units of (*b*).

Wmk. Crown CA.

1882. *Optd. with letters* "S.U." (*with stops*).

14	2 c. brown	£5	
15	4 c. rose	£100	

1882. "SU" *without stops.*

16	2 c. brown	80	0

1882–84. *Optd. with T* **2**. *Variety.* (*k*) "E" *wi*

17	**2**	2 c. brown (*a*)	£18		£
18	„	2 c. brown (*b*)	£15		£
19	„	2 c. rose (*a*)	35	0	35
20	„	2 c. rose (*b*)	30	0	30
21	„	2 c. rose (*h*)	30	0	25
22	„	2 c. rose (*i*)	30	0	25
		a. "UJONG" double			
23	„	2 c. rose (*k*)	22	6	27
24	„	8 c. orange (*a*)	£50		£
25	„	8 c. orange (*b*)	£50		£
26	„	10 c. slate (*a*)	£18		£
27	„	10 c. slate (*b*)	£15		£

On all the above "SUNGEI" and "UJON were printed as separate triplets. The 2 c. bro and the 8 c. and 10 c. were overprinted with same triplets as were used for the 4 c. rose, The "SUNGEI" triplet of this was: 18 (*b*)+(*a*)+(*b*).

The 2 c. rose was overprinted in two setti of: 1884. (*b*)+(*a*)+(*h*) *and* (*h*)+(*k*)+(*i*).

Optd. with T **3**.

28 **3** 10 c. slate (*b*) .. .. —

SUNGEI
UJONG
(4)

1883. *Optd. with T* **4**, *with stop after* "UJONG

29	**4**	2 c. brown (*b*)	20	0
30	„	2 c. brown (*h*)	20	0
31	„	2 c. brown (*i*)	20	0
31*a*	„	8 c. orange (*b*)		

1884. *Optd. with T* **4**, *without stop.*

32	**4**	2 c. rose (*b*)	20	0	25
33	„	2 c. rose (*h*)	20	0	25
34	„	2 c. rose (*k*)	20	0	25
35	„	4 c. brown (*b*)	£5		
36	„	4 c. brown (*h*)	85	0	
37	„	4 c. brown (*k*)	85	0	

"SUNGEI" and "UJONG" were printed separate triplets on Nos. 29 to 37. The tripl on the 2 c. brown were: (*b*)+(*h*)+(*i*) and on 2 c. rose and 4 c. brown (*h*)+(*k*)+(*b*).

1885–90. *Overprinted with name in various ty*

SUNGEI
UJONG
(5)

Sungei
Ujong
(6)

1885.

38	**5**	2 c. rose (without stop)	12	6	
39	**6**	2 c. rose	17	6	22
		a. Overprint double	£10		

SUNGEI
UJONG
(7)

SUNGEI
UJONG
(8)

SUNGEI
UJONG
(9)

SUNGEI
UJONG
(10)

1886.

40	**7**	2 c. rose	30	0	3
41	**8**	2 c. rose	12	6	1
		a. Opt. double			

42 **9** 2 c. rose (*long* " J ") .. 25 0 30 0
a. Opt. double ..

1887.
43 **10** 2 c. rose 8 6 10 0

1889. *As T* **5**, *but stop after* " UJONG ".
44 2 c. rose 17 6 20 0
a. Error. " UNJOG " £50 £60

SUNGEI UJONG (11)

SUNGEI UJONG (12)

1889.
45 **11** 2 c. rose 4 0 7 6

1890.
46 **12** 2 c. rose 10 0 10 0

No. 46 has two varieties in the setting—antique " G " in " SUNGEI " and antique " G " in " UJONG ".

SUNGEI UJONG Two CENTS (13)

SUNGEI UJONG *Two* CENTS (14)

SUNGEI UJONG *Two* CENTS (15)

1891. *T* **7** *of Straits, surcharged.*
47 **13** 2 c. on 24 c. green 75 0 75 0
48 **14** 2 c. on 24 c. green £7
49 **15** 2 c. on 24 c. green 60 0 70 0
50 – 2 c. on 24 c. green* .. £8

No. 49 has the antique " G " varieties as on No. 46.

*On No. 50 the word " TWO " is as in T **13** and the word " CENTS " smaller (9 instead of 11 mm.).

16  17

1891–94. *T* **16.** *Wmk. Crown CA. P* 14.
2 cents, rose 10 0 7 0
2 cents, orange (1894) .. 3 6 4 6
5 cents, blue (1893) 4 0 5 0

1894 *T* **16**, *surcharged in black.* **1 (** *or* **3) CENTS**
1 c. on 5 c. green 2 6 1 9
3 c. on 5 c. rose 2 6 3 6

1895. *T* **17.** *Wmk. Crown CA. P* 14.
3 c. dull purple and carmine .. 2 6 1 9

R—PT. I

TRENGGANU.

A State of the Federation of Malaya.

1. Sultan Zain ul ab din. 2.

1910–19. *T* **1** *and* **2** ($5 *and* $25). *Wmk. Mult. Crown CA. P* 14.
1 1 c. blue-green, O 1 3 1 6
1a 1 c. green, O 1 0 1 0
2 2 c. brown & purple, C ('15) 1 6 1 6
3 3 c. carmine-red, O .. 2 6 2 0
4 4 c. orange, O 3 6 3 6
5 4 c. red-brn. & green, C ('15) 3 6 6 0
5a 4 c. carmine-red O ('19) .. 1 0 2 6
6 5 c. grey, O 1 3 5 0
7 5 c. grey and brown, C ('15) 3 0 2 6
8 8 c. ultramarine, O .. 3 6 6 0
9 10 c. purple/*yellow* 4 6 7 0
a. On pale yellow 3 0 5 0
10 10 c. green & red/*yell.*, O ('15) 3 6 6 0
11 20 c. dull & bright purple, C 5 0 7 0
12 25 c. green & dull pur., C ('15) 6 0 8 6
13 30 c. dull pur. & blk., C ('15) 6 6 12 6
14 50 c. black/*green*, C 7 6 12 6
15 $1 black & carmine/*blue*, C 12 6 20 0
16 $3 green & red/*green*, C ('15) 55 0 70 0
17 $5 green and dull purple, C £8 £12
18 $25 rose-carmine and green, C (S. £8) £80

RED CROSS

2c.

(3)

1917 (OCT.). *T* **1** *surch. with T* **3.**
19 2 c. on 3 c. carmine-red .. 1 6 4 6
a. Comma after " 2 c." .. 10 0
b. " SS " in " CROSS " inverted .. £15
c. " CSOSS " for " CROSS " .. 45 0
d. " 2 " in thick block type .. 15 0 17 6
e. Surch. inverted £35
f. Surch. omitted (pair) .. £45 £45
20 2 c on 4 c. orange .. 2 6 10 0
a. Comma after " 2 c ". .. 25 0
b. " SS " in " CROSS " inverted .. £45
c. " CSOSS " for " CROSS " .. £10
21 2 c. on 8 c. ultramarine .. 3 0 10 0
a. Comma after " 2 c ". .. 25 0
b. " SS " in " CROSS " inverted .. £45
c. " CSOSS " for " CROSS " .. £6

1918. *Colour changed.*
28 2 c. on 4 c. brown & green 3 0 10 0
a. Surch. omitted in pair .. £25

During a temporary shortage in 1921, 2 c., 4 c. and 6 c. stamps of the Straits Settlements were authorized for use in Trengganu.

4. Sultan Suleiman. **5.**

1921. *Chalk surfaced paper. P* 14. (*a*) *Wmk. Mult. Crown CA.*

29 **4** $1 purple and blue/*blue* 10 0 12 6
30 „ $3 grn. & red/*emerald* .. 35 0 50 0
31 **5** $5 grn. & red/*pale yellow* .. 35 0 50 0

(*b*) *Wmk. Mult. Script CA.*

32 **4** 2 c. green 0 4 0 4
33 „ 4 c. carmine-red 1 0 0 4
34 „ 5 c. grey & deep brown .. 3 0 1 0
35 „ 10 c. bright blue 2 6 0 10
36 „ 20 c. dull purple & orange .. 5 0 1 3
37 „ 25 c. green and deep purple 4 0 4 0
38 „ 30 c. dull purple and black .. 6 0 3 6
39 „ 50 c. green & brt. carmine .. 4 6 4 0
40 **5** $25 purple and blue (S. £8) £95 £60
41 „ $50 green & yellow (S. £15) £260 £285
42 „ $100 green & scarlet (S. £35) £850

1922. *Optd.* " MALAYA-BORNEO EXHIBITION " *as T* 56 *of Straits Settlements.*

43 **4** 2 c. green 0 10 3 0
44 „ 4 c. carmine-red 1 9 3 0
45 **1** 5 c. grey and brown .. 1 3 5 0
46 „ 10 c. green and red/*yellow* .. 3 0 6 0
47 „ 20 c. dull and bright purple 3 6 10 0
48 „ 25 c. green and dull purple .. 4 0 10 0
49 „ 30 c. dull purple and black .. 5 0 12 6
50 „ 50 c. black/*green* 6 0 15 0
51 „ $1 black and carmine/*blue* 17 6 30 0
52 „ $3 green and red/*green* .. £7 £10
53 **2** $5 green and dull purple .. £14 £18

Minor varieties of this overprint exist as in Straits Settlements (*q.v.*).

1924–38. *New values, etc. Chalk-surfaced paper. Wmk. Mult. Script CA. P* 14.

54 **4** 1 c. black ('26) 0 4 0 3
55 „ 3 c. green ('26) 1 3 3 0
56 „ 3 c. brown ('38) 3 6 6 0
57 „ 5 c. purple/*yellow* ('26) 0 8 0 6
58 „ 6 c. orange ('24) 6 0 5 0
59 „ 8 c. grey ('38) 4 6 4 6
60 „ 12 c. bright ultramarine ('26) 3 6 4 0
61 „ 35 c. carmine/*yellow* ('26) 7 6 8 6
62 „ $1 pur. & blue/*blue* ('29) .. 17 6 15 0
63 „ $3 grn. & red/*green* ('26) .. 50 0 60 0
64 **5** $5 grn. & red/*yellow* ('38) £15 £25

The 2 c. yellow, 6 c. grey, 8 c. red and 15 c. blue were issued, but only with opt. during the Japanese occupation of Malaya. Unoverprinted specimens are due to leakages.

2 CENTS

(**6**)

1941 (1 MAY). *Nos.* 57 *and* 35 *surch. as T* **6.**

65 **4** 2 c. on 5 c. purple/*yellow* .. 4 6 4 6
66 „ 8 c. on 10 c. bright blue .. 8 0 17 6

1948 (1 DEC.). *Royal Silver Wedding. As Nos.* 30/1 *of Aden.*

67 10 c. violet 0 8 0 10
68 $5 carmine 35 0 40 0

1949 (10 OCT.). *75th Anniv. of Universal Postal Union. As Nos.* 114/7 *of Antigua.*

69 10 c. purple 1 0 1 0
70 15 c. deep blue 1 6 2 0
71 25 c. orange 2 6 3 6
72 50 c. blue-black 4 0 4 6

7. Sultan Ismail.

1949 (27 DEC.)–**55.** *Chalk-surfaced paper. Wmk Mult. Script CA. P* $17\frac{1}{2} \times 18$.

73 **7** 1 c. black 0 3 0
74 „ 2 c. orange 0 3 0
75 „ 3 c. green 1 6 2
76 „ 4 c. brown 0 4 0
76*a* „ 5 c. bright purple (1.9.52) 0 4 0 1
77 „ 6 c. grey 1 0 1
78 „ 8 c. scarlet 2 0 2
78*a* „ 8 c. green (*shades*) (1.9.52) 2 0 2
79 „ 10 c. purple 0 9 0
79*a* „ 12 c. scarlet (1.9.52) .. 2 0 2
80 „ 15 c. ultramarine 1 9 2
81 „ 20 c. black and green .. 3 0 4
81*a* „ 20 c. bright blue (1.9.52) .. 2 0 1
82 „ 25 c. purple and orange .. 1 6 3
82*a* „ 30 c. scarlet & pur. (5.9.55) 3 0 4
82*b* „ 35 c. scarlet & purple (1.9.52) 3 0 6
83 „ 40 c. red and purple ... 8 0 8
84 „ 50 c. black and blue .. 3 0 1
85 „ $1 blue and purple .. 5 0 3
86 „ $2 green and scarlet .. 10 0 12
87 „ $5 green and brown .. 30 0 35

1953 (2 JUNE). *Coronation. As No.* 47 *of Ade*

88 10 c. black and reddish purple 0 8 1

1957–63. *As Nos.* 92/102 *of Kedah, but with ins portrait of Sultan Ismail.*

89 1 c. black 0 2 0
90 2 c. orange-red 0 3 0
a. *Red-orange* (21.2.61) .. 1 0 1
91 4 c. sepia 0 4 0
92 5 c. carmine-lake 0 5 0
93 8 c. myrtle-green 0 6 1
94 10 c. deep brown 0 8 0
94*a* 10 c. dp. maroon (21.2.61) .. 0 7 0
95 20 c. blue 1 0 2
96 50 c. black and blue (*p.* $12\frac{1}{2}$) 3 0 2
a. Perf. $12\frac{1}{2} \times 13$ (17.5.60) .. 4 0 3
ab. *Black and ultram.* (20.3.62) .. 2 0 1
97 $1 ultram. & reddish pur... 4 2 3
98 $2 bronze-green and scarlet 7 9 7
99 $5 brown & bronze-green .. 25 0 20
a. Perf. $13 \times 12\frac{1}{2}$ (13.8.63) .. 18 6 18

Dates of issue: 26.6.57, 20 c., $5; 25.7.5 2 c., 50 c., $1; 4.8.57, 10 c.; 21.8.57, others.

8. *Vanda hookeriana.*

1965 (15 NOV.). *As Nos.* 166/72 *of Johore but w inset portrait of Sultan Ismail Nasiruddin Sh as in T* **8.**

100 1 c. multicoloured 0 1 0
101 2 c. multicoloured 0 2 0
102 5 c. multicoloured 0 4 0

103 6 c. multicoloured 0 4 0 7
104 10 c. multicoloured 0 6 0 10
105 15 c. multicoloured 0 7 1 0
106 20 c. multicoloured 0 10 1 4

The higher values used in Trengganu are Nos. 20/27 of Malaysia.

POSTAGE DUE STAMPS.

D 1

1937 (10 Aug.). *Wmk. Mult. Script CA.* P 14.

D1 D1 1 c. scarlet 2 6 4 0
D2 ,, 4 c. green 3 0 6 0
D3 ,, 8 c. yellow 10 0 15 0
D4 ,, 10 c. brown 15 0 20 0

JAPANESE OCCUPATION.

I. MALAYA.

For convenience we have included in one list the stamps of various States which could be used throughout Malaya and those which were issued and used in one State or district only; the latter being indicated by footnotes.

Collectors are warned against forgeries of the various overprints, particularly on the scarcer stamps.

The stamps listed below were all valid for postal use. A number of others overprinted with Types **2** or **4** were subsequently made available by favour and are known as "request stamps". Although they had postal validity they were not on sale to the public.

"Seal of Post Office of Malayan Military Dept."
(1)

(Handstamped at Singapore.)

1942 (16 Mar.). *Stamps of Straits Settlements optd. with* T **1**, *in red.*

J1 **58** 1 c. black 25 0 30 0
J2 ,, 2 c. orange 30 0 35 0
J3 ,, 3 c. green 80 0 90 0
J4 ,, 8 c. grey 40 0 40 0
J5 ,, 15 c. ultramarine 40 0 30 0

The overprint Type **1** has a double-lined frame, although the two lines are not always apparent, as in the illustration. Three chops were used, differing slightly in the shape of the characters, but forgeries also exist. It is distinguishable from Type **2** by its extra width, measuring approximately 14 mm. against 12½ mm.

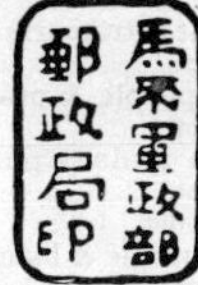
(2) (Upright.)

(Handstamped at Singapore and Kuala Lumpur.)

1942 (3 Apr.). *Stamps optd. with* T **2**.

(a) On Straits Settlements.

J6 **58** 1 c. black (R.) 6 0 6 0
a. Black opt. £10 £10
b. Violet opt. £10 £10
J7 ,, 2 c. green (V.) £75 £75
J8 ,, 2 c. orange (R.) 7 6 5 0
a. Black opt. 60 0 80 0
b. Violet opt. 60 0 80 0
c. Brown opt. .. ..
J9 ,, 3 c. green (R.) 10 0 8 6
a. Black opt. £10 £10
b. Violet opt. £10 £11
J10 ,, 5 c. brown (R.) 30 0 40 0
a. Black opt. £15 £15
J12 ,, 8 c. grey (R.) 10 0 7 6
a. Black opt. £10 £10
J13 ,, 10 c. dull purple (R.) .. 40 0 60 0
a. Brown opt. £30 £30
J14 ,, 12 c. ultramarine (R.) .. 80 0 £5
J15 ,, 15 c. ultramarine (R.) .. 12 6 8 6
a. Violet opt. £15 £15
J17 ,, 30 c. dull pur. & orge. (R.) £65 £75
J18 ,, 40 c. scar. & dull pur. (R.) 60 0 75 0
a. Brown opt. £15 £12
J19 ,, 50 c. black/*emerald* (R.) .. 40 0 45 0
J20 ,, $1 black & red/*blue* (R.) 60 0 70 0
J21 ,, $2 green and scarlet (R.) £5 £6
J22 ,, $5 green & red/*emer.* (R.) £8 £9

(b) On Negri Sembilan.

J23 **6** 1 c. black (R.) 20 0 25 0
a. Violet opt. 40 0 40 0
b. Brown opt. 25 0 35 0
c. Black opt. 50 0 65 0
J24 ,, 2 c. orange (R.) 20 0 25 0
a. Violet opt. 45 0 40 0
b. Black opt. 35 0 40 0
c. Brown opt. 40 0 50 0
J25 ,, 3 c. green (R.) 20 0 25 0
a. Violet opt. 45 0 45 0
b. Violet opt. (sideways) ..
c. Brown opt. 40 0 50 0
J27 ,, 5 c. brown 25 0 35 0
a. Brown opt. 20 0 25 0
b. Red opt. 12 6 22 6
c. Violet opt. 45 0 45 0
J29 ,, 6 c. grey £6 £7
a. Brown opt. £20 £20
J31 ,, 8 c. scarlet 40 0 80 0
J32 ,, 10 c. dull purple 80 0 90 0
a. Red opt. 50 0 60 0
b. Brown opt. £7 £7
J32*c*,, 12 c. bright ultram. (Br.) .. £30 £30
J33 ,, 15 c. ultramarine (R.) .. 25 0 20 0
a. Violet opt. 55 0 40 0
J34 ,, 25 c. dull purple & scarlet 40 0 65 0
a. Red opt. £5 £6
b. Brown opt. £10 £12
J35 ,, 30 c. dull purple and orange £8 £10
a. Brown opt. £30 £30
J36 ,, 40 c. scarlet & dull purple .. £20 £25
a. Brown opt. £50 £60
J37 ,, 50 c. black/*emerald* .. £10 £12
J38 ,, $1 black and red/*blue* .. 80 0 £5
a. Red opt. £10 £12
b. Brown opt. £20 £20
J39 ,, $5 green and red/*emerald* £18 £22
a. Red opt. £18 £22

(c) On Pahang.

J40 **7** 1 c. black 50 0 60 0
a. Red opt. 50 0 60 0
b. Violet opt. £10 £12
c. Brown opt. £8 £9
J41 ,, 3 c. green 80 0 £5
a. Red opt. £25 £30
b. Violet opt. £30 £30
J42 ,, 5 c. brown 25 0 20 0
a. Red opt. £5 £6
b. Brown opt. £8 £8
c. Violet opt. £15 £15
J44 ,, 8 c. grey £7 £7

No.	Type	Description	Unused	Used
J45	7	8 c. scarlet	35 0	20 0
		a. Red opt.	80 0	£5
		b. Violet opt.	80 0	£5
		c. Brown opt.	£5	£6
J46	,,	10 c. dull purple	50 0	70 0
		a. Red opt.	80 0	£5
		b. Brown opt.	£14	£16
J47	,,	12 c. bright ultramarine	£65	£65
		a. Red opt.	£150	£150
J48	,,	15 c. ultramarine	£5	£5
		a. Red opt.	£8	£8
		b. Violet opt.	£20	£20
		c. Brown opt.	£15	£15
J49	,,	25 c. dull purple & scarlet	40 0	60 0
J50	,,	30 c. dull purple and orange	40 0	50 0
		a. Red opt.	£10	£12
J51	,,	40 c. scarlet & dull purple	25 0	40 0
		a. Brown opt.	£7	£8
		b. Red opt.	40 0	50 0
J52	,,	50 c. black/*emerald*	£8	£12
		a. Red opt.	£20	£20
J53	,,	$1 black and red/*blue* (R.)	80 0	90 0
		a. Black opt.	£7	£8
		b. Brown opt.	£15	£16
J54	,,	$5 green & red/*emerald*	£18	£22
		a. Red opt.	£30	£35

(*d*) *On Perak.*

No.	Type	Description	Unused	Used
J55	38	1 c. black	40 0	50 0
		a. Violet opt.	80 0	£5
		b. Brown opt.	£5	£6
J57	,,	2 c. orange	20 0	25 0
		a. Violet opt.	80 0	£5
		b. Red opt.	35 0	35 0
		c. Brown opt.	80 0	80 0
J58	,,	3 c. green	50 0	65 0
		a. Violet opt.	£12	£15
		b. Brown opt.	£10	£10
		c. Red opt.	£12	£12
J59	,,	5 c. brown	15 0	12 6
		a. Brown opt.	40 0	50 0
		b. Violet opt.	£6	£8
		c. Red opt.	£6	£7
J61	,,	8 c. grey	50 0	65 0
		a. Red opt.	£12	£15
		b. Brown opt.	£12	£15
J62	,,	8 c. scarlet	25 0	£7
		a. Violet opt.		
J63	,,	10 c. dull purple	25 0	50 0
		a. Red opt.	£5	£6
J64	,,	12 c. bright ultramarine	£6	£7
J65	,,	15 c. ultramarine	40 0	75 0
		a. Red opt.	80 0	80 0
		b. Violet opt.	£8	£8
		c. Brown opt.	£8	£8
J66	,,	25 c. dull purple and scarlet	25 0	40 0
J67	,,	30 c. dull purple & orange	50 0	75 0
		a. Brown opt.	£5	£6
		b. Red opt.	50 0	65 0
J68	,,	40 c. scarlet & dull purple	£14	£18
		a. Brown opt.	£25	£25
J69	,,	50 c. black/*emerald*	40 0	40 0
		a. Red opt.	45 0	55 0
		b. Brown opt.		
J70	,,	$1 black and red/*blue*	£12	£18
		a. Brown opt.		
J71	,,	$2 green and scarlet	£50	£50
J72	,,	$5 green & red/*emerald*	£40	
		a. Brown opt.	£50	

(*e*) *On Selangor.*

No.	Type	Description	Unused	Used
J73	22	1 c. black, S	12 6	12 6
		a. Red opt., SU	20 0	25 0
		b. Violet opt., SU	25 0	50 0
J74	,,	2 c. green, U	£30	£30
		a. Violet opt., U	£60	£60
J75	,,	2 c. orange (*p.* 14×15), S	35 0	50 0
		a. Red opt., U	70 0	90 0
		b. Violet opt., U	£7	£5
		c. Brown opt., S	70 0	80 0
J76	,,	2 c. orange (*p.* 14), S	70 0	80 0
		a. Red opt., U	£6	£7
		b. Violet opt., U	£10	£10
J77	22	3 c. green, SU	20 0	40 0
		a. Red opt., SU	25 0	35 0
		b. Violet opt., S	70 0	80 0
		c. Brown opt., SU	12 6	15 0
J78	,,	5 c. brown, S	12 6	10 0
		a. Red opt., S	25 0	40 0
		b. Violet opt., SU	25 0	50 0
		c. Brown opt., SU	60 0	70 0
J79	,,	6 c. scarlet, S	£12	£14
		a. Red opt., S	£18	£18
		b. Brown opt., S	£25	
J80	,,	8 c. grey, S	25 0	35 0
		a. Red opt., SU	35 0	40 0
		b. Violet opt., U	50 0	60 0
		c. Brown opt., S	60 0	40 0
J81	,,	10 c. dull purple, S	25 0	40 0
		a. Red opt., S	65 0	65 0
		b. Brown opt., S	50 0	40 0
J82	,,	12 c. brt. ultramarine, S	50 0	65 0
		a. Red opt., S	80 0	£5
		b. Brown opt., S	£5	£5
J83	,,	15 c. ultramarine, S	25 0	35 0
		a. Red opt., SU	50 0	65 0
		b. Violet opt., U	£12	£12
		c. Brown opt., S	50 0	65 0
J84	,,	25 c. dull pur. & scar., S	£6	£7
		a. Red opt., S	£5	£6
J85	,,	30 c. dull pur. & orge., S	25 0	40 0
		a. Brown opt., S	£7	£7
J86	,,	40 c. scarlet & dull pur., S	50 0	65 0
		a. Brown opt., S	£8	£7
J87	,,	50 c. black/*emerald*, S	50 0	65 0
		a. Red opt., S	£5	£6
		b. Brown opt., S	£5	£6
J88	24	$1 black and red/*blue*	50 0	50 0
		a. Red opt.	£7	£8
J89	,,	$2 green and scarlet	70 0	80 0
		a. Red opt.	£12	£15
J91	,,	$5 green & red/*emerald*	80 0	80 0

On T **22** the overprint is normally sideways (with "top" to either right or left), but on T **24** it is always upright.

S=Sideways
U=Upright
SU=Sideways or upright (our prices being for the cheaper).

(*f*) *On Trengganu* (*all Script wmk.*).

No.	Type	Description	Unused	Used
J 92	4	1 c. black	£6	£8
		a. Red opt.	£8	£9
		b. Brown opt.	£15	£15
J 93	,,	2 c. green	£9	£10
		a. Red opt.	£10	£12
		b. Brown opt.	£15	£15
J 94	,,	2 c. on 5 c. (No. 65)	£6	£6
		a. Red opt.	70 0	70 0
J 95	,,	3 c. brown	£7	£6
		a. Brown opt.	£20	£20
J 96	,,	4 c. carmine-red	£12	£9
J 97	,,	5 c. purple/*yellow*	20 0	25 0
		a. Red opt.	40 0	
J 98	,,	6 c. orange	20 0	40 0
		a. Red opt.	40 0	
		b. Brown opt.	£10	£10
J 99	,,	8 c. grey	25 0	25 0
		a. Brown to red opt.	50 0	
J100	,,	8 c. on 10 c. (No. 66)	50 0	£5
		a. Red opt.	60 0	
J101	,,	10 c. bright blue	25 0	40 0
		a. Red opt.	50 0	
		b. Brown opt.	£10	£10
J102	,,	12 c. bright ultramarine	20 0	40 0
		a. Red opt.	35 0	
J103	,,	20 c. dull purple & orange	25 0	40 0
		a. Red opt.	35 0	
J104	,,	25 c. green & deep purple	25 0	40 0
		a. Red opt.	35 0	
		b. Brown opt.	£6	£6
J105	,,	30 c. dull purple & black	25 0	40 0
		a. Red opt.	35 0	
J106	,,	35 c. carmine/*yellow*	25 0	40 0
		a. Red opt.	35 0	

No.	Type	Description	Un.	Used
J107	**4**	50 c. green & bright carm.	80 0	£5
J108	,,	$1 purple and blue/*blue*	£100	£100
J109	,,	$3 green and red/*green* ..	£6	£7
		a. Red opt. ..	£7	
J110	**5**	$5 green & red/*yellow* ..	£10	£12
J111	,,	$25 purple and blue ..	£40	
		a. Red opt.	£100	
J112	,,	$50 green and yellow ..	£100	
J113	,,	$100 green and scarlet ..	£50	

Nos. J92/113 were issued in Trengganu only.

軍政部マラッカ州政廳之印

T 3. "Seal of the Government Office of the Malacca Military Dept." (approx. size).)

1942 (23 Apr.). *Stamps of Straits Settlements handstamped as T* **3**, *in red, each impression covering four stamps.*

No.	Type	Description	Single Un.	Used
J114	**58**	1 c. black	60 0	80 0
J115	,,	2 c. orange	70 0	80 0
J116	,,	3 c. green	70 0	85 0
J117	,,	5 c. brown	£9	£11
J118	,,	8 c. grey	£12	£10
J119	,,	10 c. dull purple	80 0	£5
J120	,,	12 c. ultramarine ..	£5	£7
J121	,,	15 c. ultramarine ..	80 0	£5
J123	,,	40 c. scarlet & dull pur. ..	£12	£14
J124	,,	50 c. black/*emerald* ..	£30	£35
J125	,,	$1 black and red/*blue*	£42	£50

Nos. J114 to J125 were issued in Malacca only. Blocks of 4 are worth from about six times the single prices.

DAI NIPPON

2602

MALAYA

(4)

1942. *Optd. with T* **4**.

(*a*) *On Straits Settlements.*

No.	Type	Description	Un.	Used
J128	**58**	2 c. orange	1 6	1 0
		a. Opt. double	25 0	35 0
		b. Opt. double, one inverted	£6	£8
J129	,,	3 c. green	80 0	£5
J130	,,	8 c. grey	6 6	6 6
		a. Opt. inverted ..	40 0	60 0
J131	,,	15 c. blue	12 6	10 0

(*b*) *On Negri Sembilan.*

No.	Type	Description	Un.	Used
J132	**6**	1 c. black..	1 6	0 2
		a. Opt. inverted ..	20 0	35 0
		b. Opt. double, one inverted	£6	£8
J133	,,	2 c. orange	1 6	2 0
J134	,,	3 c. green..	1 6	2 6
J135	,,	5 c. brown	2 0	2 6
J136	,,	6 c. grey	2 6	7 0
		a. Opt. inverted	—	£100
J137	,,	8 c. scarlet	6 0	5 0
J138	,,	10 c. dull purple ..	12 6	10 0
J139	,,	15 c. ultramarine	10 0	7 6
J140	,,	25 c. dull purple & scarlet	6 0	12 6
J141	,,	30 c. dull purple & orange	6 0	10 0
J142	,,	$1 black and red/*blue* ..	£10	£12

(*c*) *On Pahang.*

No.	Type	Description	Un.	Used
J143	**7**	1 c. black..	1 0	1 6
J144	,,	5 c. brown	2 6	4 0
J145	,,	8 c. scarlet	40 0	1 6
J146	,,	10 c. dull purple	22 6	10 0
J147	,,	12 c. bright ultramarine ..	2 6	5 0
J148	,,	25 c. dull purple & scarlet	10 0	15 0
J149	,,	30 c. dull purple & orange	2 6	5 0

(*d*) *On Perak.*

No.	Type	Description	Un.	Used
J151	**38**	2 c. orange	1 6	1 6
		a. Opt. inverted	45 0	50 0
J152	,,	3 c. green	1 6	2 0
		a. Opt. inverted	25 0	40 0
J154	,,	8 c. scarlet	2 6	0 6
		a. Opt. inverted	12 6	17 6
		b. Opt. double, one inverted	£12	£15
		c. Opt. omitted (pair with normal)	£35	
J155	,,	10 c. dull purple	12 6	20 0
J156	,,	15 c. ultramarine	7 6	6 6
J158	,,	50 c. black/*emerald* ..	6 0	8 6
J159	,,	$1 black and red/*blue*	£18	£22
J160	,,	$5 green & red/*emerald*	55 0	75 0
		a. Opt. inverted	£18	£22

(*e*) *On Selangor.*

No.	Type	Description	Un.	Used
J162	**22**	3 c. green	1 6	2 0
J165	,,	12 c. bright ultramarine	3 6	6 6
J166	,,	15 c. ultramarine ..	10 0	7 6
J168	,,	40 c. scarlet & dull purple	5 0	10 6
J170	,,	$2 green and scarlet ..	27 6	40 0

On T **22** the overprint is sideways, with "top" to left or right.

(*f*) *On Trengganu* (*all Script wmk.*).

No.	Type	Description	Un.	Used
J172	**4**	1 c. black	12 6	15 0
J173	,,	2 c. green..	£15	£15
J174	,,	2 c. on 5 c. (No. 65)	12 6	12 6
J175	,,	3 c. brown	20 0	35 0
J176	,,	4 c. carmine-red ..	12 6	20 0
J177	,,	5 c. purple/*yellow* ..	12 6	12 6
J178	,,	6 c. orange	10 0	20 0
J179	,,	8 c. grey	80 0	40 0
J180	,,	8 c. on 10 c. (No. 66)	10 0	12 6
J181	,,	12 c. bright ultramarine ..	10 0	20 0
J182	,,	20 c. dull pur. & orange ..	12 6	25 0
J183	,,	25 c. grn. & dp. purple ..	12 6	35 0
J184	,,	30 c. dull pur. & black ..	12 6	35 0
J185	,,	$3 green & red/*green* ..	80 0	£7

Nos. J172/85 were issued in Trengganu only.

DAI NIPPON

2602

MALAYA

2 Cents

(5)

SELANGOR

EXHIBITION

DAI NIPPON

2602

MALAYA

(6)

1942. *No.* 113 *of Perak surch. with T* **5**.

No.	Type	Description	Un.	Used
J186	**38**	2 c. on 5 c. brown ..	5 0	2 0

1942 (3 Nov.). *Agri-horticultural Exhibition. Nos.* 294 *and* 283 *of Straits Settlements optd. with T* **6**.

No.	Type	Description	Un.	Used
J187	**58**	2 c. orange	12 6	12 6
		a. "O" for "G" in "SELANGOR" ..	£14	£18
		b. Opt. inverted ..	£5	£6
J188		8 c. grey..	10 0	10 0
		a. "O" for "G" in "SELANGOR" ..	£12	£15
		b. Opt. inverted ..	£5	£6

Nos. J187/8 were only issued in Selangor.

DAI NIPPON

2602

(7)

DAI NIPPON

2602

(8)

1942 (13 May). *Stamps of Kedah (Script wmk.) optd.*

(a) With T **7**.

J189 **1** 1 c. black (R.) 4 0 5 0
J190 ,, 2 c. bright green (R.) .. 25 0 30 0
J191 ,, 4 c. violet (R.) 2 6 3 6
J192 ,, 5 c. yellow (R.) 3 6 2 6
a. Black opt. £20 £20
J193 ,, 6 c. carmine 3 6 6 6
J194 ,, 8 c. grey-black (R.) 5 0 4 0

(b) With T **8**.

J195 **6** 10 c. ultram. & sepia (R.) 6 0 6 0
J196 ,, 12 c. black & violet (R.) .. 20 0 40 0
J197 ,, 25 c. ultram. & pur. (R.) 10 0 10 0
a. Black opt. £15 £15
J198 ,, 30 c. green and scarlet (R.) 80 0 90 0
J199 ,, 40 c. black & pur. (R.) .. 27 6 40 0
J200 ,, 50 c. brown and blue (R.) 30 0 40 0
J201 ,, $1 black & green (R.) .. £12 £12
a. Opt. inverted £30 £30
J202 ,, $2 green & brown (R.) £9 £10
J203 ,, $5 blk. & scarlet (R.) .. 50 0 70 0
a. Black opt. £30 £35

Nos. J189 to J203a were issued in Kedah only.

奥川

(8a)

Okugawa Seal.

内延

(8b)

Ochibury Seal.

1942 (30 Mar.). *Straits Settlements stamps optd. (a) As T* **8a** *(three forms of this seal).*

J203b **58** 1 c. black 10 0 10 0
J203c ,, 2 c. orange 20 0 20 0
J203d ,, 3 c. green 15 0 25 0
J203e ,, 5 c. brown 15 0 25 0
J203f ,, 8 c. grey 20 0 20 0
J203g ,, 10 c. dull purple .. 20 0 25 0
J203h ,, 12 c. ultramarine .. 20 0 30 0
J203i ,, 15 c. ultramarine .. 25 0 25 0
J203j ,, 40 c. scarlet & dull pur. 60 0 60 0
J203k ,, 50 c. black/*emerald* .. 65 0 65 0
J203l ,, $1 black and red/*blue* £6 £6
J203m ,, $2 green and scarlet .. £10 £12
J203n ,, $5 green & red/*emerald* £25 £35

(b) With T **8b**.

J203o **58** 1 c. black 40 0 50 0
J203p ,, 2 c. orange 50 0 60 0
J203q ,, 3 c. green 50 0 60 0
J203r ,, 5 c. brown £25 £25
J203s ,, 8 c. grey 40 0 50 0
J203t ,, 10 c. dull purple .. 40 0 60 0
J203u ,, 12 c. ultramarine .. 40 0 60 0
J203v ,, 15 c. ultramarine .. 40 0 60 0

Nos. J203b/v were issued only in Penang

DAI NIPPON

2602

PENANG

(9)

DAI NIPPON

YUBIN

2 Cents

("Japanese Postal Service.")

(10)

1942 (15 Apr.). *Straits Settlements stamps optd. with T* **9**.

J204 **58** 1 c. black (R.) 1 0 1 6
a. Opt. inverted £10 £10
J205 ,, 2 c. orange 1 0 1 6
a. 'PE" for "PENANG" .. £5 £6
J206 ,, 3 c. green (R.) 1 0 1 6
J207 ,, 5 c. brown (R.) 1 0 2 6
a. "N PPON" £10
J208 ,, 8 c. grey (R.) 4 0 3 0
a. "N PPON" 70 0 80 0
J209 ,, 10 c. dull purple (R.) .. 4 0 4 0
a. Opt. double £20
J210 ,, 12 c. ultramarine (R.) .. 4 0 5 0
a. "N PPON" £25
b. Opt. double £20
J211 **58** 15 c. ultramarine (R.) .. 4 0 4 0
a. "N PPON" £10
b. Opt. inverted £25
J212 ,, 40 c. scarlet & dull pur. 6 0 8 6
J213 ,, 50 c. black/*emerald* (R.) 10 0 12 6
J214 ,, $1 black & red/*blue* .. 12 6 20 0
J215 ,, $2 green and scarlet .. 35 0 40 0
J216 ,, $5 green & red/*emerald* £30 £35

Nos. J204 to J216 were issued in Penang and Wellesley Province only.

1941 (Dec.). *Perak stamps surch. or optd. only, as in T* **10**.

J217 **38** 1 c. black 3 6 7 6
a. Opt. inverted 50 0 60 0
J218 ,, 2 c. on 5 c. brown .. 4 6 3 6
a. "DAI NIPPON YUBIN" inverted 40 0 50 0
b. Do. and "2 Cents" omitted £6 £10
J219 ,, 8 c. scarlet 5 0 3 6
a. Opt. inverted 40 0 50 0

大日本郵便

(11)

Error. 2nd character sideways

大日本郵便

(13)

大日本郵便

("Japanese Postal Service.")

(12)

6cts. (14)   6 cts. (15)   2 Cents (16)

6 cts. (17) $1.00 (18)

1943–45. *Stamps of the various Malayan territories optd. with T* **11** *or* **12** *(so-called "Kanji" characters), in black or red, some stamps surch in addition as T* **14** *to* **18**.

(a) On Straits Settlements (opt. T **11**).

J221 **58** 8 c. grey (Bk.) 1 6 1
a. Opt. inverted 65 0 70
b. Red opt. 2 0 2
J222 ,, 12 c. ultramarine .. 1 6 3
J223 ,, 40 c. scar. & dull purple .. 2 6 4

(b) On Negri Sembilan (opt. T **11**).

J224 **6** 1 c. black 0 9 1
a. Opt. inverted 35 0 40
b. Error. T 13 .. .. 27 6 40
ba. T 13 inverted £50
J225 ,, 2 c. on 5 c. brown (T **14**) 1 0 1
J226 ,, 6 c. on 5 c. brown (T **15**) 1 0 1
J227 ,, 25 c. dull purple & scarlet 4 0 5

(c) On Pahang (opt. T **11**).

J228 **7** 6 c. on 5 c. brown (T **14**) 2 6 3
J229 ,, 6 c. on 5 c. brown (T **15**) 4 0 4

(d) On Perak (opt. T **11**).

J230 **38** 1 c. black 1 0 1
a. Error. T 13 .. .. £10 £1
J232 ,, 2 c. on 5 c. brown (T **14**) 1 6 1
a. Opt. & surch. inverted .. 50 0
b. Opt. only inverted .. 50 0
c. Error. T 13 .. .. 60 0 80
J233 ,, 2 c. on 5 c. brown (T **16**) 1 6 1
a. Opt. & surch. inverted .. 50 0
b. Surch. only inverted .. 50 0
c. Error. T 13 .. .. 40 0 50
ca. Opt. & surch. inverted .. £75
cb. Surch. only inverted .. £70

J235 **38** 5 c. brown 2 0 1 6
a. Opt. inverted 70 0 80 0
b. Error. T 13 .. .. £15
J237 „ 8 c. scarlet 2 6 2 0
a. Opt. inverted 50 0 60 0
b. Error. T 13 .. .. £5
ba. T 13 inverted £60
J238 „ 10 c. dull purple 3 6 2 0
J239 „ 30 c. dull pur. & orange .. 6 6 7 6
J240 „ 50 c. black/*emerald* .. 12 6 15 0
J241 „ $5 green & red/*emerald* £5 £6

(*e*) *On Selangor.*

(i) *Opt.* **T 11** *placed horizontally either way on* **T 22** *and vertically on* **T 24.**

J242 **22** 1 c. black 2 0 2 0
J243 „ 3 c. green 1 6 2 0
a. Error. T 13 .. .. 40 0 50 0
J244 „ 12 c. bright ultramarine 1 6 4 0
a. Error. T 13 .. .. 40 0 60 0
J245 „ 15 c. ultramarine .. 10 0 10 0
a. Error. T 13 .. .. 60 0 80 0
J246 **24** $1 black and red/*blue* .. 6 0 12 6
a. Error. T 13 .. £25 £35
b. Opt. inverted .. £25 £35
J247 „ $2 green and scarlet .. 20 0 40 0
J248 „ $5 green & red/*emerald* 40 0 60 0
a. Opt. inverted .. £25 £30

(ii) *Opt.* **T 12.**

J249 **22** 1 c. black (R.) 0 6 0 9
J250 „ 2 c. on 5 c. brn. (T 15) (R.) 0 6 1 6
J251 „ 3 c. on 5 c. brown (T 15) 0 6 1 6
a. "s" in "Cts." inverted 50 0 60 0
b. Comma after "cts." .. 60 0 70 0
J252 „ 5 c. brown (R.) 0 9 1 6
J253 „ 6 c. on 5 c. brown (T 15) 0 6 1 6
J254 „ 6 c. on 5 c. brown (T 17) 0 3 0 9
a. "6" inverted £40
J255 „ 15 c. ultramarine .. 10 0 10 0
J256 „ $1.00 on 10 c. dull pur. (T 18) 0 6 3 6
J257 „ $1.50 on 30 c. dull pur. & orange (T 18) .. 0 6 3 6

(*f*) *On Trengganu* (*opt.* **T 11**).

J258 **4** 1 c. black 12 6 40 0
J259 „ 2 c. green 12 6 50 0
J260 „ 2 c. on 5 c. purple/*yellow* (No. 65) 12 6 40 0
J261 „ 5 c. purple/*yellow* .. 12 6 40 0
J262 „ 6 c. orange 20 0 50 0
J263 „ 8 c. grey 80 0 £7
J264 „ 8 c. on 10 c. bright blue (No. 66) 35 0 60 0
J265 „ 10 c. bright blue .. £8 £25
J266 „ 12 c. bright ultramarine 40 0 £6
J267 „ 20 c. dull pur. & orange 40 0 £6
J268 „ 25 c. green & dp. purple 40 0 £6
J269 „ 30 c. dull purple & black 40 0 £6
J270 „ 35 c. carmine/*yellow* .. 40 0 £6

Nos. J258/70 were issued in Trengganu only.

大日本
マライ郵便
50 セント

(**18***a*)

大日本
マライ郵便
1 ドル

(**18***b*)

大日本
マライ郵便
1½ ドル

(**18***c*)

1944 (16 Dec.). *Stamps intended for use on Red Cross letters. Surch. with T* **18***a/c*.

(*a*) *On Straits Settlements.*

J270*a* **58** 50 c. on 50 c. black/*emer.* 20 0 40 0
J270*b* „ $1 on $1 blk. & red/*bl.* 30 0 60 0
J270*c* „ $1.50 on $2 grn. & scar. 50 0 £6

(*b*) *On Johore.*

J270*d* **29** 50 c. on 50 c. dull purple and red 20 0 40 0
J270*e* **29** $1.50 on $2 green and carmine 15 0 30 0

(*c*) *On Selangor.*

J270*f* **24** $1 on $1 blk. & red/*bl.* 15 0 30 0
J270*g* „ $1.50 on $2 grn. & scar. 20 0 40 0

No. J270*a/g* were issued in Singapore but were withdrawn after one day, probably because supplies of Nos. J256/7 were received and issued on the 18th December.

19. Tapping rubber. **20.** Fruit.

21. Tin-dredger. **22.** War Memorial.

23. Huts. **24.** Japanese shrine, Singapore.

25. Sago Palms. **26.** Straits of Johore.

27. Malay Mosque, Kuala Lumpur.

(Printed by offset-litho in Batavia.)

1943. *P* 12½.

J271 **19** 1 c. grey-green (1 Oct.) 0 3 0 4
J272 **20** 2 c. pale emer. (1 June) 0 3 0 4
J273 **19** 3 c. drab (1 Oct.) .. 0 3 0 4
J274 **21** 4 c. carm.-rose (29 Apr.) 0 3 0 4
J275 **22** 8 c. dull blue (29 Apr.) .. 0 5 0 4
J276 **23** 10 c. brown-pur. (1 Oct.) 0 6 0 4
J277 **24** 15 c. violet (1 Oct.) .. 0 6 0 8
J278 **25** 30 c. olive-green (1 Oct.) 1 0 0 8

J279 **26** 50 c. blue (1 Oct.) .. 2 0 2 0
J280 **27** 70 c. blue (1 Oct.) .. 20 0 17 6

28. Ploughman.

29. Rice-planting.

(Offset-litho.)

1943 (1 Sept.). *Savings Campaign.* *P* 12½.
J281 **28** 8 c. violet 2 6 2 6
J282 „ 15 c. scarlet 2 6 2 6

1944 (15 Feb.). *"Re-birth" of Malaya.* *P* 12½.
J283 **29** 8 c. rose-red 2 6 2 6
J284 „ 15 c. magenta 2 6 2 6

POSTAGE DUE STAMPS.

Postage Due stamps of the various Malayan territories overprinted.

1942 (3 Apr.). *Handstamped with T* **2** *in black.*

(*a*) *On Malayan Postal Union.*

JD1 **D 1** 1 c. slate-purple .. 15 0 17 6
a. Red opt. 30 0 40 0
b. Brown opt. 75 0 £5
JD2 „ 3 c. green 17 6 20 0
a. Red opt. 40 0 £6
JD3 „ 4 c. green 22 6 10 0
a. Red opt. 45 0 60 0
b. Brown opt. 75 0 90 0
JD4 „ 8 c. scarlet 25 0 30 0
a. Red opt. 45 0 45 0
b. Brown opt. 60 0 75 0
JD5 „ 10 c. yellow-orange .. 30 0 37 6
a. Red opt. 30 0 40 0
b. Brown opt. 45 0 60 0
JD6 „ 12 c. ultramarine .. 32 6 35 0
a. Red opt. 50 0 65 0
JD7 „ 50 c. black 45 0 60 0
a. Red opt. £7 £9

(*b*) *On Johore.*

JD 8 **D 1** 1 c. carmine (R). .. 80 0
a. Black opt. 80 0
JD 9 „ 4 c. green (R.) .. 80 0
a. Black opt. £5
JD10 „ 8 c. orange (R.) .. £8
a. Black opt. 80 0
JD11 „ 10 c. brown (R.) .. 40 0
a. Black opt. 30 0
JD12 „ 12 c. purple (R.) .. 50 0
a. Black opt. 50 0

The above were issued only in Johore.

(*c*) *On Trengganu.*

JD13 **D 1** 1 c. scarlet 65 0 £5
JD14 „ 4 c. green £5 65 0
a. Red opt. 65 0 £5
JD15 „ 8 c. yellow 45 0 80 0
JD16 „ 10 c. brown 45 0 80 0

Nos. JD13/16 were issued in Trengganu only.

1942 (23 Apr.). *Handstamped on Malayan Postal Union with T* **3**, *in red, each impression covering four stamps.*

JD17 **D 1** 1 c. slate-purple .. £5 £5
JD18 „ 4 c. green £7 £8
JD19 „ 8 c. scarlet £60 £50
JD20 „ 10 c. yellow-orange .. £9 £11
JD21 „ 12 c. ultramarine .. £12 £15
JD22 „ 50 c. black £60 £80

Nos. JD17/22 were issued in Malacca only. Prices quoted are for single stamps. Blocks of four are worth about six times the price of a single stamp.

1942. *Optd. on Malayan Postal Union with T* **4** *in black.*

JD23 **D 1** 1 c. slate-purple .. 2 6 3 6
JD24 „ 3 c. green 5 0 7 6
JD25 „ 4 c. green 7 6 6 0
JD26 „ 8 c. scarlet 10 0 7 6
JD27 „ 10 c. yellow-orange .. 6 0 7 6
JD28 „ 12 c. ultramarine .. 6 0 7 6

1943–45. *Optd. with T* **11**.

(*a*) *On Malayan Postal Union.*

JD29 **D 1** 1 c. slate-purple .. 0 9 2 0
JD30 „ 3 c. green 0 9 3 0
JD31 „ 4 c. green 40 0 50 0
JD32 „ 5 c. scarlet 1 0 4 0
JD33 „ 9 c. yellow-orange .. 1 6 5 0
a. Opt. inverted 80 0 80 0
JD34 „ 10 c. yellow-orange .. 1 6 6 0
a. Opt. inverted 80 0 80 0
JD35 „ 12 c. ultramarine .. 2 0 7 6
JD36 „ 15 c. ultramarine .. 1 6 8 6

(*b*) *On Johore.*

JD37 **D 1** 1 c. carmine 3 0 12 6
a. Error. Optd. with T 13 50 0 80 0
JD38 „ 4 c. green 3 0 12 6
a. Error. Optd. with T 13 50 0 80 0
JD39 „ 8 c. orange 5 0 20 0
a. Error. Optd. with T 13 80 0 £5
JD40 „ 10 c. brown 6 0 25 0
a. Error. Optd. with T 13 90 0 £
JD41 „ 12 c. purple 6 0 25 0
a. Error. Optd. with T 13 90 0 £

Nos. JD37/41 were used only in Johore. Postage stamps of Johore optd. with Type **4** were authorized for use for revenue purposes only.

KELANTAN.

40 CENTS (JK 1)

$1.00 (JK 2)

Sunagawa Seal. Handa Seal.

1942 (June). *Kelantan stamps surch. as Type JK* **1** *or JK* **2** (*dollar values*).

(*a*) *With Sunagawa Seal in red.*

JK 1 **4** 1 c. on 50 c. grey-olive and orange £10 £1
JK 2 „ 2 c. on 40 c. orange and blue-green £10 £1
JK 3 „ 4 c. on 30 c. vio. & scar. £20 £2
JK 4 „ 5 c. on 12 c. blue (R.) £6 £1
JK 5 „ 6 c. on 25 c. verm. & vio. £8 £1
JK 6 „ 8 c. on 5 c. red-brn. (R.) £8 £1
JK 7 „ 10 c. on 6 c. lake .. £8 £1
JK 8 „ 12 c. on 8 c. grey-olive (R.) £8 £1
JK 9 „ 25 c. on 10 c. purple (R.) £60 £7
JK10 „ 30 c. on 4 c. scarlet .. £75 £
JK11 „ 40 c. on 2 c. green (R.) .. £8 £
JK12 „ 50 c. on 1 c. grey-olive and yellow .. .. £10 £
JK13 **1** $1 on 4 c. black and red (R., bars Bk.) .. 60 0
JK14 „ $2 on 5 c. green and red/*yellow* (R.) 60 0
JK15 „ $5 on 6 c. scarlet .. 60 0

(*b*) *With Handa Seal in red.*

JK16 **4** 12 c. on 8 c. grey-olive (R.) £10 £

1 Cents

(JK 3)

1942. *Kelantan stamps surcharged as Type* JK **3.**

(*a*) *With Sunagawa Seal in red.*

JK17	**4**	1 c. on 50 c. grey-olive and orange	£6	£6
JK18	,,	2 c. on 40 c. orange and blue-green	£6	£6
JK19	,,	5 c. on 12 c. blue (R.) ..	£5	£6
JK20	,,	8 c. on 5 c. red-brn. (R.)	£5	£5
JK21	,,	10 c. on 6 c. lake	£5	£6
JK22	,,	12 c. on 8 c. grey-ol. (R.)	£6	£7
JK23	,,	30 c. on 4 c. scarlet ..	£75	£85
JK24	,,	40 c. on 2 c. green (R.) ..	£5	£8
JK25	,,	50 c. on 1 c. grey-olive & yellow	£25	£30

(*b*) *With Handa Seal in red.*

JK26	**4**	1 c. on 50 c. grey-olive & orange	£5	£8
JK27	,,	2 c. on 40 c. orange and blue-green	£5	£8
JK28	,,	8 c. on 5 c. red-brown ..	£6	£9
JK29	,,	10 c. on 6 c. lake	£8	£10

The above stamps all exist with error " Cente " for " Cents " (No. 41 on sheet). They are worth about five times the prices for the normal stamps.

All the above were overprinted with the personal Seals of Sunagawa, the Governor or of Handa, the Assistant Governor, to indicate that these were Japanese stamps. Some of these also exist without the seals and come from remainder stocks sent to Singapore and Kuala Lumpur after Kelantan was ceded to Thailand.

THAI OCCUPATION.

Stamps issued for use in the four Malay States of Kedah, Kelantan, Perlis and Trengganu, ceded by Japan to Thailand on 19th October, 1943 and restored to British rule on the defeat of the Japanese.

I. KELANTAN.

TK 1

1943 (15 Nov.). *No gum.* *P* 11.

TK1	TK **1**	1 c. violet	75 0	£6
TK2	,,	2 c. violet	75 0	£6
TK3	,,	4 c. violet	75 0	£6
TK4	,,	8 c. violet	75 0	£5
TK5	,,	10 c. violet	75 0	£10

These stamps but with centres printed in red were for fiscal use.

II. MALAYA.

TM **1.** War Memorial.

(Litho. Survey Dept.)

1944 (15 Jan.). *Thick opaque, or thin semi-transparent paper. Gummed or ungummed.* *P* 12½ *or* 12½ × 11.

TM1	TM **1**	1 c. yellow	7 6	10 0
TM2	,,	2 c. red-brown ..	5 0	7 6
		a. Imperf. (pair) ..	£20	
TM3	,,	3 c. green	12 6	17 6
TM4	,,	4 c. purple	6 0	10 0
TM5	,,	8 c. carmine	5 0	7 6
TM6	,,	15 c. blue	7 6	12 6

MALAYSIA.

General issues intended for use throughout the new Federation. See notes at the beginning of Malaya.

1. Federation Map.

(Photo. Harrison & Sons.)

1963 (16 Sept.). *Inauguration of Federation.* *W* w. **13.** *P* 14½.

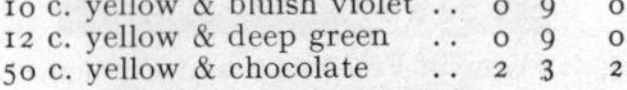

1	**1**	10 c. yellow & bluish violet ..	0 9	0 8
2	,,	12 c. yellow & deep green ..	0 9	0 9
3	,,	50 c. yellow & chocolate ..	2 3	2 6

2. Bouquet of Orchids.

(Photo. J. Enschedé & Sons.)

1963 (3 Oct.). *Fourth World Orchid Conference, Singapore. No wmk. P* 13×14.

4	**2**	6 c. multicoloured	1	0	0	9
5	,,	25 c. multicoloured	1	9	1	6

3. Sultan Idris Shah.

(Photo. Harrison.)

1963 (26 Oct.). *Installation of the Sultan of Perak. W* w. **13.** *P* 14½.

6	**3**	10 c. red, black, blue & yellow	0	7	0	10

4. Parliament House, Kuala Lumpur.

(Des. V. Whiteley. Photo. Harrison.)

1963 (4 Nov.). *Ninth Commonwealth Parliamentary Conference, Kuala Lumpur. W* w. **13.** *P* 13½.

7	**4**	20 c. deep magenta & gold ..	1	0	1	3
8	,,	30 c. deep green & gold ..	1	4	1	6

5. " Flame of Freedom " and Emblems of Goodwill, Health and Charity.

(Photo. Harrison.)

1964 (10 Oct.). *Eleanor Roosevelt Commemoration. W* w.**13.** *P* 14½×13½.

9	**5**	25 c. black, red and greenish blue	1	3	1	3
10	,,	30 c. black, red & dp. lilac	1	4	1	6
11	,,	50 c. black, red and ochre-yellow	2	0	2	3

6. Microwave Tower and I.T.U. Emblem.

(Photo. Courvoisier.)

1965 (17 May). *I.T.U. Centenary. P* 11½.

12	**6**	2 c. multicoloured	0	3	0	5
13	,,	25 c. multicoloured	1	3	1	6
14	,,	50 c. multicoloured	2	0	2	6

7. National Mosque.

(Photo. Harrison.)

1965 (27 Aug.). *Opening of National Mosque, Kuala Lumpur. W* w.**13.** *P* 14×14½.

15	**7**	6 c. carmine	0	4	0	6
16	,,	15 c. red-brown	0	7	0	9
17	,,	20 c. deep bluish green ..	0	10	1	1

8. Air Terminal.

(Photo. Harrison.)

1965 (30 Aug.). *Opening of International Airport, Kuala Lumpur. W* w.**13.** *P* 14½×14.

18	**8**	15 c. black, yellow-green and new blue	0	7	0	8
19	,,	30 c. black, yellow-green and magenta	1	1	1	4

9. Crested Green Wood Partridge. **10.** Blue-backed Fairy Bluebird.

11. Black-naped Oriole. **12.** Rhinoceros Hornbill

13. Barred Ground Dove.

14. Great Argus Pheasant.

15. Paradise Flycatcher.

16. Banded Pitta.

(Des. A. Fraser-Brunner. Photo. Harrison.)

1965 (9 Sept.). *W* w.**13**. *P* 14½.

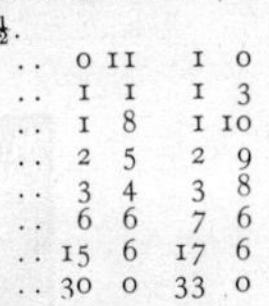

20	**9**	25 c. multicoloured ..	0	11	1	0
21	**10**	30 c. multicoloured ..	1	1	1	3
22	**11**	50 c. multicoloured ..	1	8	1	10
23	**12**	75 c. multicoloured ..	2	5	2	9
24	**13**	$1 multicoloured ..	3	4	3	8
25	**14**	$2 multicoloured ..	6	6	7	6
26	**15**	$5 multicoloured ..	15	6	17	6
27	**16**	$10 multicoloured ..	30	0	33	0

17. Sepak Raga (ball-game) and Football.

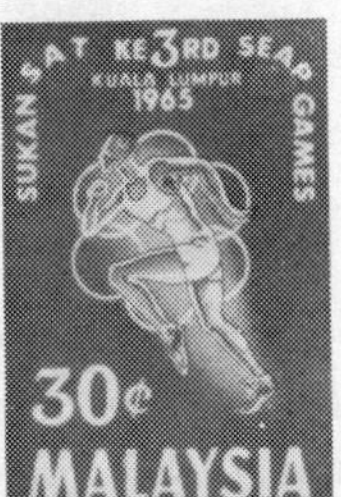

18. Running.

19. Diving.

(Des. E. A. F. Anthony. Litho. Japanese Govt. Ptg. Wks.)

1965 (14 Dec.). *Third SEAP Games. P* 13 × 13½.

28	**17**	25 c. black and olive-green	1	1	1	6
29	**18**	30 c. black and brt. purple	1	4	1	10
30	**19**	50 c. black and light blue..	2	0	2	6

20. National Monument.

(Photo. Harrison.)

1966 (8 Feb.). *National Monument, Kuala Lumpur. W* w. **13**. *P* 13½.

31	**20**	10 c. multicoloured ..	0	7	0	8
32	,,	20 c. multicoloured ..	1	0	1	2

POSTAGE DUE STAMPS.

For the time being the postage due stamps of Malayan Postal Union are valid for use throughout Malaysia.

MALDIVE ISLANDS.

MALDIVES

(1)

1906. *Stamps of Ceylon optd. with T* **1**. *Wmk. Mult. Crown CA. P* 14.

1	**44**	2 c. orange-brown, O ..	35	0	35	0
2	**45**	3 c. green, O	50	0	60	0
3	,,	4 c. orange & ultram., O ..	£6		£6	
4	**46**	5 c. dull purple, C ..	17	6	17	6
5	**48**	15 c. blue, O	£10		£10	
6	,,	25 c. bistre, O	£10		£10	

2. Minaret, Juma Mosque, Malé.

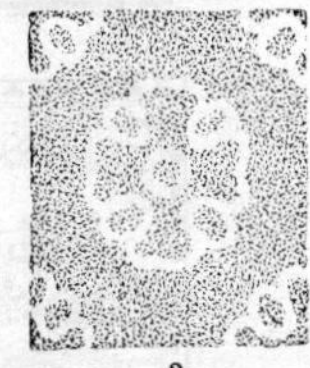

3

(Recess. De La Rue & Co.)

1909 (May). *T* **2** (18½ × 22½ *mm.*). *W* **3**. *P* 14.

8	2 c. orange-brown	3	0	1	6
9	3 c. deep myrtle	1	9	1	9
10	5 c. purple	2	6	1	6
11	10 c. carmine	3	6	2	6

4

(Photo. Harrison & Sons, Ltd.)

1933. *T* **2** *redrawn* (*reduced to* 18×21½ *mm.*). *W* **4.** *P* 15×14.

12	2 c. grey	2	0	1	6
13	3 c. red-brown	2	6	2	0
13*a*	5 c. claret (*vert. wmk.*)	27	6	35	0
13*b*	5 c. mauve (*horiz. wmk.*)	10	0	6	0
14	6 c. scarlet	4	0	4	6
15	10 c. green	1	6	1	6
16	15 c. black	3	0	3	6
17	25 c. brown	4	6	4	6
18	50 c. purple	7	6	7	6
19	1 r. deep blue	12	6	12	6

All values exist with both vert. and horiz. wmks.

(*Currency changed.* 100 *larees* = 1 *rupee.*)

5. Palm Tree and Boat.

(Recess. Bradbury, Wilkinson & Co.)

1950 (24 Dec.). *P* 13.

20 **5**	2 l. olive-green	2	0	2	0
21 ,,	3 l. blue	6	0	8	6
22 ,,	5 l. emerald-green	6	0	8	6
23 ,,	6 l. red-brown	1	0	1	0
24 ,,	10 l. scarlet	1	3	1	3
25 ,,	15 l. orange	1	9	1	9
26 ,,	25 l. purple	2	0	2	6
27 ,,	50 l. violet	3	0	4	0
28 ,,	1 r. chocolate	20	0	30	0

7. Fish.

8. Native Products.

(Recess. Bradbury, Wilkinson & Co.)

1952. *P* 13.

30 **7**	3 l. blue	3	6	5	0
31 **8**	5 l. emerald	1	9	2	0

The Maldive Islands became a republic on 1 Jan., 1953, but reverted to a sultanate in 1954.

9. Malé Harbour.

10. Fort and Building.

(Recess. Bradbury, Wilkinson & Co.)

1956 (Feb.). *P* 13½ (*T* **9**) *or* 11½×11 (*T* **10**).

32 **9**	2 l. purple	0	3	0	3
33 ,,	3 l. slate	0	3	0	4
34 ,,	5 l. red-brown	0	4	0	6
35 ,,	6 l. blackish violet	0	4	0	6
36 ,,	10 l. emerald	0	6	0	6
37 ,,	15 l. chocolate	0	6	0	9
38 ,,	25 l. rose-red	0	10	1	4
39 ,,	50 l. orange	1	3	2	6
40 **10**	1 r. bluish green	2	6	3	6
41 ,,	5 r. blue	12	6	15	0
42 ,,	10 r. magenta	22	6	25	0

11. Cycling.

12. Basketball.

(Des. C. Bottiau. Recess; athlete and value typo. Bradbury, Wilkinson & Co.)

1960 (20 Aug.). *Olympic Games.* *P* 11½×11 (*T* **11**) *or* 11×11½ (*T* **12**).

43 **11**	2 l. purple and green	0	3	0	4
44 ,,	3 l. greenish slate & purple	0	4	0	5
45 ,,	5 l. red-brown & ultram.	0	6	0	4
46 ,,	10 l. emerald-grn. & brown	0	9	0	5
47 ,,	15 l. sepia and blue	1	0	1	3
48 **12**	25 l. rose-red and olive	1	6	1	9
49 ,,	50 l. orange and violet	3	0	4	0
50 ,,	1 r. emerald and purple	5	0	6	6

13. Tomb of Sultan.

14. Custom House.

15. Cowrie Shells.

16. Old Royal Palace.

17. Road to Juma Mosque, Malé.

18. Council House.

19. New Government Secretariat.

20. Prime Minister's Office.

21. Old Ruler's Tomb.

22. Old Ruler's Tomb (distant view).

23. Maldivian Port.

(Recess. Bradbury, Wilkinson & Co.)

1960 (15 Oct.). *P* 11½ × 11.

51	**13**	2 l. purple	0	3
52	**14**	3 l. emerald-green ..	0	3
53	**15**	5 l. orange-brown ..	0	4
54	**16**	6 l. bright blue	0	4
55	**17**	10 l. carmine	0	5
56	**18**	15 l. sepia	0	7
57	**19**	25 l. deep violet	0	10
58	**20**	50 l. slate-grey	1	3
59	**21**	1 r. orange	2	6
60	**22**	5 r. deep ultramarine ..	12	6
61	**23**	10 r. grey-green	22	6

Higher values were also issued, intended mainly for fiscal use.

24. " Care of Refugees ".

(Recess. Bradbury, Wilkinson & Co.)

1960 (15 Oct.). *World Refugee Year.* *P* 11½ × 11.

62 **24** 2 l. dp. vio., orge. and grn. 0 3
63 ,, 3 l. brown, green and red 0 3
64 ,, 5 l. dp. grn., sepia and red 0 4
65 ,, 10 l. bluish green, reddish violet and red .. 0 6
66 ,, 15 l. reddish violet, grey-green and red 0 9
67 ,, 25 l. blue, red-brown and bronze-green 1 6
68 ,, 50 l. yellow-olive, rose-red and blue 2 0
69 ,, 1 r. carmine, slate and vio. 3 0

25. Coconuts.

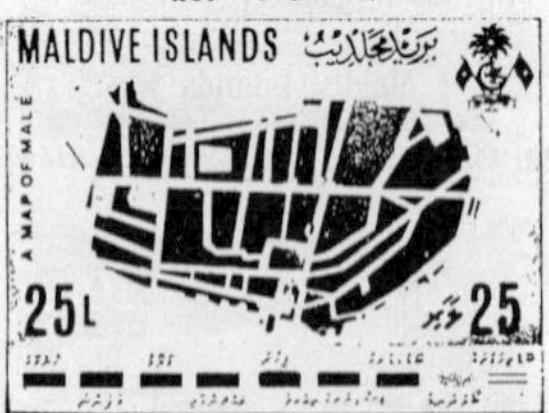

26. Map of Malé.

(Photo. Harrison & Sons.)

1961 (20 Apr.). *P* 14 × 14½ (*Nos.* 70/74) *or* 14½ × 14 (*others.*)

70 **25** 2 l. yell.-brown & dp. green 0 3
71 ,, 3 l. yellow-brn. & brt. blue 0 3
72 ,, 5 l. yellow-brn. & magenta 0 4
73 ,, 10 l. yell.-brn. & red-orange 0 6
74 ,, 15 l. yellow-brown & black 0 9
75 **26** 25 l. multicoloured 1 0
76 ,, 50 l. multicoloured 1 6
77 ,, 1 r. multicoloured 3 0

27. 5 c. stamp of 1906.

28. 3 c. stamp of 1906.

29. 2 c. stamp of 1906.

(Des. M. Shamir. Photo. Harrison & Sons.

1961 (9 Sept.). *55th Anniv. of First Maldivian Stamp.* *P* 14½ × 14.

78 **27** 2 l. brn.-pur., ultramarine and light green .. 0 3
79 ,, 3 l. brn.-pur., ultramarine and light green .. 0 3
80 ,, 5 l. brn.-pur., ultramarine and light green .. 0 4
81 ,, 6 l. brn.-pur., ultramarine and light green .. 0 4
82 **28** 10 l. grn., claret & maroon 0 6
83 ,, 15 l. grn., claret & maroon 0 7
84 ,, 20 l. grn., claret & maroon 0 8
85 **29** 25 l. claret, green & black .. 1 0
86 ,, 50 l. claret, green and black 1 6
87 ,, 1 r. claret, green and black 3 0
MS87*a* 114 × 88 mm. No. 87 (block of four). Imperf. 10 0

30. Malaria Eradication Emblem.

(Recess. Bradbury, Wilkinson.)

1962 (7 Apr.). *Malaria Eradication.* *P* 13½ × 13

88 **30** 2 l. chestnut 0 3
89 ,, 3 l. emerald 0 3
90 ,, 5 l. turquoise-blue .. 0 4
91 ,, 10 l. red 0 6
92 ,, 15 l. deep purple-brown .. 0 9
93 ,, 25 l. deep blue 0 10
94 ,, 50 l. deep green 1 6
95 ,, 1 r. purple 3 0

31. Children of Europe and America.

32. Children of Middle East and Far East.

(Des. C. Bottiau. Photo. Harrison & Sons.)

1962 (9 SEPT.). *15th Anniv. of U.N.I.C.E.F. P* 14½ × 14.

No.	Type	Description		s.	d.
96	**31**	2 l. multicoloured	..	0	3
97	,,	6 l. multicoloured	..	0	4
98	,,	10 l. multicoloured	..	0	6
99	,,	15 l. multicoloured	..	0	9
100	**32**	25 l. multicoloured	..	0	10
101	,,	50 l. multicoloured	..	1	6
102	,,	1 r. multicoloured	..	3	0
103	,,	5 r. multicoloured	..	12	0

33. Sultan Mohamed Farid Didi.

(Photo. Harrison.)

1962 (29 NOV.). *Ninth Anniv. of Enthronement of Sultan. T* **33.** *P* 14 × 14½.

No.	Description	s.	d.
104	3 l. orge.-brn. & blsh. grn.	0	3
105	5 l. orge.-brown and indigo	0	4
106	10 l. orange-brown and blue	0	9
107	20 l. orge.-brown & olive-grn.	1	3
108	50 l. orge.-brn. & dp. magenta	1	6
109	1 r. orge.-brown & slate-lilac	2	6

34. Angel Fish.

35. Moorish Idol.

36. Soldier Fish.

37. Surgeon Fish.

38. Butterfly Fish.

(Des. R. Hegeman. Photo. J. Enschedé & Sons.

1963 (2 FEB.). *Tropical Fish. P* 13½.

No.	Type	Description		s.	d.
110	**34**	2 l. multicoloured	..	0	3
111	,,	3 l. multicoloured	..	0	3
112	,,	5 l. multicoloured	..	0	4
113	**35**	10 l. multicoloured	..	0	5
114	,,	25 l. multicoloured	..	0	8
115	**36**	50 l. multicoloured	..	1	3
116	**37**	1 r. multicoloured	..	2	6
117	**38**	5 r. multicoloured	..	12	0

39. Fishes in Net.

40. Handful of Grain.

(Photo. State Ptg. Wks., Vienna.)

1963 (21 MAR.). *Freedom from Hunger.* *P* 12.

118	**39**	2 l. brown & dp. blsh. grn.	0	3
119	**40**	5 l. brown & orange-red . .	0	4
120	**39**	7 l. brown and turquoise	0	6
121	**40**	10 l. brown and blue . .	0	9
122	**39**	25 l. brown and brown-red	1	3
123	**40**	50 l. brown and violet . .	2	0
124	**39**	1 r. brown & dp. magenta	2	9

41. Centenary Emblem.

(Photo. Harrison.)

1963 (OCT.). *Centenary of Red Cross.* *P* 14 × 14½.

125	**41**	2 l. red & deep purple . .	0	3
126	,,	15 l. red & dp. bluish grn.	0	7
127	,,	50 l. red & deep brown . .	1	3
128	,,	1 r. red & indigo . .	2	6
129	,,	4 r. red & dp. brown-olive	10	0

42. Maldivian Scout Badge.

(Photo. Enschedé.)

1964. *World Scout Jamboree, Marathon* (1963) *P* 13½.

130	**42**	2 l. green and violet . .	0	3
131	,,	3 l. green and bistre-brn.	0	3
132	,,	25 l. green and blue . .	0	8
133	,,	1 r. green and crimson . .	2	6

43. Mosque, Malé.

(Recess. Bradbury, Wilkinson & Co.)

1964 (10 AUG.). "*Maldives Embrace Islam*". *W* w.**12.** *P* 11½.

134	**43**	2 l. purple	0	3
135	,,	3 l. emerald-green . .	0	3
136	,,	10 l. carmine	0	9
137	,,	40 l. deep dull purple . .	1	0
138	,,	60 l. blue	1	6
139	,,	85 l. orange-brown . .	2	2

44. Putting the Shot.

45. Running.

(Litho. Enschedé.)

1964 (OCT.). *Olympic Games, Tokio.* *W* w.**12.** *P* 14 × 13½.

140	**44**	2 l. dp. mar. & turq.-blue	0	3
141	,,	3 l. crimson and chestnut	0	3
142	,,	5 l. bronze-green and deep green	0	4
143	,,	10 l. slate-violet and reddish purple . .	0	6
144	**45**	15 l. sepia & yellow-brown	0	7
145	,,	25 l. indigo and deep blue	1	0
146	,,	50 l. deep olive-green and yellow-olive . .	1	6
147	,,	1 r. deep maroon and olive-grey	3	0
MS147*a*		126 × 140 mm. Nos. 145/7. Imperf.	10	0

46. Telecommunications Satellite.

(Des. M. Shamir. Photo. Harrison.)

1965 (1 July). *International Quiet Sun Years. P* 14½.

148	**46**	5 l. blue	0	3
149	,,	10 l. brown	0	5
150	,,	25 l. green	0	10
151	,,	1 r. deep magenta ..	2	6

MS151*a* 146 × 163 mm. Set of four sheets 35 0

Nos. 148/51 were only issued in miniature sheets of nine stamps.

On 26th July, 1965 Maldive Islands became ndependent and left the British Commonwealth. Later issues will be found listed in Part III of this Catalogue.

MALTA.

For GREAT BRITAIN stamps used in Malta see page 57.

RINTERS. Nos. 1–156. Printed by De La Rue; typographed except where stated.

1

Type **1.**

360 (Dec.)–**1863.** *No wmk. P* 14.

(i) *Blued paper.* (1 *Dec.*, 1860.)

½d. buff	£150	£90
a. Imperf. (pair)	£1000	

(ii) *White paper.* (*Nov.*, 1861–63.)

½d. pale buff	£80	£40
½d. brown-orange	£60	£35
½d. buff	£60	£35

The impression of Nos. 2 and 4 is clear, No. 3 ing the blurred and muddy printing. In os. 3 and 4, and also No. 5, specks of carmine n be detected with a magnifying glass and the ks are always muddy. Specimens also exist in hich parts of the design are pure rose, due to fective mixing of the ink.

63–67. *Wmk. Crown CC. P* 14.

½d. buff (June, 1863)	£20	£8
½d. bright orange (1864) ..	£17	£8
½d. brown-red (1867)	£30	£10

Specimens of No. 5 exist on thin, surfaced paper, and others, reissued in 1865 and 1866, are on unsurfaced paper. The ink of No. 6 is mineral and unlike No. 12, does not stain the paper. Most specimens are on thin, surfaced paper. Some shades of No. 7 may be described as chestnut. The ink of No. 7 is never muddy but clear, although sometimes in excess and this distinguishes it from No. 5, with the deep shades of which it might otherwise be confused.

1868–71. *Wmk. Crown CC. P* 12½, *rough* (*No.* 8) *or clean-cut* (*No.* 9).

8	½d. buff-brown (1868) ..	£6	£7
	a. Imperf. between (vert. pair) ..		
9	½d. yellow-orange (May, 1871)	£20	£20

1870–78. *Wmk. Crown CC. P* 14.

10	½d. dull orange (April, 1870) ..	£10	£7
11	½d. orange-buff (1873) ..	£10	£7
12	½d. golden yell. (aniline) (10.74)	£20	£25
13	½d. yellow-buff	£10	£6
14	½d. pale buff	£9	£6

1878 (July). *Wmk. Crown CC. P* 14 × 12½.

15	½d. yellow-buff	£10	£7
	a. Perf. 12½ × 14		

1880–81. *Wmk. Crown CC. P* 14.

16	½d. bright orange-yellow (4.80)	80 0	80 0
17	½d. yellow (Apr., 1881) ..	80 0	60 0

1882 (April). *Wmk. Crown CA. P* 14.

18	½d. orange-yellow	40 0	£5
19	½d. red-orange	40 0	£5

2

3

4

5

1885 (1 Jan.). *Wmk. Crown CA. P* 14.

20	**1**	½d. green	2 6	1 0
21	**2**	1d. rose	50 0	30 0
22	,,	1d. carmine	3 6	1 0
23	**3**	2d. grey	3 6	3 0
24	**4**	2½d. dull blue	30 0	2 0
25	,,	2½d. bright blue	30 0	1 6
26	,,	2½d. ultramarine	10 0	1 6
27	**3**	4d. brown	8 6	10 0
		a. Imperf. (pair) ('93) ..	£700	£600
28	,,	1s. violet	50 0	22 6
29	,,	1s. pale violet	£5	30 0

1886. *Wmk. Crown CC. P* 14.

30	**5**	5s. rose	£5	80 0

6. Gozo Fishing Boat. **7.** Ancient Maltese Galley.

8. Emblematic figure of Malta.

9. Shipwreck of St. Paul.

10. Harbour of Valletta.

One
Penny

(11)

(T **6/10** recess.)

1899 (4 Feb.). *P* 14. (*a*) *Wmk. Crown CA.*

31	**6**	4½d. sepia	22	6	22	6
32	**7**	5d. vermilion	45	0	22	6
		(*b*) *Wmk. Crown CC.*				
33	**8**	2s. 6d. olive-grey	47	6	30	0
34	**9**	10s. blue-black	£8		£7	

1901 (1 Jan.). *Wmk. Crown CA. P* 14.

35	**10**	¼d. brown	3	0	1	0
36	,,	¼d. red-brown	1	0	1	0

1902 (4 July). *Nos. 24 and 24a surch. locally at Govt. Ptg. Office with T* **11.**

37	1d. on 2½d. dull blue	0	10	1	3
	a. Surch. double	—		£150	
	b. Error. "One Pnney" ..	27	6	35	0
	ba. Surch. double, with error "One Pnney"				
38	1d. on 2½d. bright blue ..	1	3	1	6
	a. Error. "One Pnney" ..	32	6	35	0

12

1903–4. *Wmk. Crown CA. P* 14.

41	**12**	½d. green	4	6	0	4
42	,,	1d. black and red ..	4	0	0	8
43	,,	2d. purple and grey ..	17	6	15	0
44	**12**	2½d. marone and blue ..	30	0	6	0
45	,,	3d. grey and purple ..	4	6	3	6
46	,,	4d. black and brown (1904)	47	6	27	6
47	,,	1s. grey and violet ..	25	0	12	6

1904–6. *Wmk. Mult. Crown CA. P* 14.

48	**10**	¼d. red-brown, O (1905) ..	1	6	0	6
49	**12**	½d. green, O	4	6	0	3
50	,,	1d. black & red, O ('05) ..	8	6	0	10
51	,,	2d. purple & grey, O ('05)	15	0	6	0
52	,,	2½d. marone & blue, O ..	8	6	7	6
54	,,	4d. black & brown, O ('06)	20	0	17	6
55	**6**	4½d. brown ('05)	30	0	17	6
56	**7**	5d. vermilion	30	0	12	6
57	**12**	1s. grey and violet, O ..	32	6	12	6

1907–11. *Wmk. Mult. Crown CA. P* 14.

58	**10**	¼d. deep brown, O ('10) ..	1	0	0	4
59	**12**	½d. deep green, O (1909) ..	3	6	0	4
60	,,	1d. red, O	2	6	0	6
61	,,	2d. grey, O (1911) ..	6	0	5	0
62	,,	2½d. bright blue, O (1911)	8	6	3	0
62*a*	,,	4d. blk. & red/*yell.*, O (1911)	15	0	10	0
63	**6**	4½d. orange (1911) ..	10	0	8	6
64	**7**	5d. pale sage-green (1910)	12	6	15	0
67	**12**	1s. black/*green*, O (1911)	15	0	10	0
68	,,	5s. green & red/*yell.*, C ('11)	£5		£5	

13

14

15

1914–22. *Wmk. Mult. Crown CA. P* 14.

69	**13**	¼d. brown, O	0	8	0
70	,,	¼d. deep brown, O (1919)	0	6	0
71	,,	½d. green, O	2	6	0
72	,,	½d. deep green, O (1919)	0	8	0
73	,,	1d. carmine-red, O ..	3	6	0
74	,,	1d. scarlet, O (1915) ..	2	0	0
75	,,	2d. grey, O	20	0	7
76	,,	2d. deep slate, O (1919)	42	6	35
77	,,	2½d. bright blue, O ..	3	0	2
78	**14**	3d. purple/*yellow*, C (1920)	25	0	20
		a. On orange-buff	25	0	35
79	**13**	6d. dull & bright pur., C	32	6	27
80	,,	6d. dull pur. & mag., C ('19)	35	0	30
81	**14**	1s. black/*green*, C (1915)	35	0	22
		a. White back	15	0	12
		b. On blue-green, olive back ..	37	6	15
		c. On emerald surface ..	27	6	30
		d. On emerald back	37	6	32
86	**15**	2s. pur. & brt. blue/*blue*, C	80	0	60
86*a*	,,	2s. dull pur & bl.*bl*, C ('21)	85	0	70
87	,,	5s. green & red/*yellow* ..	£7		

1914–15. *Wmk. Mult. Crown CA. P* 14.

89 **10** 4d. black 50 0 25 0
90 ,, 4d. grey-black 80 0 35 0
91 **7** 5d. deep sage-green 25 0 27 6

The design of the 4d. differs in various details from that of Type **10**.

WAR TAX

(**16**)

1918. *T* **13** *and* **12** *optd. with T* **16.**

92 ½d. deep green (Jan.) 0 3 0 3
93 3d. grey and purple (March) .. 3 0 17 6

17 18

(T **17** recess.)

1919–20. *Wmk. Mult. Crown CA. P* 14.

94 **8** 2s. 6d. grey-green £6 £7
95 ,, 2s. 6d. olive-grey (1920) .. £6 £7
96 **17** 10s. black £200 £220

1921–22. *Wmk. Mult. Script CA. P* 14.

97 **13** ½d. brown, O 0 8 2 0
98 ,, ½d. green, O 0 8 2 0
99 ,, 1d. scarlet, O 0 8 0 8
100 **18** 2d. grey, O (1921) .. 10 0 3 6
101 **13** 2½d. bright blue, O .. 5 0 12 6
102 ,, 6d. dull & bright pur., C 32 6 45 0
103 **15** 2s. pur. & blue/*blue*, C .. £6 £12
104 **17** 10s. black, O £45 £65

SELF-GOVERNMENT (**19**) SELF-GOVERNMENT (**20**)

1922 (12 Jan.–Apr.). *Optd. with T* **19** *or* **20** *(large stamps), in black or red* (R.).

(*a*) *Wmk. Crown CC.*

105 **9** 10s. blue-black, O (R.) .. £25 £28

(*b*) *Wmk. Mult. Crown CA.*

106 **13** ½d. green, O 0 6 0 6
107 ,, 2½d. bright blue, O .. 7 6 12 6
108 **14** 3d. purple/*orange-buff*, C 5 0 15 0
109 **13** 6d. dull & bright pur., C 6 0 15 0
110 **14** 1s. black/*emerald*, C .. 8 0 10 0
111 **15** 2s. dull purple and blue/ *blue*, C (R.) £12 £16
112 **8** 2s. 6d. olive-grey, O .. 50 0 65 0
113 **15** 5s. green & red/*yellow*, C 90 0 £6

(*c*) *Wmk. Mult. Script CA.*

114 **13** ½d. brown, O 0 6 1 0
115 ,, ½d. green, O 0 10 1 3
116 ,, 1d. scarlet, O 0 6 0 6
117 **18** 2d. grey, O 2 6 3 0
118 **13** 2½d. bright blue, O .. 2 6 3 0
119 ,, 6d. dull & bright purple C 8 6 15 0
120 **15** 2s. dull purple and blue/ *blue*, C (R.) 70 0 80 0
121 **17** 10s. black, O (R.) .. £15 £18

One Farthing

(**21**)

1922 (15 Apr.). *No.* 100 *surch. with T* **21.**

122 ¼d. on 2d. grey 0 3 0 3

22 23

(Des. C. Dingli (T **22**) and G. Vella (**23**).)

1922 (Aug.)–**1925.** *Wmk. Mult. Script CA, (sideways on T* **22**, *except No.* 136). *P* 14.

(*a*) *Typo. Chalk-surfaced paper.*

123 **22** ¼d. brown 0 9 0 9
123*a* ,, ¼d. chocolate-brown .. 0 9 0 9
124 ,, ½d. green 0 4 0 3
125 ,, 1d. orange and purple .. 1 9 1 0
126 ,, 2d. bistre-brn. & turquoise 1 9 1 6
127 ,, 3d. bright ultramarine .. 4 6 4 6
127*a* ,, 3d. cobalt 4 0 7 6
128 ,, 4d. yellow and bright blue 4 6 6 0
129 ,, 6d. olive-green and violet 4 6 5 0
130 **23** 1s. indigo and sepia .. 8 6 8 6
131 ,, 2s. brown and blue .. 20 0 17 6
132 ,, 2s. 6d. bright mag. & black 20 0 20 0
133 ,, 5s. orange-yellow & bright ultramarine 30 0 32 6
134 ,, 10s. slate-grey and brown .. 60 0 75 0

(*b*) *Recess.*

135 **22** £1 black & carm.-red (1922) £14 £18
136 ,, £1 black & brt. carm. (1925) £12 £16

No. 135 is the first printing, with watermark sideways. No. 136 has the watermark upright.

1923–24. *Wmk. Mult. Script CA. P* 14.

137 **22** 1d. bright violet (25.4.24) 1 6 1 6
138 ,, 1½d. brown-red (1.10.23) .. 1 6 0 6

Two pence halfpenny (**24**) POSTAGE (**25**)

1925. *Surch. with T* **24.**

139 **22** 2½d. on 3d. cobalt (3 Dec.) 2 6 2 6
140 ,, 2½d. on 3d. brt. ult. (24 Dec) 3 0 4 6

1926 (Feb.). *Wmk. Mult. Script CA. P* 14.

141 **22** 2½d. ultramarine 1 3 6 0
142 ,, 3d. black/*yellow* 1 9 7 6

1926 (1 April). *Optd. with T* **25.**

143 **22** ¼d. brown 0 6 0 6
144 ,, ½d. green 0 6 0 6
145 ,, 1d. bright violet 0 9 1 3
146 ,, 1½d. brown-red 1 3 1 3
147 ,, 2d. bistre-brown & turq. 1 0 2 6
148 ,, 2½d. ultramarine 1 3 1 0
149 ,, 3d. black/*yellow* 2 6 3 6
a. Overprint inverted £12 £20
150 ,, 4d. yellow & bright blue 8 0 15 0
151 ,, 6d. olive-green and violet 3 6 3 6

152 **23** 1s. indigo and sepia .. 8 0 15 0
153 ,, 2s. brown and blue .. 75 0 90 0
154 ,, 2s. 6d. brt. mag. & blk. 35 0 40 0
155 ,, 5s. orge.-yell. & brt. ultra. 20 0 50 0
156 ,, 10s. slate-grey and brown 25 0 45 0

26

27. Valletta Harbour.

28. St. Publius.

29. Mdina (Notabile).

30

31. Neptune.

32. Ruins at Mnajdra.

33. St. Paul.

(T **26** typo., others recess. Waterlow.)

1926–27. *T* **26** (*P* 15 × 14) *and* **27** *to* **33** (*P* 12½). *Inscr.* "POSTAGE". *Wmk. Mult. Script CA.*
157 **26** ¼d. brown 0 6 0 6
158 ,, ½d. yellow-green 0 6 0 4
159 ,, 1d. rose-red 0 10 1 0
160 ,, 1½d. chestnut 1 3 0 8
161 ,, 2d. greenish grey 4 0 6 0
162 ,, 2½d. blue 6 0 2 0
162*a* ,, 3d. violet 6 6 7 6
163 ,, 4d. black and red.. .. 7 6 10 0
164 **26** 4½d. lavender and ochre .. 10 0 10 0
165 ,, 6d. violet and scarlet .. 10 0 10 0
166 **27** 1s. black 12 6 15 0
167 **28** 1s. 6d. black and green .. 20 0 17 6
168 **29** 2s. black and purple .. 20 0 27 6
169 **30** 2s. 6d. black & vermilion 32 6 35 0
170 **31** 3s. black and blue .. 32 6 45 0
171 **32** 5s. black and green .. 37 6 50 0
172 **33** 10s. black and carmine .. £5 £6

AIR MAIL	POSTAGE AND REVENUE	POSTAGE AND REVENUE.
(**34**)	(**35**)	(**36**)

1928 (1 Apr.). *Air. Optd. with T* **34.**
173 **26** 6d. violet and scarlet .. 12 6 25 0

1928 (1 Oct.–Dec.). *T* **26** *to* **33** *optd.*
174 **35** ¼d. brown 0 3 0 3
175 ,, ½d. yellow-green 0 3 0 3
176 ,, 1d. rose-red 0 8 2 0
177 ,, 1d. chestnut (Dec. '28) .. 1 6 0 8
178 ,, 1½d. chestnut 1 3 1 6
179 ,, 1½d. rose-red (Dec. '28) .. 3 6 0 4
180 ,, 2d. greenish grey .. 7 6 10
181 ,, 2½d. blue 3 6 2
182 ,, 3d. violet 5 0 3
183 ,, 4d. black and red .. 6 0 7
184 ,, 4½d. lavender and ochre .. 10 0 7
185 ,, 6d. violet and scarlet .. 12 6 10
186 **36** 1s. black (R.) 10 0 10
187 ,, 1s. 6d. black and green (R.) 15 0 17
188 ,, 2s. black and purple (R.) 22 6 25
189 ,, 2s. 6d. black & verm. (R.) 25 0 27
190 ,, 3s. black and blue (R.) .. 27 6 27
191 ,, 5s. black and green (R.) .. 65 0 80
192 ,, 10s. black and carmine (R.) 90 0 95

1930 (20 Oct.). *As Nos.* 157/172, *but inscr* "POSTAGE (&) REVENUE".
193 ¼d. brown 0 4 0
194 ½d. yellow-green 0 3 0
195 1d. chestnut 0 4 0
196 1½d. rose-red 0 6 0
197 2d. greenish grey 4 0 6
198 2½d. blue 2 6 1
199 3d. violet 2 6 2
200 4d. black and red 6 0 12
201 4½d. lavender and ochre .. 4 6 7
202 6d. violet and scarlet .. 8 6 12
203 1s. black 15 0 22
204 1s. 6d. black and green .. 20 0 22
205 2s. black and purple .. 22 6 30
206 2s. 6d. black and vermilion 35 0 40
207 3s. black and blue 40 0 45
208 5s. black and green 50 0 60
209 10s. black and carmine .. £8

1935 (6 May). *Silver Jubilee. As Nos.* 91/4 *Antigua but printed by B. W. & Co. P* 11 × 1
210 ½d. black and green 0 3 0
a. Extra flagstaff 35 0
211 2½d. brown and deep blue .. 2 6 3
a. Extra flagstaff £7
212 6d. light blue and olive-green 5 0 6
a. Extra flagstaff £6
213 1s. slate and purple .. 8 0 10
a. Extra flagstaff £12

For illustration of the "extra flagstaff variety see Bechuanaland.

1937 (12 May) *Coronation. As Nos.* 13/15 *Aden. P* 14.
214 ½d. green 0 3 0
215 1½d. scarlet 0 8 1
216 2½d. bright blue 2 6 3

7. Grand Harbour, Valletta.

38. H.M.S. *St. Angelo*.

39. Verdala Palace.

1. Victoria and Citadel, Gozo.

40. Hypogeum, Hal Saflieni.

42. De l'Isle Adam entering Mdina.

3. St. John's Co-Cathedral.

44. Ruins at Mnajdra.

45. Statue of Manoel de Vilhena.

47. St. Publius.

46. Maltese Girl wearing Faldetta.

48. Mdina Cathedral.

Palace Square, Valletta.

49. Statue of Neptune.

51. St. Paul.

(Recess. Waterlow.)

1938 (15 FEB.)–**1943.** *Wmk. Mult. Script CA (sideways on No. 217). P 12½.*

217	**37**	½d. brown	0 3	0 3
218	**38**	½d. green	0 3	0 3
218*a*	,,	½d. red-brown ('43) ..	0 6	0 3
219	**39**	1d. red-brown	2 9	1 0
219*a*	,,	1d. green ('43)	0 3	0 3
220	**40**	1½d. scarlet	0 8	0 8
220*a*	,,	1½d. blue-black ('43) ..	0 8	1 6
221	**41**	2d. blue-black	2 6	4 6
221*a*	,,	2d. scarlet ('43)	1 0	1 3
222	**42**	2½d. bright blue	2 6	4 0
222*a*	,,	2½d. violet ('43)	1 0	0 6
223	**43**	3d. violet	2 6	3 0
223*a*	,,	3d. bright blue ('43) ..	1 3	1 6
224	**44**	4½d. olive-grn. & yell.-brn	2 0	2 6
225	**45**	6d. olive-green and scarlet	2 0	2 6
226	**46**	1s. black	4 6	4 0
227	**47**	1s. 6d. blk. and olive-grn.	7 6	8 6
228	**48**	2s. green and deep blue	7 6	12 6
229	**49**	2s. 6d. black and scarlet	12 6	10 0
230	**50**	5s. black and blue-green	15 0	17 6
231	**51**	10s. black and carmine ..	35 0	35 0

1946 (3 DEC.). *Victory Commemoration. As Nos. 28/9 of Aden, but inscr. "*MALTA*" between Maltese Cross and George Cross.*

232	1d. green	0 6	0 6
233	3d. blue	1 0	1 3

SELF-GOVERNMENT
1947

(52)

1948 (25 NOV.)–**1953.** *New Constitution. As Nos. 217/231 but optd. as T* **52***; reading up on ½d. and 5s., down on other values, and smaller on ¼d. value.*

234	**37**	¼d. brown (Bk.)	0 3	0 3
235	**38**	½d. red-brown (Bk.) ..	0 3	0 3
236	**39**	1d. green (Bk.)	0 6	0 3
236*a*	,,	1d. grey (R.) (8.1.53) ..	0 6	0 4
237	**40**	1½d. blue-black (R.) ..	1 0	0 10
237*a*	,,	1½d. green (8.1.53) ..	0 6	0 6
		b. Overprint omitted ..	—	£350
238	**41**	2d. scarlet (Bk.)	1 0	0 10
238*a*	,,	2d. yellow-ochre (8.1.53)	0 8	0 10
239	**42**	2½d. violet (R.)	1 0	0 8
239*a*	,,	2½d. scarlet (8.1.53) ..	1 6	1 0
240	**43**	3d. bright blue (R.) ..	2 0	1 0
240*a*	,,	3d. violet (R.) (8.1.53) ..	1 0	0 8
241	**44**	4½d. olive-green & yellow-brown (Bk.)	2 6	5 0
241*a*	,,	4½d. olive-grn. & brt. blue (R.) (8.1.53)	3 0	3 0
242	**45**	6d. ol.-grn. and scar. (Bk.)	1 3	1 3
243	**46**	1s. black (Bk.)	3 0	2 0
244	**47**	1s. 6d. black and olive-green (Bk.)	4 6	3 0
245	**48**	2s. green & dp. blue (R.)	6 0	4 0
246	**49**	2s. 6d. black & scar. (Bk.)	7 6	6 0
247	**50**	5s. black & blue-grn. (R.)	15 0	12 6
248	**51**	10s. black & carm. (Bk.)	30 0	30 0

1949 (4 JAN.). *Royal Silver Wedding. As Nos. 30/1 of Aden, but inscr. "*MALTA*" between Maltese Cross and George Cross (recess £1).*

249	1d. green	0 6	0 6
250	£1 indigo	40 0	50 0

1949 (10 OCT.). *75th Anniv. of Universal Postal Union. As Nos. 114/7 of Antigua, but inscr. "*MALTA*" (recess).*

251	2½d. violet	0 6	0 9
252	3d. deep blue	1 6	2 0
253	6d. carmine-red	2 6	3 0
254	1s. blue-black	5 0	6 0

53. Queen Elizabeth II when Princess.

54. Virgin Mary Bestowing Scapular.

(T **53/4**. Recess. Bradbury, Wilkinson.)

1950 (1 DEC.). *Visits of Princess Elizabeth to Malta. Wmk. Mult. Script CA. P 12 × 11½*

255	**53**	1d. green	1 6	0 8
256	,,	3d. blue	4 0	4
257	,,	1s. black	6 0	7

1951 (12 JULY). *Seventh Centenary of the Scapular. Wmk. Mult. Script CA. P 12 × 11½*

258	**54**	1d. green	1 0	0
259	,,	3d. violet	2 0	1
260	,,	1s. black	5 0	5

1953 (3 JUNE). *Coronation. As No. 47 of Aden*

261	1½d. black & deep yellow-grn.	1 0	0 1

55. St. John's Co-Cathedral.

56. Altar-piece. Coll-giate Parish Church Cospicua.

(Recess. Waterlow.)

1954 (3 MAY). *Royal Visit. Wmk. Mult. Scr CA. P 12½.*

262	**55**	3d. violet	1 6	1

(Photo. Harrison.)

1954 (8 SEPT.). *Centenary of Dogma of the Immaculate Conception. Wmk. Mult. Script C Chalk-surfaced paper. P 14½ × 14.*

263	**56**	1½d. emerald	1 0	0
264	,,	3d. bright blue	1 6	1
265	,,	1s. grey-black	6 0	6

57. Monument of the Great Siege, 1565.

58. Wignacourt Aqueduct Horsetrough.

59. Victory Church.

60. War Memorial.

62. Auberge de Castile.

61. Mosta Dome.

63. The King's Scroll.

65. Neolithic Temples at Tarxien.

64. Roosevelt's Scroll.

66. Vedette.

67. Mdina Gate.

68. " Les Gavroches " (statue).

. Monument of Christ the King.

70. Grand Master Cottoner's Monument.

71. Grand Master Perellos's Monument.

72. St. Paul.

73. Baptism of Christ.

(Recess. Waterlow (2s. 6d. to £1). Bradbury, Wilkinson (others).)

1956 (23 Jan.)–**57.** *Wmk. Mult. Script CA. P* 14×13½ (*2s. 6d. to £1*), 11½ (*others*).

266	**57**	¼d. violet	0	3	0	3
267	**58**	½d. orange	0	3	0	3
268	**59**	1d. black (9.2.56) ..	0	6	0	6
269	**60**	1½d. bluish green (9.2.56)	0	5	0	5
270	**61**	2d. brown (*shades*) (9.2.56)	0	8	0	6
271	**62**	2½d. orange-brown ..	0	6	0	5
272	**63**	3d. rose-red (22.3.56) ..	0	7	0	7
273	**64**	4½d. deep blue	0	9	0	9
274	**65**	6d. indigo (9.2.56) ..	1	0	0	11
275	**66**	8d. bistre-brown	1	3	1	3
276	**67**	1s. deep reddish violet ..	1	9	1	6
277	**68**	1s. 6d. deep turq.-green ..	2	6	2	3
278	**69**	2s. olive-green	3	3	2	6
279	**70**	2s. 6d. chestnut (22.3.56)	4	0	3	9
280	**71**	5s. green (11.10.56) ..	9	6	8	6
281	**72**	10s. carm.-red (19.11.56) ..	20	0	16	6
282	**73**	£1 yellow-brown (5.1.57)	32	6	42	6

See also Nos. 314/5.

74. "Defence of Malta". **76.** Bombed Buildings.

75. Searchlights over Malta.

(Des. E. V. Cremona. Photo. Harrison.)

1957 (15 Apr.). *George Cross Commemoration. Cross in silver. Wmk. Mult. Script CA. P* 14½×14 (*3d.*) *or* 14×14½ (*others*).

283	**74**	1½d. deep dull green ..	0	9	0	9
284	**75**	3d. vermilion	1	6	1	6
285	**76**	1s. reddish brown ..	3	0	3	6

77. "Design".

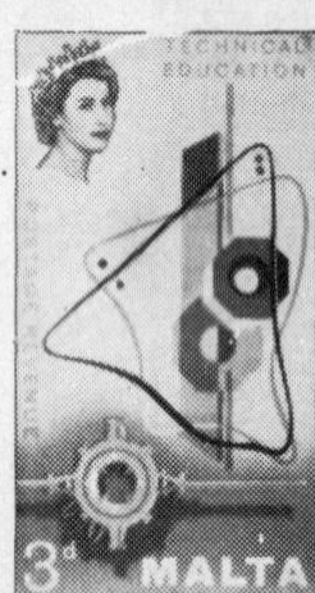

78. "Construction".

79. Technical School, Paola.

(Des. E. V. Cremona. Photo. Harrison & Sons

1958 (15 Feb.). *Technical Education in Malt W* w. **12.** *P* 14×14½ (*3d.*) *or* 14½×14 (*other*

286	**77**	1½d. black and deep green	0	9	0
287	**78**	3d. black, scarlet and grey	1	0	1
288	**79**	1s. grey, brt. pur. & black	3	0	3

80. Bombed-out Family.

81. Sea Raid on Grand Harbour, Valletta.

82. Searchlight Crew.

(Photo. Harrison & Sons.)

1958 (15 Apr.). *George Cross Commemoration. Cross in first colour, outlined in silver. W* w. **12.** *P* 14×14½ (3*d.*) *or* 14½×14 (*others*).

289	**80**	1½d. blue-green and black	0	8	0	8
290	**81**	3d. red and black ..	1	3	1	3
291	**82**	1s. reddish violet & black	3	0	3	6

3. Air Raid Casualties. **85.** Maltese under Bombardment.

84. " For Gallantry ".

(Photo. Harrison & Sons.)

59 (15 Apr.). *George Cross Commemoration. W* w. **12.** *P* 14½×14 (3*d.*) *or* 14×14½ (*others*).

2	**83**	1½d. grey-grn., blk. & gold	0	6	0	8
3	**84**	3d. reddish violet, black and gold ..	1	0	1	0
4	**85**	1s. blue-grey, blk. & gold	3	0	3	6

86. Shipwreck of St. Paul (after Palombi).

87. Consecration of St. Publius, First Bishop of Malta.

88. Departure of St. Paul (after Palombi).

89. Statue of St. Paul, Rabat, Malta.

90. Angel with the *Acts of the Apostles.*

91. St. Paul with the *Second Epistle to the Corinthians.*

(Photo. Harrison & Sons.)

1960 (9 Feb.). *19th Centenary of the Shipwreck of St. Paul.* *W* w. **12.** *P* 13 (1½*d.*, 3*d.*, 6*d.*) *or* 14 × 14½ (*others*).

No.	Type	Description	Unused	Used
295	**86**	1½d. blue, gold & yell.-brn.	1 0	0 8
		a. Gold inscr. and date omitted	£120	
296	**87**	3d. brt. pur., gold & blue	1 6	1 6
297	**88**	6d. carm., gold & pale grey	3 6	4 0
298	**89**	8d. black and gold ..	5 0	6 0
299	**90**	1s. maroon and gold ..	7 6	8 6
300	**91**	2s. 6d. blue, dp. bluish green and gold ..	20 0	22 6
		a. Gold omitted		

92. Stamp of 1860.

(Centre litho; frame recess. Waterlow.)

1960 (1 Dec.). *Stamp Centenary.* *W* w. **12.** *P* 13½.

No.	Type	Description	Unused	Used
301	**92**	1½d. buff, pale blue and green (*shades*) ..	0 9	1 0
302	,,	3d. buff, pale blue and deep carmine ..	1 8	2 0
303	,,	6d. buff, pale blue and ultramarine	3 3	3 9

93. George Cross.

94. George Cross.

95. George Cross.

(Photo. Harrison & Sons.)

1961 (15 Apr.). *George Cross Commemoration* *W* w. **12.** *P* 15 × 14.

No.	Type	Description	Unused	Used
304	**93**	1½d. black, cream & bistre	0 9	0
305	**94**	3d. olive-brown & greenish blue ..	0 9	0
306	**95**	1s. olive-green, lilac and deep reddish violet ..	3 6	3

96. " Madonna Damascena ".

97. Great Siege Monument.

98. Grand Master La Valette. **99.** Assault on Fort St. Elmo.

(Photo. Harrison & Sons.)

1962 (7 SEPT.). *Great Siege Commemoration. W* w.**12.** *P* 13×12.

307 **96** 2d. bright blue 0 6 0 6
308 **97** 3d. red 0 7 0 8
309 **98** 6d. bronze-green 1 0 1 3
310 **99** 1s. brown-purple 2 0 2 6

1963 (4 JUNE). *Freedom from Hunger. As No.* 63 *of Aden.*

311 1s. 6d. sepia 2 6 2 9

1963 (2 SEPT.). *Red Cross Centenary. As No.* 147/8 *of Antigua.*

312 2d. red and black 0 5 0 6
313 1s. 6d. red and blue 2 6 2 9

1963 (15 OCT.)–**64.** *As Nos.* 268 *and* 270, *but wmk.* w. **12.**

314 **59** 1d. black 0 9 0 6
315 **61** 2d. deep brown (25.7.64*) 1 0 0 10

* This is the earliest known date recorded in Malta.

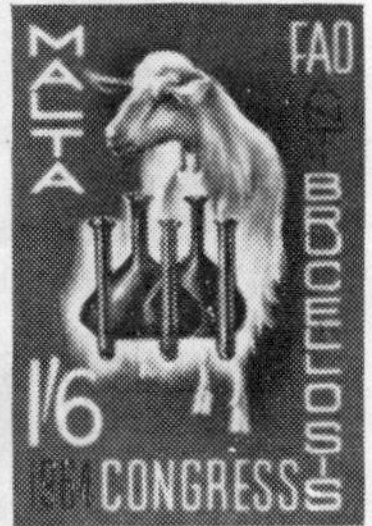

100. Bruce, Zammit and Microscope. **101.** Goat and Laboratory Equipment.

(Des. E. V. Cremona. Photo. Harrison.)

964 (14 APRIL). *Anti-Brucellosis Congress. W* w. **12.** *P* 14.

16 **100** 2d. light brown, black and bluish green .. 0 8 0 9
17 **101** 1s. 6d. black and maroon 3 6 3 6

102. "Tending the Sick".

103. St. Luke and Hospital.

104. Sacra Infermeria, Valletta.

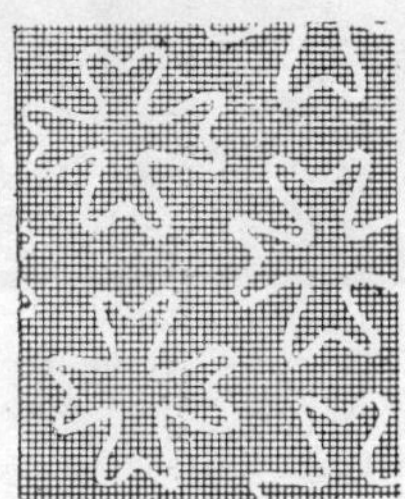

105. Maltese Cross.

(Des. E. V. Cremona. Photo. Harrison.)

1964 (5 SEPT.). *First European Catholic Doctors' Congress, Valletta. W* **105.** *P* 13½×14½.

318 **102** 2d. red, black, gold and grey-blue 1 6 2 0
319 **103** 6d. red, black, gold and bistre 3 6 4 6
320 **104** 1s. 6d. red, black, gold and reddish violet .. 8 0 9 0

106. Dove and British Crown. **107.** Dove and Pope's Tiara.

108. Dove and U.N. Emblem.

(Des. E. V. Cremona. Photo. Harrison.)

1964 (21 SEPT.). *Independence.* *W* **105.** *P* 14 × 13½.

No.	Type	Description				
321	**106**	2d. olive-brown, red and gold	0	6	0	6
322	**107**	3d. brown-purple, red and gold	0	8	0	9
323	**108**	6d. slate, red and gold ..	1	0	1	3
324	**106**	1s. blue, red and gold ..	1	9	2	0
325	**107**	1s. 6d. indigo, red & gold	2	9	3	0
326	**108**	2s. 6d. deep violet-blue, red and gold ..	5	0	6	0

109. " The Nativity ".

(Des. E. V. Cremona. Photo. De La Rue.)

1964 (3 Nov.). *Christmas.* *W* **105.** *P* 13 × 13½.

No.	Type	Description				
327	**109**	2d. bright purple & gold	2	6	3	0
328	,,	4d. bright blue and gold	5	0	6	0
329	,,	8d. deep bluish green and gold	11	6	12	6

110. Neolithic Era.

111. Punic Era.

112. Roman Era.

113. Proto Christian Era.

114. Saracenic Era.

115. Siculo Norman Era.

116. Knights of Malta.

117. Maltese Navy.

118. French Occupation.

119. British Rule.

120. Maltese Corps of the British Army.

21. International Eucharistic Congress, 1913.

122. Self-Government, 1921.

123. Gozo Civic Council.

124. State of Malta.

125. Independence.

126. HAFMED (Allied Forces, Mediterranean).

127. The Maltese Islands (map).

128. Patron Saints.

(Des. E. V. Cremona. Photo. Harrison.)

1965 (7 Jan.). *W* **105.** *P* 14 × 14½ (*vert.*) *or* 14½ (*horiz.*).

No.	Type	Value		Unused		Used	
330	**110**	½d. multicoloured	..	0	2	0	3
331	**111**	1d. multicoloured	..	0	3	0	4
332	**112**	1½d. multicoloured	..	0	4	0	4
333	**113**	2d. multicoloured	..	0	4	0	5
334	**114**	2½d. multicoloured	..	0	5	0	5
335	**115**	3d. multicoloured	..	0	6	0	7
336	**116**	4d. multicoloured	..	0	7	0	9
337	**117**	4½d. multicoloured	..	0	8	0	9
338	**118**	6d. multicoloured	..	0	10	1	0
339	**119**	8d. multicoloured	..	1	0	1	5
340	**120**	1s. multicoloured	..	1	5	2	0
341	**121**	1s. 3d. multicoloured	..	1	9	2	3
		a. Gold (centre) omitted	..				
342	**122**	1s. 6d. multicoloured	..	2	0	3	0
343	**123**	2s. multicoloured	..	2	9	3	9
344	**124**	2s. 6d. multicoloured	..	3	6	4	0
345	**125**	3s. multicoloured	..	4	0	5	0
		a. Gold (framework) omitted					
346	**126**	5s. multicoloured	..	6	9	7	6
347	**127**	10s. multicoloured	..	13	3	15	0
348	**128**	£1 multicoloured		25	0	30	0

The ½d. and 1d. had white printing plates and the plate numbers can be seen under a strong glass or if held up to the light at an angle. Two silver plates were used on the 4d., one for " KNIGHTS OF MALTA " and the other for " MALTA ". Five colours were used for the 4½d. but no plate number appears for the black plate. Two gold plates were used for the 8d. to 10s., one for the framework and the other for the gold in the central part of the designs.

129. Dante.

(Des. E. V. Cremona. Photo. Govt. Ptg. Wks., Rome.)

1965 (7 JULY). *700th Anniv. of Dante's Birth. P* 14.

349	**129**	2d. indigo	0	5	0	7
350	,,	6d. bronze-green ..	1	0	1	6
351	,,	2s. chocolate	3	3	4	0

130. Turkish Camp.

132. Turkish Armada.

134. Grand Master J. de La Valette's Arms.

131. Battle Scene.

133. Arrival of Relief Force.

135. " Allegory of Victory " (from mural by M. Preti).

136. Victory Medal.

(Des. E. V. Cremona. Photo. Harrison.)

1965 (1 SEPT.). *400th Anniv. of Great Siege. W* **105** *P* 13 (*6d.*, 1*s.*) *or* 14½ × 14 (*others*).

352	**130**	2d. olive-grn., red & blk.	0	5	0	
353	**131**	3d. olive-green, red, black and light drab ..	0	7	0	1
354	**132**	6d. multicoloured ..	1	0	1	
355	**133**	8d. red, gold, ind. & blue	1	2	1	
356	**134**	1s. red, gold and deep grey-blue	1	8	2	
357	**135**	1s. 6d. ochre, red & blk.	2	6	3	
358	**136**	2s. 6d. sepia, black, red and yellow-olive ..	4	6	5	

137. " The Three Kings ".

(Des. E. V. Cremona. Photo. Enschedé.)

1965 (7 OCT.). *Christmas. W* **105.** *P* 11 × 1

359	**137**	1d. slate-purple and red	0	4	0	
360	,,	4d. slate-purple and blue	0	9	1	
361	,,	1s. 3d. slate-purple and bright purple ..	2	3	2	

138. Sir Winston Churchill.

139. Sir Winston Churchill and George Cross.

(Des. E. V. Cremona. Photo. Harrison.)

1966 (24 Jan.). *Churchill Commemoration. W* **105.** *P* 14½ × 14.

362	**138**	2d. black, red and gold ..	0	8	1	0
363	**139**	3d. bronze-green, yellow-olive and gold ..	1	0	1	6
364	**138**	1s. maroon, red and gold	3	0	4	0
365	**139**	1s. 6d. chalky blue, violet-blue and gold ..	4	0	6	0

140. Grand Master La Valette.

141. Pope Pius V.

142. Map of Valletta.

143. Francesco Laparelli (architect).

144. Girolamo Cassar (architect).

(Des. E. V. Cremona. Photo. State Ptg. Wks., Vienna.)

1966 (28 Mar.). *400th Anniv. of Valletta. P* 12.

366	**140**	2d. multicoloured ..	0	5	0	7
367	**141**	3d. multicoloured ..	0	7	0	10
368	**142**	6d. multicoloured ..	1	0	1	2
369	**143**	1s. multicoloured ..	1	8	2	3
370	**144**	2s. 6d. multicoloured ..	4	6	5	6

POSTAGE DUE STAMPS.

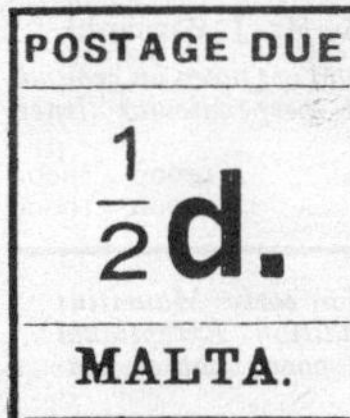

D 1

D 2

1925. *Type-set locally. Imperf.*

D 1	D 1	½d. black	0	6		0	10
D 2	,,	1d. black	0	8		1	0
D 3	,,	1½d. black	0	9		1	9
D 4	,,	2d. black	0	9		1	6
D 5	,,	2½d. black	1	0		1	9
		a. "2" of "½" omitted ..	£15			£15	
D 6	,,	3d. black/*grey*	1	6		3	6
D 7	,,	4d. black/*buff*	2	0		3	6
D 8	,,	6d. black/*buff*	2	6		5	0
D 9	,,	1s. black/*buff*	4	0		6	0
D10	,,	1s. 6d. black/*buff* ..	6	0		7	6

All the above may be had in *tête-bêche* pairs from the junction of the panes, price about four times that of a single stamp. Dangerous forgeries of No. D5*a* are in circulation.

(Typo. Bradbury, Wilkinson & Co.)

1925. *Wmk. Mult. Script CA (sideways). P* 12.

D11	D 2	½d. green	0 6	0 8
D12	,,	1d. violet	0 6	0 8
D13	,,	1½d. brown	0 10	1 3
D14	,,	2d. grey	1 3	1 0
D15	,,	2½d. orange	0 5	0 8
D16	,,	3d. blue	2 6	3 0
D17	,,	4d. olive-green	2 6	3 0
D18	,,	6d. purple	0 10	1 3
D19	,,	1s. black	1 5	2 0
D20	,,	1s. 6d. carmine	2 0	3 0

1953 (5 Nov.)–**57.** *Chalk-surfaced paper. Wmk. Mult. Script CA (sideways). P* 12.

D21	D 2	½d. emerald	0 2	0 2
D22	,,	1d. purple (*shades*)	0 3	0 4
D23	,,	1½d. yellow-brown	0 4	0 6
D23*a*	,,	2d. grey-brown (20.3.57)	0 4	0 6
D24	,,	3d. deep slate-blue	0 6	0 8
D25	,,	4d. yellow-olive	0 7	0 10

MAURITIUS.

For GREAT BRITAIN stamps used in Mauritius, see page 74.

— SIMPLIFICATION (see INTRODUCTION) — **Nos. 1 to 34.**
(1, 2). 22a, 24a. 29. 30. 32, 34.

1 ("POST OFFICE")

2 ("POST PAID")

(Engraved on copper by Mr. J. Barnard.)

1847 (21 SEPT.). *T* **1.** *Head of Queen on groundwork of diagonal and perpendicular lines. Imperf.*

1	1d. orange-red	£14000	£10000
2	2d. deep blue	£14000	£10000

NOTE.—*Our prices for early Mauritius are for stamps in fine condition. Exceptional copies are worth more, poorer copies considerably less.*

1848 (MAY). *T* **2.** 12 *varieties on the sheet. Imperf.*

A. *Earliest impressions. Design deep, sharp and clear. Diagonal lines predominate. Thick paper.*

3	1d. orange-vermilion/*yellowish*	£2250	£1200
4	2d. indigo-blue/*grey to bluish*	£2500	£1250
	a. "PENOE" for "PENCE"	—	£1750
5	2d. deep blue/*grey to bluish*	£3000	£1500
	a. "PENOE" for "PENCE"	—	£2000

B. *Early impressions. Design sharp and clear but some lines slightly weakened. Paper not so thick, grey to yellowish white or bluish.*

6	1d. vermilion	£900	£450
7	1d. orange-vermilion	£950	£475
8	2d. blue	£1000	£500
	a. "PENOE" for "PENCE"	£2250	£850
9	2d. deep blue	£1200	£600

C. *Intermediate impressions. White patches appear where design has worn. Paper yellowish white, grey or bluish, of poorish quality.*

10	1d. bright vermilion	£550	£225
11	1d. dull vermilion	£550	£225
12	1d. red	£500	£200
13	2d. deep blue	£450	£225
14	2d. blue	£375	£175
	a. "PENOE" for "PENCE" (*shades*) *from*	£700	£300
15	2d. light blue	£375	£175

D. *Worn impressions. Much of design worn away, but some diagonal lines distinct. Paper yellowish, grey or bluish, of poorish quality.*

16	1d. red/*yellowish or grey*	£225	£85
17	1d. red-brn./*yellowish or grey*	£225	£85
18	1d. red/*bluish*	£70	£70
19	1d. red-brown/*bluish*	£90	£70
20	2d. blue (*shades*) / *yellowish or grey*	£275	£125
	a. "PENOE" for "PENCE" *from*	—	£225
21	2d. grey-blue/*yellowish or grey*	£300	£135
22	2d. blue (*shades*) *bluish*	£275	£100
	a. Doubly printed		

E. *Latest impressions. Almost none of design showing except part of Queen's head and frame. Paper yellowish, grey or bluish, of poorish quality.*

23	1d. red	£85	£50
24	1d. red-brown	£110	£50
25	2d. grey-blue/*bluish*	£125	£85
	a. "PENOE" for "PENCE"	£225	£125

The stamp lettered "PENOE" is No. 7 on the sheet.

3

(Engraved on copper by Mr. Lapirot.)

1859 (MARCH). *T* **3.** 12 *varieties on the shee Imperf. Early impressions.*

26	2d. deep blue	£325	£18
27	2d. blue	£225	£17

1859 (AUG.). *Intermediate prints. Lines c background, etc., partly worn away.*

28	2d. blue	£140	£9

1859 (OCT.). *Impressions from worn plate; bluis paper.*

29	2d. blue	£70	£4

4

5

1859 (OCT.). *T* **4.** *Bluish paper. Imperf.*
(The plate of 1848 re-engraved by Mr. Sherwir

30	2d. deep blue	£900	£2

Autotype illustrations in deep blue, on sto white wove paper faced with blue, were taken 1877 from a sheet reprinted in black from t original plate.

(Lithographed in the colony by Mr. Dardenne.)

1859 (Dec.). *White laid paper. Imperf.*

No.	Type	Description	Unused	Used
31	**5**	1d. deep red	£300	£125
31a	,,	1d. red	£225	£100
32	,,	1d. dull vermilion	£150	£100
33	,,	2d. slate-blue	£300	£100
33a	,,	2d. blue	£125	£70
34	,,	2d. pale blue	£90	£60
		Retouched varieties.		
34a	**5**	2d. blue, heavy retouch on neck	—	£125
34b	,,	2d. blue, slight retouches (several varieties)	—	£90

MAURITIUS

6

FOUR-PENCE

(7)

(Recess. Perkins Bacon & Co.)

1854 (8 April). *Surch. with T* **7**. *Imperf.*

No.	Type	Description	Unused	Used
35	**6**	4d. green	£90	£55

1858–59. *No value expressed. Imperf.*

No.	Type	Description	Unused	Used
36	**6**	(4d.) green	£20	£18
37	,,	(6d.) vermilion	30 0	£5
38	,,	(9d.) dull magenta	£25	£20
		Prepared for use, but not issued.		
39	**6**	(No value), red-brown (1859)	12 6	
40	,,	(No value), blue (1858)	6 6	

Remainders of these were overprinted " L.P.E. 1890 " in *red*, perforated at the London Philatelic Exhibition and sold as souvenirs.

No. 38 *was reissued in Nov.,* 1862, *as* 1d.; *stamps obliterated* " B 53 " *were so used.*

No.	Type	Description	Unused	Used
41		(1d.) dull magenta	—	£20

MAURITIUS

SIX PENCE

8

(Recess. Perkins Bacon & Co.)

1859. *Imperf.*

No.	Type	Description	Unused	Used
42	**8**	6d. blue	£30	80 0
43	,,	1s. vermilion	£50	£8

1861. *Colours corrected. Imperf.*

No.	Type	Description	Unused	Used
44	**8**	6d. dull purple-slate	60 0	85 0
45	,,	1s. yellow-green	£23	£18

1862. *Intermediate perf.* 14 *to* 16.

No.	Type	Description	Unused	Used
46	**8**	6d. slate	65 0	50 0
		a. Imperf. between (pair)	£90	
47	,,	1s. deep green	£125	£28

MAURITIUS

THREE PENCE

9

MAURITIUS

TEN PENCE

10

(Typo. De La Rue & Co.)

1860–63. *No wmk. P* 14.

No.	Type	Description	Unused	Used
48	**9**	1d. purple-brown	£5	35 0
49	,,	2d. blue	£7	60 0
50	,,	4d. rose	£7	35 0
51	,,	6d. green (1862)	£28	£10
52	,,	6d. slate (1863)	£7	£5
53	,,	9d. dull purple	£5	75 0
54	,,	1s. buff (1862)	£12	
55	,,	1s. green (1863)	£30	£18

1863–72. *Wmk. Crown CC. P* 14.

No.	Type	Description	Unused	Used
56	**9**	1d. purple-brown (1870	30 0	17 6
57	,,	1d. brown	45 0	22 6
58	,,	1d. bistre	60 0	22 6
59	,,	2d. pale blue	60 0	20 0
60	,,	2d. bright blue	45 0	20 0
61	,,	3d. deep red	80 0	55 0
61a	,,	3d. dull red	55 0	27 6
62	,,	4d. rose	50 0	10 0
63	,,	6d. dull violet (1864)	60 0	35 0
64	,,	6d. yellow-green (1865)	90 0	45 0
65	,,	6d. blue-green	65 0	15 0
66	,,	9d. yellow-green (1872)	£6	£6
67	**10**	10d. marone (1872)	£5	25 0
68	**9**	1s. yellow	£6	27 6
69	,,	1s. orange	£6	30 0
70	,,	1s. blue (1870)	£7	40 0
71	,,	5s. rosy mauve	£6	80 0
72	,,	5s. bright mauve (1865)	£10	60 0
		Variety. Imperf. (pair).		
73	**9**	2d. blue	£100	£100

½ d

HALF PENNY

(11)

Prepared for use, but not issued.

No. 53 *surch. with T* **11**.

No.	Type	Description	Unused	Used
74	**9**	½d. on 9d. dull purple (R.)	£35	
		a. Error. " PRNNY "		
75	,,	½d. on 9d. dull purple (Bk.)	£60	

HALF PENNY

(12)

1876. *Nos.* 53 *and* 67 *surch. with T* **12**.

No.	Type	Description	Unused	Used
76		½d. on 9d. dull purple	10 0	15 0
		a. Surch. inverted	£22	
		b. Surch. double		
77		½d. on 10d. marone	7 6	17 6

HALF PENNY

(13)

One Penny

(14)

One Shilling

(15)

1877. *T* **9** *and* **10**, *wmk. Crown CC, surch. with T* **13/5**. *P* 14.

No.	Type	Description	Unused	Used
79		½d. on 10d. rose (Apr.)	15 0	25 0
80		1d. on 4d. rose-carmine (6 Dec.)	15 0	25 0
81		1s. on 5s. rosy mauve (6 Dec.)	£10	£7
82		1s. on 5s. bright mauve (6 Dec.)	£14	£10

2 CENTS

(16)

2 Rs. 50 C.

(17)

1878 (3 Jan.). *T* **10** *(with lower label blank) surch. with T* **16**. *Wmk. Crown CC. P* 14.

No.	Type	Description	Unused	Used
83		2 c. dull rose	10 0	10 0

1878. *T* **9** *surch. as T* **16** *or* **17**. *Wmk. Crown CC. P* 14.

No.	Type	Description	Unused	Used
84		4 c. on 1d. bistre	15 0	10 0
85		8 c. on 2d. blue	17 6	8 6
86		13 c. on 3d. orange-red	10 0	20 0

87	17 c. on 4d. rose	70	0	12	6
88	25 c. on 6d. slate-blue	80	0	20	0
89	38 c. on 9d. pale violet ..	20	0	30	0
90	50 c. on 1s. green	30	0	16	0
91	2 r. 50 c. on 5s. bright mauve	30	0	25	0

18  19

20  21

22  23

24  25

26

(Typo. De La Rue & Co.)

1879–80. *Wmk. Crown CC. P* 14.

92	**18**	2 c. Venetian red ..	30	0	25	0
93	**19**	4 c. orange (1879) ..	30	0	10	0
94	**20**	8 c. blue	17	6	3	6
95	**21**	13 c. slate	£5		80	0
96	**22**	17 c. rose	35	0	15	0
97	**23**	25 c. olive-yellow (1879) ..	80	0	20	0
98	**24**	38 c. bright purple	£8		£7	
99	**25**	50 c. green	8	6	8	6
100	**26**	2 r. 50 c., brown-purple ..	40	0	50	0

1882–83. *Wmk. Crown CA P* 14.

101	**18**	2 c. Venetian red ..	12	6	15	0
102	**19**	4 c. orange	32	6	2	6
103	**23**	25 c. olive-yellow (1883) ..	10	0	7	6

16 CENTS (27)

SIXTEEN CENTS (28)

1883 (26 FEB.). *No.* 96 *surch. as T* **27.**
(*a*) *Surcharge* 14 *mm. long and* 3½ *high.*
(*b*) *Surcharge* 15 *mm. long and* 3½ *high.*
(*c*) *Surcharge* 15 *mm. long and* 2½ *high.*

104	**22**	16 c. on 17 c. rose (*a*) ..	35	0	32	6
		a. Surch. double				
105	,,	16 c. on 17 c. rose (*b*) ..	47	6	27	6
106	,,	16 c. on 17 c. rose (*c*) ..	90	0	85	0

1883 (14 JULY). *Wmk. Crown CA. Surch. with T* **28.** *P* 14.

107	**22**	16 c. on 17 c. rose ..	17	6	10	0

2 CENTS

(29)

1885 (11 MAY). *No.* 98 *surch. with T* **29.**

108	**24**	2 c. on 38 c. bright purple	60	0	50	0
		a. Without bar	—		£5	
		b. Surch. inverted	£20		£20	
		c. Surch. double	£28			

30

(Typo. De La Rue & Co.)

1885–91. *Wmk. Crown CA. P* 14.

110	**18**	2 c. green	3	0	1	9
111	**19**	4 c. carmine	2	0	0	9
112	**20**	8 c. blue (1891)	6	0	5	0
113	**30**	16 c. chestnut	6	0	2	0
114	**25**	50 c. orange (1887) ..	45	0	17	6

2 CENTS

(31)

1887 (6 JULY). *No.* 95 *surch. with T* **31.**

115	**21**	2 c. on 13 c. slate (R.) ..	25	0	30	0
		a. Surch. inverted	£5		£5	
		b. Surch. double	—		£20	
		c. Surch. double, one on back of stamp	£30			

TWO CENTS (32)

TWO CENTS (33)

1891 (SEPT.). *Surch. with T* **32** *on* 4 *c.*, 17 *c.*, *and* 38 *c.* (*No.* 98), *and as T* **33** *on* 38 *c.*, (*No.* 89)

117	2 c. on 4 c. (No. 111) ..	1	9	1	[illegible]
	a. Surch. inverted	£5			
	b. Surch. double	£9		£[illegible]	
	c. Double, one inverted ..	£6		£[illegible]	
118	2 c. on 17 c. (No. 96) ..	40	0	65	[illegible]
	a. Surch. inverted	£12			
	b. Surch. double	£28		£2[illegible]	
119	2 c. on 38 c. (No. 89) ..	7	6	12	[illegible]
	a. Surch. inverted	£9			
	b. Surch. double	£24		£2[illegible]	
	c. Double, one inverted ..	£5			
120	2 c. on 38 c. (No. 98) ..	7	6	10	[illegible]
	a. Surch. inverted	£22			
	b. Surch. double	£5			
	c. Double, one inverted ..	£5			

Minor varieties are also known with portions o[f] the surcharge missing, due to defective printing

ONE CENT (34) **ONE CENT** (35)

1893 (1 Jan.). *T* **18** *and* **30** *surch. with T* **34** *and* **35** *respectively. Wmk. Crown CA. P* 14.

123 1 c. on 2 c. pale violet .. 0 8 2 0
124 1 c. on 16 c. chestnut 1 6 3 6

1893–94. *Wmk. Crown CA. P* 14.

125 **18** 1 c. pale violet 1 0 3 0
126 **30** 15 c. chestnut 1 6 1 3
127 „ 15 c. blue 10 0 2 0

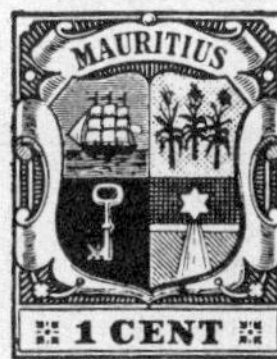

36

(Typo. De La Rue & Co.)

1895–99. *Wmk. Crown CA. P* 14.

128 **36** 1 c. dull pur. & ultram. 0 10 0 3
129 „ 2 c. dull pur. & orange.. 1 6 0 9
130 „ 3 c. dull pur. & dp. pur. 3 6 2 0
131 „ 4 c. dull pur. & emerald 1 3 0 9
131*a* „ 6 c. green and rose-red.. 4 6 2 6
132 „ 18 c. green & ultramarine 12 6 10 0

37

(Typo. De La Rue & Co.)

1898 (23 May). *Jubilee issue. T* **37**. *Wmk. CA. over Crown, sideways. P* 14.

133 36 c. orange & ultramarine.. 30 0 30 0

6 CENTS (38) **15 CENTS** (39)

1899. *Nos.* 132 *and* 133 *surcharged.*

134 **38** 6 c. on 18 c. grn. & ult. (R.) 1 9 1 9
a. Surch. inverted .. £10 £8
135 **39** 15 c. on 36 c. or. & ult. (B.) 10 0 6 0
a. Bar of surch. omitted .. £10

The space between "6" and "cents" varies from 2½ to 4 mm.

40. Admiral Mahé de La Bourdonnais, Governor of Mauritius, 1735–46.

(Recess. De La Rue & Co.)

1899 (Dec.). *Bicentenary of Birth of La Bourdonnais. Wmk. Crown CC. P* 14.

136 **40** 15 c. ultramarine 25 0 7 6

4 Cents (41) **12 CENTS** (42)

1900. *No.* 113 *surch. with T* **41**.

137 **30** 4 c. on 16 c. chestnut .. 4 0 2 6

1900. *Wmk. Crown CA. P* 14.

138 **36** 1 c. grey and black .. 1 3 1 6
139 „ 2 c. dull and bright purple 0 6 0 6
140 „ 4 c. pur. & carm./*yellow* 1 6 1 3
141 „ 15 c. green and orange .. 15 0 22 6

1902. *No.* 132 *surch. with T* **42**.

142 **36** 12 c. on 18 c. grn. & ultram. 8 6 22 6

The bar cancelling the original value seems in some cases to be one thick bar and in others two thin ones.

Postage & Revenue. (43)

1902. *Various stamps optd. with T* **43**.

143 4 c. pur. & car./*yell.* (No. 140) 1 0 0 10
144 6 c. green & red (No. 131*a*) 2 0 3 6
145 15 c. green & orange (No. 141) 2 6 2 6
146 25 c. olive-yellow (No. 103).. 6 0 10 0
147 50 c. green (No. 99) 10 0 7 6
148 2 r. 50 c. brn.-pur. (No. 100) 85 0 90 0

1902. *No.* 133 *surch. as T* **42**, *but with longer bar.*

149 12 c. on 36 c. orange & ultram. 5 0 7 6
a. Surch. inverted. .. £25 £15

The note below No. 142 also applies to No. 149.

44

(Typo. De La Rue & Co.)

1902–5. *T* **36** (*wmk. Crown CA*) *and* **44** (1 *r. wmk. Crown CC*, 2½ *and* 5 *r. wmk. Crown CA*). *P* 14.

No.	Description	Unused	Used
150	3 c. green & carmine/*yellow* ..	2 6	2 0
151	4 c. grey-green and violet ..	1 6	3 6
152	4 c. black and carmine/*blue*	4 6	0 8
153	5 c. dull & bright purple/*buff*	10 0	12 6
154	5 c. dull purple & black/*buff*	2 0	4 0
155	6 c. purple & carmine/*red* ..	2 0	2 0
156	8 c. green and black/*buff* ..	2 0	10 0
157	12 c. grey-black and carmine	6 0	3 0
158	15 c. black and blue/*blue* ('05)	20 0	10 0
159	25 c. green & carmine/*grn.* OC	12 6	22 6
160	50 c. dull grn. & dp. green/*yell.*	17 6	30 0
161	1 r. grey-black and carmine	45 0	35 0
162	2 r. 50 c. green & black/*blue*	55 0	65 0
163	5 r. purple & carmine/*red* ..	£6	£7

1904–07. *T* **36** *and* **44** (1 *r.*). *Wmk. Mult. Crown CA. P* 14.

No.	Description	Unused	Used
164	1 c. grey & black, C (1907) ..	3 6	4 6
165	2 c. dull & brt. pur., OC ('05)	2 6	0 3
166	3 c. grn. & carm./*yell.*, C ..	17 6	10 0
167	4 c. black & carm./*blue*, OC	4 6	0 10
168	6 c. purple & carm./*red*, OC	2 6	1 0
171	15 c. black & blue/*blue*, C ('07)	8 6	6 0
174	50 c. grn. & dp. grn./*yellow*. C	6 6	8 6
175	1 r. grey-blk. & car., C ('07)	35 0	30 0

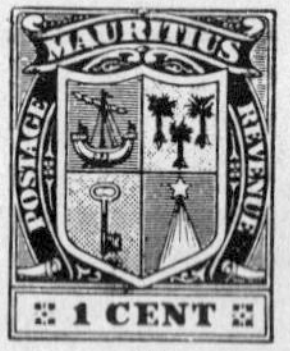

46

47

(Typo. De La Rue & Co.)

1910. *Wmk. Mult. Crown CA. P* 14.

No.	Type	Description	Unused	Used
181	**46**	1 c. black, O	0 6	0 6
182	,,	2 c. brown, O	0 6	0 4
183	,,	3 c. green, O	1 6	1 9
184	,,	4 c. pale yellow-green and carmine, O	1 6	0 6
185	**47**	5 c. grey and carmine, O	2 6	5 0
186	**46**	6 c. carmine-red, O ..	1 3	0 4
186*a*	,,	6 c. pale red, O	6 0	1 0
187	,,	8 c. orange, O	3 0	6 0
188	**47**	12 c. greyish slate, O ..	1 9	5 0
189	**46**	15 c. blue, O	2 6	0 8
190	**47**	25 c. black & red/*yell.*, C ..	12 6	20 0
191	,,	50 c. dull pur. & black, C	15 0	20 0
192	,,	1 r. black/*green*, C ..	10 6	20 0
193	,,	2 r. 50 c. blk & red/*bl.* C	40 0	60 0
194	,,	5 r. green & red/*yell.*, C ..	85 0	90 0
195	,,	10 r. green & red/*green*, C	£20	£24

In Nos. 188, 190 and 195, the value labels are as in T **49**.

48

49

(Typo. De La Rue & Co.)

1913–23. *T* **48** *and* **49** (12 *c.*, 25 *c.*, *and* 10 *r.*). *Wmk. Mult. Crown CA. P* 14.

No.	Description	Unused	Used
196	5 c. grey & carm., O (1915)	4 0	5 0
197	5 c. slate-grey & carmine, O	8 6	10 0
198	12 c. greyish slate, O (1915) ..	1 9	2 6
199	25 c. black & red/*yell.*, C ('13)	4 0	6 0
	a. White back (1916)	7 6	10 0
	b. On orange-buff ..	40 0	40 0
	c. On pale yellow (Die I) ..	40 0	25 0
	d. On pale yellow (Die II) ..	3 6	15 0
200	50 c. dull pur. & blk., C (Die I)	45 0	75 0
201	1 r. black/*blue-green*, C (*olive back*) (1917)	8 0	15 0
	a. On emerald surface ..	20 0	40 0
	b. On emerald back (Die II) ..	7 6	15 0
202	2 r. 50 c., blk. & red/*blue*, C ..	17 6	27 6
203	5 r. grn. & red/*orge.-buff*, C ..	£5	£6
	a. On pale yellow (Die I) ..	£6	£7
	b. On pale yellow (Die II) ..	£12	£12
204	10 r. green & red/*green*, C ..	£5	£6
	a. On blue-green, olive back ..	£70	
	b. On emerald surface	£5	£7
	c. On emerald back (Die I) ..	£5	£7
	d. On emerald back (Die II) ..	90 0	£5

1921–34. *Wmk. Mult. Script CA. P* 14. (*a*) *T* **46.**

No.	Description	Unused	Used
205	1 c. black, O	1 6	1 9
206	2 c. brown, O	0 4	0 4
207	4 c. pale olive-grn. & car., O	4 0	5 0
208	4 c. green, O	0 9	0 8
209	6 c. carmine, O	10 0	10 0
210	6 c. bright mauve, O ..	1 6	1 0
210*a*	8 c. orange, O	4 0	8 6
211	10 c. grey, O	6 0	6 0
212	12 c. carmine-red, O	2 6	5 0
213	15 c. blue, O	15 0	5 0
214	20 c. blue, O	6 0	7 6

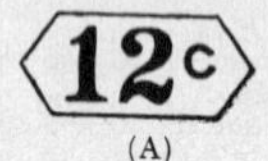

(A)

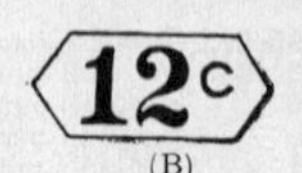

(B)

Two types of duty plate in the 12 c. In Type B, the letters of "MAURITIUS" are larger; the extremities of the downstroke and the tail of the "2" are pointed, instead of square, and the "c" is larger.

(*b*) *T* **48** *and* **49.**

No.	Description	Unused	Used
215	5 c. grey & carm., O (Die II)	0 3	0 3
215*a*	5 c. grey & carm., O (Die I) ('32)	0 6	1 0
216	12 c. grey, O (1921) (A) ..	5 0	12 6
216*a*	12 c. pale grey, O ('28) (A)	2 0	1 0
216*b*	12 c. grey, O ('34) (B) ..	1 6	0 10
217	12 c. carmine-red, O ('22) ..	3 0	12 6
218	25 c. black and red/*pale yellow*, C (Die II) ..	2 0	1 3
218*a*	25 c. black and red/*pale yellow*, C (Die I) ('32) ..	5 0	15 0
219	50 c. dull purple & black, C (Die II)	6 0	10 0
220	1 r. blk./*emer.*, C (Die II) ..	7 6	2 0
220*a*	1 r. blk./*emer.*, C (Die I) ('32)	32 6	40 0
221	2 r. 50 c. blk. & red/*blue*, C	10 0	8 6
222	5 r. green & red/*yellow*, C ..	40 0	50 0
223	10 r. grn. & red/*emer.*, C ('28)	£5	£6

1924. *T* **44**, *but Arms similar to T* **46.** *Wmk. Mult. Script CA. P* 14.

No.	Description	Unused	Used
224	50 r. dull purple & green, C	£100	£125

3

Cents

(50)

51

1925. *T* **46** *surch. as T* **50.**

225 3 c. on 4 c. green 1 6 1 9
226 10 c. on 12 c. carmine-red .. 1 9 3 6
227 15 c. on 20 c. blue 1 9 4 0

1926. *Wmk. Mult. Script CA. P* 14.

228 **46** 2 c. purple/*yellow*, O .. 0 4 0 6
229 ,, 3 c. green, O 1 0 2 6
230 ,, 4 c. brown, O 1 3 3 6
231 ,, 10 c. carmine-red, O .. 1 9 2 0
232 ,, 12 c. grey, O 4 6 7 6
233 ,, 15 c. cobalt, O 2 6 1 6
234 ,, 20 c. purple, O 5 0 10 0

1926–34. *As T* **49** (*King*). *Wmk. Mult. Script CA. P* 14.

235 1 c. black, O 1 0 1 0
236 2 c. brown, O 1 0 0 3
237 3 c. green, O 2 6 2 6
238 4 c. sage-green and carmine, O (Die II) ('27) .. 2 6 1 3
238*a* 4 c. sage-green and carmine, O (Die I) ('32) 6 0 20 0
238*b* 4 c. green, O (Die I) ('33) .. 2 6 6 0
239 6 c. sepia, O ('28) 1 6 5 0
240 8 c. orange, O 4 0 10 0
241 10 c. carmine-red, O (Die II) 1 0 2 0
241*a* 10 c. car.-red, O (Die I) ('32) 1 9 6 0
242 15 c. Prussian blue, O ('28) 5 0 4 6
243 20 c. purple, O ('27) .. 3 6 10 0
244 20 c. Prussian blue, O (Die I) ('33) 8 6 12 6
244*a* 20 c. Prussian blue, O (Die II) ('34) 12 6 12 6

1935 (6 May). *Silver Jubilee. As Nos.* 91/4 *of Antigua.*

245 5 c. ultramarine and grey .. 0 8 1 3
246 12 c. green and indigo .. 3 0 4 0
247 20 c. brown and deep blue .. 5 0 7 6
248 1 r. slate and purple .. 95 0 95 0

1937 (12 May). *Coronation. As Nos.* 13/5 *of Aden.*

249 5 c. violet 0 4 0 6
250 12 c. scarlet 0 9 1 0
251 20 c. bright blue 1 0 1 3

(Typo. De La Rue & Co.)

1938–48. *T* **51** *and similar types. Wmk. Mult. Script CA. P* 14.

252 **51** 2 c. grey 0 3 0 3
a. Perf. 15 × 14 (1943) .. 1 0 1 3
253 ,, 3 c. purple and scarlet .. 0 3 0 3
254 ,, 4 c. green 0 6 0 3
255 ,, 5 c. violet 1 6 0 9
aa. Pale violet (shades) .. 0 6 0 3
a. Perf. 15 × 14 (1943) .. 20 0 6 6
256 ,, 10 c. carmine-rose .. 1 6 2 0
a. Deep carmine-red .. 0 9 0 9
b. P. 15 × 14. Pale car m.('43) 17 6 17 6
257 ,, 12 c. salmon 1 0 1 0
a. Perf. 15 × 14 (1943) .. 30 0 17 6
258 ,, 20 c. blue 1 0 0 10
259 ,, 25 c. marone, C O .. 1 0 1 10
260 ,, 1 r. grey-brown C O .. 3 0 2 6
261 ,, 2 r. 50, pale violet, C O 8 0 12 6
a. Pale greyish violet, C .. 55 0 37 6
262 ,, 5 r. olive-green, C O .. 12 6 12 6
a. Yellow-olive, C 25 0 25 0
263 ,, 10 r. purple, C O 30 0 35 0

Dates of issue, Perf. 14: 1938—23 Feb., 5 c., 26 Feb., 4 c., 12 c., 20 c.; 2 Mar., 25 c., 1 r., 2 r. 50 (No. 261), 5 r. (No. 262), 10 r.; 9 Mar.; 2 c., 10 c. (No. 256); Oct., 3 c. 1943—10 c. (No. 256*a*). 1948—(Apr.), 2 r. 50 (No. 261*a*) and 5 r. (No. 262*a*).

1946 (20 Nov.). *Victory. As Nos.* 28/9 *of Aden.*

264 5 c. lilac 0 4 0 4
265 20 c. blue 0 8 1 3

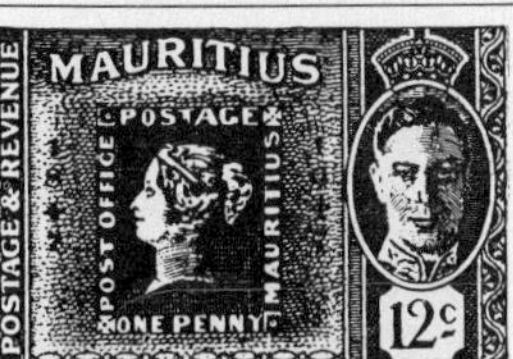

52. 1d. "Post Office" Mauritius and King George VI.

(Recess. Bradbury, Wilkinson.)

1948 (22 Mar.). *Centenary of First British Colonial Postage Stamp. P* $11\frac{1}{2} \times 11$.

266 **52** 5 c. orange & magenta .. 0 3 0 4
267 ,, 12 c. orange and green .. 0 6 0 6
268 – 20 c. blue and light blue .. 0 8 0 9
269 – 1 r. blue and red-brown .. 2 0 2 6

Design:—20 c., 1 r. As T **52** but showing 2d. "Post Office" Mauritius.

1948 (25 Oct.). *Royal Silver Wedding. As Nos.* 30/1 *of Aden.*

270 5 c. violet 0 5 0 5
271 10 r. magenta 30 0 35 0

1949 (10 Oct.). *75th Anniv. of U.P.U. As Nos.* 114/7 *of Antigua.*

272 12 c. carmine 0 9 1 0
273 20 c. deep blue 0 9 0 10
274 35 c. purple 1 6 2 0
275 1 r. sepia 3 0 3 6

53. Sugar Factory.

54. Grand Port.

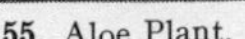

55. Aloe Plant. **56.** Tamarind Falls.

57. Rempart Mountain.

58. Transporting Cane.

59. Dodo and Map.

60. Legend of Paul and Virginia.

61. La Bourdonnais Statue.

62. Government House.

63. Pieter Both Mountain.

64. Mauritius Deer.

65. Port Louis.

66. Beach Scene.

67. Arms of Mauritius.

(Photo. Harrison & Sons, Ltd.)

1950 (1 JULY). *Wmk. Mult. Script CA* *Chalk-surfaced paper. P* 13½ × 14½ (*horiz.*) 14½ × 13½ (*vert.*).

276	**53**	1 c. bright purple ..	0	4	0
277	**54**	2 c. rose-carmine ..	0	3	0
278	**55**	3 c. yellow-green	0	10	1
279	**56**	4 c. green	0	4	0
280	**57**	5 c. blue	0	8	0
281	**58**	10 c. scarlet	0	6	0

282 **59** 12 c. olive-green 0 8 1 0
283 **60** 20 c. ultramarine 0 9 0 9
284 **61** 25 c. brown-purple .. 0 10 1 3
285 **62** 35 c. violet.. .. .. 2 0 1 0
286 **63** 50 c. emerald-green .. 2 0 2 0
287 **64** 1 r. sepia 6 0 4 6
288 **65** 2 r. 50, orange 12 6 12 6
289 **66** 5 r. red-brown 20 0 20 0
290 **67** 10 r. dull blue 30 0 32 6

1953 (2 June). *Coronation. As No.* 47 *of Aden.*
291 10 c. black and emerald .. 0 9 0 9

68. Tamarind Falls.

69. Historical Museum, Mahebourg.

(Photo. Harrison & Sons, Ltd.)

1953 (3 Nov.)–**54.** *As T* **53/67**, *but with portrait of Queen Elizabeth II in place of King George VI, as in T* **68/9**. *Wmk. Mult. Script CA. Chalk-surfaced paper. P* 13½ × 14½ (*horiz.*) *or* 14½ × 13½ (*vert.*).
293 **54** 2 c. bright carmine (1.6.54) 0 2 0 3
294 **55** 3 c. yellow-green (1.6.54) 0 3 0 6
295 **53** 4 c. bright purple .. 0 3 0 6
296 **57** 5 c. Prussian blue (1.6.54) 0 4 0 3
297 **68** 10 c. bluish green (*shades*) 0 6 0 3
298 **69** 15 c. scarlet 0 6 0 3
299 **61** 20 c. brown-purple .. 0 7 0 6
300 **60** 25 c. bright blue (*shades*).. 0 10 0 8
301 **62** 35 c. reddish violet (1.6.54) 1 0 0 10
302 **63** 50 c. bright green 1 4 1 0
302*a* **59** 60 c. deep green (*shades*) (2.8.54) 1 7 0 6
303 **64** 1 r. sepia (*shades*) .. 2 6 2 3
304 **65** 2 r. 50, orange (1.6.54) 6 6 7 6
305 **66** 5 r. red-brown (*shades*) (1.6.54) 12 0 12 6
306 **67** 10 r. dp. grey-blue (1.6.54) 22 0 18 0

70. Queen Elizabeth II and King George III (after Lawrence).

(Litho. Enschedé.)

1961 (11 Jan.). 150*th Anniv. of British Post Office in Mauritius. W* w. **12**. *P* 13½ × 14.
307 **70** 10 c. black and brown-red 1 0 1 0
308 ,, 20 c. ultram. and light blue 1 6 1 6
309 ,, 35 c. black and yellow 2 0 2 3
310 ,, 1 r. deep maroon & green 5 0 5 6

1963 (4 June). *Freedom from Hunger. As No.* 63 *of Aden.*
311 60 c. reddish violet 1 9 2 0

1963 (2 Sept.). *Red Cross Centenary. As Nos.* 147/8 *of Antigua.*
312 10 c. red and black 0 5 0 6
313 60 c. red and blue 1 6 1 9

1963 (12 Nov.)–**64.** *As Nos.* 297, 302*a and* 304 *but wmk.* w. **12**.
314 **68** 10 c. bluish green (*shades*) ('64) 0 5 0 7
315 **59** 60 c. bronze-green (28.5.64) 1 7 1 7
316 **65** 2 r. 50, orange 6 0 6 3

71. Grey White-eye.

72. Rodrigues Fody.

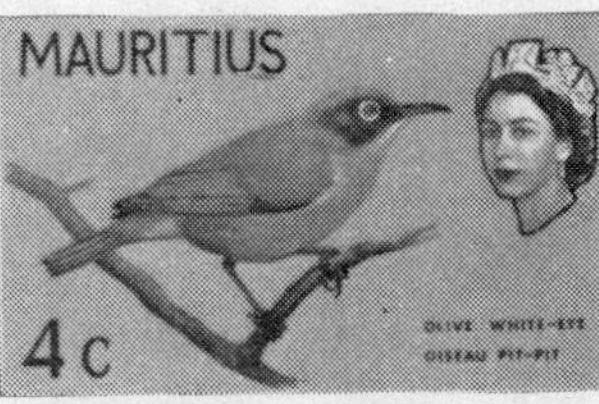

73. Olive White-eye.

74. Paradise Flycatcher.

75. Mauritius Fody.

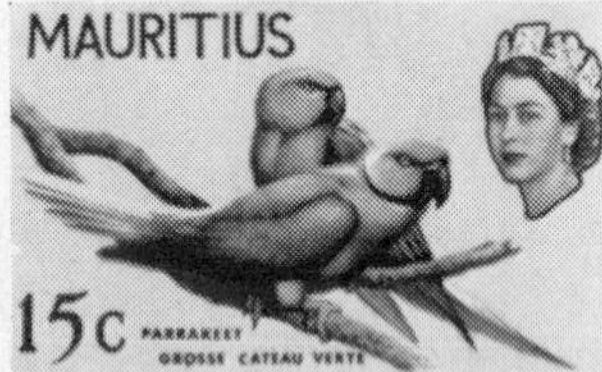

76. Parakeet.

77. Cuckoo-shrike.

78. Kestrel.

79. Pink Pigeon.

80. Merle.

81. Dutch Pigeon (extinct).

82. Mauritius Dodo (extinct).

83. Rodrigues Solitaire (extinct).

84. Red Rail (extinct).

85. Broad-billed Parrot (extinct).

(Des. D. M. Reid-Henry. Photo. Harrison.)

1965 (16 MAR.). *W* w.**12.** *P* $14\frac{1}{2} \times 14$.

317	**71**	2 c. multicoloured	..	0	1	0
318	**72**	3 c. multicoloured	..	0	2	0
319	**73**	4 c. multicoloured	..	0	2	0
320	**74**	5 c. multicoloured	..	0	3	0
321	**75**	10 c. multicoloured	..	0	4	0
322	**76**	15 c. multicoloured	..	0	5	0

323 **77** 20 c. multicoloured .. 0 6 0 8
324 **78** 25 c. multicoloured .. 0 8 0 10
325 **79** 35 c. multicoloured .. 0 10 1 0
326 **80** 50 c. multicoloured .. 1 1 1 3
327 **81** 60 c. multicoloured .. 1 4 1 6
328 **82** 1 r. multicoloured .. 2 0 2 3
329 **83** 2 r. 50, multicoloured .. 5 0 5 6
330 **84** 5 r. multicoloured .. 10 0 11 0
331 **85** 10 r. multicoloured .. 19 6 22 0

1965 (17 May). *I.T.U. Centenary. As Nos. 166/7 of Antigua.*
332 10 c. red-orange & apple-grn. 0 5 0 8
333 60 c. yellow and bluish violet 1 7 2 0

1965 (25 Oct.). *International Co-operation Year. As Nos. 168/9 of Antigua.*
334 10 c. reddish purple and turquoise-green 0 5 0 8
335 60 c. deep bluish green and lavender 1 7 2 0

1966 (24 Jan.). *Churchill Commemoration. As Nos. 170/3 of Antigua.*
336 2 c. new blue 0 2 0 3
337 10 c. deep green 0 5 0 8
338 60 c. brown 1 7 2 0
339 1 r. bluish violet 2 6 3 6

EXPRESS DELIVERY STAMPS.

EXPRESS
DELIVERY
15 c.
(E 1)

EXPRESS
DELIVERY
(INLAND)
15 c.
(E 2)

EXPRESS
DELIVERY
(INLAND)
15 c.
(E 3)

(FOREIGN)
EXPRESS
DELIVERY
18 CENTS
(E 4)

1903. *No.* 136 *surch. in red.*
E1 **E 1** 15 c. on 15 c. ultramarine 12 6 15 0
E2 **E 2** 15 c. on 15 c. ultramarine 20 0 25 0
a. "INLAND" inverted .. — £12
E3 **E 3** 15 c. on 15 c. ultramarine.. 12 6 4 6
a. Surch. double £10
b. Surch. inverted.. .. — £6
d. "A" of "INLAND" inverted £15 £18
e. Imperf. between (pair) ..
f. Surch. double, both inverted

In Type E 2 the word "INLAND" was inserted at a second printing on stamps already surcharged with Type E 1 (No. E1); Type E 3 is a new setting of the surcharge made at one printing.

1904. *T* **44** (*without value in label*), *wmk. Crown CC, surch. with Type* E **4**. *P* 14.
E4 18 c. green 8 6 12 6
a. Note of exclamation "!" for "I" in "FOREIGN" .. £15

1904. *T* **44** *surch. with Type* E **3**.
E6 15 c. grey-green (R.) 5 0 6 0
a. Surch. double £5 £5
b. Surch. inverted £10 £10
c. "LNIAND" £12 £12

Variety c, inverted is a forgery.

POSTAGE DUE STAMPS.

D 1

(Typo. Waterlow & Sons, Ltd.)

1933–54. *Wmk. Mult. Script CA. P* 15×14.
D1 **D 1** 2 c. black 0 1 0 3
D2 ,, 4 c. violet 0 2 0 4
D3 ,, 6 c. scarlet 0 3 0 6
D4 ,, 10 c. green 0 4 0 10
D5 ,, 20 c. bright blue 1 0 1 6
D6 ,, 50 c. brt. reddish purple (1.3.54) 1 1 2 6
D7 ,, 1 r. orange (1.3.54) .. 2 0 4 0

(Typo. De La Rue.)

1966 (3 Jan.). *Chalk-surfaced paper. Wmk.* w. **12**. *P* 15×14.
D12 **D 1** 20 c. blue 0 6 1 0

FISCALS USED FOR POSTAGE.

INLAND
REVENUE
(F 1)

INLAND
REVENUE
(F 2)

1889. *T* **19**, *wmk. Crown CA, optd. P* 14.
R1 **F 1** 4 c. carmine 7 6 12 6
R2 **F 2** 4 c. lilac 12 6 17 6

F 3

(Typo. De La Rue & Co.)

1896–98. *Wmk. Crown CA. P* 14.
R2*a* **F 3** 4 c. dull purple 20 0
R3 ,, 4 c. green (1898) .. 20 0

MONTSERRAT.

For GREAT BRITAIN stamps used in Montserrat, see page 65.

1

MONTSERRAT
(2)

(T **1.** Recess. De La Rue & Co.)

1876 (Sept.). *Stamps of Antigua, optd. with T* **2.** *Wmk. Crown CC. P* 14.

No.	T.	Description	Unused	Used
1	**1**	1d. red	35 0	35 0
		a. Bisected (½d.) (on cover)	—	£45
		b. Inverted "S"	£75	£75
2	,,	6d. green	85 0	60 0
		a. Bisect (used as 2½d.) (on cover)		
		b. Inverted "S"	£95	£85
3	,,	6d. blue-green	£65	
		a. Inverted "S"		

No. 1 was bisected and used for a ½d. in 1883. This bisected stamp is found surcharged with a small "½" in *black*. This is bogus. The 6d. in blue-green is only known unused.

3 (Die I.)

(Typo. De La Rue & Co.)

1880 (Jan.). *Wmk. Crown CC. P* 14.

No.	T.	Description	Unused	Used
4	**3**	2½d. red-brown	£16	£7
5	,,	4d. blue	85 0	50 0

1884–85. *Wmk. Crown CA. P* 14.

No.	T.	Description	Unused	Used
6	**3**	½d. dull green	6 6	10 0
7	**1**	1d. red	20 0	40 0
		a. Inverted "S"	£75	£80
8	,,	1d. rose-red	30 0	35 0
		a. Bisected vert. (½d.) (on cover)	—	£25
9	**3**	2½d. red-brown	£6	£5
10	,,	2½d. ultramarine	17 6	25 0
11	,,	4d. blue	£70	£20
12	,,	4d. mauve	15 0	12 6

1884 (May). *Wmk. Crown CA. P* 12.

No.	T.	Description	Unused	Used
13	**1**	1d. red	£5	85 0
		a. Inverted "S"	£85	£90
		b. Bisected (½d.) (on cover)	—	£60

The stamps for Montserrat were temporarily superseded by the general issue for Leeward Islands in 1890, but the following issues were in concurrent use with the stamps inscribed "LEEWARD ISLANDS" until July 1st 1956, when Leeward Islands stamps were withdrawn and invalidated.

4. Device of the Colony. **5**

(Typo. De La Rue & Co.)

1903. (*a*) *Wmk. Crown CA. P* 14.

No.	T.	Description	Unused	Used
14	**4**	½d. grey-green and green	3 0	10 0
15	,,	1d. grey-black and red	2 6	2 0
16	,,	2d. grey and brown	12 6	25 0
17	,,	2½d. grey and blue	10 0	17 6
18	**4**	3d. dull orange & deep pur.	15 0	30 0
19	,,	6d. dull purple and olive	22 6	35 0
20	,,	1s. green and bright purple	25 0	40 0
21	,,	2s. green & brown-orange	35 0	50 0
22	,,	2s. 6d. green and black	55 0	65 0

(*b*) *Wmk. Crown CC. P* 14.

No.	T.	Description	Unused	Used
23	**5**	5s. black and scarlet	£20	£22

1903–08. *Wmk. Mult. Crown CA. P* 14.

No.	T.	Description	Unused	Used
24	**4**	½d. grey-green & green, OC	1 9	3 6
25	,,	1d. grey-blk. & red, C ('08)	27 6	32 6
26	,,	2d. grey and brown, OC	6 0	8 0
27	,,	2½d. grey and blue, C ('06)	8 0	15 0
28	,,	3d. dull orge. & dp. pur., OC	6 6	12 6
29	,,	6d. dull purple & olive, OC	10 0	22 6
30	,,	1s. grn. & brt. pur., C ('08)	15 0	20 0
31	,,	2s. green & orange, C ('08)	60 0	75 0
32	,,	2s. 6d. grn. & black, C ('08)	75 0	85 0
33	**5**	5s. black and red, C ('07)	£18	£20

1908–13. *Wmk. Mult. Crown CA. P* 14.

No.	T.	Description	Unused	Used
35	**4**	½d. deep green O	1 3	2 6
36	,,	1d. rose-red, O	3 0	1 6
38	,,	2d. greyish slate, O	6 0	17 6
39	,,	2½d. blue, O	6 0	15 0
40	,,	3d. purple/*yellow*, C	6 0	12 6
		a. White back (1913)	15 0	27 6
43	,,	6d. dull and deep purple, C	15 0	32 6
43*a*	,,	6d. dull & bright purple, C	12 6	27 6
44	,,	1s. black/*green*, C	12 6	27 6
45	,,	2s. pur. & brt. blue/*blue*, C	45 0	55 0
46	,,	2s. 6d. black & red/*blue*, C	50 0	60 0
47	**5**	5s. red and green/*yellow*, C	£8	£10

7

(Typo. De La Rue.)

1914. *Wmk. Mult. Crown CA. P* 14.

No.	T.	Description	Unused	Used
48	**7**	5s. red and green/*yellow*, C	£16	£1

8

1916–23. *T* **8.** *Wmk. Mult. Crown CA. P* 1

No.	Description	Unused	Used
50	½d. green, O	0 9	0
51	1d. scarlet, O	1 3	1
52	1d. carmine-red, O	5 0	2
53	2d. grey, O	4 0	8
54	2½d. bright blue, O	5 0	8
55	3d. purple/*yellow*, C	6 0	12
	a. On pale yellow	5 0	10
56	4d. grey-black and red/*pale yellow*, C (1923)	12 6	22
57	6d. dull and deep purple, C	10 0	22
58	1s. blk./*blue-grn.*, C (*olive back*)	12 6	27
59	2s. purple and blue/*blue* C	22 6	37
60	2s. 6d. black & red/*blue*, C	55 0	65
61	5s. green and red/*yellow*, C	85 0	95

WAR STAMP
(9)

1917 (Oct.). *No. 50 optd. with T* **9.**
62 ½d. green (R.) 0 3 1 3

1918. *As No. 62, but optd. in black.*
63 ½d. green 0 3 1 6
64 ½d. deep green 0 3 1 6

1919. *T* **8.** *Special printing in orange. Value and "*WAR STAMP*" as T* **9** *inserted in black at one printing.*
65 1½d. black and orange .. 0 6 1 6

1922–29. *Wmk. Mult. Script CA. P* 14.
66 **8** ¼d. brown, O 0 6 1 6
67 ,, ½d. green, O 0 6 0 4
68 ,, 1d. bright violet, O .. 1 6 0 8
68*a*,, 1d. carmine O (1929) .. 1 6 2 0
69 ,, 1½d. orange-yellow, O .. 8 6 12 6
70 ,, 1½d. carmine, O 1 6 4 0
70*a*,, 1½d. red-brown O (1929) .. 2 0 1 6
71 ,, 2d. grey, O 3 0 2 6
72 ,, 2½d. deep bright blue O .. 6 0 10 0
72*a*,, 2½d. pale bright blue O ('26) 3 0 4 0
73 ,, 2½d. orange-yellow O (1923) 4 0 8 6
74 ,, 3d dull blue O (1923) .. 3 0 6 0
74*a*,, 3d. purple/*yellow*, C (1927) 5 0 10 0
75 ,, 4d. black & red/*pale yell.*, C 2 6 6 0
76 ,, 5d. dull purple and olive, C 17 6 35 0
77 ,, 6d. pale & bright purple, C 5 0 12 6
78 ,, 1s. black/*emerald*, C .. 10 0 17 6
79 ,, 2s. purple and blue/*blue*, C 12 0 25 0
80 ,, 2s. 6d. black & red/*blue*, C 30 0 30 0
81 ,, 3s. green and violet, C .. 20 0 35 0
82 ,, 4s. black and scarlet, C .. 22 6 35 0
83 ,, 5s. grn. & red/*pale yellow*, C 55 0 65 0

10. Plymouth.

(Recess. De La Rue & Co.)

1932 (18 April). *Tercentenary. Wmk. Mult. Script CA. P* 14.
84 **10** ½d. green 2 6 3 6
85 ,, 1d. scarlet 2 6 4 0
86 ,, 1½d. red-brown 8 6 10 0
87 ,, 2d. grey 7 6 12 0
88 ,, 2½d. ultramarine 8 6 15 0
89 ,, 3d. orange 12 6 20 0
90 ,, 6d. violet 22 6 32 6
91 ,, 1s. olive-brown 50 0 60 0
92 ,, 2s. 6d. purple £5 £6
93 ,, 5s. chocolate £11 £13

1935 (6 May). *Silver Jubilee. As Nos. 91/4 of Antigua, but printed by W'low & Sons. P* 11 × 12.
94 1d. deep blue and scarlet .. 1 0 1 3
95 1½d. ultramarine and grey .. 1 3 2 0
96 2½d. brown and deep blue .. 12 6 15 0
97 1s. slate and purple 27 6 32 6

1937 (12 May). *Coronation. As Nos. 13/15 of Aden. P* 14.
98 1d. scarlet 0 4 0 6
99 1½d. yellow-brown 0 6 0 8
100 2½d. bright blue 1 0 1 6

11. Carr's Bay.

12. Sea Island Cotton.

13. Botanic Station.

(Recess. De La Rue & Co.)

1938 (2 Aug.)–**1948.** *Wmk. Mult. Script CA.*
101 **11** ½d. blue-green (*p.* 13) .. 0 6 0 8
a. Perf. 14 ('42) 0 6 0 6
102 **12** 1d. carmine (*p.* 13) .. 0 8 0 8
a. Perf. 14 ('43 .. .. 0 8 0 8
103 ,, 1½d. purple (*p.* 13) .. 12 6 10 0
a. Perf. 14 ('42) 1 0 0 10
104 **13** 2d. orange (*p.* 13) .. 8 0 8 0
a. Perf. 14 ('42) 1 6 1 6
105 **12** 2½d. ultramarine (*p.* 13) .. 2 0 3 6
a. Perf. 14. ('43) 1 6 1 6
106 **11** 3d. brown (*p.* 13) .. 2 6 2 6
a. Perf. 14. *Red-brown* ('42) .. 2 0 1 6
ab. Deep brown ('43).. .. 10 0 15 0
107 **13** 6d. violet (*p.* 13).. .. 2 0 3 6
a. Perf. 14 ('43) 1 6 1 6
108 **11** 1s. lake (*p.* 13) 12 6 15 0
a. Perf. 14 ('42) 4 0 4 0
109 **13** 2s. 6d. slate-blue (*p.* 13) 7 6 10 0
a. Perf. 14 ('43) 10 0 22 6
110 **11** 5s. rose-carmine (*p.* 13).. 25 0 25 0
a. Perf. 14 ('42) 16 0 20 0
111 **13** 10s. pale blue (*p.* 12) ('48) 40 0 45 0
112 **11** £1 black (*p.* 12) ('48) .. 60 0 70 0

1946 (1 Nov.). *Victory. As Nos. 28/9 of Aden.*
113 1½d. purple 0 4 0 8
114 3d. chocolate 0 6 1 0

1949 (3 Jan.). *Royal Silver Wedding. As Nos. 30/1 of Aden.*
115 2½d. ultramarine 0 6 0 6
116 5s. carmine 10 0 15 0

1949 (10 Oct.). *75th Anniv. of Universal Postal Union. As Nos. 114/7 of Antigua.*
117 2½d. ultramarine 0 8 1 3
118 3d. brown 1 3 1 6
119 6d. purple 1 6 3 6
120 1s purple 3 0 4 0

1951 (16 Feb.). *Inauguration of B.W.I. University College. As Nos. 118/9 of Antigua.*
121 3 c. black and purple .. 0 10 0 10
122 12 c. black and violet .. 2 0 2 0

14. Government House.

15. Sea Island Cotton: Cultivation.

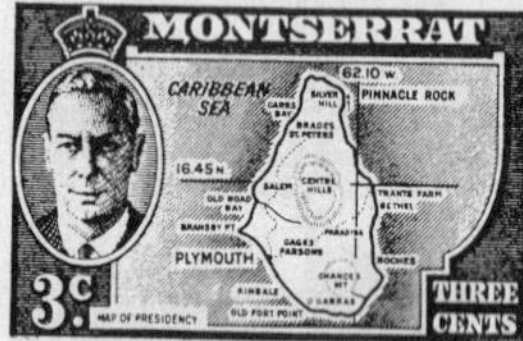

16. Map of Presidency.

17. Picking Tomatoes.

18. Badge of Presidency

19. Sea Island Cotton: Ginning.

20. St. Anthony's Church.

21. Government House.

(Recess. Bradbury Wilkinson & Co.)

1951 (17 Sept.). *Wmk. Mult. Script CA. P* 11½×11.

No.	Type	Description				
123	**14**	1 c. black	0	9	1	0
124	**15**	2 c. green	1	3	1	6
125	**16**	3 c. orange-brown ..	0	10	1	3
126	**17**	4 c. carmine	0	10	0	10
127	**20**	5 c. reddish violet ..	1	0	1	9
128	**18**	6 c. olive-brown	1	0	1	3
129	**19**	8 c. deep blue	1	3	1	6
130	**20**	12 c. blue and chocolate ..	1	6	2	6
131	**17**	24 c. carm. & yellow-grn.	2	0	3	0
132	**19**	60 c. black and carmine ..	7	6	10	6
133	**15**	$1.20, yellow-grn. & blue	17	6	20	0
134	**21**	$2.40, black and green ..	20	0	30	0
135	**18**	$[illegible].80, black and purple ..	40	0	47	6

1953 (2 June). *Coronation. As No.* 47 *of Aden.*

136	2 c. black and deep green ..	0	9	1	3

22. Government House.

(Recess. Bradbury, Wilkinson.)

1953–58. *As T* **14/21**, *but with portrait of Queen Elizabeth II as in T* **22**. *Wmk. Mult. Script CA. P* 11½×11.

No.	Type	Description				
136*a*	**16**	½ c. deep violet (I) ..	0	4	0	[illegible]
136*b*	,,	½ c. deep violet (II) ..	0	2	0	[illegible]
137	**22**	1 c. black	0	3	0	[illegible]
138	**15**	2 c. green	0	5	0	[illegible]
139	**16**	3 c. orange-brown (I) ..	1	6	1	[illegible]
139*a*	,,	3 c. orange-brown (II) ..	0	5	0	[illegible]
140	**17**	4 c. carmine-red ..	0	5	0	[illegible]
141	**20**	5 c. reddish lilac ..	0	6	0	[illegible]
142	**18**	6 c. dp. bistre-brown (I)	1	6	1	[illegible]
142*a*	,,	6 c. dp. bistre-brown (II)	0	7	0	[illegible]
143	**19**	8 c. deep bright blue ..	0	9	0	[illegible]
144	**20**	12 c. blue and red-brown	1	0	1	[illegible]
145	**17**	24 c. carm.-red and green	1	8	2	[illegible]
145*a*	**15**	48 c. yellow-olive & purple	3	3	3	[illegible]
146	**19**	60 c. black and carmine	4	6	4	[illegible]
147	**15**	$1.20, grn. & greenish bl.	8	0	9	[illegible]
148	**21**	$2.40, blk. & bluish green	16	0	18	[illegible]
149	**18**	$4.80, blk. & dp. pur. (I)		£9	[illegible]	
149*a*	,,	$4.80, blk. & dp. pur. (II)	32	6	37	[illegible]

Dates of issue: 1953—15 Oct., 1 c., 2 c., 3 c. (I). 1955—1 June, 4 c., 5 c., 6 c. (I), 8 c., 12 c., 24 c., 60 c., $1.20, $2.40, $4.80 (I). 1956—3 July, ½ c. (I). 1957—15 Oct., 48 c. 1958—1 Sept., ½ c. (II), 3 c. (II), 6 c. (II), $4.80 (II).

Types **16** and **18.** I. inscr. " Presidency ". II. inscr. " Colony ".

1958 (22 Apr.). *Inauguration of British Caribbean Federation. As Nos.* 135/7 *of Antigua.*

150	3 c. deep green	0 8	0 8
151	6 c. blue	1 3	1 3
152	12 c. scarlet	1 9	2 0

1963 (8 July). *Freedom from Hunger. As No.* 63 *of Aden.*

153	12 c. reddish violet	1 3	1 6

1963 (2 Sept.). *Red Cross Centenary. As Nos.* 147/8 *of Antigua.*

154	4 c. red and black	0 5	0 6
155	12 c. red and blue	1 0	1 3

1964 (23 April). *400th Anniversary of Birth of William Shakespeare. As No.* 164 *of Antigua.*

156	12 c. indigo	1 6	1 8

1964 (29 Oct). *As No* 138 *but wmk.* w. **12.**

157	**15** 2 c. green	0 5	0 5

1965 (17 May). *I.T.U. Centenary. As Nos.* 166/7 *of Antigua.*

158	4 c. vermilion and violet ..	0 5	0 7
159	48 c. light emerald & carmine	3 3	4 0

23. Pineapple.

24. Avocado.

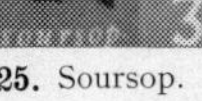

25. Soursop.

26. Pepper.

27. Mango.

28. Tomato.

29. Guava.

30. Ochro.

31. Lime.

32. Orange.

33. Banana.

34. Onion.

35. Cabbage.

36. Pawpaw.

37. Pumpkin.

38. Sweet Potato.

39. Egg Plant.

(Des. S. Goaman. Photo. Harrison.)

1965 (16 Aug.). *W* w. **12.** *P* 15 × 14.

160	**23**	1 c. multicoloured	0	2	0	2
161	**24**	2 c. multicoloured	0	3	0	3
162	**25**	3 c. multicoloured	0	4	0	4
163	**26**	4 c. multicoloured	0	4	0	4
164	**27**	5 c. multicoloured	0	5	0	5
165	**28**	6 c. multicoloured	0	6	0	6
166	**29**	8 c. multicoloured	0	7	0	8
167	**30**	10 c. multicoloured	0	9	0	10
168	**31**	12 c. multicoloured	0	10	0	11
169	**32**	20 c. multicoloured	1	3	1	6
170	**33**	24 c. multicoloured	1	5	1	8
171	**34**	42 c. multicoloured	2	5	2	8
172	**35**	48 c. multicoloured	2	9	3	0
173	**36**	60 c. multicoloured	3	6	4	0
174	**37**	$1.20, multicoloured	6	9	8	0
175	**38**	$2.40, multicoloured	13	3	15	0
176	**39**	$4.80, multicoloured	25	0	30	0

1965 (25 Oct.). *International Co-operation Year. As Nos.* 168/9 *of Antigua.*

177 2 c. reddish purple and turquoise-green 0 4 0 6
178 12 c. deep bluish green and lavender 1 0 1 6

1966 (26 Jan.). *Churchill Commemoration. As Nos.* 170/3 *of Antigua.*

179 1 c. new blue 0 4 0 5
180 2 c. deep green 0 6 0 8
181 24 c. brown 2 0 2 9
182 42 c. bluish violet 3 6 3 9

1966 (4 Feb.). *Royal Visit. As Nos.* 174/5 *of Antigua.*

183 14 c. black and ultramarine .. 1 [illegible] 1 6
184 24 c. black and magenta .. 1 8 2 0

MOROCCO AGENCIES.
(BRITISH POST OFFICES.)

I. "GIBRALTAR" PERIOD

FOR USE AT ALL BRITISH POST OFFICES IN MOROCCO.

Until 1907 all British Post Offices in Morocco were under the control of the Gibraltar P.O.

Morocco Agencies (1)   Morocco Agencies (2)

1898. *Type* **7** *of Gibraltar optd.*

I. Locally (at "Gibraltar Chronicle" office). Type **1** *(wide "*M*" and ear of "*g*" projecting upwards), in black.*

1 5 c. green 0 10 0 10
2 10 c. carmine 1 6 0 8
a. Opt. double .. .. ..
3 20 c. olive-green 2 6 3 0
a. Opt. double £38
b. Olive-green and brown .. 4 6 3 0
4 25 c. ultramarine 3 0 2 0
5 40 c. orange-brown 5 0 5 0
a. Blue opt. 50 0 50 0
6 50 c. bright lilac 30 0 30 0
a. Blue opt. 5 0 6 0
7 1 p. bistre and ultramarine .. 15 0 6 0
a. Blue opt. £10 £12
8 2 p. black and carmine .. 8 6 20 0

The *blue* overprint can be easily distinguished by looking through the stamp in front of a strong light.

OVERPRINT VARIETY: "A" for "A". Prices for un.; used 20% higher. 5 c. 45s.; 10 c. £30; 20 c. (No. 3 or 3*b*), 60s.; 25 c. £12; 40 c. £20; 50 c. £28; 1 p. £20; 2 p. £28.

This variety occurred in the first setting, No. 36 of right-hand pane. Numerous other minor varieties exist.

Morocco
(3)

II. London opt., in black. **T 2** *(narrow "*M*" and ear of "*g*" horizontal).*

9 5 c. green 0 10 0 6
10 10 c. carmine 1 3 0 4
11 20 c olive-green 3 0 3 0
12 25 c. ultramarine 6 0 3 0
13 40 c. orange-brown 17 6 10 0
14 50 c. bright lilac 12 6 6 6
15 1 p. bistre and ultramarine 17 6 12 6
16 2 p. black and carmine .. 40 0 27 6

OVERPRINT VARIETIES: Prices for un.; used 10% higher.

(A), Broad top to "M" (T **3**). No. 39 of left-hand pane. 5 c. 10s.; 10 c. 10s.; 20 c. 25s.; 25 c. 25s.; 40 c. £6; 50 c. £8; 1 p. £10; 2 p. £30.

(B). Hyphen between "n" and "c" of "Agencies". No. 17 of right-hand pane.

5 c. 10s.; 10 c. 10s.; 20 c. 25s.; 25 c. 25s. 40 c. £6; 50 c. £8; 1 p. £10; 2 p. £30.

1903–5. *As* **T 8** *of Gibraltar, but with value in Spanish currency, optd. with* **T 2.** *Wmk Crown CA. P* 14.

17 5 c. grey-grn & grn. (Jan. '03) 6 6 2
18 10 c. dull pur./*red* (Aug. '03) .. 7 6 2
19 20 c. grey-grn. & car (Sept. '04) 12 6 25
20 25 c. pur. & blk./*blue* (1 7.03) 4 0 2
21 50 c. purple & violet (3 7 05) £5 £
22 1 p. black & carm. (19.11.05) £5 £
23 2 p. black & blue (19.11 05) .. £5 £

OVERPRINT VARIETIES: Prices for un.; used 10% higher.

(A). As T **3**.

5 c. 40s.; 10 c. 40s.; 20 c. 60s.; 25 c. 60s. 50 c. £30; 1 p. £25; 2 p. £35.

(B). Hyphen between "n" and "c".

5 c. 40s.; 10 c. 40s.; 20 c. 60s.; 25 c. 60s. 50 c. £30; 1 p. £25; 2 p. £35.

1905–6. *As Nos.* 17/23, *but wmk. Mult. Crown CA.*

24 5 c. grey-green & green, OC 2 6 2
25 10 c. dull purple/*red*, OC .. 2 6 1
26 20 c. grey-grn. & car., O ('06) 7 6 12
27 25 c. pur. & blk./*blue*, C ('06) 20 0 20
28 50 c. purple & violet, C ('06) 20 0 20
29 1 p. black and carmine, C .. 40 0 60
30 2 p. black and blue, C .. 30 0 45

OVERPRINT VARIETIES: Prices for un.; used 10 per cent. higher.

(A). As T **3**.

5 c. 30s.; 10 c. 30s.; 20 c. £7; 25 c. £1 50 c. £20; 1 p. £25; 2 p. £30.

(B). Hyphen between "n" and "c".

5 c. £25.

NOTE. In 1907 control of the post offices was assumed by H.M. Postmaster-General.

ALL THE FOLLOWING ISSUES ARE OVERPRINTED ON GREAT BRITAIN.

II. BRITISH CURRENCY.

Stamps overprinted "MOROCCO AGENCIES" only were primarily intended for use on parce (and, later, air-mail correspondence), and were on sale at British P.Os. throughout Morocco, including Tangier, until 1937.

PRICES. Our prices for used stamps with these overprints are for specimens used in Morocco. These stamps could also be used in the United Kingdom, with official sanction, from the summer of 1950 onwards, and with U.K. postmarks are worth about 25 per cent. less.

MOROCCO AGENCIES (4) MOROCCO AGENCIES (5)

1907-13. *King Edward VII optd as T* **4** *and* **5** (*2s. 6d.*). (*a*) *De La Rue printings.*

31 ½d. pale green, O 0 6 1 6
32 1d. scarlet, O 1 6 1 6
33 2d. green and carmine, C .. 3 0 6 0
34 4d. green and pur.-brn., C .. 10 0 8 6
35 4d. pale orange, O (1912) .. 2 6 6 0
36 6d. dull purple, C 6 0 4 0
37 1s. green and carmine, C .. 8 0 12 6
38 2s. 6d. lilac, C 45 0 70 0
39 2s. 6d. purple, C 55 0 65 0

(*b*) *Later printings* (1913).

40 4d. bright orange, O (No. 286) 4 0 5 0
41 2s. 6d. dull pur., O (No. 315) 55 0 70 0

MOROCCO AGENCIES (6)

1914-31. *King George V.* (*i*) *Optd. with T* **4**. *W* **100**.

42 **105** ½d. green 0 6 1 0
43 **104** 1d. scarlet 0 6 0 4
44 **105** 1½d. red-brown (1921) .. 2 0 6 0
45 **106** 2d. orange (Die I) .. 1 9 1 3
46 „ 3d. blue-violet (1921) .. 1 6 2 0
47 „ 4d. grey-green (1921) .. 2 0 2 0
48 **107** 6d. reddish purple (1921) 4 6 8 6
49 **108** 1s. bistre (1917) 5 0 4 0
a. Triple opt. (two albino) .. £22

(*ii*) *Optd. with T* **6**.
(*a*) *Waterlow printing.*

50 **109** 2s. 6d. deep brown (1914) 25 0 40 0
a. Re-entry £38 £30

(*b*) *De La Rue printings.*

51 **109** 2s. 6d. chestnut (1917) .. 32 6 18 0
a. Overprint double (1917) . £32
52 **109** 2s. 6d. grey-brown .. 22 6 27 6

(*c*) *Bradbury, Wilkinson printings.*

53 **109** 2s. 6d. chocolate-brown .. 30 0 6 0
54 „ 5s rose-red (1931) .. 20 0 40 0

MOROCCO AGENCIES (7) S (A) MOROCCO AGENCIES (8) S (B)

(A) Opt. 14 mm. long; ends of "s" cut off diagonally.
(B) Opt. 15½ mm. long; ends of "s" cut off horizontally.

1925-36. *King George V, optd. with T* **7** (A) *or T* **8** (B). *W* **111**.

			A		B	
55	**105**	½d. green ..	1 9	1 6	1 0	1 9
56	„	1½d. chest. ('31)	6 0	8 6	†	
57	**106**	2d. orange ..	1 6	1 3	†	
58	**104**	2½d. blue ..	4 6	1 9	60 0	27 6
59	**106**	4d. grey-grn. (1.36)	†		12 6	25 0
60	**107**	6d. pur., O ('31)	3 0	3 6	1 9	1 9
61	**108**	1s. bistre ..	7 6	7 6	25 0	20 0

1935 (8 May). *Silver Jubilee stamps. Optd.* "MOROCCO AGENCIES" *only, as in T* **17**.

62 **123** ½d. green (B.) 1 0 2 6
63 „ 1d. scarlet (B.) 2 0 5 0
64 „ 1½d. red-brown (B.) .. 6 0 12 6
65 „ 2½d. blue (R.) 8 0 12 6

1935-37. *King George V.* (*a*) *Harrison photo ptgs. optd. with T* **8**.

66 **119** 1d. scarlet ('35) 0 10 1 3
67 **118** 1½d. red-brown ('36) .. 2 0 7 6
68 **120** 2d. orange (11.5.36) .. 0 5 0 6
69 **119** 2½d. ultramarine (11.2.36) 2 6 2 0
70 **120** 3d. violet (2.3.36) .. 1 0 0 8
71 „ 4d. dp. grey-grn. (19.5.36) 0 10 0 10
72 **122** 1s. bistre-brown ('36) .. 1 9 2 0

(*b*) *Waterlow re-engraved ptg. optd. with T* **6**.

73 **109** 2s. 6d. chocolate (No. 450) 15 0 22 6
74 „ 5s. bright rose-red (No. 451) (2.3.37) 20 0 30 0

1936. *King Edward VIII, optd.* "MOROCCO AGENCIES" *only, as in T* **18**.

(A) MOROCCO 14¼ mm. long.
(B) MOROCCO 15¼ mm. long.

			A		B	
75	**124**	1d. scarlet ..	0 3	0 4	1 3	6 0
76	„	2½d. ultram.	0 6	0 8	1 6	4 0

In 1937 unoverprinted Great Britain stamps replaced overprinted "MOROCCO AGENCIES" issues as stocks became exhausted. In 1949 overprinted issues reappeared and were in use at Tetuan (Spanish Zone), the only remaining British P.O. apart from that at Tangier.

MOROCCO AGENCIES (9) MOROCCO AGENCIES (10)

1949 (16 Aug.). *King George VI, optd. with T* **9** *or* **10** (*2s. 6d., 5s.*).

77 **128** ½d. pale green 0 4 1 0
78 „ 1d. pale scarlet 0 6 1 3
79 „ 1½d. pale red-brown .. 0 8 1 6
80 „ 2d. pale orange 0 9 1 6
81 „ 2½d. light ultramarine .. 0 10 1 6
82 „ 3d. pale violet 0 10 1 6
83 **129** 4d. grey-green 1 3 1 3
84 „ 5d. brown 1 6 3 0
85 „ 6d. purple 1 6 2 6
86 **130** 7d. emerald-green .. 1 9 3 6
87 „ 8d. bright carmine .. 2 0 4 6
88 „ 9d. deep olive-green .. 1 9 6 0
89 „ 10d. turquoise-blue .. 2 0 4 6
90 „ 11d. plum 2 3 4 6
91 „ 1s. bistre-brown 2 3 5 0
92 **131** 2s. 6d. yellow-green .. 15 0 17 6
93 „ 5s. red 25 0 30 0

1951 (3 May). *King George VI* (*Nos.* 503/7, 509/10), *optd. with T* **9** *or* **10** (*2s. 6d.*, *5s.*).

94 **128** ½d. pale orange 0 3 0 6
95 „ 1d. light ultramarine .. 0 5 1 3
96 „ 1½d. pale green 0 6 2 0
97 „ 2d. pale red-brown .. 0 10 2 6
98 „ 2½d. pale scarlet 1 0 2 6
99 **147** 2s. 6d. yellow-green .. 6 0 12 6
100 **148** 5s. red 10 0 22 6

1952-55. *Queen Elizabeth II* (*Tudor Crown wmk.*), *optd. with T* **9**.

101 **154** ½d. orange-red (31.8.53) 0 4 0 4
102 „ 1d. ultramarine (31.8.53) 0 5 0 5
103 „ 1½d. green (5.12.52) .. 0 6 0 6
104 „ 2d. red-brown (31.8.53) 1 3 1 6
105 **155** 2½d. carmine-red (5.12.52) 1 0 1 3
106 **156** 4d. ultramarine (1.3.55) 1 6 1 6
107 **157** 5d. brown (6.7.53) .. 1 6 1 6
108 „ 6d. reddish-pur. (1.3.55) 1 9 1 9
109 **158** 8d. magenta (6.7.53) .. 3 0 3 6
110 **159** 1s. bistre-brown (6.7.53) 3 0 3 6

1956 (10 Sept.). *Queen Elizabeth II* (*St. Edward's Crown wmk.*), *optd. with T* **9**.

111 **155** 2½d. carmine-red (No. 544) 3 0 3 6

Stamps overprinted "MOROCCO AGENCIES" were withdrawn from sale on December 31st, 1956.

III. SPANISH CURRENCY.

Stamps surcharged in Spanish currency were sold at British P.Os. throughout Morocco until the establishment of the French Zone and the Tangier International Zone, when their use was confined to the Spanish Zone.

MOROCCO AGENCIES
5 CENTIMOS
(11)

MOROCCO AGENCIES
6 PESETAS
(12)

1907–13. *King Edward VII, surch. as T* **11** (*5 c. to 1 p.*) *or* **12** (*3 p. to 12 p.*). (*a*) *De La Rue printings.*

112 5 c. on ½d. pale green, O .. 1 0 0 6
113 10 c. on 1d. scarlet, O .. 1 6 0 4
114 15 c. on 1½d. purple & grn., C 3 0 1 9
a. "1" of "15" omitted .. £110
115 20 c. on 2d. green & carm., C 2 6 1 9
116 25 c. on 2½d. bright blue, O 3 0 2 0
117 40 c. on 4d. grn. & pur.-brn., C 3 6 7 6
118 40 c. on 4d. orange, O (1910) 2 0 2 6
119 50 c. on 5d. pur. & blue, C .. 3 0 3 0
120 1 p. on 10d. pur. & carm., C 8 0 10 0
a. No cross on crown ..
121 3 p. on 2s. 6d. lilac, C .. 15 0 15 0
122 6 p. on 5s. carmine, O .. 35 0 35 0
123 12 p. on 10s. ultramarine, O 55 0 60 0

(*b*) *Somerset House printing.*

124 12 p. on 10s. bt. ultram. (No. 319) ('13) £6 £7

1912. *King Edward VII* (*2½d.*) *and King George V, surch. as T* **11**.

125 5 c. on ½d. green (No. 339) 0 9 0 4
126 10 c. on 1d. scarlet (No. 342) 1 0 0 6
a. No cross on crown 60 0 27 6
127 25 c. on 2½d. bt. blue (No. 283) 15 0 10 0

MOROCCO AGENCIES
3
CENTIMOS
(13)

MOROCCO AGENCIES
10
CENTIMOS
(14)

MOROCCO AGENCIES
15 CENTIMOS
(15)

MOROCCO AGENCIES
6 PESETAS
(16)

1914–26. *King George V.* (i) *Surch. as T* **11** (*5 c.*), **13** (*3 c. and 40 c.*)*, **15** (*15 c.*) *and* **14** (*remainder*). *W* **100**.

128 **105** 3 c. on ½d. green ('17) .. 2 6 3 6
129 ,, 5 c. on ½d. green .. 0 6 0 4
130 **104** 10 c. on 1d. scarlet .. 0 6 0 3
131 **105** 15 c. on 1½d. brown ('15) 0 8 0 6
132 **106** 20 c. on 2d. orange (Die I) 1 0 0 10
133 **104** 25 c. on 2½d. ultramarine 1 6 1 6
134 **106** 40 c. on 4d. grey-grn. ('17) 2 6 3 0
135 **108** 1 p. on 10d. turquoise .. 2 0 3 0

* The surcharge on Nos. 134, 148 and 158 is as T **13** for the value and T **15** for "MOROCCO AGENCIES".

(ii) *Surch. as T* **16**. *Waterlow printings.*

136 **109** 6 p. on 5s. rose-carmine 17 6 30 0
137 ,, 6 p. on 5s. pale rose-carm. £10
138 ,, 12 p. on 10s dp. blue (R.) 60 0 85 0

De La Rue printings.

139 **109** 3 p. on 2s. 6d. grey-brn. ('18) 35 0 50 0
140 ,, 3 p. on 2s. 6d. chestnut 27 6 45 0
141 ,, 12 p. on 10s. blue (R.) .. 45 0 65 0

Bradbury-Wilkinson printings.

142 **109** 3 p. on 2s. 6d. choc.-brn. ('26) 12 6 7 6

1925–31. *King George V, surch. as T* **11**, **13**, **14** *or* **15**. *W* **111**.

143 **105** 5 c. on ½d. green ('31) .. 0 4 1 6
144 **104** 10 c. on 1d. scarlet ('29) 2 6 4 0
145 **105** 15 c. on 1½d. red-brown .. 7 6 4 6
146 **106** 20 c. on 2d. orange ('31) 1 6 3 0
147 **104** 25 c. on 2½d. blue .. 1 6 1 6
148 **106** 40 c. on 4d. grey-grn. ('30) 2 0 2 0

MOROCCO AGENCIES
10 CENTIMOS
(17)

1935 (8 MAY). *Silver Jubilee, surch. as T* **17**.

149 **123** 5 c. on ½d. green (B.) .. 0 10 1 6
150 ,, 10 c. on 1d. scarlet (B.) .. 6 0 15 0
a. "CENTIMES" for "CENTIMOS" (in pair with normal) £75
151 ,, 15 c. on 1½d. red-brn. (B.) 2 0 6 0
152 ,, 25 c. on 2½d blue (R.) .. 7 6 7 6

Beware of forgeries of the error, No. 150*a*.

1935–37. *King George V, surch. as T* **11**, **13**, **14** *or* **15**.

153 **118** 5 c. on ½d. grn.(17.6.36) 0 4 1 6
154 **119** 10 c. on 1d. scarlet 0 10 1 6
155 **118** 15 c. on 1½d. red-brown .. 4 0 6 0
156 **120** 20 c. on 2d. orange ('36) .. 0 6 0 10
157 **119** 25 c. on 2½d. ultram. ('36) 8 0 12 6
158 **120** 40 c. on 4d. deep grey-green (18.5.37) .. 0 8 1 6
159 **122** 1 p. on 10d. turquoise-blue (21.4.37) .. 0 10 1 6

MOROCCO 10 AGENCIES
CENTIMOS
(18)

1936. *King Edward VIII, surch. as T* **18**. (A) *close lettering,* "MOROCCO" *14¼ mm. long.* (B) *spaced lettering,* "MOROCCO" *15¼ mm. long.*

			A		B	
160	**124**	5 c. on ½d. grn.	0 3	0 4	†	
161	,,	10 c. on 1d. scarlet ..	0 4	0 6	1 0	0
162	,,	15 c. on 1½d. red-brn.	0 6	0 8	†	
163	,,	25 c. on 2½d. ultramarine	0 8	0 8	†	

MOROCCO 15 CENTIMOS AGENCIES

(19)

1937 (13 May). *Coronation, surch. as T* **19.**

164 **126** 15 c. on 1½d. maroon (B.) 0 3 0 4

MOROCCO AGENCIES

10 CENTIMOS

(20)

MOROCCO AGENCIES

10 CENTIMOS

(21)

1937–52. *King George VI, surch. as T* **20.**

165 **128** 5 c. on ½d. green (B.) .. 0 3 0 3
166 „ 10 c. on 1d. scarlet .. 0 4 0 4
167 „ 15 c. on 1½d. red-brn. (B.) 0 4 0 6
168 „ 25 c. on 2½d. ultramarine 0 4 0 8
169 **129** 40 c. on 4d. grey-green .. 2 6 3 0
170 **130** 70 c. on 7d. emerald-green 2 3 2 6
171 „ 1 p. on 10d. turq.-blue.. 1 0 1 0

Dates of issue:—June '37, 5 c., 10 c. 25 c.; 4 Aug. '37, 15 c.; Sept. '40, 40 c., 70 c.; 16 June '52, 1 p.

1940 (6 May). *Centenary of First Adhesive Postage Stamps, surch. as T* **21.**

172 **134** 5 c. on ½d. green (B.) .. 0 10 1 0
173 „ 10 c. on 1d. scarlet (Bk.) 1 0 1 6
174 „ 15 c. on 1½d. red-brn. (B.) 1 6 1 9
175 „ 25 c. on 2½d. ultram. (Bk.) 1 9 3 0

25 CENTIMOS

MOROCCO AGENCIES

(22)

45 PESETAS MOROCCO AGENCIES

(23)

1948 (26 Apr.). *Silver Wedding, surch. with T* **22** *or* **23.**

176 **137** 25 c. on 2½d. ultramarine 0 6 0 6
177 **138** 45 p. on £1 blue 40 0 45 0

1948 (29 July). *Olympic Games, variously surch. as T* **22.**

178 **139** 25 c. on 2½d. ultramarine 0 6 0 6
179 **140** 30 c. on 3d violet 0 9 0 9
180 **141** 60 c. on 6d. bright purple 1 6 1 0
181 **142** 1 p. 20 c. on 1s. brown.. 2 6 2 6
a. Surcharge double .. £80

1951 (3 May)–**52.** *King George VI, surch. as T* **20.**

182 **128** 5 c. on ½d. pale orange.. 0 3 1 0
183 „ 10 c. on 1d. light ultram. 0 3 1 0
184 „ 15 c. on 1½d. pale green.. 0 3 1 0
185 „ 25 c. on 2½d. pale scarlet 0 3 1 0
186 **129** 40 c. on 4d. light ultramarine (26.5.52) .. 1 6 1 9

1954–55. *Queen Elizabeth II (Tudor Crown wmk.), surch. as T* **20.**

187 **154** 5 c. on ½d. orange-red (1.9.54) 0 4 0 4
188 „ 10 c. on 1d. ultram. (1.3.55) 0 6 0 6

1956. *Queen Elizabeth II (St. Edward's Crown wmk.), surch. as T* **20.**

189 **154** 5 c. on ½d. orge.-red (June) 0 6 0 6
190 **156** 40 c. on 4d. ult. (15 Aug.) 1 9 2 0

Stamps surcharged in Spanish currency were withdrawn from sale on December 31st, 1956.

IV. FRENCH CURRENCY.

Stamps surcharged in French currency were sold at British P.Os in the French Zone.

MOROCCO AGENCIES

25 CENTIMES

(24)

MOROCCO AGENCIES

1 FRANC

(25)

1917–24. *King George V, surch. as T* **24** *or* **25** (1 *fr.*) *W* **100.**

191 **105** 3 c. on ½d. green (R.) .. 0 4 3 6
192 5 c. on ½d. green .. 0 4 0 9
193 **104** 10 c. on 1d. scarlet .. 0 10 0 8
194 **105** 15 c. on 1½d. brown .. 2 0 2 0
195 **104** 25 c. on 2½d. blue .. 1 3 0 6
196 **106** 40 c on 4d. slate-green .. 1 3 0 10
197 **107** 50 c on 5d yell. brn. ('23) 2 3 3 0
198 **108** 75 c. on 9d. olive-grn. ('24) 2 3 3 0
199 „ 1 fr. on 10d. turquoise 2 6 1 9

1924–32. *King George V, surch. as T* **25,** *but closer vertical spacing.*

200 **109** 3 fr. on 2s. 6d. choc.-brn. 4 6 3 0
a. Major re-entry £38 £50
201 „ 6 fr. on 5s. rose-red ('32) 16 0 10 0

1925–34. *King George V surch. as T* **24** *or* **25,** (1 *fr.*). *W* **111.**

202 **105** 5 c. on ½d. green .. 0 4 3 0
203 **104** 10 c. on 1d. scarlet .. 0 6 0 6
204 **105** 15 c. on 1½d. red-brown.. 1 0 2 0
205 **104** 25 c. on 2½d. blue .. 0 8 1 0
206 **106** 40 c. on 4d. grey-green .. 0 9 1 3
207 **107** 50 c. on 5d. yellow-brown 1 3 1 3
208 **108** 75 c. on 9d. olive-green .. 2 0 1 0
209 „ 90 c. on 9d. olive-green .. 1 6 1 9
210 „ 1 f. on 10d. turquoise .. 1 6 1 3
211 „ 1 f. 50 c. on 1s. bistre .. 2 3 6 0

1935 (8 May). *Silver Jubilee, surch. as T* **17,** *but in French currency.*

212 **123** 5 c. on ½d. green (B.) .. 0 6 0 10
213 „ 10 c. on 1d. scarlet (B.).. 1 6 3 0
214 „ 15 c. on 1½d. red-brn. (B.) 1 0 2 0
215 „ 25 c. on 2½d. blue (R.) .. 2 0 2 0

1935–37. *King George V, surch. as T* **24** *or* **25** (1 *fr.*).

216 **118** 5 c. on ½d. green .. 0 4 0 4
217 **119** 10 c. on 1d. scar. (2.3.36) 0 6 0 6
218 **118** 15 c. on 1½d. red-brown.. 2 0 2 0
219 **119** 25 c. on 2½d. ultram. ('36) 0 10 1 0
220 **120** 40 c. on 4d. deep grey-green (2.12.36) 0 6 0 8
221 **121** 50 c. on 5d. yell.-brn. ('36) 0 8 0 10
222 **122** 90 c. on 9d. deep olive-green (17.2.37) .. 0 8 0 10
223 „ 1 f. on 10d. turquoise-blue (17.2.37) .. 0 9 0 10
224 „ 1 f. 50 on 1 s. bistre brn. (20.7.37) 1 0 1 3

1935–36. *King George V (Waterlow re-engraved ptgs.), surch. as T* **25**, *but closer vertical spacing.*
225 **109** 3 fr. on 2s. 6d. chocolate (No. 450) 6 0 4 0
226 ,, 6 fr. on 5s. bright rose-red (No. 451) (17.6.36) .. 17 6 10 0

1936. *King Edward VIII, surch. as T* **18**, *but in French currency.*
227 **124** 5 c. on ½d. green 0 3 0 3
a. Bar through "POST-AGE" .. £22
228 ,, 15 c. on 1½d. red-brown .. 0 3 0 6

1937 (13 May). *Coronation, surch. as T* **19**, *but in French currency.*
229 **126** 15 c. on 1½d. maroon (B.) 0 4 0 4

1937 (June). *King George VI, surch. as T* **20**, *but in French currency.*
230 **128** 5 c. on ½d. green (B.) .. 0 4 0 6

Stamps surcharged in French currency were withdrawn from sale on 8th January, 1938.

V. TANGIER INTERNATIONAL ZONE.

This Zone was established in 1924 and the first specially overprinted stamps issued in 1927.

PRICES. Our note re U.K. usage (at beginning of Section II) also applies to "TANGIER" optd. stamps.

TANGIER
(26)

1927. *King George V, optd. with T* **26**, *W* **111**.
231 **105** ½d. green 0 10 0 10
232 **104** 1d. scarlet 1 3 0 6
233 **105** 1½d. chestnut 1 3 1 9
234 **106** 2d. orange 1 0 1 0

1934–35. *King George V, optd. with T* **26**.
235 **118** ½d. green 0 3 0 4
236 **119** 1d. scarlet 2 0 1 6
237 **118** 1½d. red-brown 0 9 1 0

TANGIER TANGIER
(27)

1935 (8 May) *Silver Jubilee, optd. with T* **27**.
238 **123** ½d green (B.) 0 10 1 3
239 ,, 1d. scarlet 2 6 4 6
240 ,, 1½d. red-brown (B.) .. 1 6 2 0

1936. *King Edward VIII, optd. with T* **26**.
241 **124** ½d. green 0 3 0 3
242 ,, 1d. scarlet 0 3 0 3
243 ,, 1½d. red-brown 0 6 0 4

TANGIER TANGIER
(28)

1937 (13 May). *Coronation, optd. with T***28**.
244 **126** 1½d. marone (B.) .. 0 6 0 4

TANGIER
(29)

1937. *King George VI, optd. with T* **29**.
245 **128** ½d. green (B.) (June) .. 0 3 0 3
246 ,, 1d. scarlet (June) .. 0 4 0 4
247 ,, 1½d. red-brn. (B.) (4 Aug.) 0 3 0 8

TANGIER **(30)**   **TANGIER** **(31)**

1940 (6 May). *Centenary of First Adhesive Postage Stamps optd. with T* **30**.
248 **134** ½d. green (B.) 0 8 1 0
249 ,, 1d. scarlet 1 0 1 6
250 ,, 1½d. red-brown (B.) .. 1 6 1 9

1944. *King George VI, optd. with T* **29**.
251 **128** ½d. pale green (B.) .. 0 3 0 6
252 ,, 1d. pale scarlet 0 6 0 4

1946 (11 June). *Victory, optd. as T* **31**.
253 2½d. ultramarine 0 6 0 9
254 3d. violet 0 8 1 6

The opt. on No. 254 is smaller (23 × 2½ mm.).

1948 (26 Apr.). *Royal Silver Wedding, optd. with T* **30**.
255 **137** 2½d. ultramarine 0 6 0 6
a. Opt. omitted (in vertical pair with stamp optd. at top) £150
256 **138** £1 blue 40 0 55 0

No. 255*a* comes from a sheet in which the overprint is misplaced downwards resulting in the complete absence of the opt. from the six stamps of the top row. On the rest of the sheet the opt. falls at the top of each stamp instead of at the foot.

1948 (29 July). *Olympic Games, optd. with T* **30**.
257 **139** 2½d. ultramarine .. 0 8 0 6
258 **140** 3d violet .. 1 0 0 10
259 **141** 6d. bright purple .. 2 0 1 6
260 **142** 1s. brown .. 3 6 3 0

1949 (1 Jan.). *King George VI, optd. with T* **29**.
261 **128** 2d. pale orange 0 10 1 3
262 ,, 2½d. light ultramarine .. 0 6 1 0
263 ,, 3d. pale violet 0 7 0 8
264 **129** 4d. grey-green 1 6 2 6
265 ,, 5d. brown 1 9 3 0
266 ,, 6d. purple 1 0 1 0
267 **130** 7d. emerald-green .. 2 0 3 0
268 ,, 8d. bright carmine .. 2 6 4 0
269 ,, 9d. deep olive-green .. 2 0 3 0
270 ,, 10d. turquoise-blue .. 2 6 4 0
271 ,, 11d. plum 3 0 5 0
272 ,, 1s. bistre-brown .. 2 3 2 6
273 **131** 2s. 6d. yellow-green .. 7 6 15 0
274 ,, 5s. red 20 0 27 6
275 **132** 10s. ultramarine 45 0 60 0

1949 (10 Oct.). *75th Anniv. of U.P.U., optd with T* **30**.
276 **143** 2½d. ultramarine 0 10 1
277 **144** 3d. violet 1 3 1
278 **145** 6d. bright purple .. 2 0 2
279 **146** 1s. brown 4 0 6

1950–51. *King George VI, optd. wtih T* **29** *or* **30** *(shilling values).*
280 **128** ½d. pale orange 0 3 0
281 ,, 1d. light ultramarine .. 0 6 1
282 ,, 1½d. pale green 0 8 1
283 ,, 2d. pale red-brown .. 1 3 3
284 ,, 2½d. pale scarlet 0 8 1
285 **129** 4d. light ultramarine .. 1 3 1
286 **147** 2s. 6d. yellow-green .. 4 0 6
287 **148** 5s. red 10 0 10
288 **149** 10s. ultramarine 17 6 25

Dates of issue:—2.10.50, 4d.; 3.5.51, others

1952–54. *Queen Elizabeth II (Tudor Crown wmk.), optd. with T* **29.**

No.	Type	Description	Un. s.	d.	Used s.	d.
289	**154**	½d. orange-red (31.8.53)	0	4	0	4
290	,,	1d. ultramarine (31.8.53)	0	5	0	5
291	,,	1½d. green (5.12.52) ..	0	5	0	5
292	,,	2d. red brown (31.8.53)	0	6	0	10
293	**155**	2½d. carm.-red (5.12.52)..	0	6	0	6
294	,,	3d. dp. lilac (B.) (18.1.54)	0	9	0	9
295	**156**	4d. ultramarine (2.11.53)	2	0	2	6
296	**157**	5d. brown (6.7.53) ..	3	0	3	6
297	,,	6d. reddish pur. (18.1.54)	1	3	1	3
298	,,	7d. bright green (18.1.54)	3	0	3	0
299	**158**	8d. magenta (6.7.53) ..	3	0	4	0
300	,,	9d. bronze-green (8.2.54)	3	0	4	0
301	,,	10d. Prussian bl. (8.2.54)	4	0	4	6
302	,,	11d. brown-pur. (8.2.54)	4	0	6	0
303	**159**	1s. bistre-brown (6.7.53)	2	6	2	6
304	**160**	1s. 3d. green (2.11.53) ..	3	0	3	6
305	**159**	1s. 6d. grey-bl. (2.11.53)	4	0	4	6

1953 (3 June). *Coronation, optd. with T* **30.**

No.	Type	Description	Un. s.	d.	Used s.	d.
306	**161**	2½d. carmine-red.. ..	1	0	2	0
307	**162**	4d. ultramarine.. ..	1	6	3	0
308	**163**	1s. 3d. dp. yellow-green	5	0	7	6
309	**164**	1s. 6d. deep grey-blue..	7	0	12	6

1955 (23 Sept.). *Queen Elizabeth II, optd. with T* **30.**

No.	Type	Description	Un. s.	d.	Used s.	d.
310	**166**	2s. 6d. black-brown ..	10	0	10	0
311	**167**	5s. rose-red	25	0	25	0
312	**168**	10s. ultramarine.. ..	45	0	50	0

1956. *Queen Elizabeth II (St. Edward's Crown wmk.), optd. with T* **29.**

No.	Type	Description	Un. s.	d.	Used s.	d.
313	**154**	½d. orge.-red (21 March)	0	3	0	3
314	,,	1d. ultram. (13 April) ..	0	6	0	8
315	,,	1½d. green (22 Oct.) ..	1	0	1	3
316	,,	2d. red-brn. (25 July) ..	3	0	3	6
317	,,	2d. lt. red-brn. (10 Dec.)	1	6	1	9
318	**155**	2½d. carm.-red (19 Dec.)	2	0	2	6
319	,,	3d. dp. lilac (B.) (22 Oct.)	2	0	2	6
320	**156**	4d. ultramarine (25 June)	3	0	3	6
321	**157**	6d. reddish pur. (22 Oct.)	2	0	2	0
322	**160**	1s. 3d. green (26 Nov.)	5	0	6	0

1857-1957 **1857-1957**
TANGIER

TANGIER

(32) (33)

1957 (1 Apr.). *Centenary of British Post Office in Tangier. (a) Nos.* 540/2 *and* 543*b*/56 *optd. as T* **32** *or* **33** *(7d.).*

No.	Type	Description	Un. s.	d.	Used s.	d.
323	**154**	½d. orange-red	0	3	0	4
324	,,	1d. ultramarine.. ..	0	4	0	4
325	,,	1½d. green	0	5	0	5
326	,,	2d. light red-brown ..	0	6	0	8
327	**155**	2½d. carmine-red.. ..	0	8	0	9
328	,,	3d. deep lilac (B.) ..	0	9	0	10
329	**156**	4d. ultramarine.. ..	1	0	1	0
330	**157**	5d. brown	1	3	1	3
331	,,	6d. reddish purple ..	1	3	1	3
332	,,	7d. bright green ..	1	6	1	9
333	**158**	8d. magenta	1	9	2	0
334	,,	9d. bronze-green ..	1	9	2	0
		a. "TANGIER" omitted..	£1000			
335	,,	10d. Prussian blue ..	2	3	2	6
336	,,	11d. brown-purple ..	3	0	3	6
337	**159**	1s. bistre-brown ..	2	0	2	6
338	**160**	1s. 3d. green	2	6	3	0
339	**159**	1s. 6d. grey-blue ..	3	0	3	6

(*b*) *Nos.* 536/8 *optd. as T* **32.**

No.	Type	Description	Un. s.	d.	Used s.	d.
340	**166**	2s. 6d. black-brown ..	6	6	10	0
		a. Hyphen omitted ..	£35			
		b. Hyphen inserted ..	£18			
341	**167**	5s. rose-red	10	0	15	0
		a. Hyphen omitted ..	£35			
		b. Hyphen inserted ..	80	0		
342	**168**	10s. ultramarine.. ..	20	0	35	0
		a. Hyphen omitted ..	£40			
		b. Hyphen inserted ..	90	0		

Nos. 340*a*/*b*, 341*a*/*b* and 342*a*/*b* occur on stamp No. 34 in the sheet of 40 (4 × 10). They are best collected in marginal blocks of four from the bottom left corner of the sheet. Specialists recognise two forms of No. 340*b*: one where the hyphen on stamp No. 34 was inserted separately to correct the error, No. 340*a*; the other from a later printing where a new and corrected overprinting plate was used. (*Price* 60s. *un.*)

All stamps overprinted "TANGIER" were withdrawn from sale on April 30th, 1957.

MOSUL.

POSTAGE

I.E.F. 'D'

1 Anna

(1)

4 I **4** II

(*normal*). (*small*).

1919 (Feb.). *Turkish Fiscal stamps surcharged as T* **1**, *in black. P* 12½ *(except* ½ *a., P* 11½ *and* 1 *a., P* 12*).*

(*a*) Central design shows large "toughra" or sign-manual of El Ghazi 7 mm. high.

(*b*) Smaller "toughra" of Sultan Rechad 5½ mm. high.

No.	Description	Un. s.	d.	Used s.	d.
1	½ a. on 1 pi. green and red ..	2	6	2	6
2	1 a. on 20 paras, blk./*red* (*a*)	2	6	2	6
2*a*	1 a. on 20 paras, blk./*red* (*b*)	8	6	6	0
	b. Imperf. between (pair) ..	£12			
3	2½ a. on 1 pi. mauve & yell. (*b*)	3	0	3	0
	a. No bar to fraction	40	0	40	0
4	3 a. on 20 par. green (*a*) ..	3	6	3	6
5	3 a. on 20 par. grn. & orge. (*b*)	40	0	45	0
6	4 a. on 1 pi. dark violet (*a*) (I)	6	0	6	0
	a. "4" omitted..	£40			
	b. Small "4" (II)	8	6	8	6
7	8 a. on 10 par. lake (*a*) ..	8	6	8	6
	a. Surch. inverted	£12			
	b. Surch. double	£12		£12	
	c. No comma after "D" ..	50	0		
	d. Inverted. No comma after "D"				
	e. Error. 8 a. on 1 pi. dark violet	£75			

MUSCAT.

An independent Sultanate in Eastern Arabia with an Indian, and subsequently a British postal administration. The latter was closed on 30th April, 1966.

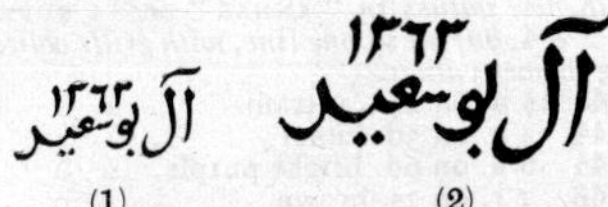

(1) (2)

1944 (20 Nov.). *Bicentenary of Al-Busaid Dynasty. Stamps of India optd.* ("AL BUSAID 1363" *in Arabic script) as T* **1** *or* **2** (*rupee values*).

1 **100a** 3 p. slate 0 3 1 0
2 ,, ½ a. purple 0 3 1 0
3 ,, 9 p. green.. .. .. 0 4 1 0
4 ,, 1 a. carmine 0 4 1 0
5 **101** 1½ a. dull violet 0 6 1 3
a. Opt. double £50
6 **101** 2 a. vermilion 0 7 1 3
7 ,, 3 a. bright violet .. 0 8 1 6
8 ,, 3½ a. bright blue 0 9 1 6
9 **102** 4 a. brown 0 10 1 6
10 ,, 6 a. turquoise-green .. 1 3 2 6
11 ,, 8 a. slate-violet 1 4 3 0
12 ,, 12 a. lake 2 0 4 0
13 **103** 14 a. purple 2 3 5 0
14 **100** 1 r. grey and red-brown.. 3 0 9 0
15 ,, 2 r. purple and brown .. 6 0 20 0

For Use in Postal Agencies of Muscat, Dubai, Doha, and Umm Said (from Feb., 1956)

1 ANNA (3)

2 RUPEES (4)

1948 (1 Apr.). *Stamps of Great Britain surch. with T* **3** (½ *a. to* 1 *r.*) *or* **4** (2 *r.*).

16 **128** ½ a. on ½d. pale green .. 0 4 0 10
17 ,, 1 a. on 1d. pale scarlet .. 0 4 0 10
18 ,, 1½ a. on 1½d. pale red-brn. 0 6 1 3
19 ,, 2 a. on 2d. pale orange .. 0 10 1 6
20 ,, 2½ a. on 2½d. light ultram. 1 0 3 6
21 ,, 3 a. on 3d. pale violet .. 0 10 1 0
22 **129** 6 a. on 6d. purple .. 1 3 1 3
23 **130** 1 r. on 1s. bistre-brown.. 4 0 5 0
24 **131** 2 r. on 2s. 6d. yellow-grn. 20 0 30 0

2½ ANNAS (5)

15 RUPEES (6)

1948 (26 Apr.). *Royal Silver Wedding. Nos.* 493/4 *of Great Britain surch. with T* **5** *or* **6**.

25 **137** 2½ a. on 2½d. ultramarine.. 0 8 1 0
26 **138** 15 r. on £1 blue 60 0 65 0

1948 (29 July). *Olympic Games. Nos.* 495/8 *of Great Britain surch. with new values in* "ANNAS" *or* "1 RUPEE", *as T* **5/6**, *but in one line on* 2½ *a.* (*vert.*) *or* 6 *a. and* 1 *r.* (*horiz.*) *and grills obliterating former values of all except* 2½ *a.*

27 **139** 2½ a. on 2½d. ultramarine 0 10 1 6
28 **140** 3 a. on 3d. violet .. 1 0 1 9
29 **141** 6 a. on 6d. bright purple 1 6 3 0
30 **142** 1 r. on 1s. brown .. 5 0 6 6
a. Surch. double £90

1949 (10 Oct.). 75*th Anniv. of Universal Postal Union. Nos.* 499/502 *of Great Britain surch. with new values in* "ANNAS" *or* "1 RUPEE", *as T* **3/4**, *but all in one line, with grills obliterating former values.*

31 **143** 2½ a. on 2½d. ultram. .. 1 0 0 10
32 **144** 3 a. on 3d. violet .. 1 3 1 3
33 **145** 6 a. on 6d. bright purple 2 6 2 6
34 **146** 1 r. on 1s. brown .. 5 0 6 0

1950–51. *Nos.* 503/9 *of Great Britain surch. as T* **3** *or* **4** (*rupee value*).

35 **128** ½ a. on ½d. pale orange .. 0 8 1 3
36 ,, 1 a. on 1d. light ultram. 0 8 0 10
37 ,, 1½ a. on 1½d. pale green .. 2 0 3 6
38 ,, 2 a. on 2d. pale red-brown 1 0 1 9
39 ,, 2½ a. on 2½d. pale scarlet.. 2 6 3 0
40 **129** 4 a. on 4d. light ultram... 2 0 3 6
41 **147** 2 r. on 2s. 6d. yellow-grn. 6 0 8 6

Dates of issue:—2.10.50, 4 a.; 3.5.51, others.

1952–54. *Stamps of Great Britain* (*Queen Elizabeth II*), *Wmk. Tudor Crown, surch. as T* **3**.

42 **154** ½ a. on ½d. orange-red .. 0 4 0 6
43 ,, 1 a. on 1d. ultramarine .. 0 5 0 6
44 ,, 1½ a. on 1½d. green .. 0 6 0 8
45 ,, 2 a. on 2d. red-brown .. 0 8 1 0
46 **155** 2½ a. on 2½d.carmine-red.. 0 9 0 9
47 ,, 3 a. on 3d. deep lilac (B.) 0 9 1 0
48 **156** 4 a. on 4d. ultramarine .. 1 0 1 6
49 **157** 6 a. on 6d. reddish purple 1 6 1 6
50 **160** 12 a. on 1s. 3d. green .. 3 0 3 0
51 **159** 1 r. on 1s. 6d. grey-blue.. 4 0 4 6

Dates of issue:—5.12.52, 1½ a., 2½ a.; 31.8.53, ½ a., 1 a., 2 a.; 2.11.53, 4 a., 12 a., 1 r.; 18.1.54, 3 a., 6 a.

1953 (10 June). *Coronation. Stamps of Great Britain surch. with new values.*

52 **161** 2½ a. on 2½d. carmine-red 1 9 4 0
53 **162** 4 a. on 4d. ultramarine .. 2 0 4 6
54 **163** 12 a. on 1s. 3d. deep yellow-green.. .. .. 6 0 10 0
55 **164** 1 r. on 1s. 6d. deep grey-blue 10 0 15 0

2 RUPEES I

2 RUPEES II

2 RUPEES III

(7)

5 RUPEES I

5 RUPEES II

(8)

Types of surcharges.

2 rupees.

Type I. *On Waterlow ptg.* Top of "R" leve with top of "2" and other letters o "RUPEES". Bars 7 mm. long.

Type II. *On Waterlow ptg.* "R" dropped ou of alignment with "2" and othe letters of "RUPEES". Bars 6½ mm long.

Type III. *On De La Rue ptg.* Top of "R below level of top of "2". Bars 7¼ mm. long and with left sid aligned with "S".

5 rupees.

Type I. *On Waterlow ptg.* Ends of letters square and sharp. There were two printings made in March and May 1957.

Type II. *On De La Rue ptg.* Type is thicker and ends of letters are relatively rounded.

For differences between Waterlow and De La Rue printings of the basic stamps see notes in Great Britain after No. 539.

1955–60. *T* **166/7** *(Waterlow ptgs.) of Great Britain (W* **165**, *St. Edward's Crown) surch. with T* **7/8**.

56 **166** 2 r. on 2s. 6d. black-brown
- Type I (23.9.55) .. 22 6 25 0
- Type II (2.57) .. 12 6 16 0
- Type III (No. 536a D.L.R.) (6.60) .. 60 0 70 0

57 **167** 5 r. on 5s. rose-red
- Type I (1.3.57) .. 25 0 25 0
- a. Wide surcharge £75
- Type II (No. 537a D.L.R.) (27.1.60) .. 50 0 60 0

No. 57*a* ("5" and "R" spaced 2¼ mm. instead of 1¼ mm.) occurred on the last stamp of Row 8 of the first "Waterlow" issue.

1956–57. *Stamps of Great Britain (Queen Elizabeth II, W* **165**, *St. Edward's Crown), surch. as T* **3**.

58 **154** 1 a. on 1d. ultram. (4.3.57) 0 9 1 3
58*a* ,, 1½ a. on 1½d. green ('56) .. — £100
59 ,, 2 a. on 2d. red-brn. (8.6.56) 1 6 2 0
60 **155** 2½ a. on 2½d. carmine-red (8.6.56) 1 6 2 0
61 ,, 3 a. on 3d. deep lilac (B.) (3.2.57) 2 6 5 0
62 **156** 4 a. on 4d. ultram. (9.12.56) 5 0 6 0
63 **157** 6 a. on 6d. red-purple (10.2.57) 2 6 4 0
64 **159** 1 r. on 1s. 6d. grey-blue (2.8.56) 3 0 3 6

For Use in Postal Agencies of Muscat, Dubai (until 6.1.61), Abu Dhabi and Das Island (from 30.3.63 to 29.3.64).

NP 1 NP (9) — 3 NP (10) — 75 NP (11)

1957 (1 Apr.)–**59**. *Value in naye paise. Stamps of Great Britain (Queen Elizabeth II, W* **165**, *St. Edward's Crown), surch. as T* **9** *(1, 15, 25, 40, 50 n.p.),* **11** *(75 n.p.) or* **10** *(others).*

65 **157** 1 n. p. on 5d. brown .. 0 2 0 3
66 **154** 3 n. p. on ½d. orange-red 0 3 0 6
67 ,, 6 n. p. on 1d. ultramarine 0 4 0 6
68 ,, 9 n. p. on 1½d. green .. 0 4 0 5
69 ,, 12 n. p. on 2d. lt. red-brn. 0 6 0 8
70 **155** 15 n. p. on 2½d. carmine-red (Type I) .. 1 0 1 6
- a. Type II (-.4.59) .. 0 10 1 0

71 ,, 20 n. p. on 3d. dp. lilac (B.) 0 8 0 8
72 **156** 25 n. p. on 4d. ultramarine 1 0 1 0
73 **157** 40 n. p. on 6d. reddish pur. 1 6 1 6
- *a. Deep claret* (-.3.59) .. 1 3 1 0

74 **158** 50 n. p. on 9d. bronze-grn. 1 6 1 9
75 **160** 75 n. p. on 1s. 3d. green .. 2 0 2 6

15 NP (12)

1957 (1 Aug.). *World Scout Jubilee Jamboree. Nos. 557/9 of Great Britain surch. in one line as T* **12** *(15 n.p.), or in two lines (others).*

76 15 n. p. on 2½d. carmine-red 1 0 1 3
77 25 n. p. on 4d. ultramarine .. 2 0 2 6
78 75 n. p. on 1s. 3d. green .. 3 0 3 6

1960–61. *Stamps of Great Britain (Queen Elizabeth II, W* **179**, *Mult. Crown), surch. as T* **8** *(1, 15, 30, 40, 50 n.p.),* **10** *(75 n.p.),* **3** *(1 r.),* **7** *(2 r., 5 r.) or* **9** *(others).*

79 **157** 1 n.p. on 5d. brown .. 0 4 0 5
80 **154** 3 n.p. on ½d. orange-red 2 0 2 6
81 ,, 5 n.p. on 1d. ultramarine 0 4 0 4
82 ,, 6 n.p. on 1d. ultramarine 3 0 4 0
83 ,, 10 n.p. on 1½d. green .. 0 5 0 5
84 ,, 12 n.p. on 2d. lt. red-brown 6 0 7 6
85 **155** 15 n.p. on 2½d. carmine-red (Type II) .. 0 6 0 7
86 ,, 20 n.p. on 3d. deep lilac (B.) 0 7 0 9
87 **156** 30 n.p. on 4½d. chestnut.. 0 11 1 0
88 **157** 40 n.p. on 6d. deep claret 1 1 1 2
89 **158** 50 n.p. on 9d. bronze-green 1 4 1 6
90 **160** 75 n.p. on 1s. 3d. green 2 0 2 6
91 **159** 1 r. on 1s. 6d. grey-blue 2 6 3 0
92 **166** 2 r. on 2s. 6d. black-brown (No. 595) .. 4 9 5 6
93 **167** 5 r. on 5s. rose-red (No. 596) 12 0 15 0

Dates of issue: 1960—1 n.p., 15 n.p.; June, 3 n.p., 6 n.p., 12 n.p.; Oct., 20 n.p., 40 n.p. 1961—8, April, others.

Nos. 16 onwards had validity in all British Postal Agencies in the Gulf.

OFFICIAL STAMPS.

1944 (20 Nov.). *Bicentenary of Al-Busaid Dynasty. Official stamps of India optd. as T* **1** *or* **2** *(1 r.).*

O 1 **O 20** 3 p. slate 0 2 0 3
O 2 ,, ½ a. purple 0 3 0 3
O 3 ,, 9 p. green 0 3 0 4
O 4 ,, 1 a. carmine 0 3 0 6
O 5 ,, 1½ a. dull violet 0 4 0 8
O 6 ,, 2 a. vermilion 0 5 0 10
O 7 ,, 2½ a. bright violet .. 0 6 1 3
O 8 ,, 4 a. brown 0 8 1 6
O 9 ,, 8 a. slate-violet .. 1 3 2 6
O10 **100** 1 r. grey and red-brown (No. O 138) .. 3 0 6 0

The Muscat Post Department took over the postal services on 30th April, 1966. Later issues will therefore be found listed in Part III of this Catalogue.

NATAL.

1

2

3

4 5

(Embossed in plain relief on coloured wove paper.)

1857 (26 MAY, *the 1d. in* **1858**). *Imperf.*

No.	Type	Description	Unused	Used
1	**1**	1d. rose	—	£90
2	,,	1d. buff	—	£90
3	,,	1d. blue	—	£95
4	**2**	3d. rose	—	£70
		a. Tête-bêche (pair)		
5	**3**	6d. green	—	£120
6	**4**	9d. blue	—	£600
7	**5**	1s. buff	—	£450

All the above have been reprinted more than once, and the early reprints of some values cannot always be distinguished with certainty from originals.

Stamps on surface-coloured paper, *P* 12½, are fiscals.

NOTE.—*The value of the above stamps depends on their dimensions, and the clearness of the embossing, but our prices are for fine used.*

6 7

(Recess. Perkins Bacon & Co.)

1859-60. *No wmk. P* 14.

No.	Type	Description	Unused	Used
9	**6**	1d. rose-red	97 6	70 0
10	,,	3d. blue	85 0	30 0

1861. *No wmk. Intermediate perf.* 14 *to* 16.

No.	Type	Description	Unused	Used
11	**6**	3d. blue	£6	27 6

1862. *No wmk. Rough perf.* 14 *to* 16.

No.	Type	Description	Unused	Used
12	**6**	3d. blue	75 0	17 6
		a. Imperf. between (pair)	£55	
		b. Imperf. (pair)	—	£70
13	,,	6d. grey	95 0	25 0

1862. *Wmk. Small Star. Rough. perf.* 14 *to* 16.

No.	Type	Description	Unused	Used
15	**6**	1d. rose-red	80 0	27 6

The 1d. and 3d. wmk. Star, *imperf.*, are only proofs, and are therefore not included. The 3d. wmk. Star, *perforated*, is believed to exist only with forged watermark.

(Recess. De La Rue & Co.)

1863. *Thick paper. No wmk. P* 13.

No.	Type	Description	Unused	Used
18	**6**	1d. lake	65 0	30 0
19	,,	1d. carmine-red	55 0	20 0

1864. *Wmk. Crown CC. P*12½.

No.	Type	Description	Unused	Used
20	**6**	1d. brown-red	90 0	30 0
21	,,	1d. rose	65 0	27 6
22	,,	1d. bright red	75 0	30 0
23	,,	6d. lilac	60 0	17 6
24	,,	6d. violet	40 0	32 6

(Typo. De La Rue & Co.)

1867 (APRIL). *Wmk. Crown CC. P* 14.

No.	Type	Description	Unused	Used
25	**7**	1s. green	75 0	25 0

1869 (23 AUG.). *Optd. horizontally in Natal.* 1*d. and* 6*d. T* **6**, *P* 12½; 1*s. T* **7**, *P* 14, *wmk. Crown CC.*; 3*d. T* **6**, *no wmk.*

POSTAGE *Tall capitals.*

No.	Description	Unused	Used
26	1d. rose	£15	75 0
27	1d. bright red	£20	75 0
28	3d. blue (No. 10)		
28*a*	3d. blue (No. 11)	£28	£18
28*b*	3d. blue (No. 12)	£20	95 0
29	6d. lilac	—	75 0
30	6d. violet	£24	65 0
31	1s. green	—	£85

Postage. *12⅝ mm. long.*

No.	Description	Unused	Used
32	1d. rose	£18	80 0
33	1d. bright red	£18	77 6
	a. Double	—	£32
34	3d. blue (No. 10)	—	£20
34*a*	3d. blue (No. 11)	£28	£14
34*b*	3d. blue (No. 12)	£25	97 6
35	6d. lilac	£18	70 0
36	6d. violet	£14	70 0
37	1s. green	—	£25

Postage. *13¾ mm. long.*

No.	Description	Unused	Used
38	1d. rose	£28	£10
39	1d. bright red	—	£10
40	3d. blue (No. 10)		
40*a*	3d. blue (No. 11)		
40*b*	3d. blue (No. 12)	£70	£24
41	6d. lilac	—	£10
42	6d. violet	£55	£9
43	1s. green	—	£160

Postage. *14½ to 15½ mm. long.*

No.	Description	Unused	Used
44	1d. rose	£25	£14
45	1d. bright red	£30	£12
46	3d. blue (No. 10)		
46*a*	3d. blue (No. 11)	—	£18
46*b*	3d. blue (No. 12)	—	£18
47	6d. lilac	—	95 0
48	6d. violet	£65	97 6
49	1s. green	—	£150

POSTAGE. *With a stop.*

No.	Description	Unused	Used
50	1d. rose	75 0	30
51	1d. bright red	£8	30
52	3d. blue (No. 10)	£15	75
53	3d. blue (No. 11)	95 0	47
54	3d. blue (No. 12)	£10	40
	a. Double	—	£6
54*b*	6d lilac	95 0	55
55	6d. violet	80 0	45
56	1s. green	90 0	55

Two sets can be made with this overprint a the top or bottom of the stamp respectively. few of the above have been chronicled with in verted or double overprints. The informatio about some of them is so meagre that we do nc put them in our lists.

POSTAGE

(8)

1870. *No.* 25 *overprinted with T* **8**, *in the colo given in brackets.*

No.	Description	Unused	Used
57	1s. green (*carmine*)*	£275	
58	1s. green (*black*)	£160	£
59	1s. green (*green*)	50 0	15

* For this stamp in orange see No. 107.

Variety. Overprint double.

No.	Description	Unused	Used
59*a*	1s. green (*black*)	£225	£

POSTAGE (9) POSTAGE POSTAGE (10) POSTAGE (11) POSTAGE

1870–73. *T* **6** (*wmk. Crown CC, P* 12½) *overprinted at each side of the stamp as T* **9**, *in the colour given.*

60	1d. bright red (*black*)	37 6	12 6
61	3d. bright blue (*red*)	45 0	15 0
62	6d. mauve (*black*)	97 6	27 6

1873 (JULY). *T* **7** (*wmk. Crown CC, P* 14) *overprinted with T* **10** *up the centre, in black.*

63	1s. purple-brown	£6	30 0

1874 (JULY). *No.* 21 *optd. with T* **11**, *in black.*

65	1d. rose	£6	40 0
	a. Overprint double		

12

13

14

15

16

(Typo. De La Rue & Co.)

874–78. *Wmk. Crown CC. P* 14.

6	**12**	1d. dull rose	15 0	2 6
7	,,	1d. bright rose	10 0	2 6
8	**13**	3d. blue	45 0	30 0
		a. Perf. 14 × 12½	£110	£65
9	**14**	4d. brown (1878)	50 0	20 0
		a. Perf. 12½	£15	22 6
0	**15**	6d. lilac	35 0	10 0
1	**16**	5s. maroon	£8	40 0
		a. Perf. 15½ × 15	£7	90 0
2	,,	5s. rose	40 0	30 0
3	,,	5s. carmine	35 0	30 0

The 5s. stamps normally have wmk. sideways.

POSTAGE (17) POSTAGE (18)

1875. *T* **6** (*wmk. Crown CC, P* 12½) *optd. with T* **17**.

76	1d. rose	85 0	35 0
	a. Opt. double	£50	£40
77	1d. bright red	£5	70 0

T **6** (*P* 12½), *and* **7** (*P* 14), *optd. with T* **18**, 14½ *mm. long, without stop. Wmk. Crown CC.*

81	1d. rose	50 0	45 0
	a. Opt. inverted	£70	£28
82	1d. yellow	60 0	60 0
83	6d. violet	55 0	8 0
	a. Opt. double	—	£45
	b. Opt. inverted	£60	£25
84	1s. green	65 0	10 0
	a. Opt. double	—	£14

½ HALF (19)

1877 (13 FEB.). *No.* 66 *surch. as T* **19**.

There are several varieties of this surcharge, of which T **19** is an example. They may be divided as follows: (*a*) "½" is 4½ mm. high, "2" has straight foot; (*b*) as last, but "½" is 4 mm. high; (*c*) as last, but "2" has curled foot; (*d*) "½" is 3½ mm. high, "2" has straight foot; (*e*) as last, but "2" has curled foot; (*f*) as last, but "2" smaller. As the "½" and "HALF" were overprinted separately, they vary in relative position, and are frequently overlapping.

88	½d. on 1d. rose (*a*)	20 0	30 0
	aa. "½" double		
88*a*	½d. on 1d. rose (*b*)	95 0	
88*b*	½d. on 1d. rose (*c*)	70 0	
89	½d. on 1d. rose (*d*)	30 0	
89*a*	½d. on 1d. rose (*e*)	40 0	
89*b*	½d. on 1d. rose (*f*)	40 0	

POSTAGE

Half-penny

(21)

1877–79. *T* **6** (*wmk. Crown CC, P* 12½) *surch. as T* **21**.

90	½d. on 1d. yellow	10 0	12 6
	a. Surch. inverted	£16	£14
	b. Surch. double	£16	£12
	c. Surch. omitted (lower stamp, vertical pair)	£60	£45
	d. "POSTAGE" omitted (in pair with normal)	£75	
	e. "S" of "POSTAGE" omitted	£12	£10
	f. "T" of "POSTAGE" omitted	£12	
91	1d. on 6d. violet	27 6	10 0
	a. "S" of "POSTAGE" omitted	£20	
92	1d. on 6d. rose	65 0	32 6
	a. Surch. inverted	—	£12
	b. Surch. double	—	£12
	c. Surch. double, one inverted ..	£18	£24
	d. Surch. four times	£25	£12
	e. "S" of "POSTAGE" omitted	£18	

No. 92c is known with one surcharge showing variety "s" of "POSTAGE" omitted.

Other minor varieties exist in these surcharges.

23

(Typo. De La Rue & Co.)

1880 (13 Oct.). *Wmk. Crown CC. P 14.*
96 **23** ½d. blue-green 6 6 8 6
a. Imperf. between (vert. pair) ..

☛ *Wmk. Crown CA. P 14 (all Nos. from 97 to 113 inclusive).*

1882–85.
97 **23** ½d. blue-green 55 0 20 0
98 ,, ½d. dull green 0 6 0 6
99 **12** 1d. rose (*shades*) 0 4 0 3
99*a* ,, 1d. carmine 7 6 1 6
100 **13** 3d. blue 40 0 15 0
101 **14** 4d. brown 4 0 2 0
102 **15** 6d. mauve 5 0 3 0

ONE HALF
PENNY.

(24)

TWO PENCE

(25)

1885 (26 Jan.). *No. 99 surch. with T* **24.**
103 **12** ½d. on 1d. rose 22 6 17 6

1886. *T* **13** *surch. with T* **25.**
104 2d. on 3d. grey 22 6 8 6

26

(Typo. De La Rue.)

1887–89.
105 **26** 2d. olive-green, Die I* .. 22 6 2 6
106 ,, 2d. olive-green, Die II .. 3 6 1 0

* The differences between Dies I and II are shown in the Introduction.

1888. *T* **7** *optd. with T* **8**, *in carmine.*
107 1s. orange 4 0 2 0
a. Opt. double .. .. ..

1889. *T* **13.** *Colour changed.*
108 3d. grey 4 0 3 0

TWOPENCE
HALFPENNY

(27)

1891. *T* **14** *surch. with T* **27.**
109 2½d. on 4d. brown 12 6 8 6
a. "TWOPENGE" 60 0 65 0
b. "HALFPENN" .. .. — £14
c. Surch. double £18 £16
d. Surch. inverted £24 £20

28

POSTAGE.

Half-Penny

(29)

(Typo. De La Rue.)

1891 (June).
113 **28** 2½d. bright blue 1 6 1 0

POSTAGE.

Varieties of long-tailed letters.

1895 (12 March). *No. 24 surch. with T* **29** *in carmine.*
114 ½d. on 6d. violet 1 6 3 0
a. "Ealf-Penny" 15 0
b. "Half-Penny" 8 6
c. No stop after "POSTAGE" .. 10 0
d. Long "P" 2 0
e. Long "T" 2 0
f. Long "A" 3 0
g. Long "P" and "T" .. 2 0
h. Long "P" and "A" .. 2 0 4 6
i. Long "T" and "A" .. 2 0 4 6
k. Long "P", "T" and "A" .. 3 0
l. Surcharge double, one vertical £28
la. Surcharge double, "Ealf-Penny"
lb. Surcharge double, "Half-Penny"

No. 114k is known without stop and also with comma instead of a stop after "POSTAGE".

HALF

(30)

1895 (18 March). *No. 99 surch. with T* **30.**
125 HALF on 1d. rose (*shades*) .. 2 0 2 6
a. Surch. double £28 £32
b. "H" with longer left limb .. 15 0

No. 125b occurs on the second, fourth, sixth, etc., stamps of the first vertical row of the right-hand pane. It was very soon corrected.

In some printings what appears to be a broken "E" (with the top limb removed) was used instead of "L" in "HALF" on the last stamp in the sheet.

31

(Typo. De La Rue.)

1902–3. *Inscr.* "POSTAGE REVENUE". *Wmk Crown CA. P 14.*
127 **31** ½d. blue-green 0 8 0
128 ,, 1d. carmine 0 8 0
129 ,, 1½d. green and black 1 0 2
130 ,, 2d. red and olive-green .. 2 0 1
131 ,, 2½d. bright blue 3 0 4
132 ,, 3d. purple and grey .. 2 0 1
133 ,, 4d. carmine and cinnamon 3 6 7
134 ,, 5d. black and orange .. 6 0 5
135 ,, 6d. green & brown-purple 6 0 2
136 ,, 1s. carmine and pale blue 8 6 2
137 ,, 2s. green and bright violet 35 0 22
138 ,, 2s. 6d. purple 42 6 27
139 ,, 4s. deep rose and maize .. 60 0 45

32

(Typo. De La Rue.)

1902-3. *Wmk. Crown CC. P* 14.
140 **32** 5s. dull blue and rose .. 60 0 30 0
141 ,, 10s. deep rose and choc. .. £7 45 0
142 ,, £1 black and bright blue £16 £6
143 ,, £1 10s. grn. & vio. (S. £5) £30 £7
144 ,, £5 mauve & blk. (S. £10) £400 £60
145 ,, £10 green & orge. (S. £30) £1600
145*a* ,, £20 red & green (S. £50) £5000

904-8. *Wmk. Mult. Crown CA. P* 14.
46 **31** ½d. blue-green 0 6 0 3
47 ,, 1d. rose-carmine 0 8 0 3
48 ,, 1d. deep carmine 1 0 0 4
49 ,, 2d. red and olive-green .. 2 0 1 3
52 ,, 4d. carmine and cinnamon 5 0 3 6
53 ,, 5d. black & orange (1908) 7 6 5 0
55 ,, 1s. carmine and pale blue 60 0 17 6
56 ,, 2s. dull. grn. & bt. violet. 65 0 30 0
57 ,, 2s. 6d. purple 60 0 35 0
62 **32** £1 10s. brown-orange and deep purple, C (1908) £225

908-9. *Inscribed* " POSTAGE POSTAGE ". *Wmk. Mult. Crown CA. P* 14.
65 **31** 6d. dull & bright purple .. 5 0 5 0
66 ,, 1s. black/*green* 8 6 7 6
67 ,, 2s. pur. & brt. blue/*blue* .. 30 0 10 0
68 ,, 2s. 6d. black & red/*blue* .. 30 0 12 6
69 **32** 5s. green and red/*yellow* 90 0 35 0
70 ,, 10s. green and red/*green* .. £8 £6
71 ,, £1 purple and black/*red* £50 £25

Collectors are warned against fiscally used high alue Natal stamps with penmarks cleaned off nd forged postmarks added.

FISCALS USED FOR POSTAGE.

369. *Embossed on coloured wove, surfaced paper. P* 12½.
01 **1** 1d. yellow 70 0 £5

373 (JULY). *Wmk. Crown CC. P* 14.
2 **7** 1s. purple-brown 30 0 70 0

75. *Wmk. Crown CC. P* 12½.
3 **6** 1d. yellow 16 0 25 0
4 ,, 6d. rose 30 0 35 0

41

(Typo. De La Rue.)

03. *Wmk. Crown CA. P* 14.
a **41** 5s. dull mauve & carm. £8 £8
,, £1 green £10 £8
206 **41** £1 10s. dull mauve & bl. £20 £20
207 ,, £5 green and red .. £35 £20
208 ,, £10 green and blue .. £75 £45

OFFICIAL STAMPS.

OFFICIAL

(**51**)

1904. *T* **31**, *wmk. Mult. Crown CA, optd. with T* **51**, *in black. P* 14.
303 ½d. blue-green 8 0 1 3
304 1d. carmine 2 0 0 10
305 2d. red and olive-green .. 20 0 12 6
306 3d. purple and grey .. 8 0 8 0
307 6d. green and brown-purple .. 37 6 22 6
308 1s. carmine and pale blue .. 80 0 60 0

The use of stamps overprinted as above was discontinued after 30 May, 1907. Stamps perforated with the letters " N.G.R. " were for use on Government Railways.

Natal now uses the stamps of South Africa.

NAURU.

NAURU (**1**) NAURU (**2**)

1916 (OCT.)–**1923**. *Stamps of Great Britain* (1912–21) *overprinted.*

(*a*) *With T* **1** (12½ *mm. long*).
1 ½d. green 0 3 0 9
a. " NAUP.U " £8
2 1d. scarlet 0 6 1 0
a. " NAUP.U " £8
3 1½d. red-brown (1923) 30 0 40 0
4 2d. orange (Die. I) 1 0 1 6
a. " NAUP.U " £8
5 2d. orange (Die II) (1923) .. 35 0 35 0
6 2½d. blue 1 6 3 0
a. " NAUP.U " £10 £8
7 3d. blue-violet 2 0 3 0
a. " NAUP.U " £10
8 4d. slate-green 3 6 5 0
a. " NAUP.U " £12
9 5d. yellow-brown 4 0 5 6
a. " NAUP.U " £12
10 6d. purple 5 0 6 0
a. " NAUP.U " £12
11 9d. agate 6 6 8 6
12 1s. bistre-brown 7 6 10 0

(*b*) *With T* **2** (13½ *mm. long*). (1923).
13 ½d. green 7 6 17 6
14 1d. scarlet 7 6 17 6
15 1½d. red-brown 7 6 15 0
16 2d. orange (Die II) 27 6 40 0

NAURU

(**3**)

Overprinted with T **3**. *Waterlow printing.*
17 5s. rose-carmine £90 £120
18 10s. indigo-blue (R.) £175 £200

De La Rue printing.
19 2s. 6d. deep brown £30 £40
20 2s. 6d. chestnut-brown .. 35 0 60 0
a. Re-entry .. .. ..
21 2s. 6d. brown 37 6 65 0
22 5s. bright carmine 37 6 65 0
23 10s. blue (R.) £6 £10

Bradbury, Wilkinson printing (1920).
24 2s. 6d. chocolate-brown .. 55 0 75 0
a. Major re-entry .. ..
25 2s. 6d. grey-brown 25 0 40 0

Nos. 1, 2, 8, 9 and 22 exist with double overprint, one albino.

PRINTERS. See note at beginning of Australia.

4

(Recess. Note Printing Branch of the Treasury, Melbourne and from 1926 by the Commonwealth Bank of Australia.)

1924–48. *T* **4.** *No wmk.* *P* 11.
I. Rough surfaced, greyish paper (1924–34).
II. Shiny surfaced, white paper (1937–47).

No.		I.		II.	
26	½d. chestnut ..	5 0	6 0	10 0	15 0
	a. Perf. 14 ('47)..	†		3 0	4 6
27	1d. green ..	6 0	6 9	6 0	8 0
28	1½d. scarlet ..	5 0	6 0	2 0	4 0
29	2d. orange ..	5 0	6 6	2 0	4 0
30	2½d. slate-blue ..	9 6	13 6	†	
30*a*	2½d. grnsh. bl. ('34)	7 6	12 6	†	
30*b*	2½d. dull blue ..	†		2 6	5 0
	ba. Imp. between (vert. pr.) ('48)	†		—	—
31	3d. pale blue ..	5 0	9 6	†	
31*a*	3d. greenish grey	†		2 6	5 0
32	4d. olive-green ..	7 6	9 6	5 6	8 0
33	5d. brown ..	7 6	9 6	3 6	5 0
34	6d. dull violet ..	13 6	15 0	4 6	7 0
35	9d. olive-brown..	16 6	19 0	13 0	17 6
36	1s. brown-lake ..	19 0	21 0	10 0	12 6
37	2s. 6d. grey-green	25 0	32 6	22 6	26 0
38	5s. claret ..	55 0	65 0	50 0	50 0
39	10s. yellow ..	70 0	80 0	50 0	60 0

HIS MAJESTY'S JUBILEE.

1910 - 1935

(5)

1935 (12 July). *Silver Jubilee.* *T* **4** (*surfaced paper*) *optd. with T* **5.**

40	1½d. scarlet	1 3	2 6
41	2d. orange	2 6	4 9
42	2½d. dull blue	4 9	6 0
43	1s. brown-lake	11 6	14 0

6

(Recess. John Ash, Melbourne.)

1937 (10 May). *Coronation.* *P* 11.

44	**6**	1½d. scarlet	0 6	0 8
45	,,	2d. orange	0 9	1 6
46	,,	2½d. blue	0 9	1 9
47	,,	1s. purple	3 0	3 6

7. Nauruan Netting Fish.

8. Anibare Bay.

12. Loading Phosphate from Cantilever.

13. Frigate Bird.

15. Nauruan Canoe.

16. "Domaneab" (Meeting-house).

17. Palm Trees. **19.** Map of Nauru.

18. Buada Lagoon.

Recess. Note Printing Branch, Commonwealth Bank, Melbourne, and from 1960 by Note Ptg. Branch, Reserve Bank of Australia, Melbourne.)

954 (6 FEB.)–**61.** *P* 13½ × 14½ (*horiz.*) *or* 14½ × 13½ (*vert.*).

8	**7**	½d. deep violet	1	0	1	0
		a. Violet (8.5.61)	0	9	0	9
9	**8**	1d. bluish green	1	0	1	0
		a. Emerald-green (8.5.61) ..	0	9	0	9
0	**12**	3½d. scarlet	1	0	1	3
1	**13**	4d. deep blue	1	0	1	3
2	**15**	6d. orange	1	6	2	0
3	**16**	9d. claret	2	0	3	0
4	**17**	1s. deep purple	2	6	4	6
5	**18**	2s. 6d. deep green ..	5	6	9	6
6	**19**	5s. magenta	10	0	17	6

Nos. 48*a* and 49*a* are on white instead of eam paper.

20. Micronesian Pigeon.

21. Poison Nut.

"Iyo" (*calophyllum*).

23. Black Lizard.

24. Capparis.

25. White Tern.

26. Coral Pinnacles.

27. Reed Warbler.

(Recess (10d., 2s. 3d.) or photo (others). Note Ptg. Branch, Reserve Bank of Australia, Melbourne.)

1963–65. *P* 13½ (*2d., 3d.,* 1*s.* 3d., 3*s.* 3d.).

57	**20**	2d. black, blue, red-brown & orange-yell. (3.5.65)	0	8	0	9
58	**21**	3d. multicoloured (16.4.64)	0	10	1	0
59	**22**	5d. multicoloured, *p* 13½ × 13 (22.4.63) ..	1	2	1	6
60	**23**	8d. black and green, *p.* 13 × 13½ (1.7.63) ..	1	9	2	3
61	**24**	10d. black, *p.* 14½ × 13½ (16.4.64)	2	0	2	6
62	**25**	1s. 3d. blue, black and yellow-green (3.5.65)..	2	6	3	3
63	**26**	2s. 3d. ultramarine, *p.* 15 × 14½ (16.4.64) ..	4	6	5	6
64	**27**	3s. 3d. multicoloured (3.5.65)	7	6	9	0

1965 (14 APR.). 50*th Anniv. of Gallipoli Landing. As T* **181** *of Australia, but slightly larger* (22 × 34½ *mm.*). *Photo.*

65	5d. sepia, black and emerald..	0	9	0	10

(100 cents = $1 Australian.)

28. Anibare Bay.

29. "Iyo" (*calophyllum*).

1966 (14 Feb.). *Decimal currency. Various stamps with values in cents and dollars as T* **28/9** *and some colours changed Helecon paper.*

No.	Type	Description	Unused	Used
66	**28**	1 c. deep blue	0 2	0 3
67	**29**	4 c. multicoloured	0 7	0 8
68	**23**	7 c. black and chestnut	0 11	1 2
69	**24**	8 c. olive-green	1 0	1 3
70	**13**	10 c. red	1 3	1 6
71	**21**	30 c. multicoloured	3 4	4 0
72	**20**	50 c. multicoloured	5 4	7 6
73	**19**	$1 magenta	10 6	16 6

NEVIS.

For GREAT BRITAIN stamps used in Nevis, see page 66.

1

2

3

4

The designs on the stamps refer to a medicinal spring on the island.

(Recess. Nissen & Parker, London.)

1861. *P* 13. (*a*) *Blued paper.*

No.	Type	Description	Unused	Used
1	**1**	1d. dull rose	£12	£8
2	**2**	4d. rose	£35	£16
3	**3**	6d. grey-lilac	£30	£28
4	**4**	1s. green	£60	£20

(*b*) *Greyish paper.*

No.	Type	Description	Unused	Used
5	**1**	1d. dull lake	40 0	55 0
6	**2**	4d. rose	£6	£6
7	**3**	6d. grey	£5	75 0
8	**4**	1s. green	£10	£7

1866. *White paper. P* 15.

No.	Type	Description	Unused	Used
9	**1**	1d. pale red	50 0	65 0
10	,,	1d. deep red	65 0	70 0
11	**2**	4d. orange	95 0	60 0
12	,,	4d. deep orange	£5	55 0
13	**4**	1s. blue-green	£16	85 0
14	,,	1s. yellow-green	£50	£12
		a. Laid paper	£550	£550
		b. No. 9 on sheet with crossed lines on hill	£100	

(Lithographed by transfer from the engraved plates. Nissen & Parker, London.)

1876. *P* 15.

No.	Type	Description	Unused	Used
15	**1**	1d. pale rose-red	20 0	30 0
		a. Imperf. (pair)	£10	
16	,,	1d. deep rose-red	32 6	45 0
17	,,	1d. vermilion-red	32 6	40 0
		a. Bisected (on cover)	—	£18
18	**2**	4d. orange-yellow	£16	70 0
		a. Imperf. between (vert. pair)	£350	
19	**3**	6d. grey	£18	£20
20	**4**	1s. pale green	95 0	£9
		a. Imperf.		
		b. Imperf. between (pair)		
		c. No. 9 on sheet with crossed lines on hill	£18	£28
21	,,	1s. deep green	£5	£12

No. 9 on the sheet of the 1s. *deep* green, has not the distinct "crossed lines on hill" of Nos. 14b and 20c, but traces of the lines are visible.

Retouches.

1d. *pale rose-red.*

	Description	Unused	Used
i.	No. 1 on sheet. Top of hill over kneeling figure redrawn by five thick lines and eight small slanting lines.	£18	£2
ii.	No. 1 on sheet. Another retouch. Three series of short vertical strokes behind the kneeling figure	£20	£2
iii.	No. 3 on sheet. Right upper corner star and border below star retouched	£18	£2
iv.	No. 9 on sheet. Retouch in same position as on No. 3 but differing in detail		
v.	No. 12 on sheet. Dress of standing figure retouched by a number of horizontal and vertical lines		

1878. *Lithographed. P* 11½.

No.	Type	Description	Unused	Used
22	**1**	1d. vermilion-red	50 0	70
		a. Bisected (on cover)	—	£2
		b. Imperf. (pair)	£10	
		c. Imperf. between (pair)		

NEVIS
ONE PENNY

5 (Die I)

REVIS. ½d.

(**6**)

(Typo. De La Rue & Co.)

1879–80. *Wmk. Crown CC. P* 14.

No.	Type	Description	Unused	Used
23	**5**	1d. lilac-mauve (1880)	40 0	30
		a. Bisected (½d.) (on cover)	—	£
24	,,	2½d. red-brown	£5	

1882. *Wmk. Crown CA. P* 14.

No.	Type	Description	Unused	Used
25	**5**	1d. lilac-mauve	35 0	30
		a. Bisected (½d.) (on cover)	—	£
26	,,	2½d. red-brown	80 0	45
27	,,	4d. blue	£7	50

1883. *No. 25 bisected vertically and surch. with T*

No.	Type	Description	Unused	Used
28		½d. on half 1d. lilac-mauve (V.)	£20	95
		a. Surch. double	—	£
		b. Surch. on half "REVENUE" stamp No. F6	—	£

29 ½d. on half 1d., lilac-mauve .. £14 95 0
a. Surch. double .. .. — £28
b. Whole stamp with surch. on right half only .. ..
c. Surch. on half "REVENUE" stamp No. F6 .. .. — £100

1883–90. *Wmk. Crown CA. P* 14.

30 **5** ½d. dull green (1883) .. 8 6 10 0
30*a* ,, 1d. dull rose 20 0 17 6
31 ,, 1d. carmine (1884) .. 8 6 10 6
32 ,, 2½d. ultramarine (1884) .. 12 6 12 0
33 ,, 4d. grey (1884) 12 6 10 6
34 ,, 6d. green (1883) £18 £15
35 ,, 6d. chestnut (1888) .. 30 0 90 0
36 ,, 1s. pale violet (1890) .. 85 0 £18

FISCALS USED FOR POSTAGE.

Revenue (F 1) REVENUE (F 2)

1882. *Stamps of* 1876 *optd. with Type* F **1.**

F1 1d. bright red 30 0
F2 1d. rose 35 0 22 6
F3 4d. orange 50 0
F4 6d. grey 60 0
F5 1s. green 65 0

Nos. 25, 27 *and* 34 *optd. with Type* F **2.**

F6 1d. lilac-mauve 30 0 30 0
F7 4d. blue 20 0 35 0
F8 6d. green 20 0 45 0

For later issues *see* St. Kitts-Nevis.

NEW BRUNSWICK.

1. Royal Crown and heraldic flowers of the United Kingdom.

(Recess. Perkins, Bacon & Co.)

51 (Sept.). *Blue paper. Imperf.*

1 3d. bright red £150 £60
,, 3d. dull red £120 £60
a. Bisected (1½d.) (on cover) .. — £250
, 6d. mustard-yellow .. .. — £275
,, 6d. yellow £250 £175
, 6d. olive-yellow £225 £150
a. Bisected (3d.) (on cover) .. — £250
,, 1s. reddish mauve £1400 £500
, 1s. dull mauve £1100 £375
a. Bisected (6d.) (on cover) .. — £2000
b. Quartered (3d.) (on cover) .. — £1500

Reprints of all three values were made in 1890 thin, hard, white paper. The 3d. is bright nge, the 6d. and 1s. violet-black.

2 3

3*a*. Charles Connell.

4

5 **6**

7. King Edward VII when Prince of Wales.

(Recess. American Bank Note Co.)

1860 (15 May)–**1863.** *No wmk. P* 12.

7 **2** 1 c. brown-purple.. .. 40 0 40 0
8 ,, 1 c. purple 30 0 40 0
9 ,, 1 c. dull claret 25 0 37 6
a. Imperf. between (horiz. pr.) £40
10 **3** 2 c. orange (1863).. .. 25 0 40 0
11 ,, 2 c. orange-yellow .. 30 0 40 0
12 ,, 2 c. deep orange 30 0 45 0
a. Imperf. between (vert. pair) £45
13 **3a** 5 c. brown £325
14 **4** 5 c. yellow-green 25 0 35 0
15 ,, 5 c. deep green 25 0 35 0
16 ,, 5 c. sap-green £28 £5
17 **5** 10 c. red 40 0 55 0
a. Bisected (5 c.) (on cover) (1860) .. .. .. — £90
18 **6** 12½ c. indigo 30 0 45 0
19 **7** 17 c. black 27 6 70 0

In March, 1868, issues of the Dominion of Canada replaced those of New Brunswick.

NEWFOUNDLAND.

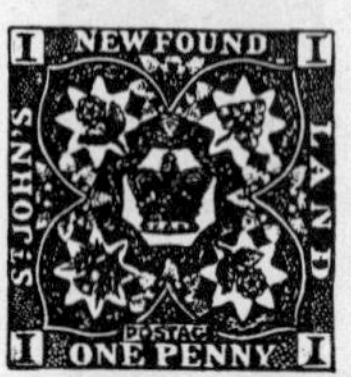

1

2

3

4

5

Royal Crown and heraldic flowers of the United Kingdom.

(Recess. Perkins, Bacon & Co.)

1857 (1 Jan.). *No wmk. Thick paper. Imperf.*

1	**1**	1d. brown-purple	60 0	£5
		a. Bisected (½d.) on cover	†	£350
2	**2**	2d. scarlet-vermilion	£1000	£450
3	**3**	3d. yellowish green	£45	£60
4	**4**	4d. scarlet-vermilion	£650	£500
		a. Bisected (2d.) (on cover)		
5	**1**	5d. brown-purple	£20	£35
6	**4**	6d. scarlet-vermilion	£650	£300
7	**5**	6½d. scarlet-vermilion	£200	£375
8	**4**	8d. scarlet-vermilion	£20	£60
		a. Bisected (4d.) (on cover)	†	£275
9	**2**	1s. scarlet-vermilion	£1400	£525
		a. Bisected (6d.) (on cover)	†	£800

The 6d. and 8d. differ from the 4d. in many details, as does also the 1s. from the 2d.

1860. *No wmk. Thinner paper. Imperf.*

10	**2**	2d. orange-vermilion	£35	£60
11	**3**	3d. green (to deep)	70 0	£20
12	**4**	4d. orange-vermilion	£250	£150
		a. Bisected (2d.) (on cover)		
13	**1**	5d. chocolate-brown	85 0	£40
14	**4**	6d. orange-vermilion	£350	£120
15	**2**	1s. orange-vermilion	£2000	£1000
		a. Bisected (6d.) (on cover)		

Stamps of this issue may be found with part of the paper-maker's watermark "STACEY WISE 1858".

The following stamp is believed to be an essay. Laid paper.

16	1s. orange-vermilion	£1500	

1861. *New colours. No wmk. Imperf.*

(a) *1st printing. Thick paper.* (July.)

17	**1**	1d. chocolate-brown	75 0	£20
		a. Red-brown	£325	
18	**2**	2d. deep rose-lake	£30	£75
19	**4**	4d. deep rose-lake	£5	£25
		a. Bisected (2d.) (on cover)		
20	**1**	5d. red-brown	50 0	£20
		a. Brown	50 0	£20
21	**4**	6d. deep rose-lake	£5	£25
		a. Bisected (3d.) (on cover)		
22	**5**	6½d. deep rose-lake	£25	£75
23	**2**	1s. deep rose-lake	£25	£75
		a. Bisected (6d.) (on cover)		

(b) *2nd printing. Thin paper.* (Nov.)

23*b*	**2**	2d. pale rose-lake	£15	£50
23*c*	**4**	4d. pale rose-lake	25 0	£15
23*d*	,,	6d. pale rose-lake	25 0	£15
23*e*	**5**	6½d. pale rose-lake	£6	£50
23*f*	**4**	8d. pale rose-lake	£6	£65
23*g*	**2**	1s. pale rose-lake	50 0	£30

Stamps of this issue may be found with part of the paper-maker's watermark "STACEY WISE 1858".

Collectors are warned against buying bisected stamps of these issues without a reliable guarantee. The same warning applies to used specimens of the stamps which are worth less in unused condition, as many unused stamps have been provided with faked postmarks.

6. Codfish.

7. Seal on ice-floe.

8. Prince Consort.

9. Queen Victoria.

10

11. Queen Victori

(Recess. American Bank Note Co., New York.)

1866 (Jan.). *P* 12. (*a*) *Thin yellowish paper.*

25	**6**	2 c. yellowish green ..	£8	50 0
		a. Bisected (1 c.) (on cover) ..	†	£500
26	**7**	5 c. brown	£50	£18
		a. Bisected (2½ c.) (on cover)		
27	**8**	10 c. black	£10	90 0
		a. Bisected (5 c.) (on cover) ..	†	£350
28	**9**	12 c. red-brown	£22	£14
		a. Bisected (6 c.) (on cover) ..		
29	**10**	13 c. orange-yellow ..	90 0	90 0
30	**11**	24 c. blue	40 0	40 0

(*b*) *Medium white paper.*

31	**6**	2 c. bluish green (to deep)	80 0	40 0
32	**8**	10 c. black	80 0	50 0
33	**9**	12 c. chestnut	22 6	27 6
33*a*	**11**	24 c. blue	£35	£20

12. King Edward VII when Prince of Wales.

I.

(Recess. National Bank Note Co., New York.)

1868. *P* 12.

34	**12**	1 c. dull purple (I)	50 0	55 0

14. Queen Victoria.

II.

(Recess. American Bank Note Co., New York.)

1868–73. *P* 12.

	12	1 c. brown-purple (II) ('71)	45 0	40 0
	14	3 c. vermilion (1870) ..	£20	£10
	,,	3 c. blue (1873)	75 0	27 6
	7	5 c. black	£15	£9
	14	6 c. rose (1870)	10 0	15 0

1876–79. *Rouletted.*

	12	1 c. lake-purple (II) (1877)	90 0	50 0
	6	2 c. bluish green (1879) ..	£10	40 0
	14	3 c. blue (1877)	£9	16 0
	7	5 c. blue (1876)	£15	25 0
		a. Imperf. (pair)		

In Type II the white oval frame line is unbroken by the scroll containing the words "ONE CENT", the letters "N.F." are smaller and closer to the scroll, and there are other minor differences.

15. King Edward VII when Prince of Wales. **16.** Codfish.

17 **18.** Seal on ice-floe.

(Recess. British-American Bank Note Co., Montreal.)

1880. *P* 12.

44	**15**	1 c. dull grey-brown ..	25 0	22 6
45	,,	1 c. dull brown	12 6	10 6
45*a*	,,	1 c. red-brown	22 6	12 6
46	**16**	2 c. yellow-green	60 0	16 0
47	**17**	3 c. pale dull blue	55 0	12 6
47*a*	,,	3 c. bright blue	£5	7 6
48	**18**	5 c. pale dull blue	85 0	12 6

19. Newfoundland dog. **20.** Atlantic Brigantine.

(Recess. British-American Bank Note Co., Montreal.)

1887. *New colours and values.* *P* 12.

49	**19**	½ c. rose-red	7 6	7 6
49*a*	**15**	1 c. blue-green	7 6	4 0
50	,,	1 c. green..	4 0	3 0
50*a*	,,	1 c. yellow-green ..	6 0	7 6
51	**16**	2 c. orange-vermilion ..	12 6	5 0
52	**17**	3 c. deep brown	12 6	8 6
53	**18**	5 c. deep blue	60 0	8 0
54	**20**	10 c. black..	45 0	40 0

21. Queen Victoria.

(Recess. British-American Bank Note Co. Ottawa.)

1890. *P* 12.

55	**21**	3 c. deep slate	17	6	1	6
		a. Imperf. (pair)				
56	,,	3 c. slate-grey (to grey) ..	30	0	1	9
		a. Imperf. between (pair) ..	£50			
57	,,	3 c. slate-violet	12	6	4	0
58	,,	3 c. grey-lilac	12	6	1	6
58*a*	,,	3 c. brown-grey	10	6	7	6
58*b*	,,	3 c. purple-grey	20	0	6	0

There is a very wide range of shades in this stamp, and those given only cover the main groups.

Stamps on pink paper are from a consignment recovered from the sea and which were affected by the salt water.

(Recess. British-American Bank Note Co., Montreal.)

1894. *Changes of colour. P* 12.

59	**19**	½ c. black	5	0	2	0
59*a*	**18**	5 c. bright blue	20	0	8	6
60	**14**	6 c. crimson-lake ..	12	6	15	0
61	**9**	12 c. deep brown	30	0	45	0

The 6c. is printed from the old American Bank Note Company's plates.

1896–97. *Reissues. P* 12.

62	**19**	½ c. orange-vermilion ..	70	0	£5	
63	**15**	1 c. deep green	7	6	6	6
63*a*	,,	1 c. deep brown	40	0		
64	**16**	2 c. green	30	0	15	0
65	**17**	3 c. deep blue	30	0	17	6
65*a*	,,	3 c. chocolate-brown ..	45	0	50	0

The above were *reissued* for postal purposes. The colours were generally brighter than those of the original stamps.

22. Queen Victoria.

23. Jean Cabot.

24. Cape Bonavista.

25. Caribou-hunting.

26. Mining.

27. Logging.

28. Fishing.

29. Cabot's ship.

30. Ptarmigan.

31. Group of Seals.

32. Salmon-fishing.

33. Seal of the Colony

34. Iceberg off St. John's.

35. Henry VII.

(Recess. American Bank Note. Co.)

1897 (24 June). 400*th Anniv. of Discovery Newfoundland and* 60*th year of Queen Victori reign. T* **22** *to* **35.** *P* 12.

66	1 c. green	1	9	2
67	2 c. bright rose	1	3	1
	a. Bisected (1 c.) on cover ..	†		£
68	3 c. bright blue	4	0	2
	a. Bisected (1½ c.) on cover ..	†		£
69	4 c. olive-green	10	0	5
70	5 c. violet	7	6	7
71	6 c. red-brown	7	0	7
	a. Bisected (3 c.) on cover ..	†		£
72	8 c. orange	12	6	12
73	10 c. sepia	12	6	12
74	12 c. deep blue	50	0	17
75	15 c. bright scarlet	50	0	22
76	24 c. dull violet-blue	27	6	32
77	30 c. slate-blue	27	6	30
78	35 c. red	50	0	60
79	60 c. black	25	0	27

The 60 c. surcharged "TWO—2—CENTS" three lines is an essay made in December, 19

ONE CENT

(36)

ONE CENT

(37)

ONE CENT

(38)

1897 (Oct.). *T* **21** *surch. with T* **36** *to* **38.**

80	**36**	1 c. on 3 c. grey-purple	15 0	17 6
		a. Double surch., one diagonal	£185	
		b. Surch. in red	£170	
		c. Surch. in red and black	£150	
81	**37**	1 c. on 3 c. grey-purple	50 0	60 0
		a. Surch. in red	£300	
		b. Surch. in red and black	£375	
82	**38**	1 c. on 3 c. grey-purple	£32	£32
		a. Surch. in red	£750	
		b. Surch. double in red		
		c. Surch. in red and black	£850	

This overprint is known on stamps of various shades.

39. Prince Edward, now Duke of Windsor.

40. Queen Victoria.

41. King Edward VII when Prince of Wales.

42. Queen Alexandra when Princess of Wales.

43. Queen Mary when Duchess of York.

44. King George V when Duke of York.

(Recess. American Bank Note Co.)

1897–1918. *P* 12.

83	**39**	½ c. olive (Aug., 1897)	1 6	2 0
		a. Imperf. (pair)	£25	
84	**40**	1 c. carmine (Dec., 1897)	1 6	1 3
85	,,	1 c. blue-grn. (June, 1898)	6 0	0 6
		a. *Yellow-green*	1 9	0 6
		b. Imperf. between (pair)	£22	
86	**41**	2 c. orange (Dec., 1897)	2 0	2 6
87	,,	2 c. scarlet (June, 1898)	5 0	0 6
		a. Imperf. (pair)	£32	
88	**42**	3 c. orange (June, 1898)	2 6	0 6
		a. Imperf. between (pair)	£32	
		b. Imperf. (pair)	£38	
		c. *Red-orange/bluish* (6.18)	22 6	7 6
89	**43**	4 c. violet (Oct., 1901)	10 0	8 6
		a. Imperf. (pair)	£32	
90	**44**	5 c. blue (June, 1899)	10 0	6 0

No. 88*c* was an emergency war-time printing made by the American Bank Note Co. from the old plate, pending receipt of the then current 3 c. from England.

45. Map of Newfoundland.

(Recess. American Bank Note Co.)

1908 (Sept.). *P* 12.

94	**45**	2 c. lake	22 6	0 6

46. King James I.

47. Arms of Colonisation Co.

48. John Guy.

49. Guy's ship.

50. Cupids.

51. Sir Francis Bacon.

52. View of Mosquito.

53. Logging Camp.

54. Paper mills.

55. King Edward VII.

56. King George V.

(Litho. Whitehead, Morris & Co., Ltd.)

1910 (15 Aug.). (*a*) *P* 12.

95	**46**	1 c. green ..		3 0	1 0
		a. "NFWFOUNDLAND"		£6	£7
		b. Imperf.between(horiz.pr.)		£45	£55
96	**47**	2 c. rose-carmine ..		3 0	1 0
97	**48**	3 c. olive		20 0	25 0
98	**49**	4 c. violet		25 0	30 0
99	**50**	5 c. bright blue		25 0	22 6
100	**51**	6 c. claret (A)		50 0	65 0
100*a*	,,	6 c. claret (B)		37 6	55 0
101	**52**	8 c. bistre-brown ..		35 0	42 6
102	**53**	9 c. olive-green		35 0	42 6
103	**54**	10 c. purple-slate ..		40 0	45 0
104	**55**	12 c. pale red-brown ..		35 0	45 0
		a. Imperf. (pair) ..		£55	
105	**56**	15 c. black		40 0	55 0

6 c. (A) "z" in "COLONIZATION" reversed thus "ƨ". (B) "z" correct.

(*b*) *P* 12 × 14.

106	**46**	1 c. green	1 9	2 0
		a. "NFWFOUNDLAND" ..	£10	
		b. Imperf. between (pair) ..	£70	£80
		c. As a. in pair imp. betwn. ..		
107	**47**	2 c. rose-carmine	3 6	0 6
		a. Imperf. between (pair) ..	£45	
108	**50**	5 c. bright blue (*p*. 14 × 12)	8 6	5 0

(*c*) *P* 12 × 11.

109	**46**	1 c. green	1 3	1 3
		a. Imp. betwn. (horiz. pair) ..	£35	
		b. Imp. betwn. (vert. pair) ..	£45	
		c. "NFWFOUNDLAND" ..	£5	£5
		d. As c. in pair imp. vert. ..		

(*d*) *P* 12 × 11½.

110	**47**	2 c. rose-carmine	£14	£16

(Dies. eng. Macdonald & Sons. Recess. A. Alexander & Sons, Ltd.)

1911 (Feb.). *Types as* **51** *to* **56**, *but recess-printed. P* 14.

111	6 c. claret (B)	40 0	42 6
112	8 c. yellow-brown	70 0	80 0
	a. Imperf. between (horiz. pair) ..	£65	
	b. Imperf. (pair)	£45	
113	9 c. sage-green	75 0	£5
	a. Imperf. between (horiz. pair) ..	£55	
114	10 c. purple-black	£5	£6
	a. Imperf. between (horiz. pair) ..	£65	
	b. Imperf. (pair)	£45	
115	12 c. red-brown	90 0	£[illegible]
116	15 c. slate-green	90 0	£[illegible]

The 9 c. exists with paper-maker's wmk.

57. Queen Mary.

58. King George V.

59. Duke of Windsor when Prince of Wales.

60. King George VI when Prince Albert.

61. Princess Mary, late Princess Royal.

62. Prince Henry, now Duke of Gloucester.

63. Prince George, late Duke of Kent.

64. Prince John.

65. Queen Alexandra.

66. Duke of Connaught.

67. Seal of Newfoundland.

(Recess. De La Rue (T **57/61** and **65**); other values, printers unknown.)

1911 (19 June). *Coronation. P* 13½ × 14 (*comb*) *or perf.* 14 (*single line*).

117	**57**	1 c. yellow-green.. ..	7	6	0	9
		a. Blue-green	1	9	0	3
118	**58**	2 c. carmine	1	9	0	3
		a. Rose-red (blurred impression)	3	0	1	6
119	**59**	3 c. red-brown	22	6	27	6
120	**60**	4 c. purple	22	6	27	6
121	**61**	5 c. ultramarine	10	0	7	6
22	**62**	6 c. slate-grey	30	0	37	6
23	**63**	8 c. greenish blue ..	£6		£8	
		a. Aniline blue	70	0	80	0
24	**64**	9 c. violet-blue	30	0	35	0
25	**65**	10 c. deep green	32	6	37	6
26	**66**	12 c. plum	32	6	37	6
27	**67**	15 c. lake	30	0	45	0
		a. Imperf. (pr. ungummed)..	£6			

The 2 c. rose-red, No. 118*a*, is a poor war-time printing.

68. Caribou.

Each value bears with " Trail of the Caribou " the name of a different action: 1 c. Suvla Bay; 3 c. Gueudecourt; 4 c. Beaumont Hamel; 6 c. Monchy; 10 c. Steenbeck; 15 c. Langemarck; 24 c. Cambrai; 36 c. Combles. 2 c., 5 c., 8 c., and 12 c. inscribed " Royal Naval Reserve, Ubique."

(Recess. De La Rue.)

919 (2 Jan.). *Newfoundland Contingent*, 1914–1918. *P* 14.

30	**68**	1 c. green (*a*) (*b*)	1	6	0	3
31	,,	2 c. scarlet (*a*) (*b*)	2	6	0	8
		a. Carmine-red (b)	2	6	0	6
32	,,	3 c. brown (*a*) (*b*)	3	0	0	3
		a. Red-brown (b)	2	6	0	3
33	,,	4 c. mauve (*a*)	5	0	1	6
		a. Purple (b)	6	0	2	6
4	,,	5 c. ultramarine (*a*) (*b*) ..	5	0	1	6
5	,,	6 c. slate-grey (*a*) ..	15	0	20	0
6	,,	8 c. bright magenta (*a*) ..	15	0	20	0
7	,,	10 c. deep grey-green (*a*)..	10	0	10	6
8	,,	12 c. orange (*a*)	25	0	30	0
9	,,	15 c. indigo (*a*)	18	0	22	6
		a. Prussian blue (a) ..	£20		£20	
0	,,	24 c. bistre-brown (*a*) ..	20	0	30	0
1	,,	36 c. sage-green (*a*) ..	25	0	37	6

Perforations. Two perforating heads were ed: (*a*) comb 14 × 13.9; (*b*) line 14.1 × 14.1.

FIRST TRANS-ATLANTIC AIR POST April, 1919.

(**69*a***)

Trans-Atlantic AIR POST, 1919. ONE DOLLAR

(**70**)

1919 (12 Apr.). *Air. T* **68** *optd. with T* **69*a***, *by Robinson & Co. Ltd., at the offices of the " Daily News."*

142	3 c. brown	£1850	£1750

These stamps franked correspondence carried by Mr. Hawker on his Atlantic flight. 18 were damaged and destroyed, 95 used on letters, 11 given as presentation copies, and the remaining 76 were sold in aid of the Marine Disasters Fund.

1919 (April.). *T* **68** *overprinted in MS.* " Aerial Atlantic Mail. J.A.R."

142*a*	3 c. brown	—	£3500

This provisional was made by the Postmaster, Mr. J. A. Robinson, for use on correspondence intended to be carried on the abortive Morgan-Raynham Trans-Atlantic flight. The mail was eventually delivered by sea.

1919 (9 June). *Air. T* **31** *surch. with T* **70** *by J. W. Withers at the offices of the " Royal Gazette."*

143	$1 on 15 c. bright scarlet ..	£20	£25
	a. No comma after " AIR POST "	£35	£40
	b. As Var. a and no stop after " 1919 "	£75	£80

These stamps were issued for use on the mail carried on the first successful flight across the Atlantic by Alcock and Brown, and on other projected Trans-Atlantic flights. (Alcock flown cover, *Price* £70.)

THREE CENTS

(**71**)

1920 (Sept.). *T* **33, 31,** *and* **34** *surch. as T* **71**, *by J. W. Withers.* (*2 c. on 30 c., with only one bar, at top of stamp.*)

(A) Bars of surch. 10½ mm. apart.

(B) Bars 13½ mm. apart.

144	2 c. on 30 c. slate-blue ..	6	0	8	6
	a. Surch. inverted	£60			
145	3 c. on 15 c. bright scarlet (A)	£5		£6	
	a. Surch. inverted	£110			
146	3 c. on 15 c. bright scarlet (B)	10	0	12	6
147	3 c. on 35 c. red	10	0	10	6
	a. Surch. inverted				
	b. Lower bar omitted	£24			
	c. " THREE " omitted ..	£200			

Our prices for Nos. 147b and 147c are for stamps with lower bar or " THREE " entirely missing. The bar may be found in all stages of incompleteness and stamps showing broken bar are not of much value.

On the other hand, stamps showing either only the top or bottom of the letters " THREE " are scarce, though not as rare as No. 147c.

The 6 c. T **27**, surcharged " THREE CENTS," in red or black, is an essay. (*Price* £30). The 2 c. on 30 c. with red surcharge is a colour trial. (*Price* £30).

AIR MAIL to Halifax, N.S. 1921.

(72)

1921 (16 Nov.). *Air. T* **34** *optd. with T* **72.**

I. $2\frac{3}{4}$ *mm. between* " AIR " *and* " MAIL ".

148	35 c. red (I)		£20	£18
		a. No stop after "1921" ..	£15	£12
		b. No stop and first "1" of "1921" below "f" of "Halifax"	£35	£30
		c. As No. 148, inverted ..	£450	
		d. As No. 148a, inverted ..	£350	
		e. As No. 148b, inverted ..	£1000	

II. $1\frac{1}{2}$ *mm. between* " AIR " *and* " MAIL ".

148*f*	35 c. red (II)		£25	£22
		g. No stop after "1921" ..	£30	£26
		h. No stop and first "1" of "1921" below "f" of "Halifax"	£35	£30
		i. As No. 148f, inverted ..	£550	
		k. As No. 148g, inverted ..	£750	
		l. As No. 148h, inverted ..	£1000	

73 Twin Hills, Tor's Cove.

74. South-West Arm, Trinity.

75. Statue of the Fighting Newfoundlander, St. John's.

76. Humber River.

77. Coast at Trinity.

78. Upper Steadies, Humber River.

79. Quidi Vidi, near St. John's.

80. Caribou crossing Lake.

81. Humber River Cañon.

82. Shell Bird Island.

83. Mount Moriah, Bay of Islands.

84. Humber River near Little Rapids.

85. Placentia.

86. Topsail Falls.

(Recess. De La Rue.)

1923 (9 July)–**24.** *P* 14 (*comb or line*).

149	**73**	1 c. green	1	6	0	
150	**74**	2 c. carmine	1	6	0	
		a. Imperf. (pair)	£32			
151	**75**	3 c. brown	1	3	0	
152	**76**	4 c. deep purple	2	6	0	
153	**77**	5 c. ultramarine	3	6	2	
154	**78**	6 c. slate	5	0	8	
155	**79**	8 c. purple	6	0	7	
156	**80**	9 c. slate-green	22	6	25	
157	**81**	10 c. violet..	8	6	6	
		a. Purple	8	0	7	
158	**82**	11 c. sage-green	10	0	10	
159	**83**	12 c. lake	10	0	12	
160	**84**	15 c. Prussian blue ..	12	6	15	
161	**85**	20 c. chestnut (28.4.24) ..	15	0	17	
162	**86**	24 c. sepia (22.4.24) ..	£5		£	

Perforations. Three perforating heads wer used: comb. 13.8 × 14 (all values); line 13.7 an 14 in various combinations (for all except 6, 9 and 11c.).

Air Mail DE PINEDO 1927

(87)

1927 (18 May). *Air. T* **35** *optd. with T* **87,** *Robinson & Co., Ltd.*

163 60 c. black (R.) £4000 £17

For the mail carried by De Pinedo to Euro 300 stamps were overprinted, 230 used in cor spondence, 66 presented to De Pinedo, Gover ment Officials, etc., and 4 damaged and destroye Stamps without overprint were also used.

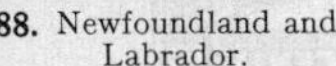

88. Newfoundland and Labrador.

89. S.S. *Caribou*.

90. King George V and Queen Mary.

91. Duke of Windsor when Prince of Wales.

92. Express Train.

93. Hotel, St. John's.

94. Heart's Content.

95. Cabot Tower St. John's.

96. ar Memorial, St. John's.

97. G.P.O., St. John's.

98. Trans-Atlantic flight.

99. Colonial Building St. John's.

100. Grand Falls, Labrador.

(Recess. De La Rue.)

1928 (3 Jan.)–**29.** "*Publicity*" *issue.* *P* 13 *to* 14.

164	**88**	1 c. deep green (*a*) ..	1	0	0	10
165	**89**	2 c. carmine (*b*)	1	6	0	8
166	**90**	3 c. brown (*b*) (*c*).. ..	1	3	0	6
167	**91**	4 c. mauve (*b*)	5	0	4	0
		a. Rose-purple ('29) ..	45	0	35	0
168	**92**	5 c. slate-grey (*b*) (*c*) ..	6	0	6	0
169	**93**	6 c. ultramarine (*b*) (*c*) ..	5	0	10	0
170	**94**	8 c. red-brown (*c*) ..	6	0	8	6
171	**95**	9 c. deep green (*c*) ..	8	6	10	6
172	**96**	10 c. deep violet (*b*) (*c*) ..	10	0	6	0
173	**97**	12 c. carmine-lake (*c*) ..	7	6	8	6
174	**95**	14 c. brown-purple (*b*) (*c*)..	8	0	7	6
175	**98**	15 c. deep blue (*c*) ..	8	0	10	6
176	**99**	20 c. grey-black (*b*) (*c*) ..	10	0	8	6
177	**97**	28 c. deep green (*c*) ..	18	6	22	6
178	**100**	30 c. sepia (*c*)	12	6	17	6

Perforations. Three perforating heads were used: (*a*) comb 14 × 13.9; (*b*) comb 13.5 × 12.75; (*c*) line 13.7 to 14 or compound.

THREE CENTS

(**101**)

(Surch. by Messrs. D. R. Thistle, St. John's.)

1929 (23 Aug.). *Surch. with T* **101.**

179	**78**	3 c. on 6 c. slate (R.) ..	3	0	6	0
		a. Surch. inverted	£45			
		b. Surch. in black	£65			

D. (1 c.) P. D. (2 c.) P.

D. (3 c.) P.

D. (4 c.) P.

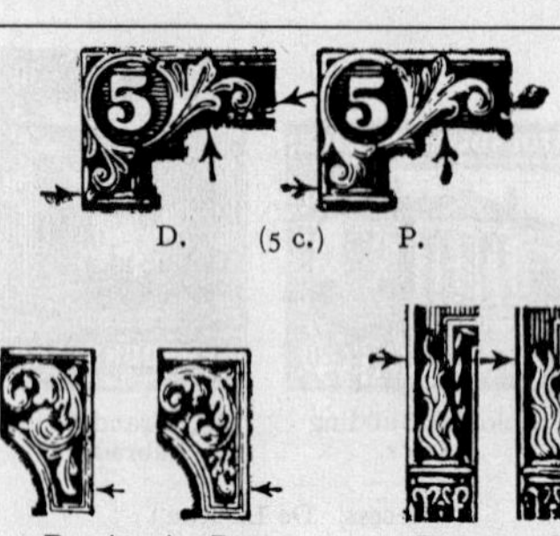

D. (5 c.) P.

D. (6 c.) P. D. (10 c.) P.

D. (15 c.) P.

D. (20 c.) P.

D. " De La Rue " printing.

P. " Perkins, Bacon " printing.

1929–31. *" Perkins, Bacon " printing. Former types re-engraved. No wmk. P* 13½ *to* 14.

180	**88**	1 c. green (*a*) (*d*) (26.9.29)	1 0	0 3
		a. Imperf. between (pair) ..	£18	
		b. Imperf. (pair)	£28	
181	**89**	2 c. scarlet (*b*) (*d*) (10.8.29)	1 0	0 3
182	**90**	3 c. red-brown (*c*) (10.8.29)	1 3	0 6
		a. Imperf. pair	£17	
183	**91**	4 c. reddish purple (*c*) (26.8.29)	3 6	1 3
		a. Imperf. (pair)	£45	
184	**92**	5 c. deep grey-green (*c*) (14.9.29)	5 0	2 0
185	**93**	6 c. ultram. (*b*) (*d*) (8.11.29)	8 0	12 6
188	**96**	10 c. violet (*c*) (5.10.29) ..	8 0	3 0
189	**98**	15 c. blue (*c*) (Jan. '30) ..	17 6	22 6
190	**99**	20 c. black (*d*) (1.1.31) ..	25 0	30 0

Perforations. Four perforating heads were used: (*a*) comb 14 × 13.9; (*b*) comb 13.6 × 13.5; (*c*) comb 13.6 × 13.8; (*d*) line 13.7 to 14 or compound.

Trans-Atlantic
AIR MAIL
By B. M.
"Columbia"
September
1930
Fifty Cents

(102)

1930 (25 Sept.). *Air. T* **68** *surch. with T* **102**, *by Messrs. D. R. Thistle.*

191	50 c. on 36 c. sage-green ..	£725	£650

Forgeries of this surcharge are known.

103. Aeroplane and dog-team.

104.
Vickers-Vimy biplane and early sailing packet

105. Routes of historic transatlantic flight

106.

(Recess. Perkins, Bacon.)

1931. *Air. T* **103** *to* **105.** *P* 14.

(*a*) *Without wmk.* (2.1.31).

192	15 c. chocolate	8 0	15
	a. Imperf. between (pair) ..	£100	
193	50 c. green	25 0	35
	a. Imperf. between (pair) ..	£150	£
194	$1 deep blue	70 0	90
	a. Imperf. between (pair) ..	£180	

(*b*) *Wmk. T* **106**, *sideways* (13.3.31).

195	15 c. chocolate	8 0	10
	a. Pair, with & without wmk..	70 0	
	b. Imperf. between (pair) ..	£100	
	ba. Do., one without wmk. (vert. pair)		
	c. Imperf. (pair)	£60	
196	50 c. green	70 0	85
	a. Imperf. between (horiz. pair)	£80	
	b. Imperf. (pair)	£100	
197	$1 deep blue	£8	£
	a. Imperf. between (vert. pair)	£275	

"WITH AND WITHOUT WMK." PAIRS listed in the issues from No. 195a. onwards must have one stamp *completely* without any trace of watermark.

1931. *"Perkins, Bacon" printing (re-engraved types).* *W* **106.** *P* 13½ *to* 14.

No.	Type		Unused	Used
198	**88**	1 c. green	1 3	0 6
		a. Imperf. betwn. (horiz. pr.)		
199	**89**	2 c. scarlet	2 0	0 6
200	**90**	3 c. red-brown	3 0	0 8
201	**91**	4 c. reddish purple	7 6	2 6
202	**92**	5 c. deep grey-green	8 0	10 0
203	**93**	6 c. ultramarine (25.3.31)	25 0	30 0
204	**94**	8 c. chestnut (1.4.31)	20 0	22 6
205	**96**	10 c. violet	10 0	15 0
206	**98**	15 c. blue	30 0	35 0
207	**99**	20 c. black	30 0	25 0
208	**100**	30 c. sepia	32 6	37 6

Perforations. Two perforating heads were used: comb 13.4 × 13.4 for 1 c.; comb 13.6 × 13.8 for other values. Some values also exist line perf.

107. Codfish.

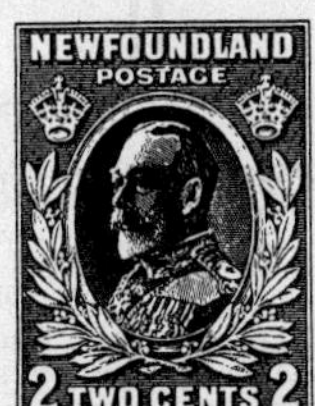

108. King George V.

109. Queen Mary.

110. Duke of Windsor when Prince of Wales.

111. Caribou.

112. Queen Elizabeth II when Princess.

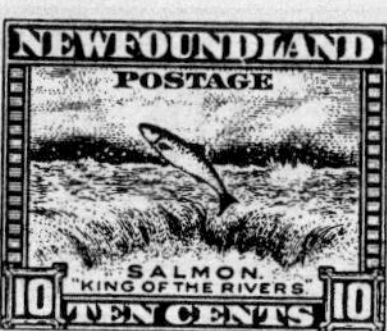

113. Salmon.

114. Newfoundland Dog.

115. Seal.

116. Cape Race.

117. Sealing Fleet.

118. Fishing Fleet.

(Recess. Perkins, Bacon & Co.)

1932 (1 Jan). *W* **106.** *P* 13½ *(comb).*

No.	Type		Unused	Used
209	**107**	1 c. green	2 0	0 10
		a. Imperf. (pair)	£20	
		b. Perf. 13 (line)	£6	£8
		ba. Imp. betwn. (vert. pr.)	£25	
210	**108**	2 c. carmine	2 6	0 6
		a. Imperf. (pair)	£20	
		b. Perf. 13 (line)	£6	£8
		c. Perf. 14 (line). Small holes		
211	**109**	3 c. orange-brown	1 0	0 6
		a. Imperf. (pair)	£20	
		b. Perf. 13 (line)	£8	
		c. Perf. 14 (line). Small holes	£8	
		ca. Imp. betwn. (vert. pr.)	£15	
212	**110**	4 c. bright violet	7 6	3 0
213	**111**	5 c. maroon	10 6	2 0
		a. Imperf. (pair)	£20	
214	**112**	6 c. light blue	22 6	27 6
215	**113**	10 c. black-brown	2 0	1 6
		a. Imperf. (pair)	£10	
216	**114**	14 c. black	5 0	6 0
		a. Imperf. (pair)	£15	
217	**115**	15 c. claret	5 0	4 0
		a. Imperf. (pair)	£20	
		b. Perf. 14 (line)	25 0	£5

218 **116** 20 c. green 3 6 4 0
a. Imperf. (pair) £12
b. Perf. 14 (line) £10
219 **117** 25 c. slate 4 0 6 0
a. Imperf. (pair) £10
b. Perf. 14 (line) 75 0 85 0
ba. Imp. betwn. (vert. pr.) .. £35
220 **118** 30 c. ultramarine .. 50 0 60 0
a. Imperf. (pair) .. £35
b. Imp. between (vert. pr.)
c. Perf. 14 (line) £35

For similar stamps perf. 12½ see Nos. 276/289.

TRANS-ATLANTIC
WEST TO EAST
Per Dornier DO-X
May, 1932.
One Dollar and Fifty Cents

(119)

1932. *Air. Surch. as T* **119**, *by Messrs. D.R. Thistle. W* **106**. *P* 14.

221 **105** $1.50 on $1 deep bue (R.) £45 £40
a. Surcharge inverted .. £850

120. Queen Mother, when Duchess of York.

121. Paper Mills.

122. Bell Island.

(Recess. Perkins Bacon.)

1932–38. *Wmk. T* **106** *(sideways on vert. designs). P* 13½ *(comb).*

222 **107** 1 c. grey 1 0 0 3
a. Imperf. (pair) .. £9
b. Perf. 14 (line) 50 0
c. P 14 (line) Small holes £6
d. Pr. with & without wmk.
223 **108** 2 c. green 1 6 0 3
a. Imperf. (pair) .. £9
b. Perf. 14 (line) 55 0
ba. Imp. btwn. (horiz. pair) £35
c. P 14 (line). Small holes 90 0
d. Pr. with & without wmk. £7
224 **110** 4 c. carmine 2 0 0 3
a. Imperf. (pair) £9
b. Perf. 14 (line) 22 6
ba. Imp. btwn. (vert. pr.) .. £20
225 **111** 5 c. violet (Die I) .. 10 0 1 0
a. Imperf. (pair) £9
b. P 14 (line). Small holes £10
c. Die II 2 6 0 4
ca. Imperf. (pair) £20
cb. Perf. 14 (line) £8
cc. Imp. btwn. (horiz. pair) £30
226 **120** 7 c. red-brown 3 0 5 0
b. Perf. 14 (line) .. ..
ba. Imp. btwn. (horiz. pair) £60
227 **121** 8 c. brownish red .. 2 6 1 3
a. Imperf. (pair) £10
228 **122** 24 c. bright blue 3 6 5 0
aa. Imperf. (pair) £22
ab. Doubly-printed .. £150
228*a* **118** 48 c. red-brown (1.1.38) .. 7 6 6 0
b. Imperf. (pair) £10

No. 223. Two dies exist of the 2 c. Die I was used for No. 210 and both dies for No. 223. The differences, though numerous, are very slight.

No. 225. There are also two dies of the 5 c., Die I only being used for No. 213 and both dies for the violet stamp. In Die II the antler pointing to the "T" of "POSTAGE" is taller than the one pointing to the "S" and the individual hairs on the underside of the caribou's tail are distinct.

For similar stamps perf. 12½ see Nos. 276/289.

L. & S. Post.

(123) "L. & S."—Land and Sea.

1933 (9 Feb.). *Optd. with T* **123**, *by Messrs. D. R. Thistle. W* **106** *sideways. P* 14.

229 **103** 15 c. chocolate 7 6 7 6
a. Pr. with & without wmk. 85 0
b. Opt. reading up .. £135

This overprint converted the air stamp into one for ordinary postal use.

124. Put to Flight.

125. Land of Hearts Delight.

126. Spotting the Herd

127. News from Home.

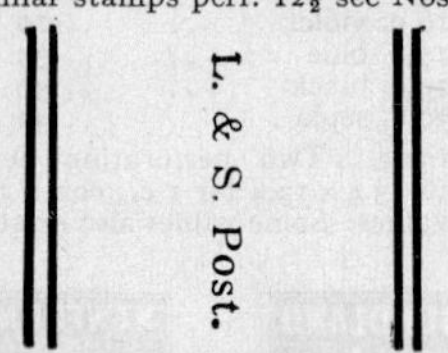

128. Labrador.

(Recess. Perkins, Bacon.)

1933 (31 May). *Air. W* **106.** *P* 14 (*a*) *or* 11½ (*b*).

230	**124**	5 c. red-brown (*a*)	.. 12 6	15 0
		a. Imperf. (pair) ..	.. £30	
		b. Imperf. between (pair) ..	£125	
231	**125**	10 c. orange-yellow (*b*)	.. 12 6	20 0
		a. Imperf. (pair) ..	.. £30	
232	**126**	30 c. light blue (*a*)	.. 40 0	50 0
		a. Imperf. (pair) ..	.. £70	
233	**127**	60 c. green (*b*)	.. 60 0	75 0
		a. Imperf. (pair) ..	.. £65	
234	**128**	75 c. yellow-brown (*a*)	.. 60 0	75 0
		a. Imperf. (pair) ..	.. £35	

1933

GEN. BALBO
FLIGHT.
$4.50
(**129**)

(Surch. by Robinson & Co., St. John's.)

1933 (24 July). *Air. Balbo Transatlantic Mass Formation Flight. Surch. with T* **129.** *Wmk.* **106.** *P* 14.

235	**128**	$4.50 on 75 c. yellow-brown	£75	£65
		a. Surch. inverted ..	..	
		b. Surch. on 10 c. orange-yellow (No. 231) ..	.. —	

130. Sir Humphrey Gilbert.

131. Compton Castle, Devon.

132. Gilbert Coat-of-Arms.

133. Eton College.

134. Anchor Token.

135. Gilbert commissioned by Elizabeth.

136. Fleet leaving Plymouth, 1583.

137. Arrival at St. John's.

138. Annexation, 5th August, 1583.

139. Royal Arms.

140. Gilbert in the *Squirrel*.

141. Map of Newfoundland.

142. Queen Elizabeth.

143. Gilbert's statue at Truro.

(Recess. Perkins, Bacon.)

1933 (3 Aug.). *350th Anniv. of the Annexation by Sir Humphrey Gilbert.* *W* **106.** *P* 13½ (*comb.*)*

No.	Type	Description	Unused	Used
236	**130**	1 c. slate	1 0	0 8
		a. Imperf. (pair)	£6	
237	**131**	2 c. green	1 0	1 0
		a. Imperf. (pair)	£8	
		b. Doubly printed	£100	
238	**132**	3 c. chestnut	1 3	1 3
239	**133**	4 c. carmine	1 9	0 9
		a. Imperf. (pair)	£8	
240	**134**	5 c. violet	3 6	3 0
241	**135**	7 c. greenish blue	14 0	20 0
		a. Perf. 14	50 0	75 0
242	**136**	8 c. vermilion	8 0	10 6
		a. Brownish red	£150	
		b. Bisected (4 c.) on cover	†	£35
243	**137**	9 c. ultramarine	8 0	10 6
		a. Imperf. (pair)	£20	
		b. Perf. 14	35 0	50 0
244	**138**	10 c. brown-lake	8 0	7 6
		a. Imperf. (pair)	£35	
		b. Perf. 14	£5	£5
245	**139**	14 c. grey-black	25 0	17 6
		a. Perf. 14	35 0	50 0
246	**140**	15 c. claret	25 0	20 0
247	**141**	20 c. grey-green	22 6	22 6
		a. Perf. 14	40 0	55 0
248	**142**	24 c. marone	50 0	55 0
		a. Imperf. (pair)	£25	
		b. Perf. 14	£5	£7
249	**143**	32 c. olive-black	60 0	65 0
		a. Perf. 14	£6	£8

**Perforations.* Two perforating heads were used: comb. 13.4 × 13.4 for all values; line 13.8 (listed above as 14) for a second printing of some values.

1935 (6 May). *Silver Jubilee. As Nos.* 91/4 *of Antigua, but ptd. by B. W. & Co.* *P* 11 × 12.

No.	Description	Unused	Used
250	4 c. rosine	1 0	0 10
251	5 c. bright violet	2 6	2 0
252	7 c. blue	3 0	3 6
253	24 c. olive-green	5 0	6 0

1937 (12 May). *Coronation Issue. As Nos.* 13/15 *of Aden but name and value uncoloured on coloured background and ptd. by B. W. & Co.* *P* 11 × 11½.

No.	Description	Unused	Used
254	2 c. green	0 4	0 6
255	4 c. carmine	1 0	0 8
256	5 c. purple	1 9	1 6

144. Codfish.

145. Map of Newfoundland.

146. Caribou.

147. Corner Brook Paper Mills.

148. Salmon.

149. Newfoundland Dog.

150. Northern Seal.

151. Cape Race.

152. Bell Island.

153. Sealing Fleet.

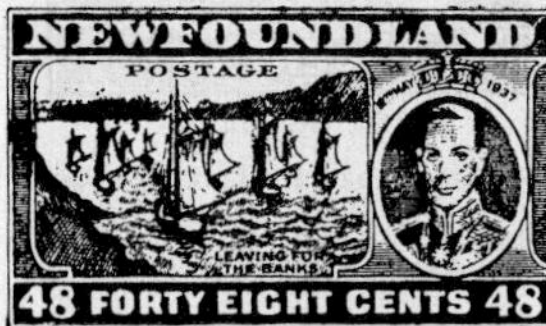

154. The Banks Fishing Fleet.

Die I. Die II.

(Recess. Perkins, Bacon.)

1937 (12 May). *Additional Coronation Issue. T* **144** *to* **154.** *W* **106.** A. *P* 14 *or* 13½ (*line*). B. *P* 13 (*comb.*)

No.			A.		B.	
257	1 c.	grey ..	0 6	0 6	£10	£12
		a. Pair with & without wmk. ..	60 0			†
258	3 c.	orge.-brn. (I)	2 6	1 6	2 0	2 6
		a. Pair with & without wmk. ..	£7			†
		b. Die I. Imp. btwn. (horiz. or vert. pr.)	£50			†
		c. Die II. ..	1 6	2 6	1 0	1 3
		d. Die II. Imp. btwn. (horiz. or vert. pr.)	£80			†
259	7 c.	brt. ultram.	1 0	1 6	£30	
		a. Pair with & without wmk. ..	—	—		†
260	8 c.	scarlet ..	2 6	3 0	5 0	6 0
		a. Pair with & without wmk. ..	£10			†
		b. Imperf. btwn. (horiz. or vert. pr.) ..	£110			†
		c. Imperf. (pair) ..	£25			
261	10 c.	deep olive ..	1 6	2 0	5 0	6 0
		a. Pair with & without wmk. ..	£9			†
262	14 c.	black ..	2 6	3 0	—	£200
		a. Pair with & without wmk. ..	£7			†
263	15 c.	claret ..	1 9	3 0	4 0	5 0
		a. Pair with & without wmk. ..	£7		—	—
		b. Imp. between (vert. pr.) ..	£50			†
264	20 c.	green ..	2 0	2 6	4 0	8 0
		a. Pair with & without wmk. ..	£15			†
		b. Imp. between (vert. pair) ..	£85			†
265	24 c.	light blue ..	2 6	3 6	7 6	17 6
		a. Pair with & without wmk. ..	£14			†
		b. Imp. between (vert. pair) ..	£110			†
266	25 c.	slate ..	3 0	4 0	£5	£5
		a. Pair with & without wmk. ..	£8			†
267	48 c.	slate-purple	5 0	6 0	60 0	80 0
		a. Pair with & without wmk. ..	£15			†
		b. Imp. between (vert. pair) ..	£95			†

See note after No. 197 re the watermark varieties.

The line perforation "A" was produced by two machines measuring respectively 13.7 and 14.1. The comb perforation "B" measures 13.3 × 13.2.

No. 258. In Die II the shading of the King's face is heavier and dots have been added down the ridge of the nose. The top frame line is thicker and more uniform.

155. King George VI.

156. Queen Mother.

157. Queen Elizabeth II as Princess.

158. Queen Mary.

(Recess. Perkins, Bacon & Co.)

1938 (12 May). *W* **106** (*sideways*). *P* 13½ (*comb.*).

No.	Type				
268	**155**	2 c.	green	1 6	0 3
			a. Pair, with and without wmk.	£40	
			b. Imperf. (pair)	£25	
269	**156**	3 c.	carmine	2 0	0 3
			a. Perf. 14 (*line*) ..	£50	£25
			b. Pair with and without wmk.	£40	
			c. Imperf. (pair)	£25	
270	**157**	4 c.	light blue	3 0	0 4
			a. Pair, with and without wmk.	£25	
			b. Imperf. (pair)	£30	
271	**158**	7 c.	deep ultramarine ..	2 0	5 0
			a. Imperf. (pair)	£25	

For similar designs, perf. 12½, see Nos. 277/281.

159. King George VI and Queen Elizabeth.

(Recess. Bradbury, Wilkinson & Co.)

1939 (17 JUNE). *Royal Visit. No wmk.* P 13½.

272	**159**	5 c. deep ultramarine ..	3 0	3 6

▲ CENTS ▲

(**160**)

1939 (20 Nov.). *No. 272 surch. as T* **160.**

273	**159**	2 c. on 5 c. dp. ultram (Br.)	2 6	2 6
274	,,	4 c. on 5 c. dp. ultram. (C.)	2 0	2 0

161. Grenfell on the *Strathcona.*

(Recess. Canadian Bank Note Co.)

1941 (1 DEC.). *Sir Wilfred Grenfell's Labrador Mission.* P 12.

275	**161**	5 c. blue	1 0	2 0

(Recess. Waterlow & Sons.)

1941–44. *W* **106** *(sideways on vert. designs).* P 12½.

276	**107**	1 c. grey	0 3	0 3
277	**155**	2 c. green	0 3	0 3
278	**156**	3 c. carmine	0 6	0 3
		a. Pair, with and without wmk.	£17	
279	**157**	4 c. blue	3 0	1 0
		a. Pair, with and without wmk.	£40	
280	**111**	5 c. violet (Die I) ..	2 6	0 6
		a. Pair, with and without wmk.		
281	**158**	7 c. deep ultramarine ..	4 0	4 0
		a. Pair, with and without wmk.	£35	
282	**121**	8 c. rose-red	2 6	2 6
		a. Pair, with and without wmk.	£40	
283	**113**	10 c. black-brown ..	2 0	1 6
284	**114**	14 c. black	3 0	3 6
285	**115**	15 c. claret	5 0	4 0
286	**116**	20 c. green	4 0	4 0
287	**122**	24 c. blue	4 6	5 0
288	**117**	25 c. slate	6 0	6 0
289	**118**	48 c. red-brown ('44) ..	7 0	7 0

Nos. 277/8 are redrawn versions of T **155/6.**
No. 280. For Die I see note relating to No. 225.

162. Memorial University College.

(Recess. Canadian Bank Note Co.)

1943 (2 JAN.). P 12.

290	**162**	30 c. carmine	4 6	3 6

163. St. John's.

(Recess. Canadian Bank Note Co.)

1943 (1 JUNE). *Air.* P 12.

291	**163**	7 c. ultramarine	1 6	1 6

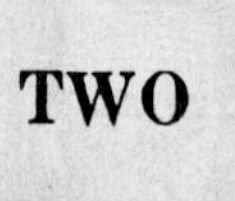

TWO

CENTS

(**164**)

165. Queen Elizabeth II when Princess.

1946 (23 MAR.). *No.* 290 *surch. with T* **164.**

292	**162**	2 c. on 30 c. carmine ..	0 9	2 0

(Recess. Waterlow & Sons.)

1947 (21 APR.). *Princess Elizabeth's 21st Birthday. W* **106** *(sideways).* P 12½.

293	**165**	4 c. light blue	1 0	1 0

166. Cabot off Cape Bonavista.

(Recess. Waterlow & Sons.)

1947 (23 JUNE). *450th Anniv. of Cabot's Discovery of Newfoundland. W* **106** *(sideways)* P 12½.

294	**166**	5 c. mauve	0 10	0 10
		a. Imperf. between (horiz. pair)		

POSTAGE DUE STAMPS.

D 1

(Litho. John Dickinson & Co., Ltd.)

1939 (1 MAY)–**49.** *P* 10.

D1	D 1	1 c. green	1 6	2 0
		a. Perf. 11 ('49)	30 0	
D2	,,	2 c. vermilion	2 6	5 0
		a. Perf. 11×9 ('46) ..	12 6	17 6
D3	,,	3 c. ultramarine	1 0	1 6
		a. Perf. 11×9 ('49) ..	17 6	
D4	,,	4 c. orange	1 0	1 6
		a. Perf. 11×9 (May '48) ..	15 0	20 0
D5	,,	5 c. brown	1 0	1 6
D6	,,	10 c. violet	2 6	6 0
		a. Perf. 11 (W 106) ('49) ..	27 6	
		ab. As last, imp. btwn. (vert. pr.)	£32	

On 1 April, 1949, Newfoundland joined the Confederation of Canada whose stamps it now uses.

NEW GUINEA.

(LATE NEW BRITAIN.)

G.R.I. 2d. (1)   G.R.I. 1s. (2)

STAMPS OF GERMAN NEW GUINEA.

Measurements are taken from the bottom of the "R" to the top of the "d" in the low values, or to the top of the figure of value in the large stamps.

Stamps of 1900, *German Colonial issue (no wmk.), surcharged as T* **1** *or* **2** *(mark values).*

FIRST PRINTING.

1914 (17 OCT.). "G.R.I." *and value* 6 *mm. apart.*

1	1d. on 3 pf. brown	£6	£6
2	1d. on 5 pf. green	30 0	30 0
3	2d. on 10 pf. carmine.. ..	60 0	60 0
4	2d. on 20 pf. ultramarine ..	60 0	60 0
	a. "2d." doubly printed without the "G.R.I."	£75	
5	2½d. on 10 pf. carmine.. ..	£6	£6
6	2½d. on 20 pf. ultramarine ..	£8	£8
7	3d. on 25 pf. blk. & red/*yell*..	£12	£12
8	3d. on 30 pf. blk. & oran./*buff*	£15	£15
9	4d. on 40 pf. blk. & carmine ..	£25	£25
	a. Surcharge double	£100	£100
	b. Surcharge inverted		
10	5d. on 50 pf. blk. & pur./*buff* ..	£40	£40
11	8d. on 80 pf. blk. & carm./*rose*	£60	£60
	a. No stop		

"G.R.I." *and value* 3½ *to* 4 *mm. apart.*

12	1s. on 1 m. carmine	£100	£100
13	2s. on 2 m. blue	£100	£100
14	3s. on 3 m. violet-black ..	£125	£125
15	5s. on 5 m. carmine and black	£325	£325
	a. No stop after "I"		
	b. No stops after "R" and "I" ..	£375	

SECOND PRINTING.

1914 (16 DEC.). "G.R.I." *and value* 5 *mm. apart.*

16	1d. on 3 pf. brown	90 0	90 0
	a. Figure "1" omitted	—	£40
	b. Surcharge double	£20	
	c. Surcharge inverted	£20	
17	1d. on 5 pf. green	25 0	25 0
	a. "d" inverted	£60	£60
	b. No stops after "G R I" ..	£15	£10
	c. Surcharge double	£40	
	d. Small "I"	50 0	50 0
	e. "1d." double..	£20	
	f. "G.I.R." for "G.R.I." ..	£200	
18	2d. on 10 pf. carmine.. ..	60 0	60 0
	a. Surcharge double	£50	
	b. Surcharge double, one inverted..	£125	£125
	c. Error. Surcharged "G.I.R. 3d."	£600	
	d. Stop before instead of after "G"		
	e. Error. "1d." for "2d." and stop before "G"	£150	£125
19	2d. on 20 pf. ultramarine ..	60 0	60 0
	a. "R" inverted	£150	£150
	b. Surcharge double	£100	
	c. Surcharge double, one inverted..	£125	£125
	d. Error. Surch. "G.R.I. 1d." ..	£300	£300
20	2½d. on 10 pf. carmine.. ..	£8	£8
21	2½d. on 20 pf. ultramarine ..	£150	£150
	a. Surcharge double, one inverted		
22	3d. on 25 pf. black & red/*yellow*	£10	£10
	a. "G.I.R." for "G.R.I." ..	£150	
23	3d. on 30 pf. blk. & orge./*buff*	£12	£12
	a. "d" inverted	—	£80
	b. Surcharge double	£100	
	c. Surcharge double, one inverted..	£125	
	d. Error. "1d." for "3d." ..	£350	
24	4d. on 40 pf. blk. & carmine ..	£8	£8
	a. Surcharge double, one inverted..	£125	
25	5d. on 50 pf. blk. & pur./*buff* ..	£20	£20
	a. Figure "5" omitted		
	b. Surcharge double		
	c. Surcharge double, one inverted..		
	d. "G.I R." for "G.R.I."		
26	8d. on 80 pf. blk. & carm./*rose*	£50	£50
	a. Surcharge double, one inverted..	£150	£150
	b. Surcharge double	£140	£140
	c. Triple surcharge	£140	£140

"G.R.I." *and value* 5½ *mm. apart.*

27	1s. on 1 m. carmine	£125	£125
28	2s. on 2 m. blue	£120	£120
	a. Surcharge double		
29	3s. on 3 m. violet-black ..	£200	£200
30	5s. on 5 m. carm. and black..	£400	£400

There appears to be also a third printing of most of the low values with 7½ mm. between "G.R.I." and top of the "d".

1915. *Nos.* 18 *and* 19 *further surch. as in T* **5.**

30*a* "1" on 2d. on 10 pf.
30*b* "1" on 2d. on 20 pf.

3

Registration Label, T **3,** *surch. and used for postage.*

3d. black and red/*buff.*

I. *With name of town in sans-serif letters and* "(Deutsch Neuguinea)".

31	Rabaul	£8	£8
	a. "G.R.I. 3d." double	£40	
	b. No bracket before "Deutsch" ..		
	c. Hyphen between "Deutsch" and "Neuguinea"	£10	
	d. No stop after "I"		
32	Herbertshöhe	£8	£8
	a. "(Deutsch Neu-Guinea)" ..	£15	
33	Kieta (hyphen btwn. "Deutsch" and "Neuguinea")	£20	£20
34	Käwieng (ditto)	£8	
	a. Without brackets	—	£20
	b. "Deutsch Neu-Guinea"		
35	Manus	£50	£50
	a. "G.R.I. 3d." double		

II. *With name of town in letters with serifs and* " (Deutsch-Neuguinea) " *hyphenated.*

36 Friedrich Wilhelmshafen .. £10 £10
 a. No hyphen £25
37 Käwieng (no hyphen between " Deutsch " and " Neu-guinea ") £10 £10
38 Manus £125 £125

SERVICE STAMPS.

O. S.

G.R.I.

1d.

(4)

SPECIAL PRINTING.

" G.R.I." *and value* 3½ *mm. apart.* *Overprinted as* T **4**.

40 1d. on 3 pf. brown 8 0 8 0
41 1d. on 5 pf. green 25 0 25 0

II. STAMPS OF MARSHALL ISLANDS.

1914 (16 DEC.). *Stamps of German Colonial issue surch. as* T **1** *and* **2** (*mark values*).

" G.R.I." *and value* 5 *mm. apart.*

50 1d. on 3 pf. brown 60 0 60 0
 a. " 1 " with straight serif .. £10
 b. Surcharge inverted £100
51 1d. on 5 pf. green 60 0 60 0
 a. No stop after " d " .. ..
 b. " 1 " and " d " wider apart ..
52 2d. on 10 pf. carmine.. .. 17 6 17 6
 a. No stop after " G " .. ..
 b. Surcharge double £75
 c. Surcharge double, one inverted £100
53 2d. on 20 pf. ultramarine .. 25 0 25 0
 a. No stop after " d " £5
 b. Surcharge double
 c. Surcharge double, one inverted.. £100
54 3d. on 25 pf. black and red/*yell.* £30 £30
 a. No stop after " d " £75 £75
 b. Surcharge double £90 £90
 c. Surcharge double, one inverted..
55 3d. on 30 pf. blk. & orge./*buff* £30 £30
 a. No stop after " d " £80
56 4d. on 40 pf. blk. & carmine.. £6 £8
 a. No stop after " d " £20 £20
 b. Surcharge inverted £100
57 5d. on 50 pf. blk. & purple/*buff* £10 £15
 a. " 5 " only for " 5d." ..
58 8d. on 80 pf. blk. & carm./*rose* £35 £35
59 1s. on 1 m. carmine £85 £85
 a. No stop after " I " .. ..
 b. Surcharge double .. ..
60 2s. on 2 m. blue £50 £50
 a. Surcharge double, one inverted.. — £200
 b. Large " S " after " 2 "
61 3s. on 3 m. violet-black .. £225 £225
 a. Surcharge double .. ..
 b. No stop after " I " .. ..
62 5s. on 5 m. carmine & black £400 £400
 a. Surcharge double, one inverted.. £600 £600

G.R.I.

1d.

(5)

1915. *Nos.* 52 *and* 53 *further surch. as in* T **5**.

63 " 1 " on 2d. on 10 pf. .. £15 £15
64 " 1 " on 2d. on 20 pf. .. £450 £300

III. AUSTRALIAN STAMPS OVERPRINTED.

N. W. PACIFIC ISLANDS. 6 (*a*)

N. W. PACIFIC ISLANDS. (*b*)

N. W. PACIFIC ISLANDS. (*c*)

8

10

11

1915–16. *Stamps of Australia optd. in black as* T **6** (*a*), (*b*) *or* (*c*).

(i) T **5***a* (*King*). W **8**. P 14. (15 March, 1915).

65 ½d. green 1 6 2 0
66 ½d. bright green 1 3 2 0
67 1d. pale rose (Die I) 2 0 2 6
68 1d. dull red (Die I) 2 6 3 0
69 1d. carmine-red (Die I) .. 2 0 2 6
 a. Top of crown missing (*a*) .. — £12
69*b* 1d. carmine-red (Die II) .. 40 0
 c. Top of crown missing (*a*) .. £15
70 4d. yellow-orange 4 0 6 6
 a. Line through " FOURPENCE " 60 0 70 0
71 4d. yellow £15 £18
72 5d. brown 6 0 9 0

(ii) T **1** (*Kangaroo*). W **10**. P 12. (15 March, 1915)

73 2d. grey 4 0 6 6
74 2½d. indigo 4 0 6 6
76 3d. yellow-olive 10 0 12 6
77 3d. greenish olive £15
78 6d. ultramarine 17 6 22 6
79 9d. violet 25 0 40 0
81 1s. green 35 0 50 0
83 5s. grey and yellow £40
84 10s. grey and pink .. .. £7 £
85 £1 brown and ultramarine .. £18 £2

(iii). T **1**. W **8**. P 12. (Oct.-Dec. 1915).

86 2d. grey 6 0
87 2½d. indigo £150
88 6d. ultramarine 5 0 6
89 9d. violet 5 0 6
90 1s. emerald 8 6 12
91 2s. brown 60 0 70
92 5s. grey and yellow 70 0 80

(iv). T **1**. W **11**. P 12. (Dec. 1915–Aug. 1916)

94 2d. grey 4 0 5
96 3d. yellow-olive 8 6 10
97 2s. brown 25 0 30
99 £1 brown and ultramarine .. £15 £1

SETTINGS. The overprint T **6** shows three main varieties differing in the letters " S " of " ISLANDS ". (*a*) Both " S S " normal. (*b*) First " S " with small head and large tail and second " S " normal. (*c*) Both " S S " with small head and large tail.

Mr. J. R. W. Purves has established, by the study of minor variations, that there are actually five settings of the overprint, including that represented by T **11***b*, but the following are the different arrangements of the letters " S ", taking these above into account.

A. Horizontal rows 1 and 2 all Type (*a*) Row 3 all Type (*b*). Rows 4 and 5 all Type (*c*).

B. (½d. green, only). As A, except that the types in the bottom row run (*c*) (*c*) (*c*) (*b*) (*c*).

C. As A, but bottom row now shows types (*a*) (*c*) (*c*) (*c*) (*b*) (*c*).

Horizontal strips and pairs showing varieties (*a*) and (*c*), or (*b*) and (*c*) *se tenant* are scarce.

The earliest printing of the 1d. and 2½d. values was made on sheets with margin attached on two sides, the later printings being on sheets from which the margins had been removed. In this printing the vertical distances between the overprints are less than in later printings, so that in the lower horizontal rows of the sheet the overprint is near the top of the stamp.

The settings used on King George stamps and on the Kangaroo type are similar, but the latter stamps being smaller the overprints are closer together in the vertical rows.

PURPLE OVERPRINTS. We no longer differentiate between purple and black overprints in the above series. In our opinion the two colours are nowadays insufficiently distinct to warrant separation.

PRICES. The prices quoted for Nos. 65 to 101 apply to stamps with opts., Types **6** (*a*) or **6** (*c*). Stamps with opt. Type **6** (*b*) are worth double. Vertical strips of three, showing (*a*), (*b*) and (*c*), can be supplied if in stock, at about five times the prices quoted for singles.

One Penny

(11*a*)

1918. *Nos. 72 and 81 surch. locally with T* **11*a*.**

100 1d. on 5d. brown £6 £5
101 1d. on 1s. green £6 £5

Types **6** (*a*), (*b*), (*c*) occur on these stamps also.

N. W. PACIFIC ISLANDS.

(11*b*)

1919–23. *Stamps of Australia, optd. with T* **11*b*** *(" P " of " PACIFIC " over space between " I " and " S " of " ISLANDS ").*

(i) *T* **5*a*** *(King).* *W* **8.** *P* 14.

102 ½d. green 1 0 1 3
103 1d. carmine-red (Die I) .. 1 6 2 0
a. Top of crown missing.. .. £7
b. Rosine. Rough paper, locally gummed (perfd. " O S ") .. £30
103*c* 1d. carmine-red (Die II) .. 35 0 40 0
d. Top of crown missing .. £12
e. Rosine. Rough paper, locally gummed (perfd. " O S ") .. £35
104 4d. yellow-orange 7 6 10 0
a. Line through " FOUR PENCE " .. .. ..
105 5d. brown 6 0 10 0

(ii) *T* **1** *(Kangaroo).* *W* **11.** *P* 12.

106 2d. grey 5 0 6 0
107 2½d. indigo 6 6 8 0
a. " 1 " of " ½ " omitted .. £110
108 2½d. blue (1922) 5 0 6 6
109 3d. greenish olive 5 0 6 6
110 6d. ultramarine 7 0 10 0
111 6d. greyish ultram. (1923) .. 15 0 20 0
112 9d. violet 15 0 17 6
113 1s. emerald 12 6 17 6
114 1s. pale blue-green 17 6 22 6
115 2s. brown 25 0 35 0
116 5s. grey and yellow 40 0 55 0
117 10s. grey and bright pink .. £6 £8
118 £1 brown and ultramarine.. £30

(iii) *T* **5*a***. *W* **6*a*** *of Australia. (Mult. Crown " A ").* *P* 14.

119 ½d. green 1 0 1 6

Type **11***b* differs from Type **6** (*a*) in the position of the " P " of " PACIFIC ", which is further to the left in Type **11***b*.

1921–22. T **5***a* *of Australia.* *W* **8**. *Colour changes and new value. Optd. with T* **11*b*.**

120 1d. bright violet 3 6 6 0
121 2d. orange 6 0 7 0
122 2d. scarlet 5 0 25 0
123 4d. violet 17 6 30 0
a. " FOURPENCE " in thinner letters £25
124 4d. ultramarine 25 0 35 0
a. " FOURPENCE " in thinner letters £22

IV. TERRITORY OF NEW GUINEA.

PRINTERS. See note at the beginning of Australia.

12. Native village.

(Recess. Note Printing Branch, Commonwealth Bank of Australia, Melbourne, from 1926 Note Ptg. Branch, Reserve Bank of Australia, Melbourne.)

1925–28. *T* **12.** *P* 11.

125 ½d. orange 2 0 2 6
126 1d. green 2 6 2 6
126*a* 1½d. orange-vermilion (1926) 2 6 2 0
127 2d. claret 3 0 2 6
128 3d. blue 6 0 4 0
129 4d. olive-green 8 6 7 6
130 6d. dull yellow-brown .. 10 0 17 6
130*a* 6d olive-bistre (1927) .. 9 0 12 6
130*b* 6d. pale yellow-bistre ('28) 12 6 15 0
131 9d. dull purple (to violet) .. 12 6 15 0
132 1s. dull blue-green .. 15 0 17 6
133 2s. brown-lake 22 6 27 6
134 5s. olive-bistre 40 0 45 0
135 10s. dull rose 65 0 70 0
136 £1 dull olive-green .. £7 £8

(13)

1931 (8 JUNE). *Air.* *T* **12** *overprinted with T* **13.** *P* 11.

137 ½d. orange 1 0 1 9

No.	Description	Unused	Used
138	1d. green	1 3	2 6
139	1½d. orange-vermilion ..	2 6	6 0
140	2d. claret	3 0	7 6
141	3d. blue	5 0	6 0
142	4d. olive-green	4 6	7 0
143	6d. pale yellow-bistre ..	5 0	8 0
144	9d. violet	6 0	12 6
145	1s. dull blue-green	8 0	12 6
146	2s. brown-lake	15 0	22 6
147	5s. olive-bistre	30 0	40 0
148	10s. bright pink	55 0	70 0
149	£1 olive-grey	£7	£8

AIR MAIL

14. Bird of Paradise. (Dates either side of value).

(15)

(Recess-printed by J. Ash, Melbourne.)

1931 (2 Aug.). *Tenth Anniv. of Australian Administration.* **T 14** *(with dates).* P 11.

No.	Description	Unused	Used
150	1d. green	1 3	1 9
151	1½d. vermilion	2 6	2 6
152	2d. claret	2 0	1 6
153	3d. blue	2 6	2 6
154	4d. olive-green	5 0	6 0
155	5d. deep blue-green ..	7 0	7 0
156	6d. bistre-brown	5 0	7 0
157	9d. violet	7 6	10 0
158	1s. pale blue-green ..	8 0	12 6
159	2s. brown-lake	10 0	17 6
160	5s. olive-brown	25 0	30 0
161	10s. bright pink	70 0	75 0
162	£1 olive-grey	£8	£8

1931 (2 Aug.). *Air.* **T 14** *optd. with* **T 15.**

No.	Description	Unused	Used
163	½d. orange	1 0	1 3
164	1d. green	1 3	1 3
165	1½d. vermilion	2 0	2 6
166	2d. claret	2 0	3 3
167	3d. blue	3 9	3 9
168	4d. olive-green	3 9	5 0
169	5d. deep blue-green ..	6 6	9 6
170	6d. bistre-brown	6 6	7 6
171	9d. violet	9 6	16 0
172	1s. pale blue-green ..	10 0	15 0
173	2s. dull lake	16 0	22 6
174	5s. olive-brown	25 0	30 0
175	10s. bright pink	95 0	95 0
176	£1 olive-grey	£10	£10

1932 (30 June)–**1934.** **T 14** *(redrawn without dates).* P 11.

No.	Description	Unused	Used
177	1d. green	1 0	1 0
178	1½d. claret	2 0	2 0
179	2d. vermilion	1 3	1 3
179a	2½d. green (14.9.34) ..	4 6	6 0
180	3d. blue	1 9	1 9
180a	3½d. aniline carm. (14.9.34) ..	7 6	8 6
181	4d. olive-green	2 0	2 6
182	5d. deep blue-green ..	2 6	2 3
183	6d. bistre-brown	2 6	4 6
184	9d. violet	7 6	12 6
185	1s. blue-green	7 6	10 0
186	2s. dull lake	10 0	12 6
187	5s. olive	30 0	35 0
188	10s. pink	£6	£6
189	£1 olive-grey	£7	90 0

1932 (30 June)–**34.** *Air.* **T 14** *(redrawn without dates), optd. with* **T 15.** P 11.

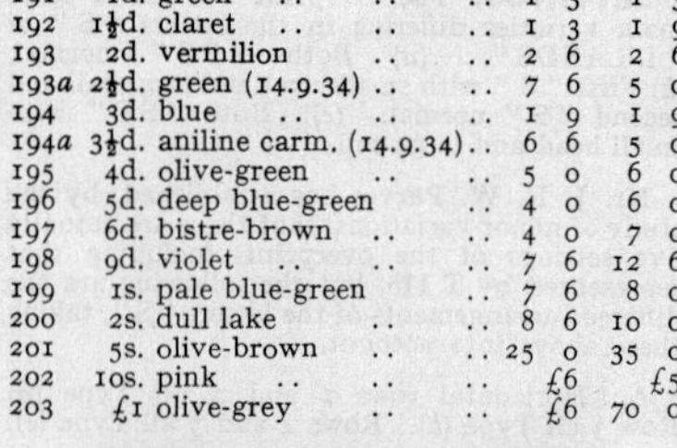

No.	Description	Unused	Used
190	½d. orange	0 8	1 0
191	1d. green	1 3	1 3
192	1½d. claret	1 3	1 9
193	2d. vermilion	2 6	2 6
193a	2½d. green (14.9.34) ..	7 6	5 0
194	3d. blue	1 9	1 9
194a	3½d. aniline carm. (14.9.34) ..	6 6	5 0
195	4d. olive-green	5 0	6 0
196	5d. deep blue-green ..	4 0	6 0
197	6d. bistre-brown	4 0	7 0
198	9d. violet	7 6	12 6
199	1s. pale blue-green ..	7 6	8 0
200	2s. dull lake	8 6	10 0
201	5s. olive-brown	25 0	35 0
202	10s. pink	£6	£5
203	£1 olive-grey	£6	70 0

16. Bulolo Goldfields.

(Recess. John Ash.)

1935 (1 May). *Air.* P 11.

No.	Type	Description	Unused	Used
204	16	£2 bright violet	£12	£8
205	,,	£5 emerald-green	£40	£20

HIS MAJESTY'S
JUBILEE.
1910 — 1935

(17)

1935 (27 June). *Silver Jubilee. As Nos.* 177 *and* 179, *but shiny paper. Optd. with* **T 17.**

No.	Description	Unused	Used
206	1d. green	2 9	5 0
207	2d. vermilion	5 0	6 6

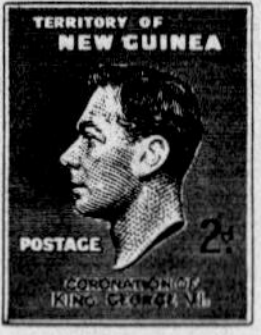

18

(Recess. John Ash, Melbourne.)

1937 (18 May). *Coronation.* P 11.

No.	Type	Description	Unused	Used
208	18	2d. scarlet	1 3	1 9
209	,,	3d. blue	0 11	1 3
210	,,	5d. green	1 3	1 9
		a. Re-entry (design completely duplicated) ..	95 0	£6
211	,,	1s. purple	2 6	3 6

(Recess. John Ash, Melbourne.)

1939 (1 Mar.). *Air. Inscr.* "AIR MAIL POSTAGE" *at foot.* P 11.

No.	Type	Description	Unused	Used
212	16	½d. orange	1 0	2 6
213	,,	1d. green	1 0	2 6
214	,,	1½d. claret	2 0	6 0
215	,,	2d. vermilion	4 0	6 0
216	,,	3d. blue	7 0	7 6
217	,,	4d. yellow-olive ..	5 0	8 6
218	,,	5d. deep green ..	7 0	6 6
219	,,	6d. bistre-brown ..	8 6	10 0
220	,,	9d. violet	10 0	17 6
221	,,	1s. pale blue-green ..	12 6	17 6
222	,,	2s. dull lake	27 6	35 0
223	,,	5s. olive-brown ..	60 0	70 0
224	,,	10s. pink	£8	£8
225	,,	£1 olive-green ..	£6	£10

OFFICIAL STAMPS.

Australian stamps perforated "O S" exist with overprint Type 6 for use in New Guinea. We do not list such varieties but can supply when in stock.

O S (O 1) O S (O 2)

1925-31. *Optd. with Type* O **1.** *P* 11.

O2	**12**	1d. green..	0 9	1 9
O2*a*	,,	1½d. orange-verm. ('31) ..	3 0	3 6
O3	,,	2d. claret..	1 0	1 6
O4	,,	3d. blue ..	0 9	1 3
O5	,,	4d. olive-green ..	2 0	2 6
O6	,,	6d. olive-bistre ..	4 0	10 0
O6*a*	,,	6d. pale yell.-bistre ('31)	6 0	10 0
O7	,,	9d. violet..	4 0	17 6
O8	,,	1s. dull blue-green ..	5 0	10 0
O9	,,	2s. brown-lake ..	7 6	20 0

1931 (2 Aug.). *Optd. with Type* O **2.** *P* 11.

O10	**14**	1d. green..	0 9	1 6
O11	,,	1½d. vermilion ..	0 9	1 6
O12	,,	2d. claret..	1 3	1 6
O13	,,	3d. blue ..	1 3	2 6
O14	,,	4d. olive-green ..	1 6	5 0
O15	,,	5d. deep blue-green ..	1 6	5 0
O16	,,	6d. bistre-brown ..	1 9	6 0
O17	,,	9d. violet..	3 6	10 0
O18	,,	1s. pale blue-green ..	5 0	12 6
O19	,,	2s. brown-lake ..	7 6	22 6
O20	,,	5s. olive-brown ..	30 0	45 0

1932 (30 June)–**1934.** *T* **14** (*redrawn without dates*), *optd. with Type* O **2.** *P* 11.

O21	1d. green ..	0 6	1 0
O22	1½d. claret ..	1 0	1 6
O23	2d. vermilion ..	1 0	1 6
O23*a*	2½d. green (14.9.34)..	2 0	3 0
O24	3d. blue ..	2 0	2 6
O24*a*	3½d. aniline carmine (14.9.34)	2 6	4 0
O25	4d. olive-green ..	2 0	4 0
O26	5d. deep blue-green ..	3 6	5 0
O27	6d. bistre-brown ..	3 6	6 0
O28	9d. violet ..	5 0	10 0
O29	1s. pale blue-green ..	6 0	10 0
O30	2s. dull lake ..	10 0	17 6
O31	5s. olive-brown ..	40 0	55 0

Civil Administration in New Guinea was suspended in 1942. On resumption, after the Japanese defeat in 1945, Australian stamps were used until the appearance of the issue for the combined territories of Papua & New Guinea (q.v.).

NEW HEBRIDES.

(ANGLO-FRENCH CONDOMINIUM.)

NEW HEBRIDES. NEW HEBRIDES

CONDOMINIUM. CONDOMINIUM

(1) (2)

1908-9. *T* **23** *and* **24** *of Fiji optd. with T* **1**, *in black; on the bicoloured stamps the word* "FIJI" *obliterated by a bar in the colour of the word. P* 14.

(*a*) *Wmk. Multiple Crown CA.*

1	½d. green & grey-green, O ('08)	2 0	4 6
2	1d. red, O ..	3 6	5 0
	a. Opt. omitted (in vert. pr. with normal) ..	£350	
3	1s. green & carmine, C (1909)	15 0	20 0

(*b*) *Wmk. Crown CA.*

4	½d. green and grey-green ('09)	17 6	20 0
5	2d. dull pur. and orange ..	3 0	3 0
6	2½d. dull pur. and blue/*blue* ..	2 6	2 6
7	5d. dull pur. and green ..	3 0	4 0
8	6d. dull pur. and carmine ..	3 0	4 0
9	1s. green and carmine.. ..	£10	£12

1911. *Types as last. Wmk. Multiple Crown CA. P* 14. *Optd. in London with T* **2.**

10	½d. green, O ..	3 0	8 6
11	1d. red, O ..	6 0	10 0
12	2d. grey, O ..	1 6	4 6
13	2½d. bright blue, O ..	2 0	4 6
14	5d. dull pur. & olive-grn., C ..	3 6	8 6
15	6d. dull and deep purple, C ..	4 6	6 0
16	1s. black/*green*, C (R.) ..	5 0	7 6

3

(Recess. De La Rue & Co.)

1911 (Aug.)–**1912.** *Wmk. Mult. Crown CA. P* 14.

18	**3**	½d. green ..	1 0	1 6
19	,,	1d. red ..	2 6	3 6
20	,,	2d. grey ..	2 6	4 6
21	,,	2½d. ultramarine ..	3 0	4 0
24	,,	5d. sage-green ..	4 6	5 0
25	,,	6d. purple ..	6 0	7 0
26	,,	1s. black/*green* ..	10 0	12 6
27	,,	2s. purple/*blue* (1912)	15 0	25 0
28	,,	5s. green/*yellow* (1912) ..	45 0	65 0

1d.

(4)

1920. *T* **3** *surch. with T* **4.**

30	1d. on 5d. sage-green ..	22 6	35 0
	a. Surch. inverted ..	£50	£50
31	1d. on 1s. black/*green* ..	7 6	15 0
32	1d. on 2s. purple/*blue*..	7 6	15 0
33	1d. on 5s. green/*yellow* ..	7 6	15 0

Stamps of French issue with similar surcharge.

(*a*) *Wmk. Mult. Crown CA.*

34	2d. on 40 c. red/*yellow* ..	12 6	30 0

(*b*) *Wmk.* "RF" *in sheet.*

35	2d. on 40 c. red/*yellow*	£14	£16

1921. *Wmk. Mult. Script CA. P* 14.

36	**3**	1d. scarlet ..	3 6	7 6
37	,,	2d. slate-grey ..	6 0	12 6
39	,,	6d. purple ..	10 0	15 0

1924. *Surch. as T* **4.**

40	**3**	1d. on ½d. green (No. 18) ..	3 0	10 0
41	,,	3d. on 1d. scarlet (No. 36) ..	5 0	10 0
42	,,	5d. on 2½d. ultram. (No. 21)	6 0	15 0
		a. Surch. inverted ..	£42	£45

5

(Recess. De La Rue.)

1925. *Wmk. Mult. Script CA.* P 14.

No.	Type	Description	s.	d.	s.	d.
43	**5**	½d. (5 c.) black	2	6	3	0
44	,,	1d. (10 c.) green	1	9	2	6
45	,,	2d. (20 c.) slate-grey ..	2	6	3	0
46	,,	2½d. (25 c.) brown	4	0	4	6
47	,,	5d. (50 c.) ultramarine ..	4	0	4	6
48	,,	6d. (60 c.) purple	7	6	10	0
49	,,	1s. (1.25 fr.) black/*emerald*	10	0	12	6
50	,,	2s. (2.50 fr.) purple/*blue* ..	15	0	25	0
51	,,	5s. (6.25 fr.) green/*yellow* ..	30	0	45	0

6. Lopevi Is. and Copra Canoe.

(Des. J. Kerhor. Recess. Bradbury, Wilkinson.)

1938 (1 June). *Wmk. Mult. Script CA.* P 12.

No.	Type	Description	s.	d.	s.	d.
52	**6**	5 c. blue-green	2	0	3	0
53	,,	10 c. orange	4	0	5	0
54	,,	15 c. bright violet	4	0	5	0
55	,,	20 c. scarlet	4	6	6	0
56	,,	25 c. reddish brown	4	6	6	0
57	,,	30 c. blue	4	6	7	6
58	,,	40 c. grey-olive	7	0	8	0
59	,,	50 c. purple	7	0	8	0
60	,,	1 f. red/*green*	17	6	17	6
61	,,	2 f. blue/*green*	22	6	22	6
62	,,	5 f. red/*yellow*	45	0	45	0
63	,,	10 f. violet/*blue*	75	0	75	0

(Recess. Waterlow.)

1949 (10 Oct.). *75th Anniv. of Universal Postal Union. As T* **21** *of Antigua, but inscribed* " NEW HEBRIDES ". *Wmk. Mult. Script CA.* P 13½–14.

No.	Description	s.	d.	s.	d.
64	10 c. red-orange	0	8	1	0
65	15 c. violet	1	0	1	0
66	30 c. ultramarine	1	9	3	6
67	50 c. purple	3	0	4	6

7. Outrigger Sailing Canoe.

8. Native carving.

9. Natives.

(Recess. Waterlow & Sons, Ltd.)

1953 (30 Apr.). *Wmk. Mult. Script CA.* P 12½.

No.	Type	Description	s.	d.	s.	d.
68	**7**	5 c. green	0	10	1	0
69	,,	10 c. scarlet	0	8	1	0
70	,,	15 c. yellow-ochre	0	9	1	6
71	,,	20 c. ultramarine	1	0	1	9
72	**8**	25 c. olive	1	9	1	3
73	,,	30 c. brown	2	6	2	6
74	,,	40 c. blackish brown ..	2	6	2	9
75	,,	50 c. violet	3	6	4	0
76	**9**	1 f. orange	6	0	5	0
77	,,	2 f. reddish purple ..	10	0	12	6
78	,,	5 f. scarlet	20	0	22	6

1953 (2 June). *Coronation. As No. 47 of Aden*

No.	Description	s.	d.	s.	d.
79	10 c. black and carmine ..	1	6	2	[illegible]

10. Sailing Ship and Map.

11. " Marianne " and " Britannia ".

(Photo. Harrison & Sons.)

1956 (20 Oct.). *Fiftieth Anniv. of Condominium. Wmk. Mult. Script CA.* P 14½ × 14.

No.	Type	Description	s.	d.	s.	d.
80	**10**	5 c. emerald	0	9	1	[illegible]
81	,,	10 c. scarlet	1	3	1	[illegible]
82	**11**	20 c. deep bright blue ..	2	6	3	[illegible]
83	,,	50 c. deep lilac	5	0	6	[illegible]

12. Port Vila: Iririki Islet.

13. River Scene and Spear Fisherman.

14. Native Woman drinking from Coconut.

Des. H. Cheffer (T **12**), P. Gandon (others). Recess. Waterlow & Sons.)

.957 (3 SEPT.). *Wmk. Mult. Script CA. P* 13½.

4 **12** 5 c. green 0 4 0 4
5 ,, 10 c. scarlet 0 7 0 10
6 ,, 15 c. yellow-ochre 1 0 1 3
7 ,, 20 c. ultramarine 1 0 1 2
8 **13** 25 c. olive 1 0 1 3
9 ,, 30 c. brown 2 0 2 6
o ,, 40 c. sepia 1 8 2 6
1 ,, 50 c. violet 2 6 3 6
2 **14** 1 f. orange 3 3 3 9
3 ,, 2 f. mauve 10 0 12 6
4 ,, 5 f. black 16 0 20 0

963 (2 SEPT.). *Freedom from Hunger. As No.* 63 *of Aden.*

5 60 c. green 3 0 3 6

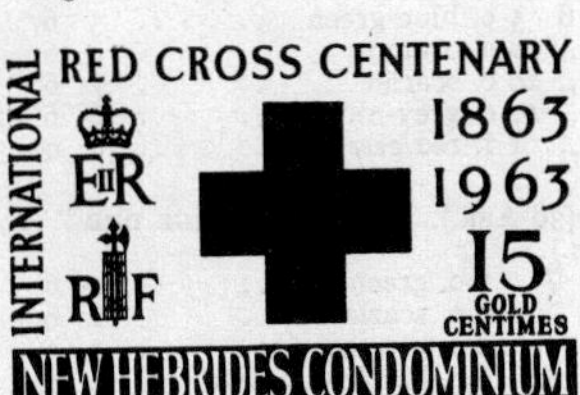

15. Red Cross Emblem.

Des. V. Whiteley. Litho. Bradbury, Wilkinson.)

963 (2 SEPT.). *Red Cross Centenary. W* w.**12.** *P* 13½.

5 **15** 15 c. red and black .. 1 0 1 3
7 ,, 45 c. red and blue 2 6 3 0

17. Cocoa Beans.

18. Copra.

19. Fishing from Pelikulo Point.

21. Nautilus.

22. Stingfish (*Pterois volitans*).

23. *Acanthurus lineatus* (fish).

25. Buff-bellied Flycatcher.

26. Thicket Warbler (*Cichlornis grosvenori*).

(Des. V. Whiteley, from drawings by J. White (10 c., 20 c.), K. Penny (40 c.), C. Robin (3 f.). Photo. Harrison. Des. J. White (15 c.), Larkins, Turrell and Thoma (30 c., 50 c., 2 f.). Recess. French National Printing Office.)

1963 (25 Nov.)–**65.** *W* w.**12** (10 *c.*, 20 *c.*, 40 *c.*, 3 *f.*) *or no wmk.* (*others*). *P* 14 (3 *f.*), 12½ (10 *c.*, 20 *c.*, 40 *c.*) *or* 13 (*others*).

99	**17**	10 c. light brown, buff and emerald (16.8.65) ..	0 6	0 9
100	**18**	15 c. yellow-bistre, red-brown and deep violet	0 8	0 10
101	**19**	20 c. black, olive-green and greenish blue (16.8.65)	0 10	1 2
103	**21**	30 c. chestnut, bistre and violet	1 3	1 8
104	**22**	40 c. vermilion and deep blue (16.8.65) ..	1 5	2 0
105	**23**	50 c. green, yellow and greenish blue ..	1 8	2 6
107	**25**	2 f. black, brown-purple and yellow-olive ..	6 6	8 0
108	**26**	3 f. deep violet, orange-brown, emerald and black (16.8.65) ..	9 6	12 6

28. I.T.U. Emblem.

(Des. M. Goaman. Litho. Enschedé.)

1965 (17 May). *I.T.U. Centenary. W* w.**12.** *P* 11×11½.

110	**28**	15 c. scarlet and drab ..	0 10	1 3
111	,,	60 c. blue and light red ..	2 3	3 0

29. I.C.Y. Emblem.

(Des. V. Whiteley. Litho. Harrison.)

1965 (24 Oct.). *International Co-operation Year. W* w.**12.** *P* 14½.

112	**29**	5 c. reddish purple and turquoise-green ..	0 7	0 10
113	,,	55 c. deep bluish green and lavender	2 9	3 6

30. Sir Winston Churchill, and St. Paul's Cathedral in Wartime.

(Des. Jennifer Toombs. Photo. Harrison.)

1966 (24 Jan.). *Churchill Commemoration. P* 14.

114	**30**	5 c. black, cerise, gold and new blue	0 7	0 10
115	,,	15 c. black, cerise, gold and deep green	1 0	1 6
116	,,	25 c. black, cerise, gold and brown	1 6	1 9
117	,,	30 c. black, cerise, gold and bluish violet ..	2 0	2 6

POSTAGE DUE STAMPS.

POSTAGE DUE

(D 1)

1925. *Optd. with Type* D **1.**

D1	**5**	1d. (10 c.) green	—	2 6
D2	,,	2d. (20 c.) slate-grey ..	—	2
D3	,,	3d. (30 c.) red	—	4
D4	,,	5d. (50 c.) ultramarine ..	—	5
D5	,,	10d. (1 fr.) carmine/*blue* ..	—	6

Set of 5 un., £10.

POSTAGE DUE

(D 2)

1938 (1 June). *Optd. with Type* D **2.**

D 6	**6**	5 c. blue-green	3 6	4
D 7	,,	10 c. orange	4 6	6
D 8	,,	20 c. scarlet	7 6	8
D 9	,,	40 c. grey-olive	12 6	15
D10	,,	1 f. red/*green*	30 0	35

1953 (30 Apr.). *Optd.* "POSTAGE DUE" (19×1 *mm.*).

D11	**7**	5 c. green	0 6	1
D12	,,	10 c. scarlet	1 0	2
D13	,,	20 c. ultramarine ..	1 3	2
D14	**8**	40 c. blackish brown ..	2 0	5
D15	**9**	1 f. orange	5 0	10

1957 (3 Sept.). *Optd.* "POSTAGE DUE" (19×1 *mm.*).

D16	**12**	5 c. green	0 4	0
D17	,,	10 c. scarlet	0 6	0
D18	,,	20 c. ultramarine ..	0 10	1
D19	**13**	40 c. sepia	1 5	2
D20	**14**	1 f. orange	3 3	5

NEW REPUBLIC, SOUTH AFRICA.

(The territory of this ephemeral State was part of Zululand, but was subsequently annexed to the South African Republic, as a new district, named Vrijheid. In January, 1903, the territory was annexed to the Colony of Natal.)

1

Printed with a rubber handstamp on paper bought in Europe and sent out ready gummed and perforated.

886 (JAN.)–1887. *T* 1. *Various dates indicating date of printing.* P 11½. (a) *Yellow paper.*

1d. black 9 JAN 86 .. .. ..
1d. violet 10 0 12 6
9 JAN 86 15 0 20 0 | 6 SEP 86 12 6
13 JAN 86 50 0 | 13 OCT 86 15 0 20 0
7 MAR 86 | 3 NOV 86
17 MAR 86 | 13 NOV 86
14 APR 86 | 24 NOV 86 17 6
24 APR 86 | 4 JAN 87
24 MAY 86 | 17 JAN 87
30 AUG 86 10 0 12 6 |
2d. violet 10 0 12 6
a. "d" omitted (13 OCT 86) ..
9 JAN 86 25 0 30 0 | 13 OCT 86 12 6 15 0
13 JAN 86 20 0 25 0 | 24 NOV 86 15 0 20 0
24 MAY 86 | 4 JAN 87
30 AUG 86 20 0 | 17 JAN 87
6 SEP 86 10 0 12 6 |
3d. violet 30 0 35 0
a. "d" omitted (13 OCT 86) ..
13 JAN 86 | 13 OCT 86 30 0 35 0
30 AUG 86 30 0 | 24 NOV 86 40 0 50 0
6 SEP 86 55 0 | 17 JAN 87
4d. violet 40 0
30 AUG 86 80 0 | 13 OCT 86 40 0
6 SEP 86 60 0
6d. violet 40 0 45 0
a. Double impression (30 AUG 86)
21 MAY 86 | 6 SEP 86 40 0
2 JUL 86 | 13 OCT 86 40 0 45 0
30 AUG 86 40 0
9d. violet 40 0
13 JAN 86 | 6 SEP 86 40 0
30 AUG 86 65 0 | 13 OCT 86 50 0
1s. violet 90 0
30 AUG 86 90 0 | 13 OCT 86 90 0
6 SEP 86 £6 |
1/s. violet 13 OCT 86 .. ..
1/6 violet 110 0
30 AUG 86 110 0 | 13 OCT 86 £9
6 SEP 86 130 0 | 26 NOV 86
1s. 6d violet 6 SEP 86
1s. 6. violet 13 OCT 86 .. £5
2s. violet 50 0
30 AUG 86 110 0 | 13 OCT 86 50 0
6 SEP 86 £6 |
2/6 violet £8
13 JAN 86 | 6 SEP 86 £8
19 AUG 86 | 13 OCT 86 £10
30 AUG 86

15 2s. 6d. violet
20 FEB 86 | 19 AUG 86
7 MAR 86
16 4s. violet 17 JAN 87 .. ..
17 5s. violet 45 0 50 0
a. "5" of "5s." omitted (7 MAR 86)
JAN 86 45 0 50 0 | 6 SEP 86
7 MAR 86 — £7 | 13 OCT 86 60 0
24 MAY 86
18 5/6 violet 40 0
20 FEB 86 | 7 MAR 86 40 0
19 5s. 6d. violet 7 MAR 86 £12
20 7/6 violet £12
13 JAN 86 | 24 MAY 86 £12
21 7s. 6d. violet .. .. ..
24 MAY 86 | 6 SEP 86
22 10s. violet .. .. — 110 0
6 SEP 86 | 24 NOV 86
13 OCT 86 — 110 0 |
23 10s. 6. violet 70 0
JAN 86 | 13 OCT 86 70 0
23a 10s. 6d. violet 7 JAN 86 ..
24 13s. violet .. .. ..
24 NOV 86 | 4 JAN 87
25 £1 violet 130 0
13 JAN 86 | 13 OCT 86 130 0
6 SEP 86
26 30s. violet £5
13 JAN 86 | 24 NOV 86 £5

(b) *Blue granite paper.*

27 1d. violet 15 0 15 0
a. "d" omitted (24 NOV 86) £15
20 JAN 86 | JUN 30 86 20 0 20 0
24 JAN 86 25 0 | 6 OCT 86
21 MAY 86 | 24 NOV 86 50 0 30 0
24 MAY 86 15 0 15 0 | 4 JAN 87 15 0 17 6
26 MAY 86 130 0 | 17 JAN 87
28 2d. violet 15 0 15 0
a. "d" omitted (24 NOV 86)
24 JAN 86 40 0 | 13 OCT 86 15 0 15 0
7 MAR 86 | 24 NOV 86 30 0
24 APR 86 | 4 JAN 87 20 0 15 0
24 MAY 86 17 6 17 6 | 20 JAN 87
30 AUG 86 15 0 17 6 |
29 3d. violet 13 OCT 86 .. .. 17 6 20 0
30 4d. violet 17 6 20 0
24 MAY 86 | 24 NOV 86 17 6 20 0
13 OCT 86 35 0 35 0 |
31 6d. violet 25 0 40 0
24 MAY 86 | 24 NOV 86 40 0 40 0
6 SEP 86 25 0 40 0 |
32 9d. violet .. .. ..
6 SEP 86 | 24 NOV 86
33 1s. violet 35 0 35 0
29 APR 86 | 6 SEP 86 90 0
21 MAY 86 35 0 35 0 | 13 OCT 86 40 0
24 MAY 86 | 24 NOV 86 80 0 80 0
34 1s. 6d. violet .. .. ..
2 JUL 86 | 6 SEP 86
35 1/6 violet £9
13 OCT 86 £9 | 24 NOV 86
36 2s. violet 110 0
21 MAY 86 | 13 OCT 86 110 0
24 MAY 86 | 24 NOV 86
37 2s. 6d. violet 19 AUG 86 £9
38 2/6 violet £12
19 AUG 86 £12 | 6 SEP 86
39 4s. violet 17 JAN 87
40 5s. 6d. violet 13 JAN 86
41 5/6 violet .. ..
13 JAN 86 | 13 JAN 87
42 7/6 violet .. ..
13 JAN 86 | 13 JAN 87
43 10s. violet .. ..
JAN 86 | 2 JUL 86
13 JAN 86
44 10s. 6d. violet .. .. .. — £7
7 JAN 86 | 13 JAN 86 — £7
45 10s. 6. violet 2 JUL 86 ..
46 12s. violet 13 JAN 86 .. £30
47 13s. violet 17 JAN 87 .. .. £35
48 £1 violet 13 JAN 86 .. £15
49 30s. violet £15
13 JAN 86 £15 | 17 JAN 87 £16

Varieties. Stamps printed tête-bêche (pairs).

50 2s. (on *yellow*), 6 SEP 86 .. £30
51 30s. (on *yellow*), 24 NOV 86
52 3d. (on *blue*), 13 OCT 86 .. £12
53 1s. (on *blue*), 21 MAY 86 .. £20
54 1s. 6d. (on *blue*), 6 SEP 86 .. £25
55 10s. (on *blue*), 2 JUL 86 .. £30

T 1, with Arms embossed. P 11½.

The motto on the embossed Arms is "EENDRAGT REGTVAARDIGHEID EN LIEFDE" (Union, Justice and Charity).

(a) Yellow paper.

56 1d. violet 15 0 17 6
20 JAN 86 | JUL 7 86
10 FEB 86 | 4 AUG 86 80 0
17 MAR 86 80 0 | 13 SEP 86 70 0
14 APR 86 40 0 | 6 OCT 86 40 0 25 0
26 MAY 86 | 3 NOV 86 15 0 17 6
28 MAY 86 | 2 DEC 86 15 0 17 6
JUN 30 86 20 0 25 0

57 2d. violet 17 6 20 0
2 DEC 86 17 6 20 0 | 20 JAN 87

58 4d. violet 30 0 40 0
2 DEC 86 £6 | DEC 86 30 0 40 0

59 6d. violet 60 0
2 DEC 86 90 0 | DEC 86 60 0

Varieties. Arms inverted.

60 1d. violet 40 0 40 0
20 JAN 86 80 0 | JUL 7 86 £6 £6
JAN 20 86 | 13 SEP 86 80 0
10 FEB 86 80 0 | 3 NOV 86 40 0 40 0
14 APR 86 £7 | 2 DEC 86 £10
26 MAY 86 £5 | JAN 20 87
JUN 30 86 40 0 40 0

61 2d. violet 35 0 40 0
24 NOV 86 | 20 JAN 87
2 DEC 86 35 0 40 0

62 4d. violet DEC 86 .. .. £6 80 0

(b) Blue granite paper.

63 1d. violet 17 6 20 0
20 JAN 86 £6 | JUL 7 86 20 0 25 0
JAN 20 86 | 4 AUG 86
10 FEB 86 | 13 SEP 86 £5
17 MAR 86 £6 | 6 OCT 86 60 0 20 0
14 APR 86 60 0 | 3 NOV 86 17 6
26 MAY 86 | 2 DEC 86 20 0
JUN 30 86 80 0 50 0

64 2d. violet 17 6 20 0
30 AUG 86 60 0 | 4 JAN 87 60 0
2 DEC 86 17 6 20 0 | 20 JAN 87 60 0

Varieties. Arms inverted.

65 1d. violet 40 0 40 0
10 FEB 86 40 0 | JUL 7 86 80 0 40 0
17 MAR 86 £5 | 6 OCT 86 £5
26 MAR 86 £8 | 3 NOV 86 40 0 40 0
23 MAY 86 150 0 | 2 DEC 86 70 0
26 MAY 86 60 0 80 0

66 2d. violet 70 0
30 AUG 86 | 20 JAN 87 £6
2 DEC 86 70 0

Varieties. Arms embossed tête-bêche (pairs).

67 1d. (on *yellow*), 3 NOV 86 .. £5 £5
68 1d. (on *yellow*), JUN 30 86 .. £10 £10
69 1d. (on *blue*), 3 NOV 86 ..
70 2d. (on *blue*), 2 DEC 86
71 4d. (on *yellow*), DEC 86 .. £10

1887 (FEB.-MAR.). *As T 1, but without date. With embossed Arms.*

(a) Blue granite paper.

72 1d. violet 15 0 16 0
a. Imperf. between (pair) .. ..
b. Stamps tête-bêche (pair) .. £15
c. Arms tête-bêche (pair) .. ..
d. Arms inverted .. ..
e. Arms omitted 25 0 25 0

73 2d. violet £6 £6
.. 6 0 8 0
a. Stamps tête-bêche (pair) .. £15
b. Arms inverted 25 0 25 0
c. Arms omitted .. .. — £5

74 3d. violet 12 6 15 0
a. Stamps tête-bêche (pair) .. £25
b. Arms tête-bêche (pair) ..
c. Arms inverted 80 0 80 0

75 4d. violet 15 0 15 0
a. Stamps tête-bêche (pair) .. £18
b. Arms tête-bêche (pair) .. £16
c. Arms inverted .. £6

76 6d. violet 12 6 15 0
a. Arms inverted .. £6

77 1/6 violet 12 6 15 0
a. Arms inverted .. ..

(b) Yellow paper (March, 1887).

78 2d. violet (*arms omitted*) .. 12 6
79 3d. violet 15 0 15 0
a. Imperf. between (pair) .. ..
b. Stamps tête-bêche (pair) .. £20 £2c
c. Arms tête-bêche (pair) .. ..
d. Arms inverted 30 0 40 0

80 4d. violet 15 0 12 6
a. Arms inverted .. 12 6 15 0

81 6d. violet 10 0 12 6
a. Arms tête-bêche (pair) .. £15
b. Arms inverted .. 60 0 40
c. Arms omitted .. ..

82 9d. violet 12 6 15
83 1s. violet 15 0 15
a. Arms inverted .. 60 0
b. Arms omitted .. 60 0

84 1/6 violet 20 0 20
85 2s. violet 40 0 30
a. Arms inverted .. — 80
b. Arms omitted .. 20 0

86 2/6 violet 25 0 30
a. Arms inverted .. 25 0 30

87 3s. violet 60 0 70
a. Arms inverted .. 70 0 80

88 4s. violet 20 0 25
a. Arms omitted (4s) ..
b. Arms omitted (4/-) ..

89 5s. violet 20 0 25
a. Imperf. between (pair) .. ..
b. Arms inverted .. .... —

90 5/6 violet 20 0 25
91 7/6 violet 30 0 35
a. Arms tête-bêche (pair) ..
b. Arms inverted ..

92 10s. violet 20 0 20
a. Imperf. between (pair) .. ..
b. Arms tête-bêche (pair) .. £6
c. Arms inverted .. 25 0
d. Arms omitted .. — 60

93 10/6 violet 25 0 30
a. Imperf. between (pair) .. ..
b. Arms inverted ..
c. Arms omitted .. ..

94 £1 violet 70 0 70
a. Stamps tête-bêche (pair) .. £20
b. Arms inverted .. 60 0

95 30s. violet £7

NEW SOUTH WALES.

— SIMPLIFICATION (see INTRODUCTION) —

Nos. 1 to 43e.

11, 25, 42. (Simplest).
5, 11, 20, 25, 30, 33, 37, 42. (More advancec

Nos. 44 to 101.

48, 55, 58, 62, 64, 67, 74, 79. (Add furth shades if desired.)
83, 85, 87. 88, 91: 95: 101.

Nos. 102 to 185.

103, 104, 106, 111, 114, 116, 120, 123, 126, 12
131, 155, 133, 135, 156, 157, 160, 161, 162, 1
145, 164, 167b, 167c, 152, 169, 170.
173. 175, 183.

Nos. 186 to 252.

191, 192, 194. 189, 202. 196, 197. 198, 19
201. 241, 203, 205.
207, 209, 210b, 211a, 214, 215, 216, 217, 2
220a, 221.

222, 223f, 225g, 226c, 228a, 229b, 232 243, 234, 235, 236, 237d.
238a, 239a. 244b, 245a, 246a: 247a, 250, 251b.

Nos. 253 to 360.
253, 256, 257, 304, 261, 262b, 305, 306, 308, 309, 268a, 312.
272, 273. 275, 276. 278, 280b. 282, 283, 284b. 285c, 298, 281. 287c, 287d.
299, 300, 301, 315, 292a, 296, 316. 328, 326.
331, 332, 333. 333d, 334, 335, 336, 337, 339, 340, 342b, 344, 345a, 346a.
349, 351, 352, 353, 354, 355, 356, 357, 348, 358, 359, 360.

Official Stamps.
401a, 402a, 404a, 405b, 406, 407a, 409, 410, 411b.
412, 413, 415b, 416b, 417, 419d, 421c, 424c, 425, 426c.
427. 428, 429, 430.
431, 432, 433, 434, 435, 436, 437, 438.
440, 441. 442, 443. 444, 448a, 445, 446, 447.

ostage Due Stamps.
One stamp of each value.

1

2

NOTE.—Prices for "Sydney Views" are for fine copies. Stamps showing the very early state of the plate, with large margins, are worth at least double, but medium specimens can be supplied at from one-third of the prices quoted, and poor copies for considerably less.

ngraved by Mr. Robert Clayton, of Sydney.)

50 (1 Jan.). *T* **1.** *Plate I. No clouds.*

(a) Soft yellowish paper.

	1d. crimson-lake	£300	£60
	1d. carmine	£250	£50
	1d. reddish rose	£225	£45
	1d. brownish red	£275	£55

(b) Hard bluish paper.

	1d. pale red	£215	£40
	1d. dull lake	£215	£40

50 (Aug.). *T* **2.** *Plate I, re-engraved by H. C. Jervis, commonly termed Plate II. With clouds.*

(a) Hard toned yellowish paper.

	1d. vermilion	£150	£30
	1d. dull carmine	£125	£25
	a. No trees on hill (No. 7)	£200	£35
	b. Hill unshaded (No. 8)	£200	£35
	c. Without clouds (No. 15)	£200	£55

(b) Hard greyish or bluish paper.

	1d. crimson-lake	£175	£35
	1d. gooseberry-red	£250	£50
	1d. dull carmine	£125	£22
	1d. brownish red	£125	£25
	a. No trees on hill (No. 7)	£170	£30
	b. Hill unshaded (No. 8)	£170	£30
	c. Without clouds (No. 15)	£170	£55

(c) Laid paper.

	1d. carmine	£225	£55
	1d. vermilion	£250	£60
	a. No trees on hill (No. 7)	—	£70
	b. Hill unshaded (No. 8)	—	£70
	c. Without clouds (No. 15)	—	£80

The varieties quoted with the letters "a", ", "c" of course exist in each shade; the ces quoted are for the commonest shade, and same applies to the following portions of this .

The numbers given in brackets throughout indicate position on sheet.

3

4

A (Pl. I).

Illustrations A, B, C, and D are sketches of the lower part of the inner circular frame, showing the characteristic variations of each plate.

(Engraved by Mr. John Carmichael.)

1850 (1 Jan.). *Plate I. Vertical-lined background.* *T* **3.** *(a) Early impressions, full details of clouds, etc.*

15	2d. greyish blue	£325	£55
16	2d. deep blue	—	£85
	a. Double lines on bale (No. 19)	—	£80

Intermediate impressions.

16*b*	2d. greyish blue	£200	£35
16*c*	2d. deep blue	£200	£40

T **4.** *(b) Later impressions, clouds, etc., mostly gone.*

17	2d. blue	£150	£16
18	2d. dull blue	£120	£16

1850 (end Jan.). *Stamps in the lower row partially retouched.*

19	2d. blue	£200	£30
20	2d. greyish blue	£175	£25

5

B (Pl. II)

(Plate entirely re-engraved by H. C. Jervis.)

1850 (Apr.). *T* **5.** *Plate II. Horizonatal-lined background. Bale on left side supporting the seated figure, dated. Dot in centre of the star in each corner.*

(a) Early impressions.

21	2d. indigo	£250	£50
22	2d. lilac-blue	—	£100
23	2d. grey-blue	£250	£40
24	2d. bright blue	£250	£40
	a. Fan as in Pl. III, but with shading outside (No. 1)	—	£50
	b. Fan as in Pl. III, but without shading, and inner circle intersects the fan (No. 2)	—	£50
	c. Pick and shovel omitted (No. 10)	—	£50
	d. "CREVIT" omitted (No. 13)	—	£60
	e. No whip (Nos. 4, 8, and 20)	—	£50

(b) Worn impressions.

25	2d. dull blue	£100	£15
26	2d. Prussian blue	£125	£20
	a. Fan as in Pl. III, but with shading outside (No. 1)	—	£25
	b. Fan as in Pl. III, but without shading, and inner circle intersects the fan (No. 2)	—	£22

c. Pick and shovel omitted (No. 10) — £22
d. "CREVIT" omitted (No. 13) .. — £30
e. No whip (Nos. 4, 8, and 20) .. — £20

1850 (Aug.). *Bottom row retouched with dots and dashes in lower spandrels.*

27 2d. Prussian blue £175 £25
28 2d. dull blue £125 £20
a. No whip (No. 20) .. .. .. — £22
b. "CREVIT" omitted (No. 13) .. — £30

C (Pl. III).

(Plate re-engraved a second time by H. C. Jervis.)

1850 (Sept.). *Plate III. Bale not dated and single-lined, except Nos. 7, 10 and 12, which are double-lined. No dots in stars.*

29 2d. ultramarine £150 £18
30 2d. deep blue £135 £15
a. No whip (Nos. 15 and 19) — £22
b. Fan with 6 segments (No. 20) .. — £22
c. Double lines on bale (No. 7, 10, and 12) .. .. .. — £18

(Plate re-engraved a third time by H. C. Jervis.)

1851 (Jan.). *Plate IV. Double-line bale, and circle in centre of each star.*

(*a*) *Hard bluish grey wove paper.*

31 2d. ultramarine £200 £30
32 2d. Prussian blue £150 £20
33 2d. bright blue £175 £25
a. Hill not shaded (No. 12) .. — £26
b. Fan with 6 segments (No. 20) .. — £26
c. No clouds (No. 22) .. .. — £26
d. Retouch (No. 13) .. .. — £26

(*b*) *Stout yellowish vertically laid paper.*

34 2d. ultramarine £150 £25
35 2d. Prussian blue £175 £24
a. Hill not shaded (No. 12) .. — £28
b. Fan with 6 segments (No. 20) .. — £28
c. No clouds (No. 22) .. .. — £28
d. Retouch (No. 13) .. .. — £28

6

D (Pl. V).

(Plate re-engraved a fourth time by H. C. Jervis.)

1851 (Apr.). *T* **6**. *Plate V. Pearl in fan.*

(*a*) *Hard greyish wove paper.*

36 2d. ultramarine £140 £22
37 2d. dull blue £120 £17
a. Pick and shovel omitted (No. 17) — £28
b. Fan with 6 segments (No. 20) .. — £28

(*b*) *Stout yellowish vertically laid paper.*

38 2d. dull ultramarine £275 £50
a. Pick and shovel omitted (No. 17) — £60
b. Fan with 6 segments (No. 20) .. — £70

7

8

(Engraved by Mr. H. C. Jervis.)

1850. *T* **7.**

(*a*) *Soft yellowish wove paper.*

39 3d. yellow-green £155 £25
40 3d. myrtle-green £400 £135
41 3d. emerald-green £200 £25
a. No whip (Nos. 18 and 19) .. — £30
b. "SIGIIIUM" for "SIGILLUM" (No. 23) .. .. — £35

(*b*) *Bluish to grey wove paper.*

42 3d. yellow-green £150 £20
43 3d. emerald-green £150 £20
b. No whip (Nos. 18 and 19) .. — £25
c. "SIGIIIUM" for "SIGILLUM" (No. 23) .. — £25

(*c*) *Yellowish to bluish laid paper.*

43*d* 3d. bright green .. £375 £5
43*e* 3d. yellowish green £375 £5
f. No whip (Nos. 18 and 19) .. — £55
g. "SIGIIIUM" for "SIGILLUM" (No. 23) .. .. — £6

(Designed by Mr. Manning; engraved on steel by Mr. John Carmichael, of Sydney.)

1851 (18 Dec.). *T* **8.** *Imperf.*

(*a*) *Thick yellowish wove paper.*

44 1d. carmine £100 £2
a. No leaves right of "SOUTH" — £3
b. Two leaves right of "SOUTH" — £4
c. "WALE" .. .. — £4

1852. (*b*) *Bluish medium wove paper.*

45 1d. carmine .. .. .. £35 £
46 1d. scarlet .. .. .. £40 £
47 1d. vermilion .. .. .. £35 £
48 1d. brick-red .. .. .. £35 £
a. No leaves right of "SOUTH" (Nos. 7 and 8) .. .. .. — £1
b. Two leaves right of "SOUTH" (No. 15) .. .. .. — £2
c. "WALE" (No. 9) .. .. .. — £2

1852 (?). (*c*) *Thick vertically laid bluish paper.*

49 1d. orange-brown £200 £4
50 1d. claret £200 £4
a. No leaves right of "SOUTH" .. — £5
b. Two leaves right of "SOUTH" — £5
c. "WALE" .. .. .. — £6

(Engraved on steel by Mr. John Carmichael.)

1851 (24 July). *T* **8.** *Plate I.*

(*a*) *Thick yellowish wove paper.*

51 2d. ultramarine .. .. £30 £

(*b*) *Fine impressions, blue to greyish medium paper.*

52 2d. ultramarine £45 45
53 2d. chalky blue £25 45
54 2d. dark blue £25 45
55 2d. greyish blue £25 35

(*c*) *Worn plate, blue to greyish medium paper.*

56 2d. ultramarine £22 35
57 2d. Prussian blue £15 40

(*d*) *Worn plate, blue wove medium paper.*

58 2d. ultramarine £20 45
59 2d. Prussian blue £17 40

9

(Plate II engraved by Mr. H. C. Jervis.)

1853 (Oct.). *T* **9.** *Plate II. Stars in corners. Imperf.*

(*a*) *Bluish medium to thick wove paper.*

60 2d. deep ultramarine £60
61 2d. indigo £75
a. "WAEES" (No. 23) .. .. — £

(b) Worn plate, hard blue wove paper.

62 2d. deep Prussian blue £50 £6
a. "WAEES" (No. 23) — £18

1855 (Sept.). *Plate III, being Plate I re-engraved by H. C. Jervis. Background of crossed lines.*

(a) Medium bluish wove paper.

63 2d. Prussian blue £25 55 0
a. "WALES" covered with wavy lines (No. 3) — £5

(b) Stout white wove paper.

64 2d. Prussian blue £22 45 0
a. "WALES" covered with wavy lines (No. 3) — 90 0

(Engraved by John Carmichael.)

1852 (3 Dec.). T **8**. *Imperf.*

(a) Medium greyish blue wove paper.

65 3d. deep green £100 £15
66 3d. green £75 £12
67 3d. dull yellow-green £60 £10
a. "WAEES" (No. 37) — £15

(b) Thick blue wove paper.

69 3d. emerald-green £75 £15
71 3d. blue-green £75 £15
a. "WAEES" (No. 37) — £18

1852 (Apr.). *As T* **8**. *Fine background. Imperf.*

(a) Medium white wove paper.

72 6d. vandyke-brown — £50
a. "WALLS" (No. 8) — £60

(b) Medium bluish grey wove paper.

73 6d. vandyke-brown £120 £20
74 6d. yellow-brown £150 £25
75 6d. chocolate-brown £120 £20
76 6d. grey-brown £90 £18
a. "WALLS" (No. 8) — £30

1853 (June). *Plate I re-engraved by H. C. Jervis. Coarse background. Imperf.*

77 6d. brown £125 £25
78 6d. grey-brown £100 £20

(Engraved by H. C. Jervis.)

1853 (May). *Medium bluish paper. Imperf.*

79 8d. dull yellow £175 £40
80 8d. orange-yellow £175 £40
81 8d. orange £250 £50
a. No bow at back of head (No. 9) — £60
b. No leaves right of "SOUTH" (No. 21) — £60
c. No lines in spandrel (Nos. 12, 22, and 32) — £45

10

NOTE.—All watermarked stamps from No. 82 to No. 172 have double-lined figures, as T **10**.

854 (Feb.). T **8**. *Wmk.* "**1**", *T* **10**. *Imperf. Yellowish wove paper.*

2 1d. red-orange £6 25 0
3 1d. orange-vermilion £6 25 0
a. No leaves right of "SOUTH" (Nos. 7 and 21) £12 60 0
b. Two leaves right of "SOUTH" (No. 15) £24 £8
c. "WALE" (No. 9) £24 £10

854 (Jan.). *Plate III. Wmk.* "**2**". *Imperf.*

4 2d. ultramarine £5 12 6
5 2d. Prussian blue £5 12 6
5 2d. chalky blue £5 12 6
a. "WALES" partly covered £25 60 0

854 (Mar.). *Wmk.* "**3**". *Imperf.*

7 3d. yellow-green £8 30 0
a. "WAEES" (No. 37) — £5
b. Error. Wmk. "2" — £200

13

(Engraved by Mr. John Carmichael.)

1856 (1 Jan.). *For Registered Letters.* T **13**. *No wmk. Imperf. Soft medium yellowish paper.*

88 (6d.) vermilion & Prussian blue £40 £10
a. Frame printed on back £250 £100
89 (6d.) salmon and indigo £60 £15
90 (6d.) orange & Prussian blue £60 £15
91 (6d.) orange and indigo £60 £15

1859 (Apr.). *Hard medium bluish wove paper, with manufacturer's wmk. in sans-serif, double-lined capitals across sheet and only showing portions of letters on a few stamps in a sheet.*

(a) Imperf.

92 (6d.) orange and Prussian blue £45 £12
92*a* (6d.) verm. and Prussian blue £70 £18

1860 (Feb.). *(b) P* 12.

93 (6d.) orange and Prussian blue £25 65 0
94 (6d.) orange and indigo £20 65 0

Coarse yellowish wove paper having the manufacturer's wmk. in Roman capitals.

(a) P 12.

95 (6d.) rose-red & Prussian blue £15 50 0
96 (6d.) rose-red and indigo £20 85 0
97 (6d.) salmon and indigo

1862. *(b) P* 13.

98 (6d.) rose-red & Prussian blue £15 70 0

1863 (May). *Yellowish wove paper. Wmk.* "**6**". *P* 13.

99 (6d.) rose-red & Prussian blue 90 0 20 0
100 (6d.) rose-red and indigo £8 25 0
101 (6d.) rose-red and pale blue 55 0 10 0

14

(Printed in the Colony from plates engraved by Messrs. Perkins, Bacon & Co.)

Two plates of the 2d. and 6d. were used. On Plate II of the 2d. the stamps are wider apart and more regularly spaced than on Plate I.

1856 (6 Apr.). T **14**. *Wmk.* "**1**". *Imperf.*

102 1d. orange-vermilion £6 30 0
103 1d. carmine-vermilion £6 27 6
104 1d. orange-red £5 27 6
a. Printed on both sides — £100

1856 (7 Jan.). T **14**. *Plate I. Wmk.* "**2**". *Imperf.*

105 2d. light ultramarine £5 7 6
106 2d. Prussian blue £5 7 6
107 2d. dull blue £5 7 6
108 2d. cobalt-blue £10 17 6
a. Error, wmk. "1"
b. Error, wmk. "5" £30 30 0
c. Error, wmk. "8"

1858. *Plate I, retouched.*
109 2d. dull blue £100 £22

1859 (Aug.). *Lithographic transfer of Plate I.*
110 2d. pale cobalt-blue .. .. — £50
a. Retouched .. .. .. — £250

Plate II. Recess. Stamps printed wider apart. (Jan. 1860.)
110*b* 2d. blue £20 25 0

1856 (10 Oct.). *As T* **14**. *Wmk.* " **3** ". *Imperf.*
111 3d. yellow-green £55 £9
112 3d. bluish green £60 £9
113 3d. dull green £60 £9
a. Error, wmk. " 2 " .. .. — £200

In the 3d. the value is in block letters on a white ground.

15 17

19 21

1855 (1 Dec.). *Wmk.* " **5** ". *Imperf.*
114 **15** 5d. dull green £40 £35

1854 (Feb.). *Wmk.* " **6** ". *Imperf.*
115 **17** 6d. deep slate £40 50 0
116 ,, 6d. greenish grey £25 40 0
117 ,, 6d. slate-green £22 50 0
a. Printed both sides ..
118 ,, 6d. bluish grey £25 70 0
119 ,, 6d. fawn £25 £6
120 ,, 6d. grey £30 60 0
121 ,, 6d. olive-grey £25 60 0
122 ,, 6d. greyish brown £30 60 0

1859 (15 Aug.). *Error. Wmk.* " **8** ".
123 **17** 6d. fawn £100 £9
124 ,, 6d. greyish brown £100 £10

1855 (1 Dec.). *Wmk.* " **8** ". *Imperf.*
125 **19** 8d. golden yellow £450 £70
126 ,, 8d. dull orange £400 £70

1854 (Feb.). *Wmk.* " **12** ". *Imperf.*
127 **21** 1s. rosy vermilion £50 85 0
128 ,, 1s. pale red £40 85 0
129 ,, 1s. brownish red £45 80 0

1857 (20 June). *Error. Wmk.* " **8** ".
130 **21** 1s. rosy vermilion .. £150 £15

1860 (Feb.)–**1863**. *Wmk. double-lined figure of value. P* 12.
131 **14** 1d. orange-red £10 17 6
a. Imperf. between (pair) ..
132 ,, 1d. scarlet 95 0 15 0
133 ,, 2d. chalky blue 95 0 12 6
134 ,, 2d. greenish blue 95 0 12 6
135 ,, 2d. Prussian blue £6 10 0
136 ,, 2d. dull blue £6 12 6
a. Retouched (from Pl. II) *From* — £25
b. Error, wmk. " 1 " .. .. — £250
139 ,, 3d. yellow-green (1860) .. £75 85 0
140 **14** 3d. blue-green £25 50 0
141 **15** 5d. dull green (1863) .. £8 80 0
142 ,, 5d. yellowish grn. (1863) .. £8 80 0
143 **17** 6d. grey-brown £18 30 0
144 ,, 6d. olive-brown £18 35 0
145 ,, 6d. greenish grey £40 60 0
146 ,, 6d. fawn £18 35 0
147 ,, 6d. mauve £25 40 0
148 ,, 6d. violet £15 15 0
a. Imperf. between (pair) ..
149 **19** 8d. orange £120 £20
150 ,, 8d. orange-red £120 £20
151 ,, 8d. yellow .. .. .. — £100
152 **21** 1s. brownish red £24 45 0
153 ,, 1s. rose-carmine £25 50 0
a. Imperf. between (pair) ..

Most of the perforated 2d. stamps from Plate I were printed after the return of the plate from London in March, 1861, where it had been repaired.

1862–72. *Wmk. double-lined figure of value. P* 13.
154 **14** 1d. scarlet (1862) 60 0 12 6
155 ,, 1d. dull red 55 0 10 0
156 ,, 3d. blue-grn. (Dec., 1862) 45 0 15 0
157 ,, 3d. yellow-green 60 0 12 6
158 ,, 3d. dull green 25 0 10 0
a. Wmk. " 6 ", yellow-green (July, '72) 80 0 15 0
b. Wmk. " 6 ", dark green .. 80 0 17 6
160 **15** 5d. bluish green 45 0 17 6
161 ,, 5d. bright yellow-green .. 65 0 30 0
162 ,, 5d. sea-green 65 0 17 6
162*a* ,, 5d. dark bluish green .. 35 0 20 0
163 **17** 6d. reddish purple (Pl. I, July, '62) 45 0 5 0
164 ,, 6d. mauve 35 0 5 0
165 ,, 6d. purple (Pl. II, 1864) .. 35 0 6 0
a. Error, wmk. "5" (July, '66) £15 40 0
b. Error, wmk. "12" (12.66) .. £8 15 0
166 ,, 6d. violet 40 0 6 0
167 ,, 6d. aniline mauve .. £70 £6
167*a* **19** 8d. deep orange 85 0 30 0
167*b* ,, 8d. yellow-orange .. £5 25 0
167*c* ,, 8d. bright yellow .. 85 0 25 0
168 **21** 1s. rose-carmine 65 0 8 6
169 ,, 1s. carmine 40 0 8 6
170 ,, 1s. crimson-lake 60 0 12 6

Perf. compound 12 × 13.
171 **14** 1d. scarlet .. .. .. — £50
172 ,, 2d. dull blue £100 £12

23

1864 (June). *T* **14**. *W* **23**. *P* 13.
173 1d. pale red 30 0 27 6

24

25

(Des. E. H. Corbould, R.I.)

1861-97. *T* **24.** *W* **25.** *Various perfs.*

174 5s. dull violet, *perf.* 12 (1861) £85 £30
175 5s. dull violet, *perf.* 13 (1863) £5 35 0
176 5s. aniline mauve, *p.* 13 ('72).. £8 45 0
177 5s. rose-lilac, *perf.* 13 (1879) £7 35 0
178 5s. deep pur., *p.* 13 (1880–88).. £6 30 0
179 5s. deep pur., *p.* 10 (1880–88) £8 20 0
180 5s. deep pur., *p.* 12 (1880–88) 60 0 25 0
181 5s. deep pur., *p.* 11 (1880–88) 50 0 17 6
182 5s. deep purple, *perf.* 12 × 10 (1880–88) £16 50 0
183 5s. red-purple, *p.* 11 (1897).. 30 0 17 6
184 5s. red-purple, *perf.* 12 (1897) 50 0 30 0
185 5s. red-pur., *p.* 11 × 12 (1897) 35 0 20 0
a. Perf. 11 × imperf. between (pair) £50

26

28

29

A. Printed by Messrs. De La Rue & Co., and perf. 14 at Somerset House, London.

1862-65. *T* **26** *and* **28.** *P* 14.

(i) *Surfaced paper.* *W* **23.**

86 1d. dull red (Pl. I, 1 Apr., '64) £6 60 0

(ii) *Surfaced paper.* *No wmk.*

87 1d. dull red (Pl. II, Jan., '65) £6 50 0
88 2d. pale blue (Mar., '62) .. £5 60 0

B. Printed from the plates of Messrs. De La Rue & Co., in the Colony.

862 (12 Apr.). *T* **28.** *Wmk. double lined* "**2**".

89 2d. blue, *perf.* 13 .. .. 60 0 5 0
a. Perf. 12 .. .. .. £12 25 0
b. Perf. 12 × 13 .. .. £50

864-65. *T* **26** *and* **28.** *W* **23.** *P* 13.

90 1d. dark red-brown (Plate I) £6 20 0
91 1d. brownish red (Plate II).. 17 6 2 0
92 1d. brick-red (Plate II) .. 17 6 2 0
a. Highly surfaced paper (1865).. £22
94 2d. pale blue £12 10 0

Plates I and II were made from the same die; hey can only be distinguished by the colour or by he marginal inscription. (See *N.S.W. Handook*, p. 232.)

865-66. *Thin wove paper.* *No wmk.* *P* 13.

95 **26** 1d. brick-red £8 22 6
96 ,, 1d. brownish red £8 22 6
97 **28** 2d. pale blue 55 0 6 0

863-69. *W* **29.**

98 **26** 1d. pale red, *perf.* 13 .. £7 20 0
99 **28** 2d. pale blue, *perf.* 12 ..
a. Perf. 13 .. .. .. 5 0 1 0
00 ,, 2d. cobalt-blue, *perf.* 13 .. 6 0 1 6
01 ,, 2d. Prussian blue, *perf.* 13 20 0 4 0

862 (Sept.). *Wmk. double-lined* "**5**" *P* 13.

02 **28** 2d. dull blue £9 35 0

32

34

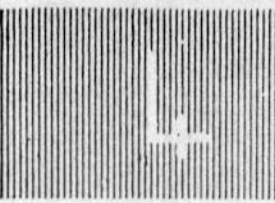

33

35

1867 (Sept.)–**1893.** *W* **33** *and* **35.**

203 **32** 4d. red-brown, *perf.* 13 .. 25 0 4 0
204 ,, 4d. pale red-brn., *perf.* 13 25 0 4 0
205 **34** 10d. lilac, *perf.* 13.. .. 6 0 6 0
a. Imperf. between (pair) £30
206 ,, 10d. lilac (1893), *perf.* 11.. 6 0 6 0
a. Perf. 10.. .. .. .. 12 6 8 6
b. Perf. 10 and 11, compound 22 6 12 6
c. Perf. 12 × 11 .. .. £10 40 0

36

37

38

NINEPENCE
(39)

From 1871 to 1903 the 9d. is formed from the 10d. by a *black* surch. (T **39**), 15 mm. long on Nos. 219 to 220h, and 13½ mm. long on subsequent issues.

1871–84. *W* **36.**

207 **26** 1d. dull red (8.71), *perf.* 13 3 0 0 6
208 ,, 1d. salmon, *perf.* 13 .. 3 0 1 0
a. Perf. 10.. .. .. £25 25 0
b. Perf. 13 × 10 .. .. 12 6 1 0
c. *Scarlet.* Perf. 10.. .. — £30
209 **28** 2d. Pruss.-bl. (11.71), *p.* 13 3 0 1 0
a. Perf. 11 × 12, comb .. £26 £6
210 ,, 2d. pale blue, *perf.* 13 .. 2 6 1 0
a. Perf. 10.. .. .. £25 25 0
b. Perf. 13 × 10 .. .. 4 0 1 0
c. Surfaced paper, perf. 13 ..
211 **14** 3d. yell.-grn. (3.74), *p.* 13 12 6 4 0
a. Perf. 10.. .. .. £5 10 0
b. Perf. 11.. .. .. £15 £10
c. Perf. 12.. .. .. — £25
d. Perf. 10 × 12 .. .. £15 £5
e. Perf. 12 × 11 .. .. £10 £6
212 ,, 3d. bright green, *perf.* 10 £10 20 0
a. Perf. 10 × 13 .. .. £6 25 0
213 **32** 4d. pale red-brown (8.77), *perf.* 13 .. .. 30 0 12 0
214 ,, 4d. red-brown, *perf.* 13 .. 27 6 7 6
a. Perf. 10 .. .. .. £25 £5
b. Perf. 13 × 10 .. .. £5 6 0

215 **15** 5d. bluish green (8.84), *p.* 10 .. 10 0 7 6
a. Perf. 12 .. .. £25 £15
b. Perf. 13 × 10 .. ..
c. Perf. 10 × 12 .. .. 22 6 12 6
216 **37** 6d. brt. mauve (1.72), *p.* 13 6 0 0 9
a. Imperf. between (horiz. pair) — £50
217 ,, 6d. pale lilac, *perf.* 13 .. 12 6 1 0
a. Perf. 10 .. .. .. £25 20 0
b. Perf. 13 × 10 .. .. 50 0 4 0
c. Imperf. between (horiz. pair)
Perf. 13 × 10 .. .. — £50
218 **19** 8d. yell. (Mar., '77), *p.* 13 .. 25 0 6 0
a. Perf. 10 .. .. .. £25 20 0
b. Perf. 13 × 10 .. .. £15 15 0
219 **34** 9d. on 10d. pale red-brown (Aug., '71) *perf.* 13 .. 12 6 5 0
220 ,, 9d. on 10d. red-brn., *p.* 13 12 6 12 6
a. Perf. 10 .. .. .. 6 0 5 0
b. Perf. 12 .. .. .. 6 0 5 0
c. Perf. 11 .. .. .. 25 0 12 6
d. Perf. 10 × 12 .. .. £25 £25
e. Perf. 10 × 11 .. .. 40 0 17 6
f. Perf. 12 × 11 .. .. 7 6 7 6
g. Perf. 11 × 12, comb .. 7 6 7 6
h. In black and blue, perf. 11 £10
221 **38** 1s. black (April, '76), *p.* 13 35 0 2 0
a. Perf. 10 .. .. .. £25 20 0
b. Perf. 10 × 13 .. .. £10 6 0
c. Perf. 11 .. .. ..
d. Imperf. between (horiz. pair) — £50

Collectors should note that the classification of perforations is that adopted by the Royal Philatelic Society, London. "Perf. 12" denotes the perforation formerly called "11½, 12" and "perf. 13" that formerly called "12½, 13." Some compound perfs. are found measuring both ways.

40

1882–93. *W* **40.**

222 **23** 1d. salmon (1882), *perf.* 10 6 0 1 0
a. Perf. 13 .. .. ..
b. Perf. 10 × 13 .. .. 50 0 5 0
223 ,, 1d. orange *to* scarlet, *p.* 13
a. Perf. 10 .. .. .. 4 0 0 9
b. Perf. 10 × 13 .. .. £10 12 6
c. Perf. 10 × 12 .. .. £25 £8
d. Perf. 10 × 11 .. .. £50 £15
e. Perf. 12 × 11 .. .. — £15
f. Perf. 11 × 12, comb .. 1 3 0 6
h. Perf. 11 .. .. .. — £20
224 **28** 2d. pale blue (1882), *p.* 13 £50 £15
a. Perf. 10 .. .. .. 6 0 0 9
b. Perf. 13 × 10 .. .. £5 5 0
225 ,, 2d. Prussian blue, *perf.* 10 8 0 0 9
a. Perf. 13 × 10 .. .. £5 5 0
b. Perf. 12 .. .. .. — £25
c. Perf. 11 .. .. .. — £15
d. Perf. 12 × 11 .. .. — £15
e. Perf. 12 × 10 .. .. £25 £6
f. Perf. 10 × 11 .. .. £50 £15
g. Perf. 11 × 12, comb .. 1 3 0 6
226 **14** 3d. yell.-grn. (1886), *p.* 10 2 0 0 9
a. Perf. 10 × 12 .. .. £10 25 0
b. Perf. 11 .. .. .. 2 6 0 9
c. Perf. 11 × 12 .. .. 2 0 0 9
d. Perf. 12 .. .. .. 4 0 1 3
da. Perf. 12 × 11 .. .. 3 6 1 0
e. Imperf. between (horiz. pair) 60 0
f. Imperf. (pair) 60 0

227 **14** 3d. bluish green, *perf.* 10 .. 3 6 0 9
a. Perf. 11 .. .. .. 3 0 0 8
b. Perf. 10 × 11 .. .. 15 0 2 0
c. Perf. 11 × 12 .. .. 3 6 1 6
d. Perf. 12 × 10 .. .. £5 3 0
228 ,, 3d. emerald-grn. ('93), *p.* 10 50 0 10 0
a. Perf. 10 × 11 .. .. 50 0 5 0
b. Perf. 12 × 10 .. .. £5 12 6
229 **32** 4d. red-brown (1882), *p.* 10 40 0 3 0
a. Perf. 10 × 12 .. .. — £15
b. Perf. 11 × 12, comb 25 0 2 0
230 ,, 4d. dark brown, *perf.* 10 25 0 3 6
a. Perf. 12 .. .. .. — £5
b. Perf. 10 × 12 .. .. — £10
c. Perf. 11 × 12, comb .. 12 6 2 0
231 **15** 5d. dull grn. (1891), *perf.* 10 8 6 3 0
a. Perf. 11 × 10 .. .. 25 0 4 0
b. Perf. 12 × 10 .. .. £5 5 0
232 ,, 5d. bright green, *perf.* 10 20 0 5 0
a. Perf. 11 .. .. .. — 7 6
b. Perf. 10 × 11 .. .. 30 0 7 6
c. Perf. 12 × 10 .. .. £10 10 0
233 ,, 5d. blue-green, *perf.* 10 .. 8 6 2 0
a. Perf. 12 .. .. .. 8 6 2 0
b. Perf. 11 .. .. .. 3 6 1 6
c. Perf. 10 × 11 .. .. 22 6 4 0
d. Perf. 11 × 12 .. .. 3 6 1 0
f. Imperf. 25 0
234 **37** 6d. pale lilac (1882), *p.* 10 5 0 0 9
a. Perf. 10 × 13 .. .. — £30
b. Perf. 10 × 12 .. .. 15 0 2 6
235 ,, 6d. mauve, *perf.* 10 .. 6 0 0 9
a. Perf. 12 .. .. .. £6 5 0
b. Perf. 11 .. .. .. £6 10 0
c. Perf. 10 × 12 .. .. 10 0 2 0
d. Perf. 11 × 12 .. .. 10 6 3
e. Perf. 10 × 11 .. .. 27 6 1 6
f. Imperf. between (horiz. pair)
Perf. 12 × 10 .. .. — £5
236 **19** 8d. yellow (1883), *perf.* 10 22 6 4
a. Perf. 12 .. .. .. £5 30
b. Perf. 11 .. .. .. 22 6 6
c. Perf. 10 × 12 .. .. 80 0 17
237 **38** 1s. black, *perf.* 10 (1883) 17 6 1
a. Perf. 11 .. .. .. £10 20
b. Perf. 10 × 12 .. ..
c. Perf. 10 × 13 .. .. — 20
d. Perf. 11 × 12, comb .. 8 6 1

41

1886–87. *W* **41.**

238 **26** 1d. scarlet, *perf.* 10 .. 10 0 6
a. Perf. 11 × 12, comb .. 3 0 2
239 **28** 2d. deep blue, *perf.* 10 .. 45 0 12
a. Perf. 11 × 12, comb .. 6 6 3
b. Imperf. .. .. ..

1891 (JULY). *Wmk.* "10" *as T* **35.** *P* 10.

240 **14** 3d. green 10 0 12
241 ,, 3d. dark green .. 2 0 2

42

NOTE. The spacin between the Crown an "NSW" is 1 mm. T **42,** as against 2 mm in T **40.**

1903–8. *W* **42.**

No.	Type	Description	Unused	Used
241*a*	**14**	3d. yellow-green, *perf.* 11	4 0	0 9
		b. Perf. 12	2 0	1 0
		c. Perf. 11×12	2 0	0 6
242	,,	3d. dull green, *perf.* 12	15 0	3 0
		a. Perf. 11×12	5 0	1 0
243	**15**	5d. dark blue-green, *p.* 11×12	2 0	1 0
		a. Perf. 11	10 0	1 0
		b. Perf. 12	15 0	6 0

43

1885–86. *T* **43.** *W* **41.**

(i) *Overprinted* "POSTAGE", *in black.*

No.	Description	Unused	Used
44	5s. green and lilac, *perf.* 13		
	a. Perf. 10		
	b. Perf. 12×10	80 0	40 0
45	10s. claret and lilac, *perf.* 13		
	a. Perf. 12	£15	£10
46	£1 claret and lilac, *perf.* 13	—	£60
	a. Perf. 12	£28	£18

(ii) *Overprinted in blue.*

No.	Description	Unused	Used
47	10s. claret and mauve, *perf.* 10	£25	£8
	a. Perf. 12	55 0	30 0
	b. Perf. 12×11	£9	
48	£1 claret and rose-lilac, *perf.* 12×10	£55	

44

Overprinted "POSTAGE" *in blue.*

394. *T* **43.** *W* **44.**

No.	Description	Unused	Used
9	10s. claret and mauve, *p.* 10	£8	45 0
9*a*	10s. claret and violet, *p.* 12	60 0	22 6
	b. Perf. 11	55 0	30 0
	c. Perf. 11×12	60 0	30 0
0	10s. aniline crimson and violet, *perf.* 12×11	60 0	35 0
	a. Perf. 12	£5	50 0
0*b*	£1 claret & violet, *p.* 12×11		

04. *T* **43,** *optd.* "POSTAGE" *in blue. Chalk-surfaced paper.* *W* **44.**

No.	Description	Unused	Used
1	10s. rosine and violet, *perf.* 12	50 0	25 0
	a. Perf. 11	65 0	20 0
	b. Perf. 12×11	65 0	20 0
2	10s. claret & viol, *p.* 12×11	£6	30 0

5. View of Sydney.

46. Emu.

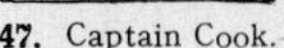

47. Captain Cook.

48. Queen Victoria and Arms of Colony.

49. Lyre bird.

50. Kangaroo.

1888–99. *W* **40.**

No.	Type	Description	Unused	Used
253	**45**	1d. lilac, *perf.* 11×12	0 6	0 4
		a. Perf. 12×11½	12 6	2 6
		b. Perf. 12	2 0	0 6
254	,,	1d. mauve, *perf.* 11×12	0 6	0 4
		a. Perf. 12×11½	5 0	0 9
		b. Perf. 12	3 0	0 6
		c. Imperf. between (pair), perf. 11×12		
255	**46**	2d. Pruss.-bl., *p.* 11×12	0 9	0 2
		a. Perf. 12×11½	6 6	0 6
		b. Perf. 12	3 0	0 2
		c. Imperf. (pair)	50 0	
		d. Imperf. between (horiz. pair), perf. 11×12	£25	
256	,,	2d. chalky-bl., *p.* 11×12	0 9	0 3
		a. Perf. 12×11½		
		b. Perf. 12	4 0	0 6
257	**47**	4d. pur.-brn., *p.* 11×12	2 6	0 6
		a. Perf. 12×11½	30 0	8 6
		b. Perf. 12	22 6	2 6
		c. Perf. 11	£30	£12
258	,,	4d. red-brown, *p.* 11×12	3 6	0 6
		a. Perf. 12×11½	8 6	0 10
		b. Perf. 12	10 0	0 9
259	,,	4d. orge.-brn., *p.* 12×11½	8 6	1 0
260	,,	4d. yell.-brn., *p.* 12×11½	8 6	1 0
261	**48**	6d. carmine, *p.* 11×12	4 0	0 6
		a. Perf. 12×11½	12 6	1 6
		b. Perf. 12	5 0	1 6
262	,,	6d. emerald-green, *perf.* 11×12 (1898)	10 0	4 0
		a. Perf. 12×11½	10 0	4 0
		b. Perf. 12	7 6	3 6
262*c*	,,	6d. orge.-yell., *p.* 11×12 (1899)	6 0	3 0
		d. Perf. 12×11½	4 6	1 3
		e. Perf. 12	10 0	3 0
263	,,	6d. yellow, *perf.* 12×11½	6 6	2 0
264	**49**	8d. lilac rose, *p.* 11×12	6 0	2 0
		a. Perf. 12×11½	45 0	15 0
		b. Perf. 12	6 0	2 6
265	,,	8d. magenta, *p.* 11×12	80 0	12 6
		a. Perf. 12×11½	6 6	2 6
		b. Perf. 12	8 0	3 0
266	**34**	9d. on 10d. red-brn. *perf.* 11×12 (1897)	6 6	5 0
		a. Perf. 12	10 0	8 6
		b. Perf. 11	6 6	6 6
		c. Double surcharge, perf. 11	£7	£6
268	,,	10d. violet, *p.* 11×12 (1897)	5 0	5 0
		a. Perf. 12×11½	4 0	4 0
		b. Perf. 12	10 0	10 0
		c. Perf. 11	10 0	10 0

No.	Type	Description	Unused	Used
269	**50**	1s. maroon, *perf.* 11×12 (1889)	4 6	1 0
		a. Perf. 12×11½	6 6	1 3
		b. Perf. 12	12 6	1 3
270	,,	1s. vio.-brn., *p.* 11×12	4 6	0 6
		a. Perf. 12×11½	30 0	2 0
		b. Perf. 12	30 0	0 9
		c. Imperf. (pair)	£50	

All these perforations, with the exception of perf. 11, are from comb machines.

1888. *W* **41.** *P* 11×12 *comb.*

No.	Type	Description	Unused	Used
271	**45**	1d. lilac	8 6	
272	,,	1d. mauve	5 0	1 3
273	**46**	2d. Prussian blue	35 0	5 0

51. Map of Australia.

52. Capt. Arthur Phillip, first Governor and Lord Carrington, Governor in 1888.

1888–89. *W* **25.** *P* 10.

No.	Type	Description	Unused	Used
274	**51**	5s. deep purple	85 0	35 0
275	,,	5s. deep violet	70 0	30 0
276	**52**	20s. cobalt blue	£8	95 0

53

1890. *W* **53.**

No.	Type	Description	Unused	Used
277	**51**	5s. lilac, *perf.* 10	30 0	15 0
		a. Perf. 11	60 0	50 0
		aa. Imperf. between (horiz. pair)		
		b. Perf. 12	£15	25 0
		c. Perf. 10×11	£8	17 6
278	,,	5s. mauve, *perf.* 10	70 0	25 0
		a. Perf. 11	60 0	30 0

54

1890. *W* **54.**

No.	Type	Description	Unused	Used
279	**52**	20s. cobalt-blue, *perf.* 10	£7	60 0
		a. Perf. 11	£10	£40
		b. Perf. 11×10		
280	,,	20s. ultramarine, *perf.* 11	£7	40 0
		a. Perf. 12	£14	85 0
		b. Perf. 11×12	£6	40 0

55. Allegorical figure of Australia.

1890 (22 Dec.). *W* **40.**

No.	Type	Description	Unused	Used
281	**55**	2½d. ultramarine, *p.* 11×12 *comb*	1 0	0 3
		a. Perf. 12×11½ comb	75 0	
		b. Perf. 12, comb	10 0	0 6

Halfpenny

(56)

Seven-pence
Halfpenny

(57)

1891 (5 Jan.). *Surch. as T* **56** *and* **57.** *Wmk. T* **40**

No.	Type	Description	Unused	Used
282	**26**	½d. on 1d. grey, *perf.* 11×12 *comb*	0 9	0
		a. Surcharge omitted		
		b. Surcharge double		
283	**37**	7½d. on 6d. brown, *p.* 10	3 0	2
		a. Perf. 11	3 6	2
		b. Perf. 12	6 0	4
		c. Perf. 11×12	3 0	2
		d. Perf. 10×12	6 0	3
284	**38**	12½d. on 1s. red, *perf.* 10	7 6	5
		a. Perf. 11	7 6	5
		b. Perf. 11×12, comb	7 6	5
		c. Perf. 12×11½, comb	4 6	4
		d. Perf. 12, comb	8 6	5

58

Die I.

1892 (21 Mar.)–**1899.** *T* **58.** *Die I. Narro*
"H" *in* "HALF". *W* **40.**

No.	Type	Description	Unused	Used
285		½d. grey, *perf.* 10	25 0	0
		a. Perf. 11	£12	10
		b. Perf. 10×12	£10	17
		c. Perf. 11×12	0 6	0
		d. Perf. 12	1 6	0
286		½d. slate, *perf.* 11×12 (1897)	0 6	0
		a. Perf. 12×11½	0 6	0
		b. Perf. 12	0 6	0
		c. Imperf. between (horiz. pair) perf. 11×12	£25	
287		½d. bluish grn., *p.* 11×12 ('99)	2 6	
		a. Perf. 12×11½	0 9	0
		b. Perf. 12	2 0	0

The perforations 11×12, 12×11½, 12, are fro
comb machines.

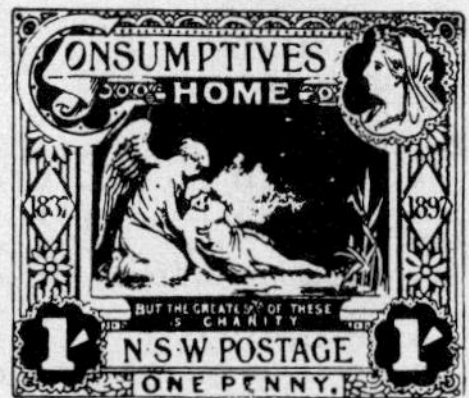

58*a*

Illustration reduced. Actual size 47×38 mm.

58*b*

Illustration reduced. Actual size 38×46 mm.

1897. *Charity. T* **58***a and* **58***b. Wmk. T* **40.** *P* 12×11 (1*d.*) *or* 11 (2½*d.*).

No.	Description	Unused	Used
287*c*	1d. (1s.), green and brown	75 0	75 0
287*d*	2½d. (2s. 6d.), gold, carmine and blue	£18	£20

These stamps, sold at 1s. and 2s. 6d. respec-ively, paid postage of 1d. and 2½d. only, the ifference being given to a Consumptives' Home.

59

60

61

Dies of the 1d.

Die I.

Die II.

1d. Die I.—The first pearl on the crown on the t side is merged into the arch, the shading der the fleur-de-lis is indistinct, the "s" of WALES" is open.

Die II.—The first pearl is circular, the vertical ading under the fleur-de-lis clear, the "s" of WALES" not so open.

Dies of the 2½d.

Die I.

Die II.

2½d. Die I.—There are 12 radiating lines in the star on the Queen's breast.

Die II.—There are 16 radiating lines in the star and the eye is nearly full of colour.

1897–99. *W* **40.**

No.	Type	Description	Unused	Used
288	**59**	1d. carm. (Die I), *p.* 11×12	2 0	0 4
		a. Perf. 12×11½	2 6	0 4
289	,,	1d. scar. (Die I), *p.* 11×12	1 6	0 4
		a. Perf. 12×11½	6 0	1 6
		b. Perf. 12	6 0	2 0
290	,,	1d. rose-carmine (Die II), *perf.* 11×12	2 0	0 2
		a. Perf. 12×11½	1 6	0 2
		b. Perf. 12	1 6	0 2
		c. Imperf. between (pair)	£25	
291	,,	1d. salmon-red (Die II), *perf.* 12×11½	1 6	0 3
		a. Perf. 12	4 6	1 0
292	**60**	2d. deep dull blue, *perf.* 11×12	1 0	0 3
		a. Perf. 12×11½	1 0	0 4
		b. Perf. 12	3 0	0 6
293	,,	2d. cobalt-bl. *perf.* 11×12	2 0	0 4
		a. Perf. 12×11½	2 6	0 3
		b. Perf. 12	4 0	0 4
294	,,	2d. ultram., *perf.* 11×12	2 0	0 3
		a. Perf. 12×11½	1 0	0 2
		b. Perf. 12	1 6	0 4
		c. Imperf. between (pair)		
295	**61**	2½d. pur. (Die I), *p.* 12×11	2 6	0 8
		a. Perf. 11½×12	6 0	0 9
		b. Perf. 11	5 0	1 6
296	,,	2½d. deep violet (Die II), *perf.* 12×11	2 6	0 8
		a. Perf. 11½×12	7 6	1 3
		b. Perf. 12	2 0	1 0
297	,,	2½d. Pruss. blue, *p.* 12×11	8 6	
		a. Perf. 11½×12	2 6	0 8
		b. Perf. 12	3 0	1 6

The perforations 11×12, 12×11½, and 12 are from comb machines, the perforation 11 is from a single-line machine.

1899 (Oct.). *Chalk-surfaced paper.* *W* **40.** *P* 12×11½ *or* 11½×12 (2½*d.*), *comb.*

No.	Type	Description	Unused	Used
298	**58**	½d. blue-green (Die I)	0 6	0 2
		a. Imperf.	15 0	12 6
299	**59**	1d. carmine (Die II)	0 6	0 2
300	,,	1d. scarlet (Die II)	0 4	0 2
301	,,	1d. salmon-red (Die II)	0 6	0 2
		a. Imperf.	12 6	12 6
302	**60**	2d. cobalt-blue	0 9	0 2
		a. Imperf.	12 6	
303	**61**	2½d. Pruss. blue (Die II)	1 0	0 2
		a. Imperf.	20 0	
303*b*	**47**	4d. red-brown	2 6	0 8
		c. Imperf.	£6	
304	,,	4d. orange-brown	2 6	0 6
305	**48**	6d. deep orange	3 6	0 6
		a. Imperf.	35 0	
306	,,	6d. orange-yellow	3 6	0 8
307	,,	6d. emerald-green	17 6	2 6
		a. Imperf.	60 0	
308	**49**	8d. magenta	4 0	2 0
309	**34**	9d. on 10d. dull brown	3 6	2 0
		a. Surcharge double	£5	70 0
		b. Without surcharge	£5	
310	,,	10d. violet	5 0	4 0
311	**50**	1s. maroon	3 6	0 9
312	,,	1s. purple-brown	3 0	3 0
		a. Imperf.	60 0	

62. Lyre bird.

63

1902. *Chalk-surfaced paper.* *W* **42.** *P* 12 × 11½ *or* 11½ × 12 (2½*d.*), *comb.*

313 **58** ½d. blue-green, (Die I) .. 3 6 0 2
a. Perf. 12 × 11 .. .. 2 6
314 **59** 1d. carmine (Die II) .. 0 6 0 2
315 **60** 2d. cobalt-blue 0 9 0 2
316 **61** 2½d. dark blue (Die II) .. 1 6 0 2
317 **47** 4d. orange-brown .. 12 6 0 6
318 **48** 6d. yellow-orange .. 8 0 1 0
319 ,, 6d. orange 6 0 1 0
320 ,, 6d. orange-buff .. 4 0 1 0
321 **49** 8d. magenta 6 0 1 3
322 **34** 9d. on 10d. brnish. orge. 3 6 4 0
323 ,, 10d. violet 15 0 6 0
324 **50** 1s. maroon 4 6 1 0
325 ,, 1s. purple-brown .. 6 0 0 8
326 **62** 2s. 6d. green 15 0 4 6

1903. *Wmk. double-lined V over Crown, Type* w. **10.**

327 **63** 9d. brown & ultramarine, *perf.* 12¼ × 12½, *comb...* 6 6 3 0
328 ,, 9d. brown & deep blue, *perf.* 12¼ × 12½, *comb...* 6 6 3 0
329 ,, 9d. brown & blue, *perf.* 11 £50 £25

Die II. Broad "H" in "HALF"

66

1905–10. *W* **66.** *P* 12 × 11½ *or* 11½ × 12 (2½*d.*) *comb, unless otherwise stated. Chalk-surfaced paper.*

330 **58** ½d. blue-green (Die I) .. 2 6 0 6
a. Perf. 11½ × 11 .. ..
331 ,, ½d. blue-green (Die II) .. 0 6 0 2
a. Perf. 11½ × 11 .. .. 1 6
332 **59** 1d. rose-carm. (Die II) .. 0 6 0 2
a. Perf. 11½ × 11 .. .. 3 6
333 **60** 2d. deep ultramarine .. 0 9 0 2
b. Perf. 11½ × 11 .. .. 1 6
333*d* ,, 2d. milky blue (1910) .. 1 0 0 2
e. Perf. 11 .. .. £6
334 **61** 2½d. Prussian blue (Die II) 1 6 0 4
335 **47** 4d. orange-brown .. 3 0 0 6
336 ,, 4d. red-brown 6 0 1 6
337 **48** 6d. dull yellow 6 0 1 0
a. Perf. 11½ × 11 .. .. 15 0
338 ,, 6d. orange-yellow .. 6 0 1 0
a. Perf. 11½ × 11 .. .. 10 0
339 ,, 6d. deep orange 2 6 0 4
a. Perf. 11 .. .. £20
339*b* **48** 6d. orange-buff 4 0 0 6
c. Perf. 11½ × 11 .. .. 7 6 4 0
340 **49** 8d. magenta 6 0 1 6
341 ,, 8d. lilac-rose 6 0 3 0
342 **34** 10d. violet 8 0 4 6
a. Perf. 11½ × 11 .. .. 6 0 3 6
b. Perf. 11 .. .. 6 0 3 0
343 **50** 1s. maroon 5 0 0 6
344 ,, 1s. purple-brown (1908) 5 0 0 6
345 **62** 2s. 6d. blue-green .. 15 0 4 0
a. Perf. 11½ × 11 .. .. 7 6 2 0
b. Perf. 11 .. .. 10 0 6 0

67

T **25.** *W* **67.**

346 20s. cobalt-blue, *perf.* 11 80 0 35 0
a. Perf. 12 .. .. .. 80 0 35 0
b. Perf. 11 × 12.. .. 70 0 30 0

1907. *Wmk. double-lined "A" and Crown* *T* w. **11.**

347 **63** 9d. brown and ultramarine *p.* 12 × 12½, *comb* 4 6 2 0
a. Perf. 11 .. .. £5 £5
348 ,, 9d. yell.-brn. & ultram. *p.* 12 × 12½, *comb* .. 4 0 1 0

1906. *Wmk.* *T* w. **11.** *P* 12 × 11½ *or* 11½ × 12 (2½*d.*), *comb, unless otherwise stated.*

349 **58** ½d. blue-green (Die I) .. 3 6 1
351 **59** 1d. dull rose (Die II) .. 1 6 1
352 **60** 2d. cobalt-blue 1 0 0
353 **61** 2½d. Pruss. blue (Die II) 20 0
354 **47** 4d. orange-brown .. 6 0 4
355 **48** 6d. orange-buff 15 0 6
356 ,, 6d. dull yellow 12 6 5
357 **49** 8d. magenta 8 6 5
358 **34** 10d. violet, *perf.* 11 .. 15 0
359 **50** 1s. purple-brown .. 10 0 6
360 **62** 2s. 6d. blue-green .. 25 0 15

OFFICIAL STAMPS.

Various stamps overprinted.

O S

(101)

There is a variety in this overprint, the spac between the letters being 8½ mm. instead 7½ mm. On the larger stamps (5s., etc.) th spacing is wider (11 to 14 mm.).

1879. *Overprinted with T* **101.** *W* **36.**

401 **26** 1d. salmon, *perf.* 10 .. £25 50
a. Perf. 13 .. .. 12 6 2
b. Perf. 10 × 13 .. .. 75 0 5
402 **28** 2d. blue, *perf.* 13 .. 12 6 2
a. Perf. 10 × 13 .. .. 75 0 5
b. Perf. 11 × 12 .. .. — £
c. Perf. 10 .. .. £20 60
403 **14** 3d. green (R.), *perf.* 13 — £
404 ,, 3d. yellow-green, *p.* 10 £15 60
a. Perf. 13 .. .. £30
b. Perf. 10 × 13 .. .. £20 £
c. Wmk. "6". Perf. 13 .. — £
405 **32** 4d. red-brown, *p.* 10 .. — £
a. Perf. 13 .. .. £15 20
b. Perf. 10 × 13 .. .. £25 25
406 **15** 5d. green, *perf.* 10 .. 12 6 15
407 **37** 6d. pale lilac, *perf.* 10 .. —
a. Perf. 13 .. .. £25 10
b. Perf. 10 × 13 .. .. —

408 **19** 8d. yellow (R.), *p.* 13 .. — £15
409 ,, 8d. yellow, *perf.* 10 .. £25 £8
a. Perf. 13 .. .. — 12 6
410 **34** 9d. on 10d. brown, *p.* 10 £20
411 **38** 1s. black (R.), *perf.* 10 .. — 40 0
a. Perf. 13 .. .. £20 12 6
b. Perf. 10×13 .. .. — 50 0

1894 (30 June). *Wmk.* **"10"**. *T* **35.**
412 **34** 10d. lilac, *perf.* 10 .. £6 £9
a. Perf. 11×10 .. .. £12 £18

1880 (15 Feb.). *Wmk.* **"5/-"**. *T* **25.**
413 **24** 5s. deep purple, *p.* 10 .. 80 0 40 0
a. Perf. 11 .. .. 60 0 40 0
b. Perf. 13 .. .. £5 50 0
c. Perf. 10×12 .. .. £5 90 0

1882. *Stamps of same date. W* **40.**
414 **26** 1d. salmon, *perf.* 10 .. 10 0 2 0
a. Perf. 10×13 .. .. — £20
415 ,, 1d. aniline scarlet, *p.* 10 5 0 0 6
a. Perf. 12×10 .. .. — £15
b. Perf. 11×12 .. .. 0 3 0 2
c. Perf. 10×13 .. .. — £20
416 **28** 2d. blue, *perf.* 10 .. 2 0 0 6
a. Perf. 10×13 .. .. £25 £7
b. Perf. 11×12 .. .. 0 8 0 4
417 **14** 3d. yellow-green, *p.* 10 2 6 1 0
a. Perf. 12 .. .. £15 £10
c. Perf. 10×12 .. .. 3 0 2 0
418 ,, 3d. bluish green, *p.* 10 .. 2 6 1 6
a. Perf. 11 .. .. — £10
b. Perf. 12 .. .. £15 £10
c. Perf. 10×12 .. .. 3 0 5 0
d. Perf. 10×11 .. .. 2 6 2 6
419 **32** 4d. red-brown, *p.* 10 .. 40 0 4 0
b. Perf. 10×12 .. .. — £10
d. Perf. 11×12 .. .. 1 6 1 6
420 ,, 4d. dark brown, *p.* 10 .. 20 0 2 0
a. Perf. 12 .. .. £25 £20
b. Perf. 10×12 .. .. £25 £10
c. Perf. 11×12 .. .. 1 0 1 0
421 **15** 5d. dull green, *p.* 10 .. 80 0 20 0
a. Perf. 11
b. Perf. 12 .. .. £10
c. Perf. 10×11 .. .. 2 6 2 6
d. Perf. 10×12 .. .. £20 £5
22 ,, 5d. blue-green, *perf.* 10 £5
23 **37** 6d. pale lilac, *perf.* 10 3 6 1 6
a. Perf. 11 .. .. 6 0 1 6
24 ,, 6d. mauve, *perf.* 10 .. 2 6 0 9
a. Perf. 12 .. .. £5
b. Perf. 10×11 .. .. 3 6 2 0
c. Perf. 10×12 .. .. 1 6 1 3
d. Perf. 11×12 .. .. £5 40 0
25 **19** 8d. yellow, *perf.* 10 .. 3 6 2 6
a. Perf. 11 .. .. 6 0 4 0
b. Perf. 12 .. .. £15 £5
c. Perf 10×12 .. .. 3 6 3 6
26 **38** 1s. black (R.), *perf.* 10 1 6 0 9
a. Perf. 11
b. Perf. 10×13 .. .. — £5
c. Perf. 11×12 .. .. 1 6 1 0

Varieties in this issue may be found with the O" sideways, or with double overprint.

Wmk. "N S W", *T* **41.**
27 **26** 1d. scarlet, *perf.* 10 .. 40 0 7 6

O S
(102)

87–90. *Long fiscal stamps, T* **43,** *optd. with T* **102,** *in black.* "POSTAGE" *in blue. W* **41.**
8 10s. claret and mauve, *p.* 10 .. £100 £50
a. Perf. 12 .. .. £15 £10

Overprinted with T **101,** *in black.*
9 10s. claret and mauve, *p.* 12 .. — £15

O S
(103)

Overprinted with T **103,** *in black.*
430 £1 claret and rose-lilac, *perf.* 12×10 .. .. .. £100

1888–89. *Overprinted as T* **101,** *in black.*
(i) *W* **40.**
431 **45** 1d. mauve, *p.* 11×12 .. 0 3 0 2
a. Perf. 12 .. .. 0 6 0 4
432 ,, 1d. lilac, *p.* 11×12 .. 0 3 0 2
a. Perf. 12 .. .. 0 9 0 6
433 **46** 2d. Prussian bl., *p.* 11×12 0 4 0 2
a. Perf. 12 .. .. 0 5 0 2
434 **47** 4d. purple-brn., *p.* 11×12 1 6 0 8
a. Perf. 12 .. .. 6 0 1 0
b. Perf. 11 .. ..
435 ,, 4d. red-brown, *p.* 11×12 0 8 0 4
a. Perf. 12 .. .. 5 0 0 9
436 **48** 6d. carmine, *p.* 11×12 .. 1 0 0 6
a. Perf. 13 .. .. 6 0 1 3
437 **49** 8d. lilac-rose, *p.* 11×12 .. 1 6 1 0
a. Perf. 12 .. .. — 10 0
438 **50** 1s. maroon, *p.* 11×12 .. 2 3 0 6
a. Perf. 12 .. .. 4 6 1 3
439 ,, 1s. pur.-brown, *p.* 11×12 2 3 0 6
a. Perf. 12 .. .. 3 6 1 0
(ii) *W* **41** (1889).
439*b* **45** 1d. mauve, *p.* 11×12 ..
439*c* **46** 2d. blue, *p.* 11×12 ..

1888–89. *Optd. as T* **101.** *W* **25.** *P* 10.
440 **51** 5s. deep purple (R.) .. £40 £40
441 **52** 20s. cobalt £100

1890 (Feb.). *As last, but W* **53** *and* **54.**
442 **51** 5s. lilac, *perf.* 10 .. .. 32 6 22 6
a. Perf. 12 .. .. 60 0 50 0
443 **52** 20s. cobalt, *perf.* 10 .. £100

1891–92. *Types of same date optd. as T* **101.** *W* **40.**
444 **26** ½d. on 1d. grey, *p.* 11×12 10 0 10 0
445 **55** 2½d. ultram., *p.* 11×12 .. 1 0 0 9
446 **37** 7½d. on 6d. brown, *p.* 10 .. 3 0 10 0
447 **38** 12½d. on 1s. red, *p.* 11×12 4 0 10 0
448 **58** ½d. grey, *perf.* 10 .. 2 0 5 0
a. Perf. 11×12 .. .. 0 4 1 0
b. Perf. 12×11½ 6 6
c. Perf. 12 .. .. 0 8 1 0

POSTAGE DUE STAMPS.

D 1

1891 (1 Jan.)–**1892.** *W* **40.**
501 D 1 ½d. green, *perf.* 10 .. 0 3 0 4
502 ,, 1d. green, *perf.* 10 .. 0 3 0 6
a. Perf. 11 .. .. 0 3 0 3
b. Perf. 12 .. .. 12 6 7 6
c. Perf. 10×12 .. .. — 3 0
d. Perf. 10×11 .. .. 5 0 1 0
e. Perf. 11×12 .. .. 0 7 0 6
503 ,, 2d. green, *perf.* 10 .. 0 6 0 4
a. Perf. 11 .. .. 0 6 0 6
b. Perf. 12 .. ..
c. Perf. 10×12 .. .. 12 6 10 0
d. Perf. 10×11 .. .. 5 0 2 0
e. Perf. 11×12 .. .. 1 0 0 6
504 ,, 3d. green, *perf.* 10 .. 2 0 1 6
a. Perf. 10×11 .. .. 2 0 1 6
505 ,, 4d. green, *perf.* 10 .. 4 6 2 6
a. Perf. 11 .. ..
b. Perf 10×11 .. .. 1 6 0 9
506 ,, 6d. green, *perf.* 10 .. 2 0 2 0
507 ,, 8d. green, *perf.* 10 .. 2 0 1 6

No.	Type	Description	Unused	Used
508	D 1	5s. green, *perf.* 10	10 0	8 6
		a. Perf. 11	£6	£6
		b. Perf. 11×12		
509	,,	10s. green, *perf.* 10	£8	
		a. Perf. 10×12	25 0	
510	,,	20s. green, *perf.* 10	£8	15 0
		a. Perf. 12	£8	
		b. Perf. 10×12	30 0	20 0

1900. *Chalk-surfaced paper.* W **40.**

No.	Type	Description	Unused	Used
511	D 1	½d. emerald-green, *p.* 11		
512	,,	1d. emerald-green, *p.* 11	3 6	2 6
		a. Perf. 12	20 0	10 0
		b. Perf. 11×12	0 6	0 3
513		2d. emerald-green, *p.* 11	3 0	3 0
		a. Perf. 11×12	1 6	1 0
514	,,	3d. emer.-grn. *p.* 11×12	5 0	2 6
515	,,	4d. emerald-green, *p.* 11	3 6	2 6

New South Wales now uses stamps of Australia.

NEW ZEALAND.

— SIMPLIFICATION (see INTRODUCTION)—

Nos. 1 to 142.

1, 2, 3. 4, 5, 6. 8, 10, 13.
35, 39, 40, 41, 43, 44.
97, 98, 99, 100. 107, 108, 106.
110, 111, 114, 115, 74, 117, 118, 119, 120, 75, 122, 125.
132. 133, 134, 136, 137, 138, 139. 140, 141.

Nos. 143 to 245.

Omit shades and perfs.
Disregard blued paper in 1874 issue.

Nos. 246 to 291.

Make one set of these two issues, selecting cheapest shades. Include marked shades if desired.

Nos. 292 to 448.

These fall into the following groups, in each of which perfs. and papers might be omitted where they occur, and only the most distinct shades taken :—

Wmk. **36a.** 292 to 305. 314 to 332.
No wmk 307 to 312. 313. 333 to 339.
Wmk. **41.** 340 to 414. (Omit 418 to 423*a*.) 428 to 429*a*.
Exhibition. 424 to 427.
Reduced sizes, etc. 430, etc. 1d., 3d., 6d., and 1s. only.

Later Issues.

Omit perfs.. papers and shades.

1

(Eng. by Humphrys. Recess. Perkins, Bacon.)

Type **1.**

1855 (18 JULY). *Wmk. Large Star, T* w. **1.** *Imperf.*

No.	Description	Unused	Used
1	1d. dull carmine (*white p.*)	£700	£425
2	2d. dull blue (*blued p.*)	£400	£70
	a. White paper	£350	£80
3	1s. pale yellow-green (*blued p.*)	£700	£250
	a. Half of 1s. used as 6d. (on cover)	—	£450
	b. White paper	£800	£300

Specimens of Nos. 2*a* and 3*b* are on paper which shows no blueing, but these no doubt come from sheets which were more or less blued in parts. These varieties must be in the identical shades of colour of the blued stamps. All 2d. and 1s. stamps, wmk. Star, dated prior to 1862, belong to this issue.

(Printed by J. Richardson, Auckland, N.Z.)

1855 (Nov.). *Blue paper. No wmk. Imperf.*

No.	Description	Unused	Used
4	1d. red	£225	£75
5	2d. blue	£160	£35
	a. Without value		
6	1s. green	£550	£185
	a. Half of 1s. used as 6d. (on cover)	—	£400

These stamps on blue paper may occasionally be found wmkd. double-lined letters, being portions of the paper-maker's name.

1857 (JAN.). *Wmk. Large Star. White paper similar to the issue of July,* 1855.

No.	Description	Unused	Used
7	1d. dull orange	—	£700

This stamp is in the precise shade of the 1d. of the 1858 printing by Richardson on *no wmk.* white paper. An unsevered pair is known with Dunedin cancellation on a cover bearing arrival postmark of Auckland dated " 19.1.1857 ".

1858-59. *Hard or soft white paper. No wmk.*

(*a*) *Imperf.*

No.	Description	Unused	Used
8	1d. dull orange (1858)	£45	£28
8*a*	2d. deep ultram. (1858)	£150	£65
9	2d. pale blue	£45	£18
10	2d. blue	£45	£18
11	2d. dull deep blue	—	£20
12	6d. bistre-brown (Aug. '59)	£175	£60
13	6d. brown	£45	£24
14	6d. pale brown	£45	£24
15	6d. chestnut	£150	£45
16	1s. dull emerald-green	£250	£10
17	1s. blue-green	£250	£10

(*b*) *Pin-roulette, about* 10.

No.	Description	Unused	Used
18	1d. dull orange	—	£10
19	2d. blue	—	£85
20	6d. brown	—	£12
21	1s. blue-green	—	£18

(*c*) *Serrated perf. about* 16 *or* 18.

No.	Description	Unused	Used
22	1d. dull orange	—	£17
23	2d. blue	—	£16
24	6d. brown	—	£15
25	6d. chestnut	—	£22
26	1s. blue-green	—	£22

(*d*) *Rouletted* 7.

No.	Description	Unused	Used
27	1d. dull orange	£185	£13
28	2d. blue	£275	£9
29	6d. brown	£135	£9
	a. Imperf. between (pair)	£275	£25
30	1s. dull emerald-green	£275	£20
31	1s. blue-green	£325	£22

Other forms of separation, in addition t those shown above, are known, both on th stamps of this issue and on those of 186 Some of the varieties are extremely rare, onl single copies being known.

1862. (*e*) *P* 13.

No.	Description	Unused	Used
31*a*	1d. dull orange	—	£17
31*b*	2d. pale blue	£250	£13
32	6d. pale brown		

(Printed by John Davies at the G.P.O., Auckland, N.Z.)

1862 (FEB.). *Wmk. Large Star.* (*a*) *Imperf.*

No.	Description	Unused	Used
33	1d. orange-vermilion	£18	£1
34	1d. vermilion	£18	£
35	1d. carmine-vermilion	£20	£1
36	2d. deep blue (Plate I)	£15	90
37	2d. slate-blue (Plate I)	£100	£
38	2d. blue (Plate I)	£12	90
39	2d. pale blue (Pl. I, worn state)	£12	90
40	3d. brown-lilac	£18	£
41	6d. black-brown	£35	£
42	6d. brown	£45	£
43	6d. red-brown	£22	£
44	1s. green	£45	£
45	1s. yellow-green	£40	£
46	1s. deep green	£50	£

1862 (JUNE). (*b*) *Rouletted* 7.

No.	Description	Unused	Used
47	1d. orange-vermilion	£185	£
48	1d. vermilion	£90	£
48*a*	1d. carmine-vermilion		

49	2d. deep blue	£70	£25
50	2d. slate-blue	£125	£60
51	2d. pale blue	£75	£25
52	3d. brown-lilac	£90	£35
53	6d. black-brown	£70	£25
54	6d. brown	£60	£20
55	6d. red-brown	£60	£20
56	1s. green	£85	£35
57	1s. yellow-green	£80	£35
58	1s. deep green..	£100	£65

1862 (Aug.). (*c*) *Serrated perf.* 14 *or* 16.

59	1d. orange-vermilion	—	£90
60	2d. deep blue	—	£80
	a. Imperf. between (pair) ..	£275	£300
61	2d. slate-blue		
62	3d. brown-lilac	—	£135
63	6d. black-brown	—	£175
64	6d. brown	—	£175
65	1s. yellow-green	—	£200

1862 (Aug.). (*d*) *Pin-perf.* 10.

66	2d. deep blue	—	£200
67	6d. black-brown	—	£200

The dates put to above varieties are the earliest that have been met with.

1862. *Wmk. Large Star.* P 13 (*at Dunedin*)

68	1d. orange-vermilion	£35	£18
69	1d. carmine-vermilion ..	£35	£18
70	2d. deep blue (Plate I) ..	£25	£5
71	2d. slate-blue (Plate I) ..	—	£100
72	2d. blue (Plate I)	£18	80 0
73	2d. pale blue (Plate I) ..	£22	£6
74	3d. brown-lilac	£45	£15
75	6d. black-brown	£30	85 0
	a. Imperf. between (horiz. pair) ..		
76	6d. brown	£30	90 0
77	6d. red-brown	£25	75 0
78	1s. dull green	£25	£15
79	1s deep green..	£40	£20
80	1s. yellow-green	£25	£15

1862. *Pelure paper. No wmk.* (*a*) *Imperf.*

81	1d. orange-vermilion	£250	£95
82	2d. ultramarine	£225	£65
83	2d. pale ultramarine	£225	£65
84	3d. lilac	£2000	
85	6d. black-brown	£80	£32
86	1s. deep green..	£225	£60

The 3d. is known only unused.

(*b*) *Rouletted* 7.

87	1d. orange-vermilion	—	£225
88	6d. black-brown	£135	£60
89	1s. deep green..	£225	£125

(*c*) P 13.

90	1d. orange-vermilion	£450	£250
91	2d. ultramarine	£225	£75
92	2d. pale ultramarine	£225	£70
93	6d. black-brown	£200	£40
94	1s. deep green..	£250	£80

(*d*) *Serrated perf.* 15.

95	6d. black-brown	—	£275

1863 (early). *Hard or soft white paper. No wmk.*

(*a*) *Imperf.*

96	2d. dull deep blue (*shades*) ..	£150	£45

(*b*) P 13.

96*a*	2d. dull deep blue (*shades*) ..	£120	£35

These stamps show slight beginnings of wear of the printing plate in the background to right of the Queen's ear, as one looks at the stamps. By the early part of 1864, the wear of the plate had spread, more or less, all over the background of the circle containing the head. The major portion of the stamps of this printing appears to have been consigned to Dunedin and to have been there perforated 13.

NZ

2

1864. *Wmk.* "N Z", *T* **2.** (*a*) *Imperf.*

97	1d. carmine-vermilion	£45	£20
98	2d. pale blue (Pl. I worn) ..	£50	£20
99	6d. red-brown	£200	£50
100	1s. green	£50	£25

(*b*) *Rouletted* 7.

101	1d. carmine-vermilion	£300	£185
102	2d. pale blue (Plate I worn)	£100	£60
103	6d. red-brown	£225	£160
104	1s. green	£120	£65

(*c*) P 13 (*at Dunedin*).

104*a*	1d. carmine-vermilion	£350	£250
105	2d. pale blue (Plate I worn)	£50	£16
106	1s. green	£80	£35
	a. Imperf. between (horiz. pair) ..	£275	

(*d*) P 12½ (*at Auckland*).

106*b*	1d. carmine-vermilion	£350	£250
107	2d. pale blue (Plate I worn)	£8	70 0
108	6d. red-brown	£16	70 0
109	1s. yellow-green	—	£250

1864–67. *Wmk. Large Star.* P 12½ (*at Auckland*).

110	1d. carmine-vermilion (1864)	£6	40 0
111	1d. pale orange-vermilion ..	£5	35 0
	a. Imperf. (pair)	£75	£65
112	1d. orange	£14	£5
113	2d. p. blue (Pl. I worn) (1864)	70 0	25 0
114	2d. dp. blue (Pl. II) (1866)	60 0	25 0
	a. Imperf. between (pair) ..	—	£150
115	2d. blue (Plate II)	60 0	25 0
	a. Retouched (Plate II) (1867) ..	£12	65 0
	b. Perf. 10 × 12½ (Plate II) ..	—	£375
	c. Imperf. (pair) (Plate II) ..	£50	£50
	d. Retouched. Imperf. (pair) ..	£70	£60
116	3d. brown-lilac (1864) ..	£65	£40
117	3d. lilac	75 0	32 6
	a. Imperf. (pair)	£32	£15
118	3d. deep mauve	£22	75 0
	a. Imperf. (pair)	£125	£60
119	4d. deep rose (1865) ..	£20	£10
120	4d. yellow (1865)	£5	60 0
121	4d. orange	£85	£50
122	6d. red-brown (1864) ..	£6	35 0
122*a*	6d. brown	110 0	35 0
	b. Imperf. (pair)	£55	£50
123	1s. deep green (1864) ..	£38	£12
124	1s. green	£30	£8
125	1s. yellow-green	£8	90 0

1871. *Wmk. Large Star.* (*a*) P 10.

126	1d. brown	£22	£6

(*b*) P 10 × 12½.

127	1d. brown	75 0	35 0
128	2d. vermilion..	£5	35 0
	a. Retouched	£15	75 0
129	6d. deep blue..	£65	£35
130	6d. blue	£65	£35
	a. Imperf. between (vert. pair) ..	£300	

(*c*) P 12½.

131	1d. brown	45 0	40 0
132	1d. pale brown	45 0	40 0
	a. Imperf. between (vert. pair) ..	—	£90
133	2d. orange	60 0	25 0
	a. Retouched	£12	60 0
134	2d. vermilion..	90 0	30 0
	a. Retouched	£18	85 0
135	6d. blue	75 0	40 0
136	6d. pale blue	75 0	40 0

In or about 1872 both 1d. and 2d. stamps were printed on some paper having a wmk. of script letters "W.T. & Co." (= Wiggins Teape & Co.) in the sheet, and other paper with the name "T. H. Saunders" in double-lined caps in the sheet: portions of these letters are occasionally found on stamps.

1872. *No wmk.* P 12½.

137	1d. brown	£22	£6
138	2d. vermilion..	70 0	35 0
	a. Retouched	£18	85 0
139	4d. orange-yellow	£15	£35

1872. *Wmk.* "N Z", *T* **2.** P 12½.

140	1d. brown	£550	£200

141	2d. vermilion	£22	£7
	a. Retouched	£35	£18

1872. *Wmk. Lozenges, with the word* " INVICTA " *in double-lined capitals in middle of sheet.* *P* 12½.

142	2d. vermilion	£220	£50
	a. Retouched	£275	£75

3

4

(Des. John Davies. Die eng. on wood in Melbourne. Printed from electrotypes at Govt. Ptg. Office, Wellington.)

1873 (1 Jan.). *T* **3.** (*a*) *Wmk.* " NZ ", *T* **2.**

143	½d. pale dull rose (*p.* 10) ..	60 0	30 0
144	½d. pale dull rose (*p.* 12½) ..	£10	70 0
145	½d. pale dull rose (*p.* 12½ × 10)	£6	60 0
	(*b*) *No wmk.*		
146	½d. pale dull rose (*p.* 10) ..	60 0	30 0
147	½d. pale dull rose (*p.* 12½) ..	£10	70 0
148	½d. pale dull rose (*p.* 12½ × 10)	£6	60 0

As the paper used for Nos. 143–145 was originally intended for fiscal stamps which were more than twice as large, about one-third of the impressions fall on portions of the sheet showing no watermark, giving rise to varieties Nos. 146–148. In later printings of No. 151 a few stamps in each sheet are without watermark. These can be distinguished from No. 147 by the shade.

1875 (Jan.). *T* **3.** *Wmk. Star, T* **4.**

149	½d. pale dull rose (*p.* 12½) ..	3 0	0 6
	a. Imperf. between (pair) ..	£12	£8
150	½d. pale dull rose (*p. nearly* 12)	70 0	6 0

1892 (June). *T* **3.** *Wmk.* " N Z *and Star* ", *T* **12a.**

151	½d. bright rose (*shades*) (*p.* 12½)	1 3	0 6
	a. No wmk.	7 6	5 0

5

6

7

8

9

10

11

12

12a

(T **5–10** eng. by De La Rue & Co. T **11** and **12** des., eng. & plates by Bock & Cousins, Wellington. Typo. Govt. Ptg. Office, Wellington.)

1874 (1 Jan.). *W* **12a.**

A. *White paper.* (*a*) *P* 12½.

152	**5**	1d. lilac	25 0	3 0
		a. Imperf.	£14	
153	**6**	2d. rose	25 0	2 0
154	**7**	3d. brown	90 0	45 0
155	**8**	4d. maroon	£12	60 0
156	**9**	6d. blue	£6	17 6
157	**10**	1s. green	£60	45 0
		(*b*) *Perf. nearly* 12.		
158	**6**	2d. rose	£14	£6
158*a*	**8**	4d. maroon		
		(*c*) *Perf. compound of* 12½ *and* 10.		
159	**5**	1d. lilac	85 0	25 0
160	**6**	2d. rose	£20	65
161	**7**	3d. brown	£6	60
162	**8**	4d. maroon	£15	£6
163	**9**	6d. blue	£5	25
164	**10**	1s. green	£60	55 0
		(*d*) *Perf. nearly* 12 × 12½.		
164*a*	**5**	1d. lilac	£18	£11
165	**6**	2d. rose	£18	£9

B. *Blued paper.* (*a*) *P* 12½.

166	**5**	1d. lilac	65 0	20
167	**6**	2d. rose	45 0	20
168	**7**	3d. brown	£6	50
169	**8**	4d. maroon	£15	90
170	**9**	6d. blue	£6	30
171	**10**	1s. green	£60	£2
		(*b*) *Perf. compound of* 12½ *and* 10.		
172	**5**	1d. lilac	£7	40
173	**6**	2d. rose	£22	60
174	**7**	3d. brown	£7	70
175	**8**	4d. maroon	£20	£
176	**9**	6d. blue	£6	40
177	**10**	1s. green	£60	£2

1875. *Wmk. Large Star.* *T* w. **1.** *P* 12½.

178	**5**	1d. deep lilac	£15	70
179	**6**	2d. rose	£7	15

1878. *W* **12a.** *P* 12 × 11½ (*comb*).

180	**5**	1d. mauve-lilac	15 0	2
181	**6**	2d. rose	17 6	1
182	**8**	4d. maroon	£6	35
183	**9**	6d. blue	45 0	17
184	**10**	1s. green	80 0	35
185	**11**	2s. deep rose	£10	£
186	**12**	5s. grey	£12	£

This perforation is made by a horizonta "comb" machine, giving a gauge of 12 hori zontally and about 11¾ vertically. Single specimens can be found apparently gauging 11½ all round or 12 all round, but these are all from the same machine. The perforation described above as "nearly 12" was from a single-line machine.

13 14 15 16 17 18 19 20 21 22

Eng. Bock & Cousins. Typo. Govt. Ptg. Office.)

882–97. *T* **13** *to* **22.** *W* **12***a*.

(*a*) *P* 12×11½.

87	½d. black (1895)	20	0	45	0
88	1d. rose	7	6	0	6
	a. Imperf. between (pair)				
89	2d. lilac	10	0	0	9
	a. Imperf. between (pair)				
90	2½d. blue (1891)	15	0	6	0
91	2½d. ultramarine	25	0	6	0
92	2½d. pale ultramarine	25	0	6	0
193	3d. yellow	17	6	5	0
194	3d. orange	17	6	5	0
195	4d. green	15	0	3	0
196	5d. olive-black (1891)	10	0	6	0
197	6d. brown	22	6	6	0
198	8d. blue	25	0	22	6
199	1s. brown-red	30	0	8	6

(*b*) *P* 11.

200	½d. black	1	3	0	3
201	1d. rose	2	0	0	3
202	2d. bright purple	2	0	0	3
203	2½d. blue	8	6	5	0
204	3d. yellow	8	6	3	0
205	3d. pale orange	8	6	3	0
206	3d. deep orange	8	6	3	0
207	4d. green	8	6	1	6
208	5d. olive-black	15	0	8	6
209	6d. deep brown	12	6	2	0
210	6d. sepia	15	0	2	6
211	8d. blue	25	0	22	6
212	1s. brown-red	30	0	6	6

(*c*) *P* 10.

213	½d. black	1	6	0	6
214	1d. rose	1	9	0	3
215	2d. mauve-lilac	5	0	0	3
216	2½d. blue	10	0	4	0
217	2½d. ultramarine	10	0	4	0
218	3d. yellow	12	6	3	0
219	3d. pale orange	12	6	3	0
220	3d. deep orange	15	0	6	0
221	4d. green	12	6	1	9
222	5d. olive-black	15	0	7	0
223	6d. sepia	17	6	3	6
	a. Imperf.				
224	8d. blue	25	0	22	6
225	1s. brown-red	30	0	6	6

(*d*) *P* 10×11.

226	½d. black	2	0	0	9
227	1d. rose	3	0	0	6
228	2d. bright purple	5	0	0	6
229	2½d. ultramarine	10	0	5	0
230	3d. yellow	15	0	6	0
231	4d. green	40	0	5	0
232	5d. olive-black	15	0	8	6
233	6d. sepia	17	6	3	6
234	1s. brown-red	30	0	7	6

(*e*) *Perf. compound of* 12½ *and* 10.

235	1d. rose	45	0	35	0
236	2d. lilac	85	0	65	0
237	2½d. blue	£6		90	0
238	3d. yellow	£12		£7	
238*a*	4d. green	£10		£7	
239	5d. olive-black	£12		£7	
239*a*	6d. sepia	£16		£12	
240	1s. brown-red	£15		£12	

(*f*) *P* 12½.

241	1d. rose	£8		£7	
242	2d. lilac	£8		£6	
243	2½d. ultramarine	£12		£12	

(*g*) *Perf. nearly* 12×12½.

244	1d. rose	£10		£10	
245	6d. deep brown	£14		£14	

The dies of the 1d., 2d., 6d., and 8d. were retouched in 1891–92 and new plates made, but the differences are not sufficiently marked to enable us to catalogue them as separate varieties. Perf. (*d*) is also known 11×10 and stamps perforated thus are rare.

Stamps of this issue with advertisements printed on the back were issued in 1893.

23. Mount Cook or Aorangi.

24. Lake Taupo and Mount Ruapehu.

25. Pembroke Peak, Milford Sound.

28. Sacred Huia birds.

26. Lake Wakatipu and Mount Earnslaw, inscribed "WAKITIPU."

29. White Terrace, Rotomahana.

27. Lake Wakatipu and Mount Earnslaw, inscribed "WAKATIPU."

31. Apterix or Kiwi.

32. Native war canoe.

33. Pink Terrace, Rotomahana.

34. Kea and Kaka, or hawk-billed parrot.

30. Otira Gorge and Mount Ruapehu.

35. Milford Sound.

36. Mount Cook.

(Recess. Waterlow & Sons.)

1898 (5 April). *No wmk. P* 12 *to* 14, 14, 15, *and* 16.

No.	Type	Description	Unused	Used
246	**23**	½d. purple-brown ..	2 0	1 0
		a. Imperf. between (pair) ..	£35	£35
247	,,	½d. purple-slate	2 0	1 6
248	,,	½d. purple-black ..	3 6	3 0
249	**24**	1d. blue and yellow-brn..	0 9	0 3
		a. Imperf. between (pair) ..	£35	£35
250	,,	1d. blue and brown ..	3 0	1 3
251	**25**	2d. lake	5 0	0 8
		a. Imperf. between (pair) ..	£35	£35
252	,,	2d. rosy lake	5 0	0 8
		a. Imperf. between (pair) ..	£35	£35
253	**26**	2½d. sky-bl. ("WAKITIPU")	3 6	10 0
254	,,	2½d. blue ("WAKITIPU")..	4 0	12 6
255	**27**	2½d. blue ("WAKATIPU")	5 0	4 0
256	,,	2½d. dp. bl. ("WAKATIPU")	6 0	6 0
257	**28**	3d. yellow-brown ..	3 6	2 0
258	**29**	4d. bright rose	6 6	4 0
259	**29**	4d. lake-rose	6 6	5
260	,,	4d. dull rose	6 6	4
261	**30**	5d. sepia	75 0	£
262	,,	5d. purple-brown ..	15 0	7
263	**31**	6d. green	17 6	12
264	,,	6d. grass-green	25 0	15
265	**32**	8d. indigo..	15 0	10
266	,,	8d. Prussian blue ..	12 6	8
267	**33**	9d. purple	10 6	10
268	**34**	1s. vermilion	20 0	7
269	,,	1s. dull red	20 0	7
		a. Imperf. between (pair) ..	£35	
270	**35**	2s. grey-green	35 0	35
		a. Imperf. between (vert. pair)	£45	
271	**36**	5s. vermilion	£7	£

1899. *Printed by the Govt. Printer at Wellingto Pirie paper. No wmk. P* 11.

No.	Type	Description	Unused	Used
272	**27**	2½d. blue	4 0	2
		a. Imperf. between (pair) ..	£25	£
273	,,	2½d. deep blue	5 0	3

274 **28** 3d. yellow-brown 3 6 1 6
a. Imperf. between (pair) .. £18 £18
275 ,, 3d. deep brown 3 6 1 6
276 **30** 5d. purple-brown 12 6 3 0
277 ,, 5d. deep purple-brown .. 12 6 3 0
a. Imperf. between (pair) .. £25 £25
278 **31** 6d. yellow-green 17 6 20 0
279 ,, 6d. deep green 12 6 15 0
280 **32** 8d. indigo 10 0 5 0
281 ,, 8d. Prussian blue .. 10 0 5 0
282 **33** 9d. deep purple 15 0 7 6
283 ,, 9d. rosy purple 12 6 6 0
284 **34** 1s. red 17 6 6 0
285 ,, 1s. dull orange-red .. 10 0 3 0
286 ,, 1s. dull brown-red .. 17 6 5 0
287 ,, 1s. bright red 20 0 10 0
288 **35** 2s. blue-green 30 0 22 6
289 ,, 2s. grey-green 35 0 22 6
290 **36** 5s. vermilion £6 £7
291 ,, 5s. carmine-red £9 £9

36a

1900. *Pirie paper. Wmk. double-lined "N Z" and Star, T* **36***a*, *sideways. P* 11.

292 **13** ½d. black (Apr.) 1 9 1 6
293 **15** 2d. bright purple (18 Apr.) 3 0 1 6

37. White Terrace, Rotomahana.

38a

38. Commemorative of the New Zealand contingent in the South African War.

(Recess. Govt. Ptg. Office, Wellington. Des. J. Nairn T **38**.)

1900–1. *W* **36***a*. *P* 11.

94 **23** ½d. deep green 3 0 0 4
94a ,, ½d. green 3 0 0 3
b. Imperf. between (pair) .. £12 £12
95 ,, ½d. yellow-green 3 0 0 4
96 ,, ½d. pale yellow-green .. 3 0 0 6
97 **37** 1d. lake 10 0 2 0
98 ,, 1d. crimson 4 0 0 6
99 ,, 1d. rose-red 4 0 0 6
a. Imperf. between (pair) ..
99b **38** 1½d. khaki* .. ..
00 ,, 1½d. brown 35 0 35 0
a. Imperf. between (pair) .. £20
b. Imperf. (pair) £30
01 ,, 1½d. chestnut 6 0 5 0
02 ,, 1½d. pale chestnut 6 0 5 0

303 **38a** 2d. dull violet 2 6 0 3
a. Imperf. between (pair) .. £30
304 ,, 2d. mauve 4 0 1 6
305 ,, 2d. purple 5 0 0 3
a. Imperf. between (pair) .. £30

The above ½d. stamps are slightly smaller than those of the previous printing. A new plate was made to print 240 stamps instead of 120 as previously, and to make these fit the watermarked paper the border design was redrawn and contracted, the centre vignette remaining as before. The stamp varies in shade from *very deep green* to *pale yellow-green*. The 2d. stamp is also from a new and smaller plate.

*No. 299*b* is the rare First Printing.

39. Lake Taupo and Mount Ruapehu.

40

1900. *No wmk. P* 11.

307 **39** 4d. indigo and brown .. 8 6 3 6
308 ,, 4d. bright blue & chestnut 8 6 3 0
309 ,, 4d. deep blue & bistre-brn. 5 0 2 0
310 **31** 6d. pale rose 7 6 3 0
a. Imperf. between (pair) .. £22
311 ,, 6d. rose-red 7 6 3 0
a. Doubly printed £40
312 ,, 6d. scarlet 15 0 10 0
a. Imperf. between (pair) .. £20

(Des. Guido Bach. Recess. Waterlow & Sons.)

1901 (1 Jan.). *Universal Penny Postage. No wmk. P* 12 *to* 16.

313 **40** 1d. carmine 1 6 0 9

(Recess. Govt. Ptg. Office, Wellington.)

1901 (Feb.). (i) *Pirie paper, thick and soft. W* **36***a*.

(*a*) *P* 11.

314 **40** 1d. carmine-lake 12 6 6 0
315 ,, 1d. deep carmine 2 0 0 6
a. Imperf. between (pair) .. £12
316 ,, 1d. carmine 2 0 0 6
a. Imperf. between (pair) .. £12

(*b*) *P* 14.

317 **23** ½d. green 5 0 1 3
318 **40** 1d. carmine 15 0 2 6
a. Imperf. between (pair) .. £12

(*c*) *Perf. compound of* 11 *and* 14.

319 **23** ½d. green 5 0 2 0
320 ,, ½d. deep green 5 0 2 0
321 **40** 1d. carmine £12 £10

(*d*) *P* 11 *and* 14 *mixed.**

322 **23** ½d. green 25 0 17 6
323 **40** 1d. carmine £7 £6

*The term "mixed" is applied to stamps from sheets which were at first perforated 14, or 14 and 11 compound, and either incompletely or defectively perforated. These sheets were patched on the back with strips of paper, and re-perforated 11 in those parts where the original perforation was defective.

1901 (Dec.). (ii). *Basted Mills, thin hard paper. W* **36***a*. (*a*) *P* 11.

324 **23** ½d. green 55 0 55 0
325 **40** 1d. carmine 45 0 55 0

(*b*) *Perf.* 14.

326 **23** ½d. green 7 6 4 0
a. Imperf. between (pair) .. £12
327 **40** 1d. carmine 3 0 0 9
a. Imperf. between (pair) .. £12

(c) Perf. compound of 11 *and* 14.

328 **23** ½d. green 6 6 6 6
329 „ ½d. deep green 6 6 6 6
330 **40** 1d. carmine 3 0 2 0

(d) Mixed perfs.

331 **23** ½d. green 65 0 70 0
332 **40** 1d. carmine 50 0 50 0

1902 (Jan.). (iii) *Cowan, thin hard paper. No wmk.*

(a) P 11.

333 **23** ½d. green £8 £8

(b) P 14.

334 **23** ½d. green 3 6 1 6
335 **40** 1d. carmine 4 0 0 9

(c) Perf. compound of 11 *and* 14.

336 **23** ½d. green £7 £7
337 **40** 1d. carmine £7 £6

(d) Mixed perfs.

338 **23** ½d. green £7 £6
339 **40** 1d. carmine £6 £6

41. " Single " Wmk.

1902 (April). (iv) *Cowan, thin hard paper. Wmk. single-lined* " N Z " *and Star.* *T* **41.**

(a) P 11.

340 **23** ½d. green 45 0 50 0
341 **40** 1d. carmine £60 £55

(b) P 14.

341*a* **23** ½d. yellow-green .. 2 0 0 4
341*b* „ ½d. pale yellow-green .. 3 0 1 3
342 „ ½d. green 2 0 0 3
a. Imperf. between (pair) .. £12
343 „ ½d. deep green 2 0 0 3
a. Imperf. between (pair) .. £12
344 **40** 1d. carmine 2 0 0 6
a. Imperf. between (pair) .. £12
345 „ 1d. pale carmine 1 6 0 6
a. Imperf. between (pair) .. £12
345*b* „ 1d. deep carmine* .. 8 6 1 6

(c) Perf. compound of 11 *and* 14.

346 **23** ½d. green 12 6 15 0
347 „ ½d. deep green 12 6 15 0
348 **40** 1d. carmine £6 80 0
348*a* „ 1d. deep carmine* .. £45 £40

(d) Mixed perfs.

349 **23** ½d. green 15 0 17 6
350 „ ½d. deep green 15 0 17 6
351 **40** 1d. carmine 25 0 20 0
351*a* „ 1d. pale carmine 25 0 20 0
351*b* „ 1d. deep carmine* .. £45 £30

* Nos. 345*b*, 348*a* and 351*b* were printed from a plate made by Waterlow & Sons, known as the " Reserve " plate. The stamps do not show evidence of wearing.

1902–9. *W* **41.**

(a) P 11. (1902–7).

352 **27** 2½d. blue 6 0 5 0
353 „ 2½d. deep blue (1905) .. 5 0 4 6
354 **28** 3d. yellow-brown .. 4 0 1 0
355 „ 3d. bistre-brown .. 4 0 1 0
356 „ 3d. pale bistre 7 6 2 0
357 **39** 4d. deep blue and deep brown/*bluish* .. 10 0 12 6
a. Imperf. between (pair) .. £25
358 **30** 5d. red brown 15 0 7 6
359 „ 5d. deep brown (1904) .. 12 6 3 0
360 „ 5d. sepia (1906) 12 6 10 0
361 **31** 6d. rose 8 0 2 0
362 „ 6d. rose-red 6 6 2 0
363 „ 6d. rose-carmine .. 8 6 3 0
a. Imperf. between (pair) .. £15
364 „ 6d. brt. carm.-pink ('05) 65 0 5 0
365 „ 6d. scarlet 20 0 5 0
366 **32** 8d. blue 8 0 4 0
367 „ 8d. steel-blue (1904) .. 8 0 4 0
a. Imperf. between (pair) .. £25
368 **33** 9d. purple 12 6 6 0
369 **34** 1s. brown-red 15 0 5 0
370 „ 1s. bright red 20 0 7 6
371 „ 1s. orange-red 10 0 2 6
372 „ 1s. orange-brown .. 15 0 3 6
373 **35** 2s. green 40 0 30 0
374 „ 2s. blue-green (1907) .. 40 0 30 0
375 **36** 5s. deep red £7 £7
376 „ 5s. vermilion (1906) .. £6 £7

Variety. Paper as that used for Nos. 187, *etc. W* **12a** (1903?).

376*a* **34** 1s. orange-red .. .. — £100

Variety. Laid paper. No wmk. (*Mar.*, 1903).

377 **35** 2s. green 80 0 90 0

(b) P 14 (1903–9).

378 **38** 1½d. chestnut (1907) .. 4 6 10 0
379 **38a** 2d. grey-purple (1903) .. 1 9 0 4
380 „ 2d. purple 1 9 0 4
a. Imperf. between (pair) .. £18
381 „ 2d. bright reddish purple 1 9 0 5
382 **27** 2½d. blue (1907) 3 0 2 0
383 „ 2½d. deep blue 3 0 2 0
384 **28** 3d. bistre-brown .. 4 6 1 0
a. Imperf. between (pair) .. £18
385 „ 3d. bistre (1906) .. 4 6 1 0
386 „ 3d. pale yellow-bistre .. 15 0 3 0
387 **39** 4d. deep blue and deep brown/*bluish* (1903) 10 0 2 6
a. Imperf. between (pair) .. £20
b. Centre inverted .. ..
388 „ 4d. blue and chestnut/ *bluish* (1906) .. 4 0 1 6
389 „ 4d. blue and ochre-brown/ *bluish* (1909) .. 5 0 1 6
390 **30** 5d. black-brown .. 17 6 8 6
391 „ 5d. red-brown (1906) .. 8 6 3 0
392 **31** 6d. brt. carm.-pink ('06) 25 0 5 0
a. Imperf. between (pair) .. £12
393 „ 6d. rose-carmine .. 30 0 6 0
394 **32** 8d. steel-blue (1907) .. 8 0 4 0
395 **33** 9d. purple (1906) .. 10 0 5 0
396 **34** 1s. orange-brown .. 15 0 5 0
397 „ 1s. orange-red 10 6 3 6
398 „ 1s. pale red (1907) .. 17 6 6 0
399 **35** 2s. green 25 0 20 0
400 „ 2s. blue-green (1907) .. 35 0 27 6
401 **36** 5s. deep red £6 £6
402 „ 5s. dull red £5 £5

(c) Perf. compound of 11 *and* 14.

402*a* **38** 1½d. chestnut £35 £35
403 **38a** 2d. purple (1903) .. £7 £6
403*a* **28** 3d. bistre-brown .. £30 £30
403*b* **39** 4d. blue & yell.-brn. .. £8 £8
403*c* **30** 5d. red-brown £25 £25
404 **31** 6d. rose-carmine (1907) £10 £10
404*a* **32** 8d. steel-blue £25 £25
404*b* **33** 9d. purple £25 £25
404*c* **36** 5s. deep red £50 £45

(d) Mixed perfs.

405 **38** 1½d. chestnut £35 £35
406 **38a** 2d. purple £5 £5
407 **28** 3d. bistre-brown .. £25 £25
408 **39** 4d. blue and chestnut/ *bluish* ('04) .. £10 £1
409 „ 4d. bl. & yell.-brn./*bluish* £9 £
409*a* **30** 5d. red-brown £25 £25
410 **31** 6d. rose-carmine .. £12 £1
411 „ 6d. bright carmine-pink £12 £1
412 **32** 8d. steel-blue £30 £3
413 **33** 9d. purple £35 £3
413*a* **35** 2s. blue-green £50 £5
414 **36** 5s. vermilion £50 £4

Two sizes of paper were used for the above stamps, viz.:—

(1) A sheet containing 240 wmks., with a space of 9 mm. between each.

(2) A sheet containing 120 wmks., with a space of 24 mm. between each vertical row.

Size (1) was used for the ½d., 1d., 2d., and 4d., and size (2) for 2½d., 5d., 9d., and 2s. The paper in each case exactly fitted the plates, and had the watermark in register, though in the case of the 4d., the plate of which contained only 80 stamps, the paper was cut up to print it. The 3d., 6d., 8d., and 1s. were printed on variety (1), but with watermark sideways: by reason of this specimens from the margins of the sheets show parts of the words "NEW ZEALAND POSTAGE" in large letters, and some copies have no watermark at all. For the 1½d. and 5s. stamps variety (1) was also used, but two watermarks appear on each stamp. The 6d. also exists on paper with the words "LISBON SUPERFINE" wmkd. once in the sheet; the paper was obtained from Parsons Bros. (now the Parsons Trading Co.), an American firm with a branch at Auckland. (*Price 20s. un. or us.*)

1904. *Printed from new plates.* *W* **41.**

(*a*) *P* 14.

415 **40** 1d. rose-carmine .. 1 6 0 6
415*a* ,, 1d. pale carmine .. 1 6 0 6

(*b*) *Perf. compound of* 11 *and* 14.

416 **40** 1d. rose-carmine .. 75 0 75 0

(*c*) *Mixed perfs.*

417 **40** 1d. rose-carmine .. 15 0 15 0
417*a* ,, 1d. pale carmine .. 15 0 15 0

The above new plates have a minute dot almost in the centre of the spaces between the stamps in the horizontal rows, but it is frequently cut out by the perfs. Stamps from these plates may be recognised by the appearance of a flaw at 4 o'clock in the rosette in the top right-hand corner, and by the fact that there is no line of shading inside the S-shaped ornament under the "N" of "NEW".

A special plate introduced in 1902 to print booklet panes also had the minute dot, but a characteristic of the booklet plate was that the pearl in the top left-hand corner was large.

In 1906 fresh printings were made from four new plates, two of which, marked in the margin "W1" and "W2", were supplied by Waterlow Bros. and Layton, and the other two, marked in the margin "R1" and "R2", by W. R. Royle & Son. The intention was to note which pair of plates wore the best and produced the best results. Stamps from these plates had the flaw at 4 o'clock. There was an inner line of shading in the S-shaped ornament under the "N" in the stamps from Plates R1 and R2. There was no shading in the three pearls near the middle of the left-hand side, in the stamps from Plates W1 and W2. (See below.)

906. *Printed from new plates by Waterlow and by Royle* (see above). *W* **41.**

(*a*) *P* 14.

18 **40** 1d. deep rose-carmine .. 5 0 0 4
aa. Imperf. between (pair) .. £10
18*a* ,, 1d. aniline carmine .. 8 6 0 9
ab. Imperf. between (pair) .. £10
18*b* ,, 1d. rose-carmine .. 5 0 0 4

(*b*) *P* 11.

18*c* **40** 1d. aniline carmine .. £35 £35

(*c*) *Perf. compound of* 11 *and* 14.

19 **40** 1d. rose-carmine .. £30 £25

(*d*) *Mixed perfs.*

19*a* **40** 1d. deep rose-carmine .. £30 £25

905–6. *Stamps supplied to penny-in-the-slot machines.* *W* **41.**

) *"Dot" plates of* 1904. (ii) *Waterlow "reserve" plate of* 1902.

) *Imperf. top and bottom; zigzag roulette* 9½ *on one or both sides, two large holes at sides.*

20 **40** 1d. rose-carmine (i) .. £6 £7

420*a* **40** 1d. deep carmine (ii) .. £9 £10

(*b*) *As last but rouletted* 14½.

420*b* **40** 1d. rose-carmine (i) .. £8 £10
420*c* ,, 1d. deep carmine (ii) ..

(*c*) *Imperf. all round, two large holes each side.*

421 **40** 1d. rose-carmine (i) .. £8
421*a* ,, 1d. deep carmine (ii) .. £8 £7

(*d*) *Imperf. all round.*

422 **40** 1d. deep carmine (ii) .. £8 £6

(*e*) *Imperf. all round. Two small indentations on back of stamp.*

422*a* **40** 1d. deep carmine (ii) .. £9 £9

(*f*) *Imperf. all round; two small pin-holes in stamp.*

422*b* **40** 1d. deep carmine (ii) .. £10 £8

1906 (MAY). *W* **41.** *P* 14 × 14½ (*comb machine*).

423 **40** 1d. bright rose-carmine .. 50 0 10 0
423*a* ,, 1d. rose-carmine .. 50 0 10 0

These 1d. stamps are known both with and without the small dot.

42. Te Arawa.

43. Maori Art.

44. Landing of Cook.

45. Annexation of New Zealand.

(Des. L. J. Steele. Eng. W. R. Bock. Typo. Govt. Ptg. Office.)

1906 (NOV.). *New Zealand Exhibition Christchurch. Wmk. single-lined "N Z" and Star. T* **41.** *P* 14.

424 **42** ½d. emerald-green .. 15 0 15 0
425 **43** 1d. vermilion 12 6 10 0
a. Claret £275
426 **44** 3d. brown and blue .. 30 0 32 6
427 **45** 6d. pink and olive-green £5 £8

The 1d. in claret was the original printing, which was considered unsatisfactory. One sheet was issued at the Exhibition P.O.

46

47 (T **28** reduced).

48 (T **31** reduced).

49 (T **34** reduced).

(New plates (except 4d.), supplied by Perkins Bacon. Recess (T **46** typo.) by Govt. Printer, Wellington.)

1907–8. *Wmk. single-lined* " N Z " *and Star, T* **41.**

No.	Type		Unused		Used	
		(*a*) *P* 14.				
428	**23**	½d. green	5	0	1	3
429	,,	½d. yellow-green	4	0	0	9
429*a*	,,	½d. deep yellow-green ..	4	0	1	0
430	**47**	3d. brown (1907) ..	10	0	4	6
431	**48**	6d. carmine-pink (1907)	12	6	3	0
432	,,	6d. red	22	6	12	6
		(*b*) *P* 14 × 13, 13½ (*comb*).				
433	**23**	½d. green (1907)	4	0	3	0
434	,,	½d. yellow-green	2	0	0	8
435	**47**	3d. brown	7	6	3	6
436	,,	3d. yellow-brown ..	8	6	4	6
437	**39**	4d. blue & yell.-brn./*bluish*	12	6	12	6
438	**48**	6d. pink	£12		60	0
439	**49**	1s. orange-red (1907) ..	35	0	17	6
		(*c*) *P* 14 × 15 (*comb*).				
440	**23**	½d. yellow-green (1907) ..	3	0	0	4
441	**46**	1d. carmine	5	0	0	6
442	**47**	3d. brown	7	6	3	0
443	,,	3d. yellow-brown ..	8	6	4	6
445	**48**	6d. carmine-pink ..	10	6	3	0
446	**49**	1s. orange-red	25	0	12	6
447	,,	1s. deep orange-brown ..	£10		£15	
		Error. Imperf. (*pair*).				
448	**23**	½d. green	£12			

The ½d. stamps of this 1907–8 issue have a minute dot in the margin between the stamps, where not removed by the perforation. (See note after No. 417*a*.)

Stamps of T **47**, **48** and **49** also have a small dot as described in note after No. 417*a*.

Stamps T **46** are typographed but the design also differs from T **40**. The rosettes in the upper corners are altered and the lines on the globe diagonal instead of vertical. The paper is chalk-surfaced.

50

51

(Eng. Perkins, Bacon & Co. Typo. in New Zealand.)

1909. *Chalky paper. Brownish gum. W* **41** *P* 14 × 15, *comb.*

No.	Type		Unused		Used	
449	**50**	½d. yellow-green	1	6	0	3
		a. Imperf. (pair)	£18			
450	**51**	1d. carmine	1	0	0	4
		a. Imperf. (pair)	£25			

½d. and 1d. stamps with blurred and heavy appearance are from booklets.

52

(Eng. W. R. Royle & Son, London, and recess-printed in New Zealand.)

1909–13. *T* **52** (*and similar types*). *W* **41.**

No.		Unused		Used	
	(*a*) *P* 14 × 14½, *comb machine.*				
452	2d. mauve	8	6	3	0
453	2d. deep mauve	12	6	3	6
454	3d. chestnut	6	0	0	9
455	4d. orange-red	6	6	7	6
456	4d. orange-yellow (1912) ..	5	6	4	6
457	5d. brown	8	6	2	0
458	5d. red-brown	6	6	1	6
459	6d. carmine	17	6	0	9
460	6d. deep carmine (29.10.13)	17	6	0	9
461	8d. indigo-blue	6	6	1	3
461*a*	8d. deep bright blue.. ..	12	6	2	0
462	1s. vermilion..	25	0	3	6
	(*b*) *P* 14, *line machine.**				
463	3d. chestnut	20	0	3	
464	4d. orange	7	6	6	
465	5d. brown	10	0	5	
466	5d. red-brown (15.9.11) ..	10	0	3	
467	6d. carmine	17	6	6	
468	8d. indigo-blue*	£90		£6	
469	1s. vermilion	25	0	5	

*In addition to showing the usual characteristics of a line perforation, these stamps may be distinguished by their vertical perforation which measures 13.8. Nos. 452 to 462 generally measure vertically 14 to 14.3. An exception is 13.8 one vertical side but 14 the other, thus avoiding confusion with No. 468.

See also No. 478 with sideways wmk.

AUCKLAND EXHIBITION, 1913.

(59)

1913. *T* **50, 51** *and* **52** *optd. with T* **59.**

No.		Unused		Used
470	½d. green	12	6	15
471	1d. carmine	15	0	15
472	3d. chestnut (*perf.* 14 × 14½)	90	0	90
473	6d. carmine (*perf.* 14 × 14½) ..	£5		£

These overprinted stamps were only available for letters in New Zealand and to Australia.

1915–16. *T* **52** (*and similar types*). *W* 41 *P* 14 × 13½.

No.		Unused		Used
474	3d. chestnut	30	0	35
	a. Vert. pr., p. 14 × 13½ & 14 × 14½	85	0	£
475	5d. red-brown	7	6	1
	a. Vert. pr., p. 14 × 13½ & 14 × 14½	25	0	35
476	6d. carmine	25	0	20
	a. Vert. pr., p. 14 × 13½ & 14 × 14½	£5		£
477	8d. indigo-blue (Mar., 1916) ..	12	6	4
	a. Vert. pr., p. 14 × 13½ & 14 × 14½	35	0	40
477*b*	8d. deep bright blue	10	0	1
	c. Vert. pr., p. 14 × 13½ & 14 × 14½	25	0	30

The 14 × 13½ perforation exists in entire sheets for the 3d., 5d. and 6d., or in conjunction with the 14 × 14½ comb in all four values. In the latter case the four top rows of the sheet are 14 × 13½, and the six lower rows show 14 × 14½.

On paper with widely spaced wmk. as used for 2½d. of pictorial issue and wmk. sideways (see note after No. 414). *P* 14, *line, as No.* 468.

478 8d. indigo-blue (Aug., 1916) 8 6 10 0
 a. No wmk. 45 0 60 0

No. 478*a* must show no trace of the wmk.

60

(Des. H. Linley Richardson, R.B.A.; plates made in London by Perkins, Bacon & Co. and stamps recess-printed in New Zealand.)

1915 (30 July)–**25.** *Wmk. single-lined* "N Z" *and Star, T* **41.** *P* 14 × 14½, *comb.* (*See note after* 490*c*.)

479 **60** 1½d. grey-slate 1 3 0 6
 a. Perf. 14 × 13½ 1 3 0 6
 b. Vert. pair 479/9a .. 8 6 12 6
480 ,, 2d. bright violet 2 6 5 0
 a. Perf 14 × 13½ 2 6 5 0
 b. Vert. pair, 480/80a .. 12 6 15 0
481 ,, 2½d. blue 3 6 1 9
 a. Perf. 14 × 13½ 2 0 1 3
 b. Vert. pair, 481/1a .. 15 0 20 0
482 ,, 3d. chocolate 3 0 0 6
 a. Perf. 14 × 13½ 4 0 0 6
 b. Vert. pair, 482/2a .. 15 0 22 6
483 ,, 4d. yellow 3 0 15 0
 a. Perf. 14 × 13½ 3 0 16 0
 b. Vert. pair, 483/3a .. 12 6 45 0
484 ,, 4½d. deep green 6 0 4 0
 a. Perf. 14 × 13½ 3 6 4 0
 b. Vert. pair, 484/4a .. 27 6 45 0
485 ,, 6d. carmine 7 0 0 9
 a. Perf. 14 × 13½ 4 0 0 4
 b. Vert. pair, 485/5a .. 65 0 80 0
 c. Imperf. three sides (pair) .. £175
 d. *Carmine-lake*, P. 14 × 13½ .. £8 £6
486 ,, 7½d. red-brown 8 0 12 6
 a. Perf. 14 × 13½ 3 0 6 0
 b. Vert. pair, 486/6a .. 30 0 70 0
487 ,, 9d. sage-green 12 6 6 0
 a. Perf. 14 × 13½ 8 6 3 0
 b. Vert. pair, 487/7a .. 60 0 80 0
 c. Imperf. three sides (pair) .. £250
 d. Imperf. (pair) £250
 e. *Yellowish olive*, P. 14 × 13½ (Dec. 1925) 15 0 6 0
488 ,, 1s. vermilion 10 0 0 9
 a. Perf. 14 × 13½ 15 0 2 0
 b. Imperf. (pair) £160
 c. Vert. pair 488/8a .. £5 £6
488*d* ,, 1s. pale orange-red .. 25 0 15 0
 da. Imperf. (pair) .. £60
 e. *Orange-brown* £35 £12

The 1½d., 2½d., 4½d. and 7½d. have value tablets as shown in T **60.** In the other values, the tablets are shortened, and the ornamental border at each side of the crown correspondingly extended.

1916. *Colours changed. W* **41.** *P* 14 × 14½, *comb.*

489 **60** 2d. yellow (15 Jan.) .. 2 6 4 0
 a. Perf. 14 × 13½ 3 6 6 0
 b. Vert. pair, 489/9a .. 8 0 17 6
490 **60** 4d. bright violet (7 April) 4 0 0 10
 a. Perf. 14 × 13½ 4 0 0 10
 b. Imperf. (pair) £85
 c. Vert. pair, 490/90a .. 20 0 35 0

The perfs. 14 × 14½ and 14 × 13½ may both be found on the same sheet in all the above values from 1½d. to 1s. and vertical pairs from the 4th and 5th horizontal rows would show both perforations *se-tenant*. (See Note after No. 477*c*).

Sheets of the 1½d., 2½d., 4d. yellow, 4d. violet, 4½d., 6d., 7½d., 9d. and 1s. are known perf. 14 × 13½ throughout, while sheets of the 4d. violet and 1s. are known perf. 14 × 14½ throughout.

Any stamps with the wmk. with perforations measuring 14 × 14 or nearly must be classed as 14 × 14½, this being an irregularity of the comb machine, and not a product of the 14-line machine.

1916 (Mar.–Aug.). *T* **60.** *On paper of pictorial issue, as* No. 478 (*wmk. sideways*) *on* 2d., 3d., 6d.

491 1½d. grey-slate (*p.* 14 × 14½) (Mar.) 1 0 1 0
 a. No wmk. 3 0 3 0
492 1½d. grey-slate (*p.* 14 × 13½) 1 3 1 3
 a. No wmk. 3 0 2 6
 b. Vert. pair, 491/492 .. .. 10 0 12 6
 c. As last. No wmk. 17 6 20 0
493 2d. yellow (*p.* 14) (June) .. 2 0 7 6
 a. No wmk. 25 0 30 0
494 3d. chocolate (*p.* 14) (June) 2 0 3 0
 a. No wmk. 25 0 25 0
495 6d. carmine (*p.* 14) (Aug.) .. 4 0 12 6
 a. No wmk. 45 0 50 0

The "no wmk." varieties must show no trace of the wmk.

60*a*

60*b*

(Die eng. W. R. Bock, Wellington. Typo. in N.Z. from plates made locally.)

1916 (April). *W* **41.** *P* 14 × 15.

496 **60*a*** 1½d. grey-black 3 0 0 6
497 ,, 1½d. black 4 0 0 6

Nos. 496 and 497 differ from No. 500 in many respects. The shading of the portrait is *diagonal* in the former and *horizontal* in the latter.

1915–19. *T* **60*b***, *typo. from steel plates by Perkins, Bacon & Co. Chalky paper. Brownish gum. W* **41.** *P* 14 × 15.

498 ½d. green (July, 1915) .. 3 0 0 3
499 ½d. yellow-green 10 0 3 0
 a. Very thick, hard, highly surfaced paper, white gum .. 20 0 20 0
500 1½d. slate (Sept., 1916) .. 2 0 0 6
501 1½d. orange-brn. (Sept. 1918) 1 3 0 3
502 2d. yellow (Sept., 1916) .. 2 0 0 6
503 2d. pale yellow 3 6 0 6
504 3d. chocolate (May, 1919) .. 8 6 0 6

The note after No. 488*e* also applies to *T* **60*b***.

WAR STAMP
(61)

1915 (24 Sept.). *Optd. with T* **61.** *P* 14 × 15.

505 **60*b*** ½d. green 0 4 0 4

62

63

POSTAGE & REVENUE VICTORY 1½d NEW ZEALAND

64

65

66

67

(Plates by Perkins, Bacon; Waterlow and De La Rue. Typo. De La Rue & Co.)

1920 (27 Jan.). *Victory.* *W* **41.** *P* 14.

506 **62** ½d. green 1 0 0 6
a. Pale yellow-green .. 17 6 12 6
508 **63** 1d. carmine-red 1 6 0 6
a. Bright carmine 3 0 1 0
510 **64** 1½d. brown-orange .. 1 6 0 6
511 **65** 3d. chocolate 7 6 7 6
512 **66** 6d. violet 15 0 10 0
513 **67** 1s. orange-red 30 0 40 0

The above stamps were placed on sale in London in November, 1919.

1921–22. *As Nos.* 479/488*d but new values.*

513*a* 5d. light blue.. .. .. 17 6 12 6
b. Perf. 14×13½ 6 0 1 0
c. Imperf. (pair) £20
514 5d. pale ultramarine .. 15 0 5 0
a. Perf. 14×13½ 10 0 4 0
b. Vert. pair 514/14a 37 6 60 0
515 8d. indigo-blue (May, 1921) 5 0 8 6
a. Perf. 14×13½ 5 0 8 6
b. Vert. pair 515/15a 20 0 35 0
516 8d. red-brown (*p.* 14×13½) (Feb., '22) 6 0 1 0

2d. 2d.

TWOPENCE

(68)

1922 (Mar.). *Surch. with T* **68.**

517 **62** 2d. on ½d. green (R.) .. 2 0 0 6

69

(Des. and eng. W. R. Bock. Typo. at Wellington.)

1923. *Restoration of Penny Postage. Chalky paper. Yellowish gum.* *W* **41.** *P* 14×15.

518 **69** 1d. carmine 0 8 0 3

1924–25. *W* **41.** *P* 14×15.

(*a*) "*Jones*" *chalky paper, white gum.*

519 **60*b*** ½d. green 6 0 1 6
520 **51** 1d. deep carmine .. 3 6 0 9
a. *Pale carmine.* Unsurfaced paper £30
521 **69** 1d. carmine 5 0 0 6
522 **60*b*** 2d. dull yellow 10 0 7 6
523 ,, 3d. deep chocolate .. 27 6 7 6

Only one half-sheet of No. 520a is known, due to faulty manufacture. This paper varies from thick to thin. It may be recognised by the watermark, as the letters "N Z" are larger than in the other papers and the "N Z" and Star are close together.

(*b*) *Medium, unsurfaced paper, brownish gum.*

524 **51** 1d. rose-carmine .. 5 6 £6

(*c*) *Medium to thick chalky paper, brownish gum. Wmk. sideways.*

526 **51** 1d. bright carmine .. 1 0 7 6
a. No wmk. 6 0 10 0

Many stamps in the sheet of No. 526 are without watermark, while others show portions of "NEW ZEALAND POSTAGE" in double-lined capitals.

1925. *No wmk. but bluish* "N Z *and Star*" *lithographed on back.* *P* 14×15.

527 **60*b*** ½d. apple-green 0 9 0 4
a. "N Z" and Star almost colourless 10 0
528 **51** 1d. rose-carmine .. 1 0 0 6
a. "N Z" and Star in black.. 47 6
b. "N Z" and Star colourless £8 £6
529 **60*b*** 2d. yellow 5 0 22 6

1925–30. *As 1924–5, but "Cowan" thick opaque chalky paper, white gum.* W **41.**

No.	Type	Description	Unused		Used	
530	**60*b***	½d. green (*p.* 14×15) ..	0	8	0	3
		a. Perf. 14	0	9	0	3
531	**51**	1d. dp. carm. (*p.* 14×15)	3	0	0	4
		a. Imperf. (pair)	£5			
532	**60*b***	1½d. orge.-brn. (*p.* 14) ('30)	7	6	3	0
		a. Perf. 14×15	40	0	25	0
533	,,	2d. yellow (*p.* 14×15) ..	2	0	0	4
		a. Perf. 14 ('30)	1	9	0	4
534	,,	3d. chocolate (*p.* 14×15)	5	0	1	0
		a. Perf. 14 ('30)	15	0	2	0

This paper differs from the "Jones" paper of Nos. 519, etc., in being very opaque, so that the watermark as a rule is barely visible. The gum in the first supply was dull, and in later supplies shiny.

"Cowan" unsurfaced paper. (*Apr.* '25.)

No.	Type	Description	Unused		Used	
535	**69**	1d. carm.-pink (*p.* 14×15)	6	0	7	6

This is a medium soft paper similar to that on which the line-engraved stamps of T **60** were printed, with very shiny gum.

"Wiggins Teape" thin, hard, chalk-surfaced paper. (*June,* '26–1930.)

No.	Type	Description	Unused		Used	
535*a*	**51**	1d. rose-carm. (*p.* 14×15)	6	0	2	0
535*b*	**60*b***	1½d. orange-brown (*perf.* 14) ('30)	20	0	10	0
535*c*	,,	2d. yellow (*p.* 14×15) ..	6	6	4	0
		d. Perf. 14 (July 1927). ..	5	0	4	0

This paper is not unlike the "Cowan" surfaced paper but has a distinct metallic ring when bent and released.

70

(Des. H. Linley Richardson. Eng. and typo. Govt. Ptg. Office, Wellington.)

1925 (17 Nov.). *Dunedin Exhibition. Thick chalky paper.* W **41.** P 14×15.

No.	Type	Description	Unused		Used	
536	**70**	½d. yellow-green/*green* ..	3	6	3	6
537	,,	1d. carmine/*rose* ..	3	6	5	0
538	,,	4d. mauve/*pale mauve* ..	30	0	35	0
		a. "POSTAGF" at right ..	£8		£8	

71 **72**

(Des. H. L. Richardson; plates by Waterlow; typo. Wellington.)

1926. W **41.** P 14.

No.	Type	Description	Unused		Used	
539	**71**	1d. rose-carmine (12.11.26)	0	6	0	3
		a. Perf. 14×15	0	8	0	4
		b. Imperf. (pair)	£12			
540	**72**	2s. deep blue	35	0	15	0
541	,,	3s. mauve	55	0	60	0

The 2s. and 3s. are on "Jones" paper.

As last. "Cowan" paper.

No.	Type	Description	Unused		Used	
542		2s. light blue	35	0	10	0
543		3s. pale mauve	75	0	60	0

73. Nurse.

(Typo. Govt. Printing Office, Wellington.)

1929–30. *Anti-Tuberculosis Fund.* T **73** (*and similar type*). W **41.** P 14.

(*a*) *Inscribed* "HELP STAMP OUT TUBERCULOSIS".

No.	Description	Unused		Used	
544	1d.+1d. scarlet (11.12.29) ..	17	6	17	6

(*b*) *Inscribed* "HELP PROMOTE HEALTH".

No.	Description	Unused		Used	
544*a*	1d.+1d. scarlet (29.10.30) ..	30	0	35	0

73*a*

(Des. H. L. Richardson. Typo. Govt. Ptg. Office.)

1931–9. *As* T **73*a*** (*various frames*). *Chalky paper.* W **41.** P 14.

No.	Description	Unused		Used	
544*b*	1s. 3d. lemon ('31) ..	15	0	12	6
544*c*	1s. 3d. orange-yellow ('32)	6	0	2	0
544*d*	2s. 6d. brown	12	6	2	6
544*e*	4s. red ('32)	12	6	3	6
544*f*	5s. green	30	0	12	6
544*g*	6s. carmine-rose ('32) ..	35	0	15	0
544*h*	7s. blue	35	0	20	0
544*i*	7s. 6d. olive-grey ('32) ..	80	0	80	0
544*k*	8s. slate-violet	40	0	20	0
544*l*	9s. orange	45	0	25	0
544*m*	10s. carmine-lake	40	0	10	0
544*n*	12s. 6d. purple ('35) ..	£6		£6	
544*o*	15s. olive-green ('32) ..	70	0	45	0
544*p*	£1 pink ('32)	£6		50	0
544*q*	25s. greenish blue ('38) ..	£40		£20	
544*r*	30s. brown ('36)	£30		£20	
544*s*	35s. orange-yellow ('37) ..	£250			
544*t*	£2 violet ('33)	£80		£12	
544*u*	£2 10s. red ('36) ..	£40		£32	
544*v*	£3 green ('32)	£50		£12	
544*w*	£3 10s. rose ('39) ..	£200		£120	
544*x*	£4 light blue	£50		£12	
544*y*	£4 10s. olive-grey ('39) ..	£90		£50	
544*z*	£5 blue ('32)	£60		£12	

We do not list values above £5 as they were mainly employed for revenue purposes.

35/-

(73*b*)

1939–40. *Types as* **73*a*** *surch. as* T **73*b*.**

No.	Description	Unused		Used	
545	3/6 on 3s. 6d. grey-green ..	30	0	20	0
545*a*	5/6 on 5s. 6d. lilac	75	0	30	0
545*b*	11/– on 11s. yellow	£12		£6	
545*c*	22/– on 22s. scarlet	£28		£20	
545*d*	35/– on 35s. orge-yell. ('39) ..	£12		£8	

For types as **73*a*** with Multiple wmk, see Nos. 634, etc.

74. Smiling Boy.

(Des. L. C. Mitchell. Dies and plates, Perkins, Bacon. Typo. Govt. Ptg. Office, Wellington.)

1931 (31 Oct.). *Health Stamps.* *T* **74.** *W* **41.** *P* 14½ × 14.

546 1d. + 1d. scarlet £5 £5
547 2d. + 1d. blue.. .. .. £5 90 0

75. New Zealand Lake Scenery.

(Des. L. C. Mitchell. Typo. Govt. Ptg. Office.)

1931 (11 Nov.). *Air.* *W* **41.** *P* 14 × 14½.

548 **75** 3d. chocolate 15 0 12 6
a. Perf. 14 × 15 .. .. £6 £10
549 ,, 4d. blackish purple .. 17 6 15 0
550 ,, 7d. brown-orange 27 6 20 0

FIVE PENCE

(**76**)

1931 (18 Dec.). *Air. Surch. with T* **76.**

551 **75** 5d. on 3d. green (R.) .. 10 0 7 6

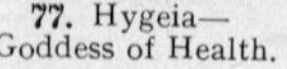

77. Hygeia—Goddess of Health.

78. The Path to Health.

(Des. R. E. Tripe and W. J. Cooch. Eng. H. T. Peat. Recess. Govt. Printing Office, Wellington.)

1932 (18 Nov.) *Health stamp.* *W* **41.** *P* 14.

552 **77** 1d. + 1d. carmine 45 0 45 0

(Des. J. Berry. Eng. H. T. Peat. Recess. Govt. Printing Office, Wellington.)

1933 (8 Nov.). *Health stamp.* *W* **41.** *P* 14.

553 **78** 1d. + 1d. carmine 30 0 30 0

TRANS-TASMAN AIR MAIL "FAITH IN AUSTRALIA."

(**79**)

1934 (Feb.). *Air. T* **75** *in new colour optd. with T* **79.** *W* **41.** *P* 14 × 14½.

554 7d. light blue (B.) 25 0 30 0

80. Crusader.

(Des. J. Berry. Recess. De La Rue & Co.)

1934 (26 Oct.). *Health stamp.* *W* **41.** *P* 14 × 13½.

555 **80** 1d. + 1d. carmine 20 0 20 0

81. Pied fantail.

82. Kiwi.

83. Maori woman.

84. Maori carved house.

85. Mt. Cook.

86. Maori girl.

87. Mitre Peak.

88. Swordfish.

89. Harvesting.

90. Tuatara lizard.

91. Maori panel.

92. Tui.

93. Capt. Cook at Poverty Bay.

94. Mt. Egmont.

Die I Die II

(Des. J. Fitzgerald (½d. and 4d.), C. H. and R. J. G. Collins (1d.), M. Matthews (1½d.), H. W. Young (2d.), L. C. Mitchell (2½d., 3d., 8d., 1s. and 3s.), W. J. Cooch and R. E. Tripe (5d.), T. I. Archer (6d.), I. F. Calder (9d.) and I. H. Jenkins (2s.). Litho. Waterlow (9d.). Recess, De La Rue (remainder).)

1935 (1 May). *W* **41.**

No.	Type	Description				
556	**81**	½d. brt. green, *p.* 14×13½	0	6	0	4
557	**82**	1d. scar. (Die I), *p.* 14×13½	0	6	0	3
		a. Perf. 13½×14	15	0	7	6
		b. Die II, *p.* 14×13½. ..	3	0	2	0
558	**83**	1½d. red-brown, *p.* 14×13½	3	0	1	3
		a. Perf. 13½×14	3	0	1	3
559	**84**	2d. orange, *p.* 14×13½ ..	1	6	0	4
560	**85**	2½d. chocolate and slate, *p.* 13–14×13½ ..	3	0	2	0
		a. Perf. 13½×14	3	0	2	0
561	**86**	3d. brown, *p.* 14×13½ ..	8	6	1	6
562	**87**	4d. black and sepia, *p.* 14	2	0	0	8
563	**88**	5d. ultram., *p.* 13–14×13½	8	6	2	6
		a. Perf. 13½×14	20	0	2	6
564	**89**	6d. scarlet, *p.* 13½×14 ..	4	0	1	6
565	**90**	8d. chocolate, *p.* 14×13½	4	0	2	9
566	**91**	9d. scarlet and black, *p.* 14×14½	4	0	1	6
567	**92**	1s. deep green, *p.* 14×13½	12	6	2	6
568	**93**	2s. ol.-grn., *p.* 13–14×13½	15	0	3	0
		a. Perf. 13½×14	25	0	5	0
569	**94**	3s. choc. & yellow-brown, *p.* 13–14×13½ ..	15	0	20	0
		a. Perf. 13½×14	20	0	15	0

In the 2½d., 5d., 2s. and 3s. perf. 13–14×13½ the horizontal perforations of each stamp are in two sizes, one half of each horizontal side measuring 13 and the other 14.

For 9d. typographed, see Nos. 626/7.

95. Bell Block Aerodrome.

(Des. J. Berry. Eng. Stamp Printing Office, Melbourne. Recess. Govt. Printing Office, Wellington.)

1935 (4 May). *Air. W* **41.** *P* 14.

No.	Type	Description				
570	**95**	1d. carmine	1	0	1	0
571	,,	3d. violet	8	6	8	6
572	,,	6d. blue	7	6	7	6

96

(Frame by J. Berry. Recess. Bradbury, Wilkinson & Co.)

1935 (7 May). *Silver Jubilee. W* **41.** *P* 11×11½.

No.	Type	Description				
573	**96**	½d. green	0	6	0	6
574	,,	1d. carmine	0	10	0	4
575	,,	6d. red-orange	12	6	15	0

97. " The Key to Health ".

(Des. S. Hall. Recess. J. Ash, Melbourne.)

1935 (30 SEPT.). *Health Stamp.* *W* **41** *P* 11.

576	**97**	1d. + 1d. scarlet	8 6	8 6

98. "Multiple Wmk."

In T **41** the wmk. units are in vertical columns widely spaced and the sheet margins are unwatermarked or wmkd. "NEW ZEALAND POSTAGE" in large letters.

In T **98** the wmk. units are arranged alternately in horizontal rows closely spaced and are continued into the sheet margins.

(Litho. Govt. Ptg. Office, Wellington (9d.). Recess. Waterlow & Sons or De La Rue & Co. (others).)

1936–43. *W* **98.**

577	**81**	½d. bright grn., *p.* 14 × 13½	0 6	0 3
578	**82**	1d. scarlet (Die II), *p.* 14 × 13½	0 8	0 3
579	**83**	1½d. red-brn. *p.* 14 × 13½	2 0	2 0
580	**84**	2d. orange *p.* 14 × 13½ ..	0 6	0 3
		a. Perf. 12½ ('41)	1 6	1 0
		c. Perf. 14 ('41)	5 0	2 0
		d. Perf. 14 × 15 ('41) ..	7 6	2 0
581	**85**	2½d. chocolate and slate, *p.* 13–14 × 13½ ..	3 0	2 0
		a. Perf. 14	2 6	1 6
		b. Perf. 14 × 13½ ('42) ..	1 0	1 0
582	**86**	3d. brown, *p.* 14 × 13½ ..	8 0	1 0
583	**87**	4d. blk. & sep., *p.* 14 × 13½	1 6	0 6
		a. Perf. 12½ ('41)	2 0	0 9
		b. Perf. 14, line ('41) ..	40 0	30 0
		c. Perf. 14 × 14½ comb. (–.7.42)	1 0	0 6
584	**88**	5d. ultram., *p.* 13–14 × 13½	3 6	1 0
		a. Perf. 12½ ('41)	4 0	1 6
		b. Perf. 14 × 13½ ('42) ..	1 6	1 6
585	**89**	6d. scarlet, *p.* 13½ × 14 ..	2 0	0 3
		a. Perf. 12½ ('41)	2 0	1 0
		b. Perf. 14½ × 14 ('42) ..	1 6	0 4
586	**90**	8d. chocolate, *p.* 14 × 13½	2 6	1 3
		aa. Wmk. sideways	15 0	3 0
		a. Perf. 12½ (*wmk. sideways*) ('41)	2 6	1 0
		b. Perf. 14 × 14½ (*wmk. sideways*) ('43) ..	2 0	0 9
587	**91**	9d. red & grey, *p.* 14 × 15 (*wmk. sideways*) ..	10 0	2 0
		a. Red and grey-black, p. 14 × 14½ (1.3.38) ..	10 0	1 6
588	**92**	1s. deep green, *p.* 14 × 13½	2 6	0 3
		a. Perf. 12½ ('41)	12 6	5 0
589	**93**	2s. olive-green *p.* 13–14 × 13½ ..	30 0	3 0
		a. Perf. 12½ ('41)	10 0	2 0
		b. Perf. 13½ × 14 ('39) ..	£15	7 6
		c. Perf. 14 × 13½ ('42) ..	7 6	2 6
590	**94**	3s. chocolate and yellow-brown, *p.* 13–14 × 13½	25 0	5 0
		a. Perf. 12½ ('41)	60 0	15 0
		b. Perf. 14 × 13½ ('42) ..	7 6	3 0

Stamps perf. 12½, 14 and 14 × 15, except the 2½d., are known as the "Blitz perfs.", having been printed and perforated by Waterlow & Sons in 1940–41 when the works of De La Rue and Co. were damaged by enemy action.

2d. Perf. 14 × 13½ varies in the sheet and is sometimes nearer 13½. Perf. 14 × 15 is sometimes nearer 14 × 14½.

2½d., 5d., 2s. and 3s. In perf. 13–14 × 13½ one half the length of each horizontal perforation measures 13 and the other 14. In perf. 14 × 13½ the horizontal perforation is regular.

4d. No. 583*b* is line-perf. measuring 14 exactly and has a blackish sepia frame. No. 583*c* is a comb-perf. measuring 14 × 14.3 or 14 × 14.2 and the frame is a warmer shade.

2s. No. 589*b* is comb-perf. and measures 13.5 × 13.75.

For 9d. typographed, see Nos. 626/7.

99. N.Z. Soldier at Anzac Cove.

(Des. L. C. Mitchell. Recess. John Ash, Melbourne.)

1936 (27 APR.). *Charity. 21st Anniv. of "Anzac". Landing at Gallipoli.* *W* **41.** *P* 11.

591	**99**	½d. + ½d. green	0 8	1 0
592	,,	1d. + 1d. scarlet	1 0	1 0

100. Wool.

101. Butter.

102. Sheep.

103. Apples.

104. Exports.

(Des. L. C. Mitchell. Recess. J. Ash, Melbourne.)

1936 (1 Oct.). *Congress of British Empire Chambers of Commerce, Wellington. N.Z. Industries Issue. W* **41.** *P* 11½.

593	**100**	½d. emerald-green	0	4	0	4
594	**101**	1d. scarlet	0	6	0	6
595	**102**	2½d. blue	3	0	3	6
596	**103**	4d. violet	3	0	3	6
597	**104**	6d. red-brown ..	5	0	5	0

105. Health Camp.

Des. J. Berry. Recess. J. Ash, Melbourne.)

936 (2 Nov.). *Health Stamp. W* **41.** *P* 11.

98	**105**	1d.+1d. scarlet	5	0	5	0

106. King George VI and Queen Elizabeth.

(Recess. Bradbury, Wilkinson & Co.)

37 (13 May). *Coronation. W* **98.** *P* 14×13½.

9	**106**	1d. carmine	0	3	0	4
0	,,	2½d. Prussian blue ..	0	6	1	0
1	,,	6d. red-orange	1	0	1	0

107. Rock-climbing.

(Des. G. Bull and J. Berry. Recess. J. Ash.)

1937 (1 Oct.). *Health Stamp. W* **41.** *P* 11.

602	**107**	1d.+1d. scarlet	7	6	8	6

108. King George VI. **108*a*.**

(Des. W. J. Cooch. Recess. Bradbury, Wilkinson & Co.)

1938–44. *W* **98.** *P* 14×13½.

603	**108**	½d. green (1.3.38) ..	1	6	0	3
603*a*	,,	½d. brn.-orange (10.7.41)	0	4	0	3
604	,,	1d. scarlet (1.7.38) ..	2	6	0	3
604*a*	,,	1d. green (21.7.41) ..	0	4	0	3
605	**108*a***	1½d. pur-brn. (26.7.38)	8	6	2	6
605*a*	,,	1½d. scarlet (1.2.44) ..	0	4	0	6
605*b*	,,	3d. blue (26.9.41) ..	0	6	0	3

For other values see Nos. 680/89.

109. Children playing.

(Des. J. Berry. Recess. Bradbury, Wilkinson & Co.)

1938 (1 Oct.). *Health Stamp. W* **98.** *P* 14×13½.

606	**109**	1d+1d. scarlet	7	6	6	0

110. Beach Ball.

(Des. S. Hall. Recess. Note Printing Branch Commonwealth Bank of Australia, Melbourne.)

1939 (16 Oct.). *Health Stamps. Surcharged with new value.* *W* **41**. *P* 11.

607	**110**	1d. on ½d.+½d. green ..	6 0	9 0
608	,,	2d. on 1d.+1d. scarlet ..	7 0	10 0

111. Arrival of the Maoris, 1350.

112. *Endeavour*, Chart of N.Z., and Capt. Cook.

113. British Monarchs.

114. Tasman with his ship and chart.

115. Signing Treaty of Waitangi, 1840.

116. Landing of Immigrants, 1840.

117. Road, rail, sea and air transport.

118. H.M.S. *Britomart* at Akaroa, 1840.

119. *Dunedin* and "frozen mutton route" to London.

120. Maori Council.

121. Gold Mining in 1861 and 1940.

122. Giant Kauri tree.

(Des. L. C. Mitchell (½d., 3d., 4d.); J. Berry (others). Recess. Bradbury, Wilkinson.)

1940 (2 Jan.–8 Mar. (8d.)). *Centenary of Proclamation of British Sovereignty.* *W* **98.** *P* 14×13½ (2½*d.*), 13½×14 (5*d.*) *or* 13½ (*others*)

609 **111** ½d. blue-green 0 3 0 3
610 **112** 1d. chocolate & scarlet 0 6 0 3
611 **113** 1½d. light blue and mauve 1 6 0 4
612 **114** 2d. blue-green & choc. 1 0 0 3
613 **115** 2½d. blue-green and blue 1 3 2 0
614 **116** 3d. purple and carmine 5 0 0 6
615 **117** 4d. chocolate and lake.. 6 0 2 0
616 **118** 5d. pale blue and brown 3 0 3 0
617 **119** 6d. emer.-green & violet 5 0 1 0
618 **120** 7d. black and red .. 12 6 15 0
619 ,, 8d. black and red .. 3 6 3 6
620 **121** 9d. olive-grn. & orange 16 0 7 6
621 **122** 1s. sage-grn. & dp. green 25 0 8 6

1940 (1 Oct.). *Health. As T* **110**, *but without extra surcharge. W* **41.** *P* 11.

622 **110** 1d.+½d. blue-green .. 6 0 8 6
623 ,, 2d.+1d. brown-orange .. 10 6 15 0

1ᴰ 1ᴰ 2ᴰ

(**123**) Inserted "2".

1941. *Surch. as T* **123.**

624 **108** 1d. on ½d. green (1.5.41) 0 6 0 6
625 **108a** 2d. on 1½d. purple-brown (–.4.41) 0 8 0 6
a. Inserted "2" £45 £35

The surcharge on No. 625 has only one figure, at top left, and there is only one square to obliterate the original value at bottom right. The variety "Inserted 2" occurs on the 10th stamp, 10th row. It is identified by the presence of remnants of the damaged "2", and by the spacing of "2" and "D" which is variable and different from the normal.

(Typo. Govt. Printing Office, Wellington.)

1941. *As T* **91**, *but smaller* (17½×20½ *mm.*). *P* 14×15. (*a*) *W* **41.**

626 **91** 9d. scarlet & blk. (–.5.41).. 12 6 2 6

(*b*) *W* **98.**

627 **91** 9d. scarlet & blk. (29.9.41) 2 6 1 0

1941

(**124**)

1941 (4 Oct.). *Health Stamps. Nos.* 622/3, *optd. with T* **124.**

628 **110** 1d.+½d. blue-green .. 3 0 3 0
629 ,, 2d.+1d. brown-orange .. 4 0 3 0

125. Boy and girl on swing.

(Des. S. Hall. Recess. Note Printing Branch, Commonweath Bank of Australia, Melbourne.)

1942 (1 Oct.). *Health Stamps. W* **41.** *P* 11.

630 **125** 1d.+½d. blue-green .. 2 0 1 9
631 ,, 2d.+1d. orange-red .. 3 0 3 0

126. Princess Margaret.

127. Queen Elizabeth II as Princess.

(Des. J. Berry. Recess. Bradbury, Wilkinson.)

1943 (1 Oct.). *Health Stamps. W* **98.** *P* 12.

632 **126** 1d.+½d. green 0 5 0 6
a. Imperf. between (vert. pair)
633 **127** 2d.+1d. red-brown .. 0 8 1 3
a. Imperf. between (vert. pair)

THREE SHILLINGS I.

THREE SHILLINGS II.

Type I. Broad seriffed capitals.
Type II. Taller capitals, without serifs.

1940–58. *T* **73a** (*various frames*). *Chalky paper. W* **98.** *P* 14.

(*a*) *Without surcharge.*

634 1s. 3d. orange-yellow .. 6 0 1 6
1s. 3d. yellow & black (Nos. 634*a*/*d*).
a. Wmk. inverted (14.6.55) .. 10 0 3 6
b. Wmk. upright (9.9.55) .. £7 £5
c. Error. *Yellow and blue.* Wmk. inverted (7.56) 35 0 50 0
d. Unsurfaced paper. P 14×13½ (11.56) 5 0 0 9
635 2s. 6d. brown 6 0 1 0
636 4s. red 7 6 2 6
637 5s. green 12 6 4 0
638 6s. carmine-rose 25 0 10 0
639 7s. light blue 25 0 10 6
640 7s. 6d. olive-grey (21.12.50) 80 0 80 0
641 8s. slate-violet 27 6 12 6
642 9s. brown-orange ('46) .. 37 6 17 6
643 10s. carmine-lake 30 0 5 0
645 15s. olive-green ('45) 45 0 30 0
646 £1 pink ('45) 70 0 10 0
a. *Rose*, p. 14×13½. Ordinary paper (20.10.58) £10 60 0
647 25s. greenish blue ('46) .. £30 £20
648 30s. brown ('46) £30 £12
650 £2 violet ('46) 50 0 30 0
651 £2 10s. red (9.8.51) £35 £25
652 £3 green ('46) 75 0 55 0
653 £3 10s. rose ('48) £225 £90
653a £4 light blue (12.2.52) .. £5 75 0
654 £5 blue ('48) 130 0 60 0

(*b*) *Surch. with value in bold figures.*

657 3/6 on 3s. 6d. grey-green (I) ('42) 17 6 17 6
657a 3/6 on 3s. 6d. do. (II) (6.53) £7 £7
658 5/6 on 5s. 6d. lilac ('44) .. 25 0 15 0
659 11/– on 11s. yellow ('42) .. £8 75 0
660 22/– on 22s. scarlet ('45) .. £25 £15

No. 634*c* was an error, as no colour change was intended, but 378,000 were printed. It has inverted wmk. and is on chalky paper. No. 634*d* exists with upright or inverted wmk.

TENPENCE 

(128)

1944 (1 May). *No.* 611 *surch. with T* **128**.
662 10d. on 1½d. lt. blue & mauve 1 4 1 6

129. Queen Elizabeth II as Princess and Princess Margaret.

(Recess. Bradbury, Wilkinson & Co.)

1944 (9 Oct.). *Health Stamps.* *W* **98.** *P* 13½.
663 **129** 1d.+½d. green 0 6 0 6
664 „ 2d.+1d. blue 0 8 0 9

130. Statue of Peter Pan, Kensington Gardens.

(Des. J. Berry. Recess. Bradbury, Wilkinson.)

1945 (1 Oct.). *Health Stamps.* *W* **98.** *P* 13½.
665 **130** 1d.+½d. green and buff .. 0 4 0 6
666 „ 2d.+1d. carmine and buff 0 6 0 8

131. Lake Matheson.

132. King George VI and Parliament House, Wellington.

133. St. Paul's Cathedral.

134. The Royal Family.

135. R.N.Z.A.F. Badge and Aeroplanes.

136. Army Badge, Tank and Plough.

137. Navy Badge, War and Trading Ships

138. N.Z. Coat-of-Arms, Foundry and Fa

139. St. George.

141. National Memorial Campanile.

140. Southern Alps and Franz Josef Glacier.

Des. J. Berry. Photo. Harrison (1½d. and 1s.). Recess. Bradbury, Wilkinson (1d. and 2d.) and Waterlow (others).)

946 (1 Apr.). *Peace issue.* *W* **98** (*sideways on* 1½*d.*). *P* 13 (1*d.*, 2*d.*), 14×14½ (1½*d.*, 1*s.*), 13½ (*others*).

67	**131**	½d. green and brown ..	0	3	0	3
68	**132**	1d. green	0	4	0	3
69	**133**	1½d. scarlet	0	4	0	3
70	**134**	2d. purple	0	5	0	3
71	**135**	3d. ultramarine and grey	0	6	0	4
72	**136**	4d. bronze-grn. and orge.	0	10	1	0
73	**137**	5d. green & ultramarine	0	8	0	9
74	**138**	6d. choc. & vermilion ..	0	10	0	9
75	**139**	8d. black and carmine ..	1	2	1	0
76	**140**	9d. blue and black ..	1	6	1	3
77	**141**	1s. grey-black	1	8	2	0

142. Soldier Helping Child over Stile.

(Des. J. Berry. Recess. Waterlow & Sons.)

46 (24 Oct.). *Health Stamps.* *W* **98.** *P* 13½.

8	**142**	1d.+½d. green & orange-brown	0	4	0	4
		a. Yellow-green and orge.-brn.	17	6	17	6
9	,,	2d.+1d. choc. & orange-brown	0	9	0	6

144. King George VI.

Plate 1.

Plate 2.

(Des. W. J. Cooch. Recess. T **108***a*, Bradbury, Wilkinson & Co.; T **144**, De La Rue & Co.)

1947–52. *W* **98** (*sideways on " shilling " values*).

(*a*) *P* 14×13½.

680	**108***a*	2d. orange	0	4	0	3
681	,,	4d. bright purple ..	0	8	0	3
682	,,	5d. slate	1	9	0	3
683	,,	6d. carmine	0	11	0	3
684	,,	8d. violet	1	6	0	4
685	,,	9d. purple-brown ..	2	0	0	4

(*b*) *P* 14.

686	**144**	1s. red-brn. & carm. (Pl. 1)	3	0	0	9
		a. Wmk. upright (Pl. 1) ..	4	0	0	9
		b. Wmk. upright (Pl. 2) ..	2	6	0	9
687	,,	1s. 3d. red-brown & blue (Pl. 2)	3	0	0	9
		a. Wmk. upright (14.1.52) ..	3	0	2	0
688	,,	2s. brn.-orge. & grn. (Pl. 1)	4	0	0	10
		a. Wmk. upright (Pl. 1) ..	6	0	2	6
689	,,	3s. red-brn. & grey (Pl. 2)	6	0	1	9

In head-plate 2 the diagonal lines of the background have been strengthened and result in the upper corners and sides appearing more deeply shaded.

145. Statue of Eros.

(Des. J. Berry. Recess. Waterlow.)

1947 (1 Oct.). *Health Stamps.* *W* **98** (*sideways*). *P* 13½.

690	**145**	1d.+½d. green	0	4	0	4
691	,,	2d.+1d. carmine ..	0	6	0	6

146. Port Chalmers, 1848.

147. Cromwell, Otago.

148. First Church, Dunedin.

149. University of Otago.

(Des. J. Berry. Recess. Bradbury, Wilkinson.)

1948 (23 Feb.). *Centennial of Otago.* *W* **98** (*sideways on* 3*d.*) *P* 13½.

692	**146**	1d. blue & green	0 3	0 3
693	**147**	2d. green and brown ..	0 6	0 6
694	**148**	3d. purple	0 8	0 8
695	**149**	6d. black and rose ..	1 3	1 3

150. Boy Sunbathing and Children Playing.

(Des. E. Linzell. Recess. Bradbury, Wilkinson.)

1948 (1 Oct.). *Health Stamps.* *W* **98.** *P* 13½.

696	**150**	1d.+½d. blue and green	0 4	0 3
697	,,	2d.+1d. purple and scar.	0 6	0 4

151. Nurse and Child.

(Des. J. Berry. Photo. Harrison & Sons.)

1949 (3 Oct.). *Health Stamps.* *W* **98.** *P* 14×14½.

698	**151**	1d.+½d. green	0 5	0 3
699	,,	2d.+1d. ultramarine ..	0 8	0 8
		a. No stop below "D" of "1 D."	55 0	65 0

1½d.

POSTAGE

(152)

1950 (28 July). *As T* **73***a*, *but without value surch. with T* **152.** *W* **98.** *P* 14.

700	**73***a*	1½d. carmine	0 4	0

153. Queen Elizabeth II and Prince Charl

(Des. J. Berry and R. S. Phillips. Photo. Harrison & Sons.)

1950 (2 Oct.). *Health Stamps.* *W* **98.** *P* 14×1

701	**153**	1d.+½d. green	0 6	0
702	,,	2d.+1d. plum	1 0	0

154. Christchurch Cathedral.

156. John Rober Godley.

155. Cairn on Lyttleton Hills.

157. Canterbury University College.

158. Aerial View of Timaru.

Des. L. C. Mitchell (2d.), J. A. Johnstone (3d. and J. Berry (others). Recess. Bradbury Wilkinson & Co.)

950 (20 Nov.). *Centennial of Canterbury, N.Z. W* **98** *(sideways on* 1d. *and* 3d.). *P* 13½.

03 **154** 1d. green and blue .. 0 4 0 6
04 **155** 2d. carmine and orange 0 6 0 8
05 **156** 3d. dark blue and blue .. 0 7 0 6
06 **157** 6d. brown and blue .. 0 11 1 0
07 **158** 1s. reddish pur. and blue 1 8 1 6

159. "Takapuna" class Yachts.

ʼes. J. Berry and R. S. Phillips. Recess. Bradbury, Wilkinson.)

51 (1 Nov.). *Health Stamps. W* **98**. *P* 13½.

8 **159** 1½d.+½d. scarlet & yellow 0 6 0 6
9 ,, 2d.+1d. dp. grn. & yellow 0 8 0 8

60. Princess Anne. **161.** Prince Charles.

(From photographs by Marcus Adams. Photo. Harrison & Sons.)

1952 (1 Oct.). *Health Stamps. W* **98**. *P* 14×14½.

710 **160** 1½d.+½d. carmine-red .. 0 8 0 8
711 **161** 2d.+1d. brown .. 1 0 1 0

3D

(162)

1952–53. *Nos.* 603*a and* 604*a surch. as T* **162**.

712 **108** 1d. on ½d. brown-orange (11.9.53) 0 3 1 3
713 ,, 3d. on 1d. grn. (12.12.52*) 0 7 0 9

*Earliest known date used.

163. Buckingham Palace.

164. Queen Elizabeth II. **166.** Westminster Abbey.

165. Coronation State Coach.

167. St. Edward's Crown and Royal Sceptre.

(Des. L. C. Mitchell (1s. 6d.), J. Berry (others). Recess. De La Rue & Co. (2d., 4d.), Waterlow & Sons (1s. 6d.). Photo. Harrison & Sons (3d., 8d.).)

1953 (25 May). *Coronation. W* **98**. *P* 13. (*2d., 4d.*), 13½ (*1s. 6d.*) *or* 14×14½ (*3d., 8d.*).

714 **163** 2d. deep bright blue .. 0 8 0 3
715 **164** 3d. brown 1 0 0 8
716 **165** 4d. carmine 1 9 3 0
717 **166** 8d. slate-grey 2 6 3 0
718 **167** 1s. 6d. purple & ultram. 4 0 4 0

168. Girl Guides.

169. Boy Scouts.

(Des. J. Berry. Photo. Harrison & Sons.)

1953 (7 Oct.). *Health Stamps.* *W* **98.** *P* 14×14½.

719	**168**	1½d.+½d. blue	0	6	0	6
720	**169**	2d.+1d. deep yell.-grn.	0	8	0	8

No. 720 exists imperf. three sides.

170. Queen Elizabeth II.

171. Queen Elizabeth II and Duke of Edinburgh.

(Des. L. C. Mitchell. Recess. Waterlow & Sons.)

1953 (9 Dec.). *Royal Visit.* *W* **98.** *P* 13×14 (*3d.*) *or* 13½ (*4d.*).

721	**170**	3d. dull purple	0	8	0	10
722	**171**	4d. deep ultramarine ..	0	10	1	0

172

173. Queen Elizabeth II. **174.**

Die I.

Die II.

(Des. L. C. Mitchell (T **172/3**), J. Berry (T **174**). Recess. De La Rue (T **173**). Bradbury, Wilkinson (others).)

1953–58. *W* **98.** *P* 14×13½ (*T* **172**), 14 (*T* **173**) *or* 13½ (*T* **174**).

723	**172**	½d. slate-black.. ..	0	3	0	3
724	,,	1d. orange	0	4	0	3
725	,,	1½d. brown-lake ..	0	5	0	4
726	,,	2d. bluish green ..	0	5	0	3
727	,,	3d. vermilion	0	7	0	4
728	,,	4d. blue	1	0	0	6
729	,,	6d. purple	2	6	0	5
730	,,	8d. carmine	1	6	1	3
731	**173**	9d. brown & brt. green	1	6	0	6
732	,,	1s. black & carmine-red (Die I)	1	9	0	
		a. Die II (1958)	£10		£6	
733	,,	1s. 6d. blk. & brt. blue	4	0	0	8
733*a*	,,	1s. 9d. black and red-orange	7	6	2	
733*b*	**174**	2s. 6d. brown	10	0	6	
734	,,	3s. bluish green ..	10	0	4	
735	,,	5s. carmine	12	6	7	
736	,,	10s. deep ultramarine ..	32	6	27	

Dates of issue:—15.12.53. 1½d.; 1.7.57 1s. 9d., 2s. 6d.; 1.3.54, others.

1s. Dies I and II. The two dies of the Queen' portrait differ in the shading on the sleeve a right. The long lines running upwards fro left to right are strong in Die I and weaker i Die II. In the upper part of the shading the fir cross-hatching is visible in Die I only betwee the middle two of the four long lines, but i Die II it extends clearly across all four lines.

In the lower part of the shading the streng of the long lines in Die I makes the cros hatching appear subdued, whereas in Die II t weaker long lines make the cross-hatching mo prominent.

Centre plates 1A, 1B, 2A and 2B are Die 3A and 3B are Die II.

For stamps as T **172** but with larger figures value see Nos. 749/54*a*.

1958 NEW PAPER. A new white opaque pap first came into use in August 1958 and w used for later printings of Nos. 733*a*, 74 751/3, O159, O161/3 and O165. It is sligh thicker than the paper previously used, b obviously different in colour (white, agai cream) and opacity (the previous paper bei *relatively* transparent).

175. Young Climber and Mts. Aspiring and Everest.

(Recess; vignette litho. Bradbury, Wilkinson.)

1954 (4 Oct.). *Health Stamps.* *W* **98.** *P* 13½.

No.	Type	Description	Unused	Used
737	**175**	1½d. + ½d. sepia and deep violet	0 6	0 6
738	,,	2d. + 1d. sepia and blue-black	0 8	0 8

176. Maori Mail-carrier. **177.** Queen Elizabeth II.

178. Douglas DC 3 Airliner.

(Des. R. M. Conly (2d.), J. Berry (3d.), A. G. Mitchell (4d.). Recess. De La Rue & Co.)

1955 (18 July). *Centenary of First New Zealand Postage Stamps.* *W* **98.** *P* 14 (2*d.*), 14 × 14½ (3*d.*) *or* 13 (4*d.*).

No.	Type	Description	Unused	Used
739	**176**	2d. sepia and deep green	0 4	0 4
740	**177**	3d. brown-red	0 6	0 6
741	**178**	4d. black & bright blue ..	0 7	0 7

179. Children's Health Camps, Federation Emblem.

(Des. E. M. Taylor. Recess. Bradbury, Wilkinson & Co.)

1955 (3 Oct.). *Health Stamps.* *W* **98** (*sideways*). *P* 13½ × 13.

No.	Type	Description	Unused	Used
742	**179**	1½d. + ½d. sepia & orange-brown	0 8	0 8
743	,,	2d. + 1d. red-brn. & grn.	1 0	1 6
744	,,	3d. + 1d. sepia and deep rose-red	1 3	1 6
		a. Centre omitted		

180. "The Whalers of Foveaux Strait".

181. "Farming".

182. *Notornis.*

(Des. E. R. Leeming (2d.), L. C. Mitchell (3d.), M. R. Smith (8d.). Recess. De La Rue.)

1956 (Jan.). *Southland Centennial.* *W* **98.** *P* 13½ × 13 (8*d.*) *or* 13 × 12½ (*others*).

No.	Type	Description	Unused	Used
745	**180**	2d. deep blue-green ..	0 6	0 6
746	**181**	3d. sepia	0 10	0 9
747	**182**	8d. slate-violet & rose-red	2 6	2 0

183

1955–59. *As Nos.* 724/30 *but larger figures of value and stars omitted from lower right corner.*

No.	Type	Description	Unused	Used
749	**183**	1d. orange (12.7.56) ..	0 6	0 4
750	,,	1½d. brown-lake (1.12.55)	1 3	0 9
751	,,	2d. bluish green (19.3.56)	0 8	0 3
752	,,	3d. vermilion (1.5.56) ..	1 6	1 6
753	,,	4d. blue (3.2.58) ..	1 3	0 6
754	,,	6d. purple (20.10.55) ..	1 9	0 6
754a	,,	8d. chestnut (1.12.59) ..	7 6	7 6

See note re white opaque paper below No. 736

184. Children Picking Apples.

(Des. L. C. Mitchell, after photo by J. F. Louden. Recess. Bradbury, Wilkinson & Co.)

1956 (24 Sept.). *Health Stamps.* *W* **98.** *P* 13×13½.

755	**184**	1½d.+½d. purple-brown ..	0	4	0	4
		a. Blackish brown	15	0	17	6
756	,,	2d.+1d. blue-green ..	0	6	0	6
757	,,	3d.+1d. claret	0	7	0	7

185. New Zealand Lamb and Map.

186. Lamb, *Dunedin* and Modern Ship.

(Des. M. Goaman. Photo. Harrison & Sons.)

1957 (15 Feb.). *75th Anniv. of First Export of N.Z. Lamb. W* 98 (*sideways on 4d.*). *P* 14×14½ (*4d.*) *or* 14½×14 (*8d.*).

758	**185**	4d. blue	2	0	2	0
759	**186**	8d. deep orange-red ..	4	6	4	6

187. Sir Truby King.

(Des. M. R. Smith. Recess. Bradbury, Wilkinson & Co.)

1957 (14 May). *50th Anniv. of Plunket Society. W* **98.** *P* 13.

760	**187**	3d. bright carmine-red ..	0	8	0	4

188. Life-savers in Action.

189. Children on Seashore.

(Des. L. Cutten (2d.); L. C. Mitchell (3d.). Recess. Waterlow & Sons.)

1957 (25 Sept.). *Health Stamps.* *W.* **98** (*sideways*). *P* 13½.

761	**188**	2d.+1d. black & emerald	0	6	0	6
		a. Wmk. upright	2	6	2	0
762	**189**	3d.+1d. ultram. & rose-red	0	8	0	8
		a. Wmk. upright	3	0	2	6
MS762*b*		Two sheets each 112×96 mm. with Nos. 761 and 762 in blocks of 6 (2×3). *Per pair*	10	0	10	0
MS762*c*		As last but with Nos. 761a and 762a. *Per pair*	20	0	20	0

Nos. 761a and 762a only exist from No. **MS**762*c*.

(**190**)

1958 (15 Jan.). *No.* 750 *surch. as T* **190.**

763	**183**	2d. on 1½d. brown-lake ..	1	0	0	
		a. Smaller dot in surch. ..	0	8	0	
		b. Error. Surch. on No. 725	60	0	65	

Diameter of dot on No. 763 is 4¼ mm.; on No. 763a 3¾ mm.

191. Girls' Life Brigade Cadet. **192.** Boys' Brigade Bugler.

(Des. J. Berry. Photo. Harrison & Sons.)

1958 (20 Aug.). *Health Stamps. W* **98.** *P* 14×14

764	**191**	2d.+1d. green	0	6	0	
765	**192**	3d.+1d. blue	0	7	0	
MS765*a*		Two sheets each 104×124 mm. with Nos. 764/5 in blocks of 6 (3×2). *Per pair*	5	6	7	

(Recess. Commonwealth Bank of Australia Note Ptg. Branch.)

1958 (27 Aug.). *30th Anniv. of First Air Crossing of the Tasman Sea. As T* **120** *of Australia, but inscr.* "NEW ZEALAND". *W* **98** *(sideways). P* 14×14½.

766 6d. deep ultramarine ... 1 6 1 0

193. Seal of Nelson.

(Des. M. J. Macdonald. Recess. Bradbury Wilkinson & Co.)

1958 (29 Sept.). *Centenary of City of Nelson. W* **98.** *P* 13½×13.

767 **193** 3d. carmine 0 6 0 5

194. "Pania" Statue, Napier.

196. Maori sheep-shearer.

195. Gannets on Cape Kidnappers.

(Photo. Harrison & Sons.)

58 (3 Nov.). *Centenary of Hawke's Bay Province. W* **98** *(sideways on 3d.). P* 14½×14 *(3d.) or* 13½×14½ *(others).*

8 **194** 2d. yellow-green 0 6 0 6
9 **195** 3d. blue 0 9 0 9
o **196** 8d. red-brown 3 6 3 6

197. "Kiwi" Jamboree Badge.

es. Mrs. S. M. Collins. Recess. Bradbury, Wilkinson & Co.)

59 (5 Jan.). *Pan-Pacific Scout Jamboree, Auckland. W* **98.** *P* 13½×13.

197 3d. sepia and carmine .. 0 8 0 6

198. Careening H.M. Bark *Endeavour* at Ship Cove.

199. Shipping wool, Wairau bar, 1857.

200. Salt Industry, Grassmere.

(Des. G. R. Bull and G. R. Smith. Photo. Harrison & Sons.)

1959 (2 Mar.). *Centenary of Marlborough Province. W* **98** *(sideways). P* 14½×14.

772 **198** 2d. green 0 6 0 6
773 **199** 3d. deep blue 0 9 0 9
774 **200** 8d. light brown 3 6 3 6

201. Red Cross Flag.

(Photo. Harrison & Sons.)

1959 (3 June). *Red Cross Commemoration. W* **98** *(sideways). P* 14½×14.

775 **201** 3d.+1d. red & ultram. .. 1 0 0 6
a. Red Cross omitted .. £450

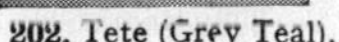

202. Tete (Grey Teal). **203.** Poaka (Pied Stilt).

(Photo. Harrison & Sons.)

1959 (16 Sept.). *Health Stamps.* *W* **98** (*sideways*). *P* 14×14½.

776 **202** 2d.+1d. greenish yellow, olive & rose-red .. 0 8 0 8
777 **203** 3d.+1d. black, pink and light blue 0 10 0 10
a. Pink ptg. omitted .. £125
b. Pink ptg. shifted to left (at least 2½ mm.) £25

MS777*c* Two sheets each 95×109 mm. with Nos. 776/7 in blocks of 6 (3×2). *Per pair* 9 0

204. " The Explorer ". **205.** " The Gold Digger".

206. " The Pioneer Woman ".

(Des. G. R. Bull and G. R. Smith. Photo. Harrison & Sons.)

1960 (16 May). *Centenary of Westland Province.* *W* **98.** *P* 14×14½.

778 **204** 2d. deep dull green 0 4 0 4
779 **205** 3d. orange-red 0 6 0 6
780 **206** 8d. grey-black 3 6 3 6

207. Manuka (Tea Tree).

208. Karaka.

209. Kowhai Ngutu-kaka (Kaka Beak).

209*a*. Titoki.

210. Kowhai.

211. Puarangi (Hibiscus). **211*a*.** Matua Tikumu (Mountain Daisy). **212.** Piklarei (Clematis).

213. Rata.

214. National Flag.

215. Timber Industry.

216. Trout.

217. Tiki.

218. Aerial Top Dressing.

219. Taniwha (Maori Rock Drawing).

220. Butter Making.

221. Tongariro National Park and Château.

21a. Tongariro National Park and Château.

2. Sutherland Falls. **224.** Pohutu Geyser.

223. Tasman Glacier.

es. Harrison & Sons (½d.), G. F. Fuller (1d., d., 6d.), A. G. Mitchell (2d., 4d., 5d., 8d., 3s., os., £1), P.O. Publicity Section (9d.), J. Berry (1s., 1s. 6d.), R. E. Barwick (1s. 3d.), . C. Boyd (1s. 9d.), D. F. Kee (2s.), L. C. itchell (2s. 6d., 5s.). Photo. De La Rue & o. (½d. to 8d., *not* 2½d. or 5d.) or Harrison & ons (others).)

1960 (11 July–1 Sept.) **64.** *W* **98** (*sideways on 2½d., 5d., 1s. 3d., 1s. 6d., 2s. 6d., 3s. and 10s.*). *P* 14 × 15 (1s. 3d., 1s. 6d., 2s., 5s., £1) or 15 × 14 (*others*).

No.	Type	Description	Unused	Used
781	**207**	½d. grey, green & cerise (1.9.60)	0 2	0 2
782	**208**	1d. orange, green, lake and brown (1.9.60).	0 3	0 2
		a. Coil. Perf. 14½ × 13. Wmk. sideways (11.63) ..	0 3	0 2
783	**209**	2d. carmine, black, yellow and green ..	0 4	0 2
784	**209a**	2½d. red, yellow, black & green (1.11.61) ..	0 5	0 2
785	**210**	3d. yell., grn., yell.-brn. & dp. greenish blue (1.9.60)	0 6	0 4
		a. Coil. Perf. 14½ × 13. Wmk. sideways (3.10.63) ..	0 6	0 4
786	**211**	4d. purple, buff, yellow-green & light blue ..	0 7	0 3
787	**211a**	5d. yellow, deep green, blk. & violet (14.5.62)	0 9	0 4
788	**212**	6d. lilac, green & deep bluish green (1.9.60)	0 10	0 3
789	**213**	8d. rose-red, yellow, green and grey (1.9.60) ..	1 0	0 9
790	**214**	9d. red & ultram. (1.9.60)	1 1	0 4
791	**215**	1s. brown & deep green	1 5	0 3
792	**216**	1s. 3d. carmine, sepia & bright blue	2 3	0 6
793	**217**	1s. 6d. olive-green and orange-brown ..	2 0	0 4
794	**218**	1s. 9d. bistre-brown ..	7 6	2 6
795	,,	1s. 9d. orange-red, blue, grn. & yell. (4.11.63)	2 5	0 8
796	**219**	2s. black & orange-buff	2 9	1 3
797	**220**	2s. 6d. yell. & lt. brown	3 6	1 6
798	**221**	3s. blackish brown ..	10 0	3 9
799	**221a**	3s. bistre, blue & green (1.4.64)	4 0	2 6
800	**222**	5s. blackish green ..	6 9	3 6
801	**223**	10s. steel-blue	13 3	6 0
802	**224**	£1 deep magenta ..	25 0	18 6

"MISSING COLOURS" (in the above issue are known in the following:—½d. (green and grey), 1d. (orange), 2d. (black and yellow), 2½d. red, yellow, green and red and green on same stamp), 3d. (yellow, green and brown), 4d. (purple and buff), 5d. (yellow), 6d. (lilac and green), 9d. (red), 1s. 3d. (carmine), and 2s. 6d. (yellow).

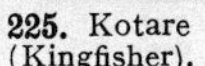

225. Kotare (Kingfisher).

226. Kereru (Wood Pigeon).

(Recess. Bradbury, Wilkinson.)

1960 (10 Aug.). *Health Stamps.* *W* **98.** *P* 13½.

No.	Type	Description	Unused	Used
803	**225**	2d. + 1d. sepia & turq.-blue	0 8	0 8
		a. Perf. 11½ × 11 ..	0 8	0 8
804	**226**	3d. + 1d. dp. purple-brown and orange ..	0 10	0 10
		a. Perf. 11½ × 11 ..	0 10	0 10
MS804*b*		Two sheets each 95 × 107 mm. with Nos. 803a and 804a in blocks of 6 (3 × 2) *Per pair*	10 0	

227. " The Adoration of the Shepherds " (after Rembrandt).

(Photo. Harrison & Sons.)

1960 (1 Nov.). *Christmas Issue.* *W* **98.** *P* 12.

805 **227** 2d. red & dp. brn./*cream* 3 0 1 6
a. Red omitted £225

228. Kotuku (White Heron).

229. Karearea (Bush Hawk).

(Recess. Bradbury, Wilkinson.)

1961 (2 Aug.). *Health Stamps.* *W* **98.** *P* 13½.

806 **228** 2d. +1d. black and purple 0 8 0 8
807 **229** 3d. +1d. deep sepia and yellow-green 0 10 0 10
MS807*a* Two sheets each 97×121 mm. with Nos. 806/7 in blocks of 6 (3×2) *Per pair* 10 0

(230) (231)

1961 (1 Sept.). *No.* 752 *surch. with T* **230** (*wide setting*).

808 **183** 2½d. on 3d. vermilion .. 0 6 0 3
a. Narrow setting (T 231). . 0 9 0 6
b. Pair, Wide and Narrow. . 50 0

The difference in the settings is in the overall width of the new value, caused by two different spacings between the "2", "½" and "d".

232. " Adoration of the Magi " (Durer).

(Photo. Harrison.)

1961 (16 Oct.). *Christmas.* *W* **98** (*sideways*). *P* 14½×14.

809 **232** 2½d. multicoloured .. 2 0 0

233. Morse Key and Port Hills, Lyttleton.

234. Modern Teleprinter.

(Des. A. G. Mitchell (3d.), L. C. Mitchell (8d. Photo. Harrison & Sons.)

1962 (1 June). *Telegraph Centenary.* *W* (*sideways*). *P* 14½×14.

810 **233** 3d. sepia and bluish green 0 10 1
a. Green omitted .. ..
811 **234** 8d. black and brown-red 3 6 3
a. Imperf. (pair) .. ..
b. Black omitted .. ..

No. 811a comes from a sheet with the thr top rows imperforate.

235. Kakariki (Parakeet).

236. Tieke (Saddleback).

(Photo. De La Rue & Co.)

1962 (3 Oct.). *Health.* *W* **98.** *P* 15×14.

812 **235** 2½d. + 1d. multicoloured 0 8
813 **236** 3d. + 1d. multicoloured 0 9
a. Orange ptg. omitted ..

MS813*b* Two sheets each 96×101 mm. with Nos. 812/3 in blocks of 6 (3×2) *Per pair* 9 6

237. " Madonna in Prayer " (after Sassoferrato).

(Photo. Harrison & Sons.)

1962 (15 Oct.). *Christmas.* *W* **98.** *P* 14½×14.
814 **237** 2½d. multicoloured .. 0 9 1 0

238. Prince Andrew. **239.**

Design after photographs by Studio Lisa, London. Recess. De La Rue.)

1963 (7 Aug.). *Health Stamps.* *W* **98.** *P* 14.
815 **238** 2½d.+1d. ultram. (*shades*) 0 8 0 8
816 **239** 3d.+1d. carmine .. 0 9 0 9
MS816*a* Two sheets each 93×100 mm. with Nos. 815/6 in blocks of 6 (3×2) *Per pair* 9 6

240. " The Holy Family " (Titian).

(Photo. Harrison.)

3 (14 Oct.). *Christmas.* *W* **98** (*sideways*). 12½.
240 2½d. multicoloured .. 0 9 0 7
a. Imperf. (pair) £120

241. Steam Locomotive " Pilgrim " and Diesel.

242. Diesel Express and Mt. Ruapehu.

(Photo. De La Rue.)

1963 (25 Nov.). *Railway Centenary.* *W* **98.** *P* 14.
818 **241** 3d. multicoloured .. 0 9 1 0
a. Blue (sky) omitted ..
819 **242** 1s. 9d. multicoloured .. 6 0 6 0
a. Red (value) omitted .. £250

1963 (3 Dec.). *Opening of COMPAC (Trans-Pacific Telephone Cable). As T* **174** *of Australia, but inscr.* " NEW ZEALAND ". *No wmk.* *P* 13½.
820 8d. red, blue, black & yellow 3 6 4 0

243. Road Map and Car Steering-wheel.

(Des. L. C. Mitchell. Photo. Harrison.)

1964 (1 May). *Road Safety Campaign.* *W* **98.** *P* 14×14½.
821 **243** 3d. blk., ochre-yell. & bl. 0 9 0 9

244. Tarapunga (gull).

245. Korora (penguin).

(Photo. Harrison.)

1964 (5 Aug.). *Health Stamps.* *W* **98.** *P* 14½.

822 **244**	2½d.+1d. multicoloured	0 7	0 9
823 **245**	3d.+1d. multicoloured	0 9	1 0
MS823*a*	Two sheets each 171×84 mm. with Nos. 822/3 in blocks of 8 (4×2) *Per pair*	12 6	

246. Rev. S. Marsden taking first Christian service at Rangihoua Bay, 1814.

(Des. L. C. Mitchell. Photo. Harrison.)

1964 (12 Oct.). *Christmas.* *W* **98** (*sideways*). *P* 14×13½.

824 **246** 2½d. multicoloured .. 0 9 0 9

7D

POSTAGE

(247)

1964 (14 Dec.). *T* **73***a* (*value unspecified*) *surch. with T* **247.**

825 7d. carmine-red 1 1 1 6

248. Anzac Cove.

249. Anzac Cove and Poppy.

(Photo. Harrison.)

1965 (14 Apr.). *50th Anniv. of Gallipoli Landing.* *W* **98.** *P* 12½.

826 **248** 4d. yellow-brown .. 0 7 0 9
827 **249** 5d. green and red .. 0 9 1 0

250. I.T.U. Emblem and Symbols.

(Photo. Harrison.)

1965 (17 May). *I.T.U. Centenary.* *W* **98.** *P* 14½×14.

828 **250** 9d. blue & pale chocolate 1 1 1 3

(From photograph by Karsh. Photo. Note Ptg. Branch, Reserve Bank of Australia.)

1965 (24 May). *Churchill Commemoration.* *As T* **186** *of Australia but inscr.* "NEW ZEALAND". *P* 13½.

829 7d. black, pale grey and light blue.. .. .. 0 11 1 0

251. Wellington Provincial Council Building

(Des. from painting by L. B. Temple (1867) Photo. Harrison.)

1965 (26 July). *Centenary of Government in Wellington.* *W* **98** (*sideways*). *P* 14½×14.

830 **251** 4d. multicoloured .. 0 7 0

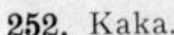

252. Kaka. **253.** Piwakawak (fantail).

(Photo. Harrison.)

1965 (4 Aug.). *Health Stamps.* *W* **98.** *P* 14×1

831 **252** 3d.+1d. multicoloured .. 0 9 0
832 **253** 4d.+1d. multicoloured .. 0 11 1
MS832*a* Two sheets each 100×109 mm. with Nos. 831/2 in blocks of 6 (3×2) *Per pair* 10 6

254. I.C.Y. Emblem.

(Litho. De La Rue.)

1965 (28 Sept.). *International Co-operation Year. W* **98** *(sideways). P* 14.
833 **254** 4d. carmine-red and light yellow-olive 0 7 0 9

255. "The Two Trinities", after Murillo.

(Photo. Harrison.)

1965 (11 Oct.). *Christmas. W* **98.** *P* 13½ × 14.
834 **255** 3d. multicoloured .. 0 6 0 8

256. Arms of New Zealand.

257. Parliament House, Wellington, and Badge.

258. Wellington from Mt. Victoria.

(Photo. De La Rue.)

1965 (30 Nov.). *11th Commonwealth Parliamentary Conference. P* 14.
835 **256** 4d. multicoloured .. 0 7 0 9
a. Blue (incl. value) omitted
836 **257** 9d. multicoloured .. 1 1 1 3
837 **258** 2s. multicoloured .. 2 9 3 0

259. "Progress" Arrowhead.

(Photo. Harrison.)

1966 (5 Jan.). *Fourth National Scout Jamboree, Trentham. W* **98.** *P* 14 × 15.
838 **259** 4d. gold & myrtle-green 0 7 0 9

EXPRESS DELIVERY STAMPS.

E 1

1903. *Value in first colour. W* **41.** *P* 11.
E1 **E 1** 6d. red and violet .. 15 0 10 0

1926–39. *Cowan thick opaque, or Wiggins, Teape hard papers. W* **41.** *(a) P* 14 × 14½.
E3 **E 1** 6d. vermilion & brt. violet 10 0 10 0

(b) P 14 × 15.
E4 **E 1** 6d. carm. & brt. violet .. 20 0 20 0
E5 „ 6d. verm. & brt. vio. ('39) 40 0 50 0

E 2. Express Mail Delivery Van.

(Des. J. Berry. Eng. Stamp Ptg. Office, Melbourne. Recess. Govt. Ptg. Office, Wellington).

1939 (16 Aug.). *W* **41.** *P* 14.
E6 **E 2** 6d. violet 3 0 3 6

POSTAGE DUE STAMPS.

D 1

(I.)

(II.)

3D. (a)   5D. (b)

(Typo. Govt. Printing Office, Wellington.)

1899 (Dec.). *W* **12a**. *P* 11. *Two types of frame, two types of* " D." *in values* (a) *and* (b.)

Type I. *Circle of 14 ornaments, 17 dots over* "N.Z.", "N.Z." *large.* (a) *Large* "D."

D1 **D 1** ½d. carmine and green .. 3 6 5 0
 a. No stop after "D" .. 35 0 35 0
D2 ,, 8d. carmine and green .. 25 0 35 0
D3 ,, 1s. carmine and green .. 20 0 30 0
D4 ,, 2s. carmine and green .. 30 0 40 0

To avoid further subdivision the 1s. and 2s. are placed with the *pence* values, although the two types of " D " do not apply to the higher values.

(b) *Small* " D ".

D6 **D 1** 5d. carmine and green .. 12 6 10 0
D7 ,, 6d. carmine and green .. 12 6 12 6
D8 ,, 10d. carmine and green .. 22 6 35 0

Type II. *Circle of 13 ornaments, 15 dots over* "N.Z.", "N.Z." *small.* (a) *Large* "D".

D 9 **D 1** ½d. vermilion and green 0 6 2 6
 a. No stop after "D" .. 35 0 35 0
D10 ,, 1d. vermilion and green 3 6 0 6
D11 ,, 2d. vermilion and green 4 0 0 8
D12 ,, 3d. vermilion and green 4 0 1 6

(b) *Small* " D ".

D14 **D 1** 1d. vermilion and green 3 0 0 6
D15 ,, 2d. vermilion and green 5 0 1 6
D16 ,, 4d. vermilion and green 12 6 6 0

D 2

(Des. W. R. Bock. Typo. Govt. Printing Office.)

1902 (28 Feb.). *No wmk. P* 11.

D17 **D 2** ½d. red and deep green .. 1 9 1 9

1904–10. *Cowan unsurfaced paper.* *W* **41** (*sideways*).

(a) *P* 11.

D18 **D 2** ½d. red and green ('04) .. 1 6 0 9
 a. Imperf. between (pair) .. £15
D19 ,, 1d. red & green (5.12.05) 6 0 4 0
D20 ,, 2d. red & green (5.4.06) 55 0 30 0

(b) *P* 14.

D21 **D 2** 1d. carm. & green ('06) .. 5 0 1 0
 a. Rose-pink & green ('10) .. 2 6 0 6
D22 ,, 2d. carm. & green ('06) .. 4 6 3 6
 a. Rose-pink & green ('10) .. 3 0 0 9

1913. *Chalky paper.* *W* **41**. *P* 14×15.

D23 **D 2** ½d. carmine and green .. 1 6 1 6
D24 ,, 1d. carmine and green .. 2 0 0 4
D25 ,, 2d. carmine and green .. 6 0 0 6

1924 (Nov.). *"Jones" chalky paper. White gum.* *W* **41.** *P* 14×15.

D26 **D 2** ½d. carmine and green .. 8 0 8 0

1925 (July). *No wmk., but bluish* " N Z " *and Star lithographed on back.* *P* 14×15.

D27 **D 2** ½d. carmine and green .. 0 6 5 0
D28 ,, 2d. carmine and green .. 1 6 6 0

1925 (Nov.)–**29.** *"Cowan" thick opaque chalky paper* (p. 14×15 *and* 14); *or* (*from* 1937) *Wiggins, Teape hard chalky paper* (p. 14×15). *W* **14.** (a) *P* 14×15.

D29 **D 2** ½d. carmine & grn. (12.27) 0 9 1 6
D30 ,, 1d. carmine and green .. 1 6 0 3
D31 ,, 2d. carmine and green .. 3 0 0 9
D32 ,, 3d. carm. & grn. ('28?) 6 6 8 6

(b) *P* 14.

D33 **D 2** ½d. carm. & grn. (10.28) 1 6 4 0
D34 ,, 1d. rose and pale yellow-green (6.28) 1 6 0 6
D35 ,, 2d. carm. & grn. (10.29) 3 6 0 9
D36 ,, 3d. carm. & grn. (5.28) .. 8 6 50 0

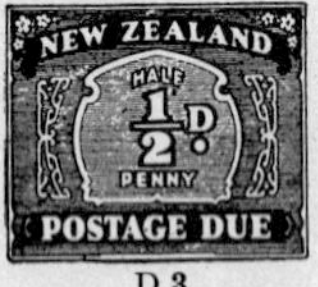

D 3

(Des. J. Berry. Typo. Govt. Printing Office, Wellington.)

1939 (17 Aug.)–**1949** (Apr.). *P* 15×14.

(a) *W* **41** *sideways.*

D37 **D 3** ½d. turquoise-green .. 0 4 0 8
D38 ,, 1d. carmine 0 6 0 4
D39 ,, 2d. bright blue 2 6 0 9
D40 ,, 3d. orange-brown .. 8 6 3 0

(b) *W* **98** *sideways.*

D42 **D 3** 1d. carmine ('49) .. 0 9 3 0
D43 ,, 2d. bright blue ('46) .. 1 3 2 6
D44 ,, 3d. orange-brown ('45) .. 2 6 1 6
 a. Wmk. upright ('47) .. 7 6 5 0

OFFICIAL STAMPS.

1892–1901. *Contemporary issues overprinted* " O. P. S. O." *diagonally.* *W* **12a.**

Violet overprint.

O40 **3** ½d. rose (p. 12½) 65 0

Rose or magenta overprint.

O41 **13** ½d. black (p. 10×11) .. 40 0
O42 ,, ½d. black (p. 10) .. 40 0
O43 **14** 1d. rose (p. 12×11½) .. 40 0
O44 ,, 1d. rose (p. 11) 40 0
O45 **15** 2d. purple (p. 11) .. 40 0
O46 ,, 2d. purple (p. 10) .. 40 0
O47 **16** 2½d. ultram. (p. 10×11) .. 45 0
O48 ,, 2½d. ultram. (p. 10) .. 50 0
O49 **19** 5d. olive-blk. (p. 12×11½) 55 0
O50 **20** 6d. brown (p. 12×11½) .. 65 0

Violet overprint. *P* 11.

O52 **40** 1d. carm. (*wmk. T* **36a**) 30 0
O52a **26** 2½d. blue (*no wmk.*) .. 70 0
O53 **27** 2½d. blue (*wmk. T* **41**) .. 50 0
O53a ,, 2½d. blue (*no wmk.*) .. 50 0
O54 **30** 5d. brown (*no wmk.*) .. 65 0
O55 **32** 8d. blue (*no wmk.*) .. 65 0
O55a **33** 9d. purple 90 0
 b. Perf. 14, 15 (No. 267) .. 90 0
O56 **35** 2s. green (*wmk. T* **41**) .. £6

Green overprint. P 11.
O57 **30** 5d. brown (*no wmk.*) .. 75 0 £8

The letters signify "On Public Service Only," and stamps so overprinted were used by the Post Office Department on official correspondence between the department and places abroad.

OFFICIAL.

(O 3)

1907. *Stamps of* 1902–7 (*W* **41.** *P* 14) *optd. with Type* O **3** (*vertically upwards*).
O59 **23** ½d. yellow-green 0 9 0 9
O60 **40** 1d. carmine 4 0 0 9
a. Perf. compound of 11 and 14 £30 £25
b. Mixed perfs. £30 £25
O61 **38a** 2d. purple 1 0 0 6
O62 ,, 2d. bright purple 1 0 0 6
a. Mixed perfs. £8 £8
O63 **28** 3d. bistre-brown 4 0 1 0
O64 **31** 6d. pink 17 6 6 0
a. Imperf. between (pair) .. £30
b. Mixed perfs. £12 £12
O65 **34** 1s. red 12 6 6 0
O66 **35** 2s. blue-green 15 0 12 6
a. Imperf. between (pair) .. £60
O67 **36** 5s. deep red 40 0 50 0
O68 F **4** £1 rose (No. F 164) .. £6 £5

1908. *Optd. as Type* O **3.** *W* **41.**
O69 **23** ½d. green (*p.* 14 × 15) .. 3 0 0 9
O70 **46** 1d. carmine (*p.* 14 × 15) .. 12 6 1 0
O71 **48** 6d. pink (*p.* 14 × 15) .. 17 6 10 0
O72 ,, 6d. pink (*p.* 14 × 13, 13½) 50 0 20 0

1910–16. *Optd. as Type* O **3.** *W* **41.** *P* 14 × 15.
O73 **50** ½d. yellow-green 5 0 0 9
O74 **51** 1d. carmine 1 6 0 6

T **52** (*and similar types*), *optd. as Type* O **3.** *W* **41.** *P* 14 × 14½.
O78 3d. chestnut 3 0 1 6
a. Perf. 14 × 13½ 50 0 35 0
b. Vert. pair, O78/8a £6 £6
O79 6d. carmine 4 6 2 0
O80 6d. deep carmine 3 0 0 9
O81 1s. vermilion 16 0 12 6

1913–14. *Optd. as Type* O **3.** *W* **41.** *P* 14.
O81*a* F **4** 2s. blue (30.9.14) .. 12 6 6 6
O82 ,, 5s. yellow-grn. (13.6.13) 20 0 12 6

The overprint on these last and on No. O69 is from a new set of type, giving a rather sharper impression than Type O **3**, but otherwise resembling it so closely as to make further illustration useless.

1915–22. *T* **60b** *and* **60a** *optd. as Type* O **3.** *Wmk. T* **41.** *P* 14 × 15.
O83 ½d. green (Oct. 12, 1915) .. 1 0 0 8
O84 1½d. slate (*local plate*), (June, '16) 1 3 0 6

T **52** *optd. as Type* O **3** *in red. P* 14 × 14½.
O85 8d. indigo-blue (May, '16) .. 4 6 6 6
a. Perf. 14 × 13½ 4 6 6 6
b. Vert. pair, O85/5a 20 0 32 6

T **60** *optd. as Type* O **3.** *P* 14 × 14½.
O86 3d. chocolate (May, 1916) .. 3 6 1 0
a. Perf. 14 × 13½ 3 6 1 0
b. Vert. pair, O86/6a 15 0 17 6
O87 6d. carmine (June, 1916) .. 2 0 0 6
a. Perf. 14 × 13½ 1 6 0 6
b. Vert. pair O87/7a 15 0 17 6
O88 8d. red-brn. (*p.* 14 × 13½) ('22) 20 0 32 6
O89 1s. vermilion (Sept., 1916) .. 3 0 0 6
a. Perf. 14 × 13½ 8 6 6 0
b. Vert. pair, O89/9a 25 0 30 0
O90 1s. pale orange-red 12 6 10 0

1916. *T* **60** *optd. as Type* O **3,** *on pictorial issue paper. Wmk. sideways. P* 14.
O93 3d. chocolate 1 0 3 0
a. No wmk. 15 0 15 0

1916–19. *T* **60b.** *P* 14 × 15. *Optd. as Type* O **3.**
O94 1½d. slate (Dec. '16) .. 1 0 0 3
O95 1½d. chestnut-brown (4.'19) .. 0 9 0 3
O96 2d. yellow (April, '17) .. 1 0 0 3
O97 3d. chocolate (Nov., '19) .. 2 6 1 3

1919–30. *Type* F **4** *optd. as Type* O **3.** *W* **41.** *P* 14½ × 14.
O98 2s. deep blue 12 6 5 0
a. No stop after "OFFICIAL" 50 0 50 0
O99 5s. yellow-green 20 0 12 6
a. No stop after "OFFICIAL" 60 0 60 0

1925. *T* **60** *optd. as Type* O **3.** *P* 14 × 13½.
O100 4d. red-violet 8 6 1 6
a. *Violet.* Perf. 14 × 14½ .. 3 6 0 4
O101 9d. sage-green 3 0 3 6

1925–31. *Optd. as Type* O **3.** "Jones" *chalky paper. White gum. W* **41.** *P* 14 × 15.
O102 **60b** ½d. green 3 6 1 9
O103 **51** 1d. deep carmine .. 7 6 2 6
O104 **60b** 3d. deep chocolate .. 6 0 4 0

No wmk. but bluish "N Z" *and Star lithographed on back.*
O105 **51** 1d. carmine-pink .. 4 6 4 0

"Cowan" *thick, opaque, chalky paper. White gum.*
O106 **60b** ½d. green (*p.* 14 × 15) .. 0 9 0 6
a. Perf. 14 .. .. 1 6 0 6
b. No stop after "OFFICIAL" (Perf. 14) 8 6 8 6
O107 **51** 1d. deep carmine .. 4 6 3 6
O108 **60b** 1½d. orge.-brn. (*p.* 14) ('30) 3 6 3 0
a. No stop after "OFFICIAL" .. 25 0 20 0
b. Perf. 14 × 15 .. .. 10 0 5 0
O109 ,, 2d. yellow (*p.* 14) ('31) 2 0 0 9
a. No stop after "OFFICIAL" .. 25 0 20 0
O110 ,, 3d. chocolate (*p.* 14 × 15) 2 0 0 4
a. No stop after "OFFICIAL" .. 25 0 20 0
b. Perf. 14 .. .. 4 0 2 0
c. Ditto, no stop after "OFFICIAL" .. 35 0 30 0

1927. *T* **71** *optd. as Type* O **3.**
O111 1d. rose-carmine (*p.* 14) .. 0 9 0 4
a. No stop after "OFFICIAL" 5 0 5 0
b. Perf. 14 × 15 .. .. 0 9 0 4

No. 542 *optd. as Type* O **3.**
O112 2s. light blue 17 6 12 6

1933. *No.* 544*f* (*Type as* **73a**) *optd. as Type* O **3.**
O113 5s. green 45 0 45 0

Official

(O 4)

1936–61. *Pictorial issue optd. horiz. or vert.* (2s.) *with Type* O **4.**
(*a*) *W* **41** (*Single* "N Z" *and Star*).
O115 **82** 1d. scarlet (Die I) (*p.* 14 × 13½) .. 1 0 0 3
a. Perf. 13½ × 14 .. 25 0 12 6
O116 **83** 1½d. red-brn. (*p.* 13½ × 14) 2 6 1 6
a. Perf. 14 × 13½ ..

O122 **92** 1s. dp. grn. (*p.* 14×13½) 10 0 7 6
O123 **73a** 5s. green (*p.* 14) .. 25 0 12 6

The watermark of O123 is almost invisible.
Only 4 copies of O116*a* exist. The 8d., previously included, was listed in error.

(*b*) *W* **98** (*Mult.* " N Z " *and Star*).

O124 **81** ½d. bright green *p.* 14×13½ .. 0 8 0 4
O125 **82** 1d. scarlet (Die II) *p.* 14×13½ .. 1 0 0 3
O126 **83** 1½d. red-brown, *p.* 14×13½ .. 2 0 1 9
O127 **84** 2d. orge., *p.* 14×13½ .. 0 6 0 2
  a. Perf. 12½ ('42) .. 22 6 4 6
  c. Perf. 14 ('42) .. 3 0 1 3
O128 **85** 2½d. chocolate and slate, *p.* 13–14×13½ .. 6 0 6 0
  a. Perf. 14 ('38) .. 1 6 1 6
O129 **86** 3d. brown, *p.* 14×13½ 5 0 0 9
O130 **87** 4d. black and sepia, *p.* 14×13½ .. 2 3 0 6
  a. Perf. 14 (Aug., '41) .. 1 9 1 0
  b. Perf. 12½ ('41) .. 1 6 1 0
  c. Perf. 14×14½ (-.10.42) 2 0 0 6
O132 **89** 6d. scarlet, *p.* 13½×14 2 6 0 3
  a. Perf. 12½ ('41) .. 2 6 1 0
  b. Perf. 14½×14 (-.7.42) .. 1 3 0 4
O133 **90** 8d. chocolate, *p.* 12½, (*wmk. sideways*) .. 1 9 1 0
  a. Perf. 14×14½ (*wmk. sideways*) ('45) .. 2 0 1 0
  b. Perf. 14×13½ . † —
O134 **91** 9d. red & grey-blk. (G.) (No. 587*a*), *p.* 14×14½ 3 0 2 0
O134*a* „ 9d. scar. & black (Bk.) (No. 627), *p.* 14×15 3 6 1 9
O135 **92** 1s. dp. grn. *p.* 14×13½ 2 6 0 4
  a. Perf. 12½ ('42) .. 3 6 0 9
O136 **93** 2s. olive-green, *p.* 13–14×13½ .. 30 0 10 0
  a. Perf. 12½ ('42) .. 15 0 4 0
  b. Perf. 13½×14 ('39) .. 70 0 10 0
  c. Perf. 14×13½ ('44) .. 10 0 5 0
O137*a* **73a** 5s. grn., C, *p.* 14 (3.43) 10 0 6 0
  b. Perf. 14 × 13½. *Yellow-green*, O (10.61) .. 8 6 7 6

The opt. on No. O132*a* was sometimes applied at the top of the stamp, instead of always at the bottom, as on No. O132.

Dates of first issue: 1936—July, No. O126; Aug., No. O130; Nov., No. O125. 1937—Feb., No. O135; May, No. O136; July, No. O124; Dec., No. O132. 1938—Jan., No. O127; 1 Mar., Nos. O129 and O134; 26 July, No. O128; Dec., No. O123. 1942—No. O133. 1943—Nos. O134*a* and O137*a*.

See notes on perforations after No. 590*b*.

1938–51. *Nos.* 603 *etc., optd. with Type* O **4.**

O138 **108** ½d. green (1.3.38) .. 1 0 0 3
O138*a* „ ½d. brown-orange ('46) 0 3 0 4
O139 „ 1d. scarlet (1.7.38) .. 1 3 0 3
O139*a* „ 1d. green (10.7.41) .. 1 0 0 4
O140 **108a** 1½d. pur.-brn. (26.7.38) 10 0 1 6
O140*a* „ 1½d. scarlet (2.4.51) .. 0 6 0 3
O140*b* „ 3d. blue (16.10.41) .. 0 8 0 2

Official

(O **5**)

1940 (2 JAN–8 MAR. (8d.)). *Centennial. Nos.* 609, *etc., optd. with Type* O **5.**

O141 ½d. blue-green (R.) .. 0 3 0 3
  a. "ff" joined, as Type O 4 .. 25 0 30 0
O142 1d. chocolate & scarlet (Bk.) 0 4 0 3
  a. "ff" joined, as Type O 4 .. 40 0 40 0
O143 1½d. light blue & mve. (Bk.) 0 5 0 8
O144 2d. blue-grn. & choc. (Bk.) 0 6 0 3
  a. "ff" joined, as Type O 4 .. 22 6 22 6
O145 2½d. blue-grn. & ultram. (Bk.) 0 6 1 0
  a. "ff" joined, as Type O 4 .. 22 6 25 0
O146 3d. purple & carmine (R.) .. 0 9 0 8
  a. "ff" joined, as Type O 4 .. 22 6 25 0
O147 4d. chocolate & lake (Bk.) .. 3 0 1 3
  a. "ff" joined, as Type O 4 .. 25 0 27 6
O148 6d. emerald-grn. & vio. (Bk.) 3 0 0 9
  a. "ff" joined, as Type O 4 .. 30 0 35 0
O149 8d. black and red (Bk.) .. 3 0 1 6
  a. "ff" joined, as Type O 4 .. 30 0 35 0
O150 9d. olive-grn. & verm. (Bk.) 2 0 1 9
O151 1s. sage-grn. & dp. grn. (Bk.) 6 0 3 0

1947–49. *Nos.* 680, *etc., optd. with Type* O **4.**

O152 **108a** 2d. orange 0 5 0 3
O153 „ 4d. bright purple .. 0 8 0 4
O154 „ 6d. carmine 1 3 0 5
O155 „ 8d. violet 1 6 0 6
O156 „ 9d. purple-brown .. 1 6 0 10
O157 **144** 1s. red-brn. & carm. (*wmk. upright*) (Pl. 1) .. 4 0 2 0
  a. Wmk. sideways (Pl. 1) ('49) 4 0 2 0
  b. Wmk. upright (Pl. 2) .. 3 6 1 0
O158 „ 2s. brown-orge. & grn. (*wmk. sideways*) (Pl. 1) 4 6 2 6
  a. Wmk. upright (Pl. 1) .. 8 0 3 6

O **6.**
Queen Elizabeth II.

6d
(O **7**)

(Des. J. Berry. Recess. Bradbury, Wilkinson.)

1954 (1 MAR.)–**63.** *W* **98.** *P* 14×13½.

O159 O **6** 1d. orange 0 3 0 2
O160 „ 1½d. brown-lake .. 1 6 1 6
O161 „ 2d. bluish green .. 1 3 0 4
O161*b* „ 2½d. olive (1.3.63) .. 0 6 0 6
O162 „ 3d. vermilion 0 8 0 6
O163 „ 4d. blue 0 9 0 8
  a. Ptd. on gummed side .. £50
O164 „ 9d. carmine 1 4 1 2
O165 „ 1s. purple .. .. 2 0 1 [illegible]
O165*b* „ 3s. slate (1.3.63) .. 5 0 6 [illegible]

See note *re* white opaque paper below No. 736

1959 (1 OCT.). *No.* O160 *surch. with Type* O **7**

O166 O **6** 6d. on 1½d. brown-lake 1 0 1

1961 (1 SEPT.). *No.* O161 *surch. as Type* O **7**

O167 O **6** 2½d. on 2d. bluish green 1 0 0

Owing to the greater use of franking machine by Government Departments, the use of officia stamps was discontinued on 31st March, 1965 but they remained on sale at the G.P.O. unt 31st December, 1965.

PROVISIONALS ISSUED AT REEFTON AND USED BY THE POLICE DEPARTMENT.

1907 (JAN.). *Current stamps of* 1906, *overwritt* "Official," *in red ink, and marked* " Gre mouth—PAID—3 " *inside a circular postmar stamp.* *P* 14.

P1 **23** ½d. green .. .. .. £12 £
P2 **40** 1d. carmine .. .. .. £12 £
P3 **38a** 2d. purple .. .. .. £18 £
P4 **28** 3d. bistre .. .. .. £12 £

P5	**31**	6d. pink	£25	£30
P6	**34**	1s. orange-red	£35	£40
P7	**35**	2s. green	—	£160

LIFE INSURANCE DEPARTMENT.

S **1**. Lighthouse.

(Des. W. B. Hudson and J. F. Rogers; eng. A. E. Cousins. Typo. Govt. Printing Office, Wellington.)

1891 (2 Jan.). *Type* S **1**. *W* **12***a*.

(a) P 12×11½.

1001	½d. bright purple	12 6	2 6
1002	1d. blue	17 6	2 6
1003	2d. brown-red	22 6	4 0
1004	3d. deep brown	42 6	15 0
1005	6d. green	60 0	35 0
1006	1s. rose	£5	50 0

(b) P 10.

1007	½d. bright purple	12 6	4 6
1008	1d. blue	7 6	2 6
1009	2d. lake	20 0	3 0

(c) P 10 *and* 11 *compound.*

1010	½d. bright purple	45 0	17 6
1011	1d. blue	15 0	6 0

(d) P 11.

1012	½d. bright purple	7 6	2 0
1013	1d. blue	6 6	0 6
1014	2d. brown-red	6 6	2 0
1015	2d. chocolate	70 0	22 6

(e) Mixed perfs.

1016	2d. brown-red	£12	£8

1902–4. *W* **41** *(sideways). (a) P* 11.

1019	S **1**	½d. bright purple ..	8 6	1 6
1020	,,	1d. blue	7 6	0 6
1021	,,	2d. brown-red ..	10 0	3 0

(b) P 11 *and* 14 *compound.*

1021*a*	S **1**	½d. bright purple ..		
1022	,,	1d. blue	20 0	3 6

Nos. 1019. 1020 and 1022 are also known without watermark from the margins of the sheets.

S 2

1905 (Dec.)–**1906**. *Design redrawn.* "V.R." *omitted. W* **41** *(sideways). (a) P* 11.

1023	S **2**	2d. brown-red	£25	45 0

(b) P 14.

1024	S **2**	1d. blue	25 0	4 6

(c) Perf. compound of 11 *and* 14.

1025	S **2**	1d. blue	£8	£6

(d) Mixed perfs.

1025*a*	S **2**	1d. blue	£10	£8

1913–37. *W* **41.** *New values and colours.*

(a) P 14×15.

1026	S **2**	½d. green	1 9	0 6
		a. Yellow-green ('25)	1 9	0 6
1027	,,	1d. carmine	5 0	0 9
		a. Carmine-pink ('25)	6 6	1 6
		b. Scarlet ('37)	2 0	0 4
1029	S **2**	1½d. black (1917) ..	6 6	5 6
1030	,,	1½d. chestnut-brn. (1919)	1 0	0 9
1031	,,	2d. bright purple ..	8 6	7 6
1031*a*	,,	2d. yellow (1920) ..	2 6	1 0
1032	,,	3d. yellow-brown ..	12 6	10 0
1033	,,	6d. carmine-pink ..	7 6	6 0

(b) P 14.

1034	S **2**	½d. yellow-green ('26) ..	1 6	0 6
1036	,,	1d. scarlet ('31) ..	2 0	0 4
1037	,,	2d. yellow ('37) ..	1 6	0 4
1038	,,	3d. brown-lake ('31) ..	2 0	1 6
1039	,,	6d. pink ('25)	7 6	6 0

In the 1½d. the word "POSTAGE" is in both the side-labels instead of at left only.

1945–47. *W* **98.** *P* 14×15.

1040	S **2**	½d. yellow-green ..	4 6	5 0
1041	,,	1d scarlet ('45) ..	1 6	0 10
1042	,,	2d. yellow ..	1 6	6 0
1043	,,	3d. brown-lake	2 6	8 6
1044	,,	6d. pink	6 0	10 0

S **3**. Castlepoint Lighthouse.

S **4**. Taiaroa Lighthouse.

S **5**. Cape Palliser Lighthouse.

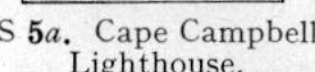

S **5***a*. Cape Campbell Lighthouse.

S **6**. Eddystone Lighthouse.

S **8**. The Brothers Lighthouse.

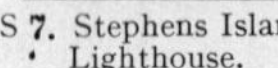

S **7.** Stephens Island Lighthouse.

S **9.** Cape Brett Lighthouse.

(Des. J. Berry. Recess. Bradbury, Wilkinson & Co.)

1947 (1 Aug.)–**65.** *W* **98** (*sideways on 1d., 2d., 2½d.*). *P* 13½.

No.	Type	Description				
1045	S **3**	½d. grey-grn. & orge.-red	1	6	1	6
1046	S **4**	1d. olive-grn. & pale bl.	0	3	0	2
1047	S **5**	2d. dark bl. & grey-blk.	0	4	0	4
1047*a*	S **5***a*	2½d. black & bright blue (4.11.63) ..	0	5	0	5
1048	S **6**	3d. mve. and pale blue	0	6	0	6
1049	S **7**	4d. brown & yell.-orge.	0	7	0	8
		a. Wmk. sideways (13.10.65)	0	7	0	8
1050	S **8**	6d. chocolate and blue	0	10	1	0
1051	S **9**	1s. red-brown and blue	1	6	2	0

See note *re* white opaque paper below No. 736.

POSTAL FISCALS.

F **1**

F **2**

F **3.**

1882 (1 April). *Type* F **1** (*1d. to 8d.*) *and Type* F **2.** *Wmk.* "N Z", *Type* F **3** *Large Star, or impressed monogram.* "N Z". (*a*) *Imperf.*

F 1	1d. lilac and red	10	0	10	0
F 2	1d. blue and red	10	0	6	0
F 3	4d. green and black ..	7	6	10	0
F 4	6d. brown and blue ..	15	0	10	0
F 5	8d. blue and black	10	0	10	0
F 6	1s. purple and red	20	0	12	6
F 7	1s. 4d. brown and blue ..	—		20	0
F 8	1s. 6d. blue and black ..	—		15	0
F 9	1s. 8d. drab and blue ..	30	0	20	0
F10	2s. red and green	30	0		
F11	2s. 4d. green and black ..				
F12	2s. 6d. brown and blue ..	—		15	0
F13	2s. 8d. blue and black ..	—		30	0
F14	3s. lilac and red	20	0	20	0
F15	3s. 4d. brown and blue ..	22	6	20	0
F16	3s. 6d. blue and black ..				
F17	3s. 8d. drab and blue ..	20	0		
F18	4s. red and green	—		20	0
F19	4s. 4d. green and black ..				
F20	4s. 6d. drab and blue ..				
F21	4s. 8d. blue and black ..				
F22	5s. 4d. drab and green ..				
F23	6s. carmine and blue ..	25	0		
F24	6s. 4d. pale blue and red ..				
F25	6s. 8d. blue and black ..	25	0	25	0
F26	7s. 6d. blue and black ..	—		12	6
F28	9s. violet and red	30	0		
F29	9s. 6d. blue and black ..	—		20	0
F30	10s. red and green	27	6	15	0
F31	15s. red and grey	—		20	0
F32	£1 red-brown and blue ..	30	0		
F33	£1 5s. red and grey ..	—		15	0
F34	30s. red and green	—		10	0
F35	35s. grey-blue and red ..	—		15	0
F36	40s. red and green	—		20	0
F37	90s. red and green				

Varieties. Wmk. Large Star.

F38	17s. 6d. blue and black ..	£10		45	0
F39	27s. 6d. blue and black ..	£9		65	0

Several varieties are known *percé en scie.*

(*b*) *P* 10, 12½, *and compound.*

F 40	1d. lilac and green ..	1	6	3	0
F 41	1d. mauve and green ..	2	0	3	0
F 42	1d. blue and brown ..				
F 44	1d. slate and green ..	5	0	5	0
F 45	1d. dull purple and green	5	0		
F 46	2d. green and red	6	0	6	0
F 48	4d. green and black ..	5	0	5	0
F 49	6d. grey-brown and blue ..	5	0		
F 50	6d. red-brown and blue ..	5	0	4	0
F 51	8d. blue and black ..	5	0	4	0
F 52	8d. blue and red	7	6		
F 53	1s. mauve and blue ..	5	0	2	6
F 54	1s. mauve and green ..	6	0	6	0
F 55	1s. purple and green ..	10	0	10	0
F 56	1s. 4d. brown and blue ..	30	0		
F 58	2s. rose and blue	12	6		
F 59	2s. 4d. green and black ..				
F 60	2s. 6d. brown and blue ..	7	6	6	0
F 61	2s. 6d. red-brown & blue ..	10	0	5	
F 63	3s. mauve and green ..	—		20	
F 64	3s. 4d. brown and blue ..	12	6	12	
F 65	4s. carmine and blue ..	15	0	10	
F 67	5s. dull violet and green ..	—		5	
F 68	5s. mauve and blue ..	—		7	
F 70	6s. red-brown and blue ..	10	0		
F 71	6s. carmine and blue ..	—		7	
F 72	6s. 8d. blue and rose ..	15	0		
F 74	7s. violet and red ..				
F 76	7s. 6d. blue and black ..	—		7	
F 78	8s. brown and blue ..				
F 80	9s. violet and red	—		30	
F 82	10s. red-brown and green ..	—		15	
F 83	10s. carmine and blue ..	—		7	
F 84	12s. 6d. brown	—		10	
F 85	15s. mauve and blue ..	—		10	
F 86	15s. grey and red	—		15	
F 87	20s. rose and blue				
F 88	£1 pink	30	0	8	
F 89	£1 2s. 6d. brown & blue ..	—		40	
F 91	£1 5s. grey and red ..	—		35	
F 92	£1 10s. brown and green ..	65	0		
F 93	£1 10s. red and green ..	—		40	
F 95	£2 orange and green ..	—		35	
F 96	£2 10s. pink and blue ..	—		50	
F 97	£3 pink and blue	—		50	
F 98	£3 red-brown and green ..	—		50	
F 99	£4 red-brown and green ..	—		45	
F100	£5 carmine and blue ..	—		60	
F101	£10 red-brown and green ..	—		60	

F 4

Type F **4.** *Value on white labels. Wmk.* " NZ " *and Star, T* **12a** *or* " NZ " *Type* F **3.** *P* 12½, 13 *or P* 11½, 12 *or P* 11.

F102	4d. red-brown	—		60	0
F103	6d. maroon	60	0	60	0
F104	8d. green (*wmk.* " NZ ") ..	—		7	6
F105	1s. rose	—		5	0
F106	1s. rose (*wmk.* " NZ ") ..	7	6	5	0
F107	2s. blue	10	0	4	0
F108	2s. 6d. grey-brown ..	10	0	3	6
F109	3s. mauve	12	6	4	0
F110	4s. brown-rose	40	0	6	0
F111	4s. dull purple	40	0	6	0
F112	4s. dull claret	25	0	6	0
F113	5s. green	20	0	4	0
F114	6s. rose	30	0	8	6
F114a	6s. rose (*wmk.* " NZ ")	—		10	0
F115	7s. blue	35	0	10	0
F116	7s. 6d. sepia	50	0	17	6
F117	8s. blue	40	0	10	6
F117a	8s. blue (*wmk.* " NZ ") ..				
F118	9s. orange	40	0	10	6
F119	9s. orange (*wmk.* " NZ ")..	—		15	0
F120	10s. Venetian red	40	0	8	6
F121	10s. Venetian red (*wmk.*"NZ")	—		15	0
F122	15s. green	60	0	12	6
F123	15s. green (*wmk.* " NZ ") ..	—		20	0
F125	£1 rose	75	0	20	0
F126	£1 rose (*wmk.* " NZ ") ..				
F127	25s. blue	—		30	0
F128	25s. blue (*wmk.* " NZ ") ..	—		40	0
F129	30s. brown	—		30	0
F130	35s. yellow	—		60	0
F131	£2 bright purple	—		20	0
F132	£2 10s. red-brown ..	—		50	0
F133	£3 green	—		25	0
F134	£3 10s. rose	—		90	0
F135	£4 ultramarine	—		70	0
F136	£4 10s. olive-brown ..	—		85	0
F137	£5 blue	—		30	0
F137a	£5 blue (*wmk.* " NZ ") ..	—		50	0
F138	£6 orange-red	—		60	0
F139	£7 Venetian red	—		50	0
F140	£8 green	—		50	0
F141	£9 rose	—		95	0
F142	£10 blue	—		70	0

Error. With " COUNTERPART " *inscribed above lower label.*

F143	2s. 6d. brown (1901) ..	35	0	45	0

All values under 15s. are Type F **4.** The 15s. to £2 10s. are of a slightly different type. The £3 to £5 have the head in a rectangle; the higher values have the head in a hexagon.

F 5

F 6

Type F **5** (1*d.*) *and various small rectangular designs as Type* F **6** (*others*). *Wmk. T* **12a.** *P* 11½, 12.

F144	1d. lilac	25	0	£5	
F145	1d. blue	12	6	5	0
F146	1s. green (LAND & DEEDS)	25	0	15	0
F147	1s. grn. & red (LAW COURTS)	25	0	30	0
F148	2s. rose & blue (LAW COURTS)	60	0		

1903–4. *Type* F **4.** *Wmk. single lined* " NZ " *and Star, T* **41.** *P* 11.

F149	2s. 6d. brown	10	0	4	6
F150	3s. mauve	12	6	4	6
F151	4s. rose	25	0	6	0
F152	6s. rose	25	0	8	6
F152a	7s. pale blue	35	0	10	0
F153	10s. brown	40	0	8	6
F154	£1 rose	75	0	20	0

1906–14. *Type* F **4.** *W* **41.** (*a*) *P* 14.

F155	2s. blue, C (1914) ..	12	6	2	6
F156	2s. 6d. brown, OC ..	10	0	3	6
F157	3s. mauve, OC	12	6	4	6
F158	4s. Venetian red, O ..	12	6	4	6
F159	5s. green, C	12	6	4	0
F159a	6s. rose, O	25	0	8	6
F160	7s. blue, OC	30	0	10	0
F160a	7s. 6d. sepia, OC ..	50	0	17	6
F161	8s. blue, OC	25	0	10	0
F162	9s. orange, O	30	0	7	6
F163	10s. brown, OC	35	0	7	6
F163a	15s. green, O	50	0	12	6
F164	£1 rose, OC	75	0	20	0
F165	£2 violet	—		30	0

(*b*) *P* 14½ × 14 (*chalk-surfaced paper*).

F166	2s. blue	6	6	3	0
F167	2s. 6d. brown	10	0	3	6
F168	3s. bright mauve	12	6	4	6
F169	4s. Venetian red	12	6	3	6
F170	5s. yellow-green (1913) ..	10	0	3	6
F171	6s. rose (1913)	20	0	8	6
F172	7s. blue	25	0	8	6
F173	8s. blue (1913)	20	0	7	6
F173a	9s. orange	25	0	10	0
F174	10s. brown	35	0	6	0
F174a	12s. 6d. purple	70	0	50	0
F175	15s. green	35	0	10	0
F176	£1 rose	70	0	20	0
F177	£2 violet	50	0		

Later printings of some values were on " Jones," " Cowan," or " Wiggins Teape " paper.

NOTE. While there are still differences of opinion as to the status of the stamps of Type F **1** and F **2**, stamps of Type F **4** and T **73a** ("Arms") were authorized to be accepted in prepayment of postage and were, in fact, with a few exceptions, the only postage stamps of high denomination in existence.

This differentiates them sharply from most other stamps listed under the heading " Postal Fiscals " in this catalogue, the use of these others being mainly for revenue purposes and their postal use exceptional.

In regard to stamps of Type F **4** the only point of difficulty is whether all values should be regarded as postage stamps in the fullest sense, or only those which were generally used for postal purposes. We have therefore left these stamps in this section of the list until there has been opportunity for fuller discussion on this point but we have transferred the stamps in the Arms design, formerly listed as Nos. F178 to F207, to the list of postage stamps, as there can be no question as to their right to that position.

ANTARCTIC EXPEDITIONS.

KING EDWARD VII LAND.

1908. *Shackleton Expedition. T* **40** *of New Zealand (p.* 14), *overprinted,* " King Edward VII Land " *in two lines, reading up.*

A1 1d. rose-carmine (No. 418*b* Royle) (G.) £25 30 0
a. Overprint double .. .. — £50
A1*b* 1d. rose-carmine (No. 418*b* Waterlow) (G.) .. ..

VICTORIA LAND.

1911. *Scott Expedition. T* **50** *and* **51** *of New Zealand overprinted* " VICTORIA LAND." *in two lines, in black.*

A2 ½d. green £50 £30
A3 1d. carmine 50 0 50 0
a. No stop after " LAND " .. £20

These issues were made under authority of the New Zealand Postal Department and, while not strictly necessary, they actually franked correspondence to New Zealand. They were sold to the public at a premium.

BRITISH POSSESSIONS UNDER NEW ZEALAND CONTROL.

AITUTAKI.

AITUTAKI.
1

Ava Pene.
2 (½d.)

Tai Pene.
3 (1d.)

Rua Pene Ma Te Ava.
4 (2½d.)

Toru Pene.
5 (3d.)

Ono Pene.
6 (6d.)

Tai Tiringi.
7 (1s.)

1903. *Stamps of New Zealand,* 1902 *issue, wmk. single-lined* " N Z " *and Star, T* **41**, *surch. with T* **1** *at top, and T* **2** *to* **7**, *in red or blue at foot.*

(*a*) *P* 14.

1 **23** ½d. green (R.) 8 6 15 0
2 **40** 1d. carmine (B.) 12 6 17 6
3 **27** 2½d. blue (R.) 8 6 17 6
a. " Ava " without stop .. 85 0 £5

(*b*) *P* 11.

5 **27** 2½d. blue (R.) 10 0 15 0
a. " Ava " without stop .. £5 £6
7 **28** 3d. yellow-brown (B.) .. 10 0 17 6
8 **31** 6d. rose-red (B.) 20 0 30 0
9 **34** 1s. bright red (B.) .. 45 0 60 0
a. " Tiringi " without stop .. £12 £15
10 ,, 1s. orange-red (B.) .. 60 0 75 0
a. " Tiringi " without stop .. £12 £15
10*b* ,, 1s. orange-brown (B.) .. £6 £7
c. " Tiringi " without stop .. £30 £35

AITUTAKI.

Ono Pene.
(7*a*)

1912–16. *Stamps of New Zealand surch., the* ½d. *and* 1d. *as on Nos.* 1/2, *the* 6d. *and* 1s. *as T* 7*a*.

11 **50** ½d. green (R.) 2 6 4 6
12 **51** 1d. carmine (B.) (1913) .. 3 6 6 6
14 **52** 6d. carm. (B.) (*p.* 14 × 14½) ('16) 12 6 20 0
15 ,, 1s. verm. (B.) (*p.* 14 × 14½) ('14) 60 0 85 0

1916–17. *T* **60** *surch. as T* 7*a*. *P* 14 × 14½.

23 6d. carmine (B.) (June, '16) .. 10 0 17 6
a. Perf. 14 × 13½ 12 6 17 6
b. Vert. pair, 23/3a 50 0 75 0
25 1s. vermilion (B.) (Mar., '17) .. 17 6 25 0
a. Perf. 14 × 13½ 17 6 25 0
b. Vert. pair, 25/25a 70 0 90 0
c. " Tai " without dot £10 £15
d. " Tiringi " no dot on second " i " £15 £20
e. " Tiringi " no dot on third " i " .. £20 £25

1917–18. *T* **60** *optd.* " AITUTAKI," *only, as in T* 7*a*. *P* 14 × 14½.

27 2½d. blue (R.) (Dec., '18) .. 3 6 6 0
a. Perf. 14 × 13½ 4 0 6 0
b. Vert. pair. 27/7a 25 0 35 0
28 3d. chocolate (B.) (Jan., '18) 5 0 8 6
a. Perf. 14 × 13½ 4 0 8 6
b. Vert. pair, 28/8a 32 6 50 0
29 6d. carmine (B.) (Dec., '17) .. 8 6 12 6
a. Perf. 14 × 13½ 8 6 12 6
b. Vert. pair, 29/9a 35 0 50 0
30 1s. vermilion (B.) (Dec., '17) 12 6 22 6
a. Perf. 14 × 13½ 15 0 25 0
b. Vert. pair, 30/30a 50 0 65 0

1917–20. *T* **60*b*** *and* **51**, *optd.* " AITUTAKI ". *only, as in T* 7*a*. *Wmk.* " N Z " *and Star, T* **41**. *P* 14 × 15.

31 ½d. green (R.) (Feb., '20) .. 1 6 3 0
32 1d. carmine (B.) (May, '20) .. 2 0 3 6
33 1½d. slate (R.) (Nov., '17) .. 4 6 6 6
34 1½d. oran.-brn. (R) (Feb.,'19) .. 4 6 6 6
35 3d. chocolate (B.) (July, '19) .. 5 0 8 6

(Des. and recess. Perkins, Bacon & Co.)

1920 (AUG.). *As T* **10** *to* **15** *of Cook Islands, but inscr.* " AITUTAKI ". *No wmk. P* 14.

36 ½d. black and deep green .. 3 6 6 0
37 1d. black and dull carmine .. 4 0 6 6
38 1½d. black and sepia 4 0 6 6
39 3d. black and deep blue .. 5 0 7 6
40 6d. red-brown and slate .. 8 6 12 6
41 1s. black and purple 15 0 20 0

(Nos. 42–44. Recess. Govt. Printing Office, Wellington.)

1927. *As Nos.* 36/37, *but wmk.* " N Z " *and Star. T* **41**. *P* 14.

42 ½d. black and green 3 6 6
43 1d. black and deep carmine .. 3 6 6

1927. *As T* **16** *of Cook Islands, but inscr* " AITUTAKI ". *Wmk.* " N Z " *and Star, T* **41** *P* 14.

44 2½d. black and dull blue .. 7 6 12

Cook Islands stamps superseded those of Aitutaki on 15 March, 1932.

NIUE.

NIUE
(1)

T **23**, **27**, *and* **40** *of New Zealand, optd.*

1902. *Handstamped with T* **1**, *in green or bluish green. Waterlow paper. Wmk. double-lined* " N Z " *and Star, T* **36a**. *P* 11.

1 1d. carmine £25 £2

A few overprints were made with a *greenish violet* ink.

NIUE.
½ PENI.
(2)

NIUE.
TAHA PENI.
3 (1d.)

NIUE.
2½ PENI.
(4)

1902. *Type-set surcharges,* **T 2, 3,** *and* **4.** *½d. and 2½d. in red, 1d. in blue.*

(1) *Waterlow paper. No wmk.* *P* 11.

2 2½d. blue 3 6 6 0
 a. No stop after "PENI" .. 50 0 65 0

(2) *Basted Mills paper. Wmk. double-lined "N Z" and Star,* **T 36a.** (*a*) *Perf.* 14.

4 ½d. green 2 6 6 0
 a. Spaced "U" and "E" .. 10 0 15 0
 b. Surch. inverted £12 £15
5 ½d. deep green 3 6 6 0
8 1d. carmine 10 0 15 0
 a. Spaced "U" and "E" .. 35 0 40 0
 b. No stop after "PENI" .. £6 £7
 c. Vars. a. and b. on same stamp .. £8 £10

(*b*) *P* 11 *and* 14 *compound.*

12 1d. carmine 2 6 6 0
 a. Spaced "U" and "E" .. 10 0 15 0
 b. No stop after "PENI" .. 25 0 40 0
 c. Vars. a. and b. on same stamp .. £5 £6

(*c*) *Mixed perfs.*

15*a* ½d. green £15
16 1d. carmine £25

(3) *Cowan paper. Wmk. single-lined "N Z" and Star,* **T 41.** (*a*) *P* 14.

17 ½d. green 2 0 3 6
 a. Spaced "U" and "E" .. 5 0 8 6
19 1d. carmine 1 6 2 6
 a. Surcharge double £35
 b. Spaced "U" and "E" .. 35 0 40 0
 c. No stop after "PENI" .. 30 0 35 0
 d. Vars. b. and c. on same stamp .. 60 0 70 0

(*b*) *Mixed perfs.*

22*a* ½d. green £25
23 1d. carmine £12
 a. Spaced "U" and "E" .. ..

NIUE. 5 — **Tolu e Pene.** 6 (3d.)

Ono e Pene. 7 (6d.) — **Taha e Sileni.** 8 (1s.)

903–4. **T 28, 31, 34** *optd. with name at top,* **T 5,** *and values at foot,* **T 6, 7,** *and* **8,** *respectively, in blue.* **W 41.** *P* 11.

4 3d. yellow-brown 10 0 17 6
5 6d. rose-red 12 6 17 6
7 1s. bright red 17 6 25 0
8 1s. orange-red 35 0 50 0

Error. "Tahae" *for* "Taha e."

9 1s. brown-red £35

NIUE.
½ PENI.
(9)

911 (Nov.). **T 50** *surch. with* **T 9.**

½d. green (C) 2 0 2 6

911. **T 52** *optd. with name at top as* **T 5** *and values at foot as* **T 7** *and* **8,** *in blue.* *P* 14 × 14½.

6d. carmine 10 0 15 0
1s. vermilion 12 6 20 0

915. **T 27** *but* **W 41.** *Surch. as* **T 4.** *P* 14.

2½d. deep blue (R.) 5 0 10 0
 a. "NIUE" 1¾ mm. high .. £6

917. **T 51** *and* **60** *surch. as* **T 3,** *in deep brown (1d.) or* "NIUE" *as* **T 5** *and value as* **T 6** *in blue (3d.).*

1d. carmine 3 6 6 0
 a. No stop after "Peni" £10
3d. chocolate (*p.* 14 × 14½) .. 40 0 55 0
 a. No stop after "Pene" £35
 b. Perf. 14 × 13½ 50 0 65 0
 c. Vert. pair 35/5b £10

NIUE.
(10)

1917–20. **T 51, 60** (*P* 14 × 14½, *etc.*) *and Type* F **4** *of New Zealand, optd. with* **T 10.**

37 1d. carmine (B.) 2 0 4 0
38 2½d. blue (R.) 3 0 5 0
 a. Perf. 14 × 13½ 4 0 6 0
 b. Vert. pair, 38/8a 15 0 30 0
39 3d. chocolate (B.) 4 0 6 0
 a. Perf. 14 × 13½ 4 0 6 0
 b. Vert. pair, 39/9a 30 0 40 0
40 6d. carmine (B.) 9 0 12 6
 a. Perf. 14 × 13½ 7 6 12 6
 b. Vert. pair, 40/40a 25 0 35 0
41 1s. vermilion (B.) 12 6 20 0
 a. Perf. 14 × 13½ 12 6 20 0
 b. Vert. pair, 41/1a 45 0 75 0
42 2s. blue (R.) (*p.* 14½ × 14) .. 35 0 45 0
43 5s. green (R.) (*p.* 14, 14½) .. 80 0 £6
 a. Perf. 14½ × 14 .. .. 60 0 £5

1917–20. **T 60b,** *surface-printed, optd. with* **T 10. W 41.** *P* 14 × 15.

44 ½d. green (R.) 1 3 2 0
45 1½d. slate (R.) 3 0 4 6
46 1½d. orange-brown (R.) .. 2 6 4 6
47 3d. chocolate (B.) 3 0 6 0

(Des., eng. and ptd. by Perkins, Bacon & Co.)

1920 (Aug.). *As* **T 10** *to* **15** *of Cook Is., but inscr.* "NIUE". *No wmk.* *P* 14.

48 ½d. black and green 1 6 2 6
49 1d. black and dull carmine .. 3 0 5 0
50 1½d. black and red 3 0 5 6
51 3d. black and blue 4 0 6 0
52 6d. red-brown and green .. 6 0 10 0
53 1s. black and sepia 12 6 17 6

1923. *Type* F **4** *of New Zealand, optd. with* **T 10.**

54 2s. 6d. pale chocolate (B.) .. 30 0 45 0
55 10s. claret (B.) £10 £15
56 £1 bright carmine-rose (B.) .. £20 £30

(Recess. Govt. Ptg. Office, Wellington.)

1925–27. *Pictorial types as* 1920, *but* **W 41.**

57 ½d. black and green ('27) .. 1 6 2 6
58 1d. black and deep carmine .. 2 0 2 6

1927. **T 72** *of New Zealand, optd. as* **T 10.** "*Jones*" *paper.*

63 2s. deep blue (R.) 35 0 45 0

As last. "*Cowan*" *paper.*

64 2s. light blue (R.) 27 6 37 6

(Recess. Govt. Ptg. Office, Wellington.)

1927. *As* **T 16** *and* **17** *of Cook Islands, but inscr.* "NIUE". **W 41.** *P* 14.

65 2½d. black and blue 4 6 6 0
66 4d. black and violet 6 0 8 6

1931. *No.* 50 *surch. as* **T 18** *of Cook Is.*

67 2d. on 1½d. black and red .. 3 0 4 0

1931–32. *Types as* **73a** *of New Zealand (various frames), optd. as* **T 10. W 41.** *P* 14.

68 2s. 6d. brown (B.) 35 0 50 0
69 5s. green (R.) 35 0 50 0
70 10s. carmine-lake (B.) £5 £7
71 £1 pink (B.) £8 £10

(Des. L. C. Mitchell. Recess. Perkins, Bacon & Co.)

1932 (16 Mar.). *As* **T 19** *to* **25** *of Cook Is., but frames include* "NIUE" *as well as* "COOK ISLANDS." *No wmk.* *P* 13.

72 ½d. black and emerald 1 6 1 3
 a. Perf. 14 × 13 .. .. .. £8
73 1d. black and deep lake 1 3 1 3
74 2d. black and red-brown 1 6 2 6
75 2½d. black and slate-blue 8 0 10 0
76 4d. black and greenish blue .. 10 0 12 6
 a. Perf. 14 .. .. .. 8 0 10 0
77 6d. black & orange-vermilion 7 6 7 6
78 1s. black and purple (*p.* 14) .. 15 0 15 0

(Recess-printed from Perkins, Bacon's plates at Govt. Ptg. Offices, Wellington, N.Z.)

1932–36. *Pictorial types as 1932, but W* **41.** *P* 14.

79 ½d. black and emerald .. 0 3 0 4
80 1d. black and deep lake .. 0 6 0 4
81 2d. black & yell.-brn. (1.4.36) 0 8 0 8
82 2½d. black and slate-blue 0 10 0 10
83 4d. black and greenish blue .. 1 6 1 6
84 6d. black and red-orge. (1.4.36) 3 6 4 0
85 1s. black and purple (1.4.36) .. 7 6 10 0

1935 (7 MAY). *Silver Jubilee. Designs as Nos.* 80, 82 *and* 84 (*colours changed*) *optd. as T* **26** *of Cook Is.* (*wider vertical spacing on 6d.*). *W* **41.** *P* 14.

86 1d. red-brown and lake .. 1 6 3 0
a. Narrow " K " in " KING " .. 10 0
b. Narrow " B " in " JUBILEE " 10 0
87 2½d. dull and deep blue (R.) .. 6 6 10 0
a. Narrow first " E " in " GEORGE " 20 0
b. Imperf. between (vert. pair) .. £40
88 6d. green and orange 15 0 22 6
a. Narrow " N " in " KING " 60 0

For illustrations of varieties, see Cook Islands.

NIUE

(13)

1937 (13 MAY). *Coronation Issue. Nos.* 599 *to* 601 *of New Zealand optd. with T* **13.**

89 1d. carmine 0 4 0 8
90 2½d. Prussian blue 0 10 1 3
91 6d. red-orange 1 6 2 6

1938 (2 MAY). *As T* **29** *to* **31** *of Cook Is., but frames inscr.* " NIUE COOK ISLANDS ". *W* **41.** *P* 14.

92 1s. black and violet 2 6 2 0
93 2s. black and red-brown .. 4 0 4 0
94 3s. light blue & emerald-green 8 6 7 6

1940 (2 SEPT.) *As T* **32** *of Cook Islands, but additionally inscr.* " NIUE ". *W* **98.** *P* 13½ × 14.

95 3d. on 1½d. black and purple 0 6 0 8

1944–46. *As T* **19** *to* **24** *and* **29** *to* **31** *of Cook Is., but additionally inscr.* " NIUE ". *W* **98.**

96 ½d. black and emerald .. 0 3 0 2
97 1d. black and deep lake .. 0 4 1 0
98 2d. black and red-brown .. 0 8 1 3
99 2½d. black and slate-blue ('46) 0 8 1 0
100 4d. black and greenish blue 1 3 1 6
101 6d. black and red-orange .. 1 3 2 0
102 1s. black and violet .. 2 0 4 0
102*a* 2s. black & red-brown ('45) 5 0 7 6
102*b* 3s. light blue and emerald-green ('45) 6 0 10 0

NIUE.

(14)

1944–57. *T* **73***a* (" *Arms*") *of New Zealand with thin opt., T* **14.** *Chalky paper. P* 14.

(*a*) *Single wmk.* " N Z " *and Star, T* **41.**

103 2s. 6d. brown (B.) .. 35 0 45 0
104 5s. green (R.) £8 £10
105 10s. pale carmine (B.) .. £8 £10
106 £1 pink (B.) £8 £10

(*b*) *Wmk. Mult.* " N Z " *and Star, T* **98.**

107 2s. 6d. brown (B.) .. 12 6 17 6
a. Ordinary paper. P 14 × 13½ (1.11.57) 3 6 5 0
108 5s. green (R.) 6 9 8 6
108*a* 10s. carmine-lake (B.) ('45) .. 13 3 20 0
108*b* £1 pink (B.) '45) 25 0 35 0

1946 (1 JUNE). *Peace. Stamps of New Zealand optd. as T* **14**, *but without stop* (*twice, reading up and down on 2d.*).

109 **132** 1d. green (Bk.) 0 4 0 5
110 **134** 2d. purple (B.) 0 5 0 8
111 **138** 6d. choc. and verm. (Bk.) 1 0 1 6
112 **139** 8d. blk. and carmine (B.) 1 3 1 9

15. Map of Niue.

16. Capt. Cook's *Resolution.*

17. Alofi Landing.

18. Native Hut.

19. Arch at Hikutavake.

20. Alofi Bay.

21. Spearing Fish.

22. Cave, Makefu.

23. Bananas.

24. Matapa Chasm.

(Des. J. Berry. Recess. Bradbury, Wilkinson.

1950 (3 JULY). *W* **98** *of New Zealand* (*sideway inverted on* 1*d.*, 2*d.*, 3*d.*, 4*d.*, 6*d. and* 1*s.* *P* 13½ × 14 (*horiz.*), 14 × 13½ (*vert.*).

113 **15** ½d. orange and blue .. 0 2 0
114 **16** 1d. brown and blue-green 0 3 0
115 **17** 2d. black and carmine .. 0 4 0
116 **18** 3d. blue and violet-blue .. 0 6 0
117 **19** 4d. olive-grn. & pur.-brn. 0 7 0
118 **20** 6d. green & brown-orange 0 10 1 [illegible]
119 **21** 9d. orange and brown .. 1 1 1
120 **22** 1s. purple and black .. 1 5 1
121 **23** 2s. brn.-orge. & dull green 2 9 3
122 **24** 3s. blue and black .. 4 0 4

1953 (25 MAY). *Coronation. As Nos.* 715 *and* 717 *of New Zealand, but inscr.* " NIUE ".
123 **164** 3d. brown 0 10 0 10
124 **166** 6d. slate-grey 1 3 1 6

PENRHYN ISLAND.

PENRHYN ISLAND.
½ PENI.
(1)

PENRHYN ISLAND.
TAI PENI.
2 (1d.)

PENRHYN ISLAND.
2½ PENI.
(3)

1902. *T* **23**, **40**, *and* **27** *of New Zealand surch. with T* **1**, **2**, *and* **3**.

(1) *Waterlow paper. No wmk. P* 11.
1 2½d. blue (R.) 2 6 6 0
a. " ½ " and " P " spaced .. 12 6 20 0

(2) *Basted Mills paper. Wmk. double-lined* " N Z " *and Star. T* **36a**. (*a*) *P* 11.
3 1d. carmine (Br.) £5 £7

(*b*) *P* 14.
4 ½d. green (R.) 1 0 2 0
a. No stop after " ISLAND " .. £6 £8
5 1d. carmine (Br.) 2 6 4 0
6 1d. pale carmine (Br.) .. 2 6 4 0

(*c*) *P* 11 × 14.
8 1d. carmine (Br.) £5 £6

(*d*) *Mixed perfs.*
9 1d. carmine (Br.) £15

(3) *Cowan paper. Wmk. single-lined* " N Z " *and Star, T* **41**. (*a*) *P* 14.
10 ½d. green (R.) 1 0 2 0
a. No stop after " ISLAND " .. 70 0 90 0
11 1d. carmine (B.) 1 6 2 0
a. No stop after " ISLAND " .. 35 0 50 0

(*b*) *Mixed perfs.*
12 ½d. green (R.) £12 £15
13 1d. carmine (B.) £5 £7

PENRHYN ISLAND.
(4)

Toru Pene.
5 (3d.)

Ono Pene.
6 (6d.)

Tahi Silingi.
7 (1s.)

1903. *Stamps of New Zealand, surch. with name at top, T* **4**, *and values at foot, T* **5/7**. *W* **41**. *P* 11.
14 **28** 3d. yellow-brown (B.) .. 10 0 17 6
15 **31** 6d. rose-red (B.) 12 6 17 6
16 **34** 1s. brown-red (B.) 25 0 35 0
17 ,, 1s. bright red (B.) 25 0 35 0
18 ,, 1s. orange-red (B.) 35 0 45 0

1914–15. *Surch. with T* **1** (½*d.*) *or optd. with T* **4** *at top and surch. with T* **6/7** *at foot.*
19 **50** ½d. yell.-green (C.) (7.14) .. 2 0 3 0
a. No stop after " ISLAND " .. 45 0 60 0
b. No stop after " PENI " .. 50 0 65 0
20 ,, ½d. yell.-green (V.) (3.15) .. 0 6 1 0
a. No stop after " ISLAND " .. 25 0 30 0
b. No stop after " PENI " .. 35 0 40 0
22 **52** 6d. carm. (B.) (Aug., '14) .. 15 0 25 0
23 ,, 1s. verm. (B.) (Sept., '14) .. 25 0 35 0

1917–20. *T* **60** *of N.Z.* (*P* 14 × 14½, *etc.*), *optd. with name only, T* **4**.
24 2½d. blue (R.) (Oct., '20) .. 2 0 5 0
a. No stop after " ISLAND " .. 40 0 55 0
b. Perf. 14 × 13½ 3 6 6 0
c. Vert. pair. 24/4b. 12 6 17 6
25 3d. chocolate (B.) (June, '18) 7 6 12 6
a. Perf. 14 × 13½ 4 6 12 6
b. Vert. pair 25/5a 30 0 45 0
26 6d. carmine (B.) (Jan., '18) .. 6 0 10 0
a. No stop after " ISLAND " .. 80 0 95 0
b. Perf. 14 × 13½ 6 0 10 0
c. Vert. pair 26/6b 30 0 45 0
27 1s. vermilion (B.) (Dec., '17) .. 15 0 20 0
a. No stop after " ISLAND " .. £5 £6
b. Perf. 14 × 13½ 10 0 15 0
c. Vert. pair 27/7b 45 0 60 0

1917–20. *T* **60b** *of N.Z., typo., optd. as T* **4**. *W* **41**. *P* 14 × 15.
28 ½d. green (R.) (Feb., '20) .. 1 0 2 0
a. No stop after " ISLAND " .. 35 0 50 0
29 1½d. slate (R.) (Nov., '17) .. 5 0 6 6
30 1½d. orange-brown (R.) (2.19) 1 6 3 6
31 3d. chocolate (B.) (July, '19) .. 3 6 6 0

(Recess. Perkins Bacon & Co., Ltd.)

1920 (AUG.). *As T* **10** *to* **15** *of Cook Islands but inscr.* " PENRHYN ". *No wmk. P* 14.
32 ½d. black and emerald 2 0 3 0
33 1d. black and deep red .. 4 0 6 0
34 1½d. black and deep violet .. 4 0 6 0
35 3d. black and red 5 0 7 6
36 6d. red-brown and sepia .. 8 6 12 6
37 1s. black and slate-blue .. 17 6 25 0

(Recess. Govt. Printing Office, Wellington.)

1927–29. *As T* **10**, **11** *and* **16** *of Cook Islands, but inscribed* " PENRHYN ", *W* **41**. *P* 14.
38 ½d. black and green 2 0 3 6
39 1d. black and deep carmine .. 3 0 4 0
40 2½d. red-brown and dull blue .. 6 0 8 6

Cook Islands stamps superseded those of Penrhyn Island on 15 March, 1932.

(For stamps of New Zealand overprinted " **RAROTONGA** " see Cook Islands, and for stamps overprinted " **SAMOA** " see list under that heading.)

ROSS DEPENDENCY.

1. H.M.S. *Erebus.*

2. Shackleton and Scott.

3. Map of Ross Dependency and New Zealand.

4. Queen Elizabeth II.

(Des. E. M. Taylor (3d.), L. C. Mitchell (4d.), R. Smith (8d.), J. Berry (1s. 6d.). Recess. De La Rue & Co.)

1957 (11 Jan.). *W* **98** *of New Zealand* (*Mult. NZ and Star*). *P* 13 (1s. 6d.) *or* 14 (*others*).

1 **1** 3d. indigo 0 6 0 8
2 **2** 4d. carmine-red 0 7 1 0
3 **3** 8d. bright carmine-red and ultramarine (*shades*) .. 1 0 1 9
4 **4** 1s. 6d. slate-purple .. 2 0 3 0

NIGER COAST PROTECTORATE.

For GREAT BRITAIN stamps used in Niger Coast, see page 78.

This district was known as the "OIL RIVERS PROTECTORATE" from 5 June, 1885, till 12 May, 1893, when the name was altered to the "NIGER COAST PROTECTORATE".

BRITISH
PROTECTORATE

OIL RIVERS
(1)

1892 (July). *Stamps of Great Britain optd. by De La Rue & Co., with T* **1**.

1 **71** ½d. vermilion 5 0 6 0
2 **57** 1d. lilac 5 0 7 0
a. Opt. reversed "OIL RIVERS" at top £100
b. Bisected (½d.) (on cover) .. † £55
3 **73** 2d. green and carmine .. 9 0 9 0
a. Bisected (1d.) (on cover) ..
4 **74** 2½d. purple/*blue* 5 0 6 0
5 **78** 5d. dull purple and blue .. 6 0 7 0
6 **82** 1s. green 60 0 50 0

Control letters. ½d. E, K, L, M.
1d. L. N, O, P, Q.

Nos. 2 to 6 surcharged locally.

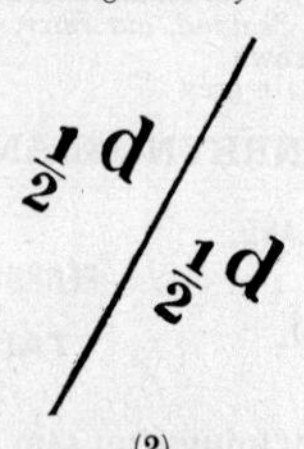

(2)

1893 (3 Sept.). *As T* **2**.

7 ½d. on half of 1d. (R.) .. 80 0 80 0
aa. Unsevered pair £20 £15
a. Surch. inverted and dividing line reversed (unsevered pair) .. — £110
b. Surch. reversed (dividing line running from left to right) ..
c. Straight top to "1" in "½" .. £8 £8
d. "½" omitted .. .. ..
e. Surch. double (in pr. with normal)
8 ½d. on half of 1d. (V.) .. £125
a. Surch. double (pair) £200

Nos. 7 and 8 exist *se-tenant*. *Price* £150 *used*.

HALF
PENNY.
(3)

HALF
PENNY.
(4)

1893 (Dec.). *With T* **3**.

9 ½d. on 2d. (V.) £12 £12
a. Surch. inverted .. ..
b. Surch. diagonal (up) .. ..
c. Surch. vertical (up or down) .. £55
10 ½d. on 2½d. (Verm.) £225
a. Surch. carmine £700

With T **4**.

11 ½d. on 2½d. (G.) £12 £12
a. Surch. double £100
b. Surch. diagonally inverted £80
12 ½d. on 2½d. (Verm.) £18 £18
13 ½d. on 2½d. (C.) £12 £12
a. Surch. omitted (in pr.) ..
14 ½d. on 2½d. (B.) £20 £20
15 ½d. on 2½d. (Bk.) £95
a. Surch. inverted .. ..
b. Surch. diagonal inverted (up or down) £100
16 ½d. on 2½d. (B.-Bk.) £80

In T **3** "HALF" measures 9½ mm. and "PENNY" 12½ mm. with space 1½ mm. between the words. Bar 14½ mm. ending below the stop. The "F" is nearly always defective.

In T **4** "HALF" is 8½ mm., "PENNY" 12½ mm spacing 2½ mm., and bar 16 mm., extending beyond the stop.

HALF
PENN.Y

HALF
PENNY

5. (Stop after "N") **6.** (No stop after "N")

With T **5**.

17 ½d. on 2½d. (Verm.) £15 £1
a. Surch. double .. .. .. — £5
b. Surch. vertical (up) .. ..

With T **6.**

18 ½d. on 2d. (V.) £30 £20
19 ½d. on 2½d. (Verm.) £8 £6
a. Surch. inverted £55
b. Surch. double.. .. .. — £50
c. Surch. diagonal (up or down) .. £50
d. Surch. omitted (in strip of 3) .. £150
e. Surch. vertical (up or down) .. £40
f. Surch. diagonal, inverted (up or down) £90

In T **5** the "P" and "Y" are raised, and the space between the words in about 4 mm. Bar is short, approx. 13½ mm. T **6** is similar but without the stop after "N".

Half Penny (7) Half Penny (8)

With T **7.**

20 ½d. on 2d. (V.) £9 £9
a. Surch. double.. .. .. — £275
b. Surch. vertical (up or down) .. £55
c. Surch. diagonal (up or down) .. £60
d. Surch. diagonal (inverted) ..
21 ½d. on 2½d. (Verm.) £8 £7
a. Surch. double.. .. .. £165
b. Surch. vertical (up or down) .. £60
c. Surch. inverted £80
d. Surch. diagonal (up or down) .. £60
e. Surch. diagonal, inverted (up) .. £165
22 ½d. on 2½d. (B.) £175 £135
23 ½d. on 2½d. (C.) .. ..
24 ½d. on 2½d. (V.) £90

With T **8.**

25 ½d. on 2½d. (Verm.) £10 £10
a. Surch. diagonal (up) .. ..
26 ½d. on 2½d. (B.) .. ..
27 ½d. on 2½d. (G.) £9 £9
28 ½d. on 2½d. (C.) .. ..

In T **7** the "a" and "e" are narrow and have a short upward terminal hook. The "l" has a very small hook. The letters "nny" have curved serifs, and the distance between the words is 5½ mm.

In T **8** the "a" and "e" are wider. The "l" has a wider hook. The letters "nny" have straight serifs, and the distance between the words is 4½ mm.

HALF PENNY. (9) HALF PENNY (10)

With T **9.**

29 ½d. on 2d. (V.) £10 £12
30 ½d. on 2d. (B.) £30 £28
a. Surch. double.. .. ..
31 ½d. on 2½d. (Verm.) £20 £20
a. Surch. double.. .. ..
32 ½d. on 2½d. (B.) £14 £14
33 ½d. on 2½d. (G.) £14 £14
a. Surch. double (G.) £50
b. Surch. double (G. and Verm.) ..
34 ½d. on 2½d. (V.) £100

With T **10.**

35 ½d. on 2½d. (G.) £12 £12
36 ½d. on 2½d. (Verm.) £135

One Shilling (11) 5/- (12)

With T **11.**

37 1s. on 2d. (V.) £15 £15
a. Surch. inverted £85
b. Surch. vertical (up or down) .. £85
c. Surch. diagonal (up or down) .. £85
d. Surch. diagonal, inverted (up or down) £125
38 1s. on 2d. (Verm.) £16 £20
a. Surch. inverted .. ..
b. Surch. diagonal (up or down) .. £175
c. Surch. vertical (up or down) .. £175
39 1s. on 2d. (Bk.) £300
a. Surch. inverted .. ..
b. Surch. vertical (up or down) .. £350

There are two main types of the "One Shilling" surcharge:—

Type A. The "O" is over the "hi" of "Shilling" and the downstrokes of the "n" in "One", if extended, would meet the "ll" of "Shilling". The "g" is always raised. Type A is known in all three colours.

Type B. The "O" is over the first "i" of "Shilling" and the downstrokes of the "n" would meet the "li" of "Shilling". Type B is known in violet and vermilion.

There is a third, minor type of the black surcharge, but the differences are very slight.

Various types of the surcharges on Nos. 9 to 39 were printed on the same sheet, and different types in different colours may be found *se-tenant*. These are of great rarity.

As T **12.**

40 5s. on 2d. (V.) £450 £550
a. Surch. inverted .. ..
b. Surch. vertical (up or down) .. £450 £550
c. Surch. diagonal (down) .. £550
41 10s. on 5d. (Verm.) £400 £450
a. Surch. inverted £400
b. Surch. vertical (up or down) .. £350
c. Surch. diagonal (down) ..
42 20s. on 1s. (V.) £4500
a. Surch. inverted .. ..
43 20s. on 1s. (Verm.) £4000
44 20s. on 1s. (Bk.) £4000

13

(Des. G. D. Drummond. Recess. Waterlow & Sons, Ltd.)

1893 (Nov. (?)). *T* **13** (*with* "OIL RIVERS" *obliterated and* "NIGER COAST" *in top margin*). *Various frames. No wmk. Thick and thin papers. P* 14, 15, *and* 12 *to* 15 *in various combinations.*

45 ½d. vermilion 4 0 6 0
46 1d. pale blue 7 0 7 6
a. Bisected, and half used for ½d.. .
b. Dull blue 6 0 7 6
ba. Dull blue.Bisected (½d.) (on cover) † £5
47 2d. green 17 6 17 6
a. Imperf. between (pair) .. — £175
b. Bisected (1d.) (on cover) .. † £55
48 2½d. carmine-lake 5 0 6 0
49 5d. grey-lilac 6 0 8 6
a. Lilac.. .. .. .. 10 0 15 0
50 1s. black 20 0 22 6

All values exist perf. 14 and perf. 15. There were three printings of each value, in June, 1893, Jan., 1894 and March, 1894.

14

(Recess. Waterlow.)

1894 (May). *T* **14** *(various frames). No wmk. P* 14, 15, 16 *and* 12 *to* 15 *in various combinations.*

51	½d. yellow-green	1	6	2	0
	a. Dark green	2	6	3	0
52	1d. orange-vermilion	6	6	7	6
	a. Vermilion	2	6	3	6
	b. Bisected diagonally (½d.) ..	—		70	0
53	2d. lake	3	0	4	0
	a. Bisected diagonally (1d.) ..				
54	2½d. blue	8	6	6	0
	a. Pale blue	4	0	4	0
55	5d. purple	5	0	6	0
	a. Deep violet	5	0	6	0
56	1s. black	7	0	9	0

All values exist perf. 15 and all except the 5d., perf. 14. The 1d. is known perf. 16.

½ (15) 1 (16)

1894. *Provisionals. Issued at Opobo.*

(May–June). *Nos.* 46*b and* 46 *bisected vertically and surch. with T* **15.**

57	" ½ " on half of 1d. dull blue (R.) (May)	£40	£12
	a. Surch. inverted (in strip of 3 with normals)	£200	
58	½ " on half of 1d. pale blue (R.) (June)	£45	£10
	a. Surch. tête-bêche (pair) ..		
	b. Surcharge inverted	£115	

(June–Oct.). *No.* 3 *bisected vertically and surch. with T* **16** *(12 mm. high).*

59	" 1 " on half of 2d. (Verm.) ..	£22	£15
	a. Surcharge double	£50	£40
	b. Surcharge inverted	—	£40
	Smaller " 1 " (4¾ mm. high).		
60	" 1 " on half of 2d. (C.) ..	—	£100
	Smaller " 1." (3¾ mm. high).		
61	" 1 " on half of 2d. (C.)		

Nos. 60 and 61 exist *se-tenant.*

(Aug.–Sept.). *No.* 52*a bisected, surch. with T* **15.**

62	½ on half of 1d. vermilion (Bk.)	£50	£20
63	½ on half of 1d. vermilion (V.)	£50	£14
64	½ on half of 1d. vermilion (B.)	£45	£12
	a. " ½ " double		

The stamp is found divided down the middle and also diagonally.

ONE

HALF PENNY

(17)

1894 (10 Aug.). *Issued at Old Calabar. No.* 54 *surch. with T* **17** *and two bars through value at foot.*

65	½d. on 2½d. blue	£10	£7
	a. Surch. double	£65	£50
	b. " OIE " for " ONE "	£50	£35
	c. Surch. double and " OIE " for " ONE "	—	£60

There are eight types in the setting of T **17**.

(Recess. Waterlow & Sons.)

1897 (Mar.)–**1898.** *Types as Nos.* 51/56 *and similar types for 6d., 2s. 6d. and 10s. Wmk. Crown CA. P* 14, 15 *and* 12 *to* 16 *in various combinations.*

66	½d. green	1	0	1	0
	a. Sage-green	1	3	2	0
67	1d. orange-vermilion	2	0	2	6
	a. Vermilion	2	0	2	0
	b. Imperf. between (pr.)				
68	2d. lake	3	0	3	0
69	2½d. slate-blue	3	6	3	6
	a. Deep bright blue				
70	5d. red-violet	12	6	17	6
	a. Purple	10	0	17	6
71	6d. yellow-brown (June, 1898)	12	6	8	6
72	1s. black	10	0	12	6
73	2s. 6d. olive-bistre	30	0	45	0
74	10s. dee? violet (June, 1898)	£5		£8	
	a. Bright violet (June, 1898) ..	£6		£8	

All values exist perf. 14 and all except the 5d. perf. 15, the latter perf. being the scarcer except in the 6d.

Owing to a temporary shortage in Southern Nigeria, the above issue was again put into use during 1902, all stamps being perf. 14, probably from the last printing made.

On 28th December, 1899, the territory occupied by the Royal Niger Company was taken over by the Imperial Government, and with Lagos and the Niger Coast Protectorate was divided into two Administrations, Northern and Southern Nigeria, later merged in Nigeria.

NIGERIA.

(Comprising the Combined Territories of Northern and Southern Nigeria and Lagos.)

1

2

(Typo. De La Rue & Co.)

1914–26. *Wmk. Mult. Crown CA. P* 14.

No.	Type	Description			
1	1	½d. green, O	0	9	0
2	,,	1d. carmine-red, O ..	0	6	0
3	,,	1d. scarlet, O (1917) ..	1	9	0
4	,,	2d. grey, O	3	0	0
5	,,	2d. slate-grey, O	6	6	1
6	,,	2½d. bright blue, O ..	3	6	2
7	2	3d. purple/*yellow*, C ..	15	0	5
		a. White back	4	0	5
		b. On lemon	8	6	4
		c. On orange-buff	10	0	4
		d. On pale yellow	12	6	2
8	,,	4d. black & red/*yellow*, C ..	12	6	12
		a. White back	3	6	6
		b. On lemon	6	0	8
		c. On orange-buff	8	0	8
		d. On pale yellow	17	6	17
9	,,	6d. dull & bright pur., C ..	7	0	5

No.	Type	Description	Unused	Used
10	1	1s. black/*green*, C ..	12 6	6 0
		a. White back ..	5 0	7 6
		b. On blue-green, olive back	25 0	10 0
		c. On emerald surface ..	20 0	6 0
		d. On emerald back ..	6 0	4 6
11	,,	2s. 6d. blk. & red/*blue*, C..	17 6	17 6
12	2	5s. green & red/*yellow*, C..	27 6	30 0
		a. White back ..	25 0	30 0
		b. On lemon	40 0	35 0
		c. On orange-buff ..	30 0	35 0
		d. On pale yellow ..	37 6	40 0
13	1	10s. green & red/*green*, C ..	70 0	70 0
		a. White back ..	85 0	70 0
		b. On blue-green, olive back ..	£70	£25
		c. On emerald surface	£8	£5
		d. On emerald back ..	80 0	70 0
14	2	£1 purple & black/*red*, C..	£10	£12
		a. Die II ('26)	£12	£14

1921–32. *Wmk. Mult. Script CA. P* 14.

A. **1921–26.** *The basic issue. Die I for the ½d., 1d., 2d., 2½d., 3d. and 6d., Die II remainder.*

No.	Type	Description	Unused	Used
15	1	½d. green, O ('21) ..	0 6	0 6
16	,,	1d. rose-carmine, O ('21)	0 8	0 6
17	,,	2d. grey, O (5.21) ..	8 6	1 9
18	,,	2½d. bright blue, O (5.21)..	3 6	3 0
19	2	3d. bright violet, O (1.24)	8 6	7 0
20	,,	4d. black and red/*pale yellow*, C (10.23) ..	2 0	1 9
21	,,	6d. dull and bright purple, C (5.21)	7 6	7 0
22	1	1s. black/*emerald*, C (7.24)	5 0	3 0
23	,,	2s. 6d. black and red/*blue*, C (8.25)	20 0	22 6
24	2	5s. grn. & red/*yel.*, C (10.26)	35 0	35 0
25	1	10s. grn. & red/*grn.*, C (4.26)	80 0	95 0

B. **1924–25.** *Change to Die II.*

No.	Type	Description	Unused	Used
25*a*	1	½d. green, O (5.25) ..	0 4	0 6
25*b*	,,	1d. rose-carmine, O (5.25)	0 4	0 3
25*c*	,,	2d. grey, O ('24) ..	3 0	0 10
25*d*	2	3d. bright violet, O (5.25)	6 0	6 6
25*e*	..	6d. dull and bright purple, C (7.24)	2 6	5 0

C. **1927–31.** *New value and colours changed. Die II.*

No.	Type	Description	Unused	Used
26	2	1½d. orange, O (1.4.31) ..	1 0	0 6
27	1	2d. chestnut, O (1.10.27)	4 6	7 6
28	,,	2d. chocolate, O (1.7.28)..	1 0	0 8
29	2	3d. bright blue, O (1.4.31)	5 0	5 0

D. **1932** (MAR.–AUG.). *Reappearance of Die I (Key Plate 23).*

No.	Type	Description	Unused	Used
29*a*	1	2d. chocolate, O (Mar.) ..	7 6	1 9
29*b*	2	4d. black and red/*pale yellow*, C	50 0	30 0
29*c*	1	2s. 6d. blk. & red/*blue*, C	17 6	20 0
29*d*	2	5s. green & red/*yellow*, C	80 0	85 0
29*e*	1	10s. green and red/*green*, C	£10	£10

1935 (6 MAY). *Silver Jubilee. As Nos.* 91/4 *of Antigua but printed by W'low & Sons. P* 11×12.

No.	Description	Unused	Used
30	1½d. ultramarine and grey ..	0 6	0 6
31	2d. green and indigo ..	1 6	1 9
32	3d. brown and deep blue ..	2 6	3 0
33	1s. slate and purple ..	7 6	8 6

3. Apapa Wharf.

4. Cocoa.

5. Tin Dredger.

6. Timber Industry.

7. Fishing Village.

8. Cotton Ginnery.

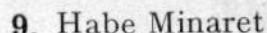

9. Habe Minaret.

10. Fulani Cattle.

11. Victoria-Buea Road.

12. Oil Palms.

13. R. Niger at Jebba.

14. Canoe Pulling.

(Recess. De La Rue & Co. Ltd.)

1936 (1 Feb.). *Wmk. Mult. Script CA.*

(*a*) *P* 11½ × 13.

34	**3**	½d. green	0	2	0	3
35	**4**	1d. carmine	0	6	0	3
36	**5**	1½d. brown	1	3	0	4
		a. Perf. 12½ × 13½	50	0	3	6
37	**6**	2d. black	3	6	1	0
38	**7**	3d. blue	3	0	2	3
		a. Perf. 12½ × 13½		£6	55	0
39	**8**	4d. red-brown	4	6	6	0
40	**9**	6d. dull violet	4	6	4	0
41	**10**	1s. sage-green	20	0	15	0
		(*b*) *P* 14.				
42	**11**	2s. 6d. blk. & ultramarine	15	0	17	6
43	**12**	5s. black and olive-green	40	0	45	0
44	**13**	10s. black and grey		£5		£5
45	**14**	£1 black and orange		£12		£12

1937 (12 May). *Coronation. As Nos.* 13/15 *of Aden, but printed by B. W. & Co. P* 11 × 11½.

46	1d. carmine	0	3	0	3
47	1½d. brown	0	5	0	8
48	3d. blue	1	0	1	6

15. King George VI.

16. Victoria-Buea Road.

17. R. Niger at Jebba.

(Recess. Bradbury, Wilkinson (T **15**), De La Rue, (others).)

1938 (1 May)–**1951.** *Wmk. Mult. Script CA. P* 12 (*T* **15**) *or* 13 × 11½ (*others*).

49	**15**	½d. green	0	3	0	3
		a. Perf. 11½ (15.2.50)	0	3	0	3
50	„	1d. carmine	22	6	6	0
		a. *Rose-red* ('41)	0	4	0	3
50*b*	„	1d. brt. purple (1.12.44)	0	4	0	3
		ba. Perf. 11½ (15.2.50)	0	4	0	3
51	„	1½d. brown	0	6	0	3
		a. Perf. 11½ (15.11.50)	0	6	0	3
52	„	2d. black	0	8	0	6
52*aa*	„	2d. rose-red (1.12.44)	0	6	0	4
		ab. Perf. 11½ (15.2.50)	0	6	0	3
52*a*	„	2½d. orange (–.4.41)	0	6	2	0
53	„	3d. blue	0	6	0	3
53*a*	„	3d. black (1.12.44)	0	6	0	6
54	„	4d. orange	37	6	17	6
54*a*	„	4d. blue (1.12.44)	0	8	1	6
55	„	6d. blackish purple	1	0	0	6
		a. Perf. 11½ (17.4.51)	0	10	0	4
56	„	1s. sage-green	1	6	1	0
		a. Perf. 11½ (15.2.50)	1	8	0	10
57	„	1s. 3d. light blue ('40)	2	0	1	6
		a. Perf. 11½ (14.6.50)	2	6	1	0
		b. Wmk. sideways (P. 11½)				
58	**16**	2s. 6d. black and blue	40	0	15	0
		a. Perf. 13½ (June '42)	7	6	6	0
		ab. Perf. 13½. *Black & deep blue* ('46)	35	0	30	0
		b. Perf. 14 (1942)	7	6	4	0
		c. Perf. 12 (15.8.51)	6	0	4	0
59	**17**	5s. black and orange	55	0	17	6
		a. Perf. 13½ (Aug. '42)	10	0	10	0
		b. Perf. 14 ('48)	10	0	10	0
		c. Perf. 12 (19.5.49)	10	0	7	6

1946 (21 Oct.). *Victory. As Nos.* 28/9 *of Aden.*

60	1½d. chocolate	0	4	0	6
61	4d. blue	0	8	1	6

1948 (20 Dec.). *Royal Silver Wedding. As Nos.* 30/1 *of Aden.*

62	1d. bright purple	0	4	0	4
63	5s. brown-orange	12	6	12	6

1949 (10 Oct.). *75th Anniv. of Universal Postal Union. As Nos.* 114/7 *of Antigua.*

64	1d. bright reddish purple	0	6	0	4
65	3d. deep blue	1	0	1	3
66	6d. purple	3	6	4	0
67	1s. olive	4	0	5	0

1953 (2 June). *Coronation. As No.* 47 *of Aden, but ptd. by B. W. & Co.*

68	1½d. black and emerald	0	6	0	4

18. Old Manilla Currency.

19. Bornu Horsemen.

20. " Groundnuts ".

21. " Tin ".

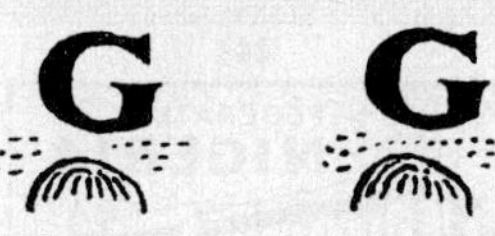

Type A. Type B.

Gap in row of dots. Unbroken row of dots.

Nos. *72a/d*. The original cylinder used was Type A (July '56); later Type B (Sept. '57). The above illustrations will help classification, but two stamps per sheet of 60 of Type A show faint dots. However, one of these has the " 2d." re-entry which does not exist in Type B sheets, and shades are distinctive.

Nos. *72b* and *72d* were released in Colony only.

22. Jebba Bridge and R. Niger.

23. " Cocoa ".

24. Ife Bronze.

25. " Timber ".

26. Victoria Harbour.

27. " Palm-oil ".

28. " Hides and Skins ".

29. New and Old Lagos.

(Des. M. Fievet. Recess. Waterlow & Sons, Ltd.)

1953 (1 Sept.)–**57.** *Wmk. Mult. Script CA. P* 14.

No.	Type	Description	Unused	Used
69	**18**	½d. black and orange ..	0 3	0 3
70	**19**	1d. black & bronze-green	0 4	0 3
71	**20**	1½d. blue-green	0 6	0 9
72	**21**	2d. black & ochre (*shades*)	0 8	0 5
72*a*	,,	2d. slate-violet (Type A) (23.7.56)	1 0	3 6
		b. Slate-blue (shades) (Type A) (*Col.*)	8 6	0 9
		c. Bluish grey (Type B) (25.9.57)	5 0	1 0
		d. Grey (shades) (Type B) (*Col.*)	0 6	0 4
73	**22**	3d. black & purple (*shades*)	0 7	0 5
74	**23**	4d. black and blue ..	0 8	0 6
75	**24**	6d. orge.-brn. & blk. (*shades*)	1 0	0 6
76	**25**	1s. black and maroon ..	2 0	0 8
77	**26**	2s. 6d. black and green ..	4 6	1 9
78	**27**	5s. black and red-orange ..	8 6	2 6
79	**28**	10s. black and red-brown ..	17 6	6 0
80	**29**	£1 black and violet ..	35 0	20 0

Nos. 72*a*/*d* and Nos. 70 and 73 (from September 1958), printed on rotary machines by subsidiary company, Imprimerie Belge de Securité, in Belgium.

ROYAL VISIT
1956
(30)

1956 (28 Jan.). *Royal Visit. No.* 72 *optd. with T* **30.**

No.	Type	Description	Unused	Used
81	**21**	2d. black and ochre ..	0 8	0 8

31. Victoria Harbour.

(Recess. Waterlow & Sons, Ltd.)

1958 (1 Dec.). *Centenary of Victoria. W* w.**12.** *P* 13½×14.

No.	Type	Description	Unused	Used
82	**31**	3d. black and purple ..	0 10	0 10

32. Lugard Hall.

33. Kano Mosque.

(Recess. Waterlow & Sons, Ltd.)

1959 (14 Mar.). *Attainment of Self-Government, Northern Region of Nigeria. W* w.**12.** *P* 13½ (*3d.*) or 13½×14 (*1s.*).

No.	Type	Description	Unused	Used
83	**32**	3d. black and purple ..	0 10	0 10
84	**33**	1s. black and green ..	3 0	3 0

INDEPENDENT FEDERATION
within the Commonwealth.

34

35. Legislative Building.

36. African paddling Canoe.

37. Federal Supreme Court.

38. Dove, Torch and Map.

(Des. R. D. Baxter (6d.), R. Crawford (3d.), L. J. Wittington (1d.), J. White (1s. 3d.), Photo. Waterlow & Sons.)

1960 (1 Oct.). *Independence.* *W* **34.** *P* 13½ (*1s. 3d.*) *or* 14 (*others*).

85	**35**	1d. black and scarlet ..	0	4	0	4
86	**36**	3d. black and greenish blue	0	8	0	6
87	**37**	6d. green and red-brown ..	1	3	1	3
88	**38**	1s. 3d. brt. blue and yellow	2	6	2	6

39. Groundnuts.

40. Coal Mining.

41. Adult Education.

42. Pottery.

43. Oyo Carver.

44. Weaving.

45. Benin Mask.

46. Hornbill.

47. Camel Train.

48. Central Bank.

49. Nigeria Museum.

50. Kano Airport.

51. Lagos Railway Station.

1961 (1 Jan.). *W* **34.** *P* 15 × 14 (*½d. to 1s. 3d.*) *or* 14½ (*others*).

89	**39**	½d. emerald	0	2	0	4
90	**40**	1d. reddish violet ..	0	3	0	2
91	**41**	1½d. carmine-red	0	4	0	4
92	**42**	2d. deep blue	0	4	0	2
93	**43**	3d. deep green	0	6	0	2
94	**44**	4d. blue	0	7	0	7
95	**45**	6d. yellow and black ..	0	10	0	3
		a. Yellow omitted	—		£150	
96	**46**	1s. yellow-green	1	5	0	6
97	**47**	1s. 3d. orange	1	9	0	9
98	**48**	2s. 6d. black and yellow	3	6	1	3
99	**49**	5s. black and emerald ..	6	9	2	6
100	**50**	10s. black and ultramarine	13	3	5	0
101	**51**	£1 black & carmine-red	25	0	17	6

PRINTERS. The above and all following issues printed in photogravure by Harrison & Sons, *except where otherwise stated.*

52. Globe and Railway Locomotive.

53. Globe and Mail-van.

54. Globe and Aircraft.

55. Globe and Ship.

(Des. M. Goaman.)

1961 (25 July). *Admission of Nigeria into U.P.U. W* **34.** *P* 14½.

102	**52**	1d. red-orange and blue ..	0	4	0	4
103	**53**	3d. olive-yellow and black	0	8	0	8
104	**54**	1s. 3d. blue and carmine-red	2	6	2	6
105	**55**	2s. 6d. deep green and blue	5	0	6	0

56. Coat-of-Arms.

57. Natural Resources Map.

58. Nigerian Eagle.

59. Eagles in Flight.

60. Nigerians and Flag.

1961 (1 Oct.). *First Anniv. of Independenc W* **34.** *P* 14½.

106	**56**	3d. multicoloured ..	0	8	0
107	**57**	4d. yell.-grn. & yellow-orge.	1	6	2
108	**58**	6d. emerald-green ..	1	0	1
109	**59**	1s. 3d. grey, emer. & blue	2	6	2
110	**60**	2s. 6d. green & grey-blue	5	0	5

61. " Health ".

62. " Culture ".

63. " Commerce ". **64.** " Communications".

65. " Co-operation ".

(Des. M. Shamir.)

962 (25 Jan.). *Lagos Conference of African and Malagasy States.* *W* **34.** *P* 14×14½.

11	**61**	1d. yellow-bistre	0	4	0	4
12	**62**	3d. deep reddish purple ..	0	8	0	8
13	**63**	6d. deep green	1	3	1	6
14	**64**	1s. brown	2	3	2	6
15	**65**	1s. 3d. blue	3	0	3	0

. Malaria Eradication Emblem and Parasites.

67. Insecticide-spraying.

68. Aerial Spraying.

69. Mother, Child and Microscope.

1962. (7 Apr.). *Malaria Eradication.* *W* **34.** *P* 14½.

116	**66**	3d. green and orange-red	0	8	0	8
117	**67**	6d. blue and bright purple	1	3	1	6
118	**68**	1s. 3d. mag. & violet-blue	2	6	3	0
119	**69**	2s. 6d. blue and yell.-brn.	5	0	5	0

70. National Monument.

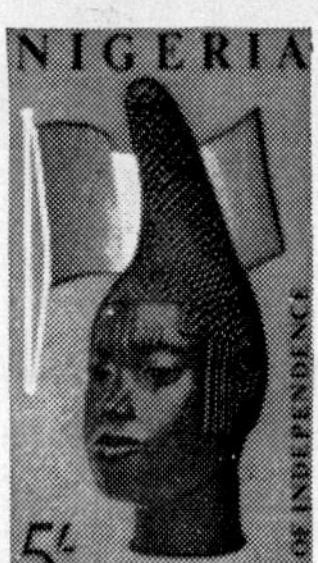

71. Benin Bronze.

(Des. Sandor Bodo (3d.), Ben Enwonwu (5s.).)

1962 (1 Oct.). *Second Anniv. of Independence.* *W* **34.** *P* 14½×14 (*3d.*) *or* 14×14½ (*5s.*).

120	**70**	3d. emerald and blue ..	0	8	0	8
		a. Emerald omitted				
121	**71**	5s. red, emerald & violet	10	0	11	6

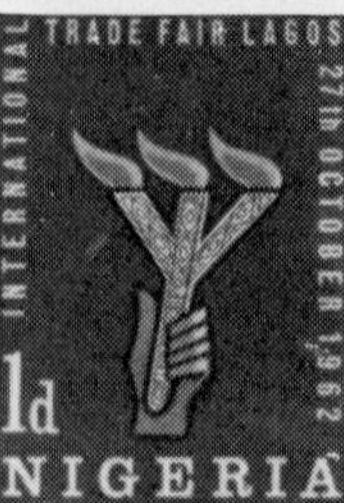

72. Fair Emblem.

73. " Cogwheels of Industry ".

74. " Cornucopia of Commerce ".

75. Oilwells and Tanker.

(Des. M. Goaman (1d., 2s. 6d.), J. O. Gbagbeolu and M. Goaman (6d.), R. Hegeman (1s.).

1962 (27 Oct.). *International Trade Fair, Lagos.* *W* **34.** *P* 14½.

122	**72**	1d. olive-brown & orge.-red	0	4	0	4
123	**73**	6d. carmine-red and black	1	3	1	3
124	**74**	1s. orange-brown & black	2	0	2	6
125	**75**	2s. 6d. ultram. and yellow	6	0	6	0

76. " Arrival of Delegates ".

78. Mace as Palm Tree.

77. National Hall.

(Des. S. Akosile (2½d.), M. Goaman (others).

1962 (5 Nov.). *Eighth Commonwealth Parliamentary Conference, Lagos.* *W* **34.** *P* 14½.

126	**76**	2½d. greenish blue ..	0	8	0	
127	**77**	4d. indigo and rose-red..	0	10	0	1
128	**78**	1s. 3d. sepia and lemon..	2	6	3	

79. Herdsman.

80. Tractor and Maize.

(Des. M. Goaman.)

1963 (21 Mar.). *Freedom from Hunger.* *W* **34.** *P*

129	**79**	3d. olive-green	0	8	0	
130	**80**	6d. magenta	1	3	1	

81. Mercury Capsule and Kano Tracking Station.

82. Satellite and Lagos Harbour.

(Des. R. Hegeman).

1963 (21 June). *"Peaceful Use of Outer Space"*. *W* **34.** *P* 14½ × 14.

131 **81** 6d. blue and yellow-green 1 3 1 3
132 **82** 1s. 3d. black and blue-grn. 2 6 3 0

83. Scouts Shaking Hands.

84. Campfire.

(*Illustrations reduced: actual size* 60 × 30 *mm.*)

(Des. S. Apostolou (3d.), G. Okiki (1s.).)

963 (1 Aug.). 11*th World Scout Jamboree, Marathon.* *W* **34.** *P* 14.

33 **83** 3d. red and bronze-green . . 0 8 0 9
4 **84** 1s. black and red . . 2 6 3 0
S134*a* 93 × 95 mm. Nos. 133/4 4 6

85. Emblem and First Aid Team.

86. Emblem and " Hospital Services ".

87. Patient (" Medical Services ") and Emblem.

(Des. M. Goaman.)

1963 (1 Sept.). *Red Cross Centenary.* *W* **34.** *P* 14½.

135 **85** 3d. red & dp. ultramarine 0 8 0 10
136 **86** 6d. red and deep green . . 1 0 1 3
137 **87** 1s. 3d. red & deep sepia . . 2 6 3 0
MS137*a* 102 × 102 mm. No. 137 (block of four) 12 6

The buildings on the 1s. 3d. and the 2s. 6d. are the Federal Supreme Court and the Parliament Building, respectively.

88. President Azikiwe and State House.

(Des. M. Shamir. Photo. Govt. Ptg. Press, Tel Aviv.)

1963 (1 Oct.). *Republic Day.* *P* 14 × 13.

138 **88** 3d. yell.-olive & grey-grn. 0 8 0 10
139 ,, 1s. 3d. yell.-brn. & sepia . . 2 6 3 0
a. Yellow-brn. (portrait) omitted
140 ,, 2s. 6d. turquoise-blue and deep violet-blue . . 5 0 5 6

89. Charter and Broken Whip.

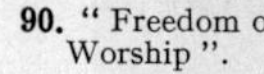

90. " Freedom of Worship ".

91. " Freedom from Want ".

92. " Freedom of Speech ".

(Photo. De La Rue.)

1963 (10 DEC.). *15th Anniv. of Declaration of Human Rights.* W **34.** *P* 13.

141	**89**	3d. vermilion	0 8	0 10
142	**90**	6d. blue-green	1 0	1 3
143	**91**	1s. 3d. ultramarine ..	2 6	3 0
144	**92**	2s. 6d. bright purple ..	5 0	5 6

93. Queen Nefertari. 94. Rameses II.

(Des. M. Shamir.)

1964 (8 MAR.). *Nubian Monuments Preservation.* W **34.** *P* $14\frac{1}{2}$.

145	**93**	6d. yellow-olive & emerald	1 3	1 6
146	**94**	2s. 6d. brown, deep olive and emerald	5 0	6 0

95. President Kennedy.

96. President Kennedy and Flags.

97. President Kennedy (U.S. Coin Head) and Flags.

(Photo. Govt. Ptg. Press, Tel Aviv (1s. 3d.); litho., Lewin-Epstein, Bat Yam, Israel (others).)

1964 (20 AUG.). *President Kennedy Memorial Issue. P* 13 × 14 (1s. 3d.) *or* 14 (*others*).

147	**95**	1s. 3d. light violet & black	2 6	2 6
148	**96**	2s. 6d. black, red, blue and green	4 9	4 9
149	**97**	5s. black, deep blue, red and green	8 6	8 6

MS149*a* 154 × 135 mm. No. 149 (block of four) Imperf. 40 0

98. President Azikiwe. 99. Herbert Macaulay.

100. King Jaja of Opobo.

(Photo. Govt. Ptg. Press, Tel Aviv (3d.); Harrison (others).)

1964 (1 Oct.). *First Anniv. of Republic. P* 14 × 13 (*3d.*) *or* 14½ (*others*).

150	**98**	3d. red-brown	0	9	0	9
151	**99**	1s. 3d. green	2	6	2	6
152	**100**	2s. 6d. deep grey-green ..	4	9	4	9

101. Boxing Gloves.

102. High-jumping.

103. Running.

104. Hurdling.

llustration of T **104** *is reduced: actual size* 60 × 30 *mm.*)

es. A. Adalade (3d.), S. Medahunsi (6d.), (M. Shamir (1s. 3d.), M. Goaman (2s. 6d.).)

64 (– Oct.). *Olympic Games, Tokio.* *W* **34.** *P* 14 (*2s. 6d.*) *or* 14½ (*others*).

3	**101**	3d. sepia and olive-green	0	9	0	9
4	**102**	6d. emerald and indigo ..	1	6	1	6
5	**103**	1s. 3d. sepia & yell.-olive	2	6	2	6
6	**104**	2s. 6d. sepia & chestnut	4	9	4	9
S156*a*		102 × 102 mm. No. 156 (block of four). Imperf. ..	20	0		

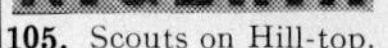

105. Scouts on Hill-top.

106. Scout Badge on Shield.

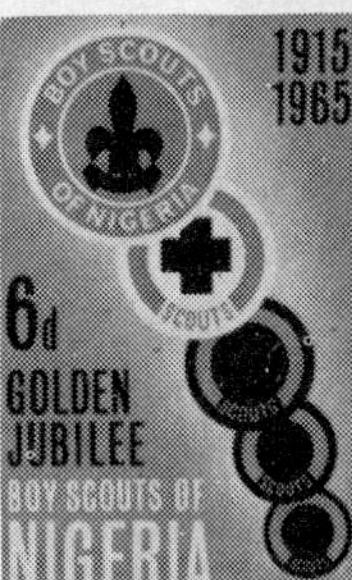

107. Scout Badges.

108. Chief Scout and Nigerian Scout.

1965 (Jan.). *50th Anniv. of Nigerian Scout Movement. P* 14 × 14½.

157	**105**	1d. brown	0	5	0	6
158	**106**	3d. red, black & emerald	0	9	1	0
159	**107**	6d. red, sepia, and yellow-green	1	6	2	0
160	**108**	1s. 3d. bistre-brown, greenish yellow and black-green	2	6	3	6
MS160a		76 × 104 mm. No. 160 (block of four). Imperf. ..	8	6		

109. " Telstar ".

110. Solar Satellite.

(Photo. Govt. Printer, Tel. Aviv.)

1965 (Apr.). *International Quiet Sun Years. P* 14 × 13.

161	**109**	6d. reddish violet and turquoise-blue ..	1	0	1	3
162	**110**	1s. 3d. green & redd. lilac	2	3	2	9

111. Native Tom-tom and Modern Telephone.

112. Microwave Aerial.

113. Telecommunications Satellite and Part of Globe.

(Photo. Enschedé.)

1965 (2 Aug.). *I.T.U. Centenary. P* 11½ × 11 (1s. 3d.) *or* 11 × 11½ (*others*).

163	**111**	3d. black, carmine and yellow-brown ..	0	6	0	8
164	**112**	1s. 3d. black, blue-green and chalky blue ..	1	9	2	6
165	**113**	5s. black, carmine, blue & bright greenish blue	6	9	8	0

114. I.C.Y. Emblem and Diesel Locomotive.

115. Students and Lagos Teaching Hospital.

116. Kainji (Niger) Dam.

(Photo. De La Rue.)

1965 (1 Sept.). *International Co-operation Year W* **34.** *P* 14 × 15.

166	**114**	3d. green, red and orange	0	6	0	
167	**115**	1s. blk., brt. blue & lemon	1	5	1	1
168	**116**	2s. 6d. green, bright blue and yellow	3	6	4	

117. Carved Frieze.

118. Stone Images at Ikom.

119. Tada Bronz

(Des. S. Apostolou (3d.), W. H. Irvine (other Photo. De La Rue.)

1965 (1 Oct.). *2nd Anniv. of Republic. P* 14 × (3d.) *or* 15 × 14 (*others*).

169	**117**	3d. blk., red & orge.-yell.	0	6	0
170	**118**	1s. 3d. red-brown, deep green & lt. ultramarine	1	9	2
171	**119**	5s. brown, blackish brown and light green ..	6	9	7

COMMONWEALTH
P. M. MEETING
11. JAN. 1966

(**120**)

1966 (12 Jan.). *Commonwealth Prime Ministe Meeting, Lagos. No.* 98 *optd. with T* **120,** *red.*

172	**48**	2s. 6d. black and yellow ..	3	6	4

POSTAGE DUE STAMPS.

D 1

(Litho. Bradbury, Wilkinson & Co.)

959 (4 Jan.). *Wmk. Mult. Script CA. P* 14½ × 14.

1	D 1	1d. red-orange	0	6	0	8
2	,,	2d. red-orange	0	8	1	0
3	,,	3d. red-orange	0	10	1	9
4	,,	6d. red-orange	1	6	2	3
5	,,	1s. grey-black	2	6	4	0

961 (1 Aug.). *W* **34.** *P* 14½ × 14.

6	D 1	1d. red	0	3	0	4
7	,,	2d. light blue	0	4	0	8
8	,,	3d. emerald	0	6	1	0
9	,,	6d. yellow	0	10	1	6
10	,,	1s. blue (*shades*) ..	1	5	2	6

NORFOLK ISLAND.

RINTERS. Nos. 1 to 42 were printed at the ote Printing Branch, Reserve Bank of Australia ntil 14 Jan. 1960, known as the Note Printing ranch, Commonwealth Bank) by recess. See ote at the beginning of Australia *re* imprints.

1. Ball Bay.

Note. Stamps of T 1, perf. 11, or in different colours, perf. 11, are in the same category as those mentioned in Australia after No. 222*a*.

47 (10 June)–**59.** *P* 14.

1		½d. orange	2	0	3	0
	,,	1d. bright violet	2	3	3	6
	,,	1½d. emerald-green	2	6	4	0
	,,	2d. reddish violet ..	2	9	4	6
	,,	2½d. scarlet	2	9	4	6
	,,	3d. chestnut	3	6	5	6
a	,,	3d. emerald-green (6.7.59)	12	6	17	6
	,,	4d. claret	4	6	7	0
	,,	5½d. indigo	6	0	8	6
	,,	6d. purple-brown	7	6	11	0
	,,	9d. magenta	9	0	12	6
	,,	1s. grey-green	12	6	16	0
	,,	2s. yellow-bistre	25	0	35	0
a	,,	2s. deep blue (6.7.59) ..	50	0	65	0

The ½d., 1d., 1½d. and 2d. were printed on ite paper from November, 1956.

Warder's Tower.

3. Airfield.

4. First Governor's Residence.

5. Barracks Entrance.

6. Salt House.

7. Bloody Bridge.

1953 (10 June). *P* 14 × 15 (*vert.*) *or* 15 × 14 (*horiz.*).

13	**2**	3½d. brown-lake	8	0	10	0
14	**3**	6½d. deep green	10	0	12	6
15	**4**	7½d. deep blue	11	6	15	0
16	**5**	8½d. chocolate	17	6	22	6
17	**6**	10d. reddish violet	16	0	20	0
18	**7**	5s. sepia	60	0	80	0

See also Nos. 30 and 35.

8. Norfolk Island Seal and Pitcairners Landing.

1956 (8 June). *Centenary of Landing of Pitcairn Islanders on Norfolk Island. P* 15 × 14½.

19	**8**	3d. deep bluish green ..	5	0	7	6
20	,,	2s. violet (*shades*)	40	0	47	6

Alternate stamps of the 2s. value were printed from a different die which is distinguishable by a dot in the bottom right corner.

(9) (10)

1958 (1 July). *Surch. with T* **9/10.**

21	**4**	7d. on 7½d. deep blue ..	12	6	17	6
22	**5**	8d. on 8½d. chocolate ..	15	0	22	6

(11)

1959 (7 Dec.). *150th Anniv. of Australian Post Office. No.* 331 *of Australia surch. with T* **11.**

23	**143**	5d. on 4d. slate (R.) ..	12	6	15	0

12. *Hibiscus insularis.* 13. *Lagunaria patersonii.*

14. White Tern.

15. Lantana.

16. Red Hibiscus.

17. Queen Elizabeth II and Cereus.

18. Fringed Hibiscus.

19. Providence Petrel.

20. Passion-flower.

21. Rose Apple.

22. Red-tailed Tropic Bird.

(Design recess; centre typo. (T **21**).)

1960–62. *P* 14½ *or* 14½ × 14 (10s.).

No.	Type		Unused s. d.	Used s. d.
24	**12**	1d. bluish green (23.5.60)	1 0	2 0
25	**13**	2d. rose and myrtle-green (23.5.60)	1 6	2 6
26	**14**	3d. green (1.5.61)	2 6	4 0
27	**15**	5d. bright purple (20.6.60)	3 6	5 6
28	**16**	8d. red (20.6.60) ..	6 0	8 6
29	**17**	9d. ultramarine (23.5.60) ..	7 6	10 0
30	**6**	10d. brown & reddish violet (27.2.61) ..	9 0	12 6
31	**18**	1s. 1d. carm.-red (16.10.61)	5 6	7 6
32	**19**	2s. sepia (1.5.61)	7 6	10 0
33	**20**	2s. 5d. deep violet (5.2.62)	9 0	11 6
34	**21**	2s. 8d. cinnamon & deep grn. (9.4.62)	10 0	12 6
35	**7**	5s. sepia & deep green (27.2.61)	20 0	25 0
36	**22**	10s. emerald-green (14.8.61)	50 0	65 0

Nos. 30 and 35 are redrawn.

(23)

2/8

2/5

(24)

(25)

1960. *As Nos.* 13/5 *but colours changed, surch. with T* **23/5.**

No.	Type		Unused s. d.	Used s. d.
37	**2**	1s. 1d. on 3½d. deep ultramarine (26.9.60)	20 0	25
38	**3**	2s. 5d. on 6½d. bluish green (26.9.60)	22 6	30
39	**4**	2s. 8d. on 7½d. sepia (29.8.60)	70 0	85

26. Queen Elizabeth II and Map.

1960 (24 Oct.). *Introduction of Local Governmen[t]. P* 14.

40	**26**	2s. 8d. reddish purple	150 0	

1960. (21 Nov.). *Christmas. As No.* 338 *Australia.*

41	5d. bright purple	12 6	15

1961 (20 Nov.). *Christmas. As No.* 341 *Australia.*

42	5d. slate-blue	11 0	13

27. "Tweed Trousers" (*Atypichthys latus*).

28. "Trumpeter".

29. " Po'ov ".

30. " Dreamfish ".

31. " Hapoeka ".

32. " Ophie " (*carangidae*).

(Photo. Harrison.)

62-63. *P* 14½ × 14.

27 6d. sepia, yellow and deep bluish green (16.7.62) .. 2 0 3 0

28 11d. red-orange, brown and blue (25.2.63) 3 0 4 0

29 1s. blue, pink and yellow-olive (17.9.62) 3 6 4 6

30 1s. 3d. blue, red-brown and green (15.7.63) .. 4 0 5 0

31 1s. 6d. sepia, violet and light blue (6.5.63) .. 4 6 5 6

32 2s. 3d. deep blue, red and greenish yellow (23.9.63) 5 6 7 6

32 (19 Nov.). *Christmas. As No.* 345 *of Australia.*

5d. ultramarine 4 0 6 0

33 (11 Nov.). *Christmas. As No.* 361 *of Australia.*

5d. red 3 9 5 0

33. Overlooking Kingston.

34. Kingston.

35. The Arches (Kingston).

36. Slaughter Bay.

(Photo. Harrison.)

1964 (24 Feb.–28 Sept.). *P* 14½ × 14.

51 **33** 5d. multicoloured .. 2 0 2 9

52 **34** 8d. multicoloured .. 2 9 3 6

53 **35** 9d. multicoloured (11.5) .. 3 0 3 9

54 **36** 10d. multicoloured (28.9) .. 3 6 4 6

37. Norfolk Pine.

(Photo. Note Ptg. Branch, Reserve Bank of Australia, Melbourne.)

1964 (1 July). *50th Anniv. of Norfolk Island as Australian Territory. P* 13½.

55 **37** 5d. black, red and orange .. 3 0 4 6

56 ,, 8d. black, red & grey-green 4 6 6 6

1964 (9 Nov.). *Christmas. As No.* 372 *of Australia.*

57 5d. green, blue, buff & violet .. 2 6 3 6

1965 (14 Apr.). *50th Anniv. of Gallipoli Landing. As T* **181** *of Australia, but slightly larger* (22 × 34½ *mm.*). *Photo.*

58 5d. sepia, black and emerald .. 2 6 3 3

1965 (25 Oct.). *Christmas. As No.* 381 *of Australia.*

59 5d. multicoloured 1 3 1 9

(New currency. 100 cents = $1 Australian.)

38. *Hibiscus insularis.*

1966 (14 Feb.). *Decimal currency. Various stamps surch. in black on silver tablets obliterating old value as in T* **38.** *Surch. typo.*

No.	Type	Description				
60	**38**	1 c. on 1d. bluish green ..	0	2	0	3
61	**13**	2 c. on 2d. rose and myrtle-green	0	4	0	5
62	**14**	3 c. on 3d. green	0	6	0	7
63	**15**	4 c. on 5d. bright purple ..	0	7	0	9
64	**16**	5 c. on 8d. red	0	9	1	0
65	**6**	10 c. on 10d. brown and reddish violet	1	3	1	6
66	**18**	15 c. on 1s. 1d. carmine-red	1	8	2	0
67	**19**	20 c. on 2s. sepia	2	3	2	9
68	**20**	25 c. on 2s. 5d. deep violet	2	9	3	6
69	**21**	30 c. on 2s. 8d. cinnamon and deep green ..	3	4	3	9
70	**7**	50 c. on 5s. sepia & dp. grn.	5	4	7	6
71	**22**	$1 on 10s. emerald-green	10	6	15	0

NORTH BORNEO.

PRINTERS. The stamps of this country up to 1894 were designed by T. Macdonald and lithographed by Blades, East and Blades, London.

1

8 Cents

(2)

EIGHT
CENTS

(3)

1883. *P* 12.

No.	Type	Description				
1	**1**	2 c. red-brown	10	0	17	6

The figure "2" varies in size.

1883. *No.* 1 *surch. as T* **2** *or* **3.**

No.	Type	Description		
2	**2**	8 c. on 2 c. red-brown ..	£25	£16
3	**3**	8 c. on 2 c. red-brown ..	£12	£6
		a. Surch. double ..		

There is grave doubt as to the authenticity of No. 2.

> **NOTE.**—Prices are separately indicated (in a third price column, in brackets, or by notes below certain issues) for remainders of the stamps of North Borneo cancelled with black bars, where these exist.
>
> It should be noted, however, that a postmark of this form was in general use for postal purposes for many years, and was used at one or two of the smaller post-offices until 1949.

4 5

1883. *P* 14.

No.	Type	Description				
4	**4**	50 c. violet ..	70	0	—	25
		a. Error. "FIFTY"	£14		—	£
5	**5**	$1 scarlet	70	0	—	25

1884. *P* 12.

No.	Type	Description			
6	**1**	4 c. pink	12	6	17
7	,,	8 c. pale green	15	0	15

1886. *P* 14.

No.	Type	Description			
8	**1**	½ c. magenta	32	6	
9	,,	1 c. orange	£12		
		a. Imperf. (pair)	70	0	
10	,,	2 c. brown	8	6	8
		a. Imperf. between (pair) ..	£8		
11	,,	4 c. pink	15	0	22
12	,,	8 c. green	15	0	22
		a. Imperf. between (pair) ..			
13	,,	10 c. blue	15	0	22
		a. Imperf. (pair)	£6		

and
Revenue

(6)

3
CENTS

(7)

3
CENTS

(8)

1886. *Nos.* 8 *and* 13 *optd. with T* **6.**

No.	Description			
14	½ c. magenta	50	0	70
15	10 c. blue	£5		

1886. *T* **1** *surch. with T* **7** *or* **8.** (*a*) *P* 12.

No.	Type	Description			
16	**7**	3 c. on 4 c. pink	£5		
17	**8**	3 c. on 4 c. pink	£150		
18	**7**	5 c. on 8 c. green	£20		£

(*b*) *P* 14.

No.	Type	Description			
19	**7**	3 c. on 4 c. pink	35	0	45
20	**8**	3 c. on 4 c. pink	£15		
21	**7**	5 c. on 8 c. green	50	0	65
		a. Surch. inverted	£70		

9

10

11

12

13

[1]886-87. *P* 14.

	9	½ c. magenta	10	0		
	,,	½ c. rose	5	0	7	0
		a. Imperf. (pair)	10	0		
	,,	1 c. orange-yellow ..	7	6	7	6
		a. Imperf. between (pair) ..				
		b. Imperf. (pair)	20	0		
	,,	1 c. orange	2	6	2	6
		a. Imperf. (pair)	10	0		
	,,	2 c. brown	3	0	3	6
		a. Imperf. (pair)	7	6		
	,,	4 c. pink	2	0	3	0
		a. Imperf. (pair)	7	6		
		b. Imperf. between (pair) ..				
	,,	8 c. green..	3	6	4	0
		a. Imperf. (pair)	10	0		
	,,	10 c. blue	6	0	10	0
		a. Imperf. between (pair) ..				
		b. Imperf. (pair)	15	0		
	10	25 c. indigo (c. 30s.) ..	75	0		
		a. Imperf. between (pair) ..				
		b. Imperf. (pair) (c. 35s.) ..	50	0		
	11	50 c. violet (c. 35s.) ..	70	0		
		a. Imperf. (pair) (c. 20s.) ..	45	0		
	12	$1 scarlet (c. 30s.) ..	£5			
		a. Imperf. (pair) (c. 25s.) ..	45	0		
	13	$2 sage-green (c. 45s.) ..	£6			
		a. Imperf. (pair) (c. 30s.) ..	70	0		

Error on sheet of 4 c.

	9	1 c. pink (strip of 3 with error in centre) ..	£5		£6	
		a. Imperf. between (pair) ..				
		b. Imperf. (in strip as No. 33)	£145			

(*b*) *P* 12.

	9	½ c. magenta	£8			
	,,	1 c. orange..	75	0	85	0

14

15

1889. *P* 14.

36	**14**	$5 bright purple ..	£5	85	0	12	6
		a. Imperf. (pair) ..	85 0	—		50	0
37	**15**	$10 brown	£8	£7		35	0
		a. Imperf. (pair) ..	£10	—		70	0
		b. "DOLLAPS" for "DOLLARS" ..	£50	—		£30	
		ba. Ditto. Imperf. (pr.)	£100	—		£60	

16

1888-92. *P* 14.

38	**16**	½ c. magenta ..	6	0	7	6	—	
38*a*	,,	½ c. rose	1	0	2	0	0	4
39	,,	1 c. orange ..	1	0	1	6	0	6
40	,,	2 c. brown	8	6	6	0	0	9
41	,,	2 c. lake-brown ..	1	6	1	3	0	6
42	,,	3 c. violet	3	0	3	0	0	8
43	,,	4 c. rose-pink ..	2	6	2	6	0	6
		a. Imperf. between (pr.)						
44	,,	5 c. slate	2	6	3	0	0	8
		a. Imperf. between (pr.)						
44*b*	,,	6 c. lake (1892) ..	4	0	5	0	1	0
45	,,	8 c. blue-green ..	4	0	4	0	0	9
45*a*	,,	8 c. yellow-green ..	10	0	10	0	1	9
46	,,	10 c. blue	5	0	6	0	1	0
46*a*	,,	10 c. dull blue ..	6	0	4	6	1	0

This set also exists imperf. (*Price 6s. per pair unused; 5s. cancelled.*)

17 18

19

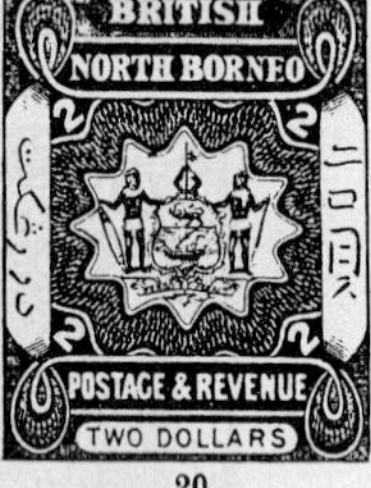

20

1888. *T* **17** *to* **20** (**10** *to* **13** *redrawn*). *P* 14.

No.	Type				
47	**17**	25 c. indigo ..	15 0	10 0	1 3
		a. Imperf. (pair)	90 0	—	5 0
48	**18**	50 c. violet ..	27 6	—	1 6
		a. Imperf. (pair)	£6	—	6 0
49	**19**	$1 scarlet	30 0	7 6	1 6
		a. Imperf. (pair)	£6	—	7 6
50	**20**	$2 dull green	40 0	—	4 0
		a. Imperf. (pair)	£7	—	10 0

The new 25 c. has the inscription "BRITISH NORTH BORNEO" in taller capitals. In the 50 c. the "0" of the numerals "50" in the two upper corners is square-shaped at the top and bottom instead of being oval. The 1 dollar has 14 pearls instead of 13 at each side, and on the 2 dollars the word "BRITISH" measures 10½ to 11 mm. in length in place of 12 mm.

Two
Cents.

(**21**)

1890. *No.* 47 *surch. in red, as T* **21**.

No.			
51	2 c. on 25 c. indigo ..	50 0	40 0
	a. Surch. inverted ..	£15	£14
52	8 c. on 25 c. indigo ..	60 0	60 0

6
cents.

(**22**)

1
cent.

(**23**)

1891–92. *Surch. with T* **22**.

No.			
54	6 c. on 8 c. (No. 27) ..	£350	£300
	a. Large "s" in "cents"	£500	
55	6 c. on 8 c. (No. 45*a*) ..	10 0	12 6
	a. Surch. inverted	£14	
	b. "эents." for "cents."	£9	
	c. "cetns." for "cents."	£9	£9
	d. Large "s" in "cents."	55 0	65 0
56	6 c. on 10 c. (No. 28) ..	30 0	15 0
	a. Surch. inverted	£5	
	b. Surch. double	£50	
	c. Surch. treble	£16	
	d. Large "s" in "cents."	80 0	80 0
57	6 c. on 10 c. (No. 46) ..	45 0	30 0
	a. Large "s" in "cents."	90 0	£5

1892-93. *Nos.* 43, 44, *and* 47 *surch. as T* **23**. (*On No.* 65 "Cents" *with capital* "C" *as in T* **21**.

No.			
63	1 c. on 4 c. pink (R.) ..	15 0	15 0
	a. Surch. double		
	b. Surch. on back and on front ..	—	£1
64	1 c. on 5 c. slate (R.) ..	5 0	5
65	8 c. on 25 c. indigo (R.)	85 0	90

24. Dyak Chief.

25. Sambar Stag (*Cervus unicolor*).

26. Sago Palm.

27. Argus Pheasan

28. Arms of the Company.

29. Malay Dhow.

30. Crocodile.

31. Mount Kinabalu.

32. Arms of the Company with supporters.

(Recess. Waterlow & Sons.)

1894. *P* 15.

No.	Type		Unused	Used
66	**24**	1 c. black & olive-bistre ..	3 6	3 6
		a. Imperf. between (pair) ..		
		b. Perf. 14	3 6	4 0
		c. Perf. 14×13½	10 0	
		d. Perf. 14, comp. 12-13 ..	10 0	10 0
67	,,	1 c. black & bistre-brown	3 6	4 0
		a. Perf. 14	3 6	
		b. Perf. 14, comp. 12-13 ..	10 0	12 6
68	**25**	2 c. black & rose-lake ..	7 6	7 6
		a. Imperf. between (pair) ..	£10	
		b. Perf. 14	30 0	
69	,,	2 c. black and lake ..	7 6	5 0
		a. Perf. 14	25 0	30 0
		b. Perf. 14, comp. 12-13 ..	10 0	
		c. Imperf. between (pair) ..		
70	**26**	3 c. olive-grn. & mauve ..	5 0	5 0
		a. Imperf. between (pair) ..	£20	
71	,,	3 c. olive-grn. & violet(*p.*14)	7 6	6 0
72	**27**	5 c. black & vermilion	7 6	7 6
		a. Imperf. between (pair) ..	£20	
		b. Perf. 14	25 0	25 0
		c. Perf. 14, comp. 12-13 ..	—	25 0
73	**28**	6 c. black & bistre-brown	20 0	20 0
		a. Perf. 14	6 0	6 0
		b. Perf. 14, comp. 12-13 ..	—	15 0
		c. Perf. 14×15		
		d. Imperf. between (pair) ..		
74	**29**	8 c. black & dull purple ..	5 0	7 6
		a. Imp. between (vert. pr.) (p. 15)	£20	
		b. Perf. 14	5 0	10 0
		c. Imp. betwn. (vert. pr.) (p. 14)	£20	
		d. Perf. 14, comp. 12-13 ..		
75	**30**	12 c. black and blue ..	30 0	30 0
		a. Perf. 14	30 0	30 0
76	,,	12 c. black & ultramarine ..	30 0	30 0
		a. Perf. 14	15 0	
		b. Imperf. between (pair) ..		
77	**31**	18 c. black & deep green ..	10 0	10 0
		a. Perf. 14	15 0	20 0
78	**32**	24 c. blue and rose-lake ..	12 6	20 0
		a. Imperf. between (pair) ..	£20	
		b. Perf. 14	20 0	15 0

NOTE.—The prices in the used column are for postally used stamps with circular postmark. Stamps cancelled with bars can be supplied at about one-third of these prices.

32*a*

32*b*

32*c*

32*d*

(Ptd. by Blades, East & Blades.)

T **32*a*** *to* **32*d***, *and T* **14** *and* **15**, *but inscribed* "THE STATE OF NORTH BORNEO". *P* 14.

No.				
81	25 c. indigo	17 6	20 0	2 6
	a. Imperf. (pair) ..	—	—	6 0
	b. Imperf. between (pair)	£30		
82	50 c. violet	17 6	20 0	2 6
	a. Imperf. (pair) ..	—	—	6 0
83	$1 scarlet	10 0	15 0	2 6
	a. Perf. 14×11 ..	£7		
	b. Imperf. (pair) ..	30 0	—	20 0
	c. Ptd. both sides ..	30 0	—	—
84	$2 dull green ..	25 0	35 0	2 6
	a. Imperf. (pair) ..	—	—	10 0
85	$5 bright purple ..	90 0	95 0	15 0
	a. Imperf. (pair) ..	—	—	40 0
86	$10 brown	£7	£6	20 0
	a. Imperf. (pair) ..	—	—	40 0

For Nos. 81 to 83 in other colours, see Labuan 80*a*, 81*a* and 82*a*.

4

CENTS

33. (3½ mm. between lines of surcharge.

1895 (June). *No.* 83 *surch. as T* **33.**

No.				
87	4 cents on $1 scarlet ..	6 0	7 6	2 6
	a. Surch. double ..	£16		
88	10 cents on $1 scarlet..	6 0	7 6	2 6
89	20 cents on $1 scarlet..	8 0	10 0	2 6
90	30 cents on $1 scarlet..	8 0	10 0	2 6
91	40 cents on $1 scarlet..	12 6	15 0	3 6

For 4 c. on $1 with wider spacing see No. 121.

34

35

36

37. Orang-Utan.

38

39

40

41. Bruang or honey-bear.

42.

43. Borneo railway train.

44

45

(Recess. Waterlow & Sons.)

1897–1902. *T* **34** *to* **45.** *New frames.* *P* 14.

No.	Description	Unused	Used
92	1 c. black and bistre-brown	5 0	4 0
	a. Perf. 15	7 6	4 0
	b. Perf. 14, comp. 12-13 ..	25 0	
	c. Perf. 13½	25 0	10 0
	d. Perf. 13½ × 14		
	e. Imperf. between (pair) ..		
93	1 c. black and ochre ..	15 0	10 0
	a. Perf. 15	6 0	6 0
94	2 c. black and lake ..	12 6	5 0
	a. Perf. 15	10 0	5 0
	b. Perf. 13	—	10 0
	c. Perf. 14, comp. 12-13 ..	—	10 0
95	2 c. black and green ..	12 6	4 0
	a. Perf. 15	—	10 0
	b. Perf. 14, comp. 12-13 ..	30 0	10 0
	c. Imperf. between (pair) ..		
96	3 c. green and rosy mauve	10 0	10
	a. Perf. 15	15 0	15
	b. Perf. 14, comp. 12-13 ..	22 6	25
	c. Perf. 13½	—	15
97	3 c. grn. & dull mauve (*p.* 15)	5 0	5
98	4 c. black and green (1900)	8 0	8
99	4 c. black & carmine (1900)	8 0	5
	a. Perf. 16	—	25
	b. Perf. 15	12 6	5
	c. Perf. 14, comp. 12-13 ..	12 6	15
100	5 c. blk. & orange-vermilion	7 6	7
	a. Perf. 15	12 6	6
	b. Perf. 14, comp. 12-13 ..	10 0	10
101	6 c. black and bistre-brown	10 0	5
	a. Perf. 15	5 0	5
	b. Perf. 13½	15 0	
102	8 c. black & brown-purple ..	12 6	
	a. Perf. 16	35 0	10
	b. Perf. 15	6 6	7
	c. Imperf. between (vert. pair)		
103	8 c. black and brown ..	6 6	
	a. Perf. 15	12 6	
104	10 c. deep brown & slate-lilac (1902)	20 0	15
	a. Imperf. between (vert. pair)		
105	10 c. brn. & grey-lilac (1902)	35 0	25

106 12 c. black and dull blue .. 35 0 25 0
a. Imperf. between (pair) ..
b. Perf. 15 .. .. .. 35 0 25 0
c. Perf. 14, comp. 12-13 .. 90 0 60 0
107 16 c. green & chestnut (1902) 17 6 12 6
a. Perf. 15 .. .. 35 0 17 6
108 18 c. black & green (*perf.* 16) 10 0 12 6
a. Imp. betwn. (pair) (*canc.*) — £6
109 24 c. blue and lake 12 6 17 6
a. Perf. 14, comp. 12-13 .. 20 0 25 0
b. Perf. 13½ 17 6

In the above the 18 c. has "POSTAL REVENUE" instead of "POSTAGE AND REVENUE" and the 24 c. has those words omitted. These stamps were replaced by others with corrected inscriptions; see Nos. 110 and 111.

NOTE.—Stamps cancelled to order can be supplied at about one-third the prices quoted above for postally used specimens, except in the case of some of the scarcer perforation varieties.

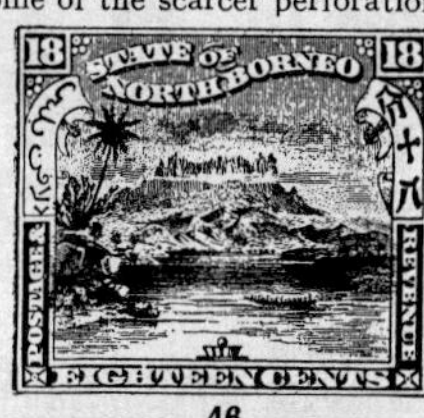

46

47

897. *Corrected inscriptions.* P 14.
10 **46** 18 c. black and green .. 17 6 17 6
a. Perf. 15. . .. .. 25 0 17 6
b. Perf. 14, comp. 13½ ..
11 **47** 24 c. blue and lake .. 25 0 25 0
a. Perf. 16. . .. .. 32 6 32 6
b. Perf. 15. . .. .. 20 0
c. Perf. 14, comp. 13½ ..

NOTE.—Price note after No. 109 applies here.

BRITISH

4

CENTS PROTECTORATE.

48. (4½ mm. between lines of surcharge.) (49)

99. *Surch. with T* **48.**
2 4 c. on 5 c. (No. 100) (*p.* 14) 10 0 12 6
a. Perf. 14 comp. 12-13 .. .. 35 0 10 0
3 4 c. on 6 c. (No. 101) (*p.* 14) 12 6 15 0
a. Perf. 15 .. .. .. 15 0 15 0
4 4 c. on 8 c. (No. 102*b*) (*p.* 15) 12 6 15 0
5 4 c. on 12 c. (No. 106*b*) (*p.* 15) 15 0 15 0
a. Imperf. between (pair) .. £25
6 4 c. on 18 c. (No. 110*a*) (*p.* 15) 15 0 15 0
7 4 c. on 24 c. (No. 111*b*) (*p.* 15) 12 6 15 0
a. Perf. 16 .. .. .. 50 0 50 0
b. Perf. 14 comp. 12-13 .. .. 20 0
c. Perf. 13½ × 14 .. .. 20 0
8 4 c. on 25 c. (No. 81) (*p.* 14) .. 12 6 15 0
a. Perf. 13½ .. .. ..
b. Imperf. between (pair) .. £40

119 4 c. on 50 c. vio. (No. 82) (*p.* 14) 30 0
120 4 c. on 50 c. mauve (*p.* 14) .. 12 6 15 0
121 4 c. on $1 (No. 83) (*p.* 14) .. 12 6 15 0
122 4 c. on $2 (No. 84) (*p.* 14) .. 17 6 25 0
123 4 c. on $5 (No. 85) (*p.* 14) .. 25 0 35 0
124 4 c. on $10 (No. 86) (*p.* 14) .. 25 0 35 0

No. 121 differs only from No. 87 in having the "4" and "cents" wider apart.

1900 (?). *Surch. as T* **48** *but* 8½ *mm. between lines of surcharge.* P 14.
125 4 c. on $5 (No. 85) 20 0 17 6
126 4 c. on $10 (No. 86) .. 17 6 17 6

1901–5. *Optd. as T* **49.** P 14.
127 1 c. (No. 92) (R.) 4 0 3 6
a. Perf. 15 .. .. .. 3 6 3 6
b. Perf. 13½ 4 0 3 6
128 2 c. (No. 95) (R.) 4 6 2 6
a. Perf. 16 .. .. .. 4 0 4 0
b. Perf. 15 .. .. .. 4 0 3 0
c. Perf. 13½ .. .. .. — 3 6
129 3 c. (No. 96) 4 0 4 6
a. Perf. 15 .. .. .. 10 0 3 6
b. Perf. 15 × 14 .. .. 30 0
130 4 c. (No. 99) (G.) 6 0 3 6
a. Perf. 15 .. .. .. 6 0 3 6
b. Perf. 13½ 5 0 4 0
131 5 c. (No. 100) (G.) .. .. — 4 0
a. Perf. 15 .. .. .. 6 0 4 0
b. Perf. 13½ 8 6 10 0
132 6 c. (No. 101) (R.) .. 15 0 20 0
a. No stop after "Protectorate" 35 0 40 0
b. Perf. 16 .. .. .. 6 0 6 0
c. Perf. 13½ 15 0 15 0
133 8 c. (No. 102) (B.) 7 6 7 6
a. Perf. 13½. No stop after "Protectorate" .. 10 0 17 6
b. Perf. 14, comp. 12-13 .. 25 0 12 6
c. Perf. 13½ × 14 .. ..
134 10 c. (No. 104) (R.) 12 6 10 0
a. Perf. 15 .. .. .. 17 6 12 6
b. Perf. 13½ .. .. .. — 10 0
c. Perf. 13½. No stop after "Protectorate" .. £9
d. Overprint double £15
135 12 c. (No. 106) (R.) 35 0 15 0
a. Perf. 13½ 25 0 15 0
136 16 c. (No. 107) 15 0 10 0
a. Perf. 15 .. .. .. 10 0 12 6
b. Perf. 14, comp. 12-13 .. 25 0 12 6
c. Perf. 13½ × 14 .. .. — 17 6
d. Perf. 14 × 13½ 25 0 20 0
137 18 c. (No. 110) (R.) 10 0 10 0
a. No stop after "Protectorate"
b. Perf. 13½ 25 0 30 0
138 24 c. (No. 111) 15 0 15 0
a. Perf. 15 .. .. .. 25 0 25 0
b. Imperf. between (pair) ..
c. Perf. 13½ 20 0 20 0
139 25 c. (No. 81) (R.) (c. 1/6) .. 12 6 15 0
a. No stop after "Protectorate" 60 0
b. Overprints tête-bêche (pair) £50
c. Overprint inverted. . .. £30
140 50 c. (No. 82) (R.) (c. 2/3) .. 12 6 15 0
a. No stop after "Protectorate" 60 0 70 0
141 $1 (No. 83) (R.) 35 0 60 0
142 $1 (No. 83) ('03) (c. 10/–) .. 35 0 45 0
a. Imperf. between (vert. pair). . £25
b. Overprint double .. ..
143 $2 (No. 84)(R.) (1905) (c. 12/6) 50 0 60 0
a. Overprint double £50
144 $5 (No. 85) (R.) (c. 14/–) .. £6 £7
145 $10 (No. 86) (R.) (c. 25/–) .. £8 £10
a. Overprint inverted. . .. £90

There was more than one setting of the overprint for some of the values. Full sheets of the 6 c. and 8 c. are known, without stop throughout.

NOTE.—Nos. 127 to 138 cancelled to order can be supplied at about one third of the prices quoted for postally used specimens. Prices for Nos. 139 to 145, cancelled, are given in brackets.

4
cents
(50)

1904–5. *Surch. locally with T* **50.**

146	4 c. on 5 c. (No. 100*a*) (*p.* 15)	17	6	15	0
147	4 c. on 6 c. (No. 101*a*) (*p.* 15)	7	6	12	6
	a. Surch. inverted	£10			
148	4 c. on 8 c. (No. 102*b*) (*p.*15)	15	0	20	0
	a. Surch. inverted	£10			
149	4 c. on 12 c. (No. 106*b*) (*p.* 15)	15	0	20	0
	a. Perf. 14	20	0	15	0
	b. Perf. 14 comp. 12				
150	4 c. on 18 c. (No. 110*a*) (*p.* 15)	20	0	20	0
151	4 c. on 24 c. (No. 111*b*) (*p.* 15)	20	0	20	0
	a. Perf. 16	15	0	20	0
	b. Perf. 14	20	0	20	0
152	4 c. on 25 c. (No. 81) (*p.* 14) ..	7	6	15	0
153	4 c. on 50 c. (No. 82) (*p.* 14) ..	10	0	15	0
154	4 c. on $1 (No. 83) (*p.* 14) ..	15	0	20	0
155	4 c. on $2 (No. 84) (*p.* 14) ..	20	0	25	0
156	4 c. on $5 (No. 85) (*p.* 14) ..	25	0	30	0
157	4 c. on $10 (No. 86) (*p.* 14) ..	25	0	30	0
	a. Surch. inverted	£35			

51. Tapir.

52. Traveller's-tree.

53. Railway at Jesselton.

54. The Sultan of Sulu, his staff and W. C. Cowie, first Chairman of the Company.

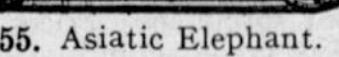

55. Asiatic Elephant.

56. Rhinoceros.

57. Ploughing with Buffalo.

58. Wild Boar.

59. Great Black Cockatoo.

60. Hornbill.

61. Wild Bull.

62. Cassowary.

(Recess. Waterlow & Sons, Ltd.)

1909 (July)–**1922.** *Centres in black.* *P* 14.

158	**51**	1 c. chocolate-brown	5	0	1	0	0
		a. Perf. 15	10	0	7	6	—
		b. Perf. 13½	10	0	6	0	—
159	,,	1 c. brown	5	0	2	0	—
		a. Perf. 15	10	0	5	0	1
160	**52**	2 c. green	2	6	1	0	0
		a. Imperf. between (pair)					
		b. Perf. 15	3	0	1	0	—
161	**53**	3 c. lake	3	0	1	6	0
162	,,	3 c. rose-lake ..	5	0	1	6	0
		a. Perf. 15	—		—		1
163	,,	3 c. green (1922) ..	5	0	0	9	—
164	**54**	4 c. scarlet	3	6	1	6	0
		a. Perf. 13½	7	6	2	6	—
		b. Perf. 15	10	0	3	6	1
165	**55**	5 c. yellow-brown ..	12	6	2	6	1
		a. Perf. 15					
166	,,	5 c. dark brown ..	10	0	3	0	—
167	**56**	6 c. olive-green ..	12	6	2	6	1
		a. Perf. 15	20	0	5	0	1
168	,,	6 c. apple-green ..	20	0	2	6	—
169	**57**	8 c. lake	5	0	2	6	1
		a. Perf. 15					
170	**58**	10 c. greyish blue ..	20	0	5	0	1
		a. Perf. 15	20	0	15	0	—
		b. Perf. 14×13½ ..					
		c. Perf. 13½	—		8	0	—
171	,,	10 c. blue	20	0	6	6	—
172	,,	10 c. turquoise-blue ..	20	0	6	6	—
		a. Perf. 15	25	0	7	6	—
173	**59**	12 c. deep blue ..	22	6	6	6	2
		a. Perf. 15					
174	**60**	16 c. brown-lake ..	22	6	12	6	4
		a. Perf. 13½	30	0	17	6	—
175	**61**	18 c. blue-green ..	30	0	25	0	6
176	**62**	24 c. mauve	40	0	12	6	3

For this issue perf. 12½ see Nos. 277, etc.

20

CENTS
(63)

1909 (Aug.). *T* **61** *surch. with T* **63.** *P* 14.
177 20 c. on 18 c. blue-green (R.) .. 10 0 2 6 0 9
a. Perf. 15 .. .. £15 £6 —

64

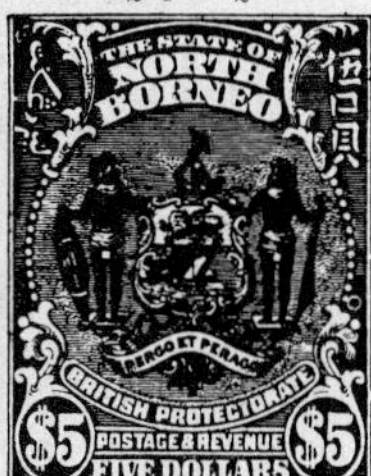

65

1911. *P* 14.
178 **64** 25 c. black and green .. 8 6 5 0
a. Perf. 15 .. .. 22 6
b. Imperf. (pair) 50 0
179 ,, 50 c. black and steel-blue 12 6 10 0
a. Perf. 15 .. .. 25 0 15 0
b. Imperf. (pair) 60 0
c. Imperf. between (pair) ..
180 ,, $1 black & chestnut .. 17 6 10 0
a. Perf. 15 .. .. 35 0 22 6
b. Imperf. (pair) 60 0
181 ,, $2 black & lilac .. 35 0 15 0
182 **65** $5 black & lake .. £5 70 0
a. Perf. 13½ .. £10
b. Imperf. (pair) .. £5
183 ,, $10 black & brick-red .. £10
a. Imperf. (pair) .. £6

BRITISH

PROTECTORATE
(66)

2

cents
(67)

912. *Nos.* 85 *and* 86 *optd. with T* **66.**
84 $5 brt. pur. (R.) (*canc.* 25s.) £60
85 $10 brown (R.) (*canc.* 25s.) .. £60

916. *Stamps of* 1909–22 *surch. as T* **67.** *P* 14.
86 2 c. on 3 c. black & rose-lake 10 0 8 6
a. "s" inverted £5
87 4 c. on 6 c. blk. & olive-grn. (R.) 7 6 10 0
a. "s" inverted £7 £8
b. "s" inserted by hand
88 10 c. on 12 c. black and deep blue (R.) 12 6 20 0
a. "s" inverted £7 £8

(68)

16 (May). *Stamps of North Borneo,* 1909–11. *optd. with T* **68.** *P* 14. *All centres in black,*
(*a*) *Cross in vermilion.*
9 1 c. brown 22 6 25 0
0 2 c. green 60 0 80 0
a. Perf. 15 .. .. .. £5 £5
1 3 c. rose-lake 40 0 50 0
2 4 c. scarlet 20 0 20 0
a. Perf. 15 .. .. .. — £12

193 5 c. yellow-brown 45 0 60 0
194 6 c. apple-green 50 0 60 0
195 8 c. lake 35 0 40 0
196 10 c. blue 80 0 90 0
197 12 c. deep blue 90 0 £5
198 16 c. brown-lake £5 £5
199 20 c. on 18 c. blue-green .. 85 0 80 0
200 24 c. dull mauve £6 £7
201 25 c. green (*p.* 15) £25 £30
(*b*) *Cross in carmine.*
202 1 c. brown 30 0 40 0
203 2 c. green 60 0 20 0
204 3 c. rose-lake 40 0 50 0
205 5 c. yellow-brown 45 0 60 0
206 6 c. apple-green 40 0 45 0
207 8 c. lake 40 0 45 0
208 10 c. blue 50 0 60 0
209 12 c. deep blue 70 0 80 0
210 16 c. brown-lake 85 0 90 0
211 20 c. on 18 c. blue-green .. £5 £5
212 24 c. dull mauve £6 £7
213 25 c. green (*p.* 15) £35 £40

RED CROSS

TWO CENTS
(69)

1918. *Stamps of* 1909–11 *surch. as T* **69.** *P* 14.
(A) *Lines of surcharge* 9 *mm. apart.*
214 **51** 1 c. brown 5 0 10 0
a. Imperf. between (pair) .. £25
215 **52** 2 c. green 3 6 4 0
a. Imperf. between (pair) .. £40
216 **53** 3 c. rose-red 8 0 12 6
a. Imperf. between (pair) .. £40
b. Perf. 15.. .. .. 60 0 70 0
217 ,, 3 c. dull rose-carmine .. £15
218 **54** 4 c. scarlet 3 6 4 6
a. Surch. inverted £20
219 **55** 5 c. deep brown 10 0 15 0
220 ,, 5 c. pale brown 10 0 20 0
221 **56** 6 c. olive-green 12 6 17 6
a. Perf. 15.. .. £20
222 **57** 8 c. lake 10 0 12 6
223 **58** 10 c. blue 15 0 22 6
224 **59** 12 c. deep blue 15 0 22 6
a. Surch. inverted £25
225 **60** 16 c. brown-lake 17 6 30 0
226 **62** 24 c. mauve 22 6 30 0
(B) *Lines of surcharge* 13–14 *mm. apart.*
227 **52** 2 c. green 60 0 70 0
228 **56** 6 c. olive-green £25 £30
229 **64** 25 c. green 35 0 50 0
230 ,, 50 c. steel-blue 35 0 50 0
231 ,, $1 chestnut 90 0 £5
232 ,, $2 lilac £6 £8
233 **65** $5 lake £45 £50
234 ,, $10 brick-red £45 £50

The above stamps were dispatched from London in three consignments, of which two were lost through enemy action at sea.

These stamps were sold at a premium of 2 c. per stamp, which went to the Red Cross Society.

FOUR CENTS
(70)

1918. *Stamps of* 1909–11 *surch. with T* **70,** *in red.* *P* 14.
235 1 c. chocolate 3 0 5 0
236 2 c. green 4 0 5 0
237 3 c. rose-lake 3 0 4 0
238 4 c. scarlet 4 0 6 0

239 5 c. brown 6 0 8 0
240 6 c. apple-green 7 6 12 6
a. Imperf. between (pair) .. £55
241 8 c. lake 7 6 12 6
242 10 c. turquoise-blue 12 6 17 6
242a 10 c. greenish blue 15 0 20 0
243 12 c. deep blue 12 6 17 6
244 16 c. brown-lake 15 0 25 0
245 24 c. mauve 17 6 30 0
246 25 c. yellow-green 25 0 35 0
247 25 c. blue-green 45 0 55 0
248 50 c. steel-blue 30 0 40 0
a. Perf. 15 .. .. .. £8
249 $1 chestnut 50 0 60 0
a. Perf. 15 .. .. ..
250 $2 lilac £5 £7
251 $5 lake £30 £35
252 $10 brick-red £30 £35

Nos. 235/52 were sold at face, plus 4 c. on each stamp for Red Cross Funds.

MALAYA-BORNEO

EXHIBITION

1922.

(71)

1922. *Stamps of* 1909–22 *optd. as T* **71.** *P* 14.

253 **51** 1 c. brown (R.) 4 6 6 0
a. Error "BORHEO" .. £25
b. Error "BORNEQ" .. £20 £30
c. Stop after "EXHBN." .. 40 0
d. Perf. 15 .. .. .. 4 6 6 0
da. Error. "BORHEO" .. £25
db. Raised stop after "1922." £10
dc. Errors "MHLAYA" and "EXHIBITICN." with stop £60
dd. Stop after "EXHBN." .. 50 0
253e ,, 1 c. brown (B.) (*p.* 15) .. £50
f. Pair, with and without opt. £85
g. Raised stop after "1922." £60
h. Error "BORHEO" .. £85
i. Error "BORNEQ" .. £85
j. Error "EXHIBITIOH" £85
k. Errors "MHLAYA" and "EXHIBITICN." with stop £120
254 ,, 1 c. orange-brown (R.) 10 0 15 0
255 **52** 2 c. green (R.) 3 6 6 0
a. Stop after "EXHBN." .. 15 0
256 **53** 3 c. rose-lake (B.) .. 5 0 7 6
a. Stop after "EXHBN." .. 22 6
257 **54** 4 c. scarlet (B.) 5 0 6 0
a. Stop after "EXHBN." .. 15 0
b. Perf. 15 .. ..
258 **55** 5 c. orange-brown (B.) .. 6 0 8 6
a. Imperf. between (pair) .. £40
b. Stop after "EXHBN." .. 15 0
c. Opt. double £85
d. Opt. double (with stop) .. £100
259 ,, 5 c. chestnut (B.) .. 10 0 12 6
260 **56** 6 c. apple-green (R.) .. 6 0 8 6
a. Stop after "EXHBN." .. 15 0
b. Opt. double £90
261 **57** 8 c. dull rose (B.) .. 6 0 8 6
262 ,, 8 c. deep rose-lake (B.) .. 6 0 7 6
a. Stop after "EXHBN." .. 22 6
263 **58** 10 c. turquoise-blue (R.) 6 0 10 0
a. Perf. 15 .. .. .. 30 0
b. Stop after "EXHBN." .. 25 0
264 ,, 10 c. greenish blue (R.) .. 8 6 12 6
a. Stop after "EXHBN." .. 30 0
265 **59** 12 c. deep blue (R.) .. 6 0 10 0
a. Stop after "EXHBN." .. 30 0
266 ,, 12 c. deep bright blue (R.) 35 0
267 **60** 16 c. brown-lake (B.) .. 8 6 12 6
a. Stop after "EXHBN." .. 40 0
b. Opt. in red £120
268 **61** 20 c. on 18 c. blue-green (B.) 15 0 20 0
a. Stop after "EXHBN." .. 85 0
269 ,, 20 c. on 18 c. blue-grn. (R.) £6
a. Stop after "EXHBN." .. £10
270 **62** 24 c. mauve (R.) 7 6 12 6
a. Stop after "EXHBN." .. 45 0
271 ,, 24 c. lilac (R.) 12 6 12 6
a. Stop after "EXHBN." .. 45 0
272 ,, 24 c. reddish lilac (R.) .. 15 0 20 0
a. Stop after "EXHBN." .. 55 0
273 **64** 25 c. blue-green (R.) .. 12 6 17 6
a. Stop after "EXHBN." .. 45 0
274 ,, 25 c. yellow-green (R.) .. 17 6 22 6
a. Stop after "EXHBN." .. 60 0
ab. Opt. double £55
b. Perf. 15 .. .. .. 45 0
c. Perf. 15. Stop after "EXHBN." £22
d. Perf. 15. Opt. double .. £45
275 ,, 50 c. steel-blue (R.) .. 15 0 20 0
a. Stop after "EXHBN." .. 75 0
b. Perf. 15 .. .. .. 75 0
c. Perf. 15. Stop after "EXHBN." £8

THREE

CENTS

(72)

1923. *T* **54** *surch. with T* **72.**

276 3 c. on 4 c. black & scarlet .. 6 0 5 0
a. Surch. double .. ..

1925–8. *As* 1909–22 (*T* **51**, *etc.*), *but perf.* 12½. *Centres in black.*

277 1 c. chocolate-brown .. 1 6 1 0
a. Imperf. between (horiz. pair) £25
278 2 c. claret 1 6 0 9
279 3 c. green ('25) 2 0 0 9
280 4 c. scarlet 3 0 0 9
a. Imperf. between (vert. pair) .. £20
b. Imperf. between (horiz. pair) .. £25
281 5 c. yellow-brown 3 0 2
282 6 c. olive-green 4 0 2
283 8 c. carmine 4 0 1
a. Imperf. between (vert. pair) .. £25
284 10 c. turquoise-blue 3 6 2
a. Imperf. between (horiz. pair) .. £30
285 12 c. deep blue 5 6 3
286 16 c. red-brown 7 6 10
287 20 c. on 18 c. blue-green (R.) 7 6 5
288 24 c. violet 12 6 15
289 25 c. green 12 6 6
290 50 c. steel-blue 18 6 12
291 $1 chestnut 35 0 22
292 $2 mauve 60 0 75
293 $5 lake ('28) £10 85
294 $10 orange-red ('28) .. £15 £

73. Head of a Murut. **74.** Orang-Utan.

75. Dyak Warrior.

76. Mount Kinabalu.

77. Clouded Leopard.

78. Arms of the Company. **80.** Arms of the Company.

79. Arms of the Company.

(Recess. Waterlow & Sons.)

31 (1 Jan.). *Fiftieth Anniv. of British North Borneo Company.* *P* 12½.

5	**73**	3 c. black and blue-green	7	6	7	6
6	**74**	6 c. black and orange ..	30	0	12	6
297	**75**	10 c. black and scarlet ..	12	6	15	0
298	**76**	12 c. black and ultram. ..	15	0	17	6
299	**77**	25 c. black and violet ..	70	0	70	0
300	**78**	$1 black & yellow-green	40	0	45	0
301	**79**	$2 black and chestnut ..	60	0	70	0
302	**80**	$5 black and purple ..	£10		£12	

81. Buffalo Transport.

82. Great Black Cockatoo.

83. Native.

84. Proboscis Monkey.

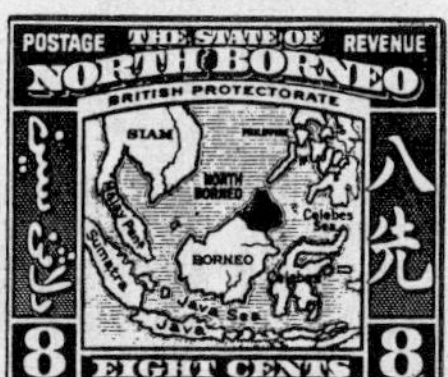

85. Mounted Bajaus.

86. Eastern Archipelago.

87. Orang-Utan.

89. Dyak.

88. Murut with Blow-pipe.

90. River Scene.

91. Native Boat.

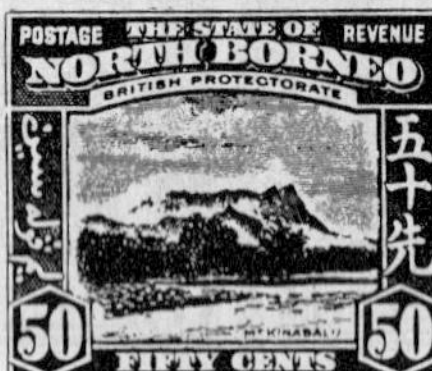

92. Mt. Kinabalu.

93. Arms of the Company. **94.**

95. Arms of the Company.

(Recess. Waterlow.)

1939 (1 Jan.). *P* 12½.

No.	Type	Description				
303	**81**	1 c. green & red-brown ..	1	0	2	0
304	**82**	2 c. purple & greenish blue	5	0	3	6
305	**83**	3 c. slate-blue and green	1	9	2	6
306	**84**	4 c. bronze-green & violet	7	6	4	0
307	**85**	6 c. deep blue & claret ..	2	6	4	0
308	**86**	8 c. scarlet	4	0	2	6
309	**87**	10 c. violet & bronze-green	10	0	5	0
310	**88**	12 c. green & bright blue..	4	0	8	6
311	**89**	15 c. blue-green & brown..	5	0	8	0
312	**90**	20 c. violet & slate-blue ..	10	0	8	6
313	**91**	25 c. green & chocolate ..	8	0	10	0
314	**92**	50 c. chocolate and violet	10	0	15	0
315	**93**	$1 brown and carmine..	22	6	25	0
316	**94**	$2 violet & olive-green..	60	0	70	0
317	**95**	$5 indigo and pale blue		£6		£8

WAR TAX (**96**) WAR TAX (**97**)

1941 (24 Feb.). *Nos.* 303/4 *optd. with T* **96/7.**

No.	Type	Description				
318	**81**	1 c. green and red-brown	0	6	1	0
319	**82**	2 c. purple & greenish blue	1	0	1	6

BMA (**98**)

1945 (17 Dec.). *British Military Administration. Nos.* 303/17 *optd. with T* **98.**

No.	Type	Description				
320	**81**	1 c. green and red-brown	0	8	1	0
321	**82**	2 c. purple & greenish blue	1	6	1	0
322	**83**	3 c. slate-blue & green ..	0	8	1	6
323	**84**	4 c. bronze-green & violet	7	6	7	6
324	**85**	6 c. deep blue & claret ..	1	0	2	6
325	**86**	8 c. scarlet	5	0	7	6
326	**87**	10 c. violet & bronze-green	5	0	4	0
327	**88**	12 c. green & bright blue..	3	0	4	0
328	**89**	15 c. blue-green & brown..	3	6	4	0
329	**90**	20 c. violet and slate-blue	6	0	5	0
330	**91**	25 c. green and chocolate..	6	0	7	6
331	**92**	50 c. chocolate and violet..	12	6	15	0
332	**93**	$1 brown and carmine..	27	6	32	[illegible]
333	**94**	$2 violet & olive-green..	35	0	40	[illegible]
		a. Opt. double				
334	**95**	$5 indigo and pale blue	45	0	65	[illegible]

These stamps and the similarly overprinted stamps of Sarawak were obtainable at all post offices throughout British Borneo (Brunei, Labuan, North Borneo and Sarawak), for use on local and overseas mail.

(**99**)

1947. *Nos.* 303 *to* 317 *optd. with T* **99** *and ba[illegible] obliterating words* "the state of" *a[illegible]* "british protectorate"

No.	Type	Description			
335	**81**	1 c. green and red-brown	0	3	0
336	**82**	2 c. purple & greenish blue	1	0	0
337	**83**	3 c. slate-blue & green (R.)	0	6	0
338	**84**	4 c. bronze-green & violet	1	6	0
339	**85**	6 c. deep blue & claret (R.)	0	6	0
340	**86**	8 c. scarlet	0	6	0
341	**87**	10 c. violet & bronze-green	2	6	0
342	**88**	12 c. green & bright blue..	0	8	1
343	**89**	15 c. blue-green and brown	0	9	0
344	**90**	20 c. violet and slate-blue	1	3	1
345	**91**	25 c. green and chocolate..	1	6	1
346	**92**	50 c. chocolate and violet	2	6	2
347	**93**	$1 brown and carmine..	4	6	6
348	**94**	$2 violet & olive-green..	12	6	15
349	**95**	$5 indigo & pale bl. (R.)	20	0	25

Dates of issue:—1.9.47, 4 c. and 8 c. 15.12.[illegible] 1 c. and 10 c. 22.12.47, other values.

1948 (1 Nov.). *Royal Silver Wedding. As Nos. 30/1 of Aden.*

350	8 c. scarlet ..	..	.. 0	6	0 8
351	$10 mauve	..	.. 40	0	45 0

1949 (10 Oct.). *75th Anniv. of Universal Postal Union. As Nos. 114/7 of Antigua.*

352	8 c. carmine..	..	.. 1	0	0 6
353	10 c. brown ..	..	.. 0	8	0 8
354	30 c. orange-brown ..	..	.. 2	0	2 6
355	55 c. blue ..	..	.. 4	0	4 6

100. Mount Kinabalu.

102. Coconut Grove.

101. Native Musical Instrument.

103. Hemp Drying.

Cattle at Kota Belud.

105. Map.

106. Logging.

107. Native Prahu, Sandakan.

109. Suluk Craft, Lahad Datu.

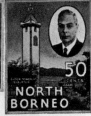

108. Bajau Chief.

110. Clock Tower Jesselton.

111. Bajau Horsemen.

112. Murut with Blowpipe.

113. Net-Fishing.

114. Arms of North Borneo.

(Photo. Harrison & Sons, Ltd.)

1950 (1 July)–**1952**. *Wmk. Mult. Script CA. Chalk-surfaced paper. P* $13\frac{1}{2} \times 14\frac{1}{2}$ *(horiz.)*, $14\frac{1}{2} \times 13\frac{1}{2}$ *(vert.)*.

356	**100**	1 c. red-brown ..	.. 0	3	0 4
357	**101**	2 c. blue ..	.. 0	3	0 3

No.	Type	Description	Un. s.	d.	Used s.	d.
358	**102**	3 c. green	0	3	0	5
359	**103**	4 c. bright purple ..	0	3	0	5
360	**104**	5 c. violet	1	6	0	10
361	**105**	8 c. scarlet	0	10	1	0
362	**106**	10 c. maroon	1	0	0	9
363	**107**	15 c. ultramarine ..	1	3	1	3
364	**108**	20 c. brown	1	6	1	6
365	**109**	30 c. olive-brown ..	2	0	1	3
366	**110**	50 c. rose-car. (JESSLETON)	3	6	5	0
366*a*	,,	50 c. rose-car. (JESSELTON) (1.5.52)	2	6	3	0
367	**111**	$1 red-orange	5	0	6	0
368	**112**	$2 grey-green	10	0	10	0
369	**113**	$5 emerald-green ..	20	0	25	0
370	**114**	$10 dull blue	35	0	42	6

1953 (3 JUNE). *Coronation. As No.* 47 *of Aden.*

No.	Description	Un. s.	d.	Used s.	d.
371	10 c. black and bright scarlet	1	0	2	0

115. Logging.

(Photo. Harrison & Sons, Ltd.)

1954–57. *Types of* 1950 (*but with portrait of Queen Elizabeth II in place of King George VI as in T* **115**). *Chalk-surfaced paper. Wmk. Mult. Script CA. P* 14½ × 13½ (*vert.*) *or* 13½ × 14½ (*horiz.*).

No.	Type	Description	Un. s.	d.	Used s.	d.
372	**100**	1 c. red-brown	0	3	0	3
373	**101**	2 c. blue	0	4	0	4
374	**102**	3 c. green (*shades*) ..	0	6	0	8
375	**103**	4 c. bright purple ..	0	5	0	5
376	**104**	5 c. reddish violet ..	1	6	0	6
377	**105**	8 c. scarlet	0	6	0	6
378	**115**	10 c. maroon	0	10	0	6
379	**107**	15 c. bright blue	1	0	0	8
380	**108**	20 c. brown	1	6	1	0
381	**109**	30 c. olive-brown ..	1	6	1	9
382	**110**	50 c. rose-carmine (Jesselton) (*shades*) ..	2	6	2	0
383	**111**	$1 red-orange	5	0	5	0
384	**112**	$2 deep green (*shades*)	12	6	12	6
385	**113**	$5 emerald-green ..	25	0	25	0
386	**114**	$10 deep blue	50	0	50	0

Plate 2 of the 30 c., released 10 Aug. 1960, had a finer, 250 screen, instead of the previous 200 (*price* 20s. *un.*).

Dates of issue : 1954—1 Mar., 10 c. ; 1 July, 5 c.; 3 Aug., 20 c., 30 c.; 1 Oct., 1 c., 8 c. 1955—1 Apr., $1 ; 16 May, 4 c., 15 c. ; 1 Oct., $2. 1956—10 Feb., 50 c. ; 1 June, 2 c. 1957—1 Feb., 3 c., $5, $10.

116. Borneo Railway, 1902.

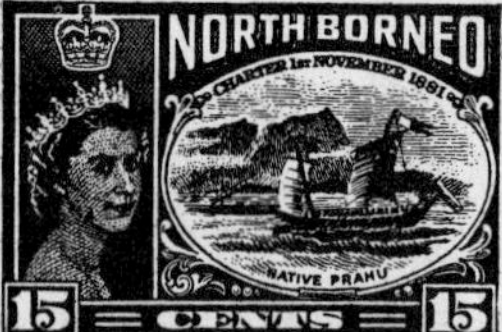

117. Native Prahu.

118. Mount Kinabalu.

119. Arms of Chartered Company.

(Recess. Waterlow & Sons.)

1956 (1 Nov.). *75th Anniv. of British North Borneo Co. Wmk. Mult. Script CA. P* 13 × 13½ (*horiz.*) *or* 13½ × 13 (*vert.*).

No.	Type	Description	Un. s.	d.	Used s.	d.
387	**116**	10 c. black & rose-carm.	1	6	1	9
388	**117**	15 c. black and red-brown	2	6	4	0
389	**118**	35 c. black & bluish grn.	4	0	6	0
390	**119**	$1 black and slate ..	10	0	12	6

120. Sambar Stag.

121. Honey Bear.

122. Clouded Leopard.

123. Dusun Woman with Gong.

124. Map of Borneo.

125. Tembadau. (Wild Bull).

126. Butterfly Orchid.

127. Sumatran Rhinoceros.

128. Murut with Blow-pipe.

129. Mount Kinabalu.

130. Dusun and Buffalo Transport.

131. Bajau Horsemen.

132. Orang-utan.

133. Hornbill.

134. Crested Wood Partridge.

135. Arms of North Borneo.

(Des. Chong Yun Fatt. Recess. Waterlow (until 1962), then De La Rue.)

1961 (1 Feb.). *W* w.**12**. *P* 13.

No.	Type	Description	Unused	Used
391	**120**	1 c. emerald & brn.-red	0 6	0 6
392	**121**	4 c. bronze-grn. & orge.	0 6	0 9
393	**122**	5 c. sepia and violet ..	1 0	0 5
394	**123**	6 c. black & blue-green	0 6	0 8
395	**124**	10 c. green and red ..	0 8	0 5
396	**125**	12 c. brown & grey-green	1 0	1 3
397	**126**	20 c. blue-grn. & ultram.	1 6	1 0
398	**127**	25 c. grey-black & scarlet	1 6	2 6
399	**128**	30 c. sepia and olive ..	1 6	1 2
400	**129**	35 c. slate-bl. & red-brn.	1 6	3 0
401	**130**	50 c. emerald & yell.-brn.	2 0	1 6
402	**131**	75 c. grey-bl. & brt. pur.	3 3	4 0
403	**132**	$1 brown & yellow-grn.	5 6	5 6
404	**133**	$2 brown and slate ..	10 0	12 6
405	**134**	$5 emerald and maroon	25 0	25 0
406	**135**	$10 carmine and blue ..	47 6	50 0

1963 (4 June). *Freedom from Hunger. As No. 63 of Aden.*

No.	Description	Unused	Used
407	12 c. ultramarine	1 0	1 0

POSTAL FISCALS.

Three Cents. Revenue (F 1)

Ten Cents. Revenue (F 2)

1886. *Regular issues surch. as Type* F **1** *or* F **2**.

No.	Description	Unused	Used
F1	3 c. on 4 c. pink (No. 6) ..	25 0	35 0
F2	5 c. on 8 c. green (No. 7) ..	25 0	35 0
F3	10 c. on 50 c. violet (No. 4) ..	40 0	60 0
	a. No stop after "Cents" ..		

POSTAGE DUE STAMPS.

NOTE.—Postage Due stamps cancelled to order can be supplied at about one-third of the prices quoted for postally used specimens. The issues of 1923 to date have not been thus cancelled.

POSTAGE DUE (D 1)

1895. *Stamps of* 1894 *optd. with Type* D **1**. *P* 15.

A. *Vertically* (*reading upwards*).

No.	Description	Unused	Used
D 1	2 c. black and rose-lake ..	15 0	17 6
D 2	2 c. black and lake	10 0	10 0
D 3	3 c. olive-green & mauve ..	6 0	10 0
D 4	5 c. black and vermilion ..	10 0	12 6
	a. Stop after "DUE" ..	35 0	
	b. Perf. 14	—	17 6
	c. Perf. 14, comp. 12-13 ..	—	17 6
D 5	6 c. black & bistre-brown ..	10 0	10 0
	a. Perf. 14	7 0	10 0
D 6	18 c. black and deep green ..	25 0	30 0
	a. Opt. reading downwards ..	£12	£12

B. *Horizontally.*

No.	Description	Unused	Used
D 7	8 c. black and dull purple ..	12 6	17 6
	a. Opt. double		
	b. Opt. inverted, perf. 14 ..	—	£6
D 8	12 c. black and blue	—	20 0
	a. Opt. double		
	b. Perf. 14	15 0	17 6
D 9	12 c. blk. & ultram. (*perf.* 14)	30 0	
D10	18 c. black and deep green ..	20 0	30 0
	a. Opt. inverted	£12	£12
	b. Perf. 11	35 0	35 0
D11	24 c. blue and rose-lake ..	—	30 0
	a. Perf. 14	15 0	25 0

1897. *Stamps of* 1897 *optd. with Type* D **1**. *P* 15.

A. *Vertically.*

No.	Description	Unused	Used
D12	2 c. black and lake	7 6	8 6
	a. Perf. 14	12 6	

B. *Horizontally.*

No.	Description	Unused	Used
D13	2 c. black and lake	12 6	15 0
D14	8 c. black and brown-purple	10 0	12 6
	a. Stop after "DUE" ..	15 0	20 0

1901. *Issue of* 1897–1902 *optd. with Type* D **1**. *P* 14.

A. *Vertically.*

No.	Description	Unused	Used
D15	2 c. black and green ..	8 6	10 0
	a. Perf. 14×13½		
	b. Perf. 14, comp. 12-13 ..	—	10 0
	c. Perf. 16		
D16	3 c. green and rosy mauve..	8 6	10 0
	a. Stop after "Due"	20 0	25 0
	b. Perf. 15	5 0	6 6
	c. Opt. double		
	d. Opt. double. Stop after "DUE"	£10	
D17	3 c. grn. & dull mve. (*p.* 15)	10 0	12 6
D18	4 c. black and carmine ..	10 0	10 0
	a. Perf. 13½	7 6	10 0
D19	5 c. black & orange-verm..	6 0	10 0
	a. Perf. 15	—	10 0
	b. Stop after "DUE" ..	20 0	
D20	6 c. black and bistre-brown	—	8 6
	a. Perf. 15	5 0	8 6
	b. Perf. 14, comp. 12-13 ..		
D21	8 c. black and brown (*p.* 15)	5 0	8 6
D22	12 c. black and dull blue ..	12 6	15 0
	a. Perf. 15		
D23	18 c. black & green (No. 108)		
D24	18 c. black & green (No. 110)	15 0	15 0
	a. Perf. 14, comp. 12-13 ..	10 0	15 0
D25	24 c. blue and lake (No. 109)	—	12 6
D26	24 c. blue and lake (*perf.* 15) (No. 111*b*) ..	15 0	17 6

B. *Horizontally.*

No.	Description	Unused	Used
D27	2 c. black and green ..	15 0	
D28	8 c. blk. & brown (*perf.* 15)	30 0	
	a. Stop after "DUE" ..		

1904–5. *Stamps of* 1901–4 *optd.* "British Protectorate," *further optd. with Type* D **1**.

A. *Vertically.*

No.	Description	Unused	Used
D29	2 c. black & green (*perf.* 16)		
D30	3 c. grn. & rosy mve. (*perf.* 14)	£8	£7
D31	5 c. blk. & orge.-ver. (*p.* 15)	£12	£8
D32	8 c. black & brown (*perf.* 14)	£12	£1
D33	24 c. blue and lake (*perf.* 14)	—	£

B. *Horizontally, at top of stamp.*

No.	Description	Unused	Used
D34	2 c. black & green (*perf.* 15)	—	£
	a. Perf. 16	£9	
D35	4 c. black & carmine (*perf.* 14)	£12	20 0

C. *Horizontally, at centre of stamp. P* 14.

No.	Description	Unused	Used
D36	2 c. black and green ..	5 0	1
	a. Perf. 15	£7	
D37	3 c. olive-grn. & rosy mauve	3 6	2
	a. Perf. 15	£8	15
D38	4 c. black and carmine ..	7 6	5
	a. Overprint double	£7	
	b. Perf. 15	5 0	6
D39	5 c. black & orge.-vermilion	5 0	2
	a. Perf. 15	10 0	10
	b. Perf. 13½	£7	10

D40 6 c. black and bistre-brown 7 6 2 6
a. Overprint inverted .. .. — £7
b. No stop after "PROTECTORATE" .. ..
c. Perf. 16 .. 20 0 20 0
D41 8 c. black and brown .. 10 0 5 0
a. No stop after "PROTECTORATE" (p. 13½) 40 0 30 0
D42 10 c. brown and slate-lilac .. 20 0 10 0
a. No stop after "PROTECTORATE" .. ..
D43 12 c. black and blue 12 6 17 6
D44 16 c. green and chestnut .. 12 6 6 0
D45 18 c. black and green .. 12 6 15 0
a. Overprint double .. .. — £6
D46 24 c. blue and lake 12 6 20 0
a. Overprint double .. .. — £6

D. *Horizontally. Optd. locally, with stop after* "DUE."
D47 1 c. blk. & bistre-brn. (*p.* 14) 12 6 20 0
a. With raised stop after "DUE" 15 0

1920–31. *Stamps of* 1909–22, *optd. with Type* D **1.** *P* 14.
A. *Horizontally at top of stamp.*
D48 4 c. black and scarlet (1920) 35 0 10 0
B. *Horizontally towards foot of stamp.*
D49 2 c. black and green .. 3 6 5 0
a. Perf. 15 .. .. .. 5 0
b. Perf. 13½ 25 0
D50 3 c. black and green .. 2 6 2 6
D51 4 c. black and scarlet .. 2 6 2 0
D52 5 c. black and yellow-brown 4 0 2 6
D53 6 c. black and olive-green .. 6 0 3 6
D54 8 c. black and rose-lake .. 3 6 2 6
D55 10 c. black & turquoise-blue 6 0 7 6
a. Perf. 15 .. .. .. 70 0
D56 12 c. black and deep blue .. 10 0 12 6
D56a 16 c. black and brown-lake .. 12 6 15 0
b. *Black and red-brown* .. 45 0

1926–31. *As* 1920–31, *but perf.* 12½.
D57 2 c. black and claret .. 1 0 2 0
D58 3 c. black and green .. 1 0 2 0
D59 4 c. black and scarlet .. 1 6 2 0
D60 5 c. black and yellow-brown 5 0 5 0
D61 6 c. black and olive-green .. 6 0 4 0
D62 8 c. black and carmine .. 6 0 5 0
D63 10 c. black & turquoise-blue 8 6 10 0
D64 12 c. black and deep blue .. 12 6 15 0
D65 16 c. black & red-brown ('31) 12 6 15 0

Nos. D49/65 exist with two types of opt.; A. Thick letters; pointed beard to "G". B. Thinner letters; "G" with square end to beard and "D" more open. No. D56*a* is Type B and D56*b*, Type A.

D **2.** Crest of the Company.

(Recess. Waterlow & Sons, Ltd.)

1939 (1 Jan.). *P* 12½.
D66 D **2** 2 c. brown 3 0 5 0
D67 " 4 c. scarlet 5 0 7 0
D68 " 6 c. violet 6 6 10 0
D69 " 8 c. green 10 0 15 0
D70 " 10 c. blue 12 6 15 0

The stamps of North Borneo were withdrawn on 30 June 1964. For later issues see Sabah.

JAPANESE OCCUPATION OF NORTH BORNEO.

The stamps listed under this heading were valid for use throughout British Borneo (i.e. in Brunei, Labuan, North Borneo and Sarawak).

1942 (June). *Stamps of N. Borneo optd. in one line as T* **1** *of Jap. Occupation of Brunei.*
J 1 **81** 1 c. grn. & red-brown .. £8 £9
J 2 **82** 2 c. purple & greenish-blue £6 £7
J 3 **83** 3 c. slate-blue & green .. £6 £7
J 4 **84** 4 c. bronze-grn. & violet £4 £6
J 5 **85** 6 c. deep blue & claret .. £6 £7
J 6 **86** 8 c. scarlet £6 £7
J 7 **87** 10 c. violet & bronze-grn. £6 £7
J 8 **88** 12 c. green & bright blue.. £10 £15
J 9 **89** 15 c. blue-green & brown.. £10 £15
J10 **90** 20 c. violet & slate-blue .. £10 £15
J11 **91** 25 c. green & chocolate .. £10 £15
J12 **92** 50 c. chocolate & violet .. £12 £17
J13 **93** $1 brown & carmine £12 £22
J14 **94** $2 violet & olive-green £25 £30
J15 **95** $5 indigo & pale blue.. £35 £40

Nos. 318 *and* 319 ("war tax") *of N. Borneo optd in one line, as last.*
J16 **81** 1 c. green & red-brown .. £10 £5
J17 **82** 2 c. purple & greenishblue £12 £6

1. Mt. Kinabalu.

2. Borneo Scene.

(Offset-litho. G. Kolff, Batavia.)

1943 (29 Apr.). *P* 12½.
J18 **1** 4 c. red 20 0 30 0
J19 **2** 8 c. blue 20 0 25 0

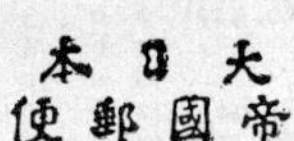

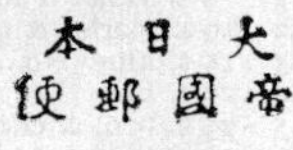

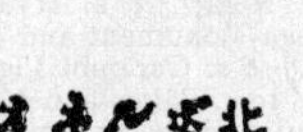

(3)

(3*a*)

("Imperial Japanese Postal Service North Borneo.")

1944 (30 Sept.). *Stamps of N. Borneo optd. as T* **3.**
J20 **81** 1 c. green and red-brown 5 0 6 0
J21 **82** 2 c. purple & grn'ish blue 5 0 6 0
J22 **83** 3 c. slate-blue & green .. 5 0 6 0
J23 **84** 4 c. bronze-grn. & violet 6 0 6 0
J24 **85** 6 c. deep blue and claret 5 0 6 0
J25 **86** 8 c. scarlet 10 0 6 0
J26 **87** 10 c. violet & bronze-green 6 0 7 6
J27 **88** 12 c. green & bright blue.. 6 0 7 6
J28 **89** 15 c. blue-green & brown.. 7 6 10 0
J29 **90** 20 c. violet and slate-blue 20 0 25 0
J30 **91** 25 c. green and chocolate 25 0 30 0
J31 **92** 50 c. chocolate and violet 50 0 60 0
J32 **93** $1 brown and carmine.. 90 0 £5

The spacing between the second and third lines of the overprint is 12 mm. on the horizontal stamps, and 15 mm. on the upright.

1944. *No.* J7 *with T* **3** *opt. in addition.*
J32*a* **87** 10 c. violet & bronze-grn. £15

The 2 c., 3 c., 8 c., 12 c. and 15 c. stamps of the 1942 issue are also known with Type **3** opt.

1945. *No.* J1 *surch. with T* **3a**.
J33 **81** $2 on 1 c. green & red-brn. £60 £75

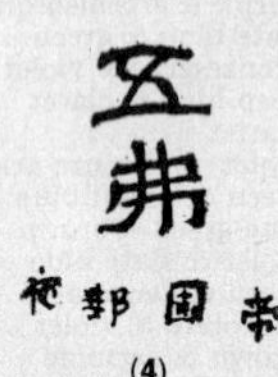

(4)

1945 (?). *North Borneo No.* 315 *surch. with T* **4**.
J34 **93** $5 on $1 brown & carmine £60 £60

5. Factory Girl.

北ボルネオ

6. (" North Borneo.")

1945. *Contemporary stamps of Japan as T* **5** (*various subjects*) *optd. with T* **6**.

No.	Description	Unused	Used
J35	1 s. red-brown (No. 404) ..	0 6	1 0
J36	2 s. scarlet (No. 383) ..	0 6	1 0
J37	3 s. emerald-green (No. 384)	0 6	1 0
J38	4 s. emerald-green (No. 408)	0 8	1 6
J39	5 s. claret (No. 409) ..	0 9	1 6
J40	6 s. orange (No. 387) ..	1 6	2 6
J41	8 s. violet & mve. (No. 389)	1 9	3 0
J42	10 s. scarlet & pink (No. 412)	2 0	3 6
J43	15 s. blue (No. 414)	2 6	4 0
J44	20 s. blue (No. 393)	50 0	50 0
J45	25 s. brn. & choc. (No. 394)	22 6	30 0
J46	30 s. turquoise-blue (No. 395)	40 0	35 0
J47	50 s. olive & bistre (No. 396)	27 6	35 0
J48	1 y. red-brn. & choc. (397)	50 0	55 0

Designs:—2 s. General Nogi; 3 s. Hydro-electric Works; 4 s. Hyuga Monument and Mt. Fuji; 5 s. Admiral Togo; 6 s. Garambi Lighthouse; 8 s. Meiji Shrine; 10 s. Palms and Map; 15 s. Airman; 20 s. Mt. Fuji and cherry blossom; 25 s. Horyuji Shrine; 30 s. Itsukushima Shrine; 50 s. Kinkakuji Shrine; 1 y. Buddha.

NORTHERN NIGERIA.

PRINTERS. All issues were typographed by De La Rue & Co.

1

2

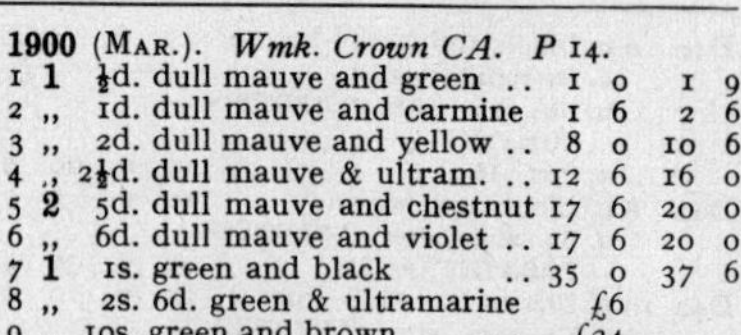

1900 (Mar.). *Wmk. Crown CA.* *P* 14.

No.	Type	Description	Unused	Used
1	**1**	½d. dull mauve and green ..	1 0	1 9
2	,,	1d. dull mauve and carmine	1 6	2 6
3	,,	2d. dull mauve and yellow ..	8 0	10 6
4	,,	2½d. dull mauve & ultram. ..	12 6	16 0
5	**2**	5d. dull mauve and chestnut	17 6	20 0
6	,,	6d. dull mauve and violet ..	17 6	20 0
7	**1**	1s. green and black ..	35 0	37 6
8	,,	2s. 6d. green & ultramarine	£6	
9	,,	10s. green and brown ..	£24	

3

4

1902 (1 July). *Wmk. Crown CA.* *P* 14.

No.	Type	Description	Unused	Used
10	**3**	½d. dull purple and green ..	0 6	0 8
11	,,	1d. dull purple and carmine	2 0	1 3
12	,,	2d. dull purple and yellow ..	4 0	5 0
13	,,	2½d. dull purple & ultram...	2 0	2 0
14	**4**	5d. dull purple & chestnut	8 6	12 6
15	,,	6d. dull purple and violet ..	15 0	10 0
16	**3**	1s. green and black ..	15 0	15 0
17	,,	2s. 6d. green and ultram...	37 6	50 0
18	,,	10s. green and brown ..	£5	£5

1904 (April). *Wmk. Multiple Crown CA.* *P* 14.
19 **4** £25 green and carmine, O ..£6000

1905 (Aug.-Oct.). *Wmk. Mult. Crown CA.* *P* 14.

No.	Type	Description	Unused	Used
20	**3**	½d. dull purple & green, OC	1 6	1 6
21	,,	1d. dull purple & carm., OC	1 6	0 8
22	,,	2d. dull purple & yell., OC	4 6	5 0
23	,,	2½d. dull purple & ultram., O	8 0	12 6
24	**4**	5d. dull pur. & chest., OC	12 6	20 0
25	,,	6d. dull pur. & violet, OC	12 6	12 6
26	**3**	1s. green and black, OC ..	20 0	20 0
27	,,	2s. 6d. green & ultram., OC	45 0	45 0

1910–11. *Wmk. Mult. Crown CA.* *P* 14.

No.	Type	Description	Unused	Used
28	**3**	½d. green, O (Apr. '10) ..	0 6	0 8
29	,,	1d. carmine, O (Jan. '10)	0 8	0 4
30	,,	2d. grey, O (Oct. '11) ..	5 0	6 0
31	,,	2½d. blue, O (Oct. '10) ..	4 6	6 0
32	**4**	3d. pur./*yell.*, C (Sept. '11)	2 0	2 6
34	,,	5d. dull pur. & olive-green, C (Feb. 11)	5 0	5 0
35	,,	6d. dull pur. and purple, C (Nov. '10)	8 6	12 6
35*a*	,,	6d. dull & brt. pur., C ('11)	6 0	7 6
36	**3**	1s. black/*grn.*, C (Nov. '10)	8 6	10 0
37	,,	2s. 6d. black and red/*blue*, C (Mar. '11)	35 0	25 0
38	**4**	5s. green and red/*yellow*, C (Sept. '11)	65 0	50 0
39	**3**	10s. green & red/*green*, C (Mar. '11)	£6	£5

5

6

1912. *Wmk Mult. Crown CA. P 14.*

No.	Type	Description	Unused	Used
40	5	½d. deep green, O	0 9	1 0
41	,,	1d. red, O	1 0	0 6
42	,,	2d. grey, O	2 0	2 0
43	6	3d. purple/*yellow*, C ..	2 6	2 6
44	,,	4d. black and red/*yellow*, C	3 0	3 0
45	,,	5d. dull pur. & olive-grn., C	5 0	6 0
46	,,	6d. dull & bright purple, C	5 0	6 0
47	,,	9d. dull purple & carm., C..	6 0	6 6
48	5	1s. black/*green*, C	8 6	8 6
49	,,	2s. 6d. black & red/*blue*, C	17 6	17 6
50	6	5s. green and red/*yellow*, C	65 0	55 0
51	5	10s. green and red/*green*, C	85 0	70 0
52	6	£1 purple and black/*red*, C	£12	£8

Since 1 January, 1914, Northern Nigeria has formed part of NIGERIA.

NORTHERN RHODESIA.

1

2

(Die eng. W. G. Fairweather. Recess. Waterlow & Sons, Ltd.)

1925 (1 APRIL)–**1929.** *Wmk. Mult. Script CA. P 12½.*

No.	Type	Description	Unused	Used
1	1	½d. green	0 3	0 4
2	,,	1d. brown	0 6	0 3
3	,,	1½d. carmine-red	1 0	1 0
4	,,	2d. yellow-brown	2 0	0 8
5	,,	3d. ultramarine	2 6	2 0
6	,,	4d. violet	3 6	2 0
7	,,	6d. slate-grey	4 0	1 6
8	,,	8d. rose-purple	22 6	27 6
9	,,	10d. olive-green	22 6	27 6
10	2	1s. yellow-brown & black..	10 0	6 0
11	,,	2s. brown & ultramarine ..	40 0	45 0
12	,,	2s. 6d. black and green ..	22 6	20 0
13	,,	3s. violet and blue ('29) ..	42 6	35 0
14	,,	5s. slate-grey and violet ..	45 0	30 0
15	,,	7s. 6d. rose-purple & black	75 0	£5
16	,,	10s. green and black ..	£5	£5
17	,,	20s. carmine-red & rose-pur.	£20	£25

1935 (6 MAY). *Silver Jubilee. As Nos. 91/4 of Antigua. P 13½ × 14.*

No.	Description	Unused	Used
18	1d. light blue and olive-green	0 6	0 6
19	2d. green and indigo ..	1 9	1 6
20	3d. brown and deep blue ..	3 0	4 0
21	6d. slate and purple	6 6	7 6

1937 (12 MAY). *Coronation. As Nos. 13/15 of Aden, but ptd. by B. W. & Co. P 11 × 11½.*

No.	Description	Unused	Used
22	1½d. carmine	0 6	0 6
23	2d. buff	0 8	1 0
24	3d. blue	1 6	2 0

3

4

(Recess. Waterlow & Sons, Ltd.)

1938 (1 MAR.)–**1952.** *Wmk. Mult. Script CA. P 12½.*

No.	Type	Description	Unused	Used
25	3	½d. green	0 3	0 3
25*a*	,,	½d. chocolate (15.11.51) ..	0 6	0 6
		b. Perf. 12½ × 14 (10.12.52) ..	0 4	0 6
26	,,	1d. brown	0 6	0 2
		a. Chocolate ('48)	1 0	0 10
26*b*	,,	1d. green (15.11.51) ..	0 4	0 4
27	,,	1½d. carmine-red	7 6	0 8
		a. Imperf. between (horiz. pair)		
27*b*	,,	1½d. yellow-brown (10.1.41)	0 5	0 2
28	,,	2d. yellow-brown	35 0	8 6
28*a*	,,	2d. carmine-red (10.1.41)	0 6	0 5
28*b*	,,	2d. purple (1.12.51) ..	0 6	0 6
29	,,	3d. ultramarine	0 8	0 8
29*a*	,,	3d. scarlet (1.12.51) ..	1 0	0 10
30	,,	4d. dull violet	1 6	0 10
30*a*	,,	4½d. blue (5.5.52)	1 6	3 6
31	,,	6d. grey	1 0	1 0
31*a*	,,	9d. violet (5.5.52) ..	3 6	4 0
32	4	1s. yellow-brn. and black	2 6	1 9
33	,,	2s. 6d. black and green ..	6 6	7 6
34	,,	3s. violet and blue ..	8 6	10 0
35	,,	5s. grey and dull violet ..	10 0	15 0
36	,,	10s. green and black ..	25 0	30 0
37	,,	20s. carm.-red and rose-pur.	45 0	55 0

1946 (26 NOV.). *Victory. As Nos. 28/9 of Aden. P 13½ × 14.*

No.	Description	Unused	Used
38	1½d. red-orange	0 6	0 8
	a. Perf. 13½	3 0	3 6
39	2d. carmine	0 8	0 10

1948 (1 DEC.). *Royal Silver Wedding. As Nos. 30/1 of Aden, but inscr.* " NORTHERN RHODESIA" *(recess 20s.).*

No.	Description	Unused	Used
40	1½d. orange	0 6	0 8
41	20s. brown-lake	40 0	45 0

1949 (10 OCT.). *75th Anniv. of U.P.U. As Nos. 114/7 of Antigua.*

No.	Description	Unused	Used
42	2d. carmine	0 6	0 8
43	3d. deep blue	0 9	1 0
44	6d. grey	2 0	2 0
45	1s. red-orange	3 6	3 6

5. Cecil Rhodes and Victoria Falls.

(Recess. De La Rue & Co.)

1953 (30 MAY). *Centenary of Birth of Cecil Rhodes. Wmk. Mult. Script CA. P 12 × 11½.*

No.	Type	Description	Unused	Used
46	5	½d. brown	1 0	1 6
47	,,	1d. green	1 9	1 9
48	,,	2d. mauve	2 0	2 0
49	,,	4½d. blue	7 6	12 6
50	,,	1s. orange and black ..	8 6	8 6

6. Arms of the Rhodesias and Nyasaland.

(Recess. Waterlow & Sons.)

1953 (30 May). *Rhodes Centenary Exhibition. Wmk. Mult. Script CA. P 14×13½.*

51		6d. violet	3 0	3 6

1953 (2 June). *Coronation. As No. 47 of Aden.*

52		1½d. black and yellow-orange	1 0	1 3

7

8

(Recess. Waterlow & Sons.)

1953 (15 Sept.). *Wmk. Mult. Script CA. P 12½×14 (pence values) or 12½×13½ (shilling values).*

53	**7**	½d. deep brown	0 4	0 6
54	,,	1d. bluish green	0 6	0 4
55	,,	1½d. orange-brown	0 8	1 0
56	,,	2d. reddish purple	0 9	0 6
57	,,	3d. scarlet	1 0	1 3
58	,,	4d. slate-lilac	1 3	1 9
59	,,	4½d. deep blue	2 6	3 6
60	,,	6d. grey-black	2 6	2 6
61	,,	9d. violet	3 0	4 6
62	**8**	1s. orange-brown and black	4 0	4 0
63	,,	2s. 6d. black and green ..	15 0	17 6
64	,,	5s. grey and dull purple ..	22 6	32 6
65	,,	10s. green and black ..	40 0	42 6
66	,,	20s. rose-red and rose-purple	70 0	85 0

For issues from 1954 to 1963, see Rhodesia and Nyasaland.

9. Arms. 10.

(Photo. Harrison & Sons.)

1963 (10 Dec.). *Arms black, gold and blue; portrait and inscriptions black; background colours below. P 14½ (T 9) or 13½×13 (T 10).*

67	**9**	½d. bright violet	0 3	0 6
		a. Value omitted		
68	,,	1d. light blue	0 4	0 5
		a. Value omitted	£6	
69	,,	2d. brown	0 5	0 6
70	,,	3d. yellow	0 7	0 3
		a. Value omitted	£30	
71	,,	4d. green	0 9	0 6
		a. Value omitted	£40	
72	,,	6d. light olive-green ..	1 0	0 9
		a. Value omitted		
73	,,	9d. yellow-brown	1 3	5 0
		a. Value omitted	£40	
74	,,	1s. slate-purple	1 9	2 0
75	,,	1s. 3d. bright purple ..	2 3	2 0
76	**10**	2s. orange	3 3	4 6
77	,,	2s. 6d. lake-brown ..	4 6	5 0
78	,,	5s. magenta	8 0	9 0
79	,,	10s. mauve	16 0	18 0
80	,,	20s. blue	30 0	37 6
		a. Value omitted	£250	

POSTAGE DUE STAMPS.

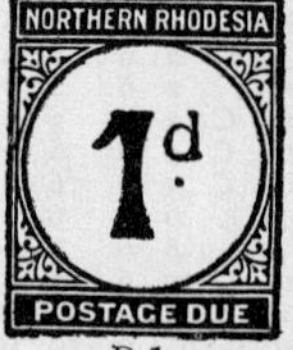

D 1

D 2

(Typo. De La Rue & Co.)

1929–52. *Wmk. Mult. Script CA. P 14.*

D1	**D 1**	1d. grey-black	5 0	4 6
		a. *Black*. Chalky paper (22.1.52)	1 0	1 6
		b. Error. St. Edward's Crown, W9b, C	£25	
D2	,,	2d. grey-black	2 6	2 6
D3	,,	3d. grey-black	7 6	6 0
		aa. *Black*. Chalky paper (22.1.52)	2 6	3 0
		a. Error. Crown missing, W9a, C	£28	
		b. Error. St. Edward's Crown, W9b, C	£25	
D4	,,	4d. grey-black	5 0	6 0

(Litho. Govt. Printer, Lusaka.)

1963 (10 Dec.). *P 12½.*

D 5	**D 2**	1d. orange	0 9	
D 6	,,	2d. deep blue	1 0	
D 7	,,	3d. lake	1 6	
D 8	,,	4d. ultramarine	2 0	
D 9	,,	6d. purple	3 0	
D10	,,	1s. light emerald	5 6	

In all values the stamps in the right-hand vertical row of the sheet are imperforate on the right.

The stamps of Northern Rhodesia were withdrawn on 23 October 1964 on attaining independence. For later issues see Zambia.

NORTH-WEST PACIFIC ISLANDS.

See NEW GUINEA.

NOVA SCOTIA.

1

2

Crown and Heraldic Flowers of United Kingdom and Mayflower of Nova Scotia.

(Recess. Perkins, Bacon & Co.)

1851 (1 Sept.)–**57.** *Bluish paper.* *Imperf.*

1	**1**	1d. red-brown (12.5.53) ..	£85	£55
		a. Bisected (½d.) (on cover) ..		
2	**2**	3d. deep blue	£65	£20
		a. Bisected (1½d.) (on cover) ..	—	£100
3	,,	3d. bright blue	£50	£18
		a. Bisected (1½d.) (on cover) ..	—	£100
4	,,	3d. pale blue	£60	£20
5	,,	6d. yellow-green	£200	£60
		a. Bisected (3d.) (on cover) ..	—	£120
		b. Quartered (1½d.) (on cover) ..		
6	,,	6d. deep green (1857)	£800	£150
		a. Bisected (3d.) (on cover) ..	—	£300
		b. Quartered (1½d.) (on cover) ..		
7	,,	1s. cold violet	£1500	£750
		a. Bisected (6d.) (on cover) ..		
		b. Quartered (3d.) (on cover) ..		
8	,,	1s. purple (1857)	£1200	£400
		a. Watermarked	£1500	£600

The watermark on No. 8*a* consists of the whole or part of a letter from the name "P. H. SAUNDERS" (the papermakers).

The stamps formerly catalogued on almost white paper are probably some from which the bluish colour has been discharged.

Reprints of all four values were made in 1890 on thin, hard, white paper. The 1d. is brown, the 3d. blue, the 6d. deep green, and the 1s. violet-black.

3

4

5

(Recess. American Bank Note Co., New York.)

1860–63. *P* 12.

(*a*) *Yellowish paper.*

	3	1 c. jet black	4	0	25	0
		a. Bisected (on cover)				
	,,	1 c. grey-black	3	6	25	0
	,,	2 c. grey-purple	30	0	45	0
a	,,	2 c. purple	60	0	40	0
	,,	5 c. blue	£15		35	0
	,,	5 c. deep blue	£15		35	0
	4	8½ c. deep green	8	6		
	,,	8½ c. yellow-green ..	6	0		
	,,	10 c. scarlet	30	0	40	0
	5	12½ c. black	17	6	30	0
a	,,	12½ c. greyish black ..	—		40	0

(*b*) *White paper.*

	3	1 c. black	8	6	35	0
		a. Imperf. between (horiz. pair)	£20			
	,,	1 c. grey	10	0	45	0
	,,	2 c. dull purple	7	6	40	0
	,,	2 c. purple	6	0	40	0
22	**3**	2 c. grey-purple	6	0	40	0
		a. Bisected (on cover) ..	—		£150	
23	,,	2 c. slate-purple	7	6	32	6
24	,,	5 c. blue	£25		30	0
25	,,	5 c. deep blue	£25		30	0
26	**4**	8½ c. deep green	50	0	75	0
27	,,	10 c. scarlet	12	6	45	0
28	,,	10 c. vermilion	17	6	50	0
		a. Bisected (on cover) ..	—		£70	
29	**5**	12½ c. black	50	0	35	0

Since 1868 Nova Scotia has used stamps of the Dominion of Canada.

NYASALAND PROTECTORATE.

(Formerly British Central Africa.

B.C.A.

(1)

1891 (April)–**1895.** *Stamps of Rhodesia optd. as T* **1.** *P* 14, 14½.

1	**1**	1d. black	3	6	4	0
2	**4**	2d. sea-green and vermilion	3	6	5	0
3	,,	4d. reddish chestnut & blk.	5	0	8	6
4	**1**	6d. ultramarine	20	0	15	0
5	,,	6d. deep blue	12	6	12	6
6	**4**	8d. rose-lake & ultramarine	15	0	25	0
6*a*	,,	8d. red and ultramarine ..	20	0	25	0
7	**1**	1s. grey-brown	12	6	12	6
8	,,	2s. vermilion	35	0	35	0
9	,,	2s. 6d. grey-purple ..	45	0	47	6
10	**4**	3s. brown and green ('95)	40	0	22	6
11	,,	4s. grey-blk. & ver. (2.'93)	55	0	45	0
12	**1**	5s. orange-yellow	50	0	60	0
13	,,	10s. deep green	85	0	£5	
14	**2**	£1 deep blue	£28		£18	
15	,,	£2 rose-red	£45			
16	,,	£5 sage-green	£85			
17	,,	£10 brown	£140			

The overprint varies on values up to 10s. Sets may be made with *thin* or *thick* letters.

B.C.A.
FOUR
SHILLINGS.

(2)

ONE PENNY.

(3)

1892–93. *Stamps of Rhodesia surch. as T* **2.**

18	**4**	3s. on 4s. grey-blk. & verm.	£15	£15
19	**1**	4s. on 5s. orange-yellow ..	£6	£6

The 4s. was issued in Aug., 1892, the 3s. in Oct., 1893.

1895. *No.* 2 *surch. at Cape Town with T* **3.**

20	**4**	1d. on 2d. sea-grn. & verm.	22	6	27	6
		a. Surch. double	£45			

Specimens are known with double surcharge, without stop after "PENNY". These are from a trial printing made at Blantyre, but it is believed that they were not issued to the public.

Supporters depict Makalolo chieftains.

5 6

(Litho. De La Rue & Co.)

1895. *No wmk. P* 14.

No.	Type	Description	Unused		Used	
21	**5**	1d. black	6	0	10	0
22	,,	2d. black and green ..	16	0	17	6
23	,,	4d. black and reddish buff	32	6	32	6
24	,,	6d. black and blue ..	32	6	18	6
25	,,	1s. black and rose	40	0	30	0
26	**6**	2s. 6d. black & brt. mag.	£6		£6	
27	,,	3s. black and yellow ..	£5		60	0
28	,,	5s. black and olive ..	£8		£5	
29	,,	£1 black & yellow-orange	£65		£24	
30	,,	£10 black & orge.-vermilion	£225			
31	,,	£25 black and blue-green ..	£600		£450	

1896 (Feb.). *Wmk. Crown CA* (*T* **5**) *or CC* (*T* **6**), *P* 14.

No.	Type	Description	Unused		Used	
32	**5**	1d. black	7	6	12	6
33	,,	2d. black and green ..	18	6	15	0
34	,,	4d. black & orange-brown	15	0	15	0
35	,,	6d. black and blue ..	15	0	10	0
36	,,	1s. black and rose	27	6	25	0
37	**6**	2s. 6d. black and magenta	£6		£6	
38	,,	3s. black and yellow ..	70	0	40	0
39	,,	5s. black and olive ..	£6		£5	
40	,,	£1 black and blue	£85		£50	
41	,,	£10 black and orange ..	£450		£175	
42	,,	£25 black and green ..	£850			

7

8

1897 (Aug.). *T* **7** (*wmk. Crown CA*) *and* **8** (*wmk. Crown CC*). *P* 14.

No.	Type	Description	Unused		Used	
43	**7**	1d. black & ultramarine ..	1	0	0	10
44	,,	2d. black & yellow ..	1	9	2	6
45	,,	4d. black and carmine ..	3	6	7	0
46	,,	6d. black & green ..	6	0	7	6
47	,,	1s. black & dull purple ..	6	0	7	6
48	**8**	2s. 6d. blk. & ultramarine	32	6	32	6
49	,,	3s. black & sea-green ..	£5		85	0
50	,,	4s. black & carmine ..	35	0	40	0
50*a*	,,	10s. black & olive-green ..	£8		£6	
51	,,	£1 black & dull purple ..	£20		£12	
52	,,	£10 black & yellow ..	£300		£90	

ONE

PENNY

(**9**)

1898. *No.* 49 *surch. with T* **9**, *in red.*

No.	Type	Description	Unused		Used	
53	**8**	1d. on 3s. black & sea-green ..	8	6	10	0
		a. Error "PNNEY"	£65			
		b. Error "PENN"	£30			
		c. Double surch.	£30		£25	

10

1898 (11 Mar.). *T* **10.** *Imperf.*

Setting I. *The vertical frame lines of the stamps cross the space between the two rows of the sheet.*

(i) *With the initials* " J.G." *or* " J.T.G." *on the back in black ink.*

No.	Description	Unused	Used
54	1d. vermilion and grey-blue ..	—	£24
	a. Without the initials	£55	
	b. Without the initials and centre inverted	£375	

(ii) *With a control number and letter, or letters, printed in plain relief at the back.*

No.	Description	Unused	Used
55	1d. vermilion and grey-blue..	—	80 c
	b. Centre omitted (vert. pr. with normal)	£160	

Setting II. *The vertical frame lines do not cros the space between the rows.*

As No. 55.

No.	Description	Unused	Used
55*a*	1d. vermilion and pale ultram.	—	40 (
	aa. Control (13 D) on face ..	—	£8
56	1d. vermilion and deep ultram.	—	32
	a. Without Control at back ..	£22	80
	b. Control doubly impressed ..		

1898 (June). *T* **10.** *Setting* II. *P* 12.

No.	Description	Unused	Used
57	1d. vermilion & pale ultram.	£22	15
57*a*	1d. vermilion & deep ultram.	—	12
	b. Without Control at back .	£22	60
	c. Two diff. Controls on back ..	—	£

The two different settings of these stamps ar each in 30 types.

1901. *Wmk. Crown CA. P* 14.

No.	Type	Description	Unused		Used
57*d*	**7**	1d. dull pur. & carmine-rose	2	6	2
57*e*	,,	4d. dull pur. & olive-green..	8	6	10
58	,,	6d. dull purple & brown ..	12	6	12

11

12

(Typo. De La Rue.)

1903–4. *T* **11** (*Wmk. Crown CA*) *and* **12** (*Wmk. Crown CC*). *P* 14.

No.	Type	Description	Unused	Used
59	**11**	1d. grey and carmine	2 6	1 0
60	,,	2d. dull & bright purple	7 6	4 0
61	,,	4d. grey-green and black	10 0	10 0
62	,,	6d. grey & reddish buff	10 0	10 0
62*a*	,,	1s. grey and blue	12 6	18 6
63	**12**	2s. 6d. grey-green & green	42 6	35 0
64	,,	4s. dull & bright purple	55 0	55 0
65	,,	10s. grey-green and black	£6	£6
66	,,	£1 grey and carmine	£25	£18
67	,,	£10 grey and blue	£350	£250

1907. *T* **11.** *Wmk. Mult. Crown CA. P* 14.

No.	Description	Unused	Used
68	1d. grey and carmine, C	3 6	2 6
69	2d. dull and bright purple, C	£1000	
70	4d. grey-green and black, C	£1000	
71	6d. grey and reddish buff, C	55 0	70 0

On 6 July, 1907 the name of the territory was altered to "NYASALAND PROTECTORATE".

13 14

(Typo. De La Rue.)

1908 (22 JULY). *Wmk. Crown CA. P* 14.

No.	Type	Description	Unused	Used
72	**13**	1s. black/*green*, C	8 6	12 6
		Wmk. Mult. Crown CA. P 14.		
73	**13**	½d. green, O	1 6	2 6
74	,,	1d. carmine, O	1 9	1 0
75	,,	3d. purple/*yellow*, C	6 0	6 0
76	,,	4d. black and red/*yellow*, C	7 6	10 0
77	,,	6d. dull pur. & brt. pur., C	6 0	10 0
78	**14**	2s. 6d. black & red/*blue*, C	30 0	40 0
79	,,	4s. carmine and black, C	45 0	60 0
80	,,	10s. green and red/*green*, C	£8	£10
81	,,	£1 purple and black/*red*, C	£40	£60
82	,,	£10 purple & ultramarine, C	£650	

15 16

(Typo. De La Rue.)

1913 (1 JUNE)–**1918.** *T* **15** *and* **16** (*2s. 6d., etc.*). *Wmk. Mult. Crown CA. P* 14.

Description	Unused	Used
½d. green, O	0 8	0 6
½d. blue-green, O (1918)	0 10	0 4
1d. carmine-red, O	2 0	0 6
1d. scarlet, O (1916)	1 0	0 4
2d. grey, O (1916)	6 0	1 0
2d. slate, O	8 0	1 6
2½d. bright blue, O	2 6	2 6
3d. purple/*yellow*, C (1914)	6 6	6 0
a. On pale yellow	5 0	5 0
4d. black and red/*yellow* C,	5 0	6 0
a. On lemon	75 0	
b. On pale yellow	10 0	10 0
6d. dull & bright purple, C	7 6	7 6

No.	Description	Unused	Used
92*a*	6d. dull pur. & brt. violet, C	7 6	7 6
93	1s. black/*green*, C (1918)	10 0	7 6
	a. On blue-green, olive back	7 6	7 6
	b. On emerald back	6 6	10 0
94	2s. 6d. blk. & red/*blue*, C('18)	12 6	12 6
95	4s. carmine & black, C ('18)	17 6	20 0
96	10s. green & red/*grn.*, C ('18)	75 0	75 0
97	10s. pale grn. & red/*green*, C	£6	£6
98	£1 purple & blk./*red*, C ('18)	£10	£7
99	£10 purple & blue, C (1914)	£275	£175

For stamps optd. "N.F." see TANGANYIKA.

1921–30. *T* **15** *and* **16** (*2s., etc.*). *Wmk. Mult. Script CA. P* 14.

No.	Description	Unused	Used
100	½d. green, O	1 0	0 4
101	1d. carmine, O	1 0	0 4
102	1½d. orange, O	2 6	4 0
103	2d. grey, O	2 0	0 6
105	3d. purple/*pale yellow*, C	2 6	2 6
106	4d. black & red/*yellow*, C	4 0	4 0
107	6d. dull & bright purple, C	5 0	5 0
108	1s. black/*emerald*, C ('30)	12 6	12 6
109	2s. purple and blue/*blue*, C	15 0	20 0
110	2s. 6d. blk. & red/*blue*, C('24)	15 0	20 0
111	4s. carmine and black, C	17 6	17 6
112	5s. green & red/*yellow*, C('29)	75 0	80 0
113	10s. green and red/*green*, C	£8	£6

17. King George V and Symbol of the Protectorate.

(Des. Major H. E. Green, D.S.O., O.B.E. Recess. Waterlow.)

1934 (JUNE)–**1935.** *Wmk. Mult. Script CA. P* 12½.

No.	Type	Description	Unused	Used
114	**17**	½d. green	0 8	0 4
115	,,	1d. brown	0 10	0 4
116	,,	1½d. carmine	2 6	2 6
117	,,	2d. pale grey	2 6	1 6
118	,,	3d. blue	3 6	2 6
119	,,	4d. brt. magenta (20.5.35)	5 6	6 6
120	,,	6d. violet	8 6	6 0
121	,,	9d. olive-bistre (20.5.35)	12 6	22 6
122	,,	1s. black and orange	12 6	15 0

1935 (6 MAY). *Silver Jubilee. As Nos.* 91/4 *of Antigua but ptd. by W'low & Sons. P* 11 × 12.

No.	Description	Unused	Used
123	1d. ultramarine and grey	1 0	1 3
124	2d. green and indigo	3 6	3 6
125	3d. brown and deep blue	7 6	8 0
126	1s. slate and purple	17 6	20 0

1937 (12 MAY). *Coronation. As Nos.* 13/15 *of Aden, but ptd. by B. W. & Co. P* 11 × 11½.

No.	Description	Unused	Used
127	½d. green	0 3	0 3
128	1d. brown	0 6	0 6
129	2d. grey-black	1 6	2 0

18. Symbol of the Protectorate.

(Recess. Waterlow & Sons.)

1938 (1 JAN.)–**1942.** *Wmk. Mult. Script CA. P* 12½.

No.	Type	Description	Unused	Used
130	**18**	½d. green	0 6	0 6
130*a*	,,	½d. brown ('42)	0 6	0 3
131	,,	1d. brown	0 8	0 3

131*a*	**18**	1d. green ('42)	0	6	0	3
132	,,	1½d. carmine	1	6	5	0
132*a*	,,	1½d. grey ('42)	0	8	1	0
133	,,	2d. grey	2	6	1	0
133*a*	,,	2d. carmine ('42) ..	0	9	0	8
134	,,	3d. blue	1	0	1	0
135	,,	4d. bright magenta ..	1	6	2	0
136	,,	6d. violet	2	0	2	0
137	,,	9d. olive-bistre	3	6	5	0
138	,,	1s. black and orange ..	5	0	2	6

19

(Typo. De La Rue & Co.)

1938 (1 Jan.). *P* 14. (*a*) *Wmk. Mult. Script CA.*

139	**19**	2s. purple & blue/*blue*, C	5	0	6	6
140	,,	2s. 6d. black & red/*blue*, C	6	0	10	0
141	,,	5s. pale grn. & red/*yell.*, C	35	0	40	0
		a. Green and red/pale yell., O	95	0	95	0
142	,,	10s. green & red/*green*, CO	35	0	40	0
		(*b*) *Wmk. Mult. Crown CA.*				
143	**19**	£1 purple & black/*red*, C	80	0	90	0

No. 141*a* has a yellow surfacing often applied in horizontal lines giving the appearance of laid paper.

20. Lake Nyasa.

21. King's African Rifles.

24. Fishing Village.

22. Tea Estate.

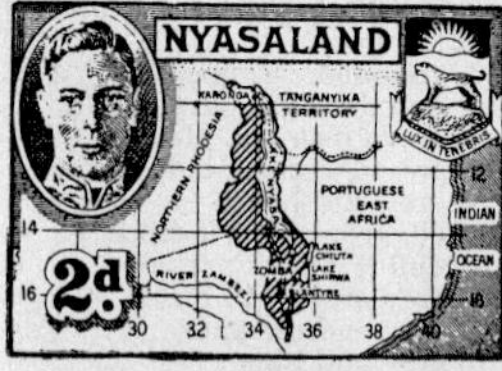

23. Map of Nyasaland.

25. Tobacco.

26. Badge of Nyasaland.

(Recess. Bradbury, Wilkinson.)

1945 (1 Sept.). *Wmk. Mult. Script CA* (*sideway on horiz. designs*). *P* 12.

144	**20**	½d. black and chocolate ..	0	6	0
145	**21**	1d. black and emerald ..	0	6	0
146	**22**	1½d. black and grey ..	0	8	0
147	**23**	2d. black and scarlet ..	0	8	0
148	**24**	3d. black and light blue ..	0	10	0
149	**25**	4d. black and claret	1	6	1
150	**22**	6d. black and violet	2	0	1
151	**20**	9d. black and olive	2	6	4
152	**23**	1s. indigo and deep green	2	6	2
153	**24**	2s. emerald and maroon ..	7	0	6
154	**25**	2s. 6d. emerald and blue	8	0	7
155	**26**	5s. purple and blue ..	12	6	12
156	**23**	10s. claret and emerald ..	20	0	22
157	**26**	20s. scarlet and black ..	45	0	45

1946 (16 Dec.). *Victory. As Nos.* 28/9 *of Ade*

158	1d. green	0	4	0
159	2d. red-orange	0	8	0

27. Symbol of the Protectorate.

Recess. Bradbury, Wilkinson.)

1947 (20 Oct.). *Wmk. Mult. Script CA. P*

160	**27**	1d. red-brn. and yell.-grn.	0	9	0

1948 (15 Dec.). *Royal Silver Wedding. As Nos. 30/1 of Aden.*

161	1d. green	0 4	0 6
162	10s. mauve	22 6	25 0

1949 (21 Nov.). *75th Anniv. of U.P.U. As Nos. 114/7 of Antigua.*

163	1d. blue-green	0 6	0 6
164	3d. greenish blue	0 10	0 10
165	6d. purple	1 9	1 6
166	1s. ultramarine	3 0	3 6

28. Arms in 1891 and 1951.

(Recess. Bradbury, Wilkinson.)

1951 (15 May). *Diamond Jubilee of Protectorate. Wmk. Mult. Script CA. P 11×12.*

67	**28**	2d. black and scarlet ..	0 10	0 10
68	,,	3d. black and turq.-blue	1 3	1 6
69	,,	6d. black and violet ..	2 0	2 6
70	,,	5s. black and indigo ..	25 0	30 0

953 (30 May). *Rhodes Centenary Exhibition. As No. 51 of Northern Rhodesia.*

71	6d. violet	3 6	4 0

953 (2 June). *Coronation. As No. 47 of Aden, but ptd. by B. W. & Co.*

72	2d. black and brown-orange	0 8	1 3

29. Grading Cotton.

(Recess. Bradbury, Wilkinson.)

953 (1 Sept.)–**54**. *As T* **20** *and* **22/7**, *but with portrait of Queen Elizabeth II, as in T* **29**. *Wmk. Mult. Script CA. P 12.*

73	**20**	½d. black and chocolate..	0 6	0 6
		a. Perf. 12×12½ (8.3.54) ..	0 4	0 8
74	**27**	1d. brown & bright green	0 8	0 6
75	**22**	1½d. blk. & dp. grey-green	0 8	1 6
76	**23**	2d. blk. & yellow-orange	1 0	1 0
		a. Perf. 12×12½ (8.3.54) ..	1 0	1 6
7	**29**	2½d. green and black ..	1 0	1 6
8	**25**	3d. black and scarlet ..	1 6	2 6
9	**24**	4½d. black and light blue..	2 6	3 6
0	**22**	6d. black and violet ..	3 0	4 0
		a. Perf. 12×12½ (8.3.54) ..	3 0	4 6
1	**20**	9d. black and deep olive	4 0	5 0
2	**23**	1s. deep blue & slate-grn.	6 0	5 0
3	**24**	2s. deep grn. & brown-red	8 6	10 6
4	**25**	2s. 6d. deep emerald and deep blue ..	12 6	15 0
5	**26**	5s. purple & Prussian blue	22 6	27 6
6	**23**	10s. carm. & deep emerald	40 0	42 6
7	**26**	20s. red and black ..	65 0	80 0

Stamps perf. 12×12½ come from sheets comb-rforated 11.8×12.25. They were also issued in ils of 480 stamps made up from sheets.

For issues between 1954 and 1963, see IODESIA AND NYASALAND.

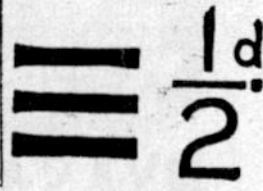

30 **(31)**

(Recess. Bradbury, Wilkinson.)

1963 (1 Nov.). *T* **30**. *Revenue stamps optd. "* POSTAGE *", or additionally surch. as T* **31**. *P 12.*

188	½d. on 1d. greenish blue ..	0 9	1 0
189	1d. green	0 9	1 0
190	2d. scarlet	1 0	1 3
191	3d. blue	2 0	2 6
192	6d. brown-purple	3 0	3 6
193	9d. on 1s. cerise	4 0	5 0
194	1s. purple	5 0	6 6
195	2s. 6d. black	10 0	12 6
196	5s. chocolate	20 0	25 0
197	10s. yellow-olive (*shades*) ..	50 0	60 0
198	£1 deep violet	£5	£6

32. Mother and Child.

33. Chambo (fish).

34. Zebu Bull.

35. Groundnuts.

36. Fishing.

37. Tea Industry.

38. Timber.

39. Turkish Tobacco Industry.

40. Cotton Industry.

41. Monkey Bay, Lake Nyasa.

42. Forestry—Afzelia.

43. Nyala.

(Des. V. Whiteley. Photo. Harrison & Sons.)

1964 (1 JAN.). *P* 14½.

199	**32**	½d. reddish violet ..	0	10	1	3
200	**33**	1d. black and green ..	1	4	1	0
201	**34**	2d. light red-brown ..	1	6	1	3
202	**35**	3d. red-brown, yellow-green and bistre-brown	1	9	1	9
203	**36**	4d. indigo & orange-yell.	2	3	2	6
204	**37**	6d. purple, yellow-green and light blue ..	2	6	2	
205	**38**	1s. brown, turquoise-blue and pale yellow ..	5	0	5	
206	**39**	1s. 3d. bronze-grn. & chest.	6	0	5	
207	**40**	2s. 6d. brown and blue ..	13	0	12	
208	**41**	5s. blue, grn., yell. & blk.	26	0	18	
209	**42**	10s. grn., orge.-brn. & blk.	45	0	45	
210	**43**	£1 dp. redsh. pur. & yell.	85	0	85	

POSTAGE DUE STAMPS.

(Typo. De La Rue.)

1950 (1 JULY). *As Type* D **1** *of Gold Coast, b inscr.* "NYASALAND". *Wmk. Mult. Scri CA. P* 14.

D1	1d. scarlet	1	6	2
D2	2d. ultramarine	2	0	2
D3	3d. green	2	6	3
D4	4d. purple	4	0	5
D5	6d. yellow-orange	6	0	7

The stamps of Nyasaland were withdrawn 30 June 1964 on attaining independence. F later issues see MALAWI.

ORANGE FREE STATE.

(CALLED ORANGE RIVER COLONY, 1900–1910).

SIMPLIFICATION (see INTRODUCTION)

Type I unsurcharged.
48, 84, 2, 68, 49, 51, 18, 5, 7, 9, 87, 20.

Type I surcharged.
3, 24, 36, 39, 53, 54, 57, 67, 69, 77, 82a,
(Add other surch. types if desired.)

V.R.I. overprints.
101 to 110 (less 105). 156 to 166 (less 160).
(214 to 223 can be included if desired.)

I. INDEPENDENT REPUBLIC.

NOTE. All stamps are perf. 14.

1

(Typo. De La Rue & Co.)

1868 (1 JAN.)–**1890.**

1	**1**	1d. pale brown	.. ..	2 6	0 9
2	,,	1d. red-brown	.. ..	3 0	0 9
3	,,	1d. deep brown	.. ..	3 6	0 9
4	,,	6d. pale rose (1868)	.. ..	10 0	5 0
5	,,	6d. rose (1871)	.. ..	7 6	4 6
6	,,	6d. rose-carmine (1877)	..	20 0	4 6
7	,,	6d. bright carmine (1890)	..	5 0	2 6
8	,,	1s. orange-buff	.. ..	15 0	8 6
		a. Double Print	.. ..	—	£85
9	,,	1s. orange-yellow	.. ..	5 0	2 6

4 (a) 4 (b) 4 (c) 4 (d)

1877. *No. 6 surcharged as above.*

10	4 on 6d. rose-carmine (*a*)	..	70 0	50 0
11	4 on 6d. rose-carmine (*b*)	..	£22	£5
12	4 on 6d. rose-carmine (*c*)	..	80 0	35 0
13	4 on 6d. rose-carmine (*d*)	..	80 0	35 0

Varieties. (i.) *Surcharge inverted.*

14	4 on 6d. rose-carmine (*a*)	..	—	£24
15	4 on 6d. rose-carmine (*b*)	..	—	£30
16	4 on 6d. rose-carmine (*c*)	..	—	£14
17	4 on 6d. rose-carmine (*d*)	..	—	£18

(ii.) *Surcharge double, one inverted.*

17*a*	4 on 6d. rose-carmine (*a* and *c*)	—	£40
17*b*	4 on 6d. rose-carmine (*b* and *d*)	—	£40

1878 (JULY). *T* 1.

18	4d. pale blue	.. ..	12 6	4 6
19	4d. ultramarine	.. ..	15 0	7 6
20	5s. green	.. ..	22 6	17 6

1d. (a) 1d. (b) 1d. (c) 1d. (d) 1d. (e)

1881 (JUNE). *No.* 20 *surch. as above, with a heavy black bar cancelling the old value.* (*a*) *Small* "1" *and* "d." (*b*) *Sloping serif.* (*c*) *Same size as* (*b*), *but* "1" *with straight horizontal serif.* (*d*) *Taller* "1" *with horizontal serif.* (*e*) *Same size as* (*d*) *but with sloping serif and thin line at foot.*

21	1d. on 5s. green (*a*)	..	40 0	17 6
22	1d. on 5s. green (*b*)	..	25 0	20 0
23	1d. on 5s. green (*c*)	..	70 0	40 0
24	1d. on 5s. green (*d*)	..	25 0	20 0
25	1d. on 5s. green (*e*)	..	£6	

There are two varieties of No. 24—one with an antique "d," the other with a Roman "d."

Varieties. (i) *Surcharge inverted.*

	1d. on 5s. green (*b*)	.. ..	—	£28
	1d. on 5s. green (*c*)	.. ..	—	£35
	1d. on 5s. green (*d*)	.. ..	£20	£20
	1d. on 5s. green (*e*)	.. ..	—	£35

(ii). *Surcharge double.*

	1d. on 5s. green (*b*)	.. ..	—	£28
	1d. on 5s. green (*c*)	.. ..		
	1d. on 5s. green (*d*)	.. ..	—	£35
	1d. on 5s. green (*e*)	.. ..		

No. 21 was the first printing in one type only. Nos. 22 to 25 constitute the second printing about a year later, and are all found on the same sheet; and as certain varieties are known with surcharge inverted and double, all probably exist.

Owing to defective printing, specimens may be found with the obliterating bar at the top of the stamps and others without the bar.

½d

1882 (AUG.). *No.* 20, *surch.* "½d" *as above and with a thin black line cancelling old value.*

	½d. on 5s. green	.. ..	4 6	5 0
	a. Surch. double	.. ..	£18	£15
	b. Surch. inverted	.. ..		
	c. Surch. double, both inverted	..		

3d (a) 3d (b) 3d (c) 3d (d) 3d (e)

1882. *No.* 19 *surch. as above with thin black line cancelling value.*

38	3d. on 4d. ultramarine (*a*)	..	60 0	50 0
	a. Surch. double	.. ..	—	£35
39	3d. on 4d. ultramarine (*b*)	..	40 0	35 0
	a. Surch. double	.. ..	—	£35
40	3d. on 4d. ultramarine (*c*)	..	40 0	35 0
	a. Surch. double	.. ..	—	£33
41	3d. on 4d. ultramarine (*d*)	..	50 0	35 0
	a. Surch. double	.. ..	—	£28
42	3d. on 4d. ultramarine (*e*)	..	£8	75 0
	a. Surch. double	.. ..	—	£35

1883–84.

48	**1**	½d. chestnut	.. ..	1 6	0 9
49	,,	2d. pale mauve	.. ..	4 0	0 4
50	,,	2d. bright mauve	.. ..	4 0	0 4
51	,,	3d. ultramarine	.. ..	6 0	5 0

For 1d. purple, see No. 68.

2d (a) 2d (b)

1888 (SEPT.–OCT.). *No.* 5 *surch. as above.*

(*a*) *Wide* "2". (*b*) *Narrow* "2".

52	2d. on 3d. ultram. (*a*) (Sept.)	..	25 0	17 6
	a. Surch. inverted	.. ..	—	£24
53	2d. on 3d. ultramarine (*b*)	..	12 6	6 0
	a. Surch. inverted	.. ..	—	£16

A variety exists having "2" with a curly tail.

1d (a) 1d (b) Id (c)

1890 (DEC.)–**1891** (MAR.). *Nos.* 51 *and* 61 *surch. as above.*

54	1d. on 3d. ultramarine (*a*)	..	2 0	1 6
	a. Surch. double	.. ..	£5	
	b. Surch. double (*a*) & (*b*)	..	£6	
	c. "1" and "d" wide apart	..	£12	£8
55	1d. on 3d. ultramarine (*b*)	..	10 0	8 0
	a. Surch. double	.. ..	£6	
57	1d. on 4d. ultramarine (*a*)	..	25 0	8 0
	a. Surch. double	.. ..	£8	£6
	b. Surch. double (*a*) & (*b*)			
58	1d. on 4d. ultramarine (*b*)	..	90 0	55 0
	a. Surch. double	.. ..	£10	
59	1d. on 4d. ultramarine (*c*)	..	£22	£18

The settings of the 1d. on 3d. and on 4d. are not identical. The variety (*c*) does not exist on the 3d.

2½d.

1892 (OCT.). *No.* 51 *surch. as above.*

67	2½d. on 3d. ultramarine	..	3 0	1 6
	a. No stop after "d"	..	40 0	

1894 (SEPT.). *Colour changed.*

68	**1**	1d. purple	.. ..	0 6	0 3

½d (a) ½d (b) ½d (c)

½d (d) ½d (e) ½d (f) ½d (g)

1896 (Sept.). *No.* 51 *surch. as above.*

69 ½d. on 3d. ultramarine (*a*) .. 2 6 3 0
70 ½d. on 3d. ultramarine (*b*) .. 6 6 7 6
71 ½d. on 3d. ultramarine (*c*) .. 7 6 8 6
72 ½d. on 3d. ultramarine (*d*) .. 7 6 8 6
73 ½d. on 3d. ultramarine (*e*) .. 7 6 8 6
74 ½d. on 3d. ultramarine (*f*) .. 4 6 5 0
75 ½d. on 3d. ultramarine (*g*) .. 3 0 4 0

Types (*a*) and (*e*) differ from types (*b*) and (*f*) respectively, in the serifs of the "1", but owing to faulty overprinting this distinction is not always clearly to be seen.

Variety. Surcharge double.

76 ½d. on 3d. ultramarine .. 20 0 15 0

The double surcharges are often different types, but are always type (*g*), or in combination with type (*g*).

Halve Penny.

1896. *No.* 51 *surch. as above.*

77 ½d. on 3d. ultramarine .. 0 6 0 6

Varieties. (i.) *Errors in setting.*

78 ½d. on 3d. (no stop) 25 0 25 0
79 ½d. on 3d. ("Peuny") .. 30 0 30 0
80 ½d. on 3d. (no bar) .. 12 0 10 0
80*a* ½d. on 3d. (no bar or stop) ..
80*b* ½d. on 3d. (no bar and "Peuny")

(ii.) *Surch. inverted.*

81 ½d. on 3d. 50 0
81*a* ½d. on 3d. (no stop) .. ..
81*b* ½d. on 3d. ("Peuny") ..

(iii.) *Surch. double, one inverted.*

81*c* ½d. on 3d. (Nos. 77 and 81) .. £12 £12
81*d* ½d. on 3d. (Nos. 77 and 81*a*) .. £30
81*e* ½d. on 3d. (Nos. 77 and 81*b*) .. £40
81*f* ½d. on 3d. (Nos. 81 and 78) ..
82 ½d. on 3d. (Nos. 81 and 79) .. — £40

No. 69 *to* 75 *additionally surcharged as last.*

82*a* "Halve Penny" on No. 69 .. 70 0
82*b* "Halve Penny" on No. 70 .. £9
ba. "Peuny" for "Penny" .. £50
bb. No bar £15
82*c* "Halve Penny" on No. 71 .. £12
82*d* "Halve Penny" on No. 72
82*e* "Halve Penny" on No. 73 .. £12
82*f* "Halve Penny" on No. 74 .. £12
82*g* "Halve Penny" on No. 75 .. £5
ga. No stop £40
gb. No bar £40

Surcharge double.

82*k* "Halve-Penny" on No. 76 .. £30
ka. No bar £40

2½

No. 51 *surch. as above.*

(*a*) *As in illustration.*
(*b*) *With Roman* "1" *and antique* "2" *in fraction.*

83 2½ on 3d. ultramarine (*a*) .. 2 6 2 6
83*a* 2½ on 3d. ultramarine (*b*) .. £8 £6

1897–1900. *T* **1.**

84 ½d. yellow 0 9 1 0
85 ½d. orange 1 0 0 6
87 1s. brown 7 6 6 0

The 6d. blue was prepared for use in the Orange Free State, but had not been brought into use when the stamps were seized in Bloemfontein. A few have been seen without the "V.R.I." overprint, but they were not authorized or available for postage. (*Price £5 un.*)

II. BRITISH OCCUPATION.

V. R. I.

4d

(31)

1900 (March). *The previous issues of Orange Free State surcharged by Messrs. Curling at Bloemfontein, as T* **31**, *in black.*

The 3d. stamps, which had already been surcharged 2½ before they were taken over by the British Government, only had the letters "V.R.I." *overprinted.*

I. First Printings of Each Value with Stops after the Letters on the Line.

101 ½d. orange 1 6 1 0
102 1d. purple 1 3 1 3
103 2d. bright mauve 1 6 1 3
104 2½ on 3d. ultram., var. (*a*) .. 8 6 7 6
105 2½ on 3d. ultram., var. (*b*) .. £10 £10
106 3d. ultramarine 1 6 1 6
107 4d. ultramarine 7 6 6 0
108 6d. bright carmine 90 0 80 0
109 6d. blue 4 0 3 0
110 1s. brown 3 6 3 0
111 5s. green 40 0 35 0

Errors. Stamps of 1868 (*old colours*) *surcharged*

112 1d. brown £12 £1
113 1s. orange-yellow .. .. — £3

Varieties. (i) *No stop after* "V".

114 ½d. orange 25 0 25
115 1d. purple 30 0 30
116 2d. bright mauve 17 6 17
117 2½ on 3d. ultramarine (*a*) .. £5 £
118 3d. ultramarine 20 0 20
119 4d. ultramarine 70 0 70
120 6d. bright carmine .. £20 £2
121 6d. blue 40 0 40
122 1s. brown 50 0 50
123 5s. green £15 £1

(ii.) *No stop after* "R".

124 1d. purple £10
125 2d. bright mauve .. ..

(iii.) *No stop after* "I".

126 ½d. orange .. .. .. £9 £
126*a* 1d. purple .. .. ..
127 2d. bright mauve .. ..

(iv.) *Figure of value omitted.*

128 ½d. orange .. .. .. £12 £
129 1d. purple £10
130 6d. bright carmine .. .. £25 £
131 6d. blue 60 0 70
132 1s. brown .. .. .. £7 £
a. Spaced stop after "s" .. £7
133 5s. green £60

(v.) *Letter* "I" *of* "V.R.I." *omitted.*

134 ½d. orange .. ..
135 1d. purple 70 0 70
a. Stop after "R" omitted .. 90 0 90

There are two varieties of No. 135—one wi raised stop after "R" (and the letters "V.R closer together than in normal overprint), t other (135*a*) without stop after "R".

(vi.) "V.R.I." *omitted.*

136 ½d. orange £15
137 1d. purple £18
138 2d. bright mauve £18
139 6d. blue .. ..
140 1s. brown £12

(vii.) "d" *omitted.*

141 1(d.) purple £22

(viii.) *Value omitted.*

142 (½d.) orange £9
143 (1d.) purple £8
144 (1s.) brown .. .. .. — £

(ix.) *Small "½".*
145 ½d. orange 80 0 80 0

(x.) *Inverted stop after "R."*
146 1d. purple £15
147 5s. green £25

(xi.) *Raised stop after "s."*
148 1s. brown 15 0 15 0

(xii.) *Wider space between figure and letter of value.*
149 1d. purple £10 £10
150 1s. brown £10
151 5s. green £10 £10

(xiii.) *"V" and "R" close.*
152 1d. purple £10

(xiv.) *Surch. double.*
153 ½d. orange 85 0

(xv.) *Surch. omitted.*
154 1d. purple £25
155 3d. ultramarine .. ..

These stamps can only be distinguished when joined to a stamp *with* surcharge. Some values may be found with the overprint shifted up or down, so that the value appears above "V.R.I."; or sideways, showing part of two overprints.

All values of this set are found with a rectangular stop instead of an oval stop after "R" of "V.R.I.".

V. R. I.

½d

32 (Thin "V.")

II. SUBSEQUENT PRINTINGS IN WHICH THE NORMAL TYPE HAS ALL STOPS ABOVE THE LINE, AS SHOWN IN T **32**.

156 ½d. orange 0 4 0 3
157 1d. purple 0 6 0 3
158 2d. bright mauve 0 8 0 6
159 2½ on 3d. ultram., var. (*a*) .. £10 £10
160 2½ on 3d. ultram., var. (*b*) .. £65
161 3d. ultramarine 0 8 1 0
162 4d. ultramarine 3 6 2 6
163 6d. bright carmine 60 0 50 0
164 6d. blue 2 0 1 6
165 1s. brown 2 6 3 0
166 5s. green 7 6 7 6

The shades of the 1d. and 2d. stamps vary considerably in these printings.

Varieties. (i.) *Stops on the line and above the line, mixed.*
167 ½d. orange 3 6 4 0
168 1d. purple 3 6 4 0
169 2d. bright mauve 8 6 12 6
169*a* 2½ on 3d. ultram., var. (*a*)
170 3d. ultramarine 12 6 15 0
171 4d. ultramarine 12 6
172 6d. bright carmine £10 £10
173 6d. blue 12 6 15 0
174 1s. brown 20 0
175 5s. green £22 £22

(ii.) *Stops on the line* (*one stamp on each pane*) *with stamp with stops above the line* (*pair*).
176 ½d. orange 15 0 15 0
177 1d. purple 30 0 30 0
178 2d. bright mauve 17 6 17 6
179 3d. ultramarine 25 0 25 0
180 4d. ultramarine 30 0 30 0
181 6d. bright carmine £15
182 6d. blue 30 0 30 0
183 1s. brown 35 0 35 0
184 5s. green £55

(iii.) *No stop after "V".*
185 ½d. orange 5 0 5 0
186 1d. purple 10 0 10 0
187 3d. ultramarine £15
188 6d. ultramarine .. ..
189 1s. brown .. .. ..

(iv.) *No stop after "R."*
190 1d. purple 20 0 20 0
191 3d. ultramarine .. ..
192 1s. brown .. .. ..

(v.) *No stop after "I."*
193 ½d. orange 50 0 50 0
194 1d. purple 25 0 30 0

(va.) *No stops after "V" and "I".*
194*a* 1d. purple £42

(vi.) *"V" of "V.R.I." omitted.*
195 ½d. orange £22

(vii.) *"I" of "V.R.I." omitted.*
196 3d. ultramarine £25

(viii.) *"s" of value omitted.*
197 1 (s.), brown £6

(ix.) *Surch. all inverted.*
198 1d. purple £18
199 2d. bright mauve £15

(x.) *Surch. double.*
200 1d. purple £6 90 0
201 3d. ultramarine £25
a. Double, one surch. diagonal .. £24
b. Diag. opt. with mixed stops ..

(xi.) *Surch. omitted* (*in pair with normal*).
202 1d. purple .. .. ..

This variety is from the junction of right and left panes, the right pane being without surcharge.

(xii.) *Short "1" in "1d."*
203 1d. purple £8 £7

(xiii.) *Short top to "5"*
204 5s. green £5 £5

(xiv.) *Small "½".*
205 ½d. orange (No. 156) .. 25 0 30 0
206 ½d. orange (No. 167) .. 25 0 30 0
207 ½d. orange (No. 176) ..

(xv.) *Wide space between "V" and "R".*
208 ½d. orange .. .. ..
209 1d. purple £5 £8

(xvi.) *Wide space between "R" and "I".*
210 1d. purple £5

(xvii.) *Wide space between figure and letter of value.*
211 1d. purple £10

(xviii.) *"I" of "V.R.I." raised.*
212 2d. bright mauve .. ..

Error. Stamp of 1868 (*old colour*) *surch. with T* **32.**
213 1s. orange-yellow £30

V. R. I.

½d

33. (Thick "V.")

(xix.) *Thick "V," stops raised* (*T* **33**).
214 ½d. orange 0 6 0 4
215 1d. purple 0 6 0 4
216 2d. bright mauve 1 6 1 6
217 2½ on 3d. ultramarine (*a*) .. £45
218 2½ on 3d. ultramarine (*b*) ..
219 3d. ultramarine 3 6 4 0
220 6d. carmine £30
221 6d. blue 6 0 8 6
222 1s. brown 8 6 10 0
223 5s. green 12 6 12 6

(xix*a*). *Thick "V" and inverted "1" for "I."*
224 1d. purple 25 0 30 0
225 2d. bright mauve 40 0 40 0
226 3d. ultramarine £7 80 0

(xix*b*.) *Thick "V". No stops after "R" and "I".*
227 1d. purple £8 80 0

(xix*c*.) *Thick* "V." *No stop after* "R".

228 1d. purple 65 0 65 0

(xix*d*.) *Thick* "V." *Surch. double.*

229 1d. purple .. .. .. — £18

Stamps with thick "V" occur in certain positions in *later* settings of the type with stops above the line (T **32**). *Earlier* settings with stops above the line have all stamps with thin "V."

Some confusion has hitherto been caused by the listing of certain varieties as though they occurred on stamps with thick "V", whereas they occur in panes of the thick "V" settings, but on stamps showing the normal thin "V".

All varieties which occur on stamps with thin "V" are now shown under that heading, whether they occur in panes of the thick "V" settings or not.

As small blocks of unsurcharged Free State stamps could be handed in for surcharging, varieties thus occur which are not found in the complete settings.

III. BRITISH COLONY.

ORANGE
RIVER
COLONY.

(**34**)

1900–2. *Cape of Good Hope stamps* (*T* **17** *and* **15** *wmk. Cabled Anchor. P* 14) *optd. with T* **34.**

230 ½d. green (Oct. 1900) .. 0 3 0 4
 a. "COLONY" (no stop) .. 12 6 15 0
 b. Opt. double .. .. ..

231 1d. carmine (July, 1902) .. 0 9 0 4
 a. "COLONY" (no stop) .. 20 0 20 0

232 2½d. ultramarine (Aug., 1900) 1 0 1 6
 a. "COLONY" (no stop) .. 40 0 40 0

In the ½d. and 2½d. the "no stop" variety was the first stamp in the left lower pane, in the 1d. the twelfth in the right lower pane. It was corrected in later printings.

4d

(**35**)

1902 (Mar.). *Surch. with T* **35.**

237 4d. on 6d. blue (No. 164) (R.) 1 6 2 0
 a. No stop after "R" .. ..
 b. No stop after "I" .. ..
 c. Thick "V" 2 6 3 6
 d. Thick "V" and inverted "1" for "I" 10 0 12 6

E. R. I.

6d

(**36**)

One Shilling

(**37**)

1902 (Aug.). *Surch. with T* **36.**

242 **1** 6d. blue 4 6 5 0
 a. Surcharge double, one inverted £25
 b. Wide space between "6" and "d" £6 20 0

1902 (Oct.). *Surch. with T* **37.**

243 **1** 1s. on 5s. green, (O.) .. 10 0 12 6
 a. Thick "V" 15 0 17 6
 b. Short top to "5" £8 75 0
 c. Surch. double .. ..

38. King Edward VII, Springbok and Gnu.

(Typo. De La Rue & Co.)

1903–4. *Wmk. Crown CA. P* 14.

247 **38** ½d. yellow-green .. 0 8 0 3
248 „ 1d. scarlet 0 6 0 3
249 „ 2d. brown 4 6 2 6
250 „ 2½d. bright blue 1 6 1 6
251 „ 3d. mauve 3 6 0 8
252 „ 4d. scarlet and sage-green 8 6 4 0
 a. Variety. Flaw on "P" .. £50
253 „ 6d. scarlet and mauve .. 5 0 2 6
254 „ 1s. scarlet and bistre .. 12 6 3 6
255 „ 5s. blue and brown (1904) 75 0 35 0

Several of the above values are found with the overprint "C.S.A.R.", in black, for use by the Central South African Railways.

1905–7. *Wmk. Mult. Crown CA. P* 14.

256 **38** ½d. yellow-green (1907) .. 1 6 0 4
257 „ 1d. scarlet 1 6 0 2
258 „ 4d. scarlet and sage-green 7 6 3 6
 a. Variety. Flaw on "P" .. £12 £10
259 „ 1s. scarlet and bistre .. 60 0 8 6

POSTCARD STAMPS.

Postage stamps of Type **1** (tree), of severa denominations, surcharged or unsurcharged, over printed with Arms similar to above illustratio and in some cases surcharged in addition, were fo use on postcards, the overprinting being don after the stamps were affixed to the cards.

FISCAL STAMPS USED FOR POSTAGE.

F 1

F 2

(Typo. De La Rue.)

1882–86. *P* 14.

F 1	**F 1**	6d. pearl-grey	2 0	7 6
F 2	,,	6d. purple-brown ..	—	7 6
F 3	**F 2**	1s. purple-brown ..	3 0	15 0
F 4	,,	1s. pearl-grey	—	30 0
F 5	,,	1s. 6d. blue	5 0	3 0
F 6	,,	2s. magenta	5 0	3 6
F 7	,,	3s. chestnut	7 6	30 0
F 8	,,	4s. grey		
F 9	,,	5s. rose	7 6	
F10	,,	6s. green	—	30 0
F11	,,	7s. violet		
F12	,,	10s. orange	15 0	
F13	,,	£1 purple	25 0	
F14	,,	£2 red-brown	15 0	
F15	,,	£5 green	40 0	15 0

ZES PENCE.

(F 3)

Surch. with Type F **3**.

F16	**F 2**	6d. on 4s. grey		
F17	,,	6d. on 8s. yellow ..	85 0	

Postage stamps overprinted for use as Telegraph stamps and used postally are omitted as it is impossible to say with certainty which stamps were genuinely used for postal purposes.

Stamps of SOUTH AFRICA are now in use.

PAKISTAN.

PAKISTAN (1) PAKISTAN (2)

1947. *Stamps of India, optd. by offset-litho. at Nasik, as T* **1** (3 *p. to* 12 *a.*) *or* **2** (14 *a. and rupee values*).

1	**100a**	3 p. slate	0 3	0 3
2	,,	½ a. purple	0 3	0 3
3	,,	9 p. green	0 4	0 3
4	,,	1 a. carmine	0 6	0 3
5	**101**	1½ a. dull violet	0 6	0 3
6	,,	2 a. vermilion	0 6	0 3
7	,,	3 a. bright violet ..	0 9	0 4
8	,,	3½ a. bright blue	1 0	2 6
9	**102**	4 a. brown	1 0	0 10
10	,,	6 a. turquoise-green ..	1 6	1 0
11	,,	8 a. slate-violet	1 9	1 0
12	,,	12 a. lake	2 0	1 3
13	**103**	14 a. purple	2 6	3 6
14	**100**	1 r. grey and red-brown	3 6	2 6
		a. Overprint omitted in pair with normal	£125	
		b. Overprint inverted ..	£40	
15	,,	2 r. purple and brown ..	6 0	4 0
16	,,	5 r. green and blue ..	12 6	6 0
17	,,	10 r. purple and claret ..	20 0	10 0
18	,,	15 r. brown and green ..	30 0	30 0
19	,,	25 r. slate-violet & purple	55 0	60 0

Numerous provisional "PAKISTAN" overprints, both hand-stamped and machine-printed, in various sizes and colours, on Postage and Official stamps, also exist.

These were made under authority of Provincial Governments, District Head Postmasters or Local Postmasters and are of considerable philatelic interest.

The 1 a. 3 p. (India, No. 269) exists only as a local issue (*price,* Peshawar opt., 1s. 9d. *un.*, 3s. *us.*).

3. Constituent Assembly Building, Karachi.

4. Karachi Airport Entrance.

5. Gateway to Lahore Fort.

6. Crescent and Stars.

(Des. A. R. Chughtai (1 r.). Recess. De La Rue.)

1948 (9 JULY). *Independence.* *P* 13½×14 *or* 11½ (1 *r.*).

20	**3**	1½ a. ultramarine	0 5	0 4
21	**4**	2½ a. green	0 6	0 6
22	**5**	3 a. purple-brown ..	0 7	0 7
23	**6**	1 r. scarlet	2 6	2 6
		a. Perf. 14×13½	40 0	40 0

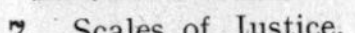

7. Scales of Justice. **8.** Star and Crescent.

9. Lloyds Barrage.

11. Karachi Port Trust.

10. Karachi Airport.

12. Salimullah Hostel, Dacca University.

13. Khyber Pass.

(Recess. Pakistan Security Ptg. Corp., Ltd., Karachi (P 13 and 13½), De La Rue & Co., Ltd. (others).)

1948 (14 Aug.)–**56**?

No.	Type	Description				
24	**7**	3 p. red (p. 12½)	0	3	0	3
		a. Perf. 13½ ('54?) ..	0	3	0	3
25	,,	6 p. violet (p. 12½) ..	0	3	0	3
		a. Perf. 13½ ('54?)	0	3	0	3
26	,,	9 p. green (p. 12½) ..	0	5	0	3
		a. Perf. 13½ ('54?)	0	4	0	3
27	**8**	1 a. blue (p. 12½) ..	0	4	0	3
28	,,	1½ a. grey-green (p. 12½) ..	0	4	0	3
29	,,	2 a. red (p. 12½)	0	6	0	3
30	**9**	2½ a. green (p. 14 × 13½) ..	0	7	0	6
31	**10**	3 a. green (p. 13½ × 14) ..	0	7	0	5
32	**9**	3½ a. brt. blue (p. 14 × 13½)	0	8	0	8
33	,,	4 a. reddish brown (p. 12½)	0	10	0	5
34	**11**	6 a. blue (p. 14 × 13½) ..	1	0	0	6
35	,,	8 a. black (p. 12½) ..	1	6	1	0
36	**10**	10 a. scarlet (p. 13½ × 14) ..	1	10	1	9
37	**11**	12 a. scarlet (p. 14 × 13½) ..	1	9	1	3
38	**12**	1 r. ultram. (p. 13½ × 14) ..	3	6	1	9
		a. Perf. 13½ ('54)	3	0	1	6
39	,,	2 r. chocolate (p. 13½ × 14)	5	0	2	6
		a. Perf. 13½ ('54?)	4	9	2	6
40	,,	5 r. carmine (p. 13½ × 14) ..	17	6	3	0
		a. Perf. 13½ (July '53) ..	13	6	3	6
41	**13**	10 r. magenta (p. 14 × 13½)	35	0	55	0
		a. Perf. 12	50	0	10	0
		b. Perf. 13 ('51)	25	0	7	6
42	,,	15 r. blue-green (p. 12) ..	37	6	15	0
		a. Perf. 14 × 13½	60	0	60	0
		b. Perf. 13 ('56?)	42	6	35	0
43	,,	25 r. violet (p. 14 × 13½) ..	70	0	75	0
		a. Perf. 12	90	0	30	0
		b. Perf. 13 ('54)	60	0	30	0

14

(Recess. De La Rue & Co., Ltd.)

1949 (11 Sept.). *First Anniv. of Death of Mr. Jinnah. T* **14** *and similar type. P* 13½ × 14.

No.	Type	Description				
44	**14**	1½ a. brown	1	6	1	6
45	,,	3 a. green	1	9	1	9
46	–	10 a. black	7	6	7	6

Design:—10 a. Inscription reads "QUAID-I-AZAM/MOHAMMAD ALI JINNAH" etc.

15. Star and Crescent.

16. Karachi Airport.

(Recess. Pakistan Security Ptg. Corp. (P 13½) De La Rue (others).)

1949–53? *Redrawn. Crescent moon with point to left as T* **15/16.**

No.	Type	Description				
47	**15**	1 a. blue (p 12½)	0	3	0	
		a. Perf. 13½ ('53?)	0	3	0	
48	,,	1½ a. grey-green (p. 12½) ..	0	8	0	
		a. Perf. 13½ ('52?)	0	4	0	
49	,,	2 a. red (p. 12½)	0	6	0	
		a. Perf 13½ ('53?)	0	5	0	
50	**16**	3 a. green (p. 13½ × 14) ..	0	8	0	
51	**11**	6 a. blue (p. 14 × 13½) ..	1	6	0	
52	,,	8 a. black (p. 12½) ..	1	3	0	
53	**16**	10 a. scarlet (p. 13½ × 14)	1	8	2	
54	**11**	12 a. scarlet (p. 14 × 13½) ..	2	3	1	

17. Pottery.

I.   II.

18. Aeroplane and Hour-glass.

19. Saracenic Leaf Pattern.

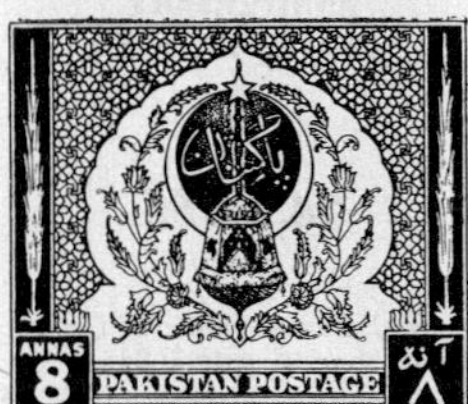

20. Archway and Lamp.

(Des. A. R. Chughtai. Recess. De La Rue, later printings, Pakistan Security Ptg. Corp.)

1951 (14 AUG.)–**56**. *Fourth Anniv. of Independence*. *P* 13.

5	**17**	2½ a. carmine	..	..	0 10	0 10
5	**18**	3 a. purple	..	..	0 8	0 8
7	**17**	3½ a. blue (I)	..	..	2 6	3 0
7a	,,	3½ a. blue (II) (Dec. '56)	..		0 10	1 0
3	**19**	4 a. green	..	..	0 10	0 6
)	,,	6 a. brown-orange		..	1 0	0 9
	20	8 a. sepia ..	..	..	1 6	0 6
	,,	10 a. violet	..	..	1 6	1 6
	18	12 a. slate	..	..	2 3	1 0

21. "Scinde Dawk" stamp and Ancient and Modern Transport.

(Recess. De La Rue.)

1952 (14 AUG.). *Indian Stamp Centenary*. *P* 13.

63	**21**	3 a. deep olive/*yellow-olive*	1 9	3 0
64	,,	12 a. deep brown/*salmon* ..	4 6	3 0

PRINTERS. All the following issues were recess-printed by the Pakistan Security Printing Corporation Ltd., Karachi, unless otherwise stated.

22. Kaghan Valley.

23. Mountains, Gilgit.

24. Badshahi Mosque, Lahore.

25. Mausoleum of Emperor Jehangir, Lahore.

26. Tea Plantation, East Pakistan.

27. Cotton Plants, West Pakistan.

28. Jute Fields and River, East Pakistan.

1954 (14 Aug.). *Seventh Anniv. of Independence. P* 13½ (14 *a.*, 1 *r.*, 2 *r.*) *or* 13 (*others*).

65	**22**	6 p. reddish violet ..	0	6	0	9
66	**23**	9 p. blue	0	8	2	6
67	**24**	1 a. carmine	0	4	0	3
68	**25**	1½ a. red	0	6	0	3
69	**26**	14 a. deep green	2	6	0	3
70	**27**	1 r. green	3	0	1	0
71	**28**	2 r. red-orange	4	6	2	0

29. View of K 2.

1954 (25 Dec.). *Conquest of K* 2 (*Mount Godwin-Austen*). *P* 13.

72	**29**	2 a. deep violet	1	6	1	6

30. Karnaphuli Paper Mill, Type I (Arabic fraction on left). Type II (Arabic fraction on right).

31. Textile Mill, West Pakistan.

32. Jute Mill, East Pakistan.

33. Main Sui Gas Plant.

1955 (14 Aug.)–**56.** *Eighth Anniv. of Indepen-dence. P* 13.

73	**30**	2½ a. scarlet (I)	1	6	2	[illegible]
73*a*	,,	2½ a. scarlet (II) (Dec. '56)	0	9	1	[illegible]
74	**31**	6 a. deep ultramarine ..	1	0	0	[illegible]
75	**32**	8 a. deep reddish violet ..	2	0	0	[illegible]
76	**33**	12 a. carmine and orange ..	2	0	0	[illegible]

TENTH
ANNIVERSARY
UNITED NATIONS

24.10.55.

(34)

1955 (24 Oct.). *Tenth Anniv. of United Nations. Nos.* 68 *and* 76 *optd. with T* **34.**

77	**25**	1½ a. red (B.)	10	0	10	
78	**33**	12 a. carmine & orange (B.)	10	0	10	

A second setting of T **34** exists in which "United Nations" is 1 mm. further to the left.

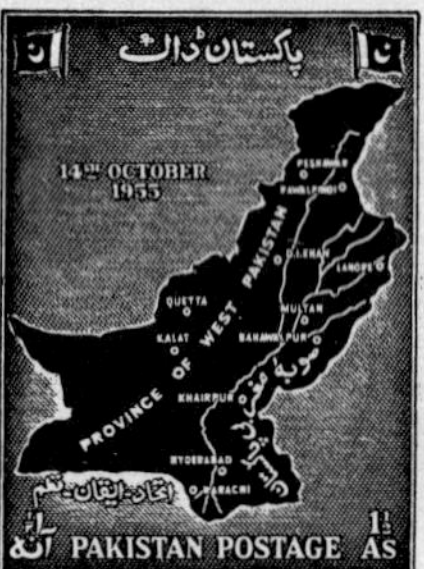

35. Map of West Pakistan.

1955 (7 Dec.). *West Pakistan Unity. P* 13.

79	**35**	1½ a. myrtle-green ..	1	0	1	[illegible]
80	,,	2 a. sepia	1	6	2	[illegible]
81	,,	12 a. deep rose-red ..	3	6	3	[illegible]

36. Constituent Assembly Building, Karachi.

(Litho. De La Rue.)

1956 (23 MAR.). *Republic Day.* *P* 13.

82	**36**	2 a. myrtle-green	0	6	0	6

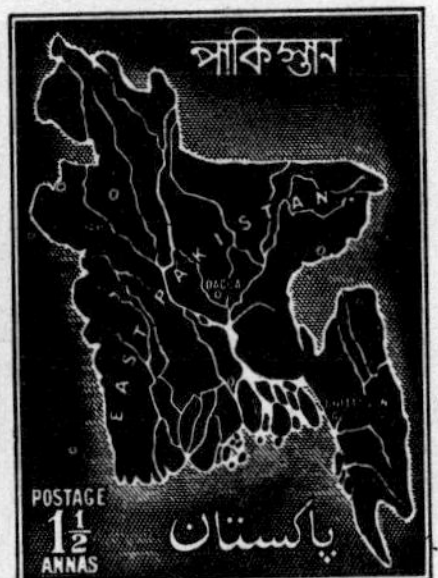

37 **38.** Map of East Pakistan.

1956 (14 AUG.). *Ninth Anniv. of Independence.* *P* 13½.

	37	2 a. scarlet	0	6	0	3

1956 (15 OCT.). *East Pakistan Unity.* *P* 13½.

	38	1½ a. myrtle-green	1	0	1	3
	,,	2 a. sepia	1	0	1	3
	,,	12 a. deep rose-red ..	3	0	3	6

39. Karnaphuli Paper Mill, East Bengal.

40. Pottery.

41. Orange Tree.

1957 (23 MAR.). *First Anniv. of Republic.* *P* 13.

87	**39**	2½ a. scarlet	0	6	0	5
88	**40**	3½ a. blue	0	10	0	9
89	**41**	10 r. myrt.-grn. & yell.-orge.	19	6	10	0

42. Pakistani Flag.

(Litho. De La Rue.)

1957 (10 MAY). *Centenary of Indian Mutiny.* *P* 13.

90	**42**	1½ a. bronze-green	0	9	1	0
91	,,	12 a. light blue	2	6	2	6

43. Pakistani Industries.

(Litho. De La Rue.)

1957 (14 AUG.). *Tenth Anniv. of Independence.* *P* 13½ × 14.

92	**43**	1½ a. ultramarine	0	9	0	9
93	,,	4 a. orange-red	1	3	1	3
94	,,	12 a. mauve	3	0	3	0

44. Coconut Tree.

1958 (23 MAR.). *Second Anniv. of Republic. P* 13.
95 **44** 15 r. red & dp. reddish pur. 30 0 20 0

45

(Photo. Harrison & Sons.)

1958 (21 APR.). *20th Anniv. of Death of Muhammad Iqbal (poet). P* 14½ × 14.
96 **45** 1½ a. yellow-olive & black .. 0 6 0 8
97 ,, 2 a. orange-brown & black 0 9 0 8
98 ,, 14 a. turquoise-blue & black 3 6 2 6

46. U.N. Charter and Globe.

PAKISTAN
BOY SCOUT
2nd NATIONAL
JAMBOREE

CHITTAGONG
Dec. 58—Jan. 59

(47)

1958 (10 DEC.). *Tenth Anniv. of Declaration of Human Rights. P* 13.
99 **46** 1½ a. turquoise-blue .. 0 6 0 6
100 ,, 14 a. sepia 2 6 2 6

1958 (28 DEC.). *Second Pakistan Boy Scouts National Jamboree, Chittagong. Nos.* 65 *and* 75 *optd. with T* **47**.
101 **22** 6 p. reddish violet 0 8 0 8
102 **32** 8 a. deep reddish violet .. 3 0 3 0

REVOLUTION
DAY
Oct. 27, 1959

(48)

49. "Centenary of An Idea".

1959 (27 OCT.). *Revolution Day. No.* 74 *optd. with Type* **48** *in red.*
103 **31** 6 a. deep ultramarine .. 1 6 1 6

1959 (19 NOV.). *Red Cross Commemoration. P* 13. *Recess; cross typo.*
104 **49** 2 a. red and green .. 0 6 0 6
105 ,, 10 a. red and deep blue .. 2 6 2 0

50. Armed Forces Badge.

(Litho. De La Rue.)

1960 (10 JAN.). *Armed Forces Day. P* 13½ × 13.
106 **50** 2 a. red, ultram. & bl.-grn. 0 6 0 6
107 ,, 14 a. red and bright blue .. 2 6 2 6

51. Map of Pakistan.

1960 (23 MAR.). *P* 13 × 13½.
108 **51** 6 p. deep purple 0 3 0
109 ,, 2 a. brown-red 0 6 0
110 ,, 8 a. deep green 1 3 1
111 ,, 1 r. blue 2 3 2

52. Uprooted Tree.

1960 (7 APR.). *World Refugee Year. P* 13.
112 **52** 2 a. rose-carmine .. 0 6 0
113 ,, 10 a. green 2 6 2

53. Punjab Agricultural College.

54. College Arms.

1960 (10 Oct.). *Golden Jubilee of Punjab Agricultural College, Lyallpur.* *P* 12½ × 14.
114 **53** 2 a. slate-blue & carm.-red 0 6 0 6
115 **54** 8 a. bluish green and reddish violet 1 9 1 9

55. "Land Reforms, Rehabilitation and Reconstruction".

(Des. M. H. Hanjra. Photo. De La Rue.)

1960 (27 Oct.). *Revolution Day.* *P* 13 × 13½.
116 **55** 2 a. green, pink & brown 0 6 0 6
117 ,, 14 a. grn., yell. & ultram. 3 0 3 0

56. Caduceus.

57. "Economic Co-operation".

(Photo. De La Rue.)

960 (16 Nov.). *Centenary of King Edward Medical College, Lahore.* *P* 13.
18 **56** 2 a. yellow, blk. & blue 0 6 0 6
19 ,, 14 a. emer., blk. & carmine 2 6 2 6

960 (5 Dec.). *International Chamber of Commerce C.A.F.E.A. Meeting, Karachi.* *P* 13.
20 **57** 14 a. orange-red 2 6 2 6

58. Zam-Zama Gun, Lahore ("Kim's Gun," after Rudyard Kipling).

entre typo., background recess. Pakistan Security Ptg. Corp.).

60 (24 Dec.). *Third Pakistan Boy Scouts National Jamboree, Lahore.* *P* 12½ × 14.
1 **58** 2 a. carmine, yellow & deep bluish green 0 9 0 9

Currency changed. 100 paisa = 1 rupee.

1 PAISA
(59)

urch. by Pakistan Security Ptg. Corp. (Nos. 23/4, 126) or by The Times Press, Karachi others).)

1 (1 Jan.). *Surch. as T* **59**.
1 p. on 1½ a. (No. 68) .. 0 3 0 3
2 p. on 3 p. (No. 24*a*) .. 0 4 0 3

124 3 p. on 6 p. (No. 108) .. 0 6 0 6
125 7 p. on 1 a. (No. 67) .. 0 9 0 9
126 13 p. on 2 a. (No. 109) .. 1 0 1 0
127 13 p. on 2 a. (No. 83) .. 1 0 1 0

ERRORS. Numerous errors exist in the above issue and also in other overprints and surcharges, including the officials. Although genuine errors, most of them were not issued to the public but came on the market by other means.

No. 122. There are two types of surcharge, with figure "1" 2½ mm. or 3 mm. tall respectively. The shorter "1" is dropped slightly below the level of "PAISA".

On the 1 p. with tall "1" and the 13 p. (No. 127), the space between the figures of value and "P" of "PAISA" varies between 1½ mm. and 3 mm.

NOTE. Stamps in the old currency were also *handstamped* with new currency equivalents and issued in various districts but these local issues are outside the scope of this catalogue.

60. Khyber Pass.

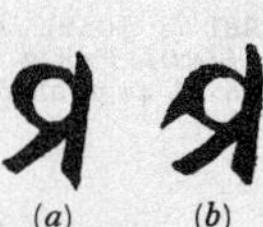

(*a*) (*b*)

61. Shalimar Gardens, Lahore.

62. Chota Sona Masjid (gateway).

Types (a) and (b) show the first letter in the top right-hand inscription; (*a*) wrongly engraved, "SH" (*b*) corrected to "P". On the 3 p. and 10 p. to 90 p. the correction was made to the *die* so that all the stamps are identical, but the other values (Nos. 131/2, 134/5) were corrected individually on the *plate* and each stamp in the sheet is slightly different.

1961–63. *No wmk.* *P* 13 (*T* **62**) *or* 14 (*others*).

(*a*) *Inscribed* "SHAKISTAN" *in Bengali.*
128 **60** 1 p. violet (1.1.61) .. 0 3 0 3
129 ,, 2 p. rose-red (1.1.61) .. 0 3 0 3
130 ,, 5 p. ultramarine (23.3.61) 0 6 0 6

(*b*) *Inscribed* "PAKISTAN" *in Bengali.*
131 **60** 1 p. violet 0 2 0 2
132 ,, 2 p. rose-red 0 3 0 3
133 ,, 3 p. reddish pur. (27.10.61) 0 2 0 2
134 ,, 5 p. ultramarine 0 6 0 6
135 ,, 7 p. emerald (23.3.61) .. 0 6 0 6
136 **61** 10 p. brown (14.8.61) .. 0 6 0 6
137 ,, 13 p. slate-violet (14.8.61) 0 8 0 6
138 ,, 25 p. deep blue (1.1.62) .. 0 10 0 8
139 ,, 40 p. deep purple (1.1.62) .. 1 3 1 0
140 ,, 50 p. deep bluish green (1.1.62) 1 6 1 0
141 ,, 75 p. carmine-red (23.3.62) 2 0 1 6
142 ,, 90 p. yellow-green (1.1.62) 2 6 1 6

143 **62** 1 r. vermilion (7.1.63) .. 3 0 2 0
144 ,, 1 r. 25, reddish vio. (3.62) 3 6 2 6
144*a* ,, 2 r. orange (7.1.63) .. 6 0 3 0
144*b* ,, 5 r. green (7.1.63) .. 13 6 6 6

See also Nos. 170 etc. and Nos. 207/10.

LAHORE STAMP
EXHIBITION
1961

(63)

1961 (12 FEB.). *Lahore Stamp Exhibition. Optd. with T* **63**.
145 **51** 8 a. deep green (R.) .. 2 0 2 0

64. Warsak Dam and Power Station.

1961 (1 JULY). *Completion of Warsak Hydro-Electric Project. P* 12½ × 14.
146 **64** 40 p. black and blue .. 1 6 1 6

65. Narcissus.

1961 (2 OCT.). *Child Welfare Week. P* 14.
147 **65** 13 p. turquoise-blue .. 1 0 1 0
148 ,, 90 p. bright purple .. 2 6 2 6

66. Ten Roses.

1961 (4 NOV.). *Co-operative Day. P* 13.
149 **66** 13 p. rose-red & dp. green 0 9 0 9
150 ,, 90 p. rose-red and blue .. 2 3 2 3

67. Police Crest and " Traffic Control."

(Photo. De La Rue.)

1961 (30 NOV.). *Police Centenary. P* 13.
151 **67** 13 p. silver, black & blue 0 8 0 8
152 ,, 40 p. silver, black & red .. 1 9 1 9

RAILWAY CENTENARY 1861-1961
68. Locomotive " Eagle " of 1861.

RAILWAY CENTENARY 1861-1961
69. Diesel Locomotive.

(Des. M. Thoma. Photo. De La Rue.)

1961 (31 DEC.). *Railway Centenary. P* 14.
153 **68** 13 p. green, blk. & yellow 0 9 1
154 **69** 50 p. yellow, black & grn. 1 9 1

FIRST JET FLIGHT
KARACHI-DACCA
13
Paisa

(70)

1962 (6 FEB.). *First Karachi-Dacca Jet Fligh No. 87 surch. with T* **70**.
155 **39** 13 p. on 2½ a. scarlet (R.) .. 1 3 1

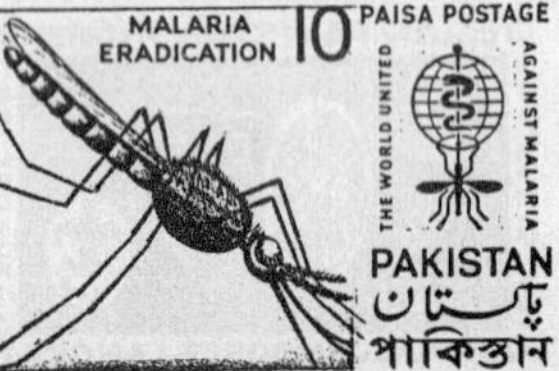

71. Mosquito.

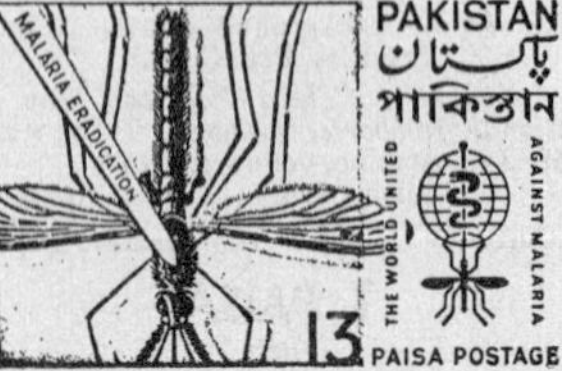

72. Mosquito Pierced by Blade.

(Photo. De La Rue.)

1962 (7 APR.). *Malaria Eradication. P* 14.
156 **71** 10 p. blk., yellow and red 0 8
157 **72** 13 p. blk., grnsh. yell. & red 1 0

73. Pakistan Map and Jasmine.

(Photo. Courvoisier.)

1962 (8 June). *New Constitution.* *P* 12.

158	**73**	40 p. yellow-green, bluish green and grey ..	1 6	1 6

74. Football.

75. Hockey.

76. Squash rackets.

77. Cricket.

2 (14 Aug.). *Sports.* *P* 12½×14.

74	7 p. black and blue ..	0 4	0 4
75	13 p. black and green ..	0 6	0 6
76	25 p. black and purple ..	0 8	0 8
77	40 p. black & orange-brown	1 0	1 0

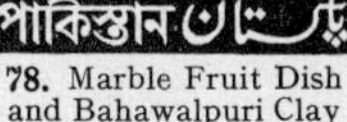

78. Marble Fruit Dish and Bahawalpuri Clay Flask.

79. Sports Equipment.

80. Camel-skin Lamp and Brassware.

81. Wooden Powder-bowl and Basket-work.

82. Inlaid Cigarette-box and Brassware.

1962 (10 Nov.). *Small Industries.* *P* 13.

163	**78**	7 p. brown-lake	0 5	0 5
164	**79**	13 p. deep green	0 8	0 9
165	**80**	25 p. reddish violet ..	1 0	1 0
166	**81**	40 p. yellow-green ..	1 0	1 0
167	**82**	50 p. deep red	1 9	1 9

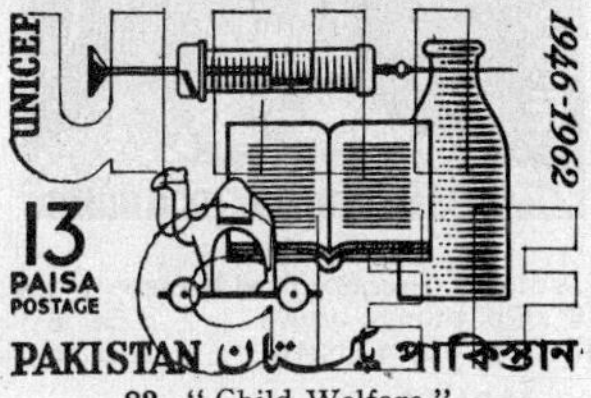

83. " Child Welfare ".

(Des. M. Thoma. Photo. De La Rue & Co.)

1962 (11 Dec.). *16th Anniv. of U.N.I.C.E.F.* *P* 14.

168	**83**	13 p. blk., lt. bl. & maroon	0 7	0 8
169	,,	40 p. blk., yell. & turq.-bl.	1 0	1 0

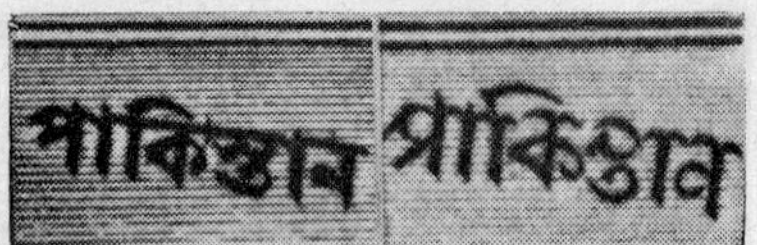

Nos. 170, etc. Nos. 131/42.

1962-65. *As T* **60/1** *but with redrawn Bengali inscription at top right. No wmk.*

170	**60**	1 p. violet ('63)	0 3	0 3
171	,,	2 p. rose-red ('64) ..	0 3	0 3
173	,,	5 p. ultramarine ('63) ..	0 3	0 3
174	,,	7 p. emerald ('64) ..	0 4	0 4
175	**61**	10 p. brown ('63)	0 5	0 5
176	,,	13 p. slate-violet	0 6	0 4
176*a*	,,	15 p. brt. purple (1.1.65)..	0 5	0 3
177	,,	25 p. deep blue ('63) ..	0 9	0 6
178	,,	40 p. deep purple ('64) ..	1 0	0 6
179	,,	50 p. dp. bluish green ('64)	1 3	0 8
180	,,	75 p. carmine-red ('64) ..	2 0	0 8
181	,,	90 p. yellow-green ('64) ..	2 2	0 10

U.N. FORCE W. IRIAN

(**84**)

1963 (15 Feb.). *Pakistan U.N. Force in West Irian. No. 176 optd. with T* **84**.

182	**61**	13 p. slate-violet (R.) ..	0 9	0 9

85. " Dancing " Horse, Camel and Bull.

(Des. S. Jahangir. Photo. Courvoisier.)

1963 (13 Mar.). *National Horse and Cattle Show. P* $11\frac{1}{2}$.

183	**85**	13 p. blue, sepia and cerise	0 8	0 8

86. Wheat and Tractor.

87. Rice.

1963 (21 Mar.). *Freedom from Hunger. P* $12\frac{1}{2} \times 14$.

184	**86**	13 p. orange-brown ..	0 8	0 8
185	**87**	50 p. bistre-brown ..	1 6	1 6

13 PAISA

INTERNATIONAL
DACCA STAMP
EXHIBITION
1963

(**88**)

1963 (23 Mar.). *2nd International Stamp Exhibition, Dacca. Surch. with T* **88**.

186	**51**	13 p. on 2 a. brown-red ..	1 3	1 6

89. Centenary Emblem.

1963 (25 June). *Centenary of Red Cross. Recess; cross typo. P* 13.

187	**89**	40 p. red and deep olive ..	1 0	1 0

90. Paharpur.

91. Mohenjodaro.

92. Taxila.

93. Mainamati.

1963 (16 Sept.). *Archaeological Series. P* 14 × 12½ (13 *p.*) *or* 12½ × 14 (*others*).

188	**90**	7 p. ultramarine	0	3	0	4
189	**91**	13 p. sepia	0	6	0	7
190	**92**	40 p. carmine	1	0	1	1
191	**93**	50 p. deep reddish violet ..	1	3	1	4

100 YEARS OF P.W.D.
OCTOBER, 1963

13
=

(94)

1963 (7 Oct.). *Centenary of Pakistan Public Works Department. No.* 133 *surch. with T* **94.**

192	**60**	13 p. on 3 p. reddish purp.	0	6	0	7

95. Atatürk's Mausoleum.

1963 (10 Nov.). *25th Anniv. of Death of Kamal Atatürk. P* 13½.

193	**95**	50 p. red	1	3	1	3

96. Globe and U.N.E.S.C.O. Emblem.

(Photo. De La Rue.)

963 (10 Dec.). *15th Anniv. of Declaration of Human Rights. P* 14.

94	**96**	50 p. brn., red & ultram...	1	6	1	6

97. Thermal Power Installations.

63 (25 Dec.). *Completion of Multan Thermal Power Station. P* 12½ × 14.

5	**97**	13 p. ultramarine	0	6	0	6

98. Multiple Star and Crescent.

1963–64. *As Nos.* 143/44*b*, *but W* **98.**

207	**62**	1 r. vermilion	2	0	1	3
208	,,	1 r. 25, reddish violet ('64)	2	6	3	6
209	,,	2 r. orange ('64)	4	0	2	6
210	,,	5 r. green ('64)	10	0	10	0

99. Temple of Thot, Queen Nefertari and Maids.

100. Temple of Abu Simbel.

1964 (30 Mar.). *Nubian Monuments Preservation. P* 13 × 13½.

211	**99**	13 p. turq.-blue and red	0	6	0	7
212	**100**	50 p. brt. purple & black	1	3	1	3

101. " Unisphere " and Pakistan Pavilion.

102. Pakistan Pavilion on " Unisphere ".

1964 (22 Apr.). *New York World's Fair. P* 12½ × 14 (13 *p.*) *or* 14 × 12½ (1 *r.* 25).

213 **101** 13 p. ultramarine 0 6 0 8
214 **102** 1 r. 25, ultramarine and red-orange 3 0 3 6

103. Shah Abdul Latif's Mausoleum.

1964 (25 June). *Bicentenary of Death of Shah Abdul Latif of Bhit. P* 13½ × 13.

215 **103** 50 p. bright blue and carmine-lake 1 3 1 3

104. Mausoleum of " Quaid-i-Azam ".

105. Mausoleum.

1964 (11 Sept.). *16th Anniv. of Death of Mr. Jinnah* (" *Quaid-i-Azam* "). *P* 13½ (15 *p.*) *or* 13 (50 *p.*).

216 **104** 15 p. emerald-green .. 0 6 0 7
217 **105** 50 p. bronze-green .. 1 3 1 3

106. Bengali and Urdu Alphabets.

1964 (5 Oct.). " *Universal Children Day* ". *P* 13.

218 **106** 15 p. brown 0 6 0 7

107. University Building.

1964 (21 Dec.). *First Convocation of the West Pakistan University of Engineering and Technology, Lahore. P* 12½ × 14.

219 **107** 15 p. chestnut 0 6 0 7

108. " Help the Blind ".

(Des. A. Chughtai. Litho.)

1965 (28 Feb.). *Blind Welfare. P* 13.

220 **108** 15 p. ultram. & yellow .. 0 6 0

109. I.T.U. Emblem and Symbols.

1965 (17 May). *I.T.U. Centenary. P* 12½ × 1

221 **109** 15 p. reddish purple .. 0 5 0

PROCESS. The following issues were *lith graphed* by the Pakistan Security Printi Corporation Ltd., *unless otherwise stated.*

110. I.C.Y. Emblem.

1965 (16 June). *International Co-operation Year. P* 13×13½.

222 **110** 15 p. black and light blue 0 5 0 6
223 ,, 50 p. green and yellow .. 1 1 1 3

111. " Co-operation ".

12. Globe and Flags of Turkey, Persia and Pakistan.

965 (21 July). *First Anniv. of Regional Development Co-operation Pact. P* 13½×13 (15 *p.*) *or* 13 (50 *p.*).

24 **111** 15 p. multicoloured .. 0 5 0 6
25 **112** 50 p. multicoloured .. 1 1 1 3

113. Soldier and Tanks.

114. Naval Officer and Destroyer.

115. Airman and " F-104 " Starfighters.

1965 (25 Dec.). *Pakistan Armed Forces. P* 13½×13.

226 **113** 7 p. bistre-brown, cinnamon, red & lt. blue 0 3 0 4
227 **114** 15 p. orange-brown, blackish brown, blue and light blue 0 5 0 6
228 **115** 50 p. black, orange-brown, ochre and light blue 1 1 1 3

116. Army, Navy and Air Force Crests.

1966 (13 Feb.). *Armed Forces Day. P* 13½×13.

229 **116** 15 p. royal blue, dull green, bright blue and buff 0 5 0 6

OFFICIAL STAMPS.

PAKISTAN

(O **1**)

1947. *Official stamps of India, Nos.* O143/50, *optd. in black as Type* O **1** *and Nos.* O138/41 *optd. as T* **2** *by offset-litho. at Nasik*

O 1	O **20**	3 p. slate	0	3	0	3
O 2	,,	½ a. purple	0	3	0	3
O 3	,,	9 p. green	0	4	0	3
O 4	,,	1 a. carmine	0	4	0	3
O 5	,,	1½ a. dull violet	0	4	0	3
O 6	,,	2 a. vermilion	0	6	0	3
O 7	,,	2½ a. bright violet ..	0	6	0	3
O 8	,,	4 a. brown	0	8	0	9
O 9	,,	8 a. slate-violet ..	1	3	1	3
O10	**100**	1 r. grey and red-brown	2	6	2	0
O11	,,	2 r. purple and brown	5	0	4	0
O12	,,	5 r. green and blue ..	15	0	15	0
O13	,,	10 r. purple and claret ..	25	0	25	0

See note after No. 19. The 1 a. 3 p. (India,

No. O146*a*) exists only as a local issue (*price*, Peshawar opt., 6s. *un.*, 8s. *us.*).

SERVICE (O 2) **SERVICE** (O 3) **SERVICE** (O 4)

NOTE. Apart from a slight difference in size, Types O 2 and O 3 can easily be distinguished by the difference in the shape of the "c". Type O 4 is taller and thinner in appearance.

PRINTERS. Type O 2 was overprinted by De La Rue and Types O 3 and O 4 by the Pakistan Security Ptg. Corp.

1948 (14 Aug.)–**54**? *Optd. with Type* O 2.

O14 **7** 3 p. red (No. 24) .. 0 3 0 3
O15 „ 6 p. violet (No. 25) (R.) 0 3 0 3
O16 „ 9 p. green (No. 26) (R.) 0 4 0 3
O17 **8** 1 a. blue (No. 27) (R.) .. 0 5 0 3
O18 „ 1½ a. grey-grn. (No. 28) (R.) 0 6 0 3
O19 „ 2 a. red (No. 29) .. 0 8 0 3
O20 **10** 3 a. green (No. 31) .. 0 8 0 4
O21 **9** 4 a. reddish brn. (No. 33) 0 9 0 6
O22 **11** 8 a. black (No. 35) (R.) .. 1 6 0 9
O23 **12** 1 r. ultram. (No. 38) 2 9 1 6
O24 „ 2 r. chocolate (No. 39) .. 5 0 2 6
O25 „ 5 r. carmine (No. 40) .. 11 0 6 0
O26 **13** 10 r. magenta (No. 41) .. 19 6 15 0
a. Perf. 12 (10.10.51) .. 45 0 20 0
b. Perf. 13 ('54?) 22 6 20 0

1949. *Optd. with Type* O 2.

O27 1 a. blue (No. 47) (R.) .. 0 4 0 3
O28 1½ a. grey-grn. (No. 48) (R.) 0 4 0 3
a. Opt. inverted .. .. — £16
O29 2 a. red (No. 49) 0 5 0 3
a. Opt. omitted (in pair with normal) .. .. ..
O30 3 a. green (No. 50) .. 0 7 0 3
O31 8 a. black (No. 52) (R.) .. 1 3 0 9

1951 (14 Aug.). *4th Anniv. of Independence. As Nos.* 56, 58 *and* 60, *but inscr.* "SERVICE" *instead of* "PAKISTAN POSTAGE".

O32 **18** 3 a. purple 0 6 0 3
O33 **19** 4 a. green 0 10 0 4
O34 **20** 8 a. sepia 1 6 0 9

1953. *Optd. with Type* O 3.

O35 3 p. red (No. 24a) .. 0 3 0 3
O36 6 p. violet (No. 25a) (R.) .. 0 3 0 3
O37 9 p. green (No. 26a) (R.) .. 0 4 0 3
O38 1 a. blue (No. 47a) (R.) .. 0 4 0 3
O39 1½ a. grey-grn. (No. 48a) (R.) 0 5 0 3
O40 2 a. red (No. 49a) ('53?) .. 0 6 0 3
O41 1 r. ultramarine (No. 38a) 2 9 1 6
O42 2 r. chocolate (No. 39a) .. 10 0 6 0
O43 5 r. carmine (No. 40a) .. 20 0 10 0
O44 10 r. mag. (No. 41b) (date?)

1954 (14 Aug.). *Seventh Anniv. of Independence. Optd. with Type* O 3.

O45 **22** 6 p. reddish violet (R.) .. 0 4 0 4
O46 **23** 9 p. blue (R.) 0 4 0 4
O47 **24** 1 a. carmine 0 4 0 4
O48 **25** 1½ a. red 0 4 0 4
O49 **26** 14 a. deep green (R.) .. 2 0 1 6
O50 **27** 1 r. green (R.) 2 6 2 0
O51 **28** 2 r. red-orange 5 0 3 6

1955 (14 Aug.). *Eighth Anniv. of Independence. Optd. with Type* O 3.

O52 **32** 8 a. dp. reddish violet (R.) 2 0 2 6

1957 (Jan.)–**59.** *Seventh Anniv. of Independence. Optd. with Type* O 4.

O53 **22** 6 p. reddish violet (R.) .. 0 2 0 2
a. Opt. inverted .. ..
O54 **23** 9 p. blue (R.) (1.59) .. 0 2 0 2
O55 **24** 1 a. carmine 0 3 0 2
a. Opt. inverted .. ..
O56 **25** 1½ a. red 0 4 0 3
O57 **26** 14 a. dp. green (R.) (2.59) 2 0 1 0
O58 **27** 1 r. green (R.) (4.58) .. 2 6 2 0
O59 **28** 2 r. red-orange (4.58) .. 5 0 3 0

1958 (Jan.)–**61.** *Optd. with Type* O 4.

O60 **7** 3 p. red (No. 24a) .. 0 3 0 2
O61 **12** 5 r. carm. (No.40a) (7.59) 10 0 7 6
O62 **41** 10 r. myrtle-green & yell.-orge. (No. 89) (R.) ('61) 22 6 20 0

1958 (Jan.)–**61.** *Eighth Anniv. of Independence. Optd. with Type* O 4.

O63 **31** 6 a. dp. ultram. (R.) (4.61) 1 6 1 6
O64 **32** 8 a. deep reddish violet (R.) 1 3 1 6

1959 (Aug.). *Ninth Anniv. of Independence. Optd. with Type O* 4.

O65 **37** 2 a. scarlet 0 6 0 6

1961 (Apr.). *Nos.* 110/111 *optd. with Type* O 4.

O66 **51** 8 a. deep green 1 9 1 6
O67 „ 1 r. blue 2 6 1 9
a. Opt. inverted £6

1961. *Optd. with Type* O 4.

O68 1 p. on 1½ a. (No. 122) .. 0 2 0 3
O69 2 p. on 3 p. (No. 123)(1.1.61) 0 3 0 3
O70 3 p. on 6 p. (No. 124) .. 0 3 0 4
O71 7 p. on 1 a. (No. 125) .. 0 4 0 4
O72 13 p. on 2 a. (No. 126) .. 0 6 0 6
O73 13 p. on 2 a. (No. 127) .. 0 5 0 5

No. O68 exists with small and large "1" (see note below Nos. 122/7, etc.).

On No. O69 the space between top of "7" and "P" of "PAISA" varies between 1½ mm. and 2¼ mm.

SERVICE
(O 5)

1961–63. *Nos.* 128/44*b optd. with Type* O 4 (*rupee values*) *or* O 5 (*others*).

(*a*) *Inscribed* "SHAKISTAN".

O74 1 p. violet (R.) (1.1.61) .. 0 3 0 3
O75 2 p. rose-red (R.) (12.1.61) 0 3 0 3
O76 5 p. ultram. (R.) (23.3.61) 0 6 0 6

(*b*) *Inscribed* "PAKISTAN".

O77 1 p. violet (R.) 0 2 0 2
O78 2 p. rose-red (R.) 0 2 0 2
O79 3 p. reddish purple (R.) (27.10.61) 0 2 0 2
O80 5 p. ultramarine (R.) .. 0 3 0 2
O81 7 p. emerald (R.) (23.3.61) 0 3 0 3
O82 10 p. brown (R.) (14.2.62) .. 0 4 0 2
a. Opt. inverted .. ..
O83 13 p. slate-vio. (R.) (14.2.61) 0 5 0 4
O85 40 p. deep purple (R.) (1.1.62) 0 11 0 9
O86 50 p. deep bluish green (R.) (1.1.62) .. .. 1 0 1 [illegible]
O87 75 p. carm.-red (R.) (23.3.62) 1 8 1 [illegible]
O88 1 r. vermilion (7.1.63) .. 2 0 1 [illegible]
O89 2 r. orange (7.1.63) .. 4 0 3 [illegible]
O90 5 r. green (R.) (7.1.63) .. 10 0 7 [illegible]

1963–65. *Nos.* 170, *etc., optd. with Type* O 5 *in red.*

O91 1 p. violet 0 1 0
O92 2 p. rose-red ('65) .. 0 1 0
O94 5 p. ultramarine 0 3 0
O96 10 p. brown ('65) 0 4 0
O97 13 p. slate-violet 0 5 0
O98 15 p. bright purple (1.1.65) .. 0 5 0
O99 50 p. dp. bluish green ('65) 1 2 0 1

BAHAWALPUR.

PRINTERS. All the following issues were recess-printed by De La Rue & Co.

1. Amir Muhammad Bahawal Khan I Abbasi.

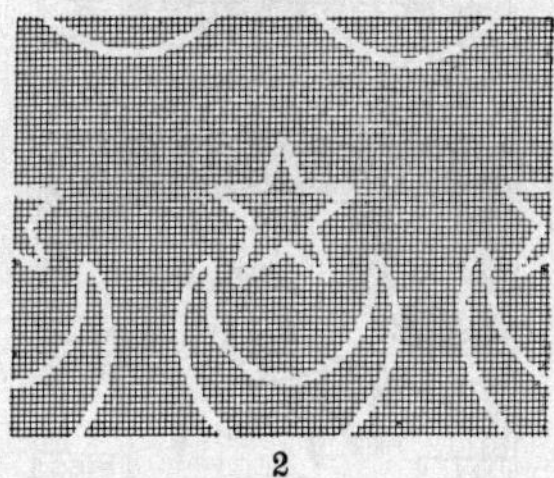

2

948. *Bicentenary Commemoration.* *W* 2 (*sideways*). *P* 12½ × 11½.

1 ½ a. black and carmine .. 4 6

3. H.H. the Ameer of Bahawalpur.

4. The Tombs of the Ameers.

5. Mosque in Sadiq-Garh.

6. Fort Derawar, from the Lake.

7. Nur-Mahal Palace.

8. The Palace, Sadiq-Garh.

9. H.H. the Ameer of Bahawalpur.

10. Three Generations of Rulers; H.H. the Ameer in centre.

1948 (1 APR.). *W* **2** (*sideways on vertical designs*). *P* 12½ (*T* **3**), 11½ × 12½ (*T* **4**, **6**, **7** *and* **8**), 12½ × 11½ (*T* **5** *and* **9**) *or* 13½ × 14 (*T* **10**).

2	**3**	3 p. black and blue	.. 0	6
3	,,	½ a. black and claret	.. 0	6
4	,,	9 p. black and green	.. 0	9
5	,,	1 a. black and carmine	.. 0	9
6	,,	1½ a. black and violet	.. 1	0
7	**4**	2 a. green and carmine	.. 1	6
8	**5**	4 a. orange and brown	.. 2	0
9	**6**	6 a. violet and blue	.. 2	6
10	**7**	8 a. carmine and violet	.. 3	0
11	**8**	12 a. green and carmine	.. 4	6
12	**9**	1 r. violet and brown	.. 5	6
13	,,	2 r. green and claret	.. 10	0
14	,,	5 r. black and violet	.. 25	0
15	**10**	10 r. scarlet and black	.. 40	0

11. H.H. The Ameer of Bahawalpur and Mr. Jinnah.

1948 (3 OCT.). *First Anniversary of Union of Bahawalpur with Pakistan.* *W* **2**. *P* 13.

16 **11** 1½ a. carmine and blue-green 1 0

12. Soldiers of 1848 and 1948.

1948 (15 OCT.). *Multan Campaign Centenary.* *W* **2**. *P* 11½.

17 **12** 1½ a. black and lake .. 1 0

1948. *As Nos.* 12/15, *but colours changed.*

18	**9**	1 r. deep green & orange..	3	6
19	,,	2 r. black and carmine ..	7	6
20	,,	5 r. chocolate and ultram.	20	0
21	**10**	10 r. red-brown and green..	35	0

13. Irrigation.

14. Wheat.

15. Cotton.

16. Sahiwal Bull.

1949 (3 MAR.). *Silver Jubilee of Accession H.H. the Ameer of Bahawalpur.* *W* **2**. *P*

22	**13**	3 p. black and ultramarine	0	2
23	**14**	½ a. black and brn.-orange	0	2
24	**15**	9 p. black and green ..	0	3
25	**16**	1 a. black and carmine ..	0	6

17. U.P.U. Monument, Berne.

1949 (10 Oct.). *75th Anniv. of Universal Postal Union. W* **2**. *P* 13.

26	**17**	9 p. black and green	o	4
		a. Perf. 17½ × 17	o	4
27	,,	1 a. black and magenta	o	6
		a. Perf. 17½ × 17	o	6
28	,,	1½ a. black and orange	o	8
		a. Perf. 17½ × 17	o	8
29	,,	2½ a. black and blue	o	10
		a. Perf. 17½ × 17	o	10

OFFICIAL STAMPS.

O **1**. Panjnad Weir.

O **2**. Camel and Calf.

O **3**. Blackbuck Antelope.

O **4**. Pelicans.

O **5**. Juma Masjid Palace, Fort Derawar.

O **6**. Temple at Pattan Munara.

1945 (1 Jan.). *Various horizontal pictorial designs, with red Arabic opt. W* **2** *P* 14.

O1	O **1**	½ a. black and green	1	0	3	0
O2	O **2**	1 a. black and carmine	3	0	5	0
O3	O **3**	2 a. black and violet	3	6		
O4	O **4**	4 a. black and olive-green	4	0		
O5	O **5**	8 a. black and brown	4	0		
O6	O **6**	1 r. black and orange	5	6		

O **7**. Baggage Camels.

1945 (10 Mar.). *Red Arabic opt. No wmk. P* 14.

O7 O **7** 1 a. black and brown .. £10

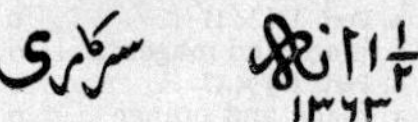

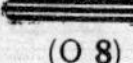
(O **8**)

1945 (Mar.). *Surch. as Type* O **8** *instead of red Arabic opt. No wmk. P* 14.

O11	O **5**	½ a. on 8 a. blk. & pur.	10	0
O12	O **6**	1½ a. on 1 r. blk. & orge.	17	6
O13	O **1**	1½ a. on 2 r. blk. & blue	30	0

SERVICE

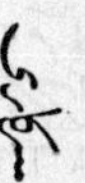
(O **9**)

1945. *Optd. with Type* O **9** *instead of red Arabic opt. No wmk. P* 14.

O14 O **1** ½ a. black and carmine .. 0 3 1 0
O15 O **2** 1 a. black and carmine .. 1 9 3 0
O16 O **3** 2 a. black and orange .. 2 0

O **10.** H.H. the Ameer of Bahawalpur.

1945. *P* 14.

O17 O **10** 3 p. black and blue .. 0 4
O18 ,, 1½ a. black and violet .. 0 9

O **11.** Allied Banners.

(Des. E. Meronti. Recess. Background litho.)

1946 (MAY). *Victory. P* 14.

O19 O **11** 1½ a. green and grey .. 5 0 10 0

1948. *Nos.* 2, 5, 7, 8 *and* 18/21 *optd. as Nos.* O1/6.

O20 **3** 3 p. black and blue (R.) .. 0 2
O21 ,, 1 a. black & carm. (Bk.) 0 4
O22 **4** 2 a. green & carm. (Bk.) 0 6
O23 **5** 4 a. orange & brn. (Bk.) 0 9
O24 **9** 1 r. dp. grn. & orge. (R.) 3 0
O25 ,, 2 r. blk. & carmine (R.) 7 6
O26 ,, 5 r. choc. & ultram. (R.) 15 0
O27 **10** 10 r. red-brn. & grn. (R.) 30 0

1949. *75th Anniv. of Universal Postal Union. Nos.* 26/9 *overprinted as Nos.* O1/6.

O28 **17** 9 p. black and green .. 0 4
a. Perf. 17½ × 17 .. .. 0 4
O29 ,, 1 a. black and magenta .. 0 6
a. Perf. 17½ × 17 .. .. 0 6
O30 ,, 1½ a. black and orange .. 0 8
a. Perf. 17½ × 17 .. .. 0 8
O31 ,, 2½ a. black and blue .. 0 10
a. Perf. 17½ × 17 .. .. 0 10

Only Pakistan stamps are now used in Bahawalpur.

LAS BELA.

1

2

(Litho. Thacker & Co., Bombay.)
Black impression. Pin-perf.

1897–98 *Thick paper*

1 **1** ½ a. on *white* 15 0 12 6

1898–1900.

2 **1** ½ a. on *greyish blue* (1898) .. 10 0 10 0
3 ,, ½ a. on *greenish grey* (1899) .. 10 0 10 0
a. "BFLA" for "BELA" .. 35 0
4 ,, ½ a. on *thin white surfaced paper* (1899) 17 6
5 ,, ½ a. on *slate* (1900) .. ..
a. Imperf. between (pair) .. 40 0

1901–2.

6 **1** ½ a. on *pale grey* 12 6 12 6
a. "BFLA" for "BELA" .. 45 0
7 ,, ½ a. on *pale green* (1902) .. 20 0 22 6
8 **2** 1 a. on *orange* 20 0 22 6

There are at least 14 settings of the above ½ a. stamps, the sheets varying from 16 to 30 stamps.

1904. *Stamps printed wider apart.*

11 **1** ½ a. on *pale blue* 15 0 17 6
a. Imperf. between (pair) .. 45 0
12 ,, ½ a. on *pale green* 15 0 17 6

There are three plates of the above two stamps, each consisting of 18 varieties.

All the coloured papers of the ½ a. show coloured fibres, to a greater or less extent, like what are termed "*granite*" papers.

The stamps of Las Bela have been obsolete since March 1907.

PALESTINE.

OCCUPIED ENEMY TERRITORIES (MILITARY) ADMINISTRATION

1 (2)

(Photo-litho. Typographical Dept., Survey o Egypt, Giza, Cairo.)

1918 (10 FEB.). *Wmk. Royal Cypher in colum (T* **100** *of Great Britain). Ungummed. Roul* 2

1 **1** 1 p. indigo £18 £1
a. Deep blue £16 £1
b. Blue .. .. .. £20 £

Control. A 18. (Prices, corner block of No. 1, £90. No. 1a, £75. No. 1b, £100.)

1918 (16 FEB.). *As last* (*ungummed*), *surch. w T* **2.**

2 **1** 5 m. on 1 p. cobalt-blue .. £9 £
a. Error. "MILLILMES" (No. 10 in sheet) £200

Control. B 18 A. (Corner block, £80

1918 (5 MAR.). *Colour changed. Gummed pap*

3 **1** 1 p. ultramarine 6 0 5

Control. C 18. (Corner block, 90s.)

1918 (5 MAR. *and* 13 MAY.) *No.* 3 *surchar with T* **2.** *Gummed paper.*

4 **1** 5 m. on 1 p. ultramarine .. 18 0 16
a. Error. Arabic surcharge wholly or partly missing (No. 11 in sheet) .. £40

Controls. C 18 B (Mar.). (Corner block, £1
D 18 C (May). (Corner block, £

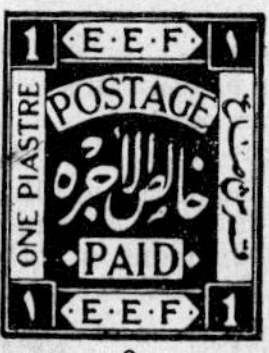

3

(Typo. Stamping Dept, Board of Inland Revenue, Somerset House, London.)

1918 (16 JULY–27 DEC.). *Wmk. Royal Cypher in column.* *P* 15 × 14.

5	**3**	1 m. sepia (16 July) ..	0 9	1 0
		a. Deep brown	1 0	1 0
6	,,	2 m. blue-green (16 July)	1 0	1 0
		a. Deep green	2 0	2 6
7	,,	3 m. yellow-brn. (17 Dec.)	1 9	2 6
		a. Chestnut	40 0	20 0
8	,,	4 m. scarlet (16 July) ..	1 9	2 6
9	,,	5 m. yellow-orge. (25 Sept.)	2 6	1 0
		a. Orange	3 0	2 0
10	,,	1 p. deep indigo (9 Nov.)	2 0	0 8
11	,,	2 p. pale olive (16 July) ..	3 6	4 0
		a. Olive	4 0	4 6
12	,,	5 p. purple (16 July) ..	8 6	9 6
13	,,	9 p. ochre (17 Dec.) ..	14 0	22 6
14	,,	10 p. ultramarine (17 Dec.)	14 0	18 0
15	,,	20 p. pale grey (27 Dec.) ..	30 0	40 0
		a. Slate-grey	50 0	65 0

There are two sizes of the design of this issue:
19 × 23 *mm.* 1, 2, and 4 m., and 2 and 5 p.
18 × 21½ *mm.* 3 and 5 m., and 1, 9, 10 and 20 p.

There are numerous minor plate varieties in this issue, such as stops omitted in "E.E.F.", malformed Arabic characters, etc.

Originally issued by the Military Authorities for use of the civil population in occupied enemy territories (including at one time or another, a large part of Asia Minor), these stamps were used in Palestine until superseded by the following issue. They were demonetised on 1 May, 1922.

CIVIL ADMINISTRATION UNDER BRITISH HIGH COMMISSIONER.

(1 July, 1920.)

فلسطين فلسطين

PALESTINE PALESTINE

פלשתינה א״י פלשתינה א״י

(4) (5)

)ptd. at Greek Orthodox Convent, Jerusalem.)

920 (1 SEPT.). *Optd. with T* **4.** (*Arabic* 8 *mm. long.*) (*a*) *P* 15 × 14.

5	**3**	1 m. sepia	5 0	7 6
7	,,	2 m. blue-green	25 0	10 0
3	,,	3 m. chestnut	12 6	8 6
		a. Error. Overprint inverted ..	£65	£90
	,,	4 m. scarlet	6 0	7 6
	,,	5 m. yellow-orange	20 0	8 0
	,,	1 p. deep indigo (Silver) ..	4 6	2 0
	,,	2 p. deep olive	7 6	9 0
	,,	5 p. deep purple	18 0	40 0
	,,	9 p. ochre	22 6	70 0
	,,	10 p. ultramarine	25 0	75 0
	,,	20 p. pale grey	45 0	110 0

(*b*) *P* 14.

	3	2 m. blue green ..	3 6	5 0
	,,	3 m. chestnut	£5	£7
	,,	5 m. orange	5 0	4 6

Two settings of T **4** are known to specialists, the first being used for all values perf. 15 × 14 except the 1 p. and the second for all values in both perfs.

Apart from minor varieties due to broken type, there are three major errors which are rare in some values. These are (*a*) two Hebrew characters at left transposed (all values of first setting only); (*b*) diamond-shaped dot over the Arabic "t" making the word read "Faleszin" for "Falestin" (2 p. to 20 p. of first setting and 1 m. and 3 m. perf. 15 × 14 and 5 m. perf. 14 of second setting); (*c*) "B" for final "E" of "PALESTINE" (2 p. to 20 p. of first setting and all values of second setting except 3 m. perf. 14).

1920 (22 SEPT.)–**1921** (21 JUNE). *Optd. with T* **5***. (*Arabic* 10 *mm. long.*)

(*a*) *P* 15 × 14.

30	**3**	1 m. sepia	3 6	4 6
31	,,	2 m. blue-green	8 6	12 6
32	,,	3 m. yellow-brown	3 0	3 6
33	,,	4 m. scarlet	4 6	6 0
34	,,	5 m. yellow-orange	4 6	2 0
35	,,	1 p. deep indigo (Silver)	£60	17 6
36	,,	2 p. olive	£7	75 0
37	,,	5 p. deep purple	60 0	16 0

(*b*) *P* 14.

38	**3**	1 m. sepia	£60	£85
39	,,	2 m. blue-green	7 6	12 6
40	,,	4 m. scarlet	£7	£10
41	,,	5 m. orange	£15	50 0
		a. Yellow-orange	6 0	5 6
42	,,	1 p. deep indigo (Silver) ..	65 0	7 6
43	,,	5 p. purple	£25	£45

* In this setting the Arabic and Hebrew characters are badly worn and blunted, the Arabic "s" and "T" are joined (i.e. there is no break in the position indicated by the arrow in our illustration); the letters of "PALESTINE" are often irregular or broken; and the space between the two groups of Hebrew characters varies from 1 mm. to over 1¾ mm.

(*For clear, sharp overprint, see Nos.* 47 *to* 59.)

فلسطين

PALESTINE

פלשתינה א״י

(6)

1920 (6 DEC.). *Optd. with T* **6**, (*Opt. measures* 19 *mm. vertically instead of* 20 *mm. and the word* "PALESTINE" *is only* 6 *mm. from Hebrew.*)

(*a*) *P* 15 × 14.

44	**3**	3 m. yellow-brown ..	£6	£7
44*a*	,,	5 m. yellow-orange ..	—	£1000

(*b*) *P* 14.

45	**3**	1 m. sepia	65 0	90 0
46	,,	5 m. orange	£45	£5

1921 (29 MAY–4 AUG.). *Optd. as T* **5†**.

(*a*) *P* 15 × 14.

47	**3**	1 m. sepia	10 0	6 6
48	,,	2 m. blue-green	15 0	10 0
49	,,	3 m. yellow-brown ..	50 0	8 6
		a. "PALESTINE" omitted ..	£250	
50	,,	4 m. scarlet	35 0	6 0
51	,,	5 m. yellow-orange	50 0	6 0
52	,,	1 p. deep indigo (Silver) ..	45 0	3 0
53	,,	2 p. olive	75 0	25 0
54	,,	5 p. purple	90 0	35 0
55	,,	9 p. ochre	90 0	£18

56 **3** 10 p. ultramarine 85 0 55 0
57 ,, 20 p. pale grey £12 £9

(*b*) *P* 14.

58 **3** 1 m. sepia .. .. .. — £240
59 ,, 20 p. pale grey £1500 £325

†In this setting the Arabic and Hebrew characters are sharp and pointed as in T **6**; there is usually a break between the Arabic "s" and "T" though this is sometimes filled with ink; and the whole overprint is much clearer. The space between the two groups of Hebrew characters is always $1\frac{7}{8}$ m. (*cf. note below* No. 43).

فلسطين

PALESTINE

פלשתינה א״י

(7)

(Overprinted by the Stamping Dept., Board of Inland Revenue, Somerset House, London.)

1921. *Optd. with T* **7** ("PALESTINE" *in sans-serif letters*). *Wmk. Royal Cypher in column. P* 15×14.

60 **3** 1 m. sepia 1 6 1 0
61 ,, 2 m. blue-green 2 0 1 3
62 ,, 3 m. yellow-brown 2 0 1 3
63 ,, 4 m. scarlet 3 6 2 0
64 ,, 5 m. yellow-orange.. .. 3 0 1 0
65 ,, 1 p. bright turquoise-blue .. 4 6 1 0
66 ,, 2 p. olive 7 0 3 0
67 ,, 5 p. deep purple 15 0 17 6
68 ,, 9 p. ochre 37 6 40 0
69 ,, 10 p. ultramarine 70 0 £55
70 ,, 20 p. pale grey £7 £125

فلسطين

PALESTINE

פלשתינה א״י

(8)

(Printed and overprinted by Waterlow & Sons, Ltd., from new plates.)

1922. *T* **3** (*redrawn*), *optd. with T* **8**. *Wmk. Mult. Script CA.* (*a*) *P* 14.

71 **3** 1 m. sepia 2 0 1 0
a. *Deep brown* 3 6 1 0
b. Overprint inverted .. .. — £1000
c. Overprint double.. .. £40 £80
72 ,, 2 m. yellow 3 0 1 0
a. *Orange-yellow* 6 0 2 0
73 ,, 3 m. greenish blue 3 0 1 0
74 ,, 4 m. carmine-pink 3 0 1 0
a. Very thin paper £7 £8
75 ,, 5 m. orange 3 0 0 6
76 ,, 6 m. blue-green 6 0 2 0
77 ,, 7 m. yellow-brown 6 0 1 9
78 ,, 8 m. scarlet 6 0 1 6
79 ,, 13 m. ultramarine 6 6 1 0
80 ,, 1 p. grey 7 0 1 3
81 ,, 2 p. olive 8 6 2 0
a. Overprint inverted .. £60 £90
b. *Ochre* £20 25 0
82 ,, 5 p. deep purple 17 6 4 6
82*a*,, 9 p. ochre £125 £20
83 ,, 10 p. light blue 85 0 20 0
a. "E.F.F." for "E.E.F." in bottom panel £100 £90
84 ,, 20 p. bright violet £18 £15

(*b*) *P* 15×14.

86 **3** 5 p. deep purple £5 15 0
87 **3** 9 p. ochre 50 0 45 0
88 ,, 10 p. light blue 40 0 8 0
a. "E.F.F." for "E.E.F." in bottom panel £70 £70
89 ,, 20 p. bright violet 65 0 40 0

In this issue the design of all denominations is the same size, viz. 18 mm.×$21\frac{1}{2}$ mm. Varieties may be found with one or other of the stops between "E.E.F." missing.

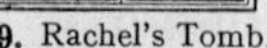

9. Rachel's Tomb.

10. Dome of the Rock.

11. Citadel, Jerusalem.

12. Sea of Galilee.

(Des. F. Taylor. Typo. Harrison & Sons, Ltd.)

1927–45. *Wmk. Mult. Script CA.* *P* $13\frac{1}{2}\times14\frac{1}{2}$ (*2 m. to 20 m.*) *or* 14.

90 **9** 2 m. greenish blue 0 4 0 3
91 ,, 3 m. yellow-green 0 4 0 3
92 **10** 4 m. rose-pink 12 6 4
93 **11** 5 m. orange 0 4 0 2
a. From coils. P$14\frac{1}{2}\times14$('36) 15 0 25
b. *Yellow* (Dec. '44) .. 1 0 1
c. *Yellow*. From coils. Perf. $14\frac{1}{2}\times14$ ('45) .. 27 6 27
94 **10** 6 m. pale green 12 6 6
a. *Deep green* 0 6 0
95 **11** 7 m. scarlet 10 0 2
96 **10** 8 m. yellow-brown .. 30 0 20
97 **9** 10 m. slate . .. 1 3 0
a. *Grey*. From coils. Perf. $14\frac{1}{2}\times14$ (Nov. '38) .. 17 6 25
b. *Grey* ('44) 0 6 0
98 **10** 13 m. ultramarine .. 15 0 1
99 **11** 20 m. dull olive-green .. 1 6 0
a. *Bright olive-green* (Dec. '44) 1 0 0
100 **12** 50 m. deep dull purple .. 4 0 1
a. *Bright pur.* (Dec. '44) .. 3 0 0
101 ,, 90 m. bistre .. .. £8 £
102 ,, 100 m. turquoise-blue .. 6 0 1
103 ,, 200 m. deep violet 12 0 3
a. *Bright violet* (1928) .. 60 0 25
b. *Blackish vio.* (Dec. '44).. 10 0 5

Three sets may be made of the above issu[e] one on thin paper, one on thicker paper with ribbed appearance, and another on thick whi[te] paper without ribbing.

2 m. stamps in the grey colour of the 10 m. a[re] changelings as also are 50 m. stamps in blue.

1932–44. *New values and colours. Wmk. Mu[lt.] Script CA. P* $13\frac{1}{2}\times14\frac{1}{2}$ (*4 m. to 15 m.*) *or* 1[4].

104 **10** 4 m. purple 0 6 0
105 **11** 7 m. deep violet 0 8 0
106 **10** 8 m. scarlet 0 9 0
107 ,, 13 m. bistre 1 6 0
108 ,, 15 m. ultramarine .. 2 6 0
a. *Grey-blue* (Dec. '44) .. 1 6 0
b. *Greenish blue* .. 1 0 0
109 **12** 250 m. brown ('41) .. 7 6 5
110 ,, 500 m. scarlet ('41) .. 15 0 10
111 ,, £P1 black ('41) .. 25 0 12

POSTAL FISCALS.

Type-set stamps inscribed "O.P.D.A." or "H.J.Z."; British 1d. stamps (No. 336); and Palestine stamps overprinted with one or other of the above groups of letters, or with the word "Devair", with or without surcharge of new value, are fiscal stamps. They are known used as postage stamps, alone, or with other stamps to make up the correct rates, and were passed by the postal authorities although they were not definitely authorised for postal use.

POSTAGE DUE STAMPS.

D 1

(Typo. Greek Orthodox Convent, Jerusalem.)

1923. *P* 11.

No.	Type	Description	Unused	Used
D1	D 1	1 m. yellow-brown	17 6	30 0
		a. Imperf. (pair)	£55	
		b. Imperf. btwn. (horiz. pr.)	£125	
D2	,,	2 m. blue-green	15 0	20 0
		a. Imperf.	£75	
D3	,,	4 m. scarlet	18 0	18 0
D4	,,	8 m. mauve	15 0	15 0
		a. Imperf.	£25	
		b. Imperf. btwn. (horiz. pr.)	—	£325
D5	,,	13 m. steel-blue	15 0	15 0
		a. Imperf. btwn. (horiz. pr.)	£125	

Perfectly centred and perforated stamps of this issue are worth considerably more than the above prices, which are for average specimens.

D 2 (MILLIEME).

D 3 (MIL.).

(Types D 2 *and* D 3. Typo. De La Rue & Co.)

924 (1 Dec.). *Wmk. Mult. Script CA. P* 14.

No.	Type	Description	Unused	Used
6	D 2	1 m. deep brown	5 0	6 0
7	,,	2 m. yellow	6 6	7 0
8	,,	4 m. green	6 0	7 0
9	,,	8 m. scarlet	7 0	5 0
10	,,	13 m. ultramarine	10 0	10 0
11	,,	5 p. violet	15 0	12 6

28–40? *Wmk. Mult. Script CA. P* 14.

No.	Type	Description	Unused	Used
12	D 3	1 m. brown	1 3	1 3
		a. Perf. 15×14 ('40?)	65 0	70 0
13	,,	2 m. yellow	1 3	1 3
14	,,	4 m. green	2 0	1 6
		a. Perf. 15×14 ('40?)	50 0	60 0
15	,,	6 m. orange-brown ('33)	4 6	3 6
16	,,	8 m. carmine	2 6	2 6
17	,,	10 m. pale grey	3 0	3 0
18	,,	13 m. ultramarine	4 6	5 0
19	,,	20 m. pale olive-green	5 0	5 0
20	,,	50 m. violet	6 0	5 0

The British Mandate terminated on 14 May, 48. For later issues of stamps and occupation ues see under Israel, Jordan and Egypt in rt III of the Stanley Gibbons Catalogue.

PAPUA.

(BRITISH NEW GUINEA.)

— SIMPLIFICATION (see INTRODUCTION) —

Nos. 1 to 46.
9, 10, 3, 12, 5, 14, 7, 8.
30, 31, 32, 27, 28, 24, 25, 26.
40, 41, 42, 38, 43, 44, 45, 46.

Later Issues.
Omit dies, perfs. and shades.

1. Lakatoi (native canoe) with Hanuabada village in the background.

2. (Horizontal.)

(Recess. De La Rue.)

1901–5. *T* **1**. *Wmk. Mult. Rosettes, T* **2**. *P* 14.

No.	Description	Unused	Used
	I. *Thick paper. Wmk. horizontal.*		
1	½d. black and yellow-green	8 6	10 0
2	1d. black and carmine	3 6	5 0
3	2d. black and violet	6 0	5 0
4	2½d. black and ultramarine	16 0	20 0
5	4d. black and sepia	30 0	25 0
6	6d. black and myrtle-green	25 0	30 0
7	1s. black and orange	40 0	50 0
8	2s. 6d. black and brown	£20	£20
	II. *Thick paper. Wmk. vertical.*		
9	½d. black and yellow-green	2 6	3 6
10	1d. black and carmine	2 6	3 0
11	2d. black and violet	4 6	5 0
12	2½d. black and ultramarine	12 6	17 6
13	4d. black and sepia	30 0	42 6
14	6d. black and myrtle-green	27 6	35 0
14*a*	1s. black and orange	40 0	60 0
14*b*	2s. 6d. black and brown	£28	£30
	III. *Thin paper. Wmk. horizontal.*		
14*c*	½d. black and yellow-green	85 0	95 0
14*d*	2½d. black and ultramarine	£8	£6
14*e*	2½d. black and dull blue	£8	£6
	IV. *Thin paper. Wmk. vertical.*		
15	½d. black and yellow-green	6 6	8 6
16	1d. black and carmine	45 0	55 0
17	2d. black and violet	30 0	20 0
18	2½d. black and ultramarine	£8	£6
18*a*	2½d. black and dull blue	£8	£8
19	4d. black and sepia	£5	£6
20	6d. black and myrtle-green	£15	£16
21	1s. black and orange	£15	£16
22	2s. 6d. black and brown	£28	£30

The 20th stamp in sheets of the ½d., 2d., and 2½d. shows a variety known as "white leaves", while stamp No. 27 of the 2d. and 2½d. and No. 28 of the ½d. and 1s. show what is known as the "unshaded leaves" variety.

Papua.
(3)

1906-7. *T* **1** *optd. P* 14. A. *With T* **3** (*large opt.*), *at Port Moresby* (8 Nov., 1906).

I. *Thick paper. Wmk. horizontal.*

No.	Description	Unused	Used
23	4d. black and sepia ..	£12	£12
24	6d. black and myrtle-green ..	20 0	30 0
25	1s. black and orange ..	17 6	20 0
26	2s. 6d. black and brown ..	£8	£10

II. *Thick paper. Wmk. vertical.*

No.	Description	Unused	Used
27	2½d. black and ultramarine ..	7 6	12 6
28	4d. black and sepia ..	£10	£10
29	6d. black and myrtle-green ..	22 6	35 0
29*a*	1s. black and orange ..	£12	£12
29*b*	2s. 6d. black and brown ..	£55	

III. *Thin paper. Wmk. vertical.*

No.	Description	Unused	Used
30	½d. black and yellow-green ..	6 0	7 6
31	1d. black and carmine ..	10 0	10 6
32	2d. black and violet ..	6 0	5 0

Papua.
(4)

B. *With T* **4** (*small opt.*), *at Brisbane* (MAY/JUNE, 1907).

I. *Thick paper. Wmk. horizontal.*

No.	Description	Unused	Used
34	½d. black and yellow-green ..	50 0	65 0
35	2½d. black and dull blue ..	85 0	85 0
36	1s. black and orange ..	75 0	85 0
37	2s. 6d black and brown ..	40 0	50 0
	a. Opt. reading downwards (pair)	£70	
	b. Double opt. reading downwards	£110	
	c. Opt. triple (horiz.)	—	£30

II. *Thick paper. Wmk. vertical.*

No.	Description	Unused	Used
38	2½d. black and ultramarine ..	6 0	7 6
	a. Opt. double		
38*b*	1s. black and orange ..	35 0	37 6
38*c*	2s. 6d. black and brown ..	£50	

III. *Thin paper. Wmk. horizontal.*

No.	Description	Unused	Used
38*d*	½d. black and yellow-green ..	70 0	75 0
39	2½d. black and ultramarine ..	15 0	25 0
	a. Opt. double		
39*b*	2½d. black and dull blue ..	60 0	70 0

IV. *Thin paper. Wmk. vertical.*

No.	Description	Unused	Used
40	½d. black and yellow-green	3 6	6 0
	a. Opt. double	£50	
41	1d. black and carmine ..	4 0	6 0
	a. Opt. reading upwards (pair) ..	£40	£40
42	2d. black and violet ..	4 0	3 0
43	4d. black and sepia ..	17 6	20 0
44	6d. black and myrtle-green ..	15 0	30 0
	a. Opt. double	£40	£50
45	1s. black and orange ..	27 6	32 6
	a. Opt. double		
46	2s. 6d. black and brown ..	25 0	32 6

In the setting of this overprint Nos. 10, 16, and 21 have the " p " of " Papua " with a defective foot or inverted " d " for " p ", and in No. 17 the " pua " of " Papua " is a shade lower than the first " a ".

PRINTERS. All the following issues were printed at Melbourne. See notes at beginning of Australia.

5

(Litho., Melbourne.)

1907-10. *T* **5** (*small* " PAPUA ").
I. *Wmk. Crown over A. Type* w. **11** *upright.*

(*a*) *P* 11.

No.	Description	Unused	Used
52	1d. blk. & rose (June, 1908)	3 0	4 0
53	2d. blk. & purple (Oct., 1908)	5 0	6 6
54	2½d. blk. & brt. ultra.(July,'08)	17 6	20 0
55	2½d. blk. & pale ultramarine	5 0	6 0
56	4d. blk. & sepia (Nov., 1907)	4 0	5 0
57	6d. black & myrtle-green (April, 1908)	12 6	15 0
58	1s. blk. & orge. (Oct., 1908)	12 6	15 0

(*b*) *P* 12½.

No.	Description	Unused	Used
59	2d. blk. & purple (Oct., 1908)	5 0	5 0
59*a*	2½d. blk. & brt. ultramarine	20 0	35 0
60	2½d. blk. & pale ultram. (7.08)	18 0	35 0
61	4d. blk. & sepia (Nov., 1907)	7 6	7 6
63	1s. blk. & orge. (Jan., 1909)	60 0	70 0

II. *Wmk. sideways.* (*a*) *P* 11.

No.	Description	Unused	Used
64	½d. black & yellow-green ..	2 6	3 6
64*a*	½d. black & deep green ..	25 0	30 0
65	1d. blk. & carm. (Jan., 1910)	10 0	4 0
66	2d. blk. & purple (Feb., 1910)	4 0	4 0
68	2½d. blk.& dull blue (Jan.,1910)	5 0	5 0
69	4d. black & sepia (Jan., 1910)	5 0	5 0
70	6d. black & myrtle-green (Dec., 1909)	17 6	10 0
71	1s. blk. & orange (Mar., 1910)	30 0	35 0

(*b*) *P* 12½.

No.	Description	Unused	Used
72	½d. blk.& yell.-grn.(Dec.,1909)	1 6	2 6
73	½d. blk. & deep green (1910)	25 0	22 6
74	1d. blk. & carmine(Dec.,1909)	6 6	5 0
75	2d. blk. & purple (Jan., 1910)	3 0	3 0
76	2½d. black & dull blue ..	8 6	10 0
77	2½d. black & ultramarine ..	35 0	42 6
78	6d. black and myrtle-green ..	£55	£45
79	1s. black & orange	10 0	10 0

(*c*) *P* 11 × 12½.

No.	Description	Unused	Used
79*a*	½d. black & yellow-green ..		
80	2d. black & purple	£30	
80*a*	4d. black & sepia		

There is a variety of this type showing a white line or " rift " in the clouds, which occurs on the twenty-third stamp of the sheet. Many of these can be supplied at four times the normal price.

The varieties showing white leaves are also to be found in the case of those values where they occurred in the original plate.

7

Type I.

Type II.

1907-10. *T* 7 (*large* " PAPUA ").

I. *Wmk. upright.* (*a*) *P* 11.

No.	Description	Unused	Used
81	½d. blk. & yellow-grn. (1907)	2 0	2

(*b*) *P* 12½ (1910).

No.	Description	Unused	Used
82	½d. black and green	2 0	2
83	1d. black and carmine ..	3 6	3
84	2d. black and dull purple ..	4 0	3
	a. " C " for " O " in " POSTAGE "	40 0	45
85	2½d. black and blue-violet ..	5 0	6
86	4d. black and sepia	5 0	6
87	6d. black and myrtle-green ..	6 6	6
88	1s. black and deep orange ..	8 6	10

89 2s. 6d. blk. & brown (Type I) 45 0 50 0
90 2s. 6d. blk. & brown (Type II) 25 0 30 0

II. *Wmk. sideways. P* 11.

91 2s. 6d. black and chocolate (Type III) ('08) 45 0 50 0

The three types of the 2s. 6d. (Nos. 89, 90 and 91) can be distinguished by the shape of the numerals and the thickness of the dividing stroke between them, that of Type I being thicker and more uneven, whilst that of Type II is very thin and sharp. In Type III (No. 91 distinguishable also by wmk. and perf.) the numerals are very thin. Type II is a transfer from the original engraved plate, while in Types I and III the figures of value were redrawn.

8

(Typo. J. B. Cooke.)

1911–15. *W* **8** *sideways.* (*a*) *P* 12½. (1911).

93 **5** ½d. yellow-green .. 2 0 3 0
93*a* „ ½d. green 2 0 2 0
94 „ 1d. rose-pink 3 0 2 0
95 „ 2d. bright mauve .. 3 0 3 6
96 „ 2½d. bright ultramarine .. 8 6 10 0
96*a* „ 2½d. dull ultramarine .. 8 6 10 0
97 „ 4d. pale olive-green .. 10 0 10 0
98 „ 6d. orange-brown .. 7 6 7 6
99 „ 1s. yellow 15 0 20 0
100 „ 2s. 6d. rose-carmine .. 35 0 42 6

(*b*) *P* 14. (June, 1915.)

101 **5** 1d. rose-pink 25 0 20 0
102 „ 1d. pale scarlet 7 6 6 0

1916. *Typo. Colour changed, and new values. W* **8** *sideways. P* 14.

103 **5** 1d. black and carmine-red.. 3 6 1 0
104 „ 3d. blk. & brt. blue-green .. 3 0 3 6
105 „ 5s. black and deep green .. 40 0 50 0

ONE PENNY

(9)

(Surch. at Port Moresby.)

1917. *Nos.* 93/100 *surch. with T* **9.**

106 1d. on ½d. yellow-green .. 2 0 2 6
106*a* 1d. on ½d. green 2 0 2 6
107 1d. on 2d. bright mauve .. 8 6 10 0
108 1d. on 2½d. ultramarine .. 5 0 6 0
109 1d. on 4d. pale olive-green 5 0 6 0
110 1d. on 6d. orange-brown .. 17 6 20 0
111 1d. on 2s. 6d. rose-carmine 6 6 7 6

Typo. T. S. Harrison, A. J. Mullett, or J. Ash.)

.919 (MAR.)–**1931.** *T* **5.** *W* **8** *sideways. P* 14.

12 ½d. myrtle and apple-green 0 9 1 0
13 1d. black and red 2 6 1 0
13*a* 1½d. pale ultram. & brn. ('25) 2 0 1 0
b. "POSTACE" for "POSTAGE" at right 17 6 17 6
14 2d. chocolate and purple .. 4 0 2 6
14*a* 2d. chocolate & lake-red ('31) 20 0 4 6
14*b* 2d. chocolate and claret ('31) 6 0 2 6
15 2½d. myrtle and ultramarine 6 0 10 0
16 4d. brown and orange .. 5 0 6 0
16*a* 5d. bluish slate and pale brown ('31) 6 0 7 6
16*b* 6d. dull and bright purple .. 5 0 7 6
c. "POSTACE" for "POSTAGE" at left 45 0
17 1s. sepia and olive-green .. 7 6 8 6
18 2s. 6d. maroon & bright pink (*Ash*) 25 0 30 0
118*a* 2s. 6d. maroon and pale pink (*Harrison*) 25 0 35 0
119 10s. grn. & pale ultram. ('25) £7 £9

Ash printings in the above and subsequent issues, where not otherwise described, can often, but not always, be distinguished from others by the white paper on which they are printed.

AIR MAIL

(10)

1929–30. *Air. T* **5** *optd. with T* **10.** *W* **8.** *P* 14.

(*a*) *Ash printing. White paper.*

120 3d. black & bright blue-green 6 0 7 6
a. Opt. omitted in horiz. pair with normal £250
b. Ditto. but vertical pair .. £150
c. Opt. vertical, on back .. £150
d. Opts. tête-bêche (pair) .. £100

(*b*) *Cooke printing. Yellowish paper.*

120*e* 3d. black & bright blue-green 6 0 10 0
f. Opt. omitted in vert. pair with normal £150

(*c*) *Harrison printing. Yellowish paper.*

120*g* 3d. sepia-black & brt. bl.-grn. 85 0 £5

(11)

1930 (15 SEPT.). *Air. T* **5** *optd. with T* **11,** *in carmine.*

121 3d. black & blue-green (*Ash*) 2 6 3 0
a. Harrison printing, yellowish paper £25
ab. Opt. double £120 £125
122 6d. dull & bright pur. (*Ash*) 8 0 12 6
a. "POSTACE" for "POSTAGE" at left (*Ash*) .. 70 0
b. Harrison printing, yellowish paper 12 6 17 6
ba. Ditto, "POSTACE" error .. 70 0
123 1s. sepia & olive-green (*Ash*) 10 0 15 0
a. Harrison printing, yellowish paper 35 0 50 0
ab. Overprint inverted £150

TWO PENCE

(12)

1931 (1 JAN.). *T* **5** *surch. with T* **12.**

124 2d. on 1½d. ult. & brn. (*Ash*) 3 6 3 6
a. "POSTACE" for "POSTAGE" at right 45 0
b. Mullett printing 12 6
c. "POSTACE" error (*Mullett*).. £5

The scarcer Mullett printing (No. 124*b*), is distinguishable by its lighter shades—the centre being a very pale ultramarine, and the frame a paler brown.

5d.

FIVE PENCE

(13)

1931. *T* **5** *surch. as T* **13** (*variously spaced*). *W* **8.**

125 5d. on 1s. sepia & olive-green (*Ash*) (26.7) 3 0 6 0
126 9d. on 2s. 6d. maroon & pink (*Ash*) 8 6 10 0
a. Harrison printing, yellowish paper (Dec.) 7 6 10 0
127 1s. 3d. on 5s. black and deep green (*Cooke*) 8 6 12 6

14
(Typo. J. Ash.)

1932. *T* **5.** *W* **14.** *P* 11.

128	9d. lilac and violet	7	6	10	0
129	1s. 3d. lilac & pale greenish bl.	12	6	15	0

15. Motuan Girl.

16. A Chieftain's Son.

17. Tree-Houses.

19. Papuan Dandy.

18. Bird of Paradise.

20. Native Mother and Child.

21. Masked Dancer.

22. Papuan Motherhood.

23. Papuan Shooting Fish.

24. *Dubu*—or Ceremonial Platform.

25. Lakatoi.

26. Papuan Art.

27. Pottery Making.

28. Native Policeman.

29. Lighting a Fire.

30. Delta House.

(Des. F. E. Williams (2s., £1 and frames of other values), E. Whitehouse (2d., 4d., 6d., 1s., and 10s.); remaining centres from photos by Messrs. F. E. Williams and Gibson. Recess. J. Ash (all values) and W. C. G. McCracken (½d., 1d., 2d., 4d.).)

1932 (14 Nov.). *No wmk.* P 11.

No.	Type	Description	Unused	Used
130	**15**	½d. black and orange	1 0	1 0
131	**16**	1d. black and green	0 6	0 6
132	**17**	1½d. black and lake	1 6	2 0
133	**18**	2d. red	5 0	1 0
134	**19**	3d. black and blue	2 6	3 0
135	**20**	4d. olive-green	5 0	5 0
136	**21**	5d. black and slate-green	4 0	4 0
137	**22**	6d. bistre-brown	6 0	6 0
138	**23**	9d. black and violet	7 6	7 6
139	**24**	1s. dull blue-green	7 6	7 6
140	**25**	1s. 3d. black & dull purple	15 0	17 6
141	**26**	2s. black and slate-green	12 6	20 0
142	**27**	2s. 6d. black & rose-mve.	22 6	35 0
143	**28**	5s. black and olive-brown	45 0	45 0
144	**29**	10s. violet	£5	£6
145	**30**	£1 black and olive-grey	£12	£8

31. Hoisting the Union Jack.

32. Scene on H.M.S. *Nelson*.

(Recess. J. Ash.)

1934 (6 Nov.). *50th Anniv. of Declaration of British Protectorate.* P 11.

No.	Type	Description	Unused	Used
146	**31**	1d. green	3 0	4 0
147	**32**	2d. scarlet	5 0	5 0
148	**31**	3d. blue	10 0	10 6
149	**32**	5d. purple	18 6	25 0

HIS MAJESTY'S JUBILEE

1910 1935

(33)

HIS MAJESTY'S
JUBILEE.
1910 — 1935

(34)

1935 (9 July). *Silver Jubilee. Optd. with T 33 or 34* (*2d.*).

No.	Type	Description	Unused	Used
150	**16**	1d. black and green	0 8	1 0
151	**18**	2d. scarlet	1 9	2 6
152	**19**	3d. black and blue	5 0	6 0
153	**21**	5d. black and slate-green	10 0	15 0

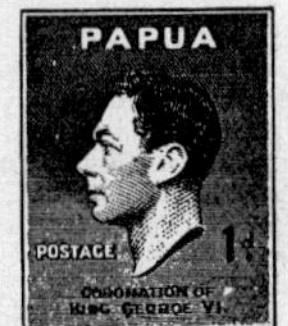

35

(Recess. J. Ash.)

1937 (14 May). *Coronation.* P 11.

No.	Type	Description	Unused	Used
154	**35**	1d. green	0 3	0 6
155	„	2d. scarlet	0 5	1 0
156	„	3d. blue	0 8	1 9
157	„	5d. purple	0 10	2 0

36. Port Moresby.

(Recess. J. Ash.)

1938 (6 Sept.). *Air. 50th Anniv. of Declaration of British Possession.* P 11.

No.	Type	Description	Unused	Used
158	**36**	2d. rose-red	3 6	5 0
159	„	3d. bright blue	6 0	8 6
160	„	5d. green	7 6	8 6
161	„	8d. brown-lake	12 6	16 6
162	„	1s. mauve	15 0	18 6

37. Native Poling Rafts.

(Recess. J. Ash.)

1939 (6 Sept.). *Air.* P 11.

No.	Type	Description	Unused	Used
163	**37**	2d. rose-red	1 9	2 0
164	„	3d. bright blue	2 6	2 6
165	„	5d. green	5 0	5 0
166	„	8d. brown-lake	6 6	6 6
167	„	1s. mauve	10 0	10 0

(Recess. W. C. G. McCracken.)

1941 (2 Jan.). *Air.* P 11½.

No.	Type	Description	Unused	Used
168	**37**	1s. 6d. olive-green	27 6	40 0

OFFICIAL STAMPS.

Stamps Perforated "O S."

We have a number of these in stock with the initials perforated through the stamps. We do not catalogue such varieties, but can send selections to collectors who are interested in them. In most cases the prices are those of used copies of the corresponding number in Catalogue.

O S

(O 1)

(Typo. by T. S. Harrison (1d. and 2s. 6d.) and J. Ash.)

1931 (29 July). *T* **5** *optd. with T* O **1**. *W* **8**. *P*14.

O 1	½d. myrtle and pale olive ..	1	0	2	0
O 2	1d. black and red	1	0	3	0
O 3	1½d. pale ultramarine & brown	3	0	5	0
	a. "POSTACE" at right ..	35	0	45	0
O 4	2d. chocolate and claret ..	4	0	5	0
O 5	3d. black and blue-green ..	4	0	6	0
O 6	4d. brown and orange ..	5	0	7	0
O 7	5d. bluish slate & pale brown	6	0	8	0
O 8	6d. dull and bright purple ..	8	6	12	6
	a. "POSTACE" at left ..	40	0	50	0
O 9	1s. sepia and olive-green ..	10	0	15	0
O10	2s. 6d. marone & pink (*Ash*)	17	6	50	0
	a. Harrison printing	20	0	45	0

1932. *T* **5** *optd. with Type* O **1**. *W* **14**. *P* 11.

O11	9d. lilac and violet	10	0	17	6
O12	1s. 3d. lilac & pl. grnsh. blue	15	0	22	6

Civil Administration, in Papua, was suspended in 1942; on resumption, after the Japanese defeat in 1945, Australian stamps were used until the appearance of the issue of the combined territories of Papua & New Guinea (*q.v.*).

PAPUA AND NEW GUINEA.

1. Tree Kangaroo.

2. Buka Head-dresses.

3. Native Youth.

4. Bird of Paradise.

5. Native Policeman.

6. Papuan Head-dress.

7. Kiriwina Chief House.

8. Kiriwina Yam House.

9. Copra Making.

10. Lakatoi.

11. Rubber Tapping.

12. Sepik Dancing Masks.

13. Native Shepherd and Flock.

14. Map of Papua and New Guinea.

15. Native Shooting Fish.

(Recess. Note Printing Branch, Commonwealth Bank, Melbourne.)

1952 (30 Oct.)–**58.** *P* 14.

1	**1**	½d. emerald	0	9	0	9
2	**2**	1d. deep brown	0	9	0	9
3	**3**	2d. blue	1	6	0	9
4	**4**	2½d. orange	4	6	6	6
5	**5**	3d. deep green	2	0	1	0
6	**6**	3½d. carmine-red	2	6	1	9
6*a*	,,	3½d. black (2.6.58)	6	6	8	6
7	**7**	6½d. dull purple (*shades*)	3	6	3	6
8	**8**	7½d. blue	15	0	20	0
9	**9**	9d. brown	7	6	7	6
10	**10**	1s. yellow-green	7	6	5	0
11	**11**	1s. 6d. deep green	11	6	8	6
12	**12**	2s. indigo	15	0	12	6
13	**13**	2s. 6d. brown-purple	20	0	16	0
14	**14**	10s. blue-black	£5		75	0
15	**15**	£1 deep brown	£7		110	0

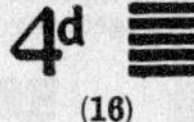

(16)

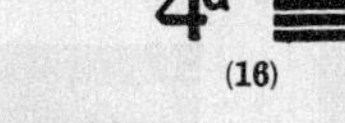

(17)

1957 (29 Jan.). *Surch. with T* **16** *and T* **17.**

16	**4**	4d. on 2½d. orange	2	6	3	6
17	**10**	7d. on 1s. yellow-green	5	0	6	0

18. Cacao Plant.

19. Klinki Plymill.

20. Cattle.

21. Coffee Beans.

(Recess. Note Ptg. Branch, Commonwealth Bank, Melbourne.)

1958 (2 June)–**60.** *P* 14.

18	**18**	4d. vermilion	2	0	2	0
19	,,	5d. green (10.11.60)	2	6	2	6
20	**19**	7d. bronze-green	12	6	12	6
21	,,	8d. dp. ultramarine (10.11.60)	35	0	40	0
22	**20**	1s. 7d. red-brown	£6		£7	
23	,,	2s. 5d. vermilion (10.11.60)	55	0	65	0
24	**21**	5s. crimson and olive-green	35	0	35	0

(22)

1959 (1 Dec.). *No.* 1 *surch. with T* **22.**

25	**1**	5d. on ½d. emerald	3	0	3	0

23. Council Chamber, Port Moresby.

(Photo. Harrison & Sons.)

1961 (10 Apr.). *Reconstitution of Legislative Council. P* 15 × 14.

26 **23** 5d. deep green and yellow .. 15 0 20 0
27 ,, 2s. 3d. deep green and light salmon £6 £7

24. Female, Goroka, New Guinea. **25.** Tribal Elder, Tari, Papua.

26. Female Dancer. **27.** Male Dancer.

(Des. Mrs. V. Prescott. Recess. Note Ptg. Branch, Reserve Bank of Australia, Melbourne.)

1961. (26 July). *P* 14½ × 14 (*1d., 3d.*) *or* 14 × 14½ (*others*).

28 **24** 1d. lake 2 0 1 6
29 **25** 3d. indigo 2 6 2 0
30 **26** 1s. bronze-green 40 0 16 0
31 **27** 2s. maroon 12 6 7 6

28. Campaign Emblem.

(Recess. Note Ptg. Branch, Reserve Bank of Australia, Melbourne.)

1962 (7 Apr.). *Malaria Eradication. P* 14.

32 **28** 5d. carm.-red and lt. blue 5 0 3 6
33 ,, 1s. red and sepia .. 13 6 17 6
34 ,, 2s. black and yellow-green 26 0 35 0

29. Map of South Pacific.

(Des. Mrs. V. Prescott. Recess. Note Ptg. Branch, Reserve Bank of Australia, Melbourne.)

1962 (9 July). *Fifth South Pacific Conference, Pago Pago. P* 14½ × 14.

35 **29** 5d. scarlet and light green .. 5 0 3 6
36 ,, 1s. 6d. dp. violet & lt. yellow 12 6 16 0
37 ,, 2s. 6d. deep green & lt. blue 22 6 32 6

30. Traffic Policeman.

(Des. Mrs. V. Prescott. Recess. Note Ptg. Branch, Reserve Bank of Australia, Melbourne.)

1962 (5 Sept.). *P* 14½ × 14.

38 **30** 3s. deep bluish green .. 10 0 9 0

31. Throwing the Javelin. **32.** High Jump.

33. Runners.

(Des. G. Hamori. Photo. Courvoisier.)

1962 (24 Oct.). *Seventh British Empire and Commonwealth Games, Perth. P* 11½.

39 **31** 5d. brown and light blue .. 7 6 9 0
40 **32** 5d. brown and orange .. 7 6 9 0
41 **33** 2s. 3d. brown & light green 25 0 35 0

Nos. 39/40 are arranged together *se-tenant* in sheets of 100.

34. Bird of Paradise. **35.** Golden Opossum

36. Rabaul.

37. Queen Elizabeth II.

(Des. S. T. Cham (10s.), A. Buckley (photo) (£1). Photo. Harrison (£1), Courvoisier (others).)

1963. *P* 14½ (£1) *or* 11½ *others.*

42	**34**	5d. yellow, chestnut and sepia (27 Mar.) ..	3	0	3	6
43	**35**	6d. red, yellow-brown and grey (27 Mar.) ..	5	0	7	0
44	**36**	10s. multicoloured (13 Feb.)	70	0	80	0
45	**37**	£1 sepia, gold and blue-green (3 July)	£5		£6	

1963 (1 May). *Red Cross Centenary. As No.* 351 *of Australia.*

46		5d. red, grey-brown and bluish-green	2	6	2	3

38. Waterfront, Port Moresby.

39. Piaggio P-166 Aircraft landing at Tapini.

(Des. J. McMahon (8d.), Mrs. V. Prescott (2s. 3d.). Recess. Note Ptg. Brch., Reserve Bank of Australia, Melbourne.)

1963 (8 May). *P* 14×13½.

47	**38**	8d. green	5	0	6	6
48	**39**	2s. 3d. ultramarine ..	15	0	18	6

40. Games Emblem.

(Des. Mrs. V. Prescott. Recess. Note Ptg. Branch, Reserve Bank of Australia, Melbourne.)

1963 (14 Aug.). *First South Pacific Games, Suva. P* 13×14½.

49	**40**	5d. bistre	8	6	12	6
50	,,	1s. deep green	15	0	20	0

41. Watam Head.

42. Watam Head.

43. Bosmun Head.

44. Medina Head.

(Des. Mrs. V. Prescott. Photo. Courvoisier.)

1964 (5 Feb.). *Native Artifacts. P* 11½.

51	**41**	11d. multicoloured ..	3	6	4	6
52	**42**	2s. 5d. multicoloured ..	7	6	8	6
53	**43**	2s. 6d. multicoloured ..	7	6	8	6
54	**44**	5s. multicoloured ..	15	0	17	6

45. Casting Vote.

(Photo. Courvoisier).

1964 (4 Mar.). *Common Roll Elections. P* 11½.

55	**45**	5d. brown and drab ..	3	6	5	0
56	,,	2s. 3d. brown & pale blue ..	12	6	15	0

HAVE YOU READ THE NOTES AT THE BEGINNING OF THIS CATALOGUE?

These often provide answers to the enquiries we receive.

46. " Health Centres ".

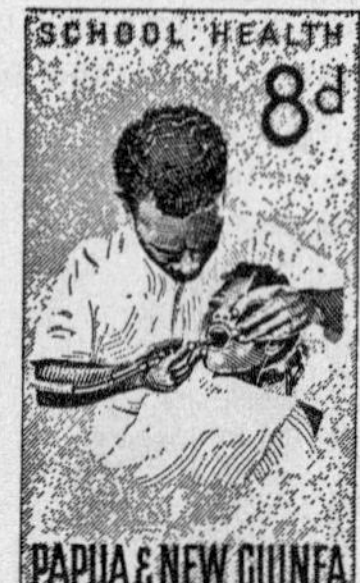

47. " School Health ".

48. " Infant, Child and Maternal Health ".

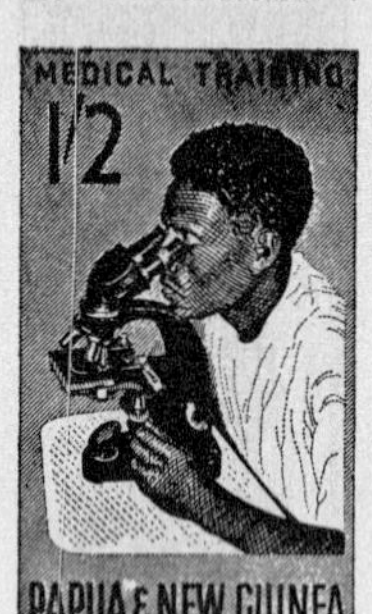

49. " Medical Training ".

(Recess. Note Ptg. Branch, Reserve Bank of Australia, Melbourne.)

1964 (5 Aug.). *Health Services. P* 14.

57	**46**	5d. violet	2	0	1	6
58	**47**	8d. bronze-green	3	6	4	6
59	**48**	1s. blue	7	6	9	0
60	**49**	1s. 2d. brown-red	8	6	10	0

50. Striped Gardener Bowerbird.

51. New Guinea Regent Bowerbird.

52. Blue Bird of Paradise.

53. Lawes' Six-wired Bird of Paradise.

54. Black-billed Sickle-billed Bird of Paradise.

55. Emperor of Germany Bird of Paradise.

56. Brown Sickle-billed Bird of Paradise.

57. Lesser Bird of Paradise.

58. Magnificent Bird of Paradise.

59. Twelve-wired Bird of Paradise.

60. Magnificent Rifle Bird.

(Photo. Courvoisier.)

1964 (28 Oct.)–**65.** *Designs multicoloured; background colours given.* *P* 11½ (1d. to 8d.) *or* 12×11½ (*others*).

61	**50**	1d. pale olive-yell. (20.1.65)	0	9	1	0
62	**51**	3d. light grey (20.1.65) ..	0	8	0	9
63	**52**	5d. pale red (20.1.65) ..	1	0	1	2
64	**53**	6d. pale green	1	3	1	6
65	**54**	8d. lilac	1	6	1	9
66	**55**	1s. salmon	1	9	2	0
67	**56**	2s. light blue (20.1.65) ..	3	3	3	6
68	**57**	2s. 3d. lt. green (20.1.65)	3	6	4	3
69	**58**	3s. pale yellow (20.1.65) ..	5	0	5	6
70	**59**	5s. cobalt (20.1.65) ..	7	6	9	0
71	**60**	10s. pale drab	14	0	16	6

61

62

63

64

All show carved canoe prows.

es. Mrs. V. Prescott. Photo. Courvoisier.)

35 (25 Mar.). *Sepik Canoe Prows in Port Moresby Museum.* *P* 11½.

61	4d. multicoloured	2	9	3	6
62	1s. 2d. multicoloured ..	6	6	8	0
63	1s. 6d. multicoloured ..	8	6	10	0
64	4s. multicoloured	20	0	24	0

1965 (14 Apr.). *50th Anniv. of Gallipoli Landing. As T* **181** *of Australia, but slightly larger* (22×34½ *mm.*). *Photo.*

76	2s. 3d. sepia, black & emerald	8	6	10	0

65. Urban Plan and Native House.

(Des. G. Hamori. Photo. Courvoisier.)

1965 (7 July). *Sixth South Pacific Conference, Lae. T* **65** *and similar horiz. design.* *P* 11½.

77	6d. multicoloured	3	6	4	6
78	1s. multicoloured	5	6	6	9

No. 78 is similar to T **65** but with the plan on the right and the house on the left. Also "URBANISATION" reads downwards.

66. Mother and Child.

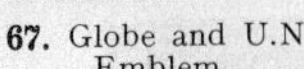

67. Globe and U.N. Emblem.

68. U.N. Emblem and Globes.

(Photo. Courvoisier.)

1965 (13 Oct.). *20th Anniv. of U.N.O.* *P* 11½.

79	**66**	6d. sepia, blue and pale turquoise-blue	4	0	5	0
80	**67**	1s. orange-brown, blue and deep reddish violet ..	5	6	7	6
81	**68**	2s. blue, blue-green and light yellow-olive ..	9	0	11	6

(New currency. 100 cents = $1 Australian.)

69. Blue Emperor.

70. White-banded Map Butterfly.

71. Mountain Swallowtail.

72. Port Moresby Terinos.

73. New Guinea Birdwing.

74. Euchenor Butterfly.

75. White-spotted Parthenos.

76. Orange Jezebel.

77. New Guinea Emperor.

78. Blue Spotted Leaf-wing.

79. Paradise Birdwing.

(Photo. Courvoisier.)

1966 (14 Feb.). *Decimal Currency.* *P* 11½.

82	**69**	1 c. multicoloured	..	0	2	0
83	**70**	3 c. multicoloured	..	0	6	0
84	**71**	4 c. multicoloured	..	0	7	0
85	**72**	5 c. multicoloured	..	0	9	1
86	**73**	10 c. multicoloured	..	1	3	1
87	**74**	15 c. multicoloured	..	1	8	2
88	**75**	20 c. multicoloured	..	2	3	2
89	**76**	25 c. multicoloured	..	2	9	3
90	**77**	50 c. multicoloured	..	5	4	7
91	**78**	$1 multicoloured	..	10	6	12
92	**79**	$2 multicoloured	..	21	0	25

POSTAGE DUE STAMPS.

POSTAL CHARGES

6d.

IXIXIXIXIX

(D 1)

POSTAL CHARGES

3s.

(D 2)

1960 (1 Mar.). *Postage stamps surcharged.*

(*a*) *With Type* D 1.

D1	8	6d. on 7½d. blue (R.)	£70	£80
		a. Surch. double	—	£250

(*b*) *As Type* D 2.

D2	7	1d. on 6½d. maroon ..	15 0	17 6
D3	1	3d. on ½d. emerald (B.) ..	20 0	25 0
		a. Surch. double	£85	
D4	8	6d. on 7½d. blue (R.) ..	30 0	35 0
		a. Surch. double	£70	
D5	6	1s. 3d. on 3½d. black (Or.)	45 0	52 6
D6	4	3s. on 2½d. orange ..	65 0	75 0

Of No. D1*a*, only a few copies are known from a sheet used at Goroka.

D 3

(Typo. Note Ptg. Branch, Reserve Bank of Australia, Melbourne.)

1960 (2 June). *W* **14** *of Papua.* *P* 14.

7	D 3	1d. orange	1 3	2 0
8	,,	3d. yellow-brown ..	1 9	2 6
9	,,	6d. blue	3 3	4 6
10	,,	9d. deep red	4 0	5 6
11	,,	1s. light emerald ..	5 0	6 6
12	,,	1s. 3d. violet	7 0	9 0
13	,,	1s. 6d. pale blue ..	9 6	13 0
14	,,	3s. yellow	16 0	20 0

PITCAIRN ISLANDS.

1. Cluster of Oranges.

2. Christian on *Bounty* and Pitcairn Is.

3. John Adams and his House.

4. Lt. Bligh and *Bounty*.

5. Pitcairn Islands and Pacific Ocean.

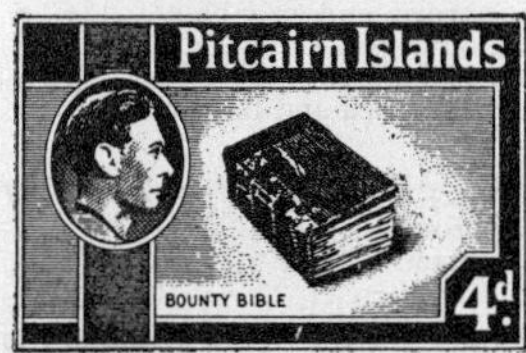

5*a*. *Bounty* Bible.

6. H.M. Armed Vessel *Bounty*.

6a. School, 1949.

7. Fletcher Christian and Pitcairn Islands.

8. Christian on *Bounty* and Pitcairn Coast.

(Recess. Bradbury, Wilkinson (1d., 3d., and 2s. 6d.), and Waterlow (other values).)

1940 (15 Oct.)–**51.** *Wmk. Mult. Script CA. P 11½×11 (1d., 3d., 4d., 8d. and 2s. 6d.) or 12½ (others).*

1	**1**	½d. orange and green ..	2	0	3	6
2	**2**	1d mauve and magenta ..	3	6	5	0
3	**3**	1½d. grey and carmine ..	5	6	9	0
4	**4**	2d. green and brown ..	6	6	11	0
5	**5**	3d. yellow-green and blue ..	8	6	15	0
5a	**5a**	4d. blk. & emer.-grn. (1.9.51)	15	0	22	6
6	**6**	6d. brown and grey-blue ..	11	0	16	0
6a	**6a**	8d. olive-grn. & mag. (1.9.51)	22	6	32	6
7	**7**	1s. violet and grey ..	15	0	22	6
8	**8**	2s. 6d. green and brown ..	50	0	70	0

1946 (2 Dec.). *Victory. As Nos. 28/9 of Aden.*

9	2d. brown	2	0	3	0
10	3d. blue	3	6	5	0

1949 (1 Aug.). *Royal Silver Wedding. As Nos. 30/1 of Aden.*

11	1½d. scarlet	3	0	4	6
12	10s. mauve	85	0	£6	

1949 (10 Oct.). *75th Anniv. of Universal Postal Union. As Nos. 114/7 of Antigua.*

13	2½d. red-brown	6	0	8	6
14	3d. deep blue	8	6	12	6
15	6d. deep blue-green	12	6	17	6
16	1s. purple	25	0	32	6

1953 (2 June). *Coronation. As No. 47 of Aden, but ptd. by B. W. & Co.*

17	4d. black & deep bluish green	6	6	9	6

9. *Cordyline terminalis* (plant).

10. Pitcairn Islands Map.

11. John Adams and *Bounty* Bible.

12. Handicrafts: Bird Model.

13. Bounty Bay.

14. Pitcairn School.

15. Pacific Ocean Map.

16. Inland Scene.

17. Handicrafts : Ship Model.

18. Island Wheelbarrow.

19. Launching New Whaleboat.

(Recess. De La Rue & Co.)

1957 (2 July)–**58.** *Wmk. Mult. Script CA. P* 13 × 12½ (*horiz.*) *or* 12½ × 13 (*others*).

No.	Type	Description	Unused s.	d.	Used s.	d.
18	**9**	½d. grn. & red'sh lilac (*shades*)	1	6	2	6
19	**10**	1d. black and yellow-green	2	9	4	0
20	**11**	2d. brown and greenish blue	3	0	5	0
21	**12**	2½d. dp. brn. & red-orange	4	0	6	6
22	**13**	3d. emerald & deep ultram.	4	0	6	6
23	**14**	4d. scarlet & dp. ultram. (I)	12	6	16	0
23*a*	,,	4d. carmine-red and deep ultram. (II) (5.11.58) ..	6	0	9	6
24	**15**	6d. pale buff and indigo ..	6	0	9	6
25	**16**	8d. deep olive-green and carmine-lake	8	0	12	6
26	**17**	1s. black & yellowish brn.	9	0	13	6
27	**18**	2s. green and red-orange ..	20	0	27	6
28	**19**	2s. 6d. ultramarine & lake (*shades*)	27	6	37	6

Nos. 23/*a*. Type I is inscribed "PITCAIRN SCHOOL"; Type II "SCHOOLTEACHER'S HOUSE".

20. Pitcairn Island and Simon Young.

21. Norfolk and Pitcairn Islands.

22. Migrant schooner *Mary Ann.*

(Photo. Harrison.)

1961 (15 Nov.). *Centenary of Return of Pitcairn Islanders from Norfolk Island. W* w.**12**. *P*14½ × 13½.

No.	Type	Description	Unused s.	d.	Used s.	d.
29	**20**	3d. black and yellow ..	7	6	11	6
30	**21**	6d. red-brown and blue ..	12	6	18	6
31	**22**	1s. red-orange & blue-grn.	17	6	25	0

1963 (4 June). *Freedom from Hunger. As No.* 63 *of Aden.*

No.	Description	Unused s.	d.	Used s.	d.
32	2s. 6d. ultramarine	15	0	20	0

1963 (4 Dec.). *As No.* 18 *but wmk.* w.**12.**

33	**9**	½d. green & reddish purple	5 0	7 6

1963 (9 Dec.). *Red Cross Centenary. As Nos.* 147/8 *of Antigua.*

34	2d. red and black	2 6	3 9
35	2s. 6d. red and blue	15 0	20 0

23. Pitcairn Is. Longboat.

24. H.M. Armed Vessel *Bounty*.

25. " Out from Bounty Bay ".

26. Frigate Bird.

27. Fairy Tern.

28. Pitcairn Sparrow.

29. Austin Bird.

30. Bosun Birds.

31. Chicken Bird.

32. Red Breast.

33. Ghost Bird.

34. Wood Pigeon.

Des. M. C. Farrar-Bell. Photo. Harrison.)

.964 (5 Aug.). *Multicoloured; background colours given below.* *W* w.**12.** *P* 14 × 14½.

.6	**23**	½d. blue-green	0 2	0 2
.7	**24**	1d. violet-blue	0 3	0 3
.8	**25**	2d. reddish violet	0 4	0 5
9	**26**	3d. yellow-ochre	0 6	0 7
0	**27**	4d. bright green	0 7	0 9
1	**28**	6d. vermilion	0 10	1 0
2	**29**	8d. purple-brown	1 0	1 3
3	**30**	10d. blue	1 3	1 6
4	**31**	1s. lemon-yellow	1 5	1 9
5	**32**	1s. 6d. drab	2 0	2 3
5	**33**	2s. 6d. orange	3 6	3 9
7	**34**	4s. reddish brown ..	5 4	5 6

35. Queen Elizabeth II.

(Portrait by Anthony Buckley. Photo. Harrison.)

65 (5 Apr.). *W* w.**12.** *P* 14 × 14½.

35	8s. multicoloured	10 9	12 0

65 (17 May). *I.T.U. Centenary. As Nos.* 166/7 *of Antigua.*

1d. mauve and orange-brown	1 0	1 6
2s. 6d. turquoise-green and bright blue	8 6	12 6

65 (15 Oct.). *International Co-operation Year. As Nos.* 168/9 *of Antigua.*

1d. reddish pur. & turq.-grn.	0 6	0 8
1s. 6d. dp. bluish grn. & lav.	3 0	4 0

66 (24 Jan.). *Churchill Commemoration. As Nos.* 170/3 *of Antigua.*

2d. new blue	0 7	0 9
3d. deep green	0 9	1 0
6d. brown	1 3	2 0
1s. bluish violet	2 0	3 3

PRINCE EDWARD ISLAND.

— SIMPLIFICATION (see Introduction) —

Nos. 1 to 47a.
9, 12, 14, 16, 18, 20: 28, 30, 31.
32. 34, 38, 37, 39, 41, 42.

1 2 3 4 5 6

(Electrotyped and printed by Charles Whiting, Beaufort House, Strand, London.)

1861 (1 Jan.). *Yellowish toned paper.* *P* 9.

1	**1**	2d. rose	£12	£9
		a. Imperf. between (horiz. pair) ..		
		b. Bisected (1d.) (on cover) ..		
2	,,	2d. rose-carmine	£12	£9
3	**2**	3d. blue	£32	£18
		a. Bisected (1½d.) (on cover) ..		
4	**3**	6d. yellow-green	£30	£20

Rouletted.

5	**1**	2d. rose		

The 2d. and 3d., perf. 9, were authorised to be bisected and used for half their nominal value.

1862. *Yellowish toned paper.* *P* 11.

6	**4**	1d. brown-orange	70 0	£12
7	**6**	9d. bluish lilac	£6	50 0
8	,,	9d. dull mauve	£6	55 0

1863–68. *Yellowish toned paper.* (*a*) *P* 11½–12.

9	**4**	1d. yellow-orange	30 0	40 0
		a. Bisected (½d.) (on cover) ..	†	£40
		b. Imperf. between (horiz. pair) ..	£28	
10	,,	1d. orange-buff	45 0	55 0
11	,,	1d. yellow	55 0	60 0
12	**1**	2d. rose	22 6	35 0
		a. Imperf. between (pair) ..		
		b. Bisected (1d.) (on cover) ..	†	£135
13	,,	2d. deep rose	20 0	32 6
14	**2**	3d. blue	30 0	45 0
		a. Imperf. between (vert. pair) ..		
		b. Bisected (1½d.) (on cover) ..		
15	,,	3d. deep blue	35 0	35 0
16	**5**	4d. black	45 0	80 0
		a. Imperf. between (horiz. pair) ..		

17 **3** 6d. yellow-green 85 0 70 0
a. Bisected (3d.) (on cover) .. ..
18 ,, 6d. blue-green (1868) .. 75 0 75 0
19 **6** 9d. lilac 50 0 60 0
20 ,, 9d. reddish mauve 45 0 45 0
a. Imperf. between (horiz. pair) .. £40
b. Bisected (4½d.) (on cover) .. † £90

(*b*) *Perf. compound of* 11 *and* 11½–12.

21 **4** 1d. yellow-orange £14 £6
22 **1** 2d. rose £14 £6
23 **2** 3d. blue £16 £6
24 **5** 4d. black £28 £20
25 **3** 6d. yellow-green £17 £14
26 **6** 9d. reddish mauve £22 £18

1867–68. *Coarse wove bluish white paper. P* 11½–12.

27 **1** 2d. rose 7 6 25 0
28 ,, 2d. rose-pink 6 0 25 0
a. Variety "TWC" 90 0
29 **2** 3d. pale blue 8 6 40 0
30 ,, 3d. blue 7 6 40 0
a. Imperf. between (horiz. pair) .. £20
31 **5** 4d. black 6 0 £5
a. Imperf. between (pair) .. £12
b. Bisected (2d.) (on cover) .. † £120
c. Perf. compound 11 and 11½-12

7

(Recess. British-American Bank Note Co., Montreal and Ottawa.)

1870 (1 June). *P* 12.

32 **7** 4½d. (3d. stg.), yellow-brown 27 6 80 0
33 ,, 4½d. (3d. stg.), deep brown .. 32 6 80 0

8

9

10

11

12

13

(Electrotyped and printed by Charles Whiting, London.)

1872 (1 Jan.). (*a*) *P* 11½–12.

34 **8** 1 c. orange.. .. .. 7 0 35 0
35 ,, 1 c. yellow-orange.. .. 6 0 35 0
36 ,, 1 c. brown-orange.. .. 10 6 40 0
37 **10** 3 c. rose 17 6 25 0
a. Stop between "PRINCE EDWARD" 35 0 45 0
b. Bisected (1½ c.) (on cover)
c. Imperf. between (pair) .. £28

(*b*) *Perf.* 12 *to* 12¼, *large holes.*

38 **9** 2 c. blue 4 0 50 0
a. Bisected (1 c.) (on cover) ..
39 **11** 4 c. yellow-green 3 0 40 0
40 ,, 4 c. deep green 6 0 40 0
41 **12** 6 c. black 3 0 45 0
a. Bisected (3 c.) (on cover) .. † £80
b. Imperf. between (horiz. pr.) £18
42 **13** 12 c. reddish mauve .. 4 0 £5

(*c*) *P* 12½–13, *smaller holes.*

43 **8** 1 c. orange 45 0
44 ,, 1 c. brown-orange.. .. 8 6 30 0
45 **10** 3 c. rose 30 0 35 0
a. Stop between "PRINCE EDWARD" 70 0 75 0
45*b* **12** 6 c. black .. .. .. — £35

(*d*) *Perf. compound of* (*a*) *and* (*c*) 11½–12 × 12½–13.

46 **8** 1 c. orange £5 £7
47 **10** 3 c. rose £7 £6
a. Stop between "PRINCE EDWARD" £24 £2

The stamps were withdrawn 1 July, 1873, when the Colony became a province of the Dominion of Canada.

QATAR.

An independent Arab Shaikhdom, with British postal administration until May 23rd, 1963.

The stamps of Muscat were formerly used at the Capital, Doha, and at Umm Said.

ALL STAMPS TO 1961 SURCHARGED ON ISSUES OF GREAT BRITAIN.

QATAR NP 1 NP (1) QATAR 3 NP (2) QATAR 75 NP (3)

1957 (1 Apr.)–**59.**

(*a*) *T* **154/60** (*St. Edward's Crown wmk. T* **165**) *surch. as T* **1** *to* **3**.

1 **1** 1 n.p. on 5d. brown .. 0 3 0
2 **2** 3 n.p. on ½d. orange-red .. 0 6 0
3 ,, 6 n.p. on 1d. ultramarine .. 0 6 0
4 ,, 9 n.p. on 1½d. green .. 0 6 0
5 ,, 12 n.p. on 2d. lt. red-brown 0 6 0
6 **1** 15 n.p. on 2½d. carm.-red (I) 0 6 0
7 **2** 20 n.p. on 3d. dp. lilac (B.).. 0 8 0
8 **1** 25 n.p. on 4d. ultramarine .. 0 8 0
9 ,, 40 n.p. on 6d. reddish purple 1 3 1
a. *Deep claret* (21.7.59) .. 2 6 3
10 ,, 50 n.p. on 9d. bronze-green 2 0 2
11 **3** 75 n.p. on 1s. 3d. green .. 2 6 3
12 ,, 1 r. on 1s. 6d. grey-blue 3 0 3

QATAR 2 RUPEES
I

II

(4)

QATAR 5 RUPEES
I

QATAR 5 RUPEES
II

(5)

QATAR 10 RUPEES
I

QATAR 10 RUPEES
II

(6)

Type I (**4/6**). Type-set overprints. Bold hick letters with sharp corners and straight :dges. Bars close together and usually slightly onger than in Type II.

Type II (**4/6**). Plate-printed overprints. Thinner letters, rounded corners and rough edges. Bars wider apart.

(*b*) *Nos.* 536/8 *surch. with T* **4/6**.

			I (1.4.57)		II (18.9.57)	
3	**166**	2 r. on 2s. 6d. blk.-brn.	15 0	17 6	35 0	40 0
4	**167**	5 r. on 5s. rose-red ..	40 0	50 0	£8	£8
5	**168**	10 r. on 10s. ultram. ..	70 0	75 0	£16	£20

QATAR
15 NP

(7)

957 (1 Aug.). *World Scout Jubilee Jamboree. Nos.* 557/9 *surch. in two lines as T* **7** (15 *n.p.*), *or in three lines* (*others*).

15 n.p. on 2½d. carmine-red ..	1	0	1	3
25 n.p. on 4d. ultramarine ..	1	9	2	0
75 n.p. on 1s. 3d. green ..	4	0	4	9

960. *Q.E. II* (*Mult. Crowns wmk. T* **179**) *surch. as T* **1** *or* **2**.

2	3 n.p. on ½d. orange-red ..	2	0	3	0
,,	6 n.p. on 1d. ultramarine ..	2	6	3	0
,,	9 n.p. on 1½d. green ..	3	0	3	6
,,	12 n.p. on 2d. lt. red-brown ..	8	0	11	0
1	15 n.p. on 2½d. carm.-red (II)	1	6	1	9
2	20 n.p. on 3d. dp. lilac (B.) ..	2	0	3	0
1	40 n.p. on 6d. deep claret ..	2	6	3	6

Dates of issue: 26 Apr., 15 n.p.; 21 June, 6 and n.p.; 28 Sept., 3, 9, 12 and 20 n.p.

8. Shaikh Ahmad bin Ali al Thani.

9. Falcon.

10. Dhow.

11. Oil Derrick.

12. Mosque.

(Des. O. C. Meronti (T **8**), M. Goaman (T **9**), M. C. Farrar-Bell (T **10**), J. Constable and O. C. Meronti (T **11/12**). Photo. Harrison & Sons (T **8/10**). Recess. De La Rue (T **11/12**).

1961 (2 Sept.). *P* 14½ (5 *n.p. to* 75 *n.p.*) *or* 13 (1 *r. to* 10 *r.*).

27	**8**	5 n.p. carmine	0 3	0 2
28	,,	15 n.p. black	0 5	0 6
29	,,	20 n.p. reddish purple ..	0 6	0 8
30	,,	30 n.p. deep green	0 9	0 10
31	**9**	40 n.p. red	0 11	1 0
32	,,	50 n.p. sepia	1 1	1 3
33	**10**	75 n.p. ultramarine ..	1 8	2 0
34	**11**	1 r. scarlet	2 0	2 6
35	,,	2 r. ultramarine ..	4 0	4 6
36	**12**	5 r. bronze-green ..	10 0	12 6
37	,,	10 r. black	19 6	22 6

The Qatar Post Department took over the postal services on May 23rd, 1963. Later stamp issues will therefore be found in Part III of the Stanley Gibbons Catalogue.

QUEENSLAND.

— **SIMPLIFICATION** (see Introduction) —

Nos. 1 to 127.

1, 2, 3. 4, 5, 6. 14, 15, 16, 17, 19, 20.
36, 37, 32, 27, 29, 49. 51, 52, 55, 58.
59, 62, 64, 65, 67, 68, 70, 72, 73.
91, 96, 100, 101, 102, 105, 109.
116, 117. 118, 120, 121, 123, 125, 127.

Nos. 128 to 165.
133, 135. 136, 138, 140, 142, 143, 146, 147, 148, 150.
151. 152, 157, 158, 155, 160. 161 to 165.

Nos. 166 to 309.
167, 168, 192, 169, 194, 170. 172, 174, 197.
219, 202, 204, 205 : 223, 206, 227, 228, 207.
184, 185, 191.
208, 210, 212, 213, 215. 229.
231, 232, 235, 236, 237, 238, 241, 244, 246, 250.
252, 253, 254.
256, 257. 262. 264a, 264b. 266. 272, 273, 275, 277, 279, 280.
283, 287, 288, 290, 291, 293, 294, 295, 296, 299, 300.

From 26 January, 1860, to 1 November, 1860, current stamps of New South Wales were used in Queensland. The stamps so used were the 1d., 2d. and 3d. diademed heads, the large square 6d., 8d. and 1s., and the "registered" stamp. Such stamps bearing a Queensland postmark may be included in a collection of the stamps of this country.

1

1*a*

(Dies engraved by Wm. Humphreys and plates made by Perkins, Bacon & Co. Recess.)
(Printed and perforated in London.)

1860 (1 Nov.). *Wmk. Large Star, T* **1a**. *Imperf.*
1 **1** 1d. carmine-rose £90 £60
2 ,, 2d. blue £275 £150
3 ,, 6d. green £225 £85

1860 (Nov.). *W* **1a**. *Perf. clean-cut* 14–15½.
4 **1** 1d. carmine-rose (1.11.1860) .. £90 £25
5 ,, 2d. blue (1.11.1860) £20 £6
a. Imperf. between (pair) ..
6 ,, 6d. green (15.11.1860) .. £20 90 0

2

1860–61. *Wmk. Small Star, T* **2**. *Perf. clean-cut* 14–15½.
7 **1** 2d. blue £30 £10
a. Imperf. between (horiz. pair) .. — £50
8 ,, 3d. brown (15 April, 1861) .. £20 £5
9 ,, 6d. green £40 £5
10 ,, 1s. violet (15 Nov., 1860) .. £35 £6
11 ,, "REGISTERED", olive-yellow (January, 1861) .. £25 £5
a. Imperf. between (pair) .. £160

The perforation of the 3d. is that known as "intermediate between clean-cut and rough".

1861 (July (?)). *W* **2**. *Clean-cut perf.* 14.
12 **1** 1d. carmine-rose £6 50 0
13 ,, 2d. blue £25 50 0

1861 (Sept.). *W* **2**. *Rough perf.* 14–15½.
14 **1** 1d. carmine-rose 60 0 40 0
15 ,, 2d. blue £6 25 0
a. Imperf. between (pair) ..
16 ,, 3d. brown 27 6 35 0
a. Imperf. between (pair) .. £85
17 **1** 6d. deep green £15 40 0
18 ,, 6d. yellow-green £18 40 0
19 ,, 1s. violet £25 90 0
20 ,, "REGISTERED" orge.-yel. 30 0 45 0

(Printed and perforated in Brisbane.)

1862–67. *Thick toned paper. No wmk.*
(*a*) *Rough perf.* 13. (1862–63).
21 **1** 1d. Indian red (16.12.1862) £30 80 0
22 ,, 1d. orange-verm. (2.1863) 80 0 27 6
a. Imperf. (pair) .. .. — £12
b. Imperf. between (pair) ..
23 ,, 2d. blue (16 Dec., 1862) .. 80 0 22 6
24 ,, 2d. pale blue £8 40 0
a. Imperf. (pair) .. .. — £12
b. Imperf. between (horiz. pair)
25 ,, 3d. brown 65 0 45 0
26 ,, 6d. apple-green (17.4.1863) .. £6 17 6
27 ,, 6d. yellow-green 80 0 15 0
a. Imperf. between (horiz. pair) .. — £65
28 ,, 6d. blue-green £7 45 0
a. Imperf. (pair) .. .. — £18
29 ,, 1s. grey (14 July, 1863) .. £6 22 6
a. Imperf. between (horiz. pair) .. — £7
b. Imperf. between (vert. pair) ..

(*b*) *P* 12½ *square holes* × *rough perf.* 13 (1867).
30 **1** 1d. orange-vermilion .. 65 0 35
31 ,, 2d. blue 75 0 27
32 ,, 3d. brown 75 0 27
33 ,, 6d. apple-green .. .. — 35
34 ,, 6d. yellow-green .. .. — 35
35 ,, 1s. grey £8 45
a. Imperf. between (horiz. pair)

(*c*) *P* 13 *round holes* (1867).
36 **1** 1d. orange-verm. (9.8.1867) 60 0 27
37 ,, 2d. blue (30 March, 1867) 75 0 12
38 ,, 2d. pale blue £10
a. Imperf. between (horiz. pair) — £7
38*b* ,, 3d. brown .. .. .. — £3
39 ,, 6d. apple-green (8.7.1867) £7 15
40 ,, 6d. yellow-green £7 15

(*d*) *P* 12½ *square holes* × *perf.* 13 *round holes* (1867
41 **1** 1d. orange-vermilion .. — 80
42 ,, 2d. blue .. .. ..
43 ,, 6d. yellow-green .. ..

1864–65. *Wmk. Star, T* **2**. (*a*) *Rough perf.* 1
44 **1** 1d. orange-verm. (Jan. '65) .. 70 0 27
a. Imperf. between (horiz. pair) £35
45 ,, 2d. pale blue (Jan.'65) .. 85 0 20
46 ,, 2d. deep blue 90 0 25
a. Imperf. between (vert. pair) .. £80
b. Bisected (1d.) (on cover) .. † £1
47 ,, 6d. yellow-green (Jan. '65) .. £9 27
48 ,, 6d. deep green £12 30
49 ,, "REGISTERED," orange-yell. (21.6.64) 50 0 35
a. Double printed £70
b. Imperf. .. ..

(*b*) *P* 12½ *square holes* × *rough perf.* 13.
50 **1** 1d. orange-vermilion .. £6 75

1866 (24 Jan.). *Wmk.* "QUEENSLAND/POSTAG —POSTAGE/STAMPS—STAMPS" *in three lines script capitals with double wavy lines above a below the wmk. and single wavy lines with proje ing sprays between each line of words. There a ornaments* ("*fleurons*") *between* "POSTAGE "POSTAGE" *and between* "STAMPS" "STAMPS *Single stamps only show a portion of one or t letters of this wmk. Rough perf.* 13.
51 **1** 1d. orange-vermilion .. £9 30
52 ,, 2d. blue 60 0 15

1866 (24 Sept.). *Lithographed on thick pap No wmk. P* 13, *round holes.*
53 **1** 4d. slate £9 35
55 ,, 4d. lilac 55 0 17
56 ,, 4d. reddish lilac 55 0 25
57 ,, 5s. bright rose £14
58 ,, 5s. pale rose £9 75
a. Imperf. between (vert. pair) —

The 4d. is from a transfer taken from the die, and the 5s. was taken from the 1s. die, t final "s" being added. The alteration in the values was made by hand on the stone, and there are many varieties, such as tall and short letters in "FOUR PENCE", some of the letters of "FOUR" smudged out, and differences in the position of the two words.

5

1868–74. *Wmk. small truncated Star, T* **5** *on each stamp, and the word* "QUEENSLAND" *in single-lined Roman capitals four times in each sheet.* (*a*) *P* 13.

59 **1** 1d. orange-verm. (18.1.'71) .. 65 0 6 0
60 ,, 2d. pale blue 70 0 6 0
61 ,, 2d. blue (3 April, 1868) .. 25 0 4 0
62 ,, 2d. bright blue 60 0 4 0
63 ,, 2d. greenish blue £6 4 6
64 ,, 2d. dark blue 75 0 6 6
a. Imperf. .. .. ..
65 ,, 3d. olive-brown (27.2.'71) .. £6 10 0
66 ,, 3d. greenish brown £8 11 6
67 ,, 3d. brown £6 12 6
68 ,, 6d. yellow-green (10.11.'71) £10 16 0
69 ,, 6d. green £10 16 0
70 ,, 6d. deep green £14 30 0
71 ,, 1s. dull claret (13.11.'72) .. £35 80 0
72 ,, 1s. brownish grey £35 75 0
73 ,, 1s. mauve (19.2.'74) .. £20 55 0

(*b*) *P* 12 (*about Feb.,* 1874).

74 **1** 1d. orange-vermilion .. £25 55 0
75 ,, 2d. blue .. .. — 60 0
76 ,, 3d. greenish brown .. .. — £17
77 ,, 3d. brown £24 £12
78 ,, 6d. deep green £80 60 0
79 ,, 1s. mauve .. .. — 80 0

(*c*) *P* 13×12.

80 **1** 1d. orange-vermilion .. — £15
81 ,, 2d. blue £70 60 0
82 ,, 3d. brown .. .. — £35

Reprints were made in 1895 of all five values on the paper of the regular issue, and perforated 13; the colours are:—1d. orange and orange-brown, 2d. dull blue and bright blue, 3d. deep brown, 6d. yellow-green, 1s. red-violet and dull violet. The "Registered" was also reprinted with these on the same paper, but perforated 12.

6

6*a*

(4d., litho. Other values recess.)

1868–75. *Wmk. Crown and Q, T* **6**. (*a*) *P* 13.

83 **1** 1d. oran.-verm. (10.11.68) 60 0 7 6
a. Imperf. .. ..
84 ,, 1d. pale rose-red (4.11.74) .. 70 0 17 6
85 ,, 1d. deep rose-red .. £6 17 6
86 ,, 2d. pale blue (4.11.74) .. 60 0 3 6
87 ,, 2d. deep blue (20.11.68) .. 50 0 3 6
a. Imperf. (pair) .. £22
b. Imperf. between (vert. pair) ..
88 ,, 3d. brown (11.6.75) .. 75 0 20 0
89 ,, 4d. yellow (1.1.75) £35 80 0
90 **1** 6d. deep green (9.4.69) .. £7 17 6
91 ,, 6d. yellow-green £5 12 6
92 ,, 6d. pale apple-grn. (1.1.75) £8 17 6
a. Imperf. £10
93 ,, 1s. mauve .. .. — 75 0

1876–78. (*b*) *P* 12.

94 **1** 1d. deep orange-vermilion 45 0 7 6
95 ,, 1d. pale orange-vermilion .. 55 0 7 6
a. Imperf. between (vert. pair) ..
96 ,, 1d. rose-red 60 0 10 0
97 ,, 1d. flesh 75 0 17 6
98 ,, 2d. pale blue £6 27 6
99 ,, 2d. bright blue 12 6 2 6
100 ,, 2d. deep blue 20 0 3 0
101 ,, 3d. brown 50 0 17 6
102 ,, 4d. yellow £20 22 6
103 ,, 4d. buff £20 22 6
104 ,, 6d. deep green £8 15 0
105 ,, 6d. green £6 8 6
106 ,, 6d. yellow-green £7 10 0
107 ,, 6d. apple-green £8 15 0
108 ,, 1s. mauve 55 0 15 0
109 ,, 1s. purple £7 10 0
a. Imperf. between (pair) ..

(*c*) *P* 13×12.

110 **1** 1d. orange-vermilion .. — £10
111 ,, 2d. deep blue .. £100 £12
112 ,, 4d. yellow ..
113 ,, 6d. deep green .. .. — £16

(*d*) *P* 12½ *square holes* × 13 *round holes.*

114 **1** 1d. orange-vermilion ..
115 ,, 2d. blue .. .. — £10

1879. *No wmk.* *P* 12.

116 **1** 6d. pale emerald-green .. £16 55 0
a. Imperf. between (horiz. pr.) — £40

Lilac burelé band at back.

117 **1** 1s. mauve (*fisc.-canc.* 20/–) £6 80 0

The *burelé* is usually very indistinct.

Reprints exist of the 1d., 2d., 3d., 6d. and 1s. on thicker paper, Wmk. Type **6***a*, and in different shades from the originals.

1881. *Lithographed from transfers from the* 1s. *die. Wmk. Crown and Q, T* **6***a*. *P* 12.

118 **1** 2s. pale blue (6 April, 1881) 65 0 45 0
119 ,, 2s. blue (*fisc.-canc.* 5/–) .. 50 0 40 0
120 ,, 2s. deep blue 80 0 27 6
121 ,, 2s. 6d. dull scarlet (28.8.1881) 85 0 60 0
122 ,, 2s. 6d. bright scarlet (*fisc.-canc.* 7/6) .. 65 0
123 ,, 5s. pale yellow-ochre (28.8.1881) 65 0 40 0
124 ,, 5s. yellow-ochre 65 0 40 0
125 ,, 10s. reddish brown (Mar., 1881) £15 £6
a. Imperf. £15
126 ,, 10s. bistre-brown £15 £6
127 ,, 20s. rose (*fisc.-canc.* 10/–) .. £15 £5

Of the 2s. and 20s. stamps there are five types of each, and of the other values ten types of each.

7

DIE I.

DIE II.

Dies I. and II. occur in the same sheet.

Die I. The whole horizontal inner line of the triangle in the upper right-hand corner merges into the outer white line of the oval above the "L."

Die II. The same line is short and does not touch the inner oval.

1879–80. *Typo.* *P* 12.

(*a*) *Wmk. Crown and Q, T* **6**.

128 **7** 1d. reddish brown (Die I.) 65 0 12 6
129 „ 1d. orange-brown (Die I.) .. 75 0 12 6
130 „ 1d. reddish brn. (Die II.) .. 75 0 12 6
a. Error. "QOEENSLAND" ..
131 „ 2d. blue (Die I.) 75 0 8 6
a. Error. "PENGE" ..
132 „ 4d. orange-yellow £20 30 0

The variety "QO" is No. 48 in the first arrangement, and No. 44 in a later arrangement on the sheets. The "PENGE" error is No 116 on Plate I.

(*b*) *No wmk., with lilac burelé band on back.*

133 **7** 1d. reddish brn. (Die I.) .. £28 75 0
134 „ 1d. reddish brn. (Die II.) .. £25 £7
a. Error. "QO" .. .. .. — £65
135 „ 2d. blue (Die I.) £35 45 0
a. Error. "PENGE" £175 £25

(*c*) *Wmk. Crown and Q, T* **6a**.

136 **7** 1d. reddish brn. (Die I.) .. 8 6 4 0
a. Imperf. between (pair) .. — £10
137 „ 1d. reddish brn. (Die II). .. 20 0 6 0
a. Error. "QO" £7
b. Imperf. between (pair) .. — £9
138 „ 1d. dull orange (Die I.) .. 8 6 5 0
139 „ 1d. dull orange (Die II.) .. 6 6 5 0
a. Error. "QO" 90 0 50 0
140 „ 1d. scarlet (Die I.) .. 6 0 2 6
141 „ 1d. scarlet (Die II.) .. 10 0 3 6
a. Error. "QO" £6 60 0
142 „ 2d. bright blue (Die I.) .. 25 0 3 6
143 „ 2d. grey-blue (Die I.) .. 15 0 2 6
a. Error. "PENGE" .. .. — £7
b. Imperf. between (pair) .. £28
144 „ 2d. pale blue (Die II.) .. 30 0 6 0
a. "TW" joined 22 6 3 0
145 „ 2d. deep blue (Die II.) .. 30 0 12 6
a. "TW" joined 22 6 2 6
146 „ 4d. orange-yellow 22 6 4 0
a. Imperf. between (pair) ..
147 „ 6d. deep green 22 6 5 0
a. Imperf. between (pair) ..
148 „ 6d. yellow-green 25 0 5 0
149 „ 1s. deep violet 20 0 7 6
150 „ 1s. pale lilac 15 0 7 6

All these values have been seen imperf. and unused, but we have no evidence that any of them were used in this condition.

The above were printed in sheets of 120, from plates made up of 30 groups of four electrotypes. There are four different types in each group, and two such groups of four are known of the 1d. and 2d., thus giving eight varieties of these two values. There was some resetting of the first plate of the 1d., and there are several plates of the 2d.; the value in the first plate of the latter value is in thinner letters, and in the last plate three types in each group of four have the "TW" of "TWO" joined, the letters of "PENCE" are larger and therefore much closer together, and in one type the "o" of "TWO" is oval, that letter being circular in the other types.

Half-penny

(8)

1880 (21 Feb.). *Surch. with T* **8**, *vert.*

151 **7** ½d. on 1d. (No. 136) (Die I.) 65 0 55 0
151*a* „ ½d. on 1d. (No. 137) (Die II.) £40 £25
b. Error. "QO" £55 £35

9

11

(Recess. Bradbury, Wilkinson & Co.)

1882–86.

A. *Thin paper.* *W* **6** *twice sideways.* *P* 12.

152 **9** 2s. bright blue 22 6 15 0
153 „ 2s. 6d. vermilion 45 0 20 0
154 „ 5s. rose 40 0 17 6
155 „ 10s. brown 50 0 45 0
156 „ £1 deep green £7 £5

B. *Thin paper.* *W* **6a** *twice sideways.* *P* 12.

157 **9** 2s. 6d. vermilion 30 0 25 0
158 „ 5s. rose 30 0 15 0
159 „ 10s. brown £9 55 0
160 „ £1 deep green 70 0 45 0

C. *Thick paper.* *W* **11**. *P* 12.

161 **9** 2s. bright blue 50 0 20 0
162 „ 2s. 6d. vermilion 17 6 17 6
163 „ 5s. rose 20 0 20 0
164 „ 10s. brown 35 0 35 0
165 „ £1 deep green 80 0 25 0

11*a*

12

1882–83. *W* **6a**. (*a*) *P* 12.

166 **11a** 1d. pale vermilion-red .. 4 0 0
167 „ 1d. deep vermilion-red .. 4 0 0
168 „ 2d. blue 6 0 0
169 „ 4d. pale yellow 10 0 0
a. "PENGE" for "PENCE" £6 60
170 „ 6d. green 5 0 0
171 „ 1s. violet 20 0 2
172 „ 1s. lilac 5 0 1
173 „ 1s. deep mauve 5 0 1
174 „ 1s. pale mauve 6 6 1

(*b*) *P* 9½×12.

176 **11a** 1d. pale red 90 0 40
177 „ 2d. blue £14 60
178 „ 1s. mauve £6 45

The above were printed from plates made up o groups of four electrotypes as previously. In th 1d. the words of value are followed by a full stop There are four types of the 4d., 6d., and 1s eight types of the 1d., and twelve types of the 2

1887–89. *W* **6a**. (*a*) *P* 12.

179 **12** 1d. vermilion-red 3 6 0
a. Imperf. 22 6 27
180 „ 2d. blue 8 6 0
181 „ 2s. deep brown 35 0 30
182 „ 2s. pale brown 30 0 25

(*b*) *P* 9½×12.

183 **12** 2d. blue £15 40

These are from new plates; four types of ea value grouped as before. The 1d. is witho stop. In all values No. 2 in each group of fo has the "L" and "A" of "QUEENSLAND" join at the foot, and No. 3 of the 2d. has "P" of wo "PENCE" with a long downstroke. Varieties a known (*perf.* 12) in which the "P" has been made normal, probably by hand on the plate.

In T **12** the shading lines do not extend entirely across, as in T **11***a*, thus leaving a white line down the front of the throat and point of the bust.

13 **14**

1890–94. *W* **6***a.* *P* 12½, 13 (*comb machine*).

No.	Type	Description	Unused	Used
184	**13**	½d. pale green	2 6	0 8
185	,,	½d. deep green	2 6	0 8
186	,,	½d. deep blue-green ..	3 0	0 10
187	**12**	1d. vermilion-red ..	0 9	0 2
188	,,	2d. blue (old plate) ..	5 0	0 4
189	,,	2d. pale blue (old plate)	3 6	0 3
190	,,	2d. pale blue (retouched plate)	3 0	1 0
191	**14**	2½d. carmine	3 0	0 6
192	**12**	3d. brown	3 0	1 0
193	**11***a*	4d. yellow	4 6	1 6
		a. "PENGE" for "PENCE"	25 0	
ɪ94	,,	4d. orange	5 0	1 6
		a. "PENGE" for "PENCE" ..	40 0	15 0
ɪ95	,,	4d. lemon	10 0	2 0
		a. "PENGE" for "PENCE"	60 0	
ɪ96	,,	6d. green	6 0	1 3
ɪ97	**12**	2s. red-brown	15 0	4 0
ɪ98	,,	2s. pale brown	15 0	7 6

The 1d. vermilion-red is known *imperf.*

This issue is perforated by a new vertical comb nachine, gauging about 12¾ × 12¾. The 3d. is rom a plate similar to those of the last issue, Io. 2 in each group of four types having "L" nd "A" joined at the foot. The ½d. and 2½d. are ikewise in groups of four types, but the differnces are very minute. In the ½d. the watermark s sideways. In the retouched plate of the 2d. he letters "L" and "A" no longer touch in Io. 2 of each group and the "P" in No. 3 is ormal.

894–95. A. *Thick paper.* *W* **11.** (*a*) *P* 12½, 13.

No.	Type	Description	Unused	Used
ɔ2	**12**	1d. vermilion-red	3 0	0 6
ɔ3	,,	1d. red-orange	2 6	0 8
ɔ4	,,	2d. blue (retouched plate)	1 6	0 8

(*b*) *P* 12.

No.	Type	Description	Unused	Used
ɔ5	**11***a*	1s. mauve	7 6	6 0

. *Unwmkd. paper; with blue burelé band at back.* *P* 12½, 13.

No.	Type	Description	Unused	Used
ɔ6	**12**	1d. deep vermilion-red ..	0 8	0 6

C. *Thin paper. Crown and Q faintly impressed.* *P* 12½, 13.

No.	Type	Description	Unused	Used
ɔ7	**12**	2d. blue (retouched plate)	5 0	

15 **16**

17 **18**

1895–96. *P* 12½, 13.

A. *W* **6***a.*

No.	Type	Description	Unused	Used
208	**15**	½d. green	0 9	0 4
209	,,	½d. deep green	0 9	0 4
		a. Printed both sides ..	30 0	
210	**16**	1d. orange-red	2 0	0 3
211	,,	1d. pale red	2 0	0 3
212	,,	2d. blue	1 6	0 2
213	**17**	2½d. carmine	4 0	3 0
214	,,	2½d. rose	4 0	2 6
215	**18**	5d. purple-brown ..	5 0	2 6

P 12.

No.	Type	Description	Unused	Used
217	**16**	1d. red		
218	,,	2d. blue	—	15 0

B. *Thick paper.* *W* **11** (*part only on each stamp*).

(*a*) *P* 12½, 13.

No.	Type	Description	Unused	Used
219	**15**	½d. green	1 0	0 8
220	,,	½d. deep green	1 0	0 8

(*b*) *P* 12.

No.	Type	Description	Unused	Used
221	**15**	½d. green	15 0	
222	,,	½d. deep green	15 0	

C. *No wmk.; with blue burelé band at back.*

(*a*) *P* 12½, 13.

No.	Type	Description	Unused	Used
223	**15**	½d. green	0 4	0 6
		a. Without burelé band ..	55 0	
224	,,	½d. deep green	1 3	

(*b*) *P* 12.

No.	Type	Description	Unused	Used
225	**15**	½d. green	20 0	
		a. Without burelé band ..	75 0	

Nos. 223*a* and 225*a* are from the margins of the sheet.

D. *Thin paper, with Crown and Q faintly impressed.* *P* 12½, 13.

No.	Type	Description	Unused	Used
227	**15**	½d. green	1 6	1 0
228	**16**	1d. orange-red .. .	2 6	1 6

19

1898. *Wmk. Crown and Q, T* **6***a.* *P* 12½, 13.

No.	Type	Description	Unused	Used
229	**19**	1d. vermilion	1 0	0 3

20 **21**

22

23

24

25

1897–1907. *Figures in all corners. W* **6***a. P* 12½, 13.

231	**20**	½d. deep green	1	0	0	8
		a. Perf. 12	—		£10	
232	**21**	1d. orange-vermilion ..	0	6	0	2
233	,,	1d. vermilion	0	6	0	2
234	,,	2d. blue	1	0	0	2
235	,,	2d. deep blue	1	0	0	2
236	**22**	2½d. rose	4	0	3	6
237	,,	2½d. purple/*blue*	2	6	0	8
238	,,	2½d. brown-purple/*blue* ..	2	0	0	6
239	,,	2½d. slate/*blue*	10	0	7	6
240	**21**	3d. brown	4	0	1	3
241	,,	3d. deep brown	2	6	1	3
242	,,	3d. reddish brown (1906)	2	6	1	3
243	,,	3d. grey-brown (1907) ..	4	0	1	6
244	,,	4d. yellow	3	0	1	0
245	,,	4d. yellow-buff	3	0	1	0
246	**23**	5d. purple-brown	2	6	1	3
247	,,	5d. dull brown (1906) ..	3	0	3	0
248	,,	5d. black-brown (1907) ..	4	0	3	6
249	**21**	6d. green	2	6	0	6
250	,,	6d. yellow-green	2	6	0	6
251	**24**	1s. pale mauve	6	0	2	6
252	,,	1s. dull mauve	5	0	2	6
253	,,	1s. bright mauve	8	6	3	0
254	**25**	2s. turquoise-green	12	6	8	6

The 1d. formerly listed *perf.* 12 × 9½, is now omitted, as later information shows that it was printed outside the Government Printing Office and was not an official issue.

1899. *W* **6***a.* (*a*) *Zigzag roulette in black.* (*b*) *The same but plain.* (*c*) *Roulette* (*a*) *and also* (*b*). (*d*) *Roulette* (*b*) *and perf.* 12½, 13. (*e*) *Roulette* (*a*) *and perf.* 12½, 13. (*f*) *Compound of* (*a*), (*b*), *and perf.* 12½, 13.

256	**21**	1d. vermilion (*a*)	8	6	8	6
257	,,	1d. vermilion (*b*)	2	0	2	6
258	,,	1d. vermilion (*c*)	7	6		
259	,,	1d. vermilion (*d*)	3	0	4	0
260	,,	1d. vermilion (*e*)	50	0		
261	,,	1d. vermilion (*f*)	75	0		

26

26*a*

1899–1906. *W* **6***a. P* 12½, 13.

262	**26**	½d. deep green	0	6	0	4
263	,,	½d. grey-green	0	6	0	4
264	,,	½d. pale green (1906) ..	0	9	0	6

Stamps of *T* **26** *without wmk.*, are proofs.

1900. *Charity. T* **26***a and horiz. design showing Queen Victoria in medallion inscr.* "PATRIOTIC FUND 1900". *W* **6**. *P* 12.

264*a*	1d. (1s.), claret	£8	£1c
264*b*	2d. (2s.), violet	£18	£2c

These stamps, sold at 1s. and 2s. respectively, paid postage of 1d. and 2d. only, the difference being contributed to a Patriotic Fund.

27

QUEENSLAND

(*a*)

QUEENSLAND

(*b*)

(Engraved and typo. in Melbourne, Victoria.)

1903. *Dates on stamps are those at whic the various colonies were established. Nam lower value tablet, and values in upper corne in second colour. Two varieties of* "QUEEN LAND" (*a*) *and* (*b*). *The letters in* (*a*) *are small than in* (*b*). *W* **10**. *P* 12½.

265	**27**	9d. brown & ultram. (*a*) ..	5	0	3
266	,,	9d. brown & ultram. (*b*) ..	5	0	3

1903. *W* **6***a. P* 12.

267	**26**	½d. green	1	0	0
268	**21**	1d. vermilion	3	0	2
269	,,	2d. blue	—		12

1905. *Recess. P* 12½, 13 (*irregular*).

270	**9**	2s. 6d. vermilion	70	0	30
271	,,	£1 deep green	£15		£

29

30

1906–10. *Litho.* A. *W* **6***a twice sideways.* (*a*) *P*

272	**9**	5s. rose	50	0	30
273	,,	£1 deep green	£6		50

(*b*) *P* 12½, 13 (*irregular*).

274	**9**	£1 deep green	£20		80

B. **W 29.,** *twice sideways.* *P* 12½, 13 (*irregular*).

275	**9**	2s. 6d. vermilion	30 0	20 0
276	,,	2s. 6d. dull orange (1910)	40 0	30 0
277	,,	5s. rose	30 0	20 0
278	,,	5s. deep rose	35 0	27 6
279	,,	10s. deep brown	50 0	40 0
280	,,	£1 bluish green	£5	70 0
280*a*	,,	£1 deep green	£18	£15

1907. *W* **6a.** *P* 12½, 13.

281	**30**	2d. blue	5 0	2 0

As compared with T **21**, the head is redrawn, the top of the crown is higher and touches the frame, as do also the back of the chignon and the point of the bust. The forehead is filled in with lines of shading, and the figures in the corners appear to have been redrawn also.

1907–12. *Wmk. Crown and double-lined. As Type* w. **11.** (*a*) *P* 12×12½.

282	**27**	9d. brown & ultram. (*a*) ..	30 0	7 6
283	,,	9d. brown & ultram. (*b*) ..	5 0	3 0
284	,,	9d. pale brown & blue (*b*) ..	6 0	3 6

(*b*) *P* 11 (1912).

285	**27**	9d. brown and blue (*b*) ..	—	£10

32

T **32** is a second redrawing of T **21.** The fore-ead is again plain, and though the top of the rown is made higher, it does not touch the frame; ut the point of the bust and the chignon still ouch. The figure in the right lower corner does ot touch the line below, and has not the battered ppearance of that in the first redrawn type. The tamps are very clearly printed, the lines of hading being distinct.

908. *W* **29.** (*a*) *P* 12½, 13.

86	**26**	½d. deep green	1 0	0 6
87	,,	½d. deep blue-green ..	0 9	0 4
38	**21**	1d. vermilion	0 9	0 2
		a. Variety. Imperf. (pair) ..	£10	
89	**30**	2d. blue	2 0	0 3
90	**32**	2d. bright blue	2 0	0 2
91	**21**	3d. pale brown	5 0	1 3
92	,,	3d. bistre-brown	5 0	1 3
93	,,	4d. yellow	7 6	3 6
94	,,	4d. grey-black	3 0	2 6
95	**23**	5d. dull brown	5 0	2 6
95*a*	,,	5d. sepia	10 0	4 0
96	**21**	6d. yellow-green	5 0	2 0
97	,,	6d. bright green	6 0	2 0
98	**24**	1s. violet	8 6	5 0
99	,,	1s. bright mauve ..	8 0	5 0
0	**25**	2s. turquoise-green ..	15 0	10 0

(*b*) *P* 13×11 *to* 12½.

1	**26**	½d. deep green		
2	**21**	1d. vermilion	1 0	0 6
3	**32**	2d. blue	3 0	
4	**21**	3d. bistre-brown	2 0	1 3
5	,,	4d. grey-black	8 6	
6	**23**	5d. dull brown	5 0	
7	**21**	6d. yellow-green	10 0	
8	**24**	1s. violet	22 6	

The perforation (*b*) is from a machine intro-aced to help cope with the demands caused by e introduction of penny postage. The three ws at top (or bottom) of the sheet show rieties gauging 13×11½, 13×11, and 13×12 spectively, these are obtainable in strips of ree showing the three variations.

11. *W* **29.** *Perf. irregular compound,* 10½ *to* 12½.

9	**21**	1d. vermilion		

This was from another converted machine, formerly used for perforating Railway stamps. The perforation was very unsatisfactory and only one or two sheets were sold.

POSTAL FISCALS.

Authorised for use from 1 *Jan.*, 1880.

51

52

1866–68. A. *No wmk.* *P* 13.

401	**51**	1d. blue	12 6	
402	,,	6d. deep violet	—	25 0
403	,,	1s. blue-green		
404	,,	2s. brown	—	40 0
405	,,	2s. 6d. dull red	—	17 6
406	,,	5s. yellow		
407	,,	10s. green	45 0	
408	,,	20s. rose		

B. *W* **52.** *P* 15.

409	**51**	1d. blue	3 0	15 0
410	,,	6d. deep violet	—	22 6
411	,,	6d. blue		
412	,,	1s. blue-green	7 6	
413	,,	2s. brown		
414	,,	10s. green		
415	,,	20s. rose		

53

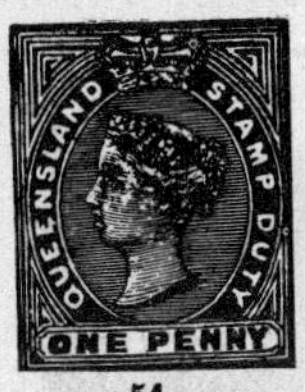

54

1871–2. *P* 12 *or* 13.

A. *Wmk. Large Crown and Q, as T* **11.**

416	**53**	1d. mauve	2 0	3 0
417	,,	6d. red-brown	4 0	6 0
418	,,	1s. green	4 0	6 0
419	,,	2s. blue	6 0	5 0
420	,,	2s. 6d. brick-red ..	12 0	12 6
421	,,	5s. orange brown ..	17 6	12 6
422	,,	10s. brown	—	30 0
423	,,	20s. rose	—	60 0

B. *No wmk. Blue burelé band at back.*

424	**53**	1d. mauve	5 0	
425	,	6d. red-brown	6 0	
426	,,	6d. mauve	10 0	
427	,,	1s. green	7 6	10 0
428	,,	2s. blue	12 6	10 0
429	,,	2s. 6d. vermilion ..		
430	,,	5s. yellow-brown ..	—	25 0
431	,,	10s. brown	—	40 0
432	,,	20s. rose	—	50 0

1878–9.

A. *No wmk. Lilac burelé band at back.* *P* 12.

433	**54**	1d. violet	—	6 0

B. *Wmk. Crown and Q, T* **6.** *P* 12.

434	**54**	1d. violet	2 0	2 6

55

1892. *Wmk. Crown and Q, T* **6**, *sideways. P* 12.

435 **55** 6d. green 15 0 50 0
436 ,, 5s. carmine 35 0 50 0
437 ,, 10s. brown 60 0

Queensland now uses Australian stamps.

RHODESIA.

I. Issues for the Area formerly covered by the British South Africa Company.

— **SIMPLIFICATION** (see Introduction) —

Nos. 119 to 185.

119, 121, 123, 125, 129, 131a, 133, 134, 137, 139, 140, 141a, 144, 145, 146, 148, 149, 151, 152, 153, 154, 155a, 157, 158, 160, 160b, 163, 165.

Nos. 186 to 322.

186, 188b, 190 192, 193, 194, 195, 286, 197, 256, 291, 201, 208, 223, 260, 225, 227, 265, 295, 230, 268, 247, 270, 233, 272, 301, 236, 274a, 304, 239, 276, 306, 252, 241, 242, 243. 280, 281.

1

2

(Recess. Bradbury, Wilkinson & Co.)

1890 (Dec.). *Thin wove paper. P* 14, 14½.

1 **1** 1d. black 2 6 2 0
2 ,, 6d. ultramarine 25 0 17 6
3 ,, 6d. deep blue 8 6 7 6
4 ,, 1s. grey-brown 17 6 10 0
5 ,, 2s. vermilion 25 0 16 0
6 ,, 2s. 6d. grey-purple .. 32 6 30 0
7 ,, 2s. 6d. purple 32 6 30 0
8 ,, 5s. orange-yellow 40 0 25 0
9 ,, 10s. deep green 50 0 60 0
10 **2** £1 deep blue £5 80 0
11 ,, £2 rose-red £12 85 0
12 ,, £5 sage-green £80 £6
13 ,, £10 brown £110 £14

* For later printing of the £2 see No. 74.

Great caution is needed in buying the high values in either used or unused condition, many stamps offered being revenue stamps cleaned and re-gummed or with forged postmarks.

The following sheet watermarks are known in the issues of 1890 and 1891–94. (1) William Collins, Sons & Co.'s paper watermarked with the firm's monogram, and "PURE LINEN WOVE BANK" in double-lined capitals. (2) As (1) with "EXTRA STRONG" and "139" added. (3) Paper by Wiggins, Teape & Co., watermarked "W T & Co" in script letters in double, lined wavy border. (4) The same firm's paper, watermarked "1011" in double-lined figures. (5) "WIGGINS TEAPE & CO LONDON" in double-lined block capitals. Many values can also be found on a slightly thicker paper without wmk. but single specimens are not easily distinguishable.

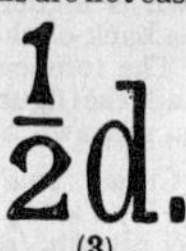

(3)

1891 (Mar.). *Nos. 2 and 4 surch. as T* **3**.

14 **1** ½d. on 6d. ultramarine .. 75 0 £5
15 ,, 2d. on 6d. ultramarine .. £6 £7
16 ,, 4d. on 6d. ultramarine .. £8 £10
17 ,, 8d. on 1s. grey-brown .. £8 £12

4

5. (Ends of scrolls behind legs of springboks.)

(T **4**, Recess. Bradbury, Wilkinson & Co.)

1891–94. *Value typo. in second colour. Thi[n] wove paper* (*wmks. as note after No.* 13) *P* 14, 14½.

18 **4** ½d. dull blue & verm. (4.'91) 2 0 2
19 ,, ½d. deep blue & vermilion .. 2 0 2
20 ,, 2d. sea-green & verm. (4.'91) 6 0 2
21 ,, 3d. grey-blk. & grn. (12.'91) 4 0 3
22 ,, 4d. chestnut & black (4.'91) 7 6 5
23 ,, 8d. rose-lake & ultram. (4.'91) 7 6 8
24 ,, 8d. red and ultramarine .. 6 0 9
25 ,, 3s. brown & green (3.'94) .. 75 0 75
26 ,, 4s. grey-black & ver. (3.'93) 42 6 47

(Recess. Perkins, Bacon & Co. from th[e] Bradbury, Wilkinson plates.)

1895. *Thick soft wove paper. P* 12½.

27 **4** 2d. green and red 12 6 5
28 ,, 4d. yellow-brown & black .. 12 6 10
a. Imperf. (pair) £40

(Centre recess; value typo. Perkins, Bacon.)

1896–97. *Wove paper. P* 14.

Die I. Plates 1 and 2.

(Small dot to the right of the tail of th[e] right-hand supporter in the coat of arms. Bod[y] of lion only partly shaded.)

29 **5** 1d. scarlet and emerald .. 7 6 2
30 ,, 2d. brown and mauve .. 6 0 2
31 ,, 3d. chocolate & ultramarine 2 0 2
32 ,, 4d. ultramarine & mauve .. 6 0 7
a. Imperf. between (pair) ..
33 ,, 6d. mauve and pink.. .. 15 0 8
34 ,, 8d. green and mauve/*buff* .. 3 6 3
a. Imperf. between (pair) ..
b. Imperf. (pair) £70
35 ,, 1s. green and blue 8 6 5
36 ,, 3s. green and mauve/*blue* .. 35 0 35
a. Imperf. (pair) £80
37 ,, 4s. orge.-red & blue/*green* 35 0 20

DIE II. PLATES 3 AND 4.

(No dot. Body of lion heavily shaded all over.)

41 **5** ½d. slate and violet .. 1 9 2 6
42 ,, 1d. scarlet and emerald .. 1 6 2 0
43 ,, 2d. brown and mauve .. 6 0 6 0
44 ,, 4d. ultramarine and mauve 45 0 12 6
45 ,, 4d. blue and mauve .. 2 0 1 0
46 ,, 6d. mauve and rose .. 3 6 1 6
47 ,, 2s. indigo and green/*buff* .. 17 6 7 6
48 ,, 2s. 6d. brown & purple/*yell.* 40 0 20 0
49 ,, 5s. chestnut and emerald .. 30 0 25 0
50 ,, 10s. slate & vermilion/*rose* .. 60 0 40 0

PROVISIONALS *used at Bulawayo during the Matabele rebellion.*

One Penny

(6)

THREE PENCE.

(7)

1896 (APRIL). *Surch. at Bulawayo with T* **6** *and* **7**.

51 **6** 1d. on 3d. (No. 21) £20 £20
a. "P" in "Penny" inverted ..
52 ,, 1d. on 4s. (No. 26) £20 £20
a. "P" in "Penny" inverted ..
b. "y" in "Penny" inverted ..
c. Single bar through original value £40 £55
53 **7** 3d. on 5s. (No. 8) .. £10 £10
a. "R" in "THREE" inverted £400
b. "T" in "THREE" inverted

BRITISH SOUTH AFRICA COMPANY.

(8)

1896 (22 MAY). *Cape of Good Hope stamps optd. by Argus Printing Co., Cape Town, with T* **8**. *Wmk. Anchor* (*3d. wmk. Crown CA*). *P* 14.

58 ½d. grey-black (No. 48*a*) .. 4 0 6 0
59 1d. rose-red (No. 58) 5 0 4 0
60 2d. deep bistre (N. 50*a*). .. 8 6 7 6
61 3d. pale claret (No. 40) .. 15 0 17 6
62 4d. blue (No. 51) 15 0 15 0
a. "COMPANY" omitted .. £300
63 6d. deep purple (No. 52*a*) .. 32 6 37 6
64 1s. yellow-ochre (No. 65) .. 75 0 75 0

. (Ends of scrolls between legs of springboks.)

(Recess. Waterlow & Sons.)

897. *P* 13½ *to* 16.

6 **9** ½d. grey-black and purple .. 2 0 3 0
7 ,, 1d. scarlet and emerald .. 4 0 4 6
8 ,, 2d. brown and mauve .. 3 6 2 0
9 ,, 3d. brown-red and slate-blue 3 6 1 6
a. Imperf. between (pair) .. £60
0 ,, 4d. ultramarine and claret .. 4 0 2 0
a. Imperf. between (pair) .. — £225
,, 6d. dull purple and pink .. 5 0 4 0
,, 8d. green and mauve/*buff* .. 10 0 6 0
a. Imperf. between (pair) .. — £50
,, £1 black & red-brown/*green* .. £20 £9

(Recess. Waterlow, from the Bradbury plate.)

1897 (JAN.). *P* 15.

74 **2** £2 rosy-red £50 £6

10 11

12

(Recess. Waterlow.)

1898–1908. *P* 13½ *to* 16.

75 **10** ½d. yellow-green 1 6 0 3
a. Imperf. between (pair .. £15
b. Imperf. (pair) £20
76 ,, ½d. deep green 27 6 1 0
77 ,, 1d. rose 1 0 0 3
a. Imperf. (pair) £40 £30
b. Imperf. between (pair) .. £16
78 ,, 1d. red 3 6 0 3
a. Imperf. between (pair) .. £8
b. Imperf. (pair) £12
79 ,, 2d. brown 2 6 0 3
80 ,, 2½d. pale dull blue (1903) .. 3 0 1 0
a. Imperf. between (pair) .. £20 £22
81 ,, 3d. claret (1908) 6 0 5 0
a. Imperf. between (pair) .. £30
82 ,, 4d. olive 5 0 1 3
a. Imperf. between (pair) .. £30
83 ,, 6d. mauve 7 0 3 6
83*a* ,, 6d. reddish purple 15 0 12 6
84 **11** 1s. bistre-buff 7 0 3 6
a. Imperf. between (pair) .. £60
84*b* ,, 1s. olive-bistre £8
c. Imperf. (pair) £65
d. Imperf. between (horiz. pair) £125
85 ,, 2s. 6d. bluish grey (Nov., 1906) 20 0 7 6
a. Imperf. between (pair) .. £40 £30
86 ,, 3s. deep violet (May, 1908) 10 0 5 0
87 ,, 5s. orange (July, 1901) .. 20 0 12 6
88 ,, 7s. 6d. black (Nov., 1901) 40 0 35 0
89 ,, 10s. dull grn. (May, 1908) .. 22 6 15 0
90 **12** £1 grey-purple (July, '01) £6 50 0
91 ,, £2 brown (May, 1908) .. £6 40 0
92 ,, £5 deep blue (July, 1901) £125 £6
93 ,, £10 lilac (7.01) £350 £15

13. Victoria Falls.

(Recess. Waterlow.)

1905 (13 July). *Visit of British Association and opening of Victoria Falls Bridge. P* 13½ *to* 15.

94 **13** 1d. red 2 0 2 6
95 „ 2½d. deep blue 7 0 7 6
96 „ 5d. claret 20 0 20 0
97 „ 1s. blue-green 20 0 22 6
a. Imperf. between (pair) £120
b. Imperf. (pair) £135
98 „ 2s. 6d. black 55 0 70 0
99 „ 5s. violet 55 0 65 0

RHODESIA.

(**14**)

1909 (15 April). *Optd. as T* **14**. *P* 14 *or* 15.

100 **10** ½d. green 0 6 0 6
a. No stop after "RHODESIA" 32 6 15 0
101 „ 1d. carmine-red 0 6 0 3
a. No stop 60 0 15 0
b. Imperf. between (pair) £12
101*c* „ 1d. scarlet 15 0 0 4
d. Imperf. between (pair) £20
102 „ 2d. brown 3 0 2 0
a. No stop 40 0 30 0
103 „ 2½d. pale dull blue 1 6 0 8
a. No stop 30 0 12 6
104 „ 3d. claret 4 0 3 0
a. No stop £5 65 0
105 „ 4d. olive 5 0 3 0
a. No stop 30 0 30 0
106 „ 6d. dull purple 12 6 5 0
a. No stop 50 0 22 6
106*b* „ 6d. reddish purple 3 0 2 6
107 **11** 1s. bistre-buff 7 6 2 6
a. No stop 40 0 30 0
108 „ 2s. 6d. bluish grey 15 0 12 6
a. No stop 30 0 30 0
109 „ 3s. deep violet 20 0 15 0
110 „ 5s. orange 30 0 20 0
a. No stop 60 0 75 0
111 „ 7s. 6d. black 40 0 22 6
112 „ 10s. dull green 35 0 30 0
a. No stop £8
113 **12** £1 grey-purple £5 75 0
a. Vertical pair, one with and one without overprint £135
b. Overprint in violet £16 £14
113*c* „ £2 brown (*bluish paper*) £250 £20

In some values the no-stop variety occurs in every stamp in a vertical row of a sheet, in other values only once in a sheet. Other varieties, such as no serif to the right of apex of "A", no serif to top of "E", etc., exist in some values.

RHODESIA.
5d

(**15**)

RHODESIA.
TWO SHILLINGS.

(**16**)

1909 (April)–**1911**. *T* **10** *and* **11** *surch. as T* **15** *and* **16** (*2s.*), *in black*.

114 5d. on 6d. reddish purple 7 6 6 0
a. Surcharge in violet 15 0
115 5d. on 6d. dull purple 7 6 6 0
116 7½d. on 2s. 6d. bluish grey 5 0 4 0
a. Surcharge in violet 15 0 8 0
117 10d. on 3s. deep violet 9 0 8 0
a. Surcharge in violet 5 0 6 0
118 2s. on 5s. orange 12 6 10 0

In the 7½d. and 10d. surcharges, the bars are spaced as in **T 16**.

½D BRITISH SOUTH AFRICA COMPANY ½D
RHODESIA

17

(Recess. Waterlow.)

1910 (11 Nov.)–**1916**. *T* **17**. (*a*) *P* 14.

119 ½d. yellow-green 1 0 0 6
a Imperf. (pair) £35 £40
120 ½d. bluish green 6 0 0 9
121 ½d. olive-green 4 0 0 6
122 ½d. dull green (1916) 4 0 7 6
123 1d. bright carmine 1 3 0 4
a. Imperf. between (pair) £65
124 1d. carmine-lake 6 0 0 6
125 1d. rose-red 2 6 0 4
126 2d. black and grey 6 0 5 0
127 2d. black-pur. & slate-grey £7 £9
128 2d. black & slate-grey 4 0 2 6
129 2d. black and slate 3 0 4 0
130 2d. black and grey-black 4 6 3 6
131 2½d. ultramarine 7 6 5 0
131*a* 2½d. bright ultramarine 4 0 6 0
132 2½d. dull blue 6 0 6 0
133 2½d. chalky blue 7 6 8 6
134 3d. purple and ochre 6 0 5 0
135 3d. purple & yellow-ochre 10 0 3 6
136 3d. magenta & yellow-ochre 42 6 25 0
137 3d. violet and ochre 17 6 15 0
138 4d. greenish black & orange 25 0 17 6
139 4d. brown-purple & orange 25 0 12 6
140 4d. black and orange 10 0 8 6
141 5d. purple-brn. & olive-grn. 22 6 20 0
141*a* 5d. purple-brn. & olive-yell. 22 6 12 6
142 5d. purple-brn. & ochre (*error*) £18 £1[illegible]
143 5d. lake-brown and olive 55 0 40 [illegible]
144 6d. red-brown and mauve 8 6 7 [illegible]
145 6d. brown and purple 10 0 8 [illegible]
145*a* 6d. bright chestnut & mauve 65 0 20 [illegible]
146 8d. black and purple 60 0 70 [illegible]
147 8d. dull purple & purple 60 0 30 [illegible]
148 8d. greenish black & purple 50 0 32 [illegible]
149 10d. scarlet & reddish mauve 25 0 17 [illegible]
150 10d. carmine and deep purple 40 0 25 [illegible]
151 1s. black and deep blue-grn. 15 0 12 [illegible]
152 1s. black & pale blue-green 10 0 8 [illegible]
152*a* 1s. purple-black & blue-grn. £12 75 [illegible]
153 2s. black & ultramarine 40 0 35 [illegible]
154 2s. black and dull blue £5 40 [illegible]
154*a* 2s. purple-black & ultram. £20 85
155 2s. 6d. black and lake 80 0
155*a* 2s. 6d. black and crimson 80 0 65
156 2s. 6d. sepia & deep crimson £7 £[illegible]
157 2s. 6d. black & rose-carmine 80 0 60
158 3s. green and violet 50 0 45
159 5s. vermilion & deep green £5 60
160 5s. scarlet & pale yell.-grn. 60 0 55
160*a* 5s. crimson and yellow-grn. £6
160*b* 7s. 6d. carmine & pale blue £5
161 7s. 6d. carmine & light blue £5 65
162 7s. 6d. carmine & brt. blue £12 £[illegible]
163 10s. deep myrtle & orange £6 £[illegible]
164 10s. blue-green & orange £12
165 £1 carm.-red & bluish black £22 £[illegible]
166 £1 rose-scarlet & bluish blk. £22 £[illegible]
166*a* £1 crimson & slate-black £25 £[illegible]
166*b* £1 scarlet & reddish mauve (*error*) £225

(*b*) *P* 15.

167 ½d. blue-green £6
168 ½d. yellow-green £6 5
169 ½d. apple-green £8 7
170 1d. carmine £5 1
171 2d. black and grey-black £8 6
172 2½d. ultramarine £5 30

No.	Description	Unused	Used
173	3d. purple & yellow-ochre	£20	20 0
174	4d. black and orange	25 0	25 0
175	5d. lake-brown & olive-green	£8	40 0
176	6d. brown and mauve	£8	25 0
177	1s. black and blue-green	£8	20 0
178	2s. black and dull blue	£40	£20
179	£1 red and black	£125	£100

(c) *P* 15 × 14 *or* 14 × 15.

No.	Description	Unused	Used
179a	½d. yellow-green	£25	
180	3d. purple & ochre	£35	£12
181	4d. black & orange	£14	
181a	1s. black & blue-green	£18	£18

(d) *P* 13½.

No.	Description	Unused	Used
182	½d. yellow-green	£5	22 6
183	1d. bright carmine	£6	40 0
184	2½d. ultramarine	17 6	30 0
185	8d. black and purple	32 6	45 0

(e) *Perf. compound of* 14 *and* 15.

No.	Description	Unused	Used
185a	1d. carmine		

Minor plate varieties in T **17** are:—½d. Double dot below "D" in right-hand value tablet. 2d. to £1. Straight stroke in Queen's right ear.

18

(Recess. Waterlow.)

1913–22. *T* **18**. *No wmk.*

(i.) *From single working plates.* (a) *P* 14.

No.	Description	Unused	Used
186	½d. blue-green	3 0	0 3
	a. Imperf. between (pair)	£18	£18
187	½d. deep green	1 9	0 3
188	½d. yellow-green	5 0	1 0
	a. Imperf. between (pair)	£20	
188b	½d. dull green	4 0	0 3
189	½d. bright green	4 0	0 4
190	1d. rose-carmine	1 3	0 3
	a. Imperf. between (pair)	£18	£18
191	1d. carmine-red	4 0	0 3
192	1d. brown-red	2 6	0 4
193	1d. red	3 6	0 4
194	1d. scarlet	2 6	0 3
195	1d. rose-red	2 0	0 10
196	1d. crimson	90 0	30 0
	a. Imperf. between (pair)	£25	
197	1½d. brown-ochre (1919)	1 6	0 4
	a. Imperf. between (pair)	£30	£30
198	1½d. bistre-brown (1917)	2 0	0 6
	a. Imperf. between (pair)	£30	£30
199	1½d. drab-brown	2 0	0 4
	a. Imperf. between (pair)	£35	
200	2½d. deep blue	5 0	7 6
201	2½d. bright blue	5 0	7 6

(b) *P* 15.

No.	Description	Unused	Used
202	½d. blue-green	5 0	3 0
203	½d. green	5 0	2 6
204	1d. carmine	£10	15 0
	a. Imperf. between (pair)	£75	
205	1d. brown-red	2 6	2 0
206	1½d. bistre-brown (1919)	12 6	4 0
206a	1½d. drab-brown	10 0	4 0
207	2½d. deep blue	15 0	15 0
208	2½d. bright blue	10 0	10 0

(c) *P* 14 × 15.

No.	Description	Unused	Used
208a	½d. green	£50	£8

(d) *P* 15 × 14.

No.	Description	Unused	Used
208b	½d. green	—	£12
208c	1½d. drab-brown		

(e) *P* 13½.

No.	Description	Unused	Used
208d	1d. red	—	£30

The remaining values were printed from double, i.e. head and duty, plates. There are at least four different head plates made from three different dies, which may be distinguished as follows :—

Die I. The King's left ear is neither shaded nor outlined ; no outline to cap.

Die II. The ear is shaded all over, but has no outline. The top of the cap has a faint outline.

Die III. The ear is shaded and outlined ; a heavy continuous outline round the cap.

(ii.) *Printed from double plates, head Die* I.

(a) *P* 14.

No.	Description	Unused	Used
209	2d. black and grey	7 6	3 0
210	3d. black and yellow	32 6	5 0
211	4d. black and orange-red	6 6	6 0
212	5d. black and green	5 0	8 6
213	6d. black and mauve	£8	20 0
213a	8d. violet and green	£125	
214	2s. black and brown	40 0	22 6

(b) *P* 15.

No.	Description	Unused	Used
215	3d. black and yellow	8 6	10 0
216	4d. black and orange-red	£8	12 6
217	6d. black and mauve	4 0	6 0
217a	8d. violet and green		
218	2s. black and brown	17 6	20 0

(iii.) *Head Die* II. (a) *P* 14.

No.	Description	Unused	Used
219	2d. black and grey	10 0	4 0
220	2d. black and brownish grey	22 6	10 0
221	3d. black and deep yellow	20 0	1 3
222	3d. black and yellow	27 6	1 6
223	3d. black and buff	5 0	2 6
224	4d. black and orange-red	10 0	3 0
225	4d. black and deep orge.-red	7 0	3 0
226	5d. black and grey-green	15 0	10 0
227	5d. black and bright green	10 0	12 6
228	6d. black and mauve	12 6	2 6
229	6d. black and purple	17 6	3 0
230	8d. violet and green	17 6	10 0
231	10d. blue and carmine-red	12 6	15 0
232	1s. black and greenish blue	17 6	10 0
233	1s. black and turquoise-blue	6 0	6 0
234	2s. black and brown	35 0	8 0
235	2s. black and yellow-brown	65 0	20 0
236	2s. 6d. indigo & grey-brown	32 6	12 6
236a	2s. 6d. pale blue and brown		
236b	3s. brown and blue	45 0	40 0
237	3s. chestnut and bright blue	45 0	40 0
238	5s. blue and yellow-green	£5	40 0
239	5s. blue and blue-green	45 0	30 0
240	7s. 6d. mauve & grey-black	£5	75 0
241	10s. crimson & yellow-green	£5	75 0
242	£1 black and purple	£12	£9
243	£1 black and violet	£16	£16

(b) *P* 15.

No.	Description	Unused	Used
244	2d. black and grey	4 0	4 0
245	4d. black & deep orange-ver.	£18	£8
246	8d. violet and green	£8	£6
247	10d. blue and red	8 6	12 6
248	1s. black and greenish blue	8 6	4 6
249	2s. 6d. indigo & grey-brown	25 0	25 0
250	3s. chocolate and blue	£30	£12
251	5s. blue and yellow-green	80 0	55 0
251a	5s. blue and blue-green	£25	
252	7s. 6d. mauve & grey-black	85 0	80 0
253	10s. red and green	£16	£14
254	£1 black and purple	£30	£20

(c) *Perf. compound of* 14 *and* 15.

No.	Description	Unused	Used
254a	2d. black and grey		

(iv.) *Head Die* III. *Toned paper, yellowish gum.*

(*a*) *P* 14.

No.	Description	Unused	Used
255	2d. black & brownish grey ..	10 0	7 6
256	2d. black and grey-black ..	2 0	1 0
	a. Imperf. between (pair) ..	£125	£100
257	2d. black and grey	2 6	1 0
258	2d. black and sepia ..	7 6	3 6
259	3d. black and yellow ..	5 0	1 3
260	3d. black and ochre ..	5 0	1 3
261	4d. black and orange-red ..	3 0	2 0
262	4d. black and dull red ..	7 6	6 0
263	5d. black and pale green ..	6 0	7 6
	a. Imperf. between (pair) ..	£200	
264	5d. black and green ..	6 0	7 6
265	6d. black and reddish mauve	7 6	3 0
266	6d. black and dull mauve ..	5 0	2 6
	a. Imperf. between (pair) ..		
267	8d. mauve & dull blue-green	30 0	20 0
268	8d. mauve & greenish blue	35 0	15 0
269	10d. indigo and carmine ..	17 6	15 0
270	10d. blue and red	12 6	15 0
271	1s. black and greenish blue	10 0	3 0
272	1s. black & pale blue-green	7 6	3 0
272*a*	1s. black and light blue ..	20 0	7 6
272*b*	1s. black and green ..	65 0	35 0
273	2s. black and brown ..	17 6	8 6
273*a*	2s. black and yellow-brown	80 0	30 0
274	2s. 6d. deep ult. & grey-brn.	35 0	20 0
274*a*	2s. 6d. pale blue and pale bistre-brown	£9	45 0
274*b*	3s. chestnut and light blue	90 0	45 0
275	5s. deep blue & blue-green	65 0	30 0
276	5s. blue & pale yellow-green	65 0	30 0
276*a*	7s. 6d. mauve & grey-black	£15	£12
277	10s. carm.-lake & yell.-green	£12	£7
278	£1 black and bright purple	£14	£12
279	£1 black and deep purple ..	£14	£12
279*a*	£1 black and violet-indigo	£16	£14
279*b*	£1 black and deep violet ..	£20	£14

(*b*) *P* 15.

No.	Description	Unused	Used
279*c*	2d. black and brownish grey	£60	£9

(*c*) *Perf. compound of* 14 *and* 15.

No.	Description	Unused	Used
279*d*	10d. blue and carmine ..		

= Half Penny (19) = Half- Penny. (20)

1917 (15 Aug.). *No.* 190, *surch. at the Northern Rhodesian Administrative Press, Livingstone, with T* **19**, *in violet or violet-black.*

No.	Description	Unused	Used
280	½d. on 1d. rose-carm. (*shades*)	2 0	3 0
	a. Surcharge inverted	£18	£20
	b. Letters "n n" spaced wider ..	12 6	15 0
	c. Letters "n y" spaced wider ..	6 0	7 6

The setting was in two rows of 10 repeated three times in the sheet.

Of variety, No. 280a, only two sheets were found.

The two colours of the surcharge occur on the same sheet.

1917 (22 Sept.). *No.* 190 *surch. as T* **20** (*new setting with hyphen, and full stop after* "Penny"), *in deep violet.*

No.	Description	Unused	Used
281	½d. on 1d. rose-carm. (*shades*)	1 6	2 0

1922–24. *T* **18.** *New printings on white paper with clear white gum.*

(i.) *Single working plates.*

(*a*) *P* 14.

No.	Description	Unused	Used
282	½d. dull green (1922) ..	1 3	0 10
	a. Imperf. between (pair) ..	£50	
283	½d. deep blue-green (1923)	3 0	1 0
284	1d. bright rose (1922) ..	3 6	1 0
285	1d. bright rose-scarlet (1923)	2 0	1 9
286	1d. aniline red (Aug., 1924)	£6	6 6
286*a*	1d. carmine-red (Jan., 1924)	60 0	17 6
	b. Imperf. between (pair) ..	£45	
287	1½d. brown-ochre (1923) ..	3 0	0 6
	a. Imperf. between (pair) ..	£45	

(*b*) *P* 15.

No.	Description	Unused	Used
288	½d. dull green (1923) ..	20 0	10 0
289	1d. bright rose-scarlet (1923)	25 0	
290	1½d. brown-ochre (1923) ..	25 0	

(ii.) *Double plates. Head Die* III.

(*a*) *P* 14.

No.	Description	Unused	Used
291	2d. black & grey-pur. (1922)	2 0	0 6
292	2d. black & slate-pur. (1923)	4 6	1 9
293	3d. black & yellow (1922) ..	10 0	8 6
294	4d. blk. & oran.-ver. (1922–3)	12 6	5 0
295	6d. jet-black & lilac (1922–3)	2 6	1 0
296	8d. mauve and pale blue-green (1922)	20 0	15 0
297	8d. violet & grey-grn. (1923)	25 0	27 6
298	10d. brt. ultram. & red (1922)	12 6	12 6
299	10d. bright ultramarine and carmine-red (1923) ..	17 6	17 6
300	1s. blk. & dull blue (1922–3)	5 0	3 6
	a. Imperf. between (pair) ..	£200	
301	2s. black & brown (1922–3)	15 0	10 0
302	2s. 6d. ultramarine & sepia (1922)	45 0	40 0
303	2s. 6d. violet-blue & grey-brown (1923)	27 6	20 0
303*a*	2s. 6d. pale blue and pale bistre-brown		
304	3s. red-brown & turquoise-blue (1922)	35 0	17 6
305	3s. red-brown & grey-blue (1923)	65 0	32 6
306	5s. bright ultramarine and emerald (1922) ..	70 0	50 0
307	5s. dp. bl. & brt. grn. (1923)	70 0	50 0
308	7s. 6d. plum & slate (1922)	£6	75 0
309	10s. crimson & bright yellow-green (1922)	£7	£5
310	10s. carm. & yell.-grn. (1923)	£8	£7
311	£1 blk. & dp. magenta (1922)	£20	£16
311*a*	£1 black & magenta (1923)	£18	£16

(*b*) *P* 15 (1923).

No.	Description	Unused	Used
312	2d. black & slate-purple ..	25 0	35 0
313	4d. black & orange-vermilion	25 0	40 0
314	6d. jet-black and lilac ..	32 6	50 0
315	8d. violet and grey-green ..	40 0	70 0
316	10d. brt. ultram. & carm.-red	50 0	90 0
317	1s. black and dull blue ..	60 0	£5
318	2s. black and brown ..	85 0	£8
319	2s. 6d. violet-blue & grey-brown	£6	£9
320	3s. red-brown & grey-blue	£7	£10
321	5s. deep blue & bright green	£8	£20
322	£1 black and magenta ..	£24	£22

The 1922 printing shows the mesh of the paper very clearly through the gum. In the 1923 printing the gum is very smooth and the mesh of the paper is not so clearly seen. Where date is given as "(1922–23)" two printings were made, which do not differ sufficiently in colour to be listed separately.

In 1924 Rhodesia was divided into Northern and Southern Rhodesia (*q.v.*) and between 1954 and 1964 these were merged in the Central African Federation (*see* Rhodesia and Nyasaland). In 1964 there were again separate issues for Northern and Southern Rhodesia but after Northern Rhodesia became independent and was renamed Zambia, Southern Rhodesia was renamed Rhodesia in October 1964.

II. ISSUES FOR THE FORMER SOUTHERN RHODESIA.

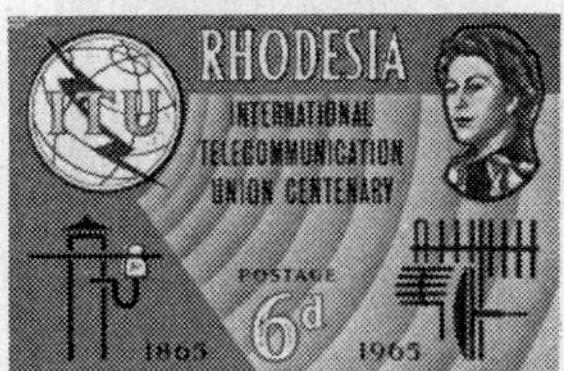

21. "Telecommunications".

(Des. V. Whiteley. Photo. Harrison.)

1965 (17 MAY). *I.T.U. Centenary.* *P* 14½.

351	**21**	6d. violet & lt. yell.-olive	1	0	1	3
352	,,	1s. 3d. violet and lilac .	2	0	2	6
353	,,	2s. 6d. violet and lt. brown	4	0	4	9

22. Bangala Dam. **23.** Irrigation Canal.

24. Cutting Sugar Cane.

(Des. V. Whiteley. Photo. Harrison.)

965 (19 JULY). *Water Conservation.* *P* 14 × 14½.

54	**22**	3d. multicoloured ..	0	8	0	8
55	**23**	4d. multicoloured ..	0	9	0	11
56	**24**	2s. 6d. multicoloured ..	4	0	4	6

5. Sir Winston Churchill, Quill, Sword and Houses of Parliament.

(Des. H. Baxter. Photo. Harrison.)

1965 (16 AUG.). *Churchill Commemoration.* *P* 14½.

357	**25**	1s. 3d. black & bright blue	10	0	17	6

26. Coat-of-Arms.

(Des. Col. C. R. Dickenson. Litho. Mardon Printers (Pvt.) Ltd., Salisbury.)

1965 (8 DEC.). "*Independence*". *P* 11.

358	**26**	2s. 6d. multicoloured ..	5	0	7	6

INDEPENDENCE
11th November
1965

(27)

INDEPENDENCE
11th November 1965 = 5/-

(28)

1966 (17 JAN.). *Nos. 92/105 of Southern Rhodesia optd. with T* **27** *or larger* (5s. *to* £1).

359	**45**	½d. yellow, yellow-green and light blue ..	0	4	0	6
360	**46**	1d. reddish violet and yellow-ochre ..	0	6	0	10
361	**47**	2d. yellow & deep violet	0	8	1	0
362	**48**	3d. chocolate & pale blue	1	0	1	6
363	**49**	4d. yell.-orge. & dp. green	1	2	1	8
364	**50**	6d. carmine-red, yellow and deep dull green ..	1	3	1	9
365	**51**	9d. red-brown, yellow and yellow-brown ..	1	4	2	0
366	**52**	1s. blue-green and ochre	1	9	2	3
		a. Opt. double				
367	**53**	1s. 3d. vermilion, violet and yellow-green ..	2	6	3	6
368	**54**	2s. blue and ochre ..	10	0	12	6
369	**55**	2s. 6d. ultram. and verm.	7	6	8	6
370	**56**	5s. lt. brown, bistre-yellow and light blue ..	25	0	35	0
371	**57**	10s. black, yellow-ochre, lt. blue & carmine-red	20	0	25	0
372	**58**	£1 brown, yellow-green, ochre and vermilion..	60	0	70	0

No. 357 *surch. with T* **28.**

373	**25**	5s. on 1s. 3d. black and bright blue (R.) ..	£9		£12	

29. Emeralds.

(Des. V. Whiteley. Photo. Harrison.)

1966 (9 Feb.). *As T* **45/51** *and* **53/8** *of Southern Rhodesia, but inscr.* "RHODESIA" *as T* **29.** *Some designs and colours changed. P* 14½ (1*d. to* 4*d.*), 13½ × 13 (6*d. to* 2*s.* 6*d.*) *or* 14½ × 14 (5*s. to* £1).

No.	Type	Value and colour	Unused s.	d.	Used s.	d.
374	**46**	1d. reddish violet and yellow-ochre	0	3	0	4
375	**49**	2d. yell.-orge. & dp. grn.	0	4	0	6
376	**48**	3d. chocolate & pale blue	0	6	0	8
377	**29**	4d. emerald and sepia ..	0	7	0	11
378	**50**	6d. carmine-red, yellow and deep dull green..	0	10	1	3
379	**47**	9d. yellow and deep violet	1	1	1	5
380	**45**	1s. yellow, yellow-green and light blue ..	1	5	1	9
381	**54**	1s. 3d. blue and ochre ..	1	9	2	3
382	**51**	1s. 6d. red-brown, yellow and yellow-green ..	2	0	2	9
383	**53**	2s. vermilion, violet and yellow-green	2	9	3	6
384	**55**	2s. 6d. blue, vermilion and turquoise-blue ..	3	6	4	6
385	**56**	5s. light brown, bistre-yellow and light blue	6	9	7	6
386	**57**	10s. black, yellow-ochre, lt. blue & carmine-red	13	3	15	0
387	**58**	£1 brown, yellow-green, ochre and vermilion..	25	0	35	0

T **45** and **47** are in larger format as T **50.**

POSTAGE DUE STAMPS.

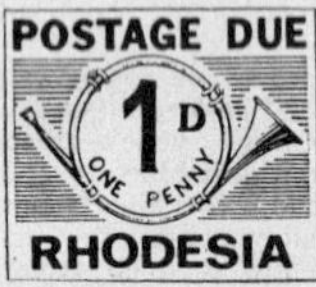

D 1

(Typo. Printing and Stationery Dept., Salisbury.)

1965 (17 June). *Roul.*

No.	Type	Value and colour	Unused s.	d.	Used s.	d.
D1	D **1**	1d. orange-red	0	3	0	5
D2	,,	2d. deep blue	0	4	0	6
D3	,,	4d. green	0	7	0	9
D4	,,	6d. plum	0	10	1	0

RHODESIA & NYASALAND.

Stamps for the Central African Federation of Northern and Southern Rhodesia and Nyasaland Protectorate.

1

2

3. Queen Elizabeth II.

(Recess. Waterlow and Sons.)

1954 (1 July)–**56.** *P* 13½ × 14 (*T* **1**), 13½ × 13 (*T* **2**) *or* 14 × 13½ (*T* **3**).

No.	Type	Value and colour	Unused s.	d.	Used s.	d.
1	**1**	½d. red-orange	0	6	0	6
		a. Coil stamp. P 12½ × 14 (6.2.56)	2	6	2	6
2	,,	1d. ultramarine	0	8	0	6
		a. Coil stamp. P 12½ × 14 (*shades*) (1.10.55)	3	6	4	0
3	,,	2d. bright green	1	0	0	8
3*a*	,,	2½d. ochre (15.2.56)	1	6	0	8
4	,,	3d. carmine-red	1	2	0	6
5	,,	4d. red-brown	2	6	1	6
6	,,	4½d. blue-green	2	6	2	6
7	,,	6d. brt. reddish pur. (*shades*)	4	0	2	0
8	,,	9d. violet	4	0	5	6
9	,,	1s. grey-black	3	6	2	0
10	**2**	1s. 3d. red-orge. & ultram.	4	6	2	0
11	,,	2s. dp. blue & yellow-brown	7	6	6	0
12	,,	2s. 6d. black and rose-red	10	6	10	6
13	,,	5s. violet and olive-green..	20	0	14	0
14	**3**	10s. dull blue-green & orge.	45	0	30	0
15	,,	£1 olive-green and lake ..	90	0	60	0

Nos. 1*a* and 2*a* printed on rotary machines by subsidiary company, Imprimerie Belge de Securité, in Belgium.

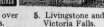

4. Aeroplane over Victoria Falls. **5.** Livingstone and Victoria Falls.

(Des. L. Hughes (3d.), V. L. Horne (1s.). Recess Waterlow.)

1955 (15 June). *Centenary of Discovery Victoria Falls. P* 13½ (3*d.*) *or* 13 (1*s*).

No.	Type	Value and colour	Unused s.	d.	Used s.
16	**4**	3d. ultramarine and deep turquoise-green	3	0	3
17	**5**	1s. purple and deep blue ..	7	0	8

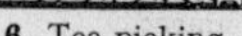

6. Tea picking. **7.** V.H.F. Mast.

8. Copper Mining.

9. Fairbridge Memorial.

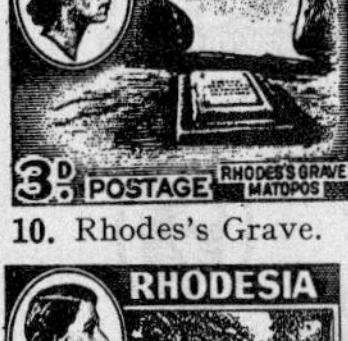

10. Rhodes's Grave.

11. Lake Bangweulu.

12. Eastern Cataract, Victoria Falls.

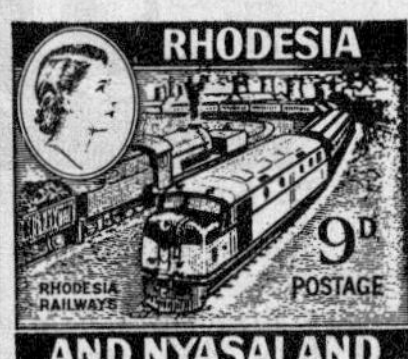

12a. Rhodesian Railway Trains.

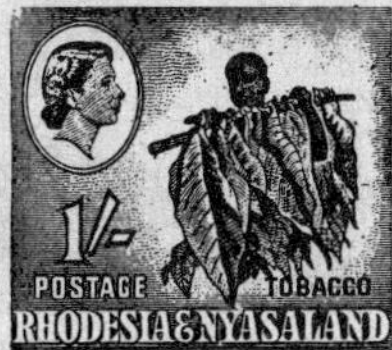

13. Tobacco.

14. Lake Nyasa.

15. Chirundu Bridge.

16. Salisbury Airport.

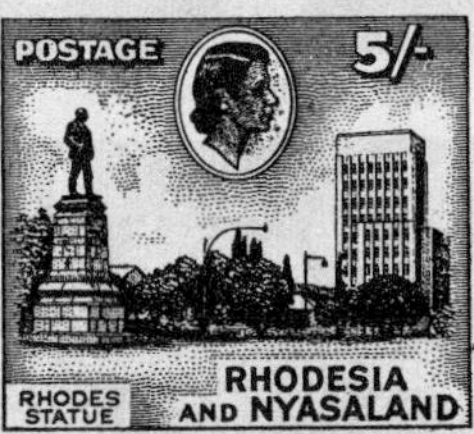

17. Rhodes Statue.

18. Mlanje.

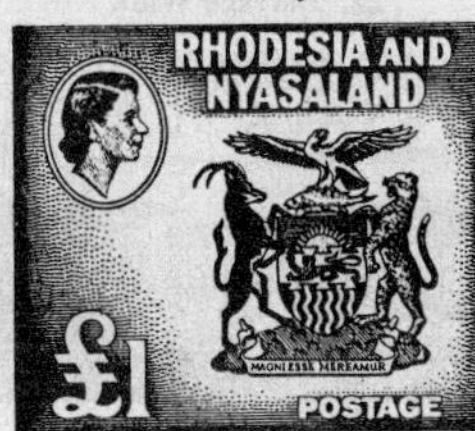

19. Federal Coat-of-Arms.

(Des. M. Kinsella (9d.). Recess. Waterlow (½d., 1d., 2d., 1s.) until 1962, then De La Rue. De La Rue (2½d., 4d., 6d , 9d., 2s., 2s. 6d.) and Bradbury, Wilkinson (others).)

1959 (12 Aug.)–**62.** *P* 13½ × 14 (*½d., 1d., 2d.*), 14½ (*2½d., 4d., 6d., 9d., 2s., 2s. 6d.*), 14 × 13½ (*3d.*), 13½ × 13 (*1s.*), 14 (*1s. 3d.*) *or* 11 (*others*).

No.	Type	Description	Unused		Used	
18	**6**	½d. black & light emerald	0	6	1	0
		a. Coil stamp. P 12½ × 14 ..	1	9	1	9
19	**7**	1d. carmine-red and black	0	6	0	6
		a. Coil stamp (*shades*). P 12½ × 14	2	0	2	0
20	**8**	2d. violet & yellow-brown	0	8	0	8
21	**9**	2½d. purple and grey-blue..	1	0	0	9
22	**10**	3d. black and blue ..	1	2	0	5
		a. Centre omitted				
23	**11**	4d. maroon and olive ..	1	4	0	8
24	**12**	6d. ultramarine and deep myrtle-green	1	9	1	6
24*a*	**12*a***	9d. orange-brn. & reddish violet (15.5.62) ..	4	0	6	0
25	**13**	1s. light green & ultram...	3	0	1	3
26	**14**	1s. 3d. emerald & dp. choc.	4	6	1	3
27	**15**	2s. grey-green & carmine	7	6	10	0
28	**16**	2s. 6d. light blue and yellow-brown	8	0	10	0

29	**17**	5s. dp. choc. & yell.-grn.	15	6	13	6
30	**18**	10s. olive-brown & rose-red	25	0	35	0
31	**19**	£1 black and deep violet	50	0	50	0

20. Kariba Gorge 1955.

21. 330kV. Power Lines.

22. Barrage Wall.

23. Barrage and Lake.

24. Interior of Power Station.

25. Barrage Wall and Queen Mother (top left).

(Photo. Harrison (3d., 6d.), De La Rue (others).)

1960 (17 May). *Opening of Kariba Hydro-Electric Scheme.* *P* 14½ × 14 (*3d., 6d.*) *or* 13 (*others*).

32	**20**	3d. blackish grn. & red-orge.	3	0	3	0
33	**21**	6d. brown & yellow-brown	4	0	4	9
34	**22**	1s. slate-blue and green ..	7	6	8	6
35	**23**	1s. 3d. light blue & orange-brown (*shades*)	10	0	11	6
36	**24**	2s. 6d. deep slate-purple & orange-red	25	0	30	0
37	**25**	5s. reddish vio. & turq.-blue	65	0	80	0

26. Miner Drilling.

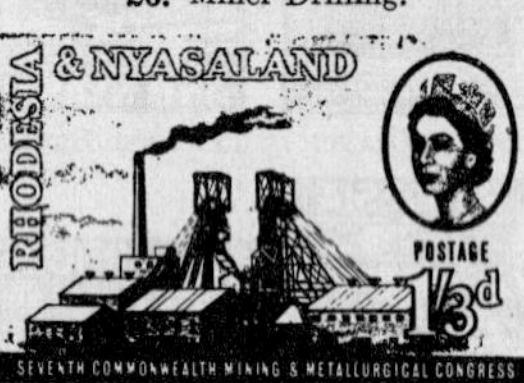

27. Surface Installations, Copper Mine.

(Des. V. Whiteley. Photo. Harrison.)

1961 (8 May). *Seventh Commonwealth Mining and Metallurgical Congress.* *P* 15 × 14.

38	**26**	6d. olive-green & orge.-brn.	3	0	5	0
39	**27**	1s. 3d. black and light blue	8	0	9	0

28. D.H. " Hercules " on Rhodesian air-strip.

29. Empire " C " Class Flying-boat taking-off from Zambesi.

30. D.H. " Comet " at Salisbury Airport.

(Des. M. Kinsella (6d., 2s. 6d.). Photo. Harrison.)

1962 (6 FEB.). *30th Anniv. of First London-Rhodesia Airmail Service. P* 14½ × 14.

40	**28**	6d. bronze-grn. & vermilion	2	0	2	6
41	**29**	1s. 3d. lt. bl., blk. & yell.	5	6	6	0
42	**30**	2s. 6d. rose-red & dp. violet	10	0	12	0

31. Tobacco Plant.

32. Tobacco Field.

33. Auction Floor.

34. Cured Tobacco.

(Des. V. Whiteley. Photo. Harrison.)

1963 (18 FEB.). *World Tobacco Congress, Salisbury. P* 14 × 14½.

43	**31**	3d. green and olive-brown ..	1	6	2	0
44	**32**	6d. green, brown and blue	2	6	3	6
45	**33**	1s. 3d. chestnut and indigo	7	0	6	0
46	**34**	2s. 6d. yellow and brown ..	12	0	15	0

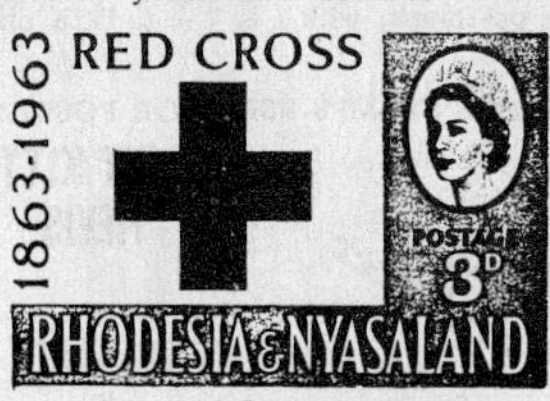

35. Red Cross Emblem.

(Photo. Harrison.)

963 (6 AUG.). *Red Cross Centenery. P* 14½ × 14.

7	**35**	3d. red	1	3	1	6

36. African " Round Table " Emblem.

(Des. V. Whiteley. Photo. Harrison.)

1963 (11 SEPT.). *World Council of Young Men's Service Clubs, Salisbury. P* 14½ × 14.

48	**36**	6d. black, gold & yell.-green	4	0	5	0
49	,,	1s. 3d. black, gold, yellow-green and lilac	6	6	8	0

POSTAGE DUE STAMPS.

The 1d. and 2d. (Nos. 2/3) exist with a rubber-stamped " POSTAGE DUE " cancellation. In the absence of proper labels these values were used as postage dues at the Salisbury G.P.O., but according to the G.P.O. the handstamp was intended as a cancellation and not as an overprint (although " unused " examples of the 1d. are known). Its use was discontinued at the end of August 1959.

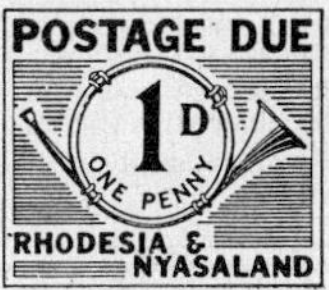

D 1

(Typo. Federal Printing & Stationery Dept., Salisbury.)

1961 (19 APR.). *P* 12½.

D1	**D 1**	1d. vermilion	1	0	1	3
		a. Imperf. between (horiz. pr.)	£55			
D2	,,	2d. deep violet-blue ..	1	3	1	9
D3	,,	4d. green	2	0	2	6
D4	,,	6d. purple..	2	9	4	6

The stamps of the Federation were withdrawn on 19th February, 1964 when all three constituent territories had resumed issuing their own stamps.

SABAH.

(FORMERLY NORTH BORNEO.)

SABAH (136) SABAH (137)

1964 (1 JULY). *Nos.* 391/406 *of North Borneo (D.L.R. printings), optd. Cents values optd. with T* **136**, *dollar values with T* **137**.

408	**120**	1 c.	emerald & brown-red	0	2	0	3
409	**121**	4 c.	bronze-green & orge.	0	4	0	5
410	**122**	5 c.	sepia & violet (*shades*)	0	5	0	6
411	**123**	6 c.	black & blue-green	0	5	0	6
412	**124**	10 c.	green and red ..	0	7	0	9
413	**125**	12 c.	brown & grey-green	0	7	0	9
414	**126**	20 c.	blue-grn. & ultram.	1	0	1	1
415	**127**	25 c.	grey-black & scarlet	1	4	1	7
416	**128**	30 c.	sepia and olive ..	1	4	1	10
417	**129**	35 c.	slate-blue & red-brn.	1	3	1	8
418	**130**	50 c.	emer. & yell.-brown	2	0	2	6
419	**131**	75 c.	grey-blue and bright purple	3	0	3	9
420	**132**	$1	brown & yellow-grn.	4	2	4	6
421	**133**	$2	brown and slate ..	7	9	9	0
422	**134**	$5	emerald and maroon	20	0	25	0
423	**135**	$10	carmine and blue ..	40	0	45	0

Old stocks bearing Waterlow imprints of the 4 c., 5 c., 20 c. and 35 c. to $10 were used for overprinting, but in addition new printings of all values by De La Rue using the original plates with the De La Rue imprint replacing the Waterlow imprint were specially made for overprinting.

138. *Vanda hookeriana.*

1965 (15 Nov.). *As Nos. 166/72 of Johore, but with Arms of Sabah inset as in T* **138.**

424	1 c. multicoloured	0	1	0	2
425	2 c. multicoloured	0	2	0	4
426	5 c. multicoloured	0	4	0	6
427	6 c. multicoloured	0	4	0	6
428	10 c. multicoloured	0	6	0	9
429	15 c. multicoloured	0	7	0	11
430	20 c. multicoloured	0	10	1	0

The higher values used in Sabah are Nos. 166/72 of Malaysia.

ST. CHRISTOPHER.

For GREAT BRITAIN stamps used in St. Christopher see page 66.

1

(Typo. De La Rue & Co.)

1870 (1 April)–**76.** *Wmk. Crown CC.* (*a*) *P* 12½.

1 **1** 1d. dull rose 50 0 40 0
  a. Wmk. sideways £12 £8
2 „ 1d. magenta 40 0 30 0
3 „ 1d. pale magenta 60 0 40 0
4 „ 6d. green £5 30 0
5 „ 6d. yellow-green £5 35 0

(*b*) *P* 14 (1875–76).

6 **1** 1d. magenta 75 0 22 6
  a. Bisected diag. or vert. (½d.) (on cover) .. .. † £22
7 „ 1d. pale magenta 50 0 22 6
8 „ 6d. green 35 0 25 0
  a. Imperf. between (pair) ..
  b. Wmk. sideways £10

1879 (Nov.). *Wmk. Crown CC. P* 14.

9 **1** 2½d. red-brown £8 £7
10 „ 4d. blue £7 40 0
  a. Wmk. sideways .. ..

1882–90. *Wmk. Crown CA. P* 14.

11 **1** ½d. dull green 4 6 4 6
12 „ 1d. dull magenta £32 £5
  a. Bisected diagonally (½d.) (on cover).. .. ..
13 „ 1d. carmine-rose 4 0 5 0
  a. Bisected (½d.) (on cover) ..
14 „ 2½d. pale red-brown .. £12 75 0
15 „ 2½d. deep red-brown .. £14 95 0
16 „ 2½d. ultramarine (1884) .. 10 0 12 6
17 „ 4d. blue £45 60 0
18 „ 4d. grey (1884) .. 8 0 8 6
19 „ 6d. olive-brown (1890) .. £15 £14
20 „ 1s. mauve (1887) .. £15 £10
21 „ 1s. bright mauve £18 £15

Halfpenny (2) **FOUR PENCE** (3)

1885 (March). *No.* 13 *bisected and No.* 8 *surch. with T* **2** (*diag.*) *and T* **3** *respectively.*

22 ½d. on half of 1d. carmine-rose 45 0 55 0
  a. Whole stamp unsevered .. £6 £8
  b. Surcharge inverted £24 £20
  c. Surcharge double .. ..
23 4d. on 6d. green 75 0 80 0
  a. Full stop after " PENCE " .. £5 £6
  b. Surcharge double £125

ONE PENNY. (4) **4d.** (5)

1886 (June). *No.* 8 *surch. with T* **4** *or* **5.**

24 1d. on 6d. green 30 0 35 0
  a. Surch. inverted £300
  b. Surch. double .. .. .. — £150
25 4d. on 6d. green 85 0 80 0
  a. No stop after " d " £12 £15
  b. Surch. double £120 £120

No. 24*b* is only known penmarked or with violet handstamp.

1887 (May). *Surch. with T* **4.**

26 **1** 1d. on ½d. dull green .. 45 0 55 0

ONE PENNY. (7)

1888 (May). *No.* 16 *surch.*

(*a*) *As T* **4** *but without bar through old value.*

27 **1** 1d. on 2½d. ultramarine ..£1350 £1150

(*b*) *With T* **7.**

28 **1** 1d. on 2½d. ultramarine .. 80 0 85 0
  a. Surch. inverted £500 £300

The 1d. of Antigua was used provisionally in St. Christopher in 1890, and can be distinguished by the postmark, which is " A 12 " in place of " A 02 ".

REVENUE STAMPS USED FOR POSTAGE.

Saint Christopher (8) **SAINT KITTS NEVIS REVENUE** (9)

1883. *Nos.* F 6 *and* F 8 *of Nevis optd. with T* **8** *in violet. Wmk. Crown CA. P* 14.

R1 1d. lilac-mauve 80 0
R2 6d. green 50 0 70

1885. *Optd. with T* **9.** *Wmk. Crown CA. P* 14.

R3 **1** 1d. rose 2 6 7
R4 „ 3d. mauve 7 6 15
R5 „ 6d. orange-brown 5 0 15
R6 „ 1s. olive 4 0 20

Other fiscal stamps with overprints as above also exist, but none of these was ever available for postal purposes.

The stamps for St. Christopher were superseded by the general issue for Leeward Islands on 31 October, 1890.

For later issues see also " St. Kitts-Nevis."

ST. HELENA.

—SIMPLIFICATION (see INTRODUCTION)—
Nos. 1 to 45.

1, 2a. 3, 5. 7, 8, 9, 10,
23, 24, 14, 22, 25, 18a. 26, 27, 28. 31, 32.
35, 36, 38, 39, 40, 41, 42, 43a, 44, 45.

1

(Recess. Perkins, Bacon & Co.)

Wmk. Large Star. Type w. **1**.

1856 (JAN.). *Imperf.*
1 **1** 6d. blue £30 £20

1861 (APRIL (?)). *Clean-cut perf.* 14 *to* 16.
2 **1** 6d. blue £45 £18

1863 (JAN.). *Rough perf.* 14 *to* 16.
2a **1** 6d. blue £18 £12

ONE PENNY (2) — FOUR PENCE (3)
ONE SHILLING (4) — ONE SHILLING (5)
ONE PENNY (6) — ONE SHILLING (7)

(Printed by De La Rue & Co.)

NOTE :—The issues which follow consist of 6d. stamps, T **1**, printed in various colours and (except in the case of the 6d. values) surcharged with a new value, as T **2** to **7**, *e.g.* stamps described as " 1d." are, in fact, 1d. on 6d. stamps, and so on.
The numbers in the Type column below refer to the *types of the lettering* of the surcharge.

The supply of 6d. stamps printed by Messrs. Perkins Bacon & Co. lasted till the year 1873.

Wmk. Crown CC.

1863 (JULY). *Thin bar approximately the same length as the words. Two varieties of the* 1d. *Imperf.*
3 **2** 1d. lake (bar 16–17 mm.) .. £7 £10
a. Surch. double £120 £55
4 ,, 1d. lake (bar 18½–19 mm.) .. £6 £6
4a ,, 1d. brown-red £22 £18
5 **3** 4d. carm. (bar. 15½–16½ mm.) £22 £18
a. Surch. double £400

Error. Surcharge omitted.
6 6d. lake (1d.) £525

864–83.
A) *Thin bar* (16½ *to* 17 *mm.*) *nearly the same length as the words.* P 12½ (1864–67).
7 **2** 1d. lake 27 6 35 0
8 **3** 3d. purple 80 0 55 0
9 ,, 4d. carmine 65 0 45 0
a. Surch. double £225 £250
o **4** 1s. deep yellow-green .. 60 0 30 0
a. Surch. double .. ..

(B) *Thick bar* (14 *to* 14½ *mm.*) *much shorter than words (except in the* 2d., *where it is nearly the same length).* (*a*) P 12½ (1865–68).
12 **2** 1d. lake 70 0 55 0
13 **3** 2d. yellow (1868) 55 0 65 0
14 ,, 3d. purple (1868) 40 0 45 0
14a ,, 3d. light purple .. £40 £45
15 ,, 4d. carmine (*words* 18 *mm.*) 75 0 50 0
16 ,, 4d. carmine-rose (*words* 19 *mm.*) .. £5 75 0
17 **5** 1s. deep yellow-green .. £14 70 0
18 ,, 5s. yellow (1868) £6 £7
18a ,, 5s. orange (1868) 50 0 55 0

Varieties. (i) *Surcharge double.*
18b **2** 1d. lake .. .. ..
18c **3** 3d. purple .. .. — £225
18d ,, 4d. carmine £200 £225
18e **5** 1s. deep yellow-green .. £450

(ii) *Surcharged with the long and short surcharges on same stamp.*
18f **3** 4d. carmine £200

(iii) *Imperf.*
18g **2** 1d. lake £90
18h **3** 2d. yellow £150
18i ,, 3d. purple £70
18j ,, 4d. carmine £225

(iv) *Surcharge omitted.*
18k 6d. carmine (4d.) .. ..
18l 6d. deep yellow-green (1s.) .. £325

No. 18l is from a sheet of the 1s. with surcharge misplaced, the fifth row of 12 stamps being thus doubly surcharged and the tenth row without surcharge.

(*b*) P 14×12½ (1882).
19 **2** 1d. lake 25 0 20 0
20 **3** 2d. yellow 60 0 45 0
21 ,, 3d. purple £10 75 0
22 ,, 4d. carm. (*words* 16½ *mm.*) 60 0 40 0

(*c*) P 14 (1883).
23 **2** 1d. lake 20 0 20 0
24 **3** 2d. yellow 27 6 30 0
25 **5** 1s. yellow-green 17 6 17 6

(C) *Words of surcharge same length as bar* (17 *to* 18 *mm.*), *the* 1d. *in thin, taller type.*

(*a*) P 12½ (1871–73).
26 **6** 1d. lake 12 6 12 6
a. Surch. in blue-black .. £18 £16
27 ,, 2d. yellow 75 0 27 6
a. Surch. in blue-black .. £225 £95
28 **7** 1s. deep green £12 15 0
a. Surch. in blue-black ..

(*b*) P 14×12½ (1882).
29 **7** 1s. deep green £9 25 0

1873–85. *No surcharge. Wmk. Crown CC.*

(*a*) P 12½.
30 **1** 6d. dull blue (1873) .. £22 £6
31 ,, 6d. ultramarine (1874) .. £20 £5

(*b*) P 14×12½ (1879).
32 **1** 6d. milky blue £5 30 0

(*c*) P 14 (*March* 1885).
33 **1** 6d. milky blue 85 0 30 0

2½d

(8)

1884–94. T **1**, *surch. similarly to* (B) *above (except* 2½d., T **8**, *and the* 1s., *in which the bar is nearly the same length as the words). The* 6d. *as before without surcharge.*

Wmk. Crown CA. P 14.
34 **3** ½d. green (*words* 17 *mm.*) .. 1 9 6 0

No.	Type	Description	Unused	Used
35	3	½d. emerald (*words 17 mm.*)	7 6	12 6
		a. "N" and "Y" spaced ..	£45	
		b. Surch. double ..	£50	
		c. Ditto, "N" and "Y" spaced*	£325	
36	,,	½d. deep green (*words 14½ mm.*) ('94)	1 0	2 0
37	2	1d. red ('87)	4 0	5 0
38	,,	1d. pale red ('87) ..	3 0	3 6
39	3	2d. yellow ('94)	2 6	7 0
40	8	2½d. ultramarine ('93) ..	3 6	8 6
		a. Surch. double	£400	
		b. Stamp doubly printed ..	£275	
41	3	3d. mauve ('87)	5 0	8 6
		a. Surch. double		
42	,,	3d. deep violet ('87) ..	7 6	10 0
		a. Surch. double	£250	
43	,,	4d. p. brown (*words 16½ mm.*) ('90)	10 0	12 6
43*a*	,,	4d. sepia (*words 17 mm.*) ..	17 6	12 6
44	–	6d. grey ('88)	10 0	10 0
45	7	1s. yellow-green ('94) ..	15 0	22 6
		a. Surch. double	£325	

Specimens of the above are sometimes found showing no watermark; these are from the bottom row of the sheet, which has escaped the watermark.

Some are found without bar and others with bar at top of stamp, due to careless overprinting.

Of the 2½d. with double surcharge only six copies exist, and of the 2½d. doubly printed, one row of 12 stamps existed on one sheet only.

**No. 35c.* No. 35*a* occurs on stamp No. 216 in the sheet. In No. 35*c* only one of the two surcharges shows the variety.

NOTE:—Nos. 36–45, both inclusive, and No. 18*a*, have been sold cancelled with a violet diamond-shaped grill with four interior bars extending over two stamps. These cannot be considered as *used* stamps, and they are consequently not priced in the list.

This violet obliteration is easily removed and many of these remainders have been cleaned and offered as unused; some are re-postmarked with a date and name in thin type rather larger than the original, a usual date being "Ap. 4.01."

9

10

(Typo. De La Rue.)

1890–97. *Wmk. Crown CA. P* 14.
Plate I for the 1½d. Plate II for the other values (for difference see Seychelles).

No.	Type	Description	Unused	Used
46	9	½d. green ('97)	2 6	3 6
47	,,	1d. carmine ('96)	4 6	5 0
48	,,	1½d. red-brown & green ('90)	6 0	7 6
49	,,	2d. orange-yellow ('96) ..	7 6	12 6
50	,,	2½d. ultramarine ('96) ..	12 6	15 0
51	,,	5d. violet ('96) ..	15 0	20 0
52	,,	10d. brown ('96)	20 0	25 0

The note below No. 45*a re* violet diamond-shaped grill cancellation also applies to Nos. 46–52.

1902. *Wmk. Crown CA. P* 14.

No.	Type	Description	Unused	Used
53	10	½d. green (Mar.)	1 0	2 6
54	,,	1d. carmine (24 Feb.) ..	5 0	6 0

11. Government House. **12.** The Wharf.

(Typo. De La Rue.)

1903 (June). *Wmk. Crown CC. P* 14.

No.	Type	Description	Unused	Used
55	11	½d. brown & grey-green ..	2 0	2 6
		a. Bluish paper	65 0	
56	12	1d. black & carmine ..	3 6	2 6
		a. Bluish paper	70 0	70 0
57	11	2d. black & sage-green ..	17 6	17 6
		a. Bluish paper	85 0	
58	12	8d. black & brown ..	25 0	27 6
59	11	1s. brown & brown-orange ..	27 6	35 0
60	12	2s. black & violet ..	55 0	60 0

13

(Typo. De La Rue.)

1908 (May). *Wmk. Mult. Crown CA. P* 14.

No.	Type	Description	Unused	Used
64	13	2½d. blue, O	4 0	8 0
66	,,	4d. blk. & red/*yellow*, OC	4 6	8 0
67	,,	6d. dull & dp. purple, OC	5 0	10 0
		Wmk. Crown CA.		
71	13	10s. green & red/*green*, C ..	£30	£35

14 15

(Typo. De La Rue.)

1912–16. *Wmk. Mult. Crown CA. P* 14.

No.	Type	Description	Unused	Used
72	14	½d. black and green ..	1 0	1
73	15	1d. black and carmine-red	2 0	1
		a. Black and scarlet (1916) ..	40 0	25
74	,,	1½d. black and orange ..	4 0	7
75	14	2d. black and greyish slate	5 0	7
76	15	2½d. black and bright blue	6 6	12
77	14	3d. black and purple/*yellow*	7 6	12
78	15	8d. black and dull purple	17 6	25
79	14	1s. black and black/*green*	25 0	32
80	15	2s. black and blue/*blue* ..	30 0	35
81	,,	3s. black and violet ..	75 0	85

No. 73*a* is on thicker paper than 73.

16

17

(Typo. De La Rue.)

1912. *Wmk. Mult. Crown CA. P* 14.

83	**16**	4d. black & red/*yellow*, C ..	10	0	22	6
84	,,	6d. dull & deep purple, C ..	6	0	20	0

1913. *Wmk. Mult. Crown CA. P* 14.

85	**17**	4d. black & red/*yellow*, O ..	6	6	10	0
86	,,	6d. dull and deep purple, O	12	6	22	6

WAR TAX ONE PENNY (18)

WAR TAX 1d. (19)

1916 (Sept.). *T* **15** *thin paper, surch. with T* **18.**

87	1d. + 1d. black and scarlet ..	0	8	1	0
	a. Surcharge double				

1919. *T* **15,** *thicker paper, surch. with T* **19.**

88	1d. + 1d. black and carmine-red (*shades*)	0	6	0	10

1922 (Jan.). *Printed in one colour. Wmk. Mult. Script CA. P* 14.

89	**15**	1d. green	2	6	7	0
90	,,	1½d. rose-scarlet	10	0	17	6
91	**14**	3d. bright blue	17	6	25	0

20. Badge of St. Helena.

(Des. T. Bruce. Typo. De La Rue.)

922–27. *T* **20.** *P* 14.

(*a*) *Wmk. Mult. Crown CA.*

92	4d. grey and black/*yellow*, C	7	6	8	6
93	1s. 6d. grey & grn./*bl.-grn.*, C	17	6	27	6
94	2s. 6d. grey & red/*yellow*, C	20	0	30	0
95	5s. grey and green/*yellow*, C	55	0	65	0
96	£1 grey and purple/*red*, C	£20		£25	

The paper of No. 93 is bluish on the surface ith a full green back.

(*b*) *Wmk. Mult. Script. CA.*

97	½d. grey and black, C ..	0	9	1	0
8	1d. grey and green, C ..	1	0	1	0
9	1½d. rose-red, C	3	0	5	0
	a. Carmine-rose.	30	0	35	0
	b. Deep carmine-red	£10		£12	
0	2d. grey and slate, C ..	2	0	3	0
1	3d. bright blue, C ..	2	6	6	0
3	5d. grn. & car./*green*, C ('27)	6	0	8	6
4	6d. grey & bright purple, C	5	0	8	6
5	8d. grey and bright violet, C	7	6	12	6
6	1s. grey and brown, C ..	12	6	17	6
7	1s. 6d. grey & green/*green*	15	0	20	0

108	2s. purple&blue/*blue*, C('27)	17	6	25	0
109	2s. 6d. grey & red/*yellow* ..	20	0	27	6
110	5s. grey and green/*yellow* ..	60	0	65	0
111	7s. 6d. grey & yell.-orge., C	60	0	75	0
112	10s. grey and olive-green, C	85	0	£5	
113	15s. grey & purple/*blue*, C ..	£65		£75	

21. Lot and Lot's wife.

22. The "Plantation".

23. Map of St. Helena.

24. Quay at Jamestown.

25. James Valley.

26. Jamestown.

27. Munden's Promontory.

28. St. Helena.

29. High Knoll.

30. Badge of St. Helena.

(Recess. Bradbury, Wilkinson & Co. Ltd.)

1934 (23 April). *Centenary of British Colonization. Wmk. Mult. Script CA. P* 12.

No.	Type	Description				
114	**21**	½d. black and purple ..	1	3	1	6
115	**22**	1d. black and green ..	1	9	2	0
116	**23**	1½d. black and scarlet ..	4	0	4	0
117	**24**	2d. black and orange ..	5	0	6	0
118	**25**	3d. black and blue ..	7	0	8	6
119	**26**	6d. black and light blue	12	6	17	6
120	**27**	1s. black and chocolate..	30	0	37	6
121	**28**	2s. 6d. black and lake ..	£5		£6	
122	**29**	5s. black and chocolate..	£8		£9	
123	**30**	10s. black and purple ..	£20		£22	

1935 (6 May). *Silver Jubilee. As Nos.* 91/4 *of Antigua. P* 13½ × 14.

124	1½d. deep blue and carmine	1	6	2	0
125	2d. ultramarine and grey ..	3	0	4	0
126	6d. green and indigo ..	12	6	12	6
127	1s. slate and purple ..	30	0	30	0

1937 (19 May). *Coronation. As Nos.* 13/15 *of Aden. P* 14.

128	1d. green	0	6	0	8
129	2d. orange	0	10	1	0
130	3d. bright blue	1	0	1	6

31. Badge of St. Helena.

(Recess. Waterlow & Sons, Ltd.)

1938 (12 May)–**44.** *Wmk. Mult. Script CA. P* 12½.

No.	Type	Description				
131	**31**	½d. violet	0	3	0	6
132	,,	1d. green	10	0	15	0
132*a*	,,	1d. yellow-orange ('40)	0	6	0	8
133	,,	1½d. scarlet	0	8	0	10
134	,,	2d. red-orange	0	10	1	0
135	,,	3d. ultramarine ..	50	0	35	0
135*a*	,,	3d. grey ('40)	1	6	1	6
135*b*	,,	4d. ultramarine ('40) ..	1	9	3	0
136	,,	6d. light blue	2	6	3	0
136*a*	,,	8d. sage-green ('40) ..	4	0	5	0
		b. Olive-green (May '44) ..	7	0	10	0
137	,,	1s. sepia..	3	6	5	0
138	,,	2s. 6d. marone	10	0	12	6
139	,,	5s. chocolate	15	0	20	0
140	,,	10s. purple	25	0	30	0

1946 (21 Oct.). *Victory. As Nos.* 28/9 *of Aden.*

141	2d. red-orange	0	6	0	8
142	4d. blue	0	8	1	0

1948 (20 Oct.). *Royal Silver Wedding. As Nos.* 30/1 *of Aden.*

143	3d. black	0	8	0	9
144	10s. violet-blue	20	0	25	0

1949 (10 Oct.). *75th Anniv. of Universal Postal Union. As Nos.* 114/7 *of Antigua.*

145	3d. carmine	0	8	1	0
146	4d. deep blue..	1	0	1	3
147	6d. olive	1	9	3	6
148	1s. blue-black	3	6	4	6

1949 (1 Nov.). *Wmk. Mult. Script CA. P* 12½

No.	Type	Description				
149	**31**	1d. black and green ..	1	3	2	[illegible]
150	,,	1½d. black and carmine ..	2	6	3	[illegible]
151	,,	2d. black and scarlet ..	2	6	3	[illegible]

1953 (2 June). *Coronation. As No.* 47 *of Aden*

152	3d. black & dp. reddish violet	1	6	2	[illegible]

32. Badge of St. Helena.

33. Flax Plantation.

34. Heart-shaped Waterfall.

35. Lace-making.

36. Drying Flax.

37. Wire Bird.

38. Flagstaff and The Barn.

39. Donkeys Carrying Flax.

40. Map of St. Helena.

41. The Castle.

42. Cutting Flax.

43. Jamestown.

44. Longwood House.
(Recess. De La Rue.)

1953 (4 Aug.). *Wmk. Mult. Script CA. P* 14.

No.	Type	Value and colour	Unused s.	d.	Used s.	d.
153	**32**	½d. black & bright green	0	4	0	6
154	**33**	1d. black and deep green	0	5	0	6
155	**34**	1½d. black & reddish purple (*shades*)	0	6	0	6
156	**35**	2d. black and claret ..	0	7	0	8
157	**36**	2½d. black and red ..	0	8	0	10
158	**37**	3d. black and brown ..	1	6	1	6
159	**38**	4d. black and deep blue	0	10	1	0
160	**39**	6d. black and deep lilac..	1	3	1	6
161	**40**	7d. black and grey-black	1	6	2	0
162	**41**	1s. black and carmine ..	2	0	2	6
163	**42**	2s. 6d. black and violet..	6	0	7	6
164	**43**	5s. black and deep brown	12	6	15	0
165	**44**	10s. black & yellow-orange	25	0	30	0

45. Stamp of 1856.

(Recess. De La Rue & Co.)

1956 (3 Jan.). *St. Helena Stamp Centenary. Wmk. Mult. Script CA. P* 11½.

166	**45**	3d. Prussian blue & carm.	2	3	2	3
167	,,	4d. Prussian blue and reddish brown	2	6	3	0
168	,,	6d. Prussian blue & deep reddish purple ..	4	0	4	6

46. Arms of East India Company.

47. *London* off James Bay.

48. Commemoration Stone.

(Recess. Waterlow & Sons.)

1959 (5 May). *Tercentenary of Settlement. W* w.**12**. *P* 12½ × 13.

169	**46**	3d. black and scarlet ..	2	6	3	0
170	**47**	6d. lt. emerald & slate-blue	4	6	5	9
171	**48**	1s. black and orange ..	7	6	10	0

ST. HELENA
Tristan Relief
9d +

(**49**)

1961 (12 Oct.). *Tristan Relief Fund. Stamps of Tristan da Cunha surch. as T* **49**.

172	**21**	2½ c. + 3d. blk. & brn.-red	*Set of* 4 *un.* £800 *us.* £475.
173	**24**	5 c. + 6d. black and blue	
174	**25**	7½ c. + 9d. black & rose-carmine	
175	**26**	10 c. + 1s. black & lt. brown	

The above stamps were withdrawn from sale on October 19th. 434 complete sets sold.

50. Cunning Fish.

51. Cape Canary.

53. Queen Elizabeth II.

52. Brittle Starfish.

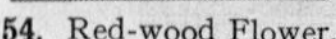

54. Red-wood Flower.

55. " Red Bird " (Weaver).

56. Trumpet Fish.

57. Feather Starfish.

58. Gum-wood Flower.

59. Fairy Tern.

60. Orange Starfish.

61. Night-blooming Cereus.

62. Deep-water Bull's-eye.

63. Queen Elizabeth II with Prince Andrew (after Cecil Beaton).

(Des. V. Whiteley. Photo. Harrison.)

1961 (12 Dec.). *W* w.**12**. *P* 11½ × 12 (*horiz.*), 12 × 11½ (*vert.*) *or* 14½ × 14 (£1).

176	**50**	1d. brt. blue, dull violet, yellow and carmine	0 3	0 3
177	**51**	1½d. yellow, green, black & light drab	0 4	0 4
178	**52**	2d. scarlet and grey ..	0 4	0 4
179	**53**	3d. light blue, black, pink & deep blue	0 6	0 7
180	**54**	4½d. yellow-green, green, brown and grey ..	0 8	0 10
181	**55**	6d. red, sepia and light yellow-olive	0 10	1 0
182	**56**	7d. red-brn., blk. & violet	0 11	1 0
183	**57**	10d. brown-purple & light blue	1 3	1 4
184	**58**	1s. greenish yellow, bluish green and brown ..	1 5	1 8
185	**59**	1s. 6d. grey, black and slate-blue	2 0	2 6
186	**60**	2s. 6d. red, pale yellow & turquoise	3 6	4 6
187	**61**	5s. yellow, brown & green	6 9	8 0
188	**62**	10s. orge.-red, blk. & blue	13 3	16 0
189	**63**	£1 chocolate & light blue	25 0	30 0

1963 (4 June). *Freedom from Hunger. As No.* 63 *of Aden.*

190	1s. 6d. ultramarine	2 6	3 0

1963 (2 Sept.). *Red Cross Centenary. As Nos.* 147/8 *of Antigua.*

191	3d. red and black	0 7	0 9
192	1s. 6d. red and blue.. ..	2 6	3 0

FIRST LOCAL POST
4th JANUARY 1965
(64)

1965 (4 Jan.). *First Local Post. Optd. with T* **64.**

193	**50**	1d. bright blue, dull violet, yellow and carmine ..	0 8	1 0
194	**53**	3d. light blue, black, pink and deep blue.. ..	1 0	1 6
195	**55**	6d. red, sepia and light yellow-olive	1 9	2 0
196	**59**	1s. 6d. grey, black and slate-blue	3 6	4 0

1965 (17 May). *I.T.U. Centenary. As Nos.* 166/7 *of Antigua.*

197	3d. blue and grey-brown ..	0 9	1 3
198	6d. brt. purple & bluish green	1 3	2 0

1965 (15 Oct.). *International Co-operation Year. As Nos. 168/9 of Antigua.*

199	1d. reddish pur. & turq.-grn.	0	4	0	6
200	6d. dp. bluish green & lav.	1	0	1	6

1966 (24 Jan.). *Churchill Commemoration. As Nos. 170/3 of Antigua.*

201	1d. new blue	0	4	0	6
202	3d. deep green	0	7	0	10
203	6d. brown	1	0	1	6
204	1s. 6d. bluish violet ..	2	6	3	6

ST. KITTS-NEVIS.

1 Christopher Columbus.

2 Medicinal Spring.

(Typo. De La Rue & Co.)

1903. *Wmk. Crown CA. P 14.*

1	**1**	½d. dull purp. & deep green	5	0	1	6
2	**2**	1d. grey-black & carmine ..	5	0	1	3
3	**1**	2d. dull purple & brown ..	10	0	22	6
4	,,	2½d. grey-black and blue ..	22	6	15	0
5	**2**	3d. deep green & orange ..	12	6	20	0
6	**1**	6d. grey-black & brt. purp.	15	0	17	6
7	,,	1s. grey-green and orange	17	6	25	0
8	**2**	2s. deep green & grey-black	22	6	27	6
9	**1**	2s. 6d. grey-black & violet	35	0	47	6
10	**2**	5s. dull purple & sage-grn.	75	0	85	0

1905–9. *Wmk. Mult. Crown CA. P 14.*

11	**1**	½d. dull pur. & dp. grn., O	12	6	12	6
12	**2**	1d. grey-black & carm., C	3	6	3	0
13	**1**	2d. dull purp. & brn., OC	5	0	6	0
14	,,	2½d. grey-black & blue, O ..	27	6	17	6
15	**2**	3d. dp. grn. & orange, OC	6	6	8	6
16	**1**	6d. grey-blk & dp. vio., O	17	6	30	0
16*a*	,,	6d. grey-black and deep purple, C (1908) ..	12	6	22	6
17	,,	1s. grey-green & orange, OC ('09)	10	0	25	0

1907–18. *Wmk. Mult. Crown CA. P 14.*

19	**1**	½d. grey-green, O ..	1	6	1	6
19*a*	,,	½d. dull blue-green, O ..	1	0	2	0
20	**2**	1d. carmine, O	3	6	1	3
20*a*	,,	1d. scarlet, O	1	6	1	6
21	**1**	2½d. bright blue, O ..	2	6	3	6
22	,,	6d. grey-black and bright purple, C ('16) ..	15	0	22	6
23	**2**	5s. dull purple & sage-grn., C (Nov. 1918) ..	65	0	90	0

WAR TAX

(3)

WAR STAMP

(3*a*)

1916 (Oct.). *Optd. with T* **3**. *Wmk. Mult. Crown CA. P 14.*

24	**1**	½d. green	0	2	0	3
25	,,	½d. grey-green	0	6	0	6

1918 (Aug.). *Special printing, optd. with T* **3a**.

26	**1**	1½d. orange	0	6	1	6

4

5

(Typo. De La Rue & Co.)

1920–22. *Wmk. Mult. Crown CA. P 14.*

27	**4**	½d. blue-green, O	2	0	1	0
28	**5**	1d. carmine, O	1	6	1	6
29	**4**	1½d. orange-yellow, O ..	2	6	2	6
30	**5**	2d. slate-grey, O	8	6	12	6
31	**4**	2½d. ultramarine, O ..	4	6	5	0
32	**5**	3d. purple/*yellow*, C ..	6	0	6	0
33	**4**	6d. dull pur. & brt. mve., C	7	6	12	6
34	**5**	1s. grey & black/*green*, C	7	6	12	6
35	**4**	2s. dull pur. & blue/*blue*, C	15	0	20	0
36	**5**	2s. 6d. grey & red/*blue*, C ..	25	0	32	6
37	**4**	5s. grn. & red/*pale yellow*, C	25	0	30	0
38	**5**	10s. green and red/*green*, C	45	0	55	0
39	**4**	£1 pur. & blk./*red*, C (1922)	£30		£35	

1921–27. *Wmk. Mult. Script CA. P 14.*

40	**4**	½d. blue-green, O	0	6	0	8
40*a*	,,	½d. yellow-green, O ..	3	6	3	6
41	**5**	1d. rose-carmine, O ..	1	0	1	0
42	,,	2d. slate-grey, O	2	0	2	0
43	**4**	2½d. pale bright blue, O ..	5	0	10	0
43*a*	,,	2½d. ultramarine, C (1927)	3	0	8	6
43*b*	,,	2½d. ultramarine, O (1927)	3	0	3	0
43*c*	,,	6d. dull & bright purple, C	5	0	6	0
44	,,	2s. purple and blue/*blue*, C	15	0	20	0
44*a*	**5**	2s. 6d. blk. & red/*blue*, C ('27)	30	0	35	0

1922–29. *Colours changed. Wmk. Mult. Script CA. P 14.*

45	**5**	1d. deep violet, O ..	3	6	1	0
45*a*	,,	1d. pale violet, O ('29) ..	1	6	1	0
45*b*	**4**	1½d. red, O (1925) ..	2	0	3	[illegible]
45*c*	,,	1½d. red-brown, O ('29) ..	1	6	1	[illegible]
46	,,	2½d. brown, O	3	6	8	[illegible]
47	**5**	3d. dull ultramarine, O ..	4	0	6	[illegible]
47*a*	,,	3d. purple/*yellow*, C ..	5	0	5	[illegible]
47*b*	,,	1s. black/*green*, C ('29) ..	15	0	15	[illegible]
47*c*	**4**	5s. grn. & red/*yell.*, C ('29)	60	0	70	[illegible]

6. Old Road Bay and Mount Misery.

(Typo. De La Rue & Co.)

1923. *Tercentenary of Colony. Chalk-surfaced paper. P 14. (a) Wmk. Mult. Script CA.*

No.	Type	Description	Unused	Used
48	**6**	½d. blk. and green	4 6	5 0
49	,,	1d. blk. and bright violet ..	5 0	5 0
50	,,	1½d. blk. and scarlet ..	8 6	10 0
51	,,	2d. blk. and slate-grey ..	10 0	7 0
52	,,	2½d. blk. and brown ..	12 6	17 6
53	,,	3d. blk. and ultramarine ..	17 6	20 0
54	,,	6d. blk. and bright purple	35 0	37 6
55	,,	1s. blk. and sage-green ..	55 0	60 0
56	,,	2s. blk. and blue/*blue* ..	65 0	75 0
57	,,	2s. 6d. blk. and red/*blue* ..	85 0	95 0
58	,,	10s. blk. and red/*emerald* ..	£50	£60

(b) Wmk. Mult. Crown CA.

No.	Type	Description	Unused	Used
59	**6**	5s. blk. and red/*pale yellow*	£25	£30
60	,,	£1 blk. and purple/*red* ..	£175	£225

1935 (6 May). *Silver Jubilee. As Nos. 91/4 of Antigua, but ptd. by W'low & Sons. P 11×12.*

No.	Description	Unused	Used
61	1d. deep blue and scarlet ..	0 8	1 0
62	1½d. ultramarine and grey ..	1 3	2 0
63	2½d. brown and deep blue ..	3 6	5 0
64	1s. slate and purple	17 6	20 0

1937 (12 May). *Coronation. As Nos. 13/15 of Aden.*

No.	Description	Unused	Used
65	1d. scarlet	0 4	0 8
66	1½d. buff	0 8	1 0
67	2½d. bright blue	1 6	2 0

Nos. 61/7 are inscribed "ST. CHRISTOPHER NEVIS".

7. King George VI.

8. King George VI and Medicinal Spring.

. King George VI and Christopher Columbus.

10. King George VI and Anguilla Island.

(Typo; centre litho. (*T* **10**). De La Rue & Co.)

1938 (15 Aug.)–**1948.** *Wmk. Mult. Script CA (sideways on T* **8** *and* **9**). *P 14 (T* **7** *and* **10**) *or 13×12 (T* **8/9**).

No.	Type	Description	Unused	Used
68	**7**	½d. green	0 8	0 8
		a. *Blue-green* ('43)	0 3	0 3
69	,,	1d. scarlet	1 0	1 0
		a. *Carmine* ('43)	0 6	0 8
		b. *Rose-red* ('47)	0 6	0 10
70	,,	1½d. orange	0 8	0 6
71	**8**	2d. scarlet and grey, O ..	25 0	20 0
		aa. *Carmine and deep grey*, C ..	15 0	22 6
		a. P. 14. *Scar. & p. grey*, OC ('41)	1 0	0 6
		ab. P. 14. *Scar. & dp. grey*, O ('43)	27 6	22 6
72	**7**	2½d. ultramarine	2 6	1 6
		a. *Bright ultramarine* ('43) ..	1 0	1 0
73	**8**	3d. dull purple & scar., OC	5 0	8 6
		a. Perf. 14, CO ('42)	1 6	1 6
74	**9**	6d. green & brt. purple, O	5 0	8 0
		a. P. 14. *Green & purple* C ('42)	40 0	40 0
		ab. P. 14. *Green & brt. purple*, OC	2 6	2 0
75	**8**	1s. black and green, O ..	8 6	8 6
		a. Perf. 14, OC ('43)	5 0	3 0
76	,,	2s. 6d. black and scarlet, O	30 0	35 0
		a. Perf. 14, CO ('42)	12 6	17 6
77	**9**	5s. green and scarlet, O ..	75 0	85 0
		a. Perf. 14, CO ('42)	15 0	17 6
77*b*	**10**	10s. blk. & ultram. (1.9.48)	25 0	30 0
77*c*	,,	£1 black & brown (1.9.48)	50 0	60 0

1946 (1 Nov.). *Victory. As Nos. 28/9 of Aden.*

No.	Description	Unused	Used
78	1½d. red-orange	0 6	0 6
79	3d. carmine	0 9	1 0

1949 (3 Jan.). *Royal Silver Wedding. As Nos. 30/1 of Aden.*

No.	Description	Unused	Used
80	2½d. ultramarine	0 6	0 6
81	5s. carmine	12 6	17 6

1949 (10 Oct.). *75th Anniv. of Universal Postal Union. As Nos. 114/7 of Antigua.*

No.	Description	Unused	Used
82	2½d. ultramarine	0 6	0 10
83	3d. carmine-red	0 9	1 6
84	6d. magenta	2 0	3 0
85	1s. blue-green	3 6	4 6

ANGUILLA ANGUILLA

TERCENTENARY 1650-1950 (11)

TERCENTENARY 1650—1950 (12)

1950 (10 Nov.). *Tercentenary of British Settlement in Anguilla. T* **7** *optd. as T* **11** *and T* **8/9**, *perf. 13×12, optd. as T* **12**.

No.	Type	Description	Unused	Used
86	**7**	1d. bright rose-red (Bk.) ..	0 6	0 8
87	,,	1½d. orange (Bk.)	0 8	0 10
		a. Error. Crown missing ..		
		b. Error. St. Edward's Crown..		
88	,,	2½d. bright ultramarine (Bk.)	0 10	1 0
89	**8**	3d. dull purple & scar. (Bk.)	1 0	2 0
90	**9**	6d. green & bt. purple (Bk.)	2 6	5 0
91	**8**	1s. black and green (R.) ..	3 6	7 0

Nos. 87a/b occur on a row in the watermark, in which the crowns and letters "CA" alternate.

1951 (16 Feb.). *Inauguration of B.W.I. University College. As Nos. 118/9 of Antigua.*

No.	Description	Unused	Used
92	3 c. black & yellow-orange ..	0 10	0 10
93	12 c. turquoise-grn. & magenta	2 6	2 6

ST. CHRISTOPHER, NEVIS AND ANGUILLA

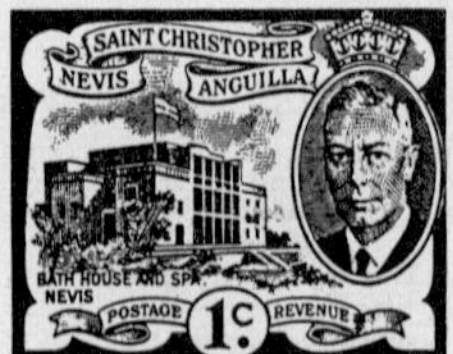

13. Bath House and Spa.

14. Warner Park.

15. Map of the Islands.

19. Sir Thomas Warner's Tomb.

16. Brimstone Hill.

17. Nevis from the Sea, North.

18. Pinney's Beach.

20. Old Road Bay.

21. Sea Island Cotton.

22. The Treasury.

23. Salt Pond.

24. Sugar Factory.

(Recess. Waterlow.)

1952 (14 JUNE). *Wmk. Mult. Script CA. P* 12½.

94	**13**	1 c. deep green & ochre..	0	4	0	8
95	**14**	2 c. green	0	6	0	8
96	**15**	3 c. carmine-red & violet	0	8	1	0
97	**16**	4 c. scarlet	0	8	0	10
98	**17**	5 c. bright blue & grey ..	0	10	1	0
99	**18**	6 c. ultramarine	1	6	1	6
100	**19**	12 c. dp. blue & reddish brn.	2	0	2	6
101	**20**	24 c. black & carmine-red	6	6	4	0
102	**21**	48 c. olive & chocolate ..	7	6	12	6
103	**22**	60 c. ochre & deep green..	8	0	15	0
104	**23**	$1.20 dp. green & ultram.	15	0	17	6
105	**24**	$4.80 green & carmine ..	40	0	47	6

1953 (2 JUNE). *Coronation. As No 47 of Aden.*

106		2 c. black and bright green..	0	6	0	10

25. Sombrero Lighthouse.

26. Map of Anguilla and Dependencies.

(Recess. Waterlow (until 1961), then De La Rue.)

1954–57. *Types of* 1952 (*but with portrait of Queen Elizabeth II in place of King George VI as in T* **25/6**). *Wmk. Mult. Script CA. P* 12½.

106*a*	**23**	½ c. deep olive	0	3	0	3
107	**13**	1 c. deep green and ochre (*shades*)	0	3	0	3
108	**14**	2 c. green (*shades*) ..	0	4	0	4
109	**15**	3 c. carmine-red & violet (*shades*)	0	5	0	5
110	**16**	4 c. scarlet	0	6	0	6
111	**17**	5 c. bright blue and grey	0	8	0	8
112	**18**	6 c. ultramarine (*shades*)	0	9	0	9
112*a*	**25**	8 c. grey-black	0	10	1	0
113	**19**	12 c. deep blue & red-brn.	1	3	1	3
114	**20**	24 c. black & carm.-red..	2	0	2	6
115	**21**	48 c. olive-bistre & choc.	4	0	4	6
116	**22**	60 c. ochre & deep green	5	0	6	0
117	**23**	$1.20, deep green and ultramarine (*shades*)	9	0	10	0
117*a*	**26**	$2.40, black & red-orange	20	0	22	6
118	**24**	$4.80, green and carmine	40	0	45	0

Dates of issue:—1954—1 Mar., 1 c., to 6 c., 2 c. 1 Dec., 24 c. to $1.20, $4.80. 1956—3 July, c. 1957—1 Feb., 8 c., $2.40.

The above stamps, from No. 1 onwards, were in concurrent use with the stamps inscribed "LEEWARD ISLANDS" until July 1st, 1956, when the general Leeward Islands stamps were withdrawn.

27. Alexander Hamilton and View of Nevis.

(Des. Miss Eva Wilkin. Recess. Waterlow.)

1957 (11 JAN.). *Bicentenary of Birth of Alexander Hamilton. Wmk. Mult. Script CA. P* 12½.

119	**27**	24 c. green and deep blue	2	9	3	9

1958 (22 APR.). *Inauguration of British Caribbean Federation. As Nos.* 135/7 *of Antigua.*

120		3 c. deep green	0	8	0	8
121		6 c. blue	1	0	1	3
122		12 c. scarlet	2	0	2	6

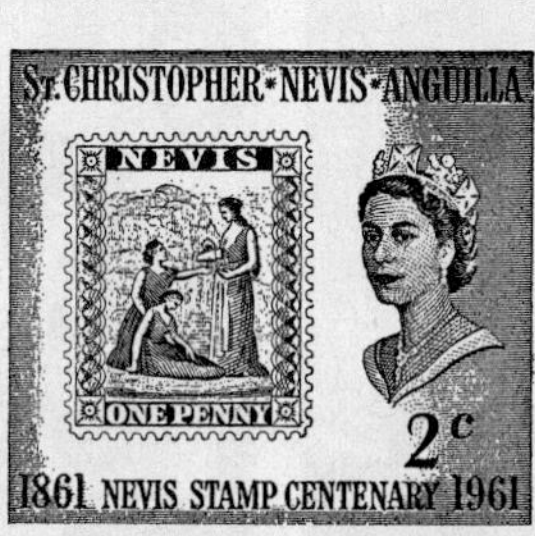

28. One Penny stamp of 1861.

29. Fourpence stamp of 1861.

30. Sixpence stamp of 1861.

31. One shilling stamp of 1861.

(Recess. Waterlow.)

1961 (15 JULY). *Nevis Stamp Centenary. W* w.**12.** *P* 14.

123	**28**	2 c. red-brown and green	1	0	1	0
124	**29**	8 c. red-brown & dp. blue	1	6	1	9
125	**30**	12 c. black & carmine-red	2	3	2	9
126	**31**	24 c. deep bluish green and red-orange	4	6	5	6

1963 (2 SEPT.). *Red Cross Centenary. As Nos.* 147/8 *of Antigua.*

127	3 c. red and black	0	5	0	6
128	12 c. red and blue	1	0	1	3

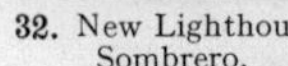

32. New Lighthouse, Sombrero.

34. Pall Mall Square, Basseterre.

33. Loading Sugar Cane, St. Kitts.

35. Gateway, Brimstone Hill Fort, St. Kitts.

40. Sea Island Cotton, Nevis.

36. Nelson's Spring, Nevis.

37. Grammar School, St. Kitts.

38. Crater, Mt. Misery, St. Kitts.

39. Hibiscus.

41. Boat-building, Anguilla.

42. White-crowned Pigeon.

44. Alexander Hamilton.

43. St. George's Church Tower, Basseterre.

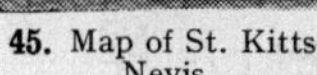

45. Map of St. Kitts-Nevis.

47. Arms of St. Christopher, Nevis and Anguilla.

46. Map of Anguilla.

(Des. V. Whiteley. Photo. Harrison.)

1963 (20 Nov.). *W* w.**12.** *P* 14.

129	**32**	½ c. sepia and light blue	0 1	0 2
130	**33**	1 c. multicoloured	0 2	0 3
131	**34**	2 c. multicoloured	0 3	0 4
132	**35**	3 c. multicoloured	0 4	0 5
133	**36**	4 c. multicoloured	0 4	0 6
134	**37**	5 c. multicoloured	0 5	0 6
135	**38**	6 c. multicoloured	0 6	0 7
136	**39**	10 c. multicoloured	0 9	0 10
137	**40**	15 c. multicoloured	0 11	1 1
138	**41**	20 c. multicoloured	1 3	1 3
139	**42**	25 c. multicoloured	1 6	1 6
140	**43**	50 c. multicoloured	2 10	3 6
141	**44**	60 c. multicoloured	3 6	4 0
142	**45**	$1 greenish yellow & bl.	5 6	6 0
143	**46**	$2.50 multicoloured	13 10	15 6
144	**47**	$5 multicoloured	26 0	29 0

ARTS
FESTIVAL
ST KITTS
1964

(48)

964 (14 Sept.). *Arts Festival.* *Optd. as T* **48.**

45	**35**	3 c. multicoloured	0 10	1 3
46	**42**	25 c. multicoloured	2 9	3 6

965 (17 May). *I.T.U. Centenary. As Nos. 166/7 of Antigua.*

47	2 c. bistre-yell. & rose-carm.	0 6	0 8
48	50 c. turq.-blue & yell.-olive	4 0	5 0

965 (15 Oct.). *International Co-operation Year. As Nos. 168/9 of Antigua.*

49	2 c. reddish pur. & turq.-grn.	0 6	0 8
50	25 c. dp. bluish green & lav.	2 0	2 6

966 (24 Jan.). *Churchill Commemoration. As Nos. 170/3 of Antigua.*

1	½ c. new blue	0 3	0 4
2	3 c. deep green	0 7	0 9
3	15 c. brown	1 3	1 6
4	25 c. bluish violet	2 0	2 6

66 (4 Feb.). *Royal Visit. As Nos. 174/5 of Antigua.*

5	3 c. black and ultramarine	0 5	0 7
6	25 c. black and magenta	1 10	2 3

ST. LUCIA.

For GREAT BRITAIN stamps used in St. Lucia, see page 66.

1

(Recess. Perkins Bacon & Co.)

1860 (18 Dec.). *T* **1.** *Wmk. Small Star, T* w. **2.** *P* 14 *to* 16.

1	(1d.) rose-red	£8	£6
	a. Imperf. between (horiz. pr.)		
	b. Double impression		
2	(4d.) blue	£30	£30
2*a*	(4d.) deep blue	£26	£26
	b. Imperf. between (horiz. pr.)		
3	(6d.) green	£35	£30
	a. Imperf. between (horiz. pr.)		
4	(6d.) deep green	£35	£30

(Printed by Messrs. De La Rue & Co.)

1863. *Wmk. Crown CC. P* 12½.

5	(1d.) lake	£5	£6
	a. Imperf.	£50	
6	(1d.) brownish lake	£7	£8
7	(4d.) indigo	£14	£20
	a. Imperf.	£70	
8	(6d.) emerald-green	£25	£22

Half penny (2) HALFPENNY (3) 2½ PENCE (4)

Prepared for use, but not issued.

T **1** *surch. as T* **2.** *Wmk. Crown CC. P* 12½.

9	½d. on (6d.) emerald-green	80 0	
10	6d. on (4d.) indigo	£100	

1864 (19 Nov.). *Wmk. Crown CC.* (*a*) *P* 12½.

11	**1**	(1d.) black	35 0	42 6
		a. Intense black	35 0	45 0
		aa. Imperf. (pair)	£35	
12	,,	(4d.) yellow	£15	£6
		a. Imperf.		
		b. Lemon-yellow	£40	
		c. Chrome yellow	£15	97 6
		d. Olive-yellow	£18	£8
13	,,	(6d.) violet	£7	80 0
		a. Mauve	£16	85 0
		aa. Imperf.	£60	
		b. Deep lilac	£12	95 0
		ba. Imperf.	£40	
14	,,	(1s.) brown-orange	£22	85 0
		a. Imperf.	£60	
		b. Orange	£25	90 0
		c. Pale orange	£22	85 0
		ca. Imperf. between (horiz. pr.)		

(*b*) *P* 14.

15	**1**	(1d.) black	40 0	45 0
		a. Imperf. between (horiz. pr.)		
16	,,	(4d.) yellow	£6	60 0
		a. Olive-yellow	£10	£8
17	,,	(6d.) mauve	£8	80 0
		a. Pale lilac	£8	50 0
		b. Violet	£18	£8
18	,,	(1s.) orange	£20	70 0
		a. Deep orange	£12	55 0
		aa. Imperf.	£40	

(c) P 13.

19 **1** (1d.) black £60

20 ,, (4d.) yellow £25 £10

a. Chrome yellow £30 £10

21 ,, (6d.) mauve £50 £10

a. Violet .. .. .. — £30

22 ,, (1s.) orange £50 £15

a. Orange-red £50 £16

1881 (Sept.). *Surch. with T* **3** *or* **4.** *Wmk. Crown CC. P* 14.

23 **1** ½d. green 75 0 90 0

24 ,, 2½d. brown-red 47 6 47 6

The 1d. black is known surcharged "1d." in violet ink by hand, but there is no evidence that this was done officially.

1882–84. *Surch. as T* **3.** *Wmk. Crown CA.*

(a) P 14.

25 **1** ½d. green (1882) 50 0 55 0

26 ,, 1d. black (C.) 37 6 40 0

a. Bisected (on cover) .. .. † £80

27 ,, 4d. yellow £16 80 0

28 ,, 6d. violet 85 0 75 0

29 ,, 1s. orange £25 £18

(b) P 12.

30 **1** 4d. yellow £25 95 0

Deep blue stamps, wmk. Crown CA, perf. 14 or 12, are fiscals from which the overprint "THREE PENCE—REVENUE", or "REVENUE", has been fraudulently removed.

5

(Typo. De La Rue.)

1882–86. *Wmk. Crown CA. P* 14. Die I.

31 **5** ½d. dull green 7 6 8 6

32 ,, 1d. carmine-rose 37 6 42 6

33 ,, 2½d. blue 25 0 10 6

34 ,, 4d. brown (1885) 27 6 15 0

a. Imperf. £35

35 ,, 6d. lilac (1886) £25 £30

a. Imperf. (pair) £60

36 ,, 1s. orange-brown (1885) .. £20 £15

Wmk. Crown CA. P 14.

1886–87. Die I.

39 **5** 1d. dull mauve 8 6 10 0

a. Imperf. (pair) £45

40 ,, 3d. dull mauve and green .. 60 0 47 6

41 ,, 6d. dull mve. & blue (1887) 18 0 25 0

42 ,, 1s. dull mve. & red (1887) 80 0 60 0

1891–98. Die II.

43 **5** ½d. dull green 1 0 1 3

44 ,, 1d. dull mauve 2 6 1 9

45 ,, 2d. ultram. & orange ('98) 7 0 7 6

46 ,, 2½d. ultramarine 6 0 4 0

47 ,, 3d. dull mauve and green 15 0 12 6

48 ,, 4d. brown 12 6 12 6

49 ,, 6d. dull mauve and blue .. 20 0 32 6

50 ,, 1s. dull mauve and red .. 18 0 20 0

51 ,, 5s. dull mauve and orange 60 0 80 0

52 ,, 10s. dull mauve and black .. £5 £6

For description and illustration of differences between Die I *and* Die II *see* Introduction.

ONE HALF PENNY (6) **½d** (7) **ONE PENNY** (8)

N Normal "N". **N** Thick "N".

Three types of T **8.**

I. All letters "N" normal.

II. Thick diagonal stroke in first "N".

III. Thick diagonal stroke in second "N".

1891–92. *Stamps of Die I surch.*

53 **6** ½d. on 3d. dull mve. & green £6 £6

a. Small "A" in "HALF" .. £10 £10

b. Small "O" in "ONE" .. £10 £10

54 **7** ½d. on half 6d. dull mauve and blue 47 6 42 6

a. No fraction bar £16 £10

b. Surch. sideways £38

c. Surch. double £45 £55

d. "2" in fraction omitted .. £32

e. Thick "1" with sloping serif £15 £16

f. Surch. triple £50

g. Figure "7" used as fraction bar £25 £25

55 **8** 1d. on 4d. brown (I) (Dec. '91) 15 0 20 0

a. Surch. double £20

b. Surch. inverted .. .. — £75

c. Type II 20 0 25 0

ca. Surch. double £20

cb. Surch. inverted .. .. — £75

d. Type III 30 0 35 0

Stamp of Die II surch.

56 **6** ½d. on 3d. dull mve. & green 70 0 60 0

a. Surch. double £70 £50

b. Surch. inverted £150 £50

c. Small "O" in "ONE" .. £10 £10

d. Small "A" in "HALF" .. £10 £10

9 10

(Typo. De La Rue.)

1902–3. *Wmk. Crown CA. P* 14.

58 **9** ½d. dull purple and green 2 6 2 0

59 ,, 1d. dull purple & carmine 2 6 2 0

60 ,, 2½d. dull purple & ultram. 20 0 22 6

61 **10** 3d. dull purple and yellow 15 0 20 0

62 ,, 1s. green and black .. 25 0 40 0

11. The Pitons.

(Recess. De La Rue.)

1902 (16 Dec.). *Wmk. Crown CC, sideways. P* 1

63 **11** 2d. green and brown .. 15 0 20

1904–10. *Wmk. Mult. Crown CA. P* 14.

64 **9** ½d. dull purple & grn., C O 2 0 3

65 ,, 1d. dull pur. & carm., C O 3 0 1

66 ,, 2½d. dull pur. & ultram., C O 12 6 15

67 **10** 3d. dull purple & yellow, O 10 0 15

68 ,, 6d. dull purple and violet, C O ('05) 25 0 35

68*b* ,, 6d. dull purple, C ('10) .. 45 0 55

69 ,, 1s. green & black, C ('05) 65 0 70

71 ,, 5s. green & carm., O ('05) 90 0

1907–9. *Wmk. Mult. Crown CA. P* 14.

No.	Type	Description	Unused s.	d.	Used s.	d.
72	**9**	½d. green, O	2	0	1	6
73	,,	1d. carmine, O	2	6	1	3
74	,,	2½d. blue, O	10	0	12	6
75	**10**	3d. purple/*yellow*, C ('09)	6	6	15	0
76	,,	6d. dull & bright pur., C	22	6	35	0
77	,,	1s. black/*green*, C ('09) ..	22	6	37	6
78	,,	5s. green & red/*yellow*, C	£5		£6	

12 **13**

14 **15**

16

(Typo. De La Rue.)

912–19. *Wmk. Mult. Crown CA. P* 14.

No.	Type	Description	Unused s.	d.	Used s.	d.
)	**12**	½d. deep green, O ..	0	6	0	6
)	,,	½d. yellow-green, O ('16)	1	0	0	8
	,,	1d. carmine-red, O ..	7	6	2	0
	,,	1d. scarlet, O ('16) ..	5	0	2	0
a	,,	1d. rose-red, O	2	6	1	3
	13	2d. grey, O	10	0	12	6
a	,,	2d. slate-grey, O ('16) ..	15	0	17	6
	12	2½d. ultramarine, O ..	8	0	8	0
a	,,	2½d. bright blue, O ('18)	8	0	7	6
b	,,	2½d. deep bright blue, O	15	0	12	6
	15	3d. purple/*yellow*, C ..	5	0	7	6
		a. On pale yellow (Die I) ..	17	6	20	0
		b. On pale yellow (Die II) ..	27	6	35	0
	14	4d. black & red/*yellow*, C	7	0	10	0
		a. White back	6	0	12	6
	15	6d. dull & bright pur., C	15	0	17	6
a	,,	6d. grey-pur.&pur.,C('18)	25	0	27	6
	,,	1s. black/*green*, C ..	20	0	25	0
		a. On blue-green, olive back ..	12	6	25	0
	16	2s. 6d. blk. & red/*blue*, C	35	0	42	6
	15	5s. green & red/*yellow*, C	65	0	75	0

WAR
TAX
(17)

WAR TAX
(18)

16 (June). *Optd. locally with T* **17**.

No.	Type	Description	Unused s.	d.	Used s.	d.
	12	1d. scarlet	12	6	17	6
		a. Opt. double	*£30		*£40	
	,,	1d. carmine	80	0	85	0

6 (Sept.). *Optd. in London with T* **18**.

No.	Type	Description	Unused s.	d.	Used s.	d.
	12	1d. scarlet	0	4	0	6

0. *T* **15.** (Die I). *Colour changed. Wmk. Mult. Crown CA. P* 14.

No.	Type	Description	Unused s.	d.	Used s.	d.
		1s. orange-brown, C	10	0	17	6

Z—PT. 1

1921–26. *Wmk. Mult. Script CA. P* 14.

No.	Type	Description	Unused s.	d.	Used s.	d.
95	**12**	½d. green, O	0	4	0	6
96	,,	1d. rose-carmine, O ..	6	6	15	0
97	**13**	2d. slate-grey, O ..	1	6	1	0
98	**12**	2½d. bright blue, O ..	4	6	6	0
98*a*	,,	2½d. dull blue, O (1926)	6	0	7	6
98*b*	**15**	3d. purple/*yellow*, C ('26)	3	0	8	6
98*c*	,,	3d. deep purple/*yellow*, C	7	6	10	0
99	**14**	4d. black & red/*yellow*, C	3	6	9	0
100	**15**	6d. grey-pur. & pur., C	6	6	10	0
101	,,	1s. orange-brown, C (II)	10	0	17	6
102	**16**	2s. 6d. blk. & red/*bl.*, C	25	0	32	6
103	**15**	5s. grn. & red/*pl. yell.*, C	35	0	45	0

1922–26. *Colours changed and new value. Wmk. Mult. Script CA. P* 14.

No.	Type	Description	Unused s.	d.	Used s.	d.
104	**12**	1d. deep brown, O ..	1	6	1	9
105	**14**	1½d. dull carmine, O ..	1	3	2	6
106	**12**	2½d. orange, O	25	0	35	0
107	**15**	3d. bright blue, O ..	12	6	20	0
108	,,	3d. dull blue, O (1926) ..	8	0	10	0

1935 (6 May). *Silver Jubilee. As Nos.* 91/4 *of Antigua. P* 13½ × 14.

No.	Type	Description	Unused s.	d.	Used s.	d.
109		½d. black and green	1	0	1	9
110		2d. ultramarine and grey ..	3	6	4	0
111		2½d. brown and deep blue ..	5	0	6	0
112		1s. slate and purple ..	17	6	20	0

19. Port Castries.

20. Columbus Square, Castries.

21. Ventine Falls.

22. Fort Rodney, Pigeon Island.

23. Inniskilling Monument.

24. Government House.

25. The Badge of the Colony.

(Recess. De La Rue & Co., Ltd.)

1936 (MAR.–APR.). *Wmk. Mult. Script CA. P* 14 *or* 13×12 (1s. *and* 10s.).

113	**19**	½d. black & bright green	0	6	0	6
		a. P. 13×12 (8.4.36) ..	2	0	2	0
114	**20**	1d. black and brown ..	0	9	0	9
		a. P 13×12 (8.4.36) ..	3	6	2	0
115	**21**	1½d. black and scarlet ..	1	6	1	3
		a. P 12×13	45	0	12	6
116	**19**	2d. black and grey ..	1	6	1	9
117	**20**	2½d. black and blue ..	2	0	2	6
118	**21**	3d. black and dull green	2	6	3	0
119	**19**	4d. black and red-brown	3	0	3	6
120	**20**	6d. black and orange ..	3	6	4	6
121	**22**	1s. black and light blue	6	0	8	6
122	**23**	2s. 6d. black and ultram.	20	0	25	0
123	**24**	5s. black and violet ..	35	0	40	0
124	**25**	10s. black and carmine ..	65	0	75	0

1937 (12 MAY). *Coronation Issue. As T* **2** *of Aden, inscr.* " ST. LUCIA ". *Recess. B. W. & Co. Wmk. Mult. Script CA. P* 11×11½.

125	1d. violet	0	6	0	8
126	1½d. carmine	0	8	0	10
127	2½d. blue	1	6	1	9

26. King George VI.

27. Columbus Square.

28. Government House.

29. The Pitons.

30. Loading Bananas.

31. Device of St. Lucia.

(Recess. Waterlow (T **26** and **30**), De La R (T **27/8**) and Bradbury Wilkinson (T **29** and **31**

1938 (22 SEPT.)–**48.** *Wmk. Mult. Script C.* (*sideways on* 2*s*.).

128	**26**	½d. green (*p.* 14½×14)..	0	3	0
		a. Perf. 12½ ('43)	0	8	0
129	,,	1d. violet (*p.* 14½×14)..	5	0	4
		a. Perf. 12½ ('38)	0	8	0
129*b*	,,	1d. scarlet (*p.* 12½) ('47)	2	6	1
		c. Perf. 14½×14 ('48) ..	1	9	1
130	,,	1½d. scarlet (*p.* 14½×14)	2	0	2
		a. Perf. 12½ ('43)	1	0	1
131	,,	2d. grey (*p.* 14½×14) ..	1	6	1
		a. Perf. 12½ ('43)	0	7	1

132 **26** 2½d. ultram. (*p.* 14½×14) 1 6 1 9
a. Perf. 12½ ('43) 1 0 0 10
132*b* „ 2½d. violet (*p.* 12½) ('47) .. 0 9 0 9
133 „ 3d. orange (*p.* 14½×14) 1 9 2 0
a. Perf. 12½ ('43) 1 9 1 3
133*b* „ 3½d. ultram. (*p.* 12½) ('47) 1 9 1 9
134 **27** 6d. claret (*p.* 13½) .. 6 0 6 0
a. Perf. 13½. *Carmine-lake* ('45) 17 6 12 6
aa. Perf. 12 *Claret* ('48) .. 10 6 10 6
134*b* **26** 8d. brown (*p.* 12½) ('46) 3 0 3 6
135 **28** 1s. brown (*p.* 13½) .. 6 0 6 0
a. Perf. 12 ('48) 10 0 10 0
136 **29** 2s. blue & pur. (*p.* 12) .. 12 6 10 0
136*a* **26** 3s. brt. pur. (*p.* 12½) ('46) 15 0 17 6
137 **30** 5s. blk. & mauve (*p.* 12½) 15 0 17 6
138 **31** 10s. black/*yellow* (*p.* 12) .. 25 0 25 0
141 **26** £1 sepia (*p.* 12½) ('46) .. 50 0 55 0

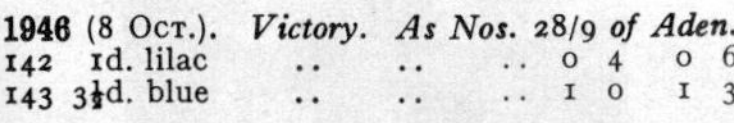

1946 (8 Oct.). *Victory. As Nos.* 28/9 *of Aden.*
142 1d. lilac 0 4 0 6
143 3½d. blue 1 0 1 3

1948 (26 Nov.). *Royal Silver Wedding. As Nos.* 30/1 *of Aden.*
144 1d. scarlet 0 6 0 8
145 £1 purple-brown 40 0 47 6

32. King George VI. **33.** Device of St. Lucia.

(Recess. Waterlow (**32**). Bradbury, Wilkinson (**33**).)

1949 (1 Oct.)–**50.** *Value in cents or dollars. Wmk. Mult. Script CA. P* 12½ (1 *c. to* 16 *c.*), 11×11½ (*others*).
46 **32** 1 c. green 0 6 0 6
a. Perf. 14 ('49) 3 0 3 6
47 „ 2 c. magenta 0 6 0 6
a. Perf. 14½×14 ('49) .. 7 6 7 6
48 „ 3 c. scarlet 0 10 0 8
49 „ 4 c. grey 0 10 0 10
a. Perf. 14½×14 .. .. — £250
50 „ 5 c. violet 1 0 1 0
51 „ 6 c. orange 0 10 0 10
52 „ 7 c. ultramarine 1 0 1 3
53 „ 12 c. claret 1 6 2 6
a. Perf. 14½×14 ('50) .. £50 £30
54 „ 16 c. brown 2 6 2 0
55 **33** 24 c. light blue 2 6 2 6
56 „ 48 c. olive-green 6 0 7 6
57 „ $1.20, purple 10 0 15 0
58 „ $2.40, blue-green .. 20 0 32 6
59 „ $4.80, rose-carmine .. 35 0 45 0

949 (10 Oct.). *75th Anniv. of Universal Postal Union. As Nos.* 114/7 *of Antigua.*
o 5 c. violet 0 6 0 8
1 6 c. orange 1 0 1 6
2 12 c. magenta 1 9 2 0
3 24 c. blue-green 3 6 4 6

51 (16 Feb.). *Inauguration of B.W.I. University College. As Nos.* 118/9 *of Antigua.*
4 3 c. black and scarlet .. 0 10 0 10
5 12 c. black & deep carmine .. 2 6 2 6

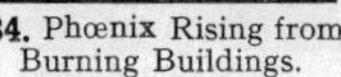

34. Phœnix Rising from Burning Buildings. (**35**)

(Flames typo., rest recess. B. W. & Co.)

1951 (19 June). *Reconstruction of Castries. Wmk. Mult. Script CA. P* 13½×13.
166 **34** 12 c. red and blue .. 5 0 6 0

1951 (25 Sept.). *New Constitution. Optd. with T* **35** *by Waterlow & Sons. P* 12½.
167 **32** 2 c. magenta 0 6 0 6
168 „ 4 c. grey 0 8 0 9
169 „ 5 c. violet 0 9 0 9
170 „ 12 c. claret 1 6 2 6

1953 (2 June). *Coronation. As No.* 47 *of Aden.*
171 3 c. black and scarlet .. 1 0 1 6

36. Queen Elizabeth II. **37.** Device of St. Lucia.

(Recess. Waterlow (T **36**) until 1936, then De La Rue. Bradbury Wilkinson (T **37**).)

1953–54. *Wmk. Mult. Script CA. P* 14½×14 (*T* **36**) *or* 11×11½ (*T* **37**).
172 **36** 1 c. green 0 3 0 3
173 „ 2 c. magenta 0 4 0 4
174 „ 3 c. red 0 5 0 4
175 „ 4 c. slate 0 5 0 5
176 „ 5 c. violet 0 6 0 6
177 „ 6 c. orange (*shades*) .. 0 9 0 9
178 „ 8 c. lake 0 9 1 0
179 „ 10 c. ultramarine (*shades*) 1 0 1 3
180 „ 15 c. red-brown (*shades*) .. 1 3 1 6
181 **37** 25 c. deep turquoise-blue 2 0 2 3
182 „ 50 c. deep olive-green .. 3 6 4 6
183 „ $1 bluish green .. 7 0 8 6
184 „ $2.50 carmine 17 6 20 0

Dates of issue:—28.10.53, 2 c.; 7.1.54, 4 c.; 1.4.54, 1 c., 5 c.; 2.9.54, others.

1958 (22 Apr.). *Inauguration of British Caribbean Federation. As Nos.* 135/7 *of Antigua.*
185 3 c. deep green 1 0 1 3
186 6 c. blue 1 6 1 9
187 12 c. scarlet 2 3 2 6

38. Columbus's *Santa Maria* off the Pitons.

39. Stamp of 1860.

(Recess. Waterlow & Sons.)

1960 (1 Jan.). *New Constitution for the Windward and Leeward Islands. W* w.**12**. *P* 13.

188	**38**	8 c. carmine-red	2 6	2 9
189	,,	10 c. red-orange	3 0	3 6
190	,,	25 c. deep blue ..	5 9	6 9

(Recess. Waterlow & Sons.)

1960 (18 Dec.). *Stamp Centenary. W* w.**12**. *P* 13½.

191	**39**	5 c. rose-red & ultram. ..	3 0	3 6
192	,,	16 c. dp. blue & yell.-grn.	3 6	4 0
193	,,	25 c. green & carm.-red ..	5 9	6 9

1963 (4 June). *Freedom from Hunger. As No.* 63 *of Aden.*

194	25 c. bluish green	2 6	3 0

1963 (2 Sept.). *Red Cross Centenary. As Nos.* 147/8 *of Antigua.*

195	4 c. red and black	0 6	0 6
196	25 c. red and blue	3 0	3 6

40. Queen Elizabeth II **41.** (after A. C. Davidson-Houston).

42. Fishing Boats.

43. Pigeon Island.

44. Reduit Beach.

45. Castries Harbour.

46. The Pitons.

47. Vigie Beach. **48.** Queen Elizabeth II

(Des. V. Whiteley. Photo. Harrison.)

1964 (1 Mar.). *W* w.**12**. *P* 14½ (*T* **40**), *other*
14½ × 14 (*vert.*) *or* 14 × 14½ (*horiz.*).

197	**40**	1 c. crimson	0 2	0
198	,,	2 c. bluish violet ..	0 3	0
199	,,	4 c. turquoise-green ..	0 4	0
200	,,	5 c. Prussian blue ..	0 5	0
201	,,	6 c. yellow-brown ..	0 6	0
202	**41**	8 c. multicoloured ..	0 7	0
203	,,	10 c. multicoloured ..	0 9	0 1
204	**42**	12 c. multicoloured ..	0 10	1
205	**43**	15 c. multicoloured ..	0 11	1
206	**44**	25 c. multicoloured ..	1 6	1
207	**45**	35 c. blue and buff ..	2 0	2
208	**46**	50 c. multicoloured ..	2 10	3
209	**47**	$1 multicoloured ..	5 6	6
210	**48**	$2.50 multicoloured ..	13 10	15

1964 (23 April). 400*th Anniv. of Birth of Willia*
Shakespeare. As No. 164 *of Antigua.*

211	10 c. blue-green	1 6	1

1965 (17 May). *I.T.U. Centenary. As Nos.* 166/7 *of Antigua.*

212 2 c. mauve and magenta .. 0 4 0 6
213 50 c. lilac and light olive-green 3 6 4 0

1965 (25 Oct.). *International Co-operation Year. As Nos.* 168/9 *of Antigua.*

214 1 c. reddish pur. & turq.-grn. 0 5 0 6
215 15 c. dp. bluish green & lav. 2 3 2 9

1966 (24 Jan.). *Churchill Commemoration. As Nos.* 170/3 *of Antigua.*

216 4 c. new blue 0 5 0 6
217 6 c. deep green 0 7 0 9
218 25 c. brown 1 10 2 3
219 35 c. bluish violet 2 6 3 0

1966 (4 Feb.). *Royal Visit. As Nos.* 174/5 *of Antigua.*

220 4 c. black and ultramarine 0 5 0 6
221 25 c. black and magenta .. 1 10 2 3

POSTAGE DUE STAMPS.

No. ..4545
ST. LUCIA.
1d.
POSTAGE DUE

D 1

1931. *No wmk. or gum. Rough perf.* 12.

(*a*) *Horizontally laid paper.*

D1 D 1 1d. black/*blue* .. 4 6 4 6
a. Wide, wrong fount "No." 10 0 10 6

(*b*) *Wove paper.*

D2 D 1 2d. black/*yellow* .. 6 0 6 0
a. Wide wrong fount "No." 25 0 27 6
b. Imperf. between (vert. pr.) £150

ST. LUCIA 1d POSTAGE DUE — D 2

ST. LUCIA 2c POSTAGE DUE — D 3

(Typo. De La Rue.)

933–47. *Wmk. Mult. Script CA. P* 14.

3 D 2 1d. black 2 6 2 6
4 ,, 2d. black 3 0 3 0
5 ,, 4d. black (28.6.47) .. 4 0 5 0
6 ,, 8d. black (28.6.47) .. 5 0 6 0

949 (1 Oct.)–**52.** *Value in cents. Wmk. Mult. Script CA. Typo. P* 14.

7 D 3 2 c. black 2 0 2 0
a. Chalky paper (27.11.52) 0 6 0 8
ab. Error. Crown missing, W9a £20
ac. Error. St. Edward's Crown, W9b .. £10
8 ,, 4 c. black 3 0 3 6
a. Chalky paper (27.11.52) 0 6 1 0
ab. Error. Crown missing, W9a £20
ac. Error. St. Edward's Crown, W9b £15
9 ,, 8 c. black 4 0 5 0
a. Chalky paper (27.11.52) 0 7 1 0
ac. Error. St. Edward's Crown, W9b £35

D10 **D 3** 16 c. black 6 0 7 6
a. Chalky paper (27.11.52) 1 0 1 6
ac. Error. St. Edward's Crown, W9b £25

1965 (9 Mar.). *As Nos.* D7/8 *but wmk.* w.**12.** *Unsurfaced paper. P* 14.

D11 D 3 2 c. black 0 3 0 4
D12 ,, 4 c. black 0 4 0 10

FISCAL STAMPS.

Allowed to be used for postage.

SHILLING
STAMP
(F 1)

1881. *T* **1.** *Wmk. Crown CC. P* 14.

(1) *Surch. as Type* F **1.**

F1 One Penny Stamp, black (C.) 35 0 20 0
a. Surch. inverted £60 £60
b. Surch. double £40 £40
F2 Four Penny Stamp, yellow .. 75 0 70 0
a. Bisected (2d.) (on cover) ..
F3 Six Pence Stamp, mauve .. £5 £5
F4 Shilling Stamp, orange .. 70 0 75 0
a. Error. "SHILEING" .. £30
b. Error. "SHILDING" .. £30 £26

One Penny
Stamp
(F 2)

(2) *Surch. as Type* F **2.**

F 7 One Penny Stamp, black (R.) 30 0 20 0
a. Surch. double £50
F 8 Four Pence Stamp, yellow .. 55 0 45 0
F 9 Six Pence Stamp, mauve .. 55 0 45 0
F10 Shilling Stamp, orange .. 75 0 60 0

HALFPENNY
Stamp
(F 3)

(3) *Surch. as Type* F **3.**

F11 Halfpenny Stamp, green .. 27 6 17 6
a. "Stamp" double £35 £35
F12 One Shilling Stamp, orange (*wmk. Crown CA*) .. 55 0 47 6
a. "Stamp" double £35 £35

FOUR PENCE
REVENUE
(F 4)

1882. *T* **1.** *Wmk. Crown CA. Surch. as Type* F **4,** *in first colour given.*

(*a*) *P* 14.

F13 1d. carmine and black .. 22 6 17 6
a. Imperf. (pair) .. £8
F14 2d. black and pale blue .. 10 6 8 6
a. Imperf. (pair) .. ..
F15 3d. carmine and deep blue .. 35 0 20 0
F16 4d. black and yellow .. 12 6 7 6
F17 6d. black and mauve .. 22 6 17 6

(*b*) *P* 12.

F18 1d. carmine and black .. 20 0 17 6
F19 3d. carmine and deep blue .. 27 6 10 6
F20 1s. black and orange .. 27 6 17 6

Revenue (F 5) REVENUE (F 6)

1883. *Nos.* 25 *and* 26 *optd. at foot with Type* F **5** *locally.*

(1) *Word* 11 *mm. long.*

F21 1d. black (C.) 15 0
  a. Opt. inverted .. ..
  b. Opt. double.. .. .. £20 £15

(2) *Word* 13 *mm.*

F22 1d. black (C.) .. .. — 40 0

(3) *Word* 15½ *mm.*

F23 ½d. green .. .. .. — 45 0
  a. "Revenue" double.. .. — £20
F24 1d. black (C.) 15 0 10 0
  a. "Revenue" double.. .. £8
  b. "Revenue" triple £20
  c. "Revenue" double, one invtd. £20 £20

Nos. 30 *and* 32 *surch. as* (3) *above.*

F25 1d. rose .. .. — 20 0
F26 4d. yellow .. .. — 40 0

1884. *Optd. with Type* F **6**. *Wmk. Crown CA. P* 14.

F27 **5** 1d. slate (C.) 10 0 6 0
  a. Imperf. (pair) .. ..
F28 ,, 1d. dull mauve (Die I) .. 10 0 4 0

ST. VINCENT.

For GREAT BRITAIN stamps used in St. Vincent, see page 66.

— SIMPLIFICATION (see INTRODUCTION) —

Nos. 1 to 66a.

5, 8, 12, 4, 11, 13, 14.
33, 18, 25, 34, 24, 35, 16, 23, 26, 19, 20, 22, 28.
29, 30, 31, 32.
40, 36, 41, 44, 64, 51, 42, 47, 60, 65, 48, 53, 57, 48a, 58, 49.
37, 39, 45, 56, 55, 66, 59, 62.

The above arrangement is purely arbitrary and collectors may prefer to arrange the stamps more nearly in order of date.

(Recess. Perkins, Bacon & Co.)

1

T **1**. *No wmk.*

1861 (8 MAY). *Intermediate perf.* 14 *to* 16.

1 1d. rose-red £125 £45
  a. Imperf. between (horiz. pair) .. £70
2 6d. deep yellow-green .. £250 £25

1862 (SEPT.). *Rough perf.* 14 *to* 16.

3 1d. rose-red 90 0 60 0
  a. Imperf. between (horiz. pair) £65
4 6d. deep green.. .. .. £8 60 0
  a. Imperf. between (horiz. pair) .. £130

1863–66. *P* 11 *to* 12½.

5 1d. rose-red 85 0 60 0
6 6d. deep green.. .. .. £30 £9

P 11 *to* 12½ × 14 *to* 16.

7 1d. rose-red £350 £135

Varieties. Imperf.

7a 1d. rose-red (*pair*) £25
7b 6d. deep green (*pair*) .. £60

The imperf. stamps are not known used.

1866. *P* 11 *to* 12½.

8 4d. deep blue £35 £12
  a. Imperf. between (pair).. ..
9 1s. slate-grey £200 £125

P 14 *to* 16.

10 1s. slate-grey £40 £16

P 11 *to* 12½ × 14 *to* 16.

11 1s. slate-grey £30 £16

1869. *P* 11 *to* 12½.

12 4d. yellow £38 £22
13 1s. indigo £45 £18
14 1s. brown £50 £20

T **1**. *Wmk. Small Star. T* w. **2**.

1871. *Rough perf.* 14 *to* 16.

15 1d. black 47 6 40 0
  a. Imperf. between (vert. pair) .. £185
16 6d. blue-green £35 £15

1872. *P* 11 *to* 12½.

17 1s. deep rose-red £85 £25

1872–73. *Perf. about* 15.

17b 1d. black 85 0 45 0
17c 6d. blue-green £40 £5
17d 6d. dull blue-green £55 £6

1873–74. *P* 11 *to* 12½ × 15.

18 1d. black 90 0 40 0
  a. Imperf. between (pair).. ..
19 1s. lilac-rose £300 £60

1875. *P* 11 *to* 12½.

20 1s. claret £75 £30

1877 (FEB.). *P* 11 *to* 12½ × 15.

21 6d. pale yellow-green £50 £10
  a. Imperf. (pair) .. ..
22 1s. vermilion £50 £15
  a. Imperf. between (pair).. ..

1877 (APR.). *Perf. about* 15.

23 6d. pale yellow-green £40 £8
23a 1s. vermilion .. .. — £250

1877 (JULY). *P* 11 *to* 12½.

24 4d. deep blue £50 £20

2

1880 (JUNE). *Wmk. Small Star, T* w. **2**. *P* 11 t
12½.

25 **1** 1d. olive-green £5 30
  a. Imperf. (pair) .. ..
26 ,, 6d. bright green £50 £1
27 ,, 1s. bright vermilion.. .. £50 £1
  a. Imperf. between (pair) ..
28 **2** 5s. rose-red £100 £11
  a. Imperf. (pair) .. ..

(3)

1880. *No. 17c divided vertically by a line of perforation, gauging 12, and surch. as T* **3.**

29 1d. on half 6d. blue-green (R.) £40 £38
a. Unsevered pair £165 £110

d 1 ½ (4)

ONE PENNY (5)

4d (6)

1881. *Nos. 26/7 surch. No. 30 divided like No. 29.*

30 **4** ½d. on half 6d. brt. grn. (R.) £20 £22
a. Unsevered pair £45 £50
b. Fraction bar omitted (pair with and without bar) .. £175 £175
31 **5** 1d. on 6d. bright green .. £45 £35
32 **6** 4d. on 1s. vermilion .. £200 £135

ST VINCENT HALFPENNY
7

1881 (Dec.). *Wmk. Small Star. T* w. **2.** *P* 11 *to* 12½.

33 **7** ½d. orange 22 6 17 6
34 **1** 1d. drab £20 37 6
35 ,, 4d. bright blue £40 £15
a. Imperf. between (pair) ..

(Printed by Messrs. De La Rue & Co.)

2½ PENCE (8)

1d 2½ PENCE (9)

1883–84. *T* **1** (2½*d. surch. T* **8**). *Wmk. Crown CA. P* 14.

6 1d. drab 32 6 15 0
7 2½d. on 1d. lake 25 0 12 6
8 4d. bright blue £38 £10
8a 4d. dull blue £70 £35

1885. *No. 37 surch. as in T* **9.**

9 1d. on 2½d. on 1d. lake .. 25 0 25 0

T **7** *and* **1.** *Wmk. Crown CA. P* 14.

0 ½d. green 1 6 1 0
0a ½d. deep green 8 6 3 0
1 1d. rose-red 6 0 5 0
2 4d. red-brown £40 75 0

1883–89. (2½*d. surch. T* **8**). *W. Crown CA.* (*a*) *P* 14.

3 **1** 1d. rose 20 0 10 0
4 ,, 1d. red 4 0 2 6
5 ,, 2½d. on 1d. milky blue .. 50 0 27 6
6 ,, 4d. purple-brown 45 0 20 0
7 ,, 4d. lake-brown 37 6 20 0
8 ,, 6d. violet £10 £12
8a ,, 1s. deep orange 50 0 60 0
2 5s. carmine-lake 45 0 55 0
a ,, 5s. brown-lake 55 0 70 0

(*b*) *P* 12.

50 **7** ½d. green 40 0 40 0
50*a* ,, ½d. orange £135
50*b* **1** 1d. rose-red £150
50*c* ,, 1d. milky bl. (without surch.) £300
51 ,, 4d. bright blue £30 50 0
52 ,, 4d. dull blue £135 £32
53 ,, 6d. bright green £28 £28
54 ,, 1s. orange-vermilion .. £5 £5
54*a* **2** 5s. carmine-lake £250

(*c*) *Imperf.* (*pair*).

54*b* **1** 1s. orange-vermilion

Nos. 50*a*, 50*b*, 50*c* and 54*a* are only known unused, and are now considered colour trials. They are very rare.

2½d. (10)

5 PENCE (11)

1890. *No. 47 surch. with T* **10.**

55 **1** 2½d. on 4d. lake-brown .. £5 £7
a. No bar in fraction £25 £22

1890–91. (2½*d. surch. T* **8**). *W Crown CA. P* 14.

55*b* **1** 2½d. on 1d. grey-blue .. 30 0 7 6
56 ,, 2½d. on 1d. blue 3 0 2 6
57 ,, 6d. dull purple 8 6 17 6
58 ,, 1s. orange-vermilion .. 15 0 27 6

1892. *Surch. with T* **11**, *in purple.*

59 **1** 5d. on 4d. lake-brown .. 25 0 30 0

T **11** is found with the first "E" double, once on some sheets.

1893. *Wmk. Crown CA. P* 14.

60 **1** 4d. yellow 6 0 8 6
60*a* ,, 4d. olive-yellow £60 £80

FIVE PENCE (12)

Surch. with T **12.** *Wmk. Crown CA. P* 14.

61 **1** 5d. on 6d. carmine-lake .. 27 6 35 0
62 ,, 5d. on 6d. deep lake .. 4 6 7 6
a. Surcharge double .. .. — £550
63 ,, 5d. on 6d. lake 7 6 12 6

1897 (13 July). *Wmk. Crown CA. P* 14.

64 **1** 2½d. blue 10 0 17 6
65 ,, 5d. sepia 15 0 25 0

1897 (6 Oct.). *Surch. as T* **12.** *W Crown CA. P* 14.

66 **1** 3d. on 1d. mauve 10 0 17 6
66*a* ,, 3d. on 1d. red-mauve .. 20 0 27 6

13

14

(Typo. De La Rue.)

1899. *Wmk. Crown CA. P* 14.

67 **13** ½d. dull mauve and green 1 6 2 0
68 ,, 1d. dull mauve & carmine 5 0 2 6
69 ,, 2½d. dull mauve and blue 10 0 20 0
70 ,, 3d. dull mauve and olive .. 12 0 20 0
71 ,, 4d. dull mauve & orange .. 12 6 20 0
72 ,, 5d. dull mauve and black 12 6 20 0
73 ,, 6d. dull mauve and brown 20 0 25 0
74 **14** 1s. green and carmine .. 27 6 35 0
75 ,, 5s. green and blue .. 95 0 £6

ST VINCENT POSTAGE & REVENUE ½d
15

ST VINCENT POSTAGE & REVENUE 2d
16

(Typo. De La Rue.)

1902. *Wmk. Crown CA. P* 14.

76 **15** ½d. dull purple and green 1 9 1 9
77 ,, 1d. dull purple & carmine 2 0 1 3
78 **16** 2d. dull purple and black 7 6 10 0
79 **15** 2½d. dull purple and blue .. 15 0 17 6
80 ,, 3d. dull purple and olive 12 6 12 6
81 ,, 6d. dull purple and brown 25 0 32 6
82 **16** 1s. green and carmine .. 40 0 55 0
83 **15** 2s. green and violet .. 55 0 65 0
84 **16** 5s. green and blue .. 75 0 85 0

1904–11. *Wmk. Mult. Crown CA. P* 14.

85 **15** ½d. dull purple and green OC ('05) 1 6 1 6
86 ,, 1d. dull purp. & carm., OC 7 0 2 6
88 ,, 2½d. dull purp. & bl., C ('06) 12 6 20 0
90 ,, 6d. dull purple & brown C (1905) 25 0 32 6
91 **16** 1s. grn. & carm., OC ('08) 25 0 32 6
92 **15** 2s. purple & bright blue/*blue*, C ('09) 42 6 55 0
93 **16** 5s. green & red/*yellow*, C (1909) 80 0 90 0
93*a* ,, £1 purple & black/*red*, C (1911) £60 £75

1d PAX ET JUSTITIA POSTAGE & REVENUE ST VINCENT
17

1d PAX ET JUSTITIA ST VINCENT
18

(Recess. De La Rue.)

1907. *Wmk. Mult. Crown CA. P* 14.

94 **17** ½d. green 1 6 1 6
95 ,, 1d. carmine 5 0 3 0
96 ,, 2d. orange 8 6 12 6
97 ,, 2½d. blue 25 0 25 0
98 ,, 3d. violet 27 6 40 0

1909. *Wmk. Mult. Crown CA. P* 14.

99 **18** 1d. carmine 5 0 5 0
100 ,, 6d. dull purple 35 0 42 6
101 ,, 1s. black/*green* 20 0 25 0

1909–11. *T* **18**, *redrawn (dot below "d," as in T* **17**). *Wmk. Mult. Crown CA. P* 14.

102 ½d. green (1910) 2 0 2 0
103 1d. carmine 1 6 0 10
104 2d. grey (1911) 5 0 6 6
105 2½d. ultramarine 6 0 8 6
106 3d. purple/*yellow* 8 0 10 0
107 6d. dull purple 12 6 17 6

ST VINCENT POSTAGE REVENUE ½d ½d
19

ONE

PENNY.
(20)

(Recess. De La Rue.)

1913. *Wmk. Mult. Crown CA. P* 14.

108 **19** ½d. green 0 8 0 8
109 ,, 1d. red 1 0 0 4
109*a* ,, 1d. rose-red 3 0 0 6
110 ,, 2d. grey 12 6 17 6
110*a* ,, 2d. slate 6 0 10 0
111 ,, 2½d. ultramarine .. 3 0 3 0
112 ,, 3d. purple/*yellow* .. 5 0 8 6
a. On lemon 10 0 17 6
b. On pale yellow 6 0 10 0
113 ,, 4d. red/*yellow* 3 6 5 0
113*a* ,, 5d. olive-green .. 10 0 17 6
114 ,, 6d. claret 7 6 8 6
115 ,, 1s. black/*green* 12 6 15 0
116 **18** 2s. blue and purple .. 22 6 30 0
117 ,, 5s. carmine and myrtle 45 0 55 0
118 ,, £1 mauve and black .. £14 £17

Nos. 116 to 118 are from new centre and frame dies, the motto "PAX ET JUSTITIA" being slightly over 7 mm. long, as against just over 8 mm. in Nos. 99 to 107. Nos. 139 to 141 are also from the new dies.

1914. *Wmk. Mult. Crown CA. P* 14.

119 **19** 1s. bistre 15 0 22 6

1915. *Surch. with T* **20**.

120 **19** 1d. on 1s. black/*green* (R.) 8 0 22 6
a. "ONE" omitted £90
b. "ONE" double £90
c. "PENNY" and bar double £65

The spacing between the two words varies from 7¾ mm. to 10 mm.

WAR

STAMP.
(21)

WAR

STAMP.
(22)

1916 (June). *Optd. locally with T* **21**. *(First and second settings; words 2 to 2½ mm. apart.*

122 **19** 1d. red 3 6 4
a. Double opt. .. .. £8 £
b. Comma for stop 10 0 15

In the first printing every second stamp has the comma for stop. The second printing of this setting has full stops only. These two printings can therefore only be distinguished in blocks or pairs.

Third setting; words only 1½ mm. apart.

123 **19** 1d. red £6

Stamps of the first setting are offered as the rare one. Care must be taken to see that the distance between the lines is not over 1½ mm.

Fourth setting; optd. with T **22**. *Words 3½ mm. apart.*

124 **19** 1d. carmine-red 2 0 3
a. Double opt. £15

WAR STAMP
(24)

1916 (Aug.)–**18.** *T* **19**, *new printing, optd. with T* **24**.

126 1d. carmine-red 1 6 1
127 1d. pale rose-red 1 0 1
128 1d. deep rose-red 0 6 1
129 1d. pale scarlet (1918) .. 0 6 1

1917 (JAN.). *Colour changed. Wmk. Mult. Crown CA. P* 14.

130 **19** 1d. scarlet 7 6 10 0

1921–32. *Wmk. Mult. Script CA. P* 14.

131 **19** ½d. green 0 6 0 6
132 „ 1d. carmine 1 6 0 10
132*a* „ 1d. red 1 0 0 8
132*b* „ 1½d. brown ('32) .. 1 6 1 6
133 „ 2d. grey 1 6 1 6
133*a* „ 2½d. bright blue (1926) .. 2 6 2 9
134 „ 3d. bright blue 7 6 12 6
135 „ 3d. purple/*yellow*, (1926) 5 0 10 0
135*a* „ 4d. red/*yellow* ('30) .. 5 0 10 0
136 „ 5d. sage-green 6 6 10 0
137 „ 6d. claret (1.11.27) .. 7 6 10 0
138 „ 1s. bistre-brown .. 8 6 12 6
139 **18** 2s. blue and purple .. 22 6 30 0
140 „ 5s. carmine and myrtle 55 0 70 0
141 „ £1 mauve & black ('28) £12 £14

1935 (6 MAY). *Silver Jubilee. As Nos.* 91/4 *of Antigua but ptd. by W'low & Sons. P* 11×12.

142 1d. deep blue and scarlet .. 0 6 1 0
143 1½d. ultramarine and grey .. 1 0 1 6
144 2½d. brown and deep blue .. 5 0 6 0
145 1s. slate and purple .. 16 0 20 0

1937 (12 MAY). *Coronation. As Nos.* 13/5 *of Aden but optd. by B.W. & Co. P* 11×11½.

146 1d. violet 0 6 0 8
147 1½d. carmine 0 8 1 0
148 2½d. blue 1 6 2 0

25

26. Young's Island and Fort Duvernette.

27. Kingstown and Fort Charlotte.

28. Bathing Beach at Villa.

29. Victoria Park, Kingstown.

(Recess. Bradbury, Wilkinson.)

1938 (11 MAR.)–**47.** *Wmk. Mult. Script CA. P* 12.

149 **25** ½d. blue and green .. 0 3 0 3
150 **26** 1d. blue and lake-brown 0 6 0 4
151 **27** 1½d. green and scarlet .. 0 6 0 6
152 **25** 2d. green and black .. 0 8 0 6
153 **28** 2½d. blue-blk. & blue-grn. 0 8 0 8
153*a* **29** 2½d. grn. & pur.-brn. ('47) 0 9 0 9
154 **25** 3d. orange and purple .. 0 10 0 10
154*a* **28** 3½d. bl.-blk. & bl.grn. ('47) 0 10 1 0
155 **25** 6d. black and lake .. 1 9 1 9
156 **29** 1s. purple and green .. 3 0 3 0
157 **25** 2s. blue and purple .. 8 6 8 6
157*a* „ 2s. 6d. red-brn. & bl. ('47) 10 0 15 0
158 „ 5s. scarlet & deep green 15 0 20 0
158*a* „ 10s. violet & brown ('47) 25 0 30 0
159 „ £1 purple and black .. 45 0 50 0

1946 (15 OCT.). *Victory. As Nos.* 28/9 *of Aden.*

160 1½d. carmine 0 6 0 6
161 3½d. blue 0 9 1 0

1948 (30 NOV.). *Royal Silver Wedding. As Nos.* 30/1 *of Aden.*

162 1½d. scarlet 0 6 0 6
163 £1 bright purple 35 0 42 6

1949 (26 MAR.)–**52.** *Value in cents and dollars. Wmk. Mult. Script CA. P* 12.

164 **25** 1 c. blue and green .. 0 3 0 6
164*a* „ 1 c. grn. & blk. (10.6.52) 0 4 0 4
165 **26** 2 c. blue and lake-brown 0 6 0 6
166 **27** 3 c. green and scarlet .. 1 6 1 0
166*a* **25** 3 c. orange and purple (10.6.52) 0 8 0 8
167 „ 4 c. green and black .. 0 8 0 8
167*a* „ 4 c. blue & grn. (10.6.52) 0 8 0 8
168 **29** 5 c. green & purple-brn. 0 9 0 9
169 **25** 6 c. orange and purple .. 0 10 1 0
169*a* **27** 6 c. green and scarlet (10.6.52) 0 10 0 10
170 **28** 7 c. blue-black and blue-green 1 9 1 9
170*a* „ 10 c. blue-black and blue-green (10.6.52) .. 1 6 1 9
171 **25** 12 c. black and lake .. 1 3 1 3
172 **29** 24 c. purple and green .. 2 0 2 6
173 **25** 48 c. blue and purple .. 4 0 6 0
174 „ 60 c. red-brown and blue 6 0 9 0
175 „ $1.20, scarlet & dp. green 12 6 17 6
176 „ $2.40, violet and brown 20 0 27 6
177 „ $4.80, purple and black 35 0 45 0

1949 (10 OCT.). *75th Anniv. of Universal Postal Union. As Nos.* 114/7 *of Antigua.*

178 5 c. blue 0 6 0 6
179 6 c. purple 0 8 1 0
180 12 c. magenta 1 6 1 9
181 24 c. blue-green 3 0 3 6

1951 (16 FEB.). *Inauguration of B.W.I. University College. As Nos.* 118/9 *of Antigua.*

182 3 c. deep green and scarlet 0 10 0 10
183 12 c. black and purple .. 2 6 2 6

1951 (21 SEPT.). *New Constitution. Optd. with T* **34** *of Dominica, by Bradbury, Wilkinson.*

184 **27** 3 c. green and scarlet .. 1 3 1 9
185 **25** 4 c. green and black .. 1 3 1 9
186 **29** 5 c. green & purple-brn. 1 3 1 9
187 **25** 12 c. black and lake .. 2 0 2 6

1953 (2 JUNE). *Coronation. As No.* 47 *of Aden.*

188 4 c. black and green.. .. 1 0 1 3

30 31

(Recess. Waterlow (until 1961), then De La Rue.)

1955 (16 Sept.). *Wmk. Mult. Script CA. P* 13½ × 14 (*T* **30**) *or* 14 (*T* **31**).

189	**30**	1 c. orange (*shades*) ..	0	3	0	3
190	,,	2 c. ultramarine (*shades*)	0	4	0	4
191	,,	3 c. slate	0	5	0	5
192	,,	4 c. brown	0	4	0	4
193	,,	5 c. scarlet	0	6	0	6
194	,,	10 c. reddish violet (*shades*)	1	0	1	0
195	,,	15 c. deep blue	1	2	1	3
196	,,	20 c. green	1	6	1	9
197	,,	25 c. black-brown ..	2	0	2	9
198	**31**	50 c. red-brown (*shades*) ..	5	0	6	0
199	,,	$1, myrtle-green (*shades*) ..	6	6	7	6
200	,,	$2.50, deep blue (*shades*) ..	15	0	20	0

1958 (22 Apr.). *Inauguration of British Caribbean Federation. As Nos.* 135/7 *of Antigua.*

201	3 c. deep green	0	6	0	6
202	6 c. blue	0	8	1	0
203	12 c. scarlet	1	3	1	9

1963 (4 June). *Freedom from Hunger. As No.* 63 *of Aden.*

204	8 c. reddish violet	1	0	1	6

1963 (2 Sept.). *Red Cross Centenary. As Nos.* 147/8 *of Antigua.*

205	4 c. red and black	0	5	0	6
206	8 c. red and blue	0	10	1	0

1964–65. *As* 1955 *but wmk.* w.**12**.

(*a*) *P* 12½ (14 Jan.–Mar. 1964).

207	**30**	10 c. deep lilac	1	0	1	3
208	,,	15 c. deep blue	3	0	3	6
209	,,	20 c. green (24.2.64*) ..	3	0	3	9
210	,,	25 c. black-brown ..	5	0	6	0
211	**31**	50 c. red-brown ..	4	0	5	0

(*b*) *P* 13 × 14 (*T* **30**) *or* 14 (*T* **31**).

212	**30**	1 c. orange (15.12.64) ..	0	3	0	4
213	,,	2 c. blue (15.12.64) ..	0	4	0	5
214	,,	3 c. slate (15.12.64) ..	0	5	0	6
215	,,	5 c. scarlet (15.12.64) ..	0	6	0	7
216	,,	10 c. deep lilac (15.12.64) ..	0	11	1	2
217	,,	15 c. deep blue (9.11.64) ..	1	1	1	4
218	,,	20 c. green ('64) ..	1	5	1	8
219	,,	25 c. black-brn. (20.10.64)	1	10	2	3
220	**31**	50 c. chocolate (18.1.65) ..	3	4	4	0

*This is the earliest known date recorded in St. Vincent although it may have been put on sale on 14.1.64.

32. Scout Badge and Proficiency Badges.

(Des. V. Whiteley. Litho. Harrison.)

1964 (23 Nov.). *50th Anniv. of St. Vincent Boy Scouts Association. W* w.**12**. *P* 14½.

221	**32**	1 c. yell.-grn. & chocolate	0	3	0	4
222	,,	4 c. blue & brown-purple	0	6	0	9
223	,,	20 c. yellow & black-violet	1	6	2	0
224	,,	50 c. red and bronze-green	3	3	4	0

33. Tropical Fruits.

34. Breadfruit and the *Providence*.

35. Doric Temple and Pond. **36.** Talipot Palm an[d] Doric Temple.

(Des. V. Whiteley. Photo. Harrison.)

1965 (23 Mar.). *Botanic Gardens Bicentenar W* w.**12**. *P* 14½ × 13½ (*horiz.*) *or* 13½ × 14 (*vert.*).

225	**33**	1 c. multicoloured ...	0	3	0
226	**34**	4 c. multicoloured ..	0	5	0
227	**35**	25 c. multicoloured ...	1	10	2
228	**36**	40 c. multicoloured ..	2	10	3

1965 (17 May). *I.T.U. Centenary. As No* 166/7 *of Antigua.*

229	4 c. light blue and light olive-green	0	5	0
230	48 c. ochre-yellow and orange	3	3	4

37. Boat-building, Bequia (inscr. "BEQUIA "

38. Friendship Beach, Bequia.

39. Terminal Building, Arnos Vale Airport.

40. Woman with Bananas.

42. Carib Stone.

41. Crater Lake.

43. Arrowroot.

46. Sea Island Cotton.

44. Owia Salt Pond.

45. Deep Water Wharf.

47. Map of St. Vincent and Islands.

48. Breadfruit.

49. Baleine Falls.

50. St. Vincent Parrot.

51. Arms of St. Vincent.

(Des. M. Goaman. Photo. Harrison.)

1965 (16 Aug.). *W* w.**12**. *P* 14½ × 13½ (*horiz.*) *or* 13½ × 14½ (*vert.*).

No.	Type	Description	Unused	Used
231	**37**	1 c. multicoloured	0 2	0 3
232	**38**	2 c. multicoloured	0 3	0 4
233	**39**	3 c. multicoloured	0 4	0 6
234	**40**	4 c. multicoloured	0 4	0 6
235	**41**	5 c. multicoloured	0 5	0 7
236	**42**	6 c. multicoloured	0 6	0 8
237	**43**	8 c. multicoloured	0 7	0 9
238	**44**	10 c. multicoloured	0 9	1 0
239	**45**	12 c. multicoloured	0 10	1 2
240	**46**	20 c. multicoloured	1 3	1 8
241	**47**	25 c. multicoloured	1 6	2 0
242	**48**	50 c. multicoloured	2 10	3 6
243	**49**	$1 multicoloured	5 6	7 6
244	**50**	$2.50, multicoloured	13 10	17 6
245	**51**	$5 multicoloured	26 0	32 0

1966 (24 Jan.). *Churchill Commemoration. As Nos.* 170/3 *of Antigua.*

No.	Description	Unused	Used
246	1 c. new blue	0 3	0 4
247	4 c. deep green	0 5	0 7
248	20 c. brown	1 6	2 0
249	40 c. bluish violet	2 10	3 3

1966 (4 Feb.). *Royal Visit. As Nos.* 174/5 *of Antigua.*

No.	Description	Unused	Used
250	4 c. black and ultramarine	0 5	0 7
251	25 c. black and magenta	1 10	2 6

SAMOA.

(Issues prior to the Anglo-German-American agreement of 1899.)

1

(Des. H. H. Glover. Litho. S. T. Leigh & Co., Sydney, N.S.W.)

1877. *P* 12½.

A. 1*st state; line above* " x " *in* " express " *not broken.*

No.	Type	Description	Unused	Used
1	**1**	1d. ultramarine	40 0	50 0
2	,,	3d. deep scarlet	40 0	50 0
3	,,	6d. bright violet	50 0	50 0
4	,,	6d. pale violet	50 0	50 0

B. 2*nd state; line above* " x " *broken, and an extra dot to the left of* " o," *in the row of small pearls over* " samoa ".

No.	Type	Description	Unused	Used
5	**1**	1d. ultramarine	40 0	50 0
6	**1**	3d. bright scarlet	40 0	50 0
7	,,	6d. bright violet	40 0	50 0
8	,,	1s. dull yellow	60 0	70 0
		a. Line above " X " not broken	70 0	80 0
9	,,	1s. orange-yellow	60 0	70 0
10	,,	2s. red-brown	80 0	90 0
11	,,	2s. chocolate	£7	£8
12	,,	5s. green	£18	£22

C. 3*rd state; line above* " x " *repaired.*

(*a*) *P* 12½.

No.	Type	Description	Unused	Used
13	**1**	1d. ultramarine	40 0	45 0
14	,,	3d. vermilion	40 0	50 0
15	,,	6d. violet	40 0	50 0
16	,,	2s. brown	£5	£6
17	,,	2s. deep brown	£5	£6
18	,,	5s. green	£12	£15
		a. Line above " X " not repaired		

(*b*) *P* 12.

No.	Type	Description	Unused	Used
19	**1**	1d. blue	25 0	30 0
20	,,	1d. deep blue	25 0	32 6
21	,,	1d. ultramarine	30 0	40 0
22	,,	3d. vermilion	25 0	50 0
23	,,	3d. carmine-vermilion	35 0	55 0
24	,,	6d. bright violet	32 6	55 0
25	,,	6d. deep violet	30 0	55 0
26	,,	9d. orange-brown	45 0	60 0
28	,,	2s. deep brown	£5	£6
29	,,	5s. yellow-green	£12	£15
30	,,	5s. deep green	£12	£15
		a. Line above " X " not repaired (Nos. 29, 30)		

Originals exist imperf., but are not known used in this state.

On sheets of the 1d., 1st state, at least eight stamps have a stop after " penny ". In the 2nd state, three stamps have the stop, and in the 3rd state, only one.

In the 1st state, all the stamps, 1d., 3d. and 6d., were in sheets of 20 and also the 1d. in the 3rd state (Nos. 13 and 19 to 21).

All values in the 2nd state (Nos. 5 to 12) and all values except the 1d. in the 3rd state (Nos. 14 to 18 and 22 to 30) were in sheets of 10.

As all sheets of all printings of the originals were imperf. at the outer edges, the only stamps which can have perforations on all four sides are Nos. 1 to 4, 13 and 19 to 21, all other originals being imperf. on one or two sides.

Remainders, in sheets of 21, of the 1d. and 6d., the *2d. rose* (which was never *issued*), and of the 3d., in sheets of 12, and of the 9d., 1s., 2s. and 5s. (probably also in sheets of 12), were found in the Samoan post office when this service closed down. The remainders are rare in complete sheets, but of very little value as singles, compared with the originals.

Reprints of all values, in sheets of 40, were made after the originals had been withdrawn from sale. These are practically worthless.

In the majority of both reprints and remainders there is a small coloured projection from the coloured curve, immediately below the middle point of the " m " of " samoa ", but a few stamps (both remainders and reprints) do not show this, while on some it is very faint. The mark is never found in the originals except in the 9d.

There are three known types of forgery, one of which is rather dangerous, the others being crude.

2. Palm Trees.

3. King Malietoa.

4

5

(Eng. Bock & Cousins. Typo. New Zealand Govt. Ptg. Office.)

1887–95. *W* **5.** (*a*) *P* 12½.

31	2	½d. purple-brown ..	.. 2 0	2 0
32	,,	1d. yellow-green ..	.. 2 0	2 6
33	,,	2d. orange ..	.. 2 6	2 6
34	3	2½d. rose (1892	.. 3 0	3 0
35	2	4d. blue ..	.. 10 0	10 0
35*a*	,,	6d. brown-lake ..	.. £45	
36	,,	1s. rose ..	.. 12 6	12 6
37	,,	2s. 6d. violet ..	.. 30 0	27 6

The 1s. rose (perf. 12½) was bisected, and each half used as a 6d. stamp from April to June, 1895. Price 15s. on piece of original. The 1s. rose, perf. 11, bisects were made later to meet a philatelic demand.

(*b*) *P* 12×11½ (1893).

38	2	½d. purple-brown ..	.. 0 9	1 0
39	,,	1d. yellow-green ..	.. 2 0	2 0
40	,,	1d. blue-green ..	.. 2 0	1 9
41	,,	2d. dull orange ..	.. 3 0	1 9
42	3	2½d. rose ..	.. 3 0	1 9
43	2	4d. blue ..	.. 6 6	2 6
44	4	5d. red (1894) ..	.. 3 6	2 6
45	2	6d. brown-lake ..	.. 5 0	4 0
46	,,	6d. maroon ..	.. 10 0	3 6
47	,,	1s. rose ..	.. 10 0	4 0
48	,,	2s. 6d. bright violet	.. 35 0	6 0

(*c*) *P* 11 (1895).

49	2	½d. purple-brown ..	.. 0 9	1 0
50	,,	½d. deep brown ..	.. 0 9	1 0
51	,,	1d. deep blue-green	.. 1 3	1 0
52	,,	1d. blue-green ..	.. 1 3	1 0
53	,,	2d. orange-yellow ..	.. 3 0	3 0
54	,,	2d. ochre ..	.. 2 0	2 6
55	,,	2d. orange ..	.. 3 0	3 0
55*a*	,,	2d. bright orange ..	.. 2 6	2 6
56	3	2½d. rose ..	.. 2 6	2 0
57	2	4d. blue ..	.. 3 0	2 6
58	,,	4d. deep blue ..	.. 3 0	3 6
59	4	5d. red ..	.. 3 0	3 0
60	2	6d. brown-lake ..	.. 4 0	4 6
61	,,	6d. maroon ..	.. 4 0	4 0
62	,,	1s. rose ..	.. 5 0	5 0
63	,,	2s. 6d. deep purple	.. 7 6	8 6
63*a*	,,	2s. 6d. mauve ..	.. 15 0	10 0
		b. Imperf. between (pair) ..	£18	

Nos. 49–63*a* and 72–74, 77–81 and 84–95, all perf. 11, are usually very unevenly perforated, owing to the large size of the pins. Evenly centred copies are extremely hard to find.

FIVE PENCE (6) FIVE PENCE (7) 5d (8)

1893 (Nov.). *No.* 43 *surch.*

4	6	5d. on 4d. blue ..	.. 50 0	50 0
		a. "FI PENCE" ..	£8	
		b. "FIVE PENOE" ...	£8	£8
5	£6	5d. on 4d. blue	£6	£6

No. 43 *surch. in red* (*a*) *as T* **8**, *but* " d " *raised,* (*b*) *with the* " d " *on a line with the* " 5 " *as illustrated.*

66		5d. on 4d. (*a*) ...	.. 20 0	20 0
		a. Surch. inverted	£20	
		b. Surch. double	£18	
67		5d. on 4d. (*b*)	.. 20 0	20 0
		a. Stop after " d "	£6	
		b. Bar omitted		

Surcharged 1½d. (9) R 3d. (10)

1895 (28 Jan.). *T* **2** *surch. with T* **9** *or* **10.**

(*a*) *P* 12×11½.

69		1½d. on 2d. dull orange (B.) ..	3 6	3 0
70		3d. on 2d. dull orange ..	7 6	6 0
		a. Surch. double ..	£7	

(*b*) *P* 11.

72		1½d. on 2d. orange (B.) ..	2 0	2 0
73		3d. on 2d. orange ..	5 0	5 0
		a. Surch. double ..	£6	
74		3d. on 2d. yellow ..	4 0	5 0
		a. Imperf. between (pair) ..	£10	

Both the above were reprinted in 1900 on stamps perf. 11. The 1½d. surcharge is in *ultramarine* and the 3d. in *green.* It is said that these have been found genuinely used.

1896. *Error of colour. P* 10×11.

76	3	2½d. black	.. 2 0	3 0
		a. Perf. 11	..	

Surcharged 2½d. (11) PROVISIONAL GOVT. (12)

1898–99. *T* **2** *surch. with T* **11.** *P* 11.

77		2½d. on 1s. rose ..	.. 2 0	2 0
78		2½d. on 1s. carmine ..	.. 2 6	3 0
79		2½d. on 1d. blue-green (R.) ..	1 6	1 6
		a. Surch. inverted ..	—	£15
80		2½d. on 1s. carmine (R.) ..	4 0	4 0
		a. Surch. double ..	£10	
81		2½d. on 2s. 6d. violet ..	3 0	4 0

There are two types of the 2½d. surcharge. In the second type the fractional line is more upright and the tail of the large numeral " 2 " is further from the line.

1899. *W* **5.** *Colours changed. P* 11.

84	2	½d. green	.. 1 9	2 6
85	,,	1d. red-brown	.. 1 9	2 6

1899. *Optd. with T* **12** (*words longer and letters shorter on* 5d.). *P* 11.

86	2	½d. blue-green (R.) ..	0 6	0 9
87	,,	½d. deep yellow-green (R.)	0 6	0 9
88	,,	1d. red-brown (B.) ..	0 6	0 9
88*a*	,,	2d. orange-yellow (R.) ..	0 9	1 0
89	,,	2d. orange (R.)	0 9	1 0
90	,,	4d. blue (R.)	1 6	2 0
91	4	5d. red (B.)	2 0	2 6
92	,,	5d. deep red (B.)	2 0	2 6
93	2	6d. lake (B.)	2 6	3 0
94	,,	1s. rose (B.)	5 0	5 0
95	,,	2s. 6d. violet (R.) ..	10 0	12 6

The Samoan group of islands was in 1900 partitioned between the German Empire (*see* German Colonies) and the United States of America. No separate stamps are issued by the latter for this territory.

The German Islands of Samoa surrendered to the New Zealand Expeditionary Force on August 29, 1914. Known as Western Samoa, they were administered by New Zealand until 1962.

G.R.I.

1d.

(13)

G.R.I.

1 Shillings.

(14)

(Surch. *Samoanische Zeitung*, Apia.)

1914 (3 Sept.). *German Colonial issue (ship) (no wmk.) surch. as T* **13** *or* **14** *(mark values)*.

No.	Description	Unused	Used
101	½d. on 3 pf. brown	20 0	17 6
	a. Surcharge double	£75	
	b. No fraction bar	£6	£5
	c. Comma after "I"	£100	£60
	d. "1" to left of "2" in "½"	£6	£5
102	½d. on 5 pf. green	50 0	35 0
	a. No fraction bar	£8	£5
	c. Comma after "I"	£20	£20
	d. Surcharge double	£60	
	e. "1" to left of "2" in "½"	£8	£8
103	1d. on 10 pf. carmine	£5	65 0
	a. Surcharge double	£60	£60
104	2½d. on 20 pf. ultram.	50 0	25 0
	a. No fraction bar	£8	£6
	b. "1" to left of "2" in "½"	£8	£6
	c. Surcharge inverted	£100	£100
	d. Comma after "I"	£50	£50
	e. Surcharge double	£100	£100
105	3d. on 25 pf. blk. & red/*yell.*	£8	80 0
	a. Surcharge double	£60	£40
	b. Comma after "I"	—	£100
106	4d. on 30 pf. blk. & orge./*buff*	£18	£10
	a. Error. 3d. on 30 pf.	£600	£500
107	5d. on 40 pf. blk. & carm.	£18	£10
	a. Error. 4d. on 40 pf.	£600	£500
108	6d. on 50 pf., blk. & pur./*buff*	60 0	45 0
	a. Surcharge double	£75	£75
	b. Inverted "9" for "6"	£8	£8
109	9d. on 80 pf. blk. & car./*rose*	£20	£12
110	"1 shillings" on 1 m. carm.	£300	£225
111	"1 shilling" on 1 m. carm.	£1500	£650
112	2s. on 2 m. blue	£275	£200
113	3s. on 3 m. violet-black	£100	£75
	a. Surcharge double	£600	£700
114	5s. on 5 m. carmine & black	£125	£90

The ½d. to 9d. were surcharged in a vertical setting of 10.

No. 108*b* is distinguishable from 108, as the "d" and the "9" are not in a line, and the upper loop of the "9" turns downwards to the left.

SAMOA.

(15)

1914 (29 Sept.). *Stamps of New Zealand, T* **50**, **51**, **52**, *and* **27**, *optd. as T* **15**, *but optd. only 14 mm. long on all except 2½d. Wmk. "N Z" and Star, T* **41**.

No.	Description	Unused	Used
115	½d. yell.-grn. (R.) (*p.* 14 × 15)	0 6	0 6
116	1d. carm. (B.) (*p.* 14 × 15)	0 6	0 6
118	2d. mauve (R.) (*p.* 14 × 14½)	2 6	3 0
119	2½d. deep blue (R.) (*p.* 14)	3 6	4 6
121	6d. carm. (B.) (*p.* 14 × 14½)	6 6	8 6
	a. Perf. 14 × 13½	25 0	30 0
	b. Vert. pair, 121/21a	50 0	65 0
122	6d. pale car. (B.) (*p.* 14 × 14½)	25 0	30 0
124	1s. verm. (B.) (*p.* 14 × 14½)	10 0	15 0

1914 (Dec.)–**1931**. *Type* **F 4** *of New Zealand optd. with T* **15**.

(*a*) *Rough perf.* 14, 14½ *(small holes)*.

No.	Description	Unused	Used
125	2s. blue (R.)	£20	£25
126	2s. 6d. brown (B.)	15 0	20 0
127	5s. yellow-green (R.)	35 0	42 6
128	10s. purple-brown (B.)	70 0	80 0
129	£1 rose (B.)	£10	£12

(*b*) *Clean cut perf.* 14½ × 14.

No.	Description	Unused	Used
130	2s. blue (R.)	15 0	20 0
130*a*	2s. 6d. brown (B.) ('31)	30 0	40 0
131	5s. yellow-green (R.)	30 0	35 0
132	10s. purple-brown (B.)	75 0	85 0
133	£1 rose (B.)	£7	£8

1916–19. *King George V stamps of New Zealand optd. as T* **15**, *but* 14 *mm. long.*

(*a*) *T* **60***b*. *Typo. P* 14 × 15.

No.	Description	Unused	Used
134	½d. yellow-green (R.)	0 6	0 8
135	1½d. slate (R.) (1917)	1 6	2 0
136	1½d. orange-brown (R.) (1919)	1 0	2 0
137	2d. yellow (R.) (1918)	2 0	1 6
138	3d. chocolate (B.)	3 6	5 0

(*b*) *T* **60**. *Recess. P* 14 × 14½, *etc.*

No.	Description	Unused	Used
139	2½d. blue (R.)	2 6	3 0
	a. Perf. 14 × 13½	1 9	1 9
	b. Vert. pair 139/9a	15 0	20 0
140	3d. chocolate (B.)	2 6	3 6
	a. Perf. 14 × 13½	3 6	5 0
	b. Vert. pair, 140/40a	20 0	27 6
141	6d. carmine (B.)	6 0	8 6
	a. Perf. 14 × 13½	6 0	12 6
	b. Vert. pair, 141/1a	20 0	30 0
142	1s. vermilion (B.)	8 6	25 0
	a. Perf. 14 × 13½	8 6	10 0
	b. Vert. pair, 142/2a	30 0	40 0

1920. *Victory. T* **62** *to* **67** *of New Zealand, optd. as T* **15**, *but* 14 *mm. long.*

No.	Description	Unused	Used
143	½d. green (R.)	1 6	2 0
144	1d. carmine (B.)	1 6	3 0
145	1½d. brown-orange (R.)	4 0	5 0
146	3d. chocolate (B.)	5 0	6 6
147	6d. violet (R.)	10 0	15 0
148	1s. orange-red (B.)	15 0	20 0

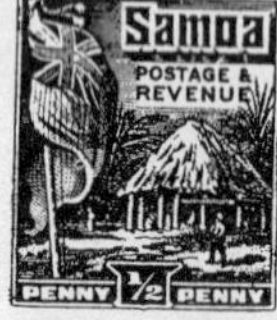

16. Native hut.

(Eng. Bradbury, Wilkinson. Recess-printed at Wellington, N.Z.)

1921 (23 Dec.). *W* **41** *of New Zealand.*

(*a*) *P* 14 × 14½.

No.	Type	Description	Unused	Used
149	**16**	½d. green	3 0	3 6
150	,,	1d. lake	1 3	2 6
151	,,	1½d. chestnut	1 9	3 6
152	,,	2d. yellow	1 6	4 6

(*b*) *P* 14 × 13½.

No.	Type	Description	Unused	Used
153	**16**	½d. green	1 0	1 0
154	,,	1d. lake	0 10	0 8
155	,,	1½d. chestnut	7 6	10 0
156	,,	2d. yellow	4 6	1 3
157	,,	2½d. grey-blue	2 6	3 6
158	,,	3d. sepia	3 6	5 0
159	,,	4d. violet	4 6	6 0
160	,,	5d. light blue	5 0	7 6
161	,,	6d. bright carmine	6 6	10 0
162	,,	8d. red-brown	10 0	15 0
163	,,	9d. olive-green	10 0	15 0
164	,,	1s. vermilion	12 6	17 6

1922–24. *As Type* **F 4** *of New Zealand optd. wit[h] T* **15**, *in red.*

No.	Description	Unused	Used
165	3s. mauve	27 6	35
166	£2 mauve	£25	£3

1926 28. *T* **72** *of New Zealand, optd. with T* **15**, *i[n] red.* (*a*) *"Jones" paper.*

No.	Description	Unused	Used
167	2s. deep blue	12 6	22
168	3s. mauve	18 6	25

(*b*) " *Cowan* " *paper.*

169	2s. light blue (1928)	.. 20 0	27 6
170	3s. pale mauve (1928)	.. 35 0	42 6

1932. *As T* **73a** (" *Arms* ") *of New Zealand optd. with T* **15.** *P* 14.

171	2s. 6d. brown (B.)	17 6	30 0
172	5s. green (R.)	40 0	60 0
173	10s. carmine (B.)	£5	£7
174	£1 pink (B.)	£7	£9
175	£2 violet (R.)	£40	
176	£5 blue (R.)	£250	

SILVER JUBILEE
OF
KING GEORGE V
1910-1935.
(**17**)

1935 (7 May.) *Silver Jubilee. Optd. with T* **17.** *P* 14 × 13½.

177	**16**	1d. lake	1 3	2 6
		a. Perf. 14 × 14½	£15	£18
178	,,	2½d. grey-blue	3 0	8 0
179	,,	6d. bright carmine	15 0	22 6

18. Samoan Girl.

19. Apia.

20. River Scene.

21. Chief and Wife.

22. Canoe and House.

23. R. L. Stevenson's home " Vailima ".

24. Stevenson's Tomb.

25. Lake Lanuto'o.

26. Falefa Falls.

(Recess. De La Rue & Co.)

1935 (7 Aug.). *W* **41** *of New Zealand* (" N Z " *and Star*). (*a*) *P* 14 × 13½, (*b*) *P* 13½ × 14 *or* (*c*) *P* 14.

180	**18**	½d. green (*a*)	0 4	0 6
181	**19**	1d. black and carmine (*b*)	0 6	0 6
182	**20**	2d. black and orange (*c*)	6 0	5 0
		a. Perf. 13½ × 14	3 0	5 0
183	**21**	2½d. black and blue (*a*)	1 0	1 0
184	**22**	4d. slate and sepia (*b*)	2 0	1 3
185	**23**	6d. bright magenta (*b*)	2 0	1 9
186	**24**	1s. violet and brown (*b*)	4 0	3 0
187	**25**	2s. green & pur.-brn. (*a*)	6 6	5 0
188	**26**	3s. blue & brown-orge. (*a*)	10 0	8 6

See also Nos. 200/3.

WESTERN
SAMOA.
(**27**)

1935. *As T* **73a** (" *Arms* ") *of New Zealand optd. with T* **27.** *W* **41.**

189	2s. 6d. brown (B.)	12 6	20 0
190	5s. green (B.)	30 0	40 0
191	10s. carmine-lake (B.)	60 0	75 0
192	£1 pink (B.)	£5	£7
193	£2 violet (R.)	£12	£15
194	£5 blue (R.)	£30	£40

See also Nos. 209/14*a*.

28. Coastal Scene.

29. Western Samoa.

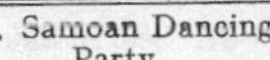

30. Samoan Dancing Party.

31. Robert Louis Stevenson.

(Des. J. Berry (1d. and 1½d.). L. C. Mitchell (2½d. and 7d.). Recess. Bradbury, Wilkinson & Co.)

1939 (29 Aug.). *25th Anniv. New Zealand Control. W* **98** *of New Zealand. P* 13½ × 14 *or* 14 × 13½ (*7d.*).

195 **28** 1d. olive-green & scarlet 1 3 1 9
196 **29** 1½d. lt. blue & red-brown 2 6 3 0
197 **30** 2½d. red-brown and blue 7 6 7 6
198 **31** 7d. violet and slate-green 17 6 17 6

32. Samoan Chief. **33.** Apia Post Office.

(Recess. Bradbury, Wilkinson & Co.)

1940 (2 Sept.). *W* **98** *of New Zealand (Mult. "N Z" and Star). P* 14 × 13½.

199 **32** 3d. on 1½d. brown .. 1 0 0 10

T **32** was not issued without surcharge.

(T **33.** Des. L. C. Mitchell. Recess. Bradbury, Wilkinson & Co. Ltd.)

1944–49. *W* **98** *of New Zealand (Mult. "N Z" and Star) (sideways on 2½d.). P* 14 *or* 13½ × 14 (*5d.*).

200 **18** ½d. green 1 0 1 6
202 **20** 2d. black and orange .. 2 6 2 0
203 **21** 2½d. black & blue ('48) .. 2 6 3 6
205 **33** 5d. sepia and blue (8.6.49) 2 6 3 0

1945–50. *As T* **73a** *("Arms") of New Zealand optd. with T* **27.** *W* **98** *of New Zealand (Mult. "N Z" and Star).*

209 2s. 6d. brown (B.) (6.45) .. 5 0 7 6
210 5s. green (B.) (5.45) 10 0 15 0
211 10s. pale carmine (B.) (4.46) .. 35 0 45 0
211*a* £1 pink (B.) (6.48) £5 £7
212 30s. brown (8.48) £10 £12
213 £2 violet (R.) (11.47) .. £10 £12
214 £3 green (8.48) £18 £22
214*a* £5 deep blue (R.) (31.1.50) .. £25 £28

See also Nos. 232/5.

WESTERN
SAMOA

(**34**)

1946 (1 June). *Peace Issue. Stamps of New Zealand optd. with T* **34** *(reading up and down at sides on 2d.).*

215 **132** 1d. green (Bk.) 0 3 0 4
216 **134** 2d. purple (B.) 0 6 0 8
217 **138** 6d. choc. & verm. (Bk.) .. 1 0 1 6
218 **139** 8d. black & carmine (B.) 1 3 1 9

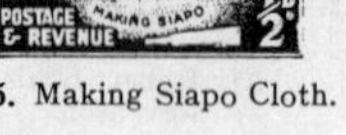

35. Making Siapo Cloth. **37.** Seal of Samoa.

36. Native Houses and Flags.

38. Malifa Falls
(wrongly inscribed " Aleisa Falls ").

39. Manumea (Tooth-billed Pig

40. Bonito Fishing Canoe.

41. Cacao Harvesting.

43. Preparing Copra.

42. Thatching a Native Hut.

44. Samoan Chieftainess.

(Recess. Bradbury, Wilkinson & Co., Ltd.)

1952 (10 Mar.). *W* **98** *of New Zealand (sideways on* 1*s. and* 3*s.). P* 13 (½*d.,* 2*d.,* 5*d. and* 1*s.) or* 13½ *(others).*

No.	Type	Description				
219	**35**	½d. claret and orange-brn.	0	4	0	6
220	**36**	1d. olive-green & green ..	0	5	0	6
221	**37**	2d. carmine-red	0	6	0	7
222	**38**	3d. pale ultram. & indigo	0	8	0	10
223	**39**	5d. brown & deep green ..	1	0	1	9
224	**40**	6d. pale ultramarine and rose-magenta ..	1	3	1	6
225	**41**	8d. carmine	1	9	2	6
226	**42**	1s. sepia and blue ..	2	3	2	6
227	**43**	2s. yellow-brown	5	0	6	0
228	**44**	3s. choc. & brown-olive ..	7	6	8	6

1953 (25 May). *Coronation. As designs of New Zealand, but inscr.* " WESTERN SAMOA ".

No.	Type	Description				
229	**164**	2d. brown	1	0	1	3
230	**166**	6d. slate-grey	1	6	1	9

WESTERN

SAMOA

(45)

1955 (14 Nov.). *As T* **73a** (" *Arms* ") *of New Zealand optd. with T* **45**, " WESTERN SAMOA " *widely spaced and without stop. W* **98** *of New Zealand (Mult.* " NZ " *and Star).*

232	5s. green (B.)..	15	0	20	0
233	10s. carmine (B.)	30	0	40	0
234	£1 pink (B.)	70	0	90	0
235	£2 violet (R.)	£8		£10	

46. Native Houses and Flags.

47. Seal of Samoa.

48. Map of Samoa, and the Mace.

(Recess. Bradbury, Wilkinson & Co.)

1958 (21 Mar.). *Inauguration of Samoan Parliament. W* **98** *of New Zealand (sideways). P* 13½ × 13 (6*d.*) *or* 13½ *(others).*

No.	Type	Description				
236	**46**	4d. cerise	1	9	2	0
237	**47**	6d. deep reddish violet ..	2	0	2	6
238	**48**	1s. deep ultramarine ..	3	0	3	6

INDEPENDENT STATE.

Samoa became independent on January 1st, 1962.

49. Samoan Fine Mat.

55. Samoan Orator.

50. Samoa College.

51. Public Library.

52. Fono House.

53. Map of Samoa.

54. Airport.

56. " Vailima ".

57. Samoan Flag.

58. Samoan Seal.

(Litho. Bradbury, Wilkinson.)

1962 (2 July). *Independence. W* **98** *of New Zealand (sideways on horiz. stamps). P* 13½.

No.	Type	Description				
239	**49**	1d. brown & rose-carmine	0	4	0	4
240	**50**	2d. brn., green, yell. & red	0	4	0	4
241	**51**	3d. brn., blue-green & blue	0	6	0	6
242	**52**	4d. mag., yell., bl. & black	0	9	0	11
243	**53**	6d. yellow and blue ..	1	0	1	2
244	**54**	8d. bluish green, yellow-green and blue ..	1	2	1	6
245	**55**	1s. brown and bluish green	1	8	2	0
246	**56**	1s. 3d. yellow-green & blue	1	9	2	3
247	**57**	2s. 6d. red and ultramarine	3	6	4	0
248	**58**	5s. ultram., yell., red & drab	6	9	7	6

59. Seal and Joint Heads of State.

(Des. L. C. Mitchell. Photo. Harrison.)

1963 (1 Oct.). *First Anniv. of Independence. W* **98** *of New Zealand. P* 14.

No.	Type	Description				
249	**59**	1d. dp. sepia and green ..	0	4	0	6
250	,,	4d. dp. sepia and blue ..	0	9	1	0
251	,,	8d. dp. sepia and rose-pink	1	6	2	0
252	,,	2s. dp. sepia and orange ..	4	0	5	0

60. Signing the Treaty.

(Des. L. C. Mitchell. Photo. Enschedé.)

1964 (1 Sept.). *2nd Anniv. of New Zealand-Samoa Treaty of Friendship. P* 13½.

No.	Type	Description				
253	**60**	1d. multicoloured ..	0	4	0	6
254	,,	8d. multicoloured ..	1	3	1	8
255	,,	2s. multicoloured ..	3	6	4	6
256	,,	3s. multicoloured ..	5	0	6	0

61. Kava Bowl.

1965 (4 Oct.). *As Nos.* 239. *etc. but W* **61** *(sideways on horiz. designs).*

No.	Type	Description				
257	**49**	1d. brown & rose-carmine	0	3	0	
260	**52**	4d. mag., yell., blue & blk.	0	7	0	
261	**53**	6d. yellow and blue ..	0	10	1	
262	**54**	8d. bluish green, yellow-green and blue ..	1	0	1	
263	**55**	1s. brown & bluish green	1	5	1	

62. Tropic Bird.

63. Flying Fish.

(Des. L. C. Mitchell. Photo. Harrison.)

1965 (29 Dec.). *Air.* W **61** (*sideways*). P 14½.

267	**62**	8d. blk., red-orge. & blue	1	0	1	3
268	**63**	2s. black and blue ..	2	9	3	3

64. Aerial View of Deep Sea Wharf.

65. Aerial View of Wharf and Bay.

(Des. Tecon. Co. (U.S.A.). Photo. Enschedé.)

1966 (2 Mar.). *Opening of First Deep Sea Wharf, Apia.* W **61** (*sideways*). P 13½.

269	**64**	1d. multicoloured ..	0	3	0	3
270	**65**	8d. multicoloured ..	1	0	1	3
271	,,	2s. multicoloured ..	2	9	3	3
272	**64**	3s. multicoloured ..	4	0	4	9

SARAWAK.

(Sarawak was placed under British protection in 1888. It was ceded to Great Britain on 1 July, 1946 and a Crown Colony until 16 Sept. 1963 when it became a state of the Federation of Malaysia.)

Sir James Brooke. 1842–11 June, 1868.
Sir Charles Brooke. 11 June, 1868–17 May, 1917.

1. Sir James Brooke.

2. Sir Charles Brooke.

The initials in the corners of T **1** and **2** stand for "James (Charles) Brooke, Rajah (of) Sarawak."

(T **1** and **2.** Die eng. Wm. Ridgway. Litho. Maclure, Macdonald & Co., Glasgow.)

1869 (1 Mar.). P 11.

1	**1**	3 c. brown/*yellow*	50	0	£10

Specimens are known printed from the engraved die in orange-brown on orange surface-coloured paper, and perf. 12. These were submitted to the Sarawak authorities as examples of the stamps and exist both with and without obliterations.

1871 (1 Jan.). P 11 (*irregular*).

2	**2**	3 c. brown/*yellow*	3	6	5	0
		a. Stop after "THREE" ..	25	0		
		b. Imperf. between (vert. pair) ..	£12			
		c. Imperf. between (horiz. pair) ..	£12			

The "stop" variety, No. 2*a*, which occurs on stamp No. 97 in the sheet, is of no more philatelic importance than any of the numerous other variations, such as narrow first "A" in "SARAWAK" (No. 17) and "R" with long tail in left lower corner (No. 90), but it has been accepted by collectors for many years, and we therefore retain it. The papermaker's wmk. "L N L" appears once or twice in sheets of No. 2.

Specimens are known, recess-printed, similar to those mentioned in note after No. 1.

1875 (1 Jan.). P 11½–12.

3	**2**	2 c. mauve/lilac (*shades*) ..	5	0	12	6
4	,,	4 c. red-brown/*yellow* ..	7	6	8	6
		a. Imperf. between (vert. pair) ..				
5	,,	6 c. green/*green*	5	0	7	6
6	,,	8 c. bright blue/*blue*	7	6	10	0
7	,,	12 c. red/*pale rose*	12	6	15	0

Nos. 3, 4, 6 and 7 have the wmk. "L N L" in the sheet, as No. 2. No. 5 is wmkd. "L N T".

All values exist imperf. and can be distinguished from the proofs by shade and impression. Stamps rouletted, pin-perf., or roughly perf. 6½ to 7 are proofs clandestinely perforated.

The 12 c. "laid" paper, formerly listed, is not on a true laid paper, the "laid" effect being accidental and not consistent.

The lithographic stones for Nos. 3 to 7 were made up from strips of five distinct impressions hence there are five types of each value differing mainly in the lettering of the tablets of value. There are flaws on nearly every individual stamp, from which they can be plated.

TWO CENTS
(3)

The 3 c. brown/*yellow* (No. 2) surcharged with T **3**, in black, appeared about 1876, but the surcharge is generally considered bogus.

4. Sir Charles Brooke.

(Typo. De La Rue & Co.)

1888 (10 Nov.)–**1897**. *No wmk.* P 14.

8	**4**	1 c. purple & black (6.6.92)	2	6	2	6
9	,,	2 c. purple and carmine ..	6	0	2	6
		a. Purple and rosine (1897) ..	7	6	2	6
10	,,	3 c. purple & blue (11.88)	4	0	3	6
11	,,	4 c. pur. & yell. (10.11.88)	17	6	22	6
12	,,	5 c. purple & grn. (12.6.91)	10	0	8	0
13	,,	6 c. pur. & brn. (11.11.88)	15	0	22	6
14	,,	8 c. green and carmine ..	8	6	8	6
		a. Green and rosine (1897) ..	20	0	17	6

15 **4** 10 c. green & pur. (12.6.93) 30 0 17 6
16 ,, 12 c. green & blue (11.11.88) 6 0 12 6
17 ,, 16 c. green & orge. (28.12.97) 30 0 32 6
18 ,, 25 c. green & brn. (19.11.88) 25 0 25 0
19 ,, 32 c. green & black (28.12.97) 32 6 37 6
20 ,, 50 c. green (26.7.97).. .. 40 0 45 0
21 ,, $1 green & black (2.11.97) 65 0 75 0

Prepared for use but not issued.

21*a* $2 green and blue £100
21*b* $5 green and violet £100
21*c* $10 green and carmine .. £100

On No. 21 the value is in black on an uncoloured ground.

The tablet of value in this and later similar issues is in the second colour given.

One Cent. (5) **one cent.** (6)

2c. (7) **5c** (8) **5c.** (9)

1889 (3 Aug.)–**1892.** *T* **4** *surcharged. P* 14.

22 **5** 1 c. on 3 c. (12.1.92).. .. 50 0 50 0
a. Surch. double £15 £12
23 **6** 1 c. on 3 c. (Feb., 1892) .. 10 0 17 6
a. No stop after " cent " .. £5
24 **7** 2 c. on 8 c. (3.8.89) .. 8 6 17 6
a. Surch. double £10
b. Surch. inverted £60
c. Surch. omitted (in pair with normal) £35
25 **8** 5 c. on 12 c. (17.2.91) .. 40 0 45 0
a. No stop after " C " 70 0 70 0
b. " C." omitted £8
c. Surch. double £38
d. Surch. double, one vertical .. £60
e. Surch. omitted (in pair with normal) £35
26 **9** 5 c. on 12 c. (17.2.91) .. 90 0 95 0
a. No stop after " C " £10 £10
b. " C." omitted £15 £18
c. Surch. double £30

ONE
CENT

(10)

1892 (23 May). *No.* 2 *surch. with T* **10.**

27 **2** 1 c. on 3 c. brown/*yellow* .. 2 6 4 0
a. Stop after " THREE " .. 30 0 35 0
b. Imperf. between (vert. pair) .. £14
c. Surch. double £8

Varieties with part of the surcharge missing are due to gum on the face of the unsurcharged stamps receiving part of the surcharge, which was afterwards washed off.

11

12

13. Sir Charles Brooke. **14.**

(Die eng. Wm. Ridgway. Recess. Perkins, Bacon & Co.)

1895 (1 Jan.–Sept.). *No wmk. P* 11½–12.

28 **11** 2 c. brown-red 15 0 15 0
a. Imperf. between (vert. pair).. £6
b. Imperf. between (horiz. pair) £6
c. Second printing. Perf. 12½ (Sept., '95) 10 0 7 6
ca. Perf. 12½. Imperf. between (horiz. pair) £8
29 **12** 4 c. black 15 0 6 0
a. Imperf. between (horiz. pair) £15
30 **13** 6 c. violet 20 0 20 0
31 **14** 8 c. green 27 6 30 0

Stamps of these types, printed in wrong colours, are trials and these, when surcharged with values in " pence ", are from waste sheets that were used by Perkins, Bacon & Co. as trial paper when preparing an issue of stamps for British South Africa.

4
Cents.
(15)

1899. *Surch as T* **15.**

32 **2** 2 c. on 3 c. brn./*yell.* (19.9.99) 3 6 7 6
a. Stop after " THREE " .. 50 0
b. Imperf. between (vert. pair).. £14
33 ,, 2 c. on 12 c. red/*pale rose* (29.6.99) 3 6 7 6
a. Surch. inverted £26 £42
34 ,, 4 c. on 6 c. green/*green* (R.) (16.11.99) 35 0 40 0
35 ,, 4 c. on 8 c. bt. blue/*blue* (R.) (29.6.99) 8 0 12 6

Re " laid paper " varieties previously listed, see note after No. 7.

A variety of surcharge with small " S " in " CENTS " may be found in the 2 c. on 12 c and 4 c. on 8 c. and a raised stop after " CENTS " on the 4 c. on 6 c.

The omission of parts of the surcharge is due to gum on the surface of the stamps (see note after No. 27).

(Typo. De La Rue & Co.)

1899 (10 Nov.)–**1908.** *Inscribed* " POSTAGE POSTAGE." *No wmk. P* 14.

36 **4** 1 c. grey-blue & rosine (1.01) 1 6 1
a. *Grey-blue and red* 1 9 0
b. *Ultramarine and rosine* .. 7 0 1
c. *Dull blue and carmine* .. 10 0 10
37 ,, 2 c. green (16.12.99) .. 1 9 1
38 ,, 3 c. dull purple (1908) .. 3 0 0
39 ,, 4 c. rose-carmine (10.11.99) 8 6 5
a. *Aniline carmine* 4 0 0 1
40 ,, 8 c. yellow & blk. (6.12.99) 6 0 3
41 ,, 10 c. ultramarine (10.11.99) 7 6 4
42 ,, 12 c. mauve (16.12.99) .. 12 6 6
a. *Bright mauve* ('05) 27 6 17
43 ,, 16 c. chest. & grn. (16.12.99) 10 0 10
44 ,, 20 c. bistre & bt. mve. (5.00) 15 0 17
45 ,, 25 c. brn. & blue (16.12.99) 12 6 17
46 ,, 50 c. sage-green & carmine (16.12.99) 35 0 35
47 ,, $1 rose-carmine & green (16.12.99) 70 0 70
a. *Rosine and pale green* .. 80 0 80

The figures of value in the $1 are in colour on an uncoloured ground.

Prepared for use but not issued.

48	**4**	5 c. olive-grey and green ..	75	0		

16

1901. *Inscribed* " POSTAGE POSTAGE ". *W* **16**, *P* 14.

49	**4**	2 c. green	35	0	17	6

Sir Charles Vyner Brooke.
17 May, 1917–1 July, 1946.

17. Sir Charles Vyner Brooke.

(Typo. De La Rue.)

1918 (26 MAR.). *No wmk. Chalky paper. P* 14.

50	**17**	1 c. slate-blue and red ..	0	10	1	0
		a. Dull blue and carmine ..	1	3	1	3
51	,,	2 c. green	2	6	2	0
52	,,	3 c. brown-purple ..	3	0	5	0
53	,,	4 c. rose-carmine ..	4	0	3	0
		a. Rose-red	4	0	6	0
54	,,	8 c. yellow and black ..	6	0	15	0
55	,,	10 c. blue (*shades*) ..	6	0	12	6
56	,,	12 c. purple	7	0	15	0
57	,,	16 c. chestnut and green ..	10	0	10	0
58	,,	20 c. olive & violet (*shades*)	7	6	10	0
59	,,	25 c. brown & bright blue..	10	0	15	0
60	,,	50 c. olive-green & carmine	12	6	10	0
61	,,	$1 bright rose and green	25	0	25	0

On the $1 the figures of value are in colour on an uncoloured ground.

Prepared for use but not issued.

62	**17**	1 c. slate-blue and slate ..	£7			

1922–23. *New colours and values. No wmk. Chalk-surfaced paper. P* 14.

63	**17**	2 c. purple (5.3.23) ..	1	6	2	6
64	,,	3 c. dull green (23.3.22) ..	1	3	1	6
65	,,	4 c. brown-purple (10.4.23)	1	3	0	8
66	,,	5 c. yellow-orange ..	1	9	2	0
67	,,	6 c. claret (–.1.22).. ..	2	6	3	0
68	,,	8 c. bright rose-red ..	3	6	6	0
69	,,	10 c. black (1923)	5	0	9	0
70	,,	12 c. bright blue (–.12.22)..	15	0	22	6
		a. Pale dull blue	15	0	20	0
71	,,	30 c. ochre-brown and slate	12	0	17	6

ONE
cent

(**18**)

1923 (JAN.). *Surch. as T* **18**.

(*a*) *First printing. Bars* 1¼ *mm. apart.*

72	**17**	1 c. on 10 c. dull blue ..	40	0	50	0
		a. " cnet " for " cent " ..	£22		£25	
73	,,	2 c. on 12 c. purple ..	8	6	25	0
		a. Thick, narrower " W " in " TWO "	30	0	35	0

(*b*) *Second printing. Bars* ¾ *mm. apart.*

74	**17**	1 c. on 10 c. blue	£6			
		a. " en " of " cent " scratched out and " ne " overprinted	£100			
75	,,	2 c. on 12 c. purple ..	65	0		
		a. Thick, narrower " W " in " TWO "	£7			

In the 2 c. on 12 c. the words of the surcharge are about 7½ mm. from the bars.

Variety 74*a* arose from a native printer " correcting " an already correct surcharge in the second printing in the endeavour exactly to reproduce the " cnet " error of the first printing.

The thick " w " variety occurs on all stamps of the last two horizontal rows of the first printing (12 stamps per sheet), and in the last two vertical rows of the second (20 stamps per sheet).

1928 (APR.)–**29**. *W* **16** (*Multiple*). *Chalk-surfaced paper. P* 14.

76	**17**	1 c. slate-blue and carmine	1	6	1	6
77	,,	2 c. bright purple ..	1	0	1	0
78	,,	3 c. green	1	6	3	0
79	,,	4 c. brown-purple ..	3	0	1	3
80	,,	5 c. yellow-orange (5.8.29)	2	6	6	0
81	,,	6 c. claret	2	6	2	0
82	,,	8 c. bright rose-red ..	5	0	8	0
83	,,	10 c. black	4	0	7	0
84	,,	12 c. bright blue	5	0	7	6
85	,,	16 c. chestnut and green ..	5	0	7	6
86	,,	20 c. olive-bistre & violet ..	5	0	8	6
87	,,	25 c. brown & bright blue..	6	0	10	0
88	,,	30 c. bistre-brown and slate	15	0	12	6
89	,,	50 c. olive-green & carmine	10	0	15	0
90	,,	$1 bright rose and green	30	0	37	6

In the $1 the value is as before.

19. Sir Chas. Vyner Brooke. **20**

(Recess. Waterlow.)

1932 (1 JAN.). *W* **20**. *P* 12½.

91	**19**	1 c. indigo	1	9	2	6
92	,,	2 c. green	2	6	3	0
93	,,	3 c. violet..	3	6	5	0
94	,,	4 c. red-orange	4	0	1	6
95	,,	5 c. deep lake	2	6	1	9
96	,,	6 c. scarlet	6	0	15	0
97	,,	8 c. orange-yellow ..	6	0	7	6
98	,,	10 c. black	6	6	10	0
99	,,	12 c. deep ultramarine ..	7	6	10	0
100	,,	15 c. chestnut	8	6	17	6
101	,,	20 c. red-orange & violet..	10	0	10	6
102	,,	25 c. oran.-yell. & chestnut	10	0	20	0
103	,,	30 c. sepia and vermilion	12	6	20	0
104	,,	50 c. carm.-red & olive-grn.	20	0	22	6
105	,,	$1 green and carmine ..	35	0	50	0

21. Sir Charles Vyner Brooke.

(Recess. Bradbury, Wilkinson.)

1934 (1 MAY)–**1941** (1 MAR.). *No wmk. P* 12.

106	**21**	1 c. purple	0	6	0	9

No.	Type	Description	Unused s.	d.	Used s.	d.
107	21	2 c. green	0	6	0	9
107a	,,	2 c. black (1.3.41)	3	6	6	0
108	,,	3 c. black	0	6	0	6
108a	,,	3 c. green (1.3.41)	0	10	3	0
109	,,	4 c. bright purple	0	8	0	8
110	,,	5 c. violet	1	3	0	9
111	,,	6 c. carmine	1	0	2	0
111a	,,	6 c. lake-brown (1.3.41)	0	8	4	0
112	,,	8 c. red-brown	1	0	2	0
112a	,,	8 c. carmine (1.3.41)	0	10	1	6
113	,,	10 c. scarlet	3	6	2	0
114	,,	12 c. blue	2	0	2	6
114a	,,	12 c. orange (1.3.41)	1	6	8	6
115	,,	15 c. orange	1	6	8	6
115a	,,	15 c. blue (1.3.41)	2	6	8	6
116	,,	20 c. olive-grn. & carmine	3	6	3	6
117	,,	25 c. violet and orange	2	0	2	6
118	,,	30 c. red-brown & violet	3	0	5	0
119	,,	50 c. violet and scarlet	7	0	8	0
120	,,	$1 scarlet and sepia	8	0	8	6
121	,,	$2 bt. purple & violet	17	6	30	0
122	,,	$3 carmine and green	20	0	32	6
123	,,	$4 blue and scarlet	30	0	40	0
124	,,	$5 scarlet & red-brn.	60	0	75	0
125	,,	$10 black and yellow	£5		110	0

For the 3 c. green, wmkd. Mult. Script CA. see No. 152a.

BMA

(22)

1945 (17 Dec.). *British Military Administration. Optd. with T 22.*

No.	Type	Description	Unused s.	d.	Used s.	d.
126	21	1 c. purple	1	0	1	6
127	,,	2 c. black (R.)	0	4	0	6
128	,,	3 c. green	0	4	1	0
129	,,	4 c. bright purple	0	6	1	0
130	,,	5 c. violet (R.)	2	6	3	6
131	,,	6 c. lake-brown	2	6	4	0
132	,,	8 c. carmine	12	6	17	6
133	,,	10 c. scarlet	3	0	5	0
134	,,	12 c. orange	4	6	8	6
135	,,	15 c. blue	4	0	2	0
136	,,	20 c. olive-green & carmine	6	0	10	0
137	,,	25 c. violet and orange (R.)	5	0	10	0
138	,,	30 c. red-brown & violet	6	0	15	0
139	,,	50 c. violet and scarlet	6	0	3	6
140	,,	$1 scarlet and sepia	10	0	15	0
141	,,	$2 bright pur. & violet	20	0	25	0
142	,,	$3 carmine and green	22	6	32	6
143	,,	$4 blue and scarlet	30	0	50	0
144	,,	$5 scarlet & red-brown	£5		£5	
145	,,	$10 black and yellow (R.)	£6		£8	

These stamps, and the similarly overprinted stamps of North Borneo, were obtainable at all post offices throughout British Borneo (Brunei, Labuan, North Borneo and Sarawak), for use on ocal and overseas mail.

23. Sir James Brooke, Sir Chas. Vyner Brooke and Sir Charles Brooke.

(Recess. Bradbury, Wilkinson.)

1946 (18 May). *Centenary Issue. P* 12.

No.	Type	Description	Unused s.	d.	Used s.	d.
146	23	8 c. lake	0	9	1	6
147	,,	15 c. blue	1	6	2	0
148	,,	50 c. black and scarlet	4	0	6	0
149	,,	$1 black and sepia	30	0	35	0

(24)

(Opt. typo. Bradbury, Wilkinson.)

1947 (16 Apr.). *Crown Colony Issue. Optd. with T* **24** *in blue-black or red. Wmk. Mult. Script. CA. P* 12.

No.	Type	Description	Unused s.	d.	Used s.	d.
150	21	1 c. purple	0	3	0	6
151	,,	2 c. black (R.)	0	4	0	8
152	,,	3 c. green (R.)	0	4	0	8
		a. Albino opt.				
153	,,	4 c. bright purple	0	6	1	6
154	,,	6 c. lake-brown	0	6	1	6
155	,,	8 c. carmine	0	6	0	8
156	,,	10 c. scarlet	0	6	1	3
157	,,	12 c. orange	0	6	1	9
158	,,	15 c. blue (R.)	1	0	1	0
159	,,	20 c. olive-grn. & carm. (R.)	1	3	1	9
160	,,	25 c. violet and orange (R.)	1	3	1	3
161	,,	50 c. violet and scarlet (R.)	1	8	1	9
162	,,	$1 scarlet and sepia	3	6	4	0
163	,,	$2 bright purple & violet	7	0	10	0
164	,,	$5 scarlet and red-brown	17	6	20	0

No. 152a shows an uninked impression of T **24.**

1948 (25 Oct.). *Royal Silver Wedding. As Nos.* 30/1 *of Aden.*

No.	Description	Unused s.	d.	Used s.	d.
165	8 c. scarlet	0	6	0	6
166	$5 brown	27	6	35	0

1949 (10 Oct.). *75th Anniv. of Universal Postal Union. As Nos.* 114/7 *of Antigua.*

No.	Description	Unused s.	d.	Used s.	d.
167	8 c. carmine	1	0	1	3
168	15 c. deep blue	1	3	1	6
169	25 c. deep blue-green	1	9	2	6
170	50 c. violet	3	0	4	6

25. Troides Brookiana.

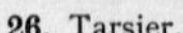

26. Tarsier. **27.** Kayan Tomb.

28. Kayan Girl and Boy. 29. Bead work.

30. Dyak Dancer.

31. Scaly Ant Eater.

32. Kenyah Boys.

33. Fire-Making.

34. Kelemantan Rice Barn.

35. Pepper Vines.

36. Iban Woman.

37. Kelabit Smithy.

38. Map of Sarawak.

39. Arms of Sarawak.

(Recess. Arms typo. Bradbury, Wilkinson.)

1950 (3 Jan.). *Wmk. Mult. Script CA. P* 11½×11 (*horiz.*) *or* 11×11½ (*vert.*).

171	**25**	1 c. black	0	6	0	6
172	**26**	2 c. red-orange	0	6	0	6
173	**27**	3 c. green	0	6	1	6
174	**28**	4 c. chocolate	0	6	0	4
175	**29**	6 c. turquoise-blue ..	0	6	1	6
176	**30**	8 c. scarlet	0	10	0	9
177	**31**	10 c. orange	2	6	3	0
178	**32**	12 c. violet..	0	10	1	6
179	**33**	15 c. blue	1	3	0	6

180	**34**	20 c. pur.-brn. & red-orge.	1	3	1	3
181	**35**	25 c. green and scarlet ..	1	4	1	6
182	**36**	50 c. brown and violet ..	2	6	2	6
183	**37**	$1 green and chocolate	5	0	6	0
184	**38**	$2 blue and carmine ..	10	0	12	6
185	**39**	$5 blk., yell., red & pur.	22	6	25	0

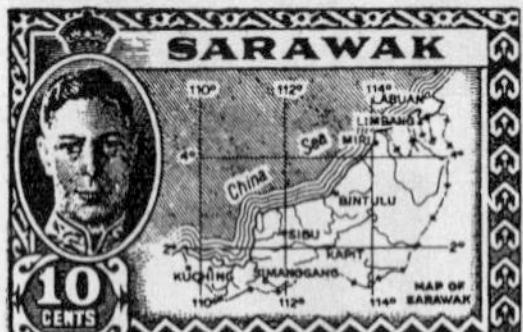

40. Map of Sarawak.

(Recess. Bradbury, Wilkinson.)

1952 (1 Feb.). *Wmk. Mult. Script CA. P* 11½×11.
186 **40** 10 c. orange 2 0 0 9

1953 (3 June). *Coronation. As No.* 47 *of Aden.*
187 10 c. blk. & deep violet-blue 1 0 1 6

41. Logging.

42. Young Orang-Utan.

43. Kayan Dancing.

44. Hornbill.

45. Shield with Spears.

46. Kenyah Ceremonial Carving.

47. Barong Panau.

48. Turtles.

49. Melanau Basket-making.

50. Astana, Kuching.

51. Queen Elizabeth II. **52.** Queen Elizabeth II (after Annigoni).

(Des. G. A. Gundersen (20 c.), K. M. Munnich (25 c.). Recess. Arms typo. ($5). Bradbury, Wilkinson.)

1955–57. $5 *as T* **39** *(but with portrait of Queen Elizabeth II in place of King George VI). Wmk. Mult. Script CA. P* 11×11½ (1 c., 2 c., 4 c.), 12×13 (30 c., 50 c., $1, $2) *or* 11½×11 *(others).*

No.	Type	Description	Unused	Used
188	**41**	1 c. green	0 6	0 10
189	**42**	2 c. red-orange	0 3	0 3
190	**43**	4 c. lake-brown (*shades*) ..	0 4	0 4
191	**44**	6 c. greenish blue ..	1 3	1 3
192	**45**	8 c. rose-red	0 6	0 5
193	**46**	10 c. deep green	1 3	1 3
194	**47**	12 c. plum	1 9	2 0
195	**48**	15 c. ultramarine	0 9	0 9
196	**49**	20 c. olive and brown ..	1 6	2 0
197	**50**	25 c. sepia and green ..	2 0	2 0
198	**51**	30 c. red-brn. & deep lilac	1 4	1 2
199	,,	50 c. black and carmine ..	2 0	2 3
200	**52**	$1 myrtle-green & orange-brown	4 2	4 6
201	,,	$2 violet & bronze-green	7 9	8 6
202	**39**	$5 black, yellow, red and deep purple	20 0	22 6

Dates of issue: 1955—1 June, 30 c. 1957—1 Oct., others.

1963 (4 June). *Freedom from Hunger. As No.* 63 *of Aden.*

No.	Description	Unused	Used
203	12 c. sepia	1 0	1 3

1964–65. *As* 1955–57 *but wmk.* w.**12.** *Perfs. as before.*

No.	Type	Description	Unused	Used
204	**41**	1 c. green (8.9.64) ..	0 2	0 2
205	**42**	2 c. red-orange (17.8.65)	0 3	0 3
206	**44**	6 c. greenish blue (8.9.64)	0 5	0 6
207	**46**	10 c. deep green (8.9.64) ..	0 7	0 9
208	**47**	12 c. plum (8.9.64) ..	0 7	0 9
209	**48**	15 c. ultramarine (17.8.65)	0 9	0 9
210	**49**	20 c. olive & brn. (9.6.64)	1 0	1 2
211	**50**	25 c. deep sepia and bluish green (8.9.64) ..	1 2	1 6

53. *Vanda hookeriana.*

965 (15 Nov.). *As Nos.* 166/72 *of Johore but with Arms of Sarawak inset as in T* **53.**

No.	Description	Unused	Used
12	1 c. multicoloured	0 1	0 1
13	2 c. multicoloured	0 2	0 2
14	5 c. multicoloured	0 4	0 4
15	6 c. multicoloured	0 4	0 5
16	10 c. multicoloured	0 6	0 7
17	15 c. multicoloured	0 7	0 7
18	20 c. multicoloured	0 10	1 0

The higher values used in Sarawak are Nos. ɔ/27 of Malaysia.

JAPANESE OCCUPATION OF SARAWAK.

The stamps listed under this heading were valid for use throughout North Borneo, (i.e. in Brunei, Labuan, North Borneo and Sarawak).

府政國帝本日大

(" Imperial Japanese Government ")
(1)

1945. *Stamps of Sarawak optd. with T* **1** *in violet.*

No.	Type	Description	Unused	Used
J 1	**21**	1 c. purple	20 0	25 0
J 2	,,	2 c. green	65 0	80 0
J 3	,,	2 c. black	60 0	80 0
J 4	,,	3 c. black	£8	£6
J 5	,,	3 c. green	40 0	50 0
J 6	,,	4 c. bright purple ..	25 0	25 0
J 7	,,	5 c. violet	30 0	40 0
J 8	,,	6 c. carmine	45 0	50 0
J 9	,,	6 c. lake-brown	40 0	50 0
J10	,,	8 c. red-brown	£5	£6
J11	,,	8 c. carmine	£6	£8
J12	,,	10 c. scarlet	30 0	40 0
J13	,,	12 c. blue	65 0	75 0
J14	,,	12 c. orange	£6	£8
J15	,,	15 c. orange	£5	£6
J16	,,	15 c. blue	60 0	75 0
J17	,,	20 c. olive-green and car..	35 0	40 0
J18	,,	25 c. violet and orange ..	35 0	40 0
J19	,,	30 c. red-brown and violet	30 0	40 0
J20	,,	50 c. violet and scarlet ..	45 0	50 0
J21	,,	$1 scarlet and sepia ..	55 0	65 0
J22	,,	$2 bright purple & violet	£6	£8
J23	,,	$3 carmine and green ..	£25	£30
J24	,,	$4 blue and scarlet ..	£8	£10
J25	,,	$5 scarlet & red-brown	£6	£8
J26	,,	$10 black and yellow ..	£9	£10

The overprint, being handstamped, exists inverted on all values.

Stamps of T **21** optd. with Japanese symbols within an oval frame are revenue stamps, while the same stamps overprinted with three Japanese characters between two vertical double rules, were used as seals.

SEYCHELLES.

For GREAT BRITAIN stamp used in Seychelles, see page 75.

PRINTERS. Nos. 1 to 127 were typographed by De La Rue & Co.

1

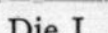

Die I. Die II.

In Die I there are lines of shading in the middle compartment of the diadem which are absent from Die II.

1890 (5 April). *Wmk. Crown CA. P 14.*

(i) Die I.

No.	T	Description		
1	1	2 c. green and carmine ..	3 6	15 0
2	,,	4 c. carmine and green ..	15 0	25 0
3	,,	8 c. brown-purple and blue	7 6	10 0
4	,,	10 c. ultramarine and brown	12 6	22 6
5	,,	13 c. grey and black ..	8 6	22 6
6	,,	16 c. chestnut and blue ..	10 0	10 0
7	,,	48 c. ochre and green ..	20 0	22 6
8	,,	96 c. mauve and carmine ..	50 0	65 0

(ii) Die II.

No.	T	Description		
9	1	2 c. green and rosine ..	2 6	3 6
10	,,	4 c. carmine and green ..	3 0	3 6
11	,,	8 c. brn.-pur. & ultramarine	7 6	8 6
12	,,	10 c. bright ultram. & brn.	8 6	8 6
13	,,	13 c. grey and black ..	8 0	8 0
14	,,	16 c. chestnut & ultramarine	25 0	15 0

3
cents
(2)

18 CENTS
(3)

4

1893 (Jan.). *Surch. as T 2.*

15	3 c. on 4 c. (No. 10) ..	2 0	3 6
	a. Surch. inverted	£12	£14
	b. Surch. double	£40	
	c. Surch. omitted (in pair with normal) ..	£175	
16	12 c. on 16 c. (No. 6) ..	6 0	6 0
	a. Surch. inverted	£32	
	b. Surch. double	£175	
17	12 c. on 16 c. (No. 14) ..	7 6	7 6
18	15 c. on 16 c. (No. 6) ..	10 0	10 0
	a. Surch. inverted	£18	£18
	b. Surch. double	£34	£36
19	15 c. on 16 c. (No. 14) ..	8 6	7 6
	a. Surch. inverted	£35	£35
	b. Surch. double	£70	£50
	c. Surch. treble		
20	45 c. on 48 c. (No. 7) ..	20 0	17 6
21	90 c. on 96 c. (No. 8) ..	40 0	55 0

Nos. 15, 16, 18 and 20 exist with "cents" omitted and with "cents" above value and are due to misplacement of the surcharge.

1893 (Nov.). *Die II. Wmk. Crown CA. P 14.*

No.	T	Description		
25	1	3 c. dull purple & orange ..	1 6	1 6
26	,,	12 c. sepia and green ..	3 6	6 0
27	,,	15 c. sage-green and lilac ..	8 6	8 6
28	,,	45 c. brown and carmine ..	35 0	50 0

1896 (1 Aug.). *No. 28 surch. as T 3.*

29	18 c. on 45 c. brown & carm.	12 6	12 6
	a. Surch. double	£90	£90
	b. Surch. treble	£55	
30	36 c. on 45 c. brown & carm.	17 6	35 0
	a. Surch. double	£120	

1897–1900. *Die II. Wmk. Crown CA. P 14.*

No.	T	Description		
32	1	2 c. orange-brn. & grn. ('00)	1 6	4 0
33	,,	6 c. carmine (1900) ..	4 0	6 0
34	,,	15 c. ultramarine (1900) ..	12 6	12 6
35	,,	18 c. ultramarine ..	10 0	15 0
36	,,	36 c. brown and carmine ..	25 0	18 6
37	4	75 c. yellow & violet (1900)	42 6	55 0
38	,,	1 r. bright mauve & dp. red	27 6	22 6
39	,,	1 r. 50 c. grey & carm. ('00)	65 0	75 0
40	,,	2 r. 25 c. brt. mauve and green (1900)	75 0	90 0

3 cents
5

6 cents
(5*a*)

1901. *Surch. with T 5 or 5a.*

41	3 c. on 10 c. (No. 12) ..	3 6	8 6
	a. Surch. double	£50	
42	3 c. on 16 c. (No. 14) ..	3 6	10 0
	a. Surch. inverted	£55	£55
	b. Surch. double	£50	
	c. "3 cents" omitted	£45	
43	3 c. on 36 c. (No. 36) ..	3 0	7 6
	a. Surch. double	£75	
	b. "3 cents" omitted	£60	£70
44	6 c. on 8 c. (No. 11)	4 0	5 0
	a. Surch. inverted	£45	£45

1902 (June). *Surch. as T 5.*

No.	T	Description		
45	1	2 c. on 4 c. (No. 10) ..	10 0	17 6
46	4	30 c. on 75 c. (No. 37) ..	20 0	30 0
		a. Narrow "0" in "30" ..	30 0	40 0
47	,,	30 c. on 1 r. (No. 38) ..	20 0	35 0
		a. Narrow "0" in "30" ..	70 0	85 0
		b. Surch. double ..	£45	
48	,,	45 c. on 1 r. (No. 38) ..	27 6	35 0
49	,,	45 c. on 2 r. 25 c. (No. 40) ..	40 0	50 0
		a. Narrow "5" in "45" ..	£14	£16

6

7

1903 (June)–**1904.** *T 6 (2 c. to 45 c.) and 7 (higher values). Wmk. Crown CA. P 14.*

53	2 c. chestnut and green ..	0 10	2 0
54	3 c. dull green	2 0	2 6
55	6 c. carmine	2 6	1 6
56	12 c. olive-sepia & dull green	6 0	8 0
57	15 c. ultramarine	7 0	10 0
58	18 c. sage-green and carmine	15 0	25 0
59	30 c. violet and dull green ..	17 6	20 0
60	45 c. brown and carmine ..	15 0	30 0
61	75 c. yellow and violet ..	15 0	27 6
62	1 r. 50 c. black and carmine	52 6	60
63	2 r. 25 c. purple and green	60 0	65

3 cents
(8)

T 6 surch. with T 8.

64	3 c. on 15 c. ultramarine ..	7 6	15
65	3 c. on 18 c. sage-green & car.	25 0	30
66	3 c. on 45 c. brown & carmine	10 0	17

1906. *Wmk. Mult. Crown CA. P 14.*

No.	T	Description		
67	6	2 c. chestnut and green ..	1 3	1
68	,,	3 c. dull green	2 6	1
69	,,	6 c. carmine	1 9	2
70	,,	12 c. olive-sepia & dull green	8 6	6
71	,,	15 c. ultramarine	6 0	12
72	,,	18 c. sage-green & carmine..	7 6	12
73	,,	30 c. violet and dull green ..	10 0	18
74	,,	45 c. brown and carmine ..	12 0	25
75	7	75 c. yellow and violet ..	25 0	35
76	,,	1 r. 50 c. black and carmine	35 0	42
77	,,	2 r. 25 c. purple and green..	65 0	75

9

10

1912. *Wmk. Mult. Crown CA. P* 14.

No.	Type	Description	Unused	Used
78	9	2 c. chestnut and green ..	2 0	4 0
79	,,	3 c. green	2 0	1 9
80	,,	6 c. aniline carmine ..	17 6	17 6
80*a*	,,	6 c. carmine-red	7 6	3 0
81	,,	12 c. olive-sepia & dull grn.	5 0	12 6
82	,,	15 c. ultramarine	6 0	7 6
83	,,	18 c. sage-green & carmine	7 0	18 6
84	,,	30 c. violet and green ..	12 6	10 0
85	,,	45 c. brown and carmine ..	10 0	22 6
86	10	75 c. yellow and violet ..	27 6	17 6
87	,,	1 r. 50 c. black & carmine	17 6	15 0
88	,,	2 r. 25 c. rose-pur. & grn.	65 0	65 0
88*a*	,,	2 r. 25 c. bright pur. & grn.	65 0	32 6

11

12

13

1917–20. *Wmk. Mult. Crown CA. P* 14.

No.	Type	Description	Unused	Used
89	11	2 c. chestnut & grn., O	0 4	2 0
90	,,	3 c. green, O (1917) ..	0 8	1 0
91	12	5 c. deep brown, O ..	1 6	4 0
92	11	6 c. carmine, O (1917)	2 6	1 0
92*a*	,,	6 c. rose, O	10 0	2 0
93	,,	12 c. grey, O	3 0	7 0
94	,,	15 c. ultramarine, O ('17)	3 6	10 0
95	,	18 c. purple/*yellow*, C ..	7 6	12 6
		a. On orange-buff ..	37 6	37 6
		b. On pale yellow (Die II) ..	15 0	17 6
96	13	25 c. blk. & red *yellow*, C	10 0	12 6
		a. On pale yellow (Die II) ..	12 6	10 0
97	11	30 c. dull. pur. & olive, C	15 0	20 0
98	,,	45 c. dull. pur. & orge., C	8 6	15 0
99	13	50 c. dull pur. & black, C	12 6	17 6
00	,,	75 c. black/*blue-green*, C (*olive back*)	10 0	17 6
		a. On emerald back (Die II) ..	15 0	25 0
01	,,	1 r. dull purple & red, C	32 6	40 0
02	,,	1 r. 50 c. reddish purple and blue/*blue*, C ..	32 6	40 0
02*a*	,,	1 r. 50 c. blue-purple & blue/*blue*, C (Die II)	42 6	50 0
03	,,	2 r. 25 c. yellow-green & violet, C	50 0	55 0
04	,,	5 r. green and blue, C ..	£5	£6

921–32. *Wmk. Mult. Script CA. P* 14.

No.	Type	Description	Unused	Used
05	11	2 c. chestnut & green, O	0 4	1 6
06	,,	3 c. green, O	0 9	1 6
07	12	5 c. deep brown, O ..	4 6	6 0
08	11	6 c. carmine, O ..	1 6	6 0
109	11	12 c. grey, O (Die II) ..	2 6	2 6
		a. Die I ('32)	3 0	4 6
110	,,	15 c. bright blue, O ..	10 0	12 6
111	,,	18 c. purple/*pale yellow*, C	6 0	12 6
112	13	25 c. blk. & red/*pale yell.*, C	6 0	12 6
113	11	30 c. dull purple & olive, C	6 0	15 0
114	,,	45 c. dull pur. & orange, C	7 6	17 6
115	13	50 c. dull purple & black, C	7 6	17 6
116	,,	75 c. black/*emerald*, C ..	15 0	20 0
117	,,	1 r. dull purple and red, C (Die II)	30 0	30 0
		a. Die I ('32)	35 0	42 6
118	,,	1 r. 50 c. pur. & blue/*blue*, C	32 6	40 0
119	,,	2 r. 25 c. yell.-grn. and violet, C	30 0	40 0
120	,,	5 r. yellow-grn. & blue, C	65 0	85 0

1922–28. *Colours changed and new values. Wmk. Mult. Script CA. P* 14.

No.	Type	Description	Unused	Used
121	11	3 c. black, O	0 6	2 0
122	,,	4 c. green, O	0 10	2 0
122*a*	,,	4 c. sage-green and carmine, O ('28) ..	10 0	22 6
123	,,	6 c. deep mauve, O ..	0 10	1 0
123*a*	13	9 c. red, O	2 0	8 6
124	11	12 c. carmine-red, O ..	2 6	3 0
125	,,	15 c. yellow, O	4 0	15 0
126	13	20 c. bright blue, O ..	6 0	10 0
127	,,	20 c. dull blue, O ..	7 6	8 6

1935 (6 May.). *Silver Jubilee. As Nos.* 91/4 *of Antigua but ptd. by B. W. & Co. P* 11 × 12.

No.	Description	Unused	Used
128	6 c. ultramarine & grey-black	1 0	1 6
	a. Extra flagstaff	£15	
129	12 c. green and indigo ..	2 0	2 6
	a. Extra flagstaff	£85	
130	20 c. brown and deep blue ..	3 0	3 6
	a. Extra flagstaff	£15	
131	1 r. slate and purple ..	10 6	15 0
	a. Extra flagstaff	£10	

For illustration of "extra flagstaff" variety see Bechuanaland.

1937 (12 May). *Coronation. As Nos.* 13/15 *of Aden, but ptd. by B. W. & Co. P* 11 × 11½.

No.	Description	Unused	Used
132	6 c. sage-green	0 4	0 6
133	12 c. orange	0 10	1 0
134	20 c. blue	1 3	1 6

14. Coco-de-mer Palm.

15. Giant Tortoise.

16. Fishing Pirogue.

(Photo. Harrison & Sons, Ltd.)

1938 (1 Jan.)–**1949.** *Wmk. Mult. Script CA. P* 14½ × 13½ (*vert.*) *or* 13½ × 14½.

No.	Type	Description	s.	d.	s.	d.
135	**14**	2 c. pur.-brn. CO (10.2.38)	0	4	0	4
136	**15**	3 c. green, C	3	6	4	0
136*a*	,,	3 c. orange, CO (-.8.41)	0	6	0	6
137	**16**	6 c. orange, C	3	6	4	0
137*a*	,,	6 c. greyish grn., C(-.8.41)	2	0	2	0
		b. Green, OC	0	9	0	9
138	**14**	9 c. scarlet, C (10.2.38)	6	0	6	0
138*a*	,,	9 c. grey-blue CO (-.8.41)	1	3	1	3
		b. Blue, OC ('45)	0	10	0	10
139	**15**	12 c. reddish violet, C ..	17	6	12	6
139*a*	,,	15 c. brn.-carm., C (-.8.41)	6	0	5	0
		b. Brown-red, O	1	6	1	6
139*c*	**14**	18 c. claret, CO (-.8.41)	1	6	1	6
140	**16**	20 c. blue, C	10	6	8	6
140*a*	,,	20 c. yell.-brn., CO (-.8.41)	1	6	1	6
141	**14**	25 c. yellow-brown, C	27	6	30	0
142	**15**	30 c. claret, C (10.2.38) ..	17	6	20	0
142*a*	,,	30 c. blue, CO (-.8.41) ..	2	6	2	6
143	**16**	45 c. choc., CO (10.2.38)	2	0	2	0
144	**14**	50 c. dull reddish violet, CO (10.2.38) ..	3	0	2	6
144*a*	,,	50 c. brt. vio., C (13.6.49)	2	6	3	0
145	**15**	75 c. slate-blue C(10.2.38)	55	0	65	0
145*a*	,,	75 c. slate-lilac, CO (-.8.41)	3	6	3	0
146	**16**	1 r. yell.-grn., C (10.2.38)	95	0	95	0
146*a*	,,	1 r. black, CO (-.8.41) ..	4	0	3	6
147	**14**	1 r. 50, ultm., CO (10.2.38)	6	0	7	6
148	**15**	2 r. 25, olive, CO (10.2.38)	10	0	12	6
149	**16**	5 r. red, CO (10.2.38) ..	25	0	25	0

The stamps on ordinary paper appeared in 1942–43.

1946 (23 Sept.). *Victory. As Nos.* 28/9 *of Aden.*

No.	Description	s.	d.	s.	d.
150	9 c. light blue	0	6	0	8
151	30 c. deep blue	1	0	1	0

1948 (11 Nov.). *Royal Silver Wedding. As Nos.* 30/1 *of Aden.*

No.	Description	s.	d.	s.	d.
152	9 c. ultramarine	0	6	0	6
153	5 r. carmine	12	6	17	6

1949 (10 Oct.). *75th Anniv. of Universal Postal Union. As Nos.* 114/7 *of Antigua, but inscr.* "SEYCHELLES" (*recess*).

No.	Description	s.	d.	s.	d.
154	18 c. bright reddish purple ..	0	10	0	10
155	50 c. purple	1	6	2	0
156	1 r. grey	3	0	4	6
157	2 r. 25, olive	8	6	9	0

17. Sail-fish.

18. Map of Indian Ocean.

(Photo. Harrison.)

1952 (3 Mar.). *Various designs as T* **14/16** *but with new portrait and crown as in T* **17/18.** *Chalk-surfaced paper. Wmk. Mult. Script CA. P* 14½ × 13½ (*vert.*) *or* 13½ × 14½ (*horiz.*).

No.	Type	Description	s.	d.	s.	d.
158	**17**	2 c. lilac	0	8	1	0
		a. Error. Crown missing ..				
		b. Error. St. Edward's Crown				
159	**15**	3 c. orange	1	0	1	6
		a. Error. Crown missing ..				
		b. Error. St. Edward's Crown				
160	**14**	9 c. chalky blue ..	1	6	2	0
		a. Error. Crown missing ..				
		b. Error. St. Edward's Crown				
161	**16**	15 c. deep yellow-green ..	1	6	2	6
		a. Error. Crown missing				
		b. Error. St. Edward's Crown				
162	**18**	18 c. carmine-lake ..	1	6	2	6
		a. Error. Crown missing				
		b. Error. St. Edward's Crown				
163	**16**	20 c. orange-yellow ..	1	6	2	6
		a. Error. Crown missing ..				
		b. Error. St. Edward's Crown				
164	**15**	25 c. vermilion	2	6	3	6
		a. Error. Crown missing ..				
		b. Error. St. Edward's Crown				
165	**17**	40 c. ultramarine	6	0	6	6
		a. Error. Crown missing ..				
		b. Error. St. Edward's Crown				
166	**16**	45 c. purple-brown ..	3	0	6	6
		a. Error. Crown missing ..				
		b. Error. St. Edward's Crown				
167	**14**	50 c. reddish violet ..	4	0	7	0
		a. Error. Crown missing ..				
		b. Error. St. Edward's Crown				
168	**18**	1 r. grey-black	5	0	7	6
		b. Error. St. Edward's Crown				
169	**14**	1 r. 50, blue	7	6	10	0
		b. Error. St. Edward's Crown				
170	**15**	2 r. 25, brown-olive ..	15	0	17	6
		b. Error. St. Edward's Crown				
171	**18**	5 r. red	20	0	30	0
		b. Error. St. Edward's Crown				
172	**17**	10 r. green	40	0	50	0

See *Introduction* re the watermark errors.

1953 (2 June). *Coronation. As No.* 47 *of Aden.*

No.	Description	s.	d.	s.	d.
173	9 c. black & deep bright blue	1	0	1	6

19. Sail-fish.

20. "Flying Fox" (fruit bat).

(Photo. Harrison & Sons, Ltd.)

1954 (1 Feb.)–**57.** *As T* **14/18** (*but with portra*[...] *of Queen Elizabeth II in place of King George VI as in T* **19**) *and T* **20.** *Chalk-surfaced pape*[...] *Wmk. Mult. Script CA. P* 14½ × 13½ (*vert.*) [...] 13½ × 14½ (*horiz.*).

No.	Type	Description	s.	d.	s.	d.
174	**19**	2 c. lilac	1	3	1	
175	**15**	3 c. orange	1	9	2	
175*a*	**20**	5 c. violet (25.10.57) ..	0	6	0	
176	**14**	9 c. chalky blue ..	1	6	1	
176*a*	,,	10 c. chalky blue (*shades*) (15.9.56)	0	6	0	
177	**16**	15 c. deep yellow-green ..	0	9	1	
178	**18**	18 c. crimson	2	6	3	
179	**16**	20 c. orange-yellow ..	0	8	0	
180	**15**	25 c. vermilion	1	0	1	

180*a*	**18**	35 c. crimson (15.9.56) ..	1	3	1	6
181	**19**	40 c. ultramarine ..	1	9	2	0
182	**16**	45 c. purple-brown ..	4	6	5	0
183	**14**	50 c. reddish violet ..	1	9	2	0
183*a*	**16**	70 c. purple-brn. (15.9.56)	2	3	2	6
184	**18**	1 r. grey-black ..	2	9	3	0
185	**14**	1 r. 50, blue	4	6	5	0
186	**15**	2 r. 25, brown-olive ..	6	6	8	6
187	**18**	5 r. red	15	0	18	6
188	**19**	10 r. green	27	6	32	6

21. " La Pierre de Possession ".

5 cents (22)

(Photo. Harrison & Sons.)

1956 (15 Nov.). *200th Anniv. of " La Pierre de Possession ". Wmk. Mult. Script CA. P* $14\frac{1}{2} \times 13\frac{1}{2}$.

189	**21**	40 c. ultramarine	3	6	4	0
190	,,	1 r. black	6	6	7	6

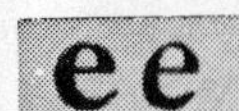

191 191*a* 191 191*b* 191 191*c*

1957 (16 Sept.). *No.* 182 *surch. with T* **22.**

191	5 c. on 45 c. purple-brown ..	3	6	5	0
	a. Italic " e "	65	0		
	b. Italic " s "	65	0		
	c. Italic " c "	40	0		
	d. Thick bars omitted ..	£300			
	e. Surcharge double	£90			

23. Mauritius 6d. Stamp with Seychelles " B 64 " Cancellation.

Recess; cancellation typo. Bradbury, Wilkinson.)

961. (11 Dec.). *Centenary of First Seychelles Post Office. W* w.**12**. *P* $11\frac{1}{2}$.

93	**23**	10 c. blue, black & purple	1	3	1	6
94	,,	35 c. blue, black and myrtle-green ..	2	6	2	9
95	,,	2 r. 25, blue, black & orange-brown ..	10	0	12	6

24. Black Parrot.

25. Vanilla Vine.

26. Fisherman.

27. Denis Island Lighthouse.

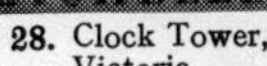

28. Clock Tower, Victoria.

31. Cascade Church.

29. Anse Royale Bay.

30. Government House.

32. Sail-fish.

38. Colony's Badge.

33. Cinnamon.

34. Copra.

35. Map.

36. Land Settlement.

37. Regina Mundi Convent.

45
CENTS
(**39**)

(Photo. Harrison.)

1962 (21 FEB.). *W* w.**12**. *P* 13½ × 14½ (*horiz. designs and* 10 *r.*) *or* 14½ × 13½ (*others*).

196 **24** 5 c. multicoloured .. 0 3 0 3
197 **25** 10 c. multicoloured .. 0 4 0 4
198 **26** 15 c. multicoloured .. 0 5 0 7
199 **27** 20 c. multicoloured .. 0 6 0 8
200 **28** 25 c. multicoloured .. 0 8 1 0
201 **29** 35 c. multicoloured .. 0 10 1 0
202 **30** 40 c. multicoloured .. 0 11 1 3
203 **31** 50 c. multicoloured .. 1 1 1 6
204 **32** 70 c. ultram. & light blue 1 6 1 9
205 **33** 1 r. multicoloured .. 2 0 2 9
206 **34** 1 r. 50, multicoloured .. 3 0 4 0
207 **35** 2 r. 25, multicoloured .. 4 8 6 0
208 **36** 3 r. 50, multicoloured .. 7 0 10 0
209 **37** 5 r. multicoloured .. 10 0 12 6
210 **38** 10 r. multicoloured .. 19 6 25 0

1963 (4 JUNE). *Freedom from Hunger. As No.* 63 *of Aden.*

211 70 c. reddish violet 3 0 3 6

1963 (16 SEPT.). *Red Cross Centenary. As Nos.* 147/8 *of Antigua.*

212 10 c. red and black 0 5 0 6
213 75 c. red and blue 2 0 2 6

1965 (15 APR.). *Surch. as T* **39**.

214 **29** 45 c. on 35 c. multicoloured 1 3 1 9
215 **32** 75 c. on 70 c. ultramarine and light blue .. 2 3 3 0

1965 (1 JUNE). *I.T.U. Centenary. As Nos.* 166/7 *of Antigua.*

216 5 c. orange and ultramarine 0 4 0 6
217 1 r. 50, mauve & apple-green 3 9 4 6

1965 (25 OCT.). *International Co-operation Year As Nos.* 168/9 *of Antigua.*

218 5 c. reddish pur. & turq.-grn. 0 4 0
219 40 c. deep bluish green & lav. 1 1 1

1966 (24 JAN.). *Churchill Commemoration. A Nos.* 170/3 *of Antigua.*

220 5 c. new blue 0 4 0
221 15 c. deep green 0 6 0
222 75 c. brown 2 0 2
223 1 r. 50, bluish violet 3 9 4

POSTAGE DUE STAMPS

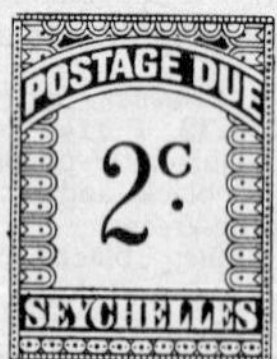

D 1

(Frame recess, value typo. Bradbury, Wilkinson

1951 (1 MAR.). *Wmk. Mult. Script CA. P* 11

D1 D **1** 2 c. scarlet and carmine 0 6 0
D2 „ 3 c. scarlet and green .. 0 3 0
D3 „ 6 c. scarlet and bistre .. 0 3 0
D4 „ 9 c. scarlet and orange .. 0 4 0
D5 „ 15 c. scarlet and violet .. 0 5 0

D6 D1 18 c. scarlet and blue .. 0 6 1 0
D7 ,, 20 c. scarlet and brown .. 0 6 1 3
D8 ,, 30 c. scarlet and claret .. 0 9 1 6

1964 (7 JULY)–**65.** *As 1951 but wmk.* w.**12.**
D 9 D1 2 c. scarlet and carmine 0 1 0 3
D10 ,, 3 c. scar. & grn. (14.9.65) 0 2 0 3

SIERRA LEONE.

CROWN COLONY AND PROTECTORATE.

PRINTERS. All issues of Sierra Leone until 1932 were typographed by De La Rue & Co.

1

The 6d. on *blue* paper, *imperf.*, is believed to be only a proof, and is therefore omitted. (*Price*, £10.)

1859 (21 SEPT.). *No wmk. P* 14.
(*a*) *Bluish paper.*
2 **1** 6d. dull purple £5 85 0
(*b*) *White paper.*
3 **1** 6d. grey lilac £16 85 0
4 ,, 6d. dull violet £14 65 0

1872. *No wmk. P* 12½.
(*a*) *Bluish paper.*
5 **1** 6d. dull violet £8 75 0
(*b*) *White paper.*
6 **1** 6d. dull violet £30 £20

2

HALF PENNY

(3)

1872–73. *Wmk. Crown CC. P* 12½.
1872 (APR.). (*a*) *Wmk. sideways.*
7 **2** 1d. rose-red 35 0 42 6
8 ,, 3d. buff 70 0 55 0
9 ,, 4d. blue 95 0 65 0
10 ,, 1s. green £5 60 0
1873 (SEPT.). (*b*) *Wmk. upright.*
11 **2** 1d. rose-red 35 0 30 0
11*a* ,, 2d. magenta 65 0 55 0
2 ,, 3d. saffron-yellow .. £30 £6
2*a* ,, 4d. blue £6 £5
2*b* ,, 1s. green £17 £8

876–77. *Wmk. Crown CC. P* 14.
3 **2** ½d. brown 7 6 15 0
4 ,, 1d. rose-red 30 0 22 6
5 ,, 1½d. lilac (1877) .. 15 0 12 6
6 ,, 2d. magenta 35 0 15 0
7 ,, 3d. buff 27 6 15 0
8 ,, 4d. blue £5 17 6
0 ,, 1s. green 50 0 35 0

883 (JUNE)–**1884.** *Wmk. Crown CA. P* 14.
1 **2** ½d. brown 37 6 42 6
1*a* ,, 1d. rose-red (26.9.83) £20 50 0
2 ,, 2d. magenta .. 60 0 15 0
3 ,, 4d. blue £45 55 0

1884–93. *Wmk. Crown CA. P* 14.
24 **2** ½d. dull green 1 6 1 3
24*a* ,, 1d. rose-carmine (1885?) .. 70 0 20 0
25 ,, 1d. carmine (July 1884) .. 4 0 2 0
26 ,, 1½d. pale violet (1893) .. 5 0 12 6
27 ,, 2d. grey 10 0 7 6
28 ,, 2½d. ultramarine (1891) .. 12 6 2 0
29 ,, 3d. yellow (1892) 7 6 8 6
30 ,, 4d. brown 6 0 6 0
31 ,, 1s. red-brown (1888) .. 15 0 17 6

1885–96. *Wmk. Crown CC. P* 14.
32 **1** 6d. dull violet (1885) .. 95 0 40 0
a. Bisected (3d.) (on cover) .. † £80
33 ,, 6d. brown-purple (1890) .. 30 0 22 6
a. Paper slightly blued .. 80 0 75 0
34 ,, 6d. purple-lake (1896) .. 15 0 20 0

1893. *Surch. with T* **3**. *P* 14.
(*a*) *Wmk. Crown CC.*
35 **2** ½d. on 1½d. pale violet .. £40 £40
a. Error. "PFNNY" .. £140
(*b*) *Wmk. Crown CA.*
37 ,, ½d. on 1½d. pale violet .. 12 6 17 6
a. Surch. inverted .. £7 £7
b. Surch. double .. £38
c. Error. "PFNNY" .. £5 £5
d. "PFNNY" inverted .. £65

4

5

1896–97. *Wmk. Crown CA. P* 14.
41 **4** ½d. dull mauve & grn. ('97) 1 3 1 0
42 ,, 1d. dull mauve & carmine 1 6 0 6
43 ,, 1½d. dull mve. & black ('97) 7 6 8 6
44 ,, 2d. dull mauve & orange 8 6 6 6
45 ,, 2½d. dull mauve & ultram. .. 6 0 2 6
46 **5** 3d. dull mauve & slate .. 17 6 15 0
47 ,, 4d. dull mauve & carm. ('97) 17 6 20 0
48 ,, 5d. dull mauve & black ('97) 17 6 20 0
49 ,, 6d. dull mauve ('97) .. 25 0 25 0
50 ,, 1s. green and black .. 22 6 20 0
51 ,, 2s. green & ultramarine .. 50 0 55 0
52 ,, 5s. green and carmine .. 90 0 95 0
53 ,, £1 purple/*red* £24 £28

6

POSTAGE AND REVENUE

(7)

1897 (MARCH). *Value in second colour. Wmk. CA over Crown,* w. 7. *Optd. with T* 7. *P* 14.
54 **6** 1d. dull purple and green .. 5 0 6 0
a. Opt. double £60 £60

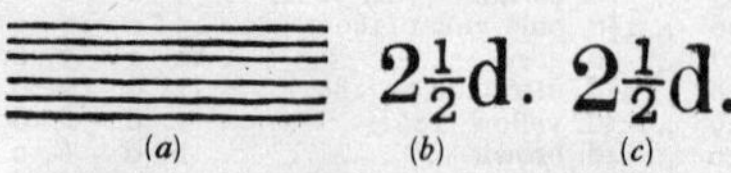

(a) (b) (c)

2½d. 2½d. 2½d.

(d) (e) (f)

T **6** *surch. in addition with* " 2½d." *below T* **7.** *Original value cancelled by 6 bars.*

55 2½d. on 3d. dull pur. & grn. (*a*) 12 6 15 0
56 2½d. on 3d. dull pur. & grn. (*c*) 60 0 70 0
57 2½d. on 3d. dull pur. & grn. (*d*) £7 £8
58 2½d. on 3d. dull pur. & grn. (*e*) £10 £12
59 2½d. on 6d. dull pur. & grn. (*a*) 10 0 12 6
60 2½d. on 6d. dull pur. & grn. (*c*) 25 0 45 0
61 2½d. on 6d. dull pur. & grn. (*d*) 60 0 70 0
62 2½d. on 6d. dull pur. & grn. (*e*) £8 £9

Variety. Surcharge double.

62*b* 2½d. (*c*) and 2½d. (*f*) on 3d. dull purple and green .. £50
62*c* 2½d. (*a*) and 2½d. (*c*) on 3d. dull purple and green .. £80

The 2½d. on 3d. and 2½d. on 6d. are printed in sheets of thirty of which there are twenty-two of (*a*), five of (*c*), two of (*d*), and one of (*e*).

POSTAGE AND
REVENUE
(8)

Similar to last, but optd. with T **8.** *The surcharge* " 2½d. " *is above T* **8**, *and there are only* 5 *bars cancelling original value instead of* 6.

63 2½d. on 1s. dull purple (*a*) .. 90 0 80 0
64 2½d. on 1s. dull purple (*b*) .. £24 £24
65 2½d. on 1s. dull purple (*c*) .. £20 £20
66 2½d. on 1s. dull purple (*d*) .. £20 £16
66*a* 2½d. on 1s. dull purple (*f*) .. £45 £40
67 2½d. on 2s. dull purple (*a*) .. £45 £40
68 2½d. on 2s. dull purple (*b*) .. £85
69 2½d. on 2s. dull purple (*c*) .. £160
70 2½d. on 2s. dull purple (*d*) .. £75
71 2½d. on 2s. dull purple (*f*) .. £300

9

10

1903. *Wmk. Crown CA. P* 14.

72 **9** ½d. dull purple & green .. 6 0 6 0
73 ,, 1d. dull purple & rosine .. 1 6 1 0
74 ,, 1½d. dull purple & black .. 8 0 15 0
75 ,, 2d. dull pur. & brn.-orange 17 6 22 6
76 ,, 2½d. dull purple & ultram. 17 6 15 0
77 **10** 3d. dull purple and grey .. 20 0 20 0
78 ,, 4d. dull purple and rosine 22 6 30 0
79 ,, 5d. dull purple and black 17 6 25 0
80 ,, 6d. dull purple 25 0 30 0
81 ,, 1s. green and black .. 50 0 60 0
82 ,, 2s. green and ultramarine 80 0 85 0
83 ,, 5s. green and carmine .. £8 £10
84 ,, £1 purple/*red* £35 £40

1904–5. *T* **9** *and* **10.** *Wmk. Mult. Crown CA. P* 14.

85 ½d. dull pur. & green, C ('04) 7 0 3 0
86 1d. dull pur. & rosine OC ('04) 2 6 0 9
86*a* 1½d. dull pur. and black, C .. 5 0 10 0
87 2d. dull pur. & brn.-orge., C 6 0 6 6
88 2½d. dull pur. & ultram., C .. 8 0 10 0
89 3d. dull purple and grey, C 10 0 10 0
90 4d. dull purple and rosine, C 7 0 8 0
91 5d. dull purple and black, C 10 0 12 6
92 6d. dull purple, C 10 0 12 6
93 1s. green and black, C .. 17 6 20 0
94 2s. green and ultramarine, C 37 6 42 6
95 5s. green and carmine, C .. £5 £6
96 £1 purple/*red*, C £35 £40

1907–10. *Wmk. Mult. Crown CA. P* 14.

97 **9** ½d. green, O (1907) .. 1 3 0 10
98 ,, 1d. carmine, O .. 4 0 0 4
99 ,, 1d. red, O (1907) .. 2 0 0 6
100 ,, 1½d. orange, O (1910) .. 4 6 7 0
101 ,, 2d. greyish slate, O .. 5 0 5 0
102 ,, 2½d. blue, O (1907) .. 5 0 6 0
103 **10** 3d. purple/*yellow*, OC .. 8 0 5 0
104 ,, 4d. black & red/*yellow*, C 10 0 7 6
105 ,, 5d. purple & ol.-green, C 12 6 15 0
106 ,, 6d. dull & bright pur., C 12 6 15 0
107 ,, 1s. black/*green*, C .. 12 6 15 0
108 ,, 2s. pur. & brt. blue/*blue*, C 40 0 45 0
109 ,, 5s. green & red/*yellow*, C £6 £7
111 ,, £1 purple & black/*red*, C £30 £35

11

12

13

14

1912–16. *Wmk. Mult. Crown CA. P* 14.

112 **11** ½d. blue-green, O .. 2 0 1 [illegible]
113 ,, ½d. yellow-green, O .. 3 0 2 [illegible]
114 ,, ½d. deep green, O .. 4 0 3 [illegible]
115 ,, 1d. carmine-red, O .. 1 0 0 [illegible]
116 ,, 1d. scarlet, O (1916) .. 3 0 0 [illegible]
116*a* ,, 1d. rose-red, O .. 1 3 0 [illegible]
117 ,, 1½d. orange, O 6 0 4
118 ,, 1½d. orange-yellow, O .. 4 0 4
119 ,, 2d. greyish slate, O .. 2 6 1
120 ,, 2½d. deep blue O .. 17 6 6
121 ,, 2½d. ultramarine, O .. 3 0 4
122 **12** 4d. black & red/*yellow*, O 5 0 9
a. On lemon 20 0 27
b. On pale yellow (Die II) .. 5 0 10
123 ,, 5d. purple & olive-grn., O 6 0 10
124 ,, 6d. dull & brt. purple, C 6 0 10
125 **13** 7d. purple & orange, C 7 6 15
126 ,, 9d. purple and black, C 9 0 15
127 **12** 10d. purple and red, C .. 10 0 20

T **14.** *Wmk. Mult. Crown CA. P* 14.

128 3d. purple/*yellow*, C .. 6 6 7 6
a. On pale yellow 10 0 10 0
129 1s. black/*green*, C .. 10 0 12 6
a. On blue-green, green back .. 7 6 10 0
130 2s. blue & purple/*blue*, C .. 17 6 12 6
131 5s. red and green/*yellow*, C 32 6 40 0
132 10s. red & green/*green*, C .. £5 £6
133 10s. carm. & bl. grn./*grn.*., C £6 £7
133*a* 10s. carm. & yell. grn./*grn.*, C £5 £6
134 £1 black and purple/*red*, C £10 £12
135 £2 blue and dull purple, C £85 £100
136 £5 orange and green, C .. £275

1921–28. *Wmk. Mult. Script CA. P* 14.

137 **11** ½d. dull green, O .. 1 3 0 9
138 ,, ½d. bright green, O .. 1 3 0 9
139 ,, 1d. bt. viol. O (Die I) ('24) 2 0 0 6
139*a* ,, 1d. bt. vio, O (Die II) ('26) 2 0 0 6
140 ,, 1½d. scarlet, O .. 3 6 2 0
141 ,, 2d. grey, O 3 6 1 3
142 ,, 2½d. ultramarine, O .. 2 0 4 0
143 **12** 3d. bright blue, O .. 2 6 1 3
144 ,, 4d. blk. & red/*pale yell.*, O 7 6 6 0
145 ,, 5d. pur. & olive-green. O 5 0 7 0
146 ,, 6d. grey-purple & bright purple, C 5 0 4 0
146*a* **13** 7d. purple & orange, C 7 0 15 0
147 ,, 9d. purple and black, C 10 0 15 0
147*a* **12** 10d. purple and red, C .. 7 6 15 0
148 **14** 1s. black/*emerald*, C .. 8 0 12 6
149 ,, 2s. blue & dull purple/*blue*, C 15 0 17 6
150 ,, 5s. red & grn./*yellow*, C 32 6 37 6
151 ,, 10s. red & grn./*green*, C 75 0 85 0
153 ,, £2 blue & dull purple, C £85 £100
154 ,, £5 orange and green, C £300

1932 (1 Mar.). *Wmk. Mult. Script CA.*

(*a*) *Recess. Waterlow. P* 12½.

155 **15** ½d. green 0 6 0 8
156 ,, 1d. violet 0 8 0 4
157 ,, 1½d. carmine 1 6 2 0
a. Imperf. between (horiz. pr.)
158 ,, 2d. brown 1 9 1 0

15. Rice Field.

16. Palms and Kola Tree.

159 **15** 3d. blue 2 6 3 0
160 ,, 4d. orange 3 0 3 6
161 ,, 5d. bronze-green .. 4 6 6 0
162 ,, 6d. light blue 6 0 5 0
163 ,, 1s. lake 12 6 15 0

(*b*) *Recess. Bradbury, Wilkinson. P* 12.

164 **16** 2s. chocolate 25 0 30 0
165 ,, 5s. deep blue 45 0 50 6
166 ,, 10s. green £5 £6
167 ,, £1 purple £12 £14

17. Arms of Sierra Leone.

18. " Freedom ".

19. Map of Sierra Leone.

20. Old Slave Market, Freetown.

21. Native Fruit Seller.

22. Government Sanatorium.

23. Bullam Canoe.

24. Punting near Banana.

25. Government Buildings.

26. Bunce Island.

27. African Elephant.

28. King George V.

29. Freetown Harbour.

(Des. Father F. Welch. Recess. Bradbury, Wilkinson & Co.)

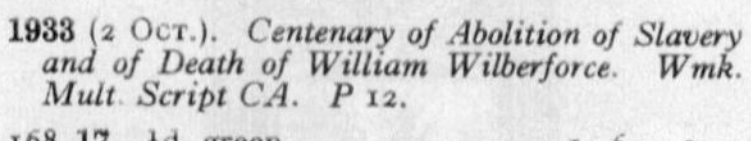

1933 (2 Oct.). *Centenary of Abolition of Slavery and of Death of William Wilberforce. Wmk. Mult. Script CA. P 12.*

No.	Type	Description	Unused s.	d.	Used s.	d.
168	**17**	½d. green	1	6	2	0
169	**18**	1d. black and brown ..	2	0	0	9
170	**19**	1½d. chestnut	7	6	8	6
171	**20**	2d. purple	6	0	3	0
172	**21**	3d. blue	8	6	7	6
173	**22**	4d. brown	12	6	15	0
174	**23**	5d. green and chestnut ..	20	0	25	0
175	**24**	6d. black & brown-orange	20	0	20	0
176	**25**	1s. violet	22	6	30	0
177	**26**	2s. brown and light blue	85	0	95	0
178	**27**	5s. black and purple ..	£25		£25	
179	**28**	10s. black & sage-green ..	£25		£25	
180	**29**	£1 violet and orange ..	£90		£100	

1935 (6 May). *Silver Jubilee. As Nos. 91/4 of Antigua, but ptd. by B. W. & Co. P 11×12.*

No.	Description	Unused s.	d.	Used s.	d.
181	1d. ultramarine & grey-blk. ..	0	6	0	8
	a. Extra flagstaff ..	30	0		
182	3d. brown and deep blue ..	4	0	4	6
	a. Extra flagstaff ..	50	0		
183	5d. green and indigo ..	4	0	5	0
	a. Extra flagstaff ..	£5			
184	1s. slate and purple	8	0	10	6
	a. Extra flagstaff	£10			

For illustration of "extra flagstaff" variety see Bechuanaland.

1937 (12 May). *Coronation. As Nos. 13/5 of Aden, but ptd. by B. W. & Co. P 11×11½.*

No.	Description	Unused s.	d.	Used s.	d.
185	1d. orange	0	4	0	4
186	2d. purple	0	9	0	10
187	3d. blue	1	3	1	6

30. Freetown from the Harbour.

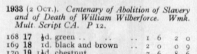

31. Rice Harvesting.

(Recess. Waterlow.)

1938 (1 May)–**1944.** *Wmk. Mult. Script CA sideways. P 12½.*

No.	Type	Description	Unused s.	d.	Used s.	d.
188	**30**	½d. black & blue-green ..	0	3	0	3
189	,,	1d. black and lake ..	0	6	0	3
		a. Imperf. between (pair) ..	—		£15	
190	**31**	1½d. scarlet	17	6	2	
190a	,,	1½d. mauve (1.2.41) ..	0	8	0	
191	,,	2d. mauve	30	0	12	
191a	,,	2d. scarlet (1.2.41) ..	0	6	0	
192	**30**	3d. black & ultram. ..	0	10	0	
193	,,	4d. black and red-brown (20.6.38)	1	6	2	
194	**31**	5d. olive-green (20.6.38)	4	0	6	
195	,,	6d. grey (20.6.38) ..	1	6	0	1
196	**30**	1s. blk. & ol.-grn.(20.6.38	2	0	1	
196a	**31**	1s. 3d. yell.-orge. ('44)	3	0	2	
197	**30**	2s. blk. & sepia (20.6.38)	5	0	4	
198	**31**	5s. red-brn. (20.6.38) ..	15	0	10	
199	,,	10s. emerald-grn.(20.6.38)	22	6	25	
200	**30**	£1 dp. blue (20.6.38) ..	42	6	37	

1946 (1 Oct.). *Victory. As Nos. 28/9 of Aden.*

No.	Description	Unused s.	d.	Used s.	d.
201	1½d. lilac	0	6	0	
202	3d. ultramarine	0	10	1	

1948 (1 Dec.). *Royal Silver Wedding. As No[s.] 30/1 of Aden.*

No.	Description	Unused s.	d.	Used s.	d.
203	1½d. bright purple	0	6	0	
204	£1 indigo	35	0	40	

1949 (10 Oct.). *75th Anniv. of U.P.U. As No[s.] 114/7 of Antigua.*

No.	Description	Unused s.	d.	Used s.	d.
205	1½d. purple	0	8	1	
206	3d. deep blue	0	10	1	
207	6d. grey	1	9	2	
208	1s. olive	3	6	5	

1953 (2 June). *Coronation. As No. 47 of Ade[n], but ptd. by B. W. & Co.*

No.	Description	Unused s.	d.	Used s.	d.
209	1½d. black and purple ..	0	9	1	

32. Cape Lighthouse.

33. Queen Elizabeth II Quay.

34. Piassava Workers.

35. Cotton Tree, Freetown.

36. Rice Harvesting.

37. Iron Ore Production, Marampa.

38. Whale Bay, York Village.

39. Bullom Boat.

40. Aeroplane and Map.

41. Orugu Bridge.

42. Kuranko Chief.

43. Law Courts, Freetown.

44. Government House.

(Recess. Waterlow & Sons.)

1956 (2 Jan.)–**61.** *Wmk. Mult. Script CA.* *P* 13½ × 13 (*horiz.*) or 14 (*vert.*).

210	**32**	½d. black & deep lilac	..	0	3	0	8
211	**33**	1d. black and olive	..	0	4	0	3

No.	Type	Description	Unused s.	d.	Used s.	d.
212	**34**	1½d. black & ultramarine	0	6	1	0
213	**35**	2d. black and brown ..	0	6	0	4
214	**36**	3d. black and bright blue	0	8	0	8
		a. Perf. 13 × 13½	20	0	17	6
215	**37**	4d. black and slate-blue..	0	10	1	0
216	**38**	6d. black and violet ..	1	0	1	0
217	**39**	1s. black and scarlet ..	2	0	2	6
218	**40**	1s. 3d. black and sepia ..	2	6	2	9
219	**41**	2s. 6d. black & chestnut	5	0	5	0
220	**42**	5s. black & deep green ..	10	0	10	0
221	**43**	10s. black and bright reddish purple	80	0	45	0
		a. *Black and purple* (19.4.61)	£9		£10	
222	**44**	£1 black and orange ..	70	0	60	0

INDEPENDENT

within the Commonwealth

45. Palm Fruit Gathering.

47. Bundu Mask.

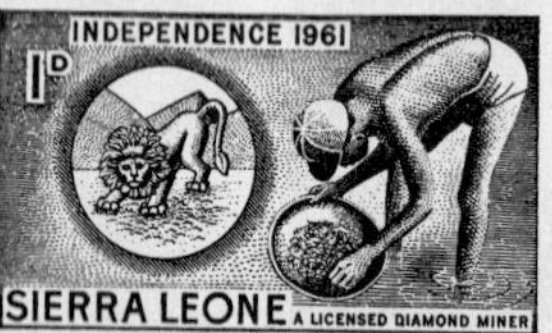

46. Licensed Diamond Miner.

48. Bishop Crowther and Old Fourah Bay College.

51. Forces Bugler.

49. Sir Milton Margai.

50. Lumley Beach.

52.

(Des. K. Penny (T **45**), Messrs. Thoma, Turrell and Larkins (T **46**, **49**), W. G. Rumley (T **47**), J. H. Vandi (T **48**), R. A. Sweet (T **50**), J. White (T **51**). Recess. Bradbury, Wilkinson & Co.).

1961 (27 Apr.). *Independence.* *W* **52.** *P* 13½.

No.	Type	Description	Unused s.	d.	Used s.	d.
223	**45**	½d. choc. & dp. bluish grn.	0	3	0	9
224	**46**	1d. orange-brown and myrtle-green ..	0	4	0	4
225	**47**	1½d. black and emerald ..	0	6	1	6
226	**48**	2d. black & ultramarine	0	8	0	6
227	**49**	3d. orange-brown & blue	0	8	0	8
228	**50**	4d. turq.-blue & scarlet ..	1	0	1	9
229	**49**	6d. black and purple ..	1	3	1	3
230	**45**	1s. chocolate & yell.-orge	2	0	2	6
231	**50**	1s. 3d. turq.-blue & vio.	2	6	2	9
232	**46**	2s. 6d. deep green & blk.	5	0	6	0
233	**47**	5s. black and red ..	8	6	10	0
234	**48**	10s. black and green ..	20	0	22	6
235	**51**	£1 carm.-red and yellow	37	6	45	0

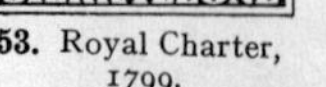

53. Royal Charter, 1799.

54. King's Yard Gate, Freetown, 1817.

55. Old House of Representatives, Freetown, 1924.

56. H.M. Yacht *Britannia* at Freetown.

(Des. C. P. Rang (T **53/4**), F. H. Burgess (T **56**). Recess. Bradbury, Wilkinson.)

1961 (25 Nov.). *Royal Visit. W* **52.** *P* 13½.

236	**53**	3d. black and rose-red ..	0	8	0	8
237	**54**	4d. black and violet ..	1	3	2	0
238	**55**	6d. black & yellow-orange	1	6	1	9
239	**56**	1s. 3d. black and blue ..	3	6	4	0

57. Campaign Emblem.

(Recess. Bradbury, Wilkinson.)

1962 (7 Apr.). *Malaria Eradication. W* **52.** *P* 11×11½.

240	**57**	3d. carmine-red ..	0	10	1	0
241	,,	1s. 3d. deep green ..	3	6	4	0

58. Fireball Lily.

59. Jina-gbo.

60. Stereospermum.

61. Black-eyed Susan.

62. Beniseed.

63. Blushing Hibiscus.

64. Climbing Lily.

65. Beautiful Crinum.

66. Blue Bells.

67. Broken Hearts.

68. Ra-ponthi.

69. Blue Plumbago.

70. African Tulip Tree.

(Des. M. Goaman. Photo. Harrison & Sons.)

1963 (1 Jan.). *Flowers in natural colours; background colours below.* W **52** (*sideways on vert. format*). *P* 14.

242	**58**	½d. bistre-brown ..	0	4	0	6
243	**59**	1d. vermilion	0	6	0	4
244	**60**	1½d. emerald-green ..	0	6	1	0
245	**61**	2d. olive-yellow	0	8	0	6
246	**62**	3d. deep bluish green ..	0	8	0	6
247	**63**	4d. violet-blue	0	10	1	9
248	**64**	6d. deep greenish blue ..	1	3	1	0
249	**65**	1s. light yellow-green ..	2	0	2	0
250	**66**	1s. 3d. bronze-green ..	2	6	2	6
251	**67**	2s. 6d. dull purple ..	4	6	4	6
252	**68**	5s. bluish violet	8	6	10	0
253	**69**	10s. bright purple ..	20	0	25	0
254	**70**	£1 light greenish blue ..	40	0	45	0

71. Threshing Machine and Corn Bins.

72. Girl with Onion Crop.

(Des. V. Whiteley. Recess. Bradbury, Wilkinsor

1963 (21 Mar.). *Freedom from Hunger.* W 5 *P* 11½ × 11.

255	**71**	3d. black and yellow-ochre	1	0	1
256	**72**	1s. 3d. sepia & emer.-green	3	0	3

2ND YEAR OF
INDEPENDENCE
19 PROGRESS 63
DEVELOPMENT

3d.

(73)

2nd Year
Independence
Progress
Development
1963

10d.

(74)

(Optd. by Govt. Printer, Freetown.)

1963 (27 APR.). *Second Anniv. of Independence. Surch. or optd. as T* **73/4**. (*a*) *Postage.*

No.	Type	Description	Unused	Used
257	**32**	3d. on ½d. black and deep lilac (R.) ..	0 9	1 0
		a. Small "c" in "INDEPENDENCE"	£5	
258	**34**	4d. on 1½d. black and ultramarine (Br.) ..	1 0	1 6
259	**32**	6d. on ½d. black and deep lilac (O.)	1 6	1 9
		a. Small "c" in "INDEPENDENCE"	£7	
260	**36**	10d. on 3d. black and bright blue (R.)	3 0	4 0
261	,,	1s. 6d. on 3d. black and bright blue (V.) ..	5 0	7 0
262	,,	3s. 6d. on 3d. black and bright blue (Ult.) ..	12 6	17 6
		(*b*) *Air. Additionally optd.* "AIR MAIL".		
263	**34**	7d. on 1½d. black and ultramarine (C.) ..	3 6	4 6
264	,,	1s. 3d. on 1½d. black and ultramarine (R.) ..	7 0	8 6
265	**41**	2s. 6d. blk. & chestnut (V.)	15 0	17 6
266	**36**	3s. on 3d. black and bright blue (B.) ..	17 6	20 0
267	,,	6s. on 3d. black and bright blue (R.) ..	30 0	35 0
268	**43**	11s. on 10s. black & bright reddish purple (C.) ..	80 0	90 0
269	**44**	11s. on £1 blk. & orange (C.)	£160	£100

75. Centenary Emblem.

76. Red Cross Emblem.

77. Centenary Emblem.

(Des. M. Goaman. Recess. Bradbury, Wilkinson.)

1963 (1 NOV.). *Centenary of Red Cross. W* **52**. *P* 11 × 11½.

No.	Type	Description	Unused	Used
270	**75**	3d. red and violet ..	0 7	0 10
271	**76**	6d. red and black ..	1 0	1 2
272	**77**	1s. 3d. red & dp. blsh. grn.	2 3	2 6

1853–1859–1963
Oldest Postal Service
Newest G.P.O.
in West Africa

1s.

(78)

1853–1859–1963
Oldest Postage Stamp
Newest G.P.O.
in West Africa

AIRMAIL

(79)

(Optd. by Govt. Printer, Freetown.)

1963 (4 NOV.). *Postal Commemorations. Various stamps optd. or surch.* (*a*) *Postage. As T* **78**.

No.	Type	Description	Unused	Used
273	**36**	3d. blk. & brt. blue (Mag.)	0 6	0 6
274	**34**	4d. on 1½d. black and ultramarine (C.) ..	0 8	0 9
275	,,	9d. on 1½d. black and ultramarine (V.) ..	1 6	1 9
276	**50**	1s. on 1s. 3d. turquoise-blue and violet (C.) ..	2 0	2 6
277	**32**	1s. 6d. on ½d. black and deep lilac (Mag.) ..	2 9	3 0
278	**36**	2s. on 3d. black and bright blue (Br.)	3 6	4 0
		(*b*) *Air. As T* **79**.		
279	**53**	7d. on 3d. black and rose-red (Br.)	2 6	3 6
280	**56**	1s. 3d. black and blue (C.)	6 0	7 6
281	**50**	2s. 6d. on 4d. turquoise-blue and scarlet ..	12 6	15 0
282	**53**	3s. on 3d. black and rose-red (V.)	15 0	17 6
283	**55**	6s. on 6d. black and yellow-orange (Ult.) ..	27 6	30 0
284	**44**	£1 black and orange (R.)	£7	£8

The events commemorated are: 1853, "First Post Office"; 1859, "First Postage Stamps"; and 1963, "Newest G.P.O." in West Africa. Nos. 273, 278 have the opt. in five lines; Nos. 279, 282 in six lines (incl. "AIRMAIL"). A number of errors and varieties exist.

80. Lion Emblem and Map.

(Recess and litho. Walsall Lithographic Co., Ltd.)

1964 (10 FEB.). *World's Fair, New York. Imperf. Self-adhesive.* (*a*) *Postage. T* **80**.

No.	Description	Unused	Used
285	1d. multicoloured	0 4	0 4
286	3d. multicoloured	0 8	0 9
287	4d. multicoloured	0 9	0 10
288	6d. multicoloured	1 0	1 3
289	1s. multicoloured	2 0	2 6
	a. "POSTAGE 1/-" omitted ..		
290	2s. multicoloured	3 6	4 0
291	5s. multicoloured	8 0	10 0
	a. "POSTAGE 5/-" omitted ..		

81. Globe and Map.

(*b*) *Air.* *T* **81.**

292	7d. multicoloured	1	3	1	6
293	9d. multicoloured	1	6	1	9
	a. " AIR MAIL 9d. " omitted				
294	1s. 3d. multicoloured ..	2	6	3	0
	a. " AIR MAIL 1/3 " omitted ..				
295	2s. 6d. multicoloured ..	4	6	5	0
296	3s. 6d. multicoloured ..	6	0	7	6
297	6s. multicoloured	10	0	12	6
298	11s. multicoloured	17	6	20	0
	a. " AIR MAIL 11/- " omitted				

Nos. 285/98 were issued in sheets of 30 (6 × 5) on green (postage) or yellow (airmail) backing paper with the emblems of Samuel Jones & Co., Ltd., self-adhesive paper-makers, on the back.

Warning. These and later self-adhesive stamps should be kept mint on their backing paper and used on cover or piece.

82. Inscription and Map.

(Recess. and litho. Walsall Lithographic Co. Ltd.)

1964 (11 MAY). *President Kennedy Memorial Issue. Imperf. Self-adhesive.*

(*a*) *Postage. Green backing paper.*

No.	Type	Description				
299	**82**	1d. multicoloured ..	0	4	0	4
300	,,	3d. multicoloured	0	8	0	9
301	,,	4d. multicoloured	0	9	0	10
302	,,	6d. multicoloured	1	0	1	3
303	,,	1s. multicoloured	2	0	2	6
304	,,	2s. multicoloured	3	6	4	0
305	,,	5s. multicoloured	8	0	10	0

83. Pres. Kennedy and Map.

(*b*) *Air. Yellow backing paper.*

No.	Type	Description				
306	**83**	7d. multicoloured ..	1	3	1	6
307	,,	9d. multicoloured ..	1	6	1	9
308	,,	1s. 3d. multicoloured ..	2	6	3	0
309	,,	2s. 6d. multicoloured ..	4	6	5	0
310	,,	3s. 6d. multicoloured ..	6	0	7	6
311	,,	6s. multicoloured ..	10	0	12	6
312	,,	11s. multicoloured ..	17	6	20	0

(New currency. 100 cents. = 1 leone.)

3c (84)

AIRMAIL **7c** (85)

LE 1·00 (86)

1964–66. *Decimal currency. Various stamps surch. locally.* (i) *First issue* (4.8.64).

(*a*) *Postage. As T* **84.**

No.	Type	Description				
313	**64**	1 c. on 6d. mult. (R.) ..	0	4	0	4
314	**53**	2 c. on 3d. blk. & rose-red	0	7	0	7
315	**62**	3 c. on 3d. multicoloured	0	6	0	6
316	**45**	5 c. on ½d. chocolate and dp. bluish green (B.)	1	0	1	
317	**71**	8 c. on 3d. black and yellow-ochre (R.) ..	1	2	1	
318	**66**	10 c. on 1s. 3d. mult. (R.)	1	5	1	
319	**65**	15 c. on 1s. multicoloured	2	0	2	
320	**55**	25 c. on 6d. black and yellow-orange (V.) ..	3	6	3	
321	**46**	50 c. on 2s. 6d. deep green and black (O.) ..	6	9	6	

(*b*) *Air. As T* **85** *or* **86** (*Nos.* 326/7).

No.	Type	Description				
322	**72**	7 c. on 1s. 3d. sepia and emerald-green (B.) ..	1	3	1	
323	**50**	20 c. on 4d. turquoise-blue and scarlet	2	9	2	
324	**48**	30 c. on 10s. black and green (R.)	4	3	4	
325	**47**	40 c. on 5s. blk. & red (B.)	5	9	5	
326	**83**	1 l. on 1s. 3d. mult. (R.) ..	15	0	20	
327	,,	2 l. on 11s. multicoloured	30	0	37	

1c (87)

TWO LEONES **Le 2·00** (88)

(ii) *Second issue* (20.1.65).

Surch. as T **87** *or* **88** (*Nos.* 332/3).

(*a*) *Postage.*

No.	Type	Description	Unused	Used
328	**49**	1 c. on 3d. orge.-brn. & bl.	0 5	0 5
329	**82**	2 c. on 1d. multicoloured	0 7	0 7
330	,,	4 c. on 3d. multicoloured	0 11	1 0
		a. Error. 4 c. on 1d. (No. 299)		
331	**61**	5 c. on 2d. olive-yellow ..	1 2	1 3
332	**68**	1 l. on 5s. bluish violet (Gold)	13 6	15 0
333	**51**	2 l. on £1 carmine-red and yellow (R.)	25 0	30 0
		a. Surch. double (B. + Bk.) ..		

(*b*) *Air.*

No.	Type	Description	Unused	Used
334	**83**	7 c. on 7d. mult. (R.) ..	1 5	1 6
335	,,	60 c. on 9d. multicoloured	8 6	9 0

(iii) *Third issue* (4.65).

Surch. in figures (*various sizes*). (*a*) *Postage.*

No.	Type	Description	Unused	Used
336	**47**	1 c. on 1½d. black and emerald (R.) ..	0 5	0 6
337	**82**	2 c. on 3d. multicoloured	0 7	0 9
338	**80**	2 c. on 4d. multicoloured	0 7	0 9
339	**59**	3 c. on 1d. vermilion ..	0 9	1 0
340	**48**	3 c. on 2d. black & ultramarine (R.)	0 9	1 0
341	**50**	5 c. on 1s. 3d. turquoise-blue and violet (R.) ..	1 3	1 9
342	**82**	15 c. on 6d. multicoloured	2 9	3 3
343	,,	15 c. on 1s. mult. (R.) ..	2 9	3 3
344	**49**	20 c. on 6d. black and purple (R.) ..	4 0	4 9
345	**64**	25 c. on 6d. deep greenish blue (R.)	5 0	6 0
346	,,	50 c. on 3d. orange-brown and blue (R.) ..	8 0	10 0
347	**80**	60 c. on 5s. mult. (V.) ..	10 6	13 6
348	**82**	1 l. on 4d. mult. (R.) ..	17 6	21 0
349	**51**	2 l. on £1 carmine-red & yellow (B.)	32 6	40 0

(*b*) *Air.*

No.	Type	Description	Unused	Used
350	**82**	7 c. on 9d. multicoloured	1 6	2 0

(iv) *Fourth issue* (11.65).

(*a*) *Postage*

No.	Type	Description	Unused	Used
351	**80**	1 c. on 6d. multicoloured ..	0 5	0 6
352	,,	1 c. on 2s. multicoloured ..	0 5	0 6
353	**82**	1 c. on 2s. multicoloured ..	0 5	0 6
354	,,	1 c. on 5s. multicoloured ..	0 5	0 6

(*b*) *Air.*

No.	Type	Description	Unused	Used
355	**81**	2 c. on 1s. 3d. mult. ..	0 7	0 9
356	**83**	2 c. on 1s. 3d. mult. ..	0 7	0 9
357	,,	2 c. on 3s. 6d. mult. ..	0 7	0 9
358	**81**	3 c. on 7d. multicoloured ..	0 9	1 0
359	**83**	3 c. on 9d. multicoloured ..	0 9	1 0
360	**81**	5 c. on 2s. 6d. mult. ..	1 3	1 9
361	**83**	5 c. on 2s. 6d. mult. ..	1 3	1 9
362	**81**	5 c. on 3s. 6d. mult. ..	1 3	1 9
363	,,	5 c. on 6s. multicoloured ..	1 3	1 9
364	**83**	5 c. on 6s. multicoloured ..	1 3	1 9

TWO
Leones

(**89**)

(v) *Fifth issue* (28.1.66).

Air. No. 374 *further surch. with T* **89**.

No.	Type	Description	Unused	Used
365	**64**	2 l. on 30 c. on 6d. ..	25 0	30 0

2c

IN MEMORIAM
TWO GREAT LEADERS

SIR MILTON MARGAI 1895-1964 SIR WINSTON CHURCHILL 1874-1965

(**90.** Margai and Churchill.)

1965 (19 May). *Sir Milton Margai and Sir Winston Churchill Commemoration. Flower stamps of* 1963 *surch. as T* **90** *on horiz. designs or with individual portraits on vert. designs as indicated. Multicoloured.* (*a*) *Postage.*

No.	Type	Description	Price
366	**59**	2 c. on 1d.	0 8
367	**62**	3 c. on 3d. Margai ..	0 10
368	**65**	10 c. on 1s. Churchill ..	1 9
369	**66**	20 c. on 1s. 3d.	3 6
370	**63**	50 c. on 4d. Margai ..	8 0
371	**68**	75 c. on 5s. Churchill ..	12 6

(*b*) *Air. Additionally optd.* "AIR MAIL".

No.	Type	Description	Price
372	**61**	7 c. on 2d.	1 6
373	**58**	15 c. on ½d. Margai ..	3 0
374	**64**	30 c. on 6d. (O. and W.) ..	6 0
375	**70**	1 l. on £1	17 6
376	**69**	2 l. on 10s. Churchill ..	30 0

91. Cola Plant and Nut.

92. Arms of Sierra Leone.

93. Inscription and Necklace.

(Des. M. Meers. Manufactured by the Walsall Lithographic Co., Ltd.)

1965 (Nov.). *Imperf. Self-adhesive.*
A. *Embossed on silver foil, backed with paper bearing advertisements. Emerald, olive-yellow and carmine; denominations in colours given. Postage.*

377	**91**	1 c. emerald	0	4	0	5
378	,,	2 c. carmine	0	7	0	8
379	,,	3 c. olive-yellow	0	9	0	10
380	,,	4 c. silver/*emerald* ..	0	10	1	0
381	,,	5 c. silver/*carmine* ..	1	0	1	3

B. *Recess on cream paper with advertisements on back.* (*a*) *Postage.*

382	**92**	20 c. multicoloured ..	2	10	3	3
383	,,	50 c. multicoloured ..	7	0	8	0

(*b*) *Air.*

384	**92**	40 c. multicoloured ..	5	9	6	3

C. *Foil-backed and photo-litho. with advertisements on white paper backing* (*see footnote*). *Air.*

385	**93**	7 c. multicoloured ..	1	3	1	6
386	,,	15 c. multicoloured ..	2	4	2	9

The above stamps were issued in single form with attached tabs to remove the backing paper, with the exception of No. 385 which was in sheets of 25 bearing a single large advertisement on the back.

SINGAPORE

A Crown Colony until the end of 1957. From August 1st, 1958, an internally self-governing territory designated the State of Singapore. From Sept. 16, 1963 part of MALAYSIA (q.v.).

1948–52. *As T* **58** *of Straits Settlements, but inscr.* "SINGAPORE" *at foot. Wmk. Mult. Script CA. Chalk-surfaced paper.* (*a*) *P* 14.

1	1 c. black	0	4	0	4
2	2 c. orange	0	4	0	4
3	3 c. green	0	6	0	8
4	4 c. brown	0	5	0	8
5	6 c. grey	0	9	0	6
6	8 c. scarlet	0	10	0	10
7	10 c. purple	0	8	0	3
8	15 c. ultramarine	1	0	0	6
9	20 c. black and green	1	6	1	0
10	25 c. purple and orange ..	2	6	0	8
11	40 c. red and purple	3	0	4	0
12	50 c. black and blue	3	0	0	9
13	$1 blue and purple ..	10	0	1	3
14	$2 green and scarlet ..	12	6	4	0
15	$5 green and brown ..	22	6	7	6

Dates of issue: 1948—1 Sept., 1 c. to 6 c., and 10 c.; 1 Oct. , 8 c., 15 c. to $1 and $5; 25 Oct., $2.

(*b*) *P* 17½ × 18.

16	1 c. black	0	2	0	3
17	2 c. orange	0	3	0	3
19	4 c. brown	0	4	0	3
19*a*	5 c. bright purple	0	6	0	3
21	6 c. grey	0	6	0	6
21*a*	8 c. green	0	8	1	6
22	10 c. purple	0	8	0	3
22*a*	12 c. scarlet	1	3	2	0
23	15 c. ultramarine	2	0	2	0
24	20 c. black and green	3	0	1	9
24*a*	20 c. bright blue	2	0	1	0
25	25 c. purple and orange ..	1	3	0	6
25*a*	35 c. scarlet and purple ..	3	0	2	6
26	40 c. red and purple	4	0	5	0
27	50 c. black and blue	2	6	0	6
28	$1 blue and purple	6	0	1	3
	a. Error. St. Edward's Crown ..				
29	$2 green and scarlet ..	10	0	3	0
	a. Error. St. Edward's Crown ..				
30	$5 green and brown ..	22	6	6	0

Dates of issue: 1949—1 July, 4 c.; 31 Oct., 2 c., 20 c. blk. & grn. and $1: 1950—9 Feb., 10 c., 15 c., 25 c. and 50 c.: 1951—24 May, 40 c. and $2; 19 Dec., $5: 1952—21 May, 1 c.; 1 Sept., 5 c., 8 c., 12 c., 20 c. blue and 35 c.; 10 Dec., 6 c.

Nos. 28a and 29a occur on rows in the watermark in which the crowns and letters "C A" alternate.

1948 (25 OCT.). *Royal Silver Wedding. As Nos.* 30/1 *of Aden.*

31	10 c. violet	0	8	0	8
32	$5 brown	35	0	30	0

1949 (10 OCT.). *75th Anniv. of Universal Posta[illegible] Union. As Nos.* 114/7 *of Antigua.*

33	10 c. purple	0	10	0	1[illegible]
34	15 c. deep blue	1	0	1	[illegible]
35	25 c. orange	1	9	2	[illegible]
36	50 c. blue-black	3	6	4	[illegible]

1953 (2 JUNE). *Coronation. As No.* 47 *of Aden*

37	10 c. black and reddish purple	0	8	0	[illegible]

1. Chinese Sampan.

2. Malay Kolek.

3. Twa-Kow.

4. Lombok Sloop.

5. Trengganu Pinas.

6. Palari.

7. Timber Tongkong.

8. Hainan Trader.

9. Cocos-Keeling Schooner.

10. *Argonaut* Aircraft.

11. Oil Tanker.

12. M.S. *Chusan*.

13. Raffles Statue.

14. Singapore River.

15. Arms of Singapore.

(Des. Dr. C. A. Gibson-Hill, except 25 c., 30 c., 50 c. and $5 (from photographs, etc.). T **1/12.** Photo. Harrison & Sons. T **13/15.** Recess; centre typo. ($5). Bradbury, Wilkinson & Co.)

1955 (4 Sept.). *Wmk. Mult. Script CA. P* 13½ × 14½ (*T* **1/12**) *or* 14 (*T* **13/15**).

38	**1**	1 c. black	0 3	0 6
39	**2**	2 c. yellow-orange ..	0 4	0 8
40	**3**	4 c. brown	0 4	0 3
41	**4**	5 c. bright purple	0 5	0 4
42	**5**	6 c. deep grey-blue ..	0 6	0 9
43	**6**	8 c. turquoise-blue ..	0 7	1 0
44	**7**	10 c. deep lilac	0 8	0 3
45	**8**	12 c. rose-carmine	1 0	2 0
46	**9**	20 c. ultramarine (*shades*) ..	1 0	0 6
47	**10**	25 c. orange-red and bluish violet (*shades*) ..	1 3	0 8
48	**11**	30 c. violet & brown-purple	1 6	0 8
49	**12**	50 c. blue and black ..	3 0	0 8
50	**13**	$1 blue and deep purple ..	4 6	0 9
51	**14**	$2 blue-green and scarlet	8 0	3 6
52	**15**	$5 yellow, red, brown and slate-black	20 0	6 0

Plates 2A and 2B of the 10 c. (12 Apr. 1960) and the blue "3A" and "3B" plates of the 50 c. "3A–2A", "3B–2B" (part of the 24 Jan. 1961 issue and later printings) were printed with a finer screen (250 dots per inch, instead of the normal 200). (*Price* 10 c., 12*s*. 6*d*. *un*.; 50 c. 2*s*. 6*d*. *un*.)

16. The Singapore Lion.

(Photo. Harrison & Sons, Ltd.)

1959 (1 June). *New Constitution.* *W* w.**12.** *P* 11½ × 12.

No.	Type	Description	Unused	Used
53	**16**	4 c. yell., sepia & rose-red	0 6	1 3
54	,,	10 c. yell., sepia & reddish purple	0 10	0 10
55	,,	20 c. yell., sepia & brt. blue	1 6	1 6
56	,,	25 c. yellow, sepia & green..	2 0	2 0
57	,,	30 c. yellow, sepia & violet	2 6	3 0
58	,,	50 c. yell., sepia & dp. slate	4 0	4 6

17. State Flag.

(Litho. J. Enschedé & Sons.)

1960 (3 June). *National Day.* *W* w.**12** (*sideways*). *P* 13½.

No.	Type	Description	Unused	Used
59	**17**	4 c. red, yellow and blue..	0 6	0 9
60	,,	10 c. red, yellow and grey..	1 0	0 6

18. Clasped Hands.

(Photo. Enschedé.)

1961 (3 June). *National Day.* *W* w.**12.** *P* 13½.

No.	Type	Description	Unused	Used
61	**18**	4 c. blk. brn. & pale yell.	0 6	0 9
62	,,	10 c. black, deep green and pale yellow	1 0	0 6

19. *Arachnis* " *Maggie Oei* " (orchid).

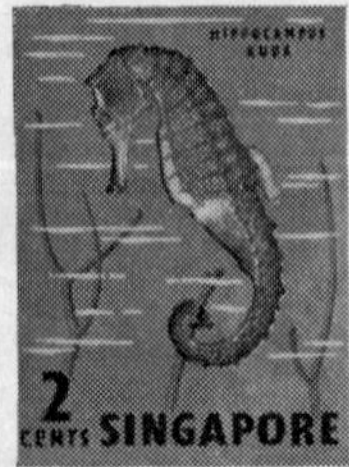

20. Sea-Horse.

21. Six-banded Barb.

22. Clown Fish.

23. Archer Fish.

24. *Vanda* " *Tan Chay Yan* " (orchid).

25. Harlequin.

26. *Grammatophyllum speciosum* (orchid).

29. *Vanda* " *Mis* *Joaquim* " (orchid).

27. Butterfly Fish. **28.** Two-spot Gourami.

30. White-rumped Shama.

31 White-throated Kingfisher.

32. Yellow-breasted Sunbird. **33.** White-bellied Sea Eagle.

(Photo. Harrison (orchids and fish), De La Rue (birds).)

1962 (31 Mar.)–**63.** *Orchid and bird designs multicoloured; background colours given. W* w.**12.** *P* 12½ (1 *c.*, 8 *c.*, 12 *c.*, 30 *c.*), 13×13½ ($2, $5), 13½×13 (50 *c.*, $1), 13½×14½ (4 *c.*, 5 *c.*, 10 *c.*, 25 *c.*) *or* 14½×13½ (2 *c.*, 6 *c.*, 20 *c.*).

63	**19**	1 c. mauve (10.3.63) ..	0	1	0	6
64	**20**	2 c. brown and green ..	0	2	0	2
65	**21**	4 c. black and orange-red	0	3	0	2
		a. Black omitted				
66	**22**	5 c. red and black ..	0	4	0	3
67	**23**	6 c. black & greenish yellow	0	4	0	3
68	**24**	8 c. pale turq.-blue (10.3.63)	0	5	0	8
69	**25**	10 c. red-orange and black	0	6	0	3
		a. Red-orange omitted ..	£35			
70	**26**	12 c. salmon (10.3.63) ..	0	6	1	0
71	**27**	20 c. orange and blue ..	0	10	0	3
		a. Orange omitted				
72	**28**	25 c. black and orange ..	0	11	0	5
73	**29**	30 c. stone (10.3.63) ..	1	1	0	5
74	**30**	50 c. apple-green (10.3.63)	1	8	0	6
75	**31**	$1 yellow (10.3.63) ..	3	4	1	3
76	**32**	$2 grey-blue (10.3.63) ..	6	6	4	0
77	**33**	$5 cobalt (10.3.63) ..	15	6	6	6

34. " The Role of Labour in Nation-Building ".

(Photo. Courvoisier.)

1962 (3 June). *National Day. P* 11½×12.

78	**34**	4 c. yellow, rose-carmine and black	0	6	0	6
79	,,	10 c. yellow, blue and black	1	0	1	0

35. Blocks of Flats, Singapore.

(Photo. Harrison.)

1963 (3 June). *National Day. W* w.**12.** *P* 12½.

80	**35**	4 c. orange-red, blk., blue and turquoise-blue ..	0	6	0	6
81	,,	10 c. orge.-red, blk., yellow-olive & turquoise-blue	1	0	0	9

36. Dancers in National Costume.

(Photo. Harrison.)

1963 (8 Aug.). *South East Asia Cultural Festival. W* w.**12.** *P* 14×14½.

82	**36**	5 c. yellow, black, blue-green and turquoise-blue ..	0	7	0	5

POSTAGE DUE STAMPS.

For postage due stamps in use since 1948, see under Malayan Postal Union.

SOMALILAND PROTECTORATE.

(BRITISH SOMALILAND)

BRITISH
SOMALILAND

(1)

1903. *Stamps of India (Queen Victoria) optd. with T* **1**, *at top of stamp.*

No.	Type	Description	Unused	Used
1	**23**	½ a. green	2 0	3 0
		a. "BRIT SH" for "BRITISH"	70 0	
2	**25**	1 a. carmine	2 6	3 0
		a. "BRIT SH" for "BRITISH"	85 0	
3	**27**	2 a. pale violet	2 0	1 6
		a. "BRIT SH" for "BRITISH"	£5	
		b. Opt. double	£30	
4	**36**	2½ a. ultramarine	5 0	10 0
		a. "BRIT SH" for "BRITISH"	£22	
5	**28**	3 a. brown-orange ..	3 0	4 0
		a. "BRIT SH" for "BRITISH"	£20	
6	**29**	4 a. slate-green	6 0	8 6
7	**21**	6 a. pale brown	8 0	10 0
8	**31**	8 a. dull mauve	10 0	12 6
9	**32**	12 a. purple/*red*	10 0	15 0
10	**37**	1 r. green and carmine ..	16 0	22 6
11	**38**	2 r. carm. & yellow-brown	42 6	55 0
12	,,	3 r. brown and green ..	45 0	55 0
13	,,	5 r. ultramarine & violet..	65 0	80 0

1903. *Stamps of India (Queen Victoria) optd. with T* **1**, *at bottom of stamp.*

No.	Type	Description	Unused	Used
18	**36**	2½ a. blue	3 6	6 0
19	**21**	6 a. pale brown	6 0	10 0
20	**32**	12 a. purple/*red*	10 0	15 0
21	**37**	1 r. green and carmine ..	15 0	20 0
22	**38**	2 r. carm. & yellow-brown	55 0	65 0
23	,,	3 r. brown and green ..	70 0	85 0
		a. Opt. inverted	£60	
24	,,	5 r. ultramarine & violet..	90 0	£6

1903. *Stamps of India (King Edward VII) optd. with T* **1**.

No.	Type	Description	Unused	Used
25	**42**	½ a. green	1 6	0 8
		a. "BRIT SH" for "BRITISH"		
26	**43**	1 a. carmine	2 0	1 3
		a. "BRIT SH" for "BRITISH"	£7	
27	**44**	2 a. mauve	6 0	10 0
		a. "BRIT SH" for "BRITISH"		
28	**46**	3 a. orange-brown ..	7 6	10 0
29	**47**	4 a. olive-green	8 0	12 6
30	**49**	8 a. magenta	10 0	15 0

2

3

(Typo. De La Rue.)

1904. *Wmk. Crown CA. P* 14.

No.	Type	Description	Unused	Used
32	**2**	½ a. dull green and green ..	0 9	1 3
33	,,	1 a. grey-black and red ..	3 6	6 0
34	**2**	2 a. dull and bright purple	4 0	7 6
35	,,	2½ a. bright blue	5 0	10 0
36	,,	3 a. chocolate & grey-green	7 6	15 0
37	,,	4 a. green and black ..	8 0	10 0
38	,,	6 a. green and violet ..	12 6	17 6
39	,,	8 a. grey-black & pale blue	17 6	22 6
40	,,	12 a. grey-blk. & orange-buff	22 6	27 6

Wmk. Crown CC. P 14.

No.	Type	Description	Unused	Used
41	**3**	1 r. green	30 0	40 0
42	,,	2 r. dull and bright purple ..	37 6	45 0
43	,,	3 r. green and black.. ..	50 0	60 0
44	,,	5 r. grey-black and red ..	80 0	90 0

1905–6. *Wmk. Mult. Crown CA. P* 14.

No.	Type	Description	Unused	Used
45	**2**	½ a. dull green & green, O	1 3	2 0
46	,,	1 a. grey-black & red, OC	3 0	2 0
47	,,	2 a. dull & brt. purple, OC	3 6	5 0
48	,,	2½ a. bright blue, O ..	7 0	10 0
49	,,	3 a. choc. & grey-green, OC	8 6	10 0
50	,,	4 a. green and black, OC	8 0	12 6
51	,,	6 a. green and violet, OC	6 0	12 6
52	,,	8 a. grey-blk. & p. blue, O	10 0	15 0
		a. Black and blue, C ..	22 6	30 0
53	,,	12 a. grey-black and orange-buff, O	10 0	15 0
		a. Black and orange-brown, C	12 6	17 6

1909. *Wmk. Mult. Crown CA. P* 14.

No.	Type	Description	Unused	Used
58	**2**	½ a. bluish green, O ..	7 6	10 0
59	,,	1 a. red, O	7 6	5 0

4

5

(Typo. De La Rue.)

1912 (Dec.)–**1919.** *Wmk. Mult. Crown CA. P* 14.

No.	Type	Description	Unused	Used
60	**4**	½ a. green, O	0 8	1 0
61	,,	1 a. red, O	2 6	1 6
61*a*	,,	1 a. scarlet, O ('17) ..	5 0	3 6
62	,,	2 a. dull & brt. purple, C	12 6	17 6
62*a*	,,	2 a. dull purple & violet-purple, C ('19) ..	20 0	25 0
63	,,	2½ a. bright blue, O ..	4 0	6 0
64	,,	3 a. choc. & grey-grn., C	4 0	6 0
65	,,	4 a. grn. & blk., C ('13) ..	5 0	6 0
66	,,	6 a. green and violet, C ..	4 0	7 6
67	,,	8 a. grey-blk. & pale blue, C	10 0	12 6
68	,,	12 a. grey-black and orange-buff, C	10 0	12 6
69	**5**	1 r. green, C	10 0	15 0
70	,,	2 r. dull pur. & pur., C ('19)	32 6	40 0
71	,,	3 r. green & blk., C ('19)	55 0	65 0
72	,,	5 r. blk. & scar., C ('19) ..	75 0	85 0

1921. *Wmk. Mult. Script CA. P* 14.

No.	Type	Description	Unused	Used
73	**4**	½ a. blue-green, O	0 6	1 3
74	,,	1 a. carmine-red, O ..	0 8	0 8
75	,,	2 a. dull & brt. purple, C ..	2 0	3 0
76	,,	2½ a. bright blue, O ..	3 0	4 6
77	,,	3 a. chocolate & green, C ..	5 0	6 6
78	,,	4 a. green and black, C ..	5 0	6 6
79	,,	6 a. green and violet, C ..	4 0	6 6
80	,,	8 a. grey-blk. & pale blue, C	6 0	8 6
81	,,	12 a. grey-blk. & orge.-buff, C	7 0	12 6
82	**5**	1 r. dull green, C	12 6	17 6
83	,,	2 r. dull purple & purple, C	25 0	32 6
84	,,	3 r. dull green & black, C	42 6	50 0
85	,,	5 r. black and scarlet, C ..	75 0	90 0

1935 (6 May). *Silver Jubilee. As Nos. 91/4 of Antigua but ptd. by W'low & Sons. P 11 × 12.*

86	1 a. deep blue and scarlet	1	6	2	6
87	2 a. ultramarine and grey	5	0	7	6
88	3 a. brown and deep blue	6	6	10	0
89	1 r. slate and purple	18	6	25	0

1937 (13 May). *Coronation. As Nos. 13/15 of Aden. P 14.*

90	1 a. scarlet	0	6	0	7
91	2 a. grey-black	1	0	1	0
92	3 a. bright blue	1	6	1	6

6. Berbera Blackhead Sheep.

7. Greater Kudu Antelope.

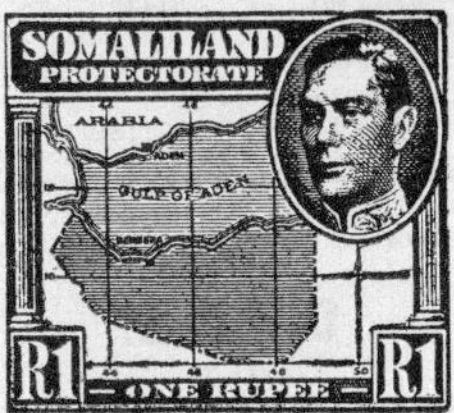

8. Somaliland Protectorate.

(Des. H. W. Claxton. Recess. Waterlow.)

1938 (10 May). *Portrait to left. Wmk. Mult. Script CA. P 12½.*

93	**6**	½ a. green	1	0	1	6
94	,,	1 a. scarlet	1	6	2	0
95	,,	2 a. maroon	1	6	3	0
96	,,	3 a. bright blue	4	6	6	0
97	**7**	4 a. sepia	5	0	7	6
98	,,	6 a. violet	6	0	8	0
99	,,	8 a. grey	7	6	12	6
100	,,	12 a. red-orange	10	0	15	0
101	**8**	1 r. green	25	0	37	6
102	,,	2 r. purple	25	0	42	6
103	,,	3 r. bright blue	20	0	35	0
104	,,	5 r. black	32	6	45	0
		a. Imperf. between (horiz. pr).				

9. Berbera Blackhead Sheep.

(Recess. Waterlow.)

1942 (27 Apr.). *As T 6/8 but with full-face portrait of King George VI, as in T* **9**. *Wmk. Mult. Script CA. P 12½.*

105	**9**	½ a. green	0	8	0	10
106	,,	1 a. scarlet	0	8	0	10
107	,,	2 a. maroon	0	10	1	0
108	,,	3 a. bright blue	1	0	1	6
109	**7**	4 a. sepia	1	3	1	9
110	**7**	6 a. violet	2	0	2	6
111	,,	8 a. grey	4	0	5	0
112	,,	12 a. red orange	4	0	5	0
113	**8**	1 r. green	6	0	8	6
114	,,	2 r. purple	8	6	12	6
115	,,	3 r. bright blue	8	6	12	6
116	,,	5 r. black	17	6	20	0

1946 (15 Oct.). *Victory. As Nos. 28/9 of Aden. P 13½ × 14.*

117	1 a. carmine	0	4	0	8
	a. Perf. 13½	2	6	10	0
118	3 a. blue	0	8	1	3

1949 (28 Jan.). *Royal Silver Wedding. As Nos. 30/1 of Aden.*

119	1 a. scarlet	0	4	0	4
120	5 r. black	17	6	17	6

1949 (10 Oct.). *75th Anniv. of U.P.U. As Nos. 114/7 of Antigua surch. with new values.*

121	1 a. on 10 c. carmine	0	4	0	6
122	3 a. on 30 c. deep blue (R.)	0	6	1	0
123	6 a. on 50 c. purple	2	0	3	6
124	12 a. on 1s. red-orange	4	0	4	6

5 Cents (10) 1 Shilling (11)

1951 (2 Apr.). *1942 issue surch. as T* **10/11**.

125	5 c. on ½ a. green	0	4	0	4
126	10 c. on 2 a. maroon	0	8	0	8
127	15 c. on 3 a. bright blue	1	0	1	3
128	20 c. on 4 a. sepia	1	3	1	0
129	30 c. on 6 a. violet	1	9	2	0
130	50 c. on 8 a. grey	2	6	2	6
131	70 c. on 12 a. red-orange	2	6	3	0
132	1s. on 1 r. green	3	0	3	6
133	2s. on 2 r. purple	4	0	7	6
134	2s. on 3 r. bright blue	7	6	8	6
135	5s. on 5 r. black (R.)	15	0	20	0

1953 (2 June). *Coronation. As No. 47 of Aden.*

136	15 c. black and green	0	9	1	0

12. Camel and Gurgi.

13. Askari. **14.** Somali Rock Pigeon.

15. Martial Eagle.

16. Berbera Blackhead Sheep.

17. Sheikh Isaaq's Tomb, Mait.

18. Taleh Fort.

(Recess. Bradbury, Wilkinson.)

1953 (15 Sept.)–**58.** *Wmk. Mult. Script CA. P* 12½.

No.	Type	Description	Unused	Used
137	**12**	5 c. slate-black	0 6	0 9
138	**13**	10 c. red-orange (*shades*) ..	0 8	0 6
139	**12**	15 c. blue-green	0 9	1 0
140	,,	20 c. scarlet	1 3	1 6
141	**13**	30 c. reddish brown ..	1 6	1 6
142	**14**	35 c. blue	2 6	2 6
143	**15**	50 c. brown & rose-carmine	3 6	3 0
144	**16**	1s. light blue	3 0	3 0
145	**17**	1s. 30 c. ultramarine and black (1.9.58) ..	4 6	4 6
146	**14**	2s. brown & bluish violet	7 6	6 0
147	**15**	5s. red-brown & emerald	17 6	20 0
148	**18**	10s. brn. & reddish violet	37 6	40 0

OPENING
OF THE
LEGISLATIVE
COUNCIL
1957

(19)

LEGISLATIVE
COUNCIL
UNOFFICIAL
MAJORITY,
1960

(20)

1957 (21 May). *Opening of Legislative Council. Nos.* 140 *and* 144 *optd. with T* **19.**

No.	Type	Description	Unused	Used
149	**12**	20 c. scarlet	1 9	2 3
150	**16**	1 s. light blue	4 6	5 6

1960 (5 Apr.). *Legislative Council's Unofficial Majority. Nos.* 140 *and* 145 *optd. as T* **20.**

No.	Type	Description	Unused	Used
151	**12**	20 c. scarlet	2 0	2 9
152	**17**	1 s. 30, ultram. & black	3 9	4 9

All Somaliland Protectorate stamps were withdrawn from sale on 25 June, 1960, when the territory became part of the independent Somali Republic, whose stamps appear in Part III of this Catalogue.

OFFICIAL STAMPS.

BRITISH

SOMALILAND

(O 1)

SERVICE

BRITISH
SOMALILAND

(O 2)

1903. *Stamps of India overprinted.*

(i) *Official stamps of* 1883–1900, *Queen's Head, with Type* O **1** (*wider spaced on* 1 *r.*).

No.	Description	Unused	Used
O 1	½ a. green	7 6	60 0
O 2	1 a. carmine	10 0	15 0
O 3	2 a. pale violet	15 0	80 0
O 4	8 a. dull mauve	40 0	£14
O 5	1 r. green and carmine ..	40 0	£10

Varieties exist on all values in which "BRITISH" measures 11 mm., and the 8 a. is known without stop after "M" in "H.M.S."

(ii) *Postage stamps of* 1902, *King's Head, with Type* O **2.**

No.	Description	Unused	Used
O 6	½ a. green	3 6	
	a. "BRIT SH" for "BRITISH"	50 0	
O 7	1 a. carmine	3 6	
	a. "BRIT SH" for "BRITISH"	70 0	
O 8	2 a. pale violet	3 6	
	a. "BRIT SH" for "BRITISH"	£8	
O 9	8 a. magenta	45 0	
	a. "BRIT SH" for "BRITISH"	£35	

Other varieties exist in which the second "E" of "SERVICE" is out of alignment, and also in which the word is in a different fount, measuring 11½ mm.

O.H.M.S.

(O 3)

1904. *Optd. with Type* O **3.**

(*a*) *Wmk. Crown CA. P* 14.

No.	Type	Description	Unused	Used
O14	**2**	½ a. dull green and green ..	12 6	60 0
		a. No stop after "M" ..	£24	
O15	,,	1 a. grey-black & carmine	17 6	20 0
		a. No stop after "M" ..	£24	
O16	,,	2 a. dull and brt. purple ..	£14	£7
		a. No stop after "M" ..	£70	
O17	,,	8 a. grey-black & p. blue	£6	£12
		a. No stop after "M" ..	£30	

(*b*) *Wmk. Mult. Crown CA. P* 14.

No.	Type	Description	Unused	Used
O18	**2**	2 a. dull & brt. purple, O	£8	
		a. No stop after "M" ..	£40	

Optd. as Type O **3.** *Wmk. Crown CC. P* 14.

No.	Type	Description	Unused	Used
O19	**3**	1 r. green	£25	£35

Of the above stamps it is doubtful if Nos. O 6 to O 9 were ever issued. Of No. O19 we have had three used copies on a portion of an official envelope. Another stamp—viz. the 1 r. *green and carmine* (*Queen's Head*)—exists overprinted with Type O **2**, but it was never issued for use. (*Price* 40s., *un.*).

SOUTH AFRICA.

The following territories combined to form the Union of South Africa in 1910 (of which they became provinces) and their issues are listed in alphabetical order in this Catalogue:—

CAPE OF GOOD HOPE (including Griqualand West)

NATAL (including New Republic and Zululand)

ORANGE FREE STATE

TRANSVAAL

Although South Africa is now a republic, outside the British Commonwealth, all its stamp issues are listed together here, purely as a matter of convenience to collectors.

Types **1** to **3** have inscriptions in English and Dutch on each stamp. From Type **5** onwards the languages used are English and Afrikaans. Sometimes this results in two different stamps for each value, appearing alternately throughout the sheet, in which case we give a three-column pricing to cover unused or used pairs, one stamp in each language, and used singles (of either language). Otherwise one design incorporates both languages.

Owing to the use of the two languages and some unusual methods of perforation, the *unused* stamps of this country are usually collected in the following forms :—

A. Stamps inscribed in both languages and having perforations round each : in singles.

B. Stamps alternately inscribed and having perforations round each stamp ; in horizontal pairs.

C. Issues in reduced sizes : in pairs or triplets, vertical or horizontal, so that the perforations surround each unit.

Used stamps : in the above forms or in singles.

1

(Des. H. S. Wilkinson. Recess. De La Rue & Co.)

1910 (4 Nov.). *Inscribed bilingually. Wmk. Multiple Rosettes. P* 14

1	**1**	2½d. deep blue	12	6	7	6
2	,,	2½d. blue	12	6	7	6

The deep blue shade is generally accompanied by a blueing of the paper.

2

3

4. Springbok's Head.

(Typo. De La Rue & Co.)

1913 (1 Sept.)–**1921**. *Inscribed bilingually. W* **4**. *P* 14.

3	**2**	½d. green	0	8	0	3
		a. Perf. 14 × Imperf. ..	7	6	2	0
		b. Stamp doubly printed ..	£90			
4	**2**	½d. blue-green	3	0	0	8
5	,,	½d. yellow-green	3	0	1	0
6	,,	1d. rose-red (*shades*) ..	1	6	0	3
		a. Perf. 14 × Imperf. (13.2.14)	8	6	5	0
7	,,	1d. carmine-red	2	6	0	6
8	,,	1d. scarlet (*shades*) ..	1	6	0	6
		a. Perf. 14 × Imperf. ..	16	0	4	0
9	,,	1½d. chest. (*shades*) (23.8.20)	1	3	0	4
		a. Tête-bêche, pair	4	0	7	6
		b. Perf. 14 × Imperf. (15.11.20)	7	6	7	6
10	**3**	2d. dull purple	2	0	0	3
		a. Perf. 14 × Imperf. (7.10.21)	8	6	2	6
11	,,	2d. deep purple	6	0	0	3
12	,,	2½d. bright blue	3	6	2	0
13	,,	2½d. deep blue	6	0	6	0
14	,,	3d. blk. & orange-red ..	5	0	1	6
15	,,	3d. blk. & dull orange-red ..	7	6	1	3
16	,,	4d. orange-yell. & olive-grn.	10	0	2	0
17	,,	4d. orange-yell. & sage-grn.	10	0	1	9
18	,,	6d. black and violet ..	10	0	1	3
18*a*	,,	6d. black & brt. violet ..	12	6	1	3
19	,,	1s. orange	12	6	1	6
19*a*	,,	1s. orange-yellow	17	6	1	9
20	,,	1s. 3d. vio. (*shades*) (1.10.20)	18	6	12	6
21	,,	2s. 6d. purple and green ..	30	0	5	0
22	,,	5s. purple and blue ..	80	0	15	0
22*a*	,,	5s. reddish pur. & light blue	90	0	27	6
23	,,	10s. deep blue & olive-green	£6		22	6
24	,,	£1 green and red (July, '16)	£30		£10	
24*a*	,,	£1 pale olive-grn. and red	£35		£12	

The 6d. of this series exists with "z" of "ZUID" wholly or partly missing due to the wear of the plate. (*Wholly missing,* 30/– *un.* 20/– *us.*)

1922 (Oct.). *Colour changed. W* **4**. *P* 14.

25	**3**	3d. ultramarine (*shades*) ..	4	0	4	0

5

(Eng. A. J. Cooper. Offset-litho. Cape Times Ltd.)

1925 (25 Feb.). *Air. Inscr. bilingually. P* 12.

26	**5**	1d. carmine	10	0	12	6
27	,,	3d. ultramarine	12	6	17	6
28	,,	6d. magenta	22	6	27	6
29	,,	9d. green	45	0	50	0

6. Springbok.

7. Van Riebeeck's Ship.

HAVE YOU READ THE NOTES AT THE BEGINNING OF THIS CATALOGUE ?

These often provide answers to the enquiries we receive.

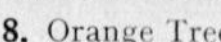

8. Orange Tree.

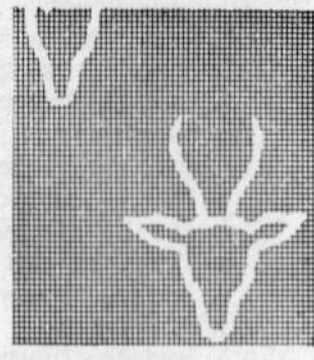

9

(Typo. first by Waterlow & Sons, later by Govt. Printer, Pretoria.)

1926. *W* **9.** *P* 14½ × 14.

No.	Type		Un. pair	Us. pair	Us. single
30	**6**	½d. black and green ..	4 0	4 0	0 3
		a. Missing "1" in "½"			
		b. Perf. 13½ × 14 ..	£6	70 0	20 0
		ba. Tête-bêche (pair) ..	£50		
31	**7**	1d. black and carmine	5 0	3 0	0 3
		a. Perf. 13½ × 14 ..	£5	70 0	20 0
		aa. Tête-bêche (pair) ..	£50		
32	**8**	6d. green and orange	25 0	12 0	1 3

No. 30a exists in Afrikaans only. Nos. 30b and 31a are from booklets of Pretoria printed stamps.

For ½d. with pale grey centre, see No. 126.

For rotogravure printing see Nos. 42, etc.

10. " Hope ".

(Recess. Bradbury, Wilkinson & Co.)

1926. *T* **10.** *Inscribed in English* (E.) *or Afrikaans* (A.). *W* **9.** *Imperf.*

		Single stamps E.	A.
33	4d. grey-bl. (*shades*)	4 0 3 6	4 0 3 6

In this value the English and Afrikaans inscriptions are on separate sheets.

This stamp is known with private perforations or roulettes.

11. Union Buildings, Pretoria.

12. Groot Schuur.

12*a*. A Native Kraal.

13. Gnus.

14. Ox-wagon inspanned

15. Ox-wagon outspanned

16. Cape Town and Table Bay.

(Recess. Bradbury, Wilkinson & Co.)

1927–28. *W* **9.** *P* 14 (*early ptgs.*) *or* 14 × 13½ (*from* 1930 *onwards*).

No.	Type		Un. pair	Us. pair	Us. single
34	**11**	2d. grey & maroon	25 0	25 0	1 3
35	**12**	3d. black and red	40 0	25 0	1 6
35*a*	**12*a***	4d. brown ..	40 0	35 0	2 6
36	**13**	1s. brn. & dp. blue	70 0	50 0	5 0
37	**14**	2s. 6d. grn. & brn.	90 0	80 0	15 0
38	**15**	5s. blk. & green ..	£6	£12	25 0
39	**16**	10s. brt. blue & brn.	£12	£6	35 0

17

(Typo. Govt. Ptg. Wks., Pretoria.)

1929 (16 Aug.). *Air. Inscribed bilingually. No wmk. P* 14×13½.

			Un. single	Us. single
40	**17**	4d. green	7 6	7 6
41	,,	1s. orange	17 6	22 6

PRINTER. All the following issues, except No. 126, are printed by rotogravure (the design having either plain lines or a dotted screen) by the Government Printer, Pretoria.

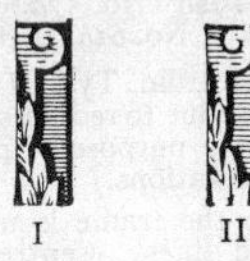

1930–45. *Types* **6** *to* **8** *and* **11** *to* **14** *redrawn,* "SUIDAFRIKA" *(in one word) on Afrikaans stamps. W* **9.** *P* 15×14 *(½d., 1d., and 6d.) or* 14.

		Un. pair	Us. pair	Us. single
42	½d. black & green ..	4 0	4 0	0 3
	a. Two English or two Afrikaans stamps *se tenant* (vert. pair)	50 0	—	—
	b. Tête bêche ..	£35	—	—
43	1d. blk. & carmine (I)	6 0	3 0	0 3
	aa. Tête bêche ..	£70	—	—
	a. Error. No wmk. ..	£7	£7	—
43*c*	1d. blk. & carmine (II)	12 0	4 0	0 3
44	2d. slate-grey & lilac (Apr. '31) ..	16 0	4 0	0 3
	aa. Tête-bêche ..	£65	—	—
44*b*	2d. blue & violet ('38)	£14	80 0	12 6
45	3d. black & red ..	45 0	40 0	3 0
45*a*	3d. blue (Oct. '33) ..	18 0	8 0	1 0
46	4d. brown	35 0	18 0	3 0
46*a*	4d. brn. (*shades*) ('36) (*again redrawn*) ..	12 0	8 0	0 6
47	6d. green & orange	50 0	8 0	1 0
48	1s. brown & deep blue (14.9.32) ..	£5	30 0	1 6
49	2s. 6d. green & brn. (24.12.32) ..	80 0	60 0	10 0
49*a*	2s. 6d. bl. & brn. ('45)	30 0	30 0	3 0

Variety: Frame omitted.

		Un. single
43*b*	1d. black (and carmine)	£25
44*a*	2d. slate-grey (and lilac)	£35

For similar designs with "SUID-AFRIKA" hyphenated, see Nos. 54 etc. and Nos. 114 etc.

The two types of the 1d. differ in the spacing of the horizontal lines in the side panels:—Type I close; Type II wide. The Afrikaans has the spacing of the words POSSEEL-INKOMSTE close in Type I and more widely spaced in Type II.

The Rotogravure printings may be distinguished from the preceding Typographed and Recess-printed issues by the following tests:—

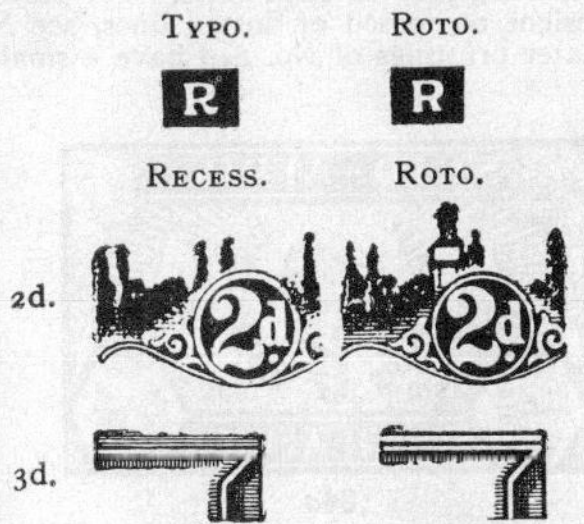

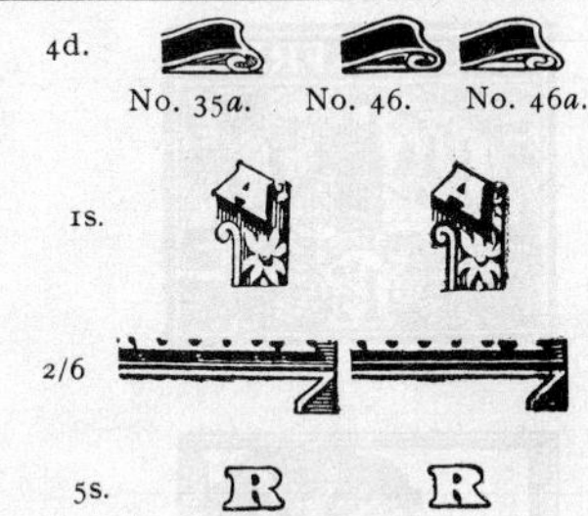

ROTOGRAVURE:

½d., 1d. & 6d. Leg of "R" in "AFR" ends squarely on the bottom line.

2d. The newly built War Memorial appears to the left of the value.

3d. Two fine lines have been removed from the top part of the frame.

4d. No. 46. The scroll is in solid colour. No. 46*a*. The scroll is white with a crooked line running through it. (No. 35*a*. The scroll is shaded by diagonal lines.)

1s. The shading of the last "A" partly covers the flower beneath.

2s. 6d. The top line of the centre frame is thick and leaves only one white line between it and the name.

5s. The leg of the "R" is straight.

Rotogravure impressions are generally coarser.

17*a*. Church of the Vow.

18. "The Great Trek".

19. A Voortrekker.

20. Voortrekker woman.

1933–36. *Voortrekker Memorial Fund. W* **9.** *P* 14.

			Un. pair	Us. pair	Us. single
50	**17*a***	½d.+½d. black and green (15.1.36) ..	3 0	5 0	1 0
51	**18**	1d.+½d. grey-black and pink ..	4 0	6 0	1 0
52	**19**	2d.+1d. grey-green and purple ..	12 6	12 6	3 0
53	**20**	3d.+1½d. grey-green and blue ..	19 0	20 0	6 0

22. Gold Mine.

22a. Groot Schuur.

I II III

23. Groot Constantia.

1933–48. " SUID-AFRIKA " (*hyphenated*) *on Afrikaans stamps.* ***W* 9.** *P* 15 × 14 (½d., 1d. *and* 6d.) *or* 14.

No.	Type		Un. pair	Us. pair	Us. single
54	**6**	½d. grey & green ..	8 0	6 0	0 4
		a. Coil stamp. Perf. 13½ × 14 ..	35 0	30 0	6 0
56		1d. grey & carmine (*shades*) ..	3 0	1 6	0 3
		a. Grey and bright rose-carmine ..	2 0	3 0	0 3
		b. Coil stamp. Perf. 13½ × 14	40 0	30 0	7 6
57	**22**	1½d. grn. & brt. gold	12 6	15 0	0 4
57*a*	,,	1½d. blue-green and dull gold ..	15 0	6 0	0 6
58	**11**	2d. blue and violet	80 0	40 0	7 0
58*a*	,,	2d. grey & dull pur.	14 0	10 0	3 0
59	**22*a***	3d. ultramarine ..	8 0	1 6	0 3
61	**8**	6d. green and vermilion (I) ..	55 0	30 0	3 0
61*a*	,,	6d. green and vermilion (II) ..	17 6	15 0	0 6
61*b*	,,	6d. green and red-orange (III) ..	20 0	15 0	2 0
62	**13**	1s. brn. & chlky. bl.	20 0	8 0	0 8
64	**15**	5s. black & green	60 0	40 0	8 0
		a. Black & blue-green	25 0	20 0	3 0
64*b*	**23**	10s. blue & sepia ..	80 0	30 0	5 0
		ba. Blue and blackish brown	55 0	20 0	5 0

The ½d. and 1d. coil stamps may be found in blocks emanating from the residue of the large rolls which were cut into sheets and distributed to Post Offices.

Varieties: (*a*) *Shading completely missing from mine dump* (*in pair with normal*).

57*aa* **22** 1½d. green and brt. gold .. £15

(*b*) *Frame omitted.*

			Un. Single
56*c*	**7**	1d. grey (and carm.)	£12
62*a*	**13**	1s. brown (& chalky-blue)	

Dates of issue:—3.7.33, No. 64. 19.4.34, No. 56. 25.9.35 No. 54. 12.11.36, No. 57. 1937, No. 61. 1938, Nos. 58, 61*a*. 1939, Nos. 62 and 64*b*. 1.3.40, No. 59. –1940, No. 57*a*. 1941, No. 58*a*. 1945, No. 64*ba*. 1946, No. 61*b*. 1948, No. 56*a*.

1d. Is printed from Type II. Frames of different sizes exist due to reductions made from time to time for the purpose of providing more space for the perforations.

3d. In No. 59 the frame is unscreened and composed of solid lines. Centre is diagonally screened. Scrolls above " 3d. " are clear lined, light in the middle and dark at sides.

6d. Die I. Green background lines faint. " SUID-AFRIKA " 16½ mm. long.

Die II. Green background lines heavy. " SUID-AFRIKA " 17 mm long, " S " near end of tablet. Scroll open.

Die III. Scroll closed up and design smaller (18 × 22 mm.).

Single specimens of the 1930 issue inscribed in English may be distinguished from those listed above as follows:—

½d. and 1d. Centres in varying intensities of black instead of grey.

2d. The letters of " SOUTH AFRICA " are wider and thicker.

3d. The trees are shorter and the sky is lined.
6d. The frame is pale orange.
1s. The frame is greenish blue.

For similar designs, but printed in screened rotogravure, see Nos. 114 to 122*a*.

24

1937–40. ***W* 9.** *P* 15 × 14.

No.	Type		Un. pair	Us. pair	Us. single
64*c*	**24**	½d. grey & green ..	8 0	4 0	0 6
		d. Grey & bl.-grn. ('40)	2 0	1 6	0 3

The lines in shading in T **24** are all horizontal and thicker than in T **6.** In Nos. 64*c* and 64*d* the design is composed of solid lines. For stamps with designs composed of dotted lines, see No. 114. Later printings of No. 64*d* have a smaller design.

24a

1935 (1 MAY). *Silver Jubilee. Inscr. bilingually. W* **9.** *P* 15×14.

			Un. pair	*Us. pair*	*Us. single*
65	**24a**	½d. blk. & blue-grn.	2 0	2 0	0 6
66	,,	1d. black & carm...	2 6	1 6	0 4
67	,,	3d. blue	27 6	40 0	12 6
68	,,	6d. green & orge. ..	27 6	40 0	12 6

In stamps with English at top the ½d., 3d. and 6d. have "SILWER JUBILEUM" to left of portrait, and "POSTAGE REVENUE" or "POSTAGE" (3d. and 6d.) in left value tablet. In the 1d., "SILVER JUBILEE" is to the left of portrait. In alternate stamps the positions of English and Afrikaans inscriptions are reversed.

JIPEX

1936

(24b)

1936 (2 Nov.). *Johannesburg International Philatelic Exhibition Optd. with T* **24b**.

			Un. sheet	*Us. sheet*
MS 69	**6**	½d. grey & green (No 54)	10 0	22 6
MS 70	**7**	1d. grey & carm. (No. 56)	8 6	22 6

Issued each in miniature sheet of six stamps with marginal advertisements.

25

1937 (12 MAY). *Coronation. W* **9** *sideways. P* 14.

			Un. pair	*Us. pair*	*Us. single*
71	**25**	½d. grey-black and blue-green ..	0 4	0 6	0 3
72	,,	1d. grey-blk. & car.	0 6	0 8	0 3
73	,,	1½d. orange & greenish blue ..	0 8	1 6	0 6
74	,,	3d. ultramarine ..	1 4	2 0	0 9
75	,,	1s. red-brown and turq.-blue ..	4 0	6 0	2 0

26. Voortrekker Ploughing.

27. Wagon crossing Drakensberg.

28. Signing of Dingaan-Relief Treaty.

29. Voortrekker Monument.

1938 (14 DEC.). *Voortrekker Centenary Memorial Fund. W* **9.** *P* 14 (*T* **26/7**) *or* 15×14.

			Un. pair	*Us. pair*	*Us. single*
76	**26**	½d.+½d. blue & grn.	3 0	5 0	1 0
77	**27**	1d.+1d. blue & car.	4 0	7 0	1 6
78	**28**	1½d.+1½d. choc. & blue-green ..	8 0	12 0	3 0
79	**29**	3d.+3d. bright blue	12 0	17 6	5 0

30. Wagon Wheel.

31. Voortrekker Family.

(Des. W. H. Coetzer.)

1938 (14 DEC.). *Voortrekker Commemoration. W* **9.** *P* 15×14.

80	**30**	1d. blue and carm.	5 0	10 0	1 6
81	**31**	1½d. greenish blue and brown ..	6 0	10 0	1 6

32. Old Vicarage, Paarl, now a museum.

33. Symbol of the Reformation.

34. Huguenot dwelling, Drakenstein mountain valley.

1939 (17 July). *250th Anniv. of Huguenot Landing S. Africa and Huguenot Commemoration Fund.* *W* **9.** *P* 14 (*T* **32/3**) *or* 15 × 14.

			Un. pair	*Us. pair*	*Us. single*
82	**32**	½d. + ½d. brn. & grn.	4 0	8 0	2 0
83	**33**	1d. + 1d. grn. & car.	6 0	12 0	2 6
84	**34**	1½d. + 1½d. blue-green and purple ..	12 0	15 0	4 0

34*a*. Gold Mine.

1941 (Aug.). *W* **9** *sideways.* *P* 14 × 15.

87	**34*a***	1½d. blue-green and yell.-buff (*shades*)	1 0	0 8	0 3
		a. Yell.-buff centre omitted ..			

35. Infantry.

36. Nurse and Ambulance.

37. Airman.

38. Sailor, Destroyer and Lifebelts.

39. Women's Auxiliary Services.

40. Artillery.

41. Electric Welding.

42. Tank Corps.

1941–42. *War Effort.* *W* **9** *sideways, perf.* 1 (*2d., 4d., 6d.*) *or upright, perf.* 15 × 14 (*others*

(*a*) *Inscr. alternately.*

			Un. pair	*Us. pair*	*Us sing*
88	**35**	½d. green (19.11.41)	0 6	0 6	0
		a. Blue-green ..	5 0	6 0	0
89	**36**	1d. carmine (3.10.41)	0 10	1 0	0
90	**37**	1½d. myrtle-green (12.1.42) ..	1 6	2 6	0
91	**39**	3d. blue (1.8.41) ..	3 0	5 0	0
92	**40**	4d. orge.brn. (20.8.41)	6 0	6 0	1
		a. Red-brown ..	20 0	15 0	1
93	**41**	6d. red-orge. (3.9.41)	8 0	12 0	2

(*b*) *Inscr. bilingually.*

			Un. single	*U sing*
94	**38**	2d. violet (15.9.41) ..	1 0	0
59	**42**	1s. brown (27.10.41) ..	5 0	4

43. Infantry.

44. Nurse.

45. Airman.

46. Sailor.

47. Women's Auxiliary Services.

48. Electric Welding.

49. Heavy gun in concrete turret.

50. Tank Corps.

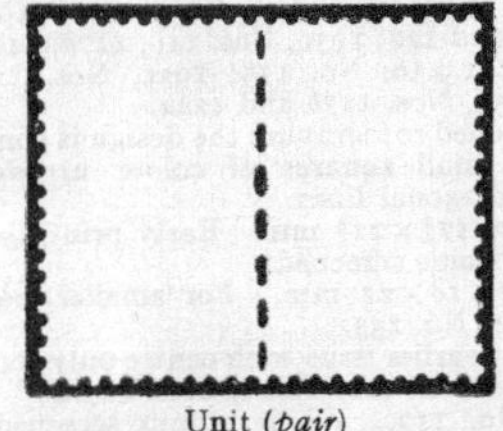

Unit (*pair*)

Unit (*triplet*)

942–44. *War Effort. Reduced sizes. In pairs perf.* 14 (P) *or strips of three, perf.* 15 × 14 (T), *subdivided by roulette* 6½. *W* **9** (*sideways on* 3*d*., 4*d. and* 1*s*.). (*a*) *Inscr. alternately.*

			Un. unit	*Us. unit*	*Us. single*
6	**43**	½d. blue-green (T)	2 0	1 6	0 3
		a. Green ('43) ..	8 0	4 0	1 0
		b. Greenish blue ('44)	4 0	3 0	0 3
		c. Roulette omitted	£16		
7	**44**	1d. carmine-red (T)	2 0	1 0	0 4
		a. Bright carmine ..	1 6	1 0	0 4
		b. Roulette omitted	£16		
8	**45**	1½d. red-brown (P)	1 6	1 6	0 2
		a. Roul. 13 instead 6½	10 0	7 6	—
		b. Roulette omitted	£15	£15	—

			Un. unit	*Us. unit*	*Us. single*
99	**46**	2d. reddish vio. (P)	6 0	4 0	1 0
		a. Violet	2 0	3 0	0 8
		b. Roulette omitted	£22		
100	**47**	3d. blue (T) ..	6 0	4 0	0 6
101	**48**	6d. red-orange (P)	4 0	4 0	0 9

(*b*) *Inscr. bilingually.*

102	**49**	4d. slate-grn. (T)	4 0	4 0	0 9
103	**50**	1s. brown (P) ..	6 0	4 6	1 6

Dates of issue:—Aug. '42, 1½d.; Oct. '42, ½d., 3d., 4d. and 6d.; Nov. '42, 1s.; 5.1.43, 1d. (No. 97); Feb. '43, 2d.; '43? 1d. (No. 97*a*).

51. Signaller.

1943 (2 Jan.). *W* **9.** *P* 15 × 14.

			Un. pair	*Us. pair*	*Us. single*
104	**51**	1s. 3d. olive-brown	5 0	8 0	1 6
		a. Blackish brown ..	4 0	8 0	0 8

52

53

1943. *Coil stamps. Redrawn. In single colours with plain background.* *W* **9.** *P* 15 × 14.

105	**52**	½d. blue-grn. (Mar.)	3 6	3 6	0 4
106	**53**	1d. carmine ..	1 6	2 6	0 4

54. Union Buildings, Pretoria.

1945–46. *Redrawn.* *W* **9.** *P* 14.

107	**54**	2d. slate & violet ..	5 0	4 0	1 3
		a. Slate and bright violet (shades) ..	2 0	1 6	1 0

In Nos. 107 and 107*a* the Union Buildings are shown at a different angle from Nos. 58 and 58*a*. Only the centre is screened i.e., composed of very small square dots of colour arranged in straight diagonal lines. For whole design screened and colours changed, see No. 116. No. 107*a* also shows "2" of "2d." clear of white circle at top.

55. Symbolical of Victory.

56. " Peace ".

57. Hope.

1945 (3 Dec.). *Victory.* *W* **9.** *P* 14.

			Un. pair	*Us. pair*	*Us. single*
108	**55**	1d. brown & carm.	0 6	0 9	0 4
109	**56**	2d. slate-blue & vio.	0 10	1 3	0 6
110	**57**	3d. deep blue & blue	1 4	2 0	0 9

58. King George VI.

59. King George VI and Queen Elizabeth.

60. Queen Elizabeth II as Princess, and Princess Margaret.

1947 (17 Feb.). *Royal Visit.* *W* **9.** *P* 15 × 14.

			Un. pair	*Us. pair*	*Us. single*
111	**58**	1d. black & carmine	0 4	0 6	0 3
112	**59**	2d. violet ..	0 8	1 0	0 4
113	**60**	3d. blue	1 0	1 6	0 6

I. SOUTH AFRICA

II. SOUTH AFRICA

1947–54. "SUID-AFRIKA" *hyphenated on Afrikaans stamps. Printed from new cylinders with design in screened rotogravure.* *W* **9.** *P* 15 × 14 (½d., 1d. *and* 6d.), 14 (*others*).

114	**24**	½d. grey and green	1 0	0 8	0 4
115	**7**	1d. grey & carmine	2 0	2 0	0 3
116	**54**	2d. slate-bl. & pur.	3 0	4 0	0 4
117	**22a**	3d. dull blue ..	3 0	4 0	0 4
117a	,,	3d. blue	3 0	4 0	0 4
		b. Deep blue ..	£6	80 0	10 0
118	**12a**	4d. brown ..	4 0	3 0	0 4
119	**8**	6d. grn. & red-orge. (III) ..	3 0	2 0	0 6
		a. Green & brown-orange (III)	3 0	2 0	0 6
120	**13**	1s. brn. & chalky bl.	4 0	2 6	0 8
		a. Blackish brown & deep ultramarine ..	8 0	6 0	0 8
121	**14**	2s. 6d. grn. & brn.	10 0	6 0	1 6
122	**15**	5s. black and pale blue-green (I)	25 0	18 0	3 0
122a	,,	5s. black & deep yellow-green (II)	28 0	15 0	3 0

Dates of issue:—1947, No. 114; 1949, Nos. 117, 121 and 122; 1950, Nos. 116, 117*a*, 119, 119*a* and 120; 1.9.50, No. 115; 1952, Nos. 118 and 120*a*; 1954, Nos. 117*b* and 122*a*.

In screened rotogravure the design is composed of very small squares of colour arranged in straight diagonal lines.

½d. Size 17¾ × 21¾ mm. Early printings have only the frame screened.

1d. Size 18 × 22 mm. For smaller, redrawn design, see No. 135.

2d. For earlier issue with centre only screened, and in different colours, see Nos. 107/*a*.

3d. No. 117. Whole stamp screened with irregular grain. Scrolls above " 3d. " solid and toneless. Printed from two cylinders.

No. 117*a*/*b*. Whole stamp diagonally screened. Printed from one cylinder. Clouds more pronounced.

4d. Two groups of white leaves below name tablet and a clear white line down left and right sides of stamp.

61. Gold Mine.

1948. *W* **9.** *In pair, perf.* 14, *subdivided by roulette* 6½.

124	**61**	1½d. blue-green & yellow-buff ..	1 6	1 0	0

62. King George VI and Queen Elizabeth.

1948 (26 APR.). *Silver Wedding. W* **9.** *P* 14.

			Un. pair	Us. pair	Us. single
125	**62**	3d. blue and silver	1 0	1 6	0 6

(Typo. Government Printer, Pretoria.)

1948. *W* **9.** *P* 14½ × 14.

126	**6**	½d. pale grey and blue-green ..	2 6	4 0	0 8

This was an economy printing made from the old plates of the 1926 issue for the purpose of using up a stock of cut paper. For the original printing in black and green, see No. 30.

63. *Wanderer* entering Durban.

1949 (2 MAY). *Centenary of Arrival of British Settlers in Natal. W* **9.** *P* 15 × 14.

127	**63**	1½d. claret	1 0	1 6	0 3

64. Hermes.

1949 (1 OCT.). *75th Anniv. of Universal Postal Union. As T* **64** *inscr.* "UNIVERSAL POSTAL UNION" *and* "WERELDPOSUNIE" *alternately. W* **9** (*sideways*). *P* 14 × 15.

128	**64**	½d. blue-green ..	0 6	0 6	0 3
129	,,	1½d. brown-red ..	1 6	0 9	0 4
130	,,	3d. bright blue ..	2 0	2 0	0 6

INSCRIPTIONS. The following stamps are all inscribed bilingually, *except where priced in pairs.*

65. Wagons Approaching Bingham's Berg.

66. Voortrekker Monument, Pretoria.

67. Bible, Candle and Voortrekkers.

(Des. W. H. Coetzer.)

1949 (1 DEC.). *Inauguration of Voortrekker Monument, Pretoria. W* **9.** *P* 15 × 14.

			Un. single	Us. single
131	**65**	1d. magenta	0 4	0 4
132	**66**	1½d. blue-green	0 6	0 6
133	**67**	3d. blue	0 10	0 8

68. Union Buildings, Pretoria.

1950 (APR.). *W* **9** (*sideways*). *P* 14 × 15.

			Un. pair	Us. pair	Us. single
134	**68**	2d. blue and violet	1 0	1 0	0 3

1951 (22 FEB.). *As No.* 115, *but redrawn with the horizon clearly defined. Size reduced to* 17¾ × 21¼ *mm.*

135	**7**	1d. grey and carmine	1 6	0 6	0 3

69. Seal and Monogram.

70. Maria de la Quellerie. **72.** Jan van Riebeeck.

71. Arrival of Van Riebeeck's Ships.

73. Landing at the Cape.

1952 (14 MAR.). *Tercentenary of Landing of Van Riebeeck. W* **9** *(sideways on* 1*d. and* 4½*d.). P* 14 × 15 (1*d. and* 4½*d.*) *or* 15 × 14 (*others*).

			Un. single		*Used single*	
136	**69**	½d. brown-purple & ol.-grey	0	3	0	6
137	**70**	1d. deep blue-green ..	0	4	0	4
138	**71**	2d. deep violet	0	6	0	4
139	**72**	4½d. blue	1	0	1	6
140	**73**	1s. brown	3	0	2	0

SATISE (74) **SADIPU** (75)

1952 (26 MAR.). *South African Tercentenary International Stamp Exhibition. No.* 137 *optd. with T* **74** *and No.* 138 *with T* **75.**

141	**70**	1d. deep blue-green ..	1	0	1	6
142	**71**	2d. deep violet	1	3	1	9

76. Queen Elizabeth II.

1953 (2 JUNE). *Coronation. W* **9** *(sideways). P* 14 × 15.

143	**76**	2d. deep violet-blue ..	0	8	0	6
		a. Ultramarine	0	6	0	4

77.

78. " Cape Triangular ".

1953 (1 SEPT.). *Centenary of First Cape of Good Hope Stamp. W* **9.** *P* 15 × 14.

144	**77**	1d. sepia and vermilion ..	0	4	0	3
145	**78**	4d. deep blue & light blue	1	3	1	3

79. Merino Ram.

80. Springbok.

81. Aloes.

1953. (1 OCT.). *W* **9.** *P* 14.

146	**79**	4½d. slate-purple & yellow	1	6	2	0
147	**80**	1s. 3d. chocolate ..	2	0	0	9
148	**81**	1s. 6d. vermilion & deep blue-green ..	3	6	1	0

82. Arms of Orange Free State and Scroll.

1954 (23 FEB.). *Centenary of Orange Free State. W* **9.** *P* 14.

149	**82**	2d. sepia & pale vermilion	0	10	0	
150	,,	4½d. purple and slate ..	1	6	1	

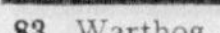

83. Warthog.

84. Gnu.

85. Leopard.

86. Zebra.

87. Rhinoceros.

88. Elephant.

89. Hippopotamus.

90. Lion.

91. Kudu.

92. Springbok.

93. Gemsbok.

94. Nyala.

95. Giraffe.

96. Sable Antelope.

1954 (14 Oct.). *W* **9** (*sideways on large vert. designs*). *P* 15×14 (*½d. to 2d.*), 14 (*others*).

No.	Type			s.	d.	s.	d.
151	**83**	½d.	deep blue-green	0	3	0	6
152	**84**	1d.	brown-lake	0	4	0	3
153	**85**	1½d.	sepia	0	6	1	0
154	**86**	2d.	plum	0	10	0	3
155	**87**	3d.	chocolate & turq.-blue	1	0	0	3
156	**88**	4d.	indigo and emerald ..	1	0	0	8
157	**89**	4½d.	blue-black & grey-blue	2	6	2	6
158	**90**	6d.	sepia and orange ..	1	3	0	4
159	**91**	1s.	deep brown and pale chocolate	2	6	0	8
160	**92**	1s. 3d.	brown & bluish green	2	6	0	9
161	**93**	1s. 6d.	brown and rose ..	3	0	3	6
162	**94**	2s. 6d.	brown-black and apple-green	5	0	2	6
163	**95**	5s.	black-brown and yellow-orange ..	10	0	4	0
164	**96**	10s.	black and cobalt ..	20	0	7	6

See also Nos. 170/7.

97. President Kruger. **98.** President Pretorius.

1955 (21 Oct.). *Centenary of Pretoria.* *W* **9** (*sideways*). *P* 14.

165	**97**	3d.	slate-green	0	6	0	6
166	**98**	6d.	maroon	1	6	1	0

99. A. Pretorius, Church of the Vow and Flag.

1955 (1 Dec.). *Voortrekker Covenant Celebrations, Pietermaritzburg.* *W* **9.** *P* 14.

			Un. pair	*Us. pair*	*Us. single*
167	**99**	2d. blue & magenta	1 0	1 6	0 3

100. Settlers' Block-wagon and House.

1958 (1 July). *Centenary of Arrival of German Settlers in South Africa.* *W* **9.** *P* 14.

			Un. single	*Used single*
168	**100**	2d. choc. and pale purple	0 8	0 3

101. Arms of the Academy.

1959 (1 MAY). *50th Anniv. of the South African Academy of Science and Art, Pretoria.* *W* **9.** *P* 14½ × 14.

169	**101**	3d. dp. blue & turq.-blue	1	0	0	8
		a. All deep blue ptg. omitted	£300			

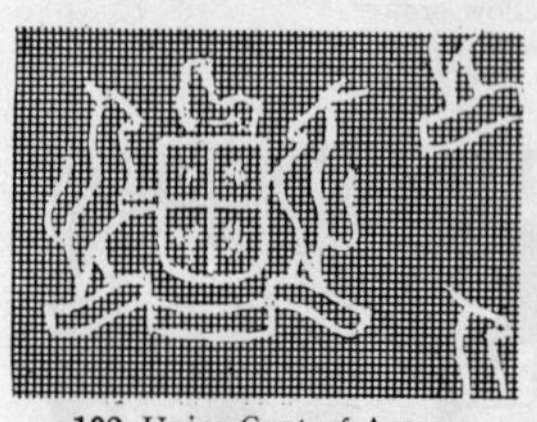

102. Union Coat-of-Arms.

1 S 1 S
I. II.

1959–61. *As Nos.* 151 *etc., but W* **102.**

170	**83**	½d. dp. greenish blue (1.61)	1	6	1	0
171	**84**	1d. brown-lake (I) (10.59)	1	0	0	4
		a. Redrawn. Type II (11.60)..	2	6	2	0
172	**87**	3d. chocolate & turquoise-blue (9.59)	2	0	0	8
173	**88**	4d. indigo & emer. (1.60)..	6	0	2	6
174	**90**	6d. sepia & orange (2.60)..	2	0	1	0
175	**91**	1s. deep brown and pale chocolate (11.59) ..	3	0	1	6
176	**94**	2s. 6d. brown-black and apple-green (12.59) ..	6	0	3	6
177	**95**	5s. black-brown & yellow-orange (10.60).. ..	20	0	15	0

Nos. 171/a. In Type II " 1d. Posgeld Postage " is more to the left in relation to " South Africa," with " 1 " almost central over " S " instead of to right as in Type I.

103. Globe and Antarctic Scene.

1959 (16 Nov.). *South African National Antarctic Expedition.* *W* **102.** *P* 14 × 15.

178	**103**	3d. blue-green & orange	0	9	0	6

104. Union Flag.

105. Union Arms

106. " Wheel of Progress".

107. Union Festival Emblem.

1960 (2 MAY). *50th Anniv. of Union of South Africa.* *W* **102.** *P* 14 × 15 (*4d., 6d.*) *or* 15 × 14 (*others*).

179	**104**	4d. orange-red and blue	0	9	0	6
180	**105**	6d. red, brown & lt. green	1	3	0	9
181	**106**	1s. deep blue & lt. yellow	2	0	1	[illegible]
182	**107**	1s. 6d. black & lt. blue ..	3	0	2	6

See also Nos. 190, 192/3.

108. Locomotives of 1860 and 1960.

1960 (2 MAY). *Centenary of South African Railways.* *W* **102.** *P* 15 × 14.

183	**108**	1s. 3d. deep blue.. ..	3	0	2	

109. Prime Ministers Botha, Smuts, Hertzog, Malan, Strijdom and Verwoerd.

1960 (31 MAY). *Union Day.* *W* **102.** *P* 15 × 14.

184	**109**	3d. brown	0	8	0	4

Currency changed. 100 cents = 1 rand.

1961 (14 FEB.). *Values in cents and rand.* *W* **102.** *P* 15 × 14 (½ *c. to* 2½ *c.*, 10 *c.*), 14 × 15 (3½ *c.*, 7½ *c.*) *or* 14 (*others*).

185	**83**	½ c. deep bluish green ..	0	6	0	4
186	**84**	1 c. brown-lake ..	0	6	0	4
187	**85**	1½ c. sepia	0	6	0	4
188	**86**	2 c. plum	0	8	0	4
189	**109**	2½ c. brown	0	9	0	4
190	**104**	3½ c. orge.-red and blue	1	3	0	9
191	**90**	5 c. sepia and orange ..	1	3	0	9
192	**105**	7½ c. red, brn., & lt. green	2	0	1	0
193	**106**	10 c. dp. blue & lt. yellow	2	6	0	9
194	**92**	12½ c. brn. & bluish green	3	0	0	9
195	**93**	20 c. brown and rose ..	5	0	3	0
196	**95**	50 c. blk.-brn. & orge.-yell.	12	6	7	0
197	**96**	1 r. black and cobalt ..	25	0	12	6

REPUBLIC.

110. Natal Kingfisher.

111. Kafferboom Flower.

12. Afrikander Bull.

113. Pouring Gold.

4. Groot Constantia.

115. Crimson-breasted Shrike.

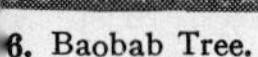

6. Baobab Tree.

117. Maize.

118. Capetown Castle Entrance.

119. Protea.

120. Secretary Bird.

121. Capetown Harbour.

122. Strelitzia.

Two types of 1 c.

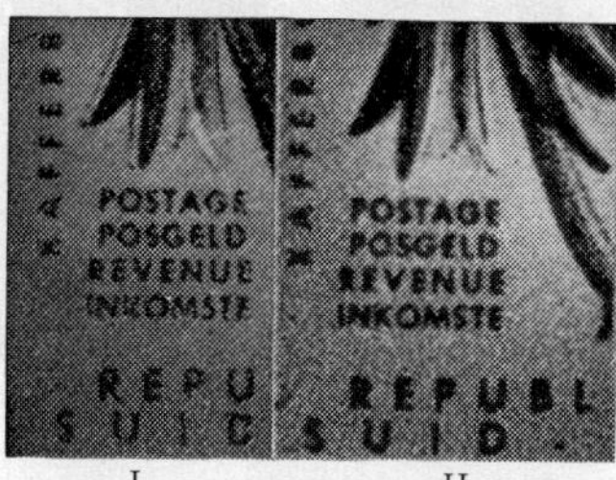

I II

Type I. Lowest point of flower between "os" of "POSTAGE".

Type II. Flower has moved fractionally to the right so that lowest point is over "s" of "POSTAGE".

Two types of 2½ c.

In Type I the lines of the building are quite faint. In Type II all lines of the building have been strengthened by re-engraving.

(Des. Mrs. T. Campbell (½ c., 3 c., 1 r.); Miss N. Desmond (1 c.); De La Rue (2½ c., 5 c., 12½ c.); H. L. Prager (50 c.); Govt. Ptg. Dept. artist (others).)

1961 (31 MAY)–**63.** *W* **102.** *P* 14 × 15 (½ *c.*, 1½ *c.*), 15 × 14 (1 *c.*) *or* 14 (*others*).

198	**110**	½ c. bright blue, carmine and brown ..	0	3	0	3
		a. Perf. 14 × 13½ (3.63) ..	0	6	0	8

199	**111**	1 c. red & olive-grey (I)	0	6	0	6
		a. Type II (1.62)	0	5	0	3
200	**112**	1½ c. red-brn. & lt. pur.	0	4	0	2
201	**113**	2 c. ultram. & yellow..	0	6	0	3
202	**114**	2½ c. violet and green (I)	1	0	0	6
		a. Type II. *Dp. violet and green* (9.61)	1	9	1	0
203	**115**	3 c. red and deep blue	0	8	0	3
204	**116**	5 c. yell. & grnish. blue	1	0	0	4
205	**117**	7½ c. yell.-brn. & lt. grn.	1	3	0	6
206	**118**	10 c. sepia and green ..	1	9	0	8
207	**119**	12½ c. red, yellow & black-green	2	3	1	3
208	**120**	20 c. turq.-blue, carmine and brown-orange	4	0	1	9
209	**121**	50 c. black & brt. blue	7	6	3	6
210	**122**	1 r. orange, olive-green and light blue ..	17	6	8	0

No. 198 was issued in coils on 18.5.63 with the spurs of the branch strengthened.

1961–63. *As Nos.* 199 *and* 201/9 *but without wmk.*

211	**111**	1 c. red & olive-grey (I)	0	6	0	6
		a. Type II (9.62)	0	4	0	3
212	**113**	2 c. ultram. & yell. (8.63)	0	6	0	5
213	**114**	2½ c. violet and green (II) (*shades*)	1	0	0	6
214	**115**	3 c. red and deep blue..	0	8	0	3
215	**116**	5 c. yell. & grnish. blue	0	10	0	4
216	**117**	7½ c. yellow-brown and light green (3.62) ..	1	1	0	6
217	**118**	10 c. sepia & grn. (*shades*)	1	9	0	5
218	**120**	20 c. turq.-blue, carmine & brn.-orge. (5.63) ..	3	6	1	9
219	**121**	50 c. black and bright blue (8.62)	6	9	3	0

See also Nos. 227, etc.

123. Blériot Monoplane and Boeing 707 Airliner over Table Mountain.

124. Folk-dancers.

1961 (1 Dec.). *50th Anniv. of First South African Aerial Post.* *W* **102.** *P* 14 × 14½.

220	**123**	3 c. blue and red ..	0	7	0	6

(Des. K. Esterhuysen.)

1962 (1 Mar.). *50th Anniv. of Volkspele (Folk-dancing) in South Africa.* *W* **102.** *P* 14 × 14½.

221	**124**	2½ c. orange-red & brown	0	7	0	6

125. The *Chapman.*

1962 (20 Aug.). *Unveiling of Precinct Stone, British Settlers Monument, Grahamstown.* *W* **102.** *P* 14½ × 14.

222	**125**	2½ c. turq.-grn. & purple	0	8	0	6
223	,,	12½ c. blue and dp. choc.	2	3	1	9

126. Red Disa (orchid), Castle Rock and Gardens.

(Des. M. F. Stern.)

1963 (14 Mar.). *50th Anniv. of Kirstenbosch Botanic Gardens, Cape Town.* *P* 13½ × 14.

224	**126**	2½ c. multicoloured ..	0	10	0	8

127.

128. Centenary Emblem and Nurse.

129. Centenary Emblem and Globe.

1963 (30 Aug.). *Centenary of Red Cro* *Wmk.* **127** (*sideways on* 2½ *c.*). *P* 14 (2½ *c.*) 15 × 14 (12½ *c.*).

225	**128**	2½ c. red, black, & reddish purple ..	0	7	0
226	**129**	12½ c. red and indigo ..	2	3	2
		a. Red Cross omitted ..			

130. Natal Kingfisher. **131.** Crimson-breasted Shrike.

132. Protea. **132a.** Strelitzia.

Redrawn types.

½ c. "½C" larger and "REPUBLIEK VAN REPUBLIC OF" smaller.

3 c. and 12½ c. Inscriptions and figures of value larger.

1 r. "REPUBLIEK VAN REPUBLIC OF" smaller and bolder and the rest of inscription bolder.

1963–65. *As 1961–63 but W* **127** *(sideways on ½ c., 2½ c., 10 c., 12½ c., 20 c.) and ½ c., 3 c., 12½ c. and 1 r. redrawn as T* **130**/**2a**.

No.	Type	Description	Unused	Used
227	**130**	½ c. bright blue, carmine and brown (21.5.64)	0 2	0 2
228	**111**	1 c. red and olive-grey (II) (9.63)	0 3	0 4
230	**113**	2 c. ultramarine and yellow (11.64) ..	0 5	0 4
231	**114**	2½ c. violet and green (II) (11.63) ..	0 6	0 6
232	**131**	3 c. red and deep blue (11.64)	0 6	0 3
235	**118**	10 c. sepia-brown and green ('64) ..	1 5	1 9
236	**132**	12½ c. red, yellow & black-green (3.64) ..	1 9	1 0
237	**120**	20 c. turq.-blue, carmine & brown-orge. ('64)	2 9	3 0
239	**122**	1 r. orange, lt. green and light blue ('64)	16 0	18 0
239a	**132a**	1 r. orange, light green and light blue ('65)	13 3	15 0

133. Assembly Building, Umtata.

1963 (11 DEC.). *First Meeting of Transkei Legislative Assembly.* *W* **127.** *P* 14½ × 14.

No.	Type	Description	Unused	Used
240	**133**	2½ c. sepia & light green..	0 7	0 6

134. "Springbok" Badge of Rugby Board. **136.** Calvin.

135. Rugby Footballer.

1964 (8 MAY). *75th Anniv. of South African Rugby Board.* *W* **127** *(sideways on 2½ c.).* *P* 14 × 15 *(2½ c.) or* 15 × 14 *(12½ c.).*

No.	Type	Description	Unused	Used
241	**134**	2½ c. yell.-brn. & dp. grn.	0 7	0 6
242	**135**	12½ c. blk. & lt. yell.-grn.	2 0	2 0

1964 (10 JULY). *400th Anniv. of Death of Calvin (Protestant Reformer).* *W* **127** *(sideways).* *P* 14.

No.	Type	Description	Unused	Used
243	**136**	2½ c. cerise, violet & brn.	0 7	0 7

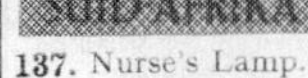

137. Nurse's Lamp. I. Screened base to lamp. II. Clear base to lamp.

138. Nurse holding Lamp.

1964 (12 OCT.). *50th Anniv. of South African Nursing Association.* *W* **127** *(sideways on 2½ c.).* *P* 14 × 14½ *(2½ c.) or* 14½ × 14 *(12½ c.).*

No.	Type	Description	Unused	Used
244	**137**	2½ c. ultramarine & dull gold (Type I) ..	0 7	0 6

245 137 2½ c. bright blue & yellow-gold (Type II) 3 6 0 6
a. *Ultram. & dull gold* .. 0 7 0 6
246 **138** 12½ c. bright blue & gold 2 0 2 0
a. Gold omitted ..

139. I.T.U. Emblem and Satellites.

140. I.T.U. Emblem and Symbols.

1965 (17 MAY). *I.T.U. Centenary.* *W* **127.** *P* 14½ × 14.
247 **139** 2½ c. orange and blue .. 0 7 0 6
248 **140** 12½ c. brown-purple & grn. 2 0 2 0

141. Pulpit in Groote Kerk, Cape Town.

142. Church Emblem.

1965 (21 OCT.). *Tercentenary of Nederduites Gereformeerde Kerk (Dutch Reformed Church) in South Africa.* *W* **127** *(sideways on 2½ c.).* *P* 14 × 14½ *(2½ c.) or* 14½ × 14 *(12½ c.).*
249 **141** 2½ c. brown & lt. yellow 0 6 0 8
250 **142** 12½ c. blk., lt. orge. & bl. 1 9 2 0

POSTAGE DUE STAMPS.

D 1

UNION OF SOUTH AFRICA
(A.)

UNION OF SOUTH AFRICA
(B.)

(Typo. De La Rue & Co.)

1914–22. *Type* D **1.** *Inscribed bilingually. Lettering as* A. *W* **4.** *P* 14.

		Un. single		*Used single*	
D1	½d. black & green (19.3.15) ..	1	9	2	6
D2	1d. blk. & scarlet (19.3.15) ..	1	3	1	0
D3	2d. blk. & reddish vio. (12.12.14)	3	0	0	10
D3*a*	2d. blk. & brt. violet (1922) ..	3	0	1	0
D4	3d. blk. & bright blue (2.2.15)	1	6	1	6
D5	5d. black & sepia (19.3.15) ..	3	0	4	0
D6	6d. black & slate (19.3.15) ..	7	6	8	6
D7	1s. red and black (19.3.15) ..	65	0	85	0

There are interesting minor varieties in some of the above values, e.g. ½d. to 3d., thick downstroke to "d"; 1d., short serif to "1"; raised "d"; 2d., forward point of "2" blunted; 3d., raised "d"; very thick "d".

(Litho. Govt. Printer, Pretoria.)

1922. *Type* D **1.** *Lettering as* A. *No wmk. Rouletted.*

D 8	½d. black & brt. grn. (6.6.22)	1	3	2	0
D 9	1d. black & rose-red (3.10.22)	2	0	2	6
D10	1½d. black & yell.-brn. (3.6.22)	3	6	5	0

(Litho. Govt. Printer, Pretoria.)

1922–26. *Type* D **1** *redrawn. Lettering as* B. *P* 14.

D11	½d. black and green (1.11.22)	0	6	0	10
D12	1d. black and rose (16.5.23)	0	10	0	9
D13	1½d. black & yell.-brn. (12.1.24)	1	9	2	[illegible]
D14	2d. black & pale vio. (16.5.23)	1	6	1	[illegible]
	a. Imperf. (pair)	£18			
D14*b*	2d. black and deep violet ..	4	0	1	[illegible]
D15	3d. black and blue (3.7.26)	3	0	4	[illegible]
D16	6d. black & slate (Sept.'23)	3	6	2	[illegible]

The locally printed stamps, perf. 14, differ both in border design and in figures of value from the rouletted stamps. All values except the 3d. and 6d. are known with closed "G" in "POSTAGE" usually referred to as the "POSTADE" variety. This was corrected in later printings.

D 2

D 3

(Typographed at Pretoria.)

1927–28. *As Type* D **2.** *Inscribed bilingually. No wmk.* *P* 13½ × 14.

D17	½d. black and green ..	1	0	2	
D18	1d. black and carmine ..	0	9	0	
D19	2d. black and mauve ..	1	6	1	
	a. Black and purple	17	6	7	
D20	3d. black and blue ..	2	0	2	
D21	6d. black and slate ..	3	6	2	

1932–42. *Type* D **2** *redrawn.* *W* **9.** *P* 15 × 14.
(a) Frame roto., value typo.

D22	½d. blk. & blue-grn. (–.–.34)	0	4	0	
D23	2d. blk. & dp. pur. (10.4.33)	1	0	0	

(b) Whole stamp roto.

		Un.	Us.
D25	1d. black & carm. (–.3.34) ..	0 6	0 6
D26	2d. blk. & dp. pur. ('40) ..	0 10	0 6
	a. Thick (double) "2d." ..	22 6	22 6
D27	3d. black & Prussian blue (3.8.32)	2 6	2 0
D28	3d. deep blue & blue ('35) ..	1 0	1 0
D28*a*	3d. indigo & milky blue ('42)	1 0	1 0
D29	6d. grn. & brn.-ochre (7.6.33)	3 0	2 6
D30	6d. green & bright orge. ('38)	3 0	2 6

In No. D26 the value, when magnified, has the meshed appearance of a photogravure screen, whereas in No. D23 the black of the value is solid.

1943–47. *Inscr. bilingually. Roto. W* **9.** *In units of three, perf.* 15 × 14 *subdivided by roulette* 6½.

		Un. unit	Us. unit	Us. single
D31 D **3**	½d. blue-grn. ('47)	2 0	2 0	0 4
D32 ,,	1d. carmine ..	1 6	2 6	0 4
D33 ,,	2d. dull violet ..	2 6	3 0	0 6
	a. Bright violet ..	3 6	3 0	0 6
D34 ,,	3d. indigo ('45) ..	3 0	4 0	1 0

D 4

D 5

948–49. *New figure of value and capital* "D". *Whole stamp roto. W* **9.** *P* 15 × 14.

		Un. single	Us. single
35 D **4**	½d. black & blue-green ..	0 6	0 10
36 ,,	1d. black and carmine ..	1 0	0 8
37 ,,	2d. black & violet ('49) ..	1 0	1 3
	a. Thick (double) "2D." ..	20 0	17 6
38 ,,	3d. deep blue and blue ..	1 9	2 0
39 ,,	6d. green & bright orange	3 6	3 6

950–58. *As Type* D **4,** *but* "SUID-AFRIKA" *hyphenated. Whole stamp roto. W* **9.** *P* 15 × 14.

		Un.	Us.
41	1d. black and carmine ..	0 8	0 6
42	2d. black and violet (*shades*)	0 8	1 0
	a. Thick (double) "2D" ..	22 6	15 0
43	3d. deep blue and blue ..	1 0	1 0
43*a*	4d. dp. myrtle-grn. & emer.	1 0	1 6
44	6d. green & bright orange ..	1 6	1 6
45	1s. blk.-brn. & purple-brown	3 6	4 0

Dates of issue :— –.5.50, Nos. D41 and D43; 4.51, No. D42; 1952, No. D44; 1958, Nos. 43*a*, D45.

61 (14 FEB.). *Values in cents as Type* D **5.** *Whole stamp roto. W* **102.** *P* 15 × 14.

		Un.	Us.
6	1 c. black and carmine ..	0 6	0 9
7	2 c. black and violet ..	0 8	1 0
8	4 c. dp. myrtle-grn. & emer.	2 0	2 0
9	5 c. deep blue and blue ..	1 3	1 9
0	6 c. green & orange-red ..	1 6	2 6
1	10 c. sepia & brown-lake ..	2 6	3 6

REPUBLIC.

. Afrikaans at top.

D **7.** English at top.

1961 (31 MAY)–**62.** *Roto. W* **102.** *P* 15 × 14.

			Un.	Us.
D52	D **6**	1 c. black & carmine ..	0 6	0 8
D53	D **7**	2 c. black & deep reddish violet ..	0 5	0 6
D54	D **6**	4 c. deep myrtle-green and light emerald	0 9	1 0
D55	D **7**	5 c. dp. blue & grey-bl.	1 9	1 6
D55*a*	,,	5 c. black and grey-blue (6.62) ..	0 10	1 0
D56	D **6**	6 c. dp. grn. & red-orge	0 11	1 6
D57	D **7**	10 c. sepia & purple-brn.	1 5	2 0

1962 (JUNE). *As No.* D52 *but inscriptions reversed.*

			Un.	Us.
D58	D **7**	1 c. black and carmine ..	0 3	0 3

OFFICIAL STAMPS.

OFFICIAL. OFFISIEEL.

(O 1)

(Approximate measurements between lines of opt. are shown in mm. in brackets.)

1926 (1 DEC.). *Optd. vertically upwards, with stops, as Type* O **1.**

			Un. single	Us. single
	(a) On 1913 issue			
O1 **3**	2d. Nos. 10/11 (12½)		20 0	7 6

	(b) On 1926 issue	Un. pair	Us. pair	Us. single
O2 **6**	½d. No. 30 (12½) ..	8 0	10 0	2 0
O3 **7**	1d. No. 31 (12½) ..	3 0	5 0	1 3
O4 **8**	6d. No. 32 (12½) ..	£5	17 6	4 0

This overprint is found on the ½d., 1d. and 6d. values of both the London and Pretoria printings. The London printings of the ½d. and 1d. stamps are considerably scarcer than the Pretoria, but the 6d. Pretoria printing is scarcer still.

1928–29. *Optd. vertically upwards, as Type* O **1,** *but without stops.*

		Un. pair	Us. pair	Us. single
O5 **11**	2d. No. 34 (17½) ..	2 0	4 0	1 3
O6 ,,	2d. No. 34 (19) ('29)	1 6	3 0	0 8
O7 **8**	6d. No. 32 (11½) ..	15 0	20 0	6 6

OFFISIEEL OFFICIAL

(O 2)

OFFICIAL OFFISIEEL

(O 3)

Overprinted vertically downwards as Type O **2.**

1929. *Typographed stamps optd. with Type* O **2.**

		Un. pair	Us. pair	Us. single
O 8 **6**	½d. No. 30 (13½) ..	0 8	1 0	0 4
	a. Stop after "OFFISIEEL" on English stamp ..	20 0	12 6	8 0
	b. Stop after "OFFISIEEL" on Afrikaans stamp ..	22 6	15 0	12 0
O 9 **7**	1d. No. 31 (13½) ..	2 0	1 6	0 6
O10 **8**	6d. No. 32 (13½) ..	6 6	6 0	2 0
	a. Stop after "OFFISIEEL" on English stamp ..	37 6	37 6	32 6
	b. Stop after "OFFISIEEL" on Afrikaans stamp	40 0	40 0	37 6

1930–47. *Rotogravure stamps* ("SUIDAFRIKA" *in one word*) *optd. with Type* O **2**.

No.	Type	Description	Un. pair	Us. pair	Us. single
O11	**6**	½d. No. 42 (9½—12)	1 6	1 6	0 3
		a. Stop after "OFFISIEEL" on English stamp ..	12 6	12 6	10 0
		b. Stop after "OFFISIEEL" on Afrikaans stamp	10 0	10 0	8 0
O12	,,	½d. No. 42 (12½) ..	2 0	1 6	0 4
O13	**7**	1d. No. 43 (12½ & 13½)	1 6	1 6	0 4
		a. Stop after "OFFISIEEL" on English stamp ..	15 0	15 0	12 6
		b. Stop after "OFFISIEEL" on Afrikaans stamp	22 6	22 6	17 6
O14	,,	1d. No. 43*c* (12½) ..	2 6	3 0	0 10
O15	**11**	2d. No. 44 (21) ..	4 0	3 6	1 0
O15*a*	,,	2d. No. 44*b* (20½)..	22 6	12 6	3 0
O16	**8**	6d. No. 47 (12½) ..	8 0	10 6	3 0
		a. Stop after "OFFISIEEL" on English stamp ..	27 6	30 0	20 0
		b. Stop after "OFFISIEEL" on Afrikaans stamp	25 0	30 0	20 0
O17	**13**	1s. No. 48 (19) ..	20 0	25 0	8 0
O18	,,	1s. No. 48 (21) ..	10 0	17 6	3 0
O19	**14**	2s. 6d. No. 49 (18)	35 0	35 0	8 0
O20	,,	2s. 6d. No. 49 (21)	40 0	40 0	10 0
O20*a*	,,	2s. 6d. No. 49*a* (19½–20) ..	15 0	12 6	4 0
		ab. Diaeresis on second "E".. ..	£35		

Nos. O8*a*/*b*, O10*a*/*b*, O11*a*/*b*, O13*a*/*b*, O16*a*/*b* and O20*a*/*b*. The pairs include one stamp with variety and the other normal.

Dates of issue:—1930, Nos. O13, O16; 1931, Nos. O11, O15; 1932, Nos. O12, O14, O17; 1933, No. O19; 1938, No. O18; 1939, Nos. O15*a*, O20; 1946, No. O20*a*; 1947, No. O20ab.

Nos. O17 to O20 were actually issued after Nos. O21 and O22, but are placed before them, in this list for convenience of reference.

1932–33. *Recess-printed stamps optd. with Type* O **2**.

No.	Type	Description	Un. pair	Us. pair	Us. single
O21	**13**	1s. No. 36 (17½, 18 & 20½) ..	20 0	40 0	15 0
		a. Stop after "OFFICIAL" on Afrikaans stamp ..	£8	£9	£8
O22	**14**	2s. 6d. No. 37 (17½ & 18) ..	25 0	40 0	12 6
		a. Stop after "OFFICIAL" on Afrikaans stamp ..	£12	£12	£12

Nos. O21*a* and O22*a*. The pairs include one stamp with variety and the other normal.

1935–51. *Rotogravure stamps* ("SUID-AFRIKA" *hyphenated*). (*a*) *Optd. with Type* O **2** ("OFFICIAL" *at right*).

No.	Type	Description	Un. pair	Us. pair	Us. single
O23	**6**	½d. No. 54 (12½)	2 6	2 6	0 8
O24	**24**	½d. No. 64*c* (11 & 12½)	2 6	1 6	0 4
O24*a*	,,	½d. No. 64*d* (12)..	1 6	1 6	0 3
O24*b*	,,	½d. No. 114 (11)..	1 0	—	—
O25	**7**	1d. No. 56 (11½–13)	1 6	1 6	0 4
O26	**22**	1½d. No. 57 (20)..	6 0	4 0	0 10
O26*a*	,,	1½d. No. 57*a* (20)	4 0	3 0	0 10
O26*b*	**34***a*	1½d. No. 87 (14½)	1 6	1 6	0 3
		ba. Diaeresis on second "E" ..	£5	60 0	—
O26*c*	,,	1½d. No. 87 (16)..	6 0	6 0	1 0
O27	**11**	2d. No. 58 (20)..	10 0	10 0	2 0
O27*a*	**54**	2d. No. 107 (20)	2 0	2 0	0 4
		ab. Diaeresis on second "E" ..	£12		
O27*b*	**54**	2d. No. 107*a* (20)	2 6	2 6	0 3
O28	**8**	6d. No. 61 (12 & 13)	70 0	70 0	15 0
O28*a*	,,	6d No. 61*a* (11½–13)	5 0	5 0	0 8
O28*b*	,,	6d. No. 61*b* (12)	5 0	5 0	0 8
O29	**13**	1s. No. 62 (20)..	6 0	8 0	1 6
		aa. Diaeresis on second "E" ..			
O29*a*	,,	1s. No. 120 (17½–18½)	7 6	7 6	1 6
O29*b*	**15**	5s. No. 64*a* (20)	30 0	30 0	7 6
O29*c*	**23**	10s. No. 64*b* (19½)	45 0	45 0	10 0

(*b*) *Optd. with Type* O **3** ("OFFICIAL" *at left*).

No.	Type	Description	Un. pair	Us. pair	Us. single
O30	**15**	5s. No. 64*a* (18)	27 6	27 6	8 0
O31	**23**	10s. No. 64*b* (19)	40 0	40 0	10 0

Dates of issue:—1935, O25; 1937, O23, O26; 1938, O24, O27, O28; 1940, O28*a*, O29, O30, O31; 1942, O26*a*; 1946? O26*ba*; 1947, O26*b*, O27*a*, O27ab, O28*b*, O29aa; 1948, O24*a*; 1949, O24*b*, O27*b*; 1950, O26*c*, O29*a*, O29*c*; 1951, O29*b*.

The pairs of Nos. O26*ba*, O27*ab* and O29*aa* include one stamp with variety and one normal.

OFFICIAL OFFISIEEL

(O 4)

OFFISIEEL OFFICIAL

(O 5)

1944. *Optd. with Type* O **4** *reading up and down and with diæresis over the second* "E" *o*[f] "OFFISIEEL".

No.	Type	Description	Un. pair	Us. pair	Us. single
O32	**24**	½d. No. 64*d* (10) ..	1 6	1 6	0 [illegible]

1944. *Optd. with Type* O **5** *reading upwards* ("OFFICIAL" *at right*).

No.	Type	Description	Un. pair	Us. pair	Us. single
O33	**11**	2d. No. 58*a* (18½)..	2 0	2 0	[illegible]

OFFICIAL OFFISIEEL

(O 6)

OFFISIEEL OFFICIAL

(O 7)

1949–50. *Optd. with Type* O **6** *reading upwar*[ds] ("OFFICIAL" *at left*).

No.	Type	Description	Un. pair	Us. pair	Us. single
O34	**34***a*	1½d. No. 87 (16)..	2 6	2 6	2
O35	**68**	2d. No. 134 (16) ('50).. ..	£100	£25	—

1950–54. *Optd. as Type O* **7**.

No.	Type	Description	Un. pair	Us. pair	Us. single
O35*a*	**24**	½d. No. 64*d* (10)	0 6	0 6	0
O35*b*	,,	½d. No. 114 (10)	0 4	0 6	0
O36	**7**	1d. No. 56*a* (10)	1 6	1 0	0
O36*a*	,,	1d. No. 115 (10)	0 6	0 6	0
O36*b*	,,	1d. No. 135 (10)	0 8	0 6	0
O37	**34***a*	1½d. No. 87 (14½)	1 0	1 0	0
O38	**68**	2d. No. 134 (14½)	1 0	1 3	0
O39	**8**	6d. No. 119 (10)	4 0	5 0	0
O39*a*	,,	6d. No. 119*a* (10)	4 0	5 0	0
O40	**13**	1s. No. 120 (19)	5 0	5 0	0
O40*a*	,,	1s. No. 120*a* (19)	£12	80 0	-
O41	**14**	2s. 6d. No. 121 (19)	10 0	8 0	1
O41*a*	**15**	5s. No. 64*a* (19)	18 0	20 0	7
O41*b*	,,	5s. No. 122 (19)	20 0	22 6	6
O41*c*	,,	5s. No. 122*a* (19)	20 0	22 6	6
O42	**23**	10s. No. 64*ba* (19)	35 0	40 0	12

Dates of issue:—1950, Nos. O36, O38/9 a[nd] O40/2; 1951, Nos. O35*a*, O36*a*, O37, O39*a* a[nd]

O41*a*; 1952, No. O36*b*; 1953, Nos. O35*b*, O40*a* and O41*b*; 1954, No. O41*c*.

On No. O36*a* the overprint is thicker.

The use of official stamps ceased in January 1955.

SOUTH ARABIAN FEDERATION.

Comprising Aden and most of the territories of the former Western Aden Protectorate plus one from the Eastern Aden Protectorate.

Currency. 100 cents = 1 shilling.

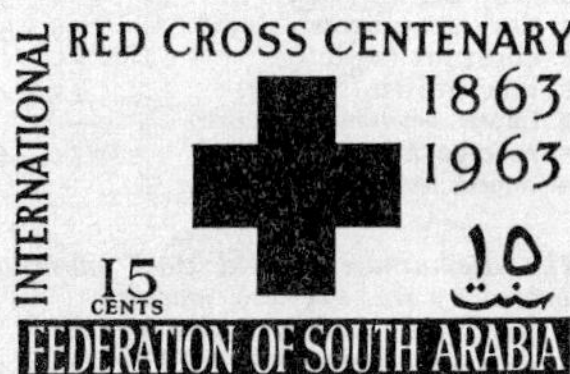

1. Red Cross Emblem.

1963 (25 Nov.). *Red Cross Centenary.* *W* w.**12.** *P* 13½.

1	**1**	15 c. red and black	0	6	0	8
2	,,	1s. 25, red and blue ..	2	6	3	0

New currency. 1,000 fils = 1 dinar.

2. Federal Crest.

3. Federal Flag.

(Des. V. Whiteley. Photo. Harrison.)

'65 (1 Apr.). *P* 14½ × 14 (*T* **1**) *or* 14½ (*T* **2**).

2	5 f. blue	0	3	0	4
,,	10 f. violet-blue	0	5	0	6
,,	15 f. turquoise-green ..	0	6	0	8
,,	20 f. green	0	8	0	10
,,	25 f. yellow-brown ..	0	10	1	0
,,	30 f. yellow-bistre	0	11	1	0
,,	35 f. chestnut	1	1	1	2
,,	50 f. red	1	5	1	4
,,	65 f. yellow-green	1	10	1	8
,,	75 f. crimson	2	3	2	6
3	100 f. multicoloured.. ..	2	9	3	3
,,	250 f. multicoloured.. ..	6	9	7	6
,,	500 f. multicoloured.. ..	13	3	15	0
,,	1 d. multicoloured.. ..	25	0	30	0

4. I.C.Y. Emblem.

(Des. V. Whiteley. Litho. Harrison.)

1965 (24 Oct.). *International Co-operation Year.* *W* w.**12.** *P* 14½.

17	**4**	5 f. reddish purple and turquoise-green	0	4	0	6
18	,,	65 f. dp. bluish green. & lav.	2	3	2	9

5. Sir Winston Churchill and St. Paul's Cathedral in Wartime.

(Des. Jennifer Toombs. Photo. Harrison.)

1966 (24 Jan.). *No wmk.* *P* 14.

19	**5**	5 f. black, cerise, gold and new blue	0	4	0	6
20	,,	10 f. black, cerise, gold and deep green	0	6	0	8
21	,,	65 f. black, cerise, gold and brown	2	3	2	9
22	,,	125 f. black, cerise, gold and bluish violet	4	6	5	6

SOUTH AUSTRALIA.

— SIMPLIFICATION (see Introduction) **—**

Nos. 1 to 151.

1, 3, 4. 6, 9, 10, 12: 13, 15, 17, 18.
21, 26, 27, 28, 31, 34, 35, 36, 37, 38, 41, 43: 62, 64, 66, 68, 71, 73, 75, 76, 78, 107, 82, 87.
111, 112, 113, 138, 139, 141, 118, 121, 123, 125, 126, 128, 131, 132. 146, 147, 151.

Nos. 152 to 181.

153, 158, 160: 164: 166: 167, 169, 172, 173, 181.

Later issues. Omit perfs and shades.

Official Stamps. Nos. 401 to 449.

406, 407, 408, 410, 411, 412, 413.
415, 417, 418, 419, 428, 421. 430, 433, 435. 436. 441, 438: 443, 445.

Later issues. Omit perfs. shades and opt. varieties.

1

2. Large Star.

(Eng. Wm. Humphrys. Recess. Perkins, Bacon.)

1855. *Printed in London. W* **2**. *Imperf.*

1 **1** 1d. dark green (26.10.55) .. £125 £35
2 ,, 2d. rose-carm. (*shades*) (1.1.55) £45 90 0
3 ,, 6d. deep blue (26.10.55) .. £100 £5

NOTE.—Proofs of the 1d. and 6d. without wmk. exist, and these are found with forged star watermarks added, and are sometimes offered as originals.

For reprints of the above and later issues, see note after No. 194.

Prepared and sent to the Colony, but not issued.

4 **1** 1s. violet £225

A printing of 500,000 of these 1s. stamps was made and delivered, but as the colour was liable to be confused with that of the 6d. stamp, the stock was destroyed on 5th June, 1857.

1856–58. *Printed by Govt. Ptr., Adelaide, from Perkins, Bacon plates. W* **2**. *Imperf.*

5 **1** 1d. dp. yellow-green (15.6.58) £225 £40
6 ,, 1d. yellow-green (11.10.58) .. — £45
7 ,, 2d. orange-red (23.4.56) .. — £7
8 ,, 2d. blood-red (14.11.56) .. £80 95 0
a. Printed on both sides
9 ,, 2d. pale red (*shades*) (31.10.57) £40 60 0
a. Printed on both sides .. — £40
10 ,, 6d. slate-blue (July, '57) .. £110 £16
11 ,, 1s. red-orange (8.7.57) .. — £50
12 ,, 1s. orange (11.6.58) .. £200 £45

1858–59. *W* **2**. *Rouletted. (This first rouletted issue has the same colours as the local imperf. issue.)*

13 **1** 1d. yellow-green (8.1.59) .. £25 50 0
14 ,, 1d. light yellow-grn. (18.3.59) £25 60 0
a. Imperf. between (pair) ..
15 ,, 2d. red (17.2.59) 85 0 12 6
a. Printed on both sides ..
17 ,, 6d. slate-blue (12.12.58) .. £18 30 0
18 ,, 1s. orange (18.3.59) £45 45 0
a. Printed on both sides .. — £50

The 2d. formerly listed as No. 16 will now be found under No. 24*a*.

3   4

TEN PENCE
(5)

1860–69. *Second rouletted issue, printed in colours only found rouletted or perforated. The 10d. is formed from the 9d. by a surcharge (T* **5**). *T* **1**, **3** *(4d. and 2s.), and* **4** *(9d.). W* **2**.

19 1d. brt. yellow-green (22.4.61) 60 0 35 0
20 1d. dull blue-green (17.12.63) 45 0 35 0
21 1d. sage-green 80 0 45 0
22 1d. pale sage-green (27.5.65).. 60 0
23 1d. deep green (1864).. .. £18 £6
24 1d. deep yellow-green (1869) £6
24*a* 2d. pale red 75 0 7 6
b. Printed on both sides .. .. — £25
25 2d. pale vermilion (3.2.63) .. 60 0 6 6
26 2d. bright verm. (19.8.64) .. 45 0 6 0
a. Imperf. between (horiz. pair) .. — £22
27 4d. dull violet (24.1.67) .. 60 0 35 0
28 6d. violet-blue (19.3.60) .. £7 10 0
29 6d. greenish blue (11.2.63) .. 70 0 12 6
30 6d. dull ultramarine (25.4.64) 70 0 10 0
a. Imperf. between (horiz. pair) — £30
31 6d. violet-ultram. (11.4.68) .. £10 12 6
32 6d. dull blue (26.8.65) .. £5 17 6
a. Imperf. between (pair) .. — £40
33 6d. Prussian blue (7.9.69) .. £40 £5
33*a* 6d. indigo .. .. ..
34 9d. grey-lilac (24.12.60) .. 55 0 20 0
a. Imperf. between (horiz. pair) ..
35 10d. in *blue*, on 9d. orange-red (20.7.66) £5 35 0
36 10d. in *blue*, on 9d. yell. (29.7.67) £10 35 0
37 10d. in *blk.*, on 9d. yell. (14.8.69) £95 65 0
a. Surch. inverted at the top .. — £225
b. Printed on both sides .. .. — £45
38 1s. yellow (25.10.61) £25 55 0
a. Imperf. between (vert. pair) ..
39 1s. grey-brown (10.4.63) £12 30 0
40 1s. dark grey-brown (26.5.63) £9 30 0
41 1s. chestnut (25.8.63) .. £9 22 6
42 1s. lake-brown (27.3.65) .. £7 25 0
a. Imperf. between (horiz. pair) .. — £25
43 2s. rose-carmine (24.1.67) .. £9 40 0
a. Imperf. between (vert. pair) .. — £40

1868–71. *Remainders of old stock subsequently perforated by the 11½–12½ machine.*

(a) Imperf. stamps. P 11½–12½.

44 2d. pale vermilion (Feb. 1868) — £150
45 2d. vermilion (18.3.68) .. — £160

(b) Rouletted stamps. P 11½–12½.

46 1d. bright green (9.11.69) .. — £40
47 2d. pale vermilion (15.8.68) .. — £60
48 6d. Prussian blue (8.11.69) .. — £25
48*a* 6d. indigo .. .. ..
49 9d. grey-lilac (29.3.71) .. £100 £20
a. Variety. Perf. × roulette .. — £16
49*b* 1s. lake-brown (23.5.70) ..

1867–70. *T* **1**, **3** *and* **4**. *W* **2**. *P 11½–12½ × roulette.*

50 1d. pale bright green (2.11.67) £12 35 0
51 1d. bright green (1868) .. £9 30 0
52 1d. grey-green (26.1.70) .. £12 60 0
a. Imperf. between (horiz. pair) ..
53 1d. blue-green (29.11.67) .. £17 65 0
54 4d. dull violet (July, 1868) .. £125 £15
55 4d. dull purple (1869) .. — £10
56 6d. bright pale blue (29.5.67) £35 40 0
57 6d. Prussian blue (30.7.67) .. £30 40 0
a. Printed on both sides ..
58 6d. indigo (1.8.69) £36 45 0
59 10d. in *blue* on 9d. yell. (2.2.69) £40 60
a. Printed on both sides .. .. — £3
60 1s. chestnut (April, 1868) .. £20 40
61 1s. lake-brown (3.3.69) .. £20 40

NOTE.—The stamps perf. 11½, 12½, or compound of the two, are here combined in one list as both perforations are on the one machine and all the varieties *may* be found in each sheet of stamps. This method of classifying the perforations by the machines is by far the most simple and convenient.

3-PENCE
(6)

1868–79. *T* **1**, **3** *and* **4**. *The 3d. is made fro[m] the 4d. by a surcharge (T* **6**). *W* **2**. *P 11½–12*

62 1d. pale bright green (8.2.68) £12 35
63 1d. grey-green (18.2.68) .. £9 70
64 1d. dark green (20.3.68) .. 75 0 25
a. Printed on both sides ..
65 1d. deep yellow-green (28.6.72) 65 0 45
66 3d. in *black*, on 4d. Prussian blue (7.2.71) .. .. — £
67 3d. in *black*, on 4d. sky-blue (12.8.70) £15 20
a. Imperf. .. .. ..
b. Rouletted .. .. ..

68 3d. in *black*, on 4d. deep ultramarine (Sept., 1872) .. 65 0 15 0
a. Double surcharge (10.9.74) .. — £120
b. Additional surch. on back .. — £225
69 4d. deep ultramarine (error "3 PENCE" surch. omitted) (26.4.79) £550 £425
70 4d. dull purple (1.2.68) .. 70 0 20 0
a. Imperf. between (horiz. pair) ..
71 4d. dull violet (1868) 60 0 15 0
72 6d. bright pale blue (23.2.68) £28 27 6
73 6d. Prussian blue (29.9.69) .. £5 10 0
74 6d. indigo (1869) £7 35 0
75 9d. claret (July 1872) .. £7 17 6
76 9d. bright mauve (1.11.72) .. £7 17 6
a. Printed on both sides .. .. — £20
77 9d. red-purple (15.1.74) .. 45 0 12 6
78 10d. in *blue*, on 9d. yell. (15.8.68) £80 50 0
a. Error. Wmk. Crown and S A (1868) .. .. .. — £60
79 10d. in *black*, on 9d. yellow (13.9.69) £15 60 0
80 1s. lake-brown (Sept., 1868) .. £12 30 0
81 1s. chestnut (8.10.72) .. £7 30 0
82 1s. dark red-brown 90 0 22 6
83 1s. red-brown (6.1.69) .. £7 25 0
84 2s. pale rose-pink (10.10.69) .. £65 £15
85 2s. deep rose-pink (Aug., 1869) — £7
86 2s. crimson-carm. (16.10.69) .. 80 0 25 0
87 2s. carmine (1869) 70 0 20 0
a. Printed on both sides .. .. — £16

1870–71. *T* **1** *and* **3.** *W* **2.** *P* 10.

88 1d. grey-green (June, 1870) .. £8 35 0
89 1d. pale bright green (9.8.70) .. £8 35 0
90 1d. bright green (1871) .. £5 30 0
91 3d. in *red*, on 4d., dull ultramarine (6.8.70) £20 90 0
92 3d. in *black*, on 4d. pale ultramarine (14.2.71) £11 25 0
93 3d. in *black*, on 4d., ultramarine (14.8.71) 60 0 35 0
93*a* 3d. in *black* on 4d. Prussian blue (16.12.71) .. ..
94 4d. dull lilac (1870) £7 27 6
95 4d. dull purple (1871) .. £6 27 6
96 6d. bright blue (19.6.70) .. £14 40 0
97 6d. indigo (11.10.71) £15 35 0
98 1s. chestnut (4.1.71) £10 40 0

1870–73. *T* **1, 3** *and* **4.** *W* **2.** *P* 10×11½–12½, 11½–12½×10, *or compound.*

99 1d. pale brt. grn. (11.10.70) .. £12 40 0
a. Printed on both sides ..
100 1d. grey-green £10 42 6
101 1d. deep green (19.6.71) .. £6 25 0
102 3d. in *black*, on 4d. pale ultramarine (9.11.70) .. £14 85 0
103 4d. dull lilac (11.5.72) .. — 20 0
104 4d. slate-lilac (5.3.73) .. £8 20 0
105 6d. Prussian blue (2.3.70) .. £6 12 6
106 6d. brt. Pruss. blue (26.10.70) £10 12 6
107 10d. in *black*, on 9d. yellow (Jan. '70) £6 30 0
108 1s. chestnut (17.6.71) .. — 65 0
109 2s. rose-pink (24.4.71) .. — £22
110 2s. carmine (2.3.72) £8 30 0

7

1871 (17 JULY). *W* **7.** *P* 10.

3 4d. dull lilac £110 £12
a. Printed on both sides ..

8. Broad Star.

8 PENCE

(**9**)

1876–1900. *T* **1, 3** *and* **4.** *W* **8.** *The 8d. is made from the 9d. by a surcharge (T* **9**). (*a*) *P* 11½–12½.

112 3d. in *black*, on 4d. ultramarine (1.6.79) 50 0 22 6
a. Double surch. .. .. — £60
113 4d. violet-slate (15.3.79) .. £8 35 0
114 4d. plum (16.4.80) 50 0 15 0
115 4d. deep mauve (8.6.82) .. 45 0 10 0
116 6d. indigo (2.12.76) £5 10 0
a. Imperf. between (horiz. pair)
117 6d. Prussian blue (July '78) 50 0 7 6
118 8d. in *black*, on 9d. brown-orange (July '76) .. 40 0 6 0
119 8d. in *blk.*, on 9d. burnt umber (1880) 50 0 5 0
120 8d. in *black*, on 9d. brown (9.3.80) 45 0 6 0
a. Imperf. between (vert. pair) .. £24
121 8d. in *blk.*, on 9d., grey-brn. (10.5.81) 40 0 10 0
a. Double surch. .. .. — £26
122 9d. purple (9.3.80) 25 0 14 0
a. Printed on both sides .. — £16
123 9d. rose-lilac (21.8.80) .. 6 6 4 6
124 9d. rose - lilac (*large holes*) (26.5.00) 6 0 5 0
125 1s. red-brown (3.11.77) .. 45 0 8 0
a. Imperf. between (horiz. pair) — £20
126 1s. reddish lake-brown (1880) 40 0 8 0
127 1s. lake-brown (9.1.83) .. 45 0 8 0
128 1s. Vandyke brown (1891) .. 70 0 20 0
129 1s. dull brown (1891) .. 27 6 8 0
130 1s. choc. (*large holes*) (6.5.97) 14 0 6 0
131 1s. sepia (*large holes*) (22.5.00) 14 0 8 0
a. Imperf. between (vert. pair) .. £7
132 2s. carmine (15.2.77) .. 18 6 8 6
a. Imperf. between (horiz. pair) ..
b. Imperf. (pair) .. ..
133 2s. rose-carmine (1885) .. 25 0 15 0
134 2s. rose-carmine. (*large holes*) (6.12.98) 18 6 12 6

The perforation with larger, clean-cut holes resulted from the fitting of the machine with new pins.

(*b*) *P* 10.

135 6d. Prussian blue (11.11.79) £6 35 0
136 6d. bright blue (1879) .. £10 20 0
136*a* 1s. reddish lake-brown .. £6

(*c*) *P* 10×11½–12½, 11½×12×10, *or compound.*

137 4d. violet-slate (21.5.79) .. £8 20 0
138 4d. dull purple (4.10.79) .. 25 0 6 0
139 6d. Prussian blue (29.12.77) 40 0 6 0
140 6d. bright blue 65 0 12 6
141 6d. bright ultramarine .. 25 0 4 0
142 1s. reddish lake-brn. (9.2.85) £5 14 0
143 1s. dull brown (29.6.86) .. £8 17 6
144 2s. carmine (27.12.77) .. 35 0 8 0
145 2s. rose-carmine (1887) .. 25 0 6 0
a. Imperf. v. between (horiz. pair). — £35

10

1901–2. *T* **1, 3** *and* **4.** *Wmk. Crown SA (wide), T* **10.** *P* 11½–12½, *large holes.*

No.	Description	Unused	Used
146	9d. claret (1.2.02)	12 6	12 6
147	1s. dull brown (12.6.01)	17 6	12 6
148	1s. dark reddish brown ('02)	17 6	17 6
	a. Imperf. between (vert. pr.) ..		
149	1s. red-brown (aniline) (18.7.02)	17 6	18 6
150	2s. crimson (29.8.01) ..	25 0	20 0
151	2s. carmine	15 0	12 6

(Plates and electrotypes by De La Rue & Co. Printed in Adelaide.)

11

12

1868–76. *T* **11** *and* **12.** *W* **10.** (*a*) *Rouletted.*

No.	Description	Unused	Used
152	2d. deep brick-red (Aug., '68)	60 0	7 6
153	2d. pale orange-red (5.10.68)	55 0	6 0
	a. Printed on both sides ..	—	£16
	b. Imperf. between (horiz. pair)..	—	£15
	(*b*) *P* 11½–12½.		
154	1d. blue-green (10.1.75) ..	£5	35 0
155	2d. pale orge.-red (5.5.69) ..	£80	£28
	(*c*) *P* 11½–12½ × *roulette.*		
156	2d. pale orge.-red (20.8.69)..	—	£14
	(*d*) *P* 10 × *roulette.*		
157	2d. pale orge.-red (7.5.70) ..	£16	40 0
	(*e*) *P* 10.		
158	1d. blue-green (April, 1870)..	27 6	7 6
159	2d. brick-red (April, 1870) ..	15 0	0 8
160	2d. orange-red (1.7.70) ..	15 0	0 6
	a. Printed on both sides ..	—	£12
	(*f*) *P* 10 × 11½–12½, 11½–12½ × 10, *or compound.*		
161	1d. blue-green (27.8.75) ..	65 0	25 0
162	2d. brick-red (19.1.71) ..	£30	17 6
163	2d. orange-red (3.2.71) ..	—	20 0
	a. Imperf. (Aug., 1876).. ..		

1869. *T* **12.** *Wmk. Large Star, T* **2.**

No.	Description	Unused	Used
	(*a*) *Rouletted.*		
164	2d. orange-red (13.3.69) ..	50 0	15 0
	(*b*) *P* 11½–12½ × *roulette.*		
165	2d. orange-red (1.8.69) ..	—	£12
	(*c*) *P* 11½–12½.		
165*a*	2d. orange-red (July, '69) ..		

1871 (15 July). *Wmk. V and Crown, T* **7.** *P* 10.

No.	Description	Unused	Used
166	**12** 2d. brick-red	75 0	17 6

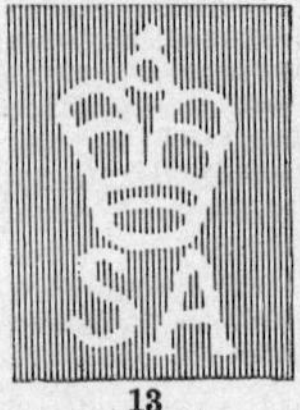

13

HALF-

PENNY

(14)

1876–85. *T* **11** *and* **12.** *Wmk. Crown SA (close), T* **13.** (*a*) *P* 10.

No.	Description	Unused	Used
167	1d. blue-green (9.2.76) ..	2 6	0 3
168	1d. yellowish grn. (Nov. '78)	4 0	0 3
169	1d. deep green (Nov. 1879)..	5 0	0 4
	a. Imperf. between (horiz. pair) ..		
170	2d. orange-red (Aug., 1876)	3 6	0 3
171	2d. dull brick-red (21.5.77)..	4 0	0 3
172	2d. blood-red (31.10.79) ..	£10	10 0
173	2d. pale red (April, 1885) ..	4 0	0 3
	(*b*) *P* 10 × 11½—12½, *or* 11½–12½ × 10, *or compound.*		
174	1d. deep green (11.2.80) ..	27 6	5 0
175	1d. blue-green (2.3.80) ..	9 0	2 6
176	2d. orange-red (4.9.77) ..	£12	12 6
177	2d. brick-red (June, 1880) ..	£12	12 6
	(*c*) *P* 11½–12½.		
178	1d. blue-green (Feb., 1884)..	—	£12
179	2d. orange-red (14.9.77) ..	—	£12
180	2d. blood-red (1.4.80) ..	—	£12

1882 (1 Jan.). *The* 1d. *green* (*W* **13,** *P* 10), *surcharged as T* **14,** *in black.*

No.	Description	Unused	Used
181	½d. on 1d., green	1 6	2 0

15

16

17

18

1883–95. *T* **15** *to* **18.** *Wmk. Crown SA (clos T* **13.** (*a*) *P* 10.

No.	Description	Unused	Used
182	½d. chocolate (1.3.83) ..	1 6	1
	a. Imperf. between (horiz. pair)		
183	½d. Venetian red (4.4.89) ..	1 0	0
184	½d. brown (1895)	1 6	0
185	3d. sage-green (Dec., '86) ..	12 6	5
186	3d. olive-green (6.6.90) ..	10 0	4
187	3d. deep green (12.4.93) ..	4 6	1
188	4d. pale violet (Mar. 1890) ..	6 6	2
189	4d. aniline violet (3.1.93) ..	9 0	3
190	6d. pale blue (Apr. '87) ..	6 0	1
191	6d. blue (5.5.87)	8 0	1
	(*b*) *P* 10 × 11½–12½, 11½–12½ × 10, *or compou*		
192	½d. pale brown (25.9.91) ..	20 0	3
193	½d. dark brown (9.9.92) ..	3 6	2
	a. Imperf. between (horiz. pair)		

(*c*) *P* 11½–12½.

194 ½d. Venetian red (12.10.90) .. 8 0 1 3

In 1884, reprints on paper wmkd. Crown SA, T **10**, were made of Nos. 1, 2, 4, 5, 12, 13, 14, 15, 19, 24, 27, 28, 32, 33, 34, 35, 36, 37, 38, 40, 43, 44, 49*a*, 53, 65, 67, 67 with surch. in red, 70, 71, 72, 73, 78, 79, 81, 83, 86, 90, 118, 119, 120, 121, 122, 155, 158, 159, 164, 181, 182. They are optd. with the word " REPRINT ".

19

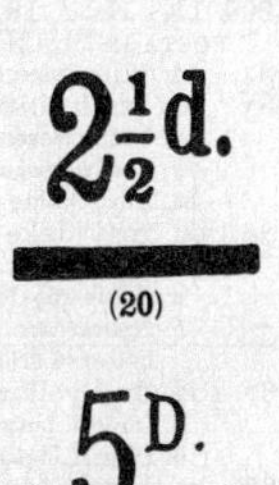

(20)

(21)

(Plates and electrotypes by De La Rue. Printed in Adelaide.)

1886–96. *T* **19** (*inscr.* " POSTAGE & REVENUE "). *W* **13.** *Parts of two or more wmks. on each stamp sometimes sideways.* A. *Perf.* 10. B. *Perf.* 11½–12½ (*small or large holes*).

		A.		B.	
195	2s. 6d. mauve ..	15 0	6 0	†	
	a. Dull violet ..	†		10 6	6 0
	b. Bright aniline vio.	†		12 6	8 6
196	5s. rose-pink ..	25 0	12 6	17 6	15 0
	a. Rose-carmine ..	†		25 0	20 0
197	10s. green	45 0	25 0	30 0	22 6
198	15s. brownish yellow ..	80 0	—	£10	£5
199	£1 blue	£6	55 0	90 0	50 0
200	£2 Venetian red	£35	£12	£35	£12
201	50s. dull pink ..	£60	£14	£60	—
202	£3 sage-green ..	£85	—	£85	—
203	£4 lemon ..	£100	—	£100	—
204	£5 grey	£200	—	£200	—
205	£5 brown (1896)	†		£200	—
206	£10 bronze ..	£275	£120	£275	£120
207	£15 silver	£600	—	£600	—
208	£20 claret ..	£750	—	£750	—

Variations exist in the length of the words and shape of the letters of the value inscription.

The 2s. 6d. dull violet, 5s. rose-pink, 10s., £1 and £5 brown exist perf. 11½–12½ with either large or small holes; the 2s. 6d. aniline, 5s. rose-carmine, 15s., £2 and 50s. with large holes only and the remainder only with small holes.

Stamps perforated 11½–12½ small holes, are, generally speaking, rather rarer than those with the 1895 (large holes) gauge.

Stamps perf. 10 were issued on 20 Dec., 1886. Stamps perf. 11½–12½ (small holes) are known with earliest dates covering the period from June, 1890 to Feb. 1896. Earliest dates of stamps with large holes range from July, 1896 to May, 1902.

1891 (1 JAN.). *T* **17** *and* **18** *in new colours surcharged as T* **20** *and* **21**, *in brown or carmine respectively. Wmk. Crown SA* (*close*), *T* **13.**

(*a*) *P* 10.

229 2½d. on 4d. pale green .. 2 0 1 0
 a. Fraction bar omitted £5 90 0

230 2½d. on 4d. deep green .. 2 6 0 9
 a. "2" and "½" closer together .. 20 0 20 0
 b. Fraction bar omitted .. ..
 c. Imperf. between (horiz. pair) ..
 d. Imperf. between (vert. pair) .. — £25
231 5d. on 6d. pale brown .. 6 0 5 0
232 5d. on 6d. dark brown .. 6 0 4 6
 a. No stop after " 5D " .. £8

(*b*) *P* 10 × 11½–12½ *or* 11½–12½ × 10.

233 2½d. on 4d. pale green .. 2 6 1 6
234 2½d. on 4d. deep green .. 3 0 2 0

(*c*) *P* 11½–12½.

235 2½d. on 4d. green 27 6

1893–4. *T* **15, 11, 12, 20** *on* **17, 17** *and* **18.** *Wmk. Crown SA* (*close*), *T* **13.** *P* 15.

236 ½d. pale brown (Jan. '93) .. 1 0 0 8
237 ½d. dark brown 1 3 0 8
 a. Perf. 12½ between, p. 15 all round, pair £8 80 0
 b. Imperf. between (horiz. pair) .. 80 0
238 1d. green (8.5.93) 1 0 0 3
239 2d. pale orange (9.2.93) .. 3 6 0 3
240 2d. orange-red 4 6 0 3
 a. Imperf. between (vert. pair) .. £10
241 2½d. on 4d. green (14.10.93) .. 4 6 2 0
 a. " 2 " and " ½ " closer .. 35 0 30 0
 b. No bar in fraction .. ..
242 4d. purple (1.1.94) 8 6 4 0
243 4d. slate-violet 8 0 3 0
244 6d. blue (20.11.93) 20 0 8 0

22

23

(Des. Tannenberg, Melbourne; plates by De La Rue & Co. Typo. Sands and McDougall, Adelaide.)

1894 (1 MAR.). *T* **22** *and* **23.** *Wmk. Crown SA* (*close*), *T* **13.** *P* 15.

245 2½d. violet-blue 10 0 1 6
246 5d. brown-purple 7 6 3 0

1895–9. *Wmk. Crown SA* (*close*), *T* **13.** *P* 13.

247 **15** ½d. pale brown (Sept. '95) 1 0 0 6
248 ,, ½d. deep brown (19.3.97) 1 0 0 6
249 **11** 1d. pale green (11.1.95) .. 1 6 0 3
250 ,, 1d. green 2 6 0 3
 a. Imperf. between (vert. pair)
251 **12** 2d. pale orange (19.1.95) 1 0 0 3
252 ,, 2d. orange-red (9.5.95) .. 1 0 0 3
253 **22** 2½d. violet-blue (11.2.95) .. 3 6 0 8
254 **16** 3d. pale ol.-grn. (26.7.97) 4 0 1 6
255 ,, 3d. dark ol.-grn. (27.11.99) 3 6 0 9
256 **17** 4d. violet (21.1.96) 1 9 0 6
257 **23** 5d. brn.-pur. (Jan. '96) .. 2 0 1 6
258 ,, 5d. purple 1 9 1 3
259 **18** 6d. pale blue (Mar. '96) .. 2 6 0 9
260 ,, 6d. blue 2 6 0 9

Varieties of the 1d. show lines and blotches of colour on the face and background. Price 2s. each, *unused*.

1897. *T* **11.** *Redrawn, lettering slightly thicker. W* **13.** *P* 13.

261 1d. pale green 1 0 0 3
 a. Imperf. between (vert. pair) ..

All later 1d. postage stamps are in this redrawn type.

24. G.P.O., Adelaide.

(½d. Typo. De La Rue & Co.)

1898–1906. *W* **13.**
A. *Perf.* 13 (1898–1900) *except* 264A/Aa.
B. *Perf.* 12 × 11½ (*comb.*) (1904–6).

No.	Type		A				B			
262	**24**	½d. yell. grn.	0	8	0	3	1	0	0	8
263	**11**	1d. rosine ..	1	0	0	3	8	0	1	0
264	,,	1d scarlet ..	3	6	1	0	3	0	0	9
		a. Deep red ..	3	0	0	9	†			
265	**12**	2d. brt. violet	0	9	0	1	3	6	0	4
266	**22**	2½d. indigo ..	5	0	0	3	5	0	0	8
267	**23**	5d. dull purple	†				2	6	1	3

Earliest dates: Perf. 13. ½d., 23 Jan. 1900; 1d. rosine, 8 Aug. 1899; 1d. scarlet, 23 Dec. 1903; 2d. 10 Oct. 1899; 2½d. 25 Mar. 1898.

Perf. 12 × 11½. ½d. July, 1905; 1d. rosine, 2 Feb. 1904; 1d. scarlet, 25 July, 1904; 2d. 11 Oct. 1904; 2½d. 4 July, 1906; 5d. Jan. 1905.

POSTAGE

25

1902–4. *As T* **19**, *but top tablet as T* **25** (*thin* "POSTAGE"). *W* **13.**

(*a*) *P* 11½–12½.

The measurements given indicate the length of the value inscription in the bottom label. The dates are those of the earliest known postmarks.

No.					
268	3d. ol.-grn. (18½ mm.) (1.8.02)	1	6	0	6
269	4d. red-orange (17 mm.) (29.11.02)	2	6	1	6
270	6d. blue-grn. (16–16½ mm.) (29.11.02)	2	6	1	3
271	8d. ultram. (19 mm.) (25.4.02)	3	6	2	6
272	8d. ultram. (16½ mm.) (22.3.04)	3	6	2	6
	a. Error. "EIGNT"	£60		£45	
273	9d. rosy lake (19.9.02) ..	2	0	2	0
	a. Imperf. between (vert. pair) ..	£15			
	b. Imperf. between (horiz. pair) ..				
274	10d. dull yellow (29.11.02) ..	3	6	3	0
275	1s. brown (18.8.02) ..	4	6	3	0
	a. Imperf. between (horiz. pair) ..				
	b. Imperf. between (vert. pair) ..				
	c. "POSTAGE" and value in red-brown	65	0	50	0
276	2s. 6d. pale violet (19.9.02) ..	25	0		
	a. Bright violet (2.2.03)	8	0	8	0
277	5s. rose (17.10.02)	35	0	25	0
278	10s. green (1.11.02)	50	0	35	0
279	£1 blue (1.11.02)	£9		35	0

(*b*) *P* 12.

280	3d. ol.-grn. (20 mm.) (15.4.04)	3	6	2	0
	a. "POSTAGE" omitted; value below "AUSTRALIA"	£15			
281	4d. oran.-red (17½–18 mm.) (18.2.03)	3	6	2	0
282	6d. blue-green (15 mm.) (14.11.03)	15	0	6	0
283	9d. rosy lake (2.12.03) ..	20	0	7	6

POSTAGE

26

TWO SHILLINGS AND SIXPENCE — V

TWO SHILLINGS AND SIXPENCE — X

FIVE SHILLINGS — Y

FIVE SHILLINGS — Z

1904–11. *As T* **19**, *but top tablet as T* **26** (*thick* "POSTAGE"). *W* **13.** *P* 12.

284	6d. blue-green (27.4.04) ..	1	6	1	6
285	8d. bright ultram. (4.7.05) ..	3	6	2	0
	a. Value closer (15¼ mm.) ..	12	6		
	b. Dull ultramarine (2.4.08) ..	6	0	5	0
	ba. Do. Value closer (15¼ mm.) ..	25	0		
286	9d. rosy lake (17–17¼ mm.) (18.7.04)	3	0	1	6
	a. Value 16½-16¾ mm. (2.06) ..	8	0	6	0
	b. Brown-lake. Perf. 12½ small holes) (6.6.11)	4	6		
287	10d. dull yellow (8.07) ..	10	0	7	0
	a. Imperf. between (horiz. pair) ..	—		£12	
	b. Imperf. between (vert. pair) ..				
288	1s. brown (12.4.04) ..	3	0	1	6
	a. Imperf. between (vert. pair) ..	£7			
	b. Imperf. between (horiz. pair) ..				
289	2s. 6d. bright violet (V) (14.7.05)	25	0	9	0
	a. Dull violet (X) (8.06)	25	0	9	0
290	5s. rose-scarlet (Y) (8.04) ..	20	0	20	0
	a. Scarlet (Z) (8.06)	20	0	20	0
	b. Pale rose. Perf. 12½ (small holes) (Z) (7.10)	32	6	25	0
291	10s. green (26.8.08)	50	0		
292	£1 blue (29.12.04)	£5			
	a. Perf. 12½ (small holes) (7.10) ..	90	0		

Types V and X of the 2s. 6d. may be distin- guished by variations in the lettering *e.g.* of Type V the "A" of "AND" and the "S" in "SIXPENCE" appear much smaller than in Type X.

In the 5s. the letters "S" of "SHILLINGS" are more closed in Type Y than in Type Z, and in Z the "G" of "SHILLINGS" is taller and the lower curve does not extend to the right of the upper curve as it does in Y.

The "value closer" variety on the 8d. occurs six times in the sheet of 60. The value normally measures 16½ mm. but in the variety it is 15¼ mm.

The 9d., 5s. and £1, perf. 12½ (small holes), are late printings made in 1910–11 to use up the Crown SA paper.

No. 286b has the value as Type C of the 9d. on Crown A paper.

27

1905–11. *W* **27.** *P* 12 × 11½ (*new comb machine*

No.	Type				
293	**24**	½d. pale green (Apr. '07) ..	0	8	0
		a. Yellow-green	2	0	0
294	**11**	1d. rosine (2.12.05) ..	1	6	0
		a. Scarlet (Apl. '11) ..	0	4	0
295	**12**	2d. bright violet (2.2.06)	2	0	0
		aa. Imperf. between (pair) ..			
		a. Mauve (Apl. '08) ..	0	6	0
296	**22**	2½d. indigo-blue (14.9.10)	8	0	2
297	**23**	5d. brown-pur. (11.3.08)	3	6	4

1906–12. *T* **19** ("POSTAGE" *thick as T* **26**). *W* **27.** *P* 12 *or* 12½ (*small holes*).

Three types of the 9d., perf. 12½, distinguishable by the distance between "NINE" and "PENCE".

A. Distance 1¾ mm. B. Distance 2¼ mm. C. Distance 2½ mm.

298 3d. sage-green (19 mm.) (26.6.06) 5 0 2 6
 a. Imperf. between (horiz. pair) ..
 b. Perf. 12½. *Sage-green* (17 mm.) (9.12.09) 6 0 2 6
 c. Perf. 12½. *Deep olive* (20 mm.) (7.10) 15 0 6 0
 d. Perf. 12½. *Yellow-olive* (16.12.11) 7 0 2 6
 da. Perf. 12½. *Bright olive-green* (19-19¾ mm.) (5.12) 7 0 2 0
 e. Perf. 11 (17 mm.) (10.7.11) .. £12
299 4d. orange-red (10.9.06) .. 6 6 4 0
 a. *Orange* 8 0 2 6
 b. Perf. 12½. *Orange* (27.10.09) .. 6 6 2 0
300 6d. blue-green (1.9.06) .. 4 0 2 6
 a. Perf. 12½ (21.4.10) 2 0 1 0
 ab. Perf. 12½. Imp. between (vert. pair) .. .. .. — £16
301 8d. bright ultram. (*P* 12½) (8.09) 8 0 6 0
 a. Value closer (8.09) 35 0 25 0
302 9d. brown-lake (3.2.06) .. 6 0 2 6
 a. Imperf. between (vert. pair) . £10
 aa. Imperf. between (horiz. pair) .. £15
 b. Deep lake (9.5.08) 25 0 6 0
 c. Perf. 12½. *Lake* (A) (5.9.09) .. 7 6 5 0
 d. Perf. 12½. *Lake* (B) (7.09) .. 9 0 6 0
 e. Perf. 12½. *Brown-lake* (C) .. 20 0 8 0
 ea. Perf. 12½. *Deep lake.* Thin pp. (C) 8 0 6 6
 f. Perf. 11 (1909) .. ..
303 1s. brown (30.5.06) .. 6 6 3 0
 a. Imperf. between (horiz. pair) .. £8
 b. Perf. 12½ (10.3.10) 3 6 1 3
304 2s. 6d. bright violet (10.6.09) 14 0 8 0
 a. Perf. 12½. *Pale violet* (6.10) .. 20 0 10 6
 ab. Perf. 12½. *Deep purple* (5.11.12) 35 0 12 6
305 5s. brt. rose (*P* 12½) (24.4.11) 30 0

The "value closer" variety of the 8d. occurred 1 times in the sheet of 60 in the later printing only. On No. 301 the value measures 16½ mm. while on No. 301a it is 15¼ mm.

The 1s. brown, perf. compound of 11½ and 12½, formerly listed is now omitted, as it must have been perforated by the 12 machine, which in places varied from 11½ to 13.

OFFICIAL STAMPS.

A. *Departmental.*

1868–74.

The following is a list of initials which are found on the stamps of the above period, in *red, blue,* and *black.* Selections can be submitted when in stock.

A. Architect; A.G. Attorney-General; A.O. Audit Office; B.D. Barracks Department; B.G. Botanic Gardens; B.M. Bench of Magistrates (Licensing Bench); C. Customs; C. D. Convict Department; C.L. Crown Lands; C.O. Commissariat Officer; C.P. Commissioner of Police; C.S. Chief Secretary; C.Sgn. Colonial Surgeon; D.B. Destitute Board; D.R. Deeds Registration; E. Engineer; E.B. Education Board; G.F. Gold Fields; G.P. Government Printer; G.S. Government Storekeeper; G.T. Goolwa Tramway; H. Hospital; H.A. House of Assembly; I.A. Immigration Agent; I.E. Intestate Estates; I.S. Inspector of Sheep; L.A. Lunatic Asylum; L.C. Legislative-Council; L.L. Legislative Librarian; L.T. Lands Titles; M. Military; M.B. Marine Board; M.R. Manager of Railways; M.R.G. Main Roads, Gambierton; N.T. Northern Territory; O.A. Official Assignee; P. Police; P.A. Protector of Aborigines; P.O. Post Office; P.S. Private Secretary; P.W. Public Works; R.B. Road Board; R.G. Registrar-General; S. Sheriff; S.C. Supreme Court; S.G. Surveyor-General; S.M. Stipendiary Magistrate; S.T. Superintendent of Telegraphs; T. Treasurer; T.R. Titles Registration; V. Volunteers; V.A. Valuator and Auctioneer; VN. Vaccination; W. Waterworks.

B. *General.*

O.S. (51) **O.S.** (52)

Contemporary stamps overprinted with T **51**, *in black.*

1874–7. *W* **2.** (*a*) *P* 10.
401 4d. dull purple (18.2.74) .. £70 £20

(*b*) *P* 11½–12½ × 10.
402 1d. green (2.1.74) .. .. — £9
403 4d. dull violet (12.2.75) .. 60 0 12 6
404 6d. Prussian blue (20.10.75) — 25 0
404*a* 2s. rose-pink .. ..
405 2s. carmine (3.12.76) .. — £9

(*c*) *P* 11½–12½.
406 1d. deep yell.-grn. (30.1.74) — 45 0
 a. Printed on both sides ..
407 3d. in *black* on 4d. ultramarine (26.6.77) .. .. .. — £15
 a. No stop after "S" .. .. — £22
408 4d. dull violet (13.7.74) .. 25 0 12 6
 a. No stop after "S" .. .. — 35 0
409 6d. bright blue (31.8.75) .. 60 0 35 0
 a. "O.S." double — 65 0
410 6d. Prussian blue (27.3.74) .. 35 0 12 6
 a. No stop after "S" .. .. — 35 0
411 9d. red-purple (22.3.76) .. £6 60 0
 a. No stop after "S" .. £8
412 1s. red-brown (5.8.74) .. 60 0 12 6
 a. "O.S." double .. .. — 40 0
 b. No stop after "S" 60 0 35 0
413 2s. crimson-carmine (13.7.75) 70 0 20 0
 a. No stop after "S" .. ..
 b. No stops .. .. .. — 45 0
 c. Stops at top of letters ..

1876–85. *W* **8.** (*a*) *P* 10.
414 6d. bright blue (1879) .. 70 0 20 0

(*b*) *P* 10 × 11½–12½, 11½–12½ × 10, *or compound.*
415 4d. violet-slate (24.1.78) .. 85 0 17 6
416 4d. plum (29.11.81) 25 0 5 0
417 4d. deep mauve 7 6 2 6
 a. No stop after "S" .. .. — 25 0
 b. No stop after "O" .. ..
 c. "O.S." double ..
 d "O.S." inverted ..
418 6d. bright blue (1877) .. 15 0 2 0
 a. "O.S." inverted ..
 b. No stop after "O" .. ..
419 6d. bright ultram. (27.3.85) 12 6 1 6
 a. "O.S." inverted .. ..
 b. "O.S" double .. ..
 c. "O.S." double, one inverted ..
 d. No stop after "S" .. ..
 e. No stops after "O" and "S"
420 1s. red-brown (27.3.83) .. 35 0 8 6
 a. "O.S." inverted .. ..
 b. No stop after "O" .. ..
 c. No stop after "S" .. ..
421 2s. carmine (16.3.81) .. 20 0 7 6
 a. "O.S." inverted .. ..
 b. No stop after "S" .. ..

(*c*) *P* 11½–12½.
422 3d. in *black* on 4d. ultram. ..
423 4d. violet-slate (14.3.76) .. £8 15 0

424 4d. deep mauve (19.8.79) .. 45 0 4 6
a. "O.S." inverted .. ..
b. "O.S." double, one inverted ..
c. No stop after "S" .. ..
425 6d. Prussian blue (June, '77) 17 6 5 0
a. "O.S." double .. .. — 45 0
b. "O.S." inverted .. ..
426 8d. in *black* on 9d. brown (9.11.76) £18 £6
a. "O.S." double £25
b. "O" only .. .. .. — £10
426*c* 9d. purple £40
427 1s. red-brown (12.2.78) .. 17 6 6 0
a. "O.S." inverted £8 £6
b. No stop after "S" £12
428 1s. lake-brown (8.11.83) .. 15 0 4 0
429 2s. rose-carmine (12.8.85) .. 25 0 7 6
a. "O.S." double .. .. — £5
b. "O.S." inverted .. .. — £6
c. No stop after "S" .. .. — 35 0

1891–1903. *Contemporary stamps optd. with* **T 52.** *W* **8.** (April, 1891.)

(*a*) *P* 11½–12½.

430 1s. lake-brown (18.4.91) .. 20 0 5 0
431 1s. Vandyke brown 30 0 12 6
432 1s. dull brown (2.7.96) .. 17 6 5 0
a. No stop after "S" .. ..
433 1s. sepia (*large holes*) (4.1.02) 10 0 3 6
a. "O.S." double .. ..
b. No stop after "S" .. ..
434 2s. carmine (20.6.00) .. 35 0 12 6
a. No stop after "S" .. ..

(*b*) *P* 10×11½–12½.

435 2s. rose-carmine (9.11.95) .. 9 0 3 6
a. No stop after "S" 40 0
b. "O.S." double .. ..

W **10.** *P* 11½–12½ (1903).

436 1s. dull brown (7.3.03) .. 12 6 3 6

1874–76. *W* **10.** "O.S", *T* **51.** (*a*) *P* 10.

437 **11** 1d. blue-green (30.9.75) .. 90 0 35 0
a. "O.S." inverted .. ..
b. No stop after "S" ..
438 **12** 2d. orange-red (18.2.74) .. 12 6 0 9
a. No stop after "S" ..
b. "O.S." double ..

(*b*) *P* 10×11½–12½, 11½–12½×10, *or compound.*

439 **11** 1d. blue-green (16.9.75) ..
a. No stop after "S" ..
440 **12** 2d. orange-red (27.9.76) .. — 12 6

(*c*) *P* 11½–12½.

441 **11** 1d. blue-green (13.8.75) .. — 30 0
a. "O.S." inverted .. ..
b. No stop after "S" .. ..
442 **12** 2d. orange-red (20.5.74) .. — £8

1876–80. *W* **13.** "O.S." *T* **51.** (*a*) *P* 10.

443 **11** 1d. blue-green (2.10.76) .. 2 6 0 4
a. "O.S." inverted .. .. — 60 0
b. "O.S." double 35 0 35 0
c. "O.S." double, one inverted
d. No stops .. .. — 25 0
e. No stop after "S" .. — 12 6
f. No stop after "O" ..
444 „ 1d. deep green 6 0 0 9
a. "O.S." double .. .. — 45 0
445 **12** 2d. orange-red (21.9.77) .. 3 0 0 3
a. "O.S." double 45 0 25 0
b. "O.S." inverted .. .. — 22 6
c. "O.S." double, both inverted — £6
d. "O.S." double, one inverted
e. No stop after "O" .. — 17 6
f. No stop after "S" ..
g. No stops after "O" & "S"
446 „ 2d. brick-red 45 0 2 6

(*b*) *P* 10×11½–12½, 11½–12½×10, *or compound.*

447 **11** 1d. deep green (14.8.80) .. — 55 0
a. "O.S." double .. ..
448 **12** 2d. orange-red (6.4.78) .. 80 0 25 0
a. "O.S." inverted .. ..
b. No stop after "S" .. ..

(*c*) *P* 11½–12½.

449 **12** 2d. orange-red (15.7.80) .. — £7

1882 (20 Feb.). *Surch. with T* **14.** *W* **13.** "O.S.", *T* **51.** *P* 10.

450 **11** ½d. on 1d. blue-green .. 5 0 1 6
a. "O.S." inverted .. ..

1888–91. *W* **13.** "O.S.", *T* **51.** *P* 10.

451 **17** 4d. violet (24.1.91) .. 8 6 3 0
452 **18** 6d. blue (15.11.88) .. 5 0 0 9
a. "O.S." double .. ..
b. No stop after "S" ..

1891. *Surch. with T* **20.** *W* **13.** "O.S.", *T* **51.**

(*a*) *P* 10.

453 **17** 2½d. on 4d. grn. (1.8.91) .. 12 6 8 6
a. "2" and "½" closer .. — 65 0
b. No stop after "S" ..
c. "O.S." omitted (in pair with normal) .. ..
d. "O.S." inverted .. ..
e. "O.S." double .. ..

(*b*) *P* 10×11½–12½, 11½–12½×10, *or compound.*

454 **17** 2½d. on 4d. grn. (1.10.91) 25 0 12 6

(*c*) *Perf.* 11½–12½.

454*a* **17** 2½d. on 4d. grn. (1.6.91)

1891–95. "O.S.", *T* **52.** (*a*) *P* 10.

455 **15** ½d. brown (2.5.94) .. 7 0 2 6
a. No stop after "S" ..
456 **11** 1d. green (22.4.91) .. 6 0 0 6
a. "O.S." double. 65 0
b. No stop after "S" .. — 12 6
c. "O.S." in blackish blue. . £7 8 6
d. "O.S." double, one inverted
457 **12** 2d. orange-red (22.4.91) 4 6 0 3
a. No stop after "S" .. — 6 0
b. "O.S." double. . ..
458 **17** 2½d. on 4d. grn. (18.8.94) 4 0 1 0
a. No stop after "S" .. — 17 6
b. "O.S." inverted .. £6
c. "2" and "½" closer .. 35 0 25
d. Fraction bar omitted ..
459 „ 4d. pale violet (13.2.91) 7 0 1
a. "O" only .. .. — 85
b. "O.S." double. .
c. No stop after "S" ..
460 „ 4d. aniline violet (31.8.93) 8 6 0
a. No stop after "S" ..
b. "O.S." double. .
461 **18** 5d. on 6d. brown (2.12.91) 4 6 3
a. No stop after "S" .. 45 0 22
b. No stop after "5D" .. £7
462 „ 6d. blue (4.4.93) .. 6 0 1
a. No stop after "S" ..
b. "O.S." in blackish blue. .

(*b*) *P* 10×11½—12½.

463 **15** ½d. pale brown (26.3.95) 5 0 2
464 **17** 2½d. on 4d. green (17.9.95) — 65
a. "O.S." double. . ..

(*c*) *P* 11½–12½.

465 **15** ½d. Venetian red (13.6.91) 15 0 4

1893–1901. "O.S.", *T* **52.** *P* 15.

466 **15** ½d. pale brown (8.6.95) 2 9 1
467 **11** 1d. green (8.9.94) .. 1 3 0
a. No stop after "S" ..
b. "O.S." double. . ..
468 **12** 2d. orange-red (16.6.94) 4 6 0
a. "O.S." double. . .. — 22
b. "O.S." inverted .. — 12
468*c* **22** 2½d. violet-blue 25 0 3
469 **17** 4d. slate-violet (4.4.95) 15 0 2
a. "O.S." double. . .. — 22
470 **23** 5d. purple (29.3.01) .. 12 6 5
471 **18** 6d. blue (20.9.93) .. 3 0 0

1895–1901. "O.S." *T* **52.** *P* 13.

472 **15** ½d. brown (17.5.98) .. 3 6 1
a. Opt. triple, twice sideways
473 **11** 1d. green (20.5.95) .. 3 6 0
a. No stop after "S" .. 17 6 12

No.	Type	Description		Unused		Used
474	12	2d. orange (11.2.96)	..	2 6		0 3
		a. No stop after " S "	..	—		12 6
		b. " O.S." double ..	..			
475	22	2½d. violet-blue (5.7.97)	..	20 0		1 6
		a. No stop after " S "	..			
476	17	4d. violet (Dec. '96)	..	4 0		0 9
		a. No stop after " S "	..	17 6		12 6
		b. " O.S." double ..	..	15 0		20 0
477	23	5d. purple (29.9.01)	..	7 6		5 0
		a. No stop after " S "	..			
478	18	6d. blue (13.9.99)	..	6 0		1 6
		a. No stop after " S "	..	17 6		

1898. " O.S.", *T* **52.** *On the redrawn design. P* 13.

No.	Type	Description		Unused		Used
479	11	1d. green (9.2.98)	..	3 0		0 6
		a. No stop after " S "	..	8 6		

O. S.

(53)

1899–1901. *Contemporary stamps (wmk. Crown SA (close),* **T 13**), *optd. with T* **53.** *P* 13.

No.	Type	Description		Unused		Used
480	24	½d. yellow-green (12.2.00)		1 3		0 6
		a. No stop after " S "	..			
		b. " O.S." inverted	..			
481	11	1d. rosine (22.9.99)	..	1 3		0 2
		a. " O.S." inverted	..			
		b. " O.S." double ..	..			
		c. No stop after " S "	..	—		17 6
482	12	2d. bright violet (1.6.00)		1 0		0 4
		a. " O.S." inverted	..	17 6		
		b. " O.S." double ..	..			
		c. No stop after " S "	..	17 6		
483	22	2½d. indigo (2.10.01)	..	5 0		0 8
		a. " O.S." inverted	..	—		30 0
		b. No stop after " S "	..	40 0		
484	17	4d. violet (18.11.00)	..	3 6		1 0
		a. " O.S." inverted	..	90 0		
		b. No stop after " S "	..	22 6		
485	18	6d. blue (8.10.00)	..	3 6		0 9
		a. No stop after " S "	..	22 6		

1891 (MAY). *T* **19.** *Wmk. Crown SA (close), T* **13.** *P* 10. *Optd. as T* **53** *but wider.*

No.	Description			Unused	Used
486	2s. 6d. pale violet ..		..	£75	£75
487	5s. pale rose ..	..	..	£75	£75

Only one small sheet (20?) of each of these stamps was printed.

South Australia now uses the stamps of AUSTRALIA.

SOUTH GEORGIA.

1. Reindeer.

2. South Sandwich Islands.

3. Sperm Whale.

4. Chinstrap and King Penguin.

5. Fur Seal.

8. Sooty Albatross.

6. Fin Whale.

7. Elephant Seal.

9. Whale-catcher.

10. Leopard Seal.

11. Shackleton's Cross.

12. Wandering Albatross.

13. Elephant and Fur Seal.

14. Plankton and Krill.

15. Blue Whale.

(Des. M. Goaman. Recess. De La Rue.)

1963 (17 July). *W* w. **12.** *P* 15.

1	**1**	½d. brown-red	0	2	0	2
2	**2**	1d. violet-blue	0	3	0	3
3	**3**	2d. turquoise-blue ..	0	4	0	4
4	**4**	2½d. black	0	5	0	5
5	**5**	3d. bistre	0	6	0	6
6	**6**	4d. bronze-green	0	7	0	8
7	**7**	5½d. deep violet	0	10	0	11
8	**8**	6d. orange	0	10	1	0
9	**9**	9d. blue	1	1	1	6
10	**10**	1s. purple	1	5	2	0
11	**11**	2s. yellow-olive & lt. blue	2	9	3	3
12	**12**	2s. 6d. blue	3	6	4	3
13	**13**	5s. orange-brown	6	9	7	6
14	**14**	10s. magenta	13	3	15	0
15	**15**	£1 ultramarine	25	0	30	0

SOUTH WEST AFRICA.

(Formerly German S.W. Africa.)

The following issues, to No. 140, are inscribed in English and Afrikaans (or Dutch) on alternate stamps throughout the sheet unless otherwise stated, and are collected in the same forms as those of South Africa. See general note at head of South Africa list.

South West	Zuid-West
Africa.	Afrika.
(1)	**(2)**

1923. *Stamps of South Africa, T* **2** *and* **3**, *optd. typographically with T* **1** *and* **2** *alternately.*

I. 14 *mm. between lines of overprint.* (2 Jan.).

		Un. pair	*Us. pair*	*Us. single*
1	½d. green	0 8	1 0	0 4
	a. "Wes" for "West" ..	65 0		
2	1d. rose-red	1 0	1 6	0 [illegible]
	a. Overprint inverted ..	£9		
	b. "Wes" for "West" ..	65 0		
	c. "Af.rica" for "Africa"	70 0		
3	2d. dull purple	2 6	3 0	0 [illegible]
	a. Overprint inverted ..	£10		
4	3d. ultramarine ..	3 0	4 0	1 [illegible]
5	4d. orge.-yell. & sage grn.	6 0	6 6	1 [illegible]
6	6d. black and violet ..	6 0	10 0	3 [illegible]
7	1s. orange-yellow ..	12 6	20 0	4 [illegible]
8	1s. 3d. pale violet ..	15 0	22 6	7 [illegible]
	a. Overprint inverted ..	£12		
9	2s. 6d. purple & green	30 0	45 0	15
10	5s. purple and blue ..	£5	£10	50
11	10s. blue and olive-grn.	£30	£18	80
12	£1 green and red ..	£15	£12	50

Minor varieties, due to wear of type includir broken "t" in "West," may be found. Varieti showing one line of overprint only, or lower li above upper line, due to misplacement, may al be found. All values may be found with fai stop after "Afrika," and the ½d., 1d., 2d. a 3d. occasionally without stop.

IA. 14 *mm. between lines, but opt. lithographed in shiny ink.*

		Un. pair	*Us. pair*	*Us. single*
12*a*	½d. green	3 0	4 6	0 9
12*b*	4d. orge.-yell.&sage-grn.	27 6	35 0	10 0
12*c*	6d. black and violet ..	20 0	32 6	10 0
12*d*	1s. orange-yellow ..	30 0	35 0	12 6
12*e*	1s. 3d. pale violet ..	30 0	40 0	12 0
12*f*	2s. 6d. purple & green	50 0	60 0	17 6

II. 10 *mm. between lines of overprint.*

(MAY, 1923.)

13	5s. purple and blue ..	95 0		
	a. "Afrika" without stop	£15		
14	10s. blue and olive-green	£10	£10	40 0
	a. "Afrika" without stop	£30	£18	£8
15	£1 green and red ..	£18	£20	£5
	a. "Afrika" without stop	£65		

Zuidwest **South West**

Afrika. **Africa.**

(3) (4)

1923–24. *Stamps of South Africa, T* **2** *and* **3**, *optd. as T* **3** ("Zuidwest" *in one word, without hyphen) and* **4** *alternately.*

III. "South West" 14 *mm. long;* "Zuidwest" 11 *mm. long;* 14 *mm. between lines of opt.* (AUG.–SEPT., 1923).

16	½d. green (Sept. 1924)	1 0	1 6	0 6
	a. "outh" for "South"	£32		
17	1d. rose-red	2 0	3 0	0 4
18	2d. dull purple ..	2 0	3 0	0 8
	a. Overprint double ..	£32		
19	3d. ultramarine ..	3 0	6 0	1 6
20	4d. orge.-yell. & sage-grn.	5 0	6 0	1 3
21	6d. black and violet ..	8 0	10 0	3 0
22	1s. orange-yellow ..	10 0	15 0	5 0
23	1s. 3d. pale violet ..	12 0	22 0	7 0
24	2s. 6d. purple & green	40 0	60 0	22 6
25	5s. purple and blue ..	60 0	65 0	22 6
26	10s. blue & olive-green	85 0	£5	35 0
27	£1 green and red ..	£12	£15	60 0

Two sets may be made with this overprint, one with bold lettering, and the other with thinner lettering and smaller stops.

V. "South West" 16 *mm. long;* "Zuidwest" 12 *mm. long;* 14 *mm. between lines of opt.* (JULY 1924).

8	2s. 6d. purple & green	30 0	60 0	20 0

I. "South West" 16 *mm. long;* * "Zuidwest" 12 *mm. long;* 9½ *mm. between lines of opt.* (DEC., 1924).

9	½d. green	1 6	3 0	1 0
	1d. rose-red	1 6	2 6	0 8
	2d. dull purple ..	2 0	2 6	0 6
2	3d. ultramarine ..	4 0	8 0	2 6
2*a*	3d. deep bright blue ..	50 0		
3	4d. orge.-yell. & sage-grn.	4 0	6 0	1 3
4	6d. black and violet ..	6 0	12 6	4 0
	1s. orange-yellow ..	5 0	15 0	5 0
	1s. 3d. pale violet ..	8 0	20 0	6 0
	2s. 6d. purple & green	15 0	37 6	12 0
	5s. purple and blue ..	40 0	90 0	35 0
	10s. blue & olive-green	80 0	£8	50 0
	£1 green and red ..	£10	£12	85 0
a	£1 pale olive-grn. & red	£10	£12	

* Two sets with this overprint may be made ıe with "South West" 16 mm. long, and the her 16½ mm. the difference occurring in the acing between the words. No. 40*a* only exists th the latter spacing.

Suidwes Afrika. **South West Africa.**

(5) (6)

1926. *Pictorial types of S. Africa overprinted with T* **5** *(on stamps inscribed in Afrikaans) and* **6** *(on stamps inscribed in English) sideways, alternately in black.*

		Un. pair	*Us. pair*	*Us. single*
41	½d. black and green ..	1 6	1 9	0 4
42	1d. black and carmine	2 0	2 0	0 6
43	6d. green and orange ..	4 0	12 0	4 0

SOUTH WEST AFRICA **SUIDWES-AFRIKA**

(7) (8)

Triangular stamps of S. Africa, imperf., optd. with T **7** (E) *or T* **8** (A.).

			Single stamps. E.	A.
44	**10**	4d. grey-blue ..	1 3 2 6	1 3 2 6

1927. *As Nos.* 41/3, *but Afrikaans opt. on stamp inscr. in English and vice versa.*

		Un. pair	*Us. pair*	*Us. single*
45	½d. black and green ..	1 0	1 3	0 4
	a. "Africa" without stop			
46	1d. black and carmine	1 6	2 0	0 6
	a. "Africa" without stop			
47	6d. green and orange ..	3 0	10 0	3 0
	a. "Africa" without stop	£8		

SOUTH WEST AFRICA

(9)

1927. *As No.* 44E, *but overprint T* **9**.

		Single stamps.
48	4d. grey-blue	4 0 5 0

1927. *Pictorial stamps of South Africa overprinted alternately as T* **5** *and* **6**, *in blue, but with lines of overprint spaced* 16 *mm.*

		Un pair	*Us. pair*	*Us. single*
49	2d. grey and purple ..	2 0	4 0	0 10
50	3d. black and red ..	2 0	5 0	1 3
51	1s. brown and blue ..	6 0	15 0	5 0
52	2s. 6d. green & brown	35 0	75 0	25 0
53	5s. black and green ..	55 0	90 0	40 0
54	10s. blue & bistre-brown	55 0	90 0	40 0

A variety of Nos. 49, 50, 51, and 54, with spacing 16½ mm. between lines of overprint, occurs in one vertical row of each sheet.

1927. *As No.* 44, *but perf.* 11½ *by John Meinert, Ltd., Windhoek.*

		Single stamps. E.	A.
55	4d. grey-blue ..	2 0 2 6	2 0 2 6
	a. Imp. btwn. (pair)	55 0	

S.W.A.

(10)

1927–30. *Optd. with T* **10.**

(*a*) *T* **3** *of South Africa.*

		Single stamps.	
56	1s. 3d. pale violet	6 0	7 6
	a. Without stop after "A" ..	45 0	
57	£1 pale olive-green and red ..	65 0	80
	a. Without stop after "A" ..	£28	

(*b*) *Pictorial stamps of South Africa.*

		Un. pair	*Us. pair*	*Us singl.*
58	½d. black and green ..	1 0	1 6	0 3
	a. Without stop after "A"	12 6		
	b. "S.W.A." opt. above value	2 6	1 6	0 6
59	1d. black and carmine	1 0	1 6	0 2
	a. Without stop after "A"	10 0		
	b. "S.W.A." opt. at top (30.4.30)	1 6		
60	2d. grey and purple ..	2 0	3 0	0 6
	a. Without stop after "A"	20 0		
	b. Opt. double, one invert.	£18	£22	
61	3d. black and red ..	3 0	4 0	1 0
	a. Without stop after "A"	16 0		
62	4d. brown (1928) ..	2 0	3 0	0 6
	a. Without stop after "A"	17 6		
63	6d. green and orange ..	4 0	6 0	1 3
	a. Without stop after "A"	20 0		
64	1s. brown and blue ..	8 0	12 0	2 0
	a. Without stop after "A"			
65	2s. 6d. green & brown	12 6	25 0	8 0
	a. Without stop after "A"	45 0		
66	5s. black and green ..	22 6	45 0	15 0
	a. Without stop after "A"	70 0		
67	10s. blue and bistre-brn.	45 0	80 0	27 6
	a. Without stop after "A"	90 0		

The overprint is normally found at the base of the ½d., 1d., 6d., 1s. 3d. and £1 values and at the top of the remainder.

1930. *Nos.* 42 *and* 43 *of South Africa* (*rotogravure printing*), *optd. with T* **10.**

68	½d. black and green ..	2 6	3 6	0 9
69	1d. black and carmine	1 6	3 0	0 8

1930. *Air. T* **17** *of South Africa optd.* (*a*) *As T* **10.**

		Un. single	*Us. single*
70	4d. green (first printing) ..	4 0	6 0
	a. No stop after "A" of "S.W.A."	£5	£5
	b. Later printings	2 6	4 0
71	1s. orange (first printing) ..	30 0	35 0
	a. No stop after "A" of "S.W.A."	£14	£14
	b. Later printings	5 0	8 0

First printing: Thick letters, blurred impression. Stops with rounded corners.

Later printings: Thinner letters, clear impression. Clean cut, square stops.

S.W.A.

(11)

(*b*) *As T* **11.**

72	4d. green	1 6	2 6
73	1s. orange	3 0	6 0

12. Gom-pauw.

13. Cape Cross.

14. Bogenfels.

15. Windhoek.

16. Waterberg.

17. Luderitz Bay.

18. Bush scene.

19. Elands.

20. Zebra and Gnus.

21. Herero huts.

22. The Welwitschia plant.

23. Okuwahaken Falls.

24. Monoplane over Windhoek.

25. Biplane over Windhoek.

(Recess. Bradbury, Wilkinson.)

1931 (5 Mar.). *T* **12** *to* **25** (*inscr. alternately in English and Afrikaans*). *W* **9** *of South Africa. P* 14×13½. (*a*) *Postage.*

No.		Un. pair	Us. pair	Us. single
74	½d. black and emerald	2 0	0 6	0 3
75	1d. indigo and scarlet	0 8	0 6	0 3
76	2d. blue and brown ..	0 8	0 8	0 3
77	3d. grey-blue & blue ..	1 4	1 6	0 6
78	4d. green and purple..	1 4	2 0	0 6
79	6d. blue and brown ..	1 6	2 0	0 6
80	1s. chocolate and blue	3 0	3 6	0 10
81	1s. 3d. violet and yell.	10 0	10 0	1 9
82	2s. 6d. carmine & grey	7 6	10 0	2 6
83	5s. sage-grn. & red-brn.	17 6	22 6	6 0
84	10s. red-brn. & emerald	50 0	60 0	10 0
85	20s. lake & blue-green..	60 0	70 0	22 6
	(*b*) *Air.*			
86	3d. brown and blue ..	20 0	45 0	15 0
87	10d. black & purple-brn.	40 0	80 0	40 0

26

(Recess. Bradbury, Wilkinson.)

1935 (6 May). *Silver Jubilee. Inscr. bilingually. W* **9** *of South Africa. P* 14×13½.

No.	Type		Un. single	Us. single
8	**26**	1d. black and scarlet ..	0 10	2 0
9	,,	2d. black and sepia ..	1 3	3 0
0	,,	3d. black and blue	27 6	35 0
1	,,	6d. black and purple ..	12 6	15 0

1935–36. *Voortrekker Memorial Fund. T* **17a** *to* **20** *of South Africa optd. with T* **10.**

No.		Un. pair	Us. pair	Us. single
2	½d.+½d. ol.-grn. & grn.	1 6	4 6	1 6
3	1d.+½d. grey-black and pink	2 6	7 6	2 6
4	2d.+1d. grey-green and purple ..	6 0	12 0	4 0
	a. Without stop after "A" ..	£12		
	3d.+1½d. grey-grn. & blue	12 0	18 0	6 0
	a. Without stop after "A" ..			

27. Mail transport.

28

(Recess. Bradbury, Wilkinson.)

1937 (1 Mar.). *W* **9** *of S. Africa. P* 14×13½.

No.	Type				
96	**27**	1½d. purple brown ..	1 4	2 6	0 3

(Recess. Bradbury, Wilkinson & Co., Ltd.)

1937 (12 May). *Coronation. W* **9** *of South Africa. P* 13½×14.

No.	Type				
97	**28**	½d. black & emerald	0 4	0 9	0 3
98	,,	1d. black & scarlet	0 6	1 0	0 4
99	,,	1½d. black & orange	0 8	1 6	0 6
100	,,	2d. black and brown	0 10	2 0	0 8
101	,,	3d. black and blue	1 4	2 6	0 10
102	,,	4d. black and purple	1 6	3 0	1 0
103	,,	6d. black & yellow	2 6	4 6	1 6
104	,,	1s. black	5 0	7 6	2 6

1938 (14 Dec.). *Voortrekker Centenary Memorial. Nos.* 76 *to* 79 *of South Africa optd. as T* **11.**

No.				
105	½d.+½d. blue and green	2 6	3 0	1 0
106	1d.+1d. blue and car.	4 0	5 0	1 3
107	1½d.+1½d. chocolate & blue-green ..	10 0	11 6	2 6
108	3d.+3d. bright blue ..	17 6	18 6	4 0

1938 (14 Dec.). *Voortrekker Commemoration. Nos.* 80/1 *of South Africa optd. as T* **11.**

No.				
109	1d. blue & carmine..	2 6	5 0	1 3
110	1½d. greenish blue and brown ..	6 0	7 6	2 6

1939 (17 July). *250th Anniv. of Landing of Huguenots in South Africa and Huguenot Commemoration Fund. Nos.* 82/4 *of South Africa optd. as T* **11.**

No.				
111	½d.+½d. brn. & green	2 6	4 6	1 6
112	1d.+1d. grn. & carm.	5 0	7 6	2 6
113	1½d.+1½d. blue-grn. & purple	10 0	12 0	3 6

SWA (29) SWA (30) SWA (31)

1941–42. *War Effort. Nos.* 88/95 *of South Africa optd. with T* **29** *or* **30** (3*d. and* 1*s.*).

(*a*) *Inscr. alternately.*

No.	Description	*Un. unit*	*Us. unit*	*Us. single*
114	½d. green	0 8	1 0	0 3
	a. Blue-green ('42)	0 8	1 0	0 3
115	1d. carmine	1 0	1 0	0 3
116	1½d. myrtle-grn. ('42)	2 6	2 0	0 6
117	3d. blue	2 0	3 0	0 8
118	4d. orange-brown	3 0	5 0	1 3
	a. Red-brown	4 0	5 0	1 3
119	6d. red-orange	3 6	7 6	2 0

(*b*) *Inscr. bilingually.*

No.	Description	*Un. single*	*Us. single*
120	2d. violet	1 3	1 3
121	1s. brown	3 0	3 6

1943–44. *War Effort* (*reduced sizes*). *Nos.* 96 *to* 103 *of South Africa, optd. with T* **29** (1½*d. and* 1*s., No.* 129), *or T* **31** (*other values*).

(*a*) *Inscr. alternately.*

No.	Description	*Un. unit*	*Us. unit*	*Us. single*
122	½d. blue-green (T)	0 9	1 0	0 3
	a. Green	1 6	1 6	0 4
	b. Greenish blue	0 9	1 0	0 3
123	1d. carmine-red (T)	1 0	1 6	0 3
	a. Bright carmine	1 0	1 6	0 3
124	1½d. red-brown (P)	0 8	1 6	0 4
125	2d. reddish violet (P)	2 6	2 6	0 10
	a. Violet	2 0	2 0	0 6
126	3d. blue (T)	2 6	3 0	0 6
127	6d. red-orange (P)	2 6	4 0	1 0
	a. Opt. inverted			
	(*b*) *Inscr. bilingually.*			
128	4d. slate-green (T)	2 6	3 6	1 0
129	1s. brn. (opt. *T* **29**) (P)	5 0	7 6	2 6
	a. Opt. *T* 31 ('44)	3 6	7 6	2 6
	b. Opt. *T* 31 inverted	£28	£28	70 0

The "units" referred to above consist of pairs (P) or triplets (T).

No. 127 exists with another type of opt. as Type **31**, but with broader "s", narrower "w" and more space between the letters.

1943 (15 JAN.). *No.* 104 *of South Africa, optd. with T* **29.**

No.	Description	*Un. pair*	*Us. pair*	*Us. single*
130	1s. 3d. olive-brown	5 0	6 0	1 0

1945. *Victory. Nos.* 108 *to* 110 *of South Africa optd. with T* **30.**

No.	Description			
131	1d. brown & carmine	0 8	1 3	0 4
132	2d. slate-blue & violet	1 0	2 0	0 7
133	3d. deep blue & blue	1 6	3 0	0 10

1947 (17 FEB.). *Royal Visit. Nos.* 111/3 *of South Africa optd. as T* **31**, *but* 8½ × 2 *mm.*

No.	Description			
134	1d. black and carmine	0 6	0 6	0 3
135	2d. violet	0 10	0 9	0 4
136	3d. blue	1 0	1 3	0 6

1948 (26 APR.). *Royal Silver Wedding. No.* 125 *of South Africa, optd. as T* **31**, *but* 4 × 2 *mm.*

No.	Description			
137	3d. blue and silver	1 0	1 0	0 4

1949 (1 OCT.). 75*th Anniv. of U.P.U. Nos.* 128 *to* 130 *of South Africa optd. as T* **30**, *but* 13 × 4 *mm.*

No.	Description			
138	½d. blue-green	0 6	0 8	0 3
139	1½d. brown-red	1 0	1 3	0 3
140	3d. bright blue	1 10	2 0	0 6

S W A

(32)

1949 (1 DEC.). *Inauguration of Voortrekker Monument, Pretoria. Nos.* 131/3 *of South Africa optd. with T* **32.**

No.	Description	*Un. single*	*Us. single*
141	1d. magenta	0 6	0 6
142	1½d. blue-green	0 6	0 6
143	3d. blue	1 0	1 0

1952 (14 MAR.). *Tercentenary of Landing of Van Riebeeck. Nos.* 136 *to* 140 *of South Africa optd. as T* **30**, *but* 8 × 3½ *mm.* (1*d.,* 4½*d.*) *or* 11 × 4 *mm.* (*others*).

No.	Description		
144	½d. brn.-purple & olive-grey	0 4	0 9
145	1d. deep blue-green	0 6	0 9
146	2d. deep violet	0 8	1 0
147	4½d. blue	1 3	3 6
148	1s. brown	2 6	4 0

PRINTERS. All the following stamps were rotogravure-printed by the Government Printer, Pretoria.

33. Queen Elizabeth II and *Catophractes Alexandri.*

1953 (2 JUNE). *Coronation. As T* **33** (*Queen and various indigenous flowers*). *P* 14.

No.	Description		
149	1d. bright carmine	2 3	2 6
150	2d. deep bluish green	3 6	4 0
151	4d. magenta	5 0	6 0
152	6d. dull ultramarine	6 6	7 6
153	1s. deep orange-brown	10 6	12 6

Designs:—2d. *Bauhinia Macrantha*, 4d. *Caralluma Nebrownii*, 6d. *Gloriosa Virescens*, 1s. *Rhigozum Tricholotum.*

34. "Two Bucks" (rock painting). **36.** "Rhinoceros Hunt" (rock painting).

37. "White Elephant and Giraffe" (rock painting). **35.** "White Lady" (rock painting).

38. Karakul Lamb. **39.** Ovambo Woman blowing Horn.

40. Ovambo Woman.

41. Herero Woman.

42. Ovambo Girl.

43. Lioness.

44. Gemsbok.

45. Elephant.

(Des. O. Schroeder (1d. to 4d.), M. Vandeneschen (4½d. to 10s.).)

1954 (15 Nov.). *W* **9** *of South Africa (sideways on vert. designs). P* 14.

154	**34**	1d. brown-red	0	6	0	4
155	**35**	2d. deep brown	0	6	0	4
156	**36**	3d. dull purple	0	8	0	4
157	**37**	4d. blackish olive	1	6	2	0
158	**38**	4½d. deep blue	1	6	2	0
159	**39**	6d. myrtle-green	1	3	1	0
160	**40**	1s. deep mauve	2	0	1	6
161	**41**	1s. 3d. cerise	2	6	2	0
162	**42**	1s. 6d. purple	3	0	3	0
163	**43**	2s. 6d. bistre-brown	7	6	7	6
164	**44**	5s. deep bright blue	12	6	12	6
165	**45**	10s. deep myrtle-green	25	0	25	0

1960. *W* **102** *of South Africa (sideways on vert. designs). P* 14.

166	**34**	1d. brown-red	0	8	0	3
167	**35**	2d. deep brown	0	9	0	4
168	**36**	3d. dull purple	1	0	0	8
169	**37**	4d. blackish olive	1	6	1	3
170	**42**	1s. 6d. purple	4	0	3	6

Currency changed. 100 cents = 1 rand.

46. G.P.O., Windhoek.

47. Finger Rock.

48. Mounted Soldier Monument.

49. Quivertree.

50. S.W.A. House, Windhoek.

50*a*. Flamingoes and Swakopmund Lighthouse.

51. Fishing Industry.

52. Flamingo.

53. German Lutheran Church, Windhoek.

54. Diamond.

55. Fort Namutoni.

55*a*. Hardap Dam.

56. Topaz.

57. Tourmaline.

58. Heliodor.

1961 (14 Feb.)–**63.** *W* **102** *of South Africa (sideways on vert. designs). P* 14.

171	**46**	½ c. brown & pale blue ..	0 3	0 3
172	**47**	1 c. sepia and mauve	0 3	0 2
173	**48**	1½ c. slate-vio. & salmon ..	0 6	0 4
174	**49**	2 c. dp. grn. and yellow	0 8	0 6
175	**50**	2½ c. red-brown & lt. blue	0 9	0 6
175*a*	**50*a***	3 c. ultramarine and rose-red (1.10.62)	0 6	0 7
176	**51**	3½ c. indigo & blue-green	0 7	0 6
177	**52**	5 c. scarlet and grey-blue	1 0	0 10
178	**53**	7½ c. sepia and lemon ..	1 1	0 10
179	**54**	10 c. blue and grnish. yell.	1 5	1 0
180	**55**	12½ c. indigo and lemon ..	1 9	1 6
180*a*	**55*a***	15 c. chocolate & light blue (16.3.63)	2 0	2 6
181	**56**	20 c. brown & red-orange	2 9	2 6
182	**57**	50 c. dp. bluish green and yellow-orange ..	6 9	6 0
183	**58**	1 r. yell., maroon & blue	13 3	12 6

1962–64. *As No.* 171, *etc,, but without watermark.*

184	**46**	½ c. brn. & pale bl. (8.62)	0 2	0 2
186	**48**	1½ c. slate-vio. & sal. (9.62)	0 4	0 3
187	**49**	2 c. dp. grn. & yell. (5.62)	0 5	0 4
188	**50**	2½ c. red-brown and light blue ('64)	0 6	0 4
190	**52**	5 c. scar. & grey-bl. (9.62)	0 10	0 8

59. " Agricultural Development ".

963 (16 Mar.). *Opening of Hardap Dam. W* **102** **1***of South Africa (sideways). P* 14.

197	**59**	3 c. chocolate & lt. green	0 9	0 8

60. Centenary Emblem and Map.

61. Centenary Emblem and part of Globe.

1963 (30 Aug.). *Centenary of Red Cross. P* 14.

198	**60**	7½ c. red, blk. and lt. blue	1 9	2 0
199	**61**	15 c. red, blk. & orge.-brn.	3 0	3 6

62. Interior of Assembly Hall.

63. Calvin.

1964 (14 May). *Opening of Legislative Assembly Hall, Windhoek. W* **102** *of South Africa. P* 14.

200	**62**	3 c. ultramarine & salmon	0 8	0 8

1964 (1 Oct.). *400th Anniv. of Death of Calvin (Protestant Reformer). P* 14.

201	**63**	2½ c. brown-purple & gold	0 9	0 9
202	,,	15 c. deep bluish green and gold	2 9	3 0

64. Mail Runner of 1890.

65. Kurt von François (founder).

(Des. D. Aschenborn.)

1965 (18 Oct.). *75th Anniv. of Windhoek. W* **127** *of South Africa (sideways). P* 14.

203	**64**	3 c. sepia and scarlet ..	0 6	0 8
204	**65**	15 c. red-brn. & blue-grn.	2 0	2 3

POSTAGE DUE STAMPS.

Postage Due stamps of Transvaal or South Africa overprinted.

1923. *Optd. with T* **1** *and* **2** *alternately.*

I. 14 *mm. between lines of overprint.*

(*a*) *On stamps of Transvaal.*

		Un. pair	*Us. pair*	*Us. single*
D1	5d. black and violet ..	5 0	10 0	3 0
	a. " Wes " for " West " ..	£7		
	b. " Afrika " (no stop) ..	90 0		

		Un. pair	Us. pair	Us. single
D2	6d. black & red-brown	8 0		
	a. "Wes" for "West"..			
	b. "Afrika" (no stop) ..	£6		

(b) *On S. African stamps* (*De La Rue printing*).

		Un. pair	Us. pair	Us. single
D3	2d. black and violet ..	12 6	22 6	7 6
	a. "Wes" for "West"..	£6	£6	
	b. "Afrika" (no stop) ..	£8		
D4	3d. black and blue ..	3 0	12 6	4 0
	a. "Wes" for "West"..	55 0		
D5	6d. black and slate ..	8 0	15 0	5 0
	a. "Wes" for "West"..	65 0		

(c) *On S. African stamps* (*Pretoria printing*).

(i) *Type* D 1 (A). *Rouletted.*

		Un. pair	Us. pair	Us. single
D6	1d. black and rose ..	1 6		
	a. "Wes" for "West" ..	25 0		
	b. "Afrika" (no stop) ..	55 0		
	c. Unrouletted between (pair)			
D7	1½d. blk. & yell.-brown	1 0	3 0	1 0
	a. "Wes" for West"..	22 6		
	b. "Afrika" (no stop) ..	20 0		

(ii) *Type D* 1 (B.). *P* 14.

		Un. pair	Us. pair	Us. single
D8	½d. black and green ..	0 8	2 0	0 6
	a. Overprint inverted ..	£12		
	b. Overprint double ..			
	c. "Wes" for "West"..	17 6		
	d. "Afrika" (no stop) ..	12 6		
D9	2d. black and violet ..	2 0	3 0	1 0
	a. "Wes" for "West"..	35 0		
	b. "Afrika" (no stop) ..	22 6		

The "Wes" variety occurs in the English overprint only, in some printings.

A variety of Nos. D1, D4, D5 and D9 with spacing 15 mm. between lines of overprint occurs on four stamps in each pane of certain printings of this setting.

Nos. D1, D4, D6, D7 and D9 exist with 2 mm. spacing between "South" and "West," and also with 2½ mm.; Nos. D2, D3 and D8 only with 2 mm. spacing; and No. D5 only with 2½ mm.

II. 10 *mm. between lines of overprint.*

(a) *On stamp of Transvaal.*

		Un. pair	Us. pair	Us. single
D10	5d. black and violet..	80 0	80 0	—

(b) *On S. African stamps* (*De La Rue printing*).

		Un. pair	Us. pair	Us. single
D11	2d. black and violet..	3 0	10 0	3 0
	a. "Afrika" (no stop)..	70 0		
D12	3d. black and blue ..	3 0		
	a. "Afrika" (no stop)..	40 0		

(c) *On S. African stamp* (*Pretoria printing*). *Type* D 1 (A), *rouletted.*

		Un. pair	Us. pair	Us. single
D13	1d. black and rose (July 1923) ..	£75		

1923–27. *Overprinted as T* **3** ("Zuidwest" *in one word without hyphen*) *and* **4**.

III. "South West" 14 *mm. long;* "Zuidwest" 11 *mm. long;* 14 *mm. between lines of overprint.* (SEPT., 1923).

(a) *On stamp of Transvaal.*

		Un. pair	Us. pair	Us. single
D14	6d. black and red-brn.	8 0		

(b) *On S. African stamps* (*Pretoria printing*). *Type* D 1 (A). (i) *Rouletted.*

		Un. pair	Us. pair	Us. single
D15	1d. black and rose ..	3 0		

(ii) *P* 14.

		Un. pair	Us. pair	Us. single
D16	½d. black and green	4 0		
D17	1d. black and rose ..	6 0	10 0	2 6

IV. "South West" 16 *mm. long;* "Zuidwest" 12 *mm. long;* 14 *mm. between lines of overprint.*

(a) *On stamp of Transvaal.*

		Un. pair	Us. pair	Us. single
D17a	5d. black & violet ..	£32	£40	

(b) *On S. African stamps* (*Pretoria printing*). *Type* D 1 (B). *P* 14.

		Un. pair	Us. pair	Us. single
D18	½d. black and green..	2 0		
D19	1d. black and rose ..	7 0	10 0	3 0
D20	6d. black and slate ..	4 0	5 0	1 9
	a. "Afrika" (no stop)..	£14		

V. *As* IV, *but* 12 *mm. between lines of overprint.*

(a) *On stamp of Transvaal.*

		Un. pair	Us. pair	Us. single
D21	5d. black and violet	7 6		

(b) *On S. African stamp* (*De La Rue printing*).

		Un. pair	Us. pair	Us. single
D22	3d. black and blue ..	7 6		

(c) *On S. African stamps* (*Pretoria printing*). *Type* D 1 (B). *P* 14.

		Un. pair	Us. pair	Us. single
D23	½d. black and green..	2 0		
D24	1½d. blk. & yell.-brn...	2 0		

VI. *As* IV, *but* 9½ *mm. between lines of overprint.*

(a) *On stamp of Transvaal.*

		Un. pair	Us. pair	Us. single
D25	5d. black and violet..	2 6	3 6	1 6
	a. "Africa" (no stop)..	40 0		

(b) *On S. African stamp* (*De La Rue printing*).

		Un. pair	Us. pair	Us. single
D26	3d. black and blue ..	8 0		

(c) *On S. African stamps* (*Pretoria printing*). *Type* D 1 (B). *P* 14.

		Un. pair	Us. pair	Us. single
D27	½d. black and green	3 0		
D28	1d. black and rose ..	0 8		
	a. "Africa" (no stop)..	£6		
D29	1½d. black & yell.-brn.	1 0		
	a. "Africa" (no stop)..	20 0		
D30	2d. black and violet..	1 0	2 0	0 8
	a. "Africa" (no stop)..	22 6		
D31	3d. black and blue ..	1 6	2 6	1 0
	a. "Africa" (no stop)..	27 6		
D32	6d. black and slate..	8 0		
	a. "Africa" (no stop)..	£6		

In Nos. D18 to D25, D29, D31 and D32, "South West" is 16 mm. long, and in Nos. D26 and D27, 16½ mm. long. Nos. D28 and D30 exist in both 16 mm. and 16½ mm. varieties. (*See note after* No. 40*a*.) In Nos. D20, D29, D31 and D32 a variety with "South West" 16½ mm. long occurs once only in each sheet of 120 stamps (in certain printings only, in the case of D20), and similarly Nos. D28 and D30 occur with the two measurements on the same sheet of certain printings.

Suidwes **South West**

Afrika. (D 1) **Africa.** (D 2)

1927. *Overprinted as Types* D 1 *and* D 2, *alternately.* 12 *mm. between lines of overprint.*

(a) *On stamp of Transvaal.*

		Un. pair	Us. pair	Us. single
D33	5d. black and violet..	10 0		

(b) *On S. African stamps* (*Pretoria printing*). *Type* D 1, *redrawn. P* 14.

		Un. pair	Us. pair	Us. single
D34	1½d. black & yell.-brn.	1 6	3 0	1 0
	a. "Africa" (no stop)..	35 0		
D35	2d. blk. & pale violet	2 0	3 0	1 0
	a. "Africa" (no stop)..	40 0		
D36	2d. black & dp. violet	3 0	5 0	1 3
	a. "Africa" (no stop)..	40 0		
D37	3d. black and blue ..	8 0	12 0	4 0
	a. "Africa" (no stop)..	80 0		
D38	6d. black and slate ..	8 0	12 0	4 0
	a. "Africa" (no stop)..	£6		

(c) *On S. African stamp* (*Pretoria printing*). *Type* D 2. *P* 14.

		Un. pair	Us. pair	Us. single
D39	1d. black and carmine	1 6	1 6	0 6
	a. "Africa" (no stop)..	15 0		

1928–29. *Optd. with T* **10**. *On S. African stamps (Pretoria printing).* *P* 14.

(*a*) *Type* D **1**, *redrawn.*

		Un. single	Us. single
D40	3d. black and blue	2 0	2 6
	a. Without stop after "A" ..	50 0	
D41	6d. black and slate	6 0	8 0
	(*b*) *Type* D **2**.		
D42	½d. black and green ..	0 4	0 4
D43	1d. black and carmine ..	0 4	0 4
	a. Without stop after "A" ..		
D44	2d. black and mauve ..	0 6	0 8
D45	3d. black and blue	1 3	1 6
D46	6d. black and slate	1 6	2 0
	a. Without stop after "A" ..	65 0	

D 3

D 4

(Litho. Bradbury, Wilkinson & Co.)

1931 (23 Feb.). *Inscribed bilingually.* *W* **9** *of South Africa.* *P* 12.

D47	D **3**	½d. black and green ..	0 3	0 6
D48	,,	1d. black and scarlet ..	0 6	0 8
D49	,,	2d. black and violet ..	0 8	0 10
D50	,,	3d. black and blue ..	0 10	1 3
D51	,,	6d. black and slate ..	1 3	2 0

(The following issues have been printed by the S.A. Government printer, Pretoria.)

1959 (18 May). *Centre typo; frame roto.* *W* **9** *of South Africa.* *P* 15 × 14.

D52	D **4**	1d. black and scarlet ..	0 9	1 0
D53	,,	2d. black & reddish vio.	0 9	1 0
D54	,,	3d. black and blue ..	1 9	2 6

1960 (Dec.). *As Nos.* D52 *and* D54 *but W* **102** *of South Africa.*

D55	1d. black and scarlet ..	3 6	4 0
D56	3d. black and blue	3 6	4 6

1961 (14 Feb.). *As Nos.* D52 *etc., but whole stamp roto. and value in cents.* *W* **102** *of South Africa.*

D57	1 c. black and blue-green ..	0 3	0 3
D58	2 c. black and scarlet ..	0 5	0 6
D59	4 c. black & reddish violet ..	0 9	1 0
D60	5 c. black and light blue ..	0 10	1 0
D61	6 c. black and green ..	0 11	1 6
D62	10 c. black and yellow ..	1 5	2 0

OFFICIAL STAMPS.

OFFICIAL South West Africa. (O 1)

OFFISIEEL Suidwes Afrika. (O 2)

1927. *Nos.* 30, 31, 10 *and* 32 *of South Africa overprinted with Type* O **1** *on English stamp and* O **2** *on Afrikaans stamp alternately.*

		Un. pair	Us. pair	Us. single
O1	½d. black and green ..	65 0	65 0	20 0
O2	1d. black & carmine ..	65 0	65 0	20 0
O3	2d. dull purple ..	£7	£5	35 0
O4	6d. green and orange ..	60 0	65 0	20 0

OFFICIAL S.W.A. (O 3)

OFFISIEEL S.W.A. (O 4)

1929. *Nos.* 30, 31, 32 *and* 34 *of South Africa optd. with Type* O **3** *on English stamp and* O **4** *on Afrikaans stamp.*

		Un. pair	Us. pair	Us. single
O5	½d. black and green ..	1 0	2 6	0 9
O6	1d. black and carmine	1 6	3 6	1 0
O7	2d. grey and purple ..	2 6	5 0	1 6
	a. Pair, stamp without stop after "OFFICIAL" ..	12 6	17 6	5 0
	b. Pair, stamp without stop after "OFFISIEEL"	10 0	17 6	5 0
	c. Pair comprising a and b	22 6	23 0	8 6
O8	6d. green and orange ..	5 0	17 6	5 0

Types O **3** and O **4** are normally spaced 17 mm. between lines on all except the 2d. value, which is spaced 13 mm.

Except on No. O7, the words "OFFICIAL" or "OFFISIEEL" normally have no stops after them.

OFFICIAL S.W.A. (O 5)

OFFISIEEL S.W.A. (O 6)

OFFICIAL. S.W.A. (O 7)

OFFISIEEL. S.W.A. (O 8)

1929. *Nos.* 30, 31 *and* 32 *of South Africa optd. with Types* O **5** *and* O **6**, *and No.* 34 *with Types* O **7** *and* O **8**, *languages to correspond.*

O 9	½d. black & green ..	0 8	1 0	0 4
O10	1d. black and carm.	1 0	1 0	0 4
O11	2d. grey and purple ..	2 6	3 0	0 9
	a. Pair, one stamp without stop after "OFFICIAL" ..	12 6		
	b. Pair, one stamp without stop after "OFFISIEEL" ..	10 0		
	c. Pair consisting of a. and b.	20 0		
O12	6d. green and orange	1 6	3 6	1 0

OFFICIAL (O 9)

OFFISIEEL (O 10)

1931. *English stamp optd. with Type* O **9** *and Afrikaans stamp with Type* O **10** *in red.*

O13	**12**	½d. black & emer.	0 8	1 3	0 4
O14	**13**	1d. indigo & scarlet	0 8	1 3	0 3
O15	**14**	2d. blue and brown	0 10	1 9	0 4
O16	**17**	6d. blue and brown	3 0	4 0	1 3

OFFICIAL (O 11)

OFFISIEEL (O 12)

1938 (1 July). *English stamp optd. with Type* O **11** *and Afrikaans with Type* O **12** *in red.*

O17	**27**	1½d. purple-brown	6 0	8 0	1 6

OFFICIAL (O 13)

OFFISIEEL (O 14)

1945–50. *English stamp optd. with Type* O **13** *and Afrikaans stamp with Type* O **14** *in red*

			Un. pair	*Us. pair*	*Us. single*
O18	**12**	½d. blk. & emerald	1 6	1 6	0 4
O19	**13**	1d. ind. & scar. ('50)	0 10	2 0	0 6
O20	**27**	1½d. pur.-brown ..	1 0	3 0	0 9
O21	**14**	2d. bl. & brn. ('47?)	£50	£50	—
O22	**17**	6d. blue & brown	1 10	3 6	1 0

OFFICIAL (O **15**) **OFFISIEEL** (O **16**)

1951 (16 Nov.)–**52.** *English stamp optd. with Type* O **15** *and Afrikaans stamp with Type* O **16**, *in red.*

O23	**12**	½d. blk. & emer. ('52)	0 10	1 0	0 4
O24	**13**	1d. indigo & scarlet	0 8	1 0	0 2
		a. Opts. transposed	35 0		
O25	**27**	1½d. purple-brown	1 0	1 3	0 6
		a. Opts. transposed	35 0		
O26	**14**	2d. blue & brown	1 4	1 6	0 6
		a. Opts. transposed	35 0		
O27	**17**	6d. blue & brown	2 6	3 0	0 8
		a. Opts. transposed	45 0		

The above errors refer to stamps with the English overprint on Afrikaans stamp and *vice versa.*

The use of official stamps ceased in January 1955.

SOUTHERN CAMEROONS.

The following issue, although ordered by the Southern Cameroons authorities, was also on sale in Northern Cameroons.

CAMEROONS
U.K.T.T.
(1)

1960 (1 Oct.)–**61.** *Stamps of Nigeria optd. with* T **1**, *in red (on Waterlow ptgs. or De La Rue, Nos. 2a, 4a, 7a only).*

1	**18**	½d. black and orange ..	0 6	1 0
2	**19**	1d. black & bronze-green	0 10	1 3
		a. Grey-black and dull bronze-green (19.9.61)	0 8	3 0
3	**20**	1½d. blue-green	0 10	2 0
4	**21**	2d. grey	0 10	2 0
		aa. Violet-grey	£10	£10
		a. Pale grey (19.9.61) ..	1 3	3 6
5	**22**	3d. black and deep lilac ..	1 6	1 9
6	**23**	4d. black and blue ..	1 6	3 6
7	**24**	6d. chestnut & black (*p.* 14)	2 0	3 0
		a. Perf. 13×13½ (19.9.61) ..	2 6	6 6
8	**25**	1s. black and maroon ..	3 0	4 0
9	**26**	2s. 6d. black and green ..	7 6	12 6
10	**27**	5s. black and red-orange	12 6	25 0
11	**28**	10s. black and red-brown ..	25 0	50 0
12	**29**	£1 black and violet ..	50 0	£6

The above stamps were withdrawn on September 30th, 1961, when Southern Cameroons became part of the independent republic of Cameroons.

SOUTHERN NIGERIA.

PRINTERS. All issues of Southern Nigeria were typographed by De La Rue & Co.

1

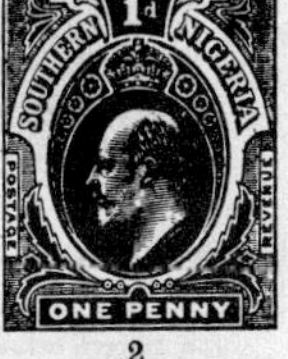

2

1901 (Mar.)–**02.** *Wmk. Crown CA.* P 14.

1	**1**	½d. black and pale green ..	1 9	2 0
1*a*	,,	½d. black and green (1902) ..	1 9	2 0
2	,,	1d. black and carmine ..	1 3	1 6
3	,,	2d black and red-brown ..	6 0	6 6
4	,,	4d. black and sage green ..	8 0	8 6
5	,,	6d. black and purple ..	10 0	15 0
6	,,	1s. green and black ..	20 0	22 6
7	,,	2s. 6d. black and brown ..	65 0	65 0
8	,,	5s. black & orange-yellow	£5	£5
9	,,	10s. black & purple/*yellow* ..	£9	£10

1903 (Mar.)–**1904.** *Wmk. Crown CA.* P 14.

10	**2**	½d. grey-black & pale green	1 6	1 3
11	,,	1d. grey-black and carmine	2 6	1 6
12	,,	2d. grey-black & chestnut	4 0	6 0
12*a*	,,	2½d. grey-black & blue ('04)	8 6	8 6
13	,,	4d. grey-black & olive-grn.	6 0	7 6
14	,,	6d. grey-black & purple ..	25 0	47 6
15	,,	1s. green and black ..	32 6	25 0
16	,,	2s. 6d. grey-black & brn.	32 6	40 0
16*a*	,,	2s. 6d. grey & yell.-brn...	£7	£20
17	,,	5s. grey black & yellow ..	80 0	80 0
18	,,	10s. grey-blk. & pur./*yellow*	£6	£6
19	,,	£1 green and violet ..	£40	£45

1904 (June)–**1908.** T **2.** *Wmk. Mult. Crown CA.* P 14.

20	½d. grey-blk. & pale grn., OC	0 8	0 9
21	1d. grey-black & carm., OC..	1 9	1 3
22	2d. grey-black & chestnut, O	4 0	4 0
22*a*	2d. pale grey & chest. O ('07)	6 0	3 6
23	2½d. grey-blk. & brt. blue, O ('05)	4 6	6 0
23*a*	3d. orange-brown and bright purple, C ('07) ..	17 6	10 0
24	4d. grey-black & olive-green OC ('05)	15 0	15 0
24*a*	4d. grey-black and pale olive-green, C (1907)	27 6	32 6
25	6d. grey-blk. & brt. pur., OC	10 0	7 6
26	1s. grey-green & black, OC..	6 0	6 0
27	2s. 6d. grey-black and brown, OC ('05)	30 0	30 0
28	5s. grey-blk. & yell., OC('05)	65 0	75 0
29	10s. grey-blk. & purple/*yellow*, C ('08)	£15	£15
30	£1 green & violet, OC ('05) ..	£23	£25

The plate for printing the central portrait was retouched early in 1907, the lines of shading on the King's cheek and particularly the fifth line counting upward from the base of the throat, which were broken in the original die, now being filled in.

All despatches from London after 7 June, 1907, were from the retouched plate. No stamps were printed on "ordinary" paper from the retouched plate. Of the stamps on chalk surfaced paper, the ½d. and 1d. were always unretouched, the 3d., 1s., 5s., and 10s. are always retouched, while the 4d., 6d., 2s. 6d. and £1 exist both unretouched and retouched.

(Die I)

(Die II)

In Die II of the 1d. the "1" of "1d." is not so thick as in Die I, while the "d" is larger and broader.

1907 (Aug.)–**1911.** T **2.** *Wmk. Mult. Crown CA.* P 14.

31	½d. pale green, O ('07) ..	2 0	0 4
31*a*	½d. blue-green, O ('10) ..	1 6	0 4
32	1d. carm., O (Die I) ('07) ..	1 3	0 8
32*a*	1d. carm.red, O (Die II) ('10)	1 0	0 3
33	2d. greyish slate, O ('09) ..	5 0	3 6
34	2½d. blue, O ('09)	5 0	12 6
35	3d. pur./*yellow*, C ('09) ..	4 0	3 0
36	4d. blk. & red/*yell.*, C ('09) ..	6 0	5 0
37	6d. dull pur. & pur. C ('09) ..	10 0	8 6

No.	Type	Description				
37a		6d. dull & brt. pur., C ('11) ..	10	0	8	6
38		1s. black/*green*, C ('09) ..	12	6	5	0
39		2s. 6d. blk. & red/*blue*, C ('09)	15	0	8	0
40		5s. grn. & red/*yell.*, C ('09) ..	80	0	85	0
41		10s. grn. & red/*grn.*, C ('09) ..	£7		£8	
42		£1 pur. & black/*red*, C ('09) ..	£18		£20	

All values of this issue were printed from the retouched head-plate.

3

1912. *Wmk. Mult. Crown CA. P* 14.

No.	Type	Description				
43	3	½d. green	1	6	1	6
44	,,	1d. red	2	0	0	8
45	,,	2d. grey	3	0	2	6
46	,,	2½d. bright blue	6	0	8	6
47	,,	3d. purple/*yellow*	3	6	2	6
48	,,	4d. black and red/*yellow* ..	7	6	7	6
49	,,	6d. dull and bright purple	7	6	4	0
50	,,	1s. black/*green*	10	0	6	0
51	,,	2s. 6d. black and red/*blue*	32	6	37	6
52	,,	5s. green and red/*yellow* ..	65	0	70	0
53	,,	10s. green and red/*green* ..	£6		£7	
54	,,	£1 purple and black/*red*	£15		£20	

Since 1914 Southern Nigeria has used the stamps of NIGERIA.

SOUTHERN RHODESIA.

1

(Recess. Waterlow.)

1924–29. *P* 14.

No.	Type	Description				
1	1	½d. blue-green	0	6	0	3
		a. Imperf. between (horiz. pair)	£28			
		b. Imperf. between (vert. pair) ..	£35			
2	,,	1d. bright rose	0	6	0	3
		a. Imperf. between (horiz. pair)	£35			
		b. Imperf. between (vert. pair) ..	£28			
		c. Perf. 12½ ('29)	15	0	40	0
3	,,	1½d. bistre-brown	0	9	1	0
		a. Imperf. between (horiz. pair)	£50			
		b. Imperf. between (vert. pair) ..	£80			
4	,,	2d. black and purple-grey ..	3	6	1	3
		a. Imperf. between (horiz. pair)	£125			
5	,,	3d. blue	3	6	4	0
6	,,	4d. black and orange-red ..	6	0	6	0
7	,,	6d. black and mauve ..	5	0	3	6
		a. Imperf. between (pair)	£125			
8	,,	8d. purple and pale green ..	10	0	20	0
9	,,	10d. blue and rose	17	6	25	0
10	,,	1s. black and light blue ..	7	6	10	0
11	,,	1s. 6d. black and yellow ..	15	0	22	6
		a. Imperf. between (pair) ..				
12	,,	2s. black and brown ..	17	6	22	6
13	,,	2s. 6d. blue and sepia ..	65	0	65	0
		a. Imperf. between (pair) ..				
14	1	5s. blue and blue-green ..	65	0	70	0
		a. Error. Blue and light blue ..	£50			

Prices for "imperf. between" varieties are for adjacent stamps from the same pane and not for those separated by wide gutter margins between vertical pairs, which come from the junction of two panes.

Collectors are warned against dangerous fakes of No. 14a, chemically produced.

2. King George V.

3. Victoria Falls.

(T **2** recess. by Bradbury, Wilkinson ; T **3** typo. by Waterlow.)

1931 (1 APRIL)–**1937.** *T* **2** (*line perf.* 12 *unless otherwise stated*) *and* **3** (*comb. perf.* 15 × 14). (*The* 11½ *perf. is comb*).

No.	Type	Description				
15	2	½d. green	0	8	0	6
		a. Perf. 11½ ('33)	0	6	0	4
		b. Perf. 14 ('35)	0	9	0	9
16	,,	1d. scarlet	0	6	0	3
		a. Perf. 11½ ('33)	1	9	0	3
		b. Perf. 14 ('35)	0	8	0	3
16c	,,	1½d. chocolate ('33) ..	60	0	65	0
		d. Perf. 11½ ('32)	1	3	1	0
17	3	2d. black and sepia ..	10	0	10	0
18	,,	3d. deep ultramarine ..	22	6	25	0
19	2	4d. black and vermilion ..	6	0	1	3
		a. Perf. 11½ ('35)	17	6	7	6
		b. Perf. 14 ('37)	55	0	50	0
20	,,	6d. black and magenta ..	8	6	1	0
		a. Perf. 11½ ('33)	17	6	2	0
		b. Perf. 14 ('36)	27	6	3	0
21	,,	8d. violet and olive-green	10	0	10	0
		a. Perf. 11½ ('34)	25	0	30	0
21b	,,	9d. verm. & olive-grn. ('34)	17	6	12	6
22	,,	10d. blue and scarlet ..	17	6	15	0
		a. Perf. 11½ ('33)	17	6	15	0
23	,,	1s. black & greenish blue ..	17	6	6	6
		a. Perf. 11½ ('36)	27	6	20	0
		b. Perf. 14 ('37)	£12		£5	
24	,,	1s. 6d. blk. & orange-yell.	17	6	20	0
		a. Perf. 11½ ('36)	47	6	45	0
25	,,	2s. black and brown ..	20	0	20	0
		a. Perf. 11½ ('33)	45	0	35	0
26	,,	2s. 6d. blue and drab ..	35	0	27	6
		a. Perf. 11½ ('33)	42	6	27	6
27	,,	5s. blue and blue-green ..	65	0	47	6
		a. Printed on gummed side ..	£45			

PRINTERS. All stamps from Types **4** to **29** were recess-printed by Waterlow except where stated.

4

1932 (MAY). *P* 12½.

No.	Type	Description				
29	4	2d. green and chocolate ..	2	0	0	1
30	,,	3d. deep ultramarine ..	8	6	3	
		a. Imperf. between (vert. pair) ..	£150		£12	

5. Victoria Falls.

1935 (6 MAY). *Silver Jubilee.* *P* 11 × 12.

31	**5**	1d. olive and rose-carmine	0	6	0	4
32	,,	2d. emerald and sepia ..	1	6	2	0
33	,,	3d. violet and deep blue ..	4	0	4	6
34	,,	6d. black and purple ..	5	6	4	0

1935–41. *Inscr.* " POSTAGE AND REVENUE ".

35	**4**	2d. green & chocolate (*p.* 12½)	5	0	5	0
		a. Perf. 14 ('41)	0	6	0	3
35*b*	,,	3d. deep blue (*p.* 14) ('38)	1	6	0	6

6. Victoria Falls and Railway Bridge.

1937 (12 MAY). *Coronation.* *P* 12½.

36	**6**	1d. olive and rose-carmine ..	0	6	0	4
37	,,	2d. emerald and sepia ..	0	8	1	0
38	,,	3d. violet and blue	6	0	8	6
39	,,	6d. black and purple ..	3	6	4	0

7. King George VI.

1937 (25 NOV.). *P* 14.

40	**7**	½d. green	0	3	0	3
41	,,	1d. scarlet	0	6	0	3
42	,,	1½d. red-brown	0	8	0	4
43	,,	4d. red-orange	1	0	0	6
44	,,	6d. grey-black	1	0	0	6
45	,,	8d. emerald-green	3	0	2	0
46	,,	9d. pale blue	2	0	2	6
47	,,	10d. purple	2	6	3	0
48	,,	1s. black and blue-green ..	2	3	1	0
49	,,	1s. 6d. black & orange-yell.	6	0	3	6
50	,,	2s. black and brown ..	5	0	2	6
51	,,	2s. 6d. ultramarine & purple	8	6	3	6
52	,,	5s. blue and blue-green ..	20	0	6	0

8. British South Africa Co.'s Arms.

9. Fort Salisbury, 1890.

10. Cecil John Rhodes (after S. P. Kendrick).

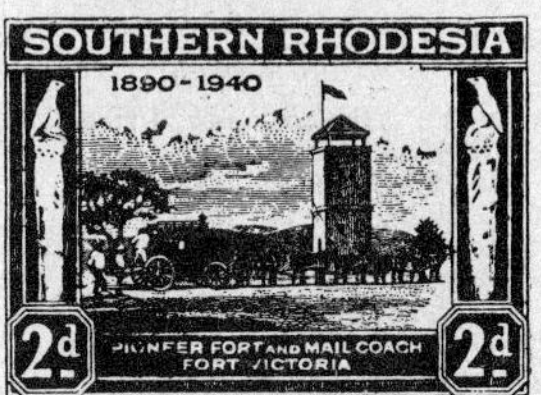

11. Fort Victoria.

12. Rhodes makes peace.

13. Victoria Falls Bridge.

14. Statue of Sir Charles Coghlan.

15. Lobengula's Kraal and Govt House, Salisbury.

(Des. Mrs. L. E. Curtis (½d., 1d., 1½d., 3d.), Mrs. I. Mount (others).)

1940 (3 June). *British South Africa Company's Golden Jubilee. P* 14.

53	**8**	½d. slate-violet and green	0	6	0	3
54	**9**	1d. violet-blue and scarlet	0	6	0	4
55	**10**	1½d. black and red-brown ..	0	8	0	6
56	**11**	2d. green and bright violet	0	8	1	0
57	**12**	3d. black and blue ..	1	0	1	3
58	**13**	4d. green and brown ..	3	6	4	0
59	**14**	6d. chocolate and green ..	2	6	3	6
60	**15**	1s. blue and green ..	3	6	4	0

16. Mounted Pioneer.

(Roto. Union Govt. Stamp Ptrs., Pretoria.)

1943 (1 Nov.). *50th Anniv. of Occupation of Matabeleland. W* **9** *of South Africa (Mult. Springbok) sideways. P* 14.

61	**16**	2d. brown and green ..	0	4	0	8

17. Queen Elizabeth II when Princess and Princess Margaret.

18. King George VI and Queen Elizabeth.

1947 (1 Apr.). *Royal Visit. P* 14.

62	**17**	½d. black and green ..	0	3	0	3
63	**18**	1d. black and scarlet ..	0	4	0	4

19. Queen Elizabeth.

SOUTHERN RHODESIA 2d VICTORY ISSUE 1939-1945 2d POSTAGE & REVENUE

20. King George VI.

21. Queen Elizabeth II when Princess.

22. Princess Margaret.

1947 (8 May). *Victory. P* 14.

64	**19**	1d. carmine	0	3	0	3
65	**20**	2d. slate	0	4	0	4
66	**21**	3d. blue	0	6	0	6
67	**22**	6d. orange	0	10	1	0

(Recess. Bradbury, Wilkinson & Co.)

1949 (10 Oct.). *75th Anniv. of Universal Postal Union. As Nos.* 115/6 *of Antigua.*

68	2d. slate-green..	1	3	1	3
69	3d. blue	2	6	2	6

23. Queen Victoria, Arms and King George VI.

1950 (12 Sept.). *Diamond Jubilee of Southern Rhodesia. P* 14.

70	**23**	2d. green and brown ..	1	0	0	6

24. "Medical Services."

25. " Agriculture."

26. " Building."

27. "Water Supplies."

28. " Transport."

(Des. A. R. Winter (2d.), Mrs. J. M. Enalim (others.).)

1953 (15 Apr.). *Centenary of Birth of Cecil Rhodes. P* 14.

71 **24** ½d. pale blue and sepia 1 0 2 6
72 **25** 1d. chestnut & blue-green 1 0 1 0
73 **26** 2d. grey-green and violet 1 6 1 9
74 **27** 4½d. dp. bl.-grn. & dp. ultra. 4 6 8 6
75 **28** 1s. black and red-brown .. 6 0 6 0

No. 74 also commemorates the Diamond Jubilee of Matabeleland.

29. Queen Elizabeth II and Arms of S. and N. Rhodesia and Nyasaland.

1953 (30 May). *Rhodes Centenary Exhibition. P* 14×13½.

6 **29** 6d. violet 3 0 3 6

30. Queen Elizabeth II.

(Recess. De La Rue.)

1953 (1 June). *Coronation. P* 12×12½.

77 **30** 2s. 6d. carmine 10 0 17 6

31. Sable Antelope.

32. Tobacco Planter.

33. Rhodes's Grave.

34. Farm Worker.

35. Flame Lily.

36. Victoria Falls.

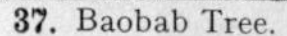

37. Baobab Tree. **38.** Lion.

39. Zimbabwe Ruins.

40. Birchenough Bridge.

41. Kariba Gorge. **42.** Basket Maker.

43. Balancing Rocks.

44. Coat-of-Arms.

(Recess; centre typo (4d.). Bradbury, Wilkinson.)

1953 (31 Aug.). *P* 13½×14 (*2d.*, *6d.*, *5s.*), 14 (*10s.*, *£1*) *or* 14×13½ (*others*).

78	**31**	½d. grey-green and claret	0	8	1	0
79	**32**	1d. green and brown ..	0	8	0	8
80	**33**	2d. deep chestnut and reddish violet	1	3	1	3
81	**34**	3d. chocolate and rose-red	1	6	2	0
82	**35**	4d. red, green & indigo ..	1	9	1	6
83	**36**	4½d. black & dp. brt. blue ..	3	0	4	0
84	**37**	6d. brown-olive and deep turquoise-green ..	3	0	1	9
85	**38**	9d. dp. blue & reddish brn.	5	0	5	0
86	**39**	1s. reddish vio. & light blue	5	0	4	0
87	**40**	2s. purple and scarlet ..	9	0	10	0
88	**41**	2s. 6d. yellow-olive and orange-brown	12	6	15	0
89	**42**	5s. yell.-brn. & dp. green ..	25	0	40	0
90	**43**	10s. red-brown and olive ..	37	6	55	0
91	**44**	£1 rose-red and black ..	70	0	90	0

For issues from 1954 to 1963 see under Rhodesia and Nyasaland.

45. Maize. **46.** Buffalo.

47. Tobacco. **48.** Kudu.

49. Citrus. **50.** Flame Lily.

51. Ansellia Orchid. **52.** Emeralds.

53. Aloe.

54. Lake Kyle.

55. Tiger Fish.

56. Cattle.

57. Guineafowl.

58. Coat of Arms.

Des. V. Whiteley. Photo. Harrison & Sons).

1964 (19 Feb.). *P* 14½ (½*d. to* 4*d.*), 13½ × 13 (6*d. to* 2*s.* 6*d.*) *or* 14½ × 14.

92	**45**	½d. yellow, yellow-green and light blue ..	0 2	0 3
93	**46**	1d. reddish violet & yellow-ochre	0 3	0 4
		a. Reddish violet omitted ..	£275	
94	**47**	2d. yellow & dp. violet	0 4	0 5
95	**48**	3d. chocolate & pale blue	0 6	0 7
96	**49**	4d. yell.-orge. & dp. grn.	0 7	0 9
97	**50**	6d. carmine-red, yellow & deep dull green ..	0 10	1 0
98	**51**	9d. red-brown, yellow and yellow-brown ..	1 1	1 6
99	**52**	1s. blue-green and ochre	1 5	2 0
		a. Green ptg. (Queen and emeralds) omitted ..		
100	**53**	1s. 3d. vermilion, violet and yellow-green ..	1 9	2 3
101	**54**	2s. blue and ochre ..	2 9	3 9
102	**55**	2s. 6d. ultram. and verm.	3 6	4 3
103	**56**	5s. lt. brown, bistre-yellow and light blue ..	6 9	7 6
104	**57**	10s. black, yellow-ochre, lt. bl. & carmine-red	13 3	15 0
105	**58**	£1 brown, yellow-green, ochre and vermilion ..	25 0	30 0

POSTAGE DUE STAMPS.

SOUTHERN

RHODESIA

(D 1)

1951–52? *Postage Due stamps of Great Britain optd. with Type* D 1.

D1	**D 1**	½d. emerald (No. D27) ..	0 6	0 8
D2	,,	1d. violet-blue (No. D36)	1 0	1 6
D3	,,	2d. agate (No. D29) ..	1 6	1 9
D4	,,	3d. violet (No. D30) ..	1 6	2 0
D5	,,	4d. blue (No. D40) ..	1 9	2 6
D6	,,	4d. dull grey-green (No. D31) ('52?)	70 0	
D7	,,	1s. deep blue (No. D33) ..	3 3	4 6

In October 1964 Southern Rhodesia was renamed Rhodesia. Issues after this date will be found listed under Rhodesia.

STELLALAND.

1. Arms of the Republic.

(Typo. by Van der Sandt, de Villiers & Co. Cape Town.)

1884 (1 Feb.). *P* 12.

1	**1**	1d. red	£6
		a. Imperf. between (pair) ..	£15
2	,,	3d. orange	25 0
		a. Imperf. between (pair) ..	£15
3	,,	4d. blue	25 0
		a. Imperf. between (pair) ..	£15
4	,,	6d. lilac-mauve	25 0
		a. Imperf. between (pair) ..	£30
5	,,	1s. green	35 0

Surcharged "Twee" in violet-lake.

6	**1**	2d. on 4d. blue	£30

Annexed by Great Britain in 1884 and now part of Bechuanaland.

SUDAN.

(Former Anglo-Egyptian Condominium)

السودان

SOUDAN

(1)

1897 (1 Mar.). 1884, 1888 *and* 1893 *issues of Egypt* (*Sphinx and Pyramid*) *optd. as T* **1**.

1	1 m. pale brown	5	0	6	0
	a. Opt. inverted	£16			
2	1 m. deep brown	5	0	6	0
3	2 m. green	6	0	7	0
4	3 m. orange-yellow	6	0	7	6
5	5 m. rose-carmine	12	6	12	6
	a. Opt. inverted	£25			
6	1 p. ultramarine	20	0	22	6
7	2 p. orange-brown	65	0	55	0
8	5 p. slate	60	0	65	0
	a. Opt. double	..			
9	10 p. mauve	55	0	60	0

Numerous forgeries exist including some which show the characteristics of the varieties mentioned below.

There are six varieties of the overprint on each value most of which can be supplied in vertical strips at double the catalogue price.

In some printings the large dot is omitted from the left-hand Arabic character on some stamps in the sheet.

The overprint was frequently misplaced, and pairs may be found with and without it, and also with the overprint diagonal.

PRINTERS. All stamps of Sudan were printed by De La Rue & Co. *except where otherwise stated.*

2. Arab Postman. 3

(Des. Col. E. A. Stanton, C.M.G. Typo.).

1898 (1 Mar.). *W* **3**. *P* 14.

No.	Type	Description				
10	2	1 m. brown and pink	1	9	1	9
11	,,	2 m. green and brown	4	0	6	0
12	,,	3 m. mauve and green	4	6	5	0
13	,,	5 m. carmine and black	1	9	1	9
14	,,	1 p. blue and brown	8	6	10	0
15	,,	2 p. black and blue	15	0	7	6
16	,,	5 p. brown and green	18	6	20	0
17	,,	10 p. black and mauve	25	0	20	0

4

1902–11. *W* **4**. *P* 14.

No.	Type	Description				
18	2	1 m. brown & carm. (5.05)	1	3	1	3
19	,,	2 m. green & brn. (11.02)	3		1	6
20	2	3 m. mauve & grn. (7.03)	2	0	2	0
21	,,	4 m. blue & bistre (20.1.07)	3	0	8	6
22	,,	4 m. verm. & brown (10.07)	7	6	10	0
23	,,	5 m. scarlet & black (12.03)	3	6	0	6
24	,,	1 p. blue & brown (12.03)	8	6	2	0
25	,,	2 p. black and blue (2.08)	25	0	10	0
26	,,	5 p. brown & grn. OC (2.08)	15	0	4	0
27	,,	10 p. blk. & mve. OC (2.11)	22	6	7	6

5 Milliemes

(5)

1903 (Sept.). *No.* 16 *surch. at Khartoum with T* **5**, *in blocks of* 30.

28	5 m. on 5 pi. brown & green	10	0	12	6
	a. Inverted	£20		£15	

1921 (22 Dec.). *As* 1902–11. *Colours changed.*

No.	Type	Description				
29	2	2 p. purple & orge.-yell., C	5	0	5	0

6 7

1921–22. *T* **6**. *Chalk-surfaced paper. Typo. W* **4**. *P* 14.

30	1 m. black & orange (4.2.22)	1	3	1	6
31	2 m. yell.-orge. & choc. (1922)	7	6	5	0
31a	2 m. yellow and chocolate	5	0	6	6
32	3 m. mauve & grn. (25.1.22)	2	0	4	0
33	4 m. grn. & choc. (21.3.22)	2	6	5	0
34	5 m. olive-brn. & blk. (4.2.22)	3	0	0	6
35	10 m. carmine & black (1922)	6	0	1	3
36	15 m. bright blue and chestnut (14.12.21)	7	6	2	6

1927–40. *W* **7**. *P* 14.

No.	Type	Description				
37	6	1 m. black & orange, CO	0	2	0	3
38	,,	2 m. orange & choc., CO	0	2	0	3
39	,,	3 m. mauve and green, CO	0	4	0	4
40	,,	4 m. green & chocolate, CO	0	4	0	5
41	,,	5 m. olive-brn. & blk., CO	0	6	0	3
42	,,	10 m. carmine & black, CO	0	8	0	3
43	,,	15 m. brt. bl. & chestnut, CO	0	9	0	6
44	2	2 p. pur. & orge.-yell. CO	1	0	0	6
44a	,,	3 p. red-brown & blue, CO	2	6	1	3
44b	,,	4 p. ultram. & black, C	2	6	1	3
45	,,	5 p. chestnut & green, CO	3	0	1	3
45a	,,	6 p. grn'ish bl. & blk., CO	4	0	2	6
45b	,,	8 p. emerald & black, CO	5	0	3	0
46	,,	10 p. black & violet, CO	6	0	2	0
46a	,,	20 p. pale blue & blue, CO	10	0	4	0

The ordinary paper of this issue is thick, smooth and opaque and is a wartime substitute for chalk-surfaced paper.

Dates of issue: 1927 (all except the following)—17.10.35, 20 p. 2.11.36, 4 p., 6 p. and 8 p. 1.1.40, 3 p.

For similar stamps, but with different Arabic inscriptions, see Nos. 96/111.

AIR MAIL (8) AIR MAIL (9)

1931. *Air stamps. Stamps of* 1927 *overprinted with T* **8** *or* **9** (2 p.).

47	5 m. olive-brn. & blk. (1.3.31)	5	0	8	
48	10 m. carmine & blk. (15.2.31)	5	0	12	
49	2 p. pur. & orge.-yell. (15.2.31)	7	0	15	

10. Statue of Gen. Gordon.

1931 (22 Aug.)–**37**. *Air. Recess.* *W* **7**. *P* 14.

No.	Type	Description				
49*a*	**10**	3 m. green & sepia (1.1.33)	17	6	17	6
50	,,	5 m. black and green ..	7	6	7	6
51	,,	10 m. black and carmine..	10	0	10	0
52	,,	15 m. red-brown & sepia..	6	6	6	6
		a. Perf. 11½ × 12½ ('37) ..	6	0	4	0
53	,,	2 p. black and orange ..	2	6	3	0
		a. Perf. 11½ × 12½ ('37) ..	50	0	70	0
53*b*	,,	2½ p. mag. & blue (1.1.33)	8	6	3	6
		c. Perf. 11½ × 12½ ('36) ..	5	0	6	0
54	,,	3 p. black and grey ..	8	0	7	6
		a. Perf. 11½ × 12½ ('37) ..	15	0	15	0
55	,,	3½ p. black and violet ..	10	0	12	6
		a. Perf. 11½ × 12½ ('37) ..	30	0	35	0
56	,,	4½ p. red-brown and grey	55	0	60	0
57	,,	5 p. black & ultramarine	15	0	15	0
		a. Perf. 11½ × 12½ ('37) ..	12	6	12	6
57*b*	,,	7½ p. green and emerald (17.10.35)	27	6	30	0
		c. Perf. 11½ × 12½ ('37) ..	22	6	25	0
57*d*	,,	10 p. brown & greenish blue (17.10.35)	40	0	20	0
		e. Perf. 11½ × 12½ ('37) ..	30	0	30	0

2½ 2½

AIR MAIL

٢½ ٢½

(11)

1932 (18 July). *Air. No.* 44 *surch. with T* **11**.

58	2½ p. on 2 p. pur. & orge.-yell.	35	0	45	0

12. Gen. Gordon.

13. Gordon Memorial College, Khartoum.

14. Gordon Memorial Service, Khartoum.

1935 (1 Jan.). 50*th Anniv. of Death of General Gordon. Recess. W* **7**. *P* 14.

No.	Type	Description				
59	**12**	5 m. green	2	0	2	0
60	,,	10 m. yellow-brown ..	2	6	5	0
61	,,	13 m. ultramarine	10	0	15	0
62	,,	15 m. scarlet	6	0	6	0
63	**13**	2 p. blue	6	0	6	0
64	,,	5 p. orange-vermilion ..	7	6	8	6
65	,,	10 p. purple	17	6	20	0
66	**14**	20 p. black	85	0	90	0
67	,,	50 p. red-brown	£10		£10	

7½ PIASTRES

قروش ٧ ½

(15)

1935. *Air. Surch. as T* **15**.

No.	Type	Description				
68	**10**	15 m. on 10 m. black and carmine (Apr.) ..	5	0	5	0
		a. Surch. double	£95			
69	,,	2½ p. on 3 m. green and sepia (Apr.) ..	12	6	12	6
		a. Second Arabic letter from left missing	£10		£10	
		b. Small "½"	40	0	50	0
70	,,	2½ p. on 5 m. black and green (Apr.)	7	6	10	0
		a. Second Arabic letter from left missing	£10		£10	
		b. Small "½"	40	0	45	0
		c. Surch. inverted	£95			
		d. ditto. with variety a. ..				
		e. ditto, with variety b. ..				
71	,,	3 p. on 4½ p. red-brown and grey (Apr.)	17	6	35	0
72	,,	7½ p. on 4½ p. red-brown and grey (Mar.)	50	0	55	0
73	,,	10 p. on 4½ p. red-brown and grey (Mar.)	37	6	45	0

The 7½ p. on 4½ p. formerly listed under No. 72a is now known to be from a proof sheet.

5 MILLIEMES

(16)

1938 (1 July). *Air. Surch. as T* **16**.

No.	Type	Description				
74	**10**	5 m. on 2½ p. (*p.* 11½ × 12½)	1	6	2	0
75	,,	3 p. on 3½ p. (*p.* 14) ..	25	0	30	0
		a. Perf. 11½ × 12½	£50		£50	

No.	Type	Description	Unused	Used
76	10	3 p. on 7½ p. (*p.* 14) ..	6 0	6 0
		a. Perf. 11½ × 12½	£50	£50
77	,,	5 p. on 10 p. (*p.* 14) ..	8 0	8 0
		a. Perf. 11½ × 12½	£50	£50

5 Mills.

٥ مليم

(17)

1940 (25 Feb.). *Surch. as T* **17**.

No.	Type	Description	Unused	Used
78	6	5 m. on 10 m. carm. & black	1 0	2 0

4½ PIASTRES

(18)

4½ Piastres

٤ ١/٢ قرش

(19)

1940–41. *Surch. with T* **18** *or* **19**.

No.	Type	Description	Unused	Used
79	6	4½ p. on 5 m. olive-brown and black (9.2.41) ..	30 0	25 0
80	2	4½ p. on 8 p. emerald and black (12.12.40) ..	25 0	20 0

20. Tuti Is., R. Nile, near Khartoum. **21.**

(Des. Miss H. M. Hebbert. Litho. Security Printing Press, Nasik, India.)

1941 (Mar.–Aug.). *P* 14 × 13½ (*T* **20**) *or P* 13½ × 14 (*T* **21**).

No.	Type	Description	Unused	Used
81	20	1 m. slate and orange ..	1 3	3 0
82	,,	2 m. orange and chocolate	1 6	3 0
83	,,	3 m. mauve and green ..	1 0	2 6
84	,,	4 m. green and chocolate ..	0 9	3 0
85	,,	5 m. olive-brown and black	0 6	0 9
86	,,	10 m. carmine and black ..	15 0	15 0
87	,,	15 m. bright blue & chestnut	1 0	1 0
88	21	2 p. purple & orge.-yellow	15 0	15 0
89	,,	3 p. red-brown and blue ..	2 6	1 6
90	,,	4 p. ultramarine and black	2 6	2 0
91	,,	5 p. chestnut and green ..	17 6	15 0
92	,,	6 p. greenish blue & black	20 0	15 0
93	,,	8 p. emerald and black ..	25 0	15 0
94	,,	10 p. slate and purple ..	35 0	30 0
95	,,	20 p. pale blue and blue ..	£5	75 0

Dates of issue: 15 m., 3 pi. and 4 pi. 25.3.41; others 10.8.41.

22

23

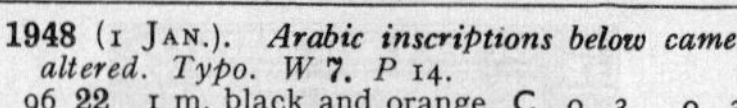

1948 (1 Jan.). *Arabic inscriptions below camel altered. Typo. W* **7**. *P* 14.

No.	Type	Description	Unused	Used
96	22	1 m. black and orange, C	0 3	0 3
97	,,	2 m. orange & choc., C ..	0 3	0 3
98	,,	3 m. mauve and green, C	0 3	0 3
99	,,	4 m. dp. grn. & choc., C	0 4	0 4
100	,,	5 m. olive-brn. & blk., C	0 4	0 3
101	,,	10 m. rose-red & blk., C ..	0 8	0 4
		a. Centre inverted ..		
102	,,	15 m. ultra. & chestnut, C	0 10	0 4
103	23	2 p. pur. & orge.-yell., C	1 3	0 8
104	,,	3 p. red-brn. & dp. bl., C	1 6	1 0
105	,,	4 p. ultram. & black, C	1 10	1 3
106	,,	5 p. brn.-orge.& dp. grn, C	3 0	2 6
107	,,	6 p. grnsh. bl. & blk., C	3 0	3 0
108	,,	8 p. bluish grn. & blk., O	4 0	5 0
109	,,	10 p. blk. & mauve, OC	5 0	5 0
110	,,	20 p. pale bl. & dp. blue, O	17 6	8 6
		a. Perf. 13, C	85 0	
111	,,	50 p. carm. & ultram., C	22 6	20 0

For similar stamps, but with different Arabic inscriptions, see Nos. 37/46*a*.

24

1948 (Oct.). *Golden Jubilee of "Camel Postman" design. Chalk-surfaced paper. Typo. W* **7**. *P* 13.

No.	Type	Description	Unused	Used
112	24	2 p. black and light blue ..	1 6	2 0

25

1948 (Dec.). *Opening of Legislative Assembly. Chalk-surfaced paper. Typo. W* **7**. *P* 13.

No.	Type	Description	Unused	Used
113	25	10 m. rose-red and black ..	1 0	0 6
114	,,	5 p. brn.-orge. & dp. grn.	3 0	2 0

26. Blue Nile Bridge, Khartoum.

27. Kassala Jebel.

28. Sagia (Water Wheel).

29. Port Sudan.

30. Gordon Memorial College.

31. Nile Post Boat.

32. Suakin.

33. G.P.O., Khartoum.

(Des. Col. W. L. Atkinson (2½ p., 6 p.), G. R. Wilson (3 p.), others from photographs. Recess.)

1950 (1 July). *Air.* *W* **7.** *P* 12.

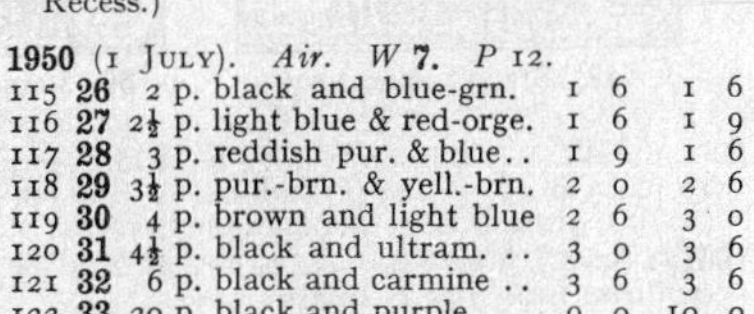

115	**26**	2 p. black and blue-grn.	1	6	1	6
116	**27**	2½ p. light blue & red-orge.	1	6	1	9
117	**28**	3 p. reddish pur. & blue..	1	9	1	6
118	**29**	3½ p. pur.-brn. & yell.-brn.	2	0	2	6
119	**30**	4 p. brown and light blue	2	6	3	0
120	**31**	4½ p. black and ultram. ..	3	0	3	6
121	**32**	6 p. black and carmine ..	3	6	3	6
122	**33**	20 p. black and purple ..	9	0	10	0

34. Ibex.

35. Shoebill.

36. Giraffe.

37. Baggara Girl.

38. Shilluk Warrior.

39. Hadendowa.

41. Cotton Picking.

40. Policeman.

42. Ambatch Canoe.

43. Nuba Wrestlers.

44. Weaving.

45. Saluka Farming.

46. Gum Tapping.

47. Darfur Chief.

48. Stack Laboratory.

50. Camel Postman.

49. Nile Lechwe.

(Des. Col. W. L. Atkinson (1 m., 2 m., 4 m., 5 m., 10 m., 3 p., 3½ p., 20 p.), Col. E. A. Stanton (50 p.), others from photographs. Typo.)

1951 (1 Sept.). *Chalk-surfaced paper.* *W* **7.** *P* 14 (*millieme values*) *or* 13 (*piastre values*).

123	**34**	1 m. black and orange ..	0	4	0	6
124	**35**	2 m. black & bright blue	0	8	0	9
125	**36**	3 m. black and green ..	2	6	3	6
126	**37**	4 m. black & yell.-green	0	8	1	0
127	**38**	5 m. black and purple ..	0	6	0	3
128	**39**	10 m. black & pale blue ..	0	8	0	4
129	**40**	15 m. black & chestnut ..	1	0	0	6
130	**41**	2 p. dp. blue & pale blue	1	0	0	8
131	**42**	3 p. brn. & pale ultram.	1	6	0	10
132	**43**	3½ p. brt. grn. & red-brn.	1	6	1	0
133	**44**	4 p. blue and black ..	1	6	1	0
134	**45**	5 p. orge.-brn. & yell.-grn.	1	9	1	3
135	**46**	6 p. blue and black ..	2	0	1	6
136	**47**	8 p. blue and brown ..	2	9	2	0
137	**48**	10 p. black and green ..	3	0	2	0
138	**49**	20 p. blue-grn. and black	6	0	5	0
139	**50**	50 p. carmine and black..	15	0	10	0

(Self Government, 1954.)

51. Camel Postman.

1954 (9 Jan.). *Self-Government. Chalk-surfaced paper. Typo. W* **7.** *P* 13.

140	**51**	15 m. orge.-brn. & brt. grn.	1	3	1	0
141	,,	3 p. blue and indigo ..	2	6	2	6
142	,,	5 p. blk. & reddish purple	4	0	3	6

Stamps as Type **51**, but dated "1953" were released in error at the Sudan Agency in London. They had no postal validity. (*Price per set, 60s. un.*)

For later issues of Sudan as an Independent Republic see Part III of the Stanley Gibbons Catalogue.

POSTAGE DUE STAMPS.

1897 (1 Mar.). *Stamps of Egypt, Type* D **3**. *Wmk. Star and Crescent, T* **12**. *P* 14, *optd. with T* **1**.
D1 2 mils. green 3 6 4 0
D2 4 mils. maroon 3 0 4 6
D3 1 pias. ultramarine 7 6 7 6
D4 2 pias. orange 12 6 15 0

Varieties are known with the large dot omitted in the first Arabic character on left.

The 4 mils. and the 2 pias. are known bisected and used for half their value.

D **1**. Gunboat *Zafir*. D **2**.

1901 (1 Jan.). *Typo. W* **4**. *P* 14.
D5 D **1** 2 m. black & brown, OC 0 9 0 9
D6 ,, 4 m. brown & green, OC 1 6 0 9
D7 ,, 10 m. grn. & mauve, OC 2 6 1 0
D8 ,, 20 m. ultram. & carm., C 6 6 4 6

1927–30. *W* **7**. *P* 14.
D 9 D **1** 2 m. blk. & brn., C ('30) 0 6 0 8
D10 ,, 4 m. brown & green, C 0 9 1 0
D11 ,, 10 m. grn. & mauve, CO 1 0 1 0

1948 (1 Jan.). *Arabic inscriptions at foot altered. Chalk-surfaced paper. Typo. W* **7**. *P* 14.
D12 D **2** 2 m. black and brown .. 0 6 0 3
D13 ,, 4 m. brown and green .. 0 9 0 6
D14 ,, 10 m. green and mauve 1 3 0 10
D15 ,, 20 m. ultram. & carmine 1 6 1 9

OFFICIAL STAMPS

1900 (8 Feb.). 5 *mils. of* 1897 *punctured* "S G" *by hand. The* "S" *has* 14 *and the* "G" 12 *holes.*
O1 5 m. rose-carmine 90 0 50 0

1901 (Jan.). 1 *m. wmk. Quatrefoil, punctured as No.* O1.
O2 1 m. brown and pink .. 70 0 60 0

O.S.G.S. **O.S.G.S.**

(O **1**) ("On Sudan Government Service".) (O **2**)

1902. *No.* 10 *optd. at Khartoum as Type* O **1** *in groups of* 30 *stamps.*
O3 **2** 1 m. brown and pink .. 6 6 8 6
a. Oval "O" No. 19 in setting of 30 .. .. .. £8
b. Round stops. Nos. 25 to 30 30 0 25 0
c. Inverted £15
d. Inverted and oval "O" .. £250
e. Inverted and round stops .. £60
f. Double £20
g. Double and round stops .. £80
h. Double and oval "O" ..

1903–12. *T* **2** *optd. as Type* O **2**, *by De La Rue & Co. in sheets of* 120 *stamps.*

(i) *Wmk. Quatrefoil.* (*Mar.*, 1906).
O4 10 pias. black and mauve .. 10 0 15 0

(ii) *Wmk. Mult. Star and Crescent.*
O5 1 m. brown & carm. (9.04) .. 1 0 0 9
a. Overprint double .. ..
O6 3 m. mauve & grn. (Feb., '04) 1 6 1 6
a. Overprint double .. ..
O7 5 m. scarlet & black (1.1.03) 1 6 0 6
O8 1 pi. blue & brown (1.1.03) 2 6 0 9
O9 2 pi. black and blue (1.1.03) 4 6 1 6
O10 5 pi. brown & green (1.1.03) 7 6 4 0
O11 10 pi. black & mauve (9.12) .. 8 0 20 0

S.G. **S.G.**

(O **3**) (O **4**)

1936–46. *Nos.* 37/43 *optd. with Type* O **3**, *and* 44/46*a with Type* O **4**. *W* **7**. *P* 14.
O12 **6** 1 m. black and orange, O 0 8 1 6
O13 ,, 2 m. orange and choc., O 0 6 1 6
O14 ,, 3 m. mauve and green, C 0 6 1 0
O15 ,, 4 m. green and choc., C .. 0 6 1 0
O16 ,, 5 m. olive-brn. & blk., CO 0 6 0 8
O17 ,, 10 m. carmine & black, C 0 8 0 10
O18 ,, 15 m. brt. bl. & chest., CO 1 0 1 3
O19 **2** 2 p. pur. & orge.-yell., CO 1 6 1 6
O19*a* ,, 3 p. red-brn. & blue, O .. 2 0 2 6
O19*b* ,, 4 p. ultram. & black, CO 2 6 3 6
O20 ,, 5 p. chest. & green, CO 3 0 3 6
O20*a* ,, 6 p. grnish. blue & blk., O 4 0 4 0
O20*b* ,, 8 p. emerald & black, O 5 0 6 0
O21 ,, 10 p. black & violet, CO 8 0 7 6
O22 ,, 20 p. pale blue & blue, O 17 6 20 0

Dates of issue :—19.9.36, 4 m. and 5 p.; Jan., '37, 3 m.; Apr., '37, 2 p.; 21.6.37, 15 m.; Oct., '37, 10 p.; Mar., '40, 5 m.; Apr. '45, 2 m., Apr., '46, 3 p., 4 p., 6 p., 8 p.; June, '46, 10 m., 20 p.; 22.11.46, 1 m.

1948 (1 Jan.). *Nos.* 96/102 *optd. with Type* O **3**, *and* 103/111 *with Type* O **4**.
O23 **22** 1 m. black and orange .. 0 3 0 3
O24 ,, 2 m. orange & chocolate 0 3 0 3
O25 ,, 3 m. mauve and green .. 0 4 0 3
O26 ,, 4 m. deep green & choc. 0 4 0 4
O27 ,, 5 m. olive-brown & black 0 4 0 3
O28 ,, 10 m. rose-red and black .. 0 8 0 4
O29 ,, 15 m. ultram. and chestnut 1 0 0 6
O30 **23** 2 p. purple & orange-yell. 1 0 0 8
O31 ,, 3 p. red-brn. & deep blue 1 6 0 10
O32 ,, 4 p. ultram. and black .. 2 0 1 0
a. Perf. 13 .. .. 30 0 30 0
O33 ,, 5 p. brn.-orge. & dp. grn. 2 6 2 0
O34 ,, 6 p. greenish blue & black 3 0 2 6
O35 ,, 8 p. bluish green & black 3 6 3 6
O36 ,, 10 p. black and mauve .. 4 6 4 0
O37 ,, 20 p. pale blue & dp. blue 10 0 7 6
O38 ,, 50 p. carmine and ultram. 22 6 18 0

1950 (1 July). *Air. Optd. with Type* O **4**.
O39 **26** 2 p. blk. & blue-grn. (R.) 1 0 1 3
O40 **27** 2½ p. light blue and red-orange (Bk.) .. 1 3 1 9
O41 **28** 3 p. reddish purple and blue (Bk.) .. 1 6 1 9
O42 **29** 3½ p. purple-brown & yellow-brown (Bk.) .. 1 9 2 0
O43 **30** 4 p. brn. & lt. blue (Bk.) 2 0 2 6
O44 **31** 4½ p. black & ultram. (R.) 3 0 3 6
O45 **32** 6 p. black & carm. (R.) 3 0 5 0
O46 **33** 20 p. black & purple (R.) 10 0 10 0

1951 (1 Sept.)–**58.** *Nos.* 123/9 *optd. with Type* O **3** *and* 130/9 *with Type* O **4**.
O47 **34** 1 m. black & orange (R.) 0 3 1 0
O48 **35** 2 m. blk. & brt. bl. (R.) .. 0 4 1 0
O49 **36** 3 m. black & green (R.) .. 2 0 2 6
O50 **37** 4 m. blk. & yell.-grn. (R.) 0 5 1 0
O51 **38** 5 m. black & purple (R.) 0 4 0 3
O52 **39** 10 m. blk. & pale bl. (R.) 0 6 0 3
O53 **40** 15 m. blk. & chest. (R.) .. 0 8 0 4
O54 **41** 2 p. dp. blue & pale blue 0 10 0 6
a. Opt. inverted £75
O55 **42** 3 p. brn. & dp. ultram. 1 3 0 10
O56 **43** 3½ p. brt. grn. & red-brn. 1 6 1 0
O57 **44** 4 p. blue and black .. 1 6 1 0
O58 **45** 5 p. orange-brown and yellow-green .. 1 9 1 3
O59 **46** 6 p. blue and black .. 2 0 1 6
O60 **47** 8 p. blue and brown .. 2 9 2 0
O61 **48** 10 p. black & green (R.) .. 3 6 2 6
O61*a* ,, 10 p. blk. & grn. (Bk.) ('58) 3 0 2 0
O62 **49** 20 p. blue-green & black 6 0 5 0
a. Opt. inverted .. ..
O63 **50** 50 p. carmine and black .. 15 0 10 0

ARMY SERVICE.

ARMY (A 1)   OFFICIAL ARMY (A 2)   Army OFFICIAL Service (A 3)

1905 (Jan.). *T* **2** *optd. at Khartoum as Type* A **1** *and* A **2**. *Wmk. Mult. Star and Crescent.*

(i) " ARMY " *reading up.*

A1 1 m. brown & carm. (A **1**) .. 8 6 4 0
a. "!" for "I" 50 0 37 6
b. Opt. Type A 2 .. .. 30 0 20 0

(ii) *Overprint horizontal.*

A2 1 m. brown & carm. (A **1**) .. £30
a. "!" for "I" £220
b. Opt. Type A 2 .. .. £120

The horizontal overprint exists with either " ARMY " or " OFFICIAL " reading the right way up. It did not fit the stamps, resulting in misplacements where more than one whole overprint appears, or when the two words are transposed.

(iii) " ARMY " *reading down.*

A3 1 m. brown & carm. (A **1**) .. 50 0 25 0
a. "!" for "I" £50 £50
b. Opt. Type A 2 .. .. £35 £35

1905 (Nov.). *As No.* A1, *but wmk. Quatrefoil.*

A4 1 m. brown and pink (A **1**) .. £10 £8
a. "!" for "I" .. .. — £200
b. Opt. Type A 2 .. .. £130

The 29th stamp in each setting of 30 (Nos. A1–A4) has an exclamation mark for first " I " in " OFFICIAL " while the 6th and 12th stamps are Type A **2**.

1906 (Jan.)–**1911**. *T* **2** *optd. as Type* A **3**.

(i) *Wmk. Mult. Star and Crescent, T* **4**.

Two varieties of the 1 *mil.*

A. 1st Ptg. 14 mm. between lines of opt.
B. Later Ptgs. 12 mm. between lines.

All other values are Type B.

A 5 1 m. brown & carm. (Type A) £15 £10
A 6 1 m. brown & carm. (Type B) 8 6 1 6
a. Opt. double. . .. .. — £60
b. Opt. inverted £30 £25
c. Pair, with and without opt.
d. " Service " omitted .. ..
A 7 2 m. green and brown .. 10 0 4 0
a. Pair, with and without opt.. . £100
b. " Army " omitted £220
A 8 3 m. mauve and green .. 8 6 3 0
a. Opt. inverted £185
A 9 5 m. scarlet and black .. 6 0 0 6
a. Opt. double. £15 £12
b. Opt. inverted .. .. — £15
c. Error " Amry " .. .. — £200
d. " A " for " A " in " Army " — £8
e. Opt. double, one inverted .. £35 £15
A10 1 pi. blue and brown .. 7 6 1 0
a. " Army " omitted £220 £250
A11 2 pi. black & blue (Jan., '09) 25 0 25 0
A12 5 pi. brown & grn. (May, '08) 70 0 30 0
A13 10 pi. black & mve. (May, '11) £40 £38

There are a number of printings of these Army Service stamps; the earlier are as Type A **3**; the 1908 printing has a narrower " A " in " Army " and the 1910–11 printings have the tail of the " y " in " Army " much shorter.

(ii) *Wmk. Quatrefoil, T* **3**.

A14 2 pi. black and blue .. 30 0 15 0
A15 5 pi. brown and green .. £7 £7
A16 10 pi. black and mauve .. £10 £10

Since 1913 a number of stamps have been issued punctured " S.G." (Sudan Government) or " AS " (Army Service), but we no longer list such varieties.

SWAZILAND.

I. Provisional Government under the joint protection of Great Britain and the South African Republic (Transvaal).

Swazieland

(**1**)

1889 (18 Oct.). *Stamps of the South African Republic (Transvaal) optd. with T* **1** *in black.*

(*a*) *P* 12½ × 12.

1 **18** 1d. carmine 15 0 17 6
a. Opt. inverted £12 £12
2 ,, 2d. olive-bistre 30 0 30 0
a. Opt. inverted .. ..
b. " Swazielan " £18 £18
3 ,, 1s. green 12 6 20 0
a. Opt. inverted £6 £5

(*b*) *P* 12½.

4 **18** ½d. grey 10 0 15 0
a. Opt. inverted £12 £12
b. " Swazielan " £22 £20
c. " Swazielan " inverted .. — £22
5 ,, 2d. olive-bistre 27 6 30 0
a. Opt. inverted £18 £18
b. " Swazielan " £20
c. " Swazielan " inverted .. — £28
6 ,, 6d. blue 20 0 27 6
7 ,, 2s. 6d. buff 75 0 80 0
8 ,, 5s. slate-blue £7 £7
a. Opt. inverted £28
b. " Swazielan " £38
c. " Swazielan " inverted ..
9 ,, 10s. fawn £35 £35

The variety without " d " occurs on the left-hand bottom corner stamp in each sheet of certain printings.

1892 (Aug.). *Optd. in carmine. P* 12½.

10 **18** ½d. grey 10 0 15 0
a. Opt. inverted £8
b. Opt. double £12

In 1894–95 reprints of the above stamps were made in the Government Printing Works at Pretoria. These have a stop after the name.

In 1894 the South African Republic was, under a convention, given powers of protection and administration over Swaziland, but it was not incorporated. On 7 Nov. of that year the stamps were recalled from use. On 5 June, 1903, authority over Swaziland was conferred on the Governor of the Transvaal, and on 1 Dec. 1906, this authority was transferred to a High Commissioner, Swaziland being considered as a British Protectorate. In 1933 stamps were again issued (*see below*).

II. British Protectorate.

2

(Des. Rev. C. C. Tugman. Recess. De La Rue

1933 (2 Jan.). *Wmk. Mult. Script CA. P* 1

11 **2** ½d. green 0 6 0
12 ,, 1d. carmine 0 8 0
13 ,, 2d. brown 1 0 1
14 ,, 3d. blue 1 6 2

No.	Type	Description	Un.		Us.	
15	**2**	4d. orange	2	6	4	0
16	,,	6d. bright purple	4	0	6	0
17	,,	1s. olive	8	0	10	0
18	,,	2s. 6d. bright violet	25	0	30	0
19	,,	5s. grey	45	0	50	0
20	,,	10s. sepia	£5		£6	

The ½d., 1d., 2d. and 6d. values exist overprinted "OFFICIAL", but authority for their use was withdrawn before any were actually used.

1935 (4 May). *Silver Jubilee. As No. 91/4 of Antigua, but ptd. by B. W. & Co. P* 11 × 12.

No.	Description	Un.		Us.	
21	1d. deep blue and scarlet	0	6	1	0
	a. Extra flagstaff	55	0		
22	2d. ultram. and grey-black	2	0	2	6
	a. Extra flagstaff	80	0		
23	3d. brown and deep blue	2	0	3	0
	a. Extra flagstaff	45	0		
24	6d. slate and purple	3	6	6	6
	a. Extra flagstaff	80	0		

For illustration of "extra flagstaff" variety see Bechuanaland.

1937 (12 May). *Coronation. As Nos. 13/15 of Aden, but ptd. by B. W. & Co. P* 11 × 11½.

No.	Description	Un.		Us.	
25	1d. carmine	0	6	0	8
26	2d. yellow-brown	1	0	1	3
27	3d. blue	1	6	1	9

3. King George VI.
(Recess. De La Rue & Co.)

1938 (1 Apr.)–**1954.** *Wmk. Mult. Script CA. P* 13½ × 13.

No.	Type	Description	Un.		Us.	
28	**3**	½d. green	0	3	0	3
		a. Perf. 13½ × 14 ('43)	0	4	0	4
29	,,	1d. carmine	0	6	0	3
		a. Perf. 13½ × 14 ('43)	0	5	0	8
30	,,	1½d. light blue	1	6	1	3
		a. Perf. 14 ('42)	1	6	1	9
		b. Perf. 13½ × 14 ('43)	0	6	0	3
31	,,	2d. brown	0	8	0	8
		a. Perf. 13½ × 14 ('43)	0	6	0	3
32	,,	3d. ultramarine	1	6	2	6
		a. *Deep blue* ('42)	2	6	3	0
		b. Perf. 13½ × 14 *ultram.* ('44)	0	10	1	0
33	,,	4d. orange	1	0	1	3
		a. Perf. 13½ × 14 ('43)	1	0	1	3
34	,,	6d. bright purple	2	6	3	0
		a. Perf. 13½ × 14 ('43)	2	6	4	0
		b. Perf. 13½ × 14 *reddish purple (shades)* ('44)	1	3	1	3
		c. Perf. 13½ × 14 *claret* (13.10.54)	1	3	1	0
35	,,	1s. olive	7	0	3	6
		a. Perf. 13½ × 14 ('43)	3	0	2	0
36	,,	2s. 6d. bright violet	6	6	8	6
		a. Perf. 13½ × 14 *violet* ('43)	5	0	7	6
		b. Perf. 13½ × 14 *reddish violet* ('47)	5	0	6	0
37	,,	5s. grey	17	6	17	6
		a. Perf. 13½ × 14 *grey* ('44)	10	0	12	6
		b. Perf. 13½ × 14 *slate* '(43)	45	0	55	0
38	,,	10s. sepia	40	0	45	0
		a. Perf. 13½ × 14 ('43)	20	0	25	0

The above perforations vary slightly from stamp to stamp, but the average measurements are respectively: 13.3 × 23.2 comb (13½ × 13), 14.2 line (14) and 13.3 × 13.8 comb (13½ × 14).

Swaziland
(4)

1945. *Victory. Nos.* 108 *to* 110 *of South Africa optd. with T* **4**.

No.	Description	Un. pair		Us. pair		Us. single	
39	1d. brown and carmine	0	6	0	9	0	3
40	2d. slate-blue & violet	0	10	1	4	0	6
41	3d. deep blue and blue	1	4	1	10	0	9

1947 (17 Feb.). *Royal Visit. As Nos.* 32/5 *of Basutoland.*

No.	Description	Un.		Us.	
42	1d. scarlet	0	3	0	4
43	2d. green	0	4	0	6
44	3d. ultramarine	0	8	1	0
45	1s. mauve	2	6	2	6

1948 (1 Dec.). *Royal Silver Wedding. As Nos.* 30/1 *of Aden.*

No.	Description	Un.		Us.	
46	1½d. ultramarine	0	6	0	8
47	10s. purple-brown	17	6	20	0

1949 (10 Oct.). *75th Anniv. of Universal Postal Union. As Nos.* 114/7 *of Antigua.*

No.	Description	Un.		Us.	
48	1½d. blue	0	6	0	8
49	3d. deep blue	1	0	1	3
50	6d. magenta	1	6	2	0
51	1s. olive	3	0	4	0

1953 (3 June). *Coronation. As No.* 47 *of Aden.*

No.	Description	Un.		Us.	
52	2d. black and yellow-brown	1	0	1	3

5. Havelock Asbestos Mine.

6. A Highveld View.

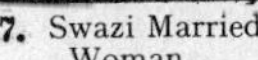

7. Swazi Married Woman.

8. Swazi Courting Couple.

9. Swazi Warrior.

10. Greater Kudu Antelope.

(Recess. Bradbury, Wilkinson.)

1956 (2 July). *Wmk. Mult. Script CA. P* 13 × 13½ (*horiz.*) *or* 13½ × 13 (*vert.*).

No.	Type	Description				
53	**5**	½d. black and orange ..	0	3	0	6
54	**6**	1d. black and emerald ..	0	4	0	4
55	**7**	2d. black and brown ..	0	5	0	6
56	**8**	3d. black and rose-red ..	0	8	0	8
57	**9**	4½d. black & dp. brt. blue ..	1	3	3	0
58	**10**	6d. black and magenta ..	1	6	1	6
59	**5**	1s. black and deep olive ..	2	6	2	6
60	**8**	1s. 3d. black and sepia ..	3	0	3	0
61	**6**	2s. 6d. emer. & carm.-red	6	6	7	6
62	**9**	5s. dp. lilac & slate-black	11	6	12	6
63	**7**	10s. black and deep lilac ..	27	6	32	6
64	**10**	£1 black & turquoise-blue	50	0	57	6

Currency changed. 100 cents = 1 rand.

½c (11) 1c (12) 2c (13) 3½c (14)

2½c (I) 2½c (II) 4c (I) 4c (II)

5c (I) 5c (II) 25c (I) 25c (II)

50c (I) 50c (II) 50c (III)

R1 (I) R1 (II) R1 (III) R2 (I) R2 (II)

1961 (14 Feb.). *T* **5** *to* **10** *surch. as T* **11** *to* **14.**

No.	Type	Description				
65	**11**	½ c. on ½d.	15	0	17	6
		a. Surch. inverted	£150			
66	**12**	1 c. on 1d.	1	3	1	6
		a. Surch. double	£125			
67	**13**	2 c. on 2d.	1	9	1	9
68	,,	2½ c. on 2d.	1	9	1	9
69	,,	2½ c. on 3d. (Type I) ..	4	6	4	6
		a. Type II	12	6	15	0
70	**14**	3½ c. on 2d. (May) ..	1	6	1	9
71	**13**	4 c. on 4½d. (Type I) ..	3	6	3	6
		a. Type II	2	6	2	6
72	,,	5 c. on 6d. (Type I) ..	3	0	3	0
		a. Type II ..	2	6	2	6
73	,,	10 c. on 1s.	65	0	60	0
		a. Surch. double (vert. pr.)* ..	£150			
74	**13**	25 c. on 2s. 6d. (Type I) ..	17	6	17	6
		a. Type II (central)	17	6	17	6
		b. Type II (bottom left) ..	£60		£65	
75	,,	50 c. on 5s. (Type I) ..	15	0	17	6
		a. Type II	80	0	85	0
		b. Type III ..	£150		£175	
76	,,	1 r. on 10s. (Type I) ..	25	0	30	0
		a. Type II	90	0	£5	
		b. Type III	£22		£22	
77	,,	2 r. on £1 (Type I) ..	£8		£8	
		a. Type II (middle left) ..	50	0	60	0
		b. Type II (bottom) ..	£25		£25	

*No. 73a is best collected as a vertical pair, due to the fall of the second surcharge.

No. 74b has the thin Type II surcharge at bottom left, in similar position to the thicker Type I, No. 74, with which it should not be confused.

No. 77b has the surcharge centrally placed at bottom. No. 77*a* has it at middle left, above "KUDU".

No. 66 with surcharge central (instead of bottom left) and No. 75a bottom left (instead of middle left) are believed to be from trial sheets released with the normal stocks. They do not represent separate printings.

(Recess. Bradbury, Wilkinson.)

1961. *Values in cents. Wmk. Mult. Script CA. P* 13 × 13½ (*horiz.*) *or* 13½ × 13 (*vert.*).

No.	Type	Description				
78	**5**	½ c. black & orange (14.2)	0	4	0	6
79	**6**	1 c. black & emerald (14.2)	0	6	0	8
80	**7**	2 c. black & brown (10.9)	0	10	1	0
81	**8**	2½ c. black & rose-red (14.2)	1	3	1	6
82	**9**	4 c. blk. & dp. brt. bl. (10.9)	1	9	2	0
83	**10**	5 c. black & mag. (10.9) ..	2	0	2	6
84	**5**	10 c. blk. & dp. olive (14.2)	3	6	4	0
85	**8**	12½ c. black & sepia (14.2) ..	4	0	5	0
86	**6**	25 c. emer. & carm.-red (1.8)	7	6	8	6
87	**9**	50 c. d.lilac & slate-blk. (10.9)	15	0	17	6
88	**7**	1 r. black & dp. lilac (10.9)	30	0	35	0
89	**10**	2 r. blk. & turq.-blue (1.8)	55	0	65	0

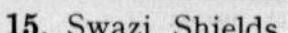

15. Swazi Shields.

16. Battle Axe.

17. Forestry.

18. Ceremonial Head-dress.

19. Musical Instrument.

20. Irrigation.

21. Widow Bird.

22. Rock Paintings.

23. Secretary Bird.

24. Pink Arum.

25. Swazi Married Woman.

26. Malaria Control.

27. Swazi Warrior.

29. Aloes.

28. Ground Hornbill.

30. Msinsi in Flower.

(Des. Mrs. C. Hughes. Photo. J. Enschedé & Sons.)

1962 (24 Apr.). *W* w.**12.** *P* 14×13 (*horiz.*) *or* 13×14 (*vert.*).

No.	Type	Value	Description	Unused s.	d.	Used s.	d.
90	**15**	½ c.	black, brown and yellow-brown ..	0	2	0	2
91	**16**	1 c.	yell.-orge. & black ..	0	3	0	2
92	**17**	2 c.	dp. bluish green, black and yellow-olive ..	0	5	0	3
93	**18**	2½ c.	black and scarlet ..	0	6	0	5
94	**19**	3½ c.	yell.-grn. & dp. grey	0	7	0	6
95	**20**	4 c.	black & turq.-green	0	9	0	8
96	**21**	5 c.	blk., red & orge.-red	0	10	0	9
97	**22**	7½ c.	deep brown & buff	1	1	1	0
98	**23**	10 c.	black & light blue ..	1	3	1	3
99	**24**	12½ c.	carm. & grey-olive	1	9	1	6
100	**25**	15 c.	black & brt. purple	2	0	1	9
101	**26**	20 c.	black and green ..	2	9	2	6
102	**27**	25 c.	black & bright blue	3	6	3	0
103	**28**	50 c.	black and rose-red ..	6	9	6	0
104	**29**	1 r.	emerald and ochre ..	13	3	12	6
105	**30**	2 r.	carm.-red & ultram.	25	0	25	0

1963 (4 June). *Freedom from Hunger. As No.* 63 *of Aden.*

No.	Value	Description	Unused s.	d.	Used s.	d.
106	15 c.	reddish violet	2	6	3	0

1963 (2 Sept.). *Red Cross Centenary. As Nos.* 147/8 *of Antigua.*

No.	Value	Description	Unused s.	d.	Used s.	d.
107	2½ c.	red and black	0	7	0	9
108	15 c.	red and blue	2	6	3	0

31. Train and Map.

(Des. R. A. H. Street. Recess. Bradbury, Wilkinson.)

1964 (5 Nov.). *Opening of Swaziland Railway. W* w.**12**. *P* 11½.

109	**31**	2½ c. emer.-grn. & purple	0	7	0	10
110	,,	3½ c. turquoise-blue and deep yellow-olive ..	0	9	1	0
111	,,	15 c. red-orange and deep chocolate	2	6	3	0
112	,,	25 c. olive-yellow and deep ultramarine	4	6	5	0

1965 (17 May). *I.T.U. Centenary. As Nos.* 166/7 *of Antigua.*

113	2½ c. light blue and bistre ..	0	7	0	10
114	15 c. bright purple and rose	2	6	3	0

1965 (25 Oct.). *International Co-operation Year. As Nos.* 168/9 *of Antigua.*

115	½ c. reddish pur.&turq.-grn.	0	3	0	5
116	15 c. dp. bluish green & lav.	2	6	3	0

1966 (24 Jan.). *Churchill Commemoration. As Nos.* 170/3 *of Antigua.*

117	½ c. new blue	0	3	0	5
118	2½ c. deep green	0	7	0	9
119	15 c. brown	2	6	3	0
120	25 c. bluish violet	4	6	5	6

POSTAGE DUE STAMPS.

D 1

Postage Due
2d
(D 2)

(Typo. De La Rue & Co.)

1933–57. *Wmk. Mult. Script CA.* P14.

D1	**D 1**	1d. carmine, O	1	6	2	0
		a. Deep carmine, C (24.10.51)	0	6	1	0
		ac. Error. St. Edward's Crown, W9b, C	£25			
D2	,,	2d. pale violet, O ..	7	6	10	0
		a. Chalky paper (22.5.57) ..	0	6	1	0

1961 (8 Feb.). *No.* 55 *surch. with Type* D **2.**

D3	**7**	2d. on 2d.	60	0	75	0

Another 2d. on 2d. Postage Due, with small surcharge as Type D **5**, was produced *after the currency change,* to meet the philatelic demand. (*Price* 10s. *unused.*)

Currency changed. 100 cents = 1 rand.

D 3

Postage Due
1c
(D 4)

Postage Due
1c
(D 5)

(Typo. De La Rue.)

1961 (14 Feb.). *Chalk-surfaced paper. Wmk. Mult. Script CA. P* 14.

D4	**D 3**	1 c. carmine	0	3	0	6
D5	,,	2 c. violet	0	5	0	10
D6	,,	5 c. green	0	10	1	3

1961. *No.* 55 *surcharged.*

A. (14 Feb.). *As Type* D **4.**

D7	**7**	1 c. on 2d.	5	0	8	6
D8	,,	2 c. on 2d.	5	0	8	6
D9	,,	5 c. on 2d.	5	0	8	6

B. (Date ?) *As Type* D **5.**

D10	**7**	1 c. on 2d.	10	0	12	6
D11	,,	2 c. on 2d.	6	0	7	6
D12	,,	5 c. on 2d.	10	0	12	6

TANGANYIKA (TANZANIA).

(Formerly German East Africa.)

I. British Occupation of Mafia Island.

Mafia Island was captured by the British from the Germans in December 1914. Letters were first sent out unstamped, then with stamps handstamped with Type M **1.** Later the military were supplied with handstamps by the post office in Zanzibar. These were used to produce Nos. M11 to M52.

G.R.
MAFIA
(M 1)

1915 (Jan.). *German East Africa Yacht types handstamped. Wmk. Lozenges, or no wmk.* (1 *r. and* 2 *r.*).

A. *In Black.* B. *In Violet.*

		A.	B.
M 1	2½ h.	£40	£45
M 2	4 h.	£40	£45
M 3	7½ h.	£40	£45
M 4	15 h.	£45	£60
M 5	20 h.	£45	£60
M 6	30 h.	£45	£60
M 7	45 h.	£45	£60
M 8	1 r.	£200	£275
M 9	2 r.	£200	£275
M10	3 r.	£200	£275

A few contemporary Zanzibar stamps (1, 3, 6 and 15 c.) are known with the above overprint

1915 (July). *German East Africa Yacht types with handstamped four-line surcharge* "G.R.—POST—6 CENTS—MAFIA" *in black, green or violet. Wmk. Lozenges or no wmk.* (1 *r and* 2 *r.*).

M11	6 c. on 2½ h. ..	£45
M12	6 c. on 4 h. ..	£45
M13	6 c. on 7½ h. ...	£45

M14 6 c. on 15 h. .. £50
M15 6 c. on 20 h. .. £50
M16 6 c. on 30 h. .. £60
M17 6 c. on 45 h. .. £60
M18 6 c. on 1 r. ..
M19 6 c. on 2 r. ..
M20 6 c. on 3 r. ..

The 5, 20 and 40 pesa values of the 1900 "Yacht" issue are also known with the above surcharge, as are the contemporary 1 c. and 6 c. Zanzibar stamps.

(M **3**)

1915 (Sept.). *German East African fiscal stamps.* "Statistik des Waaren-Verkehrs" (*Trade Statistical Charge*) *overprinted in bluish green,* "O.H.B.M.S. Mafia" *in a circle, as Type* M **3**.

M21 24 pesa, vermilion/*buff* .. }
M22 12½ heller, drab .. .. } Set of 5,
M23 25 heller, dull green .. } un. or used,
M24 50 heller, slate .. .. } £80
M25 1 rupee, lilac .. .. }

German East African "Ubersetzungs-Gebühren" (*Translation fee*) *stamp, overprinted as before.*
M26 25 heller, grey £30 £35

G. R
POST
MAFIA
(M **4**)

G. R.
Post
MAFIA.
(M **5**)

Stamps as above, but with further opt. as Type M **4**, *in green.*

M27 24 pesa, vermilion/*buff* .. }
M28 12½ heller, drab .. .. } Set of 5,
M29 25 heller, dull green .. } un. or used,
M30 50 heller, slate .. .. } £80
M31 1 rupee, lilac .. .. }
M32 25 heller, grey (No. M26) .. }

1915 (Sept.). *Stamps of India,* 1911–13, *optd.* "I.E.F." *in black, with a further opt. Type* M **4** *handstruck in green, greenish black or dull blue.*

M33 **55** 3 pies, grey 15 0 17 6
a. Opt. inverted 50 0
b. Opt. sideways 50 0
c. Pair, one stamp without opt. £8
M34 **56** ½ a. green 17 6 20 0
a. Opt. inverted 40 0
b. Opt. double 60 0
c. Opt. sideways 40 0
M35 **57** 1 a. carmine 25 0 30 0
a. Opt. sideways 40 0
b. Opt. double 50 0
c. Opt. inverted 40 0
M36 **59** 2 a. mauve 35 0 45 0
a. Opt. inverted £5
M37 **61** 2½ a. ultramarine 40 0 60 0
a. Opt. inverted £5
M38 **62** 3 a. orange-brown 40 0 40 0
a. Opt. sideways £5
b. Opt. double £5
c. Opt. inverted £5
M39 **63** 4 a. olive 65 0 80 0
a. Opt. inverted £14

M40 **65** 8 a. purple £5 £6
a. Opt. inverted £14
M41 **66** 12 a. dull claret £12 £14
a. Opt. inverted £18
M42 **67** 1 r. brown and green .. £12 £14
a. Opt. inverted £20

1916 (Oct.). *Stamps of India,* 1911–13, *opt.* "I.E.F." *in black with further opt. Type* M **5** *handstruck in green, greenish black or dull blue.*

M43 3 pies, grey £5 £5
M44 ½ a. green £5 £5
M45 1 a. carmine £6 £6
M46 2 a. mauve £6 £6
M47 2½ a. ultramarine £7 £7
M48 3 a. orange-brown £8 £8
M49 4 a. olive £8 £8
M50 8 a. purple £9 £9
M51 12 a. dull claret £10 £10
M52 1 r. brown and green .. £12 £12

II. For use of Nyasa-Rhodesian Force.

N. F.
(D)

1916. *T* **15** *of Nyasaland optd. with Type* D.

33 **15** ½d. green 2 0 3 0
34 ,, 1d. scarlet 1 3 1 9
35 ,, 3d. purple/*yellow* 7 6 8 0
a. Opt. double £65
36 ,, 4d. black and red/*yellow* .. 22 6 27 6
37 ,, 1s. black/*green* 37 6 42 6

This issue was sanctioned for use by the Nyasa-Rhodesian Force in conquered territory in German East Africa.

Of No. 35*a* only six copies were printed, these being the bottom row on one pane issued at M'bamba Bay F.P.O., German East Africa.

III. British Occupation of German East Africa.

G.E.A. (1) G.E.A. (2) G.E.A. (3)

1917–22. *Stamps of Kenya optd. with T* **1** *and* **2**. *Wmk. Mult. Crown CA.*

38 **3** 1 c. black, O (R.) 0 2 0 2
39 ,, 1 c. black, O (Verm.) .. 50 0 45 0
40 ,, 3 c. green, O 0 3 0 2
41 ,, 6 c. scarlet, O 0 4 0 3
42 ,, 10 c. orange, O 0 8 0 4
43 ,, 12 c. slate-grey, O 1 0 2 6
44 ,, 15 c. bright blue, O 1 3 1 6
45 ,, 25 c. blk. & red/*yellow*, C .. 1 6 2 0
a. On pale yellow (1921) .. 2 6 3 0
46 ,, 50 c. black and lilac, C .. 3 6 6 0
47 ,, 75 c. black/*blue-green, olive-back*, C (R.) .. 5 0 12 6
a. On emerald back 7 6 17 6
48 **4** 1 r. black/*green*, C (R.) .. 8 0 10 0
a. On emerald back 12 6 20 0
49 ,, 2 r. red and black/*blue*, C .. 17 6 25 0
50 ,, 3 r. violet and green, C .. 22 6 27 6
51 ,, 4 r. red & green/*yellow*, C .. 35 0 42 6
52 ,, 5 r. blue and dull purple, C 50 0 60 0
53 ,, 10 r. red & green/*green*, C .. £8 £9
a. On emerald back £9 £10
54 ,, 20 r. black & purple/*red*, C £14 £16
55 ,, 50 r. carmine and green, C .. £120 £140

The rupee values exist with very large stop after the "E" in "G.E.A." and also with round, or very small stop in the same position.

The later printings of the "cent" values (except 6 c.) and of the 1 r., 3 r., and 10 r., have the overprint in heavier and more regular type.

1921. *As* 1917–22 *but wmk. Mult. Script CA.*

60 **3** 12 c. slate-grey, O 1 6 5 0
61 ,, 15 c. bright blue, O 1 6 1 6
63 ,, 50 c. black & dull purple, C 15 0 20 0

No.	Type	Description	Unused	Used
66	**4**	2 r. red and black/*blue*, C ..	£5	£6
67	,,	3 r. violet and green, C ..	£6	£7
68	,,	5 r. blue and dull purple, C	£8	£10

1922. *T* **3** *of Kenya optd. by the Government printer at Dar-es-Salaam with T* **3**. *Wmk. Mult. Script. CA.*

No.	Description	Unused	Used
72	1 c. black (R.)	0 6	2 6
73	10 c. orange-yellow	1 6	6 0

IV. British Mandate.

4

5

(Recess. Bradbury, Wilkinson & Co.)

1922. *T* **4** (" cents " *values) and* **5**. *Head in black. Wmk. Mult. Script CA.*

(*a*) *P* 15 × 14.

No.	Description	Unused	Used
74	5 c. slate-purple	2 0	1 3
75	10 c. green	1 6	1 0
76	15 c. carmine-red	2 0	0 8
77	20 c. orange	3 0	0 8
78	25 c. black	17 6	22 6
79	30 c. blue	6 0	8 6
80	40 c. yellow-brown	10 0	12 6
81	50 c. slate-grey	10 0	12 6
82	75 c. yellow-bistre	15 0	20 0

(*b*) *P* 14. A. *Wmk. sideways.* B. *Wmk. upright.*

No.	Description	A. Unused	A. Used	B. Unused	B. Used
83	1s. green	17 6	20 0	12 6	17 6
84	2s. purple ..	30 0	30 0	20 0	30 0
85	3s. black	30 0	40 0	†	
86	5s. scarlet ..	50 0	75 0	50 0	50 0
87	10s. deep blue ..	£9	£10	£6	£7
88	£1 yellow-orange	£18	£18	£12	£12

In the £1 stamp the words of value are on a curved scroll running across the stamp above the words " POSTAGE AND REVENUE."

1925. *As* 1922. *Frame colours changed.*

No.	Type	Description	Unused	Used
89	**4**	5 c. green	2 0	2 6
90	,,	10 c. orange	2 6	3 0
91	,,	25 c. blue	12 6	15 0
92	,,	30 c. purple	8 6	12 6

6

7

(Typo. De La Rue & Co.)

1927–31. *Head in black. Wmk. Mult. Script CA. P* 14.

No.	Type	Description	Unused	Used
93	**6**	5 c. green	0 4	0 3
94	,,	10 c. yellow	0 6	0 3
95	,,	15 c. carmine-red	1 0	0 4
96	,,	20 c. orange-buff	1 6	0 3
97	,,	25 c. bright blue	2 0	2 0
98	,,	30 c. dull purple	4 0	3 6
98*a*	**6**	30 c. bright blue ('31) ..	17 6	6 0
99	,,	40 c. yellow-brown ..	4 0	7 6
100	,,	50 c. grey	3 0	1 6
101	,,	75 c. olive-green	10 0	15 0
102	**7**	1s. green, O	6 6	4 6
103	,,	2s. deep purple, O ..	15 0	8 6
104	,,	3s. black, O	30 0	35 0
105	,,	5s. carmine-red, C ..	30 0	25 0
106	,,	10s. deep blue, C ..	80 0	90 0
107	,,	£1 brown-orange, C ..	£10	£12

For issues between 1935 and 1961 see KENYA, UGANDA AND TANGANYIKA.

V. Independent within the Commonwealth.

8. Teacher and pupils.

9. District nurse and child.

10. Coffee-picking.

11. Harvesting Maize.

12. Tanganyikan Flag.

13. Serengeti Lions.

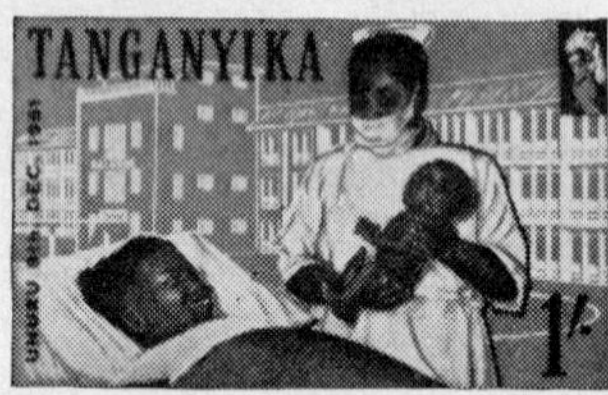

14 " Maternity ".

15. Freedom Torch over Mt. Kilimanjaro.

16. Dar-es-Salaam Waterfront.

17. Land Tillage.

18. Diamond and Mine.

Des. V. Whiteley. Photo. Harrison & Sons.)

961 (9 Dec.). *Independence.* *P* 14 × 15 (5 *c.*, 30 *c.*), 15 × 14 (10 *c.*, 15 *c.*, 20 *c.*, 50 *c.*) *or* 14½ (*others*).

08	**8**	5 c. sepia & lt. apple-grn.	0 3	0 3
09	**9**	10 c. deep bluish green ..	0 4	0 3
10	**10**	15 c. sepia and blue ..	0 5	0 3
		a. Blue omitted	£115	
11	**11**	20 c. orange-brown ..	0 6	0 4
12	**12**	30 c. blk., emerald & yell.	0 7	0 5
		a. Inscr. " UHURU 196 " ..	—	£125
13	**13**	50 c. black and yellow ..	1 0	0 10
14	**14**	1s. brn., blue & olive-yell.	1 8	1 2
15	**15**	1s. 30, red, yellow, black, brown & blue (*shades*)	2 3	1 6
16	**16**	2s. blue, yellow, green and brown	3 3	2 6
17	**17**	5s. deep bluish green and orange-red	8 0	4 9
118	**18**	10s. black, reddish purple and light blue ..	16 0	12 0
		a. Reddish purple (diamond) omitted		
119	**15**	20s. red, yellow, black, brown and green ..	30 0	23 0

19. Mr. Nyerere inaugurating Self-help Project.

20. Hoisting Flag on Mt. Kilimanjaro.

21. Presidential Emblem.

22. Independence Monument.

(Photo. Harrison & Sons.)

1962 (9 Dec.). *Inauguration of Republic.* *P* 14½.

120	**19**	30 c. emerald	0 10	0 10
121	**20**	50 c. yellow, black, green, red and blue ..	1 6	1 6
122	**21**	1s. 30, multicoloured ..	2 9	3 0
123	**22**	2s. 50, black, red & blue	5 6	6 6

23. Map of Republic.

24. Torch and Spear Emblem.

(Des. M. Goaman. Photo. Harrison & Sons.)

1964 (7 July). *United Republic of Tanganyika and Zanzibar Commemoration.* *P* 14 × 14½.

124	**23**	20 c. yellow-grn. & lt. blue	0	6	0	7
125	**24**	30 c. blue and sepia ..	0	9	1	0
126	,,	1s. 30, orange-brown and ultramarine	2	6	2	9
127	**23**	2s. 50, purple & ultram.	5	0	6	0

Despite the inscription on the stamps the above issue was only on sale in Tanganyika and had no validity in Zanzibar.

VI. Renamed Tanzania.

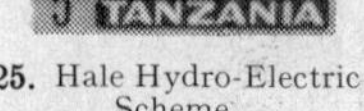

25. Hale Hydro-Electric Scheme.

26. Tanzania Flag.

27. National Servicemen.

28. Road-building.

29. Drum, Spear, Shield and Stool.

30. Giraffes, Mikumi National Park.

31. Zebras, Manyara National Park.

32. Mt. Kilimanjaro.

33. Dar-es-Salaam Harbour.

34. Skull of Zinjanthropus and Excavations, Olduvai Gorge.

35. Fishing.

36. Sisal Industry.

37. State House, Dar-es-Salaam.

38. Arms of Tanzania.

(Des. V. Whiteley. Photo. Harrison.)

1965 (9 Dec.). *P* 14 × 14½ (5 *c*., 10 *c*., 20 *c*., 50 *c*., 65 *c*.), 14½ × 14 (15 *c*., 30 *c*., 40 *c*.), *or* 14 (*others*).

No.	Type	Description				
128	**25**	5 c. ultram. & yell.-orge.	0	2	0	3
129	**26**	10 c. black, greenish yellow, green and blue ..	0	3	0	5
130	**27**	15 c. multicoloured ..	0	4	0	7
131	**28**	20 c. sepia, grey-green and greenish blue ..	0	5	0	8
132	**29**	30 c. black and red-brown	0	6	0	10
133	**30**	40 c. multicoloured ..	0	8	1	0
134	**31**	50 c. multicoloured ..	0	10	1	2
135	**32**	65 c. grn., red-brn. & blue	1	0	1	6
136	**33**	1s. multicoloured ..	1	5	2	0
137	**34**	1s. 30, multicoloured ..	1	10	2	6
138	**35**	2s. 50, blue & orge.-brn.	3	6	4	6
139	**36**	5s. lake-brown, yellow-green and blue ..	6	9	8	0
140	**37**	10s. olive-yellow, olive-green and blue ..	13	3	15	0
141	**38**	20s. multicoloured ..	25	0	30	0

NOTE. Stamps inscribed "UGANDA KENYA TANGANYIKA & ZANZIBAR" (or "TANZANIA UGANDA KENYA") will be found listed under East Africa.

OFFICIAL STAMPS.

OFFICIAL (O 1) **OFFICIAL** (O 2)

1961 (9 Dec.). *Optd. with Type* O **1** (10 *c*., 15 *c*., 20 *c*., 50 *c*.) *or larger and measuring* 17 *mm*. (5 *c*., 30 *c*.) *or with Type* O **2** (1s.) *or measuring* 22 *mm*. (5s.).

No.	Type	Description				
O1	**8**	5 c. sepia & lt. apple-grn.	0	3	0	3
O2	**9**	10 c. deep bluish green ..	0	4	0	4
O3	**10**	15 c. sepia and blue ..	0	5	0	5
O4	**11**	20 c. orange-brown ..	0	6	0	7
O5	**12**	30 c. blk., emerald & yell.	0	7	0	10
O6	**13**	50 c. black and yellow ..	1	0	1	2
O7	**14**	1s. brn., bl. & olive-yell.	1	8	1	10
O8	**17**	5s. deep bluish green and orange-red	8	0	8	6

1965 (9 Dec.). *Nos.* 128, *etc. optd. as Types* O **1** (15 *c*., 30 *c*.) *or larger*, (*measuring* 17 *mm*. 5 *c*., 10 *c*., 20 *c*., 50 *c*.), *or* O **2** (1s., 5s.).

No.	Type	Description				
O 9	**25**	5 c. ultram. & yell.-orge.	0	2	0	2
O10	**26**	10 c. black, greenish yellow, green and blue ..	0	3	0	3
O11	**27**	15 c. multicoloured ..	0	4	0	4
O12	**28**	20 c. sepia, grey-green and greenish blue ..	0	5	0	6
O13	**29**	30 c. black and red-brown	0	6	0	8
O14	**31**	50 c. multicoloured ..	0	10	1	0
O15	**33**	1s. multicoloured ..	1	5	1	6
O16	**36**	5s. lake-brown, yellow-green and blue ..	6	9	7	6

POSTAGE DUE STAMPS.

Postage Due stamps of Kenya and Uganda were issued for provisional use as such in Tanganyika on 1 July, 1933. The postmark is the only means of identification.

At present the Postage Due stamps of Kenya, Uganda and Tanganyika are still used in Tanganyika.

TASMANIA.

— SIMPLIFICATION (see Introduction) —

Nos. 1 to 129.

3, 11, 14, 15, 17. 19, 20, 22.
28, 29, 31, 33, 34, 36, 37, 38, 45, 46, 47 41.
84, 112, 99, 91, 102, 122, 124, 129, 127.

Type II.

131, 139, 135, 136.
155, 156, 160, 161, 163, 165, 167, 168, 169, 171.
178, 179, 180, 182. 193, 186, 178, 194, 195,
188, 197, 198, 226, 228. 213, 210, 211, 212.
201, 207. 255. 278a, 159a.

Types 20 to 21a.

216 to 225. 256. 257. 260, 261.

Pictorials.

229 to 236. 237, 238, 240, 241, 239.
246, 247, 242, 248, 243, 249, 245, 250. 252.

1

2

(Eng. C. W. Coard. Recess. H. and C. Best at the office of the *Courier* Newspaper.)

1853 (1 Nov.). *No wmk. Imperf. Twenty-four varieties in four rows of six each.* (*a*) *Medium soft yellowish paper with all lines clear and distinct.*

No.	Type	Description	Unused	Used
1	**1**	1d. pale blue	£125	£45
2	,,	1d. blue	£125	£45

(*b*) *Thin hard white paper with lines of the engraving blurred and worn.*

No.	Type	Description	Unused	Used
3	**1**	1d. pale blue	£110	£45
4	,,	1d. blue	£110	£45

1853–54. *No wmk. Imperf. In each plate there are twenty-four varieties in four rows of six each.*

1853. *Plate I. Finely engraved. All lines in network and background thin, clear, and well defined.*

(*a*) *First state of the plate, brilliant colours.*

No.	Type	Description	Unused	Used
5	**2**	4d. bright red-orange.. ..	£65	£28
6	,,	4d. bright brownish orange ..	—	£38

(*b*) *Second state of plate, with blurred lines and worn condition of the central background.*

No.	Type	Description	Unused	Used
7	**2**	4d. red-orange..	£45	£14
8	,,	4d. orange	£45	£14
9	,,	4d. pale orange	—	£14

1854. *Plate II. Coarse engraving, lines in network and background thicker and blurred.*

No.	Type	Description	Unused	Used
10	**2**	4d. orange	£42	£12
		a. Double print		
11	,,	4d. dull orange ..	£38	£12
12	,,	4d. yellowish orange ..	£38	£12

Variety. Laid paper, with wide vertical lines.

No.	Type	Description	Unused	Used
13		4d. red-orange	£275	

No. 13 is from a proof sheet and is only known unused.

In the 4d. Plate I, the outer frame-line is thin all round. In Plate II it is, by comparison with other parts, thicker in the lower left angle.

In 1879 reprints were made of the 1d. in blue and the 4d., Plate I, in brownish yellow, on thin, tough, white wove paper, and perforated 11½. In 1887, a reprint from the other plate of the 4d. was made in reddish brown and in black, and in 1889 of the 1d. in blue and in black, and of the 4d. (both plates) in yellow and in black on white card, imperforate. The three plates having been defaced after the issue was superseded by new types, all these reprints show two thick strokes across the Queen's Head.

3

4

(Recess. Perkins, Bacon & Co.)

1855 (Aug.). *T* **3.** *Wmk. Large Star, Type* w. **1.** *Imperf.*

14 1d. carmine £260 £75
15 2d. deep green £95 £32
16 2d. green £95 £32
17 4d. deep blue £80 95 0
18 4d. blue £75 £7

There is a proof of the 1d. on thick, no wmk. paper that is sometimes sold as the issued stamp.

(Printed by H. and C. Best, of Hobart.)

1856–57. *T* **3.** *No wmk. Imperf.*

19 1d. pale brick-red (4.56) £250 £50
20 2d. dull emerald-green (1.57) £400 £65
21 4d. deep blue £42 £7
22 4d. blue £38 £7
23 4d. pale blue — £12

1856 (Nov.). *No wmk. Pelure paper. Imperf.*

24 1d. deep red-brown £90 £40

1857–60. *Wmk. double-lined numerals* "**1**," "**2**," *or* "**4**" *as T* **4.** *Imperf.*

25 **3** 1d. deep red-brown £17 40 0
26 ,, 1d. pale red-brown £12 27 6
27 ,, 1d. brick-red £7 22 6
28 ,, 1d. dull vermilion 27 6 22 6
29 ,, 1d. carmine 40 0 22 6
a. Double print — 90 0
30 ,, 2d. dull emerald-green — 70 0
31 ,, 2d. deep green £7 50 0
32 ,, 2d. green — 37 6
a. Double print — £11
33 ,, 2d. yellow-green £12 55 0
34 ,, 2d. sage-green 80 0 45 0
35 ,, 4d. blue 65 0 17 6
a. Double print — £7
36 ,, 4d. pale blue 65 0 17 6
37 ,, 4d. bright blue 55 0 17 6
a. Printed on both sides
b. Double print — 75 0
38 ,, 4d. very deep blue — 55 0
a. Double print — £8
39 ,, 4d. cobalt-blue — 37 6

7

8

(Recess. Perkins, Bacon & Co.)

1858 (Jan.). *Wmk. double-lined numerals* "**6**" *or* "**12**". *Imperf.*

40 **7** 6d. dull lilac £27 27 6
41 **8** 1s. bright vermilion £14 35 0
42 ,, 1s. dull vermilion — 37 6

Prepared for use, but not issued.
Wmk. Large Star. Imperf.

43 6d. lilac £16

1860–67. *Printed in the Colony. Wmk. double lined* "**6**".

44 **7** 6d. dull slate-grey (3.60) £12 27 6
45 ,, 6d. grey — 32 6
46 ,, 6d. grey-violet (4.63) 95 0 32 6
a. Double print — 80 0
47 ,, 6d. dull bluish (2.65) £7 32 6
48 ,, 6d. bluish purple £11 55 0
49 ,, 6d. reddish mauve (1867) £38 £16

In 1871 reprints were made of the 6d. (in mauve) and the 1s. on white wove paper, and perforated 11½. They are found with or without "REPRINT." In 1889 they were again reprinted on white card, imperforate and perforated 12. These later impressions are also found with or without "REPRINT."

1864–70. *T* **3, 7** *and* **8** (*with double-line numeral watermarks*), *with various local roulettes and perforations.*

(*a*) **1864.** *Roughly punctured roulette about* 8, *by J. Walch, at Hobart.*

50 1d. brick-red — £12
51 1d. carmine £9 £6
52 4d. pale blue — £12
53 6d. dull lilac — £18
54 1s. vermilion — £28

(*b*) **1867** (March). *Pin-perf.* 5½ *to* 9½ *at Longford, near Launceston.*

55 1d. carmine £12 75 0
56 4d. bright blue — £18
57 6d. grey-violet — £12
58 6d. reddish mauve — £22
59 1s. vermilion

(*c*) **1867** (?). *Pin-perf.* 13½ *to* 14½.

60 1d. brick-red — £9
61 1d. dull vermilion — £9
62 1d. carmine
63 2d. yellow-green — £14
64 4d. pale blue — £9
65 6d. grey-violet — £17
66 1s. vermilion

(*d*) **1866** (?). *Oblique roulette* 10, 10½.

67 1d. brick-red — £9
68 1d. carmine £12 £7
69 2d. yellow-green — £14
70 4d. bright blue — £10
71 6d. grey-violet — £17

(*e*) **1867** (?). *Oblique roulette* 14 *to* 15, *used at Deloraine.*

72 1d. brick-red — £9
73 1d. dull vermilion — £9
74 1d. carmine — £8
75 2d. yellow-green — £14
76 4d. pale blue — £9
77 6d. grey-violet — £24
78 1s. vermilion — £27

(*f*) **1868–69.** *Serrated perf.* 19.

79 1d. carmine (*pen.-canc.* 20s.) £9 90 0
80 2d. yellow-green — £16
81 4d. deep blue £27 £8
82 4d. cobalt-blue — £8
83 6d. bluish purple — £32

1864–69. *Double-line numeral watermarks.*
I. *Perforated by J. Walch and Sons, Hobart.*

(*a*) *P* 10.

84 **3** 1d. brick-red 22 6 22 6
85 ,, 1d. vermilion 25 0 22 6
86 ,, 1d. deep carmine 20 0 22 6
87 ,, 1d. pale carmine 20 0 22 6
88 ,, 2d. sage-green £9 £8
89 ,, 2d. yellow-green £7 80 0
90 ,, 4d. blue 75 0 22 6
91 ,, 4d. pale blue 75 0 20 0
a. Double print — 55 0
92 **7** 6d. grey-violet £7 22 6

No.	Type	Stamp	Unused	Used
93	7	6d. dull bluish	95 0	22 6
94	,,	6d. bluish purple	—	27 6
95	,,	6d. reddish mauve	£16	65 0
96	8	1s. vermilion	75 0	22 6

(b) P 11½ to 12.

No.	Type	Stamp	Unused	Used
96a	3	1d. vermilion	32 6	
97	,,	1d. deep carmine	17 6	12 6
98	,,	1d. pale carmine	22 6	15 0
99	,,	2d. pale yellow-green	£7	60 0
100	,,	2d. deep yellow-green	85 0	65 0
101	,,	4d. blue	67 6	17 6
102	,,	4d. deep blue	60 0	14 0
103	,,	4d. cobalt-blue	—	32 6
104	7	6d. bluish purple	£7	25 0
105	,,	6d. reddish mauve	80 0	22 6
106	8	1s. vermilion	90 0	22 6
		a. Double print	—	£7

(c) Perf. compound 10×11½, 12.

No.	Type	Stamp	Unused	Used
107	3	1d. deep carmine	£38	
108	,,	4d. blue	—	£48

Error. Wmk. double-lined "**2**". *P* 11½–12 (Nov. 1869).

No.	Type	Stamp	Unused	Used
109	3	1d. carm. (*pen.-canc.* £12)	—	£48

II. *Perforated by R. Harris, Launceston. P* 12½, 13.

No.	Type	Stamp	Unused	Used
110	3	1d. brick-red	27 6	27 6
111	,,	1d. vermilion	22 6	22 6
112	,,	1d. deep carmine	12 6	10 0
113	,,	2d. sage-green	£9	£7
114	,,	2d. yellow-green	£12	£7
115	,,	4d. bright blue	£7	55 0
116	,,	4d. blue	£7	55 0
117	7	6d. dull bluish	£9	55 0
118	,,	6d. bluish purple	£12	55 0
119	,,	6d. reddish mauve	£22	£7
120	8	1s. vermilion	£9	80 0

III. **1871–80.** *Perforated by the Government at Hobart (a) P* 11, 11½.

No.	Type	Stamp	Unused	Used
121	7	6d. dull mauve	60 0	20 0
122	,,	6d. bright mauve	47 6	20 0
		a. Imperf. between (pair)	—	£22
123	,,	6d. dull purple	32 6	16 0
		a. Imperf. (pair)	—	£24
124	,,	6d. bright purple	45 0	15 0
		a. Double print	—	55 0
		b. Imperf. between (horiz. pair)	£28	
125	,,	6d. lilac-purple	65 0	20 0
126	8	1s. dull vermilion	65 0	17 6
		a. Imperf. between (horiz. pair)		
127	,,	1s. brownish vermilion	42 6	15 0

(b) P 12.

No.	Type	Stamp	Unused	Used
128	7	6d. bright purple	75 0	27 6
129	,,	6d. dull claret	12 6	15 0

All stamps perforated by the "Walch" machine gauge over 11½ and under 12, while those of the Government machine gauge 11½ or under.

11

12

13

14

(Plates by De La Rue & Co., Typo. in the Colony.)

1870–71. *Wmk. single lined numerals T* **12**, **13**, *or* **14**. *(a) P* 12.

No.	Type	Stamp	Unused	Used
130	11	1d. rose-red (10)	35 0	17 6
131	,,	1d. deep rose-red (10)	60 0	15 0
132	,,	1d. rose-red (4)	42 6	22 6
133	,,	2d. yellow-green (2)	42 6	12 6
134	,,	2d blue-green (2)	55 0	12 6
135	,,	4d. blue (4)	£10	£10
136	,,	10d. black (10)	6 0	6 0

(b) P 11½.

No.	Type	Stamp	Unused	Used
137	11	1d. rose-red (10)	£20	
138	,,	2d. yellow-green (2)	£8	15 0
139	,,	2d. blue-green (2)	50 0	7 6
		a. Double print		
140	,,	10d. black (10)	17 6	15 0

(c) Imperf. (pairs).

No.	Type	Stamp	Unused	Used
141	11	1d. rose-red (4)	—	£12
142	,,	1d. rose-red (10)	£20	£15
143	,,	2d. green (2)		
144	,,	10d. black (10)	£6	

The above were printed on paper borrowed from New South Wales.

15

1871–79. *W* **15**. *(a) P* 12.

No.	Type	Stamp	Unused	Used
145	11	1d. rose	85 0	10 0
146	,,	1d. carmine	£6	20 0
147	,,	2d. green	£28	£12
148	,,	3d. red-brown	75 0	35 0
149	,,	3d. deep red-brown	75 0	35 0
150	,,	4d. buff	£12	18 6
151	,,	9d. pale blue	25 0	
152	,,	5s. purple	£6	
153	,,	5s. mauve	60 0	

(b) P 11½.

No.	Type	Stamp	Unused	Used
154	11	1d. rose	3 6	1 0
155	,,	1d. bright rose	3 0	1 0
156	,,	1d. vermilion	£10	95 0
157	,,	1d. carmine	6 6	1 6
158	,,	1d. pink	6 6	1 3
159	,,	2d. deep green	22 6	1 3
160	,,	2d. yellow-green	£9	3 0
161	,,	2d. blue-green	25 0	0 8
162	,,	3d. pale red-brown	30 0	6 0
163	,,	3d. deep red-brown	35 0	7 0
		a. Imperf. between (pair)		
164	,,	3d. purple-brown	35 0	6 0
165	,,	3d. brownish purple	35 0	6 0
166	,,	4d. ochre	60 0	7 6
167	,,	4d. buff	40 0	8 6
168	,,	4d. pale yellow	35 0	7 6
169	,,	9d. blue	12 6	10 0
170	,,	5s. purple (*pen canc.* 4s.)	60 0	32 6
171	,,	5s. mauve	37 6	35 0

(c) Imperf. (pairs.)

No.	Type	Stamp	Unused	Used
172	11	1d. rose (*pen. canc.* £5)		
173	,,	2d. green	—	£7
174	,,	3d. pale red-brown	£7	
175	,,	3d. purple-brown	—	£25
176	,,	9d. blue	£6	
176a	,,	5s. purple		

16

(Typo. De La Rue & Co.)

1878. *T* **11.** *W* **16.** *P* 14.

No.	Type	Description	Unused	Used
177		1d. carmine	2 0	0 8
178		1d. rose-carmine	2 0	0 8
179		1d. scarlet	2 3	0 8
180		2d. pale green	3 6	0 6
181		2d. green	3 6	0 3
182		8d. dull purple-brown	5 0	5 0

In 1871 the 1d., 2d., 3d., 4d. blue, 9d. 10d. and 5s., *T* **11**, were reprinted on soft white wove, and perforated 11½; and in 1879 the 4d. yellow and 8d. were reprinted on thin, tough, white wove. All nine varieties are found with and without "REPRINT". In 1889 the 4d. blue was also reprinted on white card imperforate, and perforated 12. The 5s. has been reprinted in *mauve* on white card, perforated 12. These later impressions, like those of 1871 and 1879, are found with or without "REPRINT".

1880–91. *Colonial print.* *W* **16.**

(*a*) *P* 12.

No.	Type	Description	Unused	Used
183	**11**	½d. orange	2 6	2 6
184	,,	½d. deep orange	2 0	1 0
185	,,	1d. pink	18 6	7 6
		a. Imperf. (pair)	35 0	35 0
186	,,	1d. rosine	8 6	5 0
187	,,	1d. dull rosine	10 0	5 0
188	,,	3d. red-brown	3 6	3 0
		a. Imperf. (pair)	50 0	
		b. Imperf. between (pair)	£22	
189	,,	4d. deep yellow	50 0	20 0
190	,,	4d. chrome-yellow	70 0	20 0
		a. Printed both sides	50 0	

(*b*) *P* 11½.

No.	Type	Description	Unused	Used
192	**11**	½d. orange	2 6	1 3
193	,,	½d. deep orange	2 0	1 6
194	,,	1d. dull red	5 0	3 0
195	,,	1d. vermilion-red	2 6	2 6
196	,,	3d. red-brown	9 0	7 0
197	,,	4d. deep yellow	30 0	8 6
198	,,	4d. chrome-yellow	20 0	8 0
199	,,	4d. olive-yellow	70 0	27 6
200	,,	4d. buff	30 0	10 0

Halfpenny d. 2½ d. 2½

(17) (18) (2¼ mm. between "d", and "2".) (19) (3½ mm. between "d." and "2".)

1889–91. *W* **16.** (*a*) *Surch. with T* **17.** *P* 14.

No.	Type	Description	Unused	Used
201	**11**	½d. on 1d. scarlet	1 3	1 3
		a. "al" in "Half" vertical	£35	£22

A minor variety has broken "p" in "Halfpenny".

(*b*) *Surch. with T* **18.** *P* 11½.

No.	Type	Description	Unused	Used
204	**11**	2½d. on 9d. pale blue	4 6	4 6
		a. Imperf. (pair)	£7	
		b. Surch. double, one inverted	£7	£7
205	,,	2½d. on 9d. deep blue	7 6	8 6

(*c*) *Surch. with T* **19.** *P* 12.

No.	Type	Description	Unused	Used
207	**11**	2½d. on 9d. pale blue	3 0	2 0
		a. Blue surch.		

There is a reprint on the 2½d. on 9d. on stout white wove paper, perf. 12, overprinted "REPRINT".

1891. *Colonial print. Reissue with* *W* **15.**

(*a*) *P* 12.

No.	Type	Description	Unused	Used
209	**11**	½d. orange	16 0	16 0
		a. Imperf. (pair)	30 0	
210	,,	1d. dull rosine	15 0	15 0
211	,,	1d. rosine	15 0	15 0
212	,,	4d. bistre	4 6	4 6

(*b*) *P* 11½.

No.	Type	Description	Unused	Used
213	**11**	½d. orange	15 0	10 0
214	,,	½d. brown-orange	17 6	10 6
215	,,	1d. rosine	12 6	10 0

20

21

21*a*

(Typo. De La Rue & Co.)

1892–99. *W* **16.** *P* 14.

No.	Type	Description	Unused	Used
216	**20**	½d. orange and mauve	0 10	0 8
217	**21**	2½d. purple	2 6	1 6
218	**20**	5d. pale blue and brown	4 6	3 6
219	,,	6d. violet and black	6 0	5 0
220	**21*a***	10d. pur.-lake & dp. grn.	10 0	6 6
221	**20**	1s. rose and green	6 0	5 0
222	,,	2s. 6d. brown and blue	22 6	15 0
223	,,	5s. lilac and red	30 0	20 0
224	,,	10s. mauve and brown	60 0	42 6
225	,,	£1 green and yellow	£15	£11

1896. *Colonial print.* *W* **16.** *P* 12.

No.	Type	Description	Unused	Used
226	**11**	4d. pale bistre	7 6	4 0
227	,,	9d. pale blue	4 6	3 0
228	,,	9d. blue	6 0	7 6

22. Lake Marion.

23. Mount Wellington.

24. Hobart.

25. Tasman's Arch.

26. Spring River, Port Davey.

27. Russell Falls.

28. Mount Gould, Lake St. Clair.

29. Dilston Falls.

30.

1899–1912.

PICTORIAL DESIGNS.

A. Recess-printed by De La Rue, London.

1899 (Dec.)–**1900.** *W* **30.** *P* 14.

No.	Type					
229	**22**	½d. deep green	0	9	0	8
230	**23**	1d. bright lake	0	8	0	3
231	**24**	2d. deep violet	1	3	0	4
232	**25**	2½d. indigo..	3	6	3	0
233	**26**	3d. sepia	4	0	2	6
234	**27**	4d. deep orange-buff ..	6	0	3	0
235	**28**	5d. bright blue	8	6	5	0
236	**29**	6d. lake	7	6	5	0

B. Printed at the Government Printing Office Melbourne, Victoria.

I. *Wmk. V over Crown. Type* w. **10.**

1902–3. LITHOGRAPHED. *Transfers from London plates. Wmk. upright on* 1d. *P* 12½.

No.	Type					
237	**22**	½d. green (1903)	0	3	0	4
		a. Perf. 11	5	0	1	0
		b. Perf. comp. of 12½ and 11 ..	27	6	27	6
238	**23**	1d. carmine-red	0	9	0	3
239	**24**	2d. violet	0	9	0	4
		a. Perf. 11	1	0	0	4
		b. Perf. comp. of 12½ and 11 ..	37	6	20	0
		c. *Purple*	1	3	0	4
		ca. *Purple.* Perf. 11	3	0	0	3

As the V and Crown paper was originally prepared for stamps of smaller size, portions of two or more watermarks appear on each stamp.

The ½d. and 2d. may be found with wmk. upright, the normal position in these values being sideways.

We only list the main groups of shades in this and the following issues. There are variations of shade in all values, particularly in the 2d. where there is a wide range, also in the 1d. in some issues.

1902–3. ELECTROTYPED. *Plates made at Govt. Printing Office. P* 12½.

(*a*) *Wmk. sideways* (Oct. 1902).

No.	Type					
240	**23**	1d. pale red (to rose) ..	1	3	0	3
		a. Perf. 11	8	6	0	4
		b. Perf. 12½ comp. with 11 ..	60	0	20	0

Stamps from this printing with wmk. upright, are scarce, especially perf. 11.

(*b*) *Wmk. upright* (April, 1903).

No.	Type					
241	**23**	1d. rose-red	0	9	0	3
		a. Perf. 11	1	9	0	3
		b. Perf. comp. of 12½ and 11 ..	40	0	25	0
		c. *Deep carmine-red*	35	0	0	6
		ca. *Deep carmine-red.* Perf. 11 ..	—		10	0
		cb. *Deep carmine-red.* Perf. comp. of 12½ and 11				

II. *Wmk. Crown over* A. *Type* w. **11** (*sideways on oblong stamps*).

1905 (Sept.)–**1912.** LITHOGRAPHED. *Transfers from London plates.* *P* 12½.

242	**24**	2d. purple	3 6	0 8
		a. Perf. 11	3 6	0 4
		b. Perf. comp. of 12½ and 11	7 6	5 0
		c. Perf. comp. of 12½ and 12	—	20 0
		d. Perf. comp. of 11 and 12		
		e. *Dull purple*	3 6	0 6
		ea. *Dull purple.* Perf. 11	3 6	0 4
243	**26**	3d. brown	7 6	1 9
		a. Perf. 11	8 6	3 0
		b. Perf. comp. of 12½ and 11	35 0	
244	**27**	4d. orange-buff (1907)	8 0	3 0
		a. Perf. 11	6 0	2 0
		b. Perf. comp. of 12½ and 11	£6	
		c. *Brown-ochre* (wmk. sideways). Perf. 11 (1907)	18 6	7 6
		d. *Orange-yellow* (1912)	7 6	4 0
		da. *Orange-yellow.* Perf. 11 ('12)	6 0	
245	**29**	6d. lake	17 6	10 0
		a. Perf. 11	15 0	6 0
		b. Perf. comp. of 12½ and 11	70 0	

Stamps with perf. compound of 12½ and 12 or 11 and 12 are found on sheets which were sent from Melbourne incompletely perforated. The line of perforation gauging 12 was done at the Government Printing Office, Hobart.

1905–11. ELECTROTYPED. *Plates made at Govt. Printing Office.* *P* 12½.

246	**22**	½d. yellow-green (1909)	0 6	0 3
		a. Perf. 11 (1908)	0 6	0 3
		b. Perf. comp. of 12½ and 11	17 6	
		c. Perf. comp. of 11 and 12		
247	**23**	1d. rose-red	0 4	0 3
		a. Perf. 11	0 4	0 3
		b. Perf. comp. of 12½ and 11	2 6	3 0
		c. Perf. comp. of 12½ and 12	17 6	10 0
		d. Perf. comp. of 11 and 12	15 0	
		e. *Bright rose*	—	0 4
		ea. *Bright rose.* Perf. 11	2 0	0 3
		f. *Crimson* (1910)		
		fa. *Crimson.* Perf. 11		
		fb. *Crimson.* Perf. comp. of 12½ and 12		
248	**24**	2d. purple	2 0	0 3
		a. Perf. 11	3 6	0 3
		b. *Dull violet*	2 0	0 3
		ba. *Dull violet.* Perf. 11	2 0	0 3
		bb. *Dull violet.* Perf. comp. of 12½ and 11	5 0	5 0
		bc. *Dull violet.* Perf. comp. of 12½ and 11		
		bd. *Dull violet.* Perf. comp. of 11 and 12	35 0	
		c. *Bright violet* (1910)	4 6	0 8
		ca. *Bright violet.* Perf. 11	4 6	0 8
249	**26**	3d. brown (1909)	3 6	1 6
		a. Perf. 11	5 0	2 0
		b. Perf. comp. of 12½ and 11	45 0	
250	**29**	6d. dull lake (1911)	7 6	4 0
		a. Perf. 11	6 0	3 6
		b. Perf. comp. of 12½ and 11	35 0	

The note after No. 245 re perfs. compound with perf. 12 also applies here.

The ½d. and 2d. are found with wmk. upright and the 1d. with wmk. sideways, each perf. 12½ or 11.

Stamps showing blotchy or defective impression. often with shading appearing as solid colour, are from worn electrotyped plates, with the exception of Nos. 244d and 244da.

1911. *Electrotyped from new plate.* *P* 12½.

251	**24**	2d. bright violet	1 0	0 2
		a. Perf. 11	0 8	0 2
		b. Perf. comp. of 12½ and 11	35 0	

Stamps from this plate differ from Nos. 248c and 248ca in the width of the design (33 to 33¾ mm., against just over 32 mm.), in the taller, bolder letters of "TASMANIA". in the slope of the mountain in the left background, which is clearly outlined in white, and in the outer vertical frame-line at left, which appears "wavy". Compare Nos. 252, etc., which are always from this plate.

ONE PENNY

(31)

1912 (Oct.). *Nos.* 251, *etc., surch. with T* **31.** *P* 12½.

252	**24**	1d. on 2d. brt. violet (R.)	0 6	0 3
		a. Perf. 11	0 6	0 3
		b. Perf. comp. of 12½ and 11	—	£6

1912 (Dec.). *Thin paper, white gum.* (*As Victoria*, 1912.) *P* 12½.

253	**23**	1d. crimson	4 6	0 4
		a. Perf. 11	4 0	0 6
		b. Perf. comp. of 12½ and 11		
254	**26**	3d. brown	7 6	

DIFFERENCES BETWEEN LITHOGRAPHED AND ELECTROTYPED ISSUES.

LITHOGRAPHED.	ELECTROTYPED.
General appearance fine.	*Comparatively crude and coarse appearance.*
½d. All "V over Crown" wmk.	All "Crown over A" wmk.
1d. The shading on the path on the right bank of the river consists of very fine dots. In printings from worn stones the dots hardly show.	The shading on the path is coarser, consisting of large dots and small patches of colour.
The shading on the white mountain is fine (or almost absent in many stamps).	The shading on the mountain is coarse, and clearly defined.
2d. Three rows of windows in large building on shore, at extreme left, against innerframe.	Two rows of windows.
3d. Clouds very white.	Clouds dark.
Stars in corner ornaments have long points.	Stars have short points.
Shading of corner ornaments is defined by a coloured outer line.	Shading of ornaments terminates against white background.
4d. Lithographed only.	—
6d. No coloured dots at base of waterfall.	Coloured dots at base of waterfall.
Outer frame of value tablets is formed by outer line of design.	Thick line of colour between value tablets and outer line.
	Small break in inner frame below second "A" of "TASMANIA".

1903–5. *Wmk. V over Crown, Type* w. **10.** *P* 12½

255	**11**	9d. blue	2 6	2 6
		a. Perf. 11	7 6	10 0
		b. Perf. comp. of 12½ and 11	—	£18
		c. *Pale blue*	4 0	4 0
		d. *Bright blue*	7 0	5 0
		e. *Ultramarine*	£18	
		f. *Indigo*	£8	
256	**20**	1s. rose and green	7 6	6
		a. Perf. 11	22 6	

1½d.

(32)

1904 (29 Dec.). *No.* 218 (*W* **16**) *surch. with T* **32.**

257	**20**	1½d. on 5d. pale blue & brn.	0 6	0 6

Stamps with inverted surcharge or without surcharge *se tenant* with stamps with normal surcharge were obtained irregularly and were not issued for postal use.

1906–13. *Wmk. Crown over A, Type* w. **11.** *P* 12½.

258	**11**	8d. purple-brown (1907)	6 0	6 0
		a. Perf. 11	6 0	4 0
259	,,	9d. blue (1907)	6 0	6 0
		a. Perf. 11	5 0	6 0
		b. Perf. comp. of 12½ and 11 (1909)	50 0	
		c. Perf. comp. of 12½ and 12 (1909)		
		d. Perf. comp. of 11 and 12		
260	**20**	1s. rose and green (1907)	5 0	2 6
		a. Perf. 11 (1907)	7 0	8 6
		b. Perf comp. of 12½ and 11	17 6	
		c. Perf. comp. of 12½ and 12	42 6	
261	,,	10s. mauve & brn. (1906)	55 0	40 0
		a. Perf. 11	£6	
		b. Perf. comp. of 12½ and 12	85 0	

The note after No. 245 re perfs. compound with perf. 12. also applies here.

POSTAL FISCALS.

Authorized for use in 1882.

F 1 F 2

F 3 F 4

(Recess. Alfred Bock, Hobart.)

1863. *Wmk. double-lined* "**1**", *T* **4.** *Imperf.*

F1	F **1**	3d. green	45 0	
F2	F **2**	2s. 6d. carmine	50 0	
F3	F **3**	5s. sage-green	17 6	
F4	,,	5s. brown	40 0	40 0
F5	F **4**	10s. salmon	15 0	
F6	,,	10s. orange	27 6	35 0

1864. *Wmk. double-lined* "**1**", *T* **4.** (*a*) *P* 10.

F 7	F **1**	3d. green	17 6	25 0
F 8	F **2**	2s. 6d. carmine	25 0	
F 9	F **3**	5s. brown	25 0	
F10	F **4**	10s. orange	30 0	

(*b*) *P* 12.

F11	F **1**	3d. green	17 6	22 6
F12	F **2**	2s. 6d. carmine	15 0	15 0
F13	F **3**	5s. sage-green	12 6	15 0
F14	,,	5s. brown	27 6	
F15	F **4**	10s. salmon	22 6	22 6
F16	,,	10s. orange-brown	30 0	30 0

(*c*) *P* 12½, 13.

F17	F **1**	3d. green	35 0	
F18	F **2**	2s. 6d. carmine	35 0	
F19	F **3**	5s. brown	40 0	
F20	F **4**	10s. orange-brown	45 0	

(*d*) *P* 11½.

F21	F **1**	3d. green		
F22	F **2**	2s. 6d. lake	15 0	15 0
F23	F **3**	5s. sage-green	12 6	12 6
F24	F **4**	10s. salmon	20 0	20 0

In 1879 the 3d., 2s.6d., 5s. (brown), and 10s. (orange) were reprinted on thin, tough, white paper, and are found with or without "REPRINT". In 1889 another reprint was made on white card, imperforate and perforated 12. These are also found with or without "REPRINT".

Wmk. T **16.** *P* 11½, 12.

F25	F **2**	2s. 6d. lake	7 6	7 6
		a. Imperf. between (horiz. pr.)	£9	

F **5.** Duck-billed Platypus.

(Typo. De La Rue & Co.)

1880. *W* **16.** *P* 14.

F26	F **5**	1d. slate	7 6	4 0
F27	,,	3d. chestnut	5 0	1 3
F28	,,	6d. mauve	22 6	3 6
F29	,,	1s. rose-pink	35 0	10 0

All values are known imperf., but not used.

Reprints are known of the 1d. in *deep blue* and the 6d. in lilac. The former is on yellowish white, the latter on white card. Both values also exist on wove paper, perf. 12, with the word "REPRINT".

REVENUE

(F **6**)

1900 (Nov.). *Optd. with* F **6.**

A. *Types* F **2** *and* F **4.** *W* **16.**

F30	2s. 6d. carmine (*imperf.*)	£10	
	a. "REVFNUE"		
F31	2s. 6d. carmine (*perf.* 12)	£6	£6
	a. "REVFNUE"		
	b. Opt. inverted		
	c. "REVFNUE" inverted		
F32	10s. salmon (*perf.* 12)		
	a. "REVFNUE"		
F33	10s. salmon (*W* **4**, *perf.* 12)		
	a. "REVFNUE"		

B. *Type* F **5.** *W* **16.** *P* 14.

F34	3d. chestnut	10 0	7 6
	a. Double opt. one vertical		

C. *Type* F **5.** *Lithographed. P* 12.

(*a*) *Thin transparent paper. W* **15.**

F35	1d. blue	65 0	

(*b*) *Thick paper. W* **16.**

F36	1d. blue	12 6	12 6
	a. Imperf. between (horiz. pair)	£8	
	b. "REVENUE" inverted	85 0	
	c. "REVENUE" double	£20	
	d. Pale blue	10 0	12 6
F37	2d. chestnut	10 0	
	a. Value omitted	£8	
	b. Value double	£14	
F38	6d. mauve	27 6	
	a. Double print	£7	
F39	1s. pink	65 0	65 0

It is doubtful if Nos. F35 to F30 were authorized for postage, though some are known duly postmarked. No. F37 is somewhat different in design from Type F **5**.

D. *T* **20.** *W* **16.** *P* 14.

F40	£1 green and yellow	£10	£12
	a. Double opt. one vertical	£15	£18

Tasmania now uses the stamps of Australia.

TOBAGO.

For GREAT BRITAIN stamps used in Tobago, see page 66.

1

2

(T **1** and **2.** Typo. De La Rue & Co.)

1879 (1 Aug.). *Fiscal stamps issued provisionally pending the arrival of stamps inscr.* "POSTAGE". *Wmk. Crown CC. P* 14.

1 **1** 1d. rose 47 6 55 0
2 „ 3d. blue 70 0 45 0
3 „ 6d. orange 65 0 40 0
4 „ 1s. green £22 70 0
a. Bisected (6d.) (on cover) ..
5 „ 5s. slate £60 £40
6 „ £1 mauve £425

Stamps of T **1**, watermark Crown CA, are fiscals which were never admitted to postal use.

1880 (Nov.). *No.* 3 *bisected vertically and surch. with pen and ink.*

7 **1** 1d. on half of 6d. orange .. £65 £40

1880 (20 Dec.). *Wmk. Crown CC. P* 14.

8 **2** ½d. purple-brown 40 0 45 0
9 „ 1d. Venetian red 60 0 42 6
a. Bisected (½d.) (on cover) .. † £28
10 „ 4d. yellow-green £10 40 0
a. Bisected (2d.) (on cover) .. † £35
b. Malformed "CE" in "PENCE" £42 £38
11 „ 6d. stone £14 £12
12 „ 1s. yellow-ochre 35 0 40 0

2½ PENCE
(3)

1883 (Apr.). *No.* 11 *surch. with T* **3.**

13 **2** 2½d. on 6d. stone 25 0 20 0
a. Surch. double .. ..
b. Large "2" with long tail .. 80 0 80 0

1882–84. *Wmk. Crown CA. P* 14.

14 **2** ½d. purple-brown (1883) .. 7 6 25 0
15 „ 1d. Venetian red (1882) .. 10 0 10 0
a. Bisected diag. (½d.) (on cover)
16 „ 2½d. dull blue (1883) .. 12 6 9 0
16*a* „ 2½d. bright blue .. 5 0 5 0
17 „ 2½d. ultramarine (1883) .. 4 6 5 0
18 „ 4d. yellow-green (1884) .. £18 £15
a. Malformed "CE" in "PENCE"
19 „ 6d. stone (1884) £50 £45

1885–94. *Colours changed. Wmk. Crown CA. P* 14.

20 **2** ½d. dull green (1886) .. 1 3 1 3
21 „ 1d. carmine (1886) .. 1 3 1 3
22 „ 4d. grey (1885) 2 6 3 6
a. Malformed "CE" in "PENCE" 65 0
b. Imperf. (pair) £65
23 „ 6d. orange-brown (1886) 6 0 10 0
24 „ 1s. olive-yellow (1894) .. 10 0 17 6
25 „ 1s. pale olive-yellow (1894) 7 6 17 6

½ PENNY
(4)

2½ PENCE
(5)

1886–89. *Nos.* 16, 19 *and* 32 *surch. as T* **4.**

26 ½d. on 2½d. dull blue (Apr. '86) 8 6 15 0
a. Figure farther from word .. 35 0 40 0
b. Surch. double £32
c. Surch. omitted. Vert. pair with No. 26 .. .. .. £275
d. Ditto. with No. 26a £275
27 ½d. on 6d. stone (Jan. '86) .. 12 0 22 6
a. Figure farther from word .. 60 0 70 0
b. Surch. inverted £70
c. Surch. double £55
28 ½d. on 6d. orge.-brn. (Oct. '89) 80 0 90 0
a. Figure farther from word .. £22 £25
b. Surch. double £70
29 1d. on 2½d. dull blue (Jy. '89) 20 0 25 0
a. Figure farther from word .. 80 0 80 0

The surcharge is in a setting of 12 (two rows of 6) repeated five times in the pane. Nos. 7, 9 and 10 in the setting have a raised "P" in "Penny", and No. 10 also shows the wider spacing between figure and word.

1891–92. *No.* 22 *surch. with T* **5** *or* **4.**

30 ½d. on 4d. grey 40 0 50 0
a. Malformed "CE" in "PENCE" .. £20
b. Surch. double £40
31 2½d. on 4d. grey 22 6 20 0
a. Malformed "CE" in "PENCE" .. £12
b. Surch. double £40

1896. *Error of colour. Wmk. Crown CA. P* 14.

32 **2** 1s. orange-brown 17 6

½d
POSTAGE
(6)

Fiscal stamps (*T* **1**, *value in second colour, wmk. Crown CA, P* 14, *surch. with T* **6.**)

33 ½d. on 4d. lilac and carmine .. 12 6 15 0
a. Space between "½" and "d" .. 25 0 20 0

From 1896 until 1913 Trinidad stamps were used in Tobago.

For issues from 1913 see Trinidad and Tobago.

TOGO.

TOGO
Anglo-French
Occupation
(1)

I. Wide Setting. Lines 3 mm. apart. *Stamps of German Colonial issue Types* A *and* B 1900 *and* 1909–14 (5 *pf. and* 10 *pf.*).

1914 (1 Oct.). *Optd. with T* **1.**

1 3 pf. brown £50 £8
2 5 pf. green £50 £8
3 10 pf. carmine (Wmk. Lozenges) £50 £10
a. Opt. inverted .. .. — £450
b. Opt. tête-bêche in vert. pair — £750
c. Error. No wmk. .. ..
4 20 pf. ultramarine £7 60 0
5 25 pf. black and red/*yellow* .. £8 80 0
6 30 pf. black and orange/*buff* .. £8 80 0
7 40 pf. black and carmine £90 £40
8 50 pf. black and purple/*buff* .. £1800 £500
9 80 pf. black and carmine/*rose* £100 £60
10 1 m. carmine £900 £225
11 2 m. blue £1000 £500
a. "Occupation" double .. — £800
b. Opt. inverted £1200

Half penny
(2)

1914 (1 Oct.). *Nos.* 1 *and* 2 *surch. as T* **2.**

12 ½d. on 3 pf. brown £50 £10
a. Thin "y" in "penny" .. £100 £40
13 1d. on 5 pf. green £50 £10
a. Thin "y" in "penny" .. £100 £40

TOGO
Anglo-French
Occupation
(3)

II. NARROW SETTING. LINES 2 MM. APART.

1914 (*end* OCT.). *Optd. with T* **3**.

No.		Unused	Used
14	3 pf. brown	£110	£90
	a. "Occupation" omitted ..	£175	
15	5 pf. green	£125	£90
16	10 pf. carmine	£150	£150
17	20 pf. ultramarine	£10	£5
	a. Error. "TOG"	£1000	£250
18	25 pf. black and red/*yellow* ..	£10	£5
	a. Error. "TOG"	£2500	
19	30 pf. black and orange/*buff* ..	£10	£5
20	40 pf. black and carmine ..	£100	£150
21	50 pf. black and purple/*buff* ..	£2000	£750
22	80 pf. black and carmine/*rose*	£80	£150
23	1 m. carmine	£750	£300
24	2 m. blue	£1200	£550
25	3 m. violet-black		
26	5 m. lake and black		

TOGO
Anglo-French
Occupation
Half penny
(4)

Narrow setting, but including value, as T **4**.

No.		Unused	Used
27	½d. on 3 pf. brown	80 0	60 0
	a. Error. "TOG"	£100	£50
	b. Thin "y" in "penny" ..	£8	£6
28	1d. on 5 pf. green	17 6	12 6
	a. Error. "TOG"	£35	£20
	b. Thin "y" in "penny" ..	30 0	25 0

Wide setting, 3 mm. apart.

The overprint on the 3 pf. to 80 pf. was set up in five rows of 10, repeated twice on each sheet. There are many minor varieties.

The *tête-bêche* opt. in the 10 pf. is due to the sheet being turned round after the upper 50 stamps had been overprinted so that vertical pairs from the two middle rows have the opt. *tête-bêche*.

In the 20 pf. one half of a sheet was overprinted with the wide setting (3 mm.), and the other half with the narrow setting (2 mm.), so that vertical pairs from the middle of the sheet show the two varieties of the overprint.

Narrow setting, 2 mm. apart.

In the ½d. on 3 pf. brown, the 1d. on 5 pf. green, and the 20 pf. blue stamp No. 37 in each setting has the error "TOG".

The ½d. on 3 pf. and ½d. on 5 pf. have the following variety in each setting of 50:—

Thin dropped "y" with small serifs on Nos. 1, 2, 11, 21, 31, 41, and 42.

TOGO
Anglo-French
Occupation
(6)

TOGO
ANGLO-FRENCH
OCCUPATION
(7)

1915 (7 JAN.). *Optd. as T* **6**. *The words* "Anglo-French" *measure* 15 *mm. instead of* 16 *mm. as in T* **3**.

No.		Unused	Used
29	3 pf. brown	£1500	£750
30	5 pf. green	£25	£15
31	10 pf. carmine	£25	£15
	a. Error. No wmk.		
32	20 pf. ultramarine	£200	£75
33	50 pf. black and purple/*buff* ..	£2500	£1250

This printing was made on another lot of German Togo stamps, found at Sansane-Mangu.

The setting is in groups of 25 (5×5), repeated four times on a sheet.

The fifth stamp in each setting has a broken second "O" in "TOGO", resembling a badly formed "U".

For German Colonial stamps optd. "Togo Occupation franco-anglaise", see Part II of this catalogue.

1915 (MAY). *Stamps of Gold Coast, T* **9**, **10**, *and* **11**, *optd. locally with T* **7** ("OCCUPATION" 14½ *mm. long*).

No.		Unused	Used
34	½d. green	0 6	0 8
	g. Double overprint	£5	£6
35	1d. red	0 6	0 8
	g. Double overprint	£6	
	h. Overprint inverted	75 0	£6
	ha. Ditto. "TOGO" omitted ..		
36	2d. greyish slate	1 0	1 6
37	2½d. bright blue	1 6	2 6
38	3d. purple/*yellow*	2 6	2 6
	g. White back	12 6	16 0
40	6d. dull and bright purple ..	3 0	5 0
41	1s. black/*green*	6 0	8 0
	g. Overprint double	£8	
42	2s. purple and blue/*blue* ..	12 0	20 0
43	2s. 6d. black and red/*blue* ..	15 0	20 0
44	5s. grn. & red/*yell.* (*white back*)	25 0	40 0
45	10s. green and red/*green* ..	50 0	65 0
46	20s. purple and black/*red* ..	£6	£8

Varieties (*Nos. indicate positions in pane*).

A. *Small* "F" *in* "FRENCH" (25, 58, *and* 59).
B. *Thin* "G" *in* "TOGO" (24).
C. *No hyphen after* "ANGLO" (5).
D. *Two hyphens after* "ANGLO" (5).
E. "CUPATION" *for* "OCCUPATION" (33).
F. "CCUPATION" *for* "OCCUPATION" (57).

Prices are for unused. Used are worth more.

No.		A.	B.	C.	D.	E.	F.
34	½d. ..	5 0	12 6	7 0	†	£12	£10
35	1d. ..	7 6	17 6	10 0	†	†	£12
	h. Inv.	£60	£60	£60	†	†	†
36	2d. ..	7 6	25 0	£12	80 0	†	£10
37	2½d. ..	10 0	30 0	£5	£6	†	£10
38	3d. ..	10 0	30 0	£8	†	†	£12
	g. W. b.	65 0	£8	†	†	†	†
40	6d. ..	15 0	25 0	†	†	†	£20
41	1s. ..	15 0	35 0	†	†	†	£10
42	2s. ..	40 0	75 0	£8	†	†	£20
43	2s. 6d.	60 0	90 0	£8	†	†	£12
44	5s. ..	80 0	£6	£12	†	†	£12
45	10s. ..	£6	£12	†	†	†	£25
46	20s. ..	£10	£15	†	†	†	£25

TOGO
ANGLO-FRENCH
OCCUPATION
(8)

1916 (APR.). *London opt. T* **8** ("OCCUPATION" 15 *mm. long*). *Heavy type and thicker letters showing through on back.*

No.		Unused	Used
77	½d green	0 6	0 8
78	1d. red	0 6	0 8
79	2d. greyish slate	1 3	1 6
80	2½d. bright blue	1 6	2 0
81	3d. purple/*yellow*	2 0	2 6
82	6d. dull and bright purple ..	2 6	3 0
83	1s. black/*green*	5 0	6 0
	a. On blue-green, olive back ..	17 0	20 0
	b. On emerald back	£10	
84	2s. purple and blue/*blue* ..	10 0	12 6
85	2s. 6d. black and red/*blue* ..	10 0	12 6
86	5s. green and red/*yellow* ..	22 6	27 6
	a. On orange-buff	20 0	30 0
87	10s. green and red/*green* ..	45 0	55 0
	a. On blue-green, olive back ..	40 0	45 0
88	20s. purple and black/*red* ..	£6	£8

TOKELAU ISLANDS.

1. Atafu Village and Map.

2. Nukunono Hut and Map.

3. Fakaofo Village and Map.

(Des. J. Berry. Recess. Bradbury, Wilkinson.)

1948 (22 June). *Wmk.* *T* **98** *of New Zealand (Mult.* N Z *and Star).* *P* 13½.

1 **1** ½d. red-brown and purple .. 0 2 0 2
2 **2** 1d. chestnut and green .. 0 3 0 3
3 **3** 2d. green and ultramarine .. 0 4 0 4

1953 (25 May). *Coronation. As No.* 715 *of New Zealand, but inscr.* " TOKELAU ISLANDS ".

4 **164** 3d. brown 1 6 1 9

ONE SHILLING

(4)

1956 (27 Mar.). *No.* 1 *surch. with T* **4**.

5 **1** 1s. on ½d. red-brown & purple 1 5 2 0

TONGA.

PROTECTORATE.

1. King George I.

2

(Eng. Bock and Cousins. Plates made and typo. Govt. Ptg. Office, Wellington.)

1886–88. *W* **2**. *P* 12½ *(line) or* 12 × 11½ *(comb)**.

1 **1** 1d. carmine, *p*, 12½ (27.8.86) £8 40 0
a. Perf. 12½ × 10 .. ..
b. Perf. 12 × 11½ (15.7.87) .. 22 6 22 6
ba. Pale carmine (p. 12 × 11½) .. 42 6 42 6
2 **1** 2d. pale vio. *p.* 12½, (27.8.86) 42 6 32 6
a. Bright violet 50 0 32 6
b. Perf. 12 × 11½ (15.7.87) .. 37 6 25 0
ba. Bright violet (p. 12 × 11½) .. 32 6 27 6
3 ,, 6d. blue, *p.* 12½ (9.10.86) .. 25 0 17 6
a. Perf. 12 × 11½ (15.10.88) .. 25 0 15 0
ab. Dull blue (p. 12 × 11½) .. 27 6 20 0
4 ,, 1s. pale grn., *p.* 12½ (9.10.86) 65 0 25 0
a. Deep green, p. 12½ 70 0 25 0
b. Perf. 12 × 11½ (15.10.88) .. 40 0 27 6
ba. Deep green (p. 12 × 11½) .. 35 0 20 0

*See note after New Zealand, No. 186.

FOUR PENCE. (3)   **EIGHT PENCE.** (4)

(Surch. Messrs. Wilson & Horton, Auckland, N.Z.)

1891 (10 Nov.). *Nos.* 1*b and* 2*b surch.*

5 **3** 4d. on 1d. carmine 8 6 15 0
a. No stop after " PENCE " .. 60 0 65 0
6 **4** 8d. on 2d. violet 37 6 37 6
a. Short " T " in " EIGHT " .. 65 0 70 0

1891 (23 Nov.). *Optd. with stars in upper right and lower left corners. P* 12½.

7 **1** 1d. carmine 35 0 42 6
a. Three stars £5
b. Four stars £18
c. Five stars £30
d. Perf. 12 × 11½ £5
da. Three stars £12
db. Four stars £15
dc. Five stars £30
8 ,, 2d. violet 65 0 70 0
a. Perf. 12 × 11½ £7

1892 (15 Aug.). *W* **2**. *P* 12 × 11½.

9 **1** 6d. yellow-orange 25 0 30 0

5. Arms of Tonga.

6. King George I.

(Des. eng. A. E. Cousins. Typo. at Govt. Printing Office, Wellington, N.Z.)

1892 (10 Nov.). *Wmk.* *T* **2**. *P* 12 × 11½.

10 **5** 1d. pale rose 25 0 30 0
a. Bright rose 27 6 30 0
b. Bisected diagonally (½d.) (on cover) .. .. .. — £10
11 **6** 2d. olive 20 0 27 6
12 **5** 4d. chestnut 45 0 55 0
13 **6** 8d. bright mauve 60 0 55 0
14 ,, 1s. brown 60 0 55 0

½d. (7)   **2½d.** (8)

FIVE PENCE. (9)   **7½d.** (10)

1893. *Printed in new colours and surch. with T* 7/10. *(a) In carmine. P* 12½. (21 Aug.)

15 **5** ½d. on 1d. bright ultram. .. 40 0 40 0
a. Surch. omitted .. ..
16 **6** 2½d. on 2d. green 25 0 25 0
17 **5** 5d. on 4d. orange 15 0 25 0
18 **6** 7½d. on 3d. carmine .. 40 0 45 0

(*b*) *In black.* P 12 × 11½. (Nov.).

19 **5** ½d. on 1d. dull blue 40 0 45 0

20 **6** 2½d. on 2d. green 10 0 25 0

a. Surch. double . ..

SURCHARGE. HALF-PENNY

(11)

SURCHARGE, 2½d.

(12)

(Surch. at the "Star" Office, Auckland, N.Z.)

1894 (June). *Surch. with* **T 11** *or* **12.**

21 **5** ½d. on 4d. chestnut (B.) .. 6 6 12 6

a. "SURCHARCE." 15 0 30 0

22 **6** ½d. on 1s. brown 7 6 20 0

a. "SURCHARCE." 25 0 32 6

b. Surch. double £24

c. Surch. double with "SURCHARCE." .. .. ..

23 „ 2½d. on 8d. brt. mauve .. 7 6 17 6

a. No stop after "SURCHARGE" 55 0 65 0

24 „ 2½d. on 1s. green (No. 4*a*) .. 30 0 40 0

a. No stop after "SURCHARGE" £6

b. Perf. 12 × 11½ 32 6 42 6

ba. No stop after "SURCHARGE" 80 0

(Design resembling No. 11 lithographed and surcharged at "Star" Office, Auckland, N.Z.)

1895 (May). *As* **T 6** *surch. as* **T 11** *and* **12.** *No wmk.* P 12.

25 **11** 1d. on 2d. pale blue (C.) .. 35 0 40 0

26 **12** 1½d. on 2d. pale blue (C.) .. 55 0 60 0

a. Perf. 12 × 11 .. .. 45 0 50 0

27 „ 2½d. on 2d. pale blue (C.)* 65 0 70 0

a. No stop after "SURCHARGE" £12

28 „ 7½d. on 2d. pale blue (C.) .. £15

a. Perf. 12 × 11 .. .. 85 0 85 0

* The 2½d. on 2d. is the only value which normally has a stop after the word "surcharge".

13. King George II.

(Litho. "Star" Office, Auckland, N.Z.)

1895 (16 Aug.). *No wmk.* P 12.

29 **13** 1d. olive-green 30 0 37 6

a. Bisected diagonally (½d.) (on cover) .. .. — £8

b. Imperf. between (pair) .. — £225

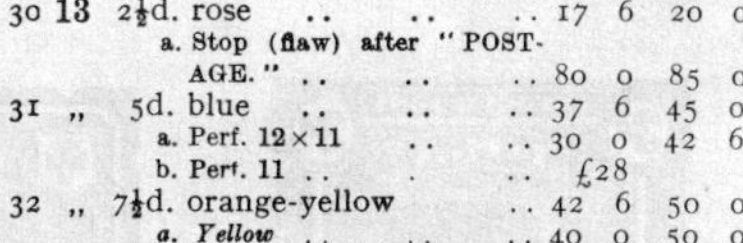

30 **13** 2½d. rose 17 6 20 0

a. Stop (flaw) after "POSTAGE." 80 0 85 0

31 „ 5d. blue 37 6 45 0

a. Perf. 12 × 11 .. .. 30 0 42 6

b. Perf. 11 .. . .. £28

32 „ 7½d. orange-yellow .. 42 6 50 0

a. *Yellow* 40 0 50 0

1895 (Sept.). **T 13** *redrawn and surcharged. No wmk.* P 12.

33 **11** ½d. on 2½d. vermilion .. 25 0 40 0

a. "SURCHARCE" .. 60 0

b. Stop after "POSTAGE." .. £6

34 „ 1d. on 2½d. vermilion .. 12 6 20 0

a. Stop after "POSTAGE." .. £5

35 **12** 7½d. on 2½d. vermilion .. 42 6 50 0

a. Stop after "POSTAGE." £8

In the ½d. surcharge there is a stop after "surcharge" and not after "penny." In the 1d. and 7½d. the stop is after the value only.

Half Penny VAEUA OE PENI

(14)

1896 (May). *Nos.* 26*a and* 28*a with typewritten surcharge* "Half-Penny-" *in violet, and Tongan surcharge in black.*

(A) *Tongan inscription reading downwards.*

(B) *Tongan inscription reading upwards.*

	A.		B.	
36 **6** ½d. on 1½d. on 2d	£10	—	£14	—
a. Perf 12 ..	£20	—	£20	—
ab Haalf" (p. 12)	†		£55	—
37 „ ½d. on 7½d. on 2d.	40 0	50 0	40 0	60 0
a. "Hafl" for "Half"	£40	—	†	
b. "Hafl" ("Penny" omitted) ..	£40	—	†	
c. "PPenny" ..	£25	—	†	
d. Stops instead of hyphens ..	£25	—	†	
e. "Halyf" ..	—	—	†	
f. "Half-Penny" inverted ..	£40	—	†	
g. No hyphen after "Penny"	—	—	†	
h. "Hwlf" ..	†		—	
j. "Penny" double	†		—	
k. "Penny" twice, with "Half" on top of upper "Penny" ..	†		—	
l. Perf. 12 ..	—	—	—	
la. No hyphen after "Half" (p. 12)	—	—	†	

There are variations in the relative positions of the words "Half" and "Penny," both vertically and horizontally.

15. Arms.

16. Ovava tree, Kana-Kubolu.

17. King George II.

18. Prehistoric Trilith at Haamonga.

19. Bread fruit.

20. Coral.

21. View of Haapai.

22. Parrot.

23. View of Vavau Harbour.

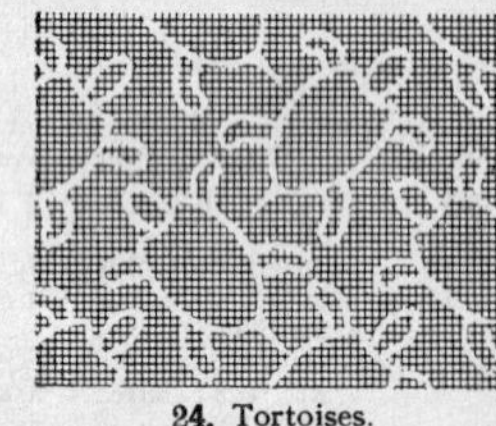

24. Tortoises.

I. No sword hilt. II. Top of hilt showing.

(Recess. De La Rue & Co.)

1897 (JUNE). *W* **24.** *P* 14.

38	**15**	½d. indigo	1	3	1	6
39	**16**	1d. black and scarlet ..	2	6	1	3
40	**17**	2d. sepia and bistre (I) ..	10	0	10	0
41	„	2d. grey and bistre (I) ..	35	0	20	0
42	„	2d. sepia and bistre (II) ..	6	0	7	6
43	„	2½d. black and blue ..	5	0	5	0
		a. No fraction bar in "½" ..	75	0	75	0
44	**18**	3d. black & yellow-green ..	5	0	7	6
45	**19**	4d. green and purple ..	25	0	22	6
46	**17**	5d. black and orange ..	17	6	25	0
47	**20**	6d. red	12	6	10	0
48	**17**	7½d. black and green ..	17	6	25	0
		a. Centre inverted	£250			
49	„	10d. black and lake ..	20	0	25	0
50	„	1s. black and red-brown ..	20	0	25	0
		a. No hyphen before "TAHA"	£15			
51	**21**	2s. black & ultramarine ..	50	0	55	0
52	**22**	2s. 6d. deep purple ..	65	0	70	0
53	**23**	5s. black and brown-red ..	50	0	55	0

The 1d., 3d., and 4d. are known bisected and used for half their value.

T - L

1 June, 1899.
(25)

26. Queen Salote.

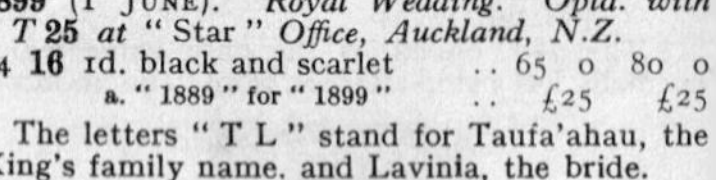

1899 (1 JUNE). *Royal Wedding. Optd. with* *T* **25** *at* "Star" *Office, Auckland, N.Z.*

54	**16**	1d. black and scarlet ..	65	0	80	0
		a. "1889" for "1899" ..	£25		£25	

The letters "T L" stand for Taufa'ahau, the King's family name, and Lavinia, the bride.

Die I.

Die II.

(Recess. De La Rue & Co.)

1920–37. *W* **24.** *P* 14.

55	**26**	2d. slate-purple and violet	12	6	15
55*a*	„	2d. black and dull purple (Die I) ('24)	8	0	8
		b. Die II ('37)	10	0	15
56	„	2½d. black and blue ..	12	6	20
57	„	5d. black & orange-verm.	17	6	25
58	„	7½d. black & yellow-green ..	8	6	15
59	„	10d. black and lake ..	17	6	22
60	„	1s. black and red-brown ..	10	0	20

In Die II the ball of the "2" is larger and t[illegible] word "PENI-E-UA" is re-engraved and slight[illegible] shorter; the "U" has a spur on the left side.

TWO PENCE

TWO PENCE

PENI-E-UA (27) **PENI-E-UA** (28)

1923 (20 Oct.)–**1924.** *Nos.* 46 *and* 48 *to* 53 *surch. as T* **27** *(vert. stamps) or* **28** *(horiz. stamps).*

No.	Description	Unused	Used
61	2d. on 5d. black & orge. (B.)	5 0	10 0
62	2d. on 7½d. black & green (B.)	35 0	40 0
63	2d. on 10d. black & lake (B.)	35 0	40 0
64	2d. on 1s. blk. & red-brn. (B.)	45 0	45 0
	a. No hyphen before " TAHA " ..	£35	
65	2d. on 2s. blk. & ultram. (R.)	17 6	35 0
66	2d. on 2s. 6d. dp. purple (R.)	20 0	25 0
67	2d. on 5s. blk. & brn. red (R.)	8 6	15 0

1934–35. *New colours. W* **24.** *P* 14.

No.	Type	Description	Unused	Used
68	**15**	½d. yellow-green	0 8	1 6
69	**26**	1½d. grey-black ('35) ..	1 3	3 0
70	,,	2½d. bright ultramarine ..	2 6	4 0

29. Queen Salote.

(Recess. De La Rue & Co.)

1938 (12 Oct.). *20th Anniv. of Queen Salote's Accession. Tablet at foot dated "* 1918–1938 *". W* **24.** *P* 14.

No.	Type	Description	Unused	Used
71	**29**	1d. black and scarlet ..	3 0	5 0
72	,,	2d. black and purple ..	15 0	12 6
73	,,	2½d. black and ultramarine	15 0	15 0

For Silver Jubilee issue in a similar design, see Nos. 83/87.

PENI-E-UA

Die III.

(Recess. De La Rue & Co.)

1942–49. *Wmk. Mult. Script CA (sideways on* 5s.). *P* 14.

No.	Type	Description	Unused	Used
74	**15**	½d. yellow-green	0 4	0 8
75	**16**	1d. black and scarlet ..	1 6	2 0
76	**26**	2d. black & purple (Die II)	1 0	1 3
		a. Die III (Apr. '49)	20 0	27 6
77	,,	2½d. bright ultramarine ..	1 0	1 6
78	**18**	3d. black and yellow-green	1 9	2 6
79	**20**	6d. red	3 6	4 6
80	**26**	1s. black and red-brown	3 0	5 0
81	**22**	2s. 6d. deep purple ..	20 0	25 0
82	**23**	5s. black and brown-red..	15 0	20 0

In Die III the foot of the " 2 " is longer than in Die II and extends towards the right beyond the curve of the loop; the letters of "PENI-E-UA" are taller and differently shaped.

UANIMA TA'U 'OE PULE 'A 'ENE AFIO 1918-1943

30

(Recess. De La Rue & Co.)

1944 (25 Jan.). *Silver Jubilee of Queen Salote's Accession. As T* **29**, *but inscr. "* 1918–1943 *" at foot, as T* **30**. *Wmk. Mult. Script CA. P* 14.

No.	Description	Unused	Used
83	1d. black and carmine ..	0 9	1 3
84	2d. black and purple	1 0	1 6
85	3d. black and green	1 9	3 0
86	6d. black and orange ..	2 6	4 0
87	1s black and brown	4 0	7 0

1949 (10 Oct.). *75th Anniv. of Universal Postal Union. As Nos.* 114/7 *of Antigua.*

No.	Description	Unused	Used
88	2½d. ultramarine	0 10	1 3
89	3d. olive	1 3	1 9
90	6d. carmine-red	1 9	2 9
91	1s. red-brown	3 6	5 0

31. Queen Salote. **33.**

32. Queen Salote.

(Photo. Waterlow & Sons.)

1950 (1 Nov.). *Queen Salote's Fiftieth Birthday. Wmk. Mult. Script CA. P* 12½.

No.	Type	Description	Unused	Used
92	**31**	1d. carmine	0 8	1 0
93	**32**	5d. green	3 0	5 0
94	**33**	1s. violet	4 6	7 0

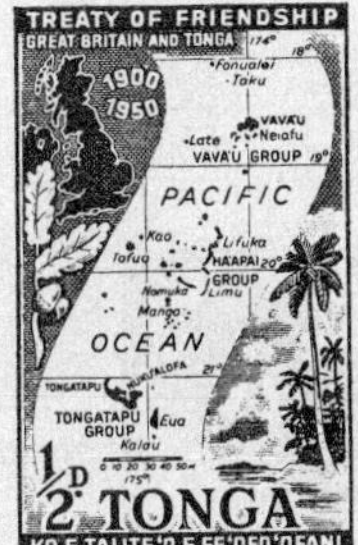

34. Map. **37.** H.M.N.Z.S. *Bellona.*

35. Palace, Nuku'alofa.

36. Beach Scene.

38. Flag.

39. Arms of Tonga and G.B.

(Recess. Waterlow.)

1951 (2 July). *50th Anniv. of Treaty of Friendship between Great Britain and Tonga. Wmk. Mult. Script CA. P* 12½ (3*d*.), 13 × 13½ (½*d*.), 13½ × 13 (*others*).

95	**34**	½d. green	1	0	1	3
96	**35**	1d. black and carmine ..	1	6	2	0
97	**36**	2½d. green and brown ..	3	0	4	0
98	**37**	3d. yellow & brt. blue ..	6	0	7	6
99	**38**	5d. carmine and green ..	7	6	10	0
100	**39**	1s. yell.-orge. & violet ..	12	6	17	6

40. Royal Palace, Nuku'alofa.

41. Shore Fishing with Throw-Net.

42. Ketches and Canoe.

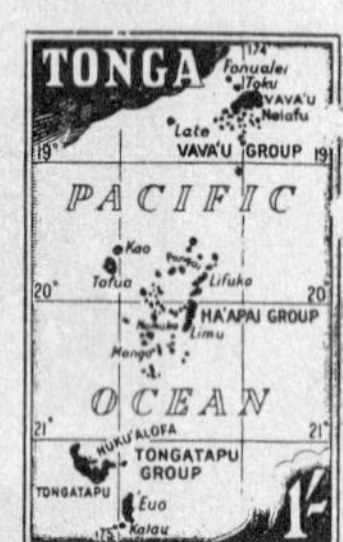

43. Swallow's Cave, Vava'u.

49. Map of Tonga Islands.

44. Map of Tongatapu.

45. Vava'u Harbour.

46. Post Office, Nuku'alofa.

47. Aerodrome, Fua'amotu.

48. Nuku'alofa Wharf.

50. Lifuka, Ha'apai.

51. Mutiny of the *Bounty*.

52. Queen Salote.

53. Arms of Tonga.

(Des. J. Berry. Centre litho., frame recess (£1); recess (others). Bradbury, Wilkinson.)

1953 (1 July). *W* **24.** *P* 11×11½ (*vert.*) *or* 11½×11 (*horiz.*).

101	**40**	1d. black and red-brown	0	3	0	3
102	**41**	1½d. blue and emerald ..	0	3	0	3
103	**42**	2d. dp. turq.-green & blk.	0	4	0	5
104	**43**	3d. blue & dp. bluish green	0	5	0	6
105	**44**	3½d. yellow & carmine-red	0	6	0	7
106	**45**	4d. yell. & dp. rose-carm.	0	6	0	8
107	**46**	5d. blue and red-brown ..	0	7	0	9
108	**47**	6d. black and deep blue	0	9	0	10
109	**48**	8d. emerald and deep reddish violet ..	0	10	1	0
110	**49**	1s. blue and black ..	1	2	1	6
111	**50**	2s. sage-green and brown	2	3	2	9
112	**51**	5s. orange-yellow and slate-lilac	5	4	6	6
113	**52**	10s. yellow and black ..	10	6	12	6
114	**53**	£1 yellow, scar., ultram. and deep bright blue	21	0	25	0

54. Stamp of 1886.

55. Whaler and Longboat.

56. Queen Salote and Post Office, Nuku'alofa.

57. Mail Steamer.

58. Mailplane over Tongatapu.

(Des. D. M. Bakeley. Photo. Harrison & Sons.)

1961 (1 Dec.). *75th Anniv. of Tongan Postal Service.* *W* **24.** *P* 14½×13½.

115	**54**	1d. carmine & brown-orange	1	6	2	0
116	**55**	2d. ultramarine	1	6	2	0
117	**56**	4d. blue-green	1	9	2	3
118	**57**	5d. violet	3	0	3	6
119	**58**	1s. red-brown	6	0	7	6

1862
TAU'ATĀINA
EMANCIPATION
1962
(59)

1962 (7 Feb.). *Centenary of Emancipation. Various stamps optd. with T* **59** *(No. 126 surch. also), in red, by R. S. Wallbank, Govt. Printer.*

120 **40** 1d. black and red-brown 3 0
121 **56** 4d. blue-green 4 0
122 **46** 5d. blue and red-brown .. 5 0
123 **47** 6d. black and deep blue .. 6 0
124 **48** 8d. emer. & dp. redd. vio. 8 0
125 **49** 1s. blue and black .. 12 6
a. Opt. inverted £450 £275
126 **43** 2s. on 3d. blue and deep bluish green 20 0
a. Missing fraction-bar in surch. £10
127 **51** 5s. orge.-yell. & slate-lilac 35 0
a. Opt. inverted £200

60. " Protein Foods ".

(Des. M. Goaman. Photo. Harrison.)

1963 (4 June). *Freedom from Hunger.* *W* **24.** *P* $14 \times 14\frac{1}{2}$.

128 **60** 11d. ultramarine 1 9 2 0

61. Coat-of-Arms.

62. Queen Salote.

63. Queen Salote.

(Des. Ida West. Walsall Lithographic Co. Ltd.)

1963 (15 July). *First Polynesian Gold Coinage Commemoration. Circular designs. Embossed on gold foil, backed with paper, inscr. overall* " TONGA THE FRIENDLY ISLANDS ". *Imperf.*

(*a*) *Postage.* $\frac{1}{4}$ *koula coin. Diameter* $1\frac{5}{8}$ *in.*

129 **61** 1d. carmine .. ..
130 **62** 2d. deep blue .. ..
131 **61** 6d. blue-green .. ..
132 **62** 9d. bright purple ..
133 **61** 1s. 6d. violet .. ..
134 **62** 2s. light emerald ..

(*b*) *Air.* (*i*) $\frac{1}{2}$ *koula coin. Diam.* $2\frac{1}{8}$ *in.*

135 **63** 10d. carmine .. ..
136 **61** 11d. blue-green .. ..
137 **63** 1s. 1d. deep blue ..

(*ii*) 1 *koula coin. Diam.* $3\frac{1}{8}$ *in.*

138 **63** 2s. 1d. bright purple ..
139 **61** 2s. 4d. light emerald ..
140 **63** 2s. 9d. violet .. ..

Set of 13 *un.* (*incl. No.* O17), £8.

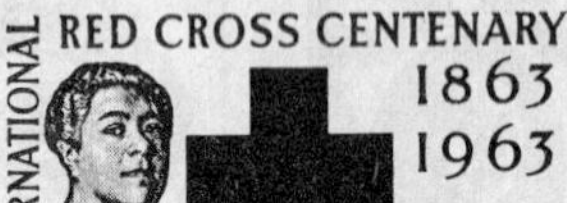

64. Red Cross Emblem.

(Des. V. Whiteley. Litho. Bradbury, Wilkinson

1963 (10 Sept.). *Red Cross Centenary.* *W* 2
P $13\frac{1}{2}$.

141 **64** 2d. red and black .. 0 8 1
142 ,, 11d. red and blue .. 2 9 3

65. Queen Salote.

66. Map of Tongatapu.

(*Illustrations reduced to approx. ¾ actual size.*)

(Des. M. Meers. Walsall Lithographic Co. Ltd.)

1964 (19 Oct.). *Pan-Pacific South-East Asia Women's Association Meeting, Nuku'alofa. Embossed on gold foil, backed with paper inscr. overall* "TONGA THE FRIENDLY ISLANDS". *Imperf.* (a) *Postage.*

143 **65** 3d. pink .. .. ..
144 ,, 9d. light blue .. ..
145 ,, 2s. yellow-green .. ..
146 ,, 5s. lilac .. .. ..

(b) *Air.*

147 **66** 10d. blue-green .. ..
148 ,, 1s. 2d. black .. ..
149 ,, 3s. 6d. cerise .. ..
150 ,, 6s. 6d. violet .. ..

Set of 8 un. 40 0

(67)

1965 (18 Mar.). "*Gold Coin*" *stamps of 1963 surch. as T* **67** *by Walsall Lithographic Co. New figures of value in gold; oblit. colours shown in brackets.* (a) *Postage.*

151 **61** 1s. 3d. on 1s. 6d. violet (R.) 1 6
152 **62** 1s. 9d. on 9d. brt. pur. (W.) 2 6
153 **61** 2s. 6d. on 6d. blue-grn. (R.) 4 0
154 ,, 5s. on 1d. carmine .. £12
155 **62** 5s. on 2d. deep blue .. 50 0
156 ,, 5s. on 2s. light emerald .. 15 0

(b) *Air.*

157 **63** 2s. 3d. on 10d. carmine .. 3 6
158 **61** 2s. 9d. on 11d. blue-grn. (W.) 4 0
159 **63** 4s. 6d. on 2s. 1d. brt. pur. (R.) £12
160 **61** 4s. 6d. on 2s. 4d. lt. emer. (R.) £10
161 **63** 4s. 6d. on 2s. 9d. violet (R.) £10

OFFICIAL STAMPS.

G.F.B.
(O 1)

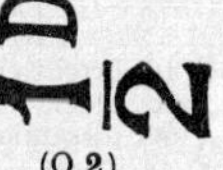
(O **2**)

(G.F.B. = Gaue Faka Buleaga = On Government Service.)

1893 (13 Feb.). *Optd. with Type* O **1**. *W* **2**. *P* 12 × 11½.

O1 **5** 1d. ultramarine (C) .. 15 0 25 0
a. Bisected diagonally (½d.) (on cover) .. .. ..
O2 **6** 2d. ultramarine (C) 25 0 40 0
O3 **5** 4d. ultramarine (C) 60 0 85 0
O4 **6** 8d. ultramarine (C) £7 £7
O5 ,, 1s. ultramarine (C) £8 £8

Above prices are for stamps in good condition and colour. Faded and stained stamps from the remainders are worth much less.

1893 (Dec.). *Nos.* O1 *to* O5 *variously surch. with new value, sideways as Type* O **2**.

O6 **5** ½d. on 1d. ultramarine .. 17 6 25 0
O7 **6** 2½d. on 2d. ultramarine .. 10 0 25 0
O8 **5** 5d. on 4d. ultramarine .. 15 0 25 0
O9 **6** 7½d. on 8d. ultramarine .. 20 0 35 0
a. "D" of "7½D." omitted ..
b. Surch. double .. ..
O10 ,, 10d. on 1s. ultramarine .. 20 0 35 0

OFFICIAL AIR MAIL
1862
TAU'ATAINA
EMANCIPATION
1962
(O 3)

1962 (7 Feb.). *Air. Centenary of Emancipation. Various stamps optd. with Type* O **3** *in red by R. S. Wallbank, Govt. Printer.*

O11 **55** 2d. ultramarine .. .. — £10
a. Error. "OFFICIAI" ..
O12 **57** 5d. violet .. .. .. — £10
a. Error. "OFFICIAI" ..
b. Error. "MAII" ..
O13 **58** 1s. red-brown .. .. — £5
a. Error. "OFFICIAI" .. — £25
b. Error. "MAII" .. .. — £25
O14 **51** 5s. orge.-yell. & slate-lilac — £60
a. Error. "MAII" .. — £65
O15 **52** 10s. yellow and black .. — £25
a. Error. "MAII" ..
O16 **53** £1 yellow, scarlet, ultram. & deep bright blue .. — £30

1963 (15 July). *Air. First Polynesian Gold Coinage Commemoration. As T* **63** *but inscr.* "OFFICIAL AIRMAIL". 1 *koula coin (diam.* 3⅛ *in.). Imperf.*

O17 **63** 15s. black .. .. ..

For price see below No. 140.

1965 (18 Mar.). *No.* O17 *surch. as T* **67**.

O18 **63** 30s. on 15s. black 55 0

TRANSJORDAN.

See Jordan in Part III of the Stanley Gibbons Catalogue.

TRANSVAAL.

Late **SOUTH AFRICAN REPUBLIC.**

— SIMPLIFICATION (see Introduction) **—**

Nos. 1 to 85.

Simplest. 64, 22, 7, 30, 38, 31.

More advanced (distinguishing between imperf., perf. and roulette and including very distinct shades):—

28, 64, 21, 53, 36, 72 76, 14.
4b, 18a, 24, 35, 7, 29, 5, 19, 23, 30, 38, 20, 31.
39, 40.

Nos. 86 to 155.

Red opt. (*omit if desired*): 87, 88, 89. 90, 91. 92.

Black opt. 98, 101, 102, 103e, 104. 113.
99, 106, 107, 108. 114a.
116, 117, 118, 139, 119, 120. 121,
122, 123, 140, 124, 125.

130, 131, 142, 132. 133, 134, 143, 135.
145b, 146, 147. 148, 149, 150.

I. FIRST REPUBLIC.

Note.—For the 1d., 3d., 6d., and 1s. stamps, T **1** and **2**, two plates of each value were made, each plate consisting of forty stamp blocks, arranged in five rows of eight in a row.

The two plates of a value were sometimes, but not always, used together, producing a sheet of eighty stamps in two panes of forty each.

One block was inverted in the original left-hand plate of the 6d. and also of the 1s. In the panes of the printed stamps this was No. 25 on the right-hand pane in the 6d. and No. 1 on the right pane of the 1s. From this cause arose the *tête-bêche* varieties of these two values in some of the printings; and later, when these stamps were overprinted, an inverted surcharge is found whenever these panes were so treated. In addition to this in the case of the 1d., 3d., 6d., and 1s. stamps it is known that at least one sheet of each of these values must have been printed with the whole surcharge inverted.

Many unauthorised imitations of these three values were made in Germany, but, with the exception of certain impressions of the 1s. value, in yellow-green on soft medium paper, they all differ from the originals in some parts of the design, particularly in the eagle and the ribbon bearing the motto under the coat of arms. To this class belong forgeries of the 1d., in red or black, in which the numerals in the top corners are enclosed in a white frame.

The exception—the 1s., in yellow-green, above mentioned—was once regarded as genuine and catalogued, but it has been proved by Mr. J. N. Luff (see his articles, "Otto's Printings," in Vols. XXXIII and XXXIV of the *Philatelic Record;* it is his "surreptitious printing J") that these were printed from an unauthorised small plate of four subjects, on each of which were certain flaws that can be easily identified in the impressions. They somewhat resemble the 1s. stamps of 1876–7, but the paper is smoother and firmer and the printing clearer.

1

2

(Typo. Adolph Otto in Gustrow, Mecklenburg-Schwerin.)

1869. *Thin paper, clear and distinct impressions.*

(*a*) *Imperf.*

No.	Type	Description	Unused	Used
1	1	1d. brown-lake	£18	
		a. Orange-red	£24	
2	,,	6d. bright ultramarine	£12	
		a. Pale ultramarine	£10	£12
3	,,	1s. deep green	£38	
		a. Tête-bêche (pair)	£1000	

(*b*) *Fine roulette,* 15½ *to* 16.

No.	Type	Description	Unused	Used
4	,,	1d. brown-lake	£5	
		a. Brick-red	70 0	
		b. Orange-red	60 0	
		c. Vermilion	65 0	
5	,,	6d. bright ultramarine	60 0	
		a. Pale ultramarine	60 0	
6	,,	1s. deep green	£6	
		a. Yellow-green	£5	
		b. Emerald-green	£5	

Stamps of this issue, genuinely used for postal purposes, are scarce.

These stamps were printed from two sets of plates, one with the stamps spaced 1¼ to 1½ mm. apart, the other with the stamps spaced 2½ to 3½ mm. apart. The former are rouletted close to the design on all the four sides, and on the 1d. of that printing the outer frame-lines do not join at the right lower corner.

(Typo. as last, in Germany).

1871 (July). *Thin paper, clear and distinct impressions.*

Fine roulette, 15½ *to* 16.

No.	Type	Description	Unused	Used
7	2	3d. pale reddish lilac	60 0	60 0
		a. Deep lilac	70 0	60 0

These fine rouletted stamps and all subsequent printings are from the plates which were subsequently sent to South Africa

Imperf. specimens of the 3d. pale reddish lilac, which are also found in *tête-à-tête* pairs, were sent out to South Africa, but there is no evidence that they were issued for postal use.

These imperf. stamps are without the small dot on the left leg of the eagle which is always found in the issued stamps.

(Typo. M. J. Viljoen at Pretoria.)

1870 (4 April.). *Printed on thin gummed paper sent out from Germany. Impressions coarse and defective.*

(*a*) *Imperf.*

No.	Type	Description	Unused	Used
8	1	1d. dull rose-red	60 0	
		a. Reddish pink	60 0	
		b. Carmine-red	50 0	
9	,,	6d. dull ultramarine	£17	
		a. Tête-bêche (pair)	£275	

(*b*) *Fine roulettes,* 15½ *to* 16.

No.	Type	Description	Unused	Used
10	1	1d. carmine-red	£50	£22
11	,,	6d. dull ultramarine	£18	£9

(*c*) *Wide roulette,* 6½.

No.	Type	Description	Unused	Used
12	1	1d. carmine-red	—	£60

1870. *Thick, hard paper, yellow streaky gum,* (*a*) *Imperf.* (26 April).

No.	Type	Description	Unused	Used
13	1	1d. pale rose-red	50 0	
		a. Carmine-red	50 0	60 0
14	,,	1s. yellow-green	£5	90 0
		a. Tête-bêche (pair)	£325	

(*b*) *Fine roulette.* 15½ *to* 16 (10 May).

No.	Type	Description	Unused	Used
15	1	6d. ultramarine	80 0	80 0
		a. Tête-bêche (pair)	£275	£250
16	,,	1s. yellow-green	£35	£40

1870 (24 May). *Third hard paper, thin yellow smooth gum. Fine roulette,* 15½ *to* 16.

No.	Type	Description	Unused	Used
17	1	1d. carmine-red	£6	

1870 (4 July). *Medium paper, blotchy heavy printing and whitish gum. Fine roulette,* 15½ *to* 16.

No.	Type	Description	Unused	Used
18	1	1d. rose-red	45 0	45 0
		a. Carmine-red	45 0	45 0
		b. *Crimson.* From over-inked plate	£6	
19	,,	6d. ultramarine	90 0	90 0
		a. Tête-bêche (pair)		
		b. *Dp. ultram.* From over-inked pl	£25	£10
20	,,	1s. deep green	£7	85 0
		a. From over-inked plate	£25	£9

Nos. 18b, 19b and 20a. were printed from over-inked plates, giving heavy, blobby impressions.

(Typo. J. P. Borrius, at Potchefstroom.)

1870 (Sept.).

I. *Stout paper, but with colour often showing through, whitish gum.*

(*a*) *Imperf.*

No.	Type	Description	Unused	Used
21	1	1d. black	£10	£1[illegible]

(*b*) *Fine roulette,* 15½ *to* 16.

No.	Type	Description	Unused	Used
22	1	1d. black	17 6	27 [illegible]
		a. Grey-black	17 6	27 [illegible]
23	,,	6d. blackish blue	£9	65 [illegible]
		a. Dull blue	£6	50 [illegible]

II. *Thin transparent paper.*
Fine roulette, 15½ *to* 16.

No.	Type	Description	Unused	Used
24	1	1d. bright carmine	£14	65 [illegible]
25	,,	1d. black	£16	£6[illegible]
26	,,	6d. ultramarine	£6	50 [illegible]
27	,,	1s. green	95 0	50 [illegible]

1872 (Dec.).
I. *Thinnish opaque paper, clear printing.*
Fine roulette, 15½ to 16.

28 **1** 1d. reddish pink 75 0 50 0
a. Carmine-red 85 0 50 0
29 **2** 3d. grey-lilac £6 50 0
30 **1** 6d. ultramarine 65 0 30 0
a. Pale ultramarine 80 0 32 6
31 ,, 1s. yellow-green 75 0 32 6
a. Green 75 0 35 0
aa. Bisected (6d.) (on cover) ..

II. *Thickish wove paper.*
(*a*) *Fine roulette, 15½ to 16.*

32 **1** 1d. dull rose £32 £5
a. Brownish rose £45 £8
b. Printed on both sides ..
33 ,, 6d. milky blue £12 60 0
a. Deep dull blue £6 45 0
aa. Imperf. (pair) £50

(*b*) *Wide roulette, 6½.*

34 **1** 6d. dull blue .. .. ..

III. *Very thick dense paper.*
Fine roulette, 15½ to 16.

35 **1** 1d. dull rose £45 £12
a. Brownish rose .. .. — £9
36 ,, 6d. dull ultramarine £18 90 0
a. Bright ultramarine £22 90 0
37 ,, 1s. yellow-green £80 £75

3

(Typo. in Germany from a new plate made by A. Otto at Gustrow.)

1874 (30 Sept.). *Thin smooth paper, clearly printed. Fine roulette, 15½ to 16.*

38 **3** 6d. bright ultramarine .. 70 0 30 0
a. Bisected (3d.) (on cover) ..

Reprints of this stamp, both unused and with forged postmarks, are in a *duller* shade of colour than the originals, andthe paper is rather thicker. Reprints also exist in fancy colours.

(Typo. P. Davis & Son, Pietermaritzburg.)

1874 (Sept.). *T* **1**. *P* 12½.
(*a*) *Thin transparent paper.*

39 **1** 1d. pale brick-red 95 0 60 0
a. Brownish red £6 60 0
40 ,, 6d. deep blue £9 70 0

(*b*) *Thicker opaque paper.*

41 **1** 1d. pale red £12 £6
42 ,, 6d. blue £10 75 0
a. Imperf. between (pair) .
b. Deep blue £10 75 0

(Typo. "The Stamp Commission" at Pretoria.)

1875 (29 April). *Very thin soft opaque paper (semi-pelure).*
(*a*) *Imperf.*

3 **1** 1d. orange-red £12 75 0
a. Pin-perf. .. ..
4 **2** 3d. lilac £9 70 0
5 **1** 6d. blue £6 47 6
a. Milky blue £12 42 6
aa. Tête-bêche (pair) £325
ab. Pin-perf. .. .. ..

(*b*) *Fine roulette, 15½ to 16.*

1 1d. orange-red £32 £15
2 3d. lilac £40 £16
1 6d. blue £32 £12

(*c*) *Wide roulette, 6½.*

1 1d. orange-red .. .. — £18
2 3d. lilac .. .. .. — £25

51 **1** 6d. blue .. .. .. — £10
a. Bright blue .. .. .. — £10
b. Milky blue .. .. ..

II. **1876** (?). *Very thin hard transparent paper (pelure).* (*a*) *Imperf.*

52 **1** 1d. brownish red 70 0 30 0
a. Orange-red 55 0 22 6
b. Dull red 55 0 55 0
53 **2** 3d. lilac 70 0 50 0
a. Deep lilac 80 0 55 0
54 **1** 6d. pale blue 65 0 55 0
a. Blue 50 0 25 0
aa. Tête-bêche (pair) .. .. — £275
b. Deep blue 55 0 25 0

(*b*) *Fine roulette, 15½ to 16.*

55 **1** 1d. orange-red £26 £14
a. Brown-red £26 £14
56 **2** 3d. lilac £32 £11
57 **1** 6d. blue £16 £9
a. Deep blue £16 £11

(*c*) *Wide roulette, 6½.*

58 **1** 1d. orange-red £50 £15
a. Bright red .. .. .. — £14
59 **2** 3d. lilac £20
60 **1** 6d. deep blue.. .. .. £55 £9

(*d*) *Pin-perf.*

61 **1** 1d. dull red £35 £22
62 **2** 3d. lilac .. .. .. — £22
63 **1** 6d. blue £18

1876. *Stout hard-surfaced paper.*
I. *Smooth, nearly white, gum.*
(*a*) *Imperf.*

64 **1** 1d. bright red 25 0 22 6
65 **2** 3d. lilac .. .. ..
66 **1** 6d. bright blue £8 30 0
a Tête-bêche (pair) .. .. — £275
b. Pale blue £8 30 0

(*b*) *Fine roulette, 15½ to 16.*

67 **1** 1d. bright red £32 £15
68 **2** 3d. lilac £20
69 **1** 6d. bright blue .. .. — £14

(*c*) *Wide roulette, 6½.*

70 **1** 1d. bright red £38 £15
71 ,, 6d. pale blue .. .. — £18

II. *Deep brown gum, staining the paper.*

72 **1** 6d. deep blue (*imperf.*) .. 75 0 22 6
a. Tête-bêche (pair)
73 ,, 6d. deep blue (*fine roulette*) .. — £32
74 ,, 6d. deep blue (*wide roulette*) £38 £18

1876–77.
I. *Coarse soft white paper, printed in the colours that were overprinted in July, 1877.*
(*a*) *Imperf.*

75 **1** 1d. brick-red £8 65 0
76 ,, 6d. deep blue £12 65 0
a. Milky blue £28 £7
77 ,, 1s. yellow-green £18 £9

(*b*) *Fine roulette, 15½ to 16.*

78 **1** 1d. brick-red .. .. — £30
79 ,, 6d. deep blue .. .. — £12
80 ,, 1s. yellow-green £45 £25

(*c*) *Wide roulette, 6½.*

81 **1** 1d. brick-red .. .. — £30
81*a* ,, 6d. deep blue .. ..
82 ,, 1s. yellow-green .. ..

(*d*) *Fine × wide roulette.*

83 **1** 1d. brick-red £50 £35

II. *Hard thick coarse yellowish paper.*

84 **1** 1d. brick-red (*imperf.*)
85 ,, 1d. brick-red (*wide roulette*)

II. FIRST BRITISH OCCUPATION.

V. R.

TRANSVAAL.

(4)

V. R.

TRANSVAAL.

(5)

T 4 is the normal overprint, but in some printings No. 11 on the pane has a wider-spaced overprint, as **T 5**.

T **1** *and* **2** (3d.) *optd. with T* **4**.

1877 (July). (A) *Opt. in red.*

(*a*) *Imperf.*

86 3d. lilac (semi-pelure) £70 £15
 a. Opt. Type 5 .. .. ..
87 3d. lilac (pelure) £65 £12
 a. Opt. Type 5 .. .. ..
 b. Opt. on back £150
 c. Opt. double, in red and in black
88 6d. blue £75 £15
 a. Opt. inverted or tête-bêche pair
 b. Opt. double .. .. ..
 c. Opt. Type 5 .. .. ..
 d. Deep blue .. .. .. — £20
89 1s. yellow-green £30 £10
 a. Bisected (6d.) (on cover) .. — £65
 b. Opt. inverted or tête-bêche pair
 c. Opt. Type 5 .. .. .. £140

(*b*) *Fine roulette*, 15½ *to* 16.

90 3d. lilac (pelure) .. .. — £65
91 6d. blue .. .. .. — £65
92 1s. yellow-green £125 £40
 a. Opt. Type 5 .. .. ..

(*c*) *Wide roulette*, 6½.

93 3d. lilac (pelure) .. .. — £65
 a. Opt. Type 5 .. .. ..
94 6d. blue .. .. .. — £65
 a. Opt. Type 5 .. .. ..
95 1s. yellow-green £125 £50
 a. Opt. inverted or tête-bêche pair

In the above, the stamps overprinted are the 3d. of the issues of April 1875 and 1876 and the 6d. and 1s. of 1876–77.

1887. (B) *Opt. in black.*

I. *Pelure paper.*

96 1d. orange-red (*imperf.*) .. £15 £7
97 1d. orange-red (*fine roulette*) — £60

II. *Hard-surfaced paper.*

98 1d. bright red (*imperf.*) .. 20 0 20 0
 a. Opt. inverted £28 £20
 b. Opt. Type 5 .. .. £38 £45
99 1d. bright red (*fine roulette*) .. £10 75 0
 a. Opt. inverted .. .. ..
 b. Opt. double .. .. ..
100 1d. bright red (*wide roulette*) £35 £12

III. *Coarse soft paper.*

(*a*) *Imperf.*

101 1d. brick-red (May, '77) .. 17 6 17 6
 a. Opt. double .. .. — £85
 b. Opt. Type 5 .. .. ..
102 3d. lilac 80 0 30 0
 a. Opt. inverted .. .. ..
 b. Deep lilac £12 £6
103 6d. dull blue £8 45 0
 a. Opt. double .. .. ..
 b. Opt. inverted £100 £15
 c. Tête-bêche (pair) .. ..
 d. Opt. Type 5 .. .. .. — £65
 da. Opt. Type 5, inverted
 e. Blue (bright to deep) .. £15 40 0
 ea. Bright blue, opt. inverted .. — £35
 f. Pin-perf. .. .. .. — £30
104 1s. yellow-green £6 50 0
 a. Opt. inverted £80 £15
 b. Tête-bêche (pair) .. ..
 c. Opt. Type 5 .. .. £80 £50
 d. Bisected (on cover) .. .. — £35

(*b*) *Fine roulette*, 15½ *to* 16.

105 1d. brick-red 95 0 85 0
106 3d. lilac £12 80 0
107 6d. dull blue £15 £6
 a. Opt. inverted .. .. — £32
 b. Opt. Type 5 .. .. ..
108 1s. yellow-green £16 £8
 a. Opt. inverted £60 £28
 b. Opt. Type 5 .. .. — £80

(*c*) *Wide roulette*, 6½.

109 1d. brick red £50 £12
110 3d. lilac .. .. .. — £40
111 6d. dull blue .. .. .. — £35
 a. Opt. inverted .. .. ..
112 1s. yellow-green £25 £10
 a. Opt. inverted £105 £35

1877 (31 Aug.). *T* **1** *optd. with T* **4** *in black.*

113 6d. blue/*rose* (*imperf.*) .. 70 0 30 0
 a. Bisected (3d.) (on cover) ..
 b. Opt. inverted 70 0 30 0
 c. Tête-bêche (pair) ..
 d. Opt. omitted ..
114 6d. blue/*rose* (*fine roulette*) .. £15 70 0
 a. Opt. inverted £30 60 0
 b. Tête-bêche (pair) .. ..
 c. Opt. omitted. .. ..
115 6d. blue/*rose* (*wide roulette*)
 a. Opt. inverted .. ..
 b. Opt. omitted .. ..

V. R. *V. R.*

Transvaal **Transvaal**

(**6**) (**7**)

1877 (July). *T* **1** *and* **2** (3d,) *optd. with T* **6** *in black.*

(*a*) *Imperf.*

116 1d. red/*blue* 70 0 35 0
 a. "Transvral" .. .. .. — £125
 b. Opt. double .. .. ..
 c. Opt. inverted £60 £25
 d. Opt. omitted .. .. ..
117 1d. red/*orange* 15 0 17 6
 a. Pin-perf. .. .. ..
 b. Printed both sides .. ..
118 3d. mauve/*buff* 40 0 25 0
 a. Opt. inverted .. .. — £40
 b. Pin-perf. .. .. ..
119 6d. blue/*green* £6 30 0
 a. Deep blue/green £8 50 0
 b. Broken "Y" for "V" in "V.R." .. .. ..
 c. Small "v" in "Transvaal" ..
 d. Stop in front of "R" (=V. . R.) .. .. — £45
 e. Tête-bêche (pair) .. ..
 f. Opt. inverted .. .. — £40
 g. Pin-perf. .. .. ..
120 6d. blue/*blue* 70 0 30
 a. Tête-bêche (pair) .. ..
 b. Opt. inverted .. .. — £4
 c. Opt. omitted .. .. — £12
 d. Opt. double .. .. .. — £15
 e. Pin-perf. .. .. ..
 f. Bisected (3d.) (on cover) .. — £1

(*b*) *Fine roulette*, 15½ *to* 16.

121 1d. red/*blue* £6 50
 a. "Transvral" .. .. — £15
122 1d. red/*orange* 35 0 35
 a. Imperf. between (pair) ..
123 3d. mauve/*buff* £7 35
 a. Imperf. between (pair) ..
 b. Opt. inverted .. .. — £16
124 6d. blue/*green* 90 0 30
 a. Bisected (3d.) (on cover) .. — £1
 b. Tête-bêche (pair) .. ..
 c. Opt. inverted .. .. — £3
 d. Opt. omitted .. .. — £1
 e. Stop in front of "R" (=V. . R.) .. .. — £
125 6d. blue/*blue* £18 60
 a. Bisected (3d.) (on cover) .. — £
 b. Imperf. between (pair) ..
 c. Opt. inverted .. .. — £
 d. Opt. omitted .. .. — £1

(c) Wide roulette, 6½.
126 1d. red/*orange* £16 £10
127 3d. mauve/*buff* .. .. — £10
128 6d. blue/*green* .. .. — £42
129 6d. blue/*blue* .. .. .. — £20
a. Opt. inverted .. ..

T **1** *and* **2** (3d.) *optd. with T* **7** *in black.*

(a) Imperf.
130 1d. red/*orange* 55 0 42 6
131 3d mauve/*buff* 55 0 32 6
a. Pin-perf. about 9 .. .. — £50
132 6d. blue/*blue* £8 37 6
a. Tête-bêche (pair) .. ..
b. Opt. inverted .. .. — £24

(b) Fine roulette, 15½ to 16.
133 1d. red/*orange* .. .. — £12
134 3d. mauve/*buff* £14 £9
a. Imperf. between (pair) ..
135 6d. blue/*blue* .. .. .. — £9
a. Opt. inverted .. .. — £60

(c) Wide roulette, 6½.
136 1d. red/*orange* .. .. — £18
137 3d. mauve/*buff* .. .. — £25
138 6d. blue/*blue* .. .. .. — £24
a. Opt. inverted .. ..

1879 (18 April). *T* **2**.
(a) Imperf. (b) Fine roulette. (c) Wide roulette.

I. *Optd. with T* **6** *in black.*
139 3d. mauve/*green (a)* £12 35 0
a. Pin-perf. .. ..
b. Opt. inverted .. .. — £65
c. Opt. double .. .. ..
140 3d. mauve/*green (b)* £55 £15
141 3d. mauve/*green (c)* .. .. — £20

II. *Optd. with T* **7** *in black.*
142 3d. mauve/*green (a)* £7 25 0
a. Opt. inverted .. .. — £65
b. Opt. omitted .. .. — £80
c. Printed both sides .. ..
143 3d. mauve/*green (b)* £38 £15
144 3d. mauve/*green (c)* .. .. — £25

V. R. V. R.

Transvaal **Transvaal**
(**8**) (**8***a*)

1879 (Aug.-Sept.). *T* **1** *and* **2** (3d.) *optd. with T* **8** *in black.*

(a) Imperf.
145 1d. red/*yellow* 60 0 42 6
a. Small "T", Type 8*a* .. £18 £14
b. Red/orange 35 0 37 6
ba. Small "T", Type 8*a* .. £14 £14
146 3d. mauve/*green* 35 0 25 0
a. Small "T", Type 8*a* .. £22 £12
147 3d. mauve/*blue* 47 6 30 0
a. Small "T", Type 8*a* .. £15 £7

(b) Fine roulette, 15½ to 16.
148 1d. red/*yellow* .. .. — £18
a. Small "T", Type 8*a* .. £60 £35
b. Red/orange .. .. — £25
ba. Small "T", Type 8*a*
149 3d. mauve/*green* £50 £20
a. Small "T", Type 8*a* ..
150 3d. mauve/*blue* .. .. — £15
a. Small "T", Type 8*a* .. — £50

(c) Wide roulette, 6½.
151 1d. red/*yellow* .. .. — £60
a. Small "T", Type 8*a* ..
b. Red/orange .. .. ..
152 3d. mauve/*green* .. ..
a. Small "T", Type 8*a* ..
153 3d. mauve/*blue* .. ..

(d) Pin-perf., about 17.
154 1d. red/*yellow* .. .. — £40
a. Small "T", Type 8*a* ..
155 3d. mauve/*blue* .. ..

9

(Recess. Bradbury, Wilkinson & Co.)

1878 (26 Aug.)–**1880**. *P* 14, 14½.
156 **9** ½d. vermilion (1880) .. 20 0 30 0
157 „ 1d. pale red-brown .. 7 6 5 0
a. Brown-red 6 0 4 6
158 „ 3d. dull rose 7 6 3 6
a. Claret 10 0 4 0
159 „ 4d. sage-green 17 6 12 6
160 „ 6d. olive-black 7 0 6 0
a. Black-brown 10 0 4 0
161 „ 1s. green 65 0 35 0
162 „ 2s. blue 90 0 35 0

The above prices are for specimens perforated on all four sides. Stamps from margins of sheets, with perforations absent on one or two sides, can be supplied for about 30% less.

1 Penny
(**10**)

1 Penny 1 Penny
(**11**) (**12**)

1 Penny 1 Penny
(**13**) (**14**)

1 PENNY *1 Penny*
(**15**) (**16**)

1879 (22 April). *No.* 160*a surch. with T* **10** *to* **16**.
(A) *In black.* (B) *In red.*

			A.		B.	
163	**10**	1d. on 6d.	£10	85 0	£25	£14
164	**11**	1d. on 6d.	75 0	47 6	£10	£8
165	**12**	1d. on 6d.	£10	85 0	£24	£15
166	**13**	1d. on 6d.	90 0	42 6	£12	£9
167	**14**	1d. on 6d.	£25	£10	—	—
168	**15**	1d. on 6d.	45 0	32 6	£6	70 0
169	**16**	1d. on 6d.	£12	90 0	£25	£15

III. SECOND REPUBLIC.

Een Penny
(**17**)

1882. *No.* 159 *surch. with T* **17**.
170 1d. on 4d. sage-green .. 5 0 5 0
a. Surch. inverted £15

1883. *Re-issue of T* **1** *and* **2** (3d.). *P* 12.
171 1d. grey (to black) 2 6 1 6
172 3d. grey-black (to black)/*rose* 10 0 8 6
a. Bisected (1d.) (on cover) .. — £20
173 3d. pale red 7 6 2 6
a. Bisected (1d) (on cover) ..
b Chestnut 37 6 5 0
c. Vermilion 27 6 8 6
174 1s. green (to deep) 15 0 5 0
a. Bisected (6d.) (on cover) .. — 90 0
b. Tête-bêche (pair) £15 80 0

Reprints are known of Nos. 172, 173, 173*b* and 173*c*. The paper of the first is *bright rose* in place of *dull rose*, and the impression is brownish black in place of grey-black to deep black. The reprints on white paper have the paper thinner than the originals, and the gum yellowish instead of white. The colour is a dull deep orange-red.

18

(Des. J. Vurtheim. Typo. Enschedé & Son, Haarlem.)

REPRINTS. Reprints of the general issues 1885–93, 1894–95, 1895–96 and 1896–97 exist in large quantities. They cannot readily be distinguished from genuine originals except by comparison with used stamps, but the following general characteristics may be noted. The reprints are all perf. 12½, large holes; the paper is whiter than that usually employed for the originals and their colours lack the lustre of those of the genuine stamps.

Forged surcharges have been made on these reprints.

1885 (13 Mar.)–**1893.** *P* 12½.

No.	Type		Unused	Used
175	**18**	½d. grey	0 3	0 3
		a. Perf. 13½	6 6	3 6
		b. Perf. 12½ × 12	2 0	0 4
		ba. Var. Perf. 11½ × 12 ..		
176	„	1d. carmine	0 8	0 3
		a. Perf. 12½ × 12	1 0	0 4
		aa. Var. Perf. 11½ × 12 ..	15 0	10 0
		b. Rose	0 4	0 3
		ba. Perf. 12½ × 12	0 8	0 3
177	„	2d. brn.-pur. (p. 12½ × 12)	1 0	0 6
178	„	2d. olive-bistre (1887) ..	1 0	0 3
		a. Perf. 12½ × 12	5 0	0 4
179	„	2½d. mauve (to bright) ('93)	2 0	0 8
180	„	3d. mauve (to bright) ..	2 0	1 9
		a. Perf. 12½ × 12	10 0	3 0
		aa. Var. Perf. 11½ × 12 ..	45 0	25 0
181	„	4d. bronze-green ..	4 0	0 8
		a. Perf. 13½	6 0	1 9
		b. Perf. 12½ × 12	25 0	2 6
		ba. Var. Perf. 11½ × 12 ..	£20	£6
182	„	6d. pale dull blue ..	2 0	0 9
		a. Perf. 13½	9 0	2 6
		b. Perf. 12½ × 12	10 0	1 3
		ba. Var. Perf. 11½ × 12 ..		
183	„	1s. yellow-green ..	6 0	1 0
		a. Perf. 13½	25 0	12 6
		b. Perf. 12½ × 12	15 0	1 3
184	„	2s. 6d. orge.-buff (to buff)	10 6	4 0
		a. Perf. 12½ × 12	18 6	10 0
185	„	5s. slate	12 6	6 0
		a. Perf. 12½ × 12	18 6	6 0
186	„	10s. fawn	37 6	6 0
187	„	£5 deep green (1892)* ..		

The variety, perf. 11½ × 12 in the 1d., 3d., 4d. and 6d. is from sheets perforated with the 12½ × 12 machine. (See note after Netherlands No. 109).

*Most specimens of No. 187 on the market are either forgeries or reprints.

HALVE PENNY

(19)

HALVE PENNY

(20)

1885. *Surch. with T* **19** *or* **20** (*½d. on 3d. mauve*).
A. *Reading down.* B. *Reading up.*

No.	Type		A. Unused	A. Used	B. Unused	B. Used
188	**2**	½d. on 3d. (No. 173)	3 6	3 6	3 6	3 6
189	**18**	½d. on 3d. (No. 180*a*)	3 6	3 6		†
		a. "PRNNY" for "PENNY" ..	50 0	—		†
		b. Second "N" in "PENNY" invert.	£8	—		†
		c. Var. Perf. 11½ × 12 ..	12 6	—		†
190	**1**	½d. on 1s. (No. 174)	12 6	17 6	12 6	17 6
		a. Tête-bêche (pair) ..		†	—	£10

No. 188 was issued on May 22, No. 189 on Sept. 28 and No. 190 in August.

In sheets of Nos. 188 and 190 one half-sheet had the surch. reading upwards and the other half-sheet downwards.

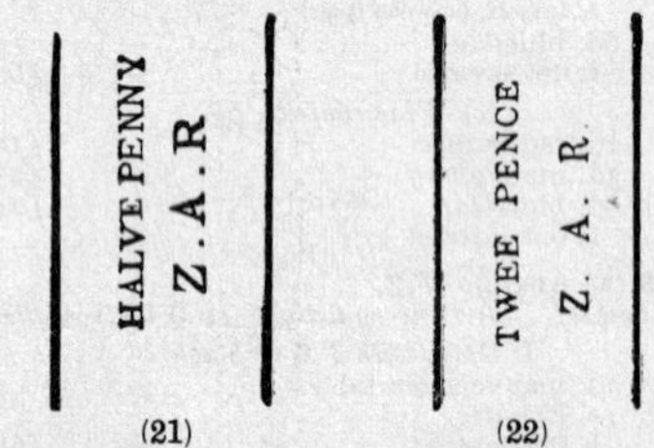

(21) (22)

1885 (1 Sept.). *No.* 160*a surcharged in red.*

No.	Type		Unused	Used
191	**21**	½d. on 6d. black-brown ..	40 0	42 6
192	**22**	2d. on 6d. black-brown ..	6 0	6 0

2d

(23)

2d

(24)

1887 (15 Jan.). *T* **18** *surch.* *P* 12½ × 12.

No.	Type		Unused	Used
193	**23**	2d. on 3d. mauve	5 0	5 0
		a. Surch. double .. .	—	£17
		b. Var. Perf. 11½ × 12 ..	12 6	12 6
194	**24**	2d. on 3d. mauve	2 6	2 6
		a. Surch. double	—	£22
		b. Var. Perf. 11½ × 12	8 6	7 6

Halve Penny

(25)

1 Penny

(26)

2½ Pence

(27)

2½ Pence

(28)

1893. *T* **18** *surcharged.* *P* 12½.

Two varieties of surcharge:
(A) *Vertical distance between bars* 12½ *mm.*
(B) *Distance* 13½ *mm.*

(1) *In red.*

No.	Type		Unused	Used
195	**25**	½d. on 2d. olive-bistre (A.) (27 May)	1 6	1
		a. Surch. inverted (A) ..	6 0	6
		b. Variety B	4 6	4
		ba. Variety B, inverted ..	18 6	

(2) *In black.*

196 **25** ½d. on 2d. olive-bistre (A) (2 July) 1 6 1 6
a. Surch. inverted (A) .. 12 6 12 6
b. Extra surch. on back inverted (A) £14
c. Variety B 3 6 3 6
ca. Variety B, inverted .. — 25 0
cb. Extra surch. on back inverted (B) .. ..

197 **26** 1d. on 6d. bl. (A) (26 Jan.) 0 8 0 9
a. Surch. double (A) .. 90 0 60 0
b. Surch. inverted (A) .. 3 6 5 0
c. Variety B 1 6 1 6
ca. Variety B inverted .. 12 6 12 6
cb. Variety B double .. — £9
d. Pair, with and without sur. £11

198 **27** 2½d. on 1s. grn. (A) (2 Jan.) 1 6 1 9
a. "2/½" for "2½" .. 55 0 55 0
b. Surch. inverted (A) .. 6 0 7 6
ba. Surch. inverted and "2/½" for "2½" £18
c. Extra surch. on back inverted (A) .. ..
d. Variety B 4 6 6 0
da. Variety B, inverted 17 6 22 6

199 **28** 2½d. on 1s. green (A) (24 June) 6 0 4 6
a. Surch. double (A) .. 70 0 70 0
b. Surch. inverted (A) .. 17 6 17 6
c. Variety B 14 0 14 0
ca. Variety B, double ..
cb. Variety B, inverted ..

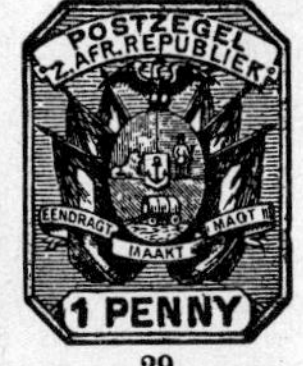

29

30

1894–95. *Waggon with shafts. P* 12½.

200 **29** ½d. grey 0 8 0 8
201 „ 1d. carmine 0 8 0 3
202 „ 2d. olive-bistre 0 8 0 6
203 „ 6d. pale dull blue .. 2 6 2 6
204 „ 1s. yellow-green 12 6 15 0

For note *re* reprints, see below T **18**.

1895–96. *Waggon with pole. P* 12½.

205 **30** ½d. pearl-grey 0 4 0 3
a. *Lilac-grey* 0 4 0 3
206 „ 1d. rose-red 0 3 0 3
207 „ 2d. olive-bistre 0 6 0 3
208 „ 3d. mauve 1 3 1 0
209 „ 4d. olive-black 3 6 3 0
210 „ 6d. pale dull blue .. 2 0 1 0
211 „ 1s. yellow-green 4 6 3 6
212 „ 5s. slate 12 6 15 0
212*a* „ 10s. pale chestnut .. 15 0 5 6

For note *re* reprints, see below T **18**.

Halve Penny

(**31**)

1d. (**32**—Round dot.)

1d. (**32a**—Square dot.)

1895 (July–Aug.). *Nos.* 211 *and* 179 *surch.*

213 **31** ½d. on 1s. green (R.) .. 0 4 0 6
a. Surch. spaced 2 0 2 6
b. "Pennij" for "Penny .. 70 0
c. Surch. inverted 10 0 10 6
d. Surch. double 60 0

214 **32** 1d. on 2½d. brt. mve. (G.) 0 3 0 3
a. Surch. inverted 17 6 17 6
b. Surch double .. ..
c. Surch. on back only ..
d. Type 32*a* 4 6 4 6
da. Type 32*a* inverted 95 0

The normal surcharge on No. 213 is spaced 3 mm. between "Penny" and the bars; on No. 213a 4 mm. approx. Copies may be found in which one or both of the bars have failed to print.

33

1895 (Aug.). *Fiscal stamp optd.* "POSTZEGEL". *P* 11½.

215 **33** 6d. bright rose (G.) .. 2 6 3 0
a. Imperf. between (pair) ..

1896–97. *P* 12½.

216 **30** ½d. green 0 3 0 3
217 „ 1d. rose-red and green .. 0 3 0 3
218 „ 2d. brown and green .. 0 3 0 6
219 „ 2½d. dull blue and green .. 0 8 0 6
220 „ 3d. purple and green .. 0 3 0 9
221 „ 4d. sage-green and green 0 3 1 0
222 „ 6d. lilac and green .. 1 0 0 8
223 „ 1s. ochre and green .. 1 6 0 6
224 „ 2s. 6d. dull violet & green 3 6 3 0

For note *re* reprints, see below T **18**.

34

(Litho. Printing Press and Publishing Co., Pretoria.)

1895 (6 Sept.). *Introduction of Penny Postage. P* 11.

225 **34** 1d. red (pale to deep) .. 0 6 0 6
a. Imperf. between (pair) .. 25 0 17 6

IV. SECOND BRITISH OCCUPATION.

V. R. I.

(**35**)

FORGERIES. The forgeries of the "V.R.I." and "E.R.I." overprints most often met with can be recognised by the fact that the type used is perfect and the three stops are always in alignment with the bottom of the letters. In the genuine overprints, which were made from old type, it is impossible to find all three letters perfect and all three stops perfect and in exact alignment with the bottom of the letters.

1900 (18 June). *Overprinted with T* **35.**

226 **30** ½d. green 0 3 0 3
f. "V.I.R." £45
227 „ 1d. rose-red and green .. 0 3 0 3
f. No stop after "R" and "I" £6 £6
228 „ 2d. brown and green .. 0 4 0 4
f. "V.I.R." £45
229 „ 2½d. dull blue and green .. 0 6 0 6
230 „ 3d. purple and green .. 0 8 0 6
231 „ 4d. sage-green and green 1 0 0 9
f. "V.I.R." £45
232 „ 6d. lilac and green .. 1 6 1 0
233 „ 1s. ochre and green .. 2 3 2 0
234 „ 2s. 6d. dull violet & grn. 4 0 3 0
235 „ 5s. slate 9 0 10 0
236 „ 10s. pale chestnut .. 12 6 12 6
237 **18** £5 green* .. ..

The error "V.I.R." occurred on stamp No. 34 in the first batch of stamps to be overprinted—a few sheets of the ½d., 2d. and 4d. The error was then corrected and stamps showing it are very rare.

*Most specimens of No. 237 on the market are forgeries.

Varieties.

A. No stop after "V". B. No stop after "R". C. No stop after "I". D. Overprint inverted. E. Overprint double.

		A	B	C	D	E
226	½d. ..	45 0	25 0	12 6	12 6	—
227	1d. ..	45 0	25 0	9 0	12 6	£6
228	2d. ..	65 0	†	75 0	25 0	—
229	2½d. ..	55 0	—	35 0	12 6	†
230	3d. ..	65 0	90 0	65 0	£7	†
231	4d. ..	90 0	£6	55 0	55 0	†
232	6d. ..	35 0	65 0	45 0	45 0	†
233	1s. ..	35 0	—	65 0	55 0	£6
234	2s. 6d. ..	50 0	£6	†	†	†
235	5s. ..	—	†	†	†	†
236	10s. ..	£6	†	£6	†	†
237	£5 ..	—	†	†	†	†

The above prices are for unused. Used are worth the same, or rather more in some cases.

E. R. I. (36)

E. R. I. Half Penny (37)

FORGERIES. See note below T **35.**

1901–2. *Optd. with T* **36.**

238 **30** ½d. green (July, '01) .. 0 4 0 6
239 „ 1d. rose-red & grn. (20.3.01) 0 4 0 4
a. "E" of opt. omitted .. £6
240 „ 3d. purple & green (6.02) 2 6 3 0
241 „ 4d. sage-grn. & grn. (6.02) 3 0 3 6
242 „ 2s. 6d. dull violet & green (10.02) 12 6 17 6

1901 (July). *Surch. with T* **37.**

243 **30** ½d. on 2d. brown & green .. 0 6 0 3
a. No stop after "E" .. 95 0

38 (Postage Revenue). **39** (Postage Postage).

(Typo. De La Rue & Co.)

1902 (1 April)–**1903.** *Wmk. Crown CA. P* 14.

244 **38** ½d. black & bluish green 0 8 0 3
245 „ 1d. black and carmine .. 0 6 0 3
246 **38** 2d. black and purple .. 1 6 0 6
247 „ 2½d. black and blue .. 2 0 3 0
248 „ 3d. black & sage-grn. ('03) 2 6 1 3
249 „ 4d. black and brown ('03) 5 0 3 0
250 „ 6d. black & orange-brown 3 0 1 9
251 „ 1s. black and sage-green 10 0 7 6
252 „ 2s. black and brown .. 37 6 37 6
253 **39** 2s. 6d. magenta & black 17 6 10 0
254 „ 5s. black & purple/*yellow* 25 0 25 0
255 „ 10s. black and purple/*red* 60 0 55 0

The colour of the "black" centres varies from brownish grey or grey to black.

1903. *Wmk. Crown CA. P* 14.

256 **39** 1s. grey-black & red-brn. 7 6 4 0
257 „ 2s. grey-black & yellow .. 17 6 15 0
258 „ £1 green and violet .. £6 £5
259 „ £5 orange-brown & violet £175 £60

1904–9. *Wmk. Mult. Crown CA. P* 14.

260 **38** ½d. blk. & bluish grn., O 2 6 1 0
261 „ 1d. black & carmine, O 2 6 0 3
262 „ 2d. blk. & purple, C ('06) 4 0 0 8
263 „ 2½d. black & blue, C O ('05) 3 6 1 6
264 „ 3d. blk. & sage-green, C ('06) 2 6 0 8
265 „ 4d. black & brown, C ('06) 3 0 0 6
266 „ 6d. black & orge., O ('05) 4 6 0 8
a. *Blk. & brown-orange*, C .. 4 6 0 6
267 **39** 1s. blk and red-brn, O ('05) 5 0 0 9
268 „ 2s. blk. & yellow, O ('06) 15 0 5 6
269 „ 2s. 6d. mag. & blk., O ('09) 20 0 6 0
270 „ 5s. blk.. & pur./*yellow*, O 35 0 6 0
271 „ 10s. blk. & pur./*red*, O('07) 70 0 12 6
272 „ £1 grn. & vio., OC ('08) £7 25 0

There is considerable variation in the "black" centres as in the previous issue.

1905–9. *Wmk. Mult. Crown CA. P* 14.

273 **38** ½d. yellow-green .. 0 6 0 3
a. *Deep green* (1908) .. 0 6 0 3
274 „ 1d. scarlet 0 6 0 3
a. Error. Wmk. Cabled Anchor, T 13 of Cape of Good Hope — £75
275 „ 2d. purple (1909) .. 2 6 0 6
276 „ 2½d. bright blue (1909) .. 10 0 5 0

The monocoloured ½d. and 1d. are printed from new combined plates. These show a slight alteration in that the frame does not touch the crown.

Many of the King's Head stamps are found overprinted or perforated "C.S.A.R.", for use on the Central South African Railways.

Fiscals with Postal Cancellations.

Various fiscal stamps are found apparently postally used, but these were used on telegrams not on postal matter.

POSTAGE DUE STAMPS.

D 1

(Typo. De La Rue & Co.)

1907. *Wmk. Mult. Crown CA. P* 14.

D1 **D 1** ½d. black and blue-green 1 0 1
D2 „ 1d. black and scarlet .. 1 3 0
D3 „ 2d. brown-orange .. 2 0 1
D4 „ 3d. black and blue .. 5 0 2
D5 „ 5d. black and violet .. 4 0 5
D6 „ 6d. black and red-brown 10 0 4
D7 „ 1s. scarlet and black .. 10 0 7

Transvaal now uses the stamps of South Afric[a]

PIETERSBURG.

These stamps were an unofficial issue of the Transvaal Government, made under President Kruger's authority while he was still in office. Issued from the middle of March, 1901, until 9th April, when the British troops occupied that district.

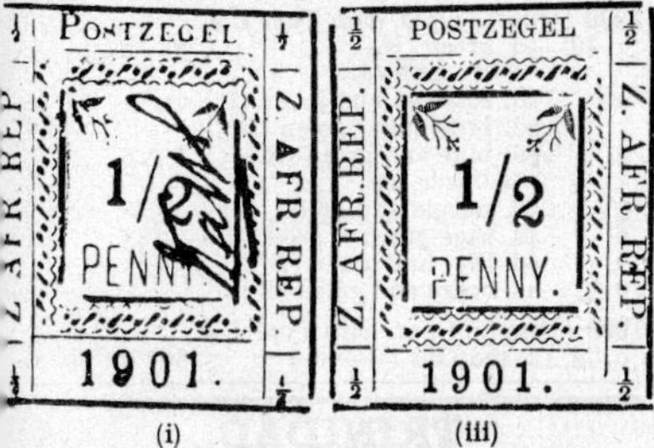

(i) (iii)

(Typo. Office of " De Zoutpansberg Wachter ", Pietersburg.)

1901 (March).

Type-set and printed in sheets of 24 (4 rows of 6), the first two rows have large " P " in " Postzegel " and large date as (i); the third row has (ii) large " P " in " Postzegel " and small date; the fourth row has small " p " in " postzegel " and small date as (iii). Black impression on coloured paper. Initialled by the Controller in black.

(*a*) *Imperf.*

1	½d. *green*	35	0
	a. Controller's initials in red ..	35	0
	b. Controller's initials omitted ..	50	0
2	1d. *rose*	12	6
3	2d. *orange*	20	0
4	4d. *blue*	35	0
5	6d. *green*	35	0
6	1s. *yellow*	40	0

No. 1*b* was issued in error, three sheets having tuck together; other values without initials re only incomplete stamps and *were not issued.*

Prices are for Type (i). Types (ii) and (iii) re worth 50% more.

Errors and varieties.

The following exist; the number in brackets eing the numbers of the positions of the stamps n the sheet (where known). Prices from 25s. pwards.

1. " Postzfgel " (No. 5): 1d., 4d., 6d.
2. " Postzeoel " (No. 9): 1d., 4d., 6d.
3. " Postzegfl " (No. 18): 4d., 6d.
4. " Postzegfl ", and no stop after " afr " on right (No. 18): 1d.
5. " Postzegei " (No. 21): 1d., 4d., 6d.
6. " Postzegei," and no stop after " z " on left (No. 16): ½d., 1s.
7. " Postzecel " and " aer " on left (No. 23): ½d.
8. " aer " on left (No. 23): 4d., 6d., 1s.
9. " aer " on left, and with " 4 " in left upper corner (No. 23): 2d.

" aer " on right (No. 10): 1d., 4d., 6d.

" afb " on left: (No. 15): ½d. (No. 8): 2d., 4d., 6d.

" afb " on right (No. 6): 1d., 4d., 6d.

" bep " on left (No. 8): 1d.

" bep " on left and no stop after "1901" (No. 11): ½d.

" reb " on left (No. 7): 1d., 4d., 6d.

Floreate ornament in left corner inverted (Nos. 20 and 24): 1d., 4d., 6d.

Floreate ornament in right corner inverted (No. 14): 1d., 2d., 4d., 6d.

Wider figure in centre and floreate ornament in left corner inverted (No. 20): 4d., 6d.

19. Wider figure in centre: (No. 20): 2d. (Nos. 19 and 20): 4d., 6d.
20. Wider figure in centre and no stop after " afr " on right (No. 19): 2d, 4d., 6d.
21. No stop after " afr " on left (No. 2): ½d., 2d., 4d., 6d., 1s.
22. No stop after " afr " on right: (Nos. 18 and 19): ½d., 1d., 2d. (No. 19): 1s.
23. " ½ " inverted in upper left-hand corner and no stop after " afr " on right: ½d.
24. No stop after " rep " on left (No. 7): 6d.
25. No stop after " z " on left (No. 16): 1d., 4d., 6d.
26. No stop after " z " on left and no bar below figure in right upper corner (No. 22): ½d.
27. No stop after " 1901 " (No. 11): ½d., 1d., 4d., 6d., 1s.
28. No bar under figure in left upper corner (No. 3): 1d.
29. No bar under figure in right upper corner (No. 22): ½d., 1d., 2d., 4d., 6d., 1s.
30. No bar over figure in left lower corner (No. 15): 1d., 4d.
31. No bar over figure in right lower corner (No. 3): 6d., 1s. (No. 4): 1d. (No. 18): ½d.
32. Figure in left lower corner inverted (No. 2): 1d.
33. " ⅛ " for " ½ " in left upper corner (No. 3): ½d.
34. No stop after " afr " on right: (Nos. 4 and 18): ½d.
35. No stop after " penny ": 1d.
36. Hyphen betwn. " afr-rep" on right (No. 24): ½d.
37. Figures in centre level (No. 17): ½d.
38. " PENNY " for " PENCE ": 2d., 4d., 6d.
39. Figure " 2 " in centre inverted: 2d.
40. " 1 " for " 2 " in left lower corner: 2d.
41. " 1 " for " 2 " in right lower corner: 2d.

(*b*) *P* 11½.

Controller's initials in red on the ½d., in black on the others.

7	½d. *green*	20	0
8	1d. *rose*	12	6
	a. Imperf. between (pair) ..	25	0
9	2d. *orange*	20	0

Prices are for Type (i). Types (ii) and (iii) are worth 50% more.

Errors and varieties.

Prices from 15s. upwards.

1. " Postzfgel " (No. 5): 1d.
2. " Postzeoel " (No. 9): 1d.
3. " Postzegfl " and no stop after " afr " on right (No. 18): 1d.
4. " Postzegei " (No. 21): 1d.
5. " aer " on right (No. 10): 1d.
6. " afb " on right (No. 6): 1d.
7. " bep " on left (No. 8): 1d.
8. " bep " on right: 1d.
9. " reb " on left (No. 7): 1d.
10. Floreate ornament in left corner inverted (Nos. 20 and 24): 1d.
11. Floreate ornament in right corner inverted (No. 14): 1d.
12. Wider figure in centre (No. 20): 2d.
13. Wider figure in centre, and no stop after " afr " on right (No. 19): 2d.
14. No stop after " afr " on left (Nos. 2 and 24): 2d.
15. No stop after " afr " on right: (Nos. 4 and 18): ½d. (No. 18): 2d. (Nos. 18 and 19): 1d.
16. No stop after " rep " on left (No. 7): 2d.
17. No stop after " z " on left (No. 16): 1d.
18. No stop after " 1901 " (No. 11): 1d., 2d.
19. No bar under figure in left upper corner (No. 3): 1d.
20. No bar under figure in right upper corner (No. 22): 1d.
21. No bar over figure in left lower corner (No. 15): 1d.

22. No bar over figure in right lower corner (No. 4): 1d.
23. Figure in left lower corner inverted (No. 2): 1d.
24. No stop after "PENNY": 1d.
25. "AFR-REP" on right (No. 24): ½d.
26. Figures in centre level (No. 17): ½d.
27. "4" in right lower corner (No. 17): 2d.

Varieties in which either of the figures of the "½" in the corners is omitted are due to imperfect printing and not to the absence of type.

LOCAL ISSUES DURING THE WAR 1900–2.

Stamps of the Transvaal Republic, unless otherwise stated, variously overprinted or surcharged.

LYDENBURG.

1900 (SEPT.). *Surch.* "V.R.I. 1d.".

1	**34**	1d. red	£32	£28

V.R.I.
3d.
(L 1)

No. 217 surch. with Type L 1, *others optd. "V.R.I." as in Type* L 1.

2	**30**	½d. green	70 0	70 0
3	,,	1d. rose-red and green ..	60 0	60 0
4	,,	2d. brown and green ..	£20	£20
5	,,	2½d. blue and green ..	—	£16
6	,,	3d. on 1d. rose-red & green	50 0	60 0
7	,,	4d. sage-green and green ..	£35	
8	,,	6d. lilac and green ..	£30	£20
9	,,	1s. ochre and green ..	£70	

RUSTENBURG.

1900 (23 JUNE). *Handstamped* **V.R.** *in violet.*

1	**30**	½d. green	70 0	70 0
2	,,	1d. rose-red and green ..	55 0	55 0
3	,,	2d. brown and green ..	90 0	90 0
4	,,	2½d. blue and green	70 0	70 0
5	,,	3d. purple and green ..	90 0	90 0
6	,,	6d. lilac and green	£8	£8
7	,,	1s. ochre and green ..	£16	£12
8	,,	2s. 6d. dull violet & green ..	—	£125

SCHWEIZER RENECKE.

BESIEGED
(SR 1)

1900 (AUG.). *Handstamped with Type* SR **1** *in black, reading vert. up or down.*

(*a*) *On stamps of Transvaal.*

1	**30**	½d. green	†	75 0
2	,,	1d. rose-red and green ..	†	70 0
3	,,	2d. brown and green ..	†	£6
4	,,	6d. lilac and green	†	£18

(*b*) *On stamps of Cape of Good Hope.*

5	**17**	½d. green	†	£7
6	,,	1d. carmine	†	£8

This was a siege issue, authorised by the commander of the British troops in the town shortly after 19th August and exhausted by the end of September 1900. All stamps were cancelled with the dated circular town postmark ("Schweizer Reneke, Z.A.R."), usually after having been stuck on paper before use. Unused, without the postmark, do not exist.

VOLKSRUST.

1902 (MAR.). *Optd.* "V.R.I.", *T* **35**. *P* 12.

1	**33**	1d. pale blue	30 0	30 0
2	,,	6d. dull carmine	45 0	40 0
3	,,	1s. olive-bistre	45 0	50 0
4	,,	1s. 6d. brown	70 0	75 0
5	,,	2s. 6d. dull purple ..	70 0	75 0

These are the normal Transvaal Revenue stamps of the period, authorised for postal use in Volksrust.

WOLMARANSSTAD.

Cancelled V-R-I. (L 3) Cancelled V-R-I. (L 4)

1900 (JUNE). *Optd. with Type* L **3**.

1	**30**	½d. green (B.)	75 0	
		a. Opt. inverted		
2	,,	1d. rose-red and green (B.)	65 0	65 0
3	,,	2d. brown and green (B.)	—	£20
4	,,	2½d. blue and green (R.) ..	£16	
		a. Opt. in blue		
5	,,	3d. purple and green (B.)	£28	
6	,,	4d. sage-green & green (B.)	£45	
7	,,	6d. lilac and green (B.) ..	£45	
8	,,	1s. ochre and green (B.) ..		

1900 (JULY). *Optd. with Type* L **4**.

9	**34**	1d. red (B.)	80 0	80 0

TRINIDAD.

—SIMPLIFICATION (see INTRODUCTION) **—**

Nos. 1 to 85.

2, 3, 5, 8, 9, 10, 11, 12.
13, 15, 17, 19, 20.
25, 28, 29 : 39, 40, 42, 44.
52, 55, 57, 58.
60, 64, 61, 62, 65, 63, 67.
69, 70, 71, 72, 73, 74, 80, 81, 84, 85.

1

1847 (24 APR.). *T* **1**. *Litho. Imperf.*

1	(5 c.) blue	£1200	£850

The "LADY MCLEOD" stamps were issued in April, 1847, by David Bryce, owner of the s.s. *Lady McLeod*, and sold at five cents each for the prepayment of the carriage of letters by his vessel between Port of Spain and San Fernando.

2. Britannia. 3.

(Recess. Perkins, Bacon & Co.)

1851 (14 AUG.)–**1856**. *No value expresse*
Imperf. Blued paper.

2	**2**	(1d.) purple-brown (1851) ..	27 6	
3	,,	(1d.) blue *to* deep blue (1851)	27 6	
4	,,	(1d.) deep blue (1853)* ..	£20	£
5	,,	(1d.) grey (1851)	£5	
6	,,	(1d.) brownish grey (1853)	85 0	
7	,,	(1d.) brownish red (1853) ..	£45	
8	,,	(1d.) brick-red (1856) ..	£16	

*No. 4 shows the paper deeply and even blued, especially on the back. It has more t appearance of having been printed on blue pap rather than on white paper that has becor blued.

1854–57. *Imperf. White paper.*

No.	Type	Description	Unused	Used
9	**2**	(1d.) deep purple (1854) ..	35 0	£7
10	,,	(1d.) dark grey (1854) ..	55 0	£9
11	,,	(1d.) blue (? date) ..		
12	,,	(1d.) rose-red (1857) ..	£80	£8

NOTE. Prices quoted for the unused of most of the above issues and Nos. 25 and 29 are for "remainders" with original gum, found in London. Old colours that have been out to Trinidad are of much greater value.

1852–60. THE LITHOGRAPHS.

The following provisional issues were lithographed in the Colony (from die engraved by Charles Petit), and brought into use to meet shortages of the Perkins Bacon stamps during the following periods:

(1) *Sept.* '52–*May* '53; (2) *March* '55–*June* '55; (3) *Dec.* '56–*Jan.* '57; (4) *Oct.* '58–*Jan.* '59; (5) *March* '60–*June* '60.

No value expressed. Imperf.

A. *First Issue* (Sept. **1852**). *Yellowish paper. Fine impression; lines of background clear and distinct.*

No.	Type	Description	Unused	Used
13	**3**	(1d.) blue	—	£190

As last, but on bluish cartridge paper (Feb. **1853**).

No.	Type	Description	Unused	Used
14	**3**	(1d.) blue	—	£225

B. *Second issue* (March **1855**). *Thinner paper. Impression less distinct than before.*

No.	Type	Description	Unused	Used
15	**3**	(1d.) pale blue *to* greenish blue	—	£90

C. *Third Issue* (December **1856**). *Background often of solid colour, but with clear lines in places.*

No.	Type	Description	Unused	Used
16	**3**	(1d.) brt. blue *to* deep blue ..	—	£95

D. *Fourth issue* (October **1858**). *Impression less distinct, and rarely showing more than traces of background lines.*

No.	Type	Description	Unused	Used
17	**3**	(1d.) very deep greenish blue	—	£60
18	,,	(1d.) slate-blue	—	£60

E. *Fifth issue* (March **1860**). *Impression shows no (or hardly any) background lines.*

No.	Type	Description	Unused	Used
19	**3**	(1d.) grey *to* bluish grey ..	—	£42
20	,,	(1d.) red (*shades*)	90 0	£65

In the worn impressions of the fourth and fifth issues, the impression varies according to the position on the stone. Generally speaking, stamps of the fifth issue have a flatter appearance and cancellations are often less well defined. The paper of both these issues is thin or very thin. In all issues except 1853 (Feb.) the gum tends to give the paper a toned appearance.

Stamps in the slate-blue shade (No. 18) also occur in the Fifth Issue, but are not readily distinguishable.

4. Britannia.

(Recess. Perkins, Bacon & Co.)

1859 (9 May). *Imperf.*

No.	Type	Description	Unused	Used
25	**4**	4d. grey-lilac	£10	£35
26	,,	4d. dull purple	—	£200
28	,,	6d. deep green	—	£50
29	,,	1s. indigo	£12	£35

1859 (Sept.). (*a*) *Pin perf.* 12½.

No.	Type	Description	Unused	Used
31	**2**	(1d.) rose-red	£42	£6
32	,,	(1d.) carmine-lake	£42	£6
33	**4**	4d. dull lilac	—	£48
34	,,	4d. dull purple	—	£48
35	,,	6d. yellow-green	£185	£22
36	,,	6d. deep green	£185	£20
37	,,	1s. purple-slate	£250	£95

(*b*) *Pin-perf.* 13½–14.

No.	Type	Description	Unused	Used
38	**2**	(1d.) rose-red	£14	75 0
39	,,	(1d.) carmine-lake	£22	60 0
40	**4**	4d. dull lilac	£79	£12
40*a*	,,	4d. brownish purple	£10	£17
41	,,	4d. dull purple	£28	£17
42	,,	6d. yellow-green	£40	£12
43	,,	6d. deep green	£38	£9
43*a*	,,	6d. bright yellow-green ..	£12	£15
		b. Imperf. between (vert. pair)	£185	
44	,,	1s. purple-slate	—	£44

(*c*) *Compound pin-perf.* 13½–14 × 12½.

No.	Type	Description	Unused	Used
45	**2**	(1d.) carmine-lake		

NOTE. The Pin-perf. stamps are very scarce with perforations on all sides and the prices quoted above are for good average specimens.

PRICES. The note after No. 12 also applies to Nos. 38, 40*a*, 43*a*, 46, 47 and 50.

1860 (Aug.). *Clean-cut perf.* 14–16½.

No.	Type	Description	Unused	Used
46	**2**	(1d.) rose-red	£12	90 0
		a. Imperf. between (horiz. pair)	£50	
47	**4**	4d. brownish lilac	£16	£9
48	,,	4d. lilac	—	£25
49	,,	6d. bright yellow-green ..	£20	£14
50	,,	6d. deep green	£25	£18

Intermediate perf. between the clean-cut and the rough.

No.	Type	Description	Unused	Used
51	**4**	1s. indigo	—	£100

1861 (June). *Rough perf.* 14–16½.

No.	Type	Description	Unused	Used
52	**2**	(1d.) rose-red	£10	50 0
53	,,	(1d.) rose	£10	50 0
54	**4**	4d. brownish lilac	£22	90 0
55	,,	4d. lilac	£40	80 0
		a. Imperf.		
56	,,	6d. yellow-green	£24	£8
57	,,	6d. deep green	£38	£6
58	,,	1s. indigo	£75	£25
59	,,	1s. deep bluish purple ..	£110	£30

(Recess. De La Rue & Co.)

1862–63. *Thick paper.* (*a*) *P* 11½, 12.

No.	Type	Description	Unused	Used
60	**2**	(1d.) crimson-lake	£7	45 0
61	**4**	4d. deep purple	£7	85 0
62	,,	6d. deep green	£55	90 0
63	,,	1s. bluish slate	£65	£14

(*b*) *P* 11½, 12, *compound with* 11.

No.	Type	Description	Unused	Used
63*a*	**2**	(1d.) crimson-lake	—	£28
63*b*	**4**	6d. deep green	—	£400

(*c*) *P* 13 (1863).

No.	Type	Description	Unused	Used
64	**2**	(1d.) lake	65 0	40 0
65	**4**	6d. emerald-green	£30	90 0
67	,,	1s. bright mauve	£275	£25

(*d*) *P* 12½ (1863).

No.	Type	Description	Unused	Used
68	**2**	(1d.) lake	50 0	55 0

1863–75. *Wmk. Crown CC. P* 12½.

No.	Type	Description	Unused	Used
69	**2**	(1d.) lake	65 0	22 6
		a. Wmk. sideways	97 6	45 0
70	,,	(1d.) rose	50 0	10 6
		a. Imperf. (pair) ..		
71	,,	(1d.) scarlet	45 0	8 6
72	,,	(1d.) carmine	60 0	10 0
73	**4**	4d. bright violet	£8	35 0
74	,,	4d. pale mauve	£16	45 0
75	,,	4d. dull lilac	70 0	35 0
77	,,	6d. emerald green	£5	50 0
78	,,	6d. deep green	£30	47 6
80	,,	6d. yellow-green	£5	20 0
81	,,	6d. apple-green	65 0	30 0
82	,,	6d. blue-green	£6	20 0
83	,,	1s. bright deep mauve ..	£20	35 0
84	,,	1s. lilac-rose	£14	25 0
85	,,	1s. mauve (aniline) ..	£10	35 0

The 1s. in a purple-slate shade is a colour changeling.

5

(Typo. De La Rue & Co.)

1869. *Wmk. Crown CC. P 12½.*
87 **5** 5s. rose-lake 90 0 65 0

1872. *Colours changed. Wmk. Crown CC. P 12½.*
88 **4** 4d. grey 90 0 15 0
89 ,, 4d. bluish grey 85 0 20 0
90 ,, 1s. chrome-yellow £8 12 6

1876. *Wmk. Crown CC. P 14.*
91 **2** (1d.) lake 12 6 4 0
a. Bisected (½d.) (on cover) .. † £15
92 ,, (1d.) rose-carmine 15 0 6 6
93 ,, (1d.) scarlet 55 0 6 6
94 **4** 4d. bluish grey 75 0 12 6
95 ,, 6d. bright yellow-green .. 65 0 10 6
96 ,, 6d. deep yellow-green .. 75 0 7 6
97 ,, 1s. chrome-yellow .. £5 20 0

P 14 × 12½.
97*a* **4** 6d. yellow-green .. .. — £425

HALFPENNY (6) **ONE PENNY** (7)

1879–82. *Surch. with T 6 or 7 in black. P 14.*
(*a*) *Wmk. Crown CC.* (*June* 1879.)
98 **2** ½d. lilac 17 6 17 6
99 ,, ½d. mauve 25 0 25 0
a. Wmk. sideways 55 0 55 0
(*b*) *Wmk. Crown CA.* (1882.)
100 **2** ½d. lilac £75 £7
101 ,, 1d. rosy carmine .. 40 0 4 6
a. Bisected (½d.) (on cover) .. † £8

1882. *Wmk. Crown CA. P 14.*
102 **4** 4d. bluish grey £7 25 0

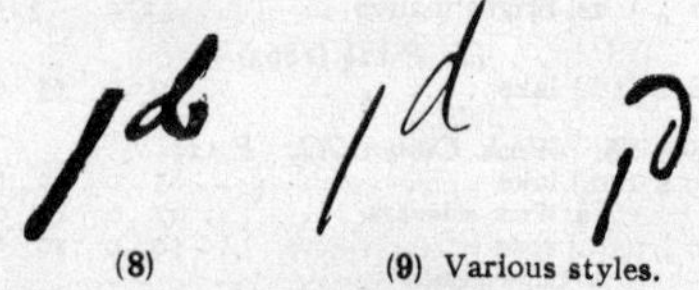

(**8**) (**9**) Various styles.

1882 (9 May). *Surcharged by hand in red or black ink and the original value obliterated by a thick or thin bar or bars, of the same colour.*
103 **8** 1d. in *black*, on 6d. (No. 95) — £110
104 **9** 1d. in *red*, on 6d. (No. 95) .. 20 0 15 0
105 ,, 1d. in *red*, on 6d. (No. 96) .. 20 0 15 0
a. Bisected (½d.) (on cover) .. † £12

10

(Typo. De La Rue & Co.)

1883–4. *Wmk. Crown CA. P 14.*
106 **10** ½d. dull green 1 0 0 4
107 ,, 1d. carmine 2 0 0 4
a. Bisected (½d.) (on cover) .. † £12
108 ,, 2½d. bright blue .. 6 0 1 0
110 ,, 4d. grey 5 0 2 6
111 ,, 6d. olive-black (1884) .. 7 6 12 6
112 ,, 1s. orange-brown (1884) 15 0 12 6

1894. *Colour changed. Wmk. Crown CC. P 14.*
113 **5** 5s. marone 30 0 50 0

11. Britannia. **12.** Britannia.

ONE PENNY (I) (round "o") **ONE PENNY** (II) (oval "o")

(Typo. De La Rue & Co.)

1896 (17 Aug.)–**1900.** *P 14.* (*a*) *Wmk. Crown CA.*
114 **11** ½d. dull purple & green .. 0 6 0 3
115 ,, 1d. dull purple & rose (I) 0 8 0 3
116 ,, 1d. dull purple & rose (II) (1900) £7 5 0
117 ,, 2½d. dull purple & blue .. 3 0 1 9
118 ,, 4d. dull purple & orange 7 6 12 6
119 ,, 5d. dull purple & mauve 10 0 17 6
120 ,, 6d. dull purple & black .. 10 0 10 6
121 ,, 1s. green and brown . 17 6 25 0
(*b*) *Wmk. CA. over Crown.*
122 **12** 5s. green and brown, O .. 65 0 75 0
123 ,, 10s. green & ultramarine, O £22 £20
124 ,, £1 green & carmine, OC £20 £18

Collectors are warned against apparently postally used copies of this issue which bear "REGISTRAR-GENERAL" obliterations and are of very little value.

13. Landing of Columbus.

(Recess. De La Rue & Co.)

1898. *Discovery of Trinidad Commemoration Wmk. Crown CC. P 14.*
125 **13** 2d. brown and dull violet 7 6 5

1901–6. *T 11 and 12. Colours changed. Wmk Crown CA or CA over Crown (5s.). P 14.*
126 1d. black/*red*, O (II) .. 0 10 0
127 5s. lilac and mauve, O .. 70 0 70
128 5s. dp. pur. & mve., OC ('06) 70 0 70

Error. Value omitted.

129 (–) black/*red* £600

A pane of sixty stamps of this error was found in a post office in Trinidad but not more than nine copies are believed to have been sold, and the rest withdrawn.

1902–3. *Colours changed. Wmk. Crown CA. P* 14.

130 **11** ½d. grey-green, O .. 1 0 0 8
131 „ 2½d. purple & blue/*blue*, O 10 0 4 6
132 „ 4d. green & blue/*buff*, OC 5 0 10 0
133 „ 1s. blk.&blue/*yell*. O('03) 17 6 10 0

1904–5. *Wmk. Mult. Crown CA. P* 14.

134 **11** ½d. grey-green, OC .. 1 6 0 10
135 „ 1d. black/*red*, OC (II) .. 1 9 0 4
136 „ 2½d. purple & blue/*blue*, C 17 6 10 0
137 „ 6d. dull pur. & blk., C ('05) 15 0 12 6
138 „ 1s. blk. & blue/*yell*. C .. 22 6 25 0
139 „ 1s. purple & blue/*golden yellow*, C 20 0 25 0

1906–9. *Wmk. Mult. Crown CA. P* 14.

139*a* **11** ½d. blue-green, O .. 3 0 1 3
140 „ 1d. rose-red, O (1907) .. 2 0 0 4
141 „ 2½d. blue, O (1906) .. 4 0 1 9
142 „ 4d. grey & red/*yellow*, C 7 6 15 0
143 „ 4d. black & red/*yellow*, C 20 0 20 0
144 „ 6d. dull & brt. purple, C 15 0 15 0
145 „ 1s. black/*green*, C .. 8 0 12 6

No. 140 is from a new die, the letters of "ONE PENNY" being short and thick, while the point of Britannia's spear breaks the uppermost horizontal line of shading in the background.

1907. *Wmk. Mult. Crown CA. P* 14.

146 **12** 5s. deep pur. & mauve, C 75 0 85 0
147 „ £1 green & carmine, C .. £22 £20

14 15

16

(Typo. De La Rue & Co.)

1909. *Wmk. Mult. Crown CA. P* 14.

148 **14** ½d. green, O 0 8 0 6
149 **15** 1d. rose-red, O 0 8 0 4
150 **16** 2½d. blue, O 10 0 10 0

TRINIDAD AND TOBAGO.

17

(Typo. De La Rue & Co.)

1913–23. *T* **17.** *Wmk. Mult. Crown CA. P* 14.

151 ½d. green, O ('13) 0 4 0 4
152 ½d. yellow-green, O ('15) .. 0 6 0 6
153 ½d. blue-green, O ('17) .. 0 6 0 4
154 ½d. blue-green/*bluish*, O (3.18) 17 6 17 6
155 1d. bright red, O ('13) .. 1 6 1 0
156 1d. red on *thick paper*, O ('16) 1 0 0 4
157 1d. pink, O ('18) 15 0 2 0
158 1d. carmine-red, O (5.18) .. 1 0 0 4
159 2½d. ultramarine, O ('13) .. 4 0 1 6
160 2½d. bright blue on *thick paper* O ('16) 5 0 4 0
161 2½d. bright blue on *thin paper*, O ('18) 10 0 6 0
162 4d. blk. & red/*yellow*, OC ('13) 4 0 8 6
a. White back (12.13) 12 6 15 0
b. On lemon ('17) .. 35 0
c. On pale yellow ('23) 12 6 15 0
163 6d. dull purple and reddish purple, C ('13) 20 0 12 6
164 6d. dull purple & deep purple, C ('18) 10 0 12 6
165 6d. dull pur. & mve., C (2.18) 12 6 17 6
166 1s. black/*green*, O ('13) .. 10 0 17 6
a. White back 8 0 20 0
b. On blue-green, olive back .. 12 6 15 0
c. On emerald back 8 0 10 0

18

(Typo. De La Rue & Co.)

1914–18. *Wmk. Mult. Crown CA. P* 14.

167 **18** 5s. dull purple & mve., C 55 0 60 0
168 „ 5s. dp. pur. & mve., C ('18) 55 0 60 0
169 „ 5s. lilac and violet, C .. 65 0 70 0
170 „ 5s. dull purple & violet, C 80 0 90 0
171 „ 5s. brown-pur. & violet, C 70 0 80 0
172 „ £1 grey-grn. & carmine, C £16 £16
173 „ £1 deep yellow-green and carmine, C ('18) .. £16 £16

The last £1 stamp is from a plate showing the lines in background much worn away.

21. 10. 15.
(19)

19. 10. 16.

(19*a*)

1915 (21 Oct.). *T* **17** *optd. with T* **19.** *Cross in deep red with outline and date in black.*

174 1d. red 1 6 3 0
a. Cross 2 mm. to right .. 40 0 40 0
b. "1" of "15" forked foot .. 15 0 25 0
c. Broken "0" in "10" .. 20 0 25 0

The varieties occur in the following positions on the *pane* of 60: a. No. 11. b. No. 42. c. No. 45. Variety a. is only found on the right-hand pane.

1916 (19 Oct.). *T* **17** *optd. with T* **19a**. *Cross in scarlet with outline and date in black.*

175 1d. scarlet 1 0 1 3
a. No stop after "16".. .. 15 0 17 6
b. "19.10.16" omitted ..

No. 175*a* appears on stamp No. 36 on the right-hand pane only.

> Note. Numerous forgeries of the various "war tax" errors listed below and other unlisted errors which are purely fakes, are offered in Trinidad and tourists and collectors buying by post should be on their guard. Many of these fakes reached England.

1917 (2 Apr.). *T* **17** *optd.*

WAR TAX *one in line.*

176 1d. red 0 9 1 3
a. Inverted £18
b. Scarlet 1 0 1 0

WAR TAX (20) WAR TAX (21)

1917 (May). *T* **17** *optd. with T* **20**.

177 ½d. green 0 3 0 6
a. Without opt. in pair w. norm. £18
178 1d. red 0 6 0 8
a. Without opt. in pair w. norm. £18
b. Scarlet 1 0 0 6
ba. Opt. double £9

The varieties without overprint were caused by the latter being shifted over towards the left so that one stamp in the lowest row of each pane escaped.

1917 (21 June). *Optd. with T* **21**.

179 **17** ½d. yellow-green .. 1 6 2 0
a. Pale green .. 2 0 2 6
b. Deep green 1 3 1 3
180 „ 1d. red 0 10 0 10

Pairs are known of the 1d. stamps, one stamp without the overprint. This was caused by a shifting of the type to the left-hand side, but only a few stamps on the right hand vertical row escaped the overprint and such pairs are very rare.

WAR TAX (22) WAR TAX (23)

1917 (21 July). *Optd. with T* **22**.

181 **17** ½d. yellow-green 3 0 6 0
a. Deep green 0 6 0 6
182 „ 1d. red (Sept.) 0 4 0 6

1917 (1 Sept.). *Optd. with T* **23** (*closer spacing between lines of opt.*).

183 **17** ½d. deep green 0 3 0 8
a. Pale yellow-green .. ..
184 „ 1d. red 15 0 20 0

WAR TAX (24) WAR TAX (25) War Tax (26)

1917 (31 Oct.). *Optd. with T* **24**.

185 **17** 1d. scarlet 0 6 0 6
a. Inverted £7

1918 (7 Jan.). *Optd. with T* **25**.

186 **17** 1d. scarlet 0 6 0 6
a. Double £15
b. Inverted £7

1918 (13 Feb.). *Optd. with T* **26**.

187 **17** ½d. bluish green 0 3 0 4
a. Without opt. in pair with normal £35
188 **17** 1d. scarlet 0 6 0 6
a. Opt. double £9
b. Rose-red (1.5.18) 1 0 1 0

1918 (14 Sept.). *New printing as T* **26**, *but* 19 *stamps on each sheet have the letters of the word* "Tax" *wider spaced, the* "x" *being to the right of* "r" *of* "War" *instead of under it. Thick bluish paper.*

189 1d. scarlet ("Tax" spaced) 3 6 2 6
a. Overprint double £18

1921–22. *Wmk. Mult. Script CA. P* 14.

206 **17** ½d. green, O 0 8 0 6
207 „ 1d. scarlet, O 0 10 1 6
208 „ 2½d. bright blue, O .. 3 6 7 6
209 „ 6d. dull & brt. purple, C.. 7 6 12 6
210 **18** 5s. dull pur. & pur., C ('21) 85 0 90 0
211 „ 5s. dp. pur. & pur., C ('22) 85 0 90 0
212 „ £1 green and carmine, C.. £16 £18

1922. *Colour changed and new values.*

213 **17** 1d. brown, O 0 8 1 3
214 „ 2d. grey, O 6 0 7 6
215 „ 3d. bright blue, O .. 7 6 10 0

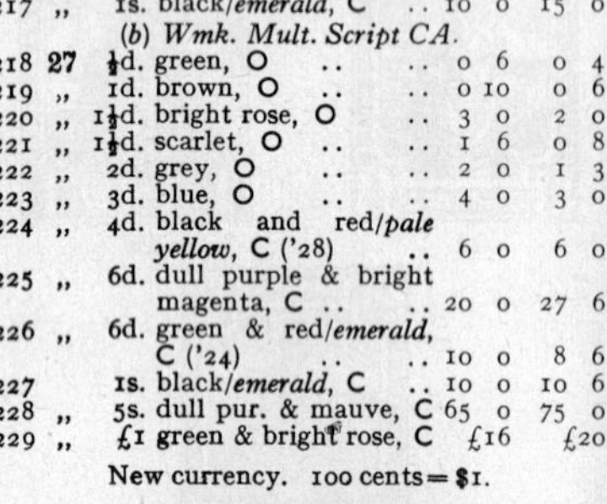

27

(Typo. De La Rue & Co.)

1922–8. *P* 14. (*a*) *Wmk. Crown Mult. CA.*

216 **27** 4d. black & red/*pale yell.*, C 3 6 5 0
217 „ 1s. black/*emerald*, C .. 10 0 15 0

(*b*) *Wmk. Mult. Script CA.*

218 **27** ½d. green, O 0 6 0 4
219 „ 1d. brown, O 0 10 0 6
220 „ 1½d. bright rose, O .. 3 0 2 0
221 „ 1½d. scarlet, O 1 6 0 8
222 „ 2d. grey, O 2 0 1 3
223 „ 3d. blue, O 4 0 3 0
224 „ 4d. black and red/*pale yellow*, C ('28) .. 6 0 6 0
225 „ 6d. dull purple & bright magenta, C 20 0 27 6
226 „ 6d. green & red/*emerald*, C ('24) 10 0 8 6
227 1s. black/*emerald*, C .. 10 0 10 6
228 „ 5s. dull pur. & mauve, C 65 0 75 0
229 „ £1 green & bright rose, C £16 £20

New currency. 100 cents = $1.

28. First Boca.

29. Imperial College of Tropical Agriculture

30. Mt. Irvine Bay, Tobago.

31. Discovery of Lake Asphalt.

32. Queen's Park, Savannah.

33. Town Hall, San Fernando.

34. Government House.

35. Memorial Park.

36. Blue Basin.

(Recess. Bradbury, Wilkinson & Co.)

1935 (1 Feb.)–**37.** *Wmk. Mult. Script CA. P* 12.

230	**28**	1 c. blue and green ..	2	0	0	3
		a. Perf. 12½ ('36)	0	6	0	3
231	**29**	2 c. ultram. & yellow-brn.	3	6	0	3
		a. Perf. 12½ ('36)	0	6	0	3
232	**30**	3 c. black and scarlet ..	0	9	0	3
		a. Perf. 12½ ('36)	1	0	0	3
233	**31**	6 c. sepia and blue ..	2	6	2	0
		a. Perf. 12½ ('37)	1	3	1	6
234	**32**	8 c. sage-green & verm.	3	0	3	0
235	**33**	12 c. black and violet ..	3	6	2	6
		a. Perf. 12½ ('37)	4	6	5	0
236	**34**	24 c. black and olive-green	8	6	5	0
		a. Perf. 12½ ('37)	8	6	12	6
237	**35**	48 c. deep green	22	6	27	6
238	**36**	72 c. myrtle-green & carm.	45	0	50	0

1935 (6 May). *Silver Jubilee. As Nos.* 91/4 *of Antigua but ptd. by B. W. & Co. P* 11 × 12.

239	2 c. ultramarine & grey-black	0	4	0	10
	a. Extra flagstaff	35	0		
240	3 c. deep blue and scarlet ..	1	0	1	6
	a. Extra flagstaff	75	0		
241	6 c. brown and deep blue ..	2	6	3	0
	a. Extra flagstaff	£8			
242	24 c. slate and purple ..	7	6	9	0
	a. Extra flagstaff	£6			

For illustration of "Extra flagstaff" variety see Bechuanaland.

1937 (12 May). *Coronation. As Nos.* 13/15 *of Aden. P* 14.

243	1 c. green	0	3	0	4
244	2 c. yellow-brown	0	6	0	6
245	8 c. orange	1	3	2	0

37. First Boca.

38. Imperial College of Tropical Agriculture.

39. Mt. Irvine Bay, Tobago.

40. Memorial Park.

41. G.P.O. and Treasury.

42. Discovery of Lake Asphalt.

43. Queen's Park, Savannah.

44. Town Hall, San Fernando.

45. Government House.

46. Blue Basin.

(Recess. Bradbury, Wilkinson & Co.)

1938 (2 May)–**1944.** *Wmk. Mult. Script CA sideways. P* 11½ × 11.

246	**37**	1 c. blue and green ..	0	3	0	3
247	**38**	2 c. blue & yellow-brn.	0	3	0	3
248	**39**	3 c. black and scarlet ..	20	0	2	6
248*a*	,,	3 c. grn. & pur.-brn. ('41)	0	6	0	3
249	**40**	4 c. chocolate	7	6	8	6
249*a*	,,	4 c. scarlet ('41) ..	1	0	0	9
249*b*	**41**	5 c. magenta (1.5.41) ..	0	8	0	3
250	**42**	6 c. sepia and blue ..	1	3	0	3
251	**43**	8 c. sage-green & verm.	1	3	1	0
252	**44**	12 c. black and purple ..	10	0	4	6
		a. Black and slate-pur. ('44)	2	0	0	10
253	**45**	24 c. black & olive-green	2	6	1	3
254	**46**	60 c. myrtle-grn. & carm.	8	6	3	6

47. King George VI.

(Recess. Bradbury, Wilkinson & Co.)

1940 (Jan.). *Wmk. Mult. Script CA. P* 12.

255	**47**	$1.20, blue-green	12	6	7	6
256	,,	$4.80, rose-carmine ..	45	0	30	0

1946 (1 Oct.). *Victory. As Nos.* 28/9 *of Aden.*

257	3 c. chocolate	0	4	0	4
258	6 c. blue	0	8	1	0

1948 (22 Nov.). *Silver Wedding. As Nos.* 30/1 *of Aden (recess* $4.80).

259	3 c. red-brown	0	6	0	6
260	$4.80, carmine	40	0	45	0

1949 (10 Oct.). *75th Anniv. of Universal Postal Union. As Nos.* 114/7 *of Antigua.*

261	5 c. bright reddish purple ..	0	6	0	6
262	6 c. deep blue	0	10	1	3
263	12 c. violet	1	9	2	0
264	24 c. olive	3	6	3	6

1951 (16 Feb.). *University College of B.W.I. As Nos.* 118/9 *of Antigua.*

265	3 c. green and red-brown ..	1	0	0	8
266	12 c. black & reddish violet ..	3	6	3	0

48. First Boca.

49. Mt. Irvine Bay, Tobago.

(Recess. Bradbury, Wilkinson & Co.)

1953 (20 APR.)–**55.** *As T* **37/47**, *but with portrait of Queen Elizabeth II in place of King George VI as in T* **48** (1 *c.*, 2 *c.*, 12 *c.*) *or* **49** (*other values*). *Wmk. Mult. Script CA. P* 12 (*dollar values*) *or* 11½ × 11 (*others*).

No.	Type	Description	s.	d.	s.	d.
267	**48**	1 c. blue & green (*shades*)	0	3	0	3
268	**38**	2 c. indigo & orge.-brown	0	4	0	3
269	**49**	3 c. dp. emer. & pur.-brn.	0	6	0	3
270	**40**	4 c. scarlet	0	6	0	6
271	**41**	5 c. magenta	0	7	0	4
272	**42**	6 c. brn. & greenish blue	1	0	0	8
273	**43**	8 c. deep yellow-green & orange-red	1	0	0	8
274	**44**	12 c. black and purple ..	1	3	0	10
275	**45**	24 c. black & yellow-olive (*shades*)	3	0	1	9
276	**46**	60 c. blackish green & carm.	7	6	3	6
277	**47**	$1.20 bluish green ..	15	0	12	6
		a. Perf 11½ (19.1.55) ..	10	6	7	6
278	,,	$4.80 cerise	90	0	70	0
		a. Perf. 11½ (16.11.55) ..	65	0	50	0

1953 (3 JUNE). *Coronation. As No.* 47 *of Aden.*

279	3 c. black and green.. ..	0	10	0	6

ONE CENT

(50)

1956 (20 DEC.) *No.* 268 *surch. with T* **50**.

280	1 c. on 2 c. ind. & orge.-brn.	15	0	15	0

1958 (22 APR.). *Inauguration of British Caribbean Federation. As Nos.* 135/7 *of Antigua.*

281	5 c. deep green	0	8	0	6
282	6 c. blue	0	10	1	0
283	12 c. scarlet	1	6	1	9

PRINTERS. From 1960 all stamps were printed in photogravure by Harrison & Sons *unless otherwise stated.*

51. Cipriani Memorial.

52. Queen's Hall.

53. Whitehall.

54. Treasury Building.

55. Governor-General's House.

56. General Hospital, San Fernando.

57. Oil Refinery.

58. Crest.

58a. Coat-of-Arms.

59. Scarlet Ibis.

60. Pitch Lake.

61. Mohammed Jinnah Mosque.

62. Anthurium Lilies.

63. Humming Bird.

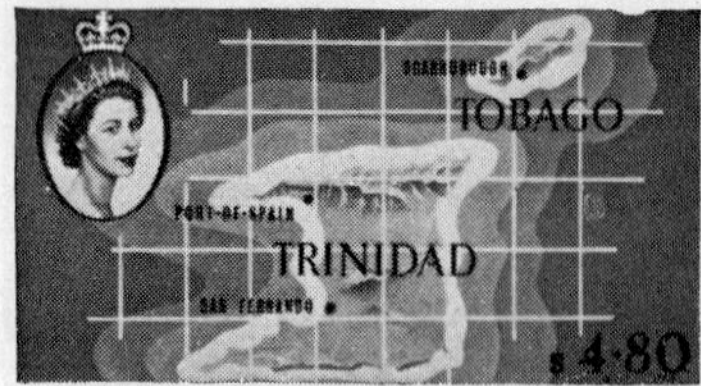

64. Map of Trinidad and Tobago.

(Des. V. Whiteley (1 c., 2 c., 12 c., 35 c., 60 c., $4.80), J. Matthews (5 c.), H. Baxter (6 c., 8 c., 10 c., 15 c.), M. Goaman (25 c., 50 c., $1.20).)

1960 (24 Sept.)–**64.** *W* w.**12.** *P* 13½ × 14½ (1 *c.*, 60 *c.*, $1.20, $4.80) *or* 14½ × 13½ (*others*).

No.	Type	Description				
284	**51**	1 c. stone and black ..	0	2	0	2
285	**52**	2 c. bright blue	0	3	0	2
286	**53**	5 c. chalky blue ..	0	5	0	3
287	**54**	6 c. red-brown	0	6	0	3
288	**55**	8 c. yellow-green	0	7	0	6
289	**56**	10 c. deep lilac	0	9	0	6
290	**57**	12 c. vermilion	0	10	0	6
291	**58**	15 c. orange	1	3	1	0
291a	**58a**	15 c. orange (15.9.64) ..	0	11	1	3
292	**59**	25 c. rose-carm. & dp. blue	1	6	1	0
293	**60**	35 c. emerald and black ..	2	0	1	6
294	**61**	50 c. yellow, grey & blue	2	10	1	9
295	**62**	60 c. vermilion, yellow-grn. and indigo	3	6	2	0
296	**63**	$1.20, multicoloured ..	6	9	8	6
297	**64**	$4.80, apple-grn. & pale blue	25	0	27	6

65. Scouts and Gold Wolf Badge.

1961 (4 Apr.). *Second Caribbean Scout Jamboree. Design multicoloured; background colours below. W* w. **12.** *P* 13½ × 14½.

No.	Type	Description				
298	**65**	8 c. light green	2	0	2	3
299	,,	25 c. light blue	4	0	4	6

INDEPENDENT

within the Commonwealth.

66. Underwater Scene after painting by Carlisle Chang.

67. Piarco Air Terminal.

68. Hilton Hotel, Port-of-Spain.

69. Bird of Paradise and Map.

70. Scarlet Ibis and Map.

1962 (31 Aug.). *Independence. W* w.**12.** *P* 14½.

No.	Type	Description				
300	**66**	5 c. bluish green ..	0	10	1	0
301	**67**	8 c. grey	1	9	1	3
302	**68**	25 c. reddish violet ..	3	6	3	6
303	**69**	35 c. brown, yellow, green and black ..	4	0	4	6
304	**70**	60 c. red, black and blue ..	6	9	7	0

71. " Protein Foods ".

(Des. M. Goaman.)

1963 (4 June). *Freedom from Hunger. W.* w.**12** *P* 14 × 13½.

No.	Type	Description				
305	**71**	5 c. brown-red	0	10	1	
306	,,	8 c. yellow-bistre ..	1	3	1	
307	,,	25 c. violet-blue	2	6	1	

72. Jubilee Emblem.

1964 (15 Sept.). *Golden Jubilee of Trinidad and Tobago Girl Guides' Association.* *W* w.**12**. *P* 14½ × 14.

308 **72** 6 c. yellow, ultramarine and rose-red .. 0 10 1 0
309 ,, 25 c. yellow, ultramarine and bright blue .. 2 3 2 9
310 ,, 35 c. yellow, ultramarine and emerald-green .. 3 6 4 0

73. I.C.Y. Emblem.

(Litho. State Ptg. Wks., Vienna.)

1965 (15 Nov.). *International Co-operation Year.* *P* 12.

311 **73** 35 c. red-brown, deep green and ochre-yellow .. 2 3 2 6

74. Eleanor Roosevelt, Flag and U.N. Emblem.

1965 (10 Dec.). *Eleanor Roosevelt Memorial Foundation.* *W* w.12. *P* 13½ × 14.

312 **74** 25 c. black, red & ultram. 1 6 2 0

75. Parliament Building.

76. Map, H.M. Yacht *Britannia* and Arms.

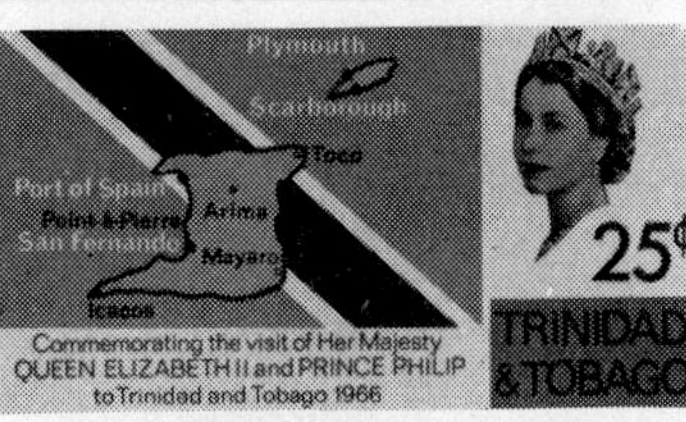

77. Map and Flag.

78. Flag and Panorama.

1966 (8 Feb.). *Royal Visit.* *W* w.**12**. *P* 13½ × 14½.

313 **75** 5 c. black, red, grn. & bl. 0 5 0 8
314 **76** 8 c. black, silver, blue & ochre 0 7 0 9
315 **77** 25 c. black, red, bright grn. and light yellow-green 1 6 2 0
316 **78** 35 c. black, red, green and light blue 2 0 2 6

POSTAGE DUE STAMPS.

TRINIDAD.

D 1

(Typo. De La Rue & Co.)

1885 (1 Jan.). *Wmk. Crown CA.* *P* 14.

D1	**D 1**	½d. slate-black	20	0	4	0
D2	,,	1d. slate-black	1	6	0	6
D3	,,	2d. slate-black	12	6	1	0
D4	,,	3d. slate-black	15	0	2	6
D5	,,	4d. slate-black	25	0	7	6
D6	,,	5d. slate-black	30	0	3	0
D7	,,	6d. slate-black	30	0	8	6
D8	,,	8d. slate-black	35	0	7	6
D9	,,	1s. slate-black	40	0	15	0

1905–6. *Wmk. Mult. Crown CA.* *P* 14.

D10	**D 1**	1d. slate-black	1	0	0	6
D11	,,	2d. slate-black	1	6	0	10
D12	,,	3d. slate-black	2	0	1	3
D13	,,	4d. slate-black	3	6	3	0
D14	,,	5d. slate-black	6	0	5	0
D15	,,	6d. slate-black	8	0	7	6
D16	,,	8d. slate-black	10	0	7	6
D17	,,	1s. slate-black	15	0	10	0

TRINIDAD AND TOBAGO.

1923–45. *Wmk. Mult. Script CA. P* 14.

D18	**D 1**	1d. black ('23)	1 6	2 0
D19	,,	2d. black ('23)	1 6	2 0
D20	,,	3d. black ('25)	2 6	3 0
D21	,,	4d. black ('29)	4 0	6 6
D22	,,	5d. black ('44)	7 6	10 0
D23	,,	6d. black ('45)	12 6	15 0
D24	,,	8d. black ('45)	12 6	20 0
D25	,,	1s. black ('45)	30 0	30 0

1947 (1 Sept.)–**61.** *Value in cents. Wmk. Mult. Script CA. P* 14.

D26	**D 1**	2 c. black, O	0 6	0 6
		aa. Chalky paper (20.1.53)	0 3	0 3
		a. Error. Crown missing. W9a, C	£20	
		b. Error. St. Edward's Crown. W9b, C	£10	
D27	,,	4 c. black, O	0 8	0 6
		a. Chalky paper (10.8.55)	0 4	0 5
D28	,,	6 c. black, O	1 0	1 0
		aa. Chalky paper (20.1.53)	0 6	0 8
		a. Error. Crown missing. W9a, C	£20	
		b. Error. St. Edward's Crown. W9b, C	£12	
D29	,,	8 c. black, O	1 6	2 0
		a. Chalky paper (10.9.58)	0 7	0 9
D30	,,	10 c. black, O	2 6	3 6
		a. Chalky paper (10.8.55)	0 9	0 10
D31	,,	12 c. black, O	2 6	3 6
		aa. Chalky paper (20.1.53)	0 10	1 0
		a. Error. Crown missing. W9a, C	£20	
		b. Error. St. Edward's Crown. W9b, C	£18	
D32	,,	16 c. black, O	3 6	5 0
		a. Chalky paper (22.8.61)	1 0	1 3
D33	,,	24 c. black, O	4 6	2 6
		a. Chalky paper (10.8.55)	1 5	1 7

"TOO LATE" STAMPS.

A handstamp with the words "TOO LATE" was used upon letters on which a too-late fee had been paid, and was sometimes used for cancelling the stamps on such letters.

OFFICIAL STAMPS.

TRINIDAD.

O S

(**S 1**)

1894. *Optd. with Type* S **1.** *Wmk. Crown CA. P* 14.

S1	**10**	½d. dull green	40 0	40 0
S2	,,	1d. carmine	40 0	40 0
S3	,,	2½d. ultramarine	50 0	50 0
S4	,,	4d. grey	65 0	60 0
S5	,,	6d. olive-black	80 0	80 0
S6	,,	1s. orange-brown	£5	£5
		Wmk. Crown CC. P 12½.		
S7	**5**	5s. rose-lake	£12	£14

OFFICIAL

(S **2**)

1909. *Optd. with Type* S **2.** *Wmk. Mult. Crown CA. P* 14.

S8	**11**	½d. green, O	1 6	2 0
S9	,,	1d. rose-red, O	0 6	0 6
		a. Double overprint	—	£16
		b. Vertical	75 0	
		c. Inverted	—	£15

1910. *Optd. with Type* S **2.** *Wmk. Mult. Crown CA. P* 14.

S10	**14**	½d. green, O	0 3	0 4

TRINIDAD AND TOBAGO.

OFFICIAL (S **3**) **OFFICIAL** (S **4**)

Nos. 151/3 *optd.*

1913. *Optd. with Type* S **3.**

S11	**17**	½d. green, O	0 8	1 0
		a. Overprint vertical		

1914. *Optd. with Type* S **4.**

S12	**17**	½d. green, O	1 6	2 6

OFFICIAL (S **5**) **OFFICIAL** S **6**)

1914–17. *Optd. with Type* S **5** (*without stop*).

S13	**17**	½d. green	1 6	1 6
S14	,,	½d. blue-green/*thick paper* ('17)	1 6	2 0

1916–17. *Optd. with Type* S **5** (*with stop*).

S15	**17**	½d. yellow-green, O	0 10	1 0
		a. Overprint double	30 0	

1917 (22 Aug.). *Optd. with Type* S **6.**

S16	**17**	½d. green/*thin paper*	0 9	1 0
S17	,,	½d. yellow-grn./*thin paper*	1 6	2 6
S18	,,	½d. blue-green/*thick paper*	0 6	0 6

TRISTAN DA CUNHA.

TRISTAN DA CUNHA

(1)

1952 (1 Jan.). *Stamps of St. Helena, optd. with T* **1.**

1	**31**	½d. violet	1 6	2 6
2	,,	1d. black and green	2 6	3 6
3	,,	1½d. black and carmine	3 0	5 0
4	,,	2d. black and scarlet	4 0	6 0
5	,,	3d. grey	5 0	7 6
6	,,	4d. ultramarine	6 0	8 6
7	,,	6d. light blue	7 6	10 6
8	,,	8d. sage-green	10 0	15 0
9	,,	1s. sepia	11 6	20 0
10	,,	2s. 6d. marone	60 0	75 0
11	,,	5s. chocolate	£6	£7
12	,,	10s. purple	£14	£16

1953 (2 June). *Coronation. As No.* 47 *of Aden.*

13	3d. black and grey-green	7 6	10 0

2. Tristan Crawfish.

3. Carting Flax for Thatching.

5. Big Beach Factory.

4. Rockhopper Penguin.

6. Mollymauk (sea-birds).

8. Tristan from the South-West.

7. Island Boat.

9. Girls on Donkeys.

10. Inaccessible Island from Tristan.

11. Nightingale Island.

12. St. Mary's Church.

13. Elephant Seal at Gough Is.

5/-

FLIGHTLESS RAIL INACCESSIBLE ISLAND

TRISTAN DA CUNHA

14. Flightless Rail.

15. Island Spinning Wheel.

(Recess. De La Rue & Co.)

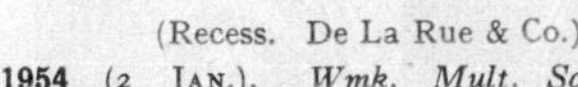

1954 (2 Jan.). *Wmk. Mult. Script CA. P* 12½ × 13 (*horiz.*) *or* 13 × 12½ (*vert.*).

14	**2**	½d. red and deep brown ..	2	6	2	0
15	**3**	1d. sepia and bluish green	3	6	3	3
16	**4**	1½d. black & reddish purple	4	0	4	0
17	**5**	2d. grey-violet & brn.-orge.	5	0	4	6
18	**6**	2½d. black & carmine-red ..	4	0	5	0
19	**7**	3d. ultram. & olive-green	4	6	5	6
20	**8**	4d. turq.-blue & deep blue	4	6	5	6
21	**9**	5d. emerald and black ..	5	0	6	0
22	**10**	6d. deep green and violet ..	5	0	6	0
23	**11**	9d. reddish violet and Venetian red	10	0	12	6
24	**12**	1s. dp. yell.-green & sepia	10	0	12	6
25	**13**	2s. 6d. dp. brn. & lt. blue	22	6	27	6
26	**14**	5s. black and red-orange ..	40	0	50	0
27	**15**	10s. brown-orange & purple	75	0	90	0

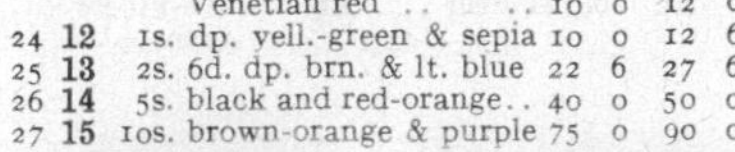

16. Starfish.

17. Concha Fish.

18. Klip Fish.

19. Heron Fish.

20. Swordfish.

21. Tristan Crawfish.

22. Soldier Fish.

23. " Five Finger " Fish.

24. Mackerel.

25. Stumpnose Fish.

26. Blue Fish.

27. Snoek.

28. Shark.

29. Atlantic Right Whale.

(Des. Mr. and Mrs. G. F. Harris. Recess. Waterlow.)

1960 (1 Feb.). *W* w. **12.** *P* 13.

No.	Type	Description				
28	**16**	½d. black & orange ..	2	0	2	9
29	**17**	1d. black & brt. purple ..	3	3	4	6
30	**18**	1½d. black & lt. turq.-blue	4	0	5	6
31	**19**	2d. black & bluish green ..	4	6	6	0
32	**20**	2½d. black and sepia ..	5	0	6	6
33	**21**	3d. black & brown-red ..	5	6	7	6
34	**22**	4d. black & yellow-olive ..	5	6	7	6
35	**23**	5d. blk. & orange-yellow ..	6	0	8	0
36	**24**	6d. black and blue ..	6	0	8	0
37	**25**	9d. black & rose-carm. ..	12	6	17	6
38	**26**	1s. black & lt. brown ..	12	6	17	6
39	**27**	2s. 6d. black & ultram. ..	27	6	40	0
40	**28**	5s. black & lt. emerald ..	50	0	70	0
41	**29**	10s. black and violet ..	95	0	130	0

1961 (15 Apr.). *As T* **16/29** *but values in South African decimal currency.*

No.	Type	Description				
42	**16**	½ c. black and orange ..	0	10	2	0
43	**17**	1 c. black and brt. purple	1	0	2	6
44	**18**	1½ c. black & lt. turq.-blue	1	3	3	6
45	**20**	2 c. black and sepia ..	1	6	3	6
46	**21**	2½ c. black and brown-red	2	0	4	6
47	**22**	3 c. black & yellow-olive..	2	6	5	0
48	**23**	4 c. black & orange-yellow	3	0	6	6
49	**24**	5 c. black and blue ..	3	6	8	6
50	**25**	7½ c. black & rose-carmine	4	6	12	6
51	**26**	10 c. black and lt. brown ..	6	0	17	6
52	**27**	25 c. black & ultramarine..	17	6	40	0
53	**28**	50 c. black and lt. emerald	35	0	80	0
54	**29**	1 r. black and violet ..	75	0	150	0

Following a volcanic eruption the island was evacuated on October 10th, 1961, but resettled in 1963.

TRISTAN DA CUNHA
RESETTLEMENT
1963
(30)

1963 (12 Apr.). *Tristan Resettlement. Stamps of St. Helena (types as shown but Wmk. Mult. Script CA), optd. with T* **30.**

No.	Type	Description				
55	**50**	1d. bright blue, dull violet, yellow and carmine ..	0	6	0	8

56	**51**	1½d. yellow, green, black and light drab	0 6	0 8
57	**52**	2d. scarlet and grey	0 8	0 9
58	**53**	3d. light blue, black, pink and deep blue	0 8	1 0
59	**54**	4½d. yellow-green, green, brown and grey	0 10	1 3
60	**55**	6d. red, sep. & lt. yell.-ol.	1 0	1 6
61	**56**	7d. red-brn., blk. & violet	1 3	1 9
62	**57**	10d. brown-purple & lt. blue	1 9	2 6
63	**58**	1s. greenish yellow, bluish green and brown ..	2 0	3 0
64	**59**	1s. 6d. grey, blk. & sl.-blue	3 0	4 6
65	**60**	2s. 6d. red, pl. yell. & turq.	5 0	7 6
66	**61**	5s. yellow, brown & green	8 6	12 6
67	**62**	10s. orge.-red, black & blue	17 6	25 0

1963 (1 Oct.). *Freedom from Hunger. As No. 63 of Aden.*

68 1s. 6d. carmine 3 6 4 6

1964 (1 Feb.). *Red Cross Centenary. As Nos. 147/8 of Antigua.*

69 3d. red and black 1 0 1 3
70 1s. 6d. red and blue 3 6 4 6

31. South Atlantic Map.

32. Flagship of Tristão da Cunha.

33. *Heemstede.*

34. New England Whaler.

35. *Shenandoah.*

36. H.M.S. *Galatea.*

37. H.M.S. *Cilicia.*

38. H.M. Yacht *Britannia.*

39. H.M.S. *Leopard.*

40. M.V. *Tjisadane.*

41. M.V. *Tristania.*

42. M.V. *Boissevain.*

43. M.S. *Bornholm.*

44. Queen Elizabeth II.

(Queen's portrait by Anthony Buckley. Des. and eng. Bradbury, Wilkinson. Recess.)

1965 (17 Feb.). *W* w.**12**. *P* 11½×11 (10s.), *or* 11×11½ ((*others*).

No.	Type	Description	Unused	Used
71	**31**	½d. black and ultramarine	0 2	0 3
72	**32**	1d. black & emerald-green	0 3	0 4
73	**33**	1½d. black and blue ..	0 4	0 4
74	**34**	2d. black and purple ..	0 4	0 5
75	**35**	3d. black and turq.-blue..	0 6	0 7
76	**36**	4½d. black and brown ..	0 8	0 9
77	**37**	6d. black and green ..	0 10	1 0
78	**38**	7d. black and rose-red ..	0 11	1 3
79	**39**	10d. black and chocolate ..	1 3	1 6
80	**40**	1s. black and carmine ..	1 5	2 0
81	**41**	1s. 6d. black & yell.-olive	2 0	3 0
82	**42**	2s. 6d. blk. & orge.-brown	3 6	4 0
83	**43**	5s. black and violet ..	6 9	7 6
84	**44**	10s. deep blue and carmine	13 3	15 0

1965 (11 May). *I.T.U. Centenary. As Nos.* 166/7 *of Antigua.*

No.	Description	Unused	Used
85	3d. orange-red and grey ..	0 7	0 11
86	6d. reddish violet and yellow-orange	1 0	1 6

1965 (25 Oct.). *International Co-operation Year. As Nos.* 168/9 *of Antigua.*

No.	Description	Unused	Used
87	1d. reddish pur. & turq.-grn.	0 4	0 6
88	6d. deep bluish green & lav...	1 0	1 6

1966 (24 Jan.). *Churchill Commemoration. As Nos.* 170/3 *of Antigua.*

No.	Description	Unused	Used
89	1d. new blue	0 4	0 6
90	3d. deep green..	0 7	0 11
91	6d. brown	1 0	1 6
92	1s. 6d. bluish violet	2 6	3 6

POSTAGE DUE STAMPS

D 1

(Typo. De La Rue & Co.

1957 (1 Feb.). *Chalk-surfaced paper. Wmk. Mult. Script C A P* 14.

No.	Type	Description	Unused	Used
D1	**D 1**	1d. scarlet..	6 6	10 0
D2	,,	2d. orange-yellow ..	2 6	17 6
D3	,,	3d. green	3 6	20 0
D4	,,	4d. ultramarine	5 0	20 0
D5	,,	5d. lake	6 0	27 6

TRUCIAL STATES.

Seven Arab Shaikdoms on the Persian Gulf and Gulf of Oman, in treaty relations with Great Britain.

The following stamps were used at the British Postal Agency at Dubai until it closed on 14th June, 1963.

1. Palms.

2. Dhow.

(Des. M. Goaman. Photo. Harrison (T **1**). Des. M. C. Farrar-Bell. Recess. De La Rue (T **2**).)

1961 (7 Jan.). *P* 15×14 (*T* **1**) *or* 13×12½ (*T* **2**).

No.	Type	Description	Unused	Used
1	**1**	5 n.p. green	0 6	0 6
2	,,	15 n.p. red-brown	0 9	0 9
3	,,	20 n.p. bright blue	1 0	1 0
4	,,	30 n.p. orange-red	1 3	1 3
5	,,	40 n.p. reddish violet ..	1 6	1 6
6	,,	50 n.p. bistre..	2 0	1 9
7	,,	75 n.p. grey	3 0	2 9
8	**2**	1 r. green..	3 6	3 0
9	,,	2 r. black..	7 0	7 0
10	,,	5 r. carmine-red	15 0	15 0
11	,,	10 r. deep ultramarine ..	30 0	27 6

TURKS ISLANDS.

1

(Recess. Perkins, Bacon & Co.)

1867 (4 APRIL). *No wmk.* *P* 11–12.

1 **1** 1d. dull rose 70 0 70 0
2 ,, 6d. black £6 £6
3 ,, 1s. dull blue £6 £6

1873–79. *Wmk. Small Star. Type* w. **2.** *P* 11–12 × 14½–15½.

4 **1** 1d. dull rose-lake (July, '73) .. 55 0 55 0
5 ,, 1d. dull red (Jan., 1879) .. 70 0 75 0
a. Imperf. between (pair) .. £275
b. Perf. 11-12 .. .. .. £140
6 ,, 1s. lilac £275 £150

1881 (1 JAN.). *Stamps of the preceding issues surcharged locally, in black.*

There are twelve different settings of the ½d., nine settings of the 2½d., and six settings of the 4d.

The halfpenny provisionals.

1/2 (2) 1/2 (3)

Setting 1. *T* **2.** *Long fraction bar. Two varieties repeated fifteen times in the sheet.*

7 ½ on 6d. black £8 £9

Setting 2. *T* **3.** *Short fraction bar. Three varieties in a vertical strip repeated ten times in sheet.*

Setting 3. *Similar to setting* 2, *but the middle stamp of the three varieties has a longer bar.*

8 ½ on 6d. black (setting 2 only) .. £5
9 ½ on 1s. dull blue £6 £10
a. Double surcharge £100

1/2 (4) 1/2 (5) 1 2 (6)

Setting 4. *T* **4** *and* **5.** *Three varieties repeated ten times in sheet. No.* 1 *is T* **4** *and Nos.* 2 *and* 3 *are T* **5.**

Setting 5. *As last, but No.* 1 *is T* **6** *(without bar).*

Setting 6. *As* 4, *but No.* 3 *is T* **5** *(without bar).*

Setting 7. *As* 4, *but No.* 1 *with long fraction bar, and No.* 2 *with sloping serif to* "**1.**"

10 ½ on 1d. dull red (S. 7 *only*) .. £90
11 ½ on 1s. dull blue (S. 6 *and* 7) £45
12 ½ on 1s. lilac (T **4**) 95 0 95 0
a. Surcharge double £30
13 ½ on 1s. lilac (T **5**) 90 0 95 0
a. Surcharge double .. ..
14 ½ on 1s. lilac (T **6**) 95 0

1/2 (7) 1/2 (8) 1/2 (9) 1/2 (10)

Setting 8. *T* **7.** *Three varieties in a vertical strip. All have a very short bar.*

15 ½d. on 1d. dull red 75 0

Setting 9. *T* **8.** *Three varieties in a vertical strip. Bars long and thick and* "**1**" *leaning a little to left.*

16 ½d. on 1d. dull red £12
a. Double surcharge .. ..

Setting 10. *T* **9** *and* **10.** *Fifteen varieties repeated twice on a sheet. Ten are of T* **9**, *five of T* **10.**

17 ½ on 1d. dull red (T **9**) .. 55 0 60 0
a. Surcharge double .. ..
18 ½ on 1d. dull red (T **10**) .. 50 0 55 0
19 ½ on 1s. lilac (T **9**) 95 0 95 0
20 ½ on 1s. lilac (T **10**) £6 £7

1/2 (11) 1/2 (12) 1 2 (13) 1/2 (14)

Setting 11. *T* **11** *to* **14.** *Fifteen varieties repeated twice in a sheet. Ten of T* **11**, *three of T* **12**, *and one each of T* **13** *and* **14.**

Setting 12. *Similar to last, but T* **13** *replaced by another T* **12.**

21 ½ on 1d. dull red (T **11**) .. 60 0
22 ½ on 1d. dull red (T **12**) .. £5
23 ½ on 1d. dull red (T **13**) .. £14
24 ½ on 1d. dull red (T **14**) .. £16
24*a* ½ on 1s. dull blue (T **11**) .. £600

The twopence-halfpenny provisionals.

2½ (15) 2½ (16)

Setting 1. *T* **15.** *Fraction in very small type.*

25 2½ on 6d. black £550

Setting 2. *T* **16.** *Large* "**2**" *on level with top of the* "**1**", *long thin bar.*

26 2½ on 6d. black £30
a. Imperf. between (pair) .. ..
b. Double surch. £90

2½ (17) 2½ (18) 2½ (19)

Setting 3. *T* **17.** *As T* **16**, *but large* "**2**" *not so high up.*

27 2½ on 1s. lilac £80

Setting 4. *T* **18.** *Three varieties in a vertical strip repeated ten times in sheet. Large* "**2**" *placed lower and small bar.*

28 2½ on 6d. black £14 £14
a. Surch. double .. .. ..

Setting 5. *T* **19.** *Three varieties in a vertical strip repeated ten times in sheet.* "**2**" *further from* "½", *small fraction bar.*

29 2½ on 1s. lilac £28 £30

(20) (21)

Setting 6. *T* **20** *and* **21**. *Fifteen varieties. Ten of T* **20** *and five of T* **21**.

30 2½ on 1s. lilac (T **20**) £500
31 2½ on 1s. lilac (T **21**) .. ..

(22) (23) (24)

Setting 7. *T* **22**. *Three varieties in a vertical strip.*

32 2½ on 6d. black £500
33 2½ on 1s. dull blue £500

Setting 8. *T* **23** *and* **24**. *Fifteen varieties. Ten of T* **23** *and five of T* **24**.

34 2½ on 1d. dull red (T **23**) .. £35
35 2½ on 1d. dull red (T **24**) .. £75
36 2½ on 1s. lilac (T **23**) £30
a. Surch. " ½ " double .. ..
37 2½ on 1s. lilac (T **24**) £45

(25) (26) (27)

Setting 9. *T* **25**, **26**, *and* **27**. *Fifteen varieties. Ten of T* **25**, *three of T* **26**, *one of T* **26** *without bar, and one of T* **27**.

38 2½ on 1s. dull blue (T **25**) .. £60
39 2½ on 1s. dull blue (T **26**) .. £250
40 2½ on 1s. dull blue (T **26**) (without bar). £300
41 2½ on 1s. dull blue (T **27**) .. £550

The fourpenny provisionals.

(28) (29) (30)

Setting 1. *T* **28**. " 4 " 8 *mm. high, pointed top.*

42 4 on 6d. black £28 £22

T **29** *and* **30**. *There are five other settings of these stamps which can only be distinguished when in blocks.*

(For particulars see Sir Edward Bacon's Handbook on this country.)

43 4 on 6d. black (T **29**) .. £5
44 4 on 6d. black (T **30**) .. £16 £14
45 4 on 1s. lilac (T **29**) £25
46 4 on 1s. lilac (T **30**) £60
47 4 on 1d. dull red (T **29**) .. £20 £20
48 4 on 1d. dull red (T **28**) .. £30 £30
a. Surch. inverted £125

31

(Typo. De La Rue & Co.)

1881. *Wmk. Crown CC sideways; upright on 4d. P* 14.

49 **1** 1d. brown-red (Oct.) .. 50 0 50 0
50 **31** 4d. ultram., Die I. (Aug.). 80 0 55 0
51 **1** 6d. olive-black (Oct.) .. £6 £6
52 ,, 1s. slate-green (Oct.) .. £14 £14

1882–84. *Wmk. Crown CA. P* 14.

53 **31** ½d. blue-grn. Die I. (2.82) 17 6 22 6
54 ,, ½d. pale green, Die I. ('84) 5 0 8 6
55 **1** 1d. orange-brown (10.83) 45 0 50 0
a. Bisected (½d.) (on cover) .. — £50
56 **31** 2½d. red-brn., Die I. (2.82) 22 6 35 0
57 ,, 4d. grey, Die I. (10.84) .. 10 0 10 0
a. Bisected (2d.) (on cover) .. — £35

1887 (July). *Wmk. Crown CA.* (*a*) *P* 12.

58 **1** 1d. crimson-lake 22 6 22 6
a. Imperf. between (pair) ..

(*b*) *P* 14.

59 **1** 6d. yellow-brown 15 0 20 0
60 ,, 1s. sepia 8 6 20 0

One Penny

(32)

1889 (May). *Surch. at Grand Turk with T* **32**.

61 **31** 1d. on 2½d. red-brown .. 17 6 27 6

1889–93. *Wmk. Crown CA. P* 14.

62 **1** 1d. crimson-lake (7.89) .. 6 0 12 6
63 ,, 1d. lake 5 0 10 0
64 ,, 1d. pale rosy lake .. 4 0 15 0
65 **31** 2½d. ultram., Die II. (4.93) 5 0 6 0

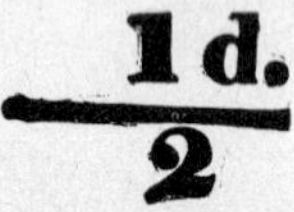

(33)

1893 (June). *No.* 57, *surcharged at Grand Turk with T* **33**.

Setting 1. *Bars between* " **1**d." *and* " **2** " *separate, instead of continuous across the rows of stamps.*

66 ½d. on 4d. grey £22 £16

Setting 2. *Continuous bars. Thin and thick bar* 10¾ *mm. apart.* " **2** " *under the* " **1** ".

67 ½d. on 4d. grey £9 £8

Setting 3. *As last, but bars* 11¾ *mm. apart.*

68 ½d. on 4d. grey £12 £12

Setting 4. *Bars* 11 *mm. apart. Five out of the six varieties in the strip have the* " **2** " *below the space between the* " **1** " *and* " d ".

69 ½d. on 4d. grey £12

There is a fifth setting, but the variation is slight.

34

(Typo. De La Rue & Co.)

1894–95. *Wmk. Crown CA. P* 14.

No.	Type	Description	Unused		Used	
70	**31**	½d. dull green, Die II (1894)	1	9	2	0
71	,,	4d. dull purple & ultramarine, Die II (May, 1895) ..	7	6	17	6
72	**34**	5d. olive-grn. & carm. (6.94)	7	6	17	6
		a. Bisected (2½d.) (on cover) ..	†		£125	

TURKS AND CAICOS ISLANDS.

35. Salt raking. **36.**

(Recess. De La Rue & Co.)

The dates on the stamps have reference to the political separation from Bahamas.

1900. *Wmk. Crown CA* (½*d. to* 1*s.*) *or Wmk. Crown CC* (2*s.*, 3*s.*). *P* 14.

No.	Type	Description	Unused		Used	
101	**35**	½d. green	3	6	7	0
102	,,	1d. red	3	6	4	0
103	,,	2d. sepia..	3	6	5	0
104	,,	2½d. blue	16	0	32	6
104*a*	,,	2½d. greyish blue ..	6	0	7	6
105	,,	4d. orange	7	6	12	6
106	,,	6d. dull mauve	7	0	14	0
107	,,	1s. purple-brown ..	9	0	14	0
108	**36**	2s. purple	£9		£10	
109	,,	3s. lake	£7		£8	

1905–08. *Wmk. Mult. Crown CA. P* 14.

No.	Type	Description	Unused		Used	
110	**35**	½d. green	2	0	3	0
111	,,	1d. red	12	6	12	6
114	,,	3d. purple/*yellow* ('08) ..	12	6	25	0

37

(Recess. De La Rue & Co.)

1909 (Sept.). *Wmk. Mult Crown CA. P* 14.

No.	Type	Description	Unused		Used	
117	**37**	½d. yellow-green	0	10	1	6
118	,,	1d. red	1	0	1	9
119	**37**	2d. greyish slate	10	0	10	0
120	,,	2½d. blue	9	0	15	0
121	,,	3d. purple/*yellow*	10	0	10	0
122	,,	4d. red/*yellow*	15	0	17	6
123	,,	6d. purple	15	0	12	6
124	,,	1s. black/*green*	12	6	15	0
125	,,	2s. red/*green*	45	0	50	0
126	,,	3s. black/*red*	55	0	60	0

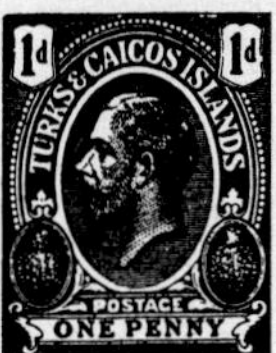

38. Melocactus Communis. **39.**

(Recess. De La Rue & Co.)

1910. *Wmk. Mult. Crown CA. P* 14.

No.	Type	Description	Unused		Used	
127	**38**	¼d. rosy mauve	0	6	1	3
128	,,	¼d. red	0	6	0	8

1913–18. *Wmk. Mult. Crown CA. P* 14.

No.	Type	Description	Unused		Used	
129	**39**	½d. green	1	0	1	0
130	,,	1d. red	3	0	3	0
130*a*	,,	1d. bright scarlet ..	2	6	2	6
130*b*	,,	1d. rose-carmine (1918)	1	3	2	6
131	,,	2d. greyish slate ..	3	6	3	0
132	,,	2½d. ultramarine ..	6	0	8	6
132*a*	,,	2½d. bright blue (1918) ..	8	6	12	6
133	,,	3d. purple/*yellow* ..	6	0	8	6
		a. On lemon	30	0		
		b. On yellow-buff	6	0	7	6
		c. On orange-buff	5	0		
		d. On pale yellow	8	6	8	6
134	,,	4d. red/*yellow*	7	6	10	0
		a. On orange-buff	8	0	9	0
		b. Carmine on pale yellow ..	6	0	12	6
135	,,	5d. pale olive-grn. (1916)	15	0	17	6
135*a*	,,	6d. dull purple ..	10	0	12	6
136	,,	1s. brown-orange ..	10	0	12	6
137	,,	2s. red/*blue-green* ..	20	0	30	0
		a. On greenish white ..	£10		£12	
		b. On emerald	22	6	32	6
138	,,	3s. black/*red*	22	6	30	0

WAR TAX

(40)

1917 (3 Jan.). ***Optd. with T* 40 *at bottom of stamp.***

No.	Type	Description	Unused		Used	
139	**39**	1d. red	0	6	2	6
		a. Overprint double	£15			
		b. " TAX " omitted				
		c. "WAR TAX" omitted in vert. pair with normal ..				
		d. Inverted overprint at top ..	£8			
140	,,	3d. purple/*yellow-buff* ..	1	9	4	0
		a. Overprint double ..	75	0		
141	,,	3d. purple/*lemon* ..	1	6	4	0
		a. Overprint double.. ..	60	0		

In both values of the first printings the stamp in the bottom left-hand corner of the sheet has a long " T " in " TAX," and the first stamp on the sixth row has " TAI " for " TAX."

1917 (Oct.). *Second printing with overprint at top or in middle of stamp.*

No.	Type	Description	Unused		Used	
142	**39**	1d. red	0	6	1	0
		a. Inverted opt. at bottom or centre	35	0		
		c. Overprint omitted, in pair with normal	£14			
		d. Double overprint, one at top, one at bottom ..	60	0		
		e. As d., but additional overprint in top margin ..	£8			
		f. Vertical pair, one as d., the other normal ..	£20			
		g. Pair, one overprint inverted, one normal	£25			
		h. Double overprint at top (in pair with normal)	£20			
		i. Overprint double	75	0	75	0
144	**39**	3d. purple/*yellow*	1	3	2	6
		a. Double	25	0		
		b. Double, one inverted ..	35	0		

1918. *Overprinted with T* **40.**
145 **89** 3d. purple/*yellow* (R.) .. 7 6 12 6

W A R
(40)

WAR
TAX
(41)

W A R
TAX
(42)

TAX
(43)

1918. *Overprinted with T* **41.**
146 **39** 1d. rose-carmine .. 1 6 1 6
146*a* ,, 1d. bright rose-scarlet .. 0 8 1 3
147 ,, 3d. purple/*yellow* .. 1 0 2 0

1919. *Optd. with T* **41.**
148 **39** 3d. pur./*orange-buff* (R.) 1 3 1 6

1919. *Local overprint. T* **40,** *in violet.*
149 **39** 1d. bright rose-scarlet .. 0 9 1 0
a. "WAR" omitted .. £8
b. Overprint double .. 27 6
c. Overprint double in pair with normal .. £8
149*d* ,, 1d. rose-carmine .. 10 0 12 6

1919. *Optd. with T* **42.**
150 **39** 1d. scarlet 0 10 1 3
a. Overprint double.. .. £8 £8
151 ,, 3d. purple/*orange-buff* .. 2 6 3 6

1919 (17 Dec.). *Optd. with T* **43.**
152 **39** 1d. scarlet .. 0 4 1 0
a. Overprint inverted ..
153 ,, 3d. purple/*orange-buff* .. 1 3 1 6

The two bottom rows of this setting have the words "WAR" and "TAX" about 1 mm. further apart.

1921 (23 April). *Wmk. Mult. Script CA.* *P* 14.
154 **38** ½d. rose-red 0 6 1 6
155 **39** ½d. green 1 0 2 0
156 ,, 1d. carmine-red 2 0 2 6
157 ,, 2d. slate-grey 2 6 5 0
158 ,, 2½d. bright blue 6 0 10 0
159 ,, 5d. sage-green 10 0 17 6
160 ,, 6d. purple 15 0 22 6
161 ,, 1s. brown-orange .. 45 0 60 0

44 **45**

(Recess. De La Rue & Co.)

1922–26. *P* 14. (*a*) *Wmk. Mult. Script CA.*
162*a* **38** ½d. black (1926) .. 0 3 0 6
163 **44** ½d. yellow-green .. 0 8 1 0
163*a* ,, ½d. bright green .. 1 3 2 0
163*b* ,, ½d. apple-green .. 2 6 3 0
164 ,, 1d. brown 1 9 2 0
165 ,, 1½d. scarlet (1925) .. 2 6 3 6
166 ,, 2d. slate 3 0 3 6
167 ,, 2½d. purple/*pale yellow* .. 1 3 2 6
168 ,, 3d. bright blue 2 6 3 6
169 ,, 4d. red/*pale yellow* .. 4 6 6 0
169*a* ,, 4d. carmine/*pale yellow* 8 6 12 6
170 ,, 5d. sage-green 6 0 8 6
171 ,, 6d. purple 6 0 8 0
172 ,, 1s. brown-orange .. 8 6 12 6
173 ,, 2s. red/*emerald* (1925) .. 22 6 27 6

(*b*) *Wmk. Mult. Crown CA.*
174 **44** 2s. red/*emerald* 45 0 60 0
175 ,, 3s. black/*red* 16 0 25 0

1928. *Inscr.* "POSTAGE & REVENUE". *Wmk. Mult. Script CA.* *P* 14.
176 **45** ½d. green 0 6 0 6
177 ,, 1d. brown 0 6 1 0
178 ,, 1½d. scarlet 1 0 1 6
179 ,, 2d. grey 1 6 1 6
180 ,, 2½d. purple/*yellow*.. .. 2 0 2 6
181 ,, 3d. bright blue 3 0 4 0
182 ,, 6d. purple 4 0 5 0
183 ,, 1s. brown-orange .. 7 6 10 0
184 ,, 2s. red/*emerald* 17 6 20 0
185 ,, 5s. green/*yellow* 45 0 50 0
186 ,, 10s. purple/*blue* 75 0 85 0

1935 (6 May). *Silver Jubilee. As Nos.* 91/4 *of Antigua, but ptd. by W'low & Sons.* *P* 11×12.
187 ½d. black and green 0 6 0 6
188 3d. brown and deep blue .. 2 6 3 0
189 6d. light blue and olive-grn. 3 0 3 6
190 1s. slate and purple .. 8 0 10 0

1937 (12 May). *Coronation. As Nos.* 13/15 *of Aden.*
191 ½d. green 0 4 0 4
192 2d. grey-black 1 0 1 3
193 3d. bright blue 1 6 2 0

46. Raking Salt. **47.** Salt Industry.

(Recess. Waterlow & Sons, Ltd.)

1938 (18 June)–**45.** *Wmk. Mult. Script CA.* *P* 12½.
194 **46** ¼d. black 0 3 0 3
195 ,, ½d. green 0 6 0 8
196 ,, 1d. red-brown 0 6 0 6
197 ,, 1½d. scarlet 0 8 1 3
198 ,, 2d. grey 1 0 0 9
199 ,, 2½d. orange 1 3 1 6
200 ,, 3d. bright blue 1 3 1 6
201 ,, 6d. mauve 7 6 8 0
201*a* ,, 6d. sepia ('45) 1 3 2 0
202 ,, 1s. yellow-bistre .. 7 6 14 0
202*a* ,, 1s. grey-olive ('45) .. 3 0 5 0
203 **47** 2s. carmine 7 6 8 6
204 ,, 5s. green 12 6 15 0
205 ,, 10s. bright violet .. 22 6 25 0

1946 (4 Nov.). *Victory. As Nos.* 28/9 *of Aden.*
206 2d. black 0 6 0 8
207 3d. blue 0 9 0 10

1948 (13 Sept.). *Royal Silver Wedding. As Nos.* 30/1 *of Aden.*
208 1d. red-brown 0 4 0 6
209 10s. mauve 20 0 27 6

50. Badge of the Islands.

51. Blue Ensign bearing Islands' Badge.

52. Turks and Caicos Islands.

53. Queen Victoria and King George VI.

(Recess. Waterlow & Sons, Ltd.)

1948 (14 Dec.). *100th Anniv. of Separation from Bahamas. Wmk. Mult. Script CA. P* 12½.

210	**50**	½d. blue-green	0 4	0 10
211	,,	2d. carmine	0 6	1 3
212	**51**	3d. blue	1 3	1 9
213	**52**	6d. violet	2 0	3 0
214	**53**	2s. black and bright blue	7 6	10 0
215	,,	5s. black and green ..	17 6	22 6
216	,,	10s. black and brown ..	30 0	35 0

1949 (10 Oct.). *75th Anniv. of Universal Postal Union. As Nos.* 114/7 *of Antigua.*

217	2½d. red-orange	0 6	0 10
218	3d. deep blue..	0 10	1 3
219	6d. brown	1 6	2 0
220	1s. olive	3 0	4 0

54. Bulk Salt Loading.

55. Salt Cay.

56. Caicos Mail.

57. Grand Turk.

58. Diving for Sponges.

59. South Creek.

60. Map.

61. Grand Turk Light.

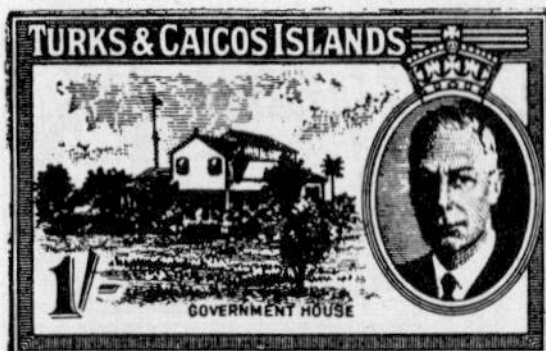

62. Government House.

63. Cockburn Harbour.

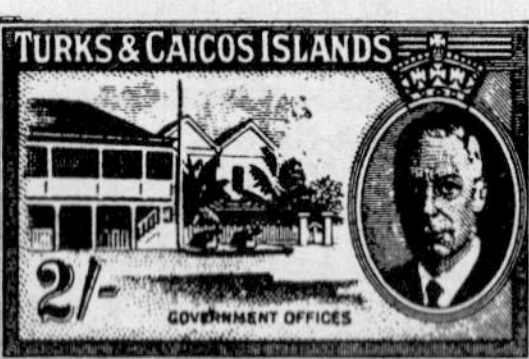

64. Government Offices.

65. Loading Salt.

66. Dependency's Badge.

(Recess. Waterlow & Sons.)

1950 (2 Aug.). *Wmk. Mult. Script CA. P* 12½.

No.	Type	Description		s.	d.	s.	d.
221	**54**	½d. green ..	.. ..	0	6	0	8
222	**55**	1d. red-brown ..	.. ..	0	9	1	0
223	**56**	1½d. deep carmine	..	1	0	1	0
224	**57**	2d. red-orange ..	..	1	0	1	0
225	**58**	2½d. grey-olive ..	..	1	3	1	6
226	**59**	3d. bright blue ..	..	1	6	1	9
227	**60**	4d. black and rose	..	2	3	3	0
228	**61**	6d. black and blue	..	3	0	3	9
229	**62**	1s. black and blue-green		3	9	5	0
230	**63**	1s. 6d. black and scarlet		6	0	7	6
231	**64**	2s. emerald and ultram.		9	6	12	6
232	**65**	5s. blue and black	..	18	6	22	6
233	**66**	10s. black and violet	..	37	6	45	0

1953 (2 June). *Coronation. As No. 47 of Aden, but ptd. by B.W. & Co.*

No.	Description		s.	d.	s.	d.
234	2d. black and orange-red	..	1	3	1	6

67. M.V. *Kirksons.*

68. Flamingoes in Flight.

(Recess. Waterlow & Sons.)

1955 (1 Feb.). *Wmk. Mult. Script CA. P* 12½.

No.	Type	Description		s.	d.	s.	d.
235	**67**	5d. black and bright green		3	6	5	0
236	**68**	8d. black and brown	..	6	0	6	6

69. Queen Elizabeth II (after Annigoni).

70. Bonefish.

71. Red Grouper.

72. Spiny Lobster.

73. Albacore.

74. Muttonfish Snapper.

75. Permit.

76. Conch.

77. Flamingoes.

78. Spanish Mackerel.

79. Salt Cay.

80. Caicos Sloop.

81. Cable Office.

82. Dependency's Badge.

(Recess. Bradbury, Wilkinson & Co.)

1957 (25 Nov.). *W* w.**12**. *P* 13½ × 14 (1*d*.), 14 (10*s*.) *or* 13½ (*others*).

237	**69**	1d. deep blue & carmine	0	3	0	3
238	**70**	1½d. grey-green & orange . .	0	4	0	3
239	**71**	2d. red-brown and olive . .	0	4	0	4
240	**72**	2½d. carmine and green . .	0	5	0	5
241	**73**	3d. turquoise-blue & pur.	0	6	0	6
242	**74**	4d. lake and black . .	0	7	0	7
243	**75**	5d. slate-green & brown	0	9	0	10
244	**76**	6d. carmine-rose & blue . .	0	10	0	10
245	**77**	8d. vermilion and black . .	1	0	1	0
246	**78**	1s. deep blue and black . .	1	5	1	6
247	**79**	1s. 6d. sepia & dp. ultra.	2	0	2	3
248	**80**	2s. deep ultram. & brown	2	9	3	6
249	**81**	5s. black and carmine . .	6	9	7	6
250	**82**	10s. black and purple . .	13	3	17	6

83. Map of the Turks and Caicos Islands.

(Photo. De La Rue & Co.)

1959 (4 July). *New Constitution. Wmk. Mult. Script CA. P* 13½ × 14.

251	**83**	6d. dp. olive & lt. orange . .	4	6	5	6
252	,,	8d. violet and light orange	5	6	6	6

84. Pelican.

(Des. Mrs. S. Hurd. Photo. Harrison and Sons.)

1960 (1 Nov.). *W* w.**12**. *P* 14×14½.
253 **84** £1 sepia and deep red .. 25 0 30 0

1963 (4 June). *Freedom from Hunger. As No. 63 of Aden.*
254 8d. carmine 1 9 2 0

1963 (2 Sept.). *Red Cross Centenary. As Nos. 147/8 of Antigua.*
255 2d. red and black 0 6 0 6
256 8d. red and blue 2 3 2 6

1964 (23 April). *400th Anniv. of Birth of William Shakespeare. As No. 164 of Antigua.*
257 8d. green 2 0 2 6

1965 (17 May). *I.T.U. Centenary. As Nos. 166/7 of Antigua.*
258 1d. vermilion and brown .. 0 4 0 6
259 2s. lt. emerald & turq.-blue 3 3 4 0

1965 (25 Oct.). *International Co-operation Year. As Nos. 168/9 of Antigua.*
260 1d. reddish pur. & turq.-grn. 0 4 0 6
261 8d. deep bluish green & lav. 1 2 1 6

1966 (24 Jan.). *Churchill Commemoration. As Nos. 170/3 of Antigua.*
262 1d. new blue 0 4 0 6
263 2d. deep green 0 5 0 7
264 8d. brown 1 2 1 6
a. Gold ptg. double £125
265 1s. 6d. bluish violet .. 2 6 3 0

1966 (4 Feb.). *Royal Visit. As Nos. 174/5 of Antigua.*
266 8d. black and ultramarine .. 1 2 1 6
267 1s. 6d. black and magenta .. 2 6 3 0

UGANDA.

BRITISH PROTECTORATE.

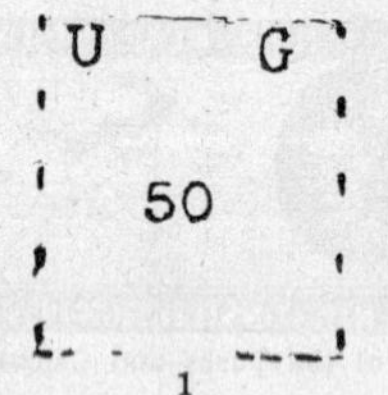

1

T **1.** *type-written by Rev. E. Millar at Mengo. Wide letters. Thin laid paper. Imperf.*

1895 (20 Mar.). A. *Wide stamps, 20 to 26 mm. wide.*
1 **1** 5 (cowries), black .. £50
2 ,, 10 (cowries), black .. £50
3 ,, 15 (cowries), black ..
4 ,, 20 (cowries), black .. — £50
5 ,, 25 (cowries), black ..
6 ,, 30 (cowries), black .. £50 £50
7 ,, 40 (cowries), black .. £75
8 ,, 50 (cowries), black .. £40
9 ,, 60 (cowries), black .. £75

1895 (May). *Provisionals. Pen-written surcharges, in black.*
10 **1** 10 on 50 (c.) black .. — £125
11 ,, 15 on 10 (c.) black .. — £125
12 ,, 15 on 20 (c.) black .. — £200
13 ,, 15 on 40 (c.) black .. — £150
14 ,, 15 on 50 (c.) black .. — £225
15 ,, 25 on 50 (c.) black .. — £175
16 ,, 50 on 60 (c.) black .. — £175

1895 (April). B. *Narrow stamps, 16 to 18 mm. wide.*
17 **1** 5 (c.) black .. .. — £50
18 ,, 10 (c.) black £50 £60
19 ,, 15 (c.) black £40 £40
20 ,, 20 (c.) black £35 £35
21 ,, 25 (c.) black £45 £45
22 ,, 30 (c.) black £60 £60
23 ,, 40 (c.) black £60
24 ,, 50 (c.) black £80
25 ,, 60 (c.) black £90

'U G'
20

2

'V.96.R'
25
'Uganda'

3

1895 (May). *T* **2**, *narrow letters. Narrow stamp. 16 to 18 mm. wide.*
26 5 (c.) black £20
27 10 (c.) black £20
28 15 (c.) black £30
29 20 (c.) black £15
30 25 (c.) black £20
31 30 (c.) black £30
32 40 (c.) black £20
33 50 (c.) black £20
34 60 (c.) black £25

End of 1895. Change of colour.
35 5 (c.) violet £20 £20
36 10 (c.) violet £20 £20
37 15 (c.) violet £20 £20
38 20 (c.) violet £20 £15
a. "G U" for "U G" ..
39 25 (c.) violet £30
40 30 (c.) violet £30
41 40 (c.) violet £30
42 50 (c.) violet £30
43 100 (c.) violet £50

Stamps of 35 (c.) and 45 (c.) have been chronicled in both colours. They were never prepared for postal use, and did not represent a postal rate, but were type-written to oblige a local collector.

1896 (June). *T* **3**. *Type-written.*
44 5 (c.) violet £10 £10
45 10 (c.) violet £10 £10
46 15 (c.) violet £10 £10
47 20 (c.) violet £8 £8
48 25 (c.) violet £20
49 30 (c.) violet £20
50 40 (c.) violet £20
51 50 (c.) violet £20
52 60 (c.) violet £50
53 100 (c.) violet £60 £70

Many of the values of the above are known *tête-bêche*.

4

5

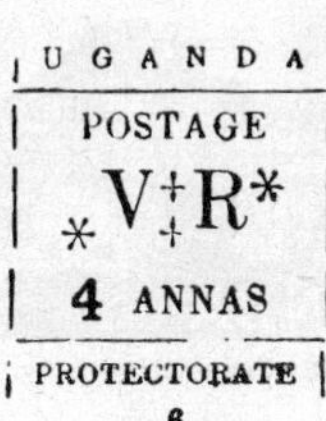

6

(Printed by the Rev. F. Rowling at Luba's, in Usoga.)

1896 (7 Nov.). *T* **4** (*thin* "**1**"), **5** (*thick* "**1**"), *and* **6** (*other values*).
A. *Normal.* B. *Small* "o" *in* "POSTAGE".

		A.		B.	
54	1 a. black (T **4**)	40 0	40 0	£5	£5
55	1 a. black (T **5**)	12 6	12 6	40 0	40 0
56	2 a. black	15 0	15 0	40 0	40 0
57	3 a. black	15 0	15 0	45 0	45 0
58	4 a. black	15 0	15 0	45 0	45 0
59	8 a. black	25 0	25 0	80 0	80 0
60	1 r. black	55 0	55 0	£12	£12
61	5 r. black	£8	£10	£20	£20

In the 2 a. and 5 a. the dagger points upwards; the stars in the 2 a. are level with the top of "VR." The 8 a. is as T **6** but with left star at top and right star at foot. The 1 r. has three stars at foot. The 5 r. has central star raised and the others at foot.

7

T **4** (1 *a.*) *and* **6** *overprinted with* "L", *in black as in T* **7**, *by the Collector at Kampala.*
A. *Normal.* B. *Small* "o" *in* "POSTAGE".

		A.		B.	
70	1 a. black	60 0	60 0	—	—
71	2 a. black	60 0	60 0	£5	£6
72	3 a. black	85 0	90 0	—	—
73	4 a. black	85 0	90 0	£7	—
74	8 a. black	£6	£6	£15	—
75	1 r. black	£8	£10	£30	—
76	5 r. black	—	—	—	—

Tête-bêche pairs of all values may be found owing to the settings being printed side by side or above one another.

8

9

(Recess. De La Rue & Co.)

1898. *P* 14. (*a*) *Wmk. Crown CA.*

84	**8**	1 a. scarlet	0 9	1 0
85	„	2 a. red-brown	1 9	2 0
86	„	3 a. pale grey	4 0	5 0
87	„	3 a. bluish grey	4 0	5 0
88	„	4 a. deep green	4 0	6 0
89	„	8 a. pale olive	7 6	10 0
89*a*	„	8 a. grey-green	7 6	10 0
		(*b*) *Wmk. Crown CC.*		
90	**9**	1 r. dull blue	15 0	20 0
90*a*	„	1 r. bright blue	30 0	30 0
91	„	5 r. brown	65 0	80 0

UGANDA
(10)

1902. *T* **11** *of British East Africa overprinted with T* **10.**

92	½ a. yellow-green	1 0	1 9
	a. Opt. omitted (pair)	£45	
	b. Opt. inverted (at foot)	£25	
	c. Opt. double	£45	
93	2½ a. deep blue (R.)	2 6	2 6
	a. Opt. double	£50	

1902. *Wmk. Crown CA. P* 14.

94	**8**	1 a. carmine-rose	1 6	1 6

For issues between 1903 and 1962 see KENYA, UGANDA AND TANGANYIKA.

11. Ripon Falls and Speke Memorial.

(Des. S. Scott. Recess. Bradbury, Wilkinson.)

1962 (28 JULY). *Centenary of Speke's Discovery of Source of the Nile. W* w.**12.** *P* 14.

95	**11**	30 c. black and red	1 3	1 3
96	„	50 c. black and slate-violet	1 6	1 6
97	„	1s. 30, black and green	2 9	2 9
98	„	2s. 50, black and blue	5 9	6 9

INDEPENDENT within the Commonwealth.

12. Murchison Falls.

13. Tobacco-Growing.

14. Coffee-Growing.

15. Ankole Cattle.

16. Cotton.

17. Mountains of the Moon

18. Mulago Hospital.

19. Cathedrals and Mosque.

20. Makerere College.

21. Copper Mining.

22. Cement Industry.

23. Parliamentary Buildings.

(Des. V. Whiteley. Photo. Harrison & Sons.)

1962 (9 Oct.). *Independence. P* 15 × 14 (5 *c. to* 50 *c.*) *or* 14½ (*others*).

99	**12**	5 c. deep bluish green ..	0	3	0	3
100	**13**	10 c. reddish brown (*shades*	0	4	0	3
101	**14**	15 c. black, red and green	0	5	0	3
102	**15**	20 c. plum and buff ..	0	6	0	4
103	**16**	30 c. blue	0	7	0	5
104	**17**	50 c. black & turq.-green..	1	0	0	10
105	**18**	1s. sepia, red & turq.-grn	1	8	1	2
106	**19**	1s. 30, yell.-orge. & vio.	2	3	1	6
107	**20**	2s. blk., carm. & lt. blue	3	3	2	6
108	**21**	5s. vermilion & dp. green	8	0	4	9
109	**22**	10s. slate and chestnut ..	16	0	12	0
110	**23**	20s. brown and blue ..	30	0	23	0

24. Crowned Crane.

(Photo. Harrison & Sons.)

1965 (20 Feb.). *International Trade Fair, Kampala.* *P* 14½ × 14.

111	**24**	30 c. multicoloured	..	0 11	1 3
112	,,	1s. 30, multicoloured	..	2 9	3 3

25. Black Bee-eater.

26. African Jacana.

27. Orange Weaver.

28. Narina Trogon.

29. Sacred Ibis.

30. Blue-breasted Kingfisher.

31. Whale-headed Stork.

32. Black-winged Red Bishop.

33. Ruwenzori Turaco.

34. African Fish Eagle. **36.** Lilac-breasted Roller.

35. Great Blue Turaco.

37. Black-collared Lovebird.

38. Crowned Crane.

(Des. Mrs. R. M. Fennessy. Photo. Harrison.)

1965 (9 Oct.). *No wmk.* *P* 15 × 14 (5 *c.*, 15 *c.*, 20 *c.*, 40 *c.*, 50 *c.*), 14 × 15 (10 *c.*, 30 *c.*, 65 *c.*), *or* 14½ (*others*).

113	**25**	5 c. multicoloured	..	0 2	0 2
114	**26**	10 c. multicoloured	..	0 3	0 3
115	**27**	15 c. multicoloured	..	0 4	0 3
116	**28**	20 c. multicoloured	..	0 5	0 3
117	**29**	30 c. multicoloured	..	0 6	0 4
118	**30**	40 c. multicoloured	..	0 8	0 6
119	**31**	50 c. multicoloured	..	0 10	0 8
120	**32**	65 c. multicoloured	..	1 0	0 10
121	**33**	1s. multicoloured	..	1 5	1 0

122	**34**	1s. 30, multicoloured	.. 1	10	1	3
123	**35**	2s. 50, multicoloured	.. 3	6	2	9
124	**36**	5s. multicoloured	.. 6	9	4	6
125	**37**	10s. multicoloured	.. 13	3	10	0
126	**38**	20s. multicoloured	.. 25	0	20	0

NOTE. Stamps inscribed " UGANDA KENYA TANGANYIKA & ZANZIBAR " (or " TANZANIA UGANDA KENYA") will be found listed under East Africa.

POSTAGE DUE STAMPS.

At present the Postage Due Stamps of Kenya, Uganda and Tanganyika are still used in Uganda.

UNION OF SOUTH AFRICA.

See SOUTH AFRICA.

VICTORIA.

— SIMPLIFICATION (**see** INTRODUCTION) —

Nos. 1 to 38.

2, 4; 5, 6, 7; 8, 9, 10; 12, 13, 14; 15; 18, 19; 20, 22, 23; 27; 28.

30, 33, 37.

Nos. 39 to 206.

39, 41*a*, 42, 43. 44*a*, 45*a*: 49, 50, 51. 52, 53, 54. 55, 64, 56, 58: 68, 69, 70, 71: 73, 75, 76: 79, 80: 83, 84: 89, 90. 92, 95.

96, 97, 98, 99, 100, 101, 102, 103, 104, 105, 106, 107, 108, 109, 110, 111, 112, 113.

120, 121: 122, 123, 124, 137, 125, 138, 139, 127: 134: 150 (also selection of other emergency printings if desired).

184, 158, 174, 179, 159, 180, 189, 160, 191*a*, 192, 203, 193, 195, 196, 162, 183, 198. 200. 201, 186. 206, 206*b*.

Nos. 207 to 454.

These issues can be greatly simplified by omitting shades, disregarding dies and perforations and by treating Wmks. V1, V2 and V3 as the same, and likewise V4 and V5.

Postage Dues.

The colour groups listed are in most cases very distinct and the catalogue list cannot be seriously reduced apart from disregarding Wmk. V3.

Unlike many British countries, Victoria, with three exceptions only, produced her own dies, plates and stamps. The exceptions were the 1d. and 6d. " Queen-on-Throne " (the dies and plates for which were produced and the stamps printed by Perkins, Bacon) and the 2d. of 1870 for which though it was printed throughout in Victoria, the die and plates were produced by De La Rue. Being the products of local endeavour in a remote country, the stamps of Victoria possess great technical interest for students although its issues are too complicated for many collectors. The present list is an attempt alike to demonstrate their interest and to clarify their complications, particularly by the inclusion of carefully written notes on various aspects of their production.

I. THE PRIVATE CONTRACT PERIOD, 1850–59. (Ham, Campbell & Co., Campbell and Fergusson, Calvert, Robinson.)

1. Queen Victoria (" Half Length ").

(Dies engraved on a single piece of steel by Thomas Ham, Melbourne.)

I. Lithographed by Thomas Ham, Melbourne.

1850 (3 JAN.). *T* **1.** *Imperf. except groups* (9) *and* (10).

1d. Thin line at top.

2d. Fine border and background.

3d. White area to left of orb.

(1) Original state of dies: 1*d.* (*tops of letters of* ' VICTORIA ' *reach to top of stamp*); 2*d.* (*fine border and background*); 3*d.* (*thicker white around left of orb, central band of orb does not protrude at left*). *No frame-lines on dies.*

1	1d. orange-vermilion	—	£125
	a. Orange-brown	—	£65
	b. Dull chocolate-brown (shades) ..	—	£65
2	2d. lilac-mauve (*shades*) ..	—	£42
3	2d. brown-lilac (*shades*) ..	£175	£35
	a. Grey-lilac	—	£35
4	3d. bright blue (*shades*) ..	—	£38
	a. Blue (shades)	—	£14
	ab. Retouched (Nos. 10 & 11 in transfer-group only)	—	£28

Periods of use: 1d., 2d. and 3d. No. 4—(January 1850); 3d. No. 4*a*, (March 1850 to October, 1851).

Note on Group (1). With the exception of No. 4*a* all the above were printed from a small stone of 30 (5 × 6), laid down without the use of an Intermediate stone. The 3d. No. 4*a* was the first ' Half Length ' to appear in sheets of 120, which was the case for all subsequent Ham printings. It was produced from an Intermediate stone of 15 (5 × 3). The 2d. No. 2 was the first printing (from Stone ' A ') and Nos. 3 and 3*a* the second (from Stone ' B '). Impressions clear and fine.

Note on margins found in the Ham printings : These stamps divide into two groups—Nos. 1 to 7—which were from 5-wide groups (or sheets) and Nos. 8 to 17—which were from 6-wide groups. The spacing between stamps horizontally is greater for Nos. 1 to 7 than Nos. 8 to 17 (and see later notes).

1d. Thick line at top.

2d. Coarse background.

3d. White area small and band protruding to left of orb.

(2) Second state of dies: 1d. (*more colour over top of letters of* ' VICTORIA '); (2d. *fine border as* (1) *but with coarse background*); 3d. (*thinner white outline around left of orb, central band of orb protrudes at left*).

5	1d. red-brown (*shades*)	£250	£35
	a. Pale dull red-brown	—	£35
6	2d. grey-lilac (*shades*)	£55	£12
	a. Dull grey	—	£12
7	3d. blue (*shades*)	—	£14
	a. Retouched (22 varieties) *from*	—	£28

Periods of use: 1d. (Feb.-Sept. 1850); 2d. (Jan.-April 1850); 3d. (Oct. 1851 to Dec. 1852).

Note on Group (2). These were all printed in sheets of 120 (10 × 12), the Printing stones for the 1d. and 2d. being produced from an Intermediate stone of 30 (5 × 6), and that for the 3d. from one of 10 (5 × 2). Impressions are clear and fine.

Frame-lines added.

(3) Third state of dies: *As in* (2) *but with frame-lines added, very close up, on all four sides.*

8	1d. dull orange-vermilion	—	£14
	a. Dull red (shades)	—	£14
9	1d. deep red-brown	—	£55
	a. Brownish red (shades) ..	—	£12
	b. Dull rose (shades)	—	£12
10	2d. grey (*shades*)	—	£14
	a. Olive-grey (shades)	—	£14
11	3d. blue (*shades*)	—	£6
	a. Deep blue (shades)	—	£6
	b. Pale greenish blue (shades) ..	—	£8

Periods of use: 1d. No. 8 (Oct. 1850 to April 1851); 1d. No. 9 (April 1851 to March 1854): 2d. (Aug.–Oct. 1850); 3d. (Dec. 1852 to April 1854).

Note on Group (3). Although the above were all printed in sheets of 120 the format was 12 × 10 —and continued so—and not 10 × 12 as in Group (2). For No. 8 (i.e. third 1d. printing) an intermediate stone of 30 (6 × 5) was used, but for all the others (i.e. fourth printings) one of 12 (6 × 2) was employed. These stamps (and those under Group (4) following) are very closely spaced as compared with the (1) and (2) groups. Group (3) represented the last state of the 1d. and 3d. dies but not of the 2d. Impressions vary from medium to fine.

White veil.

(4) *As* (3) *but altered to give, in the case of the* 1d. *and* 3d., *the so-called " white veils ", and in the case of the* 2d., *the effect of vertical drapes to the veil.*

12	1d. reddish brown	—	£12
	a. Bright pinky red (shades) ..	£35	£12
13	2d. drab	—	£14
	a. Grey-drab	—	£14
	b. Lilac-drab	—	£14
	c. Red-lilac	—	£80
	d. Void S.W corner	—	£120
14	3d. blue (*shades*)	—	90 0
	a. Deep blue (shades)	—	90 0
	b. Greenish blue (shades) ..	—	90 0
	c. Retouched (9 varieties) ..	—	£14

Periods of use: 1d. (April 1851—March 1854); 2d. (Aug.–Oct. 1850); 3d. (April–June 1854).

Note on Group (4): The alterations to the veils were made to each of the 12 impressions on the Intermediate Stones used for Group (3), and there are therefore 12 varieties of the veil in each value. Impressions are relatively coarse, particularly of the 2d. (save for No. 13*c*). Spacing of stamps is very close as in (3). In the 1d. and 2d. the shades found in Group (4) differ considerably from those met in (3).

2d. Coarse border and background.

(5) Fourth state of die. 2d. value only: *Coarse border and background. Veil details as originally.*

15	2d. red-lilac (*shades*)	—	£25
	a. Lilac	—	£25
	b. Grey	—	£25
	c. Dull brownish lilac	—	£12
	d. Retouched lower label—value omitted. (Nos. 15 to 15*c*)	—	£200
	e. Other retouches (Nos. 15 to 15*c*) (17 varieties) ..	— *from*	£28

Period of use: May–August 1850.

Note on Group (5): This comprised the sixth printing of this value and was printed from Stone " A ". For it (and also for Groups (6) and (7) below) Ham utilized an Intermediate Stone of 30 (6 × 5). This was the only printing of the 2d. value in which retouches were made to the printing stone. Impressions (save for No. 15*a*) are generally good, sometimes fine.

(6) 2d. only: *As* (5) *but with veils altered to give effect of vertical drapes.*

16 2d. lilac-grey .. .. .. — £12
a. Deep grey .. .. .. — £12
b. Brown-lilac (shades) .. .. — £8
17 2d. cinnamon (*shades*) .. £28 85 0
a. Drab (shades) .. .. .. — 85 0
b. Pale dull brown (shades) .. — £9
c. Greenish grey .. .. .. — £9
d. Olive-drab (shades) .. .. — £18
e. Buff .. .. .. — £18

Periods of use: No. 16 etc. (Nov. 1850–March 1851), No. 17 etc. (March 1851–Dec. 1852).

Note on Group (6): The 2d. Stone "B" (No. 16, etc.) and Stone "C" (No. 17, etc.) constituted Ham's seventh and eighth printings respectively. Two shades in the Stone "B" printings do not differ greatly from shades in the Stone "A" printings, but all those listed under No. 17 are entirely and peculiarly distinctive. The veil alterations were again made to each of the impressions on the Intermediate Stones so that there are 30 varieties of these.

General note on Ham printings. Ham's contract was completed in May 1850 but his 1d. and 3d. stamps remained in use up till March and June 1854 respectively. The 2d. 'Half Length' design was, however, as the result of an injury to the die, superseded by Ham's 'Queen-on-Throne' design in December 1852. In all Ham made five printings of each of the 1d. and 3d. and eight of the 2d. The paper employed by the three contractors was distinctive. For instance, for the whole of the Campbell and Fergusson printings (1d. and 3d. only) a coarse wove paper of poor quality, easily thinned and with a marked "mesh" (horizontal or vertical) was used. This paper is nothing like any paper used for the Ham or Campbell printings, and affords the best preliminary test for all 1d. and 3d. 'Half Lengths'.

II. Lithographed by J. S. Campbell & Co., Melbourne.

(7) *Wide settings. Stamps* 2½–3 *mm. apart* (1*d.*) *or* 1½–2 *mm. apart* (3*d.*).

18 1d. orange-red (*shades*) .. £34 £14
a. Rose .. .. — £55
19 3d. blue (*shades*) £22 65 0
a. Retouched (No. 17 in group) .. — £9

Periods of use: 1d. (Mar. 1854–Jan. 1855); 3d. (June, 1854–April 1855, also 1858/9).

Note on Group (7): The Campbell 1d. was printed from a stone of 192 impressions (96 × 2), and the 3d. from a stone of 320 (160 × 2). For each value an intermediate stone of 24 (6 × 4) was used. Impressions are generally good.

III. Lithographed by Campbell and Fergusson, Melbourne.

(8) *Wide settings, as* (7). *Impressions medium to poor, depending on state of printing stones. Paper used is distinctive (see final note after Ham printings).*

(*a*) *Same intermediate stones as had been employed for Group* (7).

20 1d. brown (*shades*) £22 £12
a. Brick-red (shades) .. .. — £10
b. Dull red (shades) .. .. — £10
21 1d. orange-brown (*shades*) .. — £14
a. dull rose-red (shades) .. .. — £9
b. Rose-pink .. .. .. — £14
c. Retouched (6 varieties) .. — £55
22 1d. pink (*shades*) £22 75 0
a. Rose (shades) £22 70 0
b. Lilac-rose (shades) .. .. — 75 0
c. Dull brown-red (shades) .. — £18
d. Retouched (8 varieties) .. — £55

23 3d. bright blue (*shades*) .. £28 £7
a. *Greenish blue (shades)* £22 85 0
b. Retouched (No. 17 in group) .. — £12
24 3d. Prussian blue (*shades*) .. — £12
a. Milky blue .. .. .. — £18
b. Retouched (No. 17 in group) .. — £28

Periods of use: 1d. No. 20, etc. (Stone 2, July 1854 and December 1855–May 1856): 1d. No. 21, etc. (Stone 3, Aug.–Nov. 1855); 1d. No. 22, etc. (Stones, 4, 5, Feb.–Aug. 1855 and May–Oct., 1856); 3d. No. 23, etc. (Stone "B", July 1857–Dec. 1858); 3d. No. 24 etc. (Stone "C". Nov. 1856–June 1857).

(*b*) *New intermediate stone of similar size* (6 × 4) *and spacing* 2½—3 *mm. apart horizontally.* (*Stone* "D").

25 3d. steel-blue (*shades*) .. — £7
a. Greenish blue (shades) £22 50 0
b. Blue (shades) £22 55 0
c. Deep blue (shades) £22 55 0
d. Indigo (shades) .. .. .. — 75 0

Period of use: May 1855 to November 1856. Impressions generally heavier than previous 3d.

Note on Group (8): All printing stones were of 400 impressions, consisting of an upper and lower pane of 200 (20 × 10) save in two cases, viz.: the 3d. No. 23 which was of 320 (160 × 2) and No. 24 which was probably of 200 (20 × 10) impressions. The 3d. No. 24, etc., presents a considerably worn appearance. No. 25 (steel-blue) comprised the earlier part of the printing and is, comparatively, of good appearance and impression.

IV. 3d. stamps rouletted and perforated in 1857 and 1859 respectively.

(9) ***Rouletted*** *7* ***to*** *8½* ***at G.P.O., Melbourne*** (***see later notes***).

(*a*) ***Campbell printing*** (*No.* 19).
26 3d. blue (*shades*) .. .. — £22
a. Retouched. (No. 17 in group) ..

(*b*) ***Campbell & Fergusson printing*** (*No.*23).
27 3d. bright blue (*shades*) .. — £24
a. Greenish blue (shades) .. — £20
b. Retouched. (No. 17 in group) ..

Period of use: Sept.-Dec., 1858.

(10) ***Perforated*** 12 ***by Robinson.***
(*a*) *Campbell printing* (*No.* 19).
28 3d. blue (shades) .. .. — £12
a. Retouched. (No. 17 in group).. — £28

(*b*) ***Campbell & Fergusson printing*** (*No.* 23).
29 3d. greenish blue (*shades*) .. — £55
a. Retouched. (No. 17 in group) ..

Period of use: Jan. 1859 to Jan. 1860.

Note on Groups (9) ***and*** (10)***:*** The roulettes are seldom found on all four sides. The great majority of the perforated stamps are badly off-centre.

Lithographic Reprints of the three values (the 2d. die then being in a defaced condition) were made in 1891, on paper wmk. V over Crown (Type *V* **2**) *W* **23**, perf. 12½. The 1891 Reprints of all issues were the direct result of Victoria, in that year, joining the Universal Postal Union. As a member she was expected to supply specimens of her old issues to other members. None of these being available and most of the old plates having been destroyed she was, in the majority of cases, compelled to make new plates for which, fortunately, all the original dies (save the "Emblems" (3) and the "Wood blocks" (4)) were available.

FURTHER INFORMATION on these interesting issues, including the details of the numbers printed, the plating of the Transfer Groups, the paper used, the retouches, creased transfers, "abnormal" combinations, "stitch" watermarks, etc., etc., will be found in "The Half-Lengths of Victoria", the work by J. R. W. Purves, F.R.P.S.L., on which the above list is based.

2. Queen on Throne.

1852–54. *T* 2. *Imperf.*

Corner letters: Each of the fifty subjects of the original plate show different letter combinations of A to Z, except J.

I. Dec. 1852. *Recess-printed by Thomas Ham from a steel plate of* 50 (10×5) *impressions, engraved by him by hand.*

30 2d. reddish brown	£7	55	0
a. Chestnut	—		£12
b. Purple-brown	£12	70	0

Reprints were made in 1891 (and later) using the original plate, on paper wmk. V over Crown Type V2, both imperf. and perf. 12½.

II. Dec. 1853–May 1854. *Lithographed by Campbell & Co., transfers for the stones being taken from Ham's steel plate. Period of issue: Dec.* 1853–*April* 1855 *and May* 1856–*May* 1857. *On various types of good quality paper, hand-made and machine-wove.*

(i) *Early printings: full impression, detail around back of throne generally complete. Impressions fine and clear; colours rich.*

31 2d. brownish purple	£17	45	0
a. Grey-brown	—	45	0
b. Purple-black	—	45	0
c. Dull lilac-brown (spotty print on toned)	—	55	0

Papers: The papers used for (i) and (ii) were, save in the two cases indicated, distinguished by their *whiteness,* as compared with the toned (yellowish) character of all that follow. This toning is due in part to the type of gum used but also to the larger proportion of wood pulp used in manufacture. The *hand-made* paper, which is always *white,* is found in (i) and (ii) only.

(ii) *Intermediate printings. Impressions not so full or sharp, background round top of throne not so fully defined.*

32 2d. violet-black	—	40	0
a. Grey-black	—	40	0
b. Grey-lilac	—	40	0
c. Dull brown (on toned)	—	40	0
d. Substituted transfer (in pair) ..	—		£200

(iii) *Later printings, on toned paper only. Background round top of throne generally white. Stamps lack the detail of* (i) *and* (ii) *although impression is reasonably good.*

3 2d. grey-black	£10	35	0
a. Purple-black	£10	35	0

(iv) *Last printing; on toned paper only. Background generally full as* (i) *but impression is singularly flat, and lacking in fineness and sharpness. Normal colour is distinctive.*

4 2d. grey-drab (*shades*)	—	35	0
a. Black	—		£10

Notes on the Campbell & Co. Printings.

(*a*) *Stones:* In all, 2,000,000 stamps were printed (and issued) under this contract. They were not printed on the one occasion but on several. A total of 22 transfers were taken from the steel plate, *nine* printing stones being used. Of these the first eight were of 100 impressions (one "fifty" over another "fifty") and the ninth was of 300 impressions (three "fifties" over three "fifties"). Only three of these stones were used to a point where they showed wear and in those cases the wear was nothing like that found in the Campbell & Fergusson printings. Whiteness in the background around the throne, where it occurs, is more often the result of weak pressure in the taking of the transfers.

(*b*) *Shades:* With one semi-exception (No. 32*b*) should be readily distinguished from those of the C. & F. printings.

(*c*) *Papers:* At least *six* varieties, all of good quality (comprising both hand and machine made papers) were used but they were all so different (and of so much better quality) to that employed for the C. & F. contract that, once a C. & F. stamp is acquired, no difficulty should be encountered in identifying a Campbell.

(*d*) *Vertical pairs* (they are rare) have been met from four of the Campbell stones, with *wide* distances (up to 19 mm.) between the stamps. In such cases the top stamp is from the lower row of a top transfer of fifty and the bottom stamp from the top row of a similar lower transfer.

(*e*) "*Substituted Transfers*". These (a block of four in the S.W. corner of a sheet) occurred on one out of the 22 transfers, probably on printing stone 5. The horizontal pairs read WA-HN and GM-SX respectively and the vertical pairs VZ over VZ and WA over WA respectively. They are all of the greatest rarity.

(*f*) No "*Creased Transfer*" varieties are to be met in the Campbell printings where the method followed for laying down the printing stones differed from that employed for the Campbell & Fergussons. The same is true of the "Half-Lengths" printed by these two contractors.

Some instances of *retouching* (they are rare) may be met. One stone only was affected.

III. June 1854. *Lithographed by Campbell & Fergusson; transfers for the stones again being taken from Ham's steel plate. Period of Issue: March* 1855–*May* 1856. *Printed, like the Campbell & Fergusson Half-Lengths, on a machine-wove paper of poor quality (easily thinned and torn). This factor alone provides an unfailing guide for distinguishing the products of the two contractors.*

(i) *Printings from stones which were not over-used; background around top of throne generally full and detail good.*

35 2d. lilac (*shades*)	£12	30	0
a. Purple (shades)	—	30	0
b Variety "TVO"	—		£40

(ii) *Early printings from stones which were over-used. Similar characteristics to* (i) *above, though detail is not quite so full. Distinctive shades.*

36 2d. brown	—		£12
a. Brown-purple	£18	37	6
b. Warm purple	—	37	6
c. Rose-lilac	—	37	6
d. Substituted transfer (pair) ..	—		£45

(iii) *Later printings from the same stones used for* (ii) *when in a worn condition. Impressions heavy, coarse and overcoloured; details blurred; generally white background around top of throne.*

37 2d. dull lilac-mauve	£10	27	6
a. Dull mauve	£10	27	6
b. Grey-violet	—	27	6
c. Red-lilac	—	55	0
d. Substituted transfer (pair) ..	—	£45	

(iv) *Printings from a stone giving (from the start) blotchy and unpleasing results, with poor definition. Mainly shows in extra colour patches found on most stamps.*

38 2d. dull purple	—	40	0
a. Dull grey-lilac	£15	40	0
b. On thick card paper	—	£100	

Notes on the Campbell & Fergusson Printings.

(*a*) *Stones:* 3,000,000 stamps in all were printed under this contract, of which, however, 1,500,000 (deemed to be in excess of requirements) were destroyed. A total of four printing stones (comprising 16 transfers from the steel plate) were used. The greater size of the printing and the smaller number taken of transfers of fifty (and hence of printing impressions) explains the *over-use* of certain stones, and the badly-worn prints (with filled-in colour, finer details missing, etc.) that are often met.

(*b*) *Shades:* At least 95 per cent of these printings, whatever their actual shade names, have—by comparison with the Campbell stamps—a *pink* quality. Only about 2 per cent of the Campbells, a proportion of the stamps printed from one stone only, have such a quality, but in that case the paper used was wholly different.

(*c*) *Paper* is invariably of vertical mesh. *Both* horizontal and vertical meshes are found in the Campbells.

(*d*) *Vertical pairs* with *wide* spacing have been found. They are rare: See note above on similar Campbell pairs.

(*e*) "*Substituted Transfers*": Here the entire *five* impressions comprising the left vertical row of a sheet were affected. The *horizontal* pairs (starting at the top and going down) are as follows: UY-BF, TX-MQ, DI-WA, SW-GM and CH-RW. The *vertical* pairs are UY over TX and DI over SW. They occur in various shades and stages of wear.

(*f*) "*Creased Transfer*" varieties. As in the C. & F. "Half-Length" printings, various major instances are met, including the "TVO" variety. At least two transfer groups of 50 were affected.

No retouching has been met in any printing.

3

(Die engraved and stamps lithographed by Campbell & Fergusson.)

1854–65. *T* **3.** (*a*) *Imperf.*

39 1s. blue (*shades*) (6.7.54) ..	£7	65	0
a. Greenish blue	£8	65	0
b. Indigo-blue	—	£18	

(*b*) *Rouletted* 7–7½ *at G.P.O., Melbourne (see later notes).*

40 1s. greenish blue (27.8.57) ..	—	£10
a. Blue	—	£10

(*c*) *Perf.* 12 *by Robinson, early in* 1859.

41 1s. blue (*shades*) (13.4.59) ..	95	0	22	6
a. Greenish blue	85	0	20	0
b. Indigo-blue	—		70	0

For this stamp four printing stones, each of 400 impressions (in four panes of 100), were used. These were built up from an "intermediate" stone of 40 (8 × 5) impressions. Retouches and "creased transfer" varieties also exist. At least two classes of paper were used.

This stamp was reprinted (by lithography) in 1891, wmk. V over Crown, Type V**2**, perf. 12½. The transfers were taken from the original die.

4. Queen on Throne.

(Recess. Perkins Bacon & Co.)

1856–58. *T* **4.** *Wmk. Large Star, Type* w **1.**

(*a*) *Imperf.*

42 1d. yellow-green (23.10.56) ..	£7	55	0

(*b*) *Rouletted* 5½–6½ *by F. W. Robinson, in Melbourne.*

43 6d. bright blue (1.11.58) ..	65	0	15	0
a. Light blue	£7		35	0

The gumming for the 6d. was deemed unsatisfactory and it was not used until the exhaustion of Nos. 44–48. The stock was imperf. and was rouletted by Robinson before issue. It only exists imperf., obliterated "CANCELLED" in London, in 1861.

Re-entries and re-cuts occur in both values.

These two stamps were reprinted in 1891, Wmk. V over Crown, Type V **2**, Imperf., using the original steel plates. The 1d. is found in two colours—a dull yellow-green and a bright blue-green. The 6d. has an indigo quality.

5

6

7

1854–59. *T* **5** *to* **7** (*the* "*Woodblocks*"). *Typo.*

I. *T* **5.** *6d.: Printed in sheets of* 100 *stamp representing two impressions from a plate of* 5 *woodblocks (in two panes of* 25—5 × 5), *engrave individually by S. Calvert. These all differ b are of two main types:—*

A. *Small white mark after* "VICTORIA *like an apostrophe.*

B. *No white mark after* " VICTORIA ".

(*a*) *Imperf.*

44 6d. reddish brown (13.9.54) .. £7 30 0
a. Dull orange 90 0 17 6
b. Orange-yellow 90 0 22 6

(*b*) *Rouletted* 7–9.

45 6d. reddish brown (12.8.57) .. — £7
a. Dull orange (3.12.57) .. .. — 70 0
b. Orange-yellow .. .. .. — 90 0

These stamps may be met rouletted on two sides only, and also (with finer points) on all four sides. The first class emanates from some " rouletters " used by the window-clerks at the G.P.O., Melbourne (see note after No. 62). The latter class were " perforated " by Calvert, and this gauge was also used for the Rouletted " Emblems " of early 1858.

(*c*) *Serpentine Roulette* 10½.

46 6d. orange-yellow (5.12.57) .. — £9

(*d*) *Serrated* 18–19 × *serpentine* 10½; *also serrated compound on one side with serpentine.*

47 6d. orange-yellow (19.10.57) .. — £10

(*e*) *Serrated* 18–19.

48 6d. orange-yellow .. .. — £10

Part of (*b*) and all of (*c*), (*d*) and (*e*) were " perforated " by Calvert under his contract of 14.10.57, a total of 163,000 stamps being so treated. The " pin-perf. about 10 " variety previously listed belongs to 1856 and is clearly not of official origin.

II. *T* **5.** 2s.: *For this value Calvert employed a plate of* 25 (5 × 5) *separately engraved woodblocks, two impressions of which made up the sheet of* 50.

(*a*) *Imperf.*

49 2s. dull bluish green (1.9.54) .. £55 £15

(*b*) *Rouletted* 7–7½.

50 2s. dull bluish green .. .. — £60

(*c*) *Perf.* 12 (*by Robinson*), 1859.

51 2s. dull bluish green £14 60 0
a. Pale bluish green £18 70 0

Nos. 49–51 were printed on a printed *yellow* background which is usually faint. For the blue-on-green printings of 1864–81 see Nos. 127, 130, 140 and 147. These were printed in sheets of 30, in two panes of 15 (3 × 5). The plate comprised 18 of the original woodblocks and 12 electros.

III. *T* **6.** REGISTRATION *stamp.*

(*a*) *Imperf.*

52 1s. rose-pink and blue (1.12.54) £40 £6

(*b*) *Rouletted* 7–7½.

53 1s. rose-pink and blue .. £185 £20

IV. *T* **7.** " TOO LATE " *stamp. Imperf.*

54 6d. lilac and green (1.1.55) .. £22 £12

The *same* main plate of 25 woodblock impressions (5 × 5 printed four times make up a sheet of 100) was originally used for both the " Registered " and " Too Late " stamps. For the portions printed in blue and green respectively separate stereotype plates were used of each stamp. They all represent abnormal usage.

A second woodblock plate of 25 (5 × 5) impressions from a different model was used (with the first plate) for later printings of the " Registered " only. Die 2 is distinguished by the longer head " R " of " VICTORIA " and the absence of the small white letters " V " and " R " etc. The " Registered " stamp ceased to be so used from 1.1.58 although Postmasters were then instructed to use up remaining stocks for normal postal purposes. The " Too Late " stamp was withdrawn from issue as from 1.7.57. A few used multiples are known.

8

1857–60. *T* **8** (" *Emblems* "). *Typo.*

For these stamps the dies were " woodblocks " engraved by Calvert, and the " plates " consisted of 120 individual electrotypes clamped together. In all, six settings were employed for the 4d. value and three each for the 1d. and 2d. values.

I. 1857. Printed by Calvert.

(i) ***Wmk. Large Star, Type* w 1.**

(*a*) *Imperf.*

55 1d. yellow-green (18.2.57) .. 55 0 27 6
a. Deep green £6 50 0
b. Printed on both sides .. .. — £110
56 4d. vermilion (26.1.57) £18 18 6
a. Brown-vermilion £12 15 0
b. Printed on both sides .. .. — £110
57 4d. dull red (20.7.57) £10 17 6
58 4d. dull rose (6.9.57) £10 17 6

(*b*) *Rouletted* 7–9 (*often on two sides only*).

59 1d. yellow-green £32 £14
60 4d. vermilion .. .. .. — £18
61 4d. dull red (3.9.57) .. .. — £7
62 4d. dull rose .. .. .. — 75 0

Nos. 59–62 were not rouletted by Calvert, but by one or other of three " rouletters " used by the clerks at the selling windows of the G.P.O., Melbourne. One of these " rouletters " gauged 6½–7½ and another 7¾–9. The most effective of them was purchased from one Raymond early in August, 1857.

(*c*) *P* 12.

63 1d. yellow-green .. .. — £55

This stamp and Nos. 72 and 77 were the result of the perforating (by Robinson), probably in 1860, of a few sheets of old stock.

(ii) *No wmk. On good quality medium-wove paper.*

(*a*) *Imperf.*

64 2d. pale lilac (25.5.57) .. £14 22 6
a. Grey-lilac £14 22 6

(*b*) *Rouletted* 7–9 (*often on two sides only*).

65 2d. pale lilac .. .. .. — 95 0
a. Grey-lilac .. .. .. — 95 0

See note following No. 62.

(*c*) *P* 12.

66 2d. pale lilac .. .. .. — £38
a. Grey-lilac .. .. .. — £38

See note following No. 63.

(*d*) *Serrated* 18–19.

67 2d. grey-lilac £55 £55

This variety is probably the result of an experiment by Calvert. Most of the copies seen are unused.

II. 1858: Printed by Calvert on white wove paper of good quality.

(*a*) *Rouletted all round* 8–9 (*usually fine points*).

68 1d. pale emerald (20.1.58) .. £18 35 0
a. Emerald-green £18 47 6
b. Roul. horiz. only .. .. — £55
69 4d. rose-pink (10.1.58) £20 17 6
a. Bright rose £20 17 6
b. Reddish pink .. .. .. — 25 0
c. Roul. horiz. only .. .. — £55
d. Roul. vert. only .. .. — £55

(*b*) *Imperf.* (*April* 1858).

70 1d. pale emerald £18 37 6
a. Emerald-green .. .. .. — 50 0
71 4d. rose-pink £32 80 0
a. Bright rose .. .. .. — 80 0
b. Reddish pink .. .. .. — £7

The imperf. varieties above were stamps which *should* have been rouletted by Calvert. On the cancellation of his contract they were taken over from him but since supplies were urgently required (and Robinson not having then commenced his contract) were put into use as they were. They *follow* and do not precede the roulettes.

(*c*) *P* 12.

72 1d. emerald-green .. .. — £55
a. Imperf. between (horiz. pr.) ..

III. 1858–9: Printed under contract by F. W. Robinson, first outside and later (1859) inside the Post Office Establishment.

(i) *On wove paper of a somewhat poorer quality than Calvert's. Imperf.*

73 4d. dull rose (May 58) .. .. — £12

(ii) *On smooth vertically laid paper of good quality.*

(*a*) *Imperf.*

74 4d. dull rose (May 58) .. — 95 0
a. Dull rose-red .. .. .. — 95 0
b. Dull rose-red (normal ink) .. £45 50 0

The imperforate stamps Nos. 73, 74, and 74*a* can be easily distinguished by their distinctive *heavy, coarse* impression and the *oily* nature of the ink employed. They were the *first* stamps printed by Robinson and because of the demand were rushed into circulation without being rouletted, as also was No. 74*b* which was the first stamp printed by him using a more satisfactory quality of ink.

(*b*) *Rouletted* 5½–6½.

75 2d. brown-lilac (*shades*) (Sept. 58) £18 20 0
76 4d. pale dull rose (May 58) ... — 8 6
a. Dull rose-red £9 7 6
b. Rose-red £9 7 6

(*c*) *P* 12.

77 4d. dull rose .. .. — £50
See note following No. 63.

(*d*) *Serrated* 19.

78 4d. rose-red .. .. .. — £55

(iii) *On smooth horizontally laid paper of same quality as* (ii) *above.*

(*a*) *Rouletted* 5½–6½.

79 2d. brown-lilac (*shades*) (July 58) 65 0 8 6
a. Violet (shades) (27.11.58) .. £7 8 6
b. Dull violet .. .. — 17 6
80 4d. pale dull rose .. .. — £110

(iv) *On good quality wove paper.*

(*a*) *Rouletted* 5½–6½.

81 1d. yellow-green (25.12.58) .. £32 60 0
82 4d. dull rose .. .. .. — £55

(*b*) *Perf.* 12 (*the first perforated stamps to be issued in Victoria*).

83 1d. yell.-grn. (*shades*) (11.1.59) £14 32 6
a. Imperf. × perf. (vert. pair) .. — £45
84 4d. dull rose (16.2.59) £12 7 6
Note: No. 83 is found on two classes of paper.

(v) *P* 12. *On poorer quality wove paper of coarser mesh.*

85 1d. dull green (July 59) .. £12 27 6
a. Green (Nov. 59) £12 27 6
86 4d. dull rose (19.4.59) ... .. — 6 0
a. Rose-carmine (June 59) £12 6 0
b. Rose-pink (Dec. 59) .. .. — 22 6

Save in the rouletted 1d. (where a second paper of *vertical* mesh was also employed) all the paper used for (iv) above was of *horizontal* mesh, whereas under (v) except for No. 86*b* (which was printed on a tough, thick, handmade paper) it is always of *vertical* mesh. In two printings of the 1d. *both* wove and laid papers were included.

(vi) *P* 12. *On horizontally laid papers, of coarser quality and not so smooth as those previously employed by Robinson.*

(*a*) *Laid lines closer together.*

87 1d. dull green (July 59) .. — 55 0
88 4d. rose-pink (23.12.59) .. — 22 6

(*b*) *Laid lines farther apart.*

89 1d. green (*shades*) (Oct. 59) .. £14 25 0
90 4d. rose-pink (*shades*) (Jan. 60) £9 6 0

(vii) *P* 12. *On thin glazed paper, emanating from Bordeaux.*

91 1d. deep yell.-grn. (July 1859) — £18
This stamp must have been printed *before* the "dull greens" of July 1859.

PLATES: 1857–68

The plates prepared for use between January 1857 and December 1867 (with one exception, see note after No. 51 on 2s. value) consisted of a number of individual electros (usually 120) clamped together in a "forme" and spaced and arranged to fit the pattern of the watermarked paper. Five such schemes are to be found, viz.: (*a*) from 1857 to Sept. '63 when (save for the 2d. of May 1857) the forme comprised 4 blocks of 30 (6×5) electros; (*b*) for the 2d. of May 1857 only, the sheet consisted of 20 blocks of 6 (2×3); (*c*) from Sept. 63 to Feb. 1866 when *three* separate arrangements, constant for any one value, are found. These were based on the face value of the stamps in the unit group and were as follows:—(i) For the 1d., 2d. and 4d. values the forme was composed of 8 blocks of 15 (3×5) separated by "gutters"; (ii) for the 3d., 6d. and 1s. values of 6 blocks (or 3, in the case of the 1s.) of 20 (4×5) separated by "gutters" and (iii) in the case of the 10d. of 20 blocks of 6 (3×2) separated by "gutters"; (*d*) over and following the period Jan.–July 1866, in anticipation of the introduction of the V over Crown watermarked paper, the old formes (with the exception of the 10d.) were reset and the new formes (e.g. 3d. and 6d.) arranged to give one block of 120 (12×10) evenly spaced units without "gutters". For various values, therefore, two "settings" were employed of the same electrotypes. Those interested in this subject should consult an article in *Philately from Australia* for March 1954. From 1869 to 1874 new printing plates consisted of 4 electrotypes each of 30 impressions (6×5) clamped together. These were produced via one (or two) "master" electrotypes of the same size. From 1875 (with four exceptions in the 1885 issues) all new printing plates consisted of a continuous surface electrotype of 120 (12×10) impressions. The foregoing remarks apply to normal size stamps only and require modification for other sizes.

II. GOVERNMENT STAMP PRINTING. THE FIRST PERIOD, 1860–1884.

Robinson was employed, in April 1858, to finish Calvert's uncompleted Contracts of 1857. Subsequently, under further Contracts, he printed more stamps. The work being satisfactory the Government (on 12.4.59) undertook to continue his employment and at the same time purchased the whole of his equipment, paper stocks, etc. As from 1.1.60 a Government Stamp Printing Branch was set up, Robinson was appointed its Chief Officer and there was no more Stamp Printing in terms of Private Contract. He was succeeded in 1867 by James Atkinson, and from 1883 to 1906 the same work was performed by William Bond. In December 1885 printing operations were transferred from the Post Office to the Government Printing Office and the Stamp Printer then joined the staff of the Government Printer. The Stamp Printers after Bond were J. Kemp and J. B. Cooke (1909–12), the latter being also appointed the first Commonwealth Stamp Printer.

Note: All issues of this period, 1860–84, were printed by typography from electrotypes.

9

10

11

(Dies for 3d., 4d. and 6d. (T **9**) designed and engraved by Frederick Grosse. The die for the 6d. T **11** consisted of a frame die engraved by Grosse into which was plugged a head portion, cut out of his die for the 6d. T **9**. The design, die and plate for the 1d. T **10** were all supplied by Messrs. De Gruchy and Leigh of Melbourne.)

1860–66. *T* **5, 8, 9, 10** *and* **11.** *P* 12.

(i) *On horizontally laid paper (lines further apart, as* (vi) (*b*) *above).*

92 **9** 3d. deep blue (31.1.60) .. £32 65 0
a. Light blue £165 £15

(ii) *No wmk.: On thin glazed paper emanating from Bordeaux (see also under (vii) above).*

93 **8** 1d. bright green (25.5.60) .. — 80 0
94 **9** 4d. rose (21.4.60) £28 25 0
a. Rose-pink .. .. .. — 17 6

(iii) *No wmk. On a thicker, coarser paper.*

95 **9** 4d. rose-pink (July 60) .. £28 16 0

ONE PENNY

12

(iv) 1860–66 : *Watermarked with the appropriate words of value as T* **12**. *The paper, which was hand-made, was supplied by T. H. Saunders of London.*

96 **8** 1d. pale yellowish grn. (8.7.60) 70 0 15 0
a. Yellow-green 85 0 17 6
b. Var. Wmk. "FOUR PENCE" — £185
97 **10** 1d. pale green (1.10.61) .. 95 0 15 0
a. Olive-green .. .. — 15 0
b. Pale green (deep brown gum) (Feb. '63) 95 0 15 0
98 **8** 2d. brown-lilac (7.7.61) .. — 65 0
99 ,, 2d. bluish slate (Aug. 61, June 62) £6 12 6
a. Greyish lilac (Sept. 61) .. £7 12 6
b. Slate-grey (Jan. 62) .. — 12 6
100 **9** 3d. pale blue (Jan. 61) .. 65 0 17 6
a. Light blue (Aug. 61) .. 65 0 17 6
b. Blue (dp. brn. gum) (Feb. 63) 80 0 17 6
c. Deep blue (64) 80 0 17 6
101 **9** 3d. maroon (13.2.66) .. 80 0 50 0
a. Perf. 13 .. .. .. £6 65 0
102 ,, 4d. rose-pink (1.8.60) .. — 6 0
a. Rose-red (shades) (Sept. 60) 75 0 3 0
b. Rose-carmine (Dec. 60) .. — 12 6
c. Dull rose (shades) (1861) .. 75 0 3 0
103 ,, 6d. orange (18.10.60) .. £120 £25
104 **5** 6d. black (22.6.61) .. £9 65 0
105 **9** 6d. black (20.8.61) .. £9 10 0
a. Grey-black £9 10 0
106 **11** 6d. grey (26.4.62) .. 55 0 7 0
a. Grey-black 55 0 7 0
b. Jet black (deep brown gum) (Mar. 63) 65 0 8 6

Reprints on paper wmkd. V over Crown (T **23**), perf. 12½, were made in 1891 of the 1d. Type **10**, 3d. and 4d. Type **9** and 6d. Type **11**. In all cases new plates were used, and certain "die flaws" are found on the "Reprints" which are not met on the originals.

13

1862–63. *Emergency printings due to supplies of the appropriate paper not being available.*

(*a*) *On paper wmkd.* "FIVE SHILLINGS", *T* **13**.

107 **9** 4d. dull rose-pink (11.9.62) £60 45 0
a. Dull rose .. .. .. — 45 0

(*b*) *On paper wmkd.* "THREE PENCE". *T* **12**.

108 **8** 2d. pale slate (27.12.62) .. £8 30 0
a. Bluish grey (deep brown gum) (Feb. 63) £10 30 0

Note: Certain stamps are to be met on the "words of value" papers with wmk. *reversed* under Nos. 99, 100, 102, also 173 and 176. *Inverted* wmks. may also be found in several cases. All these wmk. varieties are scarce to rare.

14

(v) 1862–64 : *Same types as before but wmkd. with the appropriate single-lined numeral of value, as T* **14**, *the paper being supplied by De La Rue. P* 12 *unless otherwise described.*

109 **10** 1d. olive-green (1.2.63) .. 40 0 8 6
a. Pale green (Sept. 63) .. 40 0 8 6
b. Apple-green (Apr. 64) .. — 12 6
110 **8** 2d. dull reddish-lilac (21.4.63) £9 22 6
111 ,, 2d. grey-lilac (Oct. 63) .. £12 30 0
a. Var: Wmk. '6' (Oct. 63) .. — £110
b. Grey-violet (shades) (Nov 63) — 27 6
c. Slate (Dec. 63) £12 35 0
112 **9** 4d. dull rose-pink (9.10.62) £6 7 0
a. Dull rose (deep brown gum) (Feb. 63) £6 7 0
b. Rose-red .. .. .. — 8 6

113 **11** 6d. grey (18.6.63) 55 0 6 0
a. Grey-black (Feb. 64) .. 55 0 6 0
b. Intense black .. .. — 6 0
114 ,, 6d. jet-black, p. 13 (Dec. 64) 55 0 6 0
a. Grey-black 55 0 6 0

July-Aug. 1863 : *Varieties due to a temporary break-down of the perforating machine.*

115 **9** 4d. dull rose-pink (imperf.) — £8
116 ,, 4d. dull rose-pink (rouletted) — £18

Notes on plate varieties found on stamps printed from plates made by Robinson.

The electros prepared by Robinson over the period 1860–66 (many, e.g. the 4d., which lasted until 1881, remaining in use for a long time after) furnish perhaps the most interesting varieties found in typographed stamps. Since the lead moulds for these were struck by hand, on semi-fused metal, and without the aid of a " collar ", the stamps present us with certain constant abnormalities, viz. *partial strikes*, *double strikes* and *internal distortion* varieties of a nature and extent not found in any other issue, as well as also providing all the more usual types of flaw found in typographed stamps. The whole of the Robinson " Beaded Ovals " and " Laureates" are plateable since the process used made it *impossible* for any stamp to be a perfect reproduction of the die. The 6d. black (Type **11**) is the most interesting of all since the die here was in two parts. This meant the adherence of lead along the line of junction, etc., and gave rise to yet further classes of plate variety. For information on this stamp see various articles in the *London Philatelist.*

Notes on the two single-line numeral watermark papers.

Two different English firms supplied the single-line numeral wmk. papers used from October 1862 onwards. The two classes of paper supplied are so distinct that they have now been given separate listing. Their characteristics are as follows:—

1. *De La Rue papers* (several consignments). Comprised *white* paper wmkd. " 1 ", " 2 ", " 4 ", " 6 " and " 8 " respectively, *blue* paper wmkd. " 1 " and *green* paper wmkd. " 2 ". In certain printings particularly in the 1d., 2d. and 4d. Laureates and the 6d. black (1863–65) on this paper, a *pelure* type—thin, hard and semi-transparent—may be found. This variety has not been separately listed but is worthy of the specialist's attention. Generally the quality of these De La Rue papers varied considerably among the different consignments.

2. *T. H. Saunders papers* (one consignment only). Comprised *white* paper wmk. " 1 ", " 4 " and " 6 " respectively, *blue* paper wmkd. " 1 ", *green* paper wmkd. " 2 ", and *pink* paper wmkd. " 10 ". It was first used in December 1865 and the white papers were exhausted by August 1867. The paper was (apart from the *blue* variety, which was rather thinner than the rest) of even quality throughout and was smoother, thicker, more brittle and (in the white variety) not so white as the De La Rue product. It will be noted that the " 2 " and " 8 " papers were supplied by De La Rue only, whereas the " 10 " paper (pink) was supplied by Saunders only. Comparison of these should assist collectors in accurate classification. The *coloured* papers lasted much longer than the white, as will be seen from the listings. The *blue* lasted until 1875, and the *green* and *pink* until 1879.

In both papers, in practically all cases, *reversed* and/or *inverted* wmks. may be met. *Sideways* wmks. have been found under Nos. 124 and 200. Stamps showing little or no wmk. are from the left or right sides of badly cut sheets.

15 16

17 18

19

(The " *Laureated* " series: Dies engraved by Frederick Grosse. Printing plates (see previous note) made by F. W. Robinson until late in 1867.)

Note. Since various printings of the 2s. Calvert (Type **5**) were also made between 1864 and 1881 these have been included where appropriate.

1863–80.

(i) 1863–64. *Early printings. Wmk with appropriate single-lined numeral as T* **14**, *on paper supplied by De La Rue. P* 12.

117 **15** 1d. pale green (8.9.64) .. 32 6 15 0
118 ,, 2d. violet (late April 64) .. 32 6 5 0
a. Dull violet (Oct. 64) .. 32 6 6 0
119 ,, 4d. deep rose (4.9.63) .. — 7 0
a. Doubly printed .. .. — £60
b. Rose-pink (Sept. 63 on) .. 45 0 4 6
c. Pink (Apr. 64) 32 6 4 6

Emergency printings on Perkins, Bacon paper wmkd. double-lined numerals " **1** " *and* " **4** " *respectively, supplied by Tasmania. P* 12.

120 **10** 1d. yellow-green (10.12.63) £8 25 0
a. Dull green (Apr. 64) .. — 25 0
b. Imperf. between (pair) .. — —
121 **15** 4d. deep rose (7.1.64) .. 85 0 8 6
a. Pale rose .. .. .. — 8 6

Like the 1d. and 4d. Perkins, Bacon types of Van Diemen's Land most of the Victorian stamps printed on the above two papers may occasionally be found with wmk. *inverted.* This applies both to the 1d. and 4d. above and also to the various " Laureates " of the 1867–68 printings. Instances are also known where the work is *reversed* and one (in No. 132) where it is *sideways.* Most of these varieties are rare.

(ii) *Printings of* Oct. 1864 *onwards. As* (i) *bu[t] P* 13.

122 **15** 1d. pale green (10.10.64) .. 22 6 8 6
a. Bluish green (Dec. 64) .. 17 6 6
aa. Doubly printed .. .. — £85
b. Green (shades) (Aug. 65) .. 17 6 7
c. Deep green (Dec. 65) .. — 6

123 **15** 2d. dull violet (Oct. 64) .. 27 6 5 0
a. Dull lilac (shades) (Apr. 65) 27 6 4 6
b. Reddish mauve (Nov. 65) .. 35 0 5 6
124 ,, 4d. dull rose (Oct. 64) .. 35 0 4 0
a. Dull rose-red (Feb. 65) .. 35 0 4 0
125 ,, 8d. orange (22.2.65) .. 77 6 35 0
126 **18** 1s. blue/*blue* (10.4.65) 110 0 7 6
127 **5** 2s. lt. blue/*grn.* (22.11.64) £5 17 6
a. Deep blue/green (65) £5 17 6

The above 1s. stamp can be immediately identified by the white patches (comprising an *albino* impression) due to the lack of a *make-ready* which are found on all stamps. The 8d. was withdrawn from issue on 11.6.69.

(iii) July–August 1865. *As before but P* 12 *or* 12 × 13 *from repaired state of* 12 *machine, with larger holes and sharper teeth than previously.*

(*a*) *Perf.* 12.

128 **15** 1d. green (*shades*) 27 6 8 6
a. Deep green 27 6 8 6
129 ,, 4d. dull rose-red (Aug. 65) £7 27 6
130 **5** 2s. dark blue/*green* .. £10 27 6

(*b*) *Perf.* 12 × 13.

131 **15** 1d. deep green .. .. — 18 6

August and December 1865. *Emergency printings* (2) *on Perkins, Bacon paper wmkd. double-lined* "**4**" *supplied by Tasmania.*

132 **15** 4d. dull reddish rose, *p.* 13 (11.8.65) 110 0 5 0
a. Perf. 12 .. .. .. — 7 0
b. Perf. 12 × 13 .. .. — 27 6
133 ,, 4d. red, *p.* 13 (6.12.65) .. £7 10 0

Oct. 1865. *Emergency printing on De La Rue paper wmkd. single-lined* " 8 ", *no* " 10 " *paper having arrived. Perf.* 13.

134 **17** 10d. grey (21.10.65) .. £9 65 0
a. Grey-black £9 65 0

(iv) Dec. 1865–66 *printings. These, in general, were of finer impression than the previous* 1865 *printings.*

A. On Saunders paper, wmkd. with the appropriate single-line numerals as T **14.**

135 **15** 1d. dp. yellow-green, *p.* 13 (Jan. 66) 17 6 6 6
a. Perf. 12 .. .. .. — 17 6
b. Perf. 12 × 13 .. .. — 15 0
136 ,, 4d. rose-red, *p.* 13 (12.12.65) 35 0 5 0
a. Perf. 12 .. .. .. — 11 6
b. Perf. 12 × 13 .. .. — 10 6
137 **17** 6d. blue, *p.* 13 (13.2.66) .. 27 6 3 0
a. Perf. 12 .. .. .. 55 0 7 0
b. Perf. 12 × 13 .. .. 27 6 4 0
c. Imperf. between (pair) .. — £55
138 ,, 10d. dull purple/*pink*, *p.* 13 (22.3.66) 37 6 5 0
a. Perf. 12 × 13 .. 50 0 8 6
b. Blackish brn./pink, *p.* 13 (69) 55 0 8 6
139 **18** 1s. indigo-blue/*blue*, *p.* 13 (70) 55 0 6 6
a. Perf. 12 (73) .. .. — 17 6
b. Brt. blue/blue, *p.* 13 (Jan. 71) 55 0 6 6
ba. Perf. 12 .. .. .. — 8 6
c. Pale dull blue/blue, *p.* 13 (Jan. 75) .. .. — 30 0
ca. Perf. 12 .. .. .. — 8 6
140 **5** 2s. dark blue/*green* (Dec. 67) £10 27 6
a. Perf. 12 (75) £14 27 6
b. Blue/green (72, 78) .. £10 17 6
c. Greenish-blue/green, *p.* 12 (75) £14 25 0
d. Deep greenish blue/green, *p.* 12½ (80) £10 25 0

The 1s. on Saunders paper was issued later than 1866 but it and the 2s. printings are included here for the sake of convenience. The Saunders green paper is distinctly *deeper* in shade and more apparently *green* than the De La Rue variety.

B. On De La Rue paper wmkd. with the appropriate single-line numerals as T **14.**

141 **15** 1d. bt. yellow-grn. (Jan. 67) — 80 0
142 ,, 2d. rosy lilac, *p.* 13 (Jan. 66) 27 6 8 6
a. Perf. 12 × 13 .. .. 55 0 8 6
143 ,, 2d. dull lilac, *p.* 13 (June 66) — 8 6
a. Perf. 12 .. .. .. — 17 6
b. Perf. 12 × 13 .. .. — 27 6
144 ,, 2d. grey, *p.* 13 (25.7.66) .. 27 6 4 6
a. Perf. 12 .. .. .. 80 0 8 0
145 **17** 6d. blue, *p.* 13 (13.2.66) .. 27 6 3 0
a. Perf. 12 .. .. .. 55 0 7 6
b. Perf. 12 × 13 .. .. 27 6 4 0
146 **18** 1s. blue/*blue*, *p.* 13 (66, 69) 55 0 7 0
a. Perf. 12 × 13 (66) 55 0 10 0
b. Bright blue/blue, *p.* 13 (67, 71) — 6 6
ba. Perf. 12 (71) .. .. — 12 6
c. Indigo/blue, *p.* 13 .. — 8 6
d. Dull blue/blue, *p.* 12 (74) .. — 12 6
e. Imperf. btwn. vert. pr. (12 × 13) — £55
147 **5** 2s. blue/*green* (68) .. 85 0 17 6
a. Greenish blue/green (73) .. 85 0 17 6
aa. Perf. 12 .. .. £10 22 6
b. Darkblue/grn., *p.* 12½ (80) 85 0 17 6

The 1d. of 1867 on De La Rue, distinguishable only by its shade, was presumably the result of the discovery of a small quantity of old stock. The 2d. and 4d. of 1866 may also be found 13 × 12 but are rare in this condition. The 10d. was withdrawn from issue on 21.6.71. There were, between 1864 and 1881, no less than 21 different printings of the 2s. blue on green. Only the main schools of colour have been listed.

1866 (SEPT.)–**67.** *Various Emergency printings, all the results of the non-arrival of the first shipment of* " *V over Crown* " *paper.*

1. *Printings on De La Rue paper wmkd. single-lined* "**8**". *P* 13.

148 **15** 1d. bt. yellow-grn. (27.12.66) £12 35 0
149 ,, 2d. grey (18.1.67) £9 7 6
150 **16** 3d. lilac (29.9.66) 55 0 45 0
151 **15** 4d. rose-red (? date) ..

Only one copy of the 4d. has been recorded and that is understood to have been lost, although its authenticity seems to have been established.

2. *Printings on Saunders paper wmkd. single-lined* "**4**". *P* 13.

152 **15** 1d. bt. yellow-grn. (6.3.67) 55 0 22 6
153 ,, 2d. grey (26.2.67) 85 0 7 6

3. *Printings on paper wmkd. single-lined* "**6**". *P* 13.

(*a*) *On De La Rue paper.*

154 **15** 1d. bt. yellow-grn. (June 67) — 65 0

(*b*) *On Saunders paper.*

155 **15** 1d. bt. yellow-grn. (June 67) £10 40 0
156 ,, 2d. grey (13.5.67) £14 15 0

20 (*V*1)

WATERMARKS. *Many stamps watermarked V and Crown may be found with watermark inverted or sideways. We do not list these as separate varieties, but copies can be supplied if in stock.*

1867–68. *Printings on first consignment of paper wmkd.* " *V over Crown* ", *T* **20**, *received in July* 1867. *P* 13.

157 **15** 1d. bt. yellow-grn. (10.8.67) 80 0 8 6
158 ,, 2d. slate-grey (*shades*) (26.8.67) 20 0 2 6
a. Grey-lilac (Jan. 68) .. — 5 0

159 **16** 3d. lilac (Aug. 67) 65 0 55 0
a. Grey-lilac (Aug. 68) .. 85 0 65 0
160 **15** 4d. dull rose (Nov. 67) ... 45 0 12 6
161 **17** 6d. dark blue (Dec. 67) .. — 3 0
162 **19** 5s. blue/*yellow* (26.12.67) £22 £18
a. Wmk. reversed .. .. — £38

The above shades (there are also paper differences) are sufficiently distinctive to enable separation of the five lower values from *later* "V over Crown" printings. The 5s. was printed from the first electros prepared by Atkinson. There were two printings, both in sheets of 25 (5 × 5). The first (1,200) was from a single vertical column of 5 electros clamped together. The second (2,000) was from a plate of 25 impressions, comprising a different "5 vertical", repeated 5 times (i.e. giving 5 types). The reversed wmk. variety belongs to the first printing and was created *deliberately* to avoid the appearance of the "page number" on the front of one stamp in every four sheets of 25.

1867 (Sept.)–**68** and **1870.** *Various Emergency printings due first to the 1867 shipment of white "V over Crown" paper being so small, later to the exhaustion and the non-arrival of the second shipment ordered, later still (1870) to a further shortage of this paper.*

1. *Printings on the Perkins, Bacon paper wmkd. double-lined "1" received from Tasmania in 1863. P 13.*

163 **15** 1d. pale yellowish green (24.9.67) 25 0 8 6
a. Deep yellow-green (June 68) — 8 6
164 „ 2d. slate (May 68) .. £12 10 0
a. Mauve (30.6.68) £12 10 0
165 **16** 3d. grey-lilac (Aug. 68) .. £14 110 0
166 **17** 6d. blue (Aug. 68) .. £7 12 6

2. *Printings on the Perkins, Bacon paper wmkd. double-lined "4" received from Tasmania in 1863. P 13.*

167 **15** 1d. pale yellow-grn. (27.5.68) £110 £14
168 „ 2d. grey-lilac (3.2.68) .. £9 5 0
a. Slate (28.3.68) £9 5 0
b. Mauve (3.7.68) .. .. — 8 6
169 „ 4d. dull rose-red (May 68) £9 8 6
170 **17** 6d. blue (20.6.68) £28 55 0
a. Indigo-blue .. .. — 65 0

3. *Printing on Saunders paper wmkd.* "six pence" *as T* **12.** *P 13.*

171 **15** 1d. pale yellow-grn. (5.6.68) £45 65 0
172 „ 2d. slate-grey .. .. — £175
173 **17** 6d. blue (23.5.68) £28 35 0
a. Indigo-blue .. .. — 45 0

Only one copy is apparently known of No. 172. From its shade it would appear to belong to an 1867–68 printing. No. 171 is known with the wmk. *sideways.*

4. *Printings on lilac paper wmkd. V over Crown from 1867 consignment. P 13.*

174 **15** 2d. mauve/*lilac* (12.8.68) .. 27 6 12 6
a. Lilac/lilac 27 6 12 6

5. 1870: *6d. value only. Printings on various wmkd. papers as indicated. P 13.*

175 **17** 6d. dull blue (three pence) (16.6.70) £18 20 0
a. Deep blue .. .. — 27 6
176 „ 6d. dull blue (four pence) (18.6.70) £44 55 0
a. Deep blue .. .. — 65 0
177 „ 6d. dull blue ("4") (21.5.70) — £110
178 „ 6d. dull blue ("2") (1870) — £110

1868 (Aug.)–**71.** *Printings on second and later consignments of V over Crown paper. W* **20.** *P 13 only.*

(i) *Printed from Robinson plates.*

179 **15** 2d. lilac (26.8.68) 17 6 2 6
a. Dull mauve (shades) (Oct. 68) 17 6 2 6
b. Lilac-grey (Jan. 69) .. — 5 0
c. Lilac-rose (Feb. 69) .. — 8 6
180 **16** 3d. yellow-orange (12.6.69) 22 6 8 6
181 **15** 4d. pale red (*anil.*) (21.4.69) — 15 0
a. Deep red (anil.) (16.7.69) .. — 15 0
b. Rose-pink (Feb. 70) .. — 12 6
182 **17** 6d. blue (*shades*) 12 6 1 6
a. Indigo-blue (69) 12 6 1 6
183 **19** 5s. indigo-blue & carmine (I) (8.10.68) £9 35 0
a. Blue and carmine (69) .. £6 17 6

Nos. 179*b*/*c* were printed from badly worn plates.

For the frame-plate of the 5s. (I) the electros of the 1867 plate, with the Crown, "victoria" and "five shillings" cut out, were employed. A new plate, also produced via cut-out portions of the 1867 plate, was brought into use for the red portion.

(ii) *Printed from new plates made by Atkinson.*

184 **15** 1d. bt. yellow-grn. (Oct. 68) 17 6 4 0
a. Bright olive-green (Jan. 69) — 4 0
b. Dull yellow-green (Apr. 69) .. — 3 0
c. Dull green (Mar. 70) .. 17 6 3 0
d. V. pale green (Oct. 70) .. — 3 0
185 „ 2d. lilac-grey (15.1.69) .. — 5 0
a. Lilac-rose (shades) (24.2.69) 35 0 5 0
b. Mauve (20.4.69) .. .. — 3 6
c. Red-lilac (shades) (May 69) .. 27 6 2 6
d. Dull lilac (shades) (June 69) 27 6 1 9
e. Silver-grey (2.9.69) £12 22 6

The Atkinson plates, produced by an improved technique, do not show the *double* and *partial strikes* and *internal distortion* varieties met on a large proportion of the stamps from the Robinson plates. Further, the later printings from the 2d. and 6d. Robinson plates show obvious signs of wear. These factors and the differing shades should make classification relatively easy. For the first two printings of the 2d. in 1869 the first of the new Atkinson plates was used in conjunction with the old Robinson plate, following which the latter was replaced by a second Atkinson plate. The dates of introduction of the Atkinson plates were 1d., Oct. 1868; 2d., Jan. 1869 and 6d., Dec. 1875.

9 9

NINEPENCE

(21)

1871. *Provisional. Surch. with T* **21**, *in blue. On Saunders paper wmkd. single-lined "10". P 13.*

186 **17** 9d. on 10d. purple-brown/*pink* (22.4.71) .. £7 17 6
a. Blackish brown/pink .. — 32 6
b. Double surcharge .. .. — £110

Perforations (to 1883).

The perforations of Victoria, particularly those of the period Oct. 1864–80, form a complex study for specialists. We have adopted in this listing a simplified classification based on *three* descriptions—Perf. 12, Perf. 13 and Perf. 12½ respectively, the latter being substituted for Perf. 13 for the period 1881 on. The position can be concisely put as follows:—

A. "*Perf.* 12"; Here the gauge is *never* quite 12 and nearer 11½. It is not found after 1883. There were two machines (both single-line), the first introduced by Robinson in Jan. 1859 and the second purchased in 1871. No "perf. 12" are found in the period mid 1866–mid 1871. At various periods, more particularly in 1865 and 1880, one or both of the machines was repaired, to give larger holes and sharper teeth over a succeeding period.

B. "*Perf.* 13": Here the gauge is invariably *over* 12 and with a sole exception (covering a section of the pins on one machine over the period 1876–80) invariably *under* 13. Generally speaking up to the end of 1880, these machines gauged 12½ to 12¾. Two classes of machine are found:

(i) *Single-line* machines. These were three in number—purchased in Oct. 1864, 1866 and 1873 respectively. Two of them were converted into combs in 1873. The other was repaired on several occasions, particularly in 1879–80, to give larger holes and sharper teeth.

(ii) *Comb* machines. First introduced in 1873 (see above). Over the period of use they gave various gauges, depending on the machine and its state of repair. They were all *vertical* combs adapted only for normal size stamps of either dimensions as likewise (until 1913) were all other comb-machines used in Victoria for perforating stamps.

C. "*Perf.* 12½": Found from late 1876 onwards, in both single-line (used mainly for the larger-size stamps) and vertical comb machines. Gradually superseded the A and B gauges. Certain stamps of the 1879–80 period are found in both B and C gauges but these are no longer differentiated as separate varieties, being only listed under the one or the other gauge. This applies also to the Postal Fiscal section.

"*Compound*" *perforations:* In previous editions certain 12 × 13 perforations were listed which were not true compounds of A and B but simply the product of one or other of the *comb* machines. Such varieties have now been eliminated. The "Compounds" now listed are all true compounds (or "mixeds") of A and B. They generally fall into two categories: (i) those of the 1865–66 period where the two machines were both used for the original perforating, one in the one direction (top and bottom) and the other in the other (sides); (ii) isolated examples, better termed "mixed" perfs., from 1873 on, where one gauge machine was used to correct off-centre perforating done by the other gauge machine. Such cases are almost invariably associated with "mends", viz. the pasting of gummed strips down the back of the faulty lines of perforation.

1871–84 Printings.

These are listed separately from the 1868–71 printings because of the perforation changes made in the period, viz. the reintroduction of the 12 gauge (1871), the introduction of comb machines (1873), the repairs of various 12 and 13 machines (1879), and the introduction of the 12½ gauge (1879–80). Many stamps issued in the latter period are found both perf, 13 and 12½ but no distinction is made. The 13 gauge disappears in 1880–81.

Papers: All printings on white paper made after April 1878 and also the last 8d. printing were on the "*glazed*" variety of paper and this furnishes another means of identification. Some shades, e.g. 6d. blue of 1878–79, are found on *both* papers.

Shades are different from those found in the 1868–71 printings.

1871–84.

(1) *Printed from Robinson plates ; W* **20** *; P* 13, 12½ *unless otherwise described.*

No.	Type	Description	Unused		Used	
187	**16**	3d. dull orange (71) ..	17	6	4	0
		a. Perf. 12 (72)	17	6	4	0
		b. Orange (74)	—		5	0
		ba. Perf. 12	—		5	0
		c. Bright orange	—		6	0
		ca. Perf. 12	—		6	0
188	**16**	3d. orange-brown (late 78)	42	6	15	0
189	,,	3d. dull orange-yellow (81)	42	6	8	6
		a. Perf. 12	—		£17	
190	**15**	4d. rose (*shades*) (71–78) ..	42	6	5	0
		a. Perf. 12	42	6	5	0
		b. Dull rose (5.3.79)	—		5	0
		ba. Perf. 12	—		5	0
		c. Dull rose-red (23.12.79) ..	—		5	0
		ca. Perf. 12	—		5	0
		d. Bt. lilac-rose (*anil.*) (3.3.80)	55	0	7	0
		da. Perf. 12	—		15	0
191	,,	4d. rosine (*anil.*) (22.9.80)	£17		17	6
		a. Perf. 12	110	0	7	6
		b. Compound p. 12 with 12½ ..	—		£55	
192	**17**	6d. Prussian blue (72, 74)	12	6	1	3
		a. Perf. 12	17	6	2	0
		b. Indigo (73)	17	6	2	6
		ba. Perf. 12	22	6	3	0
		c. Dull blue (worn plate) ..	—		1	9
193	**15**	8d. lilac-brown/*pink* (24.1.77)	35	0	8	6
		a. Purple-brown/pink (21.3.78)	55	0	8	6
		b. Chocolate/pink (6.8.78) ..	55	0	8	6
		bb. Compound p. 13 × 12 ..	—		£55	
194	,,	8d. red-brn./*pink* (20.5.78)	55	0	8	6
195	,,	8d. dark red-brn./*pink*, p. 12 (30.11.80)	45	0	12	6
196	**18**	1s. light blue/*blue* (May 75)	£7		22	6
		a. Perf. 12	—		22	6
197	**19**	5s. pale bt. blue & carmine (I) (July 77)	—		35	0
		a. Grey-blue & carmine (Aug. 78)	£10		27	6
		b. Deep lavender-blue & carmine (May 80)	£10		27	6
198	,,	5s. bright blue & red (II) (12.5.81)	£7		25	0
		a. Perf. 12	90	0	25	0
		b. Indigo-blue and red ..	—		35	0
		ba. Perf. 12	—		35	0

The 4d. "pink" previously listed is a *faded* rosine. For the 5s. (Type II) new dies were made for *each* portion of the design. All Type I stamps have a blue line under the Crown, which is missing in Type II. The latter were printed in sheets of 100 (10 × 10), as compared with 25 (5 × 5) for Type I.

1877–79. *Printings of the* 8d. *value on Saunders paper wmkd. single-lined* "10". *Perf.* 13, 12½ *unless otherwise stated.*

No.	Type	Description	Unused		Used	
199	**15**	8d. lilac-brn./*pink* (Dec. 77)	—		£55	
		a. Purple-brown/pink (20.2.78)	85	0	17	6
200	,,	8d. red-brown/*pink* (8.8.79)	55	0	12	6
		a. Perf. 12	—		27	6

The 8d. printings (save that of 1880) were *mixed* and comprised stamps on *both* V over Crown and "10" papers.

½ ½

HALF

(22)

(ii) *Printed from plates made by Atkinson. The* ½d. *made by surch. with T* **22**, *in red.*

No.	Type	Description	Unused		Used	
201	**15**	½d. on 1d. green (25.6.73)	17	6	12	6
		a. Perf. 12	27	6	17	6
		b. Grass-green	17	6	12	6
		ba. Perf. 12	27	6	17	6
		c. Short '1' at right ..	—		£10	
202	,,	1d. pale green (71) ..	17	6	3	0
		a. Perf. 12 (Oct. 71)	35	0	4	0
		b. Green (*shades*)	17	6	3	0
		ba. Perf. 12	27	6	3	6
		c. Grass-green	—		4	0
		ca. Perf. 12	—		5	0
		d. Bluish green (*shades*) ..	35	0	4	0
		da. Perf. 12	—		5	6

203	**17**	6d. dull ultram. (2.12.75)	22	6	2	3
		a. Light Prussian blue (29.12.75)	—		2	3
		b. Dull violet blue (Apr. 78) ..	—		15	0
		c. Blue (13.5.78)	35	0	1	3
		ca. Perf. 12	—		1	9
		d. Dull milky blue (7.3.79) ..	27	6	2	3
		da. Perf. 12	—		2	3
		e. Blue (light ink) (Aug. 80) ..	—		1	9
		f. Light blue (10.5.81) ..	35	0	1	9
		fa. Perf. 12	—		6	0
		g. Deep blue (15.1.82) ..	27	6	1	9

23 (*V2*)

The types of V over Crown watermark (1867–1912).

In all, *five* types were employed.

The first two types (*V1* and *V2*) belong to the contracts made with De La Rue to supply postage stamp paper. That firm lost the contract in 1895 to Waterlow and Sons, who held it until 1912. The third and fourth types are therefore products of the Waterlow contracts. The fifth type (found only in 1912) was supplied by James Spicer & Sons. The change in the pattern from *V1* to *V2* is explained by the dandy-roll (which was the property of De La Rue) requiring replacement. Since *all* the changes in pattern are also associated with changes in the nature and texture of the paper supplied, little difficulty should be encountered, with the new descriptions, in identifying the various types. Each pattern (save in a few cases of "left over" stock) succeeded the previous pattern.

Types *V1* and *V2* are mainly to be distinguished from one another by the four "points" around the top of the Crown which are found in *V1* but not in *V2*. Also, as compared with *V2*, the shapes of the top ornaments in *V1* resemble diamonds, and not ovals. It must be remembered that *V1 coloured* papers continued in use long after the exhaustion of the *V1* white paper, the earliest date met for the *V2* white paper being 15.8.82. The first *V2* coloured papers (blue and green) were not used until February 1890. In general the papers supplied by De La Rue were whiter than their successors. The quality found with the *V1* wmk. varied greatly both with and without a pronounced mesh. The quality of the *V2* papers on the other hand varied little. It is generally more "loaded" and opaque than any of the *V1* papers and the wmk. clearer when held to the light.

(iii) 1882–4. *As* (ii) *above but on paper wmkd. V over Crown* (*V2*), *W* **23.** *P* 12½.

204	**16**	3d. yellow-orange (13.4.83)	27	6	15	0
		a. Dull brownish orange ..	55	0	27	6
205	**17**	6d. dull viol.-blue (10.11.82)	12	6	1	9
		a. Indigo-blue (Nov. 83) ..	12	6	2	6
		b. Light ultramarine (Sept. 84)	12	6	4	0

The above 3d. was printed from two new plates made by Atkinson. For the 6d. the same Atkinson plates introduced in Dec. 1875 were employed.

Reprints were made, in 1891, on V over Crown paper, Type 23, perf. 12½, of the 1d., 2d., 3d., 4d., 6d., 8d., 10d., 1s. and 5s. "Laureates".

The shades are distinctive and a number of values show "die flaws" not found in the originals. The 3d. was printed in yellow, the 8d. in orange-yellow, the 10d. in greenish-slate and the 5s. in blue and red.

24

(Printed in Melbourne from a double electrotyped plate of 240 subjects supplied by Messrs. De La Rue & Co.)

1870 (28 Jan.). *Wmk. V over Crown* (*V1*), *W* **20.** *P* 13.

206	**24**	2d. brown-lilac	35	0	2	6
		a. Dull lilac-mauve (Sept. '70)	17	6	1	3
		aa. Perf. 12 (71)	27	6	1	9
		b. Mauve (worn plate, Mar. '73)	17	6	1	3
		ba. Perf. 12	27	6	1	9

25 26 27 (28)

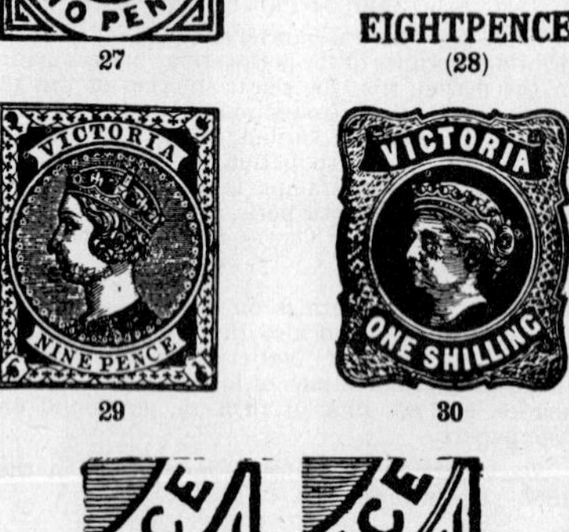

29 30

31 (Die I) **32** (Die II)

(Des. and dies eng. by William Bell and stamps printed from electrotyped plates.)

1873–84. *Two dies of 2d.: I, single-lined outer oval; II, double-lined outer oval. The 8d. is made by surch. with T* **28** *in blue. P 13 unless otherwise described.*

(*a*) *On Saunders paper, wmkd. single-lined "10".*

No.	Type	Description	Unused	Used
207	**29**	9d. pale brown/*rose* (25.3.73)	45 0	10 0
		a. P. 12	75 0	22 6
		b. Red-brown/rose (Aug. 74)	37 6	8 6

(*b*) *Wmk. V over Crown* (*V1*), *W* **20.**

No.	Type	Description	Unused	Used
208	**25**	½d. rose-red (10.2.74)	4 6	1 9
		a. Perf 12	5 6	2 6
		b Lilac-rose (74 on)	5 6	2 6
		ba. Perf. 12	5 6	2 9
		c. Rosine (shades) (Dec. 80)	3 0	1 0
		ca. Perf. 12	4 0	1 3
		d. Pale red (82)	3 6	1 3
		da. Perf. 12	4 0	1 9
		e. Mixed p. 13 and 12	—	£16
209	**26**	1d. dull bluish green (14.12.75)	8 6	1 0
		a. Perf. 12	15 0	1 3
		b. Green (shades) (77 on)	7 0	1 0
		ba. Perf. 12	8 6	1 6
		c. Yellow-green (78 and 80)	7 0	1 0
		ca. Perf. 12	—	5 6
210	**27**	2d. deep lilac-mauve, Die I (1.10.73)	8 6	0 9
		a. Perf. 12	—	5 6
		b. Dull violet-mauve	7 0	0 9
		ba. Perf. 12	—	5 6
		c. Dull mauve	8 6	0 9
		ca. Perf. 12	22 6	1 9
		d. Pale mauve (worn plate, Jan. 79)	12 6	1 0
		da. Perf. 12	—	1 9
		e. Mixed p. 13 and 12	£18	£16
211		2d. lilac-mauve, Die II (17.12.78)	12 6	0 6
		a. Perf. 12	17 6	0 9
		b. Grey-mauve (Jan. 80)	—	1 3
		ba. Perf. 12	—	2 6
		c. Pale mauve (June 80)	—	1 6
		ca. Perf. 12	—	3 6
		d. Imperf. (pair)	—	£65
		e. Imperf. between (pair)	—	£65
212	**29**	8d. on 9d. lilac-brown/*pink* (1.7.76)	£6	27 6
		a. "F.IGHT" (broken "E")	—	£22
213	,,	9d. lilac-brown/*pink*, p. 12 (1.12.75)	90 0	25 0
214	**30**	1s. indigo-bl./*blue* (16.8.76)	22 6	4 0
		a. Deep blue/blue (1877)	22 6	4 0
		aa. Perf. 12 (Oct. 80)	—	12 6
		b. Blue/blue (1878)	22 6	3 0
		ba. Perf. 12	—	12 6
		c. Ultramarine/blue (1879)	65 0	12 6
		d. Bright blue/blue (Nov. 83)	40 0	8 6

(*c*) Feb.-April 1878. *Emergency printings on various coloured papers, due to the exhaustion of white V1 paper. W* **20.** (*V1*), *P 13 only.*

No.	Type	Description	Unused	Used
215	**25**	½d. rose-red/*pink* (1.3.78)	12 6	7 0
216	**26**	1d. yellow-green/*yellow* (25.2.78)	32 6	17 6
217	,,	1d. yellow-green/*drab* (April 78)	47 6	40 0
218	**27**	2d. violet-mauve/*green* (18.2.78)	47 6	8 0
219	,,	2d. violet-mauve/*lilac* (21.2.78)	—	£26
220	,,	2d. violet-mauve/*brown* (21.3.78)	45 0	12 6

Two shades of yellow paper, termed *pale canary* and *deep canary* respectively, are found.

All supplies of *V1* paper received in Victoria after 15.3.78 were, as compared with previous supplies, highly surfaced on the printing side. An experimental printing was made on the new paper in July 1877 (1d., 2d. and 5s.) and all printings on white *V1* paper from April 1878 on were made on this glazed paper. The glazed *V1* coloured papers, with few exceptions, made their appearance later.

(*d*) 1882-3. *On white paper wmkd. V over Crown* (*V2*) *W* **23.** *P 13 only.*

No.	Type	Description	Unused	Used
221	**25**	½d. rosine (April 83)	3 0	0 9
222	**26**	1d. yellow-green (Sept. 82)	8 6	0 9

Reprints: The ½d., 1d., 2d. (Die 2), 9d. and 1s. values were reprinted in 1891, perf. 12½, the first four from new plates, made from Dies containing *die flaws* not found in the originals. The 9d. was on *V1* and the others on *V2* paper.

33

34

35

(Des. and eng. by Charles Naish (T **33** & **34**) and William Bell (T **35**). Typo. from electrotyped plates.)

1880–84. *P 12½ unless otherwise described, this description including the P 13 varieties found in* 1880.

(*a*) *W* **20** (*V1*).

No.	Type	Description	Unused	Used
223	**33**	2d. sepia (3.11.80)	17 6	0 9
		a. Perf. 12	—	£8
		b. Sepia-brown (Feb. 81)	6 0	0 6
		ba. Perf. 12	£18	£8
		c. Brown (anil.) (May 81)	17 6	0 9
		ca. Perf. 12	—	£8
		d. Dull black-brown (Oct. 81)	—	0 9
		e. Dull grey-brown (Mar. 82)	4 0	0 4
		f. Mixed p. 13 and 12	—	£35
224	,,	2d. mauve (*worn plate*) (Feb. 84)	—	17 6
225	**34**	4d. rose-carmine (Oct. 81)	15 0	4 6
		a. Rosine (Aug. 82)	15 0	4 6
226	**35**	2s. dark blue (*shades*)/*green* (8.7.81)	65 0	20 0
		a. Light blue/green (wmk. sideways) (Aug. 83)	55 0	42 6
		b. Ultramarine/green (July 84)	—	65 0
		ba. Wmk. sideways	—	110 0

(*b*) *W* **23** (*V2*).

No.	Type	Description	Unused	Used
227	**33**	2d. dull grey-brn. (15.8.82)	3 6	0 4
228	,,	2d. chocolate (Mar. 83)	3 6	0 4
		a. Perf. 12	—	50 0
229	,,	2d. mauve (20.12.83)	7 0	0 6
		a. Worn plate	12 6	0 9
		b. Perf. 12	—	£35
		c. Mixed perfs. 12½ and 12	—	£35
230	**34**	4d. rose-red (Mar. 83)	15 0	5 0

For the scarce perf. 12 stamps listed above the holes are large and the teeth sharp. See also the note about perf. 12 stamps after No. 186b.

The first printings of the 2d. in mauve were from the two plates used for the browns. Later printings were from two new plates. Reprints were made in 1891 of the 2d. (brown), 4d. (in pale red) and 2s., all on *V2* paper.

36

(Des. and die eng. Charles Naish. Typo.)

1883 (29 Oct.)–**84.** *P* 12½.

(*a*) *W* **20** (*V*1).

231 **36** 1d. green (Feb. 84) .. £9 17 6

(*b*) *W* **23** (*V*2).

232 **36** 1d. yellow-green (29.10.83) 7 6 1 0
a. Green 7 6 1 0
b. Pale green (May 1884) .. 7 6 1 0

Nos. 224 and 231 represent a printing on old stocks of paper.

III. THE "POSTAGE AND REVENUE" PERIOD, 1884–1901.

Under the provisions of the Postage Act 1883 the stamps of the three series then in use (Postage, Duty, Fee) became, as from 1.1.84, mutually interchangeable. It was, at the same time, decided to issue (as soon as possible) the *one* stamp only, for any value, to serve *all* purposes. Since there were available many more dies (and plates) inscribed "Stamp Duty" than there were of either the "Postage" or "Fee" (Stamp Statute) series it was agreed that all values should be inscribed "Stamp Duty" by the beginning of 1885. All stamps *printed* after 1.1.84 are therefore true "Postage and Revenue" stamps whereas all Stamp Duty and Fee stamps printed before that date are Postal Fiscals, since they were originally printed solely for fiscal purposes. These principles have been strictly adhered to in our listing. Little difficulty should however be met in distinguishing between the printings of the one stamp found respectively in the main list and in the "Postal Fiscal" section since there are many major differences of printing, watermark, perforation and shade. On 1.1.84 there were no "Stamp Duty" designs for the ½d., 2d., 4d., 8d. and 2s. 6d. values. Also the existing "Stamp Duty" designs for the 1d., 6d., 1s. and 2s. were deemed to be too large to be convenient for general and extensive use. For all these values it was therefore necessary to produce new and smaller designs inscribed "Stamp Duty". Pending the preparation of new dies and plates, printings were made in 1884 (for the ½d., 1d., 2d., 4d., 6d., 1s. and 2s. values) from the existing "Postage" plates. These printings are also "Postage and Revenue" stamps but have naturally been included, for the sake of convenience, in the previous period. By the beginning of 1885 printings were available, in the new designs, of all values save the 1s. and 2s., and these latter appeared later.

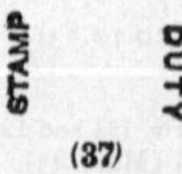

(37)

A. **1885.** *Postage Stamps optd. with T* **37.** *The 1s. and 2s. appeared in February 1885, 3d. and 4d. in November 1885. P 12½.*

(*a*) *W* **20** (*V*1).

233 **16** 3d. dull or.-yell. (Pl. 1) (B.) — £16
234 **30** 1s. ultram./*blue* .. 37 6 22 6
a. Dull blue/blue .. .. — 45 0
235 **30** 1s. deep ultram./*blue* (B.) (F.C. £8) .. .. — £55
236 **35** 2s. ultramarine/*blue* .. 35 0 20 0
a. Wmk. sideways 75 0 42 6

(*b*) *W* **23** (*V*2).

237 **16** 3d. yellow-orange Pl. 2 (B.) 20 0 15 0
a. Dull brownish-orange (B.) .. 30 0 20 0
238 **34** 4d. rose-carmine (B.) .. 20 0 15 0

The overprinted 1s. was replaced by the 1s. Type **44** on lemon. Collectors should beware of faded black overprints purporting to be the "blue". In genuine examples the blue of the overprint is difficult to distinguish in the blue of the stamp.

Reprints of the 4d. and 1s. (with and without overprint) were made in 1895–6. The 1s. is wmkd. *V*2 and the 4d. (from a new plate) is a pale red. Examples of the latter genuinely postally used are sometimes met.

38 39 40 41 42 43

(Typo. Dies for ½d., 2d., 3d., 4d., 8d. and 2s. 6d. eng. by Charles Naish, the other values being derived from these.)

B. **1884–95.** *New designs inscr. "STAMP DUTY". P 12½.* (*a*) *W* **20** (*V*1).

239 **42** 8d. rose/*pink* (*shades*) (1.1.85) 10 0 5 6
a. Rose-red/pink 10 0 5 6
240 **40** 1s. deep dull blue/*lemon* (Nov. '85) 25 0 8 6
a. Dull blue/yellow (June '86) .. 27 6 8 6
241 **42** 2s. olive/*bluish green* (May '86) 12 6 4 6

(*b*) *W* **23** (*V*2).

243 **38** ½d. pale rosine (1.1.85) .. 3 6 1 0
a. Deep rosine (July '85) .. 4 0 2 6
b. Salmon (Sept. '85) 5 0 4 6

No.	Type	Description	Unused		Used	
244	**39**	1d. yellowish green (*shades*) (1.1.85)	3	0	0	9
		a. Dull pea-green (Feb. '85)	15	0	5	6
245	**40**	2d. lilac (*shades*) (1.1.85)	4	6	0	6
		a. Mauve (Jan. '86)	6	6	0	9
		b. Rosy-mauve (June '86)	12	6	1	0
246	**39**	3d. yellowish brown (1.1.85)	5	6	1	6
		a. Pale ochre (Nov. '86)	4	6	1	0
		b. Bistre-yellow (Dec. '92)	5	6	1	6
247	**41**	4d. magenta (1.1.85)	15	0	5	0
		a. Bright mauve-rose (Jan. '87)	15	0	8	6
248	,,	4d. dull lilac (*error*) (Dec. '86)	£175		£35	
249	**39**	6d. chalky blue (1.1.85)	37	6	7	6
		a. Bright blue (Feb. '85)	22	6	5	0
		b. Cobalt (Sept. '85)	22	6	5	0
250	**42**	8d. bright scarlet/*pink* ('92)	15	0	15	0
251	,,	2s. olive-green/*pale green* (Mar. '90)	12	6	4	6
252	,,	2s. apple green (12.8.95)	10	0	10	0
253	,,	2s. blue-green (29.10.95)	10	0	7	0
254	**43**	2s. 6d. brown-orange (23.4.84)	17	6	12	6
		a. Yellow ('85)	12	6	8	6
		b. Lemon-yellow (Jan. '93)	12	6	8	6

In each of the 1d., 6d., 1s. and 2s. values six types are to be found differing, *inter alia*, in the engraving of the words of value.

4*d.* "*error*": This comprised a printing of 6,000 stamps, in 1886, in a *dull lilac* shade. It is true that only some seven unused specimens are known but it is not true (as previously stated) that it is unknown used, since a leading authority has himself seen upwards of 30 undoubted used copies, all of which have certain characteristics which distinguish them from certain colour changelings, accidental or deliberate. The records show that the whole printing of 6,000 was issued which confirms the finding of so many used copies.

The 8d. value was withdrawn from sale on 24.8.95.

Reprints were made in 1891, using one of the original plates in each case, of the ½d., 1d., 2d., 4d., 6d. and 1s. values. In the three lower values the shades are fairly distinctive. The 1s. was wmkd. *V*1. In all cases the wmk. is equally common normal and inverted and this applies to *all* the Reprints made in 1891 or later.

44 45 46 47

48 49 50 51

52 53 54 55

56 57 58

(The above illustrations are ¾ size.)

C. **1884–96.** *New printings, all typographed from electrotypes, of "STAMP DUTY" designs first issued in* 1879. (*Des. Charles Jackson and Ludwig Lang. Dies eng. by Charles Jackson, Arthur Williams, Charles Evans and possibly others, supplied* (1879) *by Messrs. Sands and McDougall of Melbourne*). *Perf.* 12½. *Wmk. sideways save where shown as upright* (U).

NOTE.—Stamps of the above designs printed by lithography or line-engraving, or similar designs not found in the following list should be looked for among the Postal Fiscals.

(*a*) *W* **20** (*V*1).

No.	Type	Description	Unused		Used	
255	**44**	1s. brt. blue/*blue*(Nov.'84)	35	0	12	6
256	,,	1s. chalky blue/*lemon* (3.3.85)	22	6	5	0
257	**46**	3s. maroon/*blue* (Aug. '84)	27	6	15	0
258	**48**	5s. reddish pur./*lemon* (June '87)	12	6	5	0
		a. Brown-red/yellow (Jan. '94)	£7		35	0
259	**52**	£1 orge./*yellow* (Sept. '84)	—		45	0
		a. Reddish orge./yell. (Dec. '90)	70	0	30	0

(*b*) *W* **23** (*V*2).

No.	Type	Description	Unused		Used	
260	**45**	1s. 6d. pink (Feb. 1885)	40	0	17	6
		a. Bright rose-carm. (May '86)	32	6	12	6
261	**46**	3s. drab (Nov. '85)	15	0	8	6
		a. Olive-drab (Oct. '93)	18	6	8	6
262	**47**	4s. red-orange (27.5.86)	13	6	6	0
		a. Yellow-orange (S, U)	20	0	8	6
263	**48**	5s. rosine (8.5.96)	16	6	8	6
264	**49**	6s. pea-green (12.11.91)	27	6	15	0
		a. Apple-green (U) (Apr. '96)	32	6	17	6
265	**50**	10s. dull bluish green (Oct. '85)	60	0	15	0
		a. Grey-green (Sept. '87)	40	0	13	6
266	**51**	15s. purple-brn. (Dec. '85)	70	0	30	0
267	,,	15s. brown (U) (May '95)	£7		£6	
268	**53**	£1 5s. pink† (U) (6.8.90)	£7		20	0
269	**54**	£1 10s. pale olive† (Oct. '88)	£8		22	6
270	**55**	£2 blue† (Aug. '88)	£8		27	6
271	**56**	45s. lilac† (15.8.90)	—		32	6
272	**57**	£5 pink (Oct. '85)	—		£6	
273	**58**	£10 lilac (July '85)	—		£6	
		a. Mauve† (July '93)	—		£5	

† Both here and later indicates that prices quoted are for stamps postmarked to order by the Victorian postal authorities for sale in sets.

59

(Illustration ¾ size).

D. **1886–1900.** *Type* **59** *and similar types. W* **23** (*V*2) *sideways* (S) *or upright* (U). *The line-engraved stamps were all printed singly direct from the dies and both the lithographed and typographed stamps in sheets of* 10 (2×5).

(i) *Lithographed. Printings of* 1886 *to* 1889.

274	£25 dull yellowish-green (S, U) (Jan. 86) ..	F.C.	£8
	a. Dull blue-green (U) (Oct. 88)	F.C.	£8
275	£50 bright violet (U) (Feb. 86)	F.C.	£10
	a. Dull purple (U) (Oct. 87) ..	F.C.	£10
276	£100 rosine (S, U) (Jan. 86) ..	F.C.	£14

(ii) *Recess-printed. Printings of Nov.* 1890 *to April* 1897.

277	£25 bright blue-green (S, U) (Nov. 90)	F.C.	£9
278	£50 black-violet (Nov. 90) ..	F.C.	£12
279	£100 crimson (aniline) (S, U) (Nov. 90)	F.C.	£12
	a. Scarlet-red† (1897)	—	£14

For earlier recess-printed printings, see under "POSTAL FISCALS".

(iii) *Typographed from Electrotyped plates. Printings of Nov.* 1897 *on.*

280	£25 dull blue-green† (U) ..	—	75 0
281	£50 bright mauve† (U) ..	—	£8
282	£100 pink-red† (U) (Oct. 1900)	—	£8

Collectors should beware of stamps with cleaned fiscal markings particularly in the higher values. Some of these bear forged cancellations but others, in fraud of the revenue, did genuine postal service.

60

61

62

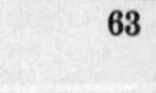

63

64

65

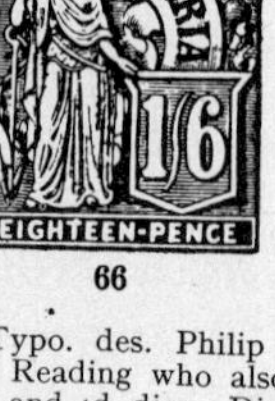

66

67

(Typo. des. Philip Astley; dies eng. Samuel Reading who also "lined" the previous 2d. and 4d. dies. Dies supplied by Fergusson and Mitchell.)

1886–96. *W* **23** (*V*2) *upright save in* ½*d.,* 1*s. and high values* (*excepting the* £6) *where it is sideways. P* 12½.

No.	Type	Description	Unused s.	d.	Used s.	d.
283	**60**	½d. lilac-grey (20.8.86) ..	4	0	2	6
		a. Grey-black	—		£6	
284	,,	½d. pink (15.2.87) ..	3	6	1	3
		a. Rosine (anil.) (Dec. '89) ..	2	6	0	9
		b. Rose-red (May '91) ..	1	9	0	6
		c. Vermilion (Mar. '96) ..	3	0	1	0
285	**61**	1d. green (26.7.86) ..	3	6	0	4
		a. Yellow-green (July '87) ..	3	0	0	3
286	**62**	2d. pale lilac (17.12.86) ..	3	6	0	4
		a. Pale mauve ('87)	1	6	0	3
		b. Deep lilac ('88, '92) ..	1	6	0	3
		c. Purple (May '94)	3	0	1	0
		d. Violet (May '95)	1	0	0	3
		e. Imperforate ('90)	—		£110	
287	**63**	4d. rose-red (1.4.87) ..	6	6	1	6
		a. Red ('93)	5	0	1	0
288	**64**	6d. bright ultram. (27.8.86)	6	0	0	9
		a. Pale ultramarine (Oct. '87) ..	4	6	0	6
		b. Dull blue (Feb. '91) ..	2	9	0	4
289	**65**	1s. dull pur.-brn. (14.3.87)	15	0	2	6
		a. Lake (Feb. '90)	22	6	3	0
		b. Carmine-lake (May '92) ..	12	6	1	6
		c. Brownish red (Jan. '96) ..	17	6	2	0
290	**66**	1s. 6d. pale blue (June '88)	55	0	37	6
291	,,	1s. 6d. orange (18.9.89) ..	8	6	6	0
		a. Red-orange	7	6	7	6
292	**67**	£5 pale blue & maroon† (7.2.88)	£10		40	0
293	,,	£6 yellow & pale blue† (1.10.87)	£15		60	0
294	,,	£7 rosine & black† (17.10.89)	£18		70	0
295	,,	£8 mauve & brn. orange† (U) (2.8.90) ..	£25		80	0
296	,,	£9 apple green & rosine† (21.8.88)	£30		90	0

Reprints of the ½d. grey and 1s. 6d. blue were made in 1894–5. They differ from the originals in shade. A £10 (*T* **67**) was prepared for use but not issued.

An imperforate sheet of the 2d. was on sale at the Mortlake Post Office in 1890 and a pair was noted in 1902.

68

69

70

(1d. die supplied, des. and eng. by Samuel Reading; 2½d. and 5d. des. by M. Tannenberg; 9d. first printed from the new Reprint plate of 1891. Typo.)

1890–96. *New designs and values.* *P* 12½.

(*a*) *W* **20** (*V*1).

297 **68** 1d. orge.-brn./*pnk.* (16.6.91) 1 3 0 9

This was an emergency printing, caused by a temporary shortage of white *V*2 paper.

(*b*) *W* **23** (*V*2).

298 **68** 1d. dull chestnut (1.1.90) 1 6 0 4
  a. Deep red-brown (Jan. '90) .. 2 6 1 6
  b. Orange-brown (Apr. '90) .. 1 9 0 3
  c. Yellow-brown ('91) .. 0 9 0 3
  d. Brown-red ('90, '92) .. 0 9 0 3
  e. Brt. yell.-orange (Jan. '94) 27 6 1 6
  f. Brownish orange (Aug. '94) 0 9 0 3
299 **69** 2½d. red-brown/*lemon* (18.12.90) 3 6 0 9
300 ,, 2½d. brown-red/*yellow* ('92) 2 6 0 6
  a. Red/yellow ('93) 2 6 0 5
301 **70** 5d. purple-brown .. 5 0 1 3
  a. Pale reddish brown ('92) .. 3 0 0 9
302 **29** 9d. apple-green (18.10.92) 15 0 8 6
303 ,, 9d. carm.-rose (18.10.95) 7 6 5 0
  a. Rosine (aniline) ('96) .. 12 6 6 0

The yellow papers used for the 2½d. value differed considerably in tint.

71

72 (*V*3).

(Eng. A. Williams (1½d.).)

1896 (June)–**1899** (Aug.). *W* **72** (*V*3). *Paper supplied by Waterlow and Sons. This paper differs noticeably from the previous De La Rue products. It is less white, softer and generally thicker, and has a coarser grain or mesh than any previous V over Crown paper. It will be noted that some coloured V2 papers of earlier manufacture were utilised during this period. Types* **60, 65, 71** *and the larger size stamps have the wmk. sideways unless marked* U (*upright*). *P* 12½.

304 **60** ½d. light scarlet (1.7.96) .. 0 9 0 4
  a. Carmine-rose (Nov. '97) .. 1 3 0 4
  b. Deep carmine-red (coarse impression '99) .. .. — 2 6
305 **68** 1d. brown-red (13.6.96) .. 0 9 0 3
  a. Brownish orange ('99) .. 0 9 0 3
306 **71** 1½d. apple-green (8.10.97) 1 0 1 6
307 **62** 2d. violet (*shades*) (12.6.96) 1 6 0 3
308 **39** 3d. ochre (Nov. '96) .. 6 0 1 0
  a. Buff (Feb. '98) 5 0 0 9
309 **63** 4d. red (June '97) .. 3 6 0 8
310 **70** 5d. red-brown (July '97) 6 0 0 9
311 **64** 6d. dull blue (Sept. '96) 2 6 0 5
312 **29** 9d. rosine (Oct. '96) .. 15 0 3 6
  a. Rose-carmine (Apr. '98) .. 12 6 3 6
  b. Dull rose (June '98) .. 7 6 2 6
313 **65** 1s. brownish red (Mar. '97) 6 0 1 9
314 **66** 1s. 6d. brown-orange (Aug. '98) 35 0 15 0
315 **42** 2s. blue-green (Apr. '97) 27 6 12 6
316 **43** 2s. 6d. yellow (Sept. '96) 27 6 15 0
  a. Yellow (U) (Sept. '98) .. 35 0 17 6
317 **46** 3s. olive-drab (Dec. '96) 27 6 15 0
  a. Olive-drab (U) (Oct. '98) .. 30 0 17 6
318 **47** 4s. orange (Sept. '97) .. 27 6 5 0
319 **48** 5s. rosine (Feb. '97) 27 6 7 6
  a. Rose-carmine (Nov. '97) .. 22 6 6 0
  b. Rosine (U) (Mar. '99) .. 40 0 10 0
320 **49** 6s. p. yell.-grn.† (Apr. '99) 27 6 10 0
321 **50** 10s. grey-green (Apr. '97) 50 0 20 0
  a. Blue-green (July '98) .. 50 0 25 0
322 **51** 15s. brown† (Apr. '97) .. 50 0 15 0
323 **59** £25 dull bluish green† (U) ('99) .. .. .. — £7
324 ,, £50 dull pur.† (U) (Nov. '97) — £6

73

74

(*Illustrations reduced. Actual size* 31½ × 38½ *mm.*)

(Des. M. Tannenberg. Eng. R. R. Mitchelhill.)

1897 (7 Oct.). *Charity.* *W* **72** (*V*3) *sideways.* *P* 12½.

325 **73** 1d. (1s.) blue 30 0 37 6
326 **74** 2½d. (2s. 6d.) red-brown .. £8 £10

These stamps, sold at 1s. and 2s. 6d. respectively, paid postage of 1d. and 2½d. only, the difference being given to a Hospital Fund.

1899 (1 Aug.)–**1900.** *Colours changed for* ½*d.,* 1*d.,* 1½*d. and* 2½*d.* *P* 12½.

(*a*) *W* **23** (*V*2).

327 **71** 1½d. brn.-red/*yell.* (1.8.99) 1 3 1 3

(*b*) *W* **72** (*V*3).

328 **60** ½d. emerald (Aug. '99) .. 2 6 0 9
329 **69** 2½d. blue (1.8.99) 1 9 1 0

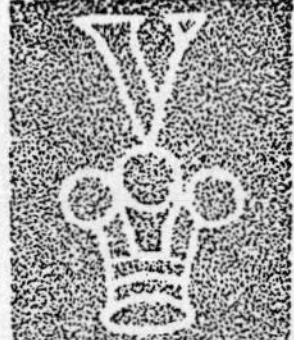
75 (*V*4)

(*c*) *W* **75** (*V*4).

*This wmk. and paper, like V*3, *was supplied by Waterlow and Sons and it continued in use until* 1905. *It was the result of an amended specification. Like the V*3 *paper it has a marked mesh but is whiter, smoother and harder. The* 1s. *and the four higher values have the wmk. sideways, the* ½d. *being found with both positions.*

No.	Type	Description	Unused		Used	
330	**60**	½d. emerald (1.8.99) ..	0	6	0	3
		a. Deep blue-green	1	6	0	6
331	**68**	1d. rosine (1.8.99) ..	0	6	0	3
		a. Rose-red (1900)	0	6	0	3
332	**62**	2d. violet (*shades*) (1.8.99)	3	0	0	4
333	**69**	2½d. blue (Feb. 1900) ..	1	3	0	9
334	**39**	3d. bistre-yell. (Sept. '99)	3	0	0	9
335	**63**	4d. rose-red (Dec. '99) ..	3	6	1	0
336	**70**	5d. red-brown (Oct. '99)..	3	0	0	9
337	**64**	6d. dull ultram. (Feb. '00)	3	6	0	9
338	**29**	9d. rose-red (Aug. '99) ..	3	6	1	9
339	**65**	1s. brown-red (May 1900)	5	0	2	0
340	**66**	1s. 6d. orange (Dec. '99)	7	6	7	6
341	**42**	2s. blue-green (June 1900)	8	6	6	0
342	**43**	2s. 6d. yellow (Jan. 1900)	12	6	5	0
343	**46**	3s. pale olive† (May 1900)	15	0	5	0
344	**48**	5s. rose-red (April 1900)	17	6	5	0
345	**50**	10s. green† (Mar. 1900) ..	30	0	7	6

76

77

(*Illustrations reduced. Actual size* 33 × 39 *mm.*)

(Eng. S. Reading.)

1900 (MAY). *Charity. W* **75** (*V*4) *sideways. P* 12½.

No.	Type	Description	Unused		Used	
346	**76**	1d. (1s.) olive-brown ..	85	0	90	0
347	**77**	2d. (2s.) emerald-green ..	£12		£15	

These stamps were sold for a Boer War Patriotic Fund, on a similar basis to the issue of 1897.

V Over Crown Wmks.: A Note on " Abnormal " Watermark Positions.

It should always be remembered that the block of 120 wmks. (12 × 10) in the sheet was designed to fit the normal size stamp in an upright position. *Other* sizes, larger and smaller, were printed, at various times, with the wmk. *both* upright and sideways. The following note concerns only varieties as they are found on stamps of normal size.

Inverted Wmks.: This description also embraces cases of wmks. lying sideways with V at right found on stamps of Type **60** etc. which are of the same dimensions (but reversed) as the usual size stamp. In printings before 1882 all inverted wmks. may be regarded as " abnormals ". In this period all sheets of 240 wmks. were, where necessary, cut into two before printing. From 1882 to mid-1896 the *only* inverted " abnormals " are found in certain of the common values where the area of the printing surface (i.e. 2 plates of 120) more or less equalled the area of the complete sheet of watermarked paper as it was supplied by De La Rue's. This was of 240 wmks., consisting of one pane of 120 wmks. over another pane of 120. In this period the sheet of 240 wmks. was not cut up before printing from single plates as had been done previously. Where only one plate was employed the sheet was fed in in one direction, taken out, and fed in in the other direction, giving in the result 120 normal and 120 inverted wmks. (This fact is of assistance when distinguishing certain Reprints.) From 1896 the same principle applied save that the complete sheets supplied were of 480 wmks. so that the only " abnormal " inverteds found are in those cases, e.g. 1d. and 2d. where the stamps were printed from a block of similar size viz. of 4 plates of 120 impressions clamped together.

Sideways Wmks.: This description includes upright wmks. on stamps of the dimensions of Type **60** etc. They usually arose through the suppliers placing the paper in the wrong direction in the bound books (and later unbound reams) of paper supplied. *Three* periods concern us in this regard.

(i) 1867–1882: Before 1867 paper was supplied in single sheets of 120 wmks. and from 1867 in double sheets of 240 wmks. From 1867 to 1882 wherever it was necessary (i.e. where only one plate was used) the double sheets were cut into half before printing. The variety may be found under the following numbers. All are extremely rare—viz. 174, 180, 190, 192, 193, 202, 214, 225.

(ii) 1882–1896. In this period no " abnormal " sideways wmks. are met since the paper supplied was not cut up before printing and since the complete sheet supplied was rectangular and *not square* in shape.

(iii) 1896–1912: Here the wmkd. paper supplied was of 480 (120 × 4) wmks. and such sheets were practically square. One meets " abnormals " under the following numbers, many of these being extremely rare—viz. 304, 305, 307, 308, 312, 313, 328, 330, 331, 332, 334, 338, 356, 357, 359, 366, 367, 368, 371, 373, 386, 400, 405, 407, 414, 417, 445, 447, 451.

Reversed Wmks.: These involved a printing on the wrong side of the paper. Since the side which should have been printed was usually ' surfaced ' to some degree these varieties almost invariably show the impression of the stamp coarser than normally and the back of the stamp smoother and glossier. From 1878 to 1896 the back of the paper supplied by De La Rues was treated with a special preparation to prevent the gum soaking through to the front. This preparation was susceptible to moisture and when printed upon and subsequently exposed to moisture occasionally shed portions of the design, so that in this period such varieties often bear the superficial appearance of having been printed on the gum, whereas in fact, up to July 1912, all gumming was done after printing. Reversed wmks., many of them very rare, have been found under the following Nos.—158, 162, 179, 181, 183, 184, 185, 187, 190, 192, 193, 197, 198, 206, 210, 211, 214, 228, 243, 244, 263, 283, 284, 285, 286, 287, 288, 289, 298, 305, 307, 310, 331, 332, 356, 357, 366, 373, 400, 401, 403, 406, 407, 408, 446, 447, 448—also in certain of the £25, £50 and £100 stamps (in both sections) and in various items in the Postal Fiscal list. In the reversed V over Crown cases—looking through the front of the stamp in a normal upright position—the double side of the ' V ' will appear on the *right* and not on the left as it should do.

IV. THE COMMONWEALTH PERIOD, 1901–12.

All postage stamps issued by the States in this period were in reality COMMONWEALTH stamps. This viewpoint has now received official endorsement (" Commonwealth of Australia Philatelic Bulletin " No. 2, Oct. 1953). Prior to the actual coming into being of the Commonwealth it had been agreed between the States that the Postal Services were to be the concern of the Commonwealth and that the postal revenue was to go to it. This decision meant, for Victoria, the separation of the Postage and the Fiscal systems. So long, however, as the Commonwealth lacked printing facilities and a Postal administration of its own the work had to be done by each State on its behalf. Separate series of Postage stamps (for which the State was obliged to account to the Commonwealth) and of Duty stamps (which were to continue as a State concern) therefore became necessary. The first Kangaroo stamps were not issued by the Commonwealth until Jan. 1913, but in the intervening period a long chain of philatelic events had contributed to make this issue possible. From the beginning of 1902 all the stamps of Tasmania and Western Australia were printed in Melbourne, on Victorian paper. Later Papua (1907) and later again South Australia (1909) were added to these. In the same year (1902) the first Commonwealth Postage Dues, printed in Sydney on New South Wales paper, appeared. In 1903 a 9d. stamp of the same "Commonwealth" design was issued in New South Wales and Queensland. In 1905 all States commenced using one or other of four types of Crown over A paper, marginally wmkd. "COMMONWEALTH OF AUSTRALIA". In 1909, printed in Melbourne, appeared new bi-coloured Postage Dues, the first stamps to be inscribed "AUSTRALIA". This followed the appointment of J. B. Cooke, the South Australian stamp printer, as Commonwealth Stamp Printer. As from 13.10.10 the stamps of any State could legally be used in any other State, and in April 1911 the first Commonwealth Postal Stationery was issued. In short, in the period 1901 to 1912, although certain States printed and issued postage stamps this was a privilege, subject at all times to Commonwealth control and direction and conducted, in respect of the nett revenue received, solely for the Commonwealth's benefit.

The Commonwealth was proclaimed as from 1st January 1901. In only three cases in the first issue, viz. the 1d., 2½d. and 5d. values was there sufficient time to alter the dies and produce new plates. In all the other cases the same plates were used as had been employed to produce the 1891 Reprints.

1901 (29 JAN.)–**1905.** *P* 12½ *or* 12×12½. (*a*) *Without the word "POSTAGE" in the design.*

(*i*) *W* **72** (*V*3).

348	**35**	2s. blue/*pink*	8	0	8	0

(*ii*) *W* **75** (*V*4).

349	**25**	½d. bluish green	0	5	0	3
		a. Var. "VICTCRIA" ..	50	0	45	0
350	**33**	2d. reddish violet	0	9	0	3
351	**16**	3d. dull orange	2	6	1	6
352	**34**	4d. bistre-yellow	3	0	2	0
353	**17**	6d. emerald	3	0	3	0
354	**30**	1s. yellow	3	0	3	0
355	**19**	5s. pale red and dp. blue	22	6	17	6

78

79

80

(*b*) *With the word "POSTAGE" in the design.* *W* **75** (*V*4).

356	**78**	1d. rose (Die I)	0	6	0	3
		a. Dull red (Dec. '01) ..	0	6	0	3
357	,,	1d. rose (Die II) (2.4.'01)	0	6	0	3
		a. Dull red (Dec. '01) ..	0	6	0	3
358	,,	1d. pale rose-red (Die III) (3.5.'05)	2	6	0	6
359	**79**	2½d. dull blue (1901) ..	1	3	0	4
		a. Deep blue (1902)	1	3	0	3
360	**80**	5d. reddish brown ..	3	6	0	6
		a. Purple-brown (1903) ..	2	6	0	6

Three dies of the 1d.: Principal differences are:

I. Horizontal lines over Queen's head fill oval surround under "VICTORIA". Found in two plates employed Jan. 1901–Feb. 1903.

II. Practically all the lines of shading to the left of and on top of the head have been "thinned", giving a lighter appearance. Some lines at the top have been cut away, leaving small white patches, particularly under the "OR". Found in ten plates in use between April 1901 and April 1905.

III. As II but with stop at lower left clearly separated from circle line at its right; spot of colour in shading between "O" and "R"; two lines of shading meet in lower left portion of "P" of "PENNY". Found in twelve plates in use between May 1905 and the end of 1912.

1901 (JUNE). *W* **75** (*V*4). *P* 12×12½.

361	**68**	1d. olive (6.6.'01)	2	6	3	0
362	**39**	3d. slate-green (20.6.'01) ..	4	0	6	0

These stamps were available for postal purposes to 30.6.'01, afterwards for fiscal purposes only.

81

82

83

84

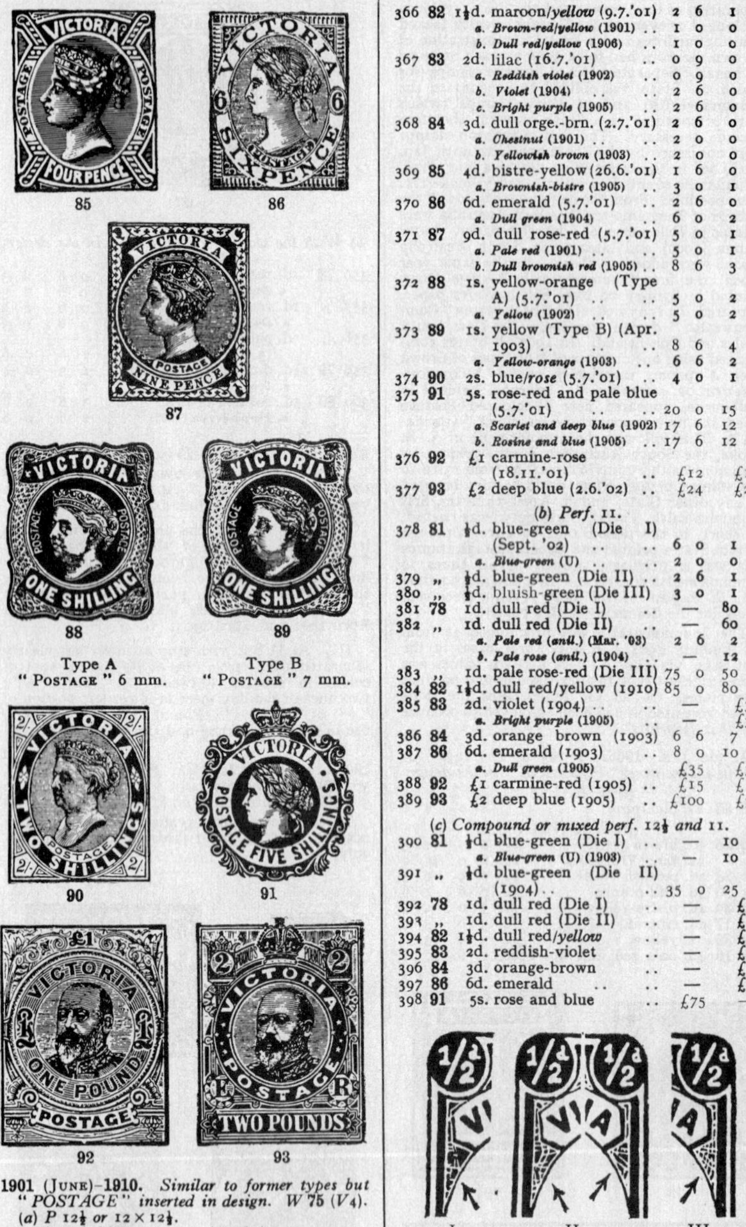

85 86

87

88 — Type A "Postage" 6 mm.

89 — Type B "Postage" 7 mm.

90 91

92 93

1901 (June)–**1910.** *Similar to former types but "POSTAGE" inserted in design. W* **75** (*V*4).

(*a*) *P* 12½ *or* 12 × 12½.

No.	Type	Description	Unused s.	d.	Used s.	d.
363	**81**	½d. blue-green (*shades*) (Die I) (26.6.01)	0	4	0	3
		a. Blue-green (U)	0	6	0	3
364	,,	½d. pale blue-grn. (Die II) (June, 04)	1	0	0	6
365	,,	½d. pale bluish green (Die III) (June, 05) ..	4	0	2	0
366	**82**	1½d. maroon/*yellow* (9.7.'01)	2	6	1	9
		a. Brown-red/yellow (1901) ..	1	0	0	6
		b. Dull red/yellow (1906) ..	1	0	0	6
367	**83**	2d. lilac (16.7.'01) ..	0	9	0	4
		a. Reddish violet (1902) ..	0	9	0	4
		b. Violet (1904)	2	6	0	9
		c. Bright purple (1905) ..	2	6	0	9
368	**84**	3d. dull orge.-brn. (2.7.'01)	2	6	0	6
		a. Chestnut (1901)	2	0	0	4
		b. Yellowish brown (1903) ..	2	0	0	4
369	**85**	4d. bistre-yellow (26.6.'01)	1	6	0	9
		a. Brownish-bistre (1905) ..	3	0	1	0
370	**86**	6d. emerald (5.7.'01) ..	2	6	0	9
		a. Dull green (1904) ..	6	0	2	6
371	**87**	9d. dull rose-red (5.7.'01)	5	0	1	9
		a. Pale red (1901)	5	0	1	9
		b. Dull brownish red (1905) ..	8	6	3	0
372	**88**	1s. yellow-orange (Type A) (5.7.'01)	5	0	2	6
		a. Yellow (1902)	5	0	2	3
373	**89**	1s. yellow (Type B) (Apr. 1903)	8	6	4	0
		a. Yellow-orange (1903) ..	6	6	2	6
374	**90**	2s. blue/*rose* (5.7.'01) ..	4	0	1	9
375	**91**	5s. rose-red and pale blue (5.7.'01)	20	0	15	0
		a. Scarlet and deep blue (1902)	17	6	12	6
		b. Rosine and blue (1905) ..	17	6	12	6
376	**92**	£1 carmine-rose (18.11.'01) ..	£12		£10	
377	**93**	£2 deep blue (2.6.'02) ..	£24		£20	

(*b*) *Perf.* 11.

No.	Type	Description	Unused s.	d.	Used s.	d.
378	**81**	½d. blue-green (Die I) (Sept. '02)	6	0	1	6
		a. Blue-green (U)	2	0	0	9
379	,,	½d. blue-green (Die II) ..	2	6	1	0
380	,,	½d. bluish-green (Die III)	3	0	1	6
381	**78**	1d. dull red (Die I) ..	—		80	0
382	,,	1d. dull red (Die II) ..	—		60	0
		a. Pale red (*anil.*) (Mar. '03)	2	6	2	6
		b. Pale rose (*anil.*) (1904) ..	—		12	6
383	,,	1d. pale rose-red (Die III)	75	0	50	0
384	**82**	1½d. dull red/yellow (1910)	85	0	80	0
385	**83**	2d. violet (1904)	—		£32	
		a. Bright purple (1905) ..	—		£32	
386	**84**	3d. orange brown (1903)	6	6	7	6
387	**86**	6d. emerald (1903) ..	8	0	10	0
		a. Dull green (1905) ..	£35		£32	
388	**92**	£1 carmine-red (1905) ..	£15		£15	
389	**93**	£2 deep blue (1905) ..	£100		£70	

(*c*) *Compound or mixed perf.* 12½ *and* 11.

No.	Type	Description	Unused s.	d.	Used s.	d.
390	**81**	½d. blue-green (Die I) ..	—		10	0
		a. Blue-green (U) (1903) ..	—		10	0
391	,,	½d. blue-green (Die II) (1904)	35	0	25	0
392	**78**	1d. dull red (Die I) ..	—		£30	
393	,,	1d. dull red (Die II) ..	—		£15	
394	**82**	1½d. dull red/*yellow* ..	—		£30	
395	**83**	2d. reddish-violet ..	—		£50	
396	**84**	3d. orange-brown ..	—		£30	
397	**86**	6d. emerald	—		£30	
398	**91**	5s. rose and blue ..	£75		—	

I. II. III.

Three dies of the ½d.: Principal differences are

I. Outer of two vertical lines of colour to lef of "v" is continuous save for a marked breal opposite top of "v". Found in two plates i use 1901–May 1904.

II. Outer vertical line to left of "V" is broken in three places; the triangular space S.W. of "V", has also been "opened up" and shows more white lines than in I. Found in two plates in use June 1904–June 1905.

III. As II but the thin vertical coloured line to right of the "A" of "VICTORIA" (previously broken in the middle) is now broken in four or five places. The triangular ornament to S.E. of the same "A" has also been "opened up", the white cross-hatching now being stronger than in I and II. Found in two plates introduced in June 1905 and in two subsequent plates introduced late in 1909.

The paper used for the 1½d. value for two printings in 1908–9 was yellow-buff in colour but in used copies the difference is not so marked as to warrant separate description.

There were two main states of the 2d. Die, the original showing the S.E. corner correctly squared and the later showing it damaged and blunter. There are other differences. The original state is found in all printings before April 1904 but not after, and the later state to a small extent (5 per cent) in the printings before April 1904 and *solely* in the printings from that date.

For the 1s. Type A the same plate was used as for the 1s. "No Postage" of 1901, the words "POSTAGE" being separately punched on. For Type B two new plates, prepared via an etched line-block, were introduced.

Certain *unlisted shades* (due to their being unsatisfactory) are found *only* punctured O.S. Marked instances of this are found in the 2d., 3d. and 4d. values.

1905–13. *Wmk. Crown over A, Type W.11. A: Medium paper, supplied, like the V4 paper, by Waterlow & Sons.*

(a) P 12½ or 12 × 12½.

No.	Type	Description	Unused	Used
399	**81**	½d. blue-green (21.10.'05)	0 6	0 3
		a. Light bluish green	0 6	0 3
400	**78**	1d. rose-red (*shades*) (16.7.'05)	0 4	0 3
		a. Pale rose (1907)	0 4	0 3
		b. Rose-carmine (Sept. '11)	2 0	0 9
401	**83**	2d. dull mauve (13.9.'05)	2 6	0 3
		a. Bright mauve (1906)	2 0	0 3
		b. Reddish violet (1907)	1 0	0 3
		c. Lilac (1910)	1 3	0 3
402	**79**	2½d. blue (April 1908)	1 6	1 0
		a. Indigo (1909)	1 6	1 0
403	**84**	3d. orge.-brn. (11.11.'05)	2 6	0 9
		a. Yellow-orange (1908)	3 6	1 3
		b. Dull orange-buff (1909)	2 6	0 9
		c. Ochre (1912)	2 6	1 0
404	**85**	4d. yellow-bistre (15.1.'06)	3 0	0 6
		a. Bistre (1908)	3 6	0 6
		b. Yellow-olive (1912)	3 6	0 6
405	**80**	5d. chocolate (14.8.'06)	3 6	1 6
		a. Dull reddish-brown (1908)	3 0	1 0
406	**86**	6d. dull green (25.10.'05)	4 0	0 9
		a. Dull yellow-green (1907)	3 6	0 6
		b. Emerald (1909)	3 6	0 6
		c. Yellowish-green (1911)	3 6	0 6
407	**87**	9d. rose-red (11.12.'05)	5 0	1 6
		a. Pale salmon-red (1906)	4 0	1 6
		b. Brown-red (1908)	5 0	1 6
		c. Pale dull rose (worn pl.)	14 0	3 6
		d. Rose-carmine new pl., (Dec. 09)	4 6	1 6
408	**89**	1s. yellow-orange (13.2.'06)	4 6	1 0
		a. Yellow (1906)	4 6	1 0
		b. Lemon (1908)	5 0	1 3
409	**91**	5s. rose-red and ultram. (U) (Dec. '07)	30 0	12 6
		a. Rose-red and blue (U) (1912)	40 0	17 6
		b. Rose-red and blue (S)	45 0	25 0
410	**92**	£1 salmon (Feb. 1907)	£16	£10
411	„	£1 dull rose (1910)	£16	£12
		a. Deep dull rose (U) (1912)	£16	£14
412	**93**	£2 dull blue (1906)	£30	£28

Perforations of period 1901–12.

In general, up to 1910, five machines were available at any one time—three single-line (two "11" and one "12½") and two vertical combs (12 × 12½). Only single-line machines were used for the 5s., £1 and £2 values. The "12½" single line was used on many occasions for the ½d. and occasionally for other values. The "11" machines were primarily employed for larger size stamps, e.g. Victorian Duty Stamps, Tasmanian Pictorials and Papua, and their use for the normal size Victorian postage stamps was in the main restricted to emergencies. At certain periods, e.g. 1909–10 one encounters the true "compounds" i.e. the products of two single-line machines, 12½ and 11 respectively. For the ½d. the vertical comb 12 × 12½ was also used, particularly in the earlier period, on the sheet turned sideways. In the result the alternate vertical margins between stamps were left imperforate and a single-line machine (either 12½ or 11) was often used to complete the perforating, in the latter case (11) giving us a variety for separate listing. "Mixed" perforations in this period are, like their predecessors of the '70s, the result of the correction—with another machine—of faultily centred lines of perforation (either single-line or comb), the back of these faulty lines being usually pasted over with gummed strips to assist in tearing down the corrected lines.

The rotary-comb machines gauging 11½ × 12¼ were brought over from South Australia by J. B. Cooke when he moved to Melbourne in 1909.

The ½d. perf. 11 and the 2½d. and 5s. first printings (all perforated with single line machines) may be met with *full imperforate base margins.* Likewise in the Crown over A issues the ½d. perf. 12½ and the 5s. perf. 12½ (1912) have been similarly found. Such varieties are, of course rare.

(b) Perf. 11.

No.	Type	Description	Unused	Used
413	**81**	½d. light bluish green	0 6	0 4
		a. Blue-green	0 9	0 6
414	**78**	1d. rose-red (1905)	1 3	0 6
		a. Pale rose (1907)	1 6	0 9
		b. Rose-carmine (1911)	5 0	5 0
415	**83**	2d. mauve (1906)	—	£30
		a. Reddish violet (1908)	70 0	45 0
		b. Lilac (1910)	37 6	25 0
416	**79**	2½d. blue (1909)	25 0	22 6
		a. Indigo (1909)	6 0	6 0
417	**84**	3d. brown (1908)	12 6	10 0
		a. Orange-buff (1909)	27 6	25 0
		b. Dull orange-yellow (1911)	—	£15
		c. Ochre (1912)	3 0	3 0
418	**85**	4d. yellow-bistre (1908)	6 6	
		a. Yellow-olive (1912)	5 0	6 0
419	**80**	5d. reddish-brown	—	£50
420	**86**	6d. emerald (1910)	4 6	4 6
		a. Yellowish green (1911)	12 6	4 6
421	**87**	9d. rose-carmine	—	£55
422	**89**	1s. yellow-orange	£38	
		a. Yellow	—	£32
423	**91**	5s. rose-red and ultram.	17 6	12 6
424	**92**	£1 salmon (1907)	£12	£12
425	**93**	£2 dull blue (1906)	£24	£20

(c) Compound or mixed perfs. 12½ and 11.

No.	Type	Description	Unused	Used
426	**81**	½d. light bluish-green (June 1909)	35 0	35 0
427	**78**	1d. rose-red	75 0	£5
428	**83**	2d. mauve	—	£32
429	**84**	3d. brown (1912)	£25	£32
		a. Ochre	—	£25
430	**85**	4d. bistre	—	£32
431	**86**	6d. yellowish green	—	£32
432	**87**	9d. dull rose-red	—	£55
433	**89**	1s. yellow-orange	—	£55

(*d*) *Rotary comb perf.* 11½ × 12½.

434 **78** 1d. pale scarlet-red (Feb. '10) 3 6 0 9
a. Rose-red (Mar. '10) .. 1 6 0 6

435 **83** 2d. lilac (*shades*) 5 0 1 6

B: *On thinner paper, ready gummed with white gum.* (*July-November* 1912).

(*a*) *P* 12½ *or* 12 × 12½.

436 **81** ½d. blue-green 3 0 1 6
437 **78** 1d. rose-red 7 6 1 6
438 **83** 2d. lilac 17 6 6 0
439 **80** 5d. brown 8 6 4 0
440 **86** 6d. emerald 8 6 4 0
441 **89** 1s. dull yellow (Nov. '12) .. 20 0 7 6
a. Pale orange (Jan. '13) .. 20 0 7 6

(*b*) *P* 11.

442 **81** ½d. blue-green 35 0 20 0
443 **78** 1d. rose-red 12 6 5 0

(*c*) *P* 11 × 12½.

444 **81** ½d. blue-green £14 £12

(*d*) *Rotary comb perf.* 11½ × 12¼.

445 **78** 1d. rose-carmine (2.7.12) .. 1 6 0 5
a. Rose-red (Oct. '12) .. 2 6 0 8

Two qualities of the "thin" paper were supplied, the first supply (earliest date 2.7.12) being thicker and with a less obvious mesh than the second (earliest date 2.10.12). The ½d. and 1d. are found on both classes of paper, the 2d. on the first only, and the 5d., 6d. and 1s. on the second only. There was a shortage pending the arrival of the second supply, and this gap was filled by the use of the "Stamp Duty" paper next described and the ONE PENNY overprint of 1.7.12. The 5d. perforated O.S. on the thin paper may be met in *dull red-brown*.

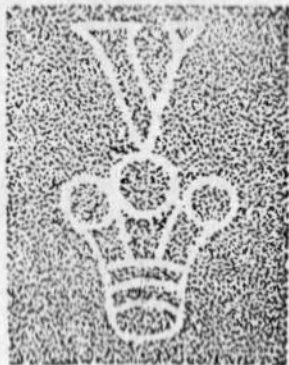

94 (*V*5).

C: *Printed on "Stamp Duty" paper,* **W 94** (*V*5). *This paper is rather softer and of a more pronounced mesh than the V*4 *paper.* (*Aug.–Oct.* 1912).

(*a*) *P* 12½ *or* 12 × 12½.

446 **81** ½d. bluish green 2 0 1 6
447 **78** 1d. rose-carmine (7.8.12) .. 2 6 0 9
448 **83** 2d. reddish-violet 3 0 1 3
a. Lilac 7 6 3 0
449 **87** 9d. carmine-red 6 0 3 0

(*b*) *P* 11.

450 **81** ½d. bluish green 25 0 20 0
451 **78** 1d. rose-carmine (Aug. '12) 45 0 15 0
452 **87** 9d. carmine-red 12 6 8 6

(*c*) *Compound perf.* 11 *with* 12½.

453 **87** 9d. carmine-red .. .. — £55

This paper was supplied by Spicer Bros. at the beginning of 1911 and continued to be used for many years in the production of Duty Stamps for this State.

ONE PENNY

(**95**)

1912 (1 July). *Surch. with T* **95** *in red. Wmk. Crown over A. P* 11½ × 12¼.

454 **83** 1d. on 2d. lilac 0 6 0 6

Late in June 1912 the first consignment of "thin" paper was exhausted and the second had not arrived. A further supply of the 1d. value was urgently required, and the expedient of overprinting current 2d. stock was employed to fill the gap. The same reason also produced the 1d. on 2d. overprints of Tasmania and Western Australia respectively.

POSTAL FISCALS.

This section embraces those printings of Duty and Fee stamps made before 1.1.84. These were made available for postal purposes as from 1.1.84. The two series were in concurrent use between December 1879 and 1884.

A. The "STAMP STATUTE" series.

This series was first issued on 26th April 1871 and it was in the main used to record the payment of various Court fees. The issue of the series ceased in April 1884.

F 1 F 2 F 3

F 4

(Illustrations ½ size.)

1870–83. *Large rectangular stamps of various designs as Types* **F 1** *to* **F 4**. *All save the 3d. and 2s. 6d. (eng. by James Turner) have the Queen's head included in the design (eng. by William Bell). Typo. at the Stamp Printing Office, Melbourne.*

(*a*) *Wmk. single-lined numerals* (1, 2, *and* 10) *as used for Postage Stamps* (1863–67). *On Saunders paper unless otherwise noted. Both sideways and upright wmks. are found in certain cases.*

F 1 1s. blue/*blue*, *p.* 13 .. .. 15 0 17 6
a. Perf. 12 .. .. .. 35 0
F 2 2s. blue/*grn.* (D.L.R.), *p.* 13 35 0 45 0
a. Perf. 12 .. .. .. 35 0 45 0
F 3 2s. deep blue/*green* (S), *p.* 13 45 0
a. Perf. 12 .. .. .. — 55 0
F 4 10s. brown-olive/*pink*, *p.* 13 (June '71) .. ..
F 5 10s. red-brown/*pink*, *p.* 13 (1879) £8 60 0
a. Perf. 12 .. .. ..

(*b*) *Wmk. V over Crown Type* **20** (*V*1)

The wmk. is usually *sideways* but in certain cases the whole of a printing was *upright*. One also meets "abnormal" upright wmks.

F 7 ½d. on 1d. pale grn. (R.), *p.* 13 7 6 8 6
F 8 1d. pale green, *p.* 13 .. 4 0 4 0
a. Green, p. 12½ (U) ('80) .. 10 0 12 6
F 9 3d. mauve, *p.* 13 (Sept. '79) 60 0 50 0
F10 4d. rose, *p.* 13 .. .. 15 0 15 0

No.	Description	Unused	Used
F11	6d. blue, *p.* 13 ('71)	18 6	17 6
	a. *Dull ultramarine, p.* 13 ('76)	5 0	6 0
	aa. Perf. 12	—	8 6
F12	1s. blue/*blue, p.* 13 (June '76)	12 6	
	a. Perf. 12	—	15 0
	b. *Ultram./blue, p.* 12½ ('82)	—	15 0
	ba. Perf. 12	—	15 0
	c. *Deep blue/blue, p.* 12½ ('83)	17 6	15 0
	ca. Perf. 12	—	15 0
F13	2s. blue/*yellow, p.* 13 (July '76)	65 0	45 0
	a. Perf. 12		
F14	2s. dp. blue/*grn., p.* 13 ('83)	40 0	27 6
	a. Perf. 12	45 0	35 0
F15	2s. 6d. orge., *p.* 13 (July '76)	—	55 0
	a. Perf. 12		
	b. *Yellow, p.* 13 (Nov. '78)	40 0	
	ba. Perf. 12	40 0	60 0
	c. *Orange-yellow, p.* 12½ ('82)		
	ca. Perf. 12		
F16	5s. blue/*yellow, p.* 13	70 0	45 0
	a. Perf. 12		
	b. *Ultram./lemon, p.* 12½ ('81)	70 0	45 0
F17	10s. brown/*pink, p.* 13 (Aug. '76)	£7	
	a. *Purple-brown/pink, p.* 12½ ('82)	£7	
	aa. Perf. 12		
F18	£1 slate-violet/*yellow* (S, U.) *p.* 13 ('71)	£7	
	a. Perf. 12 (1880)	£7	
	b. *Mauve/yellow, p.* 13 ('73)		
	ba. Perf. 12 ('81)	£7	
	bb. Perf. 12½ ('82)		
F19	£5 black and yellow-green, *p.* 12 (Nov. '71)		
	a. Perf. 13		
	b. Perf. 12½ (U)		

(*c*) 1882-3: *Wmk. V over Crown Type* **23** (*V*2).

No.	Description	Unused	Used
F20	1d. yellowish green, *p.* 12½	15 0	15 0
F21	2s. 6d. pale orange-yellow, *p.* 12½	42 6	
F22	£5 black & yellow-grn., *p.* 12		

All the values of the "Stamp Statute" series were reprinted in 1891 on paper wmkd. V1 (5s., 10s. and £1) and V2 (the rest). The colours used, in all cases, differed radically from the originals. Except for the £5, for which the old electrotypes were used, new plates were made for the Reprints, from dies which showed "die flaws" not to be found on the originals. In 1877 a 12s. 6d. value was prepared for use but although it was placed on sale at the Law Courts and was available there for some months not a single copy was sold, and it was withdrawn. Proofs are known.

B. The "STAMP DUTY" Series.

This series was used mainly to record the payment of duties on the sale of land, receipts and n merous other documents.

F 5 F 6 F 7 F 8

F 9 F 10 F 11

(Illustrations ⅔ size.)

(Dies for these issues (except 1d. of 1880) supplied by Messrs. Sands and McDougall. Des. Charles Jackson and Ludwig Lang. Eng. Charles Jackson, Arthur Williams and others (See previously). The 1d. of 1880 was eng. by Charles Naish.)

1879 (Dec.)–**1883** (Dec.). I. *December* 1879: *Litho. Stamp Printing Office, Melbourne. Wmk. V over Crown, Type* **20** (*V*1). *Sideways unless otherwise indicated* (*U*).

No.	Type	Description	Unused	Used
F23	F 5	1d. blue-green, *p.* 13	4 6	6 6
		a. Perf. 12	8 6	6 6
F24	45	1s. 6d. rosine, *p.* 13	8 6	10 0
		a. Perf. 12		
F25	46	3s. purple/*blue, p.* 13	17 6	15 0
		a. Perf. 12	—	30 0
F26	47	4s. orange-red, *p.* 13	17 6	8 6
		a. Perf. 12	17 6	8 6
F27	49	6s. apple-grn., *p.* 13 (U)	20 0	8 6
		a. Perf. 12 (U)		
F28	50	10s. brown/*rose p.* 13 (S, U)	80 0	35 0
		a. Perf. 12 (S, U)		
F29	51	15s. mauve, *p.* 13	—	60 0
F30	52	£1 red-orange, *p.* 13	—	60 0
F31	53	£1 5s. dull rose, *p.* 13 (U)	—	85 0
F32	54	£1 10s. deep grey-olive, *p.* 13 (S, U)	—	42 6
F33	–	35s. grey-violet, *p.* 13 (U)	F.C. £7	
F34	55	£2 blue, *p.* 13	—	90 0
F35	56	45s. dull brown-lilac, *p.* 13 (U)	—	90 0
F36	57	£5 rose-red, *p.* 13 (U)	—	85 0
F37	F 9	£6 blue/*pink, p.* 13 (U)	—	£14
F38	F 10	£7 violet/*blue, p.* 13 (U)	—	£14
F39	F 11	£8 brnish-red/*yellow, p.* 13 (U)	—	£14
F40	–	£9 yellow-grn./*green, p.* 13 (U)	F.C. £7	

Apart from the "Half-Lengths", the 2d. Queen-on-Throne, the first 1s. Octagonal and the £25, £50 and £100 of 1886–89 these were the only stamps of Victoria to be printed by lithography and its adoption on this occasion was dictated by the necessity for speed of production. *All* the Lithographed stamps can be distinguished from the typographed stamps of the same design by their colours which are highly distinctive. Other differences, of wmk. & perf., will be found. Some values, e.g. the 6s., 25s. and 30s. (1884–91) were available for postage over a considerable period.

II. Dec. 1879–1882: *Typographed from electrotypes at Stamp Printing Office, Melbourne.*

(1) *Wmk. V over Crown, Type* **20** (V1).

No.	Type	Description	Unused	Used
F41	F 5	1d. yellowish-green, *p.* 13 (Dec. '79)	3 6	3 6
		a. Perf. 12	5 0	5 0

F42 F 6 1d. pale bistre, *p.* 12½ (June '80) 0 9 0 9
a. Perf. 12 .. .. .. 2 0 2 0
F43 F 7 6d. dull blue, *p.* 13 (Dec. '79) 5 0 3 0
a. Perf. 12 .. ..
F44 **44** 1s. deep blue/*blue*, *p* 13 (Dec. '79) 4 0 1 9
a. Perf. 12 .. .. 5 0 3 0
b. Bright bl./bl., p. 12½ (1882) 5 0 2 6
ba. Perf. 12 .. .. — 4 6
F45 F 8 2s. deep blue/*green*, *p.* 13 (Dec. '79) .. 7 6 5 0
a. Perf. 12 .. .. — 6 0
b. Indigo/green 55 0 37 6
ba. Perf. 12 .. .. 55 0 37 6
F46 **48** 5s. claret/*yellow*, *p.* 13 (Dec. '79) 15 0 6 0
a. Perf. 12 .. .. — 8 6
b. Pale claret/yellow, p. 12½ ('80) 15 0 6 0
ba. Perf. 12 .. .. 22 6 8 6
F47 **50** 10s. chocolate/*rose*, *p.* 13 (S, U) (Dec. '79) .. — 42 6
a. Perf. 12 (S, U) ..
F48 **52** £1 yellow-orange/*yellow* *p.* 12 (1882) ..
F49 **55** £2 deep blue, *p.* 12½ (1881) — 37 6
F50 **58** £10 dull mauve, *p.* 12 (1879) ..
a. Deep red-lilac (1882) .. — £6

(ii) 1882–3: *Wmk. V over Crown, Type* **23** (*V*2).

F51 F 6 1d. ochre (*shades*), *p.* 12½ 0 9 0 9
a. Perf. 12 .. .. 2 6 1 6
F52 F 7 6d. ultramarine, *p.* 12½ 4 6 3 6
a. Perf. 12 .. .. 4 6 3 6
F53 **55** £2 blue, *p* 12 — 45 0
F54 **57** £5 rose-pink, *p.* 12 — 95 0

III. 1879–80: ***Recess-printed direct from the die.***

(i) *Wmk. V over Crown, Type* **20** (*V*1) *p.* 13.

F55 **59** £25 yellow-green (1879) F.C. £6
a. Deep grn. (1880) F.C. £6
F56 ,, £50 bright mauve (1879) F.C. £8
F57 ,, £100 crimson-lake (1879) F.C. £7

(ii) 1882–3: *Wmk. V over Crown, Type* **23** (*V*2) *p.* 12½.

F58 59 **£50 dull lilac-mauve** F.C. £10
F59 ,, £100 crimson F.C. £8
a. Perf. 12 F.C. £8

Reprints of Stamp Duty Series: The only stamps in this series to be reprinted in 1891 (on wmk. *V*2) were the two types of 1d. which by then had become obsolete. Again the colours are distinctive from the originals.

In 1879 certain other values inscribed "STAMP DUTY" (of varying heraldic designs) viz.; 7s., 8s., 9s., 11s., 12s., 13s., 14s., 16s., 17s., 18s. and 19s. were prepared for use but were not issued. Proofs are known.

POSTAGE DUE STAMPS.

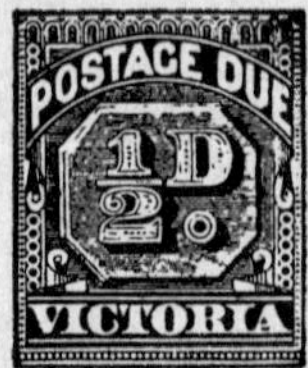

D 1

(Dies eng. Arthur Williams (values) and John McWilliams (frame). Typo.)

1890–1908. *Type* D **1**. A. *Wmk. V over Crown, Type* **23** (*V*2). *P* 12 × 12½.

(i) 1st. Nov. 1890 (*½d.,* 24.12.90).

D1 ½d. dull blue & brn. lake .. 3 0 3 0
D2 1d. dull blue & brn.-lake .. 3 0 3 0
D3 2d. dull blue & brn.-lake .. 3 6 3 0
D4 4d. dull blue & brn.-lake .. 3 6 2 6
D5 5d. dull blue & brn.-lake .. 4 6 3 0
D6 6d. dull blue & brn.-lake .. 4 6 2 0
D7 10d. dull blue & brn.-lake .. 22 6 15 0
D8 1s. dull blue & brn.-lake .. 10 0 8 0
D9 2s. dull blue & brn.-lake .. £5 70 0
D10 5s. dull blue & brn.-lake .. £6 80 0

The blue shades vary considerably.

(ii) 1890–94.

D11 ½d. dull bl. & dp. clar. (1890) 1 6 1 6
D12 1d. dull blue & brnish. red (20.1.93) 1 9 1 0
D13 2d. dull blue & brnish. red (28.3.93) 3 0 1 6
D14 4d. dull blue & pale claret (28.5.94) .. 6 0 4 0

Nos. D1 and D11 were separate printings, both made in December 1890.

(iii) 17th Jan. 1895. *Colours changed.*

D15 ½d. rosine & bluish green .. 3 6 2 6
D16 1d. rosine & bluish green .. 1 9 1 0
D17 2d. rosine & bluish green .. 1 0 0 9
D18 4d. rosine & bluish green .. 3 6 3 0
D19 5d. rosine & bluish green .. 6 6 5 0
D20 6d. rosine & bluish green .. 3 6 2 6
D21 10d. rosine & bluish green .. 7 6 6 0
D22 1s. rosine & bluish green .. 7 6 6 0

(iv) 28th March 1895

D23 2s. p. red & yellowish green 30 0 25 0
D24 5s. p. red & yellowish green 60 0 40 0

(v) **March 1896 on.**

D25 ½d. p. scarlet & yellow-green 2 6 1 6
D26 1d. p. scarlet & yellow-green 1 6 0 6
D27 2d. p. scarlet & yellow-green 1 6 0 6
D28 4d. p. scarlet & yellow-green 2 6 1 6
D29 5d. p. scarlet & yellow green 3 0 2 0

B. *W* **72** (*V*3). *P* 12½ *or* 12 × 12½.

(i) July 1897 on.

D30 1d. p. scarlet & yellow-green 0 9 0 4
D31 2d. p. scarlet & yellow-green 1 3 0 6
D32 4d. p. scarlet & yellow-green 1 6 0 9
D33 5d. p. scarlet & yellow-green 6 0 3 6
D34 6d. p. scarlet & yellow-green 3 0 2 0

(ii) July–Sept. 1899.

D35 1d. dull red & bluish green 2 6 0 9
D36 2d. dull red & bluish green 2 0 0 9
D37 4d. dull red & bluish green 3 6 1 3

C. *W* **75** (*V*4). *P* 12½ *or* 12 × 12½.

(i) 1900–1.

D38 ½d. rose-red & pale green .. 1 0 1 0
D39 1d. rose-red & pale green .. 1 0 0 6
D40 2d. rose-red & pale green .. 1 6 0 9
D41 4d. rose-red & pale green .. 3 6 1 6

(ii) 1901–2.

D42 ½d. pale red & deep green .. 1 0 0 9
D43 1d. pale red & deep green .. 1 0 0 6
D44 2d. pale red & deep green .. 1 6 0 9
D45 4d. pale red & deep green .. 3 6 1 6

(iii) 1902–3.

D46 1d. scarlet & deep green .. 1 0 0 6
D47 2d. scarlet & deep green .. 2 0 0 6
D48 4d. scarlet & deep green .. 2 6 1 0
D49 5d. scarlet & deep green .. 6 0 2 6
D50 1s. scarlet & deep green .. 10 0 5 0
D51 2s. scarlet & deep green .. £5 70 0
D52 5s. scarlet & deep green .. £6 80 0

The deep green of Nos. D46–52 has more "yellow" than that of D42–45.

(iv) 1904.

D53 ½d. rosine (*anil.*) & green .. 2 6 1 0
D54 1d. rosine (*anil.*) & green .. 1 3 0 6
D55 2d. rosine (*anil.*) & green .. 1 6 0 9
D56 4d. rosine (*anil.*) & green .. 2 6 1 6

D. *Wmk. Crown over A* (*Type W* 11). ***P* 12½ *or* 12 × 12½.**

(i) Jan. 1906.

D57 ½d. rosine (*anil.*) & p. green **6 0** **6 0**
D58 1d. rosine (*anil.*) & green .. 60 0 5 0

(ii) Mar. 1906.

D59 ½d. scarlet & p. yellow-green **1 0** **1 0**
D60 1d. scarlet & p. yellow-green **1 6** **0 9**

(iii) Dec. 1906.

D61 1d. scarlet (*anil.*) & deep yellow-green **2 6** **0 6**
D62 2d. scarlet (*anil.*) & deep yellow-green **3 6** **0 9**

(iv) 1907–8.

D63 ½d. dull scarlet & pea-green **0 9** **0 9**
D64 1d. dull scarlet & pea-green **2 6** **0 6**
D65 2d. dull scarlet & pea-green **3 6** **0 9**
D66 4d. dull scarlet & pea-green 12 6 10 0

Perf. compound 12 × 12½ *with* 11.

D67 ½d. dull scarlet & pea-green 75 0 75 0

In D59 and D60 the centre is more clearly printed than in the later printings. A 5d. value was prepared and printed on Crown over A paper but was not issued. A few copies are known postmarked to order from presentation sets.

Victoria now uses the stamps of Australia.

VIRGIN ISLANDS.

For GREAT BRITAIN stamps used in Tortola, see page 66.

1 St. Ursula. 2

(Litho. Waterlow & Sons, supplied by Messrs. Nissen & Parker.)

1866. *No wmk.* (i.) *P* 12.

(*a*) ***White wove paper.***

1 **1** 1d. green 60 0 75 0
2 „ 1d. deep green £5 £5
3 **2** 6d. rose £10 £10
4 „ 6d. deep rose £15 £16
a. Large "V" in "VIRGIN" .. £35 £40

(*b*) ***Toned paper.***

5 **1** 1d. green 80 0 90 0
6 „ 1d. deep green £11 £12
7 **2** 6d. rose-red 55 0 85 0
a. Large "V" in "VIRGIN" .. £12

(ii.) *P* 15 × 12.

7*b* **1** 1d. green £140 £275

The 1d. and 6d. perf. 12, are in sheets of twenty-five.

3 4

1867–68. *No wmk. P* 15.

The central figure in the 1*s. is in black.*

(*a*) *White wove paper.*

8 **1** 1d. blue-green 50 0 50 0
9 „ 1d. yellow-green 65 0 85 0
10 **2** 6d. pale rose £28 £32
11 **4** 1s. rose-carmine £20 £22

(*b*) *Toned paper.*

12 **1** 1d. yellow-green 80 0 85 0
13 **2** 6d. dull rose £25 £30
14 **4** 1s. rose-carmine (*blued*) .. £30 £30
14*a* „ 1s. rose-carmine £45 £55

(*c*) *Pale rose paper.*

15 **3** 4d. lake-red £5 £5

(*d*) *Buff paper.*

16 **3** 4d. lake-red 60 0 70 0
17 „ 4d. lake-brown 65 0 70 0

Nos. 11 and 14 have the double-lined frame.

5 6 (Die I)

With coloured margins. Centre in black. No wmk. P 15.

18 **5** 1s. crimson 95 0 £6
19 „ 1s. crimson (*toned* paper) .. £5 £6
20 „ 1s. crimson (*blued* paper) .. £50 £38

Error. Figure of the Virgin missing.

20*a* **5** 1s. crimson £1400

With single-lined frame.

21 **5** 1s. rose-carmine £15 £18
21*a* „ 1s. rose-carmine (*toned* paper) £15 £30

The 1d. perf. 15, is in sheets of twelve or twenty stamps. The 1s. is in sheets of twenty. The 4d. in sheets of twenty-five.

(Litho. De La Rue.)

1879. *Wmk. Crown CC* (*sideways*). *P* 14.

22 **1** 1d. green £6 £6
a. Yellow-green £14 £9
b. Wmk. upright £8 £8

(Typo. De La Rue.)

1880. *Wmk. Crown CC. P* 14.

24 **6** 1d. emerald-green 55 0 50 0
25 „ 2½d. red-brown £5 £5

1883–84. *Wmk. Crown CA. P* 14.

26 **6** ½d. yellow-buff 70 0 80 0
27 „ ½d. yellow-green 8 6 17 6
a. Imperf. (pair) £35
28 „ ½d. dull bluish green .. 15 0 25 0
29 „ 1d. pale rose 25 0 27 6
30 „ 1d. deep rose 65 0 75 0
31 „ 2½d. ultramarine (1884) .. 12 6 17 6

(Litho. De La Rue.)

1887–89. *Wmk. Crown CA. P* 14.

32 **1** 1d. red 8 0 10 0
33 „ 1d. rose-red 8 0 12 6
34 „ 1d. rose 10 0 22 6
35 **3** 4d. chestnut 40 0 45 0
36 „ 4d. pale chestnut 42 6 45 0
37 „ 4d. brown-red 35 0 52 6
38 **2** 6d. dull violet 35 0 50 0
39 „ 6d. deep violet 30 0 55 0
40 **4** 1s. sepia 95 0 97 6
41 „ 1s. brown (*to* deep) .. 60 0 65 0
41*a* „ 1s. light brown £40

The De La Rue transfers of T **1** to **4** are new transfers and differ from those of Messrs. Nissen and Parker.

4D

(7)

1888 (July). *No.* 19 *surch. with T* **7**, *in violet.*

42	4d. on 1s. black and crimson	£7	£9
	a. Surch. double..	£140	
	b. Surch. inverted (in pair with normal)		

The special issues for Virgin Islands were superseded on 31st Oct., 1890, by the general issue for Leeward Islands. In 1899, however, a new special issue (given below) appeared; it did not supersede the general issue for Leeward Islands, but was used concurrently, as were all subsequent issues, until July 1st, 1956, when the general Leeward Islands stamps were withdrawn.

8

(Recess. De La Rue & Co.)

1899. *Wmk. Crown CA. P* 14.

43	**8**	½d. yellow-green	1	6	2	6
		a. Error. "HALFPFNNY" ..	60	0	70	0
		b. Error. "HALPENNY" ..	60	0	70	0
		c. Imp. between (horiz. pair) ..	£175			
44	,,	1d. brick-red	4	6	4	6
45	,,	2½d. ultramarine	12	6	17	6
46	,,	4d. brown	15	0	20	0
		a. Error. "FOURPENCF" ..	£60		£60	
47	,,	6d. dull violet	12	6	22	6
48	,,	7d. deep green	15	0	22	6
49	,,	1s. brown-yellow	20	0	27	6
50	,,	5s. indigo	80	0	85	0

9

10

(Typo. De La Rue & Co.)

1904 (1 June). *Wmk. Mult. Crown CA. P* 14.

54	**9**	½d. dull purple and green	1	6	2	6
55	,,	1d. dull purple and scarlet	4	0	5	0
56	**10**	2d. dull purple and ochre	12	6	25	0
57	**9**	2½d. dull purple and ultram.	8	6	15	0
58	**10**	3d. dull purple and black	10	0	17	6
59	**9**	6d. dull purple and brown	10	0	17	6
60	**10**	1s. green and scarlet ..	17	6	27	6
61	,,	2s. 6d. green and black ..	45	0	60	0
62	**9**	5s. green and blue ..	85	0	£5	

11

12

(Typo. De La Rue & Co.)

1913–19. *Wmk. Mult. Crown CA. P* 14.

63	**11**	½d. green, O	1	0	2	0
64	,,	½d. yellow-green, O ('16)	1	6	2	0
65	,,	½d. blue-green and deep green, O ('19) ..	1	3	2	0
66	,,	1d. deep red, O	10	0	15	0
67	,,	1d. deep red & carmine, O	12	6	15	0
68	,,	1d. scarlet, O ('17) ..	8	0	8	6
69	,,	1d. carmine-red, O ('19)..	42	6	12	6
70	**12**	2d. grey, O	4	6	10	0
71	,,	2d. slate-grey, O ('19) ..	6	6	8	6
72	**11**	2½d. bright blue, O ..	6	6	8	6
73	**12**	3d. purple/*yellow*, C ..	5	0	8	6
74	**11**	6d. dull & bright purple, C	6	0	10	0
75	**12**	1s. black/*green*, C ..	10	0	15	0
76	,,	2s. 6d. blk. & red/*blue*, C	42	6	50	0
77	**11**	5s. green & red/*yellow*, C	60	0	70	0

WAR STAMP

(13)

1917. *Optd. with T* **13.**

78	**11**	1d. carmine	3	0	5	0
79	,,	1d. pale red/*bluish*	0	4	1	0
80	,,	1d. scarlet	0	8	2	0
81	**12**	3d. purple/*yellow*	1	0	2	6
82	,,	3d. purple/*lemon*	4	0	7	6
83	,,	3d. purple/*pale yellow* ..	2	0	4	0

1921. *As* 1913–19, *but wmk. Mult. Script CA.*

84	**11**	½d. green, O	0	10	2	6
85	,,	1d. scarlet & dp. carmine, O	2	0	3	0

14

(Typo. De La Rue & Co.)

1922–28. *T* **14.** *P* 14.

(*a*) *Wmk. Mult. Crown CA.*

86	3d. purple/*pale yellow*, C ..	1	3	3	0
87	1s. black/*emerald*, C ..	5	0	10	0
88	2s. 6d. black & red/*blue*, C..	10	0	20	0
89	5s. green & red/*pale yellow*, C	60	0	85	0

(*b*) *Wmk. Mult. Script CA.*

90	½d. dull green, O	0	3	0	6
91	1d. rose-carmine, O ..	0	8	1	3
92	2d. grey, O	2	0	2	6
93	2½d. pale bright blue, O (1922)	6	6	12	6
93*a*	2½d. bright blue, O (1927) ..	7	0	8	6
93*b*	3d. purple/*pale yellow*, C ..	2	6	6	0
94	5d. dull purple and olive, C..	20	0	32	6
95	6d. dull & bright purple, C..	4	6	8	6
96	1s. black/*emerald*, C ..	7	6	12	6
96*a*	2s. 6d. black & red/*blue*, C..	17	6	25	0
97	5s. green and red/*yellow*, C..	35	0	45	0

1923–29. *T* **14.** *Colours changed, etc. Wmk. Mult. Script CA. P* 14.

98	1d. bright violet, O (1927)	4	0	7	6
99	1d. scarlet, O (1929) ..	0	8	2	0
100	1½d. carmine-red, O (1927)	5	0	8	0
101	1½d. Venetian red, O (1928)	2	6	3	0
102	2½d. dull orange, O (1923) ..	3	0	3	6

In the 1½d. stamps the value is in colour on a white ground.

1935 (6 May). *Silver Jubilee. As Nos.* 91/4 *of Antigua but ptd. by W'low & Sons. P* 11 × 12.

103	1d. deep blue and scarlet ..	0	6	1	3
104	1½d. ultramarine and grey ..	1	0	1	6
105	2½d. brown and deep blue ..	3	6	4	0
106	1s. slate and purple ..	10	6	15	0

1937 (12 MAY). *Coronation. As T* **2** *of Aden. Recess. B. W. & Co. Wmk. Mult. Script CA. P* 11×11½.

No.	Description	Unused s.	d.	Used s.	d.
107	1d. carmine	0	6	0	8
108	1½d. yellow-brown	0	8	1	0
109	2½d. blue	1	6	2	0

15. King George VI and Badge of Colony.

(Photo. Harrison.)

1938 (1 AUG.)–**47.** *Wmk. Mult. Script CA. P* 14.

No.	Type	Description	Unused s.	d.	Used s.	d.
110	**15**	½d. green, CO	0	6	0	8
111	,,	1d. scarlet, CO	0	6	0	8
112	,,	1½d. red-brown, CO	0	8	1	0
113	,,	2d. grey, CO	0	9	0	9
114	,,	2½d. ultramarine, CO	0	10	0	10
115	,,	3d. orange, CO	1	3	1	6
116	,,	6d. mauve, CO	2	0	2	6
117	,,	1s. olive-brown, CO	5	0	6	0
118	,,	2s. 6d. sepia, CO	8	0	12	6
119	,,	5s. carmine, CO	12	6	18	6
120	,,	10s. blue, C (1.12.47)	25	0	37	6
121	,,	£1 black, C (1.12.47)	45	0	60	0

In substitute for the original chalky paper, the ordinary paper of Nos. 110/19 is thick, smooth and opaque and first appeared in August 1942 (1s. to 5s.) and in October 1943 (other values).

1946 (1 NOV.). *Victory. As Nos.* 28/9 *of Aden.*

No.	Description	Unused s.	d.	Used s.	d.
122	1½d. lake-brown	0	6	0	8
123	3d. orange	0	8	0	10

1949 (3 JAN.). *Royal Silver Wedding. As Nos.* 30/1 *of Aden.*

No.	Description	Unused s.	d.	Used s.	d.
124	2½d. ultramarine	0	6	0	6
125	£1 black	32	6	40	0

1949 (10 OCT.). *75th Anniv. of U.P.U. As Nos.* 114/7 *of Antigua.*

No.	Description	Unused s.	d.	Used s.	d.
126	2½d. ultramarine	0	8	1	0
127	3d. orange	1	0	1	3
128	6d. magenta	1	6	2	0
129	1s. olive	3	6	4	0

New currency. 100 cents=1 B.W.I. dollar.

1951. *Inauguration of B.W.I. University College. As Nos.* 118/9 *of Antigua.*

No.	Description	Unused s.	d.	Used s.	d.
130	3 c. black and brown-red	1	0	1	0
131	12 c. black and reddish violet	4	0	4	6

Dates of issue:—No. 130, 10 Apr.; No. 131, 16 Feb.

16. Map.

(Recess. Waterlow & Sons.)

1951 (2 APR.). *Restoration of Legislative Council. Wmk. Mult. Script CA. P* 14½×14.

No.	Type	Description	Unused s.	d.	Used s.	d.
132	**16**	6 c. orange	1	0	1	6
133	,,	12 c. purple	1	6	2	0
134	,,	24 c. olive	3	0	4	0
135	,,	$1.20 carmine	16	0	16	0

17. Sombrero Lighthouse

24. Badge of the Presidency.

18. Map of Jost Van Dyke.

19. Sheep Industry.

20. Map of Anegada.

21. Cattle Industry.

22. Map of Virgin Gorda.

23. Map of Tortola.

25. Dead Man's Chest.

26. Sir Francis Drake Channel.

27. Road Town.

28. Map of Virgin Islands.

(Recess. De La Rue.)

1952 (15 Apr.). *Wmk. Mult. Script. CA.* *P* 12½ × 13 (*vert.*) *or* 13 × 12½ (*horiz.*).

No.	Type	Description				
136	**17**	1 c. black	0	4	0	6
137	**18**	2 c. deep green	1	6	0	8
138	**19**	3 c. black and brown ..	0	6	0	9
139	**20**	4 c. carmine-red	1	0	1	0
140	**21**	5 c. claret and black ..	2	6	1	3
141	**22**	8 c. bright blue	1	0	1	3
142	**23**	12 c. dull violet	2	3	2	6
143	**24**	24 c. deep brown	2	0	3	0
144	**25**	60 c. yellow-green & blue..	6	0	8	6
145	**26**	$1.20 black & bright blue	10	0	12	6
146	**27**	$2.40 yellowish green and red-brown	17	6	18	6
147	**28**	$4.80 brt. blue & carmine	35	0	40	0

1953 (2 June). *Coronation. As No.* 47 *of Aden.*

148	2 c. black and green.. ..	0	9	1	0

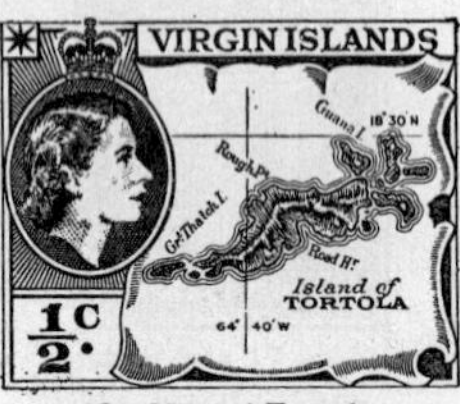

29. Map of Tortola.

30. Virgin Islands Sloop.

31. Nelthrop Red Poll Bull.

32. Road Harbour.

33. Mountain Travel.

34. Badge of the Presidency.

35. Beach Scene.

36. Boat Launching.

37. White Cedar Tree.

38. Bonito.

39. Treasury Square.

40. Brown Pelican.

41. Man-o'-War Bird.

(Recess. De La Rue & Co., Ltd.)

1956 (1 Nov.). *Wmk. Mult. Script CA. P* 13 × 12$\frac{1}{2}$ ($\frac{1}{2}$ *c. to* $1.20) *or* 12 × 11$\frac{1}{2}$ ($2.40 *and* $4.80).

No.	Type	Description	Unused	Used
149	**29**	$\frac{1}{2}$ c. black & reddish purple (*shades*)	0 6	0 6
150	**30**	1 c. turquoise-blue and slate (*shades*) ..	0 6	0 6
151	**31**	2 c. vermilion and black	1 0	0 5
152	**32**	3 c. blue and deep olive..	0 5	0 6
153	**33**	4 c. deep brown & turquoise-green ..	0 6	0 8
154	**34**	5 c. grey-black	0 7	0 8
155	**35**	8 c. yellow-orange and deep blue	0 9	0 10
156	**36**	12 c. ultram. & rose-red ..	1 0	1 3
157	**37**	24 c. myrtle-green and brown-orange ..	2 0	2 6
158	**38**	60 c. indigo & yell.-orange	7 6	5 0
159	**39**	$1.20, deep yellow-green and carmine-red .	8 6	9 0
160	**40**	$2.40, lemon & dp. dull pur.	27 6	30 0
161	**41**	$4.80, blackish brown and turquoise-blue ..	55 0	65 0

New currency. 100 cents = 1 U.S. dollar.

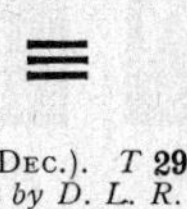

(42)

1962 (10 Dec.). *T* **29/41** *surch. in U.S. currency as T* **42** *by D. L. R. W* w.**12.**

No.	Type	Description	Unused	Used
162	**29**	1 c. on $\frac{1}{2}$ c. black and deep reddish purple ..	0 4	0 6
163	**30**	2 c. on 1 c. turquoise and slate-violet	0 6	0 6
164	**31**	3 c. on 2 c. verm. & black	0 6	0 6
165	**32**	4 c. on 3 c. bl. & dp. olive	0 8	0 10
166	**33**	5 c. on 4 c. dp. brown and turquoise-green ..	0 10	1 0
167	**35**	8 c. on 8 c. yellow-orange and deep blue ..	1 3	1 6
168	**36**	10 c. on 12 c. ultramarine and rose-red ..	1 6	1 9
169	**37**	12 c. on 24 c. myrtle-green and brown-orange ..	1 8	2 0
170	**38**	25 c. on 60 c. indigo and yellow-orange ..	3 6	4 0
171	**39**	70 c. on $1.20, dp. yell.-green and carmine-red	10 0	12 6
		a. Stop to right (In pair with normal) ..	40 0	45 0

172 **40** $1.40 on $2.40, lemon and deep dull purple .. 20 0 22 6
173 **41** $2.80 on $4.80, blackish brown & turq.-blue.. 37 6 42 6

1963 (4 June). *Freedom from Hunger. As No.* 63 *of Aden.*
174 25 c. reddish violet 3 0 3 9

1963 (2 Sept.). *Red Cross Centenary. As Nos.* 147/8 *of Antigua.*
175 2 c. red and black 0 5 0 6
176 25 c. red and blue 3 0 3 9

1964 (23 April). 400*th Anniv of Birth of William Shakespeare. As No.* 164 *of Antigua.*
177 10 c. bright blue 2 0 2 3

43. Bonito.

44. Soper's Hole.

45. Brown Pelican.

46. Dead Man's Chest.

47. Road Harbour.

48. Fallen Jerusalem.

49. The Baths, Virgin Gorda.

50. Map of Virgin Islands.

51. Tortola–St. Thomas Ferry

52. The Towers. Tortola

54. Map of Tortola.

53. Beef Island Airfield.

55. Virgin Gorda.

57. Badge of the Colony.

56 Yachts at Anchor.

(Recess. De La Rue.)

1964 (2 Nov.). *W* w.**12**. *P* 11½ × 12 ($2.80), 13 × 13½ (70 *c.*, $1, $1.40), *or* 13 × 12½ (*others*).

No.	Type	Description	Unused	Used
178	**43**	1 c. blue and olive-green	0 3	0 4
179	**44**	2 c. yellow-olive & rose-red	0 4	0 5
180	**45**	3 c. sepia & turquoise-blue	0 5	0 6
181	**46**	4 c. black & carmine-red	0 6	0 7
182	**47**	5 c. black and deep bluish green	0 8	0 9
183	**48**	6 c. black & brown-orange	0 9	0 10
184	**49**	8 c. black and magenta ..	0 11	1 0
185	**50**	10 c. lake and deep lilac ..	1 1	1 3
186	**51**	12 c. deep bluish green and deep violet-blue	1 3	1 6
187	**52**	15 c. yell.-grn. & grey-blk.	1 9	2 0
188	**53**	25 c. green and purple ..	2 6	3 6
189	**54**	70 c. black & yellow-brn.	6 9	7 6
190	**55**	$1 yellow-green & chest.	10 0	11 0
191	**56**	$1.40, light blue and rose	13 3	14 0
192	**57**	$2.80, black & brt. purple	25 0	30 0

1965 (17 May). *I.T.U. Centenary. As Nos.* 166/7 *of Antigua.*

No.	Description	Unused	Used
193	4 c. yellow and turquoise ..	0 7	0 10
194	25 c. lt. blue and orange-buff	3 0	3 9

1965 (25 Oct.). *International Co-operation Year. As Nos.* 168/9 *of Antigua.*

No.	Description	Unused	Used
195	1 c. reddish pur. & turq.-grn.	0 4	0 6
196	25 c. dp. bluish green & lav.	3 0	3 9

1966 (24 Jan.). *Churchill Commemoration. As Nos.* 170/3 *of Antigua.*

No.	Description	Unused	Used
197	1 c. new blue	0 4	0 6
198	2 c. deep green	0 5	0 7
199	10 c. brown	1 4	1 6
200	25 c. bluish violet	3 0	3 9

1966 (22 Feb.). *Royal Visit. As Nos.* 174/5 of *Antigua.*

No.	Description	Unused	Used
201	4 c. black and ultramarine ..	0 7	0 9
202	70 c. black and magenta ..	8 0	9 0

58. R.M.S. *Atrato*, 1866.

59. 1d. and 6d. Stamps of 1866.

60. Mail Transport, Beef Island, and 6d. Stamp of 1866.

61. Landing Mail at Roadtown, 1866.

(Des. R. Granger Barrett. Litho. Bradbury, Wilkinson.)

1966 (25 Apr.). *Stamp Centenary. W* w.**12** (*sideways*). *P* 13.

No.	Type	Description	Unused	Used
203	**58**	5 c. black, red, yellow & emerald	0 10	1 0
204	**59**	10 c. black, green and rose-red/*cream*	1 4	1 8
205	**60**	25 c. black, rose-red and blue/*pale green* ..	3 0	3 6
206	**61**	60 c. black, red and green/*pale blue*	7 0	8 0

WESTERN AUSTRALIA.

— SIMPLIFICATION (**see** INTRODUCTION) —
Nos. 1 to 51a.

1, 2, 4, 5, 7. 15, 17a, 18.
25, 27, 28. 41, 33, 46, 34, 35. 49, 51.

Later Issues.

Omit less distinct shades. Disregard perfs.

1 2

3 4

(Eng. and printed by Perkins Bacon & Co.)

1854 (1 AUG.). *W* **4**. *Imperf.*

1	**1**	1d. black	£25	£12

(Litho. H. Samson, Govt. Lithographer.)

1854. *W* **4** (*sideways*).

(*a*) *Imperf.*

2	**2**	4d. pale blue	£8	£8
3	,,	4d. blue	£8	£8
3*a*	,,	4d. deep dull blue	£45	£26
4	,,	4d. slate-blue	£35	£25
5	**3**	1s. pale brown	£14	£14
6	,,	1s. grey-brown	£24	£20
7	,,	1s. deep red-brown	£28	£25
8	,,	1s. salmon	—	£95

Transfer varieties of the 4d. blue.

(The numbers in brackets show the position on the sheets.)

3 aa.	Frame inverted	—	£1600
b.	Top of letters of "AUSTRALIA" cut off so that they are barely 1 mm. in height	—	£600
ba.	"PEICE" instead of "PENCE"	—	£525
bb.	"CE" of "PENCE" close together	—	£425

The above varieties come from a small early printing from Stone I (approximate quantity 36,000). Those listed below No. 3c all belong to a much larger and later printing from Stone II (approximately 360.000 in all).

3 c.	"WEST" in squeezed-down letters and "F" of "FOUR" has pointed foot (No. 37)	£35	£35
d.	"ESTERN" in squeezed-down letters and "U" of "FOUR" squeezed up (No. 57)	£65	£65
e.	Small "S" in "POSTAGE" (No. 77)	£35	£35
f.	"EN" of "PENCE" shorter (No. 104)	£20	£20
g.	"N" of "PENCE" has the first downstroke thinner and the letter slants to the right (No. 116)	£25	£25
h.	The water and part of swan damaged above "ENCE" (No. 120)	£26	£26
ha.	Tilted border (Nos. 124, 129, 134 and 139)	£22	£22
i.	"T" of "POSTAGE" shaved off to a point at foot (No. 125)	£22	£22
j.	"F" of "FOUR" slanting to left (No. 137)	£22	£22
k.	Coloured line above "AGE" of "POSTAGE" (No. 146)	£22	£22
l.	No outer line above "GE" of "POSTAGE" and a coloured line under "FOU" of "FOUR" (No. 151)	£22	£22
m.	"WESTERN" in squeezed-down letters, only 1½ mm. in height (No. 157)	£30	£30
n.	"P" of "PENCE" small head (No. 175)	£20	£20
o.	"RALIA" in squeezed-down letters only 1½ mm. in height (No. 176)	£30	£30
p.	"PE" of "PENCE" close together (No. 195)	£22	£22
q.	"N" of "PENCE" narrow (No. 196)	£22	£22
r.	Part of the right cross-stroke and down-stroke of "T" of "POSTAGE" is cut off (No. 215)	£20	£20
s.	Defective "A" in "POSTAGE" the right limb being very thin (No. 216)	£20	£20

These varieties 3c/s may be found in all shades of the blue stamps, being rare in the slate-blue. They also occur in the rouletted stamps. Nos. 3aa/bb are only found in one shade.

(*b*) *Rouletted* 8 *to* 14 *and compound.*

10	**1**	1d. black	£30	£15
11	**2**	4d. pale blue	£30	£16
12	,,	4d. blue	—	£16
12*a*	,,	4d. slate-blue	—	£40
13	**3**	1s. pale brown	£60	£35
14	,,	1s. grey-brown	£75	£32

5

(Litho. A. Hillman, Government Lithographer.)

1857. *W* **4** (*sideways*). (*a*) *Imperf.*

15	**5**	2d. brown-black/*red*	£70	£35
		a. Printed both sides	£80	£50
16	,,	2d. brn.-blk./*Indian red*	—	£45
		a. Printed both sides	£60	£50
17	,,	6d. black-bronze	£75	£45
18	,,	6d. grey-black	£75	£45
19	,,	6d. golden bronze	£150	£100

(*b*) *Rouletted* 9 *to* 14 *and compound.*

20	**5**	2d. brown-black/*red*	£100	£55
		a. Printed both sides		
21	,,	2d. brown-black/*Indian red*	—	£70
22	,,	6d. black-bronze	£90	£35
23	,,	6d. grey-black	—	£40

The 1d., 2d., 6d., and 1s. are known pin-perf.

(Printed in the colony from Messrs. Perkins, Bacon & Co.'s plates.)

1860. *W* **4** (*sideways*). (*a*) *Imperf.*

24	**1**	2d. pale orange	70 0	85 0
25	,,	2d. orange-vermilion	65 0	70 0
25*a*	,,	2d. deep vermilion	£14	£20
26	,,	4d. blue	£10	£35
27	,,	4d. deep blue	£10	£38
28	,,	6d. sage-green	£45	£32
28*a*	,,	6d. deep sage-green	—	£32

(*b*) *Rouletted* 7½ *to* 14.

29	**1**	2d. pale orange	£16	£7
30	,,	2d. orange-vermilion	£18	£7
31	,,	4d. deep blue	£120	
32	,,	6d. sage-green	—	£20

(Printed by Perkins, Bacon & Co.)

1861. *W* **4.** (*a*) *Perf. clean-cut* 14–16.

No.	Type	Description	Unused	Used
33	**1**	2d. blue	65 0	35 0
		a. Imperf. between (pair)		
34	,,	6d. purple-brown	£6	37 6
35	,,	1s. yellow-green	£14	65 0
		(*b*) *Intermediate perf.* 14–16.		
36	**1**	1d. rose	£18	£6
37	,,	2d. blue	£8	60 0
38	,,	4d. vermilion	£20	£14
39	,,	6d. purple-brown	£20	65 0
40	,,	1s. yellow-green	£28	£8
		(*c*) *P* 14–16 *very rough* (July).		
41	**1**	1d. rose-carmine	£8	45 0
41*a*	,,	2d. deep blue		
42	,,	6d. purple/*blue*	£32	£10
43	,,	1s. deep green	£55	£20
		(*d*) *P* 14.		
44	**1**	1d. rose	£6	70 0
45	,,	2d. blue	50 0	50 0
46	,,	4d. vermilion	£10	£8

The 6d. purple-brown and 1s. yellow-green are known, perf. 14, with "SPECIMEN" overprint.

(Printed by De La Rue & Co.)

1864. *T* **1.** *No wmk.* *P* 13.

No.	Description	Unused	Used
49	1d. carmine-rose	35 0	12 6
50	1d. lake	35 0	12 6
51	6d. deep lilac	£6	40 0
51*a*	6d. dull violet	£7	60 0

Both values exist on thin and on thick papers, the former being the scarcer.

Several varieties, both with wmk. (Swan) and without wmk. are to be found *imperf.*, but the majority of these were probably never issued.

1865. *Wmk. Crown CC.* *P* 12½.

No.	Type	Description	Unused	Used
52	**1**	1d. bistre	20 0	4 6
53	,,	1d. yellow-ochre	45 0	10 0
54	,,	2d. chrome-yellow	27 6	1 0
55	,,	2d. yellow	27 6	1 6
56	,,	4d. carmine	32 6	10 0
		a. Doubly printed	£525	
57	,,	6d. lilac	£7	15 0
58	,,	6d. mauve	£6	15 0
59	,,	6d. violet	£5	15 0
		a. Doubly printed		
60	,,	6d. indigo-violet	£14	75 0
61	,,	1s. bright green	65 0	20 0
62	,,	1s. sage-green	£14	35 0
		Error of colour.		
65	**1**	2d. mauve (1879)	£250	£225

ONE PENNY

(7)

1875 (Feb.). *No.* 55 *surch. with T* **7**.

No.	Type	Description	Unused	Used
67	**1**	1d. on 2d. yellow (G.)	£6	30 0
		a. Pair, one stamp no surch.		
		b. Surch. three times	—	£34
		c. "O" of "ONE" omitted		

Forged surcharges of T **7** are known on stamps wmk. Crown CC. perf. 14, and on Crown CA, perf. 12 and 14.

8

1872–78. *Wmk. Crown CC.* *P* 14.

No.	Type	Description	Unused	Used
68	**1**	1d. bistre	47 6	4 0
69	,,	1d. ochre	42 6	1 0
70	,,	1d. yellow-ochre	32 6	1 6
71	,,	2d. chrome-yellow	37 6	1 0
72	**8**	3d. pale brown	15 0	7 0
73	,,	3d. cinnamon	12 6	6 0
74	**1**	4d. carmine	£9	85 0
75	,,	6d. lilac	80 0	7 0
75*a*	,,	6d. reddish lilac	85 0	8 0

1882–90. *Wmk. Crown CA.* (*a*) *P* 12.

No.	Type	Description	Unused	Used
76	**1**	1d. yellow-ochre	55 0	3 0
77	,,	2d. chrome-yellow	75 0	2 0
		a. Imperf. between (pair)		
78	,,	4d. carmine	£7	45 0
79	,,	6d. lilac	£10	32 6
		(*b*) *P* 14.		
81	**1**	1d. yellow-ochre	7 6	0 8
82	,,	2d. chrome-yellow	10 0	0 8
83	**8**	3d. pale brown	7 6	1 9
84	,,	3d. red-brown	5 0	0 8
85	**1**	4d. carmine	32 6	22 6
86	,,	6d. lilac	45 0	5 0
87	,,	6d. reddish lilac	40 0	4 6
		(*c*) *P* 12×14.		
88	**1**	1d. yellow-ochre (1883)	£70	£6

The 3d. sage-green, wmk. Crown CA, perf. 12, is known unused, but was never issued.

½ (9) 1d. (10) 1d. (11)

1884. *T* **1** *surch. with T* **9**, *in red.*

No.	Description	Unused	Used
89	½ on 1d. yellow-ochre (No. 76)	6 0	7 0
	a. Thin bar	40 0	35 0
90	½ on 1d. yellow-ochre (No. 81)	15 0	15 0
	a. Thin bar	75 0	50 0

Inverted or double surcharges are forgeries made in London about 1886.

1885. *T* **8** *surch. in green.* *Wmk. Crown CC.* *P* 14.

(*a*) *Thick* "**1**" *with slanting top, T* **10**.

No.	Description	Unused	Used
91	1d. on 3d. pale brown	22 6	15 0
92	1d. on 3d. cinnamon	12 6	10 0
	(*b*) *Thin* "**1**" *with straight top, T* **11**.		
93	1d. on 3d. pale brown	40 0	17 6
94	1d. on 3d. cinnamon	22 6	17 6

1888. *Wmk. Crown CA.* *P* 14.

No.	Type	Description	Unused	Used
95	**1**	1d. carmine-pink	7 6	1 0
96	,,	2d. grey	12 6	3 6
97	,,	4d. red-brown	£6	32 6

12

18

14

15

1885–93. *Wmk. Crown CA.* *P* 14.

No.	Type	Description	Unused	Used
98	**12**	½d. yellow-green	0 6	0 3
98*a*	,,	½d. green	0 6	0 3
99	**13**	1d. carmine	1 3	0 3
100	**14**	2d. bluish grey	2 6	0 3
100*a*	,,	2d. grey	2 0	0 3
101	**15**	2½d. deep blue	6 0	0 6
101*a*	,,	2½d. blue	6 0	0 6
102	,,	4d. chestnut	6 6	0 6

No.	Type	Description	Unused	Used
103	**15**	5d. bistre	7 6	2 0
104	,,	6d. bright violet ..	7 6	1 0
105	,,	1s. pale olive-green ..	10 0	2 0
106	,,	1s. olive-green	6 0	1 3

ONE PENNY (16) **Half-penny** (17)

1893. *T* **8** *surcharged with T* **16**, *in green.*

No.	Description	Unused	Used
107	1d. on 3d. pale brown (No. 72)	10 0	6 0
108	1d. on 3d. cinnamon (No. 73)	10 0	8 0
	a. Double surcharge	£22	
109	1d. on 3d. brown (No. 83) ..	17 6	8 6

1895. *T* **8** *surcharged with T* **17**, *in green.*

No.	Description	Unused	Used
110	½d. on 3d. pale brown (No. 72)	8 0	8 0
110*a*	½d. on 3d. cinnamon (No. 73)	4 6	5 0
	b. Double surcharge ..	£22	

Variety. Surch. in red and in green.

No.	Description	Unused	Used
111	½d. on 3d. cinnamon (No. 73)	80 0	

The double surcharge is also found on the 3d. Crown CA, but this was printed off specially to supply a local philatelic (!) demand, and is therefore a reprint.

18 19

1899–1901. *Wmk. W. Crown A. T* **18.** *P* 14.

No.	Type	Description	Unused	Used
112	**13**	1d. carmine	0 8	0 3
		a. Imperf.		
113	**14**	2d. bright yellow ..	1 6	0 3
		a. Imperf.		
114	**19**	2½d. blue	3 6	0 6

19*a* 20

21 22

23 24

25

26

27

28

29

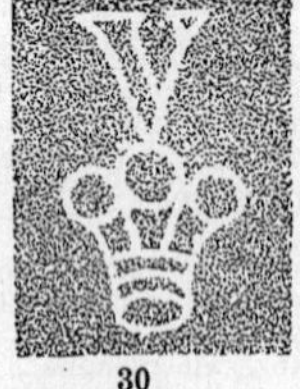
30

(Printed in Melbourne, Victoria.)

1902–11. *Wmk. V and Crown, T* **30.**
(a) P 12½ *or* 12 × 12½.

No.	Type	Description	Unused	Used
115	**19*a***	1d. carmine-rose ..	0 8	0 3
116	**20**	2d. yellow	1 9	0 3
117	**21**	4d. chestnut	4 0	0 6
117*a*	**15**	5d. bistre (1905) ..	35 0	22 6
118	**22**	8d. apple-green	8 6	6 6
119	**23**	9d. yellow-orange ..	10 0	7 6
119*a*	,,	9d. red-orange	12 6	10 0
120	**24**	10d. red	22 6	10 0
121	**25**	2s. red/*yellow*	32 6	20 0
121*a*	,,	2s. orange/*yellow* ..	32 6	17 6
122	**26**	2s. 6d. deep blue/*rose* ..	25 0	17 6
123	**27**	5s. emerald-green ..	40 0	30 0
124	**28**	10s. deep mauve ..	65 0	30 0
124*a*	,,	10s. bright purple (1911)	70 0	40 0
125	**29**	£1 orange-brown ..	£7	85 0
125*a*	,,	£1 orange (1911) ..	£12	£7

(b) P 11.

No.	Type	Description	Unused	Used
126	**19*a***	1d. carmine-rose	50 0	10 0
127	**20**	2d. yellow	75 0	10 0
128	**21**	4d. chestnut	£10	£6
129	**15**	5d. bistre (1905)	30 0	20 0
130	**23**	9d. orange (1906) ..	50 0	30 0
132	**25**	2s. red/*yellow*	60 0	50 0

(c) Perf. compound of 12½ *and* 11.

No.	Type	Description	Unused	Used
133	**19*a***	1d. carmine-rose ..	—	£5
134	**20**	2d. yellow	—	£6

Type **19*a*** is similar to Type **13** but larger.

The wmk. is generally sideways, except on the 2s. 6d., and 10s., which have the wmk. upright. It is known upright on the 1d., 2d., 4d., and 9d., perf. 12½, and on the 2d., perf. 11. On the 2s. perf. 12½, the upright wmk. is the commoner.

31

32

1905–12. *Wmk. Crown and A, T* **31** *(sideways).*

(a) P 12½ *or* 12×12½.

No.	Type	Description		Unused	Used
138	**12**	½d. green (1910)	..	1 0	0 6
139	**19a**	1d. rose-pink	..	1 0	0 3
139a	,,	1d. carmine (1910)	..	1 3	0 3
139b	,,	1d. carmine-red (1912)	..	1 0	0 3
140	**20**	2d. yellow	..	1 3	0 3
141	**8**	3d. brown	..	2 6	0 8
142	**21**	4d. bistre-brown	..	4 6	1 6
142a	,,	4d. pale chestnut	..	10 0	0 8
142b	,,	4d. bright brown-red	..	7 6	0 8
143	**15**	5d. pale olive-green	..	7 6	1 9
143a	,,	5d. olive-bistre	..	7 6	1 6
143b	**22**	8d. apple-green (1912)	..	10 0	7 0
144	**23**	9d. orange	..	10 0	3 6
144a	,,	9d. red-orange	..	12 6	4 6
145	**24**	10d. rose-orange	..	16 0	11 0
148	**27**	5s. emerald-green	..	47 6	27 6

(b) P 11.

No.	Type	Description		Unused	Used
151	**19a**	1d. rose-pink	..	3 0	2 6
151a	,,	1d. carmine-red	..	3 0	2 0
152	**20**	2d. yellow	..	5 0	4 0
153	**8**	3d. brown	..	5 0	4 0
154	**21**	4d. yellow-brown	..	£25	£7
155	**15**	5d. olive	..	20 0	8 0
156	,,	5d. pale greenish yellow		32 6	20 0
156a	,,	5d. olive-bistre	..	8 6	6 0
157	**23**	9d. orange	..	65 0	65 0
157a	,,	9d. red-orange	..	—	45 0

(c) Perf. compound of 12½ *and* 11.

No.	Type	Description		Unused	Used
161	**19a**	1d. rose-pink	..	£6	80 0
162	**20**	2d. yellow	..	£8	95 0
163	**15**	3d. brown	..	£10	£6

The 1d. and 9d. are known with upright watermark.

33

34

(Typo. De La Rue & Co.)

1906–7. *Wmk. W Crown A, T* **18.** *P* 14.

No.	Type	Description		Unused	Used
164	**33**	6d. bright violet	..	6 0	1 9
165	**34**	1s. olive-green	..	20 0	5 0

1912. *Wmk. Crown and A, T* **32.** *P* 11½×12.

No.	Type	Description		Unused	Used
168	**33**	6d. bright violet	..	6 0	3 6
169	**34**	1s. sage-green	..	18 6	7 6
		a. Perf. 12½ (single line)	..		

ONE PENNY

(35)

Nos. 140 *and* 162 *surch. with T* **35.**

(a) P 12½ *or* 12×12½.

No.	Type	Description		Unused	Used
170	**20**	1d. on 2d. yellow	..	0 10	0 6

(b) Perf. compound of 12½ *and* 11.

No.	Type	Description		Unused	Used
171	**20**	1d. on 2d. yellow	..	£12	

No 170 comes with upright or sideways wmk.

1912. *W* **31** *(upright or sideways). Thin paper and white gum (as Victoria).*

No.	Type	Description		Unused	Used
172	**8**	3d. brown (*perf.* 12½)	..	22 6	12 6
173	,,	3d. brown (*perf.* 11)	..	£6	£8

POSTAL FISCALS.

51

I. R.

TWO PENCE

(52)

1893. *Wmk. CA over Crown. P* 14.

No.	Type	Description		Unused	Used
201	**51**	1d. dull purple	..	2 0	0 9
202	,,	2d. dull purple	..	10 0	8 0
203	,,	3d. dull purple	..	12 6	2 0
204	,,	6d. dull purple	..	15 0	6 0
205	,,	1s. dull purple	..	22 6	7 0
206	,,	2s. 6d. dull purple	..	90 0	80 0
207	,,	3s. dull purple	..	£20	£10
208	,,	5s. dull purple	..	£7	£5

Wmk. Crown CC. Surch. as T **52.** *P* 14.

No.	Type	Description		Unused	Used
209	**8**	1d. on 3d. lilac	..	£8	£6
210	,,	2d. on 3d. lilac	..	7 0	7 0
211	,,	3d. on 3d. lilac	..	18 6	15 0
212	,,	6d. on 3d. lilac	..	£7	£5
213	,,	1s. on 3d. lilac	..	£18	£15

1899. *Wmk. W Crown A, T* **18.** *P* 14.

No.	Type	Description		Unused	Used
214	**51**	1d. dull purple	..	2 6	1 0
215	,,	3d. dull purple	..	4 0	1 6
216	,,	6d. dull purple	..	7 0	3 0
217	,,	1s. dull purple	..	12 6	5 0
218	,,	2s. 6d. dull purple	..	75 0	60 0
219	,,	3s. dull purple	..	£7	£5
220	,,	5s. dull purple	..	£12	£10

I R

(53)

Various stamps are known with the overprint T **53**, most of which are forgeries, although the 1d. and 2d., wmk. Crown CC, perf. 14, were so overprinted, but purely for fiscal purposes.

TELEGRAPH STAMPS USED FOR POSTAGE.

61

1886. *Wmk. Crown CC.*

No.	Type	Description		Unused	Used
301	**61**	1d. bistre (*perf.* 12½)	..	6 0	3 0
		a. Imperf.	..		
302		1d. bistre (*perf.* 14)	..	8 0	6 0
303	,,	6d. lilac (*perf.* 14)	..	15 0	15 0

OFFICIAL STAMPS.

Stamps of the various issues from 1854-85 are found with a circular hole punched out, the earlier size being about 3 mm. in diameter, and the later 4 mm. These were used on official correspondence. This system of punching ceased in 1886. Any in stock will be supplied at the same price as similar stamps without the hole. Stamps from No. 98 onward exist punctured "O S".

Western Australia now uses the stamps of AUSTRALIA.

WESTERN SAMOA.

(*See* SAMOA.)

ZAMBIA

(FORMERLY NORTHERN RHODESIA).

INDEPENDENT

within the Commonwealth.

11. Pres. Kaunda and Victoria Falls.

13. Barotse Dancer.

12. College of Further Education, Lusaka.

(Des. M. Goaman (3d., 6d.), Mrs. G. Ellison (1s. 3d.). Photo. Harrison.)

1964 (24 OCT.). *Independence.* *P* 13½ × 14½ (*6d.*) *or* 14½ × 13½ (*others*).

81	**11**	3d. sepia, yellow-green and blue	1 0	1 0
82	**12**	6d. deep violet and yellow	1 6	1 9
83	**13**	1s. 3d. red, black, sepia and orange	2 9	3 0

14. Maize-Farmer and Silo.

15. Health—Radiographer.

16. Chinyau Dancer.

18. Angoni Bull.

17. Cotton-picking.

19. Communications, Old and New.

20. Zambezi Sawmills and Redwood Flower.

21. Fishing at Mpulungu.

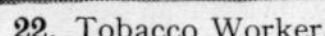

22. Tobacco Worker.

23. Tonga Basket-making.

24. Luangwa Game Reserve.

25. Education—Student.

26. Copper Mining.

27. Makishi Dancer.

(Des. Mrs. G. Ellison. Photo. Harrison.)

1964 (24 Oct.). *P* $14\frac{1}{2}$ (*$\frac{1}{2}$d. to 4d.*), $14\frac{1}{2} \times 13\frac{1}{2}$ (*1s. 3d., 2s. and £1*) *or* $13\frac{1}{2} \times 14\frac{1}{2}$ (*others*).

No.	Type	Description	s.	d.	s.	d.
84	**14**	$\frac{1}{2}$d. red, black & yell.-grn.	0	2	0	3
85	**15**	1d. brn., blk. & brt. blue	0	3	0	4
86	**16**	2d. red, dp. brn. & orange	0	4	0	5
87	**17**	3d. black and red ..	0	6	0	7
88	**18**	4d. black, brown & orange	0	7	0	9
89	**19**	6d. orange, deep brown & deep bluish green ..	0	10	1	0
90	**20**	9d. carmine, black and bright blue	1	1	1	6
91	**21**	1s. black, yellow-bistre and blue	1	5	2	0
92	**22**	1s. 3d. light red, yellow, black and blue ..	1	9	2	3
93	**23**	2s. bright blue, black, deep brown and orange ..	2	9	3	9
94	**24**	2s. 6d. black & orge.-yell.	3	6	4	0
95	**25**	5s. black, yellow & green	6	9	7	6
96	**26**	10s. black and orange ..	13	3	15	0
97	**27**	£1 blk., brn., yell. & red	25	0	30	0

28. I.T.U. Emblem and Symbols.

(Photo. Harrison.)

1965 (26 July). *I.T.U. Centenary. P* $14 \times 14\frac{1}{2}$

No.	Type	Description	s.	d.	s.	d.
98	**28**	6d. lt. reddish violet & gold	1	0	1	2
99	,,	2s. 6d. brownish grey & gold	4	6	5	6

29. I.C.Y. Emblem.

(Photo. Harrison.)

1965 (26 July). *International Co-operation Year. P* $14\frac{1}{2}$.

No.	Type	Description	s.	d.	s.	d.
100	**29**	3d. turquoise and gold ..	0	7	0	11
101	,,	1s. 3d. ultram. and gold ..	2	3	2	9

30. State House, Lusaka.

31. Fireworks, Independence Stadium.

32. Clematopsis.

33. *Tithonia diversifolia.*

(Des. Mrs. G. Ellison. Photo. Harrison.)

1965 (18 Oct.). *First Anniv. of Independence. No wmk. P* 13½ × 14½ (3*d*.), 14 × 13½ (6*d*.) *or* 13½ × 14 (*others*).

102	**30**	3d. multicoloured ..	0 7	0 9
103	**31**	6d. multicoloured ..	1 0	1 3
104	**32**	1s. 3d. multicoloured ..	2 3	2 6
105	**33**	2s. 6d. multicoloured ..	4 6	5 6

POSTAGE DUE STAMPS.

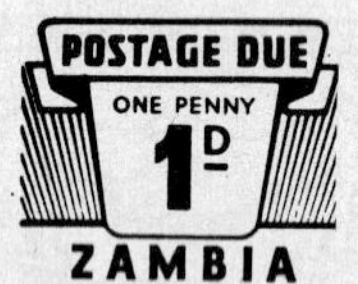

D 2

(Litho. Govt. Printer, Lusaka.)

1964 (24 Oct.). *P* 12½.

D11	**D 2**	1d. orange	0 3	0 4
D12	,,	2d. deep blue	0 4	0 5
D13	,,	3d. lake	0 6	0 8
D14	,,	4d. ultramarine	0 7	0 10
D15	,,	6d. purple	0 10	1 2
D16	,,	1s. light emerald ..	1 5	1 10

In all values the left-hand vertical row of the sheet is imperf. at left and the bottom horizontal row is imperf. at bottom. The 6d. value comes in shorter width by the measure of one perf. "tooth" and one perf. hole, the dimensions of the design being unchanged.

ZANZIBAR.

BRITISH PROTECTORATE.

Zanzibar
(1)

1895 (10 Nov.). *Contemporary stamps of India optd. with T* **1**.

A. *In blue.*

1	½ a. blue-green	£75	£55
2	1 a. plum	£55	£40
	a. "Zanzidar"		

Most of the varieties found on the same values with black overprint exist on the above.

B. *In black.*

3	½ a. blue-green	5 0	5 0
	a. "Zanzidar"	£20	£15
	b. "Zanibar"	£30	£25
4	1 a. plum	5 0	5 0
	a. "Zanzidar"	£50	£40
	b. "Zanibar"	£30	£25
5	1½ a. sepia	8 0	8 0
	a. "Zanzidar"	£60	£40
	b. "Zanibar"	£40	£35
	c. "Zanizbar"	£60	
6	2 a. pale blue	7 0	7 0
	a. Blue	8 0	8 0
	b. Opt. double	£20	
	c. "Zanzidar"	£60	
	d. "Zanibar"	£50	£40
7	2½ a. yellow-green	7 0	7 0
	a. "Zanzidar"	£35	£30
	b. "Zanibar"	£20	£20
	c. "Zapzibar"		
8	3 a. orange	15 0	17 6
	a. Brown-orange	12 6	15 0
	b. "Zanzidar"	£22	
	c "Zanizbar"	£80	
9	4 a. olive-green	15 0	15 0
	a. Slate-green	15 0	15 0
	b. "Zanzidar"	—	£40
10	6 a. pale brown	22 6	25 0
	a. Opt. double		
	b. "Zanzidar"	£50	£60
	c. "Zanibar"	£40	
	d. "Zanzibarr"	£50	
11	8 a. dull mauve	30 0	30 0
	a. Magenta	22 6	25 0
	b. "Zanzidar"		
12	12 a. purple/*red*	25 0	30 0
	a. "Zanzidar"	£80	£80
13	1 r. slate	£7	£8
	a. "Zanzidar"	£100	£100
14	1 r. green and carmine ..	32 6	37 6
	a. Opt. vert. downwards ..	£25	
15	2 r. carmine & yellow-brown	65 0	70 0
	a. "r" omitted	£60	
	b. Inverted "r"	£40	£40
16	3 r. brown and green ..	65 0	70 0
	a. "r" omitted	£60	
	b. Inverted "r"	£45	£45
17	5 r. ultramarine and violet ..	65 0	70 0
	a. Opt. double, one inverted ..	£40	
	b. "r" omitted	£60	
	c. Inverted "r"	—	£50

Many forgeries of the "Zanzibar" overprint exist, also bogus errors.

Varieties of printer's type.

The following varieties exist on all values to the 5 r. including both types of the 1 r.:—

(i) Tall second "z".
(ii) First "z" antique.

The following exist on all values to the 1 r. (both types):—

(iii) Inverted "q" for "b".
(iv) "p" with tail broken off for "n".
(v) "i" without dot.
(vi) Small second "z".
(vii) Inverted "q" for "b" and small second "z".

The following exists on the ½ a., 1½ a., 2 a. and 2½ a.:—

(viii) "ä" with diæresis for last "a".

The following exists on the 2½ a.:—

(ix) Second "z" italic.

1895–96. Provisionals.

I. *Stamps used for postal purposes.*

2½
(2)

1895 (Dec.).

No. 5 *surch. with T* **2** *in red.*

119	2½ on 1½ a. sepia	40 0	40 0
	a. "Zanizbar"	£60	£50
	b. "Zanzidar"	£60	£50
	c. Inverted "1" in "½" ..	£40	£40

2½ (3) 2½ (4) 2½ (5)

1896 (11 May). *No.* 4 *surch. in black.*

123 **3** 2½ on 1 a. plum £6 £6
124 **4** 2½ on 1 a. plum £12 £12
125 **5** 2½ on 1 a. plum £6 £6

2½ (6) 2½ (7) 2½ (8)

1896 (15 Aug.). *No.* 6 *surch. in red.*

126 **6** 2½ on 2 a. pale blue .. 50 0 50 0
a. "1" on "½" inverted .. £12 £12
b. Roman "I" in "½" .. £25 £20
127 **7** 2½ on 2 a. pale blue .. £5 £5
a. Roman "I" in "½" ..
b. "2¹" for "2½" £75
c. "2²" for "2½" .. ..
d. "2₂" for "2½" .. ..
128 **8** 2½ on 2 a. pale blue .. £30 £30

1896 (15 Nov.). *No.* 5 *surch. in red*

135 **6** 2½ on 1½ a. sepia £6 £6
a. "1" of "½" inverted .. £30 £30
b. Roman "I" in "½" .. £30
136 **7** 2½ on 1½ a. sepia £12
137 **8** 2½ on 1½ a. sepia £50

II. *Stamps prepared for official purposes, but it is doubtful whether they were issued to the public.* (*Nos.* 140–148.)

1898 (Jan.). *Surch. as before in red.*

140 **3** 2½ on 1 a. plum £12
141 **4** 2½ on 1 a. plum £20
142 **5** 2½ on 1 a. plum £12 £15
143 **3** 2½ on 1½ a. sepia £5 £5
144 **4** 2½ on 1½ a. sepia £10 £10
145 **5** 2½ on 1½ a. sepia £5 £5
146 **3** 2½ on 2 a. dull blue .. £5 £5
147 **4** 2½ on 2 a. dull blue .. £10
148 **5** 2½ on 2 a. dull blue .. £5 £5

All the varieties of printer's type of the overprint found on the general issue can, of course, be found on the surcharged stamps.

1896. *Stamps of British East Africa, T* **11**, *optd. with T***1**, *in black, except the* 2½ *a., which is in red.*

149 ½ a. yellow-green (1 June) .. 80 0 60 0
150 1 a. carmine-rose (1 June) .. 80 0 60 0
a. Overprint double £24 £20
151 2½ a. deep blue (1 June) .. £6 £6
152 4½ a. orange-yellow (12 Aug.) 50 0 50 0
153 5 a. olive-bistre (12 Aug.) .. 80 0 80 0
154 7½ a. mauve (12 Aug.) .. 80 0 80 0

The same varieties of printer's type of the overrint can be found on the above.

PRINTERS. All Zanzibar stamps up to Type **37** were printed by De La Rue & Co.

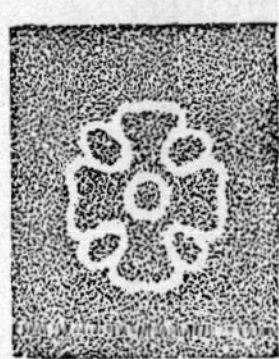

12

13

14. Sultan Seyyid Hamed-bin-Thwain.

1896 (20 Sept.). *Recess.* *W* **12.** *P* 14. *Flags in red on all values.*

156 **13** ½ a. yellow-green 1 6 1 6
157 ,, 1 a. indigo 2 6 2 6
158 ,, 1 a. violet-blue 3 6 2 6
159 ,, 2 a. red-brown 3 0 3 0
160 ,, 2½ a. bright blue 3 0 2 6
161 ,, 2½ a. pale blue 3 6 2 6
162 ,, 3 a. grey 7 0 7 0
163 ,, 3 a. bluish-grey 8 0 8 0
164 ,, 4 a. myrtle-green 7 0 8 0
165 ,, 4½ a. orange 8 0 8 0
166 ,, 5 a. bistre 8 0 8 0
a. Bisected (2½ a.) (on cover) — £20
167 ,, 7½ a. mauve 8 0 8 0
168 ,, 8 a. grey-olive 8 6 8 6
169 **14** 1 r. blue 20 0 20 0
170 ,, 1 r. deep blue 20 0 20 0
171 ,, 2 r. green 30 0 30 0
172 ,, 3 r. dull purple 60 0 50 0
173 ,, 4 r. lake 70 0 60 0
174 ,, 5 r. sepia £5 80 0

The ½, 1, 2, 2½ and 8 a. are known without wmk., these being from edges of the sheets.

1897 (5 Jan.). *No.* 164 *surcharged as before in red.*

175 **3** 2½ on 4 a. myrtle-green .. 80 0 80 0
176 **4** 2½ on 4 a. myrtle-green .. £7 £7
177 **5** 2½ on 4 a. myrtle-green .. 80 0 80 0

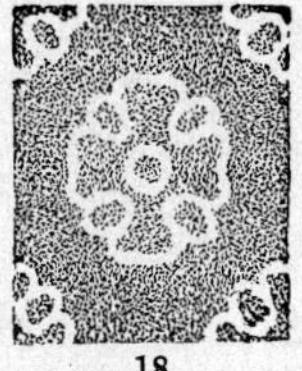

18

1898 (May). *Recess.* *W* **18.** *P* 14.

178 **13** ½ a. yellow-green .. 1 0 1 0
179 ,, 1 a. indigo 2 0 1 3
179*a* ,, 1 a. greenish black .. 3 0 1 6
180 ,, 2 a. red-brown 3 0 3 6
180*a* ,, 2 a. deep brown .. 3 0 3 6
181 ,, 2½ a. bright blue .. 2 6 1 0
182 ,, 3 a. grey 5 0 4 0
183 ,, 4 a. myrtle-green .. 5 0 4 0
184 ,, 4½ a. orange 8 0 4 0
185 ,, 5 a. bistre 10 0 6 0
185*a* ,, 5 a. pale bistre 10 0 7 6
186 ,, 7½ a. mauve 12 6 15 0
187 ,, 8 a. grey-olive 12 6 10 0

19

20. Sultan Seyyid Hamoud-bin-Mahommed bin Said.

1899 (Sept.). *Flags in red. Recess.* *W* **18.** *P* 14.

No.	Type		Unused	Used
188	**19**	½ a. yellow-green	1 0	1 3
189	,,	1 a. indigo	1 3	1 3
190	,,	2 a. red-brown	2 0	2 0
191	,,	2½ a. bright blue	2 6	2 0
192	,,	3 a. grey	4 6	5 0
193	,,	4 a. myrtle-green	4 6	5 0
194	,,	4½ a. orange	6 0	6 0
195	,,	5 a. bistre	7 0	7 0
196	,,	7½ a. mauve	10 0	12 6
197	,,	8 a. grey-olive	10 0	12 6
		W **12.** *P* 14.		
198	**20**	1 r. blue	25 0	25 0
199	,,	2 r. green	60 0	50 0
200	,,	3 r. dull purple	70 0	60 0
201	,,	4 r. lake	£5	£5
202	,,	5 r. sepia	£6	£6

1901. *Colours changed.* *W* **18.** *P* 14.

No.	Type		Unused	Used
203	**19**	1 a. carmine	1 6	0 4
204	,,	4½ a. blue-black	12 6	15 0

One (21)

Two & Half (22)

1904. *Stamps of* 1899 *and* 1901 *surch. as T* **21** *and* **22,** *in black or lake* (L.).

No.		Unused	Used
205	1 on 4½ a. orange	6 6	7 6
206	1 on 4½ a. blue-black (L.)	15 0	15 0
207	2 on 4 a. myrtle-green (L.)	50 0	50 0
208	2½ on 7½ a. mauve	45 0	45 0
209	2½ on 8 a. grey-olive	70 0	75 0

Two & Half (22*a*)

Two & Half (22*b*)

Varieties. *Thin, open* "w," *as in T* **22a.**

No.		Unused	Used
209*a*	2½ on 7½ mauve	£10	£10
	b. Serif to foot of "f" (T 22*b*)	£10	£10
	c. "Hlaf" for "Half"		
209*d*	2½ on 8 a. grey-olive	£12	£12
	e. Serif to foot of "f" (T 22*b*)	£12	£12
	f. "Hlaf" for "Half"	—	£60

23 24

Monogram of Sultan Seyyid Ali bin Hamoud bin Naherud.

1904 (8 June). *Typo.* *W* **18.** *P* 14. *Background of centre in second colour.*

No.	Type		Unused	Used
210	**23**	½ a. green	1 9	0 10
211	,,	1 a. rose-red	1 9	0 8
212	,,	2 a. brown	4 6	3 6
213	,,	2½ a. blue	4 0	2 6
214	,,	3 a. grey	6 6	6 6
215	,,	4 a. deep green	10 0	8 6
216	,,	4½ a. black	10 0	10 0
217	,,	5 a. yellow-brown	10 0	10 0
218	,,	7½ a. purple	15 0	15 0
219	,,	8 a. olive-green	15 0	15 0
220	**24**	1 r. blue and red	40 0	35 0
221	,,	2 r. green and red	90 0	90 0
222	,,	3 r. violet and red	£6	£6
223	,,	4 r. claret and red	£6	£6
224	,,	5 r. olive-brown and red	£9	£10

25 26

27. Sultan Ali bin Hamoud.

28. View of Port.

1908 (May)–**1909.** *Recess.* *W* **18.** *P* 14.

No.	Type	Description	Unused	Used
225	**25**	1 c. pearl-grey (Oct., '09)	0 4	0 6
226	,,	3 c. yellow-green ..	0 8	0 6
227	,,	6 c. rose-carmine ..	1 6	0 4
228	,,	10 c. brown (Oct., '09) ..	5 6	7 6
229	,,	12 c. violet	3 6	1 6
230	**26**	15 c. ultramarine	3 6	2 0
231	,,	25 c. sepia	6 0	3 0
232	,,	50 c. blue-green	12 6	10 0
233	,,	75 c. grey-black (Oct., '09)	15 0	17 6
234	**27**	1 r. yellow-green	25 0	17 6
235	,,	2 r. violet	45 0	45 0
236	,,	3 r. orange-bistre ..	70 0	70 0
237	,,	4 r. vermilion	£5	£5
238	,,	5 r. Antwerp blue ..	£6	£6
239	**28**	10 r. blue-green and brown	£25	£20
240	,,	20 r. black and yellow-grn.	£60	£60
241	,,	30 r. black and sepia	£110	£100
242	,,	40 r. black & orange-brown	£150	
243	,,	50 r. black and mauve	£250	
244	,,	100 r. black & Antwerp blue	£400	
245	,,	200 r. brown & greenish blue	£800	

29. Sultan Kalif bin Harub.

30. Native Craft.

31

1913. *Recess.* *W* **18.** *P* 14.

No.	Type	Description	Unused	Used
246	**29**	1 c. grey	0 3	0 6
247	,,	3 c. yellow-green	0 6	0 8
248	,,	6 c. rose-carmine ..	1 6	0 8
249	,,	10 c. brown	3 6	2 6
250	,,	12 c. violet	1 6	0 9
251	,,	15 c. blue	3 6	2 0
252	,,	25 c. sepia	4 0	3 6
253	,,	50 c. blue-green	15 0	8 6
254	,,	75 c. grey-black	8 6	7 8
255	**30**	1 r. yellow-green	15 0	10 0
256	,,	2 r. violet	40 0	35 0
257	,,	3 r. orange-bistre ..	60 0	50 0
258	,,	4 r. scarlet	75 0	60 0
259	,,	5 r. Antwerp blue ..	90 0	75 0
260	**31**	10 r. green and brown ..	£10	£10
260*a*	,,	20 r. black and green ..	£35	£30
260*b*	,,	30 r. black and brown ..	£45	£40
260*c*	,,	40 r. black and vermilion	£75	£65
260*d*	,,	50 r. black and purple ..	£100	£90
260*e*	,,	100 r. black and blue ..	£185	£150
260*f*	,,	200 r. brown and black ..	£400	£325

1914. *Wmk. Mult. Crown CA.* *P* 14.

No.	Type	Description	Unused	Used
261	**29**	1 c. grey	0 3	0 6
262	,,	3 c. yellow-green	1 0	1 0
263	,,	3 c. dull green	1 3	0 8
264	,,	6 c. deep carmine ..	1 3	0 8
265	,,	6 c. bright rose-carmine ..	0 8	0 6
266	**29**	15 c. deep ultramarine ..	1 9	3 0
268	,,	50 c. blue-green	6 0	6 0
269	,,	75 c. grey-black	8 0	10 0
270	**30**	1 r. yellow-green	8 6	6 0
271	,,	2 r. violet	20 0	20 0
272	,,	3 r. orange-bistre ..	30 0	35 0
273	,,	4 r. scarlet	60 0	60 0
274	,,	5 r. Antwerp blue ..	90 0	95 0
275	**31**	10 r. green and brown ..	£10	£10

1921–29. *Wmk. Mult. Script CA.* *P* 14.

No.	Type	Description	Unused	Used
276	**29**	1 c. slate-grey	0 10	1 3
277	,,	3 c. yellow-green	0 10	1 3
278	,,	6 c. carmine-red	1 6	1 6
279	,,	10 c. brown	4 6	5 0
280	,,	12 c. violet	2 6	3 0
281	,,	15 c. blue	4 0	5 0
282	,,	25 c. sepia	4 0	5 0
283	,,	50 c. myrtle-green ..	4 0	6 0
284	,,	75 c. slate	8 0	8 6
285	**30**	1 r. yellow-green	8 0	7 6
286	,,	2 r. deep violet	12 6	15 0
287	,,	3 r. orange-bistre ..	22 6	17 6
288	,,	4 r. scarlet	40 0	40 0
289	,,	5 r. Prussian blue ..	50 0	60 0
290	**31**	10 r. green and brown ..	95 0	95 0
291	,,	20 r. black and green ..	£30	£30
291*a*	,,	30 r. black and brown ('29)	£45	£45

1922. *Colours changed and new values.* *P* 14.

(*a*) *Wmk. Mult. Crown CA.*

No.	Type	Description	Unused	Used
292	**29**	8 c. purple/*pale yellow* ..	3 0	4 0
293	,,	10 c. myrtle/*pale yellow* ..	3 0	1 9

(*b*) *Wmk. Mult. Script CA.*

No.	Type	Description	Unused	Used
294	**29**	3 c. yellow	0 9	0 9
295	,,	4 c. green	2 6	2 6
296	,,	6 c. purple/*blue*	2 0	0 9
297	,,	12 c. carmine-red	3 6	2 6
298	,,	20 c. indigo	6 0	4 6

32. Sultan Kalif bin Harub. **33.**

1926–27. *T* **32** ("CENTS" *in seriffed capitals*). *Recess.* *Wmk. Mult. Script. CA.* *P* 14.

No.	Type	Description	Unused	Used
299	**32**	1 c. brown	0 4	0 4
300	,,	3 c. yellow-orange ..	0 6	0 6
301	,,	4 c. deep dull green ..	1 3	1 9
302	,,	6 c. violet	0 8	0 6
303	,,	8 c. slate	4 6	5 0
304	,,	10 c. olive-green	3 0	1 9
305	,,	12 c. carmine-red	3 0	1 0
306	,,	20 c. bright blue	2 0	1 0
307	,,	25 c. purple/*yellow* ('27) ..	6 0	4 0
308	,,	50 c. claret	5 0	4 6
309	,,	75 c. sepia ('27) ..	10 0	15 0

(*New currency.* 100 *cents* = 1 *shilling.*)

1936 (1 Jan.). *T* **33** ("CENTS" *in sans-serif capitals*), *and T* **30/1**, *but values in shillings.* *Recess.* *Wmk. Mult. Script CA.* *P* 14 × 13½–14.

No.	Type	Description	Unused	Used
310	**33**	5 c. green	0 6	0 6
311	,,	10 c. black	0 8	0 8
312	,,	15 c. carmine-red	0 8	1 6
313	,,	20 c. orange	1 3	1 0
314	,,	25 c. purple/*yellow* ..	1 6	1 6
315	,,	30 c. ultramarine	2 0	2 0
316	,,	40 c. sepia	2 6	2 6
317	,,	50 c. claret	3 6	3 6
318	**30**	1s. yellow-green ..	4 0	3 6
319	,,	2s. slate-violet	10 0	7 6
320	,,	5s. scarlet	20 0	20 0
321	,,	7s. 50 light blue ..	32 6	40 0
322	**31**	10s. green and brown ..	45 0	50 0

36. Sultan Kalif bin Harub.

1936 (9 DEC.). *Silver Jubilee of Sultan. Recess. Wmk. Mult. Script CA. P* 14.

No.	Type	Description				
323	**36**	10 c. black & olive-green..	1	6	2	0
324	,,	20 c. black & bright purple	2	0	2	9
325	,,	30 c. black & deep ultram.	1	9	2	3
326	,,	50 c. black & orange-verm.	2	0	3	0

37. Native Craft.

1944 (20 NOV.). *Bicentenary of Al Busaid Dynasty. Recess. Wmk. Mult. Script CA. P* 14.

No.	Type	Description				
327	**37**	10 c. ultramarine	0	6	1	0
328	,,	20 c. red	1	6	1	0
329	,,	50 c. blue-green	1	0	1	0
330	,,	1s. dull purple	1	9	2	0

VICTORY ISSUE

8TH JUNE 1946

(38)

1946 (11 NOV.). *Victory. Optd. with T* **38.**

No.	Type	Description				
331	**33**	10 c. black (R.)	0	4	0	6
332	,,	30 c. ultramarine (R.) ..	0	8	0	10

1949 (10 JAN.). *Royal Silver Wedding. As Nos.* 30/1 *of Aden.*

333	20 c. orange	0	6	0	6
334	10s. brown	17	6	20	0

1949 (10 OCT.). *75th Anniv. of U.P.U. As Nos.* 114/7 *of Antigua.*

335	20 c. red-orange	0	10	1	0
336	30 c. deep blue	1	0	1	3
337	50 c. magenta	2	0	2	6
338	1s. blue-green	3	6	4	0

39. Sultan Kalif bin Harub.

40. Seyyid Khalifa Schools, Beit-el-Ras.

(Recess. De La Rue & Co.)

1952 (26 AUG.). *Wmk. Mult. Script CA. P* 12½ (*cent values*) *or* 13 (*shilling values*).

No.	Type	Description				
339	**39**	5 c. black	0	3	0	3
340	,,	10 c. red-orange	0	4	0	3
341	,,	15 c. green (*shades*) ..	0	6	0	4
342	,,	20 c. carmine-red	0	8	0	8
343	,,	25 c. reddish purple ..	0	10	1	0
344	,,	30 c. dp. bluish grn. (*shades*)	0	10	1	0
345	,,	35 c. bright blue	1	0	1	0
346	,,	40 c. deep brown (*shades*)	1	6	1	6
347	,,	50 c. violet (*shades*) ..	1	6	1	8
348	**40**	1s. dp. green & dp. brown	2	0	3	0
349	,,	2s. bt. blue & dp. purple	4	0	5	0
350	,,	5s. black & carmine-red	10	0	12	6
351	,,	7s. 50 c. grey-blk. & emer.	20	0	27	6
352	,,	10s. carmine-red & black	25	0	30	0

41. Sultan Kalif bin Harub.

(Photo. Harrison & Sons.)

1954 (26 AUG.). *Sultan's 75th Birthday. Wmk. Mult. Script CA. Chalk-surfaced paper. P* 13×12.

No.	Type	Description				
353	**41**	15 c. deep green	1	0	1	0
354	,,	20 c. rose-red	1	0	1	6
355	,,	30 c. bright blue	2	0	2	0
356	,,	50 c. purple	3	0	3	6
357	,,	1s. 25 c. orange-red ..	7	0	8	0

42. Cloves.

43. Dhows.

44. Sultan's Barge.

45. Map of East African Coast. **46.** Minaret Mosque.

47. Dimbani Mosque. **48.** Kibweni Palace.

(Des. W. J. Jennings (T **42**), A. Farhan (T **43**), Mrs. M. Broadbent (T **44**, **46**), R. A. Sweet (T **45**), A. S. B. New (T **47**), B. J. Woolley (T **48**). Recess. Bradbury, Wilkinson & Co.)

1957 (26 Aug.). *W* w.**12**. *P* 11½ (5 *c.*, 10 *c.*), 11 × 11½ (15 *c.*, 30 *c.*, 1s. 25), 14 × 13½ (20 *c.*, 25 *c.*, 35 *c.*, 50 *c.*), 13½ × 14 (40 *c.*, 1s., 2s.) *or* 13 × 13½ (5s., 7s. 50, 10s.).

358	**42**	5 c. orange & deep green	0	3	0	3
359	,,	10 c. emerald & carm.-red	0	4	0	3
360	**43**	15 c. green and sepia ..	0	6	0	5
361	**44**	20 c. ultramarine	0	7	0	8
362	**45**	25 c. orange-brn. & black	0	8	0	8
363	**43**	30 c. carmine-red & black	0	8	0	9
364	**45**	35 c. slate and emerald ..	1	0	1	0
365	**46**	40 c. brown and black ..	1	3	1	6
366	**45**	50 c. blue and grey-green ..	1	6	1	6
367	**47**	1s. carmine and black ..	2	6	2	0
368	**43**	1s. 25, slate and carmine	3	0	3	0
369	**47**	2s. orange & deep green	4	0	4	0
370	**48**	5s. deep bright blue ..	12	6	10	6
371	,,	7s. 50, green	20	0	22	6
372	,,	10s. carmine	20	0	22	6

49. Sultan Seyyid Sir Abdulla bin Khalifa.

(Recess. Bradbury, Wilkinson.)

1961 (17 Oct.). *As T* **42/8** *but with portrait of Sultan Sir Abdulla as in T* **49**. *W* w.**12**. *P* 11½ (5 *c.*, 10 *c.*), 11 × 11½ (15 *c.*, 30 *c.*, 1 *s.* 25), 14 × 13½ (20 *c.*, 25 *c.*, 35 *c.*, 50 *c.*) 13½ × 14 (40 *c.*, 1s., 2s.) *or* 13 × 13½ (5s., 7s. 50, 10s., 20s.).

373	**49**	5 c. orange & deep green	0	6	0	6
374	,,	10 c. emer. & carmine-red	0	8	0	6
375	**43**	15 c. green and sepia ..	0	8	0	6
376	**44**	20 c. ultramarine	0	10	0	10
377	**45**	25 c. orge.-brown & black	1	0	1	0
378	**43**	30 c. carmine-red & black	1	0	1	0
379	**45**	35 c. slate and emerald ..	1	3	1	3
380	**46**	40 c. brown and black ..	1	3	1	3
381	**45**	50 c. blue and grey-green	1	6	1	6
382	**47**	1s. carmine and black ..	2	9	2	6
383	**43**	1s. 25, slate and carmine	3	6	3	0
384	**47**	2s. orange & deep green	5	0	5	0
385	**48**	5s. deep bright blue ..	12	6	11	0
386	,,	7s. 50, green	22	6	25	0
387	,,	10s. carmine	40	0	40	0
388	,,	20s. sepia	£5		110	0

50. "Protein Foods"

(Des. M. Goaman. Photo. Harrison.)

1963 (4 June). *Freedom from Hunger*. *W* w. **12**. *P* 14 × 14½.

389	**50**	1s. 30, sepia	3	6	4	6

INDEPENDENT

within the Commonwealth.

51. Zanzibar Clove.

52. "To Prosperity" (Zanzibar doorway).

53. " Religious Tolerance " (mosques and churches).

54. " Towards the Light " (Mangapwani Cave).

(Photo. Harrison.)

1963 (10 Dec.). *Independence.* *P* 12½.

390	**51**	30 c. multicoloured ..	0 9	1 0
391	**52**	50 c. multicoloured ..	1 3	1 9
392	**53**	1s. 30, multicoloured ..	3 3	4 6
393	**54**	2s. 50, multicoloured ..	5 0	7 6

REPUBLIC

within the Commonwealth.

When the Post Office opened on 14 Jan. 1964, after the revolution deposing the Sultan, the stamps on sale had the portrait cancelled by a manuscript cross. Stamps thus cancelled on cover or piece used between Jan. 14 and 17 are therefore of interest.

JAMHURI 1964

(**55** = " Republic ".)

1964 (17 Jan.). *Locally handstamped as T* **55** *in black.* (*i*) *Nos.* 373/88.

394	**49**	5 c. orange & deep green	
395	,,	10 c. emer. & carmine-red	
396	**43**	15 c. green and sepia ..	
397	**44**	20 c. ultramarine ..	
398	**45**	25 c. orange-brn. & black	
399	**43**	30 c. carmine-red & black	
400	**45**	35 c. slate and emerald ..	
401	**46**	40 c. brown and black ..	
402	**45**	50 c. blue and grey-green	*Set of* 16 *un.,* £5
403	**47**	1s. carmine and black ..	
404	**43**	1s. 25, slate and carmine	
405	**47**	2s. orange & deep green	
406	**48**	5s. deep bright blue ..	
407	,,	7s. 50, green	
408	,,	10s. carmine	
409	,,	20s. sepia	

(*ii*) *Nos.* 390/3 (*Independence*).

410	**51**	30 c. multicoloured ..	
411	**52**	50 c. multicoloured ..	*Set of* 4 *un.,* 15*s.*
412	**53**	1s. 30, multicoloured ..	
413	**54**	2s. 50, multicoloured ..	

T **55** occurs in various positions—diagonally, horizontally or vertically.

NOTE. Nos. 394 to 413 are the only stamps officially authorised to receive the handstamp, but it has also been seen on No. 389 and the Postage Dues. There are numerous errors but it is impossible to distinguish between cases of genuine oversight and those made deliberately at the request of purchasers.

JAMHURI 1964 (**56**)

JAMHURI 1964 (**57**)

1964 (28 Feb.). *Optd. by Bradbury, Wilkinson.* (*i*) *As T* **56** *on Nos.* 373/88.

414	**49**	5 c. orange & deep green	0 3	0 4
415	,,	10 c. emerald & carm.-red	0 4	0 5
416	**43**	15 c. green and sepia ..	0 5	0 6
417	**44**	20 c. ultramarine	0 6	0 7
418	**45**	25 c. orange-brn. & black	0 7	0 9
419	**43**	30 c. carmine-red & black	0 7	0 9
420	**45**	35 c. slate and emerald ..	0 9	0 10
421	**46**	40 c. brown and black ..	0 10	0 11
422	**45**	50 c. blue and grey-green ..	1 0	1 3
423	**47**	1s. carmine and black ..	1 9	2 0
424	**43**	1s. 25, slate and carmine	2 3	2 6
425	**47**	2s. orange and dp. green	3 3	4 6
426	**48**	5s. deep bright blue ..	8 0	9 0
427	,,	7s. 50, green	12 0	15 0
428	,,	10s. carmine	16 0	17 6
429	,,	20s. sepia	30 0	35 0

The opt. T **56** is set in two lines on Types **46/8.**

(*ii*) *As T***57** *on Nos.* 390/3 (*Independence*).

430	**51**	30 c. multicoloured ..	1 0	1 3
431	**52**	50 c. multicoloured ..	1 6	1 9
432	**53**	1s. 30, multicoloured ..	3 6	4 0
433	**54**	2s. 50, multicoloured ..	7 0	8 0

The opt. T **57** is set in one line on No. 432.

For the set inscribed " UNITED REPUBLIC OF TANGANYIKA & ZANZIBAR " see Nos. 124/7 of Tanganyika.

58. Axe, Spear and dagger.

59. Bow and Arrow.

60. Zanzibari with Rifle.

61. Zanzibari breaking Chains.

62. Zanzibari, Flag and Sun.

66. Flag on Map.

63. Hand breaking Chains.

64. Hand waving Flag.

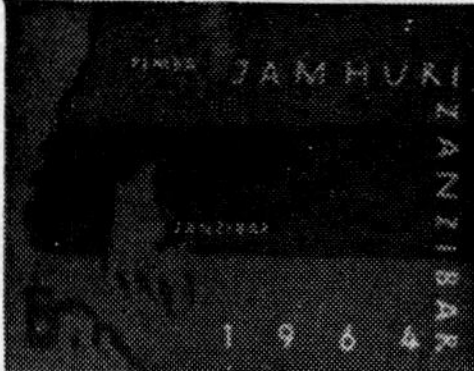

65. Map and Zanzibar and Pemba on Flag.

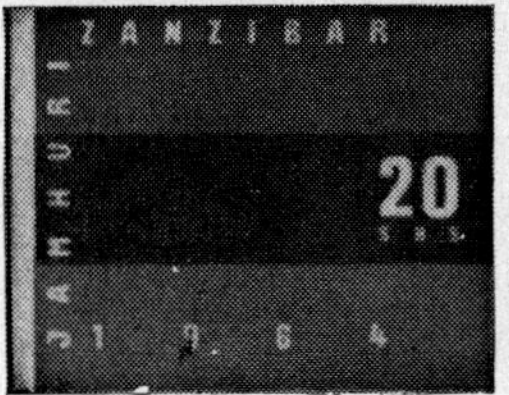

67. National Flag.

(Litho. German Bank Note Ptg. Co., Leipzig.)

1964 (21 June). *P* $13 \times 13\frac{1}{2}$ (*vert.*) *or* $13\frac{1}{2} \times 13$ (*horiz.*).

No.	Type	Value	Description	s.	d.	s.	d.
434	**58**	5 c.	blk., blue, grn., & lilac	0	2	0	3
435	**59**	10 c.	black, blue, green and yellow	0	3	0	4
436	**58**	15 c.	black, blue, green and rose-pink ..	0	4	0	5
437	**59**	20 c.	black, blue, green and olive-yellow ..	0	5	0	6
438	**60**	25 c.	black, orange, purple and carmine ..	0	6	0	7
439	**61**	30 c.	black, orange, violet and blue	0	6	0	7
440	**60**	40 c.	black, orange, violet and blue	0	8	0	9
441	**61**	50 c.	black, orange, violet and light red ..	0	10	1	0
442	**62**	1s.	black, blue, green, orange and yellow ..	1	5	1	9
443	**63**	1s. 30,	chocolate, black, green, blue & yellow	1	10	2	3
444	**64**	2s.	blue, black, green, chocolate and yellow	2	9	3	6
445	**65**	5s.	yellow-brown, blue, black and green ..	6	9	7	6
446	**66**	10s.	black, blue, green, yellow-brn. & lt. blue	13	3	15	0
447	**67**	20s.	blue, black, green and pale yellow	25	0	30	0

68. Soldier and Maps.

69. Building Construction.

(Litho. German Bank Note Ptg. Co., Leipzig.)

1965 (12 Jan.). *First Anniv. of Revolution. P* $13 \times 13\frac{1}{2}$ (*vert.*) *or* $13\frac{1}{2} \times 13$ (*horiz.*).

No.	Type	Value	Description	s.	d.	s.	d.
448	**68**	20 c.	apple-grn. & dp. grn.	0	6	0	7
449	**69**	30 c.	chocolate and yellow-orange	0	7	0	11
450	**68**	1s. 30,	light blue and ultramarine	2	3	2	9
451	**69**	2s. 50,	reddish violet and rose	4	6	4	9

70. Planting Rice.

71. Hands holding Rice.

(Litho. German Bank Note Ptg. Co., Leipzig.)

1965 (17 Oct.). *Agricultural Development. P* 13×12½.

No.	Type	Description	Unused	Used
452	**70**	20 c. sepia and blue	0 6	0 7
453	**71**	30 c. sepia and magenta	0 7	0 9
454	,,	1s. 30, sepia & yell.-orge.	2 3	2 6
455	**70**	2s. 50, sepia and emerald	4 6	5 0

72. Ship, Tractor, Factory, and Open Book and Torch.

73. Soldier.

(Litho. German Bank Note Ptg. Co., Leipzig.)

1966 (12 Jan.). *2nd Anniv. of Revolution. P* 12½×13.

No.	Type	Description	Unused	Used
456	**72**	20 c. multicoloured	0 6	0 7
457	**73**	50 c. multicoloured	1 0	1 2
458	**72**	1s. 30, multicoloured	2 3	2 6
459	**73**	2s. 50, multicoloured	4 6	5 0

NOTE. Stamps inscribed "UGANDA KENYA TANGANYIKA & ZANZIBAR (or TANZANIA UGANDA KENYA") will be found listed under East Africa.

POSTAGE DUE STAMPS

Insufficiently prepaid.
Postage due.
1 cent.

D 1

(Types D 1 and D 2 typo. by the Government Printer.)

1930–33.

(*a*) *Rouletted* 10, *with imperf. sheet edges. No gum.*

No.	Type	Description	Unused	Used
D 1	**D 1**	1 c. black/*orange*	5 0	
D 2	,,	2 c. black/*orange*	5 0	
D 3	,,	3 c. black/*orange*	5 0	
		a. "cent.s" for "cents."	30 0	
D 4	,,	6 c. black/*orange*		
		a. "cent.s" for "cents."		
D 5	,,	9 c. black/*orange*	6 0	
		a. "cent.s" for "cents."	30 0	35 0
D 6	,,	12 c. black/*orange*		
		a. "cent.s" for "cents."		
D 7	,,	12 c. black/*green*	—	£6
D 8	,,	15 c. black/*orange*	5 0	6 0
		a. "cent.s" for "cents."	30 0	35 0
D 9	**D 1**	18 c. black/*salmon*	25 0	30 0
		a. "cent.s" for "cents."	60 0	70 0
D10	,,	18 c. black/*orange*	10 0	
		a. "cent.s" for "cents."	50 0	55 0
D11	,,	20 c. black/*orange*	10 0	
		a. "cent.s" for "cents."	60 0	
D12	,,	21 c. black/*orange*	10 0	
		a. "cent.s" for "cents."	60 0	65 0
D13	,,	25 c. black/*magenta*		
		a. "cent.s" for "cents."		
D14	,,	25 c. black/*orange*		
D15	,,	31 c. black/*orange*	25 0	
		a. "cent.s" for "cents."	£7	
D16	,,	50 c. black/*orange*	60 0	
		a. "cent.s" for "cents."	£10	
D17	,,	75 c. black/*orange*	90 0	
		a. "cent.s" for "cents."	£20	

Sheets of the first printings of all values except the 1 c. and 2 c. contained one stamp showing the error "cent.s" for "cents."

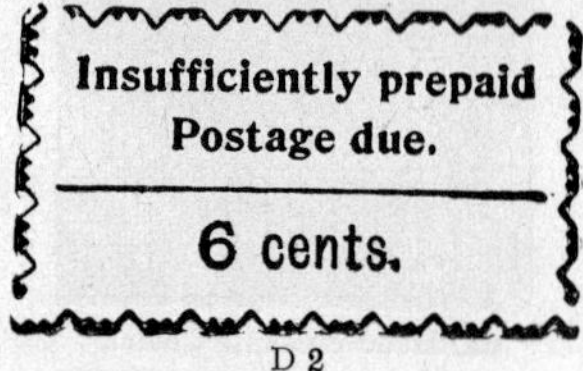

D 2

(*b*) *Rouletted* 5. *No gum.*

No.	Type	Description	Unused	Used
D18	**D 2**	2 c. black/*salmon*	5 0	
D19	,,	3 c. black/*rose*	6 0	10 0
D21	,,	6 c. black/*yellow*	8 0	
D22	,,	12 c. black/*blue*	10 0	
D23	,,	25 c. black/*rose*	25 0	
D24	,,	25 c. black/*lilac*	15 0	

D 3

(Typo. De La Rue & Co.)

1936 (1 Jan.)–**62.** *Wmk. Mult. Script CA. P* 14.

No.	Type	Description	Unused	Used
D25	**D 3**	5 c. violet, O	0 3	0 4
		a. Chalky paper (18.7.56)	0 2	0 3
D26	,,	10 c. scarlet, O	0 6	0 8
		a. Chalky paper (6.3.62)	0 3	0 6
D27	,,	20 c. green, O	1 0	1 3
		a. Chalky paper (6.3.62)	0 5	0 8
D28	,,	30 c. brown, O	1 6	1 9
		a. Chalky paper (18.7.56)	0 6	0 9
D29	,,	40 c. ultramarine, O	1 9	2 0
		a. Chalky paper (18.7.56)	0 8	1 0
D30	,,	1s. grey, O	3 6	4 6
		a. Chalky paper (18.7.56)	1 5	2 0

See footnote after No. 413.

HAVE YOU READ THE NOTES AT THE BEGINNING OF THIS CATALOGUE?

These often provide answers to the enquiries we receive.

ZULULAND.

ZULULAND (1) **ZULULAND.** (2)

1888–93. *Stamps of Great Britain optd. with T* **1.**

No.	Type	Description	Unused	Used
1	**71**	½d. vermilion	3 6	4 6
2	**57**	1d. dull purple	8 0	8 0
3	**73**	2d. green and carmine	15 0	20 0
4	**74**	2½d. purple/*blue*	22 6	30 0
5	**75**	3d. purple/*yellow*	30 0	35 0
6	**76**	4d. green and brown	30 0	35 0
7	**78**	5d. dull purple & blue ('93)	60 0	75 0
8	**79**	6d. purple/*rose-red*	50 0	50 0
9	**80**	9d. dull purple and blue	85 0	90 0
10	**82**	1s. green	£6	£7
11	**59**	5s. rose	£35	£40

No. 98 *of Natal optd. with T* **2.**

No.	Type	Description	Unused	Used
12	**23**	½d. green	25 0	35 0
		a. Overprint double	£20	
		b. Overprint inverted	£35	
		c. Without stop	50 0	60 0
		d. Opt. omtd. (pr. with normal)	£85	£100

1894 (Jan.). *No.* 102 *of Natal optd. with T* **1.**

No.	Type	Description	Unused	Used
16	**15**	6d. mauve	60 0	75 0

3

4

(Typo. De La Rue & Co.)

1894–96. *Wmk. Crown CA. P* 14.

No.	Type	Description	Unused	Used
20	**3**	½d. dull mauve & green	3 0	2 6
21	,,	1d. dull mauve & carmine	4 0	3 0
22	,,	2½d. dull mauve & ultram.	10 0	12 6
23	,,	3d. dull mauve & olive-brn.	10 0	8 6
24	**4**	6d. dull mauve & black	15 0	17 6
25	,,	1s. green	30 0	35 0
26	,,	2s. 6d. green and black	60 0	70 0
27	,,	4s. green and carmine	£5	£6
28	,,	£1 purple/*red*	£50	£40
29	,,	£5 purple and black/*red*	£400	£125

Dangerous forgeries exist of the £1 and £5.

FISCAL STAMPS USED FOR POSTAGE.

Fiscal stamps of Natal (*T* **41**, *name and value in second colour, wmk. Crown CA, P* 14) *optd. with T* **1**, *in black.*

No.	Description	Unused	Used
51	1d. dull mauve	3 0	2 6
52	1s. mauve and carmine	£8	£10
54	5s. mauve and carmine	£18	£20
55	9s. mauve and carmine	£20	£25
56	£1 green	£40	£50
57	£5 green and red	£125	£150
58	£20 green and black	£325	

The issue of Zululand stamps ceased on 30 June, 1898, the territory having been annexed to Natal on 31 December, 1897.

Please turn over for

ADDENDA AND CORRIGENDA

ADDENDA AND CORRIGENDA

GREAT BRITAIN.

248. View near Hassocks, Sussex.

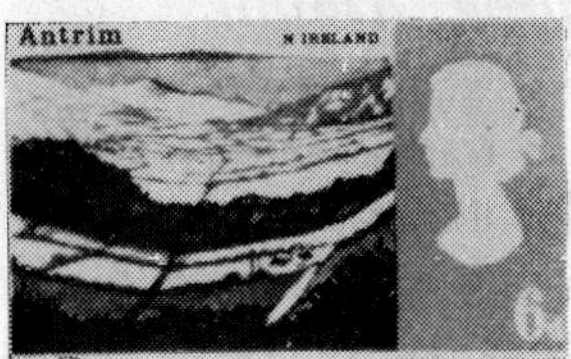

249. Antrim, Northern Ireland.

250. Harlech Castle, Wales.

251. Cairngorm Mountains, Scotland.

(Des. L. Rosomon, Queen's portrait, adapted by D. Gentleman from coinage.)

1966 (2 May). *Landscapes. Chalky paper. W* **179.** *P* 15 × 14.

689 **248**	4d. black, yellow-green and new blue ..	0 6	0 2
	p. Three phosphor bands ..	0 6	0 3
690 **249**	6d. blk., emer. & new blue	0 8	0 4
	p. Three phosphor bands ..	0 8	0 5
691 **250**	1s. 3d. greenish yellow and greenish blue ..	1 7	0 9
	p. Three phosphor bands ..	1 7	1 0
692 **251**	1s. 6d. black, orange and Prussian blue ..	1 11	1 0
	p. Three phosphor bands ..	1 11	1 3

252. Players with Ball.

253. Goalmouth Mêlée.

254. Goalkeeper saving Ball.

(Des. D. Gentleman (4d.), W. Kempster (6d.), D. Caplan (1s. 3d.). Queen's portrait adapted by D. Gentleman from coinage.)

1966 (1 June). *World Cup Football Competition. Chalky paper. W* **179.** *P* 14 × 15 *(4d.) or* 15 × 14 *(others).*

693 **252**	4d. multicoloured ..	0 6	0 3
	p. Three phosphor bands ..	0 6	0 6
694 **253**	6d. multicoloured ..	0 8	0 8
	p. Three phosphor bands ..	0 8	0 10
695 **254**	1s. 3d. multicoloured ..	1 7	2 0
	p. Three phosphor bands ..	1 7	2 3

THE 'KING GEORGE VI' ALBUM

for

BRITISH COMMONWEALTH POSTAGE STAMPS

1936-1953

A fine, Single-Volume Album

This is a single-volume, permanent, fast-bound album for the stamps of the British Commonwealth from 1936 to 1953 and covers the issues of King Edward VIII and King George VI. It caters for a straightforward collection built on popular lines. Shades, perforation varieties, etc., and the Japanese Occupation issues have been excluded, but provision is made for watermark changes, Postage Dues and Officials, etc. Arrangement is alphabetical and there is a separate, individual space for each stamp, quickly found by the illustration or printed details, so that with the *King George VI*, collecting is made easy, and the collection is always neat, attractive and interesting—to others as well as to the owner.

CONTENTS: 224 pp., size $11\frac{1}{4} \times 9$ in. Handsome, strong cloth in RED or GREEN. Fully guarded throughout to minimize bulging as the album fills. Packed in box.

No. 3385. Standard Edition. **42/-** Postage: U.K. 3/3, abd. 4/3

No. 3419. Interleaved Edition. **52/6** Postage: U.K. 3/3, abd. 4/9

AUSTRALIA.

Correction. Delete Nos. 384a and 385a which are relisted below:—

199. Queen Elizabeth II.

1966 (14 Feb.). *Coil stamps. Photo. P* 14½ × *imperf.*

404 **199** 3 c. black, lt. blue & green 0 6 0 4
405 ,, 4 c. black, light brown and light vermilion .. 0 7 0 4

BARBADOS.

Add:—As Nos. 322, 325, 330/1, 333 (1 *c.*, 4 *c.*, 15 *c.*, 25 *c.*, 50 *c.*), *but wmk. sideways.*

(322) a. Wmk. sideways (15.3.66) .. 0 2 0 3
(325) a. Wmk. sideways (15.3.66) .. 0 4 0 5
(330) a. Wmk. sideways (15.3.66) .. 0 11 1 0
(331) a. Wmk. sideways (15.3.66) .. 1 6 1 9
(333) a. Wmk. sideways (15.3.66) .. 2 10 3 6

BRITISH SOLOMON ISLANDS.

Correction. Delete the illustration above T **48** and substitute the following:—

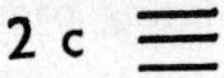

2 c

CANADA.

234. Mountain Avens and Arms of Northwest Territories.

235. Fireweed and Arms of Yukon Territory.

Add to Nos. 543/52 (*Provincial Emblems*). *New values and designs.*

553 **234** 5 c. drab, green and yellow (23.3.66) 0 8 0 9
554 **235** 5 c. blue, green and rose-red (23.3.66) .. 0 8 0 9

250. La Salle.

(Des. Brigdens Ltd., Toronto.)

1966 (13 Apr.). 300*th Anniv. of La Salle's Arrival in Canada. P* 12.

571 **250** 5 c. deep bluish green .. 0 8 0 9

CEYLON.

The above illustrates T **156.**

COOK ISLANDS.

Airmail

(62)

1966 (22 Apr.). *Air. Various stamps optd. with T* **62** *or surch. in addition.*

185 **49** 6d. red, yellow and green
186 **50** 7d. on 8d. black and blue
187 **47** 10d. on 3d. yellow, yellow-green & reddish violet
188 **51** 1s. orge.-yell.& yell.-green
189 **52** 1s. 6d. bluish violet ..
190 **54** 2s. 3d. on 3s. black and yellow-green .. ..
191 **55** 5s. bistre-brown and blue
192 **53** 10s. on 2s. bistre-brown and grey-blue ..
193 – £1 pink (No. 143) ..

IRELAND.

68. James Connolly.

69. Thomas J. Clarke.

70. P. H. Pearse.

71. " Marching to Freedom ".

72. Eamonn Ceannt.

73. Sean MacDiarmada.

74. Thomas MacDonagh.

75. Joseph Plunkett.

(Des. E. Delaney (No. 216), R. Kyne, after portraits by Sean O'Sullivan (others).)

1966 (12 Apr.). *50th Anniv. of Easter Rising. W* **22.** *P* 15.

213	**68**	3d. black & greenish blue	0	6	0	8
214	**69**	3d. black and bronze-green	0	6	0	8
215	**70**	5d. black and yellow-olive	0	9	0	10
216	**71**	5d. blk., orge. & bl.-green	0	9	0	10
217	**72**	7d. black & lt. orge.-brown	0	11	1	0
218	**73**	7d. black and blue-green..	0	11	1	0
219	**74**	1s. 5d. black & turquoise	1	11	2	3
220	**75**	1s. 5d. black & brt. green	1	11	2	3

The two designs in each denomination were issued together in sheets with each pair of designs arranged in horizontal *se-tenant* rows.

MALAWI.

1966 (1 Apr.). *As Nos.* 215/6, 222, *but wmk. Cockerel (sideways on ½d.).*

252	**32**	½d. reddish violet	0	2	0	2
253	**33**	1d. black and green ..	0	3	0	4
259	**38**	1s. brown, turquoise-blue and pale yellow ..	1	5	2	0

Nos. 252/64 have been allocated to this series.

59. British Central Africa 6d. Stamp of 1891.

(Des. V. Whiteley. Photo. Harrison.)

1966 (4 May). *75th Anniv. of Postal Services. Wmk. Cockerel. P* 14½.

265	**59**	4d. grey-blue and yellow-green	0	7	0	9
266	,,	9d. grey-blue and claret ..	1	1	1	6
267	,,	1s. 6d. grey-blue and reddish lilac	2	0	2	6
268	,,	3s. grey-blue and new blue	4	0	5	0

MALAYSIA.

21. The Yang di-Pertuan Agong (Ismail Nasiruddin Shah).

The GREAT BRITAIN Commemorative Album

Strong spring-back cover printed attractively in red, blue and black. 48 pages, size $7\frac{1}{2} \times 10\frac{3}{8}$ in., printed with full details of each issue, with illustrated space for each stamp from the first British commemorative (1924 Empire Exhibition) to the 1965 I.T.U. set.

ALBUM COMPLETE; ITEM No. 3550

PRICE 25/-
Postage extra: U.K. 3/-, abd. 2/6

EXTRA BLANK LEAVES; ITEM No. 3551

PRICE 3/6 (per 24)
Postage extra: U.K. 8d. abd. 9d.

Gibbons' **NEW COLOUR GUIDE**

Months of intensive research have gone into this new edition of our universally famous accessory. Planned to provide an authoritative standard for stamp colour naming; it is more helpful that ever **NOW SHOWING THE 100 COLOURS** most useful for stamp description. In addition there are notes on colour identification which should be of great assistance to **all** collectors. **To aid users, a black card mask is now included with each Guide, to shield stamps and samples when making colour comparison.**

PRICE 5/- post:

AVAILABLE IN FRENCH, GERMAN AND SPANISH AS WELL AS ENGLISH.

(Photo. Japanese Govt. Ptg. Wks.)

1966 (11 Apr.). *Installation of Yang di-Pertuan Agong, Tuanku Ismail Nasiruddin Shah. P* 13½.

33	**21**	15 c. black and light yellow	0 7	0 8
34	,,	50 c. black & greenish blue	1 8	1 10

NEW ZEALAND.

212a. Koromiko.

(Photo. Harrison.)

Add to Nos. 781, *etc. New value and design. W* **98** *(sideways). P* 15 × 14.

788*a*	**212a**	7d. red, green, yellow & pale red (16.3.66)	0 11	0 6

Note. The first Supplement containing new issues not in this Catalogue or the Addenda appeared in the July, 1966 number of *Gibbons Stamp Monthly*.

TANGANYIKA (TANZANIA).

39. Pres. Nyerere and First Vice-Pres. Karume within Bowl of Flame.

40. Hands supporting Bowl of Flame.

(Des. J. O. Ahmed (T **39**), G. L. Vasarhelyi (T **40**). Photo. Enschedé.)

1966 (26 Apr.). *2nd Anniv. of United Republic. P* 14 × 13.

142	**39**	30 c. multicoloured	0 6	0 10
143	**40**	50 c. multicoloured	0 10	1 2
144	,,	1s. 30, multicoloured	1 10	2 6
145	**39**	2s. 50, multicoloured	3 6	4 6

PRICE ALTERATIONS

GREAT BRITAIN		
162c	£25	£25
477	15 0	50 0
478	60 0	30 0
621	7 6	6 0
655	1 3	1 3
656	1 6	1 6
AUSTRALIA		
44	£45	£14
363	2 0	1 3
364	4 6	3 6
365	6 0	4 6
366	6 6	3 6
367	12 6	7 6
367*a*	20 0	11 6
368	18 0	9 0
369	20 0	11 0
BERMUDA		
89*a*	£40	£40
BRITISH GUIANA		
317a	£32	£22
CAYMAN ISLANDS		
84	£9	£11
95	£30	£35
160	8 6	11 0
161	15 0	18 0
161*a*	32 6	36 0
CEYLON		
180a	—	£6
509	0 10	0 11
GAMBIA		
11b	£120	
(Delete used price)		
GIBRALTAR		
108	£240	£290
GILBERT & ELLICE IS.		
23	£25	£45
IRELAND		
1a	£15	£25
10a	£30	£40
12a	*Unchanged*	
13a	£12	£14
1/15 *remainder. Increase by approx.* 50%		
17/21	*Increase* 25%	
22/29*a*	*Increase* 50%	
30/43a	*Increase* 25%	
44	£9	£12
45	£10	£12
45a	£14	
46	£15	£18
47/51	*Increase* 40%	
52a	£120	
53a	£200	
56a	£15	£17
58a	£15	£17
60a	£150	£100
61a	£22	£25
63a	£300	
63b	£60	
52/66c *remainder. Increase* 50%		
67/70a	*Increase* 50%	
72a	80 0	90 0
74b	£100	£45
71/82 *remainder. Increase* 50%		
83/88	*Increase* 25%	
89	2 0	0 6
90	2 0	2 6
91	6 6	8 0
92/4 *Each*	1 6	0 8
95	3 6	4 0
96	1 6	0 8
97	3 6	4 0
98	7 6	1 0
99	45 0	52 6
100	£6	£7
101	£22	£24
102	15 0	12 6
103	35 0	27 6
104	70 0	45 0
105	1 0	0 6
106	4 0	5 0
107	1 0	0 6
108	4 0	5 0
109	1 6	0 6
110	6 6	6 0
112a	50 0	55 0
112b	30 0	12 6
113	0 9	0 2
115	0 11	0 3
126	1 6	0 6
127	40 0	15 0
128	2 0	0 9
129	0 6	0 6
130	2 6	2 6
131	2 6	0 4
132	7 6	3 6
135	2 6	0 6
136	2 9	0 9
137	6 6	7 6
138	2 0	0 4
139	5 0	3 9
140	0 9	0 10
141	4 0	4 0
144	1 6	0 4
145	5 0	3 6
146	0 8	0 4
147	3 0	1 6
148	3 6	0 10
149	1 0	0 6
150	15 0	4 0
151	12 6	8 6
152	1 0	0 6
153	3 0	2 6
154	1 3	0 4
155	18 6	18 6
156	1 3	0 4
157	10 0	5 0
158	3 0	0 9
159	7 6	5 0
160	1 6	0 8
161	6 6	5 6
162	1 3	0 6
163	6 6	5 6
164	1 3	0 6
165	6 0	5 0
166	1 0	0 4
167	4 6	3 6
168	1 3	0 6
169	7 6	6 0
170	1 3	0 6
171	6 6	5 6
172	1 6	0 6
173	7 6	6 0
174	1 3	0 6
175	5 6	5 0
176	1 3	0 4
177	3 0	2 0
178	1 0	0 4
179	6 6	5 0
180	3 0	0 9
181	10 0	7 6
182	22 6	6 6
183	37 6	25 0
184	3 0	2 0
185	5 0	3 9
186	1 3	0 6
187	12 6	10 0
188	10 0	7 6
189	1 6	0 6
190	5 0	4 0
191	2 0	2 6
192	4 0	4 0
193	1 3	0 8
194	4 0	5 0
195	2 3	2 3
196	4 6	4 0
197	1 3	1 6
198	4 0	4 6
199	1 3	1 3
200	4 6	4 0
201	1 3	1 6
202	4 0	4 0
203	2 6	2 6
204	4 6	4 6
205	0 11	1 3
206	1 9	2 3
207	1 9	2 0
208	5 0	6 6
209	2 3	3 0
210	7 6	8 6
D1/2 *Each*	2 6	3 0
D3	2 9	3 0
D3a	12 6	
D4	8 6	6 0
D5	0 6	0 9
D10	2 6	1 6
C.1/102	*Increase* 50%	
INDIA		
O170*b*	25 0	25 0
O180	20 0	20 0
MALAWI		
223	1 8	2 6
PALESTINE		
1	£22	£15
1*a*	£20	£12
1*b*	£24	£15
Control blocks:		
1	£100	
1*a*	£85	
1*b*	£120	
2	£9	£80
2a	£220	
2 Control block	£90	
4a	£45	
Control C18B	£140	
Control D18C	£25	
35	£75	17 6
38	£80	£100
43	£30	£60

Specification

PAGE SIZE $11\frac{1}{4} \times 10\frac{1}{2}$ in.; area for stamps $9\frac{1}{4} \times 8\frac{1}{2}$ in. Stamps go on one side of page only.

PRINTED SQUARES are slightly larger than the actual stamps. Illustrations and descriptions make identification easy.

ARRANGEMENT is alphabetical, while the loose-leaf system allows collectors to arrange pages as desired. Pages for future years can be interpolated or kept separate.

SUBSIDIARY STAMP GROUPS (Postage Dues, Officials, etc.) are on separate pages which can be discarded if not wanted.

BINDERS. Popular spring-back fitting, with springs selected to take and hold up to 200 leaves. Undated covers may therefore be used with any set of leaves. TWO TYPES: Cloth (in Green or Maroon—specify when ordering) and De Luxe (Leather back and corners, in Green only).

THE QUEEN ELIZABETH REIGN

(4th Edition)

No. 3501. Set of 242 leaves only, 1953–end 1962 ... ... **40/-**

No. 3502. Leaves plus two cloth-covered spring-back binders **80/–**

No. 3503. Leaves plus two de-luxe binders in green ... **124/–**

POSTAGE EXTRA 3501, U.K. 3/–, abd. 5/7; 3502, 3503, U.K. 4/6, abd. 10/11.

FIRST SUPPLEMENT TO THE FOURTH EDITION

	Price	Postage extra U.K.	Postage extra Abroad
No. 3535. 1963 and 1964. 164 eaves	**38/6**	3/6	4/6

SECOND SUPPLEMENT TO THE FOURTH EDITION

	Price	Postage extra U.K.	Postage extra Abroad
No. 3544. 1965. 144 leaves	**35/-**	3/3	3/10